KEY TO ENTRIES

🐎 Children welcome (from age shown in brackets, if specified)

🅿 Off-street car parking (number of places shown in brackets)

✗ No smoking

📺 Television (either in every room or in a TV lounge)

🐕 Pets accepted (by prior arrangement)

✗ Evening meal available (by prior arrangement)

Ⓥ Special diets catered for (by prior arrangement - please check with owner to see if your particular requirements are catered for)

▥ Central heating throughout

♿ Suita...
with...
prov...

♿2 Gradings of ... accessibility scheme: category 1 (highest) ... accessible to wheelchair user travelling independently; 2 means accessible to wheelchair user travelling with assistance; 3 means accessible to person with limited mobility able to walk a few paces/up maximum three steps

❄ Christmas breaks a speciality

☕ Coffee/tea making facilities

cc Credit cards accepted

Use the **National Grid** reference with Ordnance Survey maps and any atlas that uses the British National Grid. The letters refer to a 100 kilometre grid square. The first two numbers refer to a North/South grid line and the last two numbers refer to an East/West grid line. The grid reference indicates their intersection point.

The **location heading** – every hamlet, village, town and city listed in this directory is represented on the local county map at the head of each section.

Penny Hassett

PH2096   🍺 *The Bull, Cat & Fiddle*

Local pubs – these are the names of nearby pubs that serve food in the evening, as suggested by local B&Bs.

The Old Rectory, Main Street, Penny Hassett, Borchester, Borsetshire, *BC69 3QJ.*
C18th former rectory, lovely garden. Convenient for countryside and Borchester. **Open:** All year
Grades: ETC 3 Diamond
01676 512480 *oldrectory@ntlworld.com*
D: £25.00-£30.00 S: £28.00-£40.00
Beds: 1D 1T **Baths:** 1 En 1 Pr 1 Sh
🐎 🅿 (2) ✗ 📺 ✗ ▥ Ⓥ ☕ ♿ cc

D: **Price range** *per person* sharing in a *double room.*
S: **Price range** for a single person in a room.

Bedrooms
F = Family
D = Double
T = Twin
S = Single

Bathrooms
En = Ensuite
Pr = Private
Sh = Shared

Grades – The English Tourism Council (**ETC**) grades B&Bs for quality in Diamonds (**1 Diamond** to **5 Diamond**, highest) and hotels in Stars (**1 Star** to **5 Star**). The Jersey Tourist Board (**JTB**) and Guernsey Tourist Board (**GTB**) use the same system. Scottish and Welsh Tourist Board (**STB** and **WTB**) grades have two parts: the Star rating is for quality (**1 Star** to **5 Star**, highest), the other part designates the type of establishment, e.g. B&B, Guest House (**GH**), Country House (**CH**) etc. Isle of Man Tourist Board (**IOMTB**) grades have two parts: the range of facilities provided is represented by 'Listed' to 1 through 5 Crowns (**Cr**); there is also a general quality grading such as Approved (**Approv**) or Commended (**Comm**). Ask at Tourist Information Centres for further information on these systems. The Automobile Association (**AA**) and Royal Automobile Club (**RAC**) both use, throughout the British–Irish Isles, the same system of Diamonds and Stars as the English Tourism Council.

Currency Converter

Here is a quick conversion table for British pounds to euros, based on January 2002 rates.

£10 = € 16.01   € 10 = £6.25
£20 = € 32.02   € 20 = £12.50
£30 = € 48.03   € 40 = £25.00
£40 = € 64.03   € 60 = £37.50

Here is a quick conversion table for British pounds to US dollars, based on January 2002 rates.

£10 = US$14.46   US$10 = £6.92
£20 = US$28.92   US$20 = £13.83
£30 = US$43.38   US$40 = £27.67
£40 = US$57.84   US$60 = £41.50

BRITAIN BED & BREAKFAST 2002

Publisher **Tim Stilwell**
Editor **Martin Dowling**

STILWELL

Publishing

Distributed in Great Britain, Ireland and the Commonwealth by Orca Book Services, Stanley House, 3 Fleets Lane, Poole, Dorset BH15 3AJ (Tel: 01202 665432); and in the USA by Seven Hills Distributors, 49 Central Avenue, Cincinatti, OH 45202 (Tel: 513 381 3881). Available from all good bookshops.

ISBN 1-900861-28-3

Published by Stilwell Publishing,
59 Charlotte Road, Shoreditch, London, EC2A 3QW.
Tel: 020 7739 7179.

Publisher: Tim Stilwell
Editor: Martin Dowling
Typesetting: Tradespools Ltd, Frome, Somerset
Front Cover Design: Crush Design Associates

Front Cover: Pear Tree Cottage, Churchstanton, Somerset is on page 284 of this directory.

Printed in France by Aubin Imprimeur, Poitiers.

Contents

Introduction

This directory is really very straightforward. It sets out to list as many B&Bs in as many places in Britain as possible, so that wherever you go, you'll be able to find one nearby.

The book was actually born out of frustration. In the summer of 1991, my wife and I walked a long distance footpath over several weekends. As neither of us are avid campers or wished to stay in expensive hotels, we decided on B&Bs for our overnight stays. But we encountered a major problem straightaway. One could not find good value bed and breakfast accommodation along the route without going to a lot of trouble. Local libraries, Directory Enquiries, six different Tourist Information Centres and a large pile of brochures yielded nothing but a hotchpotch of B&B addresses – most of them miles out of our way. In the end, we abandoned our research and did the walk in one-day stretches, high-tailing it back to our London home each evening on the train. Needless to say, the memory stayed with us.

As did this one. Earlier that year, my work for a large publishing company sent me to a conference at the National Exhibition Centre, in Birmingham. My colleagues and I wished to stay in the area together and had to book at short notice. Our office was typical of the times; the recession was in full swing and our budget did not stretch far. We asked for the local Tourist Information Centre's brochure, but it wasn't much help. It arrived three days later, had no area map and consisted mostly of hotels outside our price range. A 2-mile trek to the local reference library to trawl through the Birmingham Yellow Pages did yield a list of local guest house telephone numbers, but there was no way of knowing what facilities any of them had or how much they cost. It was like blind man's buff. Fortunately, we were lucky. We found what we wanted after only 20 calls – bed and breakfast in a thriving Coleshill pub, five miles from the Centre. We had to book our rooms unseen, though, on the landlord's word only – an uninformed decision. In their small ways, both experiences illustrated the need for a book such as Stilwell's Britain: Bed & Breakfast.

As the recession grew worse, I lost my job with the large publishing company. A year later, I set up my own small publishing company whose first project was this directory. Happily, it has been rather successful. The reason must be that many others have found themselves in similar straits – stuck for a place to stay for the evening. For lack of information, they've missed out on the good value offered by B&Bs. This book has been expressly designed with these people in mind. Its purpose is simple: to save the reader time and money. It suits anyone who wishes to plan a trip in Britain, who appreciates good value and who is open to ideas. The directory is quite deliberately not a guidebook. Its aim is that of any directory in any field: to be comprehensive, offering the widest possible choice. By this definition, Stilwell's Britain: Bed & Breakfast outstrips any guidebook. We publish the largest number of B&Bs of any book available in this country. What we don't do, though, is make up the reader's mind for them. There are plenty of other B&B books that push their particular premises as 'exclusive' or 'special'. We think that a simple glance over the salient details will allow the reader to be his or her own best judge.

We have two kinds of reader in mind. The first knows exactly where to go but not where to stay. The nearest B&B is often the best solution and a quick look at the right county map will provide the answer. The other kind of reader is not so sure where to go. A good browse through these pages, studying the colour pictures, the facilities lists and the short descriptions, will offer good ideas.

All the accommodation information in this book has been supplied by the B&B owners themselves. And all the entries are bona fide B&Bs; 99% are listed at the local Tourist Information Centre. We should make it clear that inclusion in these pages does not imply personal recommendation. We have not visited every B&B individually. What we have done is write to them. The directory lists over 6,500 entries in over 4,500 locations throughout Britain. The vast majority offer B&B for under £30 per person per night.

Owners were canvassed in the summer of 2001 and responded by the middle of October. They were asked to provide their lowest and their highest rates per person per night for 2002. The rates are thus forecasts and are subject to seasonal fluctuations due to demand. Some information may already be out of date. Grades may go up or down or be removed. British Telecom may alter exchange numbers. Proprietors may decide to sell up and move out of the business altogether. This is why the directory is year specific, published annually. In general, though, the information published here will be accurate, pertinent and useful for many a year.

Each listing in Britain: Bed & Breakfast is an advertisement. The B&B owners decide on the type of entry they want – basic or highlighted in pink to stand out on the page; with or without a colour picture – and pay accordingly.

The chief aim is to provide details that are concise and easy to understand. The only symbols used are conventional tourist symbols, common to all guide books. Similarly, the abbreviations should be clear as to what they stand for without having to refer to the keys on the first and last pages. The grades are perhaps more difficult as each inspecting organisation – the national Tourist Boards, the AA and the RAC – has its own classification system with its own definition of merit. Once again, though, the reader will soon pick out the exceptional establishments – many have high grades from each organisation. The general rule is that more facilities mean higher prices. But don't be misled into thinking that an ungraded establishment is inferior. Many B&Bs are locally registered but never apply for grades or do not wish to pay for one. They thrive on word-of-mouth and business from guests who return again and again because of the excellent hospitality. My advice is to ring around. A simple telephone call and some judicious questions will give you an impression of your host very effectively. If you write to a B&B for more details, it's a good idea to enclose a stamped, addressed envelope for a quick reply. The largest number of British B&Bs is now laid out before you – the greatest choice available in the market. We think that your tastes and preferences will do the rest.

We have deliberately arranged the book by administrative county in alphabetical order except in the cases where this would disrupt a perceived sequence (such as East, North, South and West Yorkshire). There is an exception to prove the rule – County Durham appears perversely under D, as most people look for it under this heading. Merseyside is merged into the adjacent Greater Manchester section. South, West and Mid-Glamorgan appear together under the heading of The Glamorgans. We hope this will delight those who show pride in their native or adopted counties. In April 1996, the government decided to rename administrative counties and revise many local government boundaries. Out went the 1974 creations of the Heath government – Avon, Cleveland, Hereford & Worcester, Humberside, Dyfed, Clwyd, Gwynedd, Strathclyde, Grampian, Central and Tayside – and in came older and much-loved names, such as Argyll & Bute or Pembrokeshire. While this has undoubtedly served to make many people happier (hatred of the 1974 regions was quite intense), it has proved rather a headache for travel book publishers. For example, North West Wales and North East Wales cover a plethora of unitary authorities. Also, since many of the new Scottish regions are too small to merit their own chapter, we have merged them into neighbouring regions, hence 'Lothian & Falkirk' and 'Stirling & the Trossachs'. The Glasgow & District chapter mixes several unitary authorities. The same goes for much of our Glamorgan and Monmouthshire chapters.

One feature of the book is that we insist on using the proper postal address. Many entries may carry a county name different from the one they are listed under or a post town that is some miles from their village.

These oddities arise from the Royal Mail's distribution system. They should not, under any circumstances, be used as a directional guide. In one case, the village of Laid, on Loch Eriboll, is 67 miles from its quoted post town – not a journey to make in error. Used on a letter though, this system does speed the mail up. If you need directions to a B&B (especially if you are travelling at night), the best solution is to telephone the owner and ask the way.

The county maps are intended to act as a general reference. They are intended to show the location of each entry in the directory. For a more accurate idea of the exact location of a particular B&B, use the six-figure National Grid reference published under each location's name. Used in tandem with an Ordnance Survey map (such as the excellent Landranger series) or any atlas that uses the National Grid, these numbers provide first-class route-planning references. The pubs that appear beneath each location heading are included on the recommendation of B&B owners themselves. The tankard and the knife and fork symbols show that they are local pubs where one can get a decent evening meal at a reasonable price.

You'll notice a few changes to this year's Britain: Bed & Breakfast. This is the first edition to include colour pictures. The maps have been given a revamp, too. Essentially, however, we present you with the same high-quality product our readers are accustomed to, with ease of use, geographical accuracy and excellent value.

The Editor,
Stoke Newington, December 2001.

England & Wales – *Regions*

Scotland – *Regions*

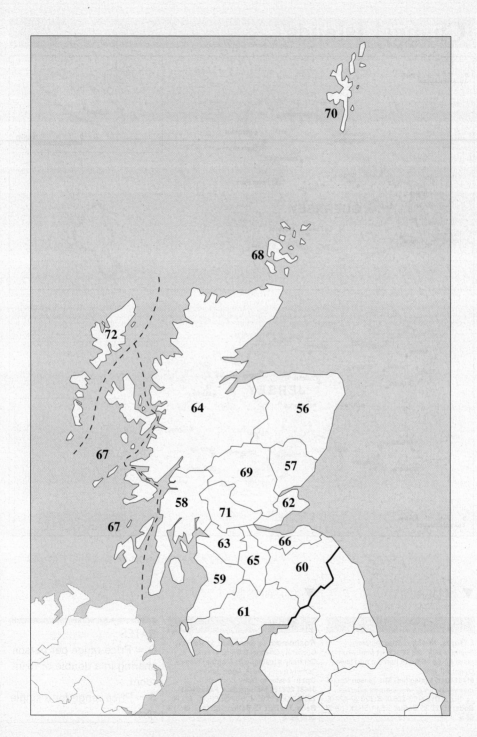

Channel Islands

▼ ALDERNEY

▼ GUERNSEY

Alderney

L'Haras, Newtown Road, Alderney,
Guernsey, C.I., *GY9 3XP*. Quiet family-run
guest house, close to harbour and town.
Open: All year
01481 823174 (also fax) Mrs Jansen *lharas@
internet.alderney.gg* www.internet.alderney.
gg/lharas **D:** £20.00–£26.00 **S:** £20.00–£24.00
Beds: 1D 2T 2S **Baths:** 2 En 1 Sh ☎ (10) ▥
▥ ♨

St Martin

Rosewood, La Grand Rue, St Martin,
Guernsey, Channel Islands, *GY4 6RU*.
Centrally situated in St Martins village -
homely guest house, large garden.
Open: Easter to Oct
01481 238329 Mr Sinkinson **Fax: 01481
239457 D:** £16.00–£20.00 **S:** £19.00–£23.00
Beds: 1F 2D 2T 1S **Baths:** 2 Sh ☎ (3) ▣ (8) ✔
▥ ▣ ▥ ♨

RATES

D = Price range per person
sharing in a double or twin
room
S = Price range for a single
room

St Peter Port

⊲ *Foresters Arms, Salerie Inn*

Marine Hotel, *Well Road, St Peter Port, Guernsey, C.I., GY1 1WS.* **Open:** All year **Grades:** GTB 3 Diamond, AA 3 Diamond, RAC 3 Diamond **01481 724978** Mrs Clegg **Fax: 01481 711729** **D:** £17.95–£26.95 **S:** £17.95–£28.95 **Beds:** 3F 3T 4D 1S **Baths:** 11 En ⊬ 🎛 Ⅴ 🛋 ♨ **cc** Friendly, comfortable hotel 30 meters from sea. Five mins walk to shops, harbour, leisure centre, theatre, etc. Lovely sun patio and relaxing lounge with sea views. Full choice English breakfast cooked fresh to order. Flexible bookings and package holidays aranged with substantial discounts.

Vale

L'Ancresse View Guest House, *La Garenne, Vale, Guernsey, C.I., GY3 5SQ.* Bordering L'Ancresse Golf Course. Main bus route to St Peter Port. **Open:** All year **01481 243963 (also fax)** Mr Peacegood *lancresse@hotmail.com* **D:** £12.00–£18.50 **S:** £12.00–£18.50 **Beds:** 1F 2D 1T ⅋ 🎛 ☗ Ⅴ 🛋 ♨

▼ JERSEY

St Aubin

Peterborough House, *Rue du Crocquet, High Street, St Aubin, Jersey, C.I., JE3 8BZ.* C17th house, personally run, conservation area, some rooms sea view. **Open:** Mar to Oct **Grades:** JTB 3 Diamond, AA 3 Diamond **01534 741568** Mr & Mrs Cabral **Fax: 01534 746787** *fernando@localdial.com* www.jerseyisland. com/staubin/peterborough **D:** £18.25–£29.00 **S:** £23.25–£34.25 **Beds:** 1F 4D 5T 4S **Baths:** 12 En 1 Sh ⅋ (10) ⊬ 🎛 Ⅴ 🛋 ♨ **cc**

Panorama, *Rue du Crocquet, St Aubin, Jersey, C.I., JE3 8BZ.* Gold merit award guest house. Exceptional standards, food, service, accommodation. **Open:** Easter to Oct **01534 742429 Fax: 01534 745940** www.jerseyisland.com/staubin/panorama **D:** £24.00–£46.00 **S:** £24.00–£72.00 **Beds:** 12T 2D 3S **Baths:** 17 En ⊬ 🎛 🛋 ♨

St Brelade

Lyndhurst, *Route de la Haule, St Brelade, Jersey, C.I., JE3 8BA.* Overlooking the golden sands of St Aubin's Bay. Superb food. **Open:** All year **01534 720317 Fax: 01534 613776 D:** £15.50–£25.50 **S:** £25.50–£35.50 **Beds:** 4F 4D 3T **Baths:** 11 Pr ⅋ (6) 🎛 Ⅴ 🛋 ♨ **cc**

Au Caprice, *Route de la Haule, St Brelade, Jersey, C.I., JE3 8BA.* Small friendly establishment situated opposite a large safe sandy beach. **Open:** Apr to Dec **01534 722083** Ms Monpetit **Fax: 01534 280058** *aucaprice@jerseymail.co.uk* www.jerseyisland.com/staubin/aucaprice **D:** £18.50–£28.00 **S:** £20.00–£29.00 **Beds:** 2F 6D 4T **Baths:** 12 En ⅋ (2) 🅿 (20) ⊬ 🎛 ✕ Ⅴ 🛋 ♨ **cc**

St Clement

Rocqueberg View, *Rue de Samares, St Clement, Jersey, JE2 6LS.* Comfortable friendly quiet house in convenient quiet location near beach. **Open:** All year **01534 852642** L & S Monks **Fax: 01534 851694 D:** £15.00–£26.00 **S:** £15.00–£46.00 **Beds:** 2F 5D 2T **Baths:** 9 En ⅋ 🅿 (9) 🎛 🛋 ♨

Planning a longer stay? Always ask for any special rates

St Helier

⊲ *The Cockles*

Bromley Guest House, *7 Winchester Street, St Helier, Jersey, C.I., JE24TH.* **Open:** All year **Grades:** JTB 3 Diamond **01534 725045 & 01534 723948** Mrs Schillaci **Fax: 01534 769712** *113555.1035@ compuserve.com* www.jersey.co. uk/hotels/bromley **D:** £16.00–£26.00 **S:** £29.00–£44.00 **Beds:** 1F 3D 3T 2S **Baths:** 7 En 2 Sh ⅋ ⊬ 🎛 Ⅴ 🛋 ♨ **cc** Jersey town guest house, open all year. Double/twin/family rooms all ensuite, single rooms basic only. Colour TV , tea/ coffee facilities. Situated only 3-4 minutes from shopping area and all amenities. Travel can be arranged from England, Scotland and Ireland.

Millbrook House, *Rue de Trachy, Millbrook, St Helier, Jersey, C.I., JE2 3JN.* **Open:** May to Oct **Grades:** AA 4 Diamond, Sparkling **01534 733036** Mr Pirouet **Fax: 01534 724317 D:** £35.00–£38.00 **S:** £35.00–£38.00 **Beds:** 5F 10D 9T 3S **Baths:** 27 En ⅋ 🅿 (20) 🎛 ✕ Ⅴ Where the air is clear, Millbrook House offers peace, quiet and character. Exceptional park and gardens with views of the sea. A good table and extensive wine list.

Seacroft, *38 Green Street, St Helier, Jersey, Channel Islands, JE2 4UG.* Close to all amenities. Small, friendly home. **Open:** All year (not Xmas/New Year) **Grades:** JTB 1 Diamond **01534 732732 D:** £18.00–£20.00 **S:** £20.00 **Beds:** 1F 5T 2D **Baths:** 3 Sh ⅋ (2) ⊬ 🎛 Ⅴ ♨

Bedfordshire

NORTHAMPTONSHIRE

CAMBRIDGESHIRE

GRAFHAM WATER

Wellingborough

Rushden

Wymington

60

Bletsoe

B E D F O R D S H I R E

Ravensden

Bedford

Wrestlingworth

Sandy

Potton

WARWICKSHIRE

Houghton Conquest

Old Warden

Biggleswade

Newport Pagnell

Cranfield

Marston Moretaine

Haynes

40

Milton Keynes

Silsoe

Woburn

Baldock

Letchworth

Milton Bryan

Hitchin

A1(M)

Leighton Buzzard

Stevenage

Totternhoe

Luton

Dunstable

LUTON

20

HERTFORDSHIRE

Welwyn Garden City

Tring

SP 00 TL

20

0   5 miles

Bedford

TL0549

Bedford Oak House, *33 Shakespear Road, Bedford, Beds, MK40 2DX.* Newly refurbished Victorian house close to town centre, comfortable accommodation. **Open:** All year (not Xmas/New Year) **01234 266972** Mr Kemp *bkemp@easynet.co.uk* **D:** £22.00–£24.00 **S:** £31.00–£35.00 **Beds:** 1D 2T 1S **Baths:** 4 En ☐ (15) ⊬ ☑ ▥ ♨

Bletsoe

TL0357

North End Farm, *Riseley Road, Bletsoe, Bedford, MK44 1QT.* A beautiful barn conversion in quiet countryside on a farm. **Open:** All year **Grades:** ETC 4 Diamond, Silver **01234 781320 & 07979 596913 (M)** Mr & Mrs Forster **Fax: 01234 781320 D:** £25.00–£50.00 **S:** £25.00–£30.00 **Beds:** 8T **Baths:** 48 En ☼ (5) ☐ (20) ⊬ ☒ ☞ ▥ ♨ cc

Cranfield

SP9542

The Queen Hotel, *40 Dartmouth Road, Olney, Buckinghamshire, MK46 4BH.* Enchanting Victorian house in bustling market town. **Open:** All year **01234 711924 (also fax)** Mrs Elsmore **D:** £27.50–£29.00 **S:** £42.00–£44.50 **Beds:** 3T 4D 2S **Baths:** 7 En 1 Sh ☐ (9) ⊬ ☑ ▥ ♨ cc

Dunstable

TL0121

Regent House Guest House, *79a High Street North, Dunstable, Beds, LU6 1JF.* Dunstable town centre, close to M1. **Open:** All year **01582 660196** Mr Woodhouse **D:** £17.00 **S:** £20.00 **Beds:** 5T 5S 1F **Baths:** 4 En ☼ ☐ (6) ☑ ☞ ☑ ▥ ♨

Haynes

TL1041

Westview, *Church End, Haynes, Bedford, Beds, MK45 3QS.* Situated within easy reach to M1 South - North + London Luton Airport. **Open:** All year **01234 742881** Mr & Mrs Baker *bevb123@ hotmail.com* **D:** £27.50–£30.00 **S:** £27.50–£30.00 **Beds:** 1T 1D 1S **Baths:** 1 En 1 Sh ☼ (5) ☐ (4) ⊬ ☑ ▥ ♨

Luton

TL0921

Belzayne, *70 Lalleford Road, Luton, Beds, LU2 9JH.* Modern semi, near airport. Old fashioned hospitality. **Open:** All year (not Xmas/New Year) **01582 736591 (also fax)** Mrs Bell **D:** £14.00–£18.00 **Beds:** 1D 2T **Baths:** 2 Sh ☼ (12) ☐ (5) ▥ ♨

Marston Moretaine

SP9941

The Coach House, *The Old Rectory, Marston Moretaine, Bedford, MK43 0NF.* Listed building, fully modernised, in 5 acres of mature gardens. **Open:** All year (not Xmas) **01234 767794 (also fax)** G S Lake *isla.lake@ uk.uumail.com* **D:** £19.50 **S:** £30.00 **Beds:** 1T 4D 1S **Baths:** 6 En ☼ ☐ (20) ☑ ▥ ♿ ♨ cc

Milton Bryan

SP9730

Town Farm, *Milton Bryan, Milton Keynes, Bucks, MK17 9HS.* Quiet, secluded farmhouse, good views, easy access Woburn and M1. **Open:** All year (not Xmas) **Grades:** ETC 4 Diamond **01525 210001 (also fax)** Mrs Harris **D:** £22.50 **S:** £25.00 **Beds:** 2T **Baths:** 2 En ☼ (12) ☐ (4) ⊬ ☑ ▥ ♨

Old Warden

TL1343

Old Warden Guest House, *Shop & Post Office, Old Warden, Biggleswade, Beds, SG18 9HQ.* Centre of quiet, picturesque village. **Open:** All year (not Xmas/New Year) **01767 627201** Mr Bruton **D:** £21.00 **S:** £25.00–£27.00 **Beds:** 2D 1T **Baths:** 3 En ☼ ☐ (5) ☑ ☑ ▥ ♨

Potton

TL2248

Rose & Crown, *Market Square, Potton, Sandy, Beds, SG19 2NP.* Former C17th coaching inn. Home cooked food and real ales. **Open:** All year **01767 260221 D:** £28.50 **S:** £40.00 **Beds:** 2F 4D 4T 4S **Baths:** 11 En ☼ ☐ ⊬ ☑ ✕ ▥ ♨ cc

---

BEDROOMS
D = Double
T = Twin
S = Single
F = Family

Ravensden

TL0853 ⬛ *Blacksmiths Arms, Horse & Jockey, Victoria Arms*

Tree-Garth, *Church End, Ravensden, Bedford, MK44 2RP.* Quiet village, 5 miles North of Bedford, warm welcome, home made fayre. **Open:** All year (not Xmas/New Year) **Grades:** ETC 4 Diamond **01234 771745 (also fax)** Mrs Edwards *treegarth@ukonline.co.uk* www.treegarth.co.uk **D:** £22.00–£23.00 **S:** £22.00–£30.00 **Beds:** 1T 1D 1S **Baths:** 1 Sh ☼ (12) ☐ (5) ⊬ ☑ ▥ ♨ cc

Sandy

TL1748

The Pantilles, *6 Swaden Everton Road, Sandy, Beds, SG19 2DA.* Converted barn in wooded valley overlooking lawns and flower gardens. **Open:** All year (not Xmas/New Year) **01767 680668** *pantiles@breathemail.net* **D:** £25.00 **S:** £35.00 **Beds:** 2D1T **Baths:** 3 En ☼ ☐ ⊬ ☞ ☞ ▥ ♨

Orchard Cottage, *1 High Street, Wrestlingworth, Sandy, Beds, SG19 2EW.* Charming C16th thatched cottage with modern extension, formerly village bakery. **Open:** All year (not Xmas) **01767 631355** Mrs Strong **D:** £21.00 **S:** £24.00 **Beds:** 1D 1T 2S **Baths:** 2 Sh ☼ ☐ (4) ⊬ ☑ ▥ ♨

Fairlawn Hotel, *70 Bedford Road, Sandy, Beds, SG19 1EP.* Small, friendly. Easy access A1 and main line railway station. **Open:** All year (not Xmas) **01767 680336 D:** £24.00–£30.00 **S:** £23.00–£26.00 **Beds:** 1F 2D 2T 3S **Baths:** 2 Pr 1 Sh ☼ ☐ (16) ☑ ☞ ✕ ☑ ▥ ♨

Highfield Farm, *Great North Road, Sandy, Beds, SG19 2AQ.* Wonderfully comfortable farmhouse in delightful grounds. Ample safe parking. **Open:** All year **01767 682332** Mrs Codd **Fax: 01767 692503** *margaret@highfield.farm.co.uk* **D:** £25.00–£30.00 **S:** £25.00–£45.00 **Beds:** 2F 2D 2T **Baths:** 3 En 1 Pr 1 Sh ☼ ☐ (10) ⊬ ☞ ☞ ▥ ♨ cc

Silsoe

TL0836

The Old George Hotel, *High Street, Silsoe, Bedford, Beds., MK45 4EP.* Old coaching inn. Village location, large garden, famous fish restaurant. **Open:** All year (not Xmas)
01525 860218 J C Bridge **D:** £24.00–£35.00 **S:** £35.00–£39.00 **Beds:** 5D 1T 1S **Baths:** 2 En 2 Sh ♿ 🅿 (50) ⌿ 🖾 ⼁ ✕ Ⓥ ⾕ ♨ cc

Totternhoe

SP9821

Country Cottage, *5 Brightwell Avenue, Totternhoe, Dunstable, Beds, LU6 1QT.* Quiet village house in countryside with views of Dunstable Downs. **Open:** All year (not Xmas)
01582 601287 (also fax) Mrs Mardell
D: £25.00 **S:** £25.00 **Beds:** 1T 1D 1S **Baths:** 2 En 1 Sh ♿ 🅿 (3) ⌿ 🖾 Ⓥ ⾕ ♨

Woburn

SP9433

11 George Street, *Woburn, Milton Keynes, Bucks, MK17 9PX.* Small, cosy, personally run, Grade II Listed cottage. Very near Woburn Abbey. **Open:** All year
01525 290405 (also fax) Mrs Tough
D: £15.00–£20.00 **S:** £15.00–£20.00 **Beds:** 1D 4F 2T 1S **Baths:** 3 Sh ♿ ⌿ 🖾 ⾕ ♨ ♨

Please respect a B&B's wishes regarding children, animals and smoking

Wrestlingworth

TL2547

Orchard Cottage, *1 High Street, Wrestlingworth, Sandy, Beds, SG19 2EW.* Charming C16th thatched cottage with modern extension, formerly village bakery. **Open:** All year (not Xmas)
01767 631355 Mrs Strong **D:** £21.00 **S:** £24.00 **Beds:** 1D 1T 2S **Baths:** 2 Sh 🅿 (4) ⌿ Ⓥ ⾕ ♨

Wymington

SP9563

The Old Rectory, *45 Rushden Road, Wymington, Rushden, Northants, NN10 9LN.* A Victorian rectory set in 5.5 acres of private grounds. A warm welcome guaranteed. **Open:** All year
01933 314486 Mrs Denton **Fax:** 01933 411266 *oldrectory.wymington@btinternet.com*
D: £20.00–£21.00 **S:** £22.00–£24.00 **Beds:** 1F 4D 3T 1S **Baths:** 8 En ♿ 🅿 (20) ⌿ 🖾 ✕ Ⓥ ⾕ ♿ ♨

Berkshire

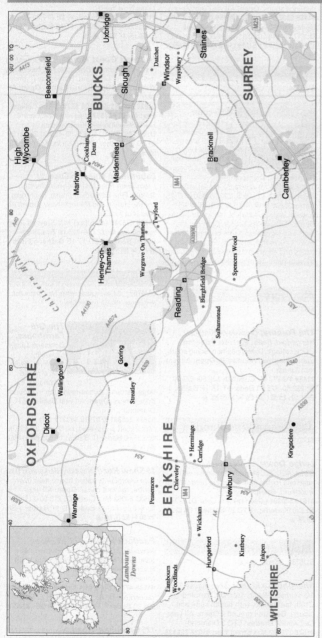

Bracknell

SU8668

53 Swaledale, Wildridings, Bracknell, Berks, RG12 7ET. Near M3 and M4 also near town centre. **Open:** All year (not Xmas/New Year)
01344 421247 T Webber **D:** £25.00 **S:** £25.00 **Beds:** 1T 1S **Baths:** 1 Sh 🖭 ⟆

Burghfield Bridge

SU6870

Boathouse, Kennet House, Burghfield Bridge, Reading, Berks, RG30 3RA. Luxury houseboat on Kennet and Avon Canal, accommodation only. **Open:** All year
0118 957 1060 Mrs Ogden **D:** £20.00 **S:** £20.00 **Beds:** 2D ⟆ 🖭 (3) ⟆ 📺 🐾 🛏

Chieveley

SU4773

19 Heathfields, Chieveley, Newbury, Berks, RG20 8TW. Quietly situated house, attractive garden, very near A34/M4, shop, pub. **Open:** Feb to Dec **Grades:** ETC 3 Diamond
01635 248179 Mrs Wood **Fax:** 01635 248799 *ingandco@aol.com* **D:** £22.50–£27.50 **S:** £22.50–£27.50 **Beds:** 1D 1T **Baths:** 1 Pr ⟆ 🖭 (3) ⟆ 📺 🐾 🛏 ⚓

The Old Farmhouse, Downend Lane, Chieveley, Newbury, Berks, RG20 8TN. Old farmhouse in large gardens. Accommodation in ground floor annexe. **Open:** All year **Grades:** ETC 4 Diamond
01635 248361 & 07970 583373 (M) Mrs Pallett *palletts@aol.com* **D:** £26.00–£30.00 **S:** £35.00 **Beds:** 1F **Baths:** 1 En ⟆ 🖭 (4) ⟆ 📺 🛏 ⚓ ♿ ⚓

Cookham

SU8985 🍴 The Harvester, Two Roses, Bel & The Dragon

Wylie Cottage, School Lane, Cookham, Maidenhead, Berks, SL6 9QJ. Detached Victorian house in Cookham village. **Open:** All year (not Xmas/New Year) **Grades:** ETC 3 Diamond
01628 520106 *crowegc@ntlworld.com* **D:** £25.00–£30.00 **S:** £28.00–£40.00 **Beds:** 1T 1D **Baths:** 1 Sh ⟆ 🖭 (2) ⟆ 📺 🐾 📺 🛏 ⚓

Planning a longer stay? Always ask for any special rates

Planning a longer stay? Always ask for any special rates

Cookham Dean
SU8684

Cartlands Cottage, *King's Lane, Cookham Dean, Maidenhead, Berks, SL6 9AY.* Self-contained guest room in garden. Rural, very quiet. **Open:** All year **Grades:** ETC 1 Diamond
01628 482196 Mr & Mrs Parkes **D:** £20.00– £27.50 **S:** £23.50–£30.00 **Beds:** 1F **Baths:** 1 Pr �♿ ▣ (2) ▥ ▥ ▥. ⚓

Curridge
SU4871   ⚓ *Bunk Inn*

Many Trees, *Curridge Road, Curridge, Thatcham, Berks, RG18 9DH.* Quiet, tranquil, perfectly situated near the A34/M4 for North, South, East and West. **Open:** All year (not Xmas/New Year)
01635 200872 Mrs Hendel **D:** £35.00–£50.00 **S:** £25.00–£35.00 **Beds:** 1T 1D 1S ▣ (6) ⚓ ▥ ▸ ▥ ▥. ⚓ ⚓

Hermitage
SU5173

The Granary, *Hermitage, Thatcham, Berks, RG18 9SD.* Charming converted barn with large garden in pretty rural hamlet. **Open:** All year (not Xmas/New Year)
01635 200249 (also fax) Mr & Mrs De Lisle-Bush **D:** £20.00–£22.50 **S:** £22.00–£25.00 **Beds:** 1T 1D 1S **Baths:** 1 Sh ⚓ (12) ▣ (3) ⚓ ▥ ▸ ▥.

Hungerford
SU3368

Anne's B&B, *59 Priory Avenue, Hungerford, Berks, RG17 0AS.* Family-run. Close to canal and railway. 5 mins M4. **Open:** All year (not Xmas/New Year) **Grades:** ETC 3 Diamond
01488 682290 Mrs Whittaker **Fax: 01488 686993** *anne@hungerfordberks.co.uk* www.hungerfordberks.co.uk **D:** £20.00– £25.00 **S:** £20.00–£25.00 **Beds:** 1T 1D 2S **Baths:** 1 En 1 Pr ⚓ ▣ (4) ⚓ ▥ ▸ ▥. ⚓

Wilton House, *33 High Street, Hungerford, Berks, RG17 0NF.* Elegant ensuite bedrooms in classic, historic English town house predating 1450. **Open:** All year (not Xmas)
01488 684228 Mrs Welfare **Fax: 01488 685037** *welfares@hotmail.com* **D:** £25.00–£27.50 **S:** £35.00–£38.00 **Beds:** 1D 1T **Baths:** 2 En ⚓ (8) ▣ (3) ⚓ ▥ ▥ ▥. ⚓

Alderborne, *33 Bourne Vale, Hungerford, Berkshire, RG17 0LL.* Modern detached family house overlooking open country. Walking distance shops. **Open:** All year (not Xmas)
01488 683228 & 07808 184156 (M) Mr & Mrs Honeybone *honeybones@hungerford.co.uk* **D:** £17.50–£18.50 **S:** £17.50–£22.50 **Beds:** 2T 1S **Baths:** 1 Pr 1 Sh ⚓ (5) ▣ (3) ⚓ ▥ ▥ ▥. ⚓

Inkpen
SU3764

Beacon House, *Bell Lane, Upper Green, Hungerford, Berks, RG17 9QJ.* **Open:** All year

Grades: AA 3 Diamond
01488 668640 Mr & Mrs Cave *l.g.cave@ classicfm.net* **D:** £22.00 **S:** £22.00 **Beds:** 1T 2S **Baths:** 2 Sh ⚓ ▣ (6) ▥ ▸ ▸ ▥ ▥. ✿ ⚓
A warm welcome awaits you at our home, Berks./Wilts/Hants border. Comfortable beds and wonderful home cooking. If the weather is inclement there are plenty of books and an artists' studio where you can try your hand at printmaking.

Kintbury
SU3866

The Forbury, *Crossways, Kintbury, Hungerford, Berks, RG17 9SU.* Extended C17th cottage. Lovely position facing south, overlooking own woodlands. **Open:** All year (not Xmas)
01488 658377 Mr Cubitt **D:** £22.50–£27.50 **S:** £22.50–£25.00 **Beds:** 1T 1S 1F **Baths:** 1 Pr 1 Sh ⚓ ▣ (10) ▥ ▸ ▸ ▥ ▥. ⚓

Lambourn Woodlands
SU3175

Lodge Down, *Lambourn , Hungerford, Berks, RG17 7BJ.* Magnificent house with spacious rooms and extensive garden with woodland. **Open:** All year
01672 540304 (also fax) Mrs Cook **D:** £22.50 **S:** £30.00 **Beds:** 1F 2D 2T **Baths:** 3 En ▣ (6) ▥ ▥. ⚓

Maidenhead
SU8781   ⚓ *Pond House*

Sheephouse Manor, *Sheephouse Road, Maidenhead, Berks, SL6 8HJ.* Charming C16th farmhouse, with health suite and jacuzzi. Beautiful grounds. **Open:** All year (not Xmas) **Grades:** ETC 3 Diamond
01628 776902 Mrs Street **Fax: 01628 625138** *info@sheephousemanor.co.uk* www.sheephousemanor.co.uk **D:** £30.00– £35.00 **S:** £49.00–£55.00 **Beds:** 1D 1T 3S **Baths:** 5 En ⚓ ▣ (7) ▥ ▸ ▸ ▥ ▥. ⚓ cc

Copperfields Guest House, *54 Bath Road, Maidenhead, Berks, SL6 4JY.* Elegant Victorian Guest House **Open:** All year (not Xmas/New Year)
01628 674941 Mrs Lindsay **D:** £27.00–£30.00 **S:** £35.00–£40.00 **Beds:** 1T 4S **Baths:** 2 En 1 Sh ▣ (5) ⚓ ▥ ▸ ▥.

Hillcrest Guest House, *19 Craufurd Rise, Maidenhead, Berks, SL6 7LR.* Near to town centre, Legoland, Henley-on-Thames, Windsor and Shire Horse Centre. **Open:** All year
01628 620086 & 01628 623572 Mrs Colligan **Fax: 01628 623572** *clifton@aroram.freeserve co.uk* www.cliftonguesthouse.co.uk **D:** £35.00–£60.00 **S:** £35.00–£60.00 **Beds:** 2F 6T 7D 5S **Baths:** 10 En 3 Sh ⚓ ▣ (20) ▥ ✕ ▥ ▥. ⚓ cc

Laburnham Guest House, *31 Laburnham Road, Maidenhead, Berks, SL6 4DB.* Fine Edwardian house, near town centre, station and M4 motorway. **Open:** All year (not Xmas)
01628 676748 (also fax) Mrs Stevens *rdgs@ waitrose.com* **D:** £23.00–£25.00 **S:** £35.00– £40.00 **Beds:** 1F 2D 1T 1S **Baths:** 5 En ⚓ ▣ (5) ⚓ ▥ ▥ ▥. ⚓

Newbury
SU4767   ⚓ *Craven Arms, White Hart, Water Rat, Red House, Plough on The Green*

The Old Farmhouse, *Downend Lane, Chieveley, Newbury, Berks, RG20 8TN.* Old farmhouse in large gardens. Accommodation in ground floor annexe. **Open:** All year **Grades:** ETC 4 Diamond
01635 248361 & 07970 583373 (M) Mrs Pallett *palletts@aol.com* **D:** £26.00–£30.00 **S:** £35.00 **Beds:** 1F **Baths:** 1 En ⚓ ▣ (4) ⚓ ▥ ▥. ⚓ ⚓

15 Shaw Road, *Newbury, Berks, RG14 1HG.* Late Georgian terraced house near town centre, rail and canal. **Open:** All year
01635 44962 Mrs Curtis **D:** £18.00–£19.00 **S:** £18.00–£19.00 **Beds:** 1D 1T **Baths:** 1 Sh ⚓ ▣ ⚓ ▥ ▥ ▥. ⚓

Paddock House, *17 Derby Road, Newbury, Berks, RG14 6DA.* Situated near town centre. Conveniently close to main Basingstoke road. **Open:** All year (not Xmas/New Year)
01635 47444 Mr & Mrs Liddell *hotelhardel@ claranet.com* **D:** £20.00–£25.00 **S:** £22.00– £28.00 **Beds:** 2T 2S **Baths:** 2 Sh ▣ ⚓ ▥ ▥ ▥.

125 Greenham Road, *Newbury, RG14 7JE.* Close to Newbury centre. Victorian home. Warm welcome. **Open:** All year
01635 47377 Mr & Mrs Kirke *a.kirke@ cwcom.net* **D:** £28.00 **S:** £20.00–£30.00 **Beds:** 1D 1S **Baths:** 1 Pr 1 Sh ⚓ ⚓ ▥ ▥ ▥. ⚓

National Grid References given are for villages, towns and cities – not for individual houses

Laurel House, *157 Andover Road, Newbury, Berks, RG14 6NB.* A warm welcome awaits you in our delightful Georgian house. **Open:** All year (not Xmas)
01635 35931 Mr & Mrs Dixon **D:** £18.00
S: £18.00 **Beds:** 1D 1T **Baths:** 1 Sh 🖪 (2) ⌀ 📺 📺 🛒 ♨

Peasemore

SU4576

Peasemore House, *Peasemore, Newbury, Berks, RG20 7JH.* **Open:** All year (not Xmas/New Year)
01635 248505 (also fax) Mrs Brown *peasemore.browns@talk21.com* **D:** £25.00
S: £25.00–£30.00 **Beds:** 1T 1D **Baths:** 2 En ♋ 🖪 ⌀ 🛏 ✕ 📺 ♨
Traditional family farmhouse with beautiful gardens set in arable downland. Peaceful village only 4 miles J13 M4/A34. Excellent walking/ riding. Spacious comfortable accommodation. Wonderful breakfasts with home-made produce.

Reading

SU7173 🍺 *Up In Arms*

Dittisham Guest House, *63 Tilehurst Road, Reading, Berks, RG30 2JL.* Centrally located quiet Georgian house, good public transport, motorway connections. **Open:** All year **Grades:** ETC 3 Diamond
0118 956 9483 Mr Harding *dittishamgh@aol.com* **D:** £22.50–£30.00 **S:** £27.50–£35.00
Beds: 2D 1T 2S **Baths:** 3 En 2 Sh ♋ 🖪 ⌀ 📺 🛏 📺 ♨ ■ cc

Donnington House B&B, *82-86 London Road, Reading, Berks, RG1 5AU.* Independently-run Hotel which is centrally located near town centre. **Open:** All year (not Xmas/New Year)
0118 926 5258 Fax: 0118 926 4593 *reservations@comfortlodge.freeserve.co.uk*
D: £40.00–£50.00 **S:** £75.00–£85.00 **Beds:** 2F 10T 9D 14S **Baths:** 17 En 5 Sh ♋ 📺 📺 ♨ cc

Greystoke Guest House, *10 Greystoke Road, Caversham, Reading, Berks, RG4 5EL.* Private home in quiet road, TV & tea/coffee making in lounge. **Open:** All year (not Xmas)
0118 947 5784 Mrs Tyler **D:** £25.00–£30.00
S: £28.00–£35.00 **Beds:** 1D 2S **Baths:** 1 Sh 🖪 (3) ⌀ 📺 📺 ♨

St Hilda's, *24 Castle Crescent, Reading, Berkshire, RG1 6AG.* Quiet Victorian home near town centre. All rooms have colour TVs & fridges. **Open:** All year
0118 961 0329 Mr & Mrs Hubbard **Fax:** 0118 954 2585 **D:** £19.00–£24.00 **S:** £20.00–£27.00
Beds: 3F 2T **Baths:** 3 Sh ♋ (1) 🖪 ⌀ 📺 🛏 📺 ♨

Spencers Wood

SU7166 🍺 *Swan Inn, Farriers' Arms*

Meadowview B&B, *Basingstoke Road, Spencers Wood, Reading, Berks, RG7 1AL.* Homely, welcoming country semi, 1/2 mile M4/J11. Garden view. **Open:** All year (not Xmas/New Year)
0118 988 3270 Mrs Patman **D:** £25.00–£30.00
S: £26.00–£30.00 **Beds:** 1D 1S **Baths:** 1 Sh 🖪 (2) ⌀ 📺 📺 ♨

Streatley

SU5980

Pennyfield, *The Coombe, Streatley, Reading, Berkshire, RG8 9QT.* Pretty village house with attractive terraced garden. Friendly, welcoming hosts. **Open:** All year (not Xmas/New Year)
01491 872048 (also fax) *mandrvanstone@hotmail.com* **D:** £22.50–£25.00 **S:** £22.50–£25.00 **Beds:** 1T 2D **Baths:** 2 En 1 Sh 🖪 (4) ⌀ 📺 📺 ♨

Sulhamstead

SU6368

The Old Manor, *Whitehouse Manor, Sulhamstead, Reading, Berks, RG7 4EA.*
Open: All year (not Xmas/New Year)
0118 983 2423 Fax: 0118 983 6262 *rags-r@theoldmanor.fsbusines.co.uk* **D:** £35.00
S: £35.00–£50.00 **Beds:** 2D 1S **Baths:** 3 En 🖪 (4) ⌀ 📺 ✕ 📺 ♨
C17th manor house with very large and beautiful beamed bedrooms. Every modern convenience in ensuite bathrooms. Elegance and tranquillity superb meals for the discerning guest.

Twyford

SU7975

Copper Beeches, *Bath Road, Kiln Green, Twyford, Reading, Berks, RG10 9UT.* Quiet house in large gardens with tennis court, warm welcome. **Open:** All year
0118 940 2929 (also fax) Mrs Gorecki
D: £22.50–£25.00 **S:** £28.00–£35.00 **Beds:** 3F 4T 1D 1S **Baths:** 1 En 3 Sh ♋ (3) 🖪 (14) 📺 📺 ♨

Somewhere To Stay, *c/o Loddon Acres, Bath Road, Twyford, Reading, Berks, RG10 9RU.* Self-contained, modern, detached ensuite accommodation. Full facilities. Lovely gardens **Open:** All year **Grades:** ETC 4 Diamond
0118 934 5880 (also fax) R Fisher *reservations@somewhere-tostay.com* www.somewhere-tostay.com **D:** £24.50–£29.00 **S:** £39.00–£49.00 **Beds:** 1F 1D 1T 1S **Baths:** 3 En 1 Pr ♋ 🖪 (6) ⌀ 📺 🛏 📺 ♨

Wargrave-on-Thames

SU7978

Windy Brow, *204 Victoria Road, Wargrave-on-Thames, Reading, Berks, RG10 8AJ.* Victorian detached house, close M4/M40, 1 mile A4, 6 miles Reading & Maidenhead. **Open:** All year (not Xmas/New Year) **Grades:** ETC 4 Diamond
0118 940 3336 Mrs Carver **Fax:** 0118 940 1260 *heathcar@aol.com* **D:** £25.00–£30.00
S: £35.00–£47.50 **Beds:** 1D 2T 2S **Baths:** 1 En 2 Sh 🖪 (5) ⌀ 📺 📺 ♨

Wickham

SU3971

St Swithins B & B, *3 St Swithins Close, Wickham, Newbury, Berks, RG20 8HJ.* A warm welcome awaits you in this home in outstanding countryside. **Open:** All year
01488 657566 & 07979 014634 (M)
Mrs Edwards **Fax:** 0870 1693325 *r.edwards@iee.org* **D:** £20.00–£25.00 **S:** £25.00–£28.00
Beds: 1T 1S **Baths:** 1 Pr ♋ 🖪 (2) ⌀ 📺 📺 ♨

Windsor

SU9676

Jean's, *1 Stovell Road, Windsor, Berks, SL4 5JB.* **Open:** All year
01753 852055 Ms Sumner **Fax:** 01753 842932 *jeanlsumner@aol.com* **D:** £25.00 **S:** £50.00
Beds: 1D 1T **Baths:** 2 En 🖪 (2) ⌀ 📺 🛏 📺 ♨ ♿ ♨
Quiet comfortable self-contained ground floor flat comprising 2 ensuite bedrooms which share a large lounge. 100 yds river and leisure centre, 7 mins riverside walk to castle, town centre and railway stations, 4 mins to buses.

Rocking Horse House, *88 St Leonards Road, Windsor, Berks, SL4 3DA.* Traditional Victorian villa home, original features, high standards, central Windsor. **Open:** All year (not Xmas/New Year)
01753 853984 (also fax) Mr & Mrs Stanton
D: £22.00–£27.00 **S:** £30.00 **Beds:** 1F/T 1D 1S **Baths:** 1 En 3 Sh 🖪 ⌀ 📺 📺 ♨

Allbrown House, *15 Princess Avenue, Windsor, Berks, SL4 3LU.* 2 minutes Windsor Park, 10 mins town centre and station. **Open:** All year
01760 441700 Mr Stewart **Fax:** 01760 440440 *info@b-and-b.uk.com* www.b-and-b.uk.com **D:** £25.00–£40.00 **S:** £25.00–£30.00 **Beds:** 1F 2T 1D 3S **Baths:** 2 Sh 🖪 (2) 📺 📺 ♨ ■ cc

The Andrews, *77 Whitehorse Road, Windsor, Berks, SL4 4PG.* Modern, comfortable private house. **Open:** All year (not Xmas)
01753 866803 Mrs Andrews **D:** £18.00–£22.50 **S:** £23.00–£25.00 **Beds:** 1D 2T **Baths:** 2 Sh ⦗ (5) 🅿 (3) ⌇ 📺 🛏.

Chasela, *30 Convent Road, Windsor, Berks, SL4 3RB.* Modern semi-detached near M4, M40, M25. Castle 1 mile and Legoland. **Open:** All year **Grades:** ETC 3 Diamond
01753 860410 Mrs Williams **D:** £22.00–£26.00 **S:** £24.00–£26.00 **Beds:** 1T 1S **Baths:** 1 Sh ⦗ (12) 🅿 (5) ⌇ 📺 🛏.

Elansey, *65 Clifton Rise, Windsor, Berks, SL4 5SX.* Modern, quiet, comfortable house. Garden, patio, Excellent breakfasts, highly recommended. **Open:** All year (not Xmas)
01753 864438 Mrs Forbutt **D:** £25.00–£30.00 **S:** £25.00–£35.00 **Beds:** 1D 1T 1S **Baths:** 1 En 1 Sh 🅿 (3) 📺 📺 🛏.

62 Queens Road, *Windsor, Berks, SL4 3BH.* Recommended, quiet. 10 mins walk castle/station. Large ground-floor family room. **Open:** All year
01753 866036 (also fax) Mrs Hughes **D:** £22.50–£25.00 **S:** £30.00–£35.00 **Beds:** 1F 1D **Baths:** 2 En ⦗ 🅿 (1) ⌇ 📺 📺 🛏 ♿3 ♨.

Langton House, *46 Alma Road, Windsor, Berks, SL4 3HA.* Victorian house, quiet tree-lined road, 5 minutes walk to town & castle. **Open:** All year (not Xmas)
01753 858299 Paul & Sonja Fogg **Fax: 01753 8582299** *bookings@langtonhouse.co.uk* www.langtonhouse.co.uk **D:** £32.50–£35.00 **S:** £55.00–£60.00 **Beds:** 2D 1T **Baths:** 2 En 1 Pr 🅿 (2) ⌇ 📺 🛏.

The Laurells, *22 Dedworth Road, Windsor, Berks, SL4 5AY.* Pretty Victorian house 3/4 mile town centre. Heathrow 20 minutes. **Open:** All year (not Xmas)
01753 855821 Mrs Joyce **D:** £20.00 **S:** £25.00 **Beds:** 2T ⦗ (5) 📺 📺 🛏 ♨.

Wraysbury
TQ0073

Honeysuckle Cottage, *61 Fairfield Approach, Wraysbury, Staines, TW19 5DR.* Picturesque cottage in the historic Thames-side village of Wraysbury. Excellent country pubs. **Open:** All year (not Xmas)
01784 482519 Mrs Vogel **Fax: 01784 482305** *B&B@berks.force9.co.uk* www.berks.force9.co.uk **D:** £22.50–£27.50 **S:** £30.00–£40.00 **Beds:** 2F 1D 1T 1S **Baths:** 4 En 1 Pr ⦗ (3) 🅿 (8) ⌇ 📺 📺 🛏 ♿ ♨ cc

BATHROOMS
En = Ensuite
Pr = Private
Sh = Shared

Bristol

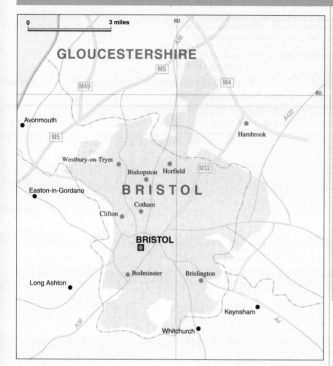

National Grid References given are for villages, towns and cities – not for individual houses

Bedminster

ST5771

Maison George, 10 Greville Road, Southville, Bristol, BS3 1LL. Large Victorian townhouse within walking distance of city centre. **Open:** All year
0117 963 9416 Mr Evans **Fax: 0117 953 5760**
D: £20.00–£30.00 **S:** £20.00–£30.00 **Beds:** 1F
1D 2T 1S **Baths:** 2 Sh ⓑ⌇⌷⌧⌦⌶

Bishopston

ST5875

Basca House, 19 Broadway Road, Bristol, BS7 8ES. Lovely Victorian house in quiet residential area. Close city centre. **Open:** All year (not Xmas/New Year) **Grades:** ETC 3
0117 942 2182 Mrs Chawdhary
carolchawdhary1@activemail.co.uk **D:** £22.50–£24.00 **S:** £25.00–£35.00 **Beds:** 2T 2S
Baths: 1 Sh ⓑ⌇⌷⌧⌦⌶

Brislington

ST6170

Kingston House, 101 Hardenhuish Road, Brislington, Bristol, BS4 3SR. Kingston House B&B is situated in a quiet residential area. **Open:** All year
0117 971 2456 & 07720 146267 (M) Ms Small
D: £22.50–£45.00 **S:** £24.00–£80.00 **Beds:** 1T
1D 1S **Baths:** 1 En 1 Pr 1 Sh ⌷(1)⌇⌷⌦⌶

Clifton

ST5674

Downs View Guest House, 38 Upper Belgrave Road, Clifton, Bristol, BS8 2XN. Centrally situated. Overlooking Durdham Down. Near Zoo and Clifton Suspension Bridge. **Open:** All year (not Xmas)
0117 973 7046 Ms Cox **Fax: 0117 973 8169**
D: £22.50–£27.50 **S:** £30.00–£35.00 **Beds:** 2F
4D 3T 6S **Baths:** 7 En 2 Sh ⓑ⌷⌦⌶⌷⌦⌶

Westbourne Hotel, 40-44 St Pauls Road, Bristol, BS8 1LR. **Open:** All year
0117 973 4214 Ms Crawshaw **Fax: 0117 974 3552** westbournehotel@bristol8.fsworld.co.uk
www.westbournehotel.bristol.co.uk
D: £32.50–£35.00 **S:** £60.00 **Beds:** 7F 4T 7D
13S **Baths:** 27 En 2 Sh ⓑ⌷(6)⌷⌧⌦⌶⌷cc
The Westbourne surpasses any other for its friendly relaxing atmosphere. Situated in the heart of Clifton, The Westbourne is a listed Georgian building within 3 minutes walk from Bristol University, Clifton Village, Whiteladies Road, with its pubs, clubs and restaurants, the city centre and shopping mall are less than a mile away. Freddies bar/beer garden and restaurant are also on site.

Cotham

ST5874

Arches Hotel, 132 Cotham Brow, Cotham, Bristol, BS6 6AE. Friendly, non-smoking city centre hotel, close to shops and restaurants. **Open:** All year (not Xmas)
0117 924 7398 (also fax) Mr Lambert ml@
arches-hotel.co.uk www.arches-hotel.co.uk
D: £21.50–£25.50 **S:** £24.50–£37.00 **Beds:** 3F
2D 1T 3S **Baths:** 4 En 2 Sh ⓑ(6)⌇⌷⌦⌶
⌷cc

Hambrook

ST6378

The Coach House, Bristol Road, Hambrook, Bristol, BS16 1RY.
Open: All year
Grades: ETC 4
Diamond
0117 956 6901 Mr & Mrs Birkett **Fax: 0117 956 7428** coachhouse.hotel@btinternet.com
D: £20.00–£40.00 **S:** £29.00 **Beds:** 5F 3T 10D
Baths: 15 En 2 Sh ⌷(30)⌇⌷⌦⌶⌶⌷cc
17-bedroom former coaching house with porthole feature windows and delightful views. Outside courtyard and games room. Village conservation area, good walks. Three local inns and restaurant. Close to central Bristol and historic Bath. 1 mile M4 Junction 19.

Horfield

ST5976

Norfolk Guest House, *577 Gloucester Road, Horfield, Bristol, BS7 0BW.* Pleasant Victorian house overlooking parklands & shops. Bus stop 100 yards.
Open: All year
0117 951 3191 (also fax) Mr Thomas
D: £38.00–£45.00 **S:** £20.00–£25.00 **Beds:** 2D 1T **Baths:** 1 En 1 Pr ⊬ 🖾 🖽 🐾

Westbury-on-Trym

ST5677

18 Charlton Road, *Westbury-on-Trym, Bristol, BS10 6NG.* Comfortable quiet house in leafy suburb of Bristol. Non-smoking.
Open: All year (not Xmas/New Year)
0117 950 0490 Mrs Duggan **D:** £18.00
S: £18.00 **Beds:** 1D 1T 1S **Baths:** 1 Sh ➢ 🅿
⊬ 🖾 🖽 🐾

Planning a longer stay? Always ask for any special rates

Buckinghamshire

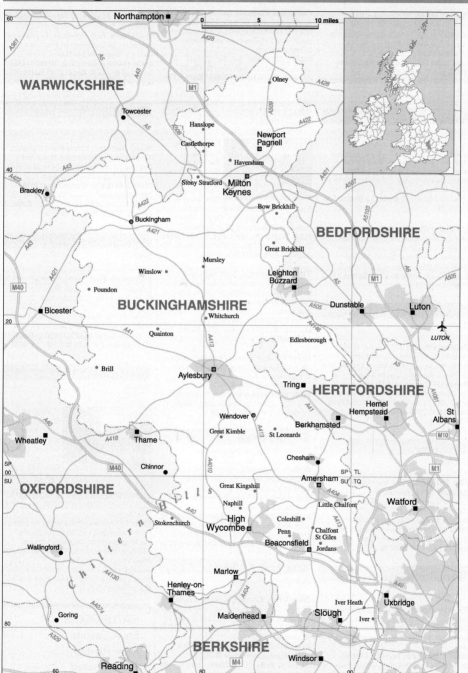

Amersham
SU9698

The Vicarage, *70 Sycamore Road, Amersham, Bucks, HP6 5DR.* Spacious, delightful home. Quiet garden. Station to London 3 minute walk. **Open:** All year (not Xmas/New Year)
01494 729993 Mrs Roderick **Fax: 01494 727553** *philip.roderick@ukonline.co.uk*
D: £24.00 **S:** £30.00 **Beds:** 1T 1S ▢ (6) ⌁ 📺 Ⓥ 🛏, ♨

Aylesbury
SP8113

62 Bierton Road, *Aylesbury, Bucks, HP20 1EJ.* Comfortable Victorian house, family home. Ten minutes from town centre. **Open:** All year (not Xmas/New Year)
01296 427980 Mrs Canover *davidcanover@yahoo.co.uk* **S:** £15.00 **Beds:** 2S **Baths:** 1 Sh ⌁ 📺 Ⓥ 🛏,

331 Tring Road, *Aylesbury, Bucks, HP20 1PJ.* High quality accommodation, spacious, ensuite. Easy parking. Close Aylesbury. Facilities. **Open:** All year
01296 424012 Mrs Mason **D:** £25.00–£27.00 **S:** £26.00–£35.00 **Beds:** 1T 1S **Baths:** 1 En 1 Pr ▢ (2) ⌁ 📺 🛏, ♨

Beaconsfield
SU9390

Beacon House, *113 Maxwell Road, Beaconsfield, Bucks, HP9 1RF.* Extended family house, use of gardens. Easy access London & Windsor. **Open:** All year
01494 672923 (also fax) Mr Dickinson *ben.dickinson@tesco.net* www.beaconhouse.org.uk **D:** £19.00–£22.50 **S:** £25.00–£35.00 **Beds:** 1D 1T 2S **Baths:** 2 En 1 Sh ⌁ (6) ▢ (5) ⌁ 📺 Ⓥ 🛏, ♨

Bletchley
SP8534

The Townhouse, *3 Westfield Road, Bletchley, Milton Keynes, Bucks, MK2 2RR.* Comfortable town house, centre of Bletchley, close to station and Milton Keynes. **Open:** All year (not Xmas)
01908 368713 (also fax) Mrs Friedman **D:** £25.00–£28.00 **S:** £28.00 **Beds:** 1T 3S **Baths:** 1 En 1 Sh ⌁ 📺 🛏, ♨

Bow Brickhill
SP9034

Plough House, *Church Road, Bow Brickhill, Milton Keynes, Bucks, MK17 9LH.* Georgian house, adjoining Woburn estates, woodland, 5 miles Milton Keynes. **Open:** All year
01908 372097 (also fax) Mrs Drabble **D:** £25.00–£30.00 **S:** £25.00–£30.00 **Beds:** 1D 1S **Baths:** 1 Sh ⌁ (10) ▢ (2) 📺 🛏 ✕ 🛏, ♨

Brill
SP6513

Poletrees Farm, *Ludgershall Road, Brill, Aylesbury, Bucks, HP18 9TZ.* Historical oak-beamed farm house with lovely garden for guests to sit in. **Open:** All year **Grades:** ETC 3 Diamond
01844 238276 (also fax) Mrs Cooper www.travel/uk.net/poletrees **D:** £26.00–£30.00 **S:** £30.00 **Beds:** 1F 2D 1T **Baths:** 1 En 1 Sh ⌁ ▢ (50) ⌁ 📺 ✕ Ⓥ 🛏, ♨ ♨

Buckingham
SP6933

Folly Farm, *Padbury, Buckingham, Bucks, MK18 2HS.* Substantial Victorian farmhouse set in open countryside between market towns of Buckingham & Winslow. **Open:** All year (not Xmas) **Grades:** ETC 3 Diamond
01296 712413 Mrs Webb **Fax: 01296 714923** **D:** £20.00–£25.00 **S:** £22.50–£25.00 **Beds:** 3D **Baths:** 3 En ▢ (6) ⌁ 📺 ✕ Ⓥ 🛏, ♨

The Hall Farm, *Lillingstone Lovell, Buckingham, Bucks, MK18 5BL.* Spacious farmhouse, rural setting M1, M40, Intercity railway within easy reach. **Open:** All year (not Xmas)
01280 860665 (also fax) Mrs Culley **D:** £18.00 **S:** £18.00 **Beds:** 1D 2T **Baths:** 3 Pr 1 Sh ⌁ ▢ (6) 📺 ♨

River View, *97 Fishers Field, Buckingham, MK18 1SF.* Elegant riverside town house. Convenient for town centre, Stowe, Claydon. **Open:** All year
01280 821265 (also fax) Mrs Dunnington **D:** £19.00–£21.00 **S:** £25.00–£27.00 **Beds:** 1T 1D **Baths:** 2 Pr ▢ (2) ⌁ 📺 🛏,

Castlethorpe
SP7944   🍺 *Globe Inn, Navigation Inn*

Balney Grounds, *Hanslope Road, Castlethorpe, Milton Keynes, Bucks, MK19 7HD.* Converted barn in open countryside 15 minutes from central Milton Keynes. **Open:** All year
01908 510208 Mrs Stacey **Fax: 01908 516119** *mary.stacey@tesco.net* www.lets-stay-mk.co.uk **D:** £25.00–£30.00 **S:** £25.00–£35.00 **Beds:** 1T 2D 1S **Baths:** 4 En ⌁ ▢ (10) ⌁ 📺 🛏 ⌁ Ⓥ 🛏, ♨

Chalfont St Giles
SU9893

Gorelands Corner, *Gorelands Lane, Chalfont St Giles, Bucks, HP8 4HQ.* Family house set in large garden. Easy access to motorways. **Open:** All year **Grades:** ETC 3 Diamond
01494 872689 (also fax) Mrs Bickford *bickfordcsg@compuserve.com* **D:** £27.50 **S:** £22.50 **Beds:** 1D 1S **Baths:** 1 En 1 Pr ⌁ ▢ (3) ⌁ 📺 🛏, ♨

Chesham
SP9601

May Tree House, *32 Hampden Avenue, Chesham, Bucks., HP5 2HL.* Comfortable family home, high standards. Courtesy car to station, pick-up/drop-off Heathrow, Gatwick. **Open:** Feb to Nov
01494 784019 A Bartle **Fax: 01494 776896** **D:** £28.00 **S:** £34.00 **Beds:** 2T 2S **Baths:** 4 En ▢ (3) ⌁ 📺 Ⓥ 🛏, ♨

Coleshill
SU9595

Pond Cottage, *Village Road, Coleshill, Amersham, Bucks, HP7 0LH.* Delightful beamed C17th listed cottage in peaceful Chiltern village. **Open:** All year
01494 728177 Mrs Wayland **Fax: 01494 729168** *pondcott@msn.com* **D:** £22.50–£27.50 **S:** £35.00–£45.00 **Beds:** 1F 3D/T 1S **Baths:** 1 En 2 Pr 1 Sh ⌁ ▢ (5) ⌁ 📺 🛏, ♨

Edlesborough
SP9719

Ridgeway End, *5 Ivinghoe Way, Edlesborough, Dunstable, Beds, LU6 2EL.* Pretty bungalow in private road, surrounded by fields and views of the Chiltern Hills. **Open:** All year (not Xmas)
01525 220405 (also fax) Mrs Lloyd **D:** £25.00–£28.00 **S:** £25.00–£28.00 **Beds:** 1F 1D 1T **Baths:** 2 En 1 Pr ⌁ (2) ▢ (3) ⌁ 📺 🛏, ♨

Great Brickhill
SP9030

Partridge House, *3 Locks Gold Club, Great Brickhill, Milton Keynes, Bucks, MK17 9BH.* **Open:** All year (not Xmas/New Year)
01525 270470 (also fax) **D:** £40.00–£47.00 **S:** £65.00–£80.00 **Beds:** 2T 1D **Baths:** 3 En ▢ ⌁ 📺 🛏, ♨ cc
Perfectly situated for exploring the many tourist attractions of Bedfordshire and Buckinghamshire, including Woburn Abbey and Safari Park, Whipsnade Zoo and Milton Keynes. Comfortable accommodation within a parkland golf course setting situated alongside The Grand Union Canal.

BATHROOMS
En = Ensuite
Pr = Private
Sh = Shared

Great Kimble
SP8205

The Swan, *Grave Lane, Great Kimble, Aylesbury, HP17 9TR.* Friendly Real Ale country inn close to historic Ridgeway walk. **Open:** All year
01844 275288 Mr Woolnough **Fax: 01494 837312 D:** £25.00–£35.00 **S:** £35.00–£45.00 **Beds:** 1F 2T 1D **Baths:** 4 En ⟳🅿(25) 📺 🛏 ✕ 📺 📖 🛴 **cc**

Great Kingshill
SU8798

Hatches Farm, *Hatches Lane, Great Kingshill, High Wycombe, Bucks, HP15 6DS.* Quiet, comfortable farmhouse. Rooms overlooking garden. Easy reach of Oxford/Windsor. **Open:** All year (not Xmas) **Grades:** ETC 2 Diamond
01494 713125 Mrs Davies **Fax: 01494 714666 D:** £16.50–£17.50 **S:** £22.00 **Beds:** 1D 1T **Baths:** 1 Sh ⟳(12) 🅿(6) 📖

Hanslope
SP8046

Woad Farm, *Tathall End, Hanslope, Milton Keynes, Bucks, MK19 7NE.* Situated on edge of village, large garden, tennis court. Milton Keynes & Northampton accessible. **Open:** All year
01908 510985 (also fax) Mr & Mrs Stacey *mail@srahstacey.freeserve.co.uk* **D:** £22.00–£24.00 **S:** £22.00–£25.00 **Beds:** 2D 1T **Baths:** 3 Sh ⟳🅿✄📺🛏✕📺📖🛴

Haversham
SP8243

The Bungalow, *The Crescent, Haversham, Milton Keynes, Bucks., MK19 7AW.* Village location within six minutes drive from central Milton Keynes. **Open:** All year
01908 311883 D: £18.00–£20.00 **S:** £18.00–£20.00 **Beds:** 2F 1T 1S 🅿(2) 📺 📖 🛴

High Wycombe
SU8693

Harfa House, *Station Road, High Wycombe, Bucks, HP13 6AD.* **Open:** All year **01494 529671 & 07956 984321 (M)** Mrs Foster-Brown **Fax: 01494 529671** *irena@harfahouse.co.uk* www.harfahouse.co.uk **D:** £15.00–£20.00 **S:** £15.00–£25.00 **Beds:** 1T 2S **Baths:** 1 Sh 📺 📖 🛴 Private, self-contained annexe to Victorian house. Comfortable, pleasant rooms with fridge and microwave. Convenient for town centre, bus, railway stations. 30 minutes to London. Excellent location for touring lovely English countryside, Marlow, Oxford, Henley, Windsor. Good pubs, restaurants nearby.

Iver Heath
TQ0282

Oaklands, *Bangors Road South, Iver Heath, Slough, Bucks, SL10 0BB.* Large family house convenient for Heathrow, Windsor, Uxbridge and Slough. **Open:** All year (not Xmas)
01753 653005 Mrs Fowler **Fax: 01753 653003 D:** £20.00 **S:** £20.00–£25.00 **Beds:** 1F 1D 2T 1S **Baths:** 1 En 2 Sh 🅿(4) ✄ 📺 📖 🛴

Jordans
SU9791

Old Jordans, *Jordans Lane, Jordans, Beaconsfield, Buckinghamshire, HP9 2SW.* Historic venue in large grounds. Traditional food and excellent hospitality. **Open:** All year **Grades:** ETC 3 Diamond
01494 874586 Fax: 01494 875657 *reception@oldjordans.org.uk* oldjordans.org.uk **D:** £25.00–£31.00 **S:** £31.00–£49.00 **Beds:** 1F 3T 9D 11S **Baths:** 15 En 4 Sh ⟳🅿✕📺📖♿❋ 🛴 **cc**

Little Chalfont
SU9997

Holmdale, *Cokes Lane, Little Chalfont, Chalfont St. Giles, Amersham, HP8 4TX.* Comfortable cottage in the Chilterns; easy access to London on trains. **Open:** All year **Grades:** ETC 4 Diamond
01494 762527 Fax: 01494 764701 *judy@holmdalebb.freeserve.co.uk* www.smoothhound.co.uk/hotels/holmdale.html **D:** £30.00–£35.00 **S:** £45.00–£50.00 **Beds:** 1D/F 1T 1S **Baths:** 3 En ⟳🅿(2) ✄ 📺 📺 📖 🛴

Marlow
SU8586 🐴 *Ploughland Marlow Donkey*

Merrie Hollow, *Seymour Court Hill, Marlow, Bucks, SL7 3DE.* **Open:** All year **Grades:** ETC 3 Diamond
01628 485663 (also fax) Mr Wells **D:** £20.00–£25.00 **S:** £25.00–£35.00 **Beds:** 1D 1T **Baths:** 1 Sh ⟳🅿(4) ✄ 📺 🛏 ✕ 📺 📖 🛴 Secluded quiet country cottage in large garden 150 yds off B482 Marlow to Stokenchurch road, easy access to M4 and M25, 35 mins from Heathrow and Oxford, private off-road car parking.

Acha Pani, *Bovingdon Green, Marlow, Bucks, SL7 2JL.* Quiet location, easy access Thames Footpath, Chilterns, Windsor, London, Heathrow. **Open:** All year **01628 483435 (also fax)** Mrs Cowling *mary@achapani.freeserve.co.uk* **D:** £18.00 **S:** £18.00 **Beds:** 1D 1T 1S **Baths:** 1 En 1 Sh ⟳(10)🅿(3) 📺 🛏 ✕ 📺 📖 🛴

16 Claremont Road, *Marlow, Bucks, SL7 1BW.* Delightful detached house, 3 minute walk from central Marlow and train. **Open:** All year **Grades:** ETC 4 Star **01628 471334** Mrs Peperell *sue@gladeend.com* www.gladeend.com **D:** £30.00–£40.00 **S:** £30.00–£50.00 **Beds:** 1F 2T 3D 1S **Baths:** 1 Sh ⟳(10) 🅿(7) ✄ 📺 📖 🛴

Sunnyside, *Munday Dean, Marlow, Bucks, SL7 3BU.* Comfortable, friendly, family home in Area of Outstanding Natural Beauty. **Open:** All year **01628 485701** Mrs O'Connor *ruthandtom@tinyworld.co.uk* **D:** £17.50 **S:** £20.00 **Beds:** 2D 1T **Baths:** 1 Sh ⟳🅿(5) ✄ 📺

Sneppen House, *Henley Road, Marlow, Bucks, SL7 2DF.* Within walking distance of town centre & river. Breakfast menu choice. Pub food nearby. **Open:** All year **01628 485227** Mr Norris **D:** £22.50 **S:** £30.00 **Beds:** 1D 1T **Baths:** 1 Sh ⟳(2)🅿(3) 📺 📖 🛴

Milton Keynes
SP8636

Kingfishers, *9 Rylstone Close, Heelands, Milton Keynes, Bucks, MK13 7QT.* Modern luxurious house. Near central Milton Keynes and station. **Open:** All year **01908 310231** Mrs Botterill **Fax: 01908 318601** *sheila-derek@m-keynes.freeserve.co.uk* **D:** £20.00 **S:** £23.00–£28.00 **Beds:** 1F 1D 1S **Baths:** 2 En 1 Pr ⟳(2)🅿(4) 📺 🛏 ✕ 📖 🛴

Furtho Manor Farm, *Old Stratford, Milton Keynes, Bucks, MK19 6BA.* Dairy and arable farm, 10 mins to central Milton Keynes. **Open:** All year (not Xmas) **01908 542139 (also fax)** Mrs Sansome **D:** £20.00–£22.00 **S:** £20.00–£25.00 **Beds:** 1D 2T **Baths:** 2 Sh ⟳🅿(6) 📺 📺 📖 ♿ 🛴

Mill Farm, *Gayhurst, Newport Pagnell, Bucks, MK16 8LT.* C17th farmhouse on working farm. Fishing and hard tennis court available. **Open:** All year **Grades:** ETC 3 Diamond, AA 3 Diamond **01908 611489 (also fax)** K Adams *adamsmillfarm@aol.com* **D:** £20.00–£25.00 **S:** £20.00–£25.00 **Beds:** 1F 2T 1D 1S **Baths:** 5 En ⟳🅿✄📺🛏📖🛴

Rovers Return, *49 Langcliffe Drive, Milton Keynes, Bucks, MK13 7LA.* Warm welcoming modern chalet-type house in tree-lined courtyard adjacent to Redway Cycle Track. **Open:** All year (not Xmas/New Year) **01908 310465** E Levins **D:** £20.00–£25.00 **S:** £23.00–£25.00 **Beds:** 1T 1S 1D **Baths:** 2 Sh ⟳(10) ✄ 📺 📺 📖 🛴

B&B owners may vary rates – be sure to check when booking

Mursley

SP8128   ⚑ *Swan Inn, Green Man*

Richmond Hill Farm, *Stewkley Lane, Mursley, Milton Keynes, Bucks, MK17 0JD.* Spacious, tranquil setting room overlooking landscaped gardens. 8 miles from the M1. **Open:** All year **Grades:** ETC 3 Diamond
01296 720385 (also fax) S J Oldham
D: £25.00 **S:** £25.00–£28.00 **Beds:** 2T
Baths: 2 Pr ⌖ 🛏 🖭 (10) ⚲ 🛏 🖭 🖭 ♨

Naphill

SU8596

Wood-peckers, *244 Main Road, Naphill, High Wycombe, Bucks, HP14 4CX.* **Open:** All year
Grades: ETC 3 Diamond
01494 563728 Mrs Brand *angela.brand@virgin.net* www.visitbritain.com **D:** £23.50–£25.00 **S:** £25.00 **Beds:** 1T 1D 1S **Baths:** 2 En 1 Pr ⌖ 🖭 (4) 🖭 🖭 ♨
Fully modernised cottage in heart of Chiltern Hills. Close to London, Windsor, Henley, Oxford, Heathrow, good public transport. Wonderful walks and scenery with places of historic interest nearby. Also can be rented as self-catering unit (6-8 people, prices on request).

Newport Pagnell

SP8743   ⚑ *Chester Arms*

Rectory Farm, *North Crawley, Newport Pagnell, Bucks, MK16 9HH.* Warm welcome on family farm. Convenient for Milton Keynes & Bedfordshire. **Open:** All year
Grades: ETC 3 Diamond
01234 391213 E Hobbs **D:** £20.00 **S:** £20.00–£25.00 **Beds:** 1T 1D **Baths:** 1 Sh ⌖ (7) 🖭 (4) ⚲ 🖭 🖭

Mill Farm, *Gayhurst, Newport Pagnell, Bucks, MK16 8LT.* C17th farmhouse on working farm. Fishing and hard tennis court available. **Open:** All year **Grades:** ETC 3 Diamond, AA 3 Diamond
01908 611489 (also fax) K Adams
adamsmillfarm@aol.com **D:** £20.00–£25.00 **S:** £20.00–£25.00 **Beds:** 1F 2T 1D 1S
Baths: 5 En ⌖ 🖭 ⚲ 🖭 🖭 ♨

The Clitheroes, *5 Walnut Close, Newport Pagnell, Bucks, MK16 8JH.* Homely atmosphere, comfortable rooms, full English breakfast, off road parking.
Open: All year (not Xmas) **Grades:** ETC 2 Diamond
01908 611643 (also fax) *shirleyderek.clitheroe@btinternet.com* **D:** £19.00 **S:** £22.00 **Beds:** 1D 1T 2 S **Baths:** 2 Sh ⌖ 🖭 (5) 🖭 🖭 ♨

Olney

SP8851

Colchester House, *26 High Street, Olney, Bucks, MK46 4BB.* Georgian town house in market town near pubs and restaurants. **Open:** All year (not Xmas)
01234 712602 Fax: 01234 240564
blenkinsops@compuserve.com **D:** £25.00
S: £25.00 **Beds:** 2D 1T **Baths:** 2 En 1 Sh 🖭 (4)
⚲ 🖭 🖭 ♨

Penn

SU9293

Little Penn Farmhouse, *Penn Bottom, Penn, High Wycombe, Bucks, HP10 8PJ.* Character family house with beautiful garden surrounded by picturesque countryside. **Open:** All year (not Xmas) **Grades:** ETC 4 Diamond
01494 813439 Mrs Harris **Fax:** 01494 817740
sally@saundersharris.co.uk **D:** £24.00 **S:** £35.00
Beds: 1D **Baths:** 1 En 🖭 (4) ⚲ 🖭 🖭 ♨

Poundon

SP6425

Manor Farm, *Poundon, Bicester, Oxon, OX6 0BB.* Extremely comfortable and welcoming. Delicious breakfasts and lovely surroundings.
Open: All year (not Xmas)
01869 277212 Mrs Collett **Fax:** 01869 277166
D: £23.00–£25.00 **S:** £25.00–£30.00 **Beds:** 1F
1D 1S **Baths:** 2 Sh ⌖ 🖭 (10) ⚲ 🖭 🖭 ♨

Quainton

SP7419

Woodlands Farmhouse, *Edgcott Road, Quainton, Aylesbury, Bucks, HP22 4DE.* C18th farmhouse offering peaceful accommodation in 11 acres of ground.
Open: All year
01296 770225 Mrs Creed **D:** £25.00–£30.00
S: £25.00–£30.00 **Beds:** 1f 2T 1D **Baths:** 4
En ⌖ 🖭 (10) ⚲ 🖭 🖭 ♨ ♨

St Leonards

SP9006

Field Cottage, *St Leonards, Tring, Herts, HP23 6NS.* Pretty secluded cottage near the Ridgeway & convenient for Wendover, Chesham & Great Missenden. **Open:** All year (not Xmas/New Year)
01494 837602 Mr & Mrs Jepson **D:** £25.00–£30.00 **S:** £25.00–£35.00 **Beds:** 1D 1T 1S
⌖ (12) 🖭 (4) ⚲ 🖭 🖭 ♨

Stokenchurch

SU7695

Gibbons Farm, *Bigmore Lane, Stokenchurch, High Wycombe, Bucks, HP14 3UR.* **Open:** All year
01494 482385 Mrs McKelvey **Fax:** 01494 485400 **D:** £25.00–£30.00 **S:** £25.00–£30.00
Beds: 2F 1D 1T 4S **Baths:** 6 En 1 Sh ⌖ 🖭 (20)
🖭 🖭 ♨ ♨
Traditional farm offering accommodation in converted barn. Set in courtyard surrounded by open countryside, this family-run B&B offers a warm and friendly welcome with Marlow and Oxford within half-hour drive, situated within 5 mins of M40, London is easily accessible.

Stony Stratford

SP7940

Fegans View, *119 High Street, Stony Stratford, Milton Keynes, Bucks, MK11 1AT.* C18th comfortable town house near local amenities. **Open:** All year
01908 562128 & 01908 564246 Mrs Levitt
D: £18.00–£20.00 **S:** £22.00–£27.00 **Beds:** 3T
1S **Baths:** 1 En 2 Sh ⌖ (1) 🖭 (5) 🖭 🖭 ♨

Wendover

SP8608

46 Lionel Avenue, *Wendover, Aylesbury, Bucks, HP22 6LP.* Family home. Lounge, conservatory, garden. English/vegetarian breakfasts. Tea/coffee always available.
Open: All year (not Xmas/New Year)
Grades: ETC 3 Diamond
01296 623426 Mr & Mrs MacDonald
D: £24.00 **S:** £25.00 **Beds:** 1T 2S **Baths:** 1 Sh
⌖ 🖭 (3) ⚲ 🖭 🛏 🖭

Whitchurch

SP8020

3 Little London, *Whitchurch, Aylesbury, Bucks, HP22 4LE.* Quiet location near Waddesdon Manor; 1 hour London, Stratford. **Open:** All year (not Xmas)
01296 641409 Mrs Gurr **D:** £20.00 **S:** £20.00
Beds: 1D 1T 1S **Baths:** 2 Sh 🖭 (3) ⚲ 🖭 🖭 ♨

Winslow

SP7627

Tuckey Farm, *Winslow, Buckingham, Bucks, MK18 3ND.* C18th farmhouse, convenient for Stowe, Waddesdon Manor, Claydon House, Silverstone. **Open:** All year (not Xmas)
01296 713208 Mrs Haynes **D:** £20.00
S: £20.00 **Beds:** 1T 2S **Baths:** 1 Sh ⌖ (5)
🖭 (4) 🖭 🖭 ♨

The Congregational Church, *15 Horn Street, Winslow, Buckingham, MK18 3AP.* Victorian church turned into fascinating home in old town centre. **Open:** All year **Grades:** ETC 3 Diamond
01296 715717 (also fax) Mrs Hood **D:** £22.50 **S:** £30.00 **Beds:** 1D 1T 1S **Baths:** 2 Sh 📺 Ⓥ ⏸, ♨

The White Cottage, *Verney Junction, Buckingham, MK18 2JZ.* Lovely country house in small hamlet. Super breakfasts, log fires. **Open:** Jan to Dec **Grades:** ETC 3 Diamond
01296 714416 Mrs Gilchrist **D:** £20.00 **S:** £20.00 **Beds:** 2D 1S **Baths:** 1 Sh 🅿 (3) 📺 ✕ Ⓥ ⏸, ♨

BEDROOMS
D = Double
T = Twin
S = Single
F = Family

Cambridgeshire

Abbotsley

TL2256

Rectory Farm, *High Street, Abbotsley, St Neots, Cambs, PE19 6UE.* **Open:** All year (not Xmas)
01767 677282 (also fax) Mr Hipwell
D: £20.00 **S:** £20.00 **Beds:** 1D 2T 1S **Baths:** 1 Sh (6)
Quiet Victorian farm house. Large gardens and ample private parking. Short stroll from centre of picturesque village with local pubs serving good food. Local countryside walks. Cambridge, Bedford, Huntingdon 30 mins drive; London 1 hour by train from St. Neots.

Balsham

TL5849

The Garden End, *10 West Wratting Road, Balsham, Cambridge, CB1 6DX.* Self-contained ground floor suite - children / pets welcome all year. **Open:** All year
01223 894021 (also fax) Mrs Greenaway
D: £18.00 **S:** £20.00 **Beds:** 1F **Baths:** 1 En 1 Pr (2)

Barham

TL1374

Ye Olde Globe and Chequers, *The Village, Barham, Huntingdon, Cambs, PE28 5AB.* **Open:** All year (not Xmas/New Year)
01480 890247 & 07860 268524 (M) Mrs Grove-Price *cheryll@globeandchequers.fsnet.co.uk*
www.globeandchequers.fsnet.co.uk
D: £21.00–£22.50 **S:** £28.00–£32.00 **Beds:** 1F 1T 1D **Baths:** 1 En 1 Sh (3)
Former Victorian village inn offering true country hospitality in idyllic rural setting. Tastefully furnished rooms with excellent facilities. Easy access A1/A14 via Junction 18. Ideally situated for Cambridge, Ely, Huntingdon, Northampton, Thrapston, Peterborough. With Grafham Water closeby. Colour brochure available.

Barway

TL5375

The Manor House, *Barway, Ely, Cambs, CB7 5UB.* Rural location near Ely and Newmarket. Generous breakfast. Large garden. **Open:** All year (not Xmas/New Year)
07968 654640 (M) Mr & Mrs Rose *boxer1@dialstart.net* **D:** £20.00 **S:** £25.00 **Beds:** 1T 1D **Baths:** 1 En 1 Pr (1) (4)

Bottisham

TL5460

27 Beechwood Avenue, *Bottisham, Cambridge, CB5 9BG.* Modern house backing farmland near Cambridge city and Newmarket racecourse. **Open:** All year (not Xmas)
01223 811493 Mrs Knight **Fax: 0870 1312396** *mike.knight@home.cam.net.uk* **D:** £22.50–£25.00 **S:** £25.00 **Beds:** 1D 2T 1S **Baths:** 1 Sh (12) (3)

Cambridge

TL4658 *Boat House*

Arbury Lodge, *82 Arbury Road, Cambridge, CB42JE.* **Open:** All year (not Xmas/ New Year)
Grades: ETC 3 Diamond
01223 364319 A J Celentano **Fax: 01223 566988** *arburylodge@ntlworld.com*
www.guesthousecambridge.com **D:** £23.00–£60.00 **S:** £30.00–£50.00 **Beds:** 1F 2T 3D 1S **Baths:** 4 En 3 Sh (8)
A comfortable family-run guest house where we pride ourselves is offering excellent service, good home cooking, cleanliness and a friendly atmosphere. We are conveniently situated about 1.5 miles north of the city centre with easy access to A14/M11.

Victoria B&B, *57 Arbury Road, Cambridge, CB4 2JB.* **Open:** All year **01223 350086 & 07803 906619 (M)** Mrs Fasano **Fax: 01223 350086**
vicmaria@globalnet.co.uk
www.victoriaguesthouse.co.uk **D:** £19.00–£30.00 **S:** £22.00–£49.00 **Beds:** 1F 1D 1T **Baths:** 1 En 1 Pr 1 Sh (4) cc
Victorian house - all rooms have TV, tea and coffee making facilities, ensuite private or shared facilities. Ideally situated for city centre, colleges and River Cam. Easy access to A14 and M11. Self-catering apartments also available.

Ashtrees Guest House, *128 Perne Road, Cambridge, Cambs, CB1 3RR.* Comfortable suburban residence with garden. Good bus to city centre. **Open:** Jan to Jan **Grades:** ETC 3 Diamond
01223 411233 (also fax) Mrs Hill **D:** £20.00–£23.00 **S:** £22.00–£38.00 **Beds:** 1F 3D 1T 2S **Baths:** 3 En 1 Sh (6) cc

Tudor Cottage, *292 Histon Road, Cambridge, CB4 3HF.* **Open:** All year **01223 565212 & 07775 667512 (M)**
Mrs Celentano **Fax: 01223 565660**
tudor.cottage@ntlworld.com **D:** £25.00–£30.00 **S:** £30.00–£35.00 **Beds:** 1D 1S **Baths:** 1 En 1 Sh (4)
Comfortable friendly Tudor style cottage situated within walking distance of city centre and colleges. Ensuite or shared facilities, central heating, colour TV, tea/coffee making facilities, excellent food and friendly personal service, off street parking easy access to A14/M11.

Dykelands Guest House, *157 Mowbray Road, Cambridge, CB1 7SP.* **Open:** All year **Grades:** ETC 3 Diamond, AA 3 Diamond
01223 244300 Ms Tweddell **Fax: 01223 566746** *dykelands@fsbdial.co.uk*
www.dykelands.com **D:** £18.50–£24.00 **S:** £28.00–£30.00 **Beds:** 3F 3D 2T 1S **Baths:** 7 En 1 Sh (6) cc
Lovely detached guest house on south side of city. Easy access from M11 and A14, yet only 1.75 miles from historic city centre. Private parking. Spacious, well furnished, comfortable rooms, 2 on ground floor, most ensuite. Good breakfasts, English/ vegetarian.

Home From Home, *78-80 Milton Road, Cambridge, Cambs, CB4 1LA.* Centrally located with access M11, A14 and Science Park.
Open: All year
01223 323555 & 07740 594306 (M)
Mrs Fasano **Fax: 01223 563509**
homefromhome@tesco.net
www.accommodationcambridge.co.uk
D: £25.00–£30.00 **S:** £40.00–£50.00 **Beds:** 1F 2D 1T **Baths:** 3 En 1 Pr (5) cc

Hamden Guest House, *89 High Street, Cherry Hinton, Cambridge, CB1 9LU.* High standard of bed & breakfast accommodation. All rooms with ensuite shower. **Open:** All year **Grades:** ETC 3 Diamond
01223 413263 Mr Casciano **Fax: 01223 245960** **D:** £25.00 **S:** £35.00 **Beds:** 1F 2D 1T 1S **Baths:** 5 En (10) (7) cc

Cristinas Guest House,
47 St Andrews Road, Cambridge, *CB4 1DH.* Quiet location, 15 minutes' walk from city centre. Hairdryers. Radio alarm clocks. **Open:** All year (not Xmas) **Grades:** ETC 3 Diamond, AA 3 Diamond **01223 365855 & 01223 327700** Mrs Celentano **Fax: 01223 365855** *Cristinas.guesthouse@ ntlworld.com* **D:** £25.00–£28.00 **S:** £37.00 **Beds:** 1F 4D 4T **Baths:** 7 En 2 Sh ⌂ 🄿 (8) 📺 ▥ 🚳2 🛉

Carolina Bed and Breakfast,
148 Perne Road, Cambridge, *CB1 3NX.* 1930's building located in a nice residential area. **Open:** All year **Grades:** ETC 3 Diamond **01223 247015 & 07771 683424 (M)** Mrs Amabile **Fax:** 01223 247015 *carolina.amabile@tesco.net* www.smoothhound. co.uk/hotels/carol/html **D:** £25.00–£30.00 **S:** £28.00 **Beds:** 1D 1T **Baths:** 2 En ⌂ 🄿 (3) ⌿ 📺 ✕ ▥ 🛉 cc

Double Two,
22 St Margarets Road, Cambridge, *CB3 0LT.* By Girton College, 1 1/2 miles Cambridge centre, near M11/A14. **Open:** All year (not Xmas/New Year) **01223 276103 (also fax)** C Noble *carol.noble@ ntlworld.com* **D:** £24.00–£26.00 **S:** £35.00– £50.00 **Beds:** 2T 1D **Baths:** 2 En 1 Sh 🄿 (2) ⌿ 📺 🐾 ▥ 🛉

El Shaddai,
41 Warkworth Street, Cambridge, Cambs, *CB1 1EG.* Centrally located, within a ten minute walk to colleges, shops and other social amenities. **Open:** All year **01223 327978** Mrs Droy **Fax: 01223 501024** *pauline@droy.freeserve.co.uk* www.droy. freeserve.co.uk **D:** £20.00–£22.50 **S:** £23.00– £25.00 **Beds:** 1F 1D 2T 1S **Baths:** 1 Sh ⌂ ⌿ 📺 ▥ 🛉

Cam Guest House,
17 Elizabeth Way, Cambridge, *CB4 1DD.* 15 mins' walk to city centre, 5 mins' to Grafton shopping centre. **Open:** All year (not Xmas/New Year) **01223 354512 Fax: 01223 353164** *camguesthouse@btinternet.com* **D:** £21.00– £30.00 **S:** £30.00 **Beds:** 3F 3D 4S **Baths:** 2 En 3 Sh ⌂ 🄿 (5) ⌿ 📺 ▥ 🛉

Castor
TL1297

Cobnut Cottage,
45 Peterborough Road, Castor, Peterborough, *PE5 7AX.* **Open:** All year **Grades:** ETC 4 Diamond **01733 380745 (also fax)** Mrs Huckle *huckle.cobnut@talk21.com* **D:** £21.00–£25.00 **S:** £27.00–£31.00 **Beds:** 1F 1T 2D **Baths:** 2 En 1 Sh ⌂ (4) 🄿 (6) ⌿ 📺 ▥ 🛉 Listed stone house close to cathedral city of Peterborough and historic Stamford. Near country park for walking, cycling, fishing, sailing, golf, self-catering cottage sleeps four available (weekly lets), all in 2/3 acre mature garden with summer house for guests' use.

Cherry Hinton
TL4855

Hamden Guest House,
89 High Street, Cherry Hinton, Cambridge, *CB1 9LU.* High standard of bed & breakfast accommodation. All rooms with ensuite shower. **Open:** All year **Grades:** ETC 3 Diamond **01223 413263** Mr Casciano **Fax: 01223 245960 D:** £25.00 **S:** £35.00 **Beds:** 1F 2D 1T 1S **Baths:** 5 En ⌂ (10) 🄿 (7) ⌿ 📺 ▥ 🛉 cc

Church End (Cambridge)
TL4856

The Ark,
30 St Matthews Street, Cambridge, *CB1 2LT.* Centrally situated. Rail/ coach stations, cinema, restaurants, shops nearby. Landlady speaks German/Spanish/ French. **Open:** All year (not Xmas/New Year) **01223 311130** Alexander Bartow Wylie *bartow.wylie@iscs.org.uk* **D:** £18.00–£22.00 **Beds:** 1T 1D **Baths:** 1 Sh ⌂ (10) ⌿ 📺 🛉

Comberton
TL3856   🍺 *Three Horseshoes*

White Horse Cottage,
28 West Street, Comberton, Cambridge, *CB3 7DS.* Restored C17th cottage near Cambridge. Pretty garden, many local attractions. **Open:** All year **01223 262914** J Wright **D:** £22.00–£35.00 **Beds:** 1F 1D ⌂ 🄿 (3) ⌿ 📺 ▥ 🛉

Coton
TL4058

Woodpeckers,
57-61 The Footpath, Coton, Cambridge, *CB3 7PX.* Modern house, quiet village. Close to Cambridge and nearby attractions. **Open:** All **01954 210455 & 07850 060688 (M)** J Young **Fax: 01954 210733** *roy@ woodpeckers61.freeserve.co.uk* **D:** £40.00–£45.00 **S:** £30.00–£33.00 **Beds:** 1T 2D **Baths:** 1 En 1 Pr 1 Sh 🄿 (4) ⌿ 📺 ▥ 🛉

Cottenham
TL4467   🍺 *Hopbind, Jolly Miller*

Denmark House,
58 Denmark Road, Cottenham, Cambridge, *CB4 8QS.* Delightful detached residence in village 6 miles Cambridge. Also self-catering. **Open:** All year **Grades:** ETC 4 Star **01954 251060 & 01954 251629** Mrs Whittaker **Fax: 01954 251629** *denmark@ house33.fsnet.co.uk* www.denmarkhouse.fsnet. co.uk **D:** £23.00–£29.00 **Beds:** 2D 1T **Baths:** 3 En ⌂ 🄿 (3) ⌿ 📺 ▥ 🛉

Dullingham
TL6257

The Old School,
Dullingham, Newmarket, Suffolk, *CB8 9XF.* Attractive conversion, spacious rooms, delightful village, nearby pub serves food. **Open:** All year **01638 507813** Mrs Andrews **Fax: 01638 507022** *gill.andrews@premeirhoildays.co.uk* **D:** £23.00–£25.00 **Beds:** 1D **Baths:** 1 En ⌂ 🄿 (2) ⌿ 📺 ▥ 🛉

Eaton Ford
TL1759

Home From Home,
1 Laxton Close, Ean Ford, St Neots, Cambs, *PE19 3AR.* Friendly family house, tea/coffee served. Ten minutes walk town. **Open:** All year **01480 383677 & 07974 969257 (M)** Mrs Francis-Macrae **Fax: 01480 383677** *gillmacrae@cheerful.com* **D:** £20.00–£22.00 **S:** £16.00–£18.00 **Beds:** 1D 1S **Baths:** 1 Sh ⌂ 🄿 (2) ⌿ 📺 🐾 ▥

Eaton Socon
TL1758

North Laurels House,
206 Great North Road, Eaton Socon, St Neots, Cambs, *PE19 8EF.* Comfortable and well presented Georgian family home. **Open:** All year **01480 385086** *jeffval@supanet.net* **D:** £20.00– £28.00 **S:** £20.00–£28.00 **Beds:** 1F 1T 1S **Baths:** 1 En 1 Sh ⌂ 🄿 (3) ⌿ 📺 ▥ 🛉

Ellington
TL1671

Grove Cottage,
Malting Lane, Ellington, Huntingdon, *PE28 0AA.* Peaceful, relaxing, self-contained suite in charming comfortable period cottage. **Open:** All year **01480 890167 (also fax)** Mr Silver *hr73@ dial.pipex.com* **D:** £20.00–£22.50 **S:** £27.50– £30.00 **Beds:** 1D **Baths:** 1 En ⌂ 🄿 (2) ⌿ ▥ 🛉

Elm
TF4606

Elm Manor,
Main Road, Elm, Wisbech, Cambs, *PE14 0AG.* Charles II manor house. Beams, inglenooks, four-posters, gardens, adjacent to local inn. **Open:** All year (not Xmas) **01945 861069 (also fax)** www.sandynye.co. uk **D:** £20.00–£22.50 **S:** £30.00–£40.00 **Beds:** 1D 1T **Baths:** 1 En 1 Pr ⌂ (8) 🄿 (2) ⌿ 📺 ▥ 🛉

All details shown are as supplied by B&B owners in Autumn 2001

Ely

TL5480 *Maltings*

82 Broad Street, *Ely, Cambs, CB7 4BE.* Comfortable rooms, central Ely. Near station, river, cathedral. Self-catering available. **Open:** All year **01353 667609** Mr & Mrs Hull **Fax: 01353 667005** **D:** £15.00–£18.00 **S:** £20.00 **Beds:** 1F 1T 1S **Baths:** 1 En 1 Pr 1 Sh ⊱ ▣ 📺 ⊁ 🎟 ⚓

Sycamore House, *91 Cambridge Road, Ely, Cambs, CB7 4HX.* Newly renovated Edwardian family home set in acre of mature gardens. **Open:** All year (not Xmas/ New Year) **Grades:** ETC 4 Diamond **01353 662139** Mrs Webster **Fax: 01353 662795** *sycamore_house@hotmail.com* **D:** £25.00–£30.00 **S:** £35.00–£40.00 **Beds:** 2T 2D **Baths:** 4 En ▣ (8) ⊁ 📺 ⊁ 🎟 ⚓

Greenways, *Prickwillow Road, Queen Adelaide, Ely, Cambs, CB7 4TZ.* Comfortable ground floor accommodation, 1 mile cathedral city of Ely. **Open:** All year **01353 666706** Mr Dunlop-Hill **D:** £22.00–£27.00 **S:** £27.00 **Beds:** 1F 1D 1T 1S **Baths:** 4 En ⊱ ▣ (6) 📺 ⊁ 🎟 & ⚓

11 Chapel Street, *Ely, Cambs, CB6 1AD.* Comfortable listed character cottage. Quiet, close to historical centre. Parking nearby. **Open:** Apr to Dec **01353 668768** Mrs Mortimer *daffmort@ talk21.com* **D:** £20.00 **S:** £20.00 **Beds:** 1D 1S **Baths:** 1 Sh ⊱ (5) ⊁ 📺 ⊁ 🎟 ⚓

Cathedral House, *17 St Mary's Street, Ely, Cambs, CB7 4ER.* Grade II Listed house, in shadow of cathedral, close to museums, restaurants, shops. **Open:** All year (not Xmas) **01353 662124 (also fax)** Mr & Mrs Farndale *farndale@cathedralhouse.co.uk* www.cathedralhouse.co.uk **D:** £25.00–£30.00 **S:** £35.00–£45.00 **Beds:** 1F 1D 1T **Baths:** 3 En ⊱ ▣ (4) ⊁ 📺 🎟 ⚓

Farcet

TL2094

Red House Farm, *Broadway, Farcet, Peterborough, PE7 3AZ.* Situated close to A1 and city centre with lovely views. **Open:** All year **01733 243129 (also fax)** *gill.emberson@ totalise.co.uk* **D:** £18.00–£20.00 **S:** £18.00–£20.00 **Beds:** 2T 1D ⊱ ▣ (6) ⊁ 📺 ⊁ × 🎟 ⚓

Fordham

TL6270 *Chequers*

Homelands, *1 Carter Street, Fordham, Ely, Cambs, CB7 5NG.* Comfort in a private house. Rooms of character. Garden & private parking. **Open:** All year (not Xmas) **01638 720363** Mrs Bycroft **D:** £25.00–£30.00 **S:** £22.00–£25.00 **Beds:** 1F 1D 1T **Baths:** 2 En ⊱ ▣ (4) ⊁ 📺 ⊁ 🎟 ⚓

Queensberry, *196 Carter Street, Fordham, Ely, Suffolk, CB7 5JU.* Country house comfort. First village off A14 Newmarket to Ely road. **Open:** All year **01638 720916** M D Roper **Fax: 01638 720233** **D:** £25.00–£30.00 **S:** £30.00–£40.00 **Beds:** 1D 1T 1S ⊱ ⊁ ▣ 📺 ⊁ 🎟 ⚓

Girton

TL4261

Finches, *144 Thorton Road, Girton, Cambridge, CB3 0ND.* A friendly welcome to our home, beautiful new ensuite rooms. **Open:** All year (not Xmas) **01223 276653** Mr & Mrs Green *liz.green.b-b@ talk21.com* **D:** £30.00–£50.00 **S:** £30.00–£50.00 **Beds:** 1D 2T ⊱ ▣ (4) ⊁ 📺 🎟 ⚓

Gorefield

TF4211

Maison De La Chien, *35 Churchill Road, Gorefield, Wisbech, Cambs, PE13 4NA.* Quiet village location overlooking farmland on the beautiful Cambridgeshire fens. **Open:** All year **01945 870789 & 07990 575219 (M)** Mrs Barnard **Fax: 01945 870789** *hols-maisonchien@faxvia.net* **D:** £15.00 **S:** £15.00 **Beds:** 1D 1T **Baths:** 1 Sh ▣ (2) ⊁ 📺 ⊁ × 🎟 ⚓

Grantchester

TL4355

Honeysuckle Cottage, *38 High Street, Grantchester, Cambridge, CB3 8PL.* Grantchester is a beauty spot, the home of politician Jeffrey Archer. **Open:** All year **01223 845977 & 07974 767807 (M)** Mr & Mrs Salt **D:** £38.00 **S:** £38.00 **Beds:** 3F 3D 3T 3S **Baths:** 3 En ⊁ 📺 × 🎟 ⚓

BATHROOMS
En = Ensuite
Pr = Private
Sh = Shared

RATES

D = Price range per person sharing in a double or twin room

S = Price range for a single room

Great Chishill

TL4238

Hall Farm, *Great Chishill, Royston, Cambridgeshire, SG8 8SH.* **Open:** All year **Grades:** ETC 4 Diamond **01763 838263 (also fax)** Mrs Wiseman www.hallfarmbb.co.uk **D:** £20.00–£30.00 **S:** £30.00–£35.00 **Beds:** 1F 1T 1D **Baths:** 1 En 1 Sh ⊱ ▣ (4) ⊁ 📺 ⊁ 🎟 ⚓ Beautiful Manor house in secluded gardens on the edge of this pretty hilltop village 11 miles south of Cambridge, wonderful views and footpaths. Duxford Air Museum 4 miles. Good local food. Working arable farm. Comfortable new beds.

Great Eversden

TL3653

The Moat House, *Great Eversden, Cambridge, CB3 7HN.* Welcoming period family home. Easy access Cambridge and East Anglia. **Open:** All year (not Xmas) **01223 262836** Mr Webster **Fax: 01223 262979** *websterassociates@ntlworld.com* **D:** £22.50 **S:** £22.50 **Beds:** 1T 1S **Baths:** 1 Pr ⊱ ▣ (4) ⊁ 📺 ⊁ 🎟 ⚓

Great Shelford

TL4652

Norfolk House, *2 Tunwells Lane, Great Shelford, Cambridge, Cambs, CB2 5LJ.* Elegant Victorian residence retaining original character plus 21st-Century comforts. **Open:** All year (not Xmas/New Year) **01223 840287** Mrs Diver **D:** £18.50–£22.50 **S:** £25.00–£30.00 **Beds:** 2T 1D **Baths:** 1 En 1 Sh ⊱ (10) ▣ (2) ⊁ 📺 🎟 ⚓

All details shown are as supplied by B&B owners in Autumn 2001

Hardwick
TL3759

Wallis Farm, *98 Main Street, Hardwick, Cambridge, CB3 7QU.* **Open:** All year **Grades:** ETC 4 Diamond
01954 210347 Mrs Sadler **Fax: 01954 210988**
wallisfarm@mcmail.com **D:** £22.50–£30.00
S: £35.00–£40.00 **Beds:** 1F 2D 3T **Baths:** 6
En ॐ 🅿 (8) ⌿ 🖵 📺 🔥 💷 & ⚄
Quiet location close to city of Cambridge. 6 ensuite rooms in converted barn with exposed beams decorated to high standard. Large gardens leading to meadows and woodland.

Helpston
TF1205

Helpston House, *Helpston, Peterborough, Cambs, PE6 7DX.* Grade II Listed stone manor house set in beautiful grounds, dating back to 1090. **Open:** All year
01733 252190 Mrs Orton **Fax: 01733 253853**
orton.helpstonhouse@btinternet.com
www.helpstonhouse.co.uk **D:** £17.50–£20.00
S: £22.00–£25.00 **Beds:** 1F 1D 1S **Baths:** 1
En 1 Sh ॐ 🅿 (6) ⌿ 🖵 ✕ 📺 💷 ⚄

Hemingford Grey
TL2970   🍺 Cock Inn

Willow Guest House, *45 High Street, Hemingford Grey, Huntingdon, Cambs, PE18 9BJ.* Large, comfortable, quiet guest house in pretty riverside village. **Open:** All year
01480 494748 Mr Webster **Fax: 01480 464456** **D:** £21.00–£24.00 **S:** £32.00–£39.00
Beds: 2F 2D 2T 1S **Baths:** 7 En ॐ 🅿 (12) ⌿ 📺 💷 ⚄

Hilton
TL2866

Prince of Wales, *Potton Road, Hilton, Huntingdon, Cambridgeshire, PE18 9NG.* Traditional village inn offering fine ales and hearty meals. **Open:** All year (not Xmas/New Year) **Grades:** ETC 4 Diamond
01480 830257 **D:** £32.00 **S:** £45.00–£50.00
Beds: 1T 1D 2S **Baths:** 4 En ॐ (5) 🅿 (6) 🖵 🔥 ✕ 📺 ⚄ cc

Histon
TL4363

Wynwyck, *55 Narrow Lane, Histon, Cambridge, CB4 9HD.* Comfortable peaceful; ideal for Cambridge, Ely, Newmarket, Duxford, Museum and East Anglia. **Open:** All year (not Xmas)
01223 232496 (also fax) Mrs Torrens
D: £23.00–£30.00 **S:** £30.00–£35.00 **Beds:** 1F 1D 2T **Baths:** 2 En 1 Sh ॐ 🅿 (4) ⌿ 🖵 📺 💷 ⚄

Huntingdon
TL2472   🍺 Victoria Inn, Dridge Hotel

Sandwich Villas Guest House, *16 George Street, Huntingdon, Cambs, PE29 3BD.* Comfortable Victorian House, close to town centre, railway and bus station. **Open:** All year
01480 458484 Mrs Sturgeon **D:** £22.50
S: £25.00–£38.00 **Beds:** 1F 1T 1D 1S
Baths: 1 En 1 Sh ॐ 🅿 (4) ⌿ 📺 💷 ⚄

Ickleton
TL4843

New Inn House, *10 Brookhampton Street, Ickleton, Duxford, Cambs, CB10 1SP.* Small village, ideal for Duxford, Cambridge and North Essex. Warm welcome. **Open:** All year (not Xmas)
01799 530463 Mrs Fletcher **Fax: 01799 531499** *jpinternational@nascr.net*
www.newinnhouse.co.uk **D:** £15.00–£19.00
S: £25.00–£30.00 **Beds:** 1D 1T **Baths:** 1 Sh
ॐ (5) 🅿 (6) ⌿ 🖵 💷 ⚄

Kirtling
TL6858

Hill Farm Guest House, *Kirtling, Newmarket, Suffolk, CB8 9HQ.* Delightful farm house in rural setting. **Open:** All year
01638 730253 (also fax) Mrs Benley
D: £25.00–£50.00 **S:** £25.00 **Beds:** 1D 1T 1S
Baths: 2 En 1 Pr 🅿 (5) 📺 🔥 💷 ⚄

Kneesworth
TL3444   🍺 Queen Adelaide

Fairhaven, *102 Old North Road, Kneesworth, Royston, Herts, SG8 5JR.* Comfortable country home near Cambridge, Wimpole Hall & Duxford War Museum. **Open:** All year (not Xmas/New Year)
01763 249471 (also fax) D Watson **D:** £20.00
S: £20.00–£25.00 **Beds:** 1T 1D 1S **Baths:** 1 Sh ॐ 🅿 (3) ⌿ 🖵 📺 💷 ⚄

RATES

D = Price range per person sharing in a double or twin room

S = Price range for a single room

Landbeach
TL4765   🍺 Travellers Rest

New Farm, *Green End, Landbeach, Cambridge, CB4 8ED.*
Open: All year
01223 863597 & 07780 982734 (M) Mrs Matthews **Fax: 01223 860258** *new_farm@hotmail.com*
www.smoothhound.co.uk/hotels/newfarm.html **D:** £20.00–£30.00 **S:** £30.00–£40.00
Beds: 1T 2D **Baths:** 2 En 1 Pr ॐ 🅿 (6) ⌿ 🖵 📺 💷 ✳ ⚄
Recently renovated to a high specification, New Farm is located on the edge of the quiet village of Landbeach, situated between Ely and Cambridge. All rooms are beautifully decorated and equipped. A must for guests who appreciate attention to detail.

Linton
TL5646

Linton Heights, *36 Wheatsheaf Way, Linton, Cambridge, Cambs, CB1 6XB.* Comfortable, friendly home, sharing lounge, convenient Duxford, Cambridge, Newmarket, Saffron Walden, Bury. **Open:** All year (not Xmas)
01223 892516 Mr & Mrs Peake **D:** £17.00–£20.00 **S:** £17.00–£20.00 **Beds:** 1T 1S
Baths: 1 Sh ॐ (6) 🅿 (2) ⌿ 🖵 📺 💷 ⚄

Cantilena, *4 Harefield Rise, Linton, Cambridge, CB1 6LS.* Quiet, spacious bungalow in historic village. Near Cambridge, Duxford, Newmarket, Stansted. **Open:** All year
01223 892988 (also fax) Mr & Mrs Clarkson
D: £20.00–£22.00 **S:** £20.00–£25.00 **Beds:** 1F 1D 1T **Baths:** 1 Sh ॐ 🅿 (3) ⌿ 🖵 📺 💷 & ⚄

Little Downham
TL5283

Bury House, *11 Main Street, Little Downham, Ely, Cambs, CB6 2ST.* Grade II Listed ex-farmhouse, large comfortable bedrooms in friendly home. **Open:** All year (not Xmas)
01353 698766 Mrs Ambrose **D:** £19.00
Beds: 1F 1T **Baths:** 1 Sh ॐ 🅿 (2) ⌿ 🖵 📺 💷 ⚄

National Grid References given are for villages, towns and cities – not for individual houses

Please respect a B&B's wishes regarding children, animals and smoking

Casa Nostra Guest House, *6 Black Bank Road, Little Downham, Ely, Cambs, CB6 2UA.* **Open:** All year 01353 862495 Mrs Milan *casanostra@ btinternet.com* **D:** £25.00 **S:** £35.00 **Beds:** 1F3T 3D **Baths:** 5 En 1 Sh ⓅⒹ(10) ⊬ ⒲× ⒱ 🌡.& ▲
Delightful modern country house, large landscaped garden, set in rural location ideal for exploring the Fens and the city of Ely. Family-run with a relaxed atmosphere. Comfortable ground-floor accommodation and an excellent breakfast. Good, secure, off-road parking.

Little Gransden
TL2754   ◀ *Duncombe Arms, Red House*

Model Farm, *Little Gransden, Sandy, Beds, SG19 3EA.* Comfortable quiet farmhouse. 14 miles west of Cambridge. **Open:** All year (not Xmas/New Year) 01767 677361 (also fax) Mrs Barlow *bandb@ modelfarm.org.uk* www.modelfarm.org.uk **D:** £22.00 **S:** £25.00 **Beds:** 3D **Baths:** 3 En Ⓢ(12)Ⓟ(6) ⊬ ⒲ ⍑ ⒱ 🌡.▲

Elms Farm, *52 Main Road, Little Gransden, Sandy, Beds, SG19 3DL.* Farm house, quiet, picturesque gardens and village. Central to many attractions. **Open:** All year (not Xmas) 01767 677459 Mrs Bygraves *joan@ elmsfarmct.freeserve.co.uk* **D:** £20.00–£25.00 **S:** £25.00–£30.00 **Beds:** 1F 1D 1T 1S **Baths:** 1 En 1 Pr 1 Sh ⓈⓅ(10) ⊬ ⒲ 🌡.▲

Longstowe
TL3055

Finch Farmhouse, *28 Fen Road, Bassingbourn, Royston, Herts, SG85 5PQ.* Charming Victorian family home 20 minutes drive from Cambridge. **Open:** All year (not Xmas/New Year) 01763 242019 (also fax) Mrs Murray *btmurray@dial.pipex.com* **D:** £21.00 **S:** £28.00 **Beds:** 1D **Baths:** 1 En Ⓢ(5) Ⓟ(3) ⊬ ⒲× ⒱ 🌡.▲

March
TL4197

Woodpecker Cottage Guest House, *20 Kingswood Road, March, Cambs, PE15 9RT.* Luxury house - landscaped gardens, hearty breakfast. Accessible London and Norfolk coast. **Open:** All year 01354 660188 Mr & Mrs Spencer **Fax:** 01354 655866 *johnliz.spencer@talk21.com* **D:** £18.50–£25.00 **S:** £22.00–£27.00 **Beds:** 2T 1D **Baths:** 1 Sh ⓈⓅ(6) ⊬ ⒲× ⒱ 🌡.✲ ▲

Marholm
TF1402

Ancient Marholm Farm, *Woodcroft Road, Marholm, Peterborough, Cambs, PE6 7HU.* Ancient farmhouse with oak beams, stone walls, set in peaceful and pastoral surroundings. **Open:** All year 01733 262824 Mrs Scott www.s-systems.co. uk/hotels/marholm.html **D:** £20.00–£35.00 **S:** £20.00–£35.00 **Beds:** 3F 1T 1S 1D **Baths:** 1 Sh ⓈⓅ(20) ⒲ ⍑ ⒱ 🌡.▲

Orton Longueville
TL1795

Longueville Guest House, *411 Oundle Road, Orton Longueville, Peterborough, Cambs, PE2 7DA.* Small, family-owned guest house, offering a warm and friendly atmosphere. **Open:** All year **Grades:** ETC 4 Diamond 01733 233442 Glover **D:** £25.00–£27.50 **S:** £35.00–£40.00 **Beds:** 1F 2T 2D **Baths:** 5 En ⓈⓅ(6) ⊬ ⒲ 🌡.▲

Orwell
TL3650   ◀ *Chequers, Royal Oak, White Horse*

Orchards End, *9 Greenford Close, Orwell, Royston, Herts, SG8 5QA.* Friendly, comfortable Tudor style family home in picturesque village. **Open:** All year (not Xmas/New Year) 01223 207202 C Sharman **Fax:** 01763 208865 *sharman@lineone.net* **D:** £22.50 **S:** £25.00 **Beds:** 1D 1S **Baths:** 1 Pr ⓈⓅ(4) ⒲ ⍑ 🌡.▲

Over
TL3770

Charter Cottage, *Horseware, Church End, Over, Cambridge, CB4 5NX.* Peaceful country cottage close to Cambridge, Ely & St Ives. **Open:** All year 01954 230056 Mr & Mrs Warren **Fax:** 01954 232300 *charter.cottage@talk21.com* **D:** £16.00 **S:** £20.00 **Beds:** 1D 1T **Baths:** 1 Sh Ⓢ(3) Ⓟ(6) ⊬ ⒲ 🌡.▲

Planning a longer stay? Always ask for any special rates

Peterborough
TL1999

Montana, *15 Fletton Avenue, Peterborough, Cambs, PE2 8AX.* Clean, friendly, family home. Close city centre. Private car park. **Open:** All year (not Xmas) **Grades:** ETC 3 Diamond 01733 567917 (also fax) Mr & Mrs Atkins www.peterboroughaccommodation.co.uk **D:** £17.50–£20.00 **S:** £19.00–£25.00 **Beds:** 1D 2T 4S **Baths:** 2 Sh Ⓟ(6) ⒲ ⍑ 🌡.▲

Aragon House, *75/77 London Road, Peterborough, Cambs, PE2 9BS.* Comfortable, friendly, easy parking and close to city centre. **Open:** All year (not Xmas) 01733 563718 (also fax) Mr & Mrs Spence *aragon@fsbdial.co.uk* www.aragonhouse.co.uk **D:** £19.00–£22.00 **S:** £20.00–£30.00 **Beds:** 1F 3D 2T 6S **Baths:** 3 En 2 Sh ⓈⓅ(8) ⊬ ⒲ ⍑ ⒱ 🌡.▲ cc

Rose-Marie, *14 Eastfield Road, Peterborough, Cambs, PE1 4AN.* The Rose Marie is a family-run guest house close to city centre. **Open:** All year 01733 557548 Mr Doyle **Fax:** 01733 764801 **D:** £15.00–£18.00 **S:** £18.00–£20.00 **Beds:** 1F 2D 1T 2S **Baths:** 1 Sh Ⓢ ⒲ ⍑ ⒱ 🌡.▲

Pidley
TL3277

Lakeside Lodge, *Fen Road, Pidley, Huntingdon, Cambs, PE28 3DF.* Located on 42 hole golf complex. Ten-pin bowling, bar/ restaurant. **Open:** All year 01487 740540 Mrs Hopkins **Fax:** 01487 740852 *info@lakeside-lodge.co.uk* www.lakeside-lodge.co.uk **D:** £20.00–£30.00 **S:** £25.00–£35.00 **Beds:** 4T 1D **Baths:** 5 En ⓈⓅ⊬ ⒲× ⒱ 🌡.& ▲ cc

Queen Adelaide
TL5580

Greenways, *Prickwillow Road, Queen Adelaide, Ely, Cambs, CB7 4TZ.* Comfortable ground floor accommodation, 1 mile cathedral city of Ely. **Open:** All year 01353 666706 Mr Dunlop-Hill **D:** £22.00–£27.00 **S:** £27.00 **Beds:** 1F 1D 1T 1S **Baths:** 4 En ⓈⓅ(6) ⒲ ⍑ 🌡.& ▲

Soham
TL5973

Greenbank, *111 Brook Street, Soham, Ely, Cambs, CB7 5AE.* Pleasant bungalow in a quiet street, convenient for Newmarket, Ely or Cambridge. **Open:** All year (not Xmas/ New Year) 01353 720929 Mrs Rump **D:** £16.00 **S:** £16.00 **Beds:** 1T 1D **Baths:** 1 Sh Ⓢ(3) Ⓟ(2) ⊬ ⒲ ⍑ ⒱ 🌡.▲ cc

Southorpe

TF0803

Midstone Farm House, *Midstone House, Southorpe, Stamford, Lincs, PE9 3BX.* Beautiful stone Georgian house in quiet location. Meet George the pot-bellied pig. **Open:** All year
01780 740136 Mrs Harrison Smith **Fax: 01780 749294** *midstonehouse@amserve.net*
D: £25.00–£30.00 **S:** £25.00–£30.00 **Beds:** 1D 1T **Baths:** 1 En 1 Pr ⌂ ⬛ ✔ ⬚ ⊶ ✕ ⬚ ⬛ ⋆

St Ives

TL3171   ◀ *The Aviator*

Forty Winks, *3 Laburnum Way, St Ives, Huntingdon, Cambs, PE17 6YW.* Central for Cromwell country. Perfect for Cambridge, East Anglia. **Open:** All year
01480 465117 & 07803 915100 (M) *40winks@ waitrose.com* **D:** £20.00–£23.00 **S:** £25.00–£30.00 **Beds:** 1F 2D **Baths:** 2 En 1 Sh ⌂ ⬛ (2) ✔ ⬚ ⊶ ⬚ ⬛ ⋆

St Neots

TL1860   ◀ *Black Bull, Chequers Inn, Old Sun, Star, Moffat House*

The Bays, *33-35 New Street, St Neots, Cambs, PE19 1AJ.* Tastefully decorated Edwardian house, close to town centre and railway. **Open:** All year (not Xmas/New Year)
01480 403701 (also fax) Mrs McKnight *thebayss@talk21.com* hometown.aol.co. uk/snmcknight/thebays.html **D:** £20.00–£24.00 **S:** £24.00–£38.00 **Beds:** 1F 1T 1D 1S **Baths:** 1 En 2 Sh ⌂ ⬛ (4) ✔ ⬚ ⬛ ⋆

The Ferns, *Berkley Street, Eynesbury, St Neots, Huntingdon, Cambs, PE19 2NE.* Welcoming family home: Picturesque C18th former farmhouse in cottage gardens. **Open:** All year (not Xmas/New Year)
01480 213884 E Raggatt *raggatt@onetel.net.uk* **D:** £18.00–£20.00 **S:** £20.00–£22.00 **Beds:** 1F 1D **Baths:** 1 En 1 Sh ⌂ ⬛ (2) ✔ ⬚ ⊶ ⬛ ⋆

Stretham

TL5074

Bridge House, *Green End, Stretham, Ely, Cambs, CB6 3LF.* Period farmhouse, river frontage, in 13 acres. Relaxed atmosphere, wildlife in profusion. **Open:** All year (not Xmas)
01353 649212 Mr Whitmore **D:** £20.00–£25.00 **S:** £25.00–£35.00 **Beds:** 2F 1D 2T **Baths:** 3 En 1 Pr ⌂ ⬛ (6) ✔ ⬚ ⊶ ⬚ ⬛ ⬚ ⋆

The Red Lion, *47 High Street, Stretham, Ely, Cambs, CB6 3JQ.* **Open:** All year (not Xmas) **Grades:** ETC 3 Diamond
01353 648132 Mrs Hayes **Fax: 01353 648327**
D: £23.00–£23.50 **S:** £34.75–£39.95 **Beds:** 3F 5D 2T 2S **Baths:** 12 En ⌂ ⬛ (18) ⬚ ⊶ ⬚ ⬛ ⋆ cc
A C18th inn centrally situated for touring or business. 4 miles from Ely, 14 miles Newmarket, 12 miles Cambridge, 30 miles from Stansted Airport. Close to major motorways, M11, A14, A428 and A. Conservatory restaurant for guests.

Swaffham Prior

TL5663

Sterling Farm, *Health Road, Swaffham Prior, Cambridge, CB5 0LA.* Convenient for visiting Newmarket, Cambridge and Ely. Anglesea Abbey 3 miles. **Open:** All year (not Xmas)
01638 741431 Mrs Harris **D:** £20.00–£25.00 **S:** £20.00–£25.00 **Beds:** 1D 1T 1S **Baths:** 1 Sh ⌂ ⬛ (8) ✔ ⬚ ⬛ ⋆

Thornhaugh

TF0700

Sacrewell Lodge Farm, *Thornhaugh, Peterborough, PE8 6HJ.* Farmhouse in quiet location surrounded by attractive gardens and farmland. **Open:** All year (not Xmas)
01780 782277 Mrs Armitage **D:** £18.00–£20.00 **S:** £15.00–£18.00 **Beds:** 1D 1T 1S **Baths:** 1 En 1 Sh ⬛ (10) ✔ ⬚ ⬛ ⋆

Ufford

TF0904

Ufford Farm, *Ufford, Stamford, Lincs, PE9 3BP.* C18th farmhouse, comfortably furnished, with open fires on edge of peaceful village. **Open:** All year
01780 740220 (also fax) Mrs Vergette *vergette@ufford1.freeserve.co.uk* **D:** £25.00–£30.00 **S:** £25.00–£30.00 **Beds:** 1T 1S **Baths:** 1 Sh ⌂ (3) ⬛ (4) ✔ ⬚ ✕ ⬚ ⬛ ⋆

All details shown are as supplied by B&B owners in Autumn 2001

Wansford

TL0799   ◀ *Haycock Hotel, Papermills*

Stoneacre, *Elton Road, Wansford, Peterborough, Cambs, PE8 6JT.* Near Peterborough and Stamford; self-catering available for long lets. **Open:** All year
Grades: ETC 4 Diamond
01780 783283 (also fax) Mr Wilkinson
D: £21.00–£26.00 **S:** £36.00–£46.00 **Beds:** 1F 1T 4D **Baths:** 4 En 1 Pr 1 Sh ⬛ (10) ⬚ ⊶ ⬚ ⬛ ⬚ ⋆

Waterbeach

TL4964   ◀ *The Slap Up*

Goose Hall Farm, *Ely Road, Waterbeach, Cambridge, CB5 9PG.* Modern farm house on 13 acres with a deer run & half acre lake. **Open:** All year (not Xmas)
01223 860235 (also fax) Mrs Lock **D:** £20.00–£22.00 **S:** £30.00–£35.00 **Beds:** 1F 1D 1T **Baths:** 3 En ⌂ (5) ⬛ (8) ⬚ ⬚ ⬛ ⋆

Wentworth

TL4777

Desiderata, *44 Main Street, Wentworth, Ely, Cambs, CB6 3QG.* Large modern house in quiet country lane; ideal for disabled. **Open:** All year
01353 776131 & 07768 827901 (M) Mrs Graham *chips.1@virgin.net* **D:** £20.00–£25.00 **S:** £25.00 **Beds:** 2D 2T **Baths:** 2 En 1 Sh ⌂ ⬛ (6) ⬚ ⬚ ⬛ ⋆ ✿ ⋆

West Perry

TL1566

38 West Perry, *West Perry, Huntingdon, Cambs, PE28 0BX.* Victorian country cottage, peaceful, interesting garden. Close Grafham Water Reservoir. **Open:** All year (not Xmas/New Year)
01480 810225 Mrs Hickling **D:** £20.00–£25.00 **S:** £20.00–£25.00 **Beds:** 2T 1S **Baths:** 1 Sh ⌂ (13) ⬛ (3) ✔ ⬚ ⬚ ⬛ ⋆

West Wratting

TL5951

The Old Bakery, *West Wratting, Cambridge, CB1 5LU.* Period cottage situated in quiet village with nice garden. **Open:** All year
01223 290492 Mr & Mrs Denny **Fax: 01223 290845** *ddtractors@zoom.co.uk* **D:** £22.50 **S:** £22.50 **Beds:** 2T 3D **Baths:** 1 En 1 Pr ⌂ ⬛ (2) ⬚ ⬛ ⋆

Whittlesey

TL2797 🍺 *Dog in a Doublet, Falcon Hotel*

Cobwebs Guest House, *21 The Delph, Whittlesey, Peterborough, Cambs, PE7 1QH.* Close to diving centre, fishing, lakes East of England Showground. **Open:** All year (not Xmas/New Year)
01733 350960 Mrs Ekins **D:** £16.00–£17.50 **S:** £17.50 **Beds:** 1F 4T **Baths:** 2 Sh 🄿 (4) 🖵 ⊁ ✕ 🖵 🏛 ఉ ఉ

Wicken

TL5670

Spinney Abbey, *Wicken, Ely, Cambs, CB7 5XQ.* Georgian Farmhouse with tennis court. Close to NT Nature Reserve. **Open:** All year (not Xmas/New Year) **Grades:** ETC 4 Diamond
01353 720971 V Fuller **Fax: 01353 720488** *spinney.abbey@tesco.net* www.spinneyabbey.co. uk **D:** £23.00–£24.00 **Beds:** 1F 1T 1D **Baths:** 2 En 1 Pr ⊱ (5) 🄿 (4) 🖵 🏛 ఉ

The Old School, *48 North Street, Wicken, Ely, Cambs, CB7 5XW.* Tastefully renovated Edwardian village school, with tea-room, gifts, Bygones shop. **Open:** All year (not Xmas/New Year)
01353 720526 Mrs Wright *wicken.oldschool@ btinternet.com* **D:** £20.00–£24.00 **S:** £25.00–£30.00 **Beds:** 1F 1D **Baths:** 1 En 1 Pr ⊱ 🄿 ⊁ 🖵 🖵 🏛 ఉ ఉ

Wisbech

TF4609 🍺 *Red Lion, Rising Sun*

Ravenscourt, *138 Lynn Road, Wisbech, Cambs, PE13 3DP.* Quality accommodation, friendly atmosphere, easy walking distance to town centre. **Open:** All year (not Xmas/New Year)
01945 585052 (also fax) Mr Parish *ravenscourt@rya-online.net* www.ravenscourtgh.fsnet.co.uk **D:** £16.00 **S:** £20.00 **Beds:** 1F 2D 1T **Baths:** 4 Pr 🄿 (3) ⊁ 🖵 🖵 🏛 ఉ

Planning a longer stay? Always ask for any special rates

Algethi Guest House, *136 Lynn Road, Wisbech, Cambs, PE13 3DP.* Small, family-run guest house near town centre. Warm welcome. **Open:** All year
01945 582278 E McManus **Fax: 01945 466456** *lizalgethi@talk21 .com* **D:** £15.00–£17.00 **S:** £15.00–£17.50 **Beds:** 2F 2T 1S **Baths:** 2 Pr ⊱ 🄿 ⊁ 🖵 ☊ ✕ 🖵 🏛 ఉ ఉ

Marmion House Hotel, *11 Lynn Road, Wisbech, Cambs, PE13 3DD.* Georgian town house hotel located in the capital of the Fens. **Open:** All year (not Xmas)
01945 582822 Mrs Lilley **Fax: 01945 475889 D:** £18.00–£22.00 **S:** £20.00–£26.00 **Beds:** 20F 10D 2T 6S **Baths:** 18 En 1 Pr 2 Sh ⊱ 🄿 🖵 🏛 ఉ cc

Witchford

TL5078

17 Common Road, *Witchford, Ely, Cambs, CB6 2HY.* Detached house and garden opposite village common. **Open:** All year (not Xmas/New Year)
01353 663918 R J Westell *rjwest@ elyfl.freeserve.co.uk* **D:** £20.00 **S:** £20.00 **Beds:** 1T 1D 1S **Baths:** 1 Sh 🄿 (1) ⊁ 🖵 🏛 ఉ

Cheshire

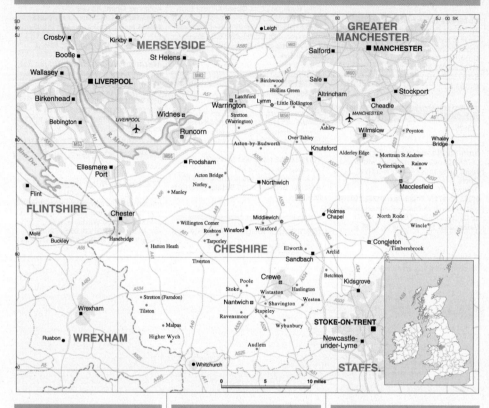

Acton Bridge
SJ5975

Manor Farm, *Cliff Road, Acton Bridge, Northwich, Cheshire, CW8 3QP.* Peaceful, elegantly furnished traditional country house. Large garden and views. **Open:** All year (not Xmas) **Grades:** ETC 4 Diamond **01606 853181** Mrs Campbell **D:** £20.00–£25.00 **S:** £20.00–£25.00 **Beds:** 1F 1T 1S **Baths:** 1 En 2 Pr ⊃ (1) 🅿 (10) ⚡ 🖻 🛏 📺 🛍 ♨

BEDROOMS
D = Double
T = Twin
S = Single
F = Family

Alderley Edge
SJ8478

Trafford House Farm, *Beswicks Lane, Row of Trees, Alderley Edge, Wilmslow, Cheshire, SK9 7SN.* Perfectly situated for exploring the many attractions in surrounding countryside. **Open:** All year **01625 582160** Mr & Mrs Blackmore **Fax: 01625 584968** www.smoothhound.co. uk/hotels/trafford.html **D:** £15.00 **S:** £20.00 **Beds:** 1F 1T 1S **Baths:** 2 Sh ⊃ 🅿 (10) ⚡ 🛏 🛍 ♨

Arclid
SJ7862

Yew Tree Farm, *Love Lane, Betchton, Sandbach, Cheshire, CW11 4TD.* Open plan bungalow - panoramic views - many local attractions - close to J17 M6. **Open:** All year **01477 500382** Mrs Hollinshead **D:** £19.00–£24.00 **S:** £20.00–£24.00 **Beds:** 1F 1D **Baths:** 1 En 1 Pr ⊃ (5) 🅿 (10) 📺 🛍 ♨

Ashley
SJ7784

Birtles Farm, *Ashley, Altrincham, Cheshire, WA14 3QH.* Delightful riverside farmhouse. Spacious bedrooms, beautifully decorated, every comfort. Peaceful yet close Manchester Airport. **Open:** All year **0161 928 0458 (also fax)** Mrs Norbury *birtlesl@supanet.com* **D:** £22.00–£23.00 **S:** £25.00–£26.00 **Beds:** 1F 1T 1D **Baths:** 2 En 1 Pr ⊃ 🅿 (10) ⚡ 📺 🛏 ✕ 📺 🛍 ♨ ♨

RATES
D = Price range per person sharing in a double or twin room
S = Price range for a single room

Aston-by-Budworth

SJ6976 🍺 *Geroge & Dragon*

Clock Cottage, *Hield Lane, Aston-by-Budworth, Northwich, Cheshire, CW9 6LP.* Lovely C17th thatched country cottage, beautiful, large, secluded garden, wooded countryside, open views. **Open:** All year (not Xmas/New Year)
01606 891271 T Tanner-Betts **D:** £18.00–£25.00 **S:** £18.00–£25.00 **Beds:** 1T 1S **Baths:** 1 Sh � 🖭 (4) ⊬ 🖻 ✕ 🖤 🛍 ♣

Audlem

SJ6643

Little Heath Farm, *Audlem, Crewe, Cheshire, CW3 0HE.* Warm traditionally furnished oak beamed farmhouse in canal side village of Audlem. **Open:** All year (not Xmas/New Year)
01270 811324 (also fax) Mrs Bennion **D:** £18.00–£24.00 **S:** £22.00–£26.00 **Beds:** 1D 1T 1F **Baths:** 1 Pr 1 En ⪼ 🖭 (3) ⊬ 🖭 ⼍ ✕ 🖤 🛍 ♣

Betchton

SJ7959 🍺 *New Inn*

Yew Tree Farm, *Love Lane, Betchton, Sandbach, Cheshire, CW11 4TD.* M6 J17. Ideally situated for Cheshire's beauty spots. **Open:** All year
01477 500626 (also fax) Mrs Hollinshead **D:** £18.00–£23.00 **S:** £20.00–£25.00 **Beds:** 2D **Baths:** 1 En 1 Pr 🖭 ⊬ 🖤 🛍 & ♣

Birchwood

SJ6492 🍺 *The Noggin*

14 Cadshaw Close, *Warrington, Warrington, Cheshire, WA3 7LR.* Modern residence situated in quiet cul-de-sac near M6 and M62. **Open:** All year
01925 818108 P Agarwal *patagarwal@hotmail.com* **D:** £20.00–£22.00 **S:** £20.00–£25.00 **Beds:** 1T 1D 2S **Baths:** 1 En 1 Sh ⪼ (12) 🖭 ⊬ 🖤 🛍 ♣

Chester

SJ4066 🍺 *Egerton Arms*

Cotton Farmhouse, *Cotton Edmunds, Chester, CH3 7PT.* **Open:** All year (not Xmas/New Year)
01244 336616 Fax: 01244 336699 *info@cottonfarm.co.uk* www.cottonfarm.co.uk
D: £25.00–£26.00 **S:** £30.00–£31.00 **Beds:** 1F 1T 1D **Baths:** 3 En ⪼ 🖭 (20) ⊬ 🖤 🛍 ♣
Complete peace at our family farmhouse set in 250 acres. Only 4 miles from the historic walled city of Chester, we offer extremely large and comfortable bedrooms with all the extras. Beeston Castle, Chirk, Liverpool and North Wales all nearby.

Dee Heights Guest House, *23 City Walls, Chester, CH1 1SB.* **Open:** All year
01244 350386 Mrs Willis **D:** £24.00 **S:** £30.00–£35.00 **Beds:** 1D **Baths:** 1 Pr ⊬ 🖤 🖤 ♣
A charming riverside house situated on the Roman walls overlooking the River Dee and Old Dee Bridge. Fresh flowers and magnificent river views. Studio bed-sitting room with French window opening onto south facing balcony. Three minutes from city centre.

Oakenholt Farm, *Chester Road, Flint, Flintshire, CH6 5SU.* Set in a beautiful location, convenient for touring Chester, North Wales & Liverpool. **Open:** All year
Grades: ETC 3 Star
01352 733264 Mrs Hulme *jenny@oakenholt.freeserve.co.uk* www.smoothhound.co.uk/oakenholt **D:** £20.00–£25.00 **S:** £25.00–£28.00 **Beds:** 1F 2D 1T **Baths:** 4 En ⪼ 🖭 ⊬ 🖤 🖤 ⼍ ✕ 🖤 🛍 ♣

Congleton

SJ8663

8 Cloud View, *Congleton, Cheshire, CW12 3TP.* Lovely family home, edge of countryside, good views. **Open:** All year (not Xmas)
01260 276048 Mrs Stewart **D:** £18.00–£20.00 **S:** £19.00–£20.00 **Beds:** 1D 1S **Baths:** 1 En 1 Sh ⪼ 🖭 (1) ⊬ 🖤 ✕ 🖤 🛍 ♣

Grosvenor Place Guest House, *2-4 Grosvenor Place, Chester, CH1 2DE.* Excellent breakfast and very clean; proprietor: Alma Wood. **Open:** All year (not Xmas)
Grades: ETC 3 Diamond
01244 324455 Mrs Wood **Fax: 01244 400225 D:** £18.00–£22.50 **S:** £25.00 **Beds:** 2F 3D 2T 3S **Baths:** 6 En 2 Sh ⪼ 🖭 🖤 ⼍ 🖤 🛍 ♣ cc

Green Cottage, *Higher Kinnerton, Chester, CH4 9BZ.* 6 miles from historic Chester, relaxing atmosphere, good food, in a Welsh rural setting. **Open:** All year
01244 660137 Mrs Milner **D:** £19.00 **S:** £24.00 **Beds:** 1D 1T **Baths:** 1 Pr ⪼ 🖭 ⊬ 🖤 🖤 🛍 ♣

Green Gables Guest House, *11 Eversley Park, Chester, Cheshire, CH2 2AJ.* Quietly situated yet 0.9 miles from town centre. Victorian property. **Open:** All year
Grades: ETC 4 Diamond
01244 372243 Mrs Perruzza **Fax: 01244 376352 D:** £19.00 **S:** £26.00 **Beds:** 1F 1D 1T 1S **Baths:** 3 En ⪼ 🖭 (5) ⊬ 🛍 ♣

Chester Court Hotel, *48 Hoole Road, Chester, CH2 3NL.* Set in its own grounds only 3/4 mile from city centre. **Open:** All year (not Xmas/New Year)
01244 320779 Mr Row **Fax: 01244 344795** *info@chestercourthotel.com* www.chestercourthotel.com **D:** £32.50–£35.00 **S:** £40.00–£45.00 **Beds:** 3F 3T 11D 3S **Baths:** 20 En ⪼ 🖭 (25) 🖤 ✕ 🖤 🛍 ♣ cc

Stone Villa, *3 Stone Place, Hoole, Chester, CH2 3NR.* A haven of quiet relaxation with individual attention and warm hospitality. **Open:** All year (not Xmas)
01244 345014 Mr Pow *adam@stonevilla.freeserve.co.uk* **D:** £25.00–£28.00 **S:** £25.00–£32.00 **Beds:** 1F 6D 2T 1S **Baths:** 9 En 1 Pr ⪼ 🖭 (10) ⊬ 🖤 🛍 & cc

Castle House, *23 Castle Street, Chester, CH1 2DS.* Pre-1580 Tudor house, plus Georgian front (1738). **Open:** All year
01244 350354 Mr Marl **D:** £24.00–£25.00 **S:** £38.00 **Beds:** 1F 1D 1T 2S **Baths:** 3 En 1 Sh ⪼ 🖭 🖤 🖤 🛍 ♣ cc

Aplas Guest House, *106 Brook Street, Chester, Cheshire, CH1 3DU.* Family-run guest house, ideally located for historic Chester. 10 mins' walk city centre. **Open:** All year
01244 312401 Mr Aplas **D:** £13.00–£17.50 **Beds:** 1F 4D 2T **Baths:** 5 En 2 Sh 🖭 (7) 🖤 🛍 ♣

RATES

D = Price range per person sharing in a double or twin room

S = Price range for a single room

BEDROOMS

D = Double

T = Twin

S = Single

F = Family

Planning a longer stay? Always ask for any special rates

The Lamb Inn, *3 Blake Street, Congleton, Cheshire, CW12 4DS.* Central location convenient for Cheshire country houses and attractions. **Open:** All year **01260 272731** Mr Kelly *john.kelly5@tesco.net* www.lambinn.org.uk **D:** £16.00–£20.00 **S:** £18.00–£25.00 **Beds:** 1F 2D 2T 1S **Baths:** 4 En 2 Sh ⛺ 🅿 (40) 🔟 ⊁ 🎑 🎬 ♨

Elworth
SJ7461

Poplar Mount Guest House, *2 Station Road, Elworth, Sandbach, Cheshire, CW11 9JG.* Friendly family-run guest house, convenient for M6 motorway. **Open:** All year **01270 761268 (also fax)** Mrs McDonald **D:** £20.00 **S:** £20.00–£28.00 **Beds:** 2F 3D 1T 2S **Baths:** 4 En 1 Sh ⛺ 🅿 (9) 🔟 × 🎑 ♨ cc

Handbridge
SJ4065

Eaton House, *36 Eaton Road, Handbridge, Chester, CH4 7EY.* Victorian town house within close walking distance of city centre. **Open:** All year (not Xmas/New Year) **01244 680349 Fax: 01244 659021** *grahamd@ aol.com* **D:** £19.00–£24.00 **S:** £20.00–£24.00 **Beds:** 1F 1D ⛺ (8) 🅿 (3) ⊁ 🔟 🎑 ♨ cc

Haslington
SJ7355

Ferndale House, *Gutterscroft, Haslington, Crewe, Cheshire, CW1 5RJ.* Victorian home, large rooms, excellent food, secure parking, convenient M6. **Open:** All year **01270 584048** L M Docherty *ferndalehouse@ tinyworld.co.uk* www.ferndalehouse.co.uk **D:** £20.00–£23.50 **S:** £20.00 ⛺ 🅿 (7) 🔟 × 🔟 🎑 ♨

Hatton Heath
SJ4561

Golborne Manor, *Platts Lane, Hatton Heath, Chester, Cheshire, CH3 9AN.* Beautifully decorated C19th manor house with glorious views and garden. **Open:** All year **01829 770310 & 07850 265425 (M)** Mrs Ikin **Fax: 01829 770370** *ann.ikin@ golbornemanor.co.uk* **D:** £58.00–£68.00 **S:** £28.00–£38.00 **Beds:** 1F 1T 1D **Baths:** 3 En 🅿 (6) ⊁ 🔟 × 🎑 🎑 ♨

Higher Wych
SJ4943   🍴 Redbrook Hunting Lodge

Mill House, *Higher Wych, Malpas, Cheshire, SY14 7JR.* Modernised mill house, peaceful valley. Convenient for Chester, Shrewsbury, Llangollen. **Open:** Jan to Nov **Grades:** ETC 3 Star **01948 780362** Mrs Smith **Fax: 01948 780566** *angela@videoactive.co.uk* **D:** £20.00 **S:** £20.00 **Beds:** 1D 1T **Baths:** 1 En 1 Sh ⛺ 🅿 (4) 🔟 × 🔟 🎑 ♨

Hollins Green
SJ6991   🍴 Black Swan, Red Lion, Rhinewood Hotel

Brook Farm, *Manchester Road, Hollins Green, Warrington, Cheshire, WA3 6HX.* A working farm and equestrian centre. Central for Manchester and Warrington. **Open:** All year (not Xmas/New Year) **0161 775 6053 (also fax)** Mr Hesford **D:** £18.00–£20.00 **S:** £21.00–£25.00 **Beds:** 2T 2D 2S **Baths:** 3 En 1 Sh 🅿 (20) 🔟 ⊁ 🎑 🎑 ♨

Latchford
SJ6187

The Maples Private Hotel, *11 Longdin Street, Latchford, WA4 1PJ.* Family-run hotel. Close village/town. Good access motorways. Friendly welcome. **Open:** All year (not Xmas/New Year) **01925 637752** S M Savory **D:** £15.00–£30.00 **S:** £10.00–£20.00 **Beds:** 1F 3T 2D 2S **Baths:** 2 En 1 Pr 1 Sh ⛺ 🅿 🔟 🎑 ♨

Little Bollington
SJ7286

Bollington Hall Farm, *Park Lane, Little Bollington, Altrincham, Cheshire, WA14 4TJ.* Close to Manchester, Dunham Massey Hall, Tatton Hall, Trans-Penine Trail & motorway network **Open:** All year (not Xmas/New Year) **0161 928 1760** Mrs Owen **D:** £18.00 **S:** £18.00 **Beds:** 1F 1D **Baths:** 1 Sh 🅿 (10) 🔟 🔟 🎑 ♨

Macclesfield
SJ9173

Moorhayes House Hotel, *27 Manchester Road, Tytherington, Macclesfield, Cheshire, SK10 2JJ.* Warm welcome. Hearty breakfast. Half a mile north of Macclesfield. **Open:** All year (not Xmas/New Year) **Grades:** ETC 3 Diamond **01625 433228 (also fax)** Helen Wood *helen@ moorhayeshouse.freeserve.co.uk* **D:** £26.00–£30.00 **S:** £35.00–£40.00 **Beds:** 1F 1T 5D 1S **Baths:** 8 En ⛺ 🅿 (14) ⊁ 🔟 ⊁ 🎑 ♨ cc

---

National Grid References given are for villages, towns and cities – not for individual houses

Penrose Guest House, *56 Birtles Road, Whirley, Macclesfield, Cheshire, SK10 3JQ.* Central for Wilmslow, Prestbury, Macclesfield. Close Intercity trains, motorway, airport. **Open:** All year **01625 615323 Fax: 01625 432284** *info@ PenroseGuestHouse.co.uk* www.PenroseGuestHouse.co.uk **D:** £20.00 **S:** £20.00 **Beds:** 1T 2S ⛺ (4) 🅿 (6) ⊁ 🔟 🎑 ♨

Malpas
SJ4847

Farm Ground Cottage, *Edge, Malpas, Cheshire, SY14 8LE.* Peaceful, comfortable Victorian Cottage in rural surroundings. Excellent touring base. **Open:** All year (not Xmas) **01948 820333 D:** £19.50–£21.00 **S:** £20.00–£22.00 **Beds:** 1D **Baths:** 1 Pr 🅿 (2) ⊁ 🔟 ⊁ × 🔟 🎑 ♨

Manley
SJ5071

Rangeway Bank Farm, *Manley, Warrington, Cheshire, WA6 9EF.* Friendly traditional farmhouse in rural Cheshire, access to Delamere Forest. **Open:** All year (not Xmas) **01928 740236** J Challoner **Fax: 01928 740703** **D:** £20.00–£25.00 **S:** £22.00–£25.00 **Beds:** 1F 1D 1T **Baths:** 2 En 1 Sh ⛺ 🅿 (6) ⊁ 🔟 ⊁ 🔟 🎑 ♨

Middlewich
SJ7066

Sandhurst Lodge, *69 Chester Road, Middlewich, Cheshire, CW10 9EW.* Charming Edwardian residence close to M6 in Cheshire heartland. **Open:** All year (not Xmas) **01606 834125** Mrs Fair **D:** £22.00–£24.00 **S:** £25.00–£30.00 **Beds:** 2F 5D 1T **Baths:** 8 En ⛺ 🅿 (8) 🔟 🎑 ♨

Mottram St Andrew
SJ8778   🍴 Bull's Head

Goose Green Farm, *Oak Road, Mottram St Andrew, Macclesfield, Cheshire, SK10 4RA.* Perfectly situated, comfortable, quiet location with lovely views. Warm welcome. **Open:** All year **Grades:** ETC 3 Diamond **01625 828814 (also fax)** D Hatch *goosegreenfarm@talk21.com* **D:** £22.00–£24.00 **S:** £22.00 **Beds:** 1T 1D 2S **Baths:** 1 En 1 Sh ⛺ (5) 🅿 (8) ⊁ 🔟 🎑 ♨ cc

Nantwich

SJ6452   🍺 *Red Cow*

Oakland House, *252 Newcastle Road, Blakelow, Shavington, Nantwich, Cheshire, CW5 7ET.* **Open:** All year **Grades:** AA 5 Diamond
01270 567134 Mr & Mrs Groom **Fax: 01270 651752 D:** £20.00–£22.50 **S:** £30.00–£34.00 **Beds:** 3T 5D 1S **Baths:** 9 En ☎ 🗗 ⌇ 🖂 ♈ ✕ Ⓥ 🛏 ఈ ✿ ⚐ cc
Family-owned and family-run. 5 miles from M6, 1.5 miles Nantwich on the A500 (jct.16). Rural location.

Lea Farm, *Wrinehill Road, Wybunbury, Nantwich, Cheshire, CW5 7HS.* Charming farmhouse set in landscaped gardens where peacocks roam. **Open:** All year (not Xmas) **Grades:** ETC 3 Diamond
01270 841429 (also fax) Mrs Callwood **D:** £19.00 **S:** £22.00 **Beds:** 1F 1D 1T **Baths:** 2 Pr 1 Sh 🗗 🖳 (22) Ⓥ 🛏 Ⓥ ఊ

The Railway Hotel, *Pillory Street, Nantwich, Cheshire, CW5 5SS.* Historic 1890 building, on the edge of beautiful Nantwich town. **Open:** All year
01270 623482 J Hobson *jhobson@freeuk.com* **D:** £25.00 **S:** £30.00–£40.00 **Beds:** 2F 1T 1S **Baths:** 4 En ☎ 🗗 🖂 ♈ 🛏 ✕ Ⓥ 🛏 ఊ cc

Kiltearn House, *33 Hospital Street, Nantwich, Cheshire, CW5 5RL.* Very old period house. Fresh flowers. Central heating throughout, cooked breakfasts. **Open:** All year **Grades:** ETC 3 Star
01270 628892 Mrs Pearson **Fax: 01270 626646** *jpearson@crewe-nantwich.gov.uk* **D:** £28.00–£33.00 **S:** £25.00–£35.00 **Beds:** 1F 1T 1D 1S **Baths:** 2 Sh ☎ 🗗 (5) Ⓥ 🛏 Ⓥ 🛏 ఊ

Stoke Grange Farm, *Chester Road, Stoke, Nantwich, Cheshire, CW5 6BT.* Canalside farmhouse. Wonderful views. Pets' Corner farmhouse. Peace and quiet. **Open:** All year
01270 625525 (also fax) Mrs West **D:** £25.00–£30.00 **S:** £30.00–£35.00 **Beds:** 1F 1T 1D **Baths:** 3 En ☎ 🗗 (10) ⌇ Ⓥ Ⓥ 🛏 ఊ

Norley

SJ5672

Wicken Tree Farm, *Blakemere Lane, Norley, Warrington, Cheshire, WA6 6NW.* High quality self-contained accommodation and B&B, surrounded by Delamere Forest. **Open:** All year
01928 788355 Mr Appleton *ches@ williamj99.freeserve.co.uk* **D:** £23.50–£25.00 **S:** £23.50–£31.00 **Beds:** 1F 5D 7T 3S **Baths:** 6 En 1 Pr 2 Sh ☎ 🗗 (14) ⌇ Ⓥ 🛏 Ⓥ 🛏 ఈ ఊ

Planning a longer stay? Always ask for any special rates

North Rode

SJ8866

Yew Tree Farm, *North Rode, Congleton, Cheshire, CW12 2PF.* Cosy farmhouse in wooded parkland, traditional home-cooked meals. **Open:** All year **Grades:** ETC 4 Diamond
01260 223569 Mrs Kidd **Fax:** 01260 223328 *kiddyewtreefarm@netscapeonline.co.uk* **D:** £20.00–£25.00 **S:** £25.00–£27.00 **Beds:** 1D 1T **Baths:** 2 En ☎ 🗗 (10) ⌇ Ⓥ ✕ Ⓥ 🛏 ఊ

Over Tabley

SJ7280

The Old Vicarage, *Moss Lane, Over Tabley, Knutsford, Cheshire, WA16 0PL.* Set in 2 acres of wooded gardens. A warm welcome awaits you. **Open:** All year (not Xmas/New Year) **Grades:** AA 4 Diamond
01565 652221 Mrs Weston **Fax:** 01565 755918 **D:** £32.50 **S:** £49.50 **Beds:** 1F 2T 2D **Baths:** 5 En ☎ (10) 🗗 (20) ⌇ Ⓥ ✕ Ⓥ 🛏 ఊ cc

Poole

SJ6455

Poole Bank Farm, *Poole, Nantwich, Cheshire, CW5 6AL.* Charming C17th timbered farmhouse, surrounded by picturesque dairy farmland. **Open:** All year
01270 625169 Ms Hocknell **D:** £18.00–£22.00 **S:** £20.00–£24.00 **Beds:** 1D 1T 1F **Baths:** 1 Pr 2 Sh ☎ 🗗 (10) Ⓥ Ⓥ ఊ

Poynton

SJ9283   🍺 *Vernon Arms*

Whitethorn, *1 Waters Reach, Poynton, Stockport, Greater Manchester, SK12 1XT.* Modern detached house. Quiet cul-de-sac close to village. **Open:** All year (not Xmas/New Year)
01625 871590 C P Williams **D:** £18.00–£20.00 **S:** £18.00–£20.00 **Beds:** 1D **Baths:** 1 Pr ⌇ Ⓥ 🛏 ఊ

Rainow

SJ9576

The Tower House, *Tower Hill, Rainow, Macclesfield, Cheshire, SK10 5TX.* Luxury accommodation in carefully restored C16th farmhouse. Superb breakfasts. **Open:** All year
01625 438022 (also fax) Mrs Buckley **D:** £25.00 **S:** £25.00–£35.00 **Beds:** 2T 1S **Baths:** 1 Pr ☎ 🗗 (4) ⌇ Ⓥ Ⓥ 🛏 ఊ

Ravensmoor

SJ6250

Pujols, *Barracks Lane, Ravensmoor, Nantwich, Cheshire, CW5 8PR.* Quiet location, easy reach M6, railways, North Wales, Peak District. **Open:** All year
01270 626528 **D:** £12.00–£15.00 **S:** £15.00–£18.00 **Beds:** 1T 1D **Baths:** 1 Sh 🗗 (2) ⌇ Ⓥ 🛏 ఊ

Runcorn

SJ5281

Panorama Hotel, *1 Castle Road, Runcorn, Cheshire, WA7 2BE.* **Open:** All year **01928 564772 (also fax)** Mr Zancudi *panoramichotel@mersinet.co.uk* **D:** £17.50–£20.00 **S:** £25.00 **Beds:** 2F 2T 6D **Baths:** 10 En ☎ 🗗 (30) Ⓥ 🛏 ✕ Ⓥ 🛏 ఈ cc
Hotel and restaurant open 7 days a week, offering a wide selection of activities from social events to weekend disco dancing. Whether you are a resident guest or just stopping over for a quick visit, you will always find a warm atmosphere to welcome you.

Fountains Hotel, *10 High Street, Runcorn, Cheshire, WA7 1AU.* Town centre Victorian building tastefully furnished. Convenient motorways and public transport. **Open:** All year
01928 569799 Mr & Mrs Gittins **Fax:** 01928 830513 **D:** £17.00 **S:** £20.00–£27.00 **Beds:** 1F 4T 1D 2S **Baths:** 8 En ☎ 🗗 Ⓥ ✕ Ⓥ 🛏 ఊ

Rushton

SJ5863

Hill House Farm, *The Hall Lane, Rushton, Tarporley, Cheshire, CW6 9AU.* Beautiful Victorian former farmhouse, comfortable accommodation, 1.5 miles from Oulton Park. **Open:** All year (not Xmas/New Year)
01829 732238 Mrs Rayner *rayner@ hillhousefarm.fsnet.co.uk* **D:** £22.00 **S:** £25.00 **Beds:** 1F 1T 1D **Baths:** 2 En 1 Pr ☎ 🗗 (10) ⌇ Ⓥ 🛏 🛏 ఊ

Please respect a B&B's wishes regarding children, animals and smoking

Shavington

SJ6951 🍺 *The Elephant, Horseshoe, Roebuck, Swan Inn*

Oakland House, *252 Newcastle Road, Blakelow, Shavington, Nantwich, Cheshire, CW5 7ET.* 5m from M6, 1.5m Nantwich on A500 (J 16). Rural location. **Open:** All year **Grades:** AA 5 Diamond
01270 567134 Mr & Mrs Groom **Fax: 01270 651752 D:** £20.00–£22.50 **S:** £30.00–£34.00 **Beds:** 3T 5D 1S **Baths:** 9 En ♿🏠🅿💷✓📺🐾✕📺 ▥🔥❀🏅cc

Stapeley

SJ6749

York Cottage, *82 Broad Lane, Stapeley, Nantwich, Cheshire, CW5 7QL.* Comfortable detached rural cottage, with garden, 2 miles from Nantwich. **Open:** All year
01270 629829 Mrs Orford **Fax: 01270 625404 D:** £18.00–£20.00 **S:** £18.00–£22.00 **Beds:** 2D 1F **Baths:** 1 Sh ♿🅿(3)✓📺🐾📺 ▥❀🏅

Stoke

SJ6552 🍺 *Dysart Arms, Boot & Slipper, Red Fox*

Stoke Grange Farm, *Chester Road, Stoke, Nantwich, Cheshire, CW5 6BT.* Canalside farmhouse. Wonderful views. Pets' Corner farmhouse. Peace and quiet. **Open:** All year
01270 625525 (also fax) Mrs West **D:** £25.00–£30.00 **S:** £30.00–£35.00 **Beds:** 1F 1T 1D **Baths:** 3 En ♿🅿(10)✓📺📺 ▥🏅

Stretton (Farndon)

SJ4452

Stretton Lower Hall, *Marsh Lane, Stretton, Tilston, Malpas, SY14 7HS.* **Open:** All year (not Xmas/New Year)
01829 250641 Fax: 01829 250596 *dradcl000@ aol.com* **D:** £25.00–£29.00 **S:** £25.00–£29.00 **Beds:** 1F 1T 1D 1S **Baths:** 1 En 1 Pr 1 Sh 🅿(20)✓📺📺 ▥🏅
C17th country house near Stretton Water Mill, Carden Park Golf Course, The Sandstone Trail and 15 minutes drive south of historic Chester. Comfortable and quiet. Large gardens and spacious parking area. 1m from Jacobean pub/restaurant.

Stretton (Warrington)

SJ6182

The School House, *Stretton Road, Stretton, Warrington, Cheshire, WA4 4NT.* Old headmaster's school house (1835). Now an upmarket B&B - semi-rural location. **Open:** All year (not Xmas/New Year)
01925 730826 D: £22.50 **S:** £35.00 **Beds:** 4F 1T 3D **Baths:** 4 En

Tarporley

SJ5462

1 Bunbury Court, *Eaton Road, Tarporley, Cheshire, CW6 0DL.* Situated in lovely Cheshire village. Close to restaurants and inns. **Open:** All year
01829 733452 Mrs Spencer **D:** £17.50 **S:** £18.50 **Beds:** 1T 1D **Baths:** 1 Sh 🅿(1)📺🐾▥🏅

Foresters Arms, *92 High Street, Tarporley, Cheshire, CW6 0AX.* A traditional country inn offering fine ales and comfortable rooms. **Open:** All year (not Xmas/New Year)
01829 733151 Mr Hulse **Fax: 01829 730020 D:** £18.00–£22.50 **S:** £18.00–£22.50 **Beds:** 4T 2D **Baths:** 2 En 3 Sh ♿(10)🅿(20)📺📺 ▥cc

Tilston

SJ4551

Tilston Lodge, *Tilston, Malpas, Cheshire, SY14 7DR.* Handsome country house with spacious grounds. Luxuriously equipped quiet bedrooms. **Open:** All year (not Xmas/New Year)
01829 250223 (also fax) Mrs Ritchie **D:** £33.00–£35.00 **S:** £43.00–£45.00 **Beds:** 1T 1D **Baths:** 2 En ♿🅿(10)✓📺📺 ▥🏅

Timbersbrook

SJ8962 🍺 *Church House, Robin Hood*

Pedley House Farm, *Pedley Lane, Timbersbrook, Congleton, Cheshire, CW12 3QD.* Free range eggs, home-made jam for breakfast. **Open:** All year (not Xmas/New Year)
01260 273650 (also fax) Mrs Gilman **D:** £18.00 **S:** £18.00–£20.00 **Beds:** 1F 1T 1D **Baths:** 3 Sh ♿🅿(3)📺📺 ▥🏅

Planning a longer stay? Always ask for any special rates

Tiverton

SJ5460

The Gables, *Tiverton, Tarporley, Cheshire, CW6 9NH.* Beautiful country cottage set amidst almost 1/2 acre of gardens. **Open:** All year
01829 733028 Mr Wilson **Fax: 01829 733399 D:** £17.50–£19.00 **S:** £25.00–£35.00 **Beds:** 3D **Baths:** 1 Sh ♿🅿(8)✓📺🐾📺 ▥🏅

Tytherington

SJ9175 🍺 *Cock & Pheasant*

Moorhayes House Hotel, *27 Manchester Road, Tytherington, Macclesfield, Cheshire, SK10 2JJ.* Warm welcome. Hearty breakfast. Half a mile north of Macclesfield. **Open:** All year (not Xmas/New Year) **Grades:** ETC 3 Diamond
01625 433228 (also fax) Helen Wood *helen@ moorhayeshouse.freeserve.co.uk* **D:** £26.00– £30.00 **S:** £35.00–£40.00 **Beds:** 1F 1T 5D 1S **Baths:** 8 En ♿🅿(14)✓📺🐾📺 ▥🏅cc

Warrington

SJ6088

Brook Farm, *Manchester Road, Hollins Green, Warrington, Cheshire, WA3 6HX.* **Open:** All year (not Xmas/New Year)
0161 775 6053 (also fax) Mr Hesford **D:** £18.00–£20.00 **S:** £21.00–£25.00 **Beds:** 2T 2D 2S **Baths:** 3 En 1 Sh 🅿(20)🐾📺 ▥🏅
Situated in a semi-rural location, close to M6, M62, M56 and 15 mins Manchester Airport. A working farm and equestrian centre. Central for Manchester and Warrington for business or leisure. Known for our 'big breakfast'.

New House Farm, *Hatton Lane, Stretton, Warrington, Cheshire, WA4 4BZ.* Fields surround cottages 1 mile, M56, J10, 4 miles south of Warrington **Open:** All year
01925 730567 & 01925 264326 Mrs Delooze *newhousefarmcottage@talk21.com* **D:** £18.00– £20.00 **S:** £18.00–£20.00 **Beds:** 1D 2T 1S **Baths:** 1 En 1 Pr 1 Sh ♿🅿(30)✓📺✕📺 ▥🏅

Braemar Guest House, *274 Manchester Road, Woolston, Warrington, WA1 4PS.* Large family house on A57 1/2 mile from J21 on M6. **Open:** All year
01925 491683 Mr Freeman **Fax: 01244 836666 D:** £20.00–£25.00 **Beds:** 2S **Baths:** 1 Sh 🅿(5)📺✕▥🏅

The Hollies, *1 Long Lane, Orford, Warrington, Cheshire, WA2 8PT.* Small & friendly. New bathroom & beds this year. Great cooked breakfasts. **Open:** All year (not Xmas/New Year)
01925 635416 (also fax) Mrs Brown **D:** £17.50–£20.00 **S:** £20.00–£22.00 **Beds:** 1F 2T 1D **Baths:** 1 Sh ♿(5)🅿(8)✓📺📺 ▥🏅

The Cottage Guest House, *37 Tanners Lane, Warrington, Cheshire, WA2 7NL.* Side street location, homely atmosphere, comfortable beds. 3 mins town centre. **Open:** All year (not Xmas/New Year) **01925 631524** Mr & Mrs Ramsdale **Fax: 01925 445400** *j.h.@3pigeons.fsnet.co.uk* **D:** £16.00–£18.00 **S:** £20.00–£22.00 **Beds:** 3T 1S **Baths:** 2 En 2 Sh ♥ ☐ (6) ⧖ ☑ ✕ ▥ ৬ ☀

Weston (Crewe)

SJ7352 ⬤ *Broughton Arms, White Lion*

Snape Farm, *Snape Lane, Weston, Crewe, Cheshire, CW2 5NB.* Quiet location within easy reach of M6. Superb farmhouse breakfasts. **Open:** All year (not Xmas/New Year) **Grades:** ETC 3 Diamond **01270 820208 (also fax)** Mrs Williamson **D:** £20.00–£25.00 **S:** £22.00–£28.00 **Beds:** 2T 1D **Baths:** 1 En 2 Sh

Willington Corner

SJ5366 ⬤ *The Boot*

Roughlow Farm, *Willington Corner, Tarporley, Cheshire, CW6 0PG.* Sandstone farmhouse. Lovely views, peaceful location. Top quality accommodation. **Open:** All year **Grades:** ETC 4 Diamond **01829 751199 (also fax)** Mrs Sutcliffe *sutcliffe@roughlow.freeserve.co.uk* www.roughlow.freeserve.co.uk **D:** £25.00–£40.00 **S:** £10.00 **Beds:** 12D **Baths:** 3 En ♥ (3) ☐ (6) ⧖ ☑ ✝ ☑ ▥ ☀

Wilmslow

SJ8480

The Grange, *Clay Lane, Handforth, Wilmslow, Cheshire, SK9 3NR.* Set in rural surroundings but close airport, motorway and trains. **Open:** All year **01625 523653** Mrs Godlee **Fax: 01625 530140** *alisongodlee@lineone.net* **D:** £20.00 **S:** £30.00 **Beds:** 3F 1T 2S **Baths:** 3 En ♥ ☐ (6) ⧖ ☑ ▥ ☀

Tulip Tree Guest House, *7 Longmeade Gdns, Wilmslow, SK9 1DA.* 2 minutes from train station. One stop Manchester airport. 40 restaurant/cafes nearby. **Open:** All year **01625 536709 & 01625 530654** Mrs Armstrong **D:** £20.00–£30.00 **S:** £25.00–£30.00 **Beds:** 1F 1T 1D 1S ☐ ⧖ ☑ ▥ ☀ ☀

Wincle

SJ9566

Hill Top Farm, *Wincle, Macclesfield, Cheshire, SK11 0QH.* Peaceful, comfortable farmhouse accommodation, set in beautiful countryside. Lovely walks. **Open:** All year (not Xmas) **01260 227257** Mrs Brocklehurst *a.brocklehurst@talk21.com* **D:** £20.00 **S:** £22.00 **Beds:** 2T 1D **Baths:** 2 En 1 Pr ♥ ☐ (4) ⧖ ☑ ✕ ☑ ▥ ☀

Winsford

SJ6566

Hermitage House, *1 Hareswood Close, Winsford, Cheshire, CW7 2TP.* Close to Oulten Park, Delamere Forest. Warm, friendly house. **Open:** All year (not Xmas/New Year) **01606 550544 (also fax)** Mrs Campbell **D:** £30.00 **S:** £20.00–£25.00 **Beds:** 1T 1D 1S **Baths:** 2 En 1 Sh ♥ ☐ (3) ☑ ✝ ✕ ☑ ▥ ☀

Wistaston

SJ6853

Greenfields, *518 Crewe Road, Wistaston, Crewe, Cheshire, CW2 6PS.* Non-smoking, pleasant residential area. Midway Crewe - Nantwich. Parking available. **Open:** All year (not Xmas/New Year) **01270 569325** Mrs Gildea **D:** £18.00–£19.00 **S:** £18.00–£19.00 **Beds:** 1T 2S **Baths:** 1 Sh ☐ (4) ⧖ ☑ ▥ ☀

Wybunbury

SJ6949

Lea Farm, *Wrinehill Road, Wybunbury, Nantwich, Cheshire, CW5 7HS.* Charming farmhouse set in landscaped gardens where peacocks roam. **Open:** All year (not Xmas) **Grades:** ETC 3 Diamond **01270 841429 (also fax)** Mrs Callwood **D:** £19.00 **S:** £22.00 **Beds:** 1F 1D 1T **Baths:** 2 Pr 1 Sh ♥ ☐ (22) ☑ ✝ ☑ ☀

Cornwall

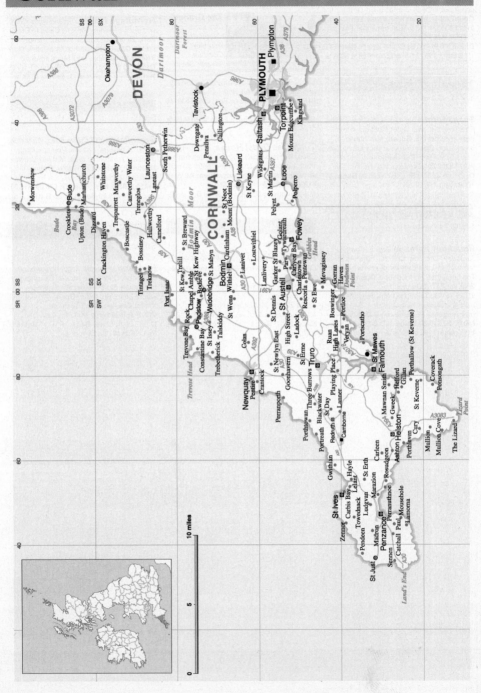

Blackwater

SW7346 ◀ The Victoria, Chiverton Arms

Rock Cottage, Blackwater, Truro, Cornwall, *TR4 8EU.* C18th beamed cob cottage. Haven for non-smokers. Full central heating. **Open:** All year (not Xmas/New Year) **Grades:** ETC 4 Diamond, AA 4 Diamond
01872 560252 (also fax) Mrs Wakeling *rockcottage@yahoo.com* **D:** £22.00–£24.00 **S:** £26.00–£28.00 **Beds:** 2D 1T **Baths:** 3 En ⊞ (3) ⍻ ⊠ Ⅲ. ≛ **cc**

Bodieve

SW9973 ◀ Swan Inn

The Mowhay, Bodieve, Wadebridge, Cornwall, *PL27 6EG.* Modern bungalow, easy reach North Coast, Camel Trail, Bodmin Moor. **Open:** All year (not Xmas/New Year)
01208 814078 Mrs Lloyd **D:** £17.50–£20.00 **S:** £17.50–£20.00 **Beds:** 1T 2D **Baths:** 1 En 1 Sh ⊞ (4) ⊠ Ⅲ. ≛

Bodmin

SX0667

Bokiddick Farm, Lanivet, Bodmin, Cornwall, *PL30 5HP.* **Open:** All year (not Xmas)
Grades: ETC 5 Diamond, Gold
01208 831481 (also fax) Mrs Hugo *gillhugo@ bokiddickfarm.co.uk* www.bokiddickfarm.co.uk **D:** £25.00 **S:** £28.00–£32.00 **Beds:** 1F 2D **Baths:** 3 En ⍾ (5) ⊞ (4) ⍻ ⊠ Ⅲ. ≛
Georgian farmhouse, oak beams, wood panelling, magnificent views, peaceful location. Central for touring all Cornwall. Close to Eden Project and NT Lanhydrock House. Working dairy farm. Delicious breakfasts cooked on Aga. On the Saints' Way Walk and Cornish Way Cycle Route.

High Cross Farm, Lanivet, Bodmin, Cornwall, *PL30 5JR.* **Open:** All year (not Xmas)
01208 831341
D: £16.00
S: £20.00
Beds: 1F 1D 1T **Baths:** 1 En 1 Sh ⍾ ⊞ (6) ⍻ ⊠ × Ⅲ. ≛
Victorian farmhouse, set within 91 acres in geographical centre of Cornwall. Ideal location for touring the north and south coasts and Bodmin Moor. Close to Eden Project, Lanhydrock, Lost Gardens of Heligan. Fishing, cycling, golf, horse riding within area.

Boscastle

SX1090 ◀ Napoleon Inn, Old Manor House

The Old Coach House, Tintagel Road, Boscastle, Cornwall, *PL35 0AS.* 350 year-old coach house near coastal path and woodland walks. **Open:** All year **Grades:** ETC 4 Diamond, AA 4 Diamond
01840 250398 Mrs & Mrs Parsons **Fax:** 01840 250346 *parsons@old-coach.co.uk* www.old-coach.co.uk **D:** £19.00–£22.00 **S:** £25.00–£36.00 **Beds:** 3F 4D 1T **Baths:** 8 En ⍾ ⊞ (9) ⍻ ⊠ ✗ ⊠ Ⅲ. ≛ & **cc**

Bridge House, Boscastle, Cornwall, *PL35 0HE.* Cornish Stone. Central, level, parking adjacent. Ensuite power showers/TV. **Open:** All year **Grades:** ETC 3 Diamond
01840 250011 **Fax: 01840** 250860 **D:** £19.00–£27.00 **S:** £19.00–£24.00 **Beds:** 2F 1T 5D **Baths:** 7 En 1 Sh ⍾ (0) ⍻ ⊠ ✗ ⊠ Ⅲ. ≛ **cc**

Tolcarne House Hotel & Restaurant, Tingel Road, Boscastle, Cornwall, *PL35 0AS.* Victorian character house with spectacular views and large grounds. **Open:** Mar to Nov
01840 250654 & 0500 131238 Mr & Mrs Crown **Fax:** 01840 250654 *crowntolhouse@ eclipse.co.uk* www.milford.co.uk/go/tolcarne. html **D:** £25.00–£32.00 **S:** £30.00–£32.00 **Beds:** 1F 2T 4D 2S **Baths:** 9 En ⍾ (10) ⊞ (12) ⊠ ⍾ ✗ Ⅲ. ≛ **cc**

Pencarmol, The Harbour, Boscastle, Cornwall, *PL35 0HA.* Pencarmol is a 300-year-old Listed house dramatically situated overlooking Boscastle Harbour. **Open:** Feb to Oct
01840 250435 Mrs Murphy *enquiries@ pencarmol.co.uk* www.pencarmol.co.uk **D:** £20.00–£22.50 **S:** £25.00–£30.00 **Beds:** 1F 2D **Baths:** 3 En ⊞ (3) ⍻ ⊠ ⊠ Ⅲ. ≛

Bossiney

SX0688

The Old Borough House, Bossiney, Tintagel, Cornwall, *PL34 0AY.* Traditional C16th Cornish house close to coastal path, luxury bedrooms. **Open:** All year (not Xmas)
01840 770475 (also fax) Mrs Bryant *borough@fsbdial.co.uk* **D:** £25.00–£30.00 **S:** £35.00 **Beds:** 3D 1T **Baths:** 3 En 1 Pr ⍾ (12) ⊞ (10) ⍻ ⊠ ✗ ⊠ Ⅲ. & **cc**

Please respect a B&B's wishes regarding children, animals and smoking

Boswinger

SW9840

The Granary, Boswinger, Gorran, St Austell, Cornwall, *PL26 6LL.* Comfortable bedrooms. Scrumptious breakfasts/suppers. Spectacular sea views. Warm welcome. **Open:** All year (not Xmas/New Year)
01726 844381 S Chubb *hoildays@ thegranaryboswinger.freeserve.co.uk* www.cornwallbandb.co.uk **D:** £16.00–£19.00 **S:** £18.00–£22.00 **Beds:** 2D 1T **Baths:** 2 Pr 1 Sh ⍾ ⊞ (3) ⊠ ✗ ⊠ Ⅲ. ≛

Bude

SS2106 ◀ The Carriers, Brendon Arms, Falcon

Brendon Arms, Falcon Terrace, Bude, Cornwall, *EX23 8SD.* **Open:** All year (not Xmas/New Year) **Grades:** ETC 2 Diamond
01288 354542 (also fax) Ms Brendon *sophia@sophiafrbrendon.demon.co.uk* www.brendonarms.co.uk **D:** £25.00–£29.00 **S:** £25.00–£29.00 **Beds:** 3T 4D **Baths:** 7 En ⊞ ⊠ ✗ Ⅲ. ≛ **cc**
Situated in a picturesque part of Bude, just a short stroll from the beach, The Brendon Arms offers very comfortable ensuite bed and breakfast accommodation, an extensive bar food menu, including local seafood, and a good range of beers.

Seagulls, 11 Downs View, Bude, Cornwall, *EX23 8RF.* **Open:** All year (not Xmas/New Year)
Grades: ETC 3 Diamond
01288 352059 Mr Watkiss **Fax: 01288 359259** *contactus@seagullsguesthouse.co.uk* www.seagullsguesthouse.co.uk **D:** £16.00–£22.00 **S:** £16.00–£27.00 **Beds:** 1F 4D 1S **Baths:** 5 En 1 Sh ⍾ ⍻ ⊠ Ⅲ. ≛ **cc**
Delightful Victorian guest house overlooking golf course, situated a few minutes' walk from glorious beaches, Coastal Path and town centre. Ideal for touring. Pretty, comfortable rooms, tastefully decorated. Delicious full English breakfast, freshly cooked using local produce. Friendly relaxed atmosphere.

Planning a longer stay? Always ask for any special rates

BEDROOMS
D = Double
T = Twin
S = Single
F = Family

Surf Haven, *31 Downs View, Bude, Cornwall, EX23 8RG.* Every comfort, 200 yards from beach, overlooking golf course. Walks galore. **Open:** All year (not Xmas)
01288 353923 (also fax) Mrs Drew
surfhaven@bude33.fsnet.co.uk www.surfhaven.co.uk **D:** £17.00–£26.00 **S:** £20.00–£30.00
Beds: 7D/T **Baths:** 7 En ▣ (6) ⊬ ▥ ⊁ ▥, ⚤

Harefield Cottage, *Upton, Bude, Cornwall, EX23 0LY.* Luxurious cottage with outstanding views. Ideal for walking/touring holiday. **Open:** All year
01288 352350 Mrs Trewin **Fax: 01288 352712**
sally@coast-countryside.co.uk
www.coast-countryside.co.uk **D:** £22.00–£44.00 **S:** £22.00–£30.00 **Beds:** 2D 1T
Baths: 3 En ▤ ▣ (4) ⊬ ▥ ⊁ × ▥, ⚤

St Merryn, *Coastview, Bude, Cornwall, EX23 8AG.* A large dormer bungalow with good sized ground floor bedrooms.
Open: All year
01288 352058 Miss Abbot **Fax: 01288 359050**
st.merryn@ukonline.co.uk www.stmerryn.org.uk **D:** £15.00–£17.00 **S:** £20.00–£25.00
Beds: 1F 1D 1T 1S **Baths:** 2 Sh ▤ ▣ (4) ⊬ ▥ ⊁ ▥, & ⚤

Sunrise Guest House, *6 Burn View, Bude, Cornwall, EX23 8BY.* Delightful features, high standards of hospitality. Centrally located. All rooms ensuite. **Open:** Feb to Nov
01288 353214 & 07714 274650 (M)
Mr Masters **D:** £18.00–£23.00 **S:** £18.00–£25.00 **Beds:** 1F 3D 1T 1S **Baths:** 6 En ▤ (3) ▣ (2) ⊬ ▥ ▥, & ⚤

Callington
SX3669

Dozmary, *Tors View Close, Tavistock Road, Callington, Cornwall, PL17 7DY.* Spacious dormer bungalow in quiet cul-de-sac near town centre. **Open:** All year (not Xmas) **Grades:** ETC 3 Diamond
01579 383677 Mrs Wills *dozmarybb@aol.com*
D: £17.00–£18.00 **S:** £20.00–£21.00 **Beds:** 1F 1D 1T **Baths:** 2 En 1 Pr ▤ ▣ (4) ⊬ ▥ ▥, ⚤

Camelford
SX1083   🍴 *Darlington Arms, Maltsters' Arms, Masons' Arms, New Inn, Old School House, Oscar's, Red Lion, Slipway Hotel, White Hart*

The Old Manse, *11 Victoria Road, Camelford, Cornwall, PL32 9XA.* Stunning, listed building. Spacious, comfortable accommodation. **Open:** All year (not Xmas/New Year)
01840 211066 & 07712 202976 (M) Mr Allen
D: £20.00–£23.00 **S:** £23.00–£25.00 **Beds:** 1T 1D 1S **Baths:** 2 En ▤ ▣ (2) ⊬ ▥ ▥, ⚤

Canworthy Water
SX2291   🍴 *Combe Barton Inn*

Deer Park, *Canworthy Water, Launceston, Cornwall, PL15 8UW.* Warm welcome to 200 year old farmhouse. Peaceful rural location. Ideal for coast and Bodmin Moor. **Open:** All year (not Xmas/New Year)
01566 781325 Mr & Mrs Strickland **D:** £15.00 **S:** £15.00 **Beds:** 1F 1D **Baths:** 1 Pr ▤ ▣ (3) ⊬ ▥ ⊁ ▥, ⚤

Carbis Bay
SW5238   🍴 *Badger Inn, Cornish Arms, Cornishman*

St Merryn Hotel, *Trelyon, Carbis Bay, St Ives, Cornwall, TR26 2PN.*
Open: All year
01736 795767
Fax: 01736 797248
D: £20.00–£27.00 **S:** £20.00–£27.00 **Beds:** 6F 1T 9D 3S **Baths:** 19 En ▤ ▣ (24) ▥ × ▥ ▥, ⚤ cc
Standing in its own spacious grounds and gardens on the main St Ives road, the hotel occupies an ideal position overlooking St Ives Bay. Well stocked, comfortable licensed bar. Large private car park at rear of hotel, with easy access.

Headland House, *Headland Road, Carbis Bay, St Ives, Cornwall, TR26 2NS.* Family-run Victorian house with stunning views of St Ives Bay. **Open:** All year
01736 796647 (also fax) Mrs Antonini
headlandhouse@btinternet.com **D:** £18.00–£25.00 **S:** £18.00–£25.00 **Beds:** 3F 1T 3D **Baths:** 5 En 1 Sh ▤ ▣ (10) ▥ ⊁ ▥ ▥, ⚤

Planning a longer stay? Always ask for any special rates

Cardinham
SX1268

The Stables, *Cardinham, Bodmin, Cornwall, PL30 4EG.* Peaceful location on edge of Bodmin Moor. Ideal area for walking & cycling. **Open:** All year
01208 821316 Mr Moseley *gerald@stablebarns.freeserve.co.uk* **D:** £16.00–£19.00
S: £16.00–£25.00 **Beds:** 3T 1D 1S **Baths:** 2 En 2 Pr 1 Sh ▤ (4) ▣ (4) ⊬ ▥ × ▥ ▥, ⚤

Carleen
SW6130

Poldown Camping Park, *Carleen, Helston, Cornwall, TR13 9NN.* Charming cottage with pretty rooms in beautiful garden. Centrally situated.
Open: June to Sept
01326 574560 (also fax) Mr Rhodes
primrose@poldown.co.uk www.chycor.co.uk/camping/poldown/bnb **D:** £16.00
S: £20.00 **Beds:** 2D **Baths:** 1 Sh ▤ ▣ (2) ▥ ⊁ ▥, ⚤

Carlyon Bay
SX0552   🍴 *Britannia Inn, Rashleigh Arms, Cliff Head*

Amberley, *Crinnis Close, Carlyon Bay, St Austell, Cornwall, PL25 3SE.* Ideal for Eden Project. Golf course and beach nearby.
Open: All year (not Xmas/New Year)
01726 815174 Mrs Pipe *raypipe@ntlworld.com*
D: £17.00 **S:** £20.00 **Beds:** 2T **Baths:** 1 Sh ▣ (2) ⊬ ▥ ▥, ⚤

16 Hadden Way, *Carlyon Bay, St Austell, Cornwall, PL25 3QG.* Lovely accommodation/gardens. Quiet coastal area betwixt beaches and Eden Project. **Open:** Easter to Oct
01726 815566 Mrs Buckingham
www.buckingham.fsbusiness.co.uk
D: £19.00–£21.00 **S:** £25.00–£30.00 **Beds:** 1D
Baths: 1 En ▤ (12) ▣ (2) ⊬ ▥ ▥, ⚤

Catchall
SW4228

Coth A Noweth, *Catchall, Penzance, Cornwall, TR19 6AQ.* Detached house; stream borders large garden. Convenient for Penwith's attractions. **Open:** Easter to Sept **Grades:** AA 2 Diamond
01736 810572 Mrs Craigue **D:** £15.00–£17.00
S: £15.00 **Beds:** 2F 1D 1T **Baths:** 1 Sh ▤ ▣ (7) ▥ ▥ ▥, ⚤

All details shown are as supplied by B&B owners in Autumn 2001

Chapel Amble
SW9975

Kivells, *Chapel Amble, Wadebridge, PL27 6EP.* Comfortable, attractive house and gardens set amid peaceful countryside. **Open:** Easter to Oct **01208 841755** Mr & Mrs Hosegood *info@ kivellsbandb.co.uk* www.kivellsbandb.co.uk **D:** £20.00–£24.00 **S:** £20.00–£26.00 **Beds:** 1T 2D **Baths:** 1 En 1 Sh ☺ (12) ▣ (5) ⚡ ▦ ▥ ♨

Charlestown
SX0351 ◀ *Rashleigh Amrs, Pier House, Polgooth Inn*

Ardenconnel, *179 Charlestown Road, Charlestown, St Austell, Cornwall, PL25 3NN.* Beautiful Victorian house situated in the unchanged C18th port of Charlestown. **Open:** All year **01726 75469** Mr Callis *ardenconnel@ hotmail.com* **D:** £21.00–£25.00 **S:** £29.00–£33.00 **Beds:** 1F 1T 1D **Baths:** 1 En 1 Pr ☺ ▣ (2) ⚡ ▦ ▥ ▦ ♨

Colan
SW8661

Colan Barton Farmhouse, *Colan, Newquay, Cornwall, TR8 4NB.* C17th farmhouse set in stunning countryside. Self-contained cottage adjacent. Warm welcome. **Open:** Apr to Sept **Grades:** AA 4 Diamond **01637 874395** Mrs Machan-Weaver **Fax: 01637 881388** *colanbarton.hotmail.com@ barclays.net* **D:** £16.00–£24.00 **S:** £21.00–£29.00 **Beds:** 3F 1T 1D **Baths:** 1 En 1 Pr ☺ ▣ (6) ⚡ ▦ ▥ ♨

Constantine Bay
SW8574

Chyloweth, *Constantine Bay, Padstow, Cornwall, PL28 8JQ.* Quiet location close to sandy beaches and Trevose Golf Club. **Open:** All year **Grades:** ETC 3 Diamond **01841 521012** R & S Vivian *ROGER.VIVIAN@ ukgateway.net* **D:** £20.00–£25.00 **S:** £25.00–£27.50 **Beds:** 1T 1D **Baths:** 2 En ☺ ▣ (2) ⚡ ▦ ▥ ▦ ♨

Coverack
SW7818 ◀ *The Paris, Fodder Barn*

Boak House, *Coverack, Helston, Cornwall, TR12 6SH.* Seaside guest house overlooking harbour and cove. Sea views from rooms. **Open:** Easter to Nov **01326 280608** Mrs Watters www.bedandbreakfastcornwall. com/members-house/boakhouse.htm **D:** £18.50–£19.00 **Beds:** 2F 1T 1D 1S **Baths:** 1 Sh ☺ ▣ (2) ▥ ♨ ✕ ♨

Wych Elm, *Ponsongath, Coverack, Helston, Cornwall, TR12 6SQ.* Idyllic quiet setting close secluded Lankidden Cove. Backwoodsmen's bliss! **Open:** All year (not Xmas) **01326 280576** Mrs Whitaker **D:** £18.00 **S:** £20.00 **Beds:** 1T **Baths:** 1 En ☺ (8) ▣ (2) ⚡ ▥ ♨ ✕ ▥ ▦

Tamarisk Cottage, *North Corner, Coverack, Helston, Cornwall, TR12 6TG.* C18th cottage overlooking bay. On footpath. Parking and wash basin. **Open:** Easter to Oct **01326 280638** Mrs Carey **D:** £17.00 **S:** £17.00 **Beds:** 1T 1D 1S **Baths:** 1 Sh ☺ (8) ▣ (2) ♨ ▥ ♨

Crackington Haven
SX1496 ◀ *Coombe Barton Inn, Widemouth Manor, Bullers' Arms, Wilsey Down Hotel*

Hallagather, *Crackington Haven, Bude, Cornwall, EX23 0LA.* Ancient farmhouse, warm, welcoming. Substantial buffet style breakfast. Spectacular scenery. **Open:** Feb to Nov **01840 230276 (also fax)** Mrs Anthony **D:** £17.50–£24.00 **S:** £18.00–£26.00 **Beds:** 1F 1D 1S **Baths:** 3 En ☺ (11) ▣ (6) ⚡ ▥ ▥ ▦ ♨

Venn Park Farm, *Crackington Haven, Bude, Cornwall, EX23 0LB.* Relaxation opportunity. Sea/countryside views. 2 miles beach. Coastal/moorland walks. **Open:** All year **01840 230159 (also fax)** Jane Wilson **D:** £18.00–£22.00 **S:** £18.00–£24.00 **Beds:** 1F 2D **Baths:** 2 En 1 Pr ☺ ▣ ⚡ ▥ ♨ ✕ ▦ ❄ ♨

RATES

D = Price range per person sharing in a double or twin room

S = Price range for a single room

Crantock
SW7960 ◀ *Old Albion, Cornishman, Bowgie Inn, Smugglers Den*

Carden Cottage, *Halwyn Hill, Crantock, Newquay, Cornwall, TR8 5RR.* **Open:** All year (not Xmas/New Year) **01637 830806** Mr Clark **D:** £20.00–£22.00 **S:** £20.00–£22.00 **Beds:** 1T 2D **Baths:** 3 En ☺ (10) ▣ (4) ⚡ ▥ ▥ ▦ ♨ A beautiful place with king-size beds, tea and coffee, soap and towels and a full English breakfast, situated in the heart of the village, with two pubs, a church and a few minutes walk from a lovely sandy beach.

Highfield Lodge Hotel, *Halwyn Road, Crantock, Newquay, Cornwall, TR8 5TR.* Friendly non-smoking hotel in picturesque village with sandy beach **Open:** All year (not Xmas/New Year) **Grades:** ETC 3 Diamond **01637 830744 Fax: 01637 830568** www.highfieldlodge.co.uk **D:** £18.00–£23.00 **S:** £18.00–£26.00 **Beds:** 1T 7D 1S **Baths:** 6 En 1 Sh ▣ (12) ▥ ✕ ▦ ♨ cc

Crooklets
SS2006

Inn on the Green, *Crooklets Beach, Crooklets, Bude, Cornwall, EX23 8NF.* **Open:** All year (not Xmas/New Year) **01288 356013** Mr & Mrs Bellward **Fax: 01288 356244** *innonthegreen46@btinternet.com* www.innonthegreen46.co.uk **D:** £24.00–£30.00 **S:** £30.00–£42.00 **Beds:** 2F 10T 7D 5S **Baths:** 17 En 3 Sh ☺ ▣ (4) ▥ ♨ ✕ ▥ ▦ ♨ cc This family-run hotel, has a reputation for comfort and service. Only 100 metres from the beach and a short walk from town centre. Wholesome locally produced food is served, & a well stocked bar is open every day.

B&B owners may vary rates – be sure to check when booking

Planning a longer stay? Always ask for any special rates

Cury

SW6721 🖣 *Old Inn, Wheel Inn*

Colvennor Farmhouse, Cury, Helston, Cornwall, TR12 7BJ. Delightful former farmhouse. Peaceful setting. Perfect location for exploring. Excellent hospitality. **Open:** All year (not Xmas/New Year) **Grades:** AA 4 Diamond
01326 241208 Mrs Royds *colvennor@aol.com* **D:** £20.00–£23.00 **S:** £25.00–£28.00 **Beds:** 1T 2D **Baths:** 3 En 🅿 (3) ⚲ 📺 🔟 🞣, ☕

Nanplough Farm, Cury, Whitecross, Helston, Cornwall, TR12 7BQ. Large Victorian farmhouse. Overlooking wooded valley. Beach 1 mile. **Open:** All year
01326 241088 Mr Lepper *william.lepper@ btclick.com* **D:** £22.00–£28.00 **Beds:** 1F 1D **Baths:** 2 En 🏂 🅿 🔟 🞣, ☕

Tregaddra Farmhouse, Cury, Helston, Cornwall, TR12 7BB. Farmhouse B&B quiet, peaceful, set in Area of Outstanding Natural Beauty. **Open:** All year (not Xmas)
01326 240235 (also fax) Mrs Lugg
www.tregaddra.freeserve.co.uk **D:** £20.00–£25.00 **S:** £20.00–£25.00 **Beds:** 2F 4D 1T **Baths:** 6 En 1 Pr 🏂 🅿 (10) ⚲ 📺 ✕ 🔟 cc

Dizzard

SX1698 🖣 *Wainhouse Inn, Coombe Barton Inn*

Trengayor Farm, Dizzard, Bude, Cornwall, EX23 0NX. Secluded 1900 farmhouse, close Coastal Path, Cycle Route. Coastal views. **Open:** All year (not Xmas/New Year)
01840 230427 Mr Jackson **D:** £18.00 **S:** £18.00 **Beds:** 1D 1S **Baths:** 1 Sh 🏂 🅿 (6) ⚲ 🔟 🞣, ☕

Downgate

SX3672 🖣 *Springer Spaniel*

Niggles Nook Guest House, Sandercock Close, Downgate, Callington, Cornwall, PL17 8JS. Modern bungalow set in lovely countryside. Midway north/south coasts. **Open:** All year
01579 370813 S Bartlett **D:** £15.00 **S:** £15.00 **Beds:** 2D **Baths:** 1 Sh 🏂 🅿 (2) ⚲ 📺 🔟 🞣, ☕

Falmouth

SW8032 🖣 *Four Winds, Greenbank Hotel*

Telford Guest House, 47 Melvill Road, Falmouth, Cornwall, TR11 4DG. Ideal base for Cornish holidays. Friendly, personal service assured. **Open:** Feb to Nov
01326 314581 (also fax) A Eschenauer
telford-falmouth@goformet.co.uk
www.smoothhound.co.uk/hotels/telfordg. html **D:** £18.00–£20.00 **Beds:** 1T 4D **Baths:** 5 En 🅿 (5) ⚲ 📺 🞣, ☕

Melvill House Hotel, 52 Melvill Road, Falmouth, Cornwall, TR11 4DQ. **Open:** All year (not Xmas)

Grades: AA 4 Diamond
01326 316645 Mr & Mrs Crawford **Fax:** 01326 211608 *crawfords@crawfords.eurobell.co.uk* www.melvill-house-falmouth.co.uk
D: £19.00–£24.50 **S:** £19.00–£25.00 **Beds:** 2F 3D 2T **Baths:** 7 En 🏂 🅿 (9) ⚲ 📺 🔟 🞣, ☕ cc
Friendly hotel run by Franco-Scottish couple. It has spacious, comfortable and attractive rooms with views of the sea and harbour. Excellent home cooking, table licence, special diets catered for. Lots of ideas for trips and visits for all ages.

Wellington House, 26 Melvill Road, Falmouth, Cornwall, TR11 4AR. Edwardian elegance, perfectly located for harbour, beaches, Maritime Museum, town! **Open:** All year
01326 319947 Mrs Riddette-Jones
www.bedbreadfastcornwall.co.uk **D:** £17.50–£25.00 **S:** £20.00–£30.00 **Beds:** 1F 1T 1D 1S **Baths:** 3 En 1 Pr 🏂 🅿 (4) ⚲ 📺 🔟 🞣, ☕ cc

Ambleside Guest House, 9 Marlborough Road, Falmouth, Cornwall, TR11 3LP. Victorian guest house. Relaxed and friendly. **Open:** All year
01326 319630 Mr Walker **D:** £18.00 **S:** £18.00 **Beds:** 1F 2D 1T 1S **Baths:** 1 Sh 🏂 🅿 📺 🞣, 🔟

Chelsea House Hotel, 2 Emslie Road, Falmouth, Cornwall, TR11 4BG. Enjoy panoramic sea views, close to town and beaches. **Open:** Mar to Oct **Grades:** ETC 3 Diamond
01326 212230 Mr & Mrs Parkes **D:** £20.00–£28.00 **S:** £30.00–£40.00 **Beds:** 2F 1T 3D 1S **Baths:** 7 En 🏂 (4) 🅿 (4) ⚲ 📺 ✕ 🞣, ☕ cc

Trevaylor, 8 Pennance Road, Falmouth, Cornwall, TR11 4EA. Close town and beaches, disabled facilities, sea views, table licence. **Open:** All year (not Xmas/New Year)
01326 313041 **Fax:** 01326 316899 *stay@ trevaylor.co.uk* www.trevaylor.co.uk **D:** £18.00–£25.00 **S:** £20.00–£35.00 **Beds:** 2F 3T 3D 1S **Baths:** 9 En 🏂 🅿 (9) ⚲ 📺 🔟 ✕ 🔟 🞣, ☕ cc

Dolvean Hotel, 50 Melvill Road, Falmouth, Cornwall, TR11 4DQ. Traditional Victorian hotel with old-fashioned standards of care and courtesy. **Open:** All year (not Xmas)
01326 313658 Mrs Crocker **Fax:** 01326 313995 *reservations@dolvean.freeserve.co.uk* www.dolvean.co.uk **D:** £23.00–£27.00 **S:** £25.00–£30.00 **Beds:** 1F 6D 3T 2S **Baths:** 12 En 🏂 (12) 🅿 (12) ⚲ 📺 🔟 🞣, ☕ cc

Beachwalk House, 39 Castle Drive, Falmouth, Cornwall, TR11 4NF. Fabulous views, seafront position, overlooks Falmouth Bay, beaches and castle. **Open:** All year (not Xmas)
01326 319841 Mr & Mrs Clarke **D:** £18.00–£20.00 **S:** £20.00–£25.00 **Beds:** 3D 1T **Baths:** 4 En 🏂 🅿 (4) 📺 🔟 🞣, ☕

Trevu House Hotel, 45 Melvill Road, Falmouth, Cornwall, TR11 4DG. Small select, non-smoking hotel. Superb for town, Princess Pavilion & beautiful gardens. **Open:** All year (not Xmas)
01326 312852 Mrs Eustice **Fax:** 01326 318631 *elaine.eddy@lineone.net* www.trevu-house-hotel.co.uk **D:** £17.50–£21.50 **S:** £17.50–£21.50 **Beds:** 1F 2D 3T 3S **Baths:** 9 En 🏂 (5) 🅿 ⚲ 📺 🔟 🞣, ☕

Rosemullion Hotel, Gyllyngvase Hill, Falmouth, Cornwall, TR11 4DF. Imposing Tudor-style building with balcony rooms, sea view, king-size beds. **Open:** All year
01326 314690 Mrs Jones **Fax:** 01326 210098 **D:** £21.50–£26.00 **S:** £24.50–£26.00 **Beds:** 3T 9D 1S **Baths:** 1 En 2 Pr 🅿 ⚲ 📺 🔟 🞣, ☕

Fowey

SX1251 🖣 *The Lugger, Galleon, Ship, King of Prussia*

St Keverne, 4 Daglands Road, Fowey, Cornwall, PL23 1JL. Comfortable Edwardian house close to town centre, with river views. **Open:** All year (not Xmas)
01726 833164 Mrs Eardley *carol@ stkeverne1.fsnet.co.uk* **D:** £22.00 **S:** £22.00 **Beds:** 2D **Baths:** 2 En 🅿 (1) ⚲ 📺 🔟 🞣, ☕

Pendower, 11 Park Road, Fowey, Cornwall, PL23 1EB. River views both rooms. 7 mins town. 5 miles Eden Project. **Open:** Apr to Oct
01726 833559 Mrs Dorkins **D:** £20.00–£22.00 **S:** £23.00–£25.00 **Beds:** 1T 1D **Baths:** 2 Pr 🏂 🅿 (2) ⚲ 📺 🔟 🞣

Safe Harbour Hotel, Lostwithiel Road, Fowey, Cornwall, PL23 1BD. Friendly inn, river views, car parking, quiet lounge bar, full menu available. **Open:** All year
01726 833379 **D:** £21.00–£25.00 **S:** £25.00 **Beds:** 2F 2D 1T **Baths:** 5 En 🏂 🅿 (8) ⚲ 📺 🔟 ✕ 🞣, ☕

Garker

SX0454

Restineas Cottage, Garker, St Austell, Cornwall, PL26 8YA. Country cottage set in two acre garden and grounds. Peaceful surroundings. **Open:** All year (not Xmas/ New Year)
01726 812171 (also fax) Mrs Sampson **D:** £20.00–£25.00 **S:** £30.00–£35.00 **Beds:** 1D **Baths:** 1 Pr 🅿 (1) ⚲ 📺 ✕ 🞣, ☕

Planning a longer stay? Always ask for any special rates

Gillan

SW7824 New Inn, Shipwright's Arms, Five Pilchards, Three Tuns, White Hart

Porthvean, Gillan, Manaccan, Helston, Cornwall, TR12 6HL. Specially suitable Coastal Footpath walkers. Views, Gillan Creek and Helford. **Open:** All year (not Xmas/New Year)
01326 231204 E A Whale **D:** £16.50 **S:** £16.50 **Beds:** 1T **Baths:** 1 En ▣ (2) ⚡ ☑ ➤ 🛏 ▥ ₤

Golant

SX1254 Fisherman's Arms, Royal Oak

Bellscat, Golant, Fowley, Cornwall, PL23 1LA. A gentleman's residence situated in stunning countryside overlooking the River Fowey. **Open:** All year (not Xmas/New Year)
01726 833404 *carol_white@ bellscat.freeserve.co.uk* cornwall-online.co.uk
D: £22.50–£25.00 **S:** £15.00–£30.00 ☎ (12) ▣ ⚡ ☑ ▣ ▥ ₤

Goonhavern

SW7853

September Lodge, Wheal Hope, Goonhavern, Truro, Cornwall, TR4 9QJ. Modern house with countryside views. Ideally situated for touring Cornwall. **Open:** All year (not Xmas/New Year)
jc.septlodge@virgin.net **D:** £20.00 **S:** £25.00– £28.00 **Beds:** 1F 1D **Baths:** 2 En ☎ ▣ (10) ⚡ ☑ ➤ ☑ ▥ ₤ Mr Philipps

Gorran Haven

SX0041 Llawnroc Inn

Homestead, 34 Chute Lane, Gorran Haven, St Austell, Cornwall, PL26 6NU. Cottage/beach 100m overlooking garden. Parking. Easy reach Heligan/Eden. **Open:** All year
01726 842567 Mr & Mrs Smith **D:** £25.00 **S:** £50.00 **Beds:** 1T 1D **Baths:** 2 Pr ▣ ⚡ ▥

Piggys Pantry, The Willows, Gorran Haven, St Austell, Cornwall, PL26 6JG. Detached family bungalow. Close to beach, Heligan Gardens and Eden Project. **Open:** All year
01726 843545 G Mott *piggyspantry@ hotmail.com* www.piggyspantry.co.uk **D:** £20.00 **S:** £25.00 **Beds:** 1T 1D 1S **Baths:** 1 Sh ▣ ⚡ ☑ ➤ ☑ ▥ ₤

Please respect a B&B's wishes regarding children, animals and smoking

Grampound

SW9348

Perran House, Grampound, Truro, Cornwall, TR2 4RS. **Open:** All year
Grades: ETC 3 Diamond, AA 3 Diamond
01726 882066 Mr Diboll **Fax: 01726 882936**
perran-house@faxvia.net **D:** £18.00–£20.00 **S:** £16.00–£17.00 **Beds:** 3D 1T 2S **Baths:** 3 En 1 Sh ☎ ▣ (8) ⚡ ☑ ☑ ▥ ₤
Delightful C17th cottage in the pretty village of Grampound within a conservation area. Centrally located for touring, visiting the many nearby gardens including the Lost Gardens of Heligan and the Eden Project. Also within easy reach of the coastal footpaths.

Gweek

SW7026 Sweet Inn

Barton Farm, Gweek, Helston, Cornwall, TR13 0QH. **Open:** All year (not Xmas/New Year)
01326 572557 *bartonfarm@talk21.com* www.cornwall-online.co.uk/barton-farm
D: £16.00–£18.00 **S:** £17.50–£20.00 **Beds:** 1T 2D **Baths:** 1 Pr 1 Sh ☎ ▣ (5) ⚡ ☑ ☑ ₤
Attractive open beamed farmhouse, a mile from Gweek the head of the beautiful Helford River. Ideal base for exploring all of South West Cornwall from the Lizard to Lands End with its lovely coves, beaches, gardens and coastal walks.

1 Rose Terrace, Gweek, Helston, Cornwall, TR12 6UG. A delightful waterside terraced cottage. Seal Sanctuary within the village. **Open:** All year
01326 221345 Miss Jacobs **D:** £23.00–£24.00 **S:** £23.00–£24.00 **Beds:** 1T 1D **Baths:** 1 Sh ▣ (1) ⚡ ☑ ₤

Gwithian

SW5841

Calize Country House, Prosper Hill, Gwithian, Hayle, Cornwall, TR27 5BW. Country house overlooking sea. Rural location near beautiful beaches/countryside. **Open:** All year
01736 753268 (also fax) Mrs Bailey *penny.bailey@talk21.com* members.tripod. com/PennyBailey/index.html **D:** £16.00– £19.00 **S:** £15.50–£19.00 **Beds:** 3D 2T **Baths:** 3 En 1 Sh ☎ (10) ▣ (5) ⚡ ☑ ➤ 🛏 ▥ ₤

Nanterrow Farm, Gwithian, Hayle, Cornwall, TR27 5BP. **Open:** All year (not Xmas)
01209 712282 Mrs Davies *nanterrow@ hotmail.com* www.nanterrowfarm.co.uk
D: £16.00–£20.00 **S:** £18.00–£22.00 **Beds:** 1F 1D 1S **Baths:** 2 Sh ☎ ▣ (4) ☑ ➤ 🛏 ☑ ₤
Come and enjoy a relaxing stay on our traditional working farm situated in a quiet traffic-free valley 1.5 miles from St Ives Bay. 3 miles of sandy beaches; good area for coastal walks; many other local attractions. Good farmhouse fare.

Hallworthy

SX1887

Wilsey Down Hotel, Hallworthy, Camelford, Cornwall, PL32 9SH. Warm welcome, friendly hotel, views over Bodmin Moor, near to coast. **Open:** All year
01840 261205 J Bremdon **D:** £18.00–£24.00 **S:** £15.00–£18.00 **Beds:** 1F 2T 2D **Baths:** 2 En 1 Pr 1 Sh ☎ ▣ (50) ☑ ✕ ₤ cc

Hayle

SW5537 Bluff Inn, Star Inn, Bucket of Blood

54 Penpol Terrace, Hayle, Cornwall, TR27 4BQ. Large mid-terraced Victorian cottage. Close to Bird Paradise. **Open:** Easter to Nov
01736 752855 A Cooper **D:** £18.00–£22.00 **S:** £20.00–£25.00 **Beds:** 1T 1D **Baths:** 1 Sh ☎ ▣ (2) ⚡ ☑ ☑ ▥ ₤

Helford

SW7526 Shipwrights' Arms, New Inn

Pengwedhen, Helford, Helston, Cornwall, TR12 6JZ. Riverbank gardens. Quay. Verandah with stunning sea and estuary views. **Open:** Easter to Oct
01326 231481 J Davies *nandjdavies@ hotmail.com* **D:** £22.00 **S:** £22.00 **Beds:** 1T 1D 1S **Baths:** 1 Pr 1 Sh ☎ ▣ (3) ☑ ☑ ▥ ₤

Helston

SW6627

Lyndale Guest House, Greenbank, Meneage Road, Helston, Cornwall, TR13 8JA. Pretty cottage style guest house. Central for touring/walking coastal footpath. **Open:** All year
01326 561082 Mrs Tucker **Fax: 01326 565813** *enquiries@lyndale1.freeserve.co.uk* **D:** £16.50– £20.50 **S:** £23.00–£26.00 **Beds:** 1F 3D 2T 1S **Baths:** 3 En 1 Sh ☎ ▣ (6) ☑ ➤ ✕ ☑ ▥ ₤ cc

Planning a longer stay? Always ask for any special rates

High Street

SW9653

Manor Farm, *High Street, Burngullow, St Austell, Cornwall, PL26 7TQ.* Beautiful Grade II Listed manor house. Eden Project, Heligan 6 miles. **Open:** All year (not Xmas/New Year)
01726 72242 (also fax) S Manuell
suzannemanuell@tinyworld.co.uk **D:** £21.00–£22.00 **S:** £25.00–£30.00 **Beds:** 1F 1D
Baths: 2 En ☎ ⓟ (10) ⅙ 📺 Ⅴ ▥ ♨

Kingsand

SX4350

Cliff House, *Devon Port Hill, Kingsand, Torpoint, Cornwall, PL10 1NT.* Listed comfortable house. Sea and country views. Great wholefood cookery. **Open:** All year
01752 823110 Mrs Heasman **Fax:** 01752 822595 *info@cliffhse.abel.co.uk* cliffhse.abel.co.uk **D:** £21.00–£25.00 **S:** £25.00–£35.00
Beds: 3F 3T 2D **Baths:** 3 En 3 Pr ⓟ (3) ⅙ 📺 ✕ ▥ ✿ ♨

Ladock

SW8950

Swallows Court, *Treworyan, Ladock, Truro, Cornwall, TR2 4QD.* Beautifully converted stone barn, peaceful location, delicious breakfasts, friendly atmosphere. **Open:** Mar to Sept
01726 883488 Mrs Harvey **D:** £19.00–£22.00 **S:** £22.00–£25.00 ☎ ⓟ ⅙ 📺 ▥ ♨

Lamorna

SW4425

Tremeneth Hotel, *Lamorna, Penzance, Cornwall, TR19 6XL.* Set in the heart of a wooded valley. **Open:** Easter to Oct
01736 731367 (also fax) J J Rowley
D: £22.00–£26.00 **S:** £18.00–£20.00 **Beds:** 3D 1T 1S 1F **Baths:** 5 En 1 Sh ☎ (2) ⓟ (8) 📺 🐾 ✕ Ⅴ ▥ ✿ ♨

Laneast

SX2284

Stitch Park, *Laneast, Launceston, Cornwall, PL15 8PN.* Situated close to Bodmin Moor with magnificent views towards Dartmoor. **Open:** All year
01566 86687 Mrs Handford **D:** £16.50–£18.00 **S:** £16.50–£18.00 **Beds:** 1T 1D **Baths:** 2 En ⓟ (6) ⅙ 📺 ✕ Ⅴ ▥ ♨

Lanivet

SX0364

High Cross Farm, *Lanivet, Bodmin, Cornwall, PL30 5JR.* Victorian farmhouse, set within 91 acres in geographical centre of Cornwall. **Open:** All year (not Xmas)
01208 831341 D: £16.00 **S:** £20.00 **Beds:** 1F 1D 1T **Baths:** 1 En 1 Sh ☎ ⓟ (6) ⅙ 📺 ✕ Ⅴ ▥ ♨

Bokiddick Farm, *Lanivet, Bodmin, Cornwall, PL30 5HP.* Georgian farmhouse, oak beams, wood panelling, magnificent views, peaceful location. **Open:** All year (not Xmas) **Grades:** ETC 5 Diamond, Gold
01208 831481 (also fax) Mrs Hugo *gillhugo@bokiddickfarm.co.uk* www.bokiddickfarm.co.uk **D:** £25.00 **S:** £28.00–£32.00 **Beds:** 1F 2D
Baths: 3 En ☎ (5) ⓟ (4) ⅙ 📺 ▥ ♨

Tremeere Manor, *Lanivet, Bodmin, Cornwall, PL30 5BG.* Spacious farmhouse in lovely surroundings. Easy access coasts and moors. **Open:** Feb to Nov
01208 831513 Mrs Oliver **Fax: 01208 832417** *oliver.tremeere.manor@farming.co.uk* **D:** £15.00–£20.00 **S:** £16.00–£20.00 **Beds:** 2D 1T
Baths: 1 En 1 Sh ☎ ⓟ (6) ⅙ 📺 ▥ ♨

Lanlivery

SX0759   🍺 *Crown Inn*

Longfield House, *Lanlivery, Bodmin, Cornwall, PL30 5BT.* Quiet family house. Panoramic countryside views. 4 miles Eden Project. **Open:** All year (not Xmas/New Year)
01208 873439 Mrs Haley **D:** £20.00 **S:** £30.00 **Beds:** 1F 2D **Baths:** 3 En ☎ ⓟ ⅙ 📺 ✕ ▥ ♨

Lynnwood, *Lanlivery, Bodmin, Cornwall, PL30 5BX.* Modern bungalow in landscaped gardens. 3 miles from Eden Project. **Open:** All year
01208 872326 A J Penk **D:** £15.00–£20.00 **S:** £15.00–£20.00 **Beds:** 1T 2D **Baths:** 1 En 1 Sh ☎ ⓟ (3) ⅙ 📺 🐾 ✕ Ⅴ ▥ ♨

Higher Pennant, *Lanlivery, Bodmin, PL30 5DD.* Friendly, relaxed, rural accommodation. Ideal family break with horse-riding available. **Open:** All year
01208 873252 Mr Chester *dave@higherpennant.freeserve.co.uk* **D:** £20.00
S: £20.00–£30.00 **Beds:** 1F 1D 1S **Baths:** 2 En 1 Pr ☎ ⓟ 📺 🐾 ✕ Ⅴ ▥ ✿ ♨

Lanner

SW7140

Lanner Inn, *Lanner, Redruth, Cornwall, TR16 6EH.* Old traditional country inn, comfortable accommodation, a warm welcome in a true local. **Open:** All year (not Xmas/New Year)
01209 215611 J L Wilson **Fax: 01209 214065** *lannerinn@btinternet.com* lannerinn.com **D:** £18.00–£25.00 **S:** £20.00–£30.00 **Beds:** 2F 1T 2D **Baths:** 2 En 1 Sh ☎ ⓟ (30) 📺 ✕ Ⅴ ♨ **cc**

BEDROOMS
D = Double
T = Twin
S = Single
F = Family

Planning a longer stay? Always ask for any special rates

Launceston

SX3384   🍺 *Countryman, Harris Arms, Arscott Arms, White Hart, Elliott Arms*

Oakside, *South Petherwin, Launceston, Cornwall, PL15 7LJ.* **Open:** Mar to Nov
01566 86733 Mrs Crossman **D:** £16.00–£20.00 **S:** £16.00–£20.00 **Beds:** 1F 1D 1T **Baths:** 1 En 3 Sh ☎ (2) ⓟ (4) ⅙ 📺 ▥ & ♨ Panoramic views of Bodmin Moor from bungalow nestling peacefully in beautiful surroundings 1 min from A30 Trunk Road Exeter M5. Ideal base for touring, Eden Project, all Cornwall. English breakfasts a speciality, attractively furnished, well-equipped rooms. Many legendary landmarks nearby.

11 Castle Street, *Launceston, Cornwall, PL15 8BA.* Georgian St. Town facilities. Castle views. Gourmet breakfasts. Parking. Period Furnishings. **Open:** Easter to Oct **Grades:** ETC 4 Diamond
01566 773873 Mrs Bowles **D:** £17.50–£25.00 **S:** £20.00–£25.00 **Beds:** 2T 1D **Baths:** 1 En 1 Sh ⅙ 📺 Ⅴ ▥ ♨

Tremaine Chapel, *Tremaine, Launceston, Cornwall, PL15 8SA.* Quiet hamlet central for exploring coasts, Dartmoor and Bodmin Moor. **Open:** All year (not Xmas/New Year)
01566 781590 Mrs Walker **D:** £17.00–£20.00 **S:** £19.00–£22.00 **Beds:** 1D **Baths:** 1 Pr ⓟ (2) ⅙ 📺 Ⅴ ▥ ♨

Newport Villa Guest House, *34 St Stephens Hill, Launceston, Cornwall, PL15 8HW.* Old house near town, steam railway, golf course. Warm welcome. **Open:** All year
01566 775242 L Ackroyd **D:** £18.00–£22.50 **S:** £18.50–£22.00 **Beds:** 1F 1T 1D 2S **Baths:** 1 Pr 2 Sh ☎ ⓟ (4) 📺 ✕ Ⅴ ▥ ♨

Lower Dutson Farm, *Dutson, Launceston, Cornwall, PL15 9SP.* 1st farmhouse in Cornwall on A388, central to tour Devon & Cornwall. **Open:** All year (not Xmas/New Year)
01566 776456 (also fax) Mrs Broad *francisbroad@btclick.com* **D:** £19.00–£20.00 **Beds:** 1D **Baths:** 1 En ⅙ 📺 Ⅴ ♨

Country Friends, *St Leonards House, Polson Bridge, Launceston, Cornwall, PL15 9QR.* C16th Devon longhouse, comfortable, quiet rooms. Evening meal optional. **Open:** All year **01566 774479 (also fax)** Mr & Mrs Mardon *berylmardon@globalnet.co.uk* **D:** £24.00 **S:** £24.00 **Beds:** 1F 1T 1S **Baths:** 3 En ⅀ ▯(5) ▥ ⊁ ✕ ▨ ▥. ఉ. ⚲

Trethorne Leisure Farm, *Kennards House, Launceston, Cornwall, PL15 8QE.* Warm, friendly farmhouse accommodation which overlooks our 18-hole golf course. **Open:** All year (not Xmas) **01566 86324 & 01566 86992** Mrs Davey **Fax: 01566 86981** *trethorneleisure@eclipse.co.uk* www.cornwall-online.co.uk/trethorne **D:** £21.00–£22.00 **S:** £20.00–£22.00 **Beds:** 3F 2D 1T **Baths:** 6 Pr ⅀ ▯(20) ▥ ⊁ ✕ ▨ ▥. ⚲

Bradbridge Farm, *Boyton, Launceston, Cornwall, PL15 9RL.* On Devon/Cornwall border, fishing, walks, wildlife, golf, riding, beach nearby. **Open:** Easter to Oct **01409 271264** Mrs Strout **D:** £16.00 **S:** £16.00 **Beds:** 1D 1T 1S ⅀ ▯ ⊁ ▥ ⊁ ⊁ ✕ ▥. ⚲

Tregerrie, *Trebursye Road, Launceston, Cornwall, PL15 7EL.* Welcoming, modern farmhouse overlooking Launceston. Ideal for touring Devon, Cornwall. **Open:** Mar to Nov **01566 775884** Mrs Cobbledick **D:** £16.50– £20.00 **S:** £18.00–£22.00 **Beds:** 2D **Baths:** 1 En 1 Pr ⅀ ▯(4) ▥ ▥ ▥. ⚲

Landrayne Manor, *Coads Green, Launceston, Cornwall, PL15 7LZ.* A superb country property providing extremely comfortable accommodation in Cornwall's rural heart. **Open:** All year **01566 782528** Mrs Loe *loe@ landreyne.fsnet.co.uk* **D:** £24.00–£28.00 **S:** £24.00–£34.00 **Beds:** 1T 2D 1S **Baths:** 2 En 1 Pr ⅀ ▯ ✕ ▥ ▥. ✿ ⚲

Lelant

SW5437 🍺 *Badger Inn, Old Quay House, Watermill*

Hindon Hall, *Lelant, St Ives, Cornwall, TR26 3EN.* **Open:** All year (not Xmas/New Year) **01736 753046 (also fax)** Mrs O'Sullivan *hindonhall@talk21.com* www.hindonhall.co.uk **D:** £23.00–£30.00 **Beds:** 4D **Baths:** 4 En ▯(10) ⊁ ▥ ▥ ▥. ⚲ Upmarket luxury B&B in delightful village 2.5 miles from St Ives. Beautiful rooms have superking, 4-poster and antique beds, lots of extras and panoramic views over RSPB estuary. Delicious breakfasts. Nearby beaches, golf, walking, gardens, Eden 45 mins.

Liskeard

SX2564

Hyvue House, *Barras Cross, Liskeard, Cornwall, PL14 6BN.* Family-run exclusively for non-smokers on outskirts of town overlooking Bodmin Moor. **Open:** All year **01579 348175** Mrs Demmer **D:** £20.00 **S:** £20.00–£25.00 **Beds:** 2D 1T **Baths:** 3 En 3 Pr ▯(6) ⊁ ▥ ▥ ▥. ⚲

Elnor Guest House, *1 Russell Street, Liskeard, Cornwall, PL14 4BP.* Many nearby attractions, good local restaurants. Lovely scenery, station near, licensed. **Open:** Jan to Dec **01579 342472** Mr Slocombe & Mrs G G M Slocombe **Fax: 01579 345673** *elnor@ btclick.com* **D:** £20.00–£23.00 **S:** £30.00–£35.00 **Beds:** 1F 2D 2T 4S **Baths:** 7 En 1 Sh ⅀ ▯(8) ▥ ▥.

Looe

SX2553 🍺 *Plough Inn, Jolly Sailor, Harbour Moon, Tom Sawyer's*

Talehay, *Tremaine, Pelynt, Looe, Cornwall, PL13 2LT.* **Open:** All year **01503 220252 (also fax)** Mr & Mrs Brumpton *pr.brumpton@ukonline.co.uk* www.talehay.co. uk **D:** £23.00–£25.00 **S:** £33.00 **Beds:** 1F 1D 1T **Baths:** 3 En ⅀ ▯(12) ⊁ ▥ ⊁ ▥ ▥. ⚲ Charming C17th former farmstead. Large ensuite rooms with beautiful views. A quiet haven with countryside/coastal walks nearby. Delicious breakfasts served with our own freerange eggs & home-made marmalade. An ideal comfortable base for exploring the delights of Cornwall & close to Eden Project.

Trevanion Hotel, *Hannafore Road, Looe, Cornwall, PL13 2DE.* Turn-of-the-20th-Century residence, overlooking river, beach, harbour. 20m headland. **Open:** All year **Grades:** ETC 3 Diamond **01503 262003** Mr Fildes **Fax: 01503 265408** *hotel@looecornwall.co.uk* www.looecornwall.co. uk **D:** £18.00–£26.50 **S:** £22.00–£28.50 **Beds:** 2F 6D 2S **Baths:** 10 En ⅀ ▯(5) ▥ ✕ ▥ ▥. ⚲ cc

Schooner Point Guest House, *1 Trelawney Terrace, Polperro Road, Looe, Cornwall, PL13 2AG.* **Open:** All year **01503 262670 (also fax)** Mr & Mrs Warren *enquiries@ schoonerpoint.co.uk* www.schoonerpoint.co.uk **D:** £14.00–£20.00 **S:** £14.00–£17.00 **Beds:** 1F 2D 1T 2S **Baths:** 2 En 1 Sh ⅀ ▯(2) ▥ ⊁ ▥ ▥. ⚲ Perfectly situated overlooking the Estuary with views towards East Looe, our family-run guest house offers a warm and friendly welcome. Close to the town centre and beaches, we are the ideal base for exploring the South West including the Eden Project.

Sea Haze, *Polperro Road, Looe, PL13 2JS.* Country/ sea views friendly, 30 mins from Eden, good food. **Open:** All year (not Xmas) **01503 262708 (also fax)** Mr & Mrs Dearsley *dearsley@tinyonline.co.uk* **D:** £17.00–£20.00 **S:** £17.00–£20.00 **Beds:** 1T 3D **Baths:** 2 En 2 Sh ▯(7) ⊁ ▥ ▥ ▥. ఉ3 ⚲

Marwinthy Guest House, *East Cliff, Looe, Cornwall, PL13 1DE.* Small friendly guest house, on Coastal Footpath overlooking beach. In Which? Guide. **Open:** All year **01503 264382** E Mawby *eddie.mawby@ lineone.net* www.marwinthy.co.uk **D:** £18.00 **Beds:** 2F 2D 1T **Baths:** 2 Pr 1 Sh ⅀(4) ▥ ⊁ ▥. ⚲

Grasmere Guest House, *St Martins Road, Looe, Cornwall, PL13 1LP.* Clean comfortable friendly guest house with splendid river views. **Open:** All year (not Xmas/New Year) **01503 262556** Mr Eveleigh **D:** £15.00–£17.00 **S:** £15.00–£20.00 **Beds:** 2F 3D **Baths:** 1 En 1 Sh ⅀(3) ▯(5) ▥ ✕ ▥. ⚲

Tidal Court, *3 Church Street, Looe, Cornwall, PL13 2EX.* Situated in floral award-winning street, 50 yards harbour, central for coast & woodland walks. **Open:** All year (not Xmas) **01503 263695** Mrs Hocking **D:** £16.00–£21.00 **S:** £16.00–£25.00 **Beds:** 3F 1D 1T 1S **Baths:** 5 En 1 Pr ⅀ ▯(3) ▥ ⊁ ▥ ▥. ⚲

The Beach House, *Marine Drive, Looe, Cornwall, PL13 2DH.* On sea front/coastal path, uninterrupted views Looe Bay. Boating, fishing, diving, rambling, birdwatching. **Open:** All year **01503 262598 Fax: 01503 262298** *enquires@ thebeachhouse.uk.com* www.thebeachhouse.uk. com **D:** £20.00–£28.00 **S:** £25.00–£38.00 **Beds:** 2T 3D **Baths:** 4 En 1 Pr ⅀(12) ▯(5) ⊁ ▥ ▥. ⚲ cc

Lostwithiel
SX1059

Treview House, Redlake, Lostwithiel, Cornwall, *PL22 0ND.* Charming country house set amidst woodlands. Ideal location for visiting Eden Project. **Open:** All year (not Xmas/New Year)
01208 872664 (also fax) Mrs Phipps *sue@ treview.freeserve.co.uk* **D:** £20.00–£25.00
S: £25.00 **Beds:** 1T 1D 1S **Baths:** 2 En 1 Pr
P (4) 🛇 📺 Ⓥ 📖 ☕

Benthams, Grenville Road, Lostwithiel, Cornwall, *PL22 0RA.* Large house, 5 miles from Eden Project. Central for Cornwall. **Open:** All year
01208 872472 Mrs Sanders
sanders.benthams@virgin.net **D:** £20.00–£25.00
S: £20.00–£25.00 **Beds:** 2D 1T 1S **Baths:** 1 Pr 1 Sh ⛵ 📺 (6) 🛇 📺 Ⓥ ☕

Ludgvan
SW5033

Menwidden Farm, Ludgvan, Penzance, Cornwall, *TR20 8BN.* Comfortable farmhouse, centrally situated in peaceful countryside. Friendly welcome guaranteed. **Open:** Easter to Oct **Grades:** ETC 3 Diamond
01736 740415 Mrs Quick **D:** £17.50–£21.00
S: £17.50–£21.00 **Beds:** 3D 1T 1S **Baths:** 1 En 2 Sh ⛵ 📺 (8) 🛇 📺 ★ ✕ ☕

Madron
SW4432

Tregoddick House, Madron, Penzance, Cornwall, *TR20 8SS.* Charming house in small village, close to all amenities. **Open:** All year (not Xmas)
01736 362643 Mrs Scoble **Fax:** 01736 332920
D: £17.00–£18.00 **S:** £17.00–£18.00 **Beds:** 2T
Baths: 2 Pr ⛵ (2) **P** (2) 🛇 📺 📖 ☕

Marazion
SW5130

Chymorvah Private Hotel, Marazion, Cornwall, *TR17 0DQ.* **Open:** All year (not Xmas/New Year) **Grades:** ETC 3 Diamond, RAC 3 Diamond
01736 710497 Mrs Bull **Fax:** 01736 710508
www.smoothhound.co.uk/hotels/chymorva. html **D:** £26.00–£30.50 **S:** £26.00–£30.50
Beds: 3F 1T 4D 1S **Baths:** 9 En 1 Sh ⛵ (0)
P (12) 🛇 📺 ★ ✕ Ⓥ 📖 ☕ cc
Small, family-run Victorian hotel with one of the finest sea views in Cornwall to St Michael's Mount and beyond. One acre of grounds with private access to secluded beach. Aga cooking using green produce. Your successful holiday is our priority!

Marhamchurch
SS2203

Hilton Farm House, Marhamchurch, Bude, Cornwall, *EX23 OHE.* C16th farmhouse set in 25 acres with panoramic views of countryside & sea. **Open:** All year
01288 361521 (also fax) Mr & Mrs Goodman
ian@hiltonfarmhouse.freeserve.co.uk **D:** £16.00–£25.00 **S:** £20.00–£24.00 **Beds:** 1F 1D 1S
Baths: 2 En 1 Pr ⛵ **P** (18) 📺 ★ Ⓥ 📖 ☕ ☕

Mawnan Smith
SW7728 🍺 Red Lion

Carwinion Vean, Grove Hill, Mawnan Smith, Falmouth, Cornwall, *TR11 5ER.* Lovely country house near beautiful Helford River, gardens, coastal footpaths and beaches.
Open: All year (not Xmas)
01326 250513 Mrs Spike **D:** £20.00–£25.00
S: £20.00–£25.00 **Beds:** 1F 3D 3T **Baths:** 3 En 2 Sh ⛵ (5) **P** (6) 📺 ★ Ⓥ 📖 ☕

The White House, 28 Castle View Park, Mawnan Smith, Falmouth, Cornwall, *TR11 5HB.* Friendly family guest house near village centre and easy access from coast.
Open: All year
01326 250768 Mrs Grant **D:** £18.00–£20.00
S: £20.00–£25.00 **Beds:** 1F 1D 1T 1S
Baths: 1 En 1 Sh ⛵ **P** (2) 📺 ✕ Ⓥ 📖 ☕

B&B owners may vary rates – be sure to check when booking

Maxworthy
SX2592

Wheatley Farm, Maxworthy, Launceston, Cornwall, *PL15 8LY.* Country farmhouse. Superb food, near coast, every comfort. Perfect holiday. **Open:** Easter to Oct
01566 781232 (also fax) Mrs Griffin
wheatley@farming.co.uk www.wheatleyfrm.co. uk **D:** £18.00–£23.00 **S:** £23.00–£25.00
Beds: 1F 3D 1T **Baths:** 5 En ⛵ **P** (5) 🛇 📺 ✕ Ⓥ 📖 ☕ cc

Mevagissey
SX0145 🍺 Fountain Inn, Rising Sun, Salamander

Kerryanna, Valley Road, Mevagissey, St Austell, Cornwall, *PL26 6RZ.* Stunning position overlooking village, close to Heligan and Eden.
Open: Easter to Oct **Grades:** ETC 4 Diamond
01726 843558 (also fax) Mrs Hennah
linda.hennah@btinternet.com www.kerryana.co. uk **D:** £24.00–£28.00 **Beds:** 2T 4D **Baths:** 6 En ⛵ (5) **P** (6) 📺 📖 ☕ cc

Mevagissey House, Vicarage Hill, Mevagissey, St Austell, *PL26 6SZ.* Peaceful Georgian house in three acres, close to Eden Project. **Open:** Mar to Oct
01726 842427 Mrs Dodds **Fax:** 01726 844327
D: £20.00–£25.00 **S:** £30.00–£35.00 **Beds:** 1F 1T 1D **Baths:** 3 En ⛵ **P** (8) 📺 ★ 📖 ☕

Tregorran, Cliff Street, Mevagissey, St Austell, Cornwall, *PL26 6QW.* Most rooms have stunning sea or landscape views across the village. **Open:** All year (not Xmas/New Year)
01726 842319 *patricia@parsloop.freeserve.co.uk*
www.tregorran.homestead.com/home.html
D: £20.00–£25.00 **Beds:** 1F 1T 4D **Baths:** 5 En 1 Pr ⛵ **P** 🛇 📺 ★ Ⓥ 📖 ☕

Morwenstow
SS2015 🍺 Old Smithy, New Inn, London Inn, Bush Inn

Little Bryaton, Morwenstow, Bude, Cornwall, *EX23 9SU.* Tranquil old farmhouse. Warm welcome, candlelit dinner. Beaches, cliffs nearby. **Open:** All year
01288 331755 Mrs Hudson *little.bryaton@ dial.pipex.com* www.little.bryaton.dial.pipex. com **D:** £21.00–£24.00 **S:** £21.00–£24.00
Beds: 1F 1T 1D **Baths:** 3 En ⛵ **P** 📺 ★ ✕ Ⓥ 📖 ☕ ☕

Please respect a B&B's wishes regarding children, animals and smoking

Meadow Park, Lee Barton, Morwenstow, Bude, Cornwall, *EX23 9ST.* Superb views on family farm. Traditional farmhouse cooking, friendly atmosphere. **Open:** Mar to Nov
01288 331499 Mrs Hobbs **D:** £16.50–£17.50 **S:** £16.50–£18.00 **Beds:** 1F 1D 1S **Baths:** 1 Pr ⚥ 🄿 (4) 📺 ✕ 📖 ᵇ

Mount (Bodmin)
SX1568

Mount Pleasant Farm, Mount, Bodmin, Cornwall, *PL30 4EX.* Comfortable converted farmhouse, central for Eden project. Indoor heated pool. **Open:** Easter to Sept
01208 821342 (also fax) Mr & Mrs Capper
colette@capper61.fsnet.co.uk
www.peacefulholiday.co.uk **D:** £30.00–£35.00 **S:** £40.00–£45.00 **Beds:** 1T 4D **Baths:** 5 En ⚥ (5) 🄿 (10) ✄ 📺 ✕ 📖 ᵇ cc

Mount Edgcumbe
SX4552

Friary Manor Hotel, Maker Heights, Mount Edgcumbe, Millbrook, Torpoint, Cornwall, *PL10 1JB.* C17th former Vicarage. Close to sea and smugglers' villages. **Open:** All year
01752 822112 Mr & Mrs Bartlett **Fax:** 01752 822804 *106220.3641@compuserve.com*
D: £22.50–£29.00 **S:** £35.00–£41.50 **Beds:** 3F 3D 3T 2S **Baths:** 6 En 1 Pr ⚥ 🄿 (25) 📺 ✕ 📖 ❄ ᵇ cc

Mousehole
SW4626

Carn Du Hotel, Mousehole, Penzance, Cornwall, *TR19 6SS.* Peaceful comfortable hotel. Superb views, food, accommodation overlooking Mount's Bay. **Open:** All year
01736 731233 (also fax) Mr Field **D:** £25.00–£35.00 **S:** £35.00–£45.00 **Beds:** 4D 3T **Baths:** 6 En 1 Pr ⚥ 🄿 (12) 📺 ✕ 📖 ᵇ cc

Mullion
SW6719 🍺 Old Inn

Campden House, The Commons, Mullion, Helston, Cornwall, *TR12 7HZ.* One acre of gardens. Home-grown vegetables when in season. **Open:** All year (not Xmas)
01326 240365 Mr & Mrs Hyde **D:** £16.50–£17.50 **S:** £16.50–£17.50 **Beds:** 2F 5D 1T 2S **Baths:** 2 Sh ⚥ 🄿 (9) 📺 ❄ ✕ 📺 ᵇ

Meaver Farm, Mullion, Helston, Cornwall, *TR12 7DN.* Traditional 300 year old farmhouse; exposed beams, log fire, delightful breakfasts. **Open:** All year **Grades:** ETC 4 Diamond, Silver
01326 240128 J Stanland **Fax: 01326 240011** *meaverfarm@eclipse.co.uk* www.meaverfarm. freeserve.co.uk **D:** £21.00–£24.00 **S:** £25.00–£30.00 **Beds:** 1T 2D **Baths:** 3 En 🄿 (3) ✄ 📺 ❄ ❄ ᵇ

Colvennor Farmhouse, Cury, Helston, Cornwall, *TR12 7BJ.* Delightful former farmhouse. Peaceful setting. Perfect location for exploring. Excellent hospitality. **Open:** All year (not Xmas/New Year) **Grades:** AA 4 Diamond
01326 241208 Mrs Royds *colvennor@aol.com* **D:** £20.00–£23.00 **S:** £25.00–£28.00 **Beds:** 1T 2D **Baths:** 3 En 🄿 (3) ✄ 📺 📺 ᵇ

Mullion Cove
SW6617

Criggan Mill, Mullion Cove, Helston, Cornwall, *TR12 7EU.* Timber lodges 200 yards from fishing harbour and coastal footpath. **Open:** Easter to Oct
01326 240496 Mr Bolton **Fax: 0870 1640549** *info@criggan-mill.co.uk* www.crigganmill.co.uk **D:** £17.00–£22.00 **S:** £20.00–£25.00 **Beds:** 5F 6D 4T **Baths:** 3 En ⚥ (1) 🄿 📺 ❄ ✕ ᵇ cc

Newquay
SW8161 🍺 Springbok, Skinners

Pengilley, 12 Trebarwith Crescent, Newquay, Cornwall, *TR71DX.* **Open:** All year
01637 872039
jan@pengilley-guesthouse.com
www.pengilley-guesthouse.com **D:** £17.00–£23.00 **S:** £17.00–£25.00 **Beds:** 2F 2D 1T 1S **Baths:** 4 En 2 Sh ⚥ (5) 📺 ❄ ✕ 📺 ᵇ
A friendly atmosphere awaits you at Pengilley, one minute from town, beach, close to shops and Newquay's famous nightlife and restaurants. For those wishing to try surfing, an introduction to Newquay's coolest surf school - West Coast Surfari.

Planning a longer stay? Always ask for any special rates

Alicia, 136 Henver Road, Newquay, Cornwall, *TR7 3EQ.* Perfectly situated to explore the Cornish coastline & Newquay's Golden Sands.
Open: All year
01637 874328 Mrs Limer *aliciaguesthouse@ mlimer.fsnet.co.uk* www.cornishlight.freeserve. co.uk/alicia.htm **D:** £18.00–£25.00 **S:** £20.00–£27.50 **Beds:** 1T 3D 1F **Baths:** 3 En 2 Sh ⚥ 🄿 (6) ✄ 📺 ❄ ✕ 📺 📖 ᵇ

Chichester Guest House, 14 Bay View Terrace, Newquay, Cornwall, *TR7 2LR.* Good coffee, we provide walking, mineral collecting and archaeology weeks. **Open:** All year (not Xmas)
01637 874216 (also fax) Miss Harper *sheila.harper@virgin.net* freespace.virgin. net/sheila.harper **D:** £16.50 **S:** £16.50 **Beds:** 2F 2D 2T 1S **Baths:** 2 Sh 🄿 (6) 📺 ✕ 📺 📖 ᵇ

The Bangaroo Guest House, 23 Tolcarne Road, Newquay, Cornwall, *TR7 2NQ.* Near town centre and beaches. Licensed. No restrictions. **Open:** All year
01637 874798 (also fax) Ms Beechey www.bangaroo.free-online.co.uk **D:** £30.00–£40.00 **S:** £15.00–£20.00 **Beds:** 2F 3T ⚥ 📺 ❄ 📺 📖 ❄ ᵇ

The Croft Hotel, 37 Mount Wise, Newquay, Cornwall, *TR7 2BL.* Ideally situated close to beaches, pubs & clubs, coach & rail stations. **Open:** All year (not Xmas)
01637 871520 L Duffin www.the-crofthotel. co.uk **D:** £14.00–£25.00 **S:** £20.00–£40.00 **Beds:** 4F 2T 2D **Baths:** 4 En 2 Pr 1 Sh ⚥ 🄿 ✄ 📺 ✕ 📺 📖 ᵇ cc

Padstow
SW9175 🍺 London Inn, Cornish Arms, Brocks, Customs House, Farmers' Arms

Mother Ivey Cottage, Trevose Head, Padstow, Cornwall, *PL28 8SL.* **Open:** All year
01841 520329 (also fax) Mrs Woosnam Mills *woosnammills@compuserve.com* **D:** £22.50 **S:** £25.00 **Beds:** 2T **Baths:** 2 En ⚥ (6) 🄿 📺 ❄ ✕ 📺 ᵇ
Traditionally-built Cornish clifftop house with stunning sea views, overlooking Trevose Head with a beach below. The area is renowned for swimming, fishing, surfing and walking. A championship golf course - Trevose - is nearby. The Cornwall Coastal Path is adjacent.

Althea Library B&B, 27 High Street, Padstow, Cornwall, PL28 8BB.
Converted library, short walk from harbour, old part of town. **Open:** All year (not Xmas) **Grades:** ETC 4 Diamond, Silver
01841 532717 J Beare *enquiries@althea library.co.uk* www.althealibrary.co.uk
D: £27.00–£30.00 **Beds:** 2D 1T **Baths:** 3 En ▣ (3) ⌀ ⊠ ⊡ ▥. ♨ **cc**

Hemingford House, 21 Grenville Road, Padstow, Cornwall, PL28 8EX.
Comfortable relaxed style. Hearty breakfast. 10 minutes walk to harbour. **Open:** All year
01841 532806 (also fax) Mr Tamblin *peter@ ptamblin.freeserve.co.uk* www.padstow-bb.co.uk
D: £22.50–£27.50 **S:** £25.00–£30.00 **Beds:** 1T 2D **Baths:** 1 En 1 Pr 1 Sh ⌇(12)▣(1)⌀⊠⌀ ⊡ ▥. ♨

Par
SX0753

Hidden Valley Gardens, Treesmill, Par, Cornwall, PL24 2TU.
Secluded location. Near Eden Project and Fowey, in own grounds. **Open:** Easter to Oct
01208 873225 **D:** £20.00–£22.00 **S:** £22.00–£24.00 **Beds:** 2D **Baths:** 2 En ▣ (7) ⌀ ▥. ♨

Paul
SW4527

Kerris Farm, Paul, Penzance, Cornwall, TR19 6UY.
Peaceful dairy farm, rural views, central to Minack Theatre, St Ives. **Open:** Easter to Oct
01736 731309 *susangiles@btconnect.com* www.cornwall-online.co.uk/kerris-farm
D: £15.00–£20.00 **S:** £16.00–£18.00 **Beds:** 1F 1D 1T **Baths:** 1 En 1 Sh ⌇ ▣ (4) ⌀ ✕ ⊠ ♨

Pelynt
SX2055   ⚑ *Jubilee Inn*

Talehay, Tremaine, Pelynt, Looe, Cornwall, PL13 2LT.
Charming C17th former farmstead. Large ensuite rooms with beautiful views. **Open:** All year
01503 220252 (also fax) Mr & Mrs Brumpton *pr.brumpton@ukonline.co.uk* www.talehay.co. uk **D:** £23.00–£25.00 **S:** £33.00 **Beds:** 1F 1D 1T **Baths:** 3 En ⌇ ▣ (12) ⌀ ⊠ ✝ ⊠ ▥. ♨

Colwells House, Pelynt, Looe, Cornwall, PL13 2JX.
Family run country house. Polperro 3 miles. **Open:** All year (not Xmas/New Year)
01503 220201 Mrs Harvey **D:** £17.00–£22.00 **S:** £25.00 **Beds:** 1F 1T 2D **Baths:** 1 En 2 Sh ⌇ (12) ▣ (7) ⌀ ⊠ ⊠ ▥. ♨

Little Larnick Farm, Pelynt, Looe, Cornwall, PL13 2NB.
Character farmhouse and barn accommodation in the beautiful Looe valley. **Open:** All year **Grades:** ETC 4 Diamond
01503 262837 (also fax) Mrs Eastley *littlelarnick@btclick.com* **D:** £20.00–£24.00 **S:** £25.00–£28.00 **Beds:** 1F 1T 4D **Baths:** 6 En ⌇ (3) ▣ (6) ⌀ ⊠ ▥. ♨ **cc**

Pendeen
SW3834   ⚑ *Radjel Inn, North Inn, Trewellard Arms*

The Old Count House, Boscaswell Downs, Pendeen, Penzance, Cornwall, TR19 7ED.
Old granite house in quiet village, on the dramatic North Coast. **Open:** Easter to Oct
01736 788058 Mrs Dymond **D:** £16.00–£18.00 **S:** £16.00–£18.00 **Beds:** 2D **Baths:** 1 Sh ⌇ (2) ▣ (4) ⌀ ⊠ ▥. ♨

Pensilva
SX2969

Wheal Tor Hotel, Caradon Hill, Pensilva, Liskeard, Cornwall, PL14 5PJ.
Highest inn in Cornwall. Set in rugged Bodmin Moor location. **Open:** All year
01579 362281 Mr & Mrs Chapman **Fax: 01579 363401** *pdc@whealtorhotel.freeserve.co.uk* www.wheal-tor-hotel.co.uk **D:** £22.50–£27.50 **S:** £30.00–£32.50 **Beds:** 1F 2T 3D **Baths:** 4 En 2 Sh ⌀ ⊠ ✝ ⊠ ▥. ♿ ♨ **cc**

Pentewan
SX0147   ⚑ *Crown Inn, Ship Inn, Fountains, Polgooth Inn*

Piskey Cove, The Square, Pentewan, St Austell, Cornwall, PL26 6DA.
Open: All year (not Xmas/New Year)
01726 843781 (also fax) Ms Avery *gillian@ averya.freeserve.co.uk* **D:** £25.00–£35.00 **S:** £25.00–£38.00 **Beds:** 1F 2T 3D **Baths:** 3 En 1 Pr ⌇ ▣ (2) ⌀ ✝ ✕ ⊠ ♨ **cc**
Close to the Eden Project and Heligan Gardens. Family run and situated in peaceful, pretty coastal village. Ideal base for cosy winter, refreshing spring, British summer and beautiful autumn breaks, to visit Cornwall's sites. Complimentary and sports therapy in house.

Pentire
SW7861   ⚑ *Lewinnick Lodge, Olde Dolphin*

Golden Bay Hotel, Pentire Avenue, Pentire, Newquay, Cornwall, TR7 1PD.
Unwind and relax in this surprisingly affordable, small, quality hotel. **Open:** All year
01637 873318 *enquiries@goldenbayhotel.co.uk* www.goldenbayhotel.co.uk **D:** £18.00–£30.00 **S:** £24.00–£40.00 **Beds:** 2F 1T 7D **Baths:** 10 En ▣ (10) ⌀ ✝ ▥. ♨ **cc**

Penzance
SW4730   ⚑ *The Coldstreamer*

Lynwood Guest House, 41 Morrab Road, Penzance, Cornwall, TR18 4EX.
Open: All year **Grades:** ETC 3 Diamond
01736 365871 (also fax) Mrs Stacey *Lynwoodpz@aol.com* www.penzance.co. uk/lynwood-guesthouse **D:** £13.50–£17.50 **S:** £13.50–£17.50 **Beds:** 2F 2D 2T 2S **Baths:** 4 En 2 Pr 3 Sh ⌇ (5) ⌀ ✝ ⊠ ▥. ♨ **cc**
Family-run Victorian guest house. Internationally recommended for good food, cleanliness. Close to all amenities. Ideally situated for visiting Land's End, St Michael's Mount, Minack Theatre, art galleries and the Lizard Peninsula.

Trewella Guest House, 18 Mennaye Road, Penzance, Cornwall, TR18 4NG.
Large Victorian house. Recommended for good food. Ideal touring centre. **Open:** Mar to Oct
01736 363818 D Glenn *shan.dave@lineone.net* **D:** £18.00–£19.00 **S:** £16.00–£23.00 **Beds:** 2F 4D 2S **Baths:** 6 En 1 Sh ⌇ (5) ⌀ ⊠ ▥. ♨

Carnson House Private Hotel, East Terrace, Market Jew Street, Penzance, Cornwall, TR18 2TD.
Centrally located, friendly, small hotel near station and harbour. **Open:** All year
01736 365589 Mr & Mrs Smyth **Fax: 01736 365594** *carnson@netcomuk.co.uk* www.carnson-house.co.uk **D:** £18.00–£24.50 **S:** £20.00 **Beds:** 3D 2T 2S **Baths:** 3 Pr 1 Sh ⌇ (6) ⌀ ⊠ ▥. ♨

Penalva Guest House, Alexandra Road, Penzance, Cornwall, TR18 4LZ.
Victorian guest house. Walking distance from sea front & town centre. **Open:** All year **Grades:** AA 3 Diamond
01736 369060 (also fax) Mrs Buswell **D:** £15.00–£22.00 **S:** £15.00–£22.00 **Beds:** 1F 2D 1T 1S **Baths:** 4 En 1 Pr ⌇ (5) ⌀ ⊠ ⊠ ▥. ♨

Kimberley House, 10 Morrab Road, Penzance, Cornwall, TR18 4EZ.
Convenient bus and railway station. Minutes walk town and seafront. **Open:** Feb to Dec
01736 362727 Mr & Mrs Bashford **D:** £15.00–£21.00 **S:** £15.00–£18.00 **Beds:** 2F 2D 3T 1S **Baths:** 3 En 2 Pr 3 Sh ⌇ (5) ▣ (3) ⌀ ⊠ ⊠ ▥. ♨

Menwidden Farm, Ludgvan, Penzance, Cornwall, *TR20 8BN.* Comfortable farmhouse, centrally situated in peaceful countryside. Friendly welcome guaranteed. **Open:** Easter to Oct **Grades:** ETC 3 Diamond
01736 740415 Mrs Quick **D:** £17.50–£21.00 **S:** £17.50–£21.00 **Beds:** 3D 1T 1S **Baths:** 1 En 2 Sh ♥ 🖪 (8) ⮴ ☒ ⼲ ✕ ⚓

Woodstock Guest House, 29 Morrab Road, Penzance, Cornwall, *TR18 4EZ.* Central Penzance. Ideal for touring & visiting the Land's End Peninsula. **Open:** All year
01736 369049 (also fax) Mr & Mrs Hopkins *woodstocp@aol.com* www.cruising-america.com/woodstock **D:** £14.00–£20.00 **S:** £14.00–£20.00 **Beds:** 1F 2T 3D 2S **Baths:** 4 En 1 Pr 1 Sh ⮴ ☒ ⼲ ☒ ▥. ✳ ⚓ cc

Mount Royal Hotel, Chyandour Cliff, Penzance, Cornwall, *TR18 3LQ.* Small family-run hotel facing the sea & overlooking the entrance of Penzance harbour. **Open:** Mar to Oct **Grades:** AA 3 Diamond, RAC 3 Diamond
01736 362233 (also fax) Mr Cox *mountroyal@talk21.com* **D:** £22.50–£27.50 **S:** £25.00–£27.50 **Beds:** 3F 3D 2T **Baths:** 5 En 2 Sh ♥ (1) 🖪 (10) ⮴ ☒ ☒ ▥.

Pendennis Hotel, Alexandra Road, Penzance, Cornwall, *TR18.* Victorian licensed hotel built 1830 in a quiet tree-lined residential area. **Open:** All year
01736 363823 (also fax) Mrs Cook *ray@pendennishotel.freeserve.co.uk* **D:** £15.00–£22.00 **S:** £15.00–£22.00 **Beds:** 5F 2D **Baths:** 7 En 1 Sh ♥ ☒ ✕ ☒ ▥. ⚓ cc

Chy an Gof Guest House, 10 Regent Terrace, Penzance, Cornwall, *TR18 4DW.* Listed Regency house overlooking Penzance promenade & the lovely Mount's Bay **Open:** All year
01736 332361 (also fax) Mr & Mrs Schofield *scholfield@callnetuk.com* **D:** £22.00 **S:** £22.00 **Beds:** 2T 2S **Baths:** 4 En 🖪 (4) ☒ ☒ ▥. ⚓

Perranporth
SW7554

Tremore, Liskey Hill Crescent, Perranporth, Cornwall, *TR6 0HP.* **Open:** All year (not Xmas)
01872 573537 (also fax) Ms Crofts *tremore@totalise.co.uk* www.tremore.co.uk **D:** £19.00–£22.00 **S:** £20.00–£25.00 **Beds:** 3D 1T 1S **Baths:** 3 En 2 Sh ♥ (11) 🖪 (6) ⮴ ☒ ☒ ▥. ⚓
A warm welcome awaits in our well-established and highly recommended guest house. Totally non-smoking, close to the Eden Project. Special diets catered for. Off-road parking. Ideal for touring. Excellent value. Try us, you won't be disappointed.

Chy an Kerensa, Cliff Road, Perranporth, Cornwall, *TR6 0DR.* Panoramic coastal views from lounge/bar, dining-room. 200 metres beach/village centre. **Open:** All year **Grades:** ETC 3 Diamond
01872 572470 (also fax) Mrs Woodcock **D:** £17.00–£24.00 **S:** £17.00–£24.00 **Beds:** 3F 2D 2T 2S **Baths:** 6 En 3 Sh ♥ 🖪 (4) ☒ ⼲ ☒ ▥. ⚓

Perranuthnoe
SW5329 · *Victoria Inn*

Ednovean Farm, Perranuthnoe, Penzance, Cornwall, *TR20 9LZ.* C17th barns. Stunning views, Italian garden. **Open:** All year (not Xmas/New Year) **Grades:** ETC 5 Diamond
01736 711883 Mr & Mrs Taylor **Fax:** 01736 710480 *info@ednoveanfarm.co.uk* www.ednoveanfarm.co.uk **D:** £27.00–£35.00 **S:** £50.00–£60.00 **Beds:** 3D **Baths:** 3 En 🖪 (3) ⮴ ☒ ☒ ▥. ⚓ cc

Ednovean House, Perranuthnoe, Penzance, Cornwall, *TR20 9LZ.* Beautiful 180-year-old country house standing above Perranuthnoe village in 1 acre lovely gardens. **Open:** All year (not Xmas/New Year)
01736 711071 Mr & Mrs Whittington *clive@ednoveanhouse.co.uk* www.ednoveanhouse.co.uk **D:** £20.00–£27.00 **S:** £24.00–£25.00 **Beds:** 2T 4D 2S **Baths:** 6 En 2 Sh ♥ (7) 🖪 (10) ☒ ⼲ ▥. ⚓ cc

Playing Place
SW8141

Clestwyth, 20 Penhalls Way, Playing Place, Truro, Cornwall, *TR3 6EX.* Attractive house, tastefully furnished, peaceful mature gardens, ideal sightseeing location. **Open:** All year
01872 864120 Mr Mallinson *mallinson@clestwyth.freeserve.co.uk* **D:** £17.50–£19.50 **S:** £21.00–£25.00 **Beds:** 1T 1D **Baths:** 1 En 1 Sh ♥ 🖪 (4) ⮴ ☒ ☒ ▥. ⚓

Polperro
SX2050

Little Tregue, Langreek Road, Polperro, Cornwall, *PL13 2PR.* Pretty country cottage near sea & village, tranquil surroundings, great breakfasts. **Open:** All year (not Xmas/New Year)
01503 272758 (also fax) Ms Kellaway *little-tregue@cornwall-online.co.uk* www.cornwall-online.co.uk/little-tregue **D:** £15.00–£20.00 **S:** £15.00–£30.00 **Beds:** 1F 1T **Baths:** 2 En 1 Sh ♥ 🖪 (30) ☒ ⼲ ☒ ⚓

Crumplehorn Inn, Polperro, Cornwall, *PL13 2RJ.* Inn & watermill in quaint Cornish fishing village. B&B, S/C, 2-8. **Open:** All year
01503 272348 Andrew & Joanne Taylor *host@crumplehorn-inn.co.uk* www.crumplehorn-inn.co.uk **D:** £22.50–£32.50 **S:** £27.50–£60.00 **Beds:** 4F 3T 3D **Baths:** 10 Pr ♥ 🖪 ☒ ▥ ⼲ ✕ ☒ ▥. ✳ ⚓ cc

Ponsongath
SW7517

Wych Elm, Ponsongath, Coverack, Helston, Cornwall, *TR12 6SQ.* Idyllic quiet setting close secluded Lankidden Cove. Backwoodsmen's bliss! **Open:** All year (not Xmas)
01326 280576 Mrs Whitaker **D:** £18.00 **S:** £20.00 **Beds:** 1T **Baths:** 1 En ♥ (8) 🖪 (2) ⮴ ☒ ⼲ ✕ ☒ ▥.

Port Isaac
SW9980 · *Golden Lion*

Bay Hotel, 1 The Terrace, Port Isaac, Cornwall, *PL29 3SG.* Small, friendly Victorian hotel overlooking bay with wonderful views. **Open:** All year
01208 880380 & 0500 515242 Mr Hawkes & J Burns *jacki.burns@talk21.com* **D:** £24.00–£36.00 **S:** £23.00–£32.00 **Beds:** 8D **Baths:** 8 En ♥ 🖪 (9) ☒ ⼲ ☒ ▥. ⚓

Porthallow (St Keverne)
SW7923

Gallen-Treath Guest House, Porthallow (Helston), St Keverne, Helston, Cornwall, *TR12 6PL.* Warm, friendly welcome. Spectacular coastal location. **Open:** All year
01326 280400 Ms Strickland *gallen-treath@btclick.com* www.gallen-treath.com **D:** £22.00–£24.00 **S:** £30.00–£40.00 **Beds:** 1F 1T 2D 1S **Baths:** 5 En 1 Sh ♥ (6) 🖪 (6) ☒ ⼲ ✕ ☒ ▥. ✳ ⚓

Porthleven
SW6225 · *Ship Inn, Harbour Hotel*

Greystones, 40 West End, Porthleven, Helston, Cornwall, *TR13 9JL.* Overlooking sea. Close, harbour/beach/shops/restaurants/pubs. Dogs welcome. **Open:** All year (not Xmas)
01326 565583 & 07720 588194 (M) Mrs Woodward **Fax:** 01326 565583 **D:** £15.00–£20.00 **S:** £20.00–£25.00 **Beds:** 1F 1D 1S **Baths:** 1 Sh ♥ ☒ ⼲ ☒ ⚓

Please respect a B&B's wishes regarding children, animals and smoking

Tamarind, *Shrubberies Hill, Porthleven, Helston, Cornwall, TR13 9EA.* Overlooking Mounts Bay, near Coastal Path, picturesque views, village nearby. **Open:** Mar to Nov **01326 574303** www.bedbreakfastcornwall.com/members/tamarind/tamarind/htm **D:** £19.00–£22.00 **S:** £20.00–£22.00 **Beds:** 1T 1D **Baths:** 1 Pr 1 Sh ⊃ ⊠ ⊬ ⊠ ♉ ⊞ ⊞ ⚲

Seefar, *Peverell Terrace, Porthleven, Helston, Cornwall, TR13 9DZ.* Traditional Cornish Victorian mine captain's house, overlooking sea. **Open:** Mar to Nov **Grades:** ETC 3 Diamond **01326 573778** Mr & Mrs Hallam *seefar@talk21.com* **D:** £16.00–£22.00 **S:** £16.00 **Beds:** 2D 1T 1S **Baths:** 2 En 1 Pr 1 Sh ⊃ ⊞ (1) ⊬ ⊠ ♉ ⊞ ⚲

Porthtowan

SW6847   ◁ *Commodore Inn*

Buzby View, *Forthvean Road, Porthtowan, Truro, Cornwall, TR4 8AY.* Large modern bungalow set in beautiful secluded gardens. **Open:** Easter to Oct **01209 891178 (also fax)** Mrs Parkinson *buzbyview@freenet.co.uk* www.chycor.co.uk/bnb/busby/index.htm **D:** £20.00 **S:** £20.00 **Beds:** 1T 2D 1S **Baths:** 1 Sh ⊃ (12) ⊞ (10) ⊠ ⊠ ⊞

Portloe

SW9339

Pine Cottage, *Portloe, Truro, Cornwall, TR2 5QU.* Friendly welcome, peaceful fishing village, award-winning home cooking. **Open:** Easter to Oct **01872 501385** Mrs Holdsworth **D:** £30.00–£35.00 **S:** £35.00–£40.00 **Beds:** 1D 1T **Baths:** 1 En 1 Pr ⊃ × ⊠

Portreath

SW6545   ◁ *Basset Arms, Waterfront, Fox & Hounds, Portreath Arms*

Fountain Springs, *Glenfeadon House, Portreath, Redruth, Cornwall, TR16 4JU.* Listed Georgian house. Peaceful valley. Gardens, aviary, wooded/cliff walks. **Open:** Feb to Dec **01209 842650 (also fax)** A Keast **D:** £20.00 **S:** £20.00–£25.00 **Beds:** 3F 2D 1T 1S **Baths:** 6 En 1 Sh ⊃ ⊞ (12) ⊬ ⊠ ♉ ⊞ ⚲ ⚲

Planning a longer stay? Always ask for any special rates

Cliff House, *The Square, Portreath, Redruth, Cornwall, TR16 4LB.* 200-year-old whitewashed cottage; clean and comfortable. **Open:** All year (not Xmas) **01209 842008** Mrs Healan **D:** £20.00 **S:** £20.00–£25.00 **Beds:** 1D 1T 2S **Baths:** 2 En 2 Pr ⊃ (7) ⊞ (4) ⊠ ⊞ ⚲

Bensons, *1 The Hillside, Portreath, Redruth, Cornwall, TR16 4LL.* Beautiful accommodation - panoramic sea views - quiet, warm, friendly and comfortable. **Open:** Easter to Sept **Grades:** AA 4 Diamond **01209 842534** Mr & Mrs Smythe **Fax:** 01209 843578 **D:** £20.00 **S:** £25.00 **Beds:** 2D 2S **Baths:** 4 En ⊃ (12) ⊞ (6) ⊬ ⊠ ⊞ ⚲

Portscatho

SW8735   ◁ *Standard Inn, Plume & Feathers, Roseland Inn, New Inn, King's Head*

Hillside House, *8 The Square, Portscatho, Truro, Cornwall, TR2 5HW.* **Open:** All year **01872 580526** Mrs Hart **Fax:** 01872 580527 **D:** £20.00 **S:** £20.00 **Beds:** 1F 2D 1T **Baths:** 1 Pr 1 Sh ⊃ ⊞ ♉ ⊞ ⚲ Charming Georgian house in centre of unspoilt picturesque fishing village. Beaches, harbour, Coastal Path only yards away. Comfortable bedrooms, loads of hot water, excellent Aga cooking. Children, dogs and walkers welcome. Those choosing to visit will find a special place.

Redruth

SW6942

Lanner Inn, *Lanner, Redruth, Cornwall, TR16 6EH.* **Open:** All year (not Xmas/New Year) **01209 215611** J L Wilson **Fax:** 01209 214065 *lannerinn@btinternet.com* lannerinn.com **D:** £18.00–£25.00 **S:** £20.00–£30.00 **Beds:** 2F 1T 2D **Baths:** 2 En 1 Sh ⊃ ⊞ (30) ⊠ × ⊠ ⚲ cc An old traditional country inn, offering comfortable accommodation with a warm welcome in a true local. Centrally situated within easy distance of all Cornish attractions, we also specialise in real ales and can be found in Camra Good Beer Guide 2001.

San Paula, *Tolgus Mount, Redruth, Cornwall, TR15 3TA.* **Open:** All year **01209 211191** Mrs Ormandy **D:** £18.00–£20.00 **Beds:** 1T 2D **Baths:** 3 En ⊃ ⊞ ⊬ ⊠ ⊠ ⊞ ⚲ Our farmhouse, built about 1840, is set in its own grounds of seven acres of paddocks and mature trees, surrounded by traditional Cornish hedges. There are family beaches within two miles, and a good selection of local visitor attractions.

Lower Poldice Cottage, *St Day, Redruth, Cornwall, TR16 5PP.* Central for beaches, touring, walks, cycling. Warm welcome, comfortable surroundings. **Open:** All year **01209 820438 (also fax)** J K Oates **D:** £16.50–£21.00 **S:** £16.50–£21.00 **Beds:** 1T 2D **Baths:** 1 En 1 Sh ⊃ ⊞ (8) ⊬ ⊠ × ⊠ ⊞ ⚲

Lyndhurst Guest House, *80 Agar Road, Redruth, Cornwall, TR15 3NB.* Comfortable spacious house, friendly welcome. Close to Cornish history and beaches. **Open:** All year **Grades:** RAC 3 Diamond **01209 215146** M Smith-Potter **Fax:** 01209 217643 *sales@lyndhurst-guesthouse.net* www.lyndhurst-guesthouse.net **D:** £19.00–£21.00 **S:** £17.00–£19.00 **Beds:** 1F 1T 1D 3S **Baths:** 4 En 1 Sh ⊃ ⊞ (6) ⊠ × ⊠ ⊞ ⚲ cc

Rescorla

SW9848

Yazumez, *Rescorla, St Austell, Cornwall, PL26 8YT.* Dormer bungalow near Eden Project, beaches, moors, countryside. Central location. **Open:** All year **01726 852043 (also fax)** **D:** £15.00 **S:** £15.00 **Beds:** 1F 2D **Baths:** 2 En 1 Pr ⊃ ⊞ (3) ⊠ ♉ × ⊠ ⊞ ⚲

Rock

SW9476

Silvermead, *Rock, Wadebridge, Cornwall, PL27 6LB.* 10 bedroom licensed family-run guest house overlooking Camel Estuary. **Open:** All year **Grades:** ETC 3 Diamond, AA 3 Diamond **01208 862425** Mrs Martin **Fax:** 01208 862919 **D:** £20.00–£26.00 **S:** £20.00–£47.00 **Beds:** 2F 3D 2T 2S **Baths:** 6 En 1 Sh ⊃ ⊞ (9) ⊠ ♉ × ⊠ ⊞ ⚲

Roskarnon House Hotel, *Rock, Wadebridge, Cornwall, PL27 6LD.* Edwardian hotel, overlooking estuary, 100 metres from ferry to Padstow. **Open:** Mar to Oct **01208 862785** Mr Veall **D:** £25.00–£35.00 **S:** £30.00–£40.00 **Beds:** 2F 4D 4T 2S **Baths:** 10 En 1 Sh ⊃ (5) ⊞ (14) ⊬ ⊠ ♉ × ⊠ ⊞ ⚲ ⚲

Tztizikama Lodge, *Rock Road, Rock, Wadebridge, Cornwall, PL27 6NP.* Stylish accommodation near the Camel Estuary and the North Cornish coast. **Open:** All year (not Xmas) **01208 862839** Mr Cox & Alison Jones *tztizikama.stilwell@btinternet.com* www.cornwall-online.co.uk/tztizikama-lodge **D:** £22.00–£27.00 **S:** £32.00–£37.00 **Beds:** 1F 1D 1T **Baths:** 3 En ⊃ ⊞ ⊬ ⊠ ♉ ⊞ ⚲ cc

Rosudgeon

SW5529

Carthew House, *Kenneggy Downs, Rosudgeon, Penzance, Cornwall, TR20 9AT.* Home from Home, Warm, friendly. Ideal touring beaches, cycling. Non-smoking. **Open:** Easter to Oct
01736 762437 (also fax) Mrs Webb *jan@ kenneggy.freeserve.co.uk* **D:** £14.00–£25.00
S: £14.00–£25.00 **Beds:** 1T 1D 1S **Baths:** 1
En 1 Sh 🅿✗📺📶🖥🏧

Ruan High Lanes

SW9039

Trenona Fram, *Ruan High Lanes, Truro, Cornwall, TR2 5JS.* Victorian farmhouse on mixed working farm. Enjoy our Cornish hospitality. **Open:** Mar to Oct
01872 501339 (also fax) Mrs Carbis
pamelacarbis@cs.com www.connexions.co. uk/trenona **D:** £17.00–£22.00 **S:** £22.00–£27.00 **Beds:** 4F **Baths:** 3 En 1 Pr 🚭🅿(6)✗📺🏧📶

Saltash

SX4259 🍺 *Ploughboy*

The Old Cottage, *Barkers Hill, St Stephens, Saltash, Cornwall, PL12 4QA.* Charming old beamed cottage, hearty breakfasts. **Open:** All year (not Xmas)
01752 845260 Mrs Plant *roger.plant@virgin.net*
D: £15.00 **S:** £15.00 **Beds:** 1D 2S **Baths:** 1
Sh 🚭🅿(2)✗📺🏧

Mill Park House, *Pill, Saltash, Cornwall, PL12 6LQ.* Victorian farmhouse. Ideal for touring Devon and Cornwall. **Open:** All year (not Xmas/New Year)
01752 843234 Mrs Wadge *mikedebkatem@ yahoo.co.uk* **D:** £16.00–£20.00 **S:** £17.00–£22.00 **Beds:** 1F 1T 1D **Baths:** 1 En 1 Sh 🚭
🅿(2)📺🏧

Sennen

SW3525 🍺 *Old Success, Star Inn, First & Last, Logan Rock*

The Old Manor Hotel, *Sennen, Lands End, Penzance, Cornwall, TR19 7AD.* **Open:** All year
01736 871280
Mr O'Grady **Fax: 1736871280** *info@ oldmanor.net* www.oldmanor.net **D:** £25.00–£30.00 **S:** £20.00–£30.00 **Beds:** 2F 1T 2D 2S **Baths:** 6 En 1 Pr 🚭(2)🅿(10)📺✗📶🖥🏧🍴cc
This C18th, granite built, Cornish manor house offers a warm welcome and comfortable accommodation. Located amidst coastal and rural scenery, less than a mile from Land's End and a short walk to Sennen Cove and the South West coastal path.

Treeve Moor House, *Sennen, Penzance, Cornwall, TR19 7AE.* **Open:** All year (not Xmas/New Year)
01736 871284 & 07771 914660 (M)
Miss Trenary **Fax: 01736 871284** *info@ firstandlastcottages.co.uk*
www.firstandlastcottages.co.uk **D:** £18.00–£25.00 **S:** £28.00–£35.00 **Beds:** 1F 1T 1D
Baths: 2 En 1 Pr 🚭🅿(3)✗📺📶🏧
Located within sight of Land's End in a tranquil, secluded setting with uninterrupted sea views. Footpath direct from the house to the sandy beach at Sennen Cove. Minack Theatre and excellent pubs nearby. Haven for birdwatchers and walkers.

Sunny Bank Hotel, *Seaview Hill, Sennen, Lands End, Penzance, Cornwall, TR19 7AR.* Comfortable detached hotel, close beaches, Minack Theatre, good food, licensed. **Open:** Jan to Nov
01736 871278 Mr & Mrs Comber **D:** £15.00–£20.00 **S:** £15.00–£25.00 **Beds:** 2F 5D 2T 2S
Baths: 2 Sh 🚭🅿(15)📺✗📶🏧

South Petherwin

SX3181

Oakside, *South Petherwin, Launceston, Cornwall, PL15 7LJ.* Panoramic views of Bodmin Moor from bungalow nestling peacefully in beautiful surroundings. **Open:** Mar to Nov
01566 86733 Mrs Crossman **D:** £16.00–£20.00 **S:** £16.00–£20.00 **Beds:** 1F 1D 1T
Baths: 1 En 3 Sh 🚭(2)🅿(4)✗📺🖥♿🏧

St Austell

SX0252 🍺 *Polgooth Inn, Hewas Inn*

Crossways, *6 Cromwell Road, St Austell, Cornwall, PL25 4PS.* Beaches, golf, Heligan, Eden Project, coastal walks nearby. Contractors welcome. **Open:** All year
01726 77436 Mrs Nancarrow **Fax: 01726 66877 D:** £25.00 **Beds:** 3D 1T 1F **Baths:** 5 En
🅿✗📺🍴📶🏧

National Grid References given are for villages, towns and cities – not for individual houses

Poltarrow Farm, *St Mewan, St Austell, Cornwall, PL26 7DR.* Charming farmhouse, with pretty ensuite rooms, delicious breakfast, indoor swimming pool. **Open:** All year (not Xmas/New Year)
01726 67111 (also fax) Mrs Nancarrow *enquire@poltarrow.co.uk* www.poltarrow.co.uk
D: £23.00–£25.00 **S:** £28.00–£30.00 **Beds:** 1F 3D 1T **Baths:** 4 En 1 Pr 🚭🅿(10)📺📶🖥🏧cc

Cornerways Guest House, *Penwinnick Road, St Austell, Cornwall, PL25 5DS.* Cornerways stands in its own grounds surrounded by garden/ large car park. **Open:** All year
01726 61579 B J Edwards **Fax: 01726 66871** *nwsurveys@aol.com* **D:** £16.50–£19.00
S: £16.50–£22.50 **Beds:** 1F 1T 1S **Baths:** 2 En 1 Sh 🅿(10)📺🍴📶🖥🏧

St Blazey

SX0655 🍺 *Ship Inn*

Nanscawen Manor House, *Prideaux Road, St Blazey, Par, Cornwall, PL24 2SR.* Lovely Georgian home; peaceful countryside. 3 ensuite bedrooms, swimming pool. **Open:** All year
Grades: ETC 5 Diamond
01726 814488 Mr & Mrs Martin *keith@ nanscawen.com* www.nanscawen.com
D: £39.00–£42.00 **S:** £68.00–£74.00 **Beds:** 2D 1T **Baths:** 3 En 🚭(12)🅿(8)✗📺📶🖥🏧cc

St Breward

SX0977 🍺 *Old Inn, Blisland Inn*

Treswallock Cottage, *St Breward, Bodmin, Cornwall, PL30 4PL.* Peaceful moorland setting. Panoramic views. Central for touring Cornwall. Gardens. **Open:** All year
01208 851508 *pauline@ treswallock-cottage.fsnet.co.uk*
www.treswallock-cottage.fsnet.co.uk
D: £22.50–£25.00 **S:** £30.00 **Beds:** 2D
Baths: 2 En 🅿(4)✗📺✗📶🏧

St Day

SW7342

Lower Poldice Cottage, *St Day, Redruth, Cornwall, TR16 5PP.* Central for beaches, touring, walks, cycling. Warm welcome, comfortable surroundings. **Open:** All year
01209 820438 (also fax) J K Oates
D: £16.50–£21.00 **S:** £16.50–£21.00 **Beds:** 1T 2D **Baths:** 1 En 1 Sh 🚭🅿(8)✗📺✗📶🏧

St Dennis

SW9558

Boscawen Hotel, Foe Street, St Dennis, St Austell, Cornwall, PL26 8AD. Easy access north and south coast, near Cornwall's Eden Project. **Open:** All year **01726 822275** K Mason **D:** £17.50–£25.00 **S:** £15.00–£20.00 **Beds:** 1F 1T 1D 1S **Baths:** 1 En 2 Sh 🅿 🛏 📺 🛏 ✗ Ⓥ 📖 🌢

St Erme

SW8449

Trevispian Vean Farm Guest House, St Erme, Truro, Cornwall, TR4 9BL. 300 old working farm - family run - lovely views of Cornish countryside. **Open:** Feb to Nov **01872 279514** Mr & Mrs Dymond **Fax:** 01872 263730 www.guesthousestruro.com **D:** £18.50 **S:** £24.00 **Beds:** 2F 5D 2T **Baths:** 9 Pr 🛏 🅿 (12) 🛏 📺 Ⓥ 🌢

St Erth

SW5535

Lanuthnoe Barns, St Erth Hill, St Erth, Hayle, Cornwall, TR27 6HX. Picturesque converted barn, peaceful village location yet 1.5 miles to sea. **Open:** All year **01736 755529** Mrs Crutchfield **D:** £18.00 **Beds:** 1F 1D **Baths:** 1 Pr 🛏 🅿 (4) 📺 🛏 ✗ 📖 🌢 ✳ 🌢

St Ewe

SW9746

Corran Farm, St Ewe, St Austell, Cornwall, PL26 6ER. Quality B&B in open countryside, adjoining Heligan Gardens. Eden nearby. **Open:** All year (not Xmas) **01726 842159** Mrs Lobb terryandkathy@ corranfarm.fsnet.co.uk **D:** £17.00–£19.00 **S:** £20.00–£22.00 **Beds:** 1T 1D **Baths:** 1 En 1 Pr 🛏 🅿 (4) 🛏 📺 Ⓥ 📖 🌢

St Issey

SW9271

Trevorrick Farm, St Issey, Wadebridge, Cornwall, PL27 7QH. Near Camel Trail and Padstow, centrally situated in North Cornwall for touring. **Open:** All year (not Xmas) **01841 540574 (also fax)** Mr Mealing **D:** £18.00–£25.00 **S:** £27.00–£36.00 **Beds:** 1F 1D 1T **Baths:** 3 En 🛏 🅿 (6) 🛏 📺 Ⓥ 📖 🌢 cc

BEDROOMS

D = Double
T = Twin
S = Single
F = Family

St Ives

SW5140 🍴 Engine Inn, Sloop Inn, Sheaf of Wheat

Rivendell, 7 Porthminster Terrace, St Ives, Cornwall, TR26 2DQ. **Open:** All year **01736 794923** Ms Walker **D:** £16.00–£26.00 **S:** £16.00–£21.00 **Beds:** 1F 4D 1T 1S **Baths:** 3 En 1 Sh 🛏 🅿 (6) 🛏 📺 ✗ Ⓥ 📖 ✳ 🌢

Highly recommended family-run guest house. Superb sea views from many rooms. Close to town, beaches, bus and rail stations. Friendly hospitality, excellent food. As featured in the TV drama Wycliffe.

The Primrose Valley Hotel, St Ives, Cornwall, TR26. **Open:** All year **01736 794939 (also fax)** info@ primroseonline.co.uk www.primroseonline.co. uk **D:** £24.50–£40.00 **S:** £24.50–£50.00 **Beds:** 4F 2T 4D **Baths:** 10 En 🛏 🅿 (9) 🛏 ✗ Ⓥ 📖 🌢 cc A popular independent family friendly hotel with both stunning views over St Ives and on the level with direct access to Porthminster Beach (less than one minute!) Sun terrace, licensed bar, evening meals with home-made specials and fantastic handpicked wine list.

Downlong Cottage Guest House, 95 Back Road East, St Ives, Cornwall, TR26 1PF. **Open:** All year (not Xmas) **01736 798107 D:** £20.00–£25.00 **S:** £25.00 **Beds:** 1F 4D 1T **Baths:** 4 En 1 Sh 🛏 (11) 📺 📖 🌢 Ideally situated in the heart of Downlong, the old fishing quarter of picturesque St Ives, Downlong Cottage is only minutes away from the harbour and beaches. St Ives is famous for its artists and galleries including the Tate.

Chy-An-Creet Hotel, The Stennack, St Ives, Cornwall, TR26 2HA. Warm welcome, relaxing home comfort, excellent touring and walking base. **Open:** Jan to Nov **Grades:** ETC 3 Diamond, AA 3 Diamond **01736 796559 (also fax)** Mr & Mrs Tremelling judith@chy.co.uk www.chy.co.uk **D:** £21.00–£28.00 **S:** £21.00–£28.00 **Beds:** 2F 4D 2T 1S **Baths:** 9 En 🅿 (9) 📺 🛏 ✗ Ⓥ 🌢 cc

Planning a longer stay? Always ask for any special rates

Carlill, 9 Porthminster Terrace, St Ives, Cornwall, TR26 2DQ. Friendly, comfortable, licensed, family-run guest house. Good food. Highly recommended. **Open:** All year (not Xmas) **01736 796738** Mrs Bowden Lynne@ lgtpa.freeserve.co.uk **D:** £16.00–£25.00 **S:** £18.00–£25.00 **Beds:** 2F 2D 2T 1S **Baths:** 3 En 2 Pr 2 Sh 🛏 (5) 🅿 (6) 🛏 🛏 ✗ Ⓥ 📖 🌢

Monteray Guest House, 7 Clodgy View, St Ives, Cornwall, TR26 1JG. Warm welcome. Sea views, near town, harbour coastal path, galleries. **Open:** Feb to Nov **01736 794248 D:** £19.00–£25.00 **S:** £20.00–£25.00 **Beds:** 1F 3D 1S **Baths:** 2 En 1 Pr 2 Sh 🛏 🅿 (2) 🛏 📺 Ⓥ 📖 🌢 cc

The Old Vicarage Hotel, Parc-An-Creet, St Ives, Cornwall, TR26 2ES. Large Victorian vicarage, beautifully converted, peaceful location, wooded grounds. **Open:** Easter to Nov **01736 796124** J Sykes **Fax:** 01736 796343 holidays@oldvicaragehotel.co.uk www.oldvicaragehotel.co.uk **D:** £23.00–£28.00 **S:** £28.00–£49.00 **Beds:** 3F 4T 1S **Baths:** 3 En 4 Pr 🛏 🅿 (8) 📺 🛏 📖 🌢 cc

Blue Hayes, Trelyon Avenue, St Ives, Cornwall, TR26 2AD. Country house by the sea. Beautiful sandy beaches few mins' walk along coastal path. **Open:** Feb to Nov **01736 797129** Mr Herring malcolm@ bluehayes.fsbusiness.co.uk www.bluehayes.co. uk **D:** £39.00–£60.00 **S:** £49.00–£70.00 **Beds:** 1F 5T 1S **Baths:** 7 En 🛏 (10) 🅿 (10) 🛏 📺 ✗ 📖 🌢 cc

Whitewaves, 4 Sea View, St Ives, Cornwall, TR26 2DH. Small, warm, friendly, family-run, non-smoking guest house in quiet private road. **Open:** All year (not Xmas) **01736 796595 (also fax)** Mrs Webb jan@ whitewaves.in2home.co.uk **D:** £14.00–£20.00 **S:** £14.00–£20.00 **Beds:** 1F 3D 1T 2S **Baths:** 3 Sh 🛏 🅿 🛏 📺 Ⓥ 📖 🌢

St Just-in-Penwith

SW3631

Boswedden House Hotel, Cape Cornwall, St Just-in-Penwith, Penzance, Cornwall, TR19 7NJ. Spacious Georgian mansion. Quiet country setting. Large garden, warm welcome. **Open:** All year **01736 788733 (also fax)** Miss Griffiths relax@ boswedden.org.uk www.boswedden.org.uk **D:** £20.00–£25.00 **S:** £20.00–£30.00 **Beds:** 1F 2D 3T 2S **Baths:** 8 En 🛏 🅿 🛏 🛏 📺 Ⓥ 📖 🌢 cc

B&B owners may vary rates – be sure to check when booking

Boscean Country Hotel

Boscean Country Hotel, *St Just-in-Penwith, Penzance, Cornwall, TR19 7QP.* **Open:** All Year (not Xmas) **Grades:** ETC 4 Diamond
01736 788748 (also fax) Mr & Mrs Wilson
boscean@aol.com www.connexions.co.uk/boscean/index.htm **D:** £23.00–£24.00
S: £31.00 **Beds:** 3F 4D 5T **Baths:** 12 En ♿ �P (15) ⊠ × ⊠ ▥ ♨ cc
A warm & hospitable welcome awaits you at Boscean - a magnificent country house in three acres of private walled garden, set amidst some the most dramatic scenery in West Cornwall. Home cooking, using fresh local and home-grown produce.

St Keverne

SW7921 *White Hart, Three Tuns, Five Pilchards, New Inn*

Trevinock, *St Keverne, Helston, Cornwall, TR12 6QP.* Excellent food, accommodation beautiful, unspoilt coastal area, warm welcome. Parking. **Open:** Easter to Oct
01326 280498 Mrs Kelly **D:** £18.00–£22.00
S: £18.00–£22.00 **Beds:** 1D 2S **Baths:** 1 En 1 Sh ♿ �P (5) ⊬ ⊠ ↟ × ⊠ ♨

St Kew

SX0177

Tregellist Farm, *Tregellist, St Kew, Bodmin, Cornwall, PL30 3HG.* Set in beautiful countryside with splendid views. Close to Camel Trail. **Open:** All year (not Xmas/New Year)
01208 880537 Mrs Cleave **Fax:** 01208 881017
D: £20.00–£24.00 **S:** £24.00–£26.00 **Beds:** 1F 3D 1T **Baths:** 5 En ♿ �P (6) ⊠ × ⊠ ▥ ♨

BEDROOMS

D = Double
T = Twin
S = Single
F = Family

St Kew Highway

SX0375 *St Kew Inn, Maltsters' Arms, Red Lion*

Porchester House, *St Kew Highway, Bodmin, Cornwall, PL30 3ED.* In rural village, secluded detached house with large conservatory/aviary. **Open:** All year (not Xmas)
01208 841725 Mr Ashley **D:** £25.00 **Beds:** 1D 1T **Baths:** 1 En 1 Pr ⚟ (4) ⊬ ⊠ ↟ × ▥ ♨

Brookfields, *Hendra Lane, St. Kew Highway, Bodmin, Cornwall, PL30 3EQ.* **Open:** All year (not Xmas/New Year)
01208 841698 Mr Caswell **Fax:** 01208 841174
robbie.caswell@btinternet.co.uk
www.brookfields-stkew.co.uk **D:** £20.00–£25.00 **S:** £25.00 **Beds:** 1F 1T 1D **Baths:** 3 En ♿ ⚟ (10) ⊬ ⊠ ⊠ ▥ ♨
Quality en-suite accommodation in picturesque North Cornwall. Modern country home with panoramic rural views. Wonderful setting, welcoming, fine rooms, great breakfasts. Centrally located for coasts, beaches, golf, walking, cycling, moors, towns, stately homes, attractions - and the Eden Project. Families welcome.

St Keyne

SX2460 *Highwayman Inn, Old Plough*

Wallis Holiday Barn, *St Keyne, Liskeard, Cornwall, PL14 4RP.* Rural Victorian house in 3 acres. Breakfast in conservatory with views. **Open:** All year (not Xmas/New Year)
01579 345412 (also fax) Ms Sharp
wallisbarn@hotmail.com **D:** £16.00 **S:** £21.00
Beds: 1T 1D **Baths:** 1 Sh ⚟ (2) ⊬ ⊠ ▥ ♨

St Mabyn

SX0473

Chrismar, *Wadebridge Road, St Mabyn, Bodmin, Cornwall, PL30 3BH.* Family house in village overlooking countryside.
Well positioned Camel Trail, Eden Project. **Open:** Easter to Oct
01208 841518 Mrs Frances **D:** £15.00–£18.00
S: £13.00–£15.00 **Beds:** 1F 1D 1S **Baths:** 1 Sh ♿ ⚟ (4) ⊬ ⊠ × ▥ ♨

Cles Kernyk, *Wadebridge Road, St Mabyn, Bodmin, Cornwall, PL30 3BH.* Relax in quiet North Cornwall village. Handy for beaches/moors. **Open:** All year (not Xmas)
01208 841258 Mr & Mrs Jago *sue@mabyn.freeserve.co.uk* **D:** £15.00–£20.00
S: £15.00–£20.00 **Beds:** 1F 1D 1S **Baths:** 1 Sh ♿ ⚟ (3) ⊠ ♨

St Martin

SX2655

Tregoad Farm Camping and Caravanning Park, *St Martin, Looe, Cornwall, PL13 1PB.* Tregoad Farmhouse offers quiet and restful accommodation 1.5 miles from the heart of Looe. **Open:** May to Sept
01503 262718 Mr Werkmeister **Fax:** 01503 264777 *www.tregoadfarmccp@aol.com*
www.cornwall-online.co.uk/tregoad
D: £25.00–£30.00 **S:** £25.00–£30.00 **Beds:** 1T 1D **Baths:** 2 En ⚟ ⊬ ⊠ × ▥ ♨ cc

St Neot

SX1867 *London Inn*

Lampen Mill, *St Neot, Liskeard, Cornwall, PL14 6PB.* **Open:** All year
01579 321119 (also fax) Mrs Pearce *heather@lampen.ndo.co.uk* www.lampen.ndo.co.uk
D: £25.00–£28.00 **S:** £28.00–£30.00 **Beds:** 1F 1T 1D **Baths:** 3 En ♿ ⚟ ⊬ ⊠ ⊠ ▥ ♨
Lampen Mill is a lovingly converted cornmill nestling in complete seclusion in 8 acres of natural woodland. An ideal location for touring Cornwall and Devon, close to Bodmin Moor, the Eden Project and National Trust Properties. Warm welcome is assured.

Lampen Farm, *St Neot, Liskeard, Cornwall, PL14 6PB.* Delightful, spacious C16th farmhouse in a tranquil setting on edge of Bodmin Moor. **Open:** All year
01579 320284 D: £17.00–£22.00 **S:** £20.00–£25.00 **Beds:** 1F 1T 1D **Baths:** 2 En 1 Pr ♿ ⚟ (4) ⊬ ⊠ ⊠ ▥ ♨

Dye Cottage, *St Neot, Liskeard, Cornwall, PL14 6NG.* Charming C17th cottage, oak beams, flagstone floors, lovely gardens by river. **Open:** All year (not Xmas)
01579 321394 S M Williams **Fax:** 0870 169 2029 *dyecott@lineone.net* www.cornwall-info.co.uk/dye-cottage **D:** £16.50–£17.00 **S:** £16.50–£17.00 **Beds:** 1D 2S **Baths:** 1 Sh ♿ ⚟ (1) ⊬ ⊠ ↟ ⊠ ▥ ♨

BATHROOMS

En = Ensuite
Pr = Private
Sh = Shared

National Grid References given are for villages, towns and cities – not for individual houses

St Newlyn East
SW8256

Trewerry Mill, *Trerice, St Newlyn East, Newquay, Cornwall, TR8 5GS.* Picturesque C17th watermill in peaceful riverside gardens, 4m from coast. **Open:** Feb to Nov **01872 510345 (also fax)** D & T Clark *trewerry.mill@which.net* www.connexions.co.uk/trewerry.mill **D:** £20.00–£24.00 **S:** £20.00–£24.00 **Beds:** 1F 2D 1T 2S **Baths:** 3 En 3 Sh ⛄ (7) ⊞ (12) 🛏 📺 🖛 🛒 🕯

St Wenn
SW9665

Tregolls Farm, *St Wenn, Bodmin, Cornwall, PL30 5PG.* **Open:** All year (not Xmas) **01208 812154 (also fax)** Mrs Hawkey *tregollsfarm@btclick.com* tregollsfarm.co.uk **D:** £15.00–£20.00 **S:** £15.50–£17.00 **Beds:** 2D 1T 1S **Baths:** 1 En 1 Sh ⛄ 🛒 ⊞ (10) 🖛 📺 × ⊞ 🛒 🕯

Tregolls is a Grade II Listed building, on a beef and sheep farm in mid Cornwall. We have a farm trail which links up to the Saints' Way Footpath. Convenient for visiting Padstow, Lanhydrock House, Heligan Garden and the Eden Project.

Talskiddy
SW9165

Pennatillie Farm, *Talskiddy, St Columb Major, TR9 6EF.* Secluded delightful 450 acre dairy farm. Excellent accommodation and food. **Open:** All year **01637 880280 (also fax)** Mrs Colgrove **D:** £16.00–£18.00 **S:** £16.00–£18.00 **Beds:** 3D **Baths:** 3 En ⛄ 📺 ⊞ 📺 🖛 × ⊞ 🛒 🕯

The Lizard
SW7012

Parc Brawse House, *Penmenner Road, The Lizard, Helston, Cornwall, TR12 7NR.* Old Cornish house with extensive sea views and secluded garden. **Open:** All year **01326 290466 (also fax)** Mrs Brookes *lindabrookes@cwcom.net* www.s-h-systems.co.uk/hotels/parcbraw **D:** £16.50–£23.00 **S:** £16.50–£29.00 **Beds:** 1F 1T 4D 1S **Baths:** 4 Pr 2 Sh ⛄ ⊞ (7) 📺 🖛 × ⊞ 🛒 🕯 ☀ 🕯 cc

Three Burrows
SW7447

Lands Vue Country House, *Lands Vue, Three Burrows, Truro, Cornwall, TR4 8JA.* Special welcome for all our guests at a peaceful country home. **Open:** All year (not Xmas) **01872 560242** Mrs Hutchings **Fax:** **01872 560950 D:** £20.00–£24.00 **S:** £25.00–£32.00 **Beds:** 1D 2T **Baths:** 3 En ⛄ (12) ⊞ (4) ⛄ 📺 📺 🛒 🕯

Tintagel
SX0588   ⊞ *Cornishman, Mill House Inn*

Bosayne Guest House, *Atlantic Road, Tintagel, Cornwall, PL34 0DE.* Warm, friendly family-run guest house with sea views, serving a great breakfast. **Open:** All year **Grades:** ETC 3 Diamond **01840 770514** Mr Clark *clark@clarky100.freeserve.co.uk* www.bosayne.co.uk **D:** £16.00–£20.00 **S:** £16.00–£18.00 **Beds:** 2F 3D 1T 3S **Baths:** 4 En 1 Pr 2 Sh ⛄ ⛄ 📺 🛏 × ⊞ 🛒 🕯 ☀ 🕯

Tintagel Arms Hotel, *Fore Street, Tintagel, Cornwall, PL34 0DB.* 200 year old stone building on site of Chapel of St Dennis. **Open:** All year **01840 770780** Mr Hunter **D:** £20.00–£25.00 **S:** £25.00–£30.00 **Beds:** 1F 4D 2T **Baths:** 7 En ⊞ (8) 📺 📺 🛒 🕯 cc

Pendrin House, *Atlantic Road, Tintagel, Cornwall, PL34 0DE.* Beautiful Victorian house close to many amenities, castle and beaches. **Open:** Mar to Nov **01840 770560 (also fax)** Mrs Howe *pendrin@tesco.net* **D:** £16.00–£19.00 **S:** £16.00 **Beds:** 2F 2T 4D 1S **Baths:** 3 En 3 Sh ⛄ ⊞ (5) ⛄ 📺 🛏 × 📺 🛒 🕯 🕯

Towednack
SW4838

Chytodden Farm, *Towednack, St Ives, Cornwall, TR26 3AT.* Comfortable accommodation in peaceful surroundings, good food. Car essential. **Open:** Easter to Oct **01736 795029** Mr & Mrs Hollow **D:** £15.00 **S:** £15.00 **Beds:** 1F 1D **Baths:** 1 Sh ⊞ 🕯

Trebetherick
SW9378   ⊞ *St Kew Inn, Port Gaverne Hotel*

Daymer House, *Daymer Bay, Trebetherick, Wadebridge, PL27 6SA.* Large country house by the beach. Close famous golf course & lovely coastal walks. **Open:** All year (not Xmas/New Year) **01208 862639** Mrs Burrows **D:** £27.50–£30.00 **S:** £15.50–£27.50 **Beds:** 1T 2D 1S **Baths:** 1 En 1 Pr ⛄ (11) ⊞ (3) ⛄ 📺 📺 🕯

Treknow
SX0586

Atlantic View Hotel, *Treknow, Tintagel, Cornwall, PL34 0E.* Victorian house, glorious position, set 300 yards from cliff top. **Open:** Feb to Dec. **01840 770221 Fax:** **01840 770995** *atlantic-view@eclipse.co.uk* www.holidayscornwall.com **D:** £28.00–£32.00 **S:** £32.00 **Beds:** 2F 1T 6D **Baths:** 9 En ⛄ ⊞ (10) 📺 🛏 × ⊞ 🛒 🕯 cc

Hillscroft, *Treknow, Tintagel, Cornwall, PL34 0EN.* Scenic views across Trebarwith Valley. Use of garden & summer house. **Open:** All year (not Xmas/New Year) **01840 770551** Mrs Nutt *Pat@bascastle.fsnet.co.uk* **D:** £16.00–£20.00 **S:** £16.00–£20.00 **Beds:** 1T 2D **Baths:** 2 En 1 Sh ⛄ (8) ⊞ (6) 📺 🛏 📺 🛒 🕯

Challoch Guest House, *Treknow, Tintagel, Cornwall, PL34 0EN.* Small friendly guest house, superb views, near beautiful surfing beach. **Open:** Easter to Oct **01840 770273** Mrs May **D:** £17.00–£19.00 **S:** £19.00–£20.00 **Beds:** 2D 1T ⛄ ⊞ 📺 🛏 🕯

Trelill
SX0477

Trevorrian Farm, *Trelill, Bodmin, Cornwall, PL30 3HZ.* Dairy farm. Near Port Isaac. Wonderful views over peaceful countryside. **Open:** Easter to Oct **01208 850434 (also fax)** Mrs Kingdon **D:** £20.00–£25.00 **S:** £30.00 **Beds:** 2D **Baths:** 1 En 1 Sh ⊞ (4) ⛄ 📺 × ⊞ 🕯 🕯

Treneglos
SX2088

The Old Vicarage, *Treneglos, Launceston, Cornwall, PL15 8UQ.* Renowned for hospitality and excellent food. Highest standards throughout. **Open:** Mar to Nov **01566 781351 (also fax)** Mrs Fancourt *maggie@fancourt.freeserve.co.uk* www.fancourt.freeserve.co.uk **D:** £25.00 **S:** £25.00 **Beds:** 2D 1S **Baths:** 2 En ⊞ (10) ⛄ 📺 🛒 🕯

Tresparrett
SX1491

Oaklands, *Tresparrett, Boscastle, Cornwall, PL32 9SX.* 2 miles north of picturesque Boscastle. Superb, quiet, spacious ground floor accommodation. **Open:** Easter to Sept **01840 261302** Mrs Routly **D:** £16.00–£19.00 **S:** £16.00–£20.00 **Beds:** 1T 2D **Baths:** 1 En 1 Sh ⛄ (11) ⊞ (4) ⛄ 📺 📺 🛒 🕯

Planning a longer stay? Always ask for any special rates

Planning a longer stay? Always ask for any special rates

Trevone Bay
SW8876

Well Parc Hotel, *Trevone Bay, Padstow, Cornwall, PL28 8QN.* Family run hotel and inn. Friendly, excellent food, fine ales. **Open:** All year (not Xmas/New Year)
01841 520318 Mrs Mills **D:** £23.00–£32.00 **S:** £23.00–£32.00 **Beds:** 4F 1T 4D 1S **Baths:** 5 En 2 Sh �🛇 🅿 📺 ✕ 🆅 ♨

Truro
SW8244   🍺 *Heron Inn, Wheel Inn*

Rock Cottage, *Blackwater, Truro, Cornwall, TR4 8EU.* **Open:** All year (not Xmas/New Year) **Grades:** ETC 4 Diamond, AA 4 Diamond
01872 560252 (also fax) Mrs Wakeling *rockcottage@yahoo.com* **D:** £22.00–£24.00 **S:** £26.00–£28.00 **Beds:** 2D 1T **Baths:** 3 En 🅿 (3) ⚡ 📺 🍴 ♨ cc
C18th beamed cob cottage. Haven for non-smokers. Full central heating. Bedrooms with colour television, radio, beverage tray, hairdryer. Sitting/TV room. Cosy dining room. Village location 6 miles Truro, 3 miles ocean. Delightful gardens. Mastercard/Visa/Delta/Switch.

The Donnington Guest House, *43 Treyew Road, Truro, Cornwall, TR1 2BY.* **Open:** All year
01872 222552

Fax: 01872 222 394 *eathorne-gibbons@ donnington-guesthouse.freeserve.co.uk* donnogton-guesthouse.co.uk. **D:** £18.00–£22.00 **S:** £18.00–£26.00 **Beds:** 2F 1T 2D 1S **Baths:** 4 En 2 Pr ⚡ 🅿 (6) 📺 🍴 ✕ 🆅 🍴 ♨
Elegant Victorian house with lovely views over cathedral and countryside, providing excellent accommodation, service and facilities for discerning visitors. Perfectly situated to explore the historic delights of Cornwall and the amazing Eden Project. Our mouth-watering breakfast will make your day.

Trevispian Vean Farm Guest House, *St Erme, Truro, Cornwall, TR4 9BL.* 300 old working farm - family run - lovely views of Cornish countryside. **Open:** Feb to Nov
01872 279514 Mr & Mrs Dymond **Fax:** 01872 263730 www.guesthousetruro.com **D:** £18.50 **S:** £24.00 **Beds:** 2F 5D 2T **Baths:** 9 Pr ⚡ 🅿 (12) ⚡ 📺 🆅 ♨

Patmos, *8 Burley Close, Truro, Cornwall, TR1 2EP.* Beautiful friendly home, close to centre. River view. Excellent breakfast. **Open:** All year
01872 278018 Mrs Ankers *brian.ankers@ lineone.net* **D:** £16.00–£19.00 **S:** £16.00–£20.00 **Beds:** 1D 1T **Baths:** 1 En 1 Pr ⚡ 🅿 (5) ⚡ 📺 🆅 🍴 ♨

Tywardreath
SX0854

Polbrean House, *Woodland Avenue, Tywardreath, Par, Cornwall, PL24 2PL.* Comfortable Victorian house. Close to beaches, Fowey, Eden Project & Heligan Gardens. **Open:** All year (not Xmas)
01726 812530 Mrs Ball **D:** £20.00 **S:** £25.00 **Beds:** 2D 1S **Baths:** 1 Sh ⚡ 🅿 (4) ⚡ 📺 🆅 🍴 ♨

Upton (Bude)
SS2004

Harefield Cottage, *Upton, Bude, Cornwall, EX23 0LY.* Luxurious cottage with outstanding views. Ideal for walking/touring holiday. **Open:** All year
01288 352350 Mrs Trewin **Fax:** 01288 352712 *sally@coast-countryside.co.uk* www.coast-countryside.co.uk **D:** £22.00–£44.00 **S:** £22.00–£30.00 **Beds:** 2D 1T **Baths:** 3 En ⚡ 🅿 (4) ⚡ 📺 🍴 ✕ 🆅 🍴 ♨

Veryan
SW9139   🍺 *New Inn, Roseland Inn.*

The New Inn, *Veryan, Truro, Cornwall, TR2 5QA.* **Open:** All year (not Xmas)
01872 501362
Mr Gayton **Fax:** 01872 501078 *jack@ veryan44.freeserve.co.uk* www.veryan44. freeserve.co.uk **D:** £25.00 **S:** £25.00–£35.00 **Beds:** 1D 1T 1S **Baths:** 2 En 1 Sh ⚡ ✕ 🆅 🍴 ♨ cc
The inn is based on a pair of C16th cottages. The single bar is welcoming and unspoilt. Situated in a beautiful village close by safe bathing beaches. Renowned locally for a high standard of catering.

Planning a longer stay? Always ask for any special rates

Wadebridge
SW9872   🍺 *Ring o' Bells Inn, Halfway House, Carpenters Arms, Atlantic Hotel, Ship Inn, Molesworth Arms*

Keresen, *St Giles Drive, Wadebridge, PL27 6DS.* 6 miles from coastal walks and beautiful beaches. Comfortable accommodation. **Open:** All year (not Xmas/New Year)
01208 813975 & 07775 873364 (M) Mr & Mrs Braithwaite **D:** £18.00–£20.00 **S:** £18.00–£20.00 **Beds:** 1T 2D **Baths:** 1 Sh 🅿 (3) ⚡ 📺 🍴 ♨

Porteath Barn, *St Minver, Wadebridge, Cornwall, PL27 6RA.* Recently converted barn in 8 acres. Own path to beach. **Open:** All year
01208 863605 Ms Bloor *mbloor@ukonline.co.uk* **D:** £22.00–£28.00 **S:** £25.00–£30.00 **Beds:** 2T 1D **Baths:** 2 Sh ⚡ (12) 🅿 ⚡ 🐕 ✕ 🆅 🍴 ♨

Whitstone
SX2698

West Nethercroft, *Whitstone, Holsworthy, Devon, EX22 6LD.* Warm welcome. Relaxing home from home break. Delicious farmhouse foods. **Open:** All year (not Xmas/New Year)
01288 341394 Mrs Hopper **D:** £15.00–£17.50 **S:** £15.00–£17.50 **Beds:** 1F 1D 1S **Baths:** 1 Sh ⚡ 🅿 📺 🐕 ✕ 🆅 ♨

Widegates
SX2857

Tresorya, *Widegates, Looe, Cornwall, PL13 1QL.* Cottage conveniently situated, main Looe road. Enjoy beautiful landscaped gardens. **Open:** All year (not Xmas)
01503 240258 Mrs Southwood *info@ tresorya.co.uk* www.tresorya.co.uk **D:** £18.00–£25.00 **S:** £20.00–£27.00 **Beds:** 1F 1T 1D 1S **Baths:** 1 En 1 Sh ⚡ 🅿 (10) ⚡ 🐕

National Grid References given are for villages, towns and cities – not for individual houses

Treveria Farm, *Widegates, Looe, Cornwall, PL13 1QR.* Delightful manor offering luxurious accommodation in spacious and elegant rooms. **Open:** Easter to Oct
01503 240237 (also fax) Mrs Kitto **D:** £20.00–£22.00 **S:** £25.00–£30.00 **Beds:** 2D 1T **Baths:** 3 Pr ▣ (3) ⊬ ☒ ☑ ▦ ♨

Withiel

SW9965

Tregawne, *Withiel, Bodmin, Cornwall, PL30 5NR.* C18th farmhouse lovingly restored and situated on beautiful Ruthern Valley, Eden Project 15 mins. **Open:** All year
01208 831552 Mr Jackson **Fax: 01208 832122**
D: £25.00–£35.50 **S:** £35.00–£47.50 **Beds:** 1F 1T 1D ⊱ ▣ ☒ ↑ ✕ ☑ ▦ ♨ ♨ cc

Zennor

SW4538   ◀ *Gurnard's Head, Tinners' Arms*

Boswednack Manor, *Zennor, St Ives, Cornwall, TR26 3DD.* Peaceful, vegetarian, non-smoking. Organic gardens, superb views, sea sunsets. **Open:** Easter to Oct
01736 794183 Mrs Gynn **D:** £17.00–£22.00 **S:** £18.00–£23.00 **Beds:** 1F 2D 1T 1S **Baths:** 2 En 1 Sh ⊱ ▣ (6) ⊬ ☑ ♨

Trewey Farm, *Zennor, St Ives, Cornwall, TR26 3DA.* Working farm. Peaceful attractive surroundings. Warm welcome, excellent food. **Open:** Feb to Nov
01736 796936 Mrs Mann **D:** £19.00–£22.00 **S:** £19.00–£22.00 **Beds:** 2F 2D 1T 1S **Baths:** 1 Sh ⊱ ▣ (6) ☑ ↑ ☑ ♨ cc

Rosmorva, *Boswednack, Zennor, St Ives, Cornwall, TR26 3DD.* Lovely views from garden. Superb walking on cliffs and moorland. **Open:** All year
01736 796722 Ms Hamlett **D:** £17.00–£20.00 **S:** £17.00–£20.00 **Beds:** 1F 1T **Baths:** 1 En 1 Pr ⊱ (4) ▣ (3) ⊬ ▦ ♨

The Old Chapel Backpackers, *Zennor, St Ives, Cornwall, TR26 3BY.* Perfectly situated on SW Footpath between Land's End and St Ives. **Open:** All year
01736 798307 (also fax) Ms Whitelock
zennorbackpackers@btinternet.com
www.backpackers.co.uk **D:** £12.50–£14.00 **S:** £12.50–£14.00 **Beds:** 1F 5S **Baths:** 6 Sh ⊱ ▣ ⊬ ↑ ✕ ☑ ▦ ♨ ♨

RATES
D = Price range per person sharing in a double or twin room
S = Price range for a single room

Cumbria

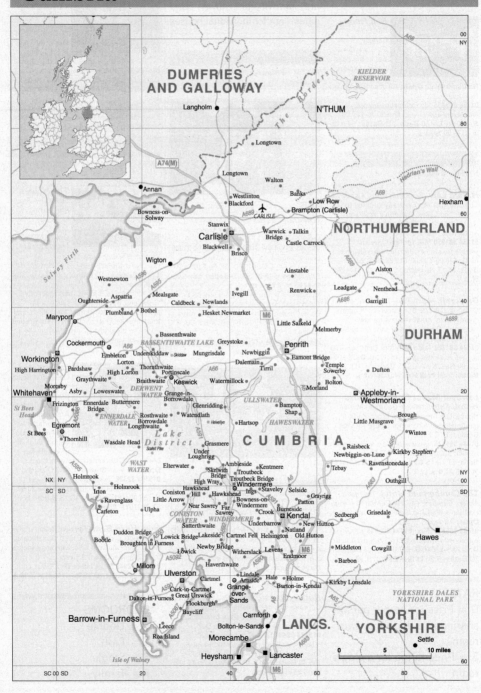

Ainstable

NY5346

Bell House, *Ainstable, Carlisle, Cumbria, CA4 9RE.* Set in the Eden Valley. Explore the Lakes, Hadrian's Wall. **Open:** All year (not Xmas/New Year) **01768 896255** Ms Robinson *mrobinson@bellhouse.fsbusiness.co.uk* **D:** £20.00–£22.50 **S:** £20.00–£22.50 **Beds:** 1D **Baths:** 1 En ⛺ 🅿 (1) ⅍ 📺 🐾 ▥ ⚓

Alston

NY7146   🍺 *Angel Inn*

Harbut Law, *Brampton Road, Alston, Cumbria, CA9 3BD.* Centrally situated to explore the Lakes, Hadrian's Wall and Northumberland. **Open:** All year (not Xmas/New Year) **01434 381950** Mrs Younger *thomas@younger.fsnet.co.uk* www.cumbria-cottages.co.uk **D:** £18.00–£21.00 **S:** £20.00–£25.00 **Beds:** 2F 1T 3D **Baths:** 2 En ⛺ 🅿 (3) ⅍ 📺 📺 ▥ ⚓

Greycroft, *Middle Park, The Raise, Alston, Cumbria, CA9 3AR.* Bungalow set in open country side, great views & handy footpaths. **Open:** All year (not Xmas/New Year) **Grades:** ETC 4 Diamond, Silver **01434 381383 (also fax)** Mrs Dent *enquiry@greycroft.co.uk* www.greycroft.co.uk **D:** £21.00–£23.00 **S:** £26.00–£28.00 **Beds:** 1F 1D **Baths:** 2 En ⛺ 🅿 ⅍ 📺 ✗ ▥ ♿ ⚓

Lowbyer Manor Country House Hotel, *Alston, CA9 3JX.* Georgian Manor House. Log fires. Library. Woodlands, gardens, secure parking. **Open:** All year **Grades:** ETC 2 Star **01434 381425** *stAy@lowbyer.com* www.lowbyer.com **D:** £32.00–£36.00 **S:** £32.00–£36.00 **Beds:** 3T 7D 1S **Baths:** 11 En 🅿 (10) ⅍ 📺 🐾 ✗ 📺 ▥ ❄ ⚓ cc

The Cumberland Hotel, *Townfoot, Alston, Cumbria, CA9 3HX.* Central to walks, Hadrian's Wall and North East. Family-run. **Open:** All year **01434 381875 Fax: 01434 382035** *postweigh@aol.com* www.cumbria1st.com/towns/hotelst **D:** £22.00–£26.00 **S:** £27.00–£31.00 **Beds:** 3F 2D **Baths:** 5 En ⛺ 🅿 ⅍ 📺 🐾 ✗ 📺 ▥ ⚓ cc

RATES

D = Price range per person sharing in a double or twin room
S = Price range for a single room

National Grid References given are for villages, towns and cities – not for individual houses

Ambleside

NY3704   🍺 *Wateredge Inn, White Lion, Unicorn, Salutation*

Hillsdale Hotel, *Church Street, Ambleside, Cumbria, LA22 0BT.* **Open:** All year (not Xmas) **015394 33174** Mr Staley **Fax: 015394 31226** *gstaley@hillsdale.freeserve.co.uk* www.hillsdale.freeserve.co.uk **D:** £18.00–£30.00 **S:** £18.00–£25.00 **Beds:** 1F 2T 5D 1S **Baths:** 6 En 2 Sh ⛺ ⅍ 📺 🐾 📺 ▥ ⚓ cc Hillsdale is a family-run B&B situated in a quiet location in the heart of Ambleside. Restaurants & pubs are a minute's walk away. We serve a hearty breakfast. Our rooms are clean & stylish and we offer a warm & friendly stay.

Borwick Lodge, *Hawkshead, Ambleside, Cumbria, LA22 0PU.* **Open:** All year **Grades:** ETC 4 Diamond, Silver **015394 36332 (also fax)** Mr & Mrs Haskell *borwicklodge@talk21.com* www.borwicklodge.com **D:** £25.00–£36.00 **S:** £35.00 **Beds:** 1F 4D 1T **Baths:** 6 En ⛺ (8) 🅿 (8) ⅍ 📺 📺 ▥ ⚓ Award-winning 'accommodation of the highest standards'. A rather special C17th country house.

Rothay House, *Rothay Road, Ambleside, Cumbria, LA22 2EE.* Quality establishment, professional care, first class breakfast. Private car park. **Open:** Feb to Dec **015394 32434** Mr & Mrs Lees *email@rothay-house.fsnet.co.uk* www.rothay-house.fsnet.co.uk **D:** £24.00–£28.00 **S:** £30.00–£35.00 **Beds:** 1F 1T 4D **Baths:** 6 En ⛺ (2) 🅿 (9) 📺 📺 ▥ ⚓ cc

---

The Old Vicarage, *Vicarage Road, Ambleside, Cumbria, LA22 9DH.* **Open:** All year **015394 33364** Mrs Burt **Fax:** **015394 34734** *the.old.vicarage@kencomp.net* **D:** £25.00–£30.00 **S:** £30.00–£40.00 **Beds:** 2F 6D 2T **Baths:** 10 En ⛺ 🅿 (15) ⅍ 🐾 📺 ▥ ♿ ❄ ⚓ Quality bed and breakfast accommodation in a peaceful location in central Ambleside. Large car park. Pets welcome. All bedrooms are well-appointed and have multi-channel TV, hairdryers, radio alarm, mini fridge, kettle, private bath/shower and WC.

The Howes, *Stockghyll Brow, Ambleside, Cumbria, LA22 0QZ.* **Open:** All year **015394 32444** *enquiries@thehowes-ambleside.co.uk* www.thehowes-ambleside.co.uk **D:** £22.00–£28.00 **Beds:** 1T 1D **Baths:** 2 En 🅿 (5) ⅍ 📺 🐾 📺 ▥ ♿ ⚓ We are close to the beautiful Stockghyll Waterfalls, but only 3 mins walk from Ambleside centre. Perfect for walkers and tourists alike. Our rooms are on the ground floor and breakfast is served within the privacy of your own room.

Lattendales, *Compston Road, Ambleside, Cumbria, LA22 9DJ.* Central Ambleside, comfortable en-suite accommodation. English or vegetarian breakfast. Discounted midweek breaks. **Open:** All year **Grades:** ETC 3 Diamond **015394 32368** *admin@latts.freeserve.co.uk* www.latts.freeserve.co.uk **D:** £19.00–£26.00 **S:** £19.00–£21.00 **Beds:** 4D 2S **Baths:** 4 En 1 Sh ⛺ (10) ⅍ 📺 📺 ▥ ⚓ cc

How Head Barn, *Fairview Road, Ambleside, Cumbria, LA22 9ED.* Spectacular views over Lakeland fells, with easy access to Ambleside. **Open:** All year **015394 32948** Mrs Walker **D:** £15.00 **S:** £16.50 **Beds:** 1D 2S ⛺ (1) ⅍ 📺 ✗ 📺 ▥ ⚓

BEDROOMS

D = Double
T = Twin
S = Single
F = Family

Fern Cottage, *6 Waterhead Terrace, Ambleside, Cumbria, LA22 0HA.* Homely Lakeland stone terraced cottage, two minutes from Lake Windermere. **Open:** All year (not Xmas) **Grades:** ETC 3 Diamond **015394 33007** S M Rushby **D:** £15.00–£17.00 **S:** £18.00–£20.00 **Beds:** 2D 1T **Baths:** 1 Sh ఔ (4) ⅍ ⊡ ⊁ ⊻ ▥ ⚲

Appleby-in-Westmorland

NY6820 ◀ *The Stag, Royal Oak, New Inn, Crown & Cushion*

Bongate House, *Appleby-in-Westmorland, Cumbria, CA16 6UE.* **Open:** Mar to Nov **Grades:** ETC 4 Diamond **017683 51245** Mrs Dayson **Fax: 017683 51423** *bongatehouse@aol.com.* **D:** £19.50–£22.50 **S:** £19.50–£30.00 **Beds:** 1F 3T 3D 1S **Baths:** 5 En 1 Sh ఔ (5) ▣ (8) ⊡ ⊁ ⊻ ▥ ⚲ This large Georgian guest house is in an acre of secluded gardens. Taste good food in a relaxed atmosphere, ideal base to tour Dales, Borders and, of course, the Settle to Carlisle railway. Make your holiday one to remember.

Slakes Farm, *Milburn, Appleby-in-Westmorland, Cumbria, CA16 6DP.* **Open:** Easter to Oct **Grades:** ETC 3 Diamond **017683 61385** C Braithwaite *oakleaves5491@ aol.com* **D:** £21.00–£22.00 **S:** £25.00 **Beds:** 1T 1D **Baths:** 2 En ▣ ⊁ ⊡ × Slakes Farm was built in 1734. It is situated in the beautiful Eden Valley, with views of the Pennines and Lake District Fells. Good local produce, own bread and preserves. A warm welcome with tea and homemade biscuits on arrival. Open fire.

Limnerslease, *Bongate, Appleby-in-Westmorland, Cumbria, CA16 6UE.* Family-run guest house 10 mins town centre. Lovely golf course and many walks. **Open:** All year (not Xmas) **017683 51578** Mrs Coward **D:** £18.00–£19.00 **Beds:** 2D 1T **Baths:** 1 Pr 1 Sh ఔ (13) ▣ (3) ⊡ ⊁ ⊻ ▥ ⚲

Planning a longer stay? Always ask for any special rates

Planning a longer stay? Always ask for any special rates

Howgill House, *Bongate, Appleby-in-Westmorland, Cumbria, CA16 6UW.* Ideally situated for Lakes, Dales, Eden Valley. Comfortable. **Open:** Easter to Oct **017683 53459 & 017683 51240** Mrs Pigney *linda@pigney.fsbusiness.co.uk* **D:** £15.00–£20.00 **S:** £15.00–£20.00 **Beds:** 1T 2D **Baths:** 1 Sh ఔ ▣ (6) ⊁ ⊡ ⊻ ⚲

Wemyss House, *48 Boroughgate, Appleby-in-Westmorland, Cumbria, CA16 6XG.* Georgian house in small country town. **Open:** Easter to Oct **017683 51494** Mrs Hirst *nickhirst@aol.com* **D:** £17.00 **S:** £17.00 **Beds:** 1D 1T 1S **Baths:** 2 Sh ఔ ▣ (2) ⊡ ⊻ ▥ ⚲

Arnside

SD4578

Willowfield Hotel, *The Promenade, Arnside, Carnforth, Lancs, LA5 0AD.* Non-smoking family-run hotel in superb estuaryside location. **Open:** All year **Grades:** ETC 4 Diamond **01524 761354** Mr Kerr *janet@ willowfield.net.1.co.uk* www.willowfield.uk.com **D:** £26.50–£29.00 **S:** £26.50–£42.00 **Beds:** 2F 3D 4T 2S **Baths:** 9 En 1 Pr 2 Sh ఔ ▣ (8) ⊁ ⊡ × ⊻ ▥ ⚲ ⊱ **cc**

Aspatria

NY1441 ◀ *The Beeches*

Castlemont, *Aspatria, Carlisle, Cumbria, CA72JU.* Castlemont is a large Victorian family residence in 2 acres of garden. **Open:** All year **016973 20205** Mr & Mrs Lines *castlemont@ tesco.net* **D:** £19.00–£23.00 **S:** £22.00–£26.00 **Beds:** 1F 1D 1T **Baths:** 1 En 2 Sh ఔ ▣ ⊁ ⊡ ⊻ ▥ ⚲ **cc**

The Retreat, *Lakeside, Brayton, Aspatria, Carlisle, Cumbria, CA5 3PT.* Modern guest house. Central location, great view, bike hire. Patio, gardens. **Open:** All year **016973 21900** Mr & Mrs Stitt www.gstitt.fsnet. co.uk **D:** £20.00–£22.00 **S:** £20.00–£22.00 **Beds:** 1T 1D 1S **Baths:** 1 En ఔ ▣ (10) ⊁ ⊡ ⊁ × ⊻ ▥ ⚲

Bampton

NY5218

Crown and Mitre, *Bampton Grange, Bampton, Penrith, Cumbria, CA10 2QR.* Family-run hotel set in undiscovered part of Lake District. **Open:** All year **01931 713225** Mrs Frith **D:** £20.00 **S:** £20.00 **Beds:** 2F 3T 5D 2S **Baths:** 5 En ఔ ▣ (5) ⊁ × ⊻ ▥ ⚲

Banks

NY5664 ◀ *White Lion, Blacksmiths Arms, Gilsland Spa Hotel*

South View, *Banks, Brampton, Cumbria, CA82JH.* Quiet location on Hadrian's Wall overlooking the picturesque Irthing Valley. **Open:** All year (not Xmas/New Year) **Grades:** ETC 3 Diamond **016977 2309** Mrs Hodgson *sandrahodgson@ southviewbanks.f9.co.uk* www.southviewbanks. f9.co.uk **D:** £20.00–£24.00 **S:** £22.00–£25.00 **Beds:** 1T 1D **Baths:** 2 En ఔ (12) ▣ (4) ⊡ ▥ ⚲

Barbon

SD6282

Kemps Hill, *Moorthwaite Lane, Barbon, Kirkby Lonsdale, Cumbria, LA6 2LP.* Ideally situated between the Lake District and Yorkshire Dales. **Open:** All year **015242 76322** Mr & Mrs Groves **Fax: 015242 76544** *info@kempshill.co.uk* www.kempshill.co. uk **D:** £20.00 **S:** £30.00 **Beds:** 2D **Baths:** 2 En ▣ ⊁ ⊡ ⊁ × ⊻ ▥ ⚲

Barrow-in-Furness

SD1969 ◀ *Brown Cow*

Glen Garth Hotel, *359 Abbey Road, Barrow-in-Furness, Cumbria, LA13 9JY.* Beautiful Victorian mansion with friendly service. All rooms well appointed. **Open:** All year **01229 825374 Fax: 01229 811744 D:** £27.45–£34.95 **S:** £49.90–£59.90 **Beds:** 2F 1T 5D 7S **Baths:** 15 En

Bassenthwaite

NY2332 ◀ *Sun Inn, Snooty Fox, Oddfellows Arms, Wheatsheaf*

Parkergate, *Bassenthwaite, Keswick, Cumbria, CA12 4QG.* Wonderful views of mountains and lake. Cosy. Tranquil and relaxing. **Open:** All year (not Xmas) **017687 76376** Mr & Mrs Phillips **Fax: 017687 76911** *phillips@parkergate.freeserve.co.uk* **D:** £20.00–£27.00 **S:** £25.00–£30.00 **Beds:** 1F 2D 1T **Baths:** 3 En 1 Pr ఔ (5) ▣ (4) ⊁ ⊡ ⊁ × ⊻ ▥ ⚲

Willow Cottage, *Bassenthwaite, Keswick, Cumbria, CA12 4QP.* Converted barn nestling at the foot of Skiddaw rural village. **Open:** All year (not Xmas/New Year) **017687 76440** Mrs Beaty **D:** £22.50–£25.00 **S:** £32.50–£35.00 **Beds:** 1T 1D **Baths:** 2 En ▣ (2) ⊁ ⊻ ▥ ⚲

Bassenthwaite Hall Farm,
Bassenthwaite, Keswick, Cumbria, CA12 4QP.
Charming, olde worlde, farmhouse -
excellent accommodation. By a stream
with ducks! **Open:** All year
017687 76393 (also fax) Mrs Trafford
D: £16.00–£20.00 **S:** £25.00–£30.00 **Beds:** 1D
1T **Baths:** 2 Sh ⌂ (10) 🅿 (4) ⊁ 📺 📺 ▥ ⚓

Baycliff
SD2972   ◀ *Fisherman's Arms*

Far Haven,
*Coast Road,
Baycliff,
Ulverston,
Cumbria,
LA12 9RJ.* Rural
setting
overlooking Morecambe Bay. Ideal for
exploring South Lakes. **Open:** All year
01229 869507 Mr & Mrs Hill **D:** £18.00–£20.00
S: £18.00–£25.00 **Beds:** 1D 1S **Baths:** 1 Sh
🅿 (2) ⊁ 📺 ⚓

Blackford
NY3962   ◀ *Crown & Thistle, Coach & Horses*

Gill Farm, *Blackford, Carlisle, Cumbria,
CA6 4EL.* Welcome to our C18th farmhouse
on working farm, set in quiet peaceful
countryside. **Open:** All year
01228 675326 & 07808 571586 (M)
Mrs Nicholson **D:** £18.00–£23.00 **S:** £19.00–
£23.00 **Beds:** 1F 1T 1D **Baths:** 1 En 2 Sh ⌂
🅿 (7) 📺 🕭 ✕ ▥ ❋ ⚓

The Hill Cottage, *Blackford, Carlisle,
Cumbria, CA6 4DU.* Country house, one
minute M6/A74. Spacious modern ground
floor rooms. **Open:** All year (not Xmas/New
Year)
01228 674739 Martin **D:** £18.50–£19.00
S: £21.00–£23.00 **Beds:** 1T 1D **Baths:** 1 Sh
⌂ (6) 🅿 (4) ⊁ 📺 📺 ▥ ⚓

Blackwell
NY4053

Blackwell Farm, *Lowry Street, Blackwell,
Carlisle, Cumbria, CA2 4SH.* Warm and
comfortable family farm close to M6
junction 42. **Open:** All year (not Xmas)
01228 524073 Ms Westmorland
blackwellfarm@ukf.net **D:** £18.00 **S:** £20.00
Beds: 1F 1D ⌂ 🅿 (4) 📺 🕭 📺 ▥ ⚓

Bolton
NY6323

Glebe House, *Bolton, Appleby in
Westmorland, Cumbria, CA16 6AW.* Former
C17th farmhouse, quiet location,
comfortable rooms, hearty breakfast.
Open: All year (not Xmas)
017683 61125 Mrs Cotton *derick.cotton@
btinternet.com* www.btinternet.com/~derick.
cotton **D:** £15.00–£20.00 **S:** £15.00–£20.00
Beds: 2D 1T **Baths:** 1 En 1 Sh ⌂ 🅿 (8) ⊁ 📺
🕭 ✕ ▥ ▥ ⚓

Bootle
SD1188

The Stables, *Bootle, Millom, Cumbria,
LA19 5TJ.* Spacious accommodation, lovely
views, two rivers, mountains, fells. Home-
cooking. **Open:** All year
01229 718644 Mrs Light **D:** £16.00–£18.50
S: £17.50–£25.00 **Beds:** 1F 2D **Baths:** 2 En 1
Sh ⌂ 🅿 (6) 📺 🕭 ✕ ▥ ▥ ⚓

Borrowdale
NY2417

Greenbank Country House Hotel,
Borrowdale, Keswick, Cumbria, CA12 5UY.
Open: Feb to Jan (not Xmas)
017687 77215 Mrs Wood **D:** £30.00–£36.00
S: £45.00 **Beds:** 1F 2T 7D **Baths:** 10 En ⌂ (2)
🅿 (15) 📺 ✕ ▥ ▥ ⚓ cc
Greenbank is quietly situated in the heart of
Borrowdale. Superb walking area and
lovely views. 10 ensuite bedrooms with tea
and coffee-making facilities etc. Two
lounges with log fires. Excellent cuisine and
warm welcome.

**Ashness
Cottage,**
*Borrowdale,
Keswick,
Cumbria,
CA12 5UN.* Cosy
cottage, in
pleasant grounds, near Ashness Bridge,
overlooking Derwent Water. **Open:** All year
(not Xmas)
017687 77244 Mrs Hamilton-Wright
D: £16.00 **S:** £20.00 **Beds:** 1D 1T **Baths:** 1
Sh ⌂ (10) 🅿 (2) ⊁ 📺 ▥ ⚓

Mary Mount, *Country House Hotel,
Borrowdale, Keswick, Cumbria, CA12 5UU.*
Country house in gardens and woodlands
on shores of Derwent Water. **Open:** All year
017687 77223 Mrs Mawdsley *marymount@
bigfoot.com* visitweb.com/marymount
D: £27.00–£32.00 **S:** £27.00–£32.00 **Beds:** 3F
6T 4D 1S **Baths:** 14 En ⌂ 🅿 (25) 📺 🕭 ✕ ▥ ▥
& ❋ ⚓ cc

Bothel
NY1838

Bothel Parks Farm, *Bothel, Carlisle,
Cumbria, CA5 2HX.* Comfortable farmhouse
on working farm near Lakes and Scottish
borders. **Open:** Easter to Oct
016973 20567 Mrs Bowe **D:** £15.00 **S:** £16.00
Beds: 1F 1D **Baths:** 1 Sh ⌂ 🅿 (6) ⊁ 📺 📺 ⚓

RATES
D = Price range per person
sharing in a double or twin
room
S = Price range for a single
room

Bowness-on-Solway
NY2262

Maia Lodge, *Bowness-on-Solway,
Wigton, Cumbria, CA7 5BH.* Panoramic views
of Solway Firth and Scottish Borders. End of
Hadrian's Wall. **Open:** All year (not Xmas)
Grades: ETC 3 Diamond
016973 51955 Mrs Chettle *d.chettle@virgin.net*
D: £18.00 **S:** £21.00 **Beds:** 1F 1D 1T **Baths:** 2
Sh ⌂ (5) 🅿 (4) ⊁ 📺 ✕ ▥ ⚓

The Old Rectory, *Bowness-on-Solway,
Carlisle, Cumbria, CA7 5AF.* Fully ensuite old
rectory at end of Hadrian's Wall.
www.wallsend.net. **Open:** All year (not
Xmas)
016973 51055 Mr & Mrs Knowles *wallsend@
btinternet.com* www.wallsend.net **D:** £20.00–
£25.00 **S:** £20.00–£25.00 **Beds:** 1F 2D 1S
Baths: 4 En ⌂ (5) 🅿 (6) ⊁ 📺 🕭 ✕ ▥ ⚓

Bowness-on-Windermere
SD4097   ◀ *Punch Bowl, Queen's Head, Village Inn*

The Fairfield, *Brantfell Road, Bowness-
on-Windermere, Windermere, Cumbria,
LA23 3AE.* **Open:** Feb to Oct **Grades:** ETC 4
Diamond
015394 46565 (also fax) Mr & Mrs Hood
Ray&barb@the-fairfield.co.uk www.the-fairfield.
co.uk **D:** £26.00–£33.00 **S:** £36.00–£43.00
Beds: 2F 5D 1T 1S **Baths:** 8 En 1 Pr ⌂ 🅿 (12)
⊁ 📺 📺 ▥ ⚓
Small friendly family-run hotel in Bowness
at the end of the Dales Way. Ensuite rooms
with colour TVs. Leisure facilities. Ideal
venue to end your walk. Private car park.
Genuine hospitality in a homely
atmosphere.

Rosemount, Lake Road, Bowness-on-Windermere, Windermere, Cumbria, LA23 2EQ. **Open:** All year **Grades:** AA 3 Diamond
015394 43739 Mr Thomas **Fax: 015394 48978** *rosemt3739@aol.com*
www.lakedistrictguesthouse.com **D:** £20.00–£30.00 **S:** £20.00–£30.00 **Beds:** 3F 10D 1T 3S **Baths:** 15 En 2 Pr ☎ 🅿 (12) ⚡ ⊠ 📺 🛏, ♨ ✕ cc
Firm, comfortable beds and breakfasts worth getting up for at this impressive Victorian guest house with elegant public rooms. Between Windermere and Bowness, yet seconds from a wood where the loudest thing you'll hear is a stream seeking the lake.

Lingwood, Birkett Hill, Bowness-on-Windermere, Windermere, Cumbria, LA23 3EZ. Friendly, comfortable, family guest house within 400 yards of lake. **Open:** All year **Grades:** ETC 4 Diamond ·
015394 44680 Mr & Mrs Atkinson *enquiries@ lingwood-guesthouse.co.uk*
www.lingwood-guesthouse.co.uk **D:** £19.00–£30.00 **S:** £30.00–£38.00 **Beds:** 2F 3D 1T **Baths:** 4 En 2 Pr ☎ 🅿 (6) 📺 📶 🛏, ♨ cc

Holly Cottages, Rayrigg Road, Bowness-on-Windermere, Windermere, Cumbria, LA23 3BZ. In the centre of town. Lake and all facilities nearby. **Open:** All year (not Xmas)
015394 44250 (also fax) Mr Bebbington *rayrig98@aol.co.uk* **D:** £25.00–£30.00 **Beds:** 4D **Baths:** 4 En 🅿 (4) ⚡ 🛏 ✕ ⊠ 📺 🛏.

Elim House, Bisky Howe Road, Bowness-on-Windermere, Windermere, Cumbria, LA23 2JP. Warm, friendly and peaceful family-run guest house with award winning garden. **Open:** All year **Grades:** AA 3 Diamond
015394 42021 *lakedistrict@ elimhouse.freeserve.co.uk* **D:** £16.00–£50.00 **S:** £20.00–£50.00 **Beds:** 2F 11D 2T **Baths:** 7 En 2 Sh ☎ (7) 🅿 (6) 📺 📶 📺 🛏, ♨ 🛏

Annisgarth House, 2 Annisgarth, Bowness-on-Windermere, Windermere, Cumbria, LA23 2HF. Views of lake and mountains. Private parking. Quiet location. **Open:** Mar to Dec
015394 48049 (also fax) Mrs Erwig **D:** £16.00–£22.00 **S:** £21.00–£27.00 **Beds:** 1T 1D **Baths:** 1 En 1 Sh ☎ 🅿 (3) 📺 🛏 📺, 🛏

All details shown are as supplied by B&B owners in Autumn 2001

Brooklands, Ferry View, Bowness-on-Windermere, Windermere, Cumbria, LA23 3JB. Fine views of Lakes and Fells. Warm welcome. Lakeland breakfast. **Open:** All year **Grades:** ETC 3 Diamond
015394 42344 R D Renwick *enquiries@ brooklandsguesthouse.net*
www.brooklandsguesthouse.net **D:** £18.00–£25.00 **S:** £25.00–£30.00 **Beds:** 2F 1T 2D **Baths:** 5 En ☎ 🅿 (6) 📺 🛏 ✕ ⊠ 📺, ♨ ♨ cc

Virginia Cottage, Kendal Road, Bowness-on-Windermere, Windermere, Cumbria, LA23 3EJ. C19th house set in heart of village. Friendly welcome assured. **Open:** All year
015394 44891 Mr Tyler **Fax: 015394 44855** *paul-deb@virginia-cottage.freeserve.co.uk* **D:** £18.00–£36.00 **S:** £20.00–£30.00 **Beds:** 1F 1T 8D 1S **Baths:** 9 En 2 Pr ☎ 🅿 (9) ⚡ ⊠ 🛏 📺 🛏, ♨ cc

Langthwaite, Crook Road, Ferry View, Bowness-on-Windermere, Windermere, Cumbria, LA23 3JB. Beautiful bungalow. Luxurious, quiet accommodation, breakfast in conservatory, warm welcome. **Open:** Feb to Nov
015394 43329 Mr Newham *howard.t.newham@ amserve.net* www.theaa.co.uk **D:** £20.00–£26.00 **S:** £30.00–£40.00 **Beds:** 2D 1T **Baths:** 3 En 🅿 (4) ⚡ ⊠ 📺 🛏, 🛏

Braithwaite

NY2323

Coledale Inn, Braithwaite, Keswick, Cumbria, CA12 5TN. Georgian inn with spectacular mountain views. Situated in peaceful countryside village. **Open:** All year
017687 78272 Mr Mawdsley **D:** £22.00–£30.00 **S:** £17.00–£25.00 **Beds:** 5F 1T 5D 1S **Baths:** 12 En ☎ 🅿 (15) 📺 📶 ✕ ⊠ 📺, ♨ 🛏 cc

Brampton (Carlisle)

NY5360

Kirby Moor Country House Hotel, Longtown Road, Brampton (Carlisle), Cumbria, CA8 2AB. Built in C19th in idyllic surroundings overlooking the beautiful Castlestead Estates. **Open:** All year **Grades:** ETC 2 Star
016977 3893 **D:** £35.00 **S:** £45.00 **Beds:** 2F 1T 3D **Baths:** 7 En ☎ 🅿 (20) 📺 📶 ✕ ⊠ 📺, ♨ cc

Brisco

NY4251

Staggs Cottage, Brisco, Carlisle, CA4 0QS. Open views. Close Carlisle, Hadrian's Wall, Northern Lakes. Painters welcome. **Open:** All year (not Xmas/New Year)
01228 547419 Mrs Gray **D:** £19.00–£26.00 **S:** £19.00–£26.00 **Beds:** 2T **Baths:** 1 En 1 Pr ☎ 🅿 ⚡ ⊠ 📺 🛏, 🛏

Crossroads House, Brisco, Carlisle, Cumbria, CA4 0QZ. Peaceful house set in the country with superb views and 100 ft Roman well. **Open:** All year (not Xmas/New Year)
01228 528994 (also fax) Mr & Mrs Wilson **D:** £21.00–£23.00 **S:** £21.00–£23.00 **Beds:** 1F 1T 2D 1S **Baths:** 1 En 2 Sh ☎ 🅿 (6) ⚡ ⊠ ✕ 📺 🛏, 🛏

Brough

NY7914 ⚲ *Golden Fleece*

Riverview, Brough, Kirkby Stephen, Cumbria, CA17 4BZ. Friendly welcome. Clean, comfortable, attractive bedrooms. Pleasant location, great breakfasts. **Open:** All year (not Xmas/New Year) **Grades:** ETC 3 Diamond
017683 41894 (also fax) H Holmes *riverviewbb@btinternet.com* **D:** £18.00–£20.00 **S:** £20.00–£25.00 **Beds:** 1F 1D **Baths:** 2 En ☎ 🅿 (3) ⚡ ⊠ 🛏 📺 🛏, 🛏

Broughton in Furness

SD2187 ⚲ *Newfield Inn*

The Dower House, High Duddon, Duddon Bridge, Broughton In Furness, Cumbria, LA20 6ET. Exceptional location, peaceful, secluded country house. Comfortable rooms & warm welcome. **Open:** All year (not Xmas/New Year) **Grades:** ETC 3 Diamond
01229 716279 (also fax) Mrs Nichols **D:** £23.00–£27.00 **S:** £30.00 **Beds:** 1F 1T 3D 1S **Baths:** 4 En 1 Pr ☎ 🅿 (8) 📺 📺 🛏, 🛏 cc

Browside, Seathwaite, Broughton in Furness, Cumbria, LA20 6EF. Beautifully situated between Harter and Coniston Fells. River bathing. **Open:** All year
01229 716612 D: £14.00 **S:** £14.00 **Beds:** 1D 1S **Baths:** 1 Sh ☎ 🅿 (2) 🛏 🛏

Burneside

SD5095

Gateside House Farm, Windermere Road, Burneside, Kendal, Cumbria, LA9 5SE. Gateside Farm is a working dairy and sheep farm. **Open:** All year
015397 22036 (also fax) Mrs Ellis **D:** £18.00–£23.00 **S:** £18.00–£23.00 **Beds:** 1F 3D 1T **Baths:** 3 En 2 Sh ☎ 🅿 (5) 📺 ✕ ⊠ 📺, 🛏

BEDROOMS

D = Double

T = Twin

S = Single

F = Family

Burton-in-Kendal

SD5376

Coat Green Farm, *Burton-in-Kendal, Carnforth, Lancs, LA6 1JG.* Comfortable farmhouse accommodation on a working farm. Quiet rural location. **Open:** Easter to Nov
01524 781535 (also fax) Mrs Duckett
D: £16.00–£18.00 **S:** £18.00 **Beds:** 1F 1D 1S
Baths: 1 Sh ♿ 🖪 ✔ 📺 🎅 ⬛ ♨

Buttermere

NY1717

Trevene, *Buttermere, Cockermouth, Cumbria, CA13 9XA.* Peaceful house surrounded by ideal walking country, close to Lakes.
Open: All year (not Xmas)
017687 70210 (also fax) Mrs Knight *roland@ trevene.co.uk* www.trevene.co.uk **D:** £19.00
S: £20.00 **Beds:** 1F 1D 1T **Baths:** 1 Sh ♿ (6)
🖪 (3) ✔ 📺 🎅 ⬛ ♨

Caldbeck

NY3239 🍺 *Royal Oak, Oddfellows Arms, Snooty Fox, Old Crown*

Parkend Country Hotel, *Parkend, Caldbeck, Wigton, Cumbria, CA7 8HH.*
Open: All year
016974 78494 C Slinger **D:** £25.00–£32.00
S: £32.00–£40.00 **Beds:** 1F 2T 3D **Baths:** 6 En ♿ 🖪 (16) 📺 🎅 ✗ 📺 ⬛ ♨ cc
C17th converted farmhouse set in the tranquil northern Lake District Fells. Ideal for walkers who enjoy their comforts. Situated on the Coast to Coast Cycle Route. Good home-cooked food in olde worlde surroundings.

The Briars, *Friar Row, Caldbeck, Wigton, Cumbria, CA7 8DS.* In Caldbeck village, right on Cumbria Way. 2 mins' walk pub. **Open:** All year (not Xmas)
016974 78633 Mrs Coulthard **D:** £18.50–£20.00 **S:** £18.50–£20.00 **Beds:** 1D 1T 1S
Baths: 1 En 1 Sh 🖪 (4) ✔ 📺 🎅 ⬛ ♨

Cark-in-Cartmel

SD3676 🍺 *The Engine, Rose & Crown*

Eeabank House, *123 Station Road, Cark-in-Cartmel, Grange-over-Sands, Cumbria, LA11 7NY.* C17th coaching house inn, licensed bar, log fires, Old England is here.
Open: All year (not Xmas/New Year)
015395 58156 (also fax) Mr Reece
D: £22.00–£24.00 **S:** £20.00–£22.00 **Beds:** 1F 1T 3D 2S **Baths:** 2 En 1 Pr 1 Sh ♿ 🖪 📺 🎅 ✗ 📺 ⬛ ♿ ♨

Carleton (Holmrook)

SD0898

Coachman's Cottage, *Carleton Hall, Carleton, Holmrook, Cumbria, CA19 1YX.* Converted coach house, oak beams, good food, warm welcome. **Open:** All year (not Xmas)
019467 24369 Mrs Marshall
www.coachmans-cottage.co.uk **D:** £16.00–£20.00 **S:** £16.00–£20.00 **Beds:** 3F 1D 1S
Baths: 1 En 2 Sh ♿ 🖪 (5) ✔ 📺 📺 ⬛ ♨

Carlisle

NY3955 🍺 *Cranemakers*

Dalroc, *411 Warwick Road, Carlisle, Cumbria, CA1 2RZ.* **Open:** All year (not Xmas/New Year) **Grades:** ETC 3 Star
01228 542805 Mrs Irving www.dalroc.co.uk
D: £16.00–£18.00 **S:** £16.00–£18.00 **Beds:** 1T 1D 1S ♿ (7) 🖪 📺 ✗ ⬛ ♨
Welcome to this small, friendly home in lovely gardens. Midway between motorway M6 (43) and city centre. Close to restaurants, auction, golf course, riverside walks and all amenities. Good base for Lakes, Borders of Scotland and Hadrian's Wall.

Craighead, *6 Hartington Place, Carlisle, Cumbria, CA1 1HL.* **Open:** All year (not Xmas) **Grades:** ETC 3 Diamond
01228 596767 Mrs Smith **D:** £17.00 **S:** £16.00 **Beds:** 1F 2D 1T 1S **Baths:** 1 En 2 Sh ♿ 📺 🎅 📺 ⬛ ♨
You will receive a warm welcome at Craighead, a Grade II Listed spacious Victorian town house with comfortable rooms and original features. CTV, tea/coffee tray in all rooms. Minutes' walk to city centre bus and rail stations and all amenities. Friendly personal service.

White Lea Guest House, *191 Warwick Road, Carlisle, CA1 1LP.* **Open:** All year
Grades: ETC 3 Diamond
01228 533139 & 07901 525376 (M)
Ms Denison **Fax:** 01228 533139 **D:** £16.00–£18.00 **S:** £18.00–£20.00 **Beds:** 2F 2T
Baths: 1 En 2 Sh ♿ 🖪 (2) ✔ 📺 🎅 ✗ 📺 ⬛ ♨
White Lea is a Victorian house built in 1900, featuring original plaster heads of a lady in the hallway. Short walk to historic Carlisle city with the Castle, Cathedral and Tullie House museum. Golf courses nearby. One mile from M6 (J43).

Angus Hotel & Almonds Bistro, *14 Scotland Road, Stanwix, Carlisle, Cumbria, CA3 9DG.*
Open: All year
Grades: AA 4 Diamond
01228 523546 & 0800 0262046 Mr Webster
Fax: 01228 531895 *angus@ hadrians-wall.fsnet.co.uk* www.angus-hotel. fsnet.co.uk **D:** £23.00–£30.00 **S:** £30.00–£48.00 **Beds:** 4F 3D 4T 3S **Baths:** 11 En 3 Sh ♿ 🖪 (6) 📺 🎅 ✗ 📺 ⬛ ♨ cc
Victorian town house, foundations on Hadrian's Wall. Excellent food, Les Routiers Awards, local cheeses, home baked bread. Genuine warm welcome from owners. Licensed, draught beer, lounge, meeting room, Internet cafe, direct dial telephones, secure garaging. Group rates for cyclists available.

New Pallyards, *Hethersgill, Carlisle, Cumbria, CA6 6HZ.*
Open: All year
Grades: ETC 4 Diamond
01228 577308 (also fax) Mrs Elwen *info@ newpallyards.freeserve.co.uk* www.newpallyards. freeserv.co.uk **D:** £22.00–£23.90 **S:** £27.00–£29.00 **Beds:** 1F 2T 2D 1S **Baths:** 6 En ♿ 🖪 📺 🎅 ✗ 📺 ⬛ ♨ ✱ cc
N/E of Carlisle in M6-A7 corridor. Ideal stopover or longer visit to explore our wonderful countryside such as Hadrians Wall, Gretna Green, Kielder Forest. Country farmhouse accommodation, National Gold Award, all ensuite, some ground floor. Licensed.

Gill Farm,
Blackford, Carlisle, Cumbria, CA6 4EL. **Open:** All year **01228 675326 &** **07808 571586 (M)** Mrs Nicholson **D:** £18.00–£23.00 **S:** £19.00–£23.00 **Beds:** 1F 1T 1D **Baths:** 1 En 2 Sh ☎ 🗗 (7) 🖂 ⅋ 🖺 🎞 ☀ 🛱
Welcome to our C18th farmhouse on working farm, set in quiet peaceful countryside.

Crossroads House, Brisco,
Carlisle, Cumbria, CA4 0QZ. **Open:** All year (not Xmas/New Year) **01228 528994 (also fax)** Mr & Mrs Wilson **D:** £21.00–£23.00 **S:** £21.00–£23.00 **Beds:** 1F 1T 2D 1S **Baths:** 1 En 2 Sh ☎ 🗗 (6) ⅋ 🖂 ✕ 🖾 🎞
A warm welcome awaits you at this peaceful house set in the country with superb views and 100 ft Roman well. Ideally situated for touring Lakes and Hadrian's Wall with easy access from M6 motorway. High standards, excellent breakfasts and licensed.

Howard Lodge, 90 Warwick Road,
Carlisle, Cumbria, CA1 1JU. **Open:** All year **Grades:** ETC 4 Diamond, AA 3 Diamond **01228 529842** Mr Hendrie **D:** £15.00–£25.00 **S:** £20.00–£30.00 **Beds:** 2F 1D 2T 1S **Baths:** 6 En 1 Sh ☎ 🗗 (6) 🖂 ⅋ ✕ 🖾 🎞 🛱
Friendly family-run guest house in comfortable Victorian town house in conservation area. Spacious rooms, all fully ensuite with satellite TV, welcome tray, hairdryer and clock radio. Large breakfasts. 5 minutes walk from station and city centre. Evening meals by prior arrangement. Private car park.

Howard House, 27
Howard Place, Carlisle, Cumbria, CA1 1HR. Elegant Victorian town house, 5 minutes walk to city centre. **Open:** All year (not Xmas/New Year) **01228 529159 & 01228 512550** Mrs Fisher **Fax:** 01228 512550 howardhouse@bigfoot.co.uk **D:** £18.00–£22.00 **S:** £18.00–£22.00 **Beds:** 1F 1T 2D 3S **Baths:** 2 En 1 Pr 1 Sh 🖂 🖾 🎞 🛱 cc

Courtfield Guest House, 169 Warwick
Road, Carlisle, Cumbria, CA1 1LP. Short walk to historic city centre. Close to M6, J43. **Open:** All year (not Xmas) **01228 522767** Mrs Dawes **D:** £18.00–£22.00 **S:** £25.00 **Beds:** 1F 2D 2T **Baths:** 5 En ☎ (4) ⅋ 🖂 🖾 🎞 🛱

Ashleigh House, 46
Victoria Place, Carlisle, Cumbria, CA1 1EX. Beautifully decorated town house. Two minutes from city centre. **Open:** All year (not Xmas/New Year) **01228 521631** Mr Dawes **D:** £19.00–£22.50 **S:** £25.00–£30.00 **Beds:** 3F 1T 2D 1S **Baths:** 7 En ☎ (5) 🖂 🖾 🛱 cc

Avondale, 3 St Aidans Road, Carlisle,
Cumbria, CA1 1LT. Attractive comfortable Edwardian house. Quiet central position convenient M6 J43. **Open:** All year (not Xmas) **Grades:** ETC 4 Diamond **01228 523012 (also fax)** Mr & Mrs Hayes beeanbee@hotmail.com www.bed-breakfast-carlisle.co.uk **D:** £20.00 **S:** £20.00–£40.00 **Beds:** 1D 2T **Baths:** 1 En 1 Pr ☎ 🗗 (3) ⅋ 🖂 ✕ 🖾 🎞 🛱

Cornerways Guest House, 107
Warwick Road, Carlisle, Cumbria, CA1 1EA. Large Victorian town house. **Open:** All year (not Xmas) **01228 521733** Mrs Fisher **D:** £14.00–£18.00 **S:** £16.00–£18.00 **Beds:** 2F 1D 4T 3S **Baths:** 3 En 2 Sh ☎ 🗗 (4) 🖂 ⅋ ✕ 🖾 🛱

Kingstown Hotel, 246 Kingstown Road,
Carlisle, CA3 0DE. A licensed hotel just off the M6/J44 providing high-quality accommodation. **Open:** All year **01228 515292 (also fax)** Mrs Marshall **D:** £27.50 **S:** £40.00 **Beds:** 1F 4D 2T **Baths:** 7 En ☎ 🗗 (14) 🖂 ✕ 🖾 🎞 ⅍ ☀ 🛱 cc

Claremont, 30 London Road, Carlisle,
Cumbria, CA1 2EL. Ideal location to tour the North Lakes and Southwest Scotland. **Open:** All year (not Xmas/New Year) **Grades:** ETC 3 Diamond **01228 524691** Mrs Rayson **D:** £15.00–£17.00 **S:** £20.00–£22.00 **Beds:** 2F 1T 2D 4S **Baths:** 1 Pr 2 Sh ☎ 🖂 🖾 🎞 🛱

East View Guest House, 110 Warwick
Road, Carlisle, Cumbria, CA1 1JU. 10 minutes' walking distance from city centre, railway station & restaurants. **Open:** All year (not Xmas) **01228 522112 (also fax)** Mrs Glease www.eastviewguesthouse.com **D:** £18.00–£20.00 **S:** £20.00–£25.00 **Beds:** 3F 2D 1T 1S **Baths:** 7 En ☎ 🗗 (4) ⅋ 🖂 🖾 🎞 🛱

Chatsworth Guest House, 22
Chatsworth Square, Carlisle, Cumbria, CA1 1HF. City centre Grade II Listed building, close to all amenities. **Open:** All year (not Xmas) **01228 524023 (also fax)** Mrs Mackin **D:** £19.00–£22.00 **S:** £25.00 **Beds:** 1F 1D 2T 1S **Baths:** 5 En ☎ 🗗 (2) ⅋ 🖂 🖾 🎞 🛱

Planning a longer stay? Always ask for any special rates

RATES
D = Price range per person sharing in a double or twin room
S = Price range for a single room

Cherry Grove, 87 Petteril Street, Carlisle,
Cumbria, CA1 2AW. Lovely red brick building close to golf club and town. **Open:** All year **01228 541942** Mr & Mrs Houghton petteril87@ aol.com **D:** £17.50–£20.00 **S:** £20.00–£30.00 **Beds:** 3F 2D **Baths:** 5 En ☎ 🗗 (3) ⅋ 🖂 ⅋ 🖾 🎞 🛱

Corner House Hotel & Bar, 4 Grey
Street, Carlisle, CA1 2JP. Refurbished family-run hotel. Base for golf, walking, cycling, touring Lakes, Roman wall, Settle-Carlisle Railway. **Open:** All year **01228 533239** Mrs Anderson **Fax:** 01228 546628 **D:** £17.50–£22.00 **S:** £20.00–£30.00 **Beds:** 3F 4D 4T 3S **Baths:** 14 En ☎ 🖂 ⅋ ✕ 🖾 🎞 ⅍ ☀ 🛱 cc

Cambro House, 173 Warwick Road,
Carlisle, Cumbria, CA1 1LP. Attractively decorated and well-maintained guest house. Each ensuite bedroom includes TV. **Open:** All year **01228 543094 (also fax)** Mr & Mrs Mawson cambrohouse@amserve.net **D:** £17.00–£20.00 **S:** £20.00–£25.00 **Beds:** 2D 1T **Baths:** 3 En 🗗 (2) ⅋ 🖂 🖾 🛱

Cartmel
SD3878 🍺 Cavendish Arms, Royal Oak, King's Arms, Pig & Whistle

Bank Court Cottage, The Square,
Cartmel, Grange-over-Sands, Cumbria, LA11 6QB. We offer a warm welcome to our pretty character cottage. **Open:** All year (not Xmas) **015395 36593 (also fax)** Mrs Lawson **D:** £19.50–£26.00 **S:** £22.50 **Beds:** 1D 1T **Baths:** 1 Sh ☎ ⅋ 🖂 ⅋ ✕ 🖾 🎞 🛱

Cartmel Fell
SD4187

Lightwood Farmhouse, Cartmel Fell,
Grange-over-Sands, Cumbria, LA11 6NP. Dating back to 1656, many original features, 2 acres of gardens, extensive views. **Open:** All year (not Xmas) **015395 31454 (also fax)** Ms Cervetti **D:** £24.00–£28.00 **S:** £30.00–£35.00 **Beds:** 2F 2D 2T **Baths:** 6 En ☎ 🗗 (8) ⅋ 🖂 ✕ 🖾 🎞 🛱 cc

Please respect a B&B's wishes regarding children, animals and smoking

BEDROOMS
D = Double
T = Twin
S = Single
F = Family

Castle Carrock
NY5455

Gelt Hall Farm, *Castle Carrock, Brampton, Carlisle, Cumbria, CA4 9LT.* **Open:** All year **01228 670260** Ms Robinson **D:** £17.50 **S:** £16.00–£17.50 **Beds:** 1F 1D 1T **Baths:** 2 Sh ⍟⎙⌦⎙⊠✕☰⠿.
Farmhouse dating back to C17th. Near Hadrian's Wall, good stop-off on way to Scotland, near Gretna Green. Scenic walks and bird sanctuary, 2 miles golf course and Talkin Tarn boating lake.

Catlowdy
NY4576

Bessiestown, *Catlowdy, Longtown, Carlisle, Cumbria, CA6 5QP.* **Open:** All year (not Xmas) **Grades:** ETC 5 Diamond, Sllver, AA 5 Diamond **01228 577219 & 01228 577019 (also fax)** Mr & Mrs Sisson *bestbb2000@cs.com* www.bessiestown.co.uk **D:** £27.50–£30.00 **S:** £35.00 **Beds:** 1F 2T 3D **Baths:** 6 Pr ⍟⎙⌦⎙⌦⊠✕⎙☰⠿.&3 ⍠ cc
As featured on TV, multi-award winning Best Guest House, offering warm, lighthearted welcome, peace and quiet, delightful public rooms, beautiful ensuite bedrooms, luxury honeymoon suite, delicious food. Open all year with indoor heated swimming pool May-Sept. Easy access M6, M74, A7.

Craigburn Farm, *Catlowdy, Carlisle, Cumbria, CA6 5QD.* **Open:** All year (not Xmas/New Year) **Grades:** ETC 4 Diamond **01228 577214** Mrs Lawson **Fax: 01228 577014** *louiselawson@hotmail.com* www.craigburnfarmhouse.co.uk **D:** £24.00–£25.00 **S:** £29.00–£30.00 **Beds:** 1F 2T 3D **Baths:** 6 En ⍟⎙⊠(20)⎙✕⎙☰⠿.⍠cc
Friendly relaxed atmosphere awaits you at our family-run farmhouse set in quiet green countryside. Delicious food, residential licence, beautiful ensuite bedrooms all make for a peaceful stopover to and from Scotland. Ideal for visiting Hadrian's Wall, Scottish Borders or Lakes.

Cockermouth
NY1230 ⍟ *The Trout, Wheatsheaf, Bitter End*

The Rook Guest House, *9 Castlegate, Cockermouth, Cumbria, CA13 9EU.* Cosy C17th town house. Spiral staircase. Convenient for all amenities. **Open:** All year (not Xmas) **01900 828496** Mrs Waters **D:** £16.00–£18.00 **S:** £20.00 **Beds:** 2D 1T **Baths:** 1 En 1 Pr 1 Sh ⍟(5)⌦⎙⊠⎙☰⠿.

Coniston
SD3097 ⍟ *Crown Inn, Ship Inn, Sun Inn, Black Bull*

Ship Inn, *Bowmanstead, Coniston, Cumbria, LA21 8HB.* **015394 41224** Mrs Jackson **D:** £22.50–£25.00 **S:** £25.00–£30.00 **Beds:** 1F 3D **Baths:** 2 Sh ⍟⎙(10)⎙✕⎙☰⠿.⍠cc
Traditional Country Inn with original oak beams and real log fire. Perfectly situated for exploring Coniston Fells and surrounding areas of the Lake District. You can be assured of a warm welcome, comfortable accommodation and good food.

Planning a longer stay? Always ask for any special rates

Kirkbeck House, *Lake Road, Coniston, Cumbria, LA21 8EW.* Comfortable friendly accommodation close to lake and amenities. Yummy breakfast. **Open:** All year **015394 41358** Mrs Potter *ann@kirkbeck.co.uk* www.kirkbeck.co.uk **D:** £16.00 **S:** £16.00 **Beds:** 1F 1D 1T ⍟⎙(3)⎙⎙☰⠿.

Crown Hotel, *Coniston, Cumbria, LA21 8EA.* Situated in the picturesque village of Coniston within easy reach of the famous lake. **Open:** All year (not Xmas) **Grades:** ETC 4 Diamond, RAC 4 Diamond **015394 41243** Mr Tiidus **Fax: 015394 41804** *info@crown-hotel-coniston.com* www.crown-hotel-coniston.com **D:** £30.00–£40.00 **S:** £40.00–£50.00 **Beds:** 6D 6T **Baths:** 12 En ⍟⎙⊠(20)⎙✕⎙☰⠿.⍠cc

Waverley, *Lake Road, Coniston, Cumbria, LA21 8EW.* Clean and friendly, excellent value. Large Victorian house. **Open:** All year (not Xmas) **015394 41127 (also fax)** Mrs Graham **D:** £16.00 **S:** £16.00 **Beds:** 1F 1D 1T **Baths:** 1 Pr 2 Sh ⍟⎙(3)⌦⎙↑⎙☰⠿.

Thwaite Cottage, *Waterhead, Coniston, Cumbria, LA21 8AJ.* Beautiful C17th cottage. Peaceful location near head of Coniston Water. **Open:** All year (not Xmas) **015394 41367** Mrs Aldridge *m@thwaitcot.freeserve.co.uk* www.thwaitcot.freeserve.co.uk **D:** £21.00–£24.00 **Beds:** 2D 1T **Baths:** 1 En 2 Pr ⍟⎙(3)⌦⎙⎙☰⠿.

Lakeland House, *Tilberthwaite Avenue, Coniston, Cumbria, LA21 8ED.* Friendly, family-run, village centre, lounge, log fire, groups welcome. **Open:** All year (not Xmas) **015394 41303** Mrs Holland *lakelandhouse_coniston@hotmail.com* **D:** £16.00–£35.00 **S:** £16.00–£35.00 **Beds:** 5F 2D 1T 1S **Baths:** 3 En 3 Sh ⍟⎙⎙⎙☰⠿.⍠cc

Oaklands, *Yewdale Road, Coniston, Cumbria, LA21 8DX.* Beautiful spacious Lakeland house, near village centre, private parking. **Open:** All year (not Xmas/New Year) **015394 41245 (also fax)** Mrs Myers **D:** £20.00–£25.00 **S:** £20.00–£25.00 **Beds:** 1T 2D **Baths:** 1 En 1 Sh ⎙(4)⌦⎙⎙☰⠿.

Cowgill
SD7587

The Sportsman's Inn, *Cowgill, Dent, Sedbergh, Cumbria, LA10 5RG.* Family owned freehouse 1670, scenic location, rooms overlooking River Dee. **Open:** All year **015396 25282** Mr & Mrs Martin *ronmartin@bun.com* **D:** £17.50–£23.50 **S:** £17.50–£23.50 **Beds:** 1F 2D 3T **Baths:** 3 Sh ⍟⎙(10)↑✕⎙☰.

Crook
SD4695

Mitchelland Farm Bungalow, *Crook, Kendal, Cumbria, LA8 8LL.* Wheelchair accessible spacious working farm bungalow. Wonderful views near Windermere. **Open:** All year
015394 47421 Mr Higham **D:** £22.00–£26.00 **S:** £25.00–£30.00 **Beds:** 1T 1D **Baths:** 1 En 1 Pr ⌂ 🅿 (5) ⏰ 🖤 🌳 🎔 🖳 & 🏊

Dalemain
NY4726 🍴 *Horse & Farrier*

Park House Farm, *Dalemain, Penrith, Cumbria, CA11 0HB.* Glorious views, excellent stop-off for M6. Peaceful surroundings. **Open:** Mar to Nov **Grades:** ETC 3 Diamond
017684 86212 (also fax) Mrs Milburn *park.house@faxuia.net* www.the-eden-in-cumbria. co.uk/parkhouse **D:** £19.00–£22.00 **S:** £19.00–£22.00 **Beds:** 1F 1T 1D **Baths:** 1 En 1 Sh ⌂ 🅿 ⏰ 🖳 🏊 cc

Dalton-in-Furness
SD2374

Park Cottage, *Park, Dalton-in-Furness, Cumbria, LA15 8JZ.* **Open:** All year
01229 462850 Mr & Mrs Nicholson *nicholson.parkcottage@quista.net* www.parkcottagedalton.co.uk **D:** £18.50–£20.00 **S:** £22.00–£26.00 **Beds:** 1F 2D **Baths:** 3 En 🅿 (6) ⏰ 🖤 🎔 🖳 🏊
Surrounded by woodland and farmland, this C17th beamed cottage enjoys a peaceful location and overlooks Burlington Lake. Birdwatchers' paradise. Excellent ensuite bedrooms have good views. Comfortable residents' lounge. Hearty Cumbrian breakfasts. Easy access to South Lakeland, fells and coast. Highly recommended, many repeat bookings.

Dent
SD7086 🍴 *Sun Inn, George & Dragon*

Rash House, *Dent Foot, Dent, Sedbergh, Cumbria, LA10 5SU.* Charming C18th farmhouse situated in picturesque Dentdale. **Open:** All year (not Xmas)
015396 20113 (also fax) Mrs Hunter **D:** £16.00–£18.00 **S:** £18.00–£20.00 **Beds:** 1F 1D **Baths:** 1 Sh ⌂ 🅿 (2) ⏰ 🎔 ✕ 🖳 🏊

Smithy Fold, *Whernside Manor, Dent, Sedbergh, Cumbria, LA10 5RE.* Relax in this beautiful setting and we'll make it memorable. **Open:** All year
Grades: ETC 3 Diamond
015396 25368 A J Cheetham *cheetham@ smithyfold.co.uk* www.smithyfold.co.uk **D:** £18.00 **S:** £18.00 **Beds:** 1F 1T 2D **Baths:** 1 Sh ⌂ (3) 🅿 (20) ⏰ 🎔 🖤 🖳 🏊

Garda View Guest House, *Dent, Sedbergh, Cumbria, LA10 5QL.* Village centre, friendly family house. Hearty breakfasts, walking information available. **Open:** All year (not Xmas)
015396 25209 Mrs Smith *dentstores@cwcom.net* **D:** £17.00 **S:** £17.00 **Beds:** 2D 1T 1S **Baths:** 1 Sh ⌂ 🅿 (2) ⏰ 🎔 🖳 🏊

Duddon Bridge
SD1988 🍴 *High Cross Inn, Black Cock, King's Head, Blacksmith's Arms*

The Dower House, *High Duddon, Duddon Bridge, Broughton In Furness, Cumbria, LA20 6ET.* Exceptional location, peaceful, secluded country house. Comfortable rooms & warm welcome. **Open:** All year (not Xmas/New Year)
Grades: ETC 3 Diamond
01229 716279 (also fax) Mrs Nichols **D:** £23.00–£27.00 **S:** £30.00 **Beds:** 1F 1T 3D 1S **Baths:** 4 En 1 Pr ⌂ 🅿 (8) ⏰ 🖳 🖤 🏊 cc

Dufton
NY6825

Sycamore House, *Dufton, Appleby-in-Westmorland, Cumbria, CA16 6DB.* Listed cottage, cosy living room, close to pub and shop. **Open:** Easter to Dec
017683 51296 Mrs O'Halloran *o_halloran@ hotmail.com* www.sycamorehouse.org.uk **D:** £18.00–£20.00 **S:** £17.00–£20.00 **Beds:** 3D **Baths:** 1 En 1 Sh ⌂ 🅿 (2) ⏰ 🎔 🖳

Eamont Bridge
NY5228

River View, *6 Lowther Glen, Eamont Bridge, Penrith, Cumbria, CA10 2BP.* Beautiful riverside bungalow near Lake Ullswater. Comfortable beds, good breakfasts. **Open:** All year
01768 864405 Mrs O'Neil **D:** £18.00–£22.00 **S:** £20.00–£22.00 **Beds:** 1T 2D 2S **Baths:** 1 En ⌂ 🅿 (4) ⏰ 🎔 🖤 🖳 & 🏊

Egremont
NY0110 🍴 *White Mare*

Far Head of Haile, *Haile, Egremont, CA22 2PE.* **Open:** All year (not Xmas/New Year)
01946 841205 Mr Greening **Fax: 01946 841781** *farhead@supanet.com* www.smoothhound.co.uk/hotels/farhead. html **D:** £14.50 **S:** £15.50–£16.50 **Beds:** 1F 4D 7S **Baths:** 1 En 4 Sh 🅿 (14) ⏰ 🖤 🖳 🏊
Explore the quieter Western Lakes, mountains and coast. See Georgian Whitehaven and its newly developed harbour, Quest and Rum Story, Egremont's Florence iron ore mine, Muncaster Castle, Ravenglass and miniature railway. Cyclists welcome. Between Ennerdale and Westwater, overlooking fells. Quiet, friendly, comfortable bed and breakfast accommodation. Log fires, off the beaten track. Large car park. Non smoking.

Ghyll Farm Guest House, *Egremont, Cumbria, CA22 2UA.* **Open:** All year (not Xmas)
01946 822256 Mrs Holliday **D:** £15.00 **S:** £15.00 **Beds:** 2T 2S **Baths:** 2 Sh ⌂ 🅿 (6) ⏰ 🖳 🏊
Comfortable, clean, friendly farmhouse. Good breakfast, private off-road parking. Try a fishing holiday on River Irt at Holmrook and catch salmon and sea trout. Reasonable rates. While the men fish, the ladies can visit our beautiful lakes etc.

Elterwater
NY3204

Britannia Inn, *Elterwater, Langdale, Ambleside, Cumbria, LA22 9HP.* Traditional Lakeland inn overlooking village green. Cosy bars with log fires. **Open:** All year (not Xmas)
015394 37210 J A Fry **Fax: 015394 37311** www.britinn.co.uk www.britinn.co.uk **D:** £24.00–£39.00 **S:** £24.00–£30.00 **Beds:** 9D 3T **Baths:** 9 En 3 Sh ⌂ 🅿 (10) ⏰ 🎔 ✕ 🖳 🏊 cc

Embleton
NY1630

Orchard House, *Embleton, Cockermouth, Cumbria, CA13 9XP.* Detached Edwardian country house with 3/4 acre garden. Mountain views. **Open:** All year
017687 76347 (also fax) Mrs Newton *info@ orchardhouse.uk.net* www.orchardhouse.uk. net **D:** £18.00–£20.00 **S:** £20.00–£25.00 **Beds:** 2D **Baths:** 2 En ⌂ (7) 🅿 (8) ⏰ 🖤 🎔 🖳 🏊

Planning a longer stay? Always ask for any special rates

Endmoor
SD5385

Summerlands Tower, Summerlands, Endmoor, Kendal, Cumbria, LA8 0ED. Victorian country house with fine rooms and gardens. 3 miles from M6/J36. **Open:** Easter to Nov
015395 61081 (also fax) Mr & Mrs Green m_.green@virgin.net **D:** £24.00–£29.50 **S:** £29.00–£34.50 **Beds:** 2T 1D **Baths:** 1 En 1 Pr ⇘ (12) 🅿 (3) ⊬ 🖥 🆅 📖 ♨

Ennerdale Bridge
NY0715

The Shepherds Arms Hotel, Ennerdale Bridge, Cleator, Cumbria, CA23 3AR. Small friendly hotel in the Lake District National Park which has been completely refurbished. **Open:** All year **Grades:** ETC 2 Star
01946 861249 (also fax) Mr Stanfield enquiries@shepherdsarmshotel.co.uk www.shepherdsarmshotel.co.uk **D:** £29.50 **S:** £32.00–£37.50 **Beds:** 1F 3D 3T 1S **Baths:** 6 En 2 Pr ⇘ 🅿 (6) 🆅 🐾 🆅 📖 ♨ cc

Eskdale Green
NY1400   🍴 Bower House, Brook House, Santon Bridge, Burn Moor

The Ferns, Eskdale Green, Holmrook, Cumbria, CA19 1UA. Homely accommodation in large Victorian residence. Near lakes and mountains. **Open:** All year
019467 23217 (also fax) Mr & Mrs Prestwood j.prestwood@talk21.com **D:** £18.00–£25.00 **S:** £22.00–£25.00 **Beds:** 2D 1T **Baths:** 1 En 2 Sh ⇘ 🅿 (4) ⊬ 🆅 📖 ♨

Far Sawrey
SD3895

Sawrey Hotel, Far Sawrey, Ambleside, Cumbria, LA22 0LQ. C18th country inn. Log fires. Bar in old stables. **Open:** All year (not Xmas)
015394 43425 (also fax) Mr Brayshaw **D:** £29.50 **S:** £29.50 **Beds:** 3F 8D 5T 2S **Baths:** 18 Pr 1 Sh ⇘ 🅿 (30) 🆅 🐾 🆅 📖 ♨ cc

Flookburgh
SD3675

Fieldhead Farm House, Flookburgh, Grange-over-Sands, Cumbria, LA11 7LN. A C17th farmhouse on edge of ancient fishing village. **Open:** All year
015395 58651 **D:** £17.00–£20.00 **S:** £17.00–£20.00 **Beds:** 2D 1S 1T 1F **Baths:** 1 Sh ⇘ 🅿 (3) ⊬ 🆅 ✗ 🆅 📖 ♨

Planning a longer stay? Always ask for any special rates

Frizington
NY0317

14 Lingley Fields, Frizington, Cumbria, CA26 3RU. Village house set in cottage-style garden. Choice of breakfast. **Open:** All year
01946 811779 Mrs Hall **D:** £16.00–£20.00 **S:** £16.00–£20.00 **Beds:** 1F 1T **Baths:** 1 En 1 Sh ⇘ 🅿 ⊬ ✗ 🆅 📖 ♨

Garrigill
NY7441

Ivy House, Garrigill, Alston, Cumbria, CA9 3DU. C17th converted farmhouse. Comfortable, friendly atmosphere. Picturesque north Pennines village. **Open:** All year
01434 382501 Mrs Humble **Fax:** 01434 382660 ivyhouse@garrigill.com www.garrigill.com **D:** £17.50–£22.00 **S:** £26.00–£29.00 **Beds:** 2F 3T 2D 3S **Baths:** 3 En ⇘ 🅿 (10) ⊬ 🆅 🐾 ✗ 🆅 📖 ⚒ ♨ cc

Glenridding
NY3816   🍴 White Lion, Travellers' Rest, Ratchers Bar

Beech House, Glenridding, Penrith, Cumbria, CA11 0PA. Very popular walking area next to Ullswater, close to Helvellyn. **Open:** All year
017684 82037 (also fax) Mr & Mrs Reed reed@beechouse.com www.beechhouse.com **D:** £18.00–£25.00 **S:** £18.00–£20.00 **Beds:** 1F 4D 2S **Baths:** 2 En ⇘ 🅿 (8) ⊬ 🆅 🐾 🆅 📖 🚻 ♨ cc

Grange-in-Borrowdale
NY2517

Scawdel, Grange-in-Borrowdale, Keswick, Cumbria, CA12 5UQ. Comfortable accommodation with magnificent mountain views. Ideal walking/touring base. **Open:** All year
017687 77271 J Reinecke info@scawdel.co.uk www.scawdel.co.uk **D:** £16.50–£20.00 **S:** £20.00–£30.00 **Beds:** 3D **Baths:** 2 En 1 Sh 🅿 (4) ⊬ 🆅 🐾 🆅 📖 ♨

Grayrigg, Grange-in-Borrowdale, Keswick, Cumbria, CA12 5UQ. Situated just below Peace How at foot of Maiden Moor, in a quiet location. **Open:** All year (not Xmas)
017687 77607 Mrs Figg **D:** £19.00–£22.00 **S:** £19.00–£30.00 **Beds:** 1F 1D 1T **Baths:** 2 En 1 Pr ⇘ 🅿 (4) ⊬ 🆅 🆅 📖 ♨

Grange-over-Sands
SD4077   🍴 Punch Bowl, Masons' Arms, Royal Oak, Crown Inn, Derby Arms, Lindale Inn

Mayfields, 3 Mayfield Terrace, Kents Bank Road, Grange-over-Sands, Cumbria, LA11 7DW. Perfectly situated for Lakes, Dales, Cartmel & Furness Peninsular. Very warm welcome. **Open:** All year **Grades:** ETC 4 Diamond, AA 4 Diamond
015395 34730 Mr Thorburn **D:** £25.00 **S:** £32.00 **Beds:** 1T 1D 1S **Baths:** 2 En 1 Pr ⇘ 🅿 (3) ⊬ 🆅 ✗ 🆅 📖 ♨

Grasmere
NY3307   🍴 The Swan, Red Lion

Titteringdales Guest House, Pye Lane, Grasmere, Ambleside, Cumbria, LA22 9RQ. Quietly situated in the village of Grasmere with good off-road parking. **Open:** All year (not Xmas/New Year)
015394 35439 Mr Scott titteringdales@grasmere.net www.grasmere.net **D:** £18.50–£25.00 **Beds:** 6D 1T **Baths:** 6 En 1 Pr 🅿 (7) ⊬ 🆅 📖 ♨ cc

Ash Cottage, Red Lion Square, Grasmere, Ambleside, Cumbria, LA22 9SP. Detached guest house in central Grasmere. Gardens. **Open:** All year **Grades:** ETC 4 Diamond
015394 35224 ashcottage@demon.co.uk **D:** £24.00–£30.00 **S:** £25.00–£32.00 **Beds:** 1F 3T 3D 1S ⇘ (8) 🅿 (10) 🆅 🐾 ✗ 🆅 📖 ♨

Oak Lodge, Easedale Road, Grasmere, Ambleside, Cumbria, LA22 9QJ. Quiet location with open views of the Easedale Valley. **Open:** Feb to Dec
015394 35527 Mrs Dixon **D:** £22.00–£26.00 **S:** £30.00 **Beds:** 2D 1T **Baths:** 3 En ⇘ (10) 🅿 (3) ⊬ 🆅 🆅 📖 ♨

Grayrigg
SD5797

Punchbowl House, Grayrigg, Kendal, Cumbria, LA8 9BU. Spacious and comfortable former Victorian farmhouse in the centre of the village. **Open:** Mar to Dec **Grades:** ETC 4 Diamond, Silver
01539 824345 (also fax) Mrs Johnson **D:** £20.00–£25.00 **S:** £20.00–£40.00 **Beds:** 2D 1T **Baths:** 1 En 1 Sh 🅿 (4) ⊬ 🆅 ✗ 🆅 📖 ♨

Planning a longer stay? Always ask for any special rates

National Grid References given are for villages, towns and cities – not for individual houses

Graythwaite
NY1123

Low Graythwaite Hall, Graythwaite, Ulverston, Cumbria, *LA12 8AZ.* Historic statesman's house, old panelling, fine furnishings, open log fires. **Open:** Feb to Jan
015395 31676 (also fax) D: £22.00–£30.00 **S:** £25.00–£30.00 **Beds:** 1F 1T 1D **Baths:** 2 En ⌂ 🅿 (20) 📺 🏋 ✕ 📺 💷 ☂

Great Urswick
SD2774

The Stables, At The Derby Arms, Great Urswick, Ulverston, Cumbria, *LA12 0SP.*
Converted stable in friendly country village, within easy reach of Lake District. **Open:** All year
01229 586348 Mr Dickinson **Fax: 01229 585223** *thederbyarms@yahoo.co.uk*
www.geocities.com/thederbyarms **D:** £20.00–£25.00 **S:** £30.00–£40.00 **Beds:** 2T 2D **Baths:** 4 En 🅿 (10) 📺 💷 ☂

Greystoke
NY4430 🍺*The Sportsman, Boot & Shoe, Clickham Inn*

Lattendales Farm, Greystoke, Penrith, Cumbria, *CA11 0UE.* Comfortable C17th farmhouse in pleasant quiet village.
Open: Feb to Nov
017684 83474 Mrs Ashburner **D:** £17.00–£18.00 **Beds:** 1T 2D **Baths:** 1 Sh ⌂ 🅿 ✖ 📺 🏋 💷

Orchard Cottage, Church Road, Greystoke, Penrith, Cumbria, *CA11 0TW.* Comfortable, peaceful bedrooms overlooking gardens. M6/jct. 40 just 4.5 miles. **Open:** All year
017684 83264 Mrs Theakston **Fax: 017684 80015 D:** £22.00 **S:** £22.00 **Beds:** 1F 1D **Baths:** 1 En 1 Pr 📺 📺 💷

Grisedale
SD7792

Aldershaw, Grisedale, Sedbergh, Cumbria, *LA10 5PS.* Superb Daleside renovated farmhouse, oak-beamed. Delicious food. **Open:** All year (not Xmas)
015396 21211 Mr & Mrs Robinson **D:** £17.50–£25.00 **S:** £20.00–£27.00 **Beds:** 1D 1T 1S **Baths:** 1 En 1 Sh ⌂ 🅿 (3) 📺 🏋 ✕ 📺 💷 ☂

Hale
SD5078

Yewdale, Hale, Milnthorpe, Cumbria, *LA7 7BL.* **Open:** All year (not Xmas)
015395 62457 Mrs Westworth
t.westworth@virgin.net **D:** £22.50–£25.00 **S:** £18.00–£22.50 **Beds:** 1D 2T 1S **Baths:** 1 En 2 Sh ⌂ 🅿 (4) 📺 🏋 💷 ☂
High-class accommodation in AONB, 180 degree spectacular views, excellent location for outdoor pursuits, RSPB reserve nearby, Windermere 15 min, Yorkshire Dales 20 min. Perfect midway break between England/Scotland. A warm welcome & superb breakfast assured. 5 miles from M6/J35.

Hartsop
NY4013

Patterdale, Fellside, Hartsop, Patterdale, Penrith, Cumbria, *CA11 0NZ.* C17th stone built farmhouse, close to lakes and high mountains. **Open:** All year (not Xmas/New Year)
017684 82532 Mrs Knight **D:** £16.00–£18.00 **S:** £20.00–£24.00 **Beds:** 2T **Baths:** 1 Sh ⌂ 🅿 (2) ✖ 📺 🏋 📺 💷 ☂

Haverthwaite
SD3483

Rusland Pool Hotel and Restaurant, Haverthwaite, Newby Bridge, Ulverston, Cumbria, *LA12 8AA.* Friendly, informal atmosphere. Central to popular local walks. **Open:** All year **Grades:** ETC 3 Star
01229 861384 *enquiries@ruslandpool.co.uk* www.ruslandpool.co.uk **D:** £26.00–£39.50 **S:** £40.00–£59.00 **Beds:** 4F 4T 10D **Baths:** 18 En ⌂ 🅿 (35) 📺 ✕ 📺 💷 ♿ ✳ ☂ cc

Hawkshead
SD3597 🍺*The Outgate, Queen's Head, Red Lion, Drunken Duck, King's Arms*

School House Cottage, Hawkshead, Ambleside, Cumbria, *LA22 0NT.*
Open: All year
015394 36401 D: £21.00 **Beds:** 2D **Baths:** 2 En 🅿 (2) 📺 🏋 📺 💷 ☂
A warm welcome to Hawkshead, said to be the prettiest village in the Lakes. Ideal for walking, touring, cycling. Close to Grizedale Forest, Tarn Hows, Beatrix Potter country. Quiet location, comfortable rooms, hearty breakfast, private garden with sun loungers.

Borwick Lodge, Hawkshead, Ambleside, Cumbria, *LA22 0PU.* Award-winning 'accommodation of the highest standards'. A rather special C17th country house. **Open:** All year **Grades:** ETC 4 Diamond, Silver
015394 36332 (also fax) Mr & Mrs Haskell *borwicklodge@talk21.com* www.borwicklodge.com **D:** £25.00–£36.00 **S:** £35.00 **Beds:** 1F 4D 1T **Baths:** 6 En ⌂ (8) 🅿 (8) ✖ 📺 📺 💷 ☂

Beechmount, Near Sawrey, Hawkshead, Ambleside, Cumbria, *LA22 0JZ.* Charming, spacious country house situated in Beatrix Potter's picturesque village. **Open:** All year
015394 36356 Mrs Siddall www.beechmountcountryhouse.co.uk **D:** £20.00–£22.00 **S:** £25.00–£30.00 **Beds:** 3D **Baths:** 3 Pr ⌂ 🅿 (3) 📺 🏋 📺 💷 ☂

Hawkshead Hill
SD3398

Yewfield Vegetarian Guest House, Hawkshead Hill, Ambleside, *LA22 0PR.* Peaceful retreat in 30 acres grounds, impressive Gothic house overlooking Esthwaite Vale. **Open:** Feb to Nov
015394 36765 Mr Hook www.yewfield.co.uk **D:** £20.00–£37.00 **S:** £25.00–£33.00 **Beds:** 1T 2D **Baths:** 3 En ⌂ (9) 🅿 (6) ✖ 📺 💷 ☂ cc

Helsington
SD5090

Helsington Laithes Manor, Helsington, Kendal, Cumbria, *LA9 5RJ.* Historic Listed Manor House in 3 acre grounds, 5 minutes M6/J36. **Open:** All year (not Xmas/New Year)
01539 741253 & 07767 342696 (M) Fax: 01539 741346 *themanor@helsington.uk.com* www.helsington.uk.com **D:** £20.00–£25.00 **S:** £25.00–£30.00 **Beds:** 1F 1T 3D **Baths:** 2 En 1 Pr ⌂ (5) 🅿 (5) ✖ 📺 📺 💷 ☂

Hesket Newmarket
NY3338 🍺*The Oddfellows, Old Crown*

Newlands Grange, Hesket Newmarket, Caldbeck, Wigton, Cumbria, *CA7 8HP.* Comfortable, oak beamed farmhouse offering all home cooking. All welcome. **Open:** All year (not Xmas)
016974 78676 Mrs Studholme **D:** £16.50–£19.50 **S:** £16.50–£19.50 **Beds:** 1F 1D 1T 1S **Baths:** 1 En 1 Sh ⌂ 🅿 📺 🏋 ✕ 💷 ☂

Please respect a B&B's wishes regarding children, animals and smoking

High Harrington
NY0025

Riversleigh Guest House, *39 Primrose Terrace, High Harrington, Workington, Cumbria, CA14 5PS.* Riverside house overlooking gardens, 5 mins from station and marina. **Open:** All year **01946 830267** Mrs Davies **D:** £15.00–£20.00 **S:** £15.00–£20.00 **Beds:** 1F 1T 1D **Baths:** 2 En 1 Pr ☎ (5) ▣ (8) ⿻ �📺 Ⓥ ▥ ⚱

High Lorton
NY1625

Owl Brook, *Whinlatter Pass, High Lorton, Cockermouth, Cumbria, CA13 9TX.* Green slate bungalow, designed by owners. Pine ceilings. Oak floors. **Open:** All year **01900 85333** Mrs Roberts **D:** £16.50–£17.50 **S:** £16.50–£17.50 **Beds:** 3D **Baths:** 1 Sh ☎ (0) ▣ (2) ⿻ 📺 ✕ ✕ Ⓥ ▥ ❀ ⚱

High Wray
SD3799

Tock How Farm, *High Wray, Ambleside, Cumbria, LA22 0JF.* Traditional farmhouse overlooking to Lake Windermere and the surrounding Fells. **Open:** All year **015394 36106 & 07971 984232 (M)** Mrs Irvine **D:** £19.50–£23.00 **S:** £21.00–£25.00 **Beds:** 1F 1D **Baths:** 2 En ☎ ▣ (4) ⿻ 📺 Ⓥ ▥ ⚱

Holme
SD5279

Marwin House, *Duke Street, Holme, Carnforth, Cumbria, LA6 1PY.* Gateway to Lake District, Yorkshire Dales. M6 (J36) 5 minutes. **Open:** All year **01524 781144 (also fax)** **D:** £16.00–£18.00 **S:** £17.00–£19.00 **Beds:** 1F 1T **Baths:** 1 Sh ☎ ▣ (3) ⿻ 📺 Ⓥ ▥ ⚱

Holmrook
SD0799

Hill Farm, *Holmrook, Cumbria, CA19 1UG.* Working farm - beautiful views overlooking River Irt and Wasdale Fells. **Open:** All year (not Xmas) **019467 24217** Mrs Leak **D:** £14.00 **S:** £14.00 **Beds:** 2F **Baths:** 2 Sh ☎ ▣ 📺 ✕ ▥ ⚱

Ings
SD4498   ⚫ *Watermill, Railway Hotel*

St Annes Farm, *Ings, Kendal, Cumbria, LA8 9QG.* Clean, friendly. Windermere 2 miles. Good breakfast. **Open:** Easter to Oct **01539 821223** Mrs Allen **D:** £17.00 **Beds:** 2D **Baths:** 1 Sh ☎ (5) ▣ (2) ⿻ Ⓥ

All details shown are as supplied by B&B owners in Autumn 2001

Irton
NY1000

Cookson Place Farm, *Irton, Holmrook, Cumbria, CA19 1YQ.* Working farm. Quiet area within easy reach of Wasdale, Eskdale. **Open:** All year (not Xmas) **019467 24286** Mrs Crayston **D:** £13.00–£14.00 **S:** £14.00 **Beds:** 1F 1T **Baths:** 1 Sh ▣ ⿻ 📺 Ⓥ ▥ ❀ ⚱

Ivegill
NY4143

Streethead Farm, *Ivegill, Carlisle, Cumbria, CA4 0NG.* Distant hills, real fires, home-baking, convenient for Lakes or Scotland. **Open:** All year (not Xmas) **016974 73327 (also fax)** Mrs Wilson **D:** £20.00–£22.00 **S:** £22.00–£25.00 **Beds:** 2D **Baths:** 2 En ☎ (7) ▣ (2) 📺 ▥ ⚱

Croft End Hurst, *Ivegill, Carlisle, Cumbria, CA4 0NL.* Rural bungalow situated midway between J41/42 of M6. **Open:** All year **Grades:** ETC 3 Diamond **017684 84362** Mrs Nichol **D:** £17.00–£19.00 **S:** £17.00 **Beds:** 1D 1T **Baths:** 1 Sh ☎ (1) ▣ (4) ⿻ 📺 ▥ ♿ ⚱

Kendal
SD5192   ⚫ *Station Inn, Punch Bowl*

Sonata, *19 Burnside Road, Kendal, Cumbria, LA9 4RL.* **Open:** All year **Grades:** ETC 3 Diamond **01539 732290 (also fax)** Mr Wilkinson *chris@ sonataguesthouse.freeserve.co.uk* www.sonataguesthouse.co.uk **D:** £23.00 **S:** £25.00–£30.00 **Beds:** 1F 2D 1T **Baths:** 4 En ☎ ⿻ ✕ ✕ Ⓥ ▥ ⚱ cc Friendly, family-run, Georgian, terraced guest house with comfortable, ensuite bedrooms containing radio, alarm, colour TV, complimentary beverage facilities, hairdryer and independently controlled central heating. Shopping centres 3 mins walk, Windermere 10 mins drive.

Lakeland Natural Vegetarian Guest House, *Low Slack, Queens Road, Kendal, Cumbria, LA9 4PH.* **Open:** All year **Grades:** ETC 3 Diamond **01539 733011 (also fax)** *relax@ lakelandnatural.co.uk* www.lakelandnatural. co.uk **D:** £28.00 **S:** £32.00 **Beds:** 1F 2T 2D **Baths:** 5 En ☎ ▣ (7) ⿻ 📺 ✕ ✕ Ⓥ ▥ ⚱ cc Spacious Victorian home, with stunning views overlooking Kendal and the surrounding fells. Adjacent woodland walks and golf course. Only 5 mins' walk from the town centre. Non-smoking. Brilliant breakfasts and imaginative evening meals using largely organic produce. Licensed.

Bridge House, *65 Castle Street, Kendal, Cumbria, LA9 7AD.* **Open:** All year **015397 22041 & 07813 679411** **(M)** Mrs Brindley *sheila@bridgehouse-kendal.co.uk* www.bridgehouse-kendal.co.uk **D:** £20.00–£25.00 **S:** £25.00 **Beds:** 1D 1T **Baths:** 1 En 1 Sh ☎ ⿻ 📺 ✕ ▥ ⚱ Beautiful Georgian Listed building a short walk from Kendal Castle and the River Kent. Home made bread and preserves a speciality. Complimentary Kendal mint cake for our visitors. A lovely private garden for guests' use. A warm and friendly welcome.

The Glen, *Oxenholme, Kendal, Cumbria, LA9 7RF.* **Open:** All year (not Xmas/New Year) **015397 26386** Mrs Green *greenintheglen@ easicom.com* **D:** £19.00–£26.00 **S:** £25.00–£30.00 **Beds:** 1F 1T 2D **Baths:** 3 En ☎ (6) ▣ (10) ⿻ 📺 ✕ ✕ Ⓥ ▥ ⚱ On the outskirts of Kendal in a quiet location under 'the Helm' (local walk and view point of Lakeland fells), but within a short walk of pub and restaurant. For that special occasion a four poster, jacuzzi and spa (ensuite).

Natland Mill Beck Farm, Kendal, Cumbria, *LA9 7LH.* C17th working farm, large garden. Close to Kendal & local attractions. **Open:** Mar to Nov **Grades:** ETC 3 Diamond **015397 21122** Mrs Gardner **D:** £19.50–£21.00 **Beds:** 1T 1D 1S **Baths:** 1 En 1 Pr 1 Sh ⚲ 🅿 ✯ 📺 📶 ♨

Birslack Grange, Hutton Lane, Levens, Kendal, Cumbria, *LA8 8PA.* Converted farm buildings in rural setting overlooking the scenic Lyth Valley. **Open:** All year (not Xmas) **015395 60989** Mrs Carrington-Birch *birslackgrange@msn.com* www.birslackgrange. co.uk **D:** £20.00–£22.00 **S:** £22.00–£28.00 **Beds:** 1F 2D 2T 2S **Baths:** 4 En 2 Sh ⚲ (3) 🅿 (6) ✯ 📺 ✯ ✕ 📶 ⅙ ♨

The Headlands Hotel, 53 Milnthorpe Road, Kendal, Cumbria, *LA9 5QG.* Family run (private) hotel. Ideal town location for all amenities. **Open:** All year **01539 732464 (also fax)** Mr & Mrs Kellington *info@headlands-kendal.fsnet.co.uk* www.headlands-hotel.co.uk **D:** £20.00–£24.00 **S:** £20.00–£35.00 **Beds:** 2F 1T 3D **Baths:** 5 En 1 Pr ⚲ 🅿 ✯ 📺 ✕ 📶 ✱ ♨ cc

Airethwaite House, 1 Airethwaite, Horncop Lane, Kendal, Cumbria, *LA9 4SP.* Spacious Victorian guest house. Original features, antique furniture. Lovely views. Town centre 5 mins. **Open:** All year **01539 730435** Mrs Dean *info@ airethwaitehouse.co.uk* www.arethwaitehouse. co.uk **D:** £20.00–£22.00 **S:** £25.00 **Beds:** 3D/ T **Baths:** 3 En ⚲ 🅿 (3) ✯ 📺 📶 ♨

High House Farm, Oxenholme Lane, Natland, Kendal, Cumbria, *LA9 7QH.* Tranquil Lakeland village, C17th farmhouse. **Open:** All year (not Xmas) **Grades:** ETC 4 Diamond, Silver, AA 4 Diamond **015395 61177** Mrs Sunter **Fax: 015395 61520** **D:** £24.50–£29.50 **S:** £29.50–£32.50 **Beds:** 2D 1T **Baths:** 3 En 🅿 (9) ✯ 📺 📶 ♨

Fairways, 102 Windermere Road, Kendal, Cumbria, *LA9 5EZ.* Victorian guest house, ensuite rooms, TV. Edge of Lake District. **Open:** All year **Grades:** ETC 3 Diamond **015397 25564** Mrs Paylor *mp@ fairwaysl.fsnet.co.uk* **D:** £19.00–£20.00 **S:** £20.00–£25.00 **Beds:** 1F 2D 1S **Baths:** 3 En 1 Pr ⚲ (2) 🅿 (4) ✯ 📺 📺 📶 ✱ ♨

Sundial House, 51 Milnthorpe Road, Kendal, Cumbria, *LA9 5QG.* Quality guest house, private car park, 5 mins from town centre. **Open:** All year (not Xmas) **01539 724468** Mr & Mrs Richardson **Fax: 01539 736900 D:** £17.50–£25.00 **S:** £18.50–£22.50 **Beds:** 1F 1D 1T 1S **Baths:** 1 En 2 Sh ⚲ 🅿 (8) 📺 ✯ 📺 📶 ♨

Hillside Guest House, 4 Beast Banks, Kendal, Cumbria, *LA9 4JW.* Large Victorian guest house, town centre. Ideal for Lake District & Yorkshire Dales. **Open:** Mar to Nov **015397 22836** Mrs Denison **D:** £18.00–£21.00 **S:** £18.00–£22.00 **Beds:** 3D 1T 3S **Baths:** 5 En 4 Pr 1 Sh ⚲ (4) 🅿 (4) 📺 📺 📶 ♨

Punchbowl House, Grayrigg, Kendal, Cumbria, *LA8 9BU.* Spacious and comfortable former Victorian farmhouse in the centre of the village. **Open:** Mar to Dec **Grades:** ETC 4 Diamond, Silver **01539 824345 (also fax)** Mrs Johnson **D:** £20.00–£25.00 **S:** £20.00–£40.00 **Beds:** 2D 1T **Baths:** 1 En 1 Sh 🅿 (4) ✯ 📺 ✕ 📶 ♨

Cragg Farm, New Hutton, Kendal, Cumbria, *LA8 0BA.* Situated 4 miles Kendal, warm welcome, excellent accommodation. Breakfast provided. **Open:** Mar to Nov **Grades:** ETC 3 Diamond **01539 721760 (also fax)** Mrs Knowles *knowles.cragg@ukgateway.net* **D:** £17.00–£19.00 **S:** £17.00–£19.00 **Beds:** 1F 1D 1S **Baths:** 1 Sh ⚲ 🅿 ✯ 📺 📺 📶 ♨

Highgate Hotel, 128 Highgate, Kendal, Cumbria, *LA9 4HE.* Grade II* Listed town centre B&B, built 1769. Private car park. **Open:** All year (not Xmas/New Year) **01539 724229 (also fax)** Mr Dawson www.highgatehotel.co.uk **D:** £21.50–£23.50 **S:** £27.00–£29.00 **Beds:** 1F 4D 2T 3S **Baths:** 10 En ⚲ 🅿 (10) ✯ 📶 ♨ cc

Mitchelland House, Off Crook Road, Kendal, Cumbria, *LA8 8LL.* Delightful country location, only 5 minutes Lake Windermere and all attractions. **Open:** All year (not Xmas) **015394 48589** *marie.mitchelland@talk21.com* **D:** £18.00–£24.00 **S:** £21.00–£26.00 **Beds:** 1F 1D 1T **Baths:** 1 En 1 Sh ⚲ 🅿 (10) 📺 ✯ 📺 📶 ♨

Magic Hills House, 123 Appleby Road, Kendal, Cumbria, *LA9 6HF.* Late Victorian family house, comfortably furnished, tastefully decorated. 10 mins' walk to centre. **Open:** All year (not Xmas) **01539 736248** C.K Moseley *ckm@ ukgateway.net* **D:** £18.50–£22.50 **S:** £21.00–£27.00 **Beds:** 2D 1T **Baths:** 1 En 1 Pr 1 Sh ⚲ (12) ✯ 📺 📺 📶 ♨

National Grid References given are for villages, towns and cities – not for individual houses

Kentmere

NY4504

Maggs Howe, Kentmere, Kendal, Cumbria, *LA8 9JP.* Detached former farmhouse in beautiful, quiet, unspoilt cul-de-sac valley. **Open:** All year (not Xmas) **01539 821689** Mrs Hevey www.smoothhound.co.uk/hotels/maggs. html **D:** £18.00–£20.00 **S:** £18.00–£20.00 **Beds:** 1F 1D 1T **Baths:** 1 En 1 Sh ⚲ 🅿 (6) 📺 ✯ ✕ 📶 ♨

Keswick

NY2623   🚂 Station Inn, Punch Bowl, Derwentwater Hotel, Masons, King's Head, Two Dogs Inn, The George, Farmers' Arms, Four In Hand, Swan Hotel, Swinside Inn, Keswick Lodge, Bank Tavern

Cragside Guest House, 39 Blencathra Street, Keswick, Cumbria, *CA12 4HX.* **Open:** All year **Grades:** AA 3 Diamond **017687 73344 & 017687 80410** *sue@ cragsideguest-house.fsnet.co.uk* cragsideguest-house.fsnet.co.uk **D:** £18.50–£20.00 **S:** £25.00–£30.00 **Beds:** 1F 1T 3D **Baths:** 4 En 1 Sh ⚲ (5) ✯ 📺 ✯ 📺 📶 ♨ Sue and Mike invite you to bring your family and pets to stay at our friendly Victorian home with views of the local fells and close to Keswick town centre. Enjoy easy access to great walks and stunning scenery.

RATES

D = Price range per person sharing in a double or twin room

S = Price range for a single room

RATES

D = Price range per person sharing in a double or twin room

S = Price range for a single room

Shemara Guest House, 27 Bank Street, Keswick, Cumbria, CA12 5JZ **Open:** All year **017687 73936 Fax: 017687 80785**
shemaraguesthouse@yahoo.co.uk www.shemara. u.k.com **D:** £19.50–£25.00 **S:** £25.00 **Beds:** 1F 1T 5D **Baths:** 7 En ॐ (2) 🅟 (4) ⌦ 🖵 🏧 ⌧ 🆅 🗏 ♨ cc
A warm, friendly welcome awaits you at our award-winning guest house. All rooms are furnished to a very high standard and have stunning views of the mountains. A full Cumbrian or continental breakfast is served in our cosy dining room.

Hedgehog Hill, 18 Blencathra Street, Keswick, Cumbria, CA12 4HP. **Open:** All year **Grades:** ETC 3 Diamond
017687 74386 Fax: 017687 80622 *info@ hedgehoghill.co.uk* www.hedgehoghill.co.uk
D: £21.00–£24.00 **S:** £17.50–£18.50 **Beds:** 4D 2S **Baths:** 4 En 1 Sh ⌦ 🆅 🖵 🗏 ♨ cc
You are assured a warm welcome from your hosts Nel and Keith. Ideally situated for exploring the Lake District. Located in a quiet street close to all amenities, stunning fell views from most rooms. Freshly prepared breakfast with choice.

Anderville, 19 Helvellyn Street, Keswick, Cumbria, CA12 4EN. **Open:** All year (not Xmas) **017687 72578**
(also fax) *wpaul595@aol.com* www.anderville.co.uk **D:** £15.00–£18.00 **S:** £15.00–£16.00 **Beds:** 1T 2D 1S **Baths:** 3 En 1 Pr ॐ ⌦ 🆅 🏧 ⌧ 🆅 🗏 ♨
'Anderville' offers quiet comfortable guest house accommodation, situated just two minutes from the town centre. Parks and Lake Derwentwater are just a short stroll away as is the 'Theatre by the Lake'. Open all year with the exception of Xmas day. Evening meals available. Your hosts Paul and Anita Wilson welcome you.

Chaucer House Hotel, Derwentwater Place, Keswick, Cumbria, CA12 4DR. **Open:** Feb to Dec **Grades:** AA
2 Star, RAC 2 Star
017687 72318 & 017687 73223
Mr Pechartscheck **Fax: 017687 75551**
enquiries@chaucer-house.demon.co.uk www.chaucer-house.co.uk **D:** £32.00–£46.00 **S:** £32.00–£41.00 **Beds:** 4F 9D 12T 8S **Baths:** 29 En 4 Pr ॐ 🅿 ⌦ 🏧 🆅 🖵 🗏 ♨ cc
Lakeland hospitality at its best. Quiet setting, surrounded by spectacular mountains. Close to theatre, market place & lake. Relaxed, informal atmosphere. Freshly prepared evening meal available. Friendly, professional staff always available to help you enjoy your stay, plan tours and walks.

Littlefield, 32 Eskin Street, Keswick, Cumbria, CA12 4DG. **Open:** All year **017687 72949** Miss Maddock *littlefield@*
keswick98.fsnet.co.uk keswick98.fsnet.co.uk **D:** £17.00–£18.00 **S:** £17.00–£18.00 **Beds:** 1T 2D 2S **Baths:** 1 Sh ॐ 🅟 (3) ⌦ 🆅 🏧 ⌧ 🆅 🗏 ♨
Very conveniently situated for the centre of Keswick and Derwentwater. We have a very comfortable guests' lounge with many books, maps and walking guides available for visitors. A warm welcome is assured from Ali and Maureen the proprietors.

All details shown are as supplied by B&B owners in Autumn 2001

Birch How, 41 Brundholme Terrace, Station Road, Keswick, Cumbria, CA12 4NB. **Open:** All year **017687 73404** *birchhow@aol.com* www.members. aol. com/birchhow
D: £17.50–£22.00 **S:** £20.00–£30.00 **Beds:** 1T 2D **Baths:** 2 En 1 Sh 🅟 (3) ⌦ 🆅 🏧 ⌧ 🆅 🗏 ♨
Birch How is a small, friendly guest house close to Fitz Park, and very convenient for town centre. Within easy reach of Derwent Water, the Borrowdale Valley, and many other local beauty areas. Advice can be given on local walks.

Sunnyside Guest House, 25 Southey Street, Keswick, Cumbria, CA12 4EF. **Open:** All year (not Xmas) **Grades:** ETC 4 Diamond, AA 4 Diamond, RAC 4 Diamond
017687 72446 Mrs Newton **Fax: 017687 74444** *raynewton@survey.u-net.com* www.survey. u-net.com **D:** £20.00–£25.00 **S:** £25.00 **Beds:** 1F 4D 1T 1S **Baths:** 5 En 2 Pr ॐ 🅟 (7) ⌦ 🆅 🏧 🗏 ♨
This tastefully decorated Victorian building is situated just five minutes walk from the town centre and ten minutes walk from the lake, yet provides quiet and comfortable accommodation throughout. Relaxing guest lounge with views of Skiddaw.

Badgers Wood Guest House, 30 Stanger Street, Keswick, Cumbria, CA12 5JU. **Open:** All year (not Xmas) **017687 72621** Ms Godfrey *enquiries@ badgers-wood.co.uk* www.badgers-wood.co.uk
D: £18.00–£23.00 **S:** £18.00 **Beds:** 3D 1T 2S **Baths:** 4 En 1 Sh ⌦ 🆅 🆅 🗏 ♨
Comfortable, quiet, friendly, ideally situated for walking, climbing and sightseeing. Badgers Wood is close to bus station, town centre and eating places. All our bedrooms have mountain views. We can offer you ensuite or standard rooms.

Planning a longer stay? Always ask for any special rates

Planning a longer stay? Always ask for any special rates

Abacourt House, 26 Stanger Street, Keswick, Cumbria, CA12 5JU. Lovingly restored Victorian town house. Perfectly situated for all amenities. **Open:** All year (not Xmas/New Year) **Grades:** ETC 4 Diamond **017687 72967** *abacourt@btinternet.com* www.abacourt.co.uk **D:** £22.00 **Beds:** 5D **Baths:** 5 En 🅿 (5) ⌇ 📺 🖤 🛏 🖳 👶

Long Close Farm, Underskiddaw, Keswick, Cumbria, CA12 4QD. Period farmhouse enjoying exceptional views over mountains and Bassenthwaite Lake. **Open:** All year **017687 72851 (also fax)** Mrs Evers *longclosefarm@bushinternet.com* **D:** £17.00–£25.00 **S:** £20.00–£25.00 **Beds:** 1D 2T **Baths:** 1 En 1 Sh 🅿 📺 🖤 🖳 👶

Derwentdale Guest Hotel, 8 Blencathra Street, Keswick, Cumbria, CA12 4HP. Friendly, family-run guest house close to lake and parks. **Open:** All year **017687 74187 (also fax)** Mrs Riding **D:** £17.50–£21.00 **S:** £17.50–£18.00 **Beds:** 3D 1T 2S **Baths:** 2 En 3 Pr 🐾 ⌇ 📺 🖤 🖳 👶

Glendale Guest House, 7 Eskin Street, Keswick, Cumbria, CA12 4DH. Comfortable Victorian house. Close to town, lake, park and fells. **Open:** All year **017687 73562** Mr Lankester *info@ glendalekeswick.co.uk* www.glendalekeswick.co. uk **D:** £18.00–£22.00 **S:** £19.00–£22.00 **Beds:** 1F 2D 1S **Baths:** 3 En 2 Sh 🐾 ⌇ 📺 🖤 🖳 👶

The Paddock Guest House, Wordsworth Street, Keswick, Cumbria, CA12 4HU. Delightful 1800's residence. Close to town, lake, parks and fells. **Open:** All year **Grades:** ETC 4 Diamond **017687 72510** www.keswickguesthouse.com **D:** £19.00–£21.00 **S:** £25.00–£40.00 **Beds:** 1F 1T 4D **Baths:** 6 En 🐾 🅿 (5) ⌇ 📺 🖤 🖳 👶 cc

Edwardene, 26 Southey Street, Keswick, Cumbria, CA12 4EF. The Edwardene Hotel offers central, stylish, luxurious accommodation at affordable rates. **Open:** All year **Grades:** ETC 2 Star, AA 2 Star **017687 73586 & 0800 163983** Mr Holman **Fax:** **017687 73824** *info@edwardenehotel.com* www.edwardenehotel.com **D:** £26.00–£29.00 **S:** £37.00–£43.00 **Beds:** 1F 2T 6D 2S **Baths:** 11 Pr 🐾 (1) 🅿 (2) ⌇ 📺 🛏 🗙 🖳 👶 ⚹ 👶 cc

Daresfield, Chestnut Hill, Keswick, Cumbria, CA12 4LS. Warm welcome, splendid views, walks advice, doll-making studio. **Open:** All year (not New Year) **017687 72531** V Spencer *daresfiedl@ hotmail.com* **D:** £16.00 **S:** £16.00 **Beds:** 1T 1D 1S **Baths:** 2 Sh 🐾 🅿 (3) ⌇ 📺 🛏 🖤 🖳 👶 👶

Ivy Lodge, 32 Penrith Road, Keswick, Cumbria, CA12 4HA. Superb rooms. Convenient for parks, theatre and lake. **Open:** All year **017687 75747** *pdwells@compuserve.com* **D:** £18.00–£23.00 **S:** £25.00–£28.00 **Beds:** 1F 1T 1D **Baths:** 3 En 🐾 🅿 (10) ⌇ 📺 🛏 🗙 🖳 👶

Clarence House, 14 Eskin Street, Keswick, Cumbria, CA12 4DQ. Lovely detached Victorian house, excellent ensuite accommodation. Cleanliness guaranteed. No smoking. **Open:** All year (not Xmas) **017687 73186** Mr & Mrs Robertson **Fax:** **017687 72317** *clarenceho@aol.com* www.members.aol.com/clarenceho/index. html **D:** £20.00–£28.00 **S:** £20.00–£28.00 **Beds:** 1F 4D 3T 1S **Baths:** 8 Pr 🐾 (5) ⌇ 📺 🖳 👶

Lynwood House, 35 Helvellyn Street, Keswick, Cumbria, CA12 4EP. Victorian-style with modern comforts. Traditional or home-made organic breakfasts. **Open:** All year **017687 72398** Mr Picken *lynwoodho@aol.com* **D:** £17.00–£20.50 **S:** £18.50–£23.00 **Beds:** 1F 2D 1S **Baths:** 1 En 🐾 (3) ⌇ 📺 🖳 👶

Berkeley Guest House, The Heads, Keswick, Cumbria, CA12 5ER. Friendly, relaxed guest house with superb mountain views from each comfortable room. **Open:** Jan to Dec **017687 74222** Mrs Crompton *berkeley@ tesco.net* berkeley_keswick.homepage.com **D:** £17.00–£24.00 **S:** £20.00 **Beds:** 1F 2D 1T 1S **Baths:** 3 En 2 Sh 🐾 (3) ⌇ 📺 🖳 👶

Lairbeck Hotel, Vicarage Hill, Keswick, Cumbria, CA12 5QB. Secluded setting, superb mountain views. Spacious parking. No single supplements. **Open:** Mar to Jan **017687 73373** Mr Coy **Fax:** **017687 73144** *swell@lairbeckhotel-keswick.co.uk* www.lairbeckhotel-keswick.co.uk **D:** £30.00–£38.00 **S:** £30.00–£38.00 **Beds:** 1F 8D 1T 4S **Baths:** 14 En 🐾 (5) 🅿 (16) ⌇ 📺 🗙 🖳 👶 ⚹ 👶

Hawcliffe House, 30 Eskin Street, Keswick, Cumbria, CA12 4DG. Warm welcome assured. Short walk to lake and town centre. **Open:** All year **017687 73250** D McConnell **D:** £16.00–£18.00 **S:** £16.00–£18.00 **Beds:** 1T 2D 2S **Baths:** 2 Sh ⌇ 📺 🛏 🖳 👶

Watendlath, 15 Acorn Street, Keswick, Cumbria, CA12 4EA. Few mins Keswick centre, quiet retreat, renowned superb traditional English breakfasts. **Open:** All year **017687 74165** **D:** £17.00–£20.00 **S:** 2F 2D **Beds:** 3 En 1 Sh **Baths:** Y ⌇ ⌇ 📺 ⚹ cc

Brookfield, Penrith Road, Keswick, Cumbria, CA12 4LJ. A warm welcome awaits you at this family-run Victorian guest house. **Open:** All year **017687 72867** Mr Gregory *ronnie.sally@ talk21.com* www.expage.com/ronniesally **D:** £16.00–£20.00 **S:** £16.00–£20.00 **Beds:** 2F 2D **Baths:** 4 En 🐾 🅿 (4) ⌇ 📺 🛏 🗙 🖳 👶

Claremont House, Chestnut Hill, Keswick, Cumbria, CA12 4LT. Built about 150 years ago as lodge house to Fieldside Estate, 1m Keswick. **Open:** Easter to Nov **017687 72089** Peter & Jackie Werfel *claremontbb@btinternet.com* www.claremonthousekeswick.co.uk **D:** £21.00–£25.00 **Beds:** 3D 1T **Baths:** 4 En 🐾 (12) 🅿 (5) ⌇ 📺 🖤 🖳 👶

Spooney Green, Spooney Green Lane, Keswick, Cumbria, CA12 4PJ. Only 15 minutes' walk into Keswick, foothills of Skiddaw, a relaxing country retreat. **Open:** All year **017687 72601** Ms Wallace *spooneygreen@ beeb.net* **D:** £20.00–£25.00 **S:** £25.00–£40.00 **Beds:** 1T 1D **Baths:** 1 En 1 Pr 🐾 🅿 (5) ⌇ 📺 🛏 🗙 🖳 👶

Kirkby Lonsdale
SD6178

Wyck House, 4 Main Street, Kirkby Lonsdale, Carnforth, Lancs, LA6 2AE. Quality accommodation in a Victorian town house, close to amenities. **Open:** All year **015242 71953 (also fax)** Pat & Brian Bradley *wyckhouse@studioarts.co.uk* www.studioarts.co. uk/wyckhouse.htm **D:** £20.00–£22.50 **S:** £18.50–£30.00 **Beds:** 1F 1T 2D 2S **Baths:** 3 En 1 Sh 🐾 🅿 (3) ⌇ 📺 🖳 👶

Barnfield Farm, Tunstall, Kirkby Lonsdale, Carnforth, Lancs, LA6 2QP. 1702 family farmhouse on a 200-acre working farm. **Open:** All year (not Xmas/New Year) **015242 74284 (also fax)** J Stephenson **D:** £17.00–£17.50 **S:** £17.50–£20.00 **Beds:** 1F 1D **Baths:** 1 Sh 🐾 🅿 (2) ⌇ 📺 🖳 👶

Kirkby Stephen
NY7708 🍺 *Bay Horse, King's Arms, Crogin Castle*

Fletcher House, Fletcher Hill, Kirkby Stephen, Cumbria, CA17 4QQ. **Open:** Apr to Oct **017683 71013** Mrs Bradwell *fletcherhouse@ btinternet.com* **D:** £20.00–£30.00 **S:** £25.00 **Beds:** 2T 2D **Baths:** 2 En 2 Pr 🅿 (4) ⌇ 📺 🖳 👶 Situated in the lovely Upper Eden Valley near to the Yorkshire Dales and the Lake District. Ideal for walkers, cyclists and motorists. Enjoy your stay in a comfortable house with a good choice of breakfast and daily home baked bread.

Lockholme, *48 South Road, Kirkby Stephen, Cumbria, CA17 4SN.* Victorian home, ideally situated for breaking a journey or exploring. **Open:** All year (not Xmas/New Year)
017683 71321 Mrs Graham *lockholme@ supanet.com* www.lockholme.supanet.com
D: £16.00–£18.00 **S:** £16.00–£22.00 **Beds:** 1F 1T 1D 1S **Baths:** 2 En 1 Sh ➣ ⚡ ⏲ ⎚ ♈ ⎚ ⊞ ⚓

Lakeside
SD3787

The Knoll Country Guest House, *Lakeside, Newby Bridge, Ulverston, Cumbria, LA12 8AU.* **Open:** All year
015395 31347 Ms Meads and Ms T Watson *info@theknoll-lakeside.co.uk* www.theknoll-lakeside.co.uk **D:** £26.00–£45.00 **S:** £40.00 **Beds:** 6D 2T **Baths:** 8 En ⚡ ⎚ ⚡ ⎚ ⏲ ⎚ ⊞ ✳ ⚓ cc
The Knoll - a delightful Victorian house, set amidst peaceful wooded countryside at the south end of Lake Windermere, offering a relaxed night's sleep and hearty breakfast. Only 5 minutes walk from main attractions, an ideal base for relaxing or exploring.

Leadgate
NY7043

Brownside House, *Leadgate, Alston, Cumbria, CA9 3EL.* Warm welcome awaits at peaceful house in the country with superb views. **Open:** All year
01434 382169 & 01434 382100 Mrs Le Marie **Fax: 01434 382169** *brownside_hse@hotmail.com* www.cumbria1st. com/brown_side/indexhtm **D:** £18.00 **S:** £18.00 **Beds:** 1D 2T 1S **Baths:** 1 Sh ➣ ⚡ (4) ⚡ ⎚ ♈ ✕ ⎚ ⊞ ⚓ cc

Leece
SD2469

Winander, *Leece, Ulverston, Cumbria, LA12 0QP.* Converted barn in quiet village location in Lake District peninsula. **Open:** All year (not Xmas)
01229 822353 Mr Cockshott **D:** £18.00–£23.00 **S:** £21.00–£26.00 **Beds:** 1T 1D **Baths:** 1 Pr 1 Sh ➣ (5) ⚡ (3) ⚡ ⎚ ✕ ⎚ ⊞ ⚓

Levens
SD4886

Glen Robin, *Church Road, Levens, Kendal, Cumbria, LA8 8PS.* Beautiful house with lovely views, delicious breakfasts, peace and quiet. **Open:** All year (not Xmas)
015395 60369 (also fax) D: £16.00–£20.00 **S:** £16.00–£20.00 **Beds:** 1D 1T 1S **Baths:** 1 Sh ➣ (3) ⚡ (3) ⚡ ⎚ ⎚ ⊞ ⚓

Lindale
SD4180

Greenacres Country Guest House, *Lindale, Grange-over-Sands, Cumbria, LA11 6LP.* Warm hospitality, lovely rooms, ideal for Lakes, Dales and coast. **Open:** All year (not Xmas/New Year) **Grades:** ETC 4 Diamond
015395 34578 (also fax) www.accomodata. co.uk/091098.htm **D:** £25.00–£28.00 **S:** £25.00–£30.00 **Beds:** 1F 1T 2D **Baths:** 4 En ➣ ⚡ (5) ⚡ ⎚ ✕ ⎚ ⊞ ⚓ cc

Little Arrow
SD2895

Browside, *Little Arrow, Coniston, Cumbria, LA21 8AU.* Panoramic views across Coniston Water to Brantwood, Grizedale Forest & Ambleside Fells. **Open:** Feb to Nov
015394 41162 Mrs Dugdale **D:** £18.00–£22.00 **S:** £20.00–£25.00 **Beds:** 1T 1D **Baths:** 2 En ➣ ⚡ ⚡ ⎚ ⎚ ⊞ ⚓

Little Musgrave
NY7513

Smithfield Barn, *Little Musgrave, Kirkby Stephen, Cumbria, CA17 4PG.* Modern barn conversion. Tranquil setting. beautiful views over unspoilt countryside. **Open:** All year
017683 41002 E Hodgson **D:** £19.00 **S:** £19.00 **Beds:** 2D **Baths:** 1 En 1 Pr ➣ ⚡ ⚡ ⎚ ♈ ✕ ⎚ ⊞ ⚓

Little Salkeld
NY5636

Bank house Farm and Stables, *Bankhouse, Little Salkeld, Penrith, Cumbria, CA10 1NN.* Converted barns on stable yard. Village location in Eden Valley. **Open:** All year
01768 881257 D: £20.00–£30.00 **S:** £25.00–£30.00 **Beds:** 3F 3T 3D **Baths:** 6 En 3 Sh ➣ ⚡ (20) ⎚ ♈ ⎚ ⊞ ⚓ ⚓

Longthwaite
NY2514   ⚑ *Scafell Hotel, Lanstrath Hotel*

Castle Lodge, *Peat Howe, Longthwaite, Borrowdale, Keswick, Cumbria, CA12 5XE.* Cosy, charming Lakeland cottage. Olde Worlde with modern conveniences. **Open:** All year (not Xmas/New Year)
017687 77346 Mrs Weir www.castle-lodge.co. uk **D:** £18.00–£23.00 **S:** £21.00 **Beds:** 1F 1T 1D 1S **Baths:** 1 En 1 Sh ➣ ⚡ ⎚ ♈ ⎚ ⊞ ⚓

Longtown
NY3868

New Pallyards, *Hethersgill, Carlisle, Cumbria, CA6 6HZ.* Ideal stopover or longer visit to explore our wonderful countryside. **Open:** All year **Grades:** ETC 4 Diamond
01228 577308 (also fax) Mrs Elwen *info@ newpallyards.freeserve.co.uk* www.newpallyards. freeserv.co.uk **D:** £22.00–£23.90 **S:** £27.00–£29.00 **Beds:** 1F 2T 2D 1S **Baths:** 6 En ➣ ⚡ ⎚ ♈ ✕ ⎚ ⊞ ✳ ⚓ cc

Lorton
NY1525

Cragg End Farm, *Rogerscale, Lorton Vale, Cockermouth, Cumbria, CA13 0RG.* Beautiful views, ideal situation for walking. Quiet, working, family farm. **Open:** All year
01900 85658 Mrs Steel **D:** £20.00 **S:** £20.00 **Beds:** 1F 1D 2T **Baths:** 3 Sh ➣ ⚡ ⚡ ⎚ ♈ ✕ ⎚

The Old Vicarage, *Church Lane, Lorton, Cockermouth, Cumbria, CA13 9UN.* Elegant Victorian country house with stunning views, wooded grounds, log fires. **Open:** All year (not Xmas)
01900 85656 (also fax) Mr Humphreys *enquiries@oldvicarage.co.uk* www.oldvicarage. co.uk **D:** £22.00–£32.00 **S:** £22.00–£30.00 **Beds:** 5D 3T **Baths:** 8 En ➣ ⚡ (10) ⚡ ✕ ⎚ ⊞ ⚓ cc

Low Row
NY5863   ⚑ *Railway Inn*

High Nook Farm, *Low Row, Brampton, Cumbria, CA8 2LU.* Comfortable farmhouse built in 1857. **Open:** June to Oct
016977 46273 Mrs Foster **D:** £28.00–£30.00 **S:** £15.00 **Beds:** 1D **Baths:** 1 Sh ➣ ⚡ (2) ⎚ ♈

Loweswater
NY1420

Brook Farm, *Thacktwaite, Loweswater, Cockermouth, Cumbria, CA13 0RP.* Comfortable, quiet, working farmhouse. Good food! open fire, pretty garden. **Open:** Easter to Nov
01900 85606 (also fax) Mrs Hayton **D:** £20.00–£21.00 **S:** £20.00–£21.00 **Beds:** 1F 1D **Baths:** 1 Sh ➣ ⚡ (3) ⚡ ⎚ ♈ ✕ ⚓

Askhill Farm, *Loweswater, Cockermouth, Cumbria, CA13 0SU.* Beef & sheep rearing farm, quiet valley, Loweswater. Ideal country walking area. **Open:** Easter to Oct
01946 861640 Mrs Vickers **D:** £18.00–£20.00 **S:** £19.00–£21.00 **Beds:** 1F 1D **Baths:** 1 Sh ➣ ⚡ (3) ⚡ ⎚ ✕ ⎚ ⊞ ⚓

Lowick

SD2986

Garth Row, Lowick Green, Lowick, Ulverston, Cumbria, *LA12 8EB.* Traditional Lakeland house. Warm welcome. Super, peaceful setting. Quality accommodation. **Open:** All year (not Xmas/New Year) **01229 885633** Mrs Wickens *b&b@ garthrow.freeserve.co.uk* **D:** £18.00–£20.00 **S:** £23.00–£25.00 **Beds:** 1F 1D **Baths:** 1 Sh ⑤ 🅿 (4) ⊁ 📺 🛏 📺 🛢 🕭

Lowick Bridge

SD2986

Red Lion Inn, Lowick Bridge, Ulverston, Cumbria, *LA12 8EF.* In the unspoilt part of English Lake District. Cosy atmosphere. **Open:** All year **01229 885366 (also fax)** *redlion@ lowick.fslife.co.uk* **D:** £17.50–£25.00 **S:** £25.00– £30.00 **Beds:** 2D **Baths:** 2 En ⑤ 🅿 📺 🛏 ✕ 📺 🛢 🕭 cc

Maryport

NY0336

10 Selby Terrace, Maryport, Cumbria, *CA15 6NF.* Welcoming Victorian town house. Good food. 20 minutes Lakes. Fishing. **Open:** All year **01900 813595** Mrs Renac **D:** £14.00 **S:** £14.00–£15.00 **Beds:** 2F 1D 1S **Baths:** 2 Sh ⑤ ⊁ 📺 📺 🛢 🕭

Mealsgate

NY2041

Appletree House, Mealsgate, Wigton, Cumbria, *CA7 1JP.* Conveniently situated for exploring Northern Lakes and Solway Coast. **Open:** All year (not Xmas) **016973 71200** Mrs Exley **D:** £18.00 **S:** £18.00 **Beds:** 1D 1T **Baths:** 1 Sh ⑤ 🅿 (3) ⊁ 📺 🛢

Melmerby

NY6137   🍺 *Shepherds Inn*

Bolton Farmhouse, Melmerby, Penrith, Cumbria, *CA10 1HF.* C17th oak-beamed farmhouse. Wonderful views. Friendly. Comfortable. Good sightseeing. **Open:** All year **01768 881851 & 07702 933952 (M)** *www.eden-valley.net/boltonfarmhouse* **D:** £16.00 **S:** £16.00 **Beds:** 1T 1D 1S **Baths:** 1 Sh ⑤ 🅿 (4) 📺 🛏 📺 🛢 🕭

Gale Hall Farm, Melmerby, Penrith, Cumbria, *CA10 1HN.* Large comfortable farmhouse near Pennines and Lake District. **Open:** June to Nov **01768 881254** Mrs Toppin **S:** £15.00 **S:** £15.00 **Beds:** 1F 1T 1S **Baths:** 1 Sh ⑤ 🅿 (3) 📺 🛏 📺

Middleton

SD6286

Tossbeck Farm, Middleton, Carnforth, Lancashire, *LA6 2LZ.* A friendly welcome awaits you at Tossbeck, mixed farm in unspoilt Lune Valley. **Open:** Easter to Oct **015242 76214 D:** £17.00–£19.00 **S:** £22.00– £25.00 **Beds:** 1F 1D **Baths:** 1 En 1 Pr ⑤ 🅿 (2) ⊁ 📺 🛏 🛢 🕭

Moresby

NX9921

Moresby Hall, Moresby, Whitehaven, Cumbria, *CA28 6PJ.* A Grade I Listed character building. Spacious and well-equipped rooms. **Open:** All year **01946 696317** Mrs Saxon **Fax: 01946 692666** *saxon@moresbyhall.co.uk* www.moresbyhall.co.uk **D:** £22.50–£32.50 **S:** £25.00–£35.00 **Beds:** 1F 1T 2D **Baths:** 2 En 2 Pr ⑤ (10) 🅿 (6) ⊁ 📺 ✕ 📺 🛢 ✲ 🕭 cc

Morland

NY5923

Mill Beck Cottage, Water Street, Morland, Penrith, Cumbria, *CA10 3AY.* **Open:** All year (not Xmas/New Year) **01931 714567** Mrs Jackson **Fax: 01931714567 D:** £22.00–£25.00 **S:** £22.00– £25.00 **Beds:** 1T 1D **Baths:** 1 Pr ⑤ (12) ⊁ 📺 ✕ 📺 🛢 🕭
Traditional riverside cottage, unspoilt village and countryside, comfortable rooms, good beds. Morning sun, excellent food. Perfectly situated for the Lakes, Pennines and Yorkshire Dales, 45 mins. M6 10 minutes. Tranquility supported by good pubs and peaceful villages, of which Morland is one of the oldest.

Mungrisdale

NY3630   🍺 *Mill Inn, White Horse, Troutbeck Hotel*

Near Howe Hotel, Mungrisdale, Penrith, Cumbria, *CA11 0SH.* Small hotel in beautiful area. Warm welcome awaits you. **Open:** All year (not Xmas) **Grades:** ETC 3 Diamond **017687 79678 (also fax)** Mrs Weightman **D:** £19.00–£24.00 **S:** £24.00 **Beds:** 3F 3D 1T **Baths:** 5 En 2 Sh ⑤ 🅿 (20) 📺 🛏 ✕ 📺 🛢 🕭

Natland

SD5289   🍺 *Punch Bowl, Station Inn*

High House Farm, Oxenholme Lane, Natland, Kendal, Cumbria, *LA9 7QH.* Tranquil Lakeland village, C17th farmhouse. **Open:** All year (not Xmas) **Grades:** ETC 4 Diamond, Silver, AA 4 Diamond **015395 61177** Mrs Sunter **Fax: 015395 615120 D:** £24.50–£29.50 **S:** £29.50–£32.50 **Beds:** 2D 1T **Baths:** 3 En 🅿 (9) ⊁ 📺 📺 🛢 🕭

Near Sawrey

SD3795

High Green Gate Guest House, Near Sawrey, Ambleside, Cumbria, *LA22 0LF.* Converted farmhouse in Beatrix Potter's village countryside, farm position. **Open:** Apr to Oct **015394 36296** Miss Fletcher **D:** £23.00– £26.00 **S:** £23.00 **Beds:** 4F 1D **Baths:** 3 Pr 1 Sh ⑤ 🅿 (7) 📺 🛏 ✕ 📺 🛢 🕭

Nenthead

NY7843

The Miners Arms, Nenthead, Alston, Cumbria, *CA9 3PF.* Friendly family pub. Real ales, real food, real fires. **Open:** All year **01434 381427** Miss Clark www.theminersarms.org.uk **D:** £15.00 **S:** £15.00 **Beds:** 2F 2D 2T 2S ⑤ 🅿 ⊁ 📺 🛏 ✕ 📺 🛢 🕭 cc

Mill Cottage Bunkhouse, Nenthead, Alston, Cumbria, *CA9 3PD.* Bunkhouse in spectacular landscape, part of Nenthead Mines heritage site. **Open:** All year **01434 382771 & 01434 382037** *administration.office@virgin.net* www.freespace. virgin.net.np.ht **D:** £12.00 **S:** £12.00 **Beds:** 2F ⑤ 🅿 (4) ⊁ ✕ 📺 🛢 🕭

New Hutton

SD5691   🍺 *Station Inn*

Cragg Farm, New Hutton, Kendal, Cumbria, *LA8 0BA.* Situated 4 miles Kendal, warm welcome, excellent accommodation. Breakfast provided. **Open:** Mar to Nov **Grades:** ETC 3 Diamond **01539 721760 (also fax)** Mrs Knowles *knowles.cragg@ukgateway.net* **D:** £17.00–£19.00 **S:** £17.00–£19.00 **Beds:** 1F 1D 1S **Baths:** 1 Sh ⑤ 🅿 ⊁ 📺 📺 🛢 🕭

Newbiggin (Stainton)

NY4629

Tymparon Hall, Newbiggin , Penrith, Cumbria, *CA11 0HS.* Secluded farm house. 3/ 4 mile A66 close M6/J40 & Ullswater. **Open:** Feb to Nov **017684 83236** Ms Taylor *margaret@ pearson.freeserve.co.uk* www.pearson. freeserve.co.uk **D:** £21.00–£25.00 **S:** £21.00– £25.00 **Beds:** 1F 1D 1T **Baths:** 2 En 1 Pr ⑤ 🅿 ⊁ 📺 🛏 ✕ 📺 🛢 🕭

Newbiggin-on-Lune

NY7005   🍺 *Black Swan*

Tranna Hill, Newbiggin-on-Lune, Kirkby Stephen, Cumbria, *CA17 4NY.* Beautiful views from lovely rooms - good walking area, 5 miles M6. **Open:** Easter to Oct **Grades:** ETC 3 Diamond **015396 23227 & 07989 892368 (M)** B Boustead *trannahill@hotmail.com* **D:** £18.00 **S:** £20.00 **Beds:** 1T 1D **Baths:** 1 En 1 Pr ⑤ 🅿 (4) ⊁ 📺 ✕ 🛢 🕭

Church View Farmhouse, *Newbiggin-on-Lune, Kirkby Stephen, Cumbria, CA17 4NS.* Comfortable, beamed C17th farmhouse in peaceful village. Good walking country. **Open:** All year (not Xmas/New Year) **015396 23283 (also fax)** *kedwards@ couttsinfo.com* **D:** £17.00–£18.00 **S:** £17.00–£18.00 **Beds:** 2D **Baths:** 1 Sh ▣ (2) ⅙ ⊡ ✕ ⅤⅤ ▥ ⚲

Newby Bridge

SD3786   *Crown Inn, Swan Inn, Newby Bridge Hotel*

Hill Crest, *Backbarrow, Newby Bridge, Ulverston, Cumbria, LA12 8QP.* Traditional Lakeland house, magnificent views, country location - quality accommodation, homely. **Open:** All year (not Xmas) **Grades:** ETC 4 Diamond **015395 31766** Mrs Jenkinson **Fax: 015395 31986 D:** £20.00–£25.00 **S:** £25.00–£35.00 **Beds:** 1F 3D 1T **Baths:** 2 En 1 Pr ⅙ ▣ (3) ⅙ ⊡ Ⅴ ▥ ⚲

Miller Beck, *Newby Bridge, Ulverston, Cumbria, LA12 8NE.* Typical Lakeland house from 1920, backing onto Lake Windermere. Warm welcome, good breakfasts. **Open:** All year (not Xmas) **015395 31329** E I Foster **D:** £22.50–£25.00 **S:** £30.00–£35.00 **Beds:** 1D 1T 1S **Baths:** 2 En ⅙ (8) ▣ (10) ⅙ ⊡ ⅙ ⅤⅤ ▥ ⚲

Alloa Guest House, *Newby Bridge, Cumbria, LA12 8LZ.* Secluded luxury bungalow with all amenities. Excellent home cooking. Superb lake views. **Open:** All year (not Xmas/New Year) **015395 30391 (also fax) D:** £20.00–£25.00 **S:** £25.00–£30.00 **Beds:** 1F 1T 1D **Baths:** 2 En 1 Pr ⅙ (2) ▣ (10) ⅙ ⊡ ✕ ⅤⅤ ▥ ⅙ ⚲

Lyndhurst Country House, *Newby Bridge, Ulverston, Cumbria, LA12 8ND.* Warm welcome for walkers, cyclists, vegetarian/vegans. Bird watchers' paradise. **Open:** Easter to Nov **015395 31245** Mr & Mrs Evans *lyndhurst@ gofree.co.uk* www.lyndhurstguesthouse.co.uk **D:** £19.00–£24.00 **Beds:** 1T 2D **Baths:** 3 En ⅙ ▣ (3) ⅙ ⊡ ✕ ⅤⅤ ▥ ⚲

Newlands

NY2420

Uzzicar Farm, *Newlands, Keswick, Cumbria, CA12 5TS.* Clean, cosy, comfortable farmhouse with character, situated in idyllic surroundings. **Open:** All year (not Xmas) **017687 78367** Mrs Simpson **D:** £17.00–£19.00 **S:** £20.00 **Beds:** 1D 1F **Baths:** 1 Sh ⅙ ▣ ⅙ ⅤⅤ ▥ ⚲

Old Hutton

SD5688

Blaven, *Middleshaw Head Barn, Old Hutton, Kendal, Cumbria, LA8 0LZ.* Peaceful, hilly location. Lovely streamside Lakeland house, very convenient for M6 J36/37. **Open:** All year **01539 734894** Mrs Beale & Mr Green **Fax: 01539 727447** *blaven@greenarrow.demon.co.uk* www.superdigs.co.uk **D:** £25.00–£32.00 **S:** £28.00–£42.00 **Beds:** 1S 1T 1F **Baths:** 1 En 1 Pr ⅙ ▣ (4) ⅙ ⊡ ⅙ ✕ ▥ ⚲ ✿ cc

Oughterside

NY1140

The Manor House Guest House, *Oughterside, Aspatria, Cumbria, CA7 2PT.* Georgian manor farmhouse. Spacious rooms and grounds. Peaceful. Comfortable. Welcoming. **Open:** All year (not New Year) **01697 322420 (also fax)** Mr & Mrs Mortimer *richardandjudy@themanorhouse.net* www.themanorhouse.net **D:** £21.00–£25.00 **S:** £25.00–£30.00 **Beds:** 2F 1T 2D **Baths:** 3 En 1 Sh ⅙ ▣ (5) ⅙ ⊡ ⅙ ✕ ⅤⅤ ▥ ⚲

Outhgill

NY7801

Faraday Cottage, *Outhgill, Kirkby Stephen, Cumbria, CA17 4JU.* Historic cottage. Heart of Mallerstang Valley, walkers' paradise. **Open:** All year (not Xmas/New Year) **017683 72351** Mrs Porter **D:** £15.00 **S:** £15.00 **Beds:** 1T 1D **Baths:** 1 Sh ⅙ ▣ (2) ⅙ ⊡ ⅙ ✕ ⅤⅤ ▥ ⚲

Pardshaw

NY0924   *Old Posting House*

Pardshaw Hall, *Pardshaw, Cockermouth, Cumbria, CA13 0SP.* New barn conversion. Reduced rates. Children welcome. All ensuite. **Open:** All year **01900 822607** Mrs Richardson **D:** £20.00 **S:** £20.00 **Beds:** 1F 1D 1S **Baths:** 3 En ⅙ (3) ▣ (3) ⊡ ⅙ ⅤⅤ ▥ ⚲

Patton

SD5496

High Barn, *Shaw End, Patton, Kendal, Cumbria, LA8 9DU.* Beautiful barn conversion on the Dales Way. Peaceful setting. Home cooking. **Open:** All year **01539 824625** Mrs Sanderson *hibarn@ hotmail.com* **D:** £16.00 **S:** £16.00 **Beds:** 2D **Baths:** 1 En 1 Pr ▣ (2) ⅙ ⊡ ✕ ⅤⅤ ▥ ⚲

Penrith

NY5130   *Crown Inn, White Horse, Sportsman, Clickham Inn, Newby Inn, Queens Head*

Norcroft Guest House, *Graham Street, Penrith, Cumbria, CA11 9LQ.* **Open:** All year **Grades:** RAC 4 Diamond **01768 862365 (also fax)** Ms Simmons **D:** £21.00–£23.00 **S:** £22.00–£26.00 **Beds:** 2F 3T 3D 1S **Baths:** 9 En ⅙ ▣ (9) ⅙ ⊡ ✕ ⅤⅤ ▥ ⅙1 ⚲ cc Spacious, charming Victorian house with relaxed friendly atmosphere. Ideal for holiday centre or stop over for English Lakes and Scottish Borders (M6 Junction 40, 5 min drive away). Ample private parking and secure cycle storage. C2C route on doorstep.

Makalolo, *Barco Avenue, Penrith, Cumbria, CA11 8LU.* Spacious modern house, beamed lounge, conservatory, views of Lakeland hills. Local Authority Approved. **Open:** All year **01768 891519** Mr Dawson **D:** £16.00–£20.00 **S:** £25.00–£28.00 **Beds:** 1T 1D **Baths:** 1 En 1 Pr ▣ (6) ⅙ ⊡ ✕ ⅤⅤ ▥ ⚲

Albany House, *5 Portland Place, Penrith, Cumbria, CA11 7QN.* Friendly, comfortable Victorian house, good breakfast, town centre, M6 5 minutes. **Open:** All year **01768 863072 (also fax)** Mrs Blundell **D:** £17.50–£25.00 **S:** £20.00–£27.50 **Beds:** 4F 1D **Baths:** 2 En 2 Sh ⅙ ▣ (1) ⊡ ⅤⅤ ▥ ⚲

Blue Swallow, *11 Victoria Road, Penrith, Cumbria, CA11 8HR.* Victorian town house situated in lovely market town of Penrith. **Open:** All year (not Xmas) **Grades:** ETC 3 Diamond **01768 866335 (also fax)** Mrs Hughes *blueswallows@lineone.net* www.blueswallow.co.uk **D:** £17.00–£20.00 **S:** £22.00–£27.00 **Beds:** 1F 2D 2T **Baths:** 3 En 1 Sh ⅙ ▣ (5) ⊡ Ⅴ ▥ ⚲

Brooklands Guest House, *2 Portland Place, Penrith, Cumbria, CA11 7QN.* Fine Victorian town house 100m town centre, retaining many of the original features. **Open:** All year **01768 863395 Fax: 01768 864895** *leon.j.kirk@ btinternet.com* **D:** £18.00–£22.50 **S:** £20.00–£22.00 **Beds:** 1F 2S 3D/T **Baths:** 2 Sh 3 En ⅙ ▣ (1) ⊡ ⅙ ⅤⅤ ▥ ⚲

BEDROOMS

D = Double

T = Twin

S = Single

F = Family

Plumbland

NY1439

Chapel House, Plumbland, Aspatria, Carlisle, Cumbria, CA5 2HA. Well-located between Keswick, Cockermouth & the Solway with excellent access to the Lakes. **Open:** All year (not Xmas/New Year) **01697 321480** Mr & Mrs Wells *gilda.wells@ talk21.com* members.tripod.co. uk/wells-2/b-b.html **D:** £17.50 **S:** £17.50 **Beds:** 1T 1D **Baths:** 2 En ♿ ⊞ (3) ⊬ 📺 🕇 🛒 ♨

Portinscale

NY2523

Thirnbeck Guest House, Portinscale, Keswick, Cumbria, CA12 5RD. Comfortable Georgian guest house with fine views over Derwent Water. **Open:** All year (not Xmas) **017687 72869** Martin & Lynn Savage *mls@ thirnbeck.fsnet.co.uk* **D:** £23.00 **S:** £23.00 **Beds:** 4D 1T 1S **Baths:** 5 En 1 Pr ♿ (4) 🖪 (4) ⊬ 📺 🕇 🛒 ♨

Rickerby Grange, Portinscale, Keswick, Cumbria, CA12 5RH. Set within own garden, private parking. In the pretty village of Portinscale. **Open:** All year **017687 72344** Mrs Bradley *val@ ricor.demon.co.uk* www.ricor.demon.co.uk **D:** £28.00–£30.00 **S:** £28.00–£30.00 **Beds:** 3F 9D 2S **Baths:** 14 En ♿ (5) 🖪 (14) ⊬ 📺 🕇 🛒 ♨ ❋ ♨

Skiddaw Croft, Portinscale, Keswick, Cumbria, CA12 5RD. Comfortable & friendly B&B in charming village. Splendid lake & mountain views. **Open:** All year **017687 72321 (also fax)** J Downer *skiddawcroft@talk21.com* **D:** £20.00–£25.00 **S:** £20.00–£25.00 **Beds:** 1F 1T 2D 2S **Baths:** 4 En 1 Sh ♿ 🖪 (6) ⊬ 📺 🕇 🛒 ♨

Raisbeck

NY6407

New House Farm, Raisbeck, Orton, Penrith, Cumbria, CA10 3SD. Quiet, picturesque. Panoramic views. For walking and camping and caravanning. **Open:** All year **015396 24324** Mrs Winder **D:** £17.50–£18.50 **S:** £18.50 **Beds:** 2T 1D 2S ♿ 🖪 ⊬ × 🛒 ♨

Ravenglass

SD0896

Rosegarth, Main Street, Ravenglass, Cumbria, CA18 1SQ. Warm and friendly welcome, most rooms with estuary view. **Open:** All year (not Xmas/New Year) **01229 717275** Mrs Muxlow *rosegarth@ talk21.com* **D:** £18.00–£23.00 **S:** £18.00–£23.00 **Beds:** 1F 2T 3D 1S **Baths:** 2 Sh ♿ 🖪 (6) 📺 🕇 × 🛒 ♨

Muncaster Country Guest House, Ravenglass, Cumbria, CA18 1RD. A very comfortable & welcoming country guest house adjoining Muncaster Estate & open countryside. **Open:** Mar to Oct **01229 717693 (also fax)** Mr Putnam **D:** £20.00–£24.00 **S:** £22.00–£28.00 **Beds:** 1F 3D 2T 3S **Baths:** 2 En 2 Sh ♿ (1) 🖪 (16) ⊬ 📺 🕇 🛒 ♨ ♨

Ravenstonedale

NY7203

Bowber Head, Ravenstonedale, Kirkby Stephen, Cumbria, CA17 4NL. C17th farmhouse, open views, centre for classic coach tours. **Open:** All year **015396 23254 (also fax)** Mr Hamer *hols@ www.cumbriaclassiccoaches.co.uk* www.cumbriaclassiccoaches.co.uk **D:** £20.00–£22.00 **S:** £20.00–£22.00 **Beds:** 1F 2D 2T **Baths:** 1 En 2 Pr ♿ 🖪 (6) ⊬ 📺 🕇 × 🛒 ♨ ♨ ♨

Renwick

NY5943

Scalehouse Farm, Scalehouses, Renwick, Penrith, Cumbria, CA10 1JY. Old farmhouse with period features, open fires and beams, tastefully renovated. **Open:** All year (not Xmas) **01768 896493 (also fax)** **D:** £14.00–£18.00 **S:** £16.00–£20.00 **Beds:** 2D 1T **Baths:** 1 Pr 1 Sh ♿ 🖪 (6) ⊬ 📺 × 🛒 ♨

Roa Island

SD2364

Villa Marina, Roa Island, Barrow-in-Furness, Cumbria, LA13 0QL. Victorian gentleman's residence situated on Morecambe Bay. **Open:** All year (not Xmas/New Year) **01229 822520** Mrs Allen **D:** £15.00–£20.00 **S:** £20.00–£25.00 **Beds:** 1F 2T **Baths:** 1 En 1 Sh ♿ 🖪 (4) ⊬ 📺 🕇 🛒 ♨

Rosthwaite (Borrowdale)

NY2514

Royal Oak Hotel, Rosthwaite, Keswick, Cumbria, CA12 5XB. **Open:** All year **Grades:** ETC 1 Star **017687 77214 (also fax)** Mr Dowie *royaloak@ ukgateway.net* www.royaloakhotel.co.uk **D:** £26.00 **S:** £25.00 **Beds:** 6F 5D 2T 2S **Baths:** 12 En 3 Sh ♿ 🖪 (15) 📺 🕇 × 🛒 ♨ ♨ A former Lakeland 'longhouse', our traditional family-run hotel is set in the heart of beautiful Borrowdale. With good home-cooking, open fire and friendly service, we provide the perfect base from which to explore the Northern Lakes.

The How, Rosthwaite, Keswick, Cumbria, CA12 5BX. **Open:** Mar to Nov **017687 77692** **D:** £19.00–£20.50 **S:** £22.00–£23.00 **Beds:** 1T 2D **Baths:** 2 Sh 🖪 (4) 📺 🕇 🛒 ♨ Rosthwaite is in the beautiful Borrowdale Valley about six miles from Keswick. Fell and riverside walking. Country house in well-kept garden. Comfortable lounge with television, log fire when required. Breakfast room. Superb views.

Yew Craggs, Rosthwaite, Keswick, Cumbria, CA12 5XB. Central Borrowdale, spectacular views, car park, riverside location (by the bridge). **Open:** Mar to Oct **017687 77260** Mr & Mrs Crofts *yewcraggs@ aol.com* www.members.aol.com/yewcraggs **D:** £18.00–£23.00 **S:** £25.00 **Beds:** 2F 3D **Baths:** 1 Sh ♿ (6) 🖪 (6) ⊬

Satterthwaite

SD3392

Force Mill Farm, Satterthwaite, Ulverston, Cumbria, LA12 8LQ. C17th riverside farmhouse, near Grizedale Forest, Lakes and Fells. **Open:** All year **01229 860205 (also fax)** **D:** £20.00 **S:** £20.00–£25.00 **Beds:** 1F 1T 2D **Baths:** 4 En ♿ 🖪 (6) ⊬ 📺 🕇 × 🛒 ♨ ♨

Sedbergh

SD6592   🍴 Dalesman

Stable Antiques, 15 Back Lane, Sedbergh, Cumbria, LA10 5AQ. C18th wheelwright's cottage with wonderful views of Howgill Fells. **Open:** All year **Grades:** ETC 2 Diamond **015396 20251** Miss Thurlby *ourworld.compuserve. com/homepages/sedburgh* **D:** £18.00–£19.00 **S:** £18.00–£19.00 **Beds:** 1D 1T **Baths:** 1 Sh ♿ (10) 📺 🕇 🛒 ♨ cc

Holmecroft, Station Road, Sedbergh, Cumbria, LA10 5DW. Recommended by 'Which' Good Bed and Breakfast Guide. **Open:** All year (not Xmas) **015396 20754 (also fax)** Mrs Sharrocks *ssharrocks@breathemail.net* ourworld.compuserve. com/homepages/sedbergh **D:** £19.00 **S:** £19.00 **Beds:** 1D 1T 1S **Baths:** 1 Sh ♿ 🖪 (6) ⊬ 📺 🛒 ♨

Selside
SD5399

Hollowgate, *Selside, Kendal, Cumbria,*
LA8 9LG. C16th comfortable farmhouse.
Open: Easter to Oct
01539 823258 Mrs Knowles *hollowgate@*
talk21.com **D:** £17.00–£17.50 **S:** £17.00–
£17.50 **Beds:** 2D 1S Ⓥ

Shap
NY5615

The Crown Inn, *Main Street, Shap,*
Penrith, Cumbria, CA10 3NL. **Open:** Feb to
Dec
01931 716229 Mrs Beardall *crowninnshap@*
totalise.co.uk www.shap-cumbria.com.
D: £19.50–£22.50 **S:** £19.50–£22.50 **Beds:** 1F
1D 1S **Baths:** 1 Sh ⌂ �ℙ (15) Ⓥ ❄ ✕ Ⓥ ▥ ⚲
A warm welcome awaits you at our
charming C18th inn where your comfort is
our priority. Historic Shap is ideally situated
for the Lakes, Pennines and Howgills - just
two miles from the M6 (Junction 39).
Perfect for breaking long journeys!

Fell House, *Shap, Penrith, Cumbria,*
CA10 3NY. **Open:** All year
01931 716343 Mr & Mrs Smith *johnsmith@*
fellhouse.freeserve.co.uk
www.shapaccommodation.co.uk **D:** £17.00–
£20.00 **S:** £18.50–£24.00 **Beds:** 3F 1D 1T
Baths: 1 En 2 Sh ⌂ ⊞ Ⓥ ❄ Ⓥ ▥ ⚲
Large Victorian house in small friendly
village steeped in history. Ideal base for
touring Lakes and Dales, also convenient
stop en-route to Scotland. Excellent
walking in area, also view golden eagles at
Haweswater or sail or windsurf at
Ullswater. Pets welcome.

Brookfield, *Shop, Penrith, Cumbria,*
CA10 3PZ. Renowned for good food, comfort
and personal attention. Ensuite, licensed.
Open: All year (not Xmas/New Year)
Grades: AA 4 Diamond
01931 716397 (also fax) Mrs Brunskill
D: £19.00–£25.00 **S:** £19.00–£25.00 **Beds:** 3F
5D 3T 1S **Baths:** 4 En 4 Pr 1 Sh ⊞ (20) ✌ Ⓥ ✕
Ⓥ ▥ ⚲

Skelwith Bridge
NY3403 ⚑ *Skelwith Bridge, Talbot Bar,*
Wainwright's Bar, Britannia Inn

Greenbank,
Skelwith Bridge,
Ambleside,
Cumbria,
LA22 9NW.
Comfortable,
friendly B and B
in superb central Lakes location. **Open:** Feb
to Nov **Grades:** ETC 4 Diamond, Silver
015394 33236 Mr Green *greenbank@bigwig.net*
www.visitgreenbank.co.uk **D:** £22.00–£25.00
S: £32.00–£35.00 **Beds:** 2D 1T **Baths:** 3 En
⌂ (8) ⊞ (5) ✌ Ⓥ Ⓥ ▥ ⚲

St Bees
NX9711 ⚑ *Queen's Hotel, Manor House*

Stonehouse
Farm, *Main*
Street, St Bees,
Cumbria,
CA27 0DE. Modern
Georgian
farmhouse in
centre of village,
next to railway station. **Open:** All year (not
Xmas)
01946 822224 Mrs Smith **D:** £16.00–£20.00
S: £20.00 **Beds:** 1F 2D 2T 1S **Baths:** 4 En 1
Sh ⌂ ⊞ (20) Ⓥ ❄ Ⓥ ▥ ⚲

Fairladies Barn Guest House, *Main*
Street, St Bees, CA27 0AD. Large converted
barn located in centre of seaside village.
Open: All year
01946 822718 Mrs Carr **D:** £16.00 **S:** £16.00
Beds: 1F 5D 3T 1S **Baths:** 6 En 2 Sh ⌂ ⊞ (10)
Ⓥ Ⓥ ▥ ⚲

Outrigg House, *St Bees, Cumbria,*
CA27 0AN. Georgian house with unique
character, situated in centre of village.
Open: All year (not Xmas/New Year)
01956 822348 (also fax) Mrs Moffat
D: £17.00–£18.00 **S:** £17.00–£18.00 **Beds:** 1F
1T 1D 1S **Baths:** 1 Sh ⌂ ⊞ (2) ✌ Ⓥ Ⓥ ▥ ⚲

Tomlin Guest House, *1 Tomlin House,*
St Bees, Cumbria, CA27 0EN. Comfortable
Victorian house convenient to beach and St
Bees Head. **Open:** All year (not Xmas)
01946 822284 Mrs Whitehead **Fax:** 01946
824243 *id.whitehead@which.net* **D:** £15.00–
£18.00 **S:** £18.00 **Beds:** 1F 2D 1T **Baths:** 2 En
2 Sh ⌂ ⊞ (2) ✌ Ⓥ ❄ Ⓥ ▥ ⚲

Stanwix
NY3957

No. 1, *1 Etterby Street, Stanwix, Carlisle,*
Cumbria, CA3 9JB. Homely accommodation
in easy reach of Hadrian's Wall & Scotland,
Lakes. **Open:** All year (not Xmas/New Year)
01228 547285 Ms Nixon **D:** £17.00–£20.00
S: £17.00–£20.00 **Beds:** 1D 2S ⌂ (4) ⊞ (1) ✌
Ⓥ ✕ Ⓥ ▥ ⚲

Staveley
SD4698 ⚑ *Eagle & Child, Water Mill, Duke William,*
Railway Hotel

Stock Bridge Farm, *Staveley, Kendal,*
Cumbria, LA8 9LP. Modernised comfortable
C17th farmhouse in picturesque village
close to Lakes. **Open:** Mar to Oct
01539 821580 Mrs Fishwick **D:** £17.00–
£18.00 **S:** £17.00 **Beds:** 1F 4D 1T 1S **Baths:** 1
Sh ⌂ ⊞ (6) Ⓥ ❄ Ⓥ ▥

Sunny Wood, *Kentmere Road, Staveley,*
Kendal, Cumbria, LA8 9JF. Away from the
crowds. Friendly family home overlooking
the Fells. **Open:** All year
01539 821236 **D:** £16.00 **S:** £20.00–£25.00
Beds: 1T 1D **Baths:** 1 Sh ⌂ ⊞ (3) ✌ Ⓥ ❄ Ⓥ
▥ ⚲

Heywood, *Kentmere Road, Staveley,*
Kendal, Cumbria, LA8 9JF. Peaceful spacious
bungalow in hamlet with views of Kentmere
Valley. **Open:** Feb to Nov
01539 821198 **D:** £18.00–£20.00 **S:** £20.00
Beds: 1D **Baths:** 1 En ⊞ (1) ✌ ▥ ⚲

Talkin
NY5457

Hullerbank, *Talkin, Brampton, Cumbria,*
CA8 1LB. **Open:** All year (not Xmas/New
Year) **Grades:** ETC 3 Diamond
016977 46668 (also fax) Mrs Stobbart *info@*
hullerbank.freeserve.co.uk www.smoothhound.
co.uk/hotels/huller.html **D:** £23.50–£24.00
S: £30.00 **Beds:** 2T 1D **Baths:** 2 En 1 Pr ⊞ (6)
✌ Ⓥ ▥ ⚲ cc
Centrally situated for Hadrian's Wall,
Scotland & Lake District. Hullerbank is an
attractive pink washed farmhouse dated
1635-1751. Adjoining the house we have 14
acres of pasture on which we keep pedigree
sheep. 9 miles from Carlisle M6/J43,
motorway, 3 miles from Brampton.

Blacksmith Arms, *Talkin, Brampton, Cumbria, CA8 1LE.* Village inn, restaurant, cask ales. **Open:** All year **Grades:** ETC 3 Diamond
016977 3452 Mrs Jackson **Fax: 016977 3396 D:** £22.00 **S:** £30.00 **Beds:** 2T 3D **Baths:** 2 En ⛺ 🅿 (20) 📺 ✕ 🆅 ▥ ♿ **cc**

Tebay
NY6104

Primrose Cottage, *Orton Road, Tebay, Penrith, Cumbria, CA10 3TL.* Adjacent M6/J38. 4 poster bed, jacuzzi bathroom, suitable for disabled visitors. **Open:** All year **Grades:** ETC 4 Diamond, RAC 4 Diamond
015396 24791 Mrs Jones *info@ primrosecottagecumbria.co.uk* www.primrosecottagecumbria.co.uk **D:** £20.00–£25.00 **S:** £20.00–£30.00 **Beds:** 2D 1T **Baths:** 1 En 2 Pr ⛺ 🅿 (6) 📺 🐾 ✕ 🆅 ▥ ♿

Temple Sowerby
NY6127

Skygarth Farm, *Temple Sowerby, Penrith, Cumbria, CA10 1SS.* **Open:** Easter to Nov
017683 61300 (also fax) Mrs Robinson *enquire@skygarth.co.uk* www.skygarth.co.uk **D:** £17.00 **S:** £17.00 **Beds:** 2F 1S **Baths:** 1 Sh ⛺ 🅿 (4) 📺 ✕ ▥ ♿
Traditional family-run farm, 500 yards from A66. Ideal stopover South-Scotland. A warm welcome assured in C17th farmhouse with spacious comfortable rooms, guest lounge, garden. Enjoy a generous meal, walk by the River Eden. Sleep peacefully, wake to a hearty breakfast.

Thornhill
NY0108

The Old Vicarage Guest House, *Thornhill, Egremont, Cumbria, CA22 2NY.* C19th vicarage of character, within easy reach Fells and Lakes. **Open:** All year (not Xmas)
01946 841577 Mrs Graham **D:** £15.00–£17.00 **S:** £15.00–£17.00 **Beds:** 3F **Baths:** 2 Sh ⛺ 🅿 (6) 📺 🐾 🆅 ▥ ♿

Thornthwaite
NY2225 ⬛ *Swan Inn, Coledale Inn, Royal Oak, Swinside Inn*

Thwaite Howe Hotel, *Thornthwaite, Keswick, Cumbria, CA12 5SA.* Beautiful small country house hotel backing onto Thornthwaite Forest, views over Derwent Valley. **Open:** Mar to Oct
017687 78281 Mr & Mrs Marshall **D:** £28.00–£35.00 **S:** £48.00–£58.00 **Beds:** 5D 3T 1F 1S **Baths:** 8 En ⛺ (12) 🅿 (10) 📺 🐾 ✕ ▥ ♿ **cc**

Ladstock Country House Hotel, *Thornthwaite, Keswick, Cumbria, CA12 5RZ.* Tremendous views to Skiddaw. Excellent food and service. **Open:** All year (not Xmas) **Grades:** ETC 2 Diamond, AA 2 Diamond, RAC 2 Diamond
017687 78210 Fax: 017687 78088 D: £20.00–£40.00 **S:** £30.00–£45.00 **Beds:** 2F 8T 9D 2S **Baths:** 19 En 2 Pr ⛺ 🅿 (60) 📺 ✕ 🆅 ▥ ♿ **cc**

Tirril
NY5026

The Queens Head Inn, *Tirril, Penrith, Cumbria, CA10 2JF.* C1719, once owned by Wordsworth, own brewery, food awards. **Open:** All year (not Xmas)
01768 863219 Fax: 01768 863243 *bookings@ queensheadinn.co.uk* www.queensheadinn.co.uk **D:** £22.50–£25.00 **S:** £30.00–£35.00 **Beds:** 1F 5D 1T **Baths:** 4 En 1 Pr 1 Sh ⛺ 🅿 (40) 📺 ✕ 🆅 ▥ ♿ **cc**

Troutbeck Bridge
NY3900

High View, *Sun Hill Lane, Troutbeck Bridge, Windermere, Cumbria, LA23 1HJ.* Elevated bungalow enjoying panoramic views. Centrally located for all attractions. **Open:** All year **Grades:** ETC 4 Diamond, Silver
015934 44618 Mrs Ramsay **Fax: 015934 42731** *info@accommodationlakedistrict.com* www.accommodationlakedistrict.com **D:** £19.50–£24.00 **S:** £19.50–£24.00 **Beds:** 1F 1D **Baths:** 2 En ⛺ 🅿 ✂ 📺 🆅 ▥ ♿

Troutbeck (Penrith)
NY3826 ⬛ *Troutbeck Hotel, White Horse, Sportsman Inn, Horse & Farrier*

Greenah Crag Farm, *Troutbeck, Penrith, Cumbria, CA11 0SQ.* **Open:** Feb to Nov **Grades:** ETC 4 Diamond
017684 83233 D: £22.50–£27.50 **S:** £28.00–£35.00 **Beds:** 2D 1T **Baths:** 2 En 1 Sh ⛺ 🅿 ✂ 📺 🆅 ▥ ♿
Warm welcome to our old farmhouse. Guests' sitting room with woodburner. Oak-beamed dining room, memorable breakfast. Ideal for exploring Lakes, Eden Valley, Carlisle, Borders. Quiet secluded rural location, only 8 miles from motorway. Keswick 10, Ullswater 6.

Planning a longer stay? Always ask for any special rates

Troutbeck (Windermere)
NY4002 ⬛ *Queen's Head, Mortal Man*

High Fold Farm, *Troutbeck, Windermere, Cumbria, LA23 1PG.* **Open:** All year **Grades:** ETC 4 Star
015394 32200 Fax: 015394 34970 D: £20.00–£27.00 **S:** £25.00–£35.00 **Beds:** 2F 1T 2D **Baths:** 3 En 1 Sh ⛺ 🅿 (6) ✂ 🆅 🐾 🆅 ▥ ♿
Unbeatable views of Troutbeck Valley. Well furnished comfortable accommodation of the highest standards in a tranquil setting. Excellent breakfasts. Ideal centre for walkers, for touring. Located in one of the Lakes' prettiest villages, only 3 miles from Ambleside and Windermere.

Yew Grove, *Troutbeck, Windermere, Cumbria, LA23 1PG.* Comfortable C18th stone house, beautiful village, valley and mountain views. **Open:** All year (not Xmas)
015394 33304 Mr Pratt **D:** £20.00–£24.00 **S:** £22.00–£23.00 **Beds:** 1F 1D 1T 1S **Baths:** 1 En 1 Pr 1 Sh ⛺ 🅿 (3) ✂ 🆅 🆅 ▥ ♿

Ulpha
SD1993

Oak Bank, *Ulpha, Duddon Valley, Broughton in Furness, Cumbria, LA20 6DZ.* Victorian house in peaceful valley, relax indoors or ramble. **Open:** All year (not Xmas) **Grades:** ETC 2 Diamond
01229 716393 Mrs Batten www.duddonvalley.co.uk **D:** £20.00 **S:** £22.00 **Beds:** 2D 1T **Baths:** 3 Sh ⛺ 🅿 (8) 📺 🐾 ♿

Ulverston
SD2878 ⬛ *New Inn, Black Dog, Rose & Crown*

Sefton House, *Queen Street, Ulverston, Cumbria, LA12 7AF.* Georgian town house in the busy market town of Ulverston. **Open:** All year (not Xmas)
01229 582190 Mrs Glaister **Fax: 01229 581773** *romo@seftonhouse.co.uk* **D:** £20.00–£22.50 **S:** £27.50–£30.00 **Beds:** 1F 1D 1S 1T **Baths:** 4 En ⛺ 🅿 (15) 📺 ▥ ♿ **cc**

Church Walk House, *Church Walk, Ulverston, Cumbria, LA12 7EW.* Tastefully decorated Georgian house in town centre. Comfortable and relaxing. **Open:** All year (not Xmas/New Year) **Grades:** ETC 4 Diamond
01229 582211 M Chadderton *churchwalk@ mchadderton.freeserve.co.uk* **D:** £20.00–£26.00 **S:** £20.00–£26.00 **Beds:** 1T 2D **Baths:** 2 En 1 Pr ⛺ ✂ 📺 🐾 🆅 ▥ ♿

Under Loughrigg
NY3404

Foxghyll, *Lake Road, Under Loughrigg, Ambleside, Cumbria, LA22 9LL.* Large country house. 2 acre garden, 4 poster bed, spa bath. **Open:** All year
015394 33292 Mrs Mann *foxghyll@hotmail.com* **D:** £23.50–£27.00 **S:** £23.50–£27.00 **Beds:** 1D 2T **Baths:** 3 En ⛺ (5) 🅿 (7) 📺 🐾 🆅 ▥ ♿

Underbarrow

SD4692

Tranthwaite Hall, *Underbarrow, Kendal, Cumbria, LA8 8HG.* Tranthwaite Hall is something special dating back to C11th. Excellent accommodation. **Open:** All year
015395 68285 Mrs Swindlehurst
tranthwaitehall@hotmail.com
www.tranthwaitehall.freeserve.co.uk
D: £22.00–£25.00 **S:** £25.00–£30.00 **Beds:** 1F 1D 1T **Baths:** 2 En ⌂ 🖪 (4) ⚡ 🖻 🖽 ▥ ▴

Underskiddaw

NY2328

Long Close Farm, *Underskiddaw, Keswick, Cumbria, CA12 4QD.* Period farmhouse enjoying exceptional views over mountains and Bassenthwaite Lake.
Open: All year
017687 72851 (also fax) Mrs Evers
longclosefarm@bushinternet.com **D:** £17.00–£25.00 **S:** £20.00–£25.00 **Beds:** 1D 2T **Baths:** 1 En 1 Sh 🖪 🖻 🖽 ▥ ▴

Walton

NY5264 🍺 *The Centurion*

Town Head Farm, *Walton, Brampton, Cumbria, CA8 2DJ.* Cosy 200 year old farmhouse with panoramic views. Near Hadrian's Wall. **Open:** All year (not Xmas/New Year)
016977 2730 Ms Armstrong **D:** £16.00–£17.00 **S:** £17.00–£18.00 **Beds:** 1T 1D **Baths:** 1 Sh ⌂ 🖪 ⚡ 🖻 🖽 ▴

High Rigg Farm, *Walton, Brampton, Cumbria, CA8 2AZ.* Listed beautiful Georgian farmhouse with breathtaking views of Pennines & Lake District. **Open:** All year (not Xmas)
016977 2117 Mrs Mounsey **D:** £16.00–£18.00 **S:** £18.00 **Beds:** 2F **Baths:** 1 Pr 1 Sh ⌂ 🖪 (4) ⚡ 🖻 ✕ 🖽 ▥ ▴

Warwick Bridge

NY4756

Brookside B&B, *Warwick Bridge, Carlisle, Cumbria, CA4 8RE.* Delightful sandstone Listed building. Original miller's house, homely atmosphere, comfortable beds. **Open:** All year (not Xmas)
01228 560250 D Wearing *brookside@contactme.co.uk* **D:** £17.00–£20.00 **S:** £20.00–£24.00 **Beds:** 2D 1T **Baths:** 1 En 1 Sh ⌂ 🖪 (3) 🖻 ✕ 🖽 ▴

Wasdale Head

NY1808

Burnthwaite Farm, *Wasdale Head, Seascale, Cumbria, CA20 1EX.* Perfectly situated for walkers and climbers, peaceful valley, farmhouse breakfast. **Open:** All year
019467 26242 Mrs Buchanan **D:** £25.00–£27.50 **S:** £27.50–£30.00 **Beds:** 2F 4D 1S **Baths:** 2 En 2 Sh ⌂ 🖪 (12) ✕ 🖽 ▴

Watendlath

NY2716

Fold Head Farm, *Watendlath, Keswick, Cumbria, CA12 5UN.* Comfortable friendly accommodation on working farm in beautiful unspoiled valley. **Open:** Mar to Nov
017687 77255 Mrs Richardson **D:** £17.00–£18.00 **S:** £17.00–£18.00 **Beds:** 1F 2D **Baths:** 1 Sh ⌂ 🖪 🖻 🖽 ✕ 🖽 ▴

Watermillock

NY4422 🍺 *Herdwick Inn, Brackenrigg Inn, Horse & Farrier, Queen's Head, The Sun*

Gowbarrow Lodge, *Watermillock on Ullswater, Penrith, Cumbria, CA11 0JP.*
Open: All year
017684 86286 D: £27.50 **S:** £35.00 **Beds:** 2F 2T 8D **Baths:** 8 En ⌂ 🖪 🖻 🖽 ▴ cc
Gowbarrow Lodge offers superior ensuite rooms with lake/fell views over Lake Ullswater. Excellent full English breakfast for £27.50 pppn and £35 ppnsr. Comfortable lounge & bar for relaxing. Ideally situated 7 miles from M6 junction 40, for walking, lake amenities & good local eating places.

Mellfell House Farm, *Watermillock, Penrith, Cumbria, CA11 0LS.* **Open:** All year (not Xmas)
017684 86295 (also fax) Mrs Goddard
www.mellfell.co.uk **D:** £13.50–£17.50 **S:** £13.50–£20.00 **Beds:** 1F 1D 1T **Baths:** 2 Sh ⌂ 🖪 (6) ⚡ 🖻 ✕ 🖻 🖽 ▴
Beautiful old farmhouse high above Ullswater, log fires, relaxed atmosphere.

Planning a longer stay? Always ask for any special rates

Land End Country Lodge, *Watermillock, Ullswater, Penrith, Cumbria, CA11 0NB.* **Open:** All year **Grades:** ETC 3 Diamond
017684 86438 Miss Holmes **Fax:** **017684 86959** *infolandends@btinternet.com*
www.landends.btinternet.co.uk **D:** £26.00–£30.00 **S:** £30.00–£32.00 **Beds:** 4D 2T 2S **Baths:** 8 En ⌂ 🖪 (15) 🖻 🖽 ▥ ▵ ▴
Tastefully restored traditional farmhouse with pretty courtyard in 25 acres with 2 lakes, lovely trees and lots of wildlife, including red squirrels. Quality rooms, cosy lounge and honesty bar make this a perfect place to relax. Ullswater's dramatic scenery 1 mile.

Westlinton

NY3964

Lynebank, *Westlinton, Carlisle, Cumbria, CA6 6AA.* Family-run, excellent food, ideal stop for England/Scotland journey.
Open: All year
01228 792820 (also fax) Mrs Butler *info@lynebank.co.uk www.lynebank.co.uk*
D: £18.00–£22.00 **S:** £20.00–£24.00 **Beds:** 2F 3D 1T 3S **Baths:** 9 En ⌂ 🖪 (15) 🖻 ✕ 🖽 ▥ ▴ cc

Westnewton

NY1344 🍺 *Swan Inn*

The Swan Inn, *Westnewton, Carlisle, Cumbria, CA7 3PQ.* Traditional C18th country inn. Picturesque village location. Exposed beams in some bedrooms. **Open:** All year
016973 20627 J Hitchen **Fax:** **016973 20036**
D: £18.00–£20.00 **S:** £18.00–£20.00 **Beds:** 1F 3T **Baths:** 2 En 1 Sh ⌂ 🖪 (7) 🖻 ✕ 🖽 ▥ 🖽 ▴

Windermere

SD4198 🍺 *Hole in the Wall, Lamplighter Bar, Queens Hotel, Grey Walls Hotel, Greys Inn*

Heatherbank, *13 Birch Street, Windermere, Cumbria, LA23 1EG.*
Open: All year (not Xmas) **Grades:** ETC 3 Diamond
015394 46503 (also fax) Mrs Houghton
heatherbank@btinternet.com **D:** £19.00–£27.00 **S:** £20.00–£30.00 **Beds:** 3D 2T **Baths:** 5 En 🖪 (4) ⚡ 🖻 🖽 ▥ 🖽 ▴ cc
Heatherbank is a quiet, comfortable, non-smoking, Lakeland stone guest house. Situated in the centre of Windermere village, it is within 5 mins walk of the rail/bus station. Heatherbank is noted for its superb English breakfast.

BATHROOMS
En = Ensuite
Pr = Private
Sh = Shared

Eastbourne Guest House, Biskey
Howe Road, Windermere, Cumbria, LA23 2JR.
Open: Feb to Dec **Grades:** ETC 4 Diamond
015394 43525 (also fax) Mr Whitfield *mail@*
eastbourne-guesthouse.co.uk
www.eastbourne-guesthouse.co.uk
D: £22.00–£35.00 **S:** £26.00–£35.00 **Beds:** 1F
1T 5D 1S **Baths:** 7 En 1 Pr ⏍ (5) ▣ (6) ⌿ ▥ ▣
▦ ♨ **cc**
Our traditional Lakeland guest house is
situated below the Biskey Howe Viewpoint
in a quiet, central location. Our aim is to
offer you high quality well-furnished
ensuite accommodation with excellent
value for money. Joyce and John will
ensure a warm, friendly welcome into a
relaxed and cosy atmosphere.

Braemount House, Sunny Bank Road,
Windermere, Cumbria, LA23 2EN. **Open:** All
year (not Xmas) **Grades:** ETC 4 Diamond
015394 45967 (also fax) *braemount.house@*
virgin.net freespace.virgin.net/braemount.
house **D:** £23.00–£30.00 **S:** £23.00–£30.00
Beds: 3F 5D 1T **Baths:** 9 En ⏍ (9) ⌿ ▥ ▯
▥ ▦ ♨ **cc**
Our guest book reads 'immaculate
accommodation and lots of extras not
normally available', 'excellent, especially
breakfast in bed', 'great once again',
'wonderful', 'lovely room, brilliant
hospitality, yummy breakfast', 'we will be
back', and many more. Why not come and
read it?

**Beckmead
House,** 5 Park
Avenue,
Windermere,
Cumbria,
LA23 2AR.
Open: All year
Grades: ETC 3 Diamond
015394 42757 (also fax) *beckmead_house@*
yahoo.com www.dot-t.co.uk/beckmead
D: £16.00–£24.00 **S:** £16.00–£24.00 **Beds:** 1F
1T 2D 1S **Baths:** 2 En 1 Pr 1 Sh ⏍ ▣ ▥ ▦ ♨
cc
A warm, friendly welcome awaits you in our
traditional stone-built Victorian house.
Tastefully decorated & furnished to a high
standard. Delicious, hearty breakfasts.
Ideally situated for enjoying the many
attractions of the Lake District, i.e. boating,
walking, golf, historic houses, restaurants
etc.

Ivy Bank,
Holly Road,
Windermere,
Cumbria,
LA23 2AF.
Open: All year
(not Xmas/New
Year)
Grades: ETC 4 Diamond
015394 42601 Mr Clothier *ivybank@clara.co.uk*
www.ivybank.clara.co.uk **D:** £18.00–£25.00
Beds: 1F 1T 3D **Baths:** 5 En ⏍ ▣ (6) ⌿ ▥ ▥
▦ ♨ **cc**
Pretty Victorian stone-built home in quiet
location close to village centre and station.
Attractively decorated and comfortably
furnished. Substantial choice for breakfast.
Beautiful viewpoints within 30 minutes
walk. Private car park, storage for cycles.
Free use of local leisure club.

The Queens Cottage, Queens Hotel,
Victoria Street, Windermere, Cumbria,
LA23 1AB. **Open:** All year
015394 43713 **Fax:** 015394 44261 **D:** £17.00–
£28.00 **S:** £20.00–£27.00 **Beds:** 1T 4D
Baths: 5 En ⏍ ▣ ⌿ ▥ ✕ ▥ ▦ ♨ **cc**
Windermere, a beautiful area, is an ideal
base for exploring nearby lake and fells and
all the Lake District. The Queens Cottage
and traditional pub - the Queens Hotel -
with private parking are in the centre, close
to buses and trains.

**Holly Lodge
Guest House,**
6 College Road,
Windermere,
Cumbria,
LA23 1BX. Family-
run centrally
situated traditional Lakeland guest house.
Good English breakfasts. **Open:** All year
(not Xmas) **Grades:** ETC 3 Diamond, AA 3
Diamond
015394 43873 (also fax) Tim & Alison Doyle
doyle@hollylodge20.fsnet.co.uk
www.hollylodge20.fsnet.co.uk **D:** £19.00–
£27.00 **S:** £19.00–£27.00 **Beds:** 2F 5D 3T 1S
Baths: 6 En 2 Bath ⏍ ▣ (7) ▥ ✝ ▦ ♨

Fir Trees, Lake
Road,
Windermere,
Cumbria,
LA23 2EQ.
Perfectly
situated midway
between
Windermere and the Lake. Scrumptious
breakfasts. **Open:** All year **Grades:** ETC 4
Diamond, AA 4 Diamond
015394 42272 **Fax:** 015394 42512 *enquiries@*
fir-trees.com www.fir-trees.com **D:** £20.00–
£34.00 **S:** £30.00–£45.00 **Beds:** 2F 1T 5D
Baths: 7 En 1 Pr ⏍ ▣ (8) ⌿ ▥ ▥ ▦ ♨ **cc**

Meadfoot,
New Road,
Windermere,
Cumbria,
LA23 2LA.
Detached
house, large
garden, patio and summerhouse. Warm
welcome assured. **Open:** Jan to Dec
Grades: ETC 3 Diamond
015394 42610 T Shaw **Fax:** 015394 45280
enquiries@meadfoot-guesthouse.co.uk
www.meadfoot-guesthouse.co.uk **D:** £17.50–
£27.00 **S:** £22.50–£27.00 **Beds:** 1F 4D 1T 1S
Baths: 7 En ⏍ ▣ (7) ⌿ ▥ ✝ ▥ ▦ ♿ ♨

**Beckside
Cottage,** 4
Park Road,
Windermere,
Cumbria,
LA23 2AW.
Comfortable
B&B with full
ensuite bedrooms in Windermere village.
Open: All year **Grades:** ETC 3 Diamond
015394 42069 Mr & Mrs Lowe **D:** £16.00–
£22.00 **S:** £17.00–£23.00 **Beds:** 1F 2D 1S
Baths: 4 En ⏍ (6) ▣ (3) ▥ ▥ ▦ ✳ ♨

High View,
Sun Hill Lane,
Troutbeck
Bridge,
Windermere,
Cumbria,
LA23 1HJ.
Elevated bungalow enjoying panoramic
views. Centrally located for all attractions.
Open: All year **Grades:** ETC 4 Diamond,
Silver
015934 44618 Mrs Ramsay **Fax:** 015394
42731 *info@accommodationlakedistrict.com*
www.accommodationlakedistrict.com
D: £19.50–£24.00 **S:** £19.50–£24.00 **Beds:** 1F
1D **Baths:** 2 En ⏍ ▣ ⌿ ▥ ▥ ▦ ♨

F irgarth, Ambleside Road, Windermere,
Cumbria, LA23 1EU. Comfortable Victorian
country house, fine views, opposite riding
stables. **Open:** All year **Grades:** ETC 3
Diamond, AA 3 Diamond
015394 46974 Mr & Mrs Lucking **Fax:** 015394
42384 **D:** £18.00–£24.50 **S:** £19.00–£26.50
Beds: 1F 3D 3T 1S **Baths:** 8 Pr ⏍ ▣ (9) ▥ ✝
▥ ▦ ♨ **cc**

Ashleigh Guest House, 11 College Road, Windermere, Cumbria, LA23 1BU. Comfortable Victorian guest house situated in the village of Windermere. **Open:** All year **Grades:** ETC 4 Diamond
015394 42292 Mr & Mrs Smith *ashleighhouse@ windermere44.fsnet.co.uk* **D:** £19.00–£21.00 **S:** £23.00–£25.00 **Beds:** 2F 2D 1S **Baths:** 5 En ॐ ⊬ ⊡ ⊻ ▥ ⚓

Applegarth Hotel, College Road, Windermere, LA23 1BU. Victorian hotel of character. Excellent location, friendly bar, warm welcome. **Open:** All year **Grades:** ETC 3 Diamond
015394 43206 Mr & Mrs Hydes **Fax: 015394 46636** *enquiries@applegarthhotel.com* www.applegarthhotel.com **D:** £20.00–£40.00 **S:** £22.00–£40.00 **Beds:** 4F 3T 10D 3S **Baths:** 18 En ॐ ⊡ ⊡ ⊁ ⋈ × ⊡ ▥ ⚓ cc

Annisgarth House, 2 Annisgarth, Bowness-on-Windermere, Windermere, Cumbria, LA23 2HF. Views of lake and mountains. Private parking. Quiet location. **Open:** Mar to Dec
015394 48049 (also fax) Mrs Erwig **D:** £16.00–£22.00 **S:** £21.00–£27.00 **Beds:** 1T 1D **Baths:** 1 En 1 Sh ॐ ⊡ (3) ⊡ ⋈ ▥ ⚓

Linthwaite House, Crook Road, Windermere, Cumbria, LA23 3EZ. Sublime hilltop setting. Beautiful gardens overlooking Lake Windermere. Delicious food. **Open:** All year **Grades:** ETC 3 Star
015394 44680 *riseholme215@aol.com* **D:** £45.00–£125.00 **S:** £90.00–£115.00 **Beds:** 1F 4T 12D 1S **Baths:** 12 En

The Archway, 13 College Road, Windermere, Cumbria, LA23 1BU. Comfortable Victorian guest house, choice of breakfasts, good touring base. **Open:** All year **Grades:** ETC 4 Diamond
015394 45613 Fax: 015394 45328 *archway@ btinternet.com* www.communiken. com/archway **D:** £20.00–£30.00 **S:** £30.00–£45.00 **Beds:** 2T 2D **Baths:** 4 En ॐ (10) ⊬ ⊡ × ⊻ ▥ ⚓

Laurel Cottage, Park Road, Windermere, Cumbria, LA23 2BJ. A superb place to stay to tour this beautiful corner of England. **Open:** All year (not Xmas/New Year) **015394 43053** W Taylor **D:** £22.00–£26.00 **S:** £22.00–£28.00 **Beds:** 1F 2T 2D 1S ॐ ⊬ ⊡ ⋈ ⊻ ▥ ⚓

Beech Hill Hotel, Newby Bridge Road, Windermere, LA23 3LR. Perfect lakeside setting ideal for business or leisure. Fantastic food. **Open:** All year **015394 42137** J Santanera **Fax: 015394 43745** *beechhill@richardsonshotels.co.uk* www.richardsonshotels.co.uk **D:** £45.00– £100.00 **S:** £45.00–£100.00 **Beds:** 2F 12T 38D 6S **Baths:** 58 En ॐ ⊡ (80) ⊬ ⊡ ⋈ × ⊡ ▥ ⚓ cc

Osborne Guest House, 3 High Street, Windermere, Cumbria, LA23 1AF. Family-run guest house. Central Windermere. Excellent food, warm welcome. **Open:** All year
015394 46452 J Every *jennyevery@aol.com* **D:** £18.00–£28.00 **S:** £20.00–£28.00 **Beds:** 2F 2D **Baths:** 3 En 1 Sh ॐ ⊬ ⊡ ⋈ ⊻ ▥ ⚓

Westbury House, 27 Broad Street, Windermere, Cumbria, LA23 2AB. Victorian house, centre of Windermere. Near lake, shops, trains. Lovely food. **Open:** All year **015394 46839 & 015394 44575** Mrs Baker **Fax: 015394 42784** *westhouse@commundo.net* **D:** £14.00–£23.00 **S:** £16.00–£30.00 **Beds:** 2F 3D 1T **Baths:** 4 En 1 Sh ॐ (2) ⊡ (5) ⊡ ⊻ ▥ ⚓ cc

Kenilworth Guest House, Holly Road, Windermere, Cumbria, LA23 2AF. Comfortable Victorian house, two minutes centre Windermere. Convenient centre for exploring Lakeland's beautiful scenery. **Open:** All year
015394 44004 Mr Roberts **Fax: 015394 46554** **D:** £16.00 **S:** £16.00 **Beds:** 1F 2T 2D 1S **Baths:** 3 En 3 Sh ॐ ⊡ (3) ⊬ ⊡ ⋈ ⊻ ▥ ⚓ ⚓

Villa Lodge, Cross Street, Windermere, Cumbria, LA23 1AE. Extremely comfortable traditional accommodation in peaceful area overlooking Windermere village. **Open:** All year
015394 43318 (also fax) Mr Rooney *rooneym@btconnect.com* www.villa-lodge.co.uk **D:** £22.00–£35.00 **S:** £22.00–£30.00 **Beds:** 5D 1T 2S **Baths:** 8 En ॐ ⊡ (8) ⊬ ⊡ ⋈ × ⊡ ▥ ⚓ ⚓ cc

Winton

NY7811   ⚘ Bay Horse

South View Farm, Winton, Kirkby Stephen, Cumbria, CA17 4HS. Lovely farmhouse situated in quiet village, easy access to the Lakes and Dales. **Open:** All year
017683 71120 & 07801 432184 (M) Mrs Marston *southviewwinton@hotmail.com* **D:** £15.00 **S:** £15.00 **Beds:** 1F 1D 1S ॐ ⊡ (2) ⊡ ⋈ × ⊻ ⚓

Witherslack

SD4384

Fernhill Vegetarian Country House, Witherslack, Grange Over Sands, Cumbria, LA11 6RX. Idyllic country house and garden. Excellent organic vegetarian food. **Open:** All year
01359 552237 *alibramall@lineone.net* **D:** £30.00–£35.00 **S:** £30.00–£45.00 **Beds:** 2D 1S **Baths:** 1 En 1 Pr 1 Sh ⊡ (10) ⊬ ⋈ × ⊻ ▥ ⚓

Workington

NX9927

Fernleigh House, 15 High Seaton, Workington, Cumbria, CA14 1PE. Georgian house, lovely garden, warm and friendly welcome, excellent breakfasts. **Open:** All year
01900 605811 Ms Bewsher **D:** £17.00–£45.00 **S:** £17.00 **Beds:** 1F 2T 1S ॐ ⊡ ⊡ ⊻ ▥ ⚓ ⚓

Derbyshire

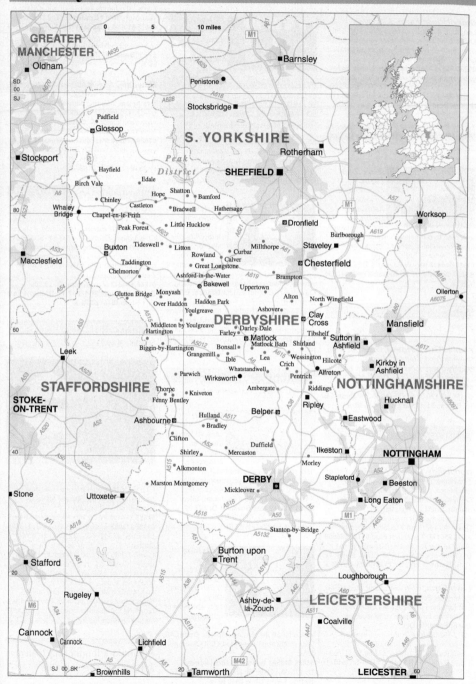

Alkmonton

SK1838

Dairy House Farm, *Alkmonton, Longford, Ashbourne, Derbyshire, DE6 3DG.* Old farmhouse: comfortable rooms, guests' own lounges & dining room. Lovely walled garden. **Open:** All year **01335 330359 (also fax)** Mrs Harris *andy@ dairyhousefarm.force9.co.uk* www.digitalpages. co.uk/dairyhousefarm **D:** £25.00 **S:** £23.00–£25.00 **Beds:** 1T 4S **Baths:** 4 En 1 Pr 🛏 (16) 🄿 (8) 🏊 🍽 ✕ 🔟 ▦ ♨

Alsop en le Dale

SK1655

Dove Top Farm, *Coldeaton, Alsop en le Dale, Ashbourne, Derbyshire, DE6 1QR.* Friendly welcome to our peaceful working farm. Ideal for walking, cycling & trekking. **Open:** Easter to Sept **01335 310472** Mrs Wainwright **D:** £18.00 **S:** £20.00 **Beds:** 1F 1D **Baths:** 2 En 🛏 🄿 🔟 ✕ 🔟 ▦ ♨

Alton

SK3664

Fernlea Guest House, *Cedar Hill, Alton, Stoke-on-Trent, Staffs, ST10 4BH.* Stone country guest house 5 mins Alton Towers. Families most welcome. **Open:** Mar to Nov **01538 702327 (also fax)** Mrs Nother **D:** £16.50–£20.00 **S:** £25.00–£30.00 **Beds:** 2F 1D **Baths:** 3 En 🛏 🄿 (3) 🔟 🍽 ▦ ♨

Ambergate

SK3451 🍺 *Bull's Head, Hurt Arms*

Woodlands, *Sawmills, Ambergate, Belper, Derbyshire, DE56 2JQ.* Comfortable old farmhouse, centrally situated for touring Derbyshire. One mile from Ambergate Station. Guest lounge, fishing. Smallholding with interesting garden. **Open:** All year (not Xmas/New Year) **01773 856178** D & G Hirst **Fax:** 01773 836559 *dhirst316@aol.com* www.woodlands.cjb.net **D:** £16.00–£24.00 **S:** £19.00–£27.00 **Beds:** 1F 1T 1D **Baths:** 1 En 1 Sh 🛏 🄿 (6) 🔟 ✕ 🔟 ▦ ♨

Lawn Farm, *Whitewells Lane, Holly Lane, Ambergate, Belper, Derbyshire, DE56 2DN.* Comfortable farmhouse accommodation on working farm; quiet rural location. **Open:** Easter to Oct **01773 852352** Mrs Oulton *carol.oulton@ farming.co.uk* members.farmline. com/jhoulton **D:** £17.50–£22.50 **S:** £20.00–£30.00 **Beds:** 1F 1D **Baths:** 1 En 1 Sh 🛏 🄿 (4) 🏊 🔟 ♨

Ashbourne

SK1846 🍺 *Royal Oak, Cock Inn*

Compton House, *27-31 Compton, Ashbourne, Derbyshire, DE6 1BX.* **Open:** All year

Grades: AA 3 Diamond **01335 343100** Mrs Maher **Fax: 01335 348100 D:** £19.00–£23.00 **S:** £20.00–£25.00 **Beds:** 1F 3D 1T **Baths:** 4 En 🛏 🄿 (6) 🔟 🍽 ✕ 🔟 ♨ Originally three terraced cottages now converted into one rather individual home, offering good food and quality accommodation with a warm and friendly atmosphere. A delightful garden for you to enjoy a relaxing hour. Parking within an enclosed rear garden.

Hurtswood, *Sandybrook, Ashbourne, Derbyshire, DE6 2AQ.* Comfortable rooms, excellent breakfasts, superb views, extensive off-road parking. **Open:** All year (not Xmas) **Grades:** ETC 3 Diamond **01335 342031** Mrs Hadley & Mrs S Loveridge **Fax: 01335 347467** *gl.hurtswood@virgin.net* www.hurtswood.co.uk **D:** £23.50 **S:** £27.50–£30.00 **Beds:** 1T 4D 1S **Baths:** 6 En 🄿 🏊 🔟 🔟 ▦ ♨

Ashford-in-the-Water

SK1969 🍺 *Bull's Head, Ashford Arms*

Chy-An-Dour, *Vicarage Lane, Ashford-in-the-Water, Bakewell, Derbyshire, DE45 1QL.* Quality accommodation. Quiet position overlooking picturesque village. Friendly welcome. **Open:** All year (not Xmas) **Grades:** ETC 4 Diamond, Silver **01629 813162** Mrs Rowland **D:** £23.00–£27.00 **S:** £30.00–£35.00 **Beds:** 3D 1T **Baths:** 4 En 🄿 (4) 🏊 🔟 ▦

Gritstone House, *Greaves Lane, Ashford-in-the-Water, Bakewell, Derbyshire, DE45 1QH.* Host of attractive features to welcome all discerning tourists. **Open:** All year (not Xmas) **Grades:** ETC 4 Diamond, Silver **01629 813563 (also fax)** Mrs Lindsay **D:** £20.00–£25.00 **S:** £30.00 **Beds:** 2D 1T **Baths:** 1 En 1 Sh 🏊 🔟 🔟 ▦ ♨

Woodland View, *John Bank Lane, Ashford-in-the-Water, Bakewell, Derbyshire, DE45 1PY.* Renovated farmhouse set in 4 acres. 10 minutes walk to village. **Open:** All year (not Xmas) **Grades:** ETC 3 Diamond **01629 813008 (also fax)** Neil Ellis *woodview@ neilellis.free-online.co.uk* www.woodlandviewbandb.co.uk **D:** £18.00–£22.00 **Beds:** 2D **Baths:** 1 En 1 Pr 🄿 (4) 🔟 🍽 ▦,

Rowdale, *Ashford-in-the-Water, Bakewell, Derbyshire, DE45 1NX.* C17th Listed farmhouse, friendly, comfortable, large gardens, generous breakfasts. www.rowdale.co.uk **Open:** All year (not New Year) **Grades:** RAC 3 Diamond, Silver **01629 640260** Mrs Mills *info@rowdale.co.uk* www.rowdale.co.uk **D:** £20.00–£25.00 **S:** £25.00–£27.50 **Beds:** 3D 2T **Baths:** 3 En 2 Pr 🛏 🄿 (20) 🔟 🍽 🔟 ▦ ♨

Ashover

SK3463

Old School Farm, *Uppertown, Ashover, Chesterfield, Derbyshire, S45 0JF.* Spacious, comfortable, working farm, home from home, peaceful and friendly. **Open:** Easter to Oct **Grades:** ETC 4 Diamond, RAC 4 Diamond, Sparkling **01246 590813** Mrs Wooton **D:** £22.00 **S:** £22.00 **Beds:** 2F 1D 1T 1S **Baths:** 3 En 1 Pr 1 Sh 🛏 🄿 (6) 🔟 ▦ ♨

Bakewell

SK2168 🍺 *Aitch's*

Croft Cottages, *Coombs Road, Bakewell, Derbyshire, DE45 1AQ.* **Open:** All year **Grades:** AA 4 Diamond **01629 814101** Pat & Des Weatherley **Fax: 01629 815083** *croftco@btinternet.com* **D:** £23.00–£30.00 **S:** £25.00–£35.00 **Beds:** 1F 2D 1T **Baths:** 3 En 1 Pr 🛏 (4) 🔟 🍽 🔟 ▦ ♨ Lovely C17th cottage, peaceful riverside location; town centre pubs, restaurants and shops two minute stroll. Excellently equipped accommodation, including luxurious private suite, for special occasions or just to unwind. Guests return regularly for splendid breakfasts, comfort and relaxation. Try us!

Planning a longer stay? Always ask for any special rates

BATHROOMS

En = Ensuite
Pr = Private
Sh = Shared

Bene-Dorme, *The Avenue, Bakewell, Derbyshire, DE45 1EQ.* A friendly welcome in our traditional built house in quiet cul-de-sac. **Open:** All year (not Xmas)
01629 813192 & 07712 490703 (M) Mrs Twigg
Fax: 01629 814208 *judithtwigg@callnetuk.com*
www.benedorme.co.uk **D:** £22.00–£25.00
S: £33.00 **Beds:** 2D 1T **Baths:** 3 En 🖪 (4) ⠟ 🖾
🖭 ⬛, ♨

Loughrigg, *Burton Close Drive, Bakewell, Derbyshire, DE45 1BG.* Extensive landscaped gardens, magnificent views, splendid walking, peaceful. Breakfast menu.
Open: All year (not Xmas) **Grades:** ETC 4 Diamond, Silver
01629 813173 Mrs Morris *john@ bakewell55.freeserve.co.uk* **D:** £24.00–£26.00 **S:** £25.00–£30.00 **Beds:** 2D **Baths:** 1 En 1 Pr ⠵ (10)
🖪 (2) ⠟ 🐾 🖭 ⬛, ♨ ⬥

Wye Close, *5 Granby Croft, Bakewell, Derbyshire, DE45 1ET.* Edwardian house in a quiet location in the centre of Bakewell.
Open: All year (not Xmas/New Year)
Grades: ETC 3 Diamond
01629 813702 (also fax) Ms Wilson
h.wilson@talk21.com www.h.wilson.care4free.
net **D:** £19.00 **S:** £20.00 **Beds:** 1T 1D
Baths: 1 Sh 🖪 (3) ⠟ 🖾 🖭 ⬛, ♨

1 Coach House Mews, *Bagshaw Hill, Bakewell, Derbyshire, DE45 1DL.* Quiet courtyard location - near town centre. Lovely views. Excellent breakfasts.
Open: All year (not Xmas/New Year)
01629 814847 (also fax) Mrs Northin
northin@onetel.uk **D:** £23.00–£25.00 **S:** £30.00–£35.00 **Beds:** 1T **Baths:** 1 Pr 🖪 (1) ⠟ 🖾 🖭 ⬛, ♨

Easthorpe, *Buxton Road, Bakewell, Derbyshire, DE45 1DA.* A Gothic-style family home, ideal for walkers. Near Chatsworth.
Open: All year (not Xmas)
01629 814929 M Peters **D:** £20.00–£24.00
S: £28.00–£32.00 **Beds:** 1F 1T 1D **Baths:** 3 En ⠵ 🖪 (2) ⠟ 🖾 🐾 ⬛, ♨

BEDROOMS

D = Double
T = Twin
S = Single
F = Family

Bamford

SK2083 🍺 *Angler's Rest, Marquis of Granby, Yorkshire Bridge, Derwent Arms, Rising Sun*

Pioneer House, *Station Road, Bamford, Hope Valley, Derbyshire, S33 0BN.* **Open:** All year **Grades:** ETC 4 Diamond
01433 650638 Mrs Treacher *pioneerhouse@ yahoo.co.uk* www.pioneerhouse.co.uk
🖪 (3) ⠟ 🖾 🖭 ⬛, ♨ **Beds:** 2D 1T **Baths:** 3 En
Relax in the friendly atmosphere of our comfortable, lovingly restored home. Our beautifully decorated and spacious ensuite bedrooms have colour television and hospitality tray. Located between Hathersage, Hope and Castleton we are surrounded by breathtaking scenery, stately homes and heritage sites.

Barlborough

SK4777

Stone Croft, *15 Church Street, Barlborough, Chesterfield, Derbyshire, S43 4ER.* A Grade II house built in 1670. Full of charm. **Open:** All year
01246 810974 Mrs Widdowson **D:** £16.00–£18.00 **S:** £18.00–£20.00 **Beds:** 1F **Baths:** 1 En ⠵ 🖪 (6) ⠟ 🖾 🐾 ✕ 🖭 ⬛, ♨

Barrow-upon-Trent

SK2763 🍺 *Bowling Green*

Red House Carriage Museum, *Old Road, Darley Dale, Matlock, Derbyshire, DE4 2ER.* Quiet, relaxing location. Ideal base for all country pursuits. **Open:** All year
01629 733583 Mrs Dale **D:** £20.00–£27.50
S: £25.00–£35.00 **Beds:** 1F 1T 1D 1S
Baths: 2 En 1 Sh 🖪 (4) ⠟ 🖾 ⬛, ♨

RATES

D = Price range per person sharing in a double or twin room
S = Price range for a single room

Belper

SK3547

Chevin Green Farm, *Chevin Road, Belper, Derbyshire, DE56 2UN.*
Open: All year (not Xmas)

Grades: AA 4 Diamond
01773 822328 Mr Postles *spostles@ globalnet.co.uk* www.chevingreenfarm.co.uk
D: £20.00–£23.00 **S:** £23.00–£26.00 **Beds:** 1F 3D 2T **Baths:** 6 En ⠵ 🖪 (10) ⠟ 🖾 🖭 ⬛, ♨ cc
Farmhouse set in 38 acres, in picturesque hillside scenery (the Chevin) looking across Derwent Valley. Ensuite rooms, guests' own lounge and dining room, generous breakfasts, peace and tranquillity. Central for all Derbyshire and its attractions.

Biggin-by-Hartington

SK1559

Biggin Hall, *Biggin-by-Hartington, Buxton, Derbyshire, SK17 0DH.*
Open: All year

Grades: ETC 2 Star
01298 84451 Mr Moffett **Fax: 01298 84681**
bigginhall@compuserve.com www.bigginhall.co.uk **D:** £30.00–£62.00 **S:** £55.00–£90.00
Beds: 10T 9D **Baths:** 19 En ⠵ (11) 🖪 🖾 🐾 ✕ 🖭 ⬛, ✽ ♨ cc
C17th Grade II* listed hall sympathetically restored, keeping fine old character while giving house room to contemporary comforts and antiques, log fires, fresh home cooking. Beautiful unclouded walks from the grounds. Traffic free cycling trails. Close Chatsworth, Haddon Hall etc.

Birch Vale

SK0186

Spinney Cottage B&B, *Spinner Bottom, Birch Vale, High Peak, SK22 1BL.* Tastefully furnished country home, excellent walking & biking area, 1 mile Hayfield. **Open:** All year (not Xmas)
Grades: ETC 4 Diamond
01663 743230 🖪 **D:** £20.00–£22.00 **S:** £20.00–£25.00 **Beds:** 1D 1T 1S **Baths:** 2 En 1 Pr ⠵ ⠟ 🖾 ⬛, ♨

Bonsall

SK2758

Town Head Farmhouse, *70 High Street, Bonsall, Matlock, Derbyshire, DE4 2AR.* Converted friendly C18th farmhouse set in peaceful pretty village. **Open:** All year
01629 823762 Mrs Cordin *townhead70@ hotmail.com* **D:** £20.00–£22.00 **S:** £24.00–£30.00 **Beds:** 3D 2T **Baths:** 5 En ⠵ 🖪 (6) 🖾 ⬛, ♨

Bradley

SK2246

Yeldersley Old Hall Farm, *Yeldersley Lane, Bradley, Ashbourne, Derbyshire, DE6 1PH.* Relax and unwind in peaceful surroundings at our Grade II Listed farmhouse. **Open:** Easter to Nov **01335 344504 (also fax)** Mrs Hinds *janethindsfarm@yahoo.co.uk* **D:** £20.00–£25.00 **S:** £25.00–£26.00 **Beds:** 2D 1T **Baths:** 2 En 1 Pr ⓟ (7) ⊬ 🖵 🞀 🟃

Bradwell

SK1781

Stoney Ridge, *Granby Road, Bradwell, Hope Valley, S33 9HU.* **Open:** All year **Grades:** ETC 4 Diamond, Silver, AA 4 Diamond **01433 620538** Mrs Plant **Fax: 01433 623154** *toneyridge@aol.com* www.cressbrook.co. uk/hopev/stoneyridge **D:** £28.00 **S:** £31.00 **Beds:** 3D 1T **Baths:** 3 En 1 Pr ⟆ (10) ⓟ (4) 🖵 🞀 🖵 🞀, ✻ 🟃 cc
Our large split-level bungalow overlooks The Peakland Village of Bradwell with overviews of Hope Valley. Our heated indoor pool is available to guests teatime and before breakfast.

Ashbrook, *Brookside, Bradwell, Hope Valley, S33 9HF.* Idyllic peaceful location lovely gardens with fish pond, stunning views. **Open:** All year (not Xmas) **01433 620803** J Maskrey **D:** £19.00–£25.00 **S:** £20.00–£25.00 **Beds:** 2D 1T **Baths:** 2 Sh ⟆ ⓟ (2) ⊬ 🖵 🖵 🞀 🟃

Brampton

SK3670

Brampton Guest House, *75 Old Road, Brampton, Chesterfield, Derbyshire, S40 2QU.* Victorian house in quiet cul-de-sac close to Chatsworth. **Open:** All year **01246 276533** Mr Thompson **Fax: 01246 211636** *guesthouse@ oldroadbrampton.freeserve.co.uk* www.ztour. com/top/brampton.guesthouse.htm **D:** £14.00–£16.00 **S:** £14.00–£18.50 **Beds:** 2F 1D 1S **Baths:** 3 Pr 1 Sh ⟆ ⓟ (4) 🖵 🖵 🞀

BATHROOMS

En = Ensuite
Pr = Private
Sh = Shared

Buxton

SK0573 🍺 *King's Head, Three Horseshoes, Ramsey's Bar*

Grosvenor House Hotel, *1 Broad Walk, Buxton, Derbyshire, SK17 6JE.* **Open:** All year **Grades:** ETC 4 Diamond, AA 4 Diamond **01298 72439 (also fax)** Mr & Mrs Fairbairn **D:** £25.00–£37.50 **S:** £45.00–£50.00 **Beds:** 2F 5D 1T **Baths:** 8 En ⟆ (8) ⊬ 🖵 🖵 🞀 🟃
Idyllically set in the heart of historic spa town, overlooking Pavilion Gardens/Opera house. Bedrooms ensuite, non-smoking, hearty full English breakfast. Ideal centre for exploring Peak District & Derbyshire Dales. Within easy walking distance of numerous pubs & restaurants. Which? Recommended.

Harefield, *15 Marlborough Road, Buxton, Derbyshire, SK17 6RD.* **Open:** All year (not Xmas/New Year) **Grades:** ETC 4 Diamond, Silver **01298 24029 (also fax)** *hardie@ harefield1.freeserve.co.uk* www.harefield1. freeserve.co.uk **D:** £23.00–£25.00 **S:** £23.00–£25.00 **Beds:** 2T 3D 1S **Baths:** 5 En 1 Pr ⓟ (8) ⊬ 🖵 ✕ 🖵 🞀 🟃
Elegant Victorian property set on its own grounds overlooking Buxton. Quiet location just a few minutes walk from the historic town centre. An ideal base for exploring the beautiful Peak District. Friendly atmosphere, delicious food and lovely gardens to enjoy.

Templeton Guest House, *Compton Road, Buxton, Derbyshire, SK17 9DN.* Family-run licensed guest house superbly situated for exploring Peak District. **Open:** All year **01298 25275** G Spicer **D:** £18.50–£20.00 **S:** £21.50–£24.00 **Beds:** 2D 1T **Baths:** 3 En ⟆ ⓟ (6) 🖵 ✕ 🖵 🞀 🟃

Buxton Wheelhouse Hotel, *19 College Road, Buxton, Derbyshire, SK17 9DZ.* Elegant Victorian establishment. Refurbished spacious bedrooms. Central. Warm welcome, excellent value. **Open:** All year (not Xmas) **01298 24869 (also fax)** Ms Thompson Price *lyndsie@buxton-wheelhouse.com* www.buxton-wheelhouse.com **D:** £22.00–£27.00 **S:** £27.00–£35.00 **Beds:** 3F 3D 2T 1S **Baths:** 9 En ⓟ (10) ⊬ 🖵 🖵 🞀 cc

---

Nithen Cottage, *123 Park Road, Buxton, Derbyshire, SK17 6SP.* Beautiful Victorian house. Luxurious accommodation. Wonderful breakfasts. Close town centre. **Open:** All year (not Xmas/New Year) **Grades:** ETC 4 Diamond, Silver Award **01298 24679 D:** £23.00–£25.00 **S:** £33.00–£35.00 **Beds:** 2D **Baths:** 1 En 1 Pr ⊬ 🖵 🖵 🞀

The Old Manse Private Hotel, *6 Clifton Road, Silverlands, Buxton, Derbyshire, SK17 6QL.* Quietly situated Victorian hotel. Delicious food. Warm welcome. Friendly atmosphere **Open:** All year **Grades:** AA 3 Diamond **01298 25638 (also fax)** P A Cotton *old_manse@yahoo.co.uk* www.oldmanse.co.uk **D:** £18.00–£25.00 **S:** £18.00–£25.00 **Beds:** 2F 4D 1S **Baths:** 7 En 2 Sh ⟆ ⓟ (3) 🖵 🞀 ✕ 🖵 🞀 ✻ 🟃 cc

Abbey Guest House, *43 South Avenue, Buxton, Derbyshire, SK17 6NQ.* In the centre of Buxton. Small and friendly, great value. **Open:** All year **01298 26419** *aghbuxton@aol.com* **D:** £15.00 **S:** £15.00 **Beds:** 1F 1T **Baths:** 1 Sh ⟆ ⓟ (1) 🖵 🞀 ✕ 🖵 🞀 🟃

Hilldeen, *97 Dale Road, Buxton, Derbyshire, SK17 6PD.* Family-run business, established 15 yrs. Pavilion, gardens, Opera House 10 mins walk. **Open:** All year (not Xmas/New Year) **01298 23015** Mrs Taylor **D:** £19.00 **S:** £20.00–£22.00 **Beds:** 1F 1T 1D 1S **Baths:** 5 En ⟆ ⓟ 🖵 🞀 🖵 🟃

The Victorian Guest House, *3a Broad Walk, Buxton, Derbyshire, SK17 6JE.* Unique quiet elegant home, refurbished 1999, overlooking Pavilion Gardens/Opera House. **Open:** All year **01298 78759** Mrs Whiston **Fax: 01298 74732** *buxvic@x-stream.co.uk* **D:** £25.00–£32.50 **S:** £35.00 **Beds:** 2F 5D 2T **Baths:** 9 En ⟆ ⓟ (10) ⊬ 🖵 🖵 🞀 🟃

Fairhaven, *1 Dale Terrace, Buxton, Derbyshire, SK17 6LU.* Victorian premises in historical Buxton, surrounded by picturesque Peak District. **Open:** All year **01298 24481 (also fax)** *paulandcatherine@ fairhavenguesthouse.freeserve.co.uk* www.fairhavenbedandbreakfast.com **D:** £17.00–£19.00 **S:** £19.00–£23.00 **Beds:** 1F 2T 2D 1S **Baths:** 1 Pr 2 Sh ⟆ ⊬ 🖵 🖵 🞀 cc

Compton House Guest House, *4 Compton Road, Buxton, Derbyshire, SK17 9DN.* Warm & friendly atmosphere. Comfortable rooms, good food, excellent value. **Open:** All year **01298 26926 (also fax)** Mr Hesp **D:** £16.00–£20.00 **S:** £20.00–£30.00 **Beds:** 2F 2D 1T 1S **Baths:** 4 En 1 Sh ⟆ 🖵 ✕ 🖵 🖵 🞀 🟃

Ford Side House, *125 Lightwood Road, Buxton, Derbyshire, SK17 6RW.* Peaceful elegant Edwardian house for non-smokers. Premier residential area. **Open:** Easter to Oct
01298 72842 Mr & Mrs Roberts **D:** £19.00–£20.00 **S:** £25.00–£30.00 **Beds:** 3D 1T **Baths:** 3 En ⌂ (10) ▯ (3) ⚊ ▥ ⊁ ▣ ▥ ⚊

Calver

SK2374

Hydrangea Cottage, *Hall Fold, Main Street, Calver, Hope Valley, S32 3XL.* Luxurious accommodation, beautiful garden and views. Quiet location near Chatsworth.
Open: All year (not Xmas)
01433 630760 Mrs Hall **D:** £25.00 **S:** £50.00 **Beds:** 1D **Baths:** 1 Pr ▯ (1) ⚊ ▥ ▣ ▥ ⚊

Castleton

SK1582 ⚑ *George Hotel, Castle Hotel, Peak Hotel, Cheshire Cheese, Nag's Head, Poachers' Arms*

Hillside House, *Pindale Road, Castleton, Hope Valley, S33 8WU.* Peaceful location, panoramic views, hearty breakfasts. Clean, spacious family house. **Open:** All year (not Xmas) **Grades:** ETC 4 Diamond
01433 620312 (also fax) Mrs Webster **D:** £22.50–£24.00 **Beds:** 2D **Baths:** 2 En ▯ (3) ⚊ ▥ ▣ ▥ ⚊

Willow Croft, *Pindale Road, Castleton, Hope Valley, Derbyshire, S33 8WU.* Perfectly situated for exploring the area. Warm welcome, wonderful views. **Open:** All year (not Xmas/New Year)
01433 620400 D: £22.50–£25.00 **S:** £25.00–£30.00 **Beds:** 2D **Baths:** 2 En ⌂ ▯ (6) ⚊ ▥ ▣ ▥ ⚊

Bray Cottage, *Market Place, Castleton, Hope Valley, S33 8WQ.* Charming C18th cottage, excellent accommodation, hearty breakfast, very friendly atmosphere.
Open: All year (not Xmas)
01433 621532 Mrs Heard **D:** £21.00 **S:** £23.00 **Beds:** 2D **Baths:** 1 En 1 Pr ⌂ ▯ (1) ⚊ ▥ ⊁ ▥ ▣ ⚊

Bargate Cottage, *Market Place, Castleton, Hope Valley, Derbyshire, S33 8WQ.* Comfortable C17th cottage overlooking picturesque village green. Warm welcome.
Open: All year (not Xmas)
01433 620201 F Saxon **Fax: 01433 621739 D:** £21.50–£23.50 **S:** £37.00 **Beds:** 1T 2D **Baths:** 3 En ⌂ (12) ▯ (5) ⚊ ▥ ▣ ▥ ⚊

Cryer House, *Castleton, Hope Valley, S33 8WG.* C17th rectory with cottage garden & views of church and castle. **Open:** All year (not Xmas)
01433 620244 Mrs Skelton *FleeSkel@aol.com* **D:** £21.00–£23.50 **S:** £30.00 **Beds:** 1F 1D **Baths:** 1 En 1 Pr ⌂ ▥ ⊁ ▣ ▥ ⚊

Chapel-en-le-Frith

SK0680 ⚑ *Wanted Inn, New Inn, Roebuck, King's Arms, Devonshire Arms, Lamb Inn, Jolly Carter, Rose & Crown, Hanging Gate, Crown & Mitre*

Slack Hall Farm, *Castleton Road, Chapel-en-le-Frith, High Peak, SK23 6QS.* C17th farmhouse on family-run working farm, comfortable friendly accommodation. **Open:** All year (not Xmas/New Year) **Grades:** ETC 3 Diamond
01298 812845 (also fax) Mrs Hayward **D:** £19.00–£20.00 **Beds:** 1F 1D **Baths:** 2 En ⌂ ▯ (2) ⚊ ▥ ▥ ⚊

Potting Shed, *Bank Hall, Chapel-en-le-Frith, High Peak, Derbyshire, SK23 9UB.* Breakfast in plant lovers' conservatory, gorgeous views, oak beams, antique furniture. **Open:** All year (not Xmas/New Year)
01298 812656 & 0161 338 8134 Mr Ashton **D:** £22.50–£25.00 **S:** £35.00–£40.00 **Beds:** 2D **Baths:** 2 En ▯ (3) ⚊ ▥ ▥ ⚊

Chelmorton

SK1169

Ditch House, *Chelmorton, Buxton, Derbyshire, SK17 9SG.* Cottage with superb views. Close to Buxton, Bakewell and Chatsworth.
Open: All year **Grades:** ETC 4 Diamond
01298 85719 (also fax) Ms Simmonds **D:** £20.00–£30.00 **S:** £25.00–£30.00 **Beds:** 1T 1D **Baths:** 2 En ▯ (4) ⚊ ▥ ▣ ▥ ✳ ⚊

Chesterfield

SK3871

Buckinghams Hotel, *85-87 Newbold Road, Newbold, Chesterfield, Derbyshire, S41 7PU.* A pair of Victorian houses which have been sympathetically converted.
Open: All year
01246 201041 Fax: 01246 550059 *info@ buckinghams-table.com* buckingham-table.com **D:** £60.00–£75.00 **S:** £40.00–£50.00 **Beds:** 2S 2F 4T 2D **Baths:** 10 En ⌂ ▯ (5) ▥ × ▥ ▣ ⚊ cc

Planning a longer stay? Always ask for any special rates

Locksley, *21 Tennyson Avenue, Chesterfield, Derbyshire, S40 4SN.* Comfortable friendly atmosphere; pleasant location near town centre. **Open:** All year (not Xmas)
01246 273332 Mrs Parker **D:** £15.00 **S:** £17.00 **Beds:** 1D 1T/S **Baths:** 1 Sh

Anis Louise Guest House, *34 Clarence Road, Chesterfield, Derbyshire, S40 1LN.* Town centre location. Convenient for local cafes, restaurants and amenities. **Open:** All year
01246 235412 Mr Connell *neil@ anislouise.co.uk* www.anislouise.co.uk **D:** £18.00–£19.50 **S:** £21.00 **Beds:** 1F 2D 1T 1S **Baths:** 5 En ⌂ (8) ▯ (5) ⚊ ▥ ▣ ⚊

Abbeydale Hotel, *Cross Street, Chesterfield, Derbyshire, S40 4TD.* Comfortable, friendly, Victorian town hotel, quiet location. Clean, bright, well-appointed. **Open:** All year
01246 277849 Mrs Harper **Fax: 01246 558223** *elaine@abbey66.freeserve.co.uk* **D:** £25.00–£30.00 **S:** £39.00–£43.00 **Beds:** 1F 5D 1T 4S **Baths:** 11 En ⌂ (1) ▯ (14) ▥ ⊁ × ▥ ▣ ⚊ &3 ⚊ cc

Chinley

SK0482

Craigside, *4 Buxton Road, Chinley, High Peak, SK23 6DJ.* Warm welcome, small, clean, comfortable. Good walking and cycling location. **Open:** All year (not Xmas)
01663 750604 Mrs Cameron **D:** £16.00–£20.00 **S:** £16.00–£20.00 **Beds:** 1D 1T 1S **Baths:** 1 Sh ⌂ ▯ (2) ▥ ⊁ ▣ ▥ ⚊

Clay Cross

SK3963

Ashview Lodge, *171 High Street, Clay Cross, Chesterfiled, Derbyshire, S45 9DZ.* Overlooking beautiful country views. Many attractions for town and country. **Open:** All year
01246 860992 Mrs Morley **D:** £15.00–£17.50 **S:** £15.00–£17.50 **Beds:** 4T 1D 2S **Baths:** 2 Sh ⌂ (5) ▯ (7) ▥ × ▥ ⚊

Clifton

SK1644 ⚑ *Royal Oak, Cock Inn*

Stone Cottage, *Green Lane, Clifton, Ashbourne, Derbyshire, DE6 1BX.* A charming cottage, perfectly situated, Peak District, Derbyshire Dales, Alton Towers. **Open:** All year (not Xmas/New Year)
01335 343377 Mrs Whittle **Fax: 01335 347117** *awhittle@tinyonline.co.uk* **D:** £20.00–£30.00 **S:** £25.00–£35.00 **Beds:** 1F 1T 3D ⌂ ▯ ⚊ ▥ × ▥ ▣ ⚊ cc

Crich

SK3554   🍺 *Derwent Hotel*

Clovelly Guest House, *Roe's Lane,
Crich, Matlock, Derbyshire, DE4 5DH.* Friendly
family home near to Tramway Museum and
local attractions. **Open:** All year
01773 852295 & 07932 694025 (M) Mrs Lester
D: £18.00 **S:** £14.00 **Beds:** 1D 1S ⛌ 🄿 (3) 📺
🐾✕ 🆅 🛢 ⚘ 🖢

Curbar

SK2574

Bridgend,
*Dukes Drive,
Curbar, Calver,
Hope Valley,
S32 3YP.* Quiet
bungalow near
village shops
and pub, 3 miles from Chatsworth.
Open: All year
01433 630226 Mrs Hunt *HUNT@
g3fwb.freeserve.co.uk* **D:** £18.00–£20.00
S: £20.00–£25.00 **Beds:** 1D 1T **Baths:** 1 Sh
⛌ 🄿 ⚥ 🐾 🐾 🆅 🛢 ⚘ 🖢

Derby

SK3535

**Hill House
Hotel,** *294
Burton Road,
Derby, DE23 6AD.*
Newly
refurbished 10
bedroom hotel
near city centre,
exceptional
value. **Open:** All
year (not Xmas/
New Year)
01332 361523
(also fax) Ms Fearn *enquiries@
hillhousehotel.co.uk* www.hillhousehotel.co.uk
D: £17.50–£20.00 **S:** £20.00–£25.00 **Beds:** 1F
2D 3T 4S **Baths:** 5 Pr 1 Sh 🄿 (10) 📺 🐾 🆅 🛢 🖢

Dronfield

SK3578

Cassita, *off Snape Hill Lane, Dronfield,
Derbyshire, S18 2GL.* Quietly situated
bungalow. Annexed accommodation.
Central for Derbyshire or Sheffield. Friendly
welcome. **Open:** All year (not Xmas/New
Year)
01246 417303 (also fax) D: £18.50 **S:** £22.00
Beds: 1T **Baths:** 1 En 🄿 (1) ⚥ 🆅 🛢 🖢

Duffield

SK3443

The Kings Head Inn, *1 Town Street,
Duffield, Belper, Derbyshire, DE56 4EH.* A very
old Derbyshire inn set in a local village.
Open: All year
01332 841370 Mr Staley **D:** £25.00 **S:** £25.00
Beds: 1F 1D **Baths:** 2 En ⛌ 🄿 ⚥ 🐾 🖢

Edale

SK1285   🍺 *Hope Inn, Cheshire Cheese, Rambler
Country House Hotel*

Brookfield, *Edale, Hope Valley, S33 7ZL.*
Peaceful, high-quality accommodation,
outstanding views, ideal walking and
touring base. **Open:** Easter to Oct
Grades: ETC 3 Diamond
01433 670227 Mrs Chapman **D:** £18.00
S: £20.00 **Beds:** 1D 1T **Baths:** 1 Sh 🄿 (3) ⚥
📺 🆅 🛢 🖢

Mam Tor House, *Grindsbrook, Edale,
Hope Valley, Derbyshire, S33 7ZA.* Edwardian
family home, 2 minutes from start of
Pennine Way. **Open:** All year
01433 670253 Mrs Jackson **D:** £17.50–£20.00
S: £17.50–£20.00 **Beds:** 1F 2T ⛌ 🄿 (4) 📺 🐾✕
🆅 🛢 ♿ 🖢

Stonecroft, *Grindsbrook, Edale, Hope
Valley, S33 7ZA.* Luxury country house
accommodation in spectacular situation
amongst Derbyshire Hills. **Open:** All year
(not Xmas)
01433 670262 (also fax) Mrs Reid
www.cressbrook.co.uk/edale/stonecroft
D: £26.00–£29.00 **S:** £36.00–£39.00 **Beds:** 2D
Baths: 1 En 1 Pr ⛌ (12) 🄿 (2) ⚥ ✕ 🆅 🛢 🖢
cc

Farley

SK2961

Robertswood, *Farley Hill, Matlock,
Derbyshire, DE4 3LL.* Handsome Victorian
family home, set in own grounds,
spectacular views across Derwent Valley.
Open: All year **Grades:** ETC 5 Diamond,
Silver
01629 55642 (also fax) Mr & Mrs Andrew
robertswood@supanet.com www.robertswood.
com **D:** £25.00–£30.00 **S:** £36.00–£42.00
Beds: 6D 2T **Baths:** 8 En ⛌ (10) 🄿 (8) ⚥ 📺 ✕
🆅 🛢 ⚘ 🖢 cc

Fenny Bentley

SK1750

Cairn Grove, *Ashes Lane, Fenny Bentley,
Ashbourne, Derbyshire, DE6 1LD.* Spacious
limestone house in 1 acre grove.
Convenient for Buxton, Chatsworth,
Haddon, White Peak. **Open:** All year
01335 350538 Mrs Wheeldon *keith.wheeldon@
virgin.net* **D:** £18.00–£25.00 **S:** £22.00–£27.00
Beds: 1T 2D **Baths:** 2 En 1 Pr ⛌ 🄿 (6) ⚥ 🐾
🆅 🛢 🖢

RATES

D = Price range per person
sharing in a double or twin
room

S = Price range for a single
room

Glossop

SK0492   🍺 *The Bull, Grouse, Lantern Pike, Royal
Oak*

Rock Farm, *Monks Road, Glossop,
Derbyshire, SK13 6JZ.* Secluded Peak District
farmhouse. Panoramic views. Good
walking. Excellent service. **Open:** All year
(not Xmas/New Year) **Grades:** AA 4
Diamond
01457 861086 Ms Child *pfc@
rockfarm99.freeserve.co.uk* www.rockfarm99.
freeserve.co.uk **D:** £19.00 **S:** £22.00 **Beds:** 1F
1D **Baths:** 1 Sh 🄿 (3) ⚥ 📺 🐾 🆅 🛢 🖢

Kings Clough Head Farm, *Monks
Road, Glossop, Derbyshire, SK13 6ED.* Stone
farmhouse. Panoramic views. Comfortable
accommodation. Half hour Buxton,
Manchester. **Open:** All year (not Xmas)
Grades: ETC 2 Diamond
01457 862668 Mrs Keegan **D:** £18.00
S: £18.00 **Beds:** 1T 1D 1S **Baths:** 1 Sh ⛌
🄿 (4) 📺 🐾 🛢 🖢

Glutton Bridge

SK0866

Dowall Hall Farm, *Glutton Bridge,
Buxton, Derbyshire, SK17 0RW.* A warm
welcome awaits you at our C17th
farmhouse, in our secluded valley.
Open: All year (not Xmas/New Year)
01298 83297 Mrs Etches **D:** £16.00–£20.00
S: £17.00–£20.00 **Beds:** 1F 1D **Baths:** 1 En 1
Pr ⛌ 🄿 ⚥ 📺 ✕ 🆅 🛢 🖢

Grangemill

SK2457

**Avondale
Farm,**
*Grangemill,
Matlock,
Derbyshire,
DE4 4HT.* Quality
B&B in tastefully
converted barn. Ground floor level. Close
Chatsworth. **Open:** All year (not Xmas/New
Year) **Grades:** ETC 4 Diamond, Silver
01629 650820 Mrs Wragg *avondale@
tinyworld.co.uk* **D:** £23.00–£26.00 **S:** £36.00
Beds: 1T **Baths:** 1 En 🄿 (1) ⚥ 📺 🆅 🛢 🖢

Great Longstone

SK2071   🍺 *Crispin Inn*

Willow Croft, *Station Road, Great
Longstone, Bakewell, Derbyshire, DE45 1TS.*
First class accommodation, award-winning
village, warm welcome, choice of
breakfasts. **Open:** Jan to Dec
01629 640576 (also fax) Mrs McGovern
www.willowcroft.com@bushinternet.com
D: £20.00–£25.00 **S:** £20.00–£27.50 **Beds:** 1F
1T 1D **Baths:** 3 En ⛌ (0) 🄿 (4) ⚥ 📺 🐾 🆅 🛢 🖢
♿ 🖢

Fieldsview, *Station Road, Great Longstone, Bakewell, Derbyshire, DE45 1TS.* Spacious house. Ideal location for walking and touring. Close Chatsworth. **Open:** All year (not Xmas/New Year) **Grades:** ETC 4 Diamond
01629 640593 Mrs Coase **Fax:** 0870 0568861 *mikes@ga-memik.demon.co.uk* **D:** £19.00–£20.00 **S:** £25.00–£30.00 **Beds:** 1T 2D **Baths:** 1 Sh ▣ (4) ⌿ ⊤⋁ ✕ ▦ ♨

Haddon Park

SK2367

Haddon Park Farm, *Bakewell, Derbyshire, DE45ND.* Farmhouse two miles Bakewell, close to Chatsworth and Haddon Hall. **Open:** All year
01629 814854 Mrs Cooper **D:** £20.00–£22.00 **S:** £25.00 **Beds:** 1D 1T **Baths:** 1 Pr 1 Sh ▣ (2) ⌿ ⊤⋁ ♨

Hartington

SK1260 ⚓ *Bull's Head, George Hotel, Waterloo Inn.*

Bank Top Farm, *Hartington, Buxton, Derbyshire, SK17 0AD.* Welcome farmhouse stay. Explore rural Derbyshire by walking, cycling from our door **Open:** All year
01298 84859 J Pilkington **Fax:** 01298 84205 *owenjane@farming.co.uk* **D:** £21.00–£30.00 **S:** £24.00–£30.00 ▧ ▣ ⌿ ⊤⋁ ⊢ ✕ ⋁ ▦ ✻ ♨

Wolfscote Grange Farm, *Hartington, Buxton, Derbyshire, SK17 0AX.* Wolfscote farmhouse, steeped in history, nestles on edge of Dove Valley. **Open:** All year (not Xmas)
01298 84342 (also fax) Mrs Gibbs *wolfscote@ btinternet.com* www.peakdistrictfarmhols.co. uk **D:** £25.00 **Beds:** 1F 1D 1T **Baths:** 2 En 1 Pr ▧ ▣ ⊤⋁ ✕ ▦ ♨

Bank House, *Hartington, Buxton, Derbyshire, SK17 0AL.* Central village location, excellent walking, cycling. Near many attractions, 15 miles Alton Towers. **Open:** All year (not Xmas)
01298 84465 Mrs Harrison **D:** £18.00–£25.00 **S:** £20.00–£25.00 **Beds:** 1F 2D 1T 1S **Baths:** 3 En 2 Sh ▧ ▣ (2) ⊤⋁ ✕ ▦ ♨

Hathersage

SK2381 ⚓ *The Plough, Barrel, Scotsman's Pack, Sir William*

Polly's B&B, *Moorview Cottage, Cannonfields, Jaggers Lane, Hathersage, Hope Valley, S32 1AG.* Warm, friendly, first-class accommodation in quiet location, very imaginative breakfast menu. **Open:** All year
01433 650110 P Fisher **D:** £19.00–£23.00 **S:** £25.00–£28.00 **Beds:** 2D 1T **Baths:** 3 En ▧ (4) ▣ (3) ⌿ ⊤⋁ ⊢ ⋁ ▦ ✻ ♨

Planning a longer stay? Always ask for any special rates

Cannon Croft, *Cannonfields, Hathersage, Hope Valley, Derbyshire, S32 1AG.* **Open:** All year
Grades: ETC 4 Diamond Gold
01433 650005 (also fax) Mrs Oates *soates@ cannoncroft.fsbusiness.co.uk* www.cannoncroft. fsbusiness.co.uk **D:** £22.00–£25.00 **S:** £30.00–£42.00 **Beds:** 2T 2D **Baths:** 4 En ▧ (12) ▣ (5) ⌿ ⊤⋁ ⋁ ▦ ♨
Enjoy panoramic views from the conservatory. Famous for our welcome, decor and varied menu (try our sundancer eggs, whiskey porridge etc). Flower arrangers' garden. Excellent choice of local dining within 10 mins' walk. Visit Chatsworth, walk, climb cycle, enjoy.

Hillfoot Farm, *Castleton Road, Hathersage, Hope Valley, Derbyshire, S32 1EG.* Originally C16th inn and toll house on the old Jaggers Pack Horse route. **Open:** All year **Grades:** ETC 4 Diamond
01433 651673 Mrs Wilcockson *lorna@ wilcockson0.fsnet.co.uk* www.hillfootfarm.com **D:** £20.00–£25.00 **S:** £25.00–£50.00 **Beds:** 2D 2T **Baths:** 4 En ▣ (10) ⌿ ⊤⋁ ▦ ✻ ♨

Moorgate, *Castleton Road, Hathersage, Hope Valley, S32 1EH.* Fringe of Hathersage in Peak National Park - touring, walking, climbing. **Open:** All year **Grades:** ETC 3 Diamond
01433 650293 Mrs Veevers **D:** £16.00 **S:** £19.00 **Beds:** 1D 1T 1S **Baths:** 1 Sh ▧ ▣ (3) ⌿ ⊤⋁ ▦ ♨

Hayfield

SK0386 ⚓ *Pack Horse, Royal Hotel, Sportsman, Lantern Pike*

Spinney Cottage B&B, *Spinner Bottom, Birch Vale, High Peak, SK22 1BL.* Tastefully furnished country home, excellent walking & biking area, 1 mile Hayfield. **Open:** All year (not Xmas) **Grades:** ETC 4 Diamond
01663 743230 **D:** £20.00–£22.00 **S:** £20.00–£25.00 **Beds:** 1D 1T 1S **Baths:** 2 En 1 Pr ▧ ⌿ ⊤⋁ ▦ ♨

Pool Cottage, *Park Hall, Hayfield, High Peak, SK22 2NN.* Unusual Victorian greenhouse. Converted house, secluded. South facing woodland setting. **Open:** May to Dec
01663 742463 Mr Dean **D:** £20.00–£22.00 **Beds:** 1F 1T 1S **Baths:** 2 En 1 Pr ▧ ▣ ⌿ ⊤⋁ ⊢ ▦ ♨

Hilcote

SK4457

Hillcote Hall, *Hilcote Lane, Hilcote, Alfreton, Derbyshire, DE55 5HR.* Listed country house with easy access to M1 and Derbyshire. **Open:** Mar to Nov
01773 812608 Mrs Doncaster **D:** £18.00 **S:** £20.00 **Beds:** 1F 1D ▧ ▣ (4) ⌿ ⊤⋁ ⋁ ♨

Hope

SK1683 ⚓ *The Poachers, Cheshire Cheese, Woodroffe Arms*

Underleigh House, *Edale Road, Hope, Hope Valley, S33 6RF.* A stunning, tranquil setting in the heart of magnificent walking country. **Open:** All year (not Xmas/New Year) **Grades:** ETC 4 Diamond, Silver
01433 621372 Mrs Taylor **Fax:** 01433 621 324 *underleigh.house@btinternet.com* www.underleigh.house.co.uk **D:** £30.00–£33.00 **S:** £33.00–£46.00 **Beds:** 4D 2T **Baths:** 6 En ▧ (12) ▣ (6) ⌿ ⊤⋁ ▦ ♨ **cc**

The Woodroffe Arms Hotel, *1 Castleton Road, Hope, Hope Valley, Derbyshire, S33 6SB.* Situated in Hope in heart of the Peak District. Open fire. **Open:** All year
01433 620351 Mr Thompson **Fax:** 01433 623465 *tanya.thomson@online.net* www.woodroffearms.co.uk **D:** £27.00–£29.50 **S:** £35.00–£39.00 **Beds:** 1T 2D **Baths:** 3 En ▧ ▣ (20) ⌿ ⊤⋁ ✕ ⋁ ▦ ♨ ✻ **cc**

Round Meadow Barn, *Parsons Lane, Hope , Hope Valley, Derbyshire, S33 6RA.* Converted barn, magnificent views all round. Ideal walking, hang-gliding, rock-climbing, mountain-biking. **Open:** All year
01433 621347 Mrs Taylor **D:** £20.00–£23.00 **S:** £25.00–£28.00 **Beds:** 1F 1T **Baths:** 2 Sh ▧ ▣ (12) ⌿ ⊤⋁ ⊢ ⋁ ♨

Hulland

SK2446 ⚓ *Black Horse, Railway, Crosskeys*

Hulland Nurseries, *The Green, Hulland, Ashbourne, Derbyshire, DE6 3EP.* Grade II Listed farmhouse close to Carsington Water, children welcome. **Open:** All year (not Xmas/New Year) **Grades:** ETC 3 Diamond
01335 370052 J V Barr **D:** £22.50–£30.00 **S:** £20.00–£30.00 **Beds:** 2F 1D **Baths:** 2 En 1 Pr ▧ (0) ▣ (6) ⌿ ⊤⋁ ✕ ⋁ ▦ ♨

RATES

D = Price range per person sharing in a double or twin room
S = Price range for a single room

Kniveton

SK2050   🍴 *The Ketch, Red Lion*

New House Farm, *Longrose Lane, Kniveton, Ashbourne, Derbyshire, DE6 1JL.* Working organic farm. Many local attractions. 'Peak Practice' country. Also camping, caravans, self-catering. **Open:** All year
01335 342429 Mrs Smail **D:** £11.50–£20.00 **S:** £13.50–£30.00 **Beds:** 2F 1T 1D ⛱(0) 🅿(10) ⛺ 🅃 🏍 🆅 🕮 🛡

Lea

SK3257

The Coach House, *Lea, Matlock, Derbyshire, DE4 5GJ.* Converted farm buildings, central location for walking and touring Derbyshire. **Open:** All year
01629 534346 (also fax) Mr & Mrs Hobson *alanandbarbara@coachhouselea.co.uk* www.coachhouselea.co.uk **D:** £18.50–£27.50 **S:** £22.50–£30.00 **Beds:** 2T 1D **Baths:** 1 En 1 Sh ⛱ 🅿 🅃 🏍 ✕ 🆅 🛡 cc

Little Hucklow

SK1678

Ye Olde Bull's Head, *Little Hucklow, Tideswell, Buxton, Derbyshire, SK17 8RT.* Unspoilt C12th inn with cosy log fires and panoramic views. **Open:** All year
01298 871097 (also fax) Mr Denton *accom@ yeoldebullshead.freeserve.co.uk* www.yeoldebullshead.freeserve.co.uk **D:** £25.00–£30.00 **S:** £30.00–£60.00 **Beds:** 2D **Baths:** 2 En ⛱ 🅿 ⛺ 🅃 ✕ 🆅 🕮 🔥 ❀ 🛡 cc

Litton

SK1675

Beacon House, *Litton, Buxton, Derbyshire, SK17 8QP.* Farm smallholding overlooking Tansley Dale. Quietly situated, walks from the door. **Open:** Feb to Nov
01298 871752 Mrs Parsons **D:** £19.00–£21.00 **Beds:** 2D **Baths:** 2 En 🅿(4) ⛺ 🅃 🏍 🆅 🕮 🛡

Marston Montgomery

SK1337

Waldley Manor, *Marston Montgomery, Doveridge, Ashbourne, Derbyshire, DE6 5LR.* Relax in this C16th manor farmhouse. Quiet location, access to commuter roads. **Open:** All year (not Xmas/New Year)
01889 590287 Ms Whitfield **D:** £20.00–£25.00 **S:** £20.00–£25.00 **Beds:** 1F 1D **Baths:** 2 En ⛱ 🅿 🅃 🆅 🕮 🛡

Planning a longer stay? Always ask for any special rates

Matlock

SK3060   🍴 *Boat House, Crown, Grouse, Royal Oak*

Roberts-wood, *Farley Hill, Matlock, Derbyshire, DE43LL.* **Open:** All year
Grades: ETC 5 Diamond, Silver
01629 55642
(also fax) Mr & Mrs Andrew *robertswood@ supanet.com* www.robertswood.com **D:** £25.00–£30.00 **S:** £36.00–£42.00 **Beds:** 6D 2T **Baths:** 8 En ⛱(10) 🅿(8) ⛺ ✕ 🆅 🕮 ❀ 🛡 cc
A handsome Victorian family home. Its friendly young owners offer their guests a tranquil, relaxed atmosphere, with traditional values. Set in its own grounds, it commands spectacular views across the Derwent Valley. Perfectly located for the Great Houses and attractions.

Bank House, *12 Snitterton Road, Matlock, Derbyshire, DE4 3LZ.* Beamed C17th stone cottage with double/family converted stable suite. **Open:** All year **Grades:** ETC 5 Diamond, Silver
01629 56101 (also fax) Mrs Donnell **D:** £21.00–£25.00 **S:** £25.00 **Beds:** 1F 1D **Baths:** 1 En 1 Pr ⛱ 🅿(2) ⛺ 🅃 🆅 🕮 🛡

Glendon, *Knowleston Place, Matlock, Derbyshire, DE4 3BU.* Conveniently situated, well-equipped accommodation in a relaxed atmosphere. **Open:** Jan to Nov **Grades:** AA 4 Diamond
01629 584732 Mrs Elliott **D:** £20.00–£25.00 **S:** £25.00 **Beds:** 1F 2D 1T **Baths:** 2 En 2 Sh ⛱(3) 🅿(5) ⛺ 🅃 🆅 🕮 🛡

Riverbank House, *Derwent Avenue, Matlock, Derbyshire, DE4 3LX.* Victorian house nestling on the banks of the River Derwent. **Open:** All year (not Xmas/New Year) **Grades:** ETC 4 Diamond
01629 582593 Mr & Mrs Newberry **Fax:** 01629 580885 *bookings@riverbankhouse.co.uk* **D:** £23.50–£30.00 **S:** £25.00–£31.00 **Beds:** 2F 1T 3D **Baths:** 6 En ⛱ 🅿 ⛺ ✕ 🆅 🕮 🛡

Edgemount, *16 Edge Road, Matlock, Derbyshire, DE4 3NH.* Quality accommodation. Quiet, picturesque central position. Near holiday attractions. (Comfort assured). **Open:** All year (not Xmas) **Grades:** ETC 2 Diamond
01629 584787 Mrs Allen **D:** £17.50–£20.00 **S:** £17.00–£20.00 **Beds:** 1D 1F 1S **Baths:** 1 Sh ⛱(5) 🅿(2) ⛺ 🅃 🏍 🆅 🕮 🛡

Norden House, *Chesterfield Road, Two Dales, Matlock, Derbyshire, DE4 2EZ.* Converted barn, village outskirts. Friendly, cosy accommodation, pub nearby. Tasty home cooking. **Open:** All year (not Xmas) **Grades:** ETC 4 Diamond
01629 732074 Mrs Pope **Fax:** 01629 735805 *david.a.pope@talk21.com* www.geocities.com/nordenhouse **D:** £20.00–£26.00 **S:** £37.00–£40.00 **Beds:** 2D **Baths:** 2 En ⛱ 🅿(2) ⛺ 🅃 🏍 ✕ 🆅 🕮 🛡

Kensington Villa, *84 Dale Road, Matlock, Derbyshire, DE4 3LU.* Warm welcome, comfortable accommodation, substantial breakfast, central for touring area. **Open:** All year (not Xmas) **Grades:** AA 3 Diamond
01629 57627 Mrs Gorman *info@ kensington.villa.co.uk* **D:** £20.00 **S:** £20.00 **Beds:** 2D 1T **Baths:** 1 Sh ⛱ 🅿(3) ⛺ 🅃 🆅 🕮 🛡

Farley Farm, *Farley, Matlock, Derbyshire, DE4 5LR.* Working farm, lovely countryside, easy access Chatsworth/walks. Pets welcome. **Open:** All year (not Xmas/New Year)
01629 582533 & 07801 756409 (M) M Brailsford **D:** £20.00–£25.00 **S:** £22.00–£25.00 **Beds:** 1F 1D **Baths:** 2 En ⛱ 🅿(10) 🅃 🏍 ✕ 🆅 🕮 🛡

Ellen House, *37 Snitterton Road, Matlock, Derbys, DE43LZ.* Friendly hosts offer hospitality and comfort in attractively extended Edwardian home. **Open:** All year **Grades:** ETC 4 Diamond
01629 55584 Mrs Lewis **D:** £21.00–£25.00 **S:** £30.00–£40.00 **Beds:** 1T 2D **Baths:** 3 En ⛱ 🆅 🅃 🆅 🕮 🛡

Matlock Bath

SK2958

Sunnybank Guest House, *Clifton Road, Matlock Bath, Matlock, Derbyshire, DE4 3PW.* Spacious Victorian residence offering peace and comfort in wonderful location. **Open:** All year (not Xmas)
01629 584621 Mr & Mrs Ward *sunward@ lineone.net* **D:** £20.00–£33.00 **S:** £20.00–£30.00 **Beds:** 1F 2D 1T 1S **Baths:** 4 En 1 Pr ⛱ 🆅 ✕ 🆅 🕮 🛡

BATHROOMS

En = Ensuite
Pr = Private
Sh = Shared

Ashdale Guest House, *92 North Parade, Matlock Bath, Matlock, Derbyshire, DE4 3NS.* Listed Victorian villa, central Matlock Bath. Level walking to station etc. **Open:** All year **01629 57826** Mrs Lomas *ashdale@ matlockbath.fsnet.co.uk* www.ashdaleguesthouse.co.uk **D:** £22.00–£25.00 **S:** £25.00–£28.00 **Beds:** 2F 1T 1D **Baths:** 4 En ➰ 🏱 (4) ⚡ 🖭 ⊁ × 🖤 🛲 ⚘ cc

Old Museum Guest House, *170-172 South Parade, Matlock Bath, Matlock, Derbyshire, DE4 3NR.* Friendly family-run guest house. Ensuite double rooms with four-poster beds. **Open:** All year (not Xmas) **01629 57783 (also fax)** Mr & Mrs Bailey *lindsayandstewartbailey@tinyworld.co.uk* **D:** £15.00 **S:** £20.00 **Beds:** 1F 2D **Baths:** 3 En ➰ 🖭 × 🖤 🛲 ⚘

Mercaston

SK2643

Mercaston Hall, *Mercaston, Ashbourne, Derbyshire, DE6 3BL.* A warm welcome in comfortable historic farmhouse set in peaceful attractive countryside. **Open:** All year (not Xmas) **01335 360263** Mrs Haddon **Fax: 01335 361399** *Mercastonhall@btinternet.com* **D:** £20.00–£22.50 **S:** £25.00–£28.00 **Beds:** 2D 1T **Baths:** 2 En 1 Pr ➰ (8) 🏱 (6) 🖭 ⊁ 🖤 🛲 ⚘

Mickleover

SK3033

Bonehill Farm, *Etwall Road, Mickleover, Derby, DE3 5DN.* Comfortable Georgian farmhouse in countryside, 3 miles from centre of Derby. **Open:** All year **Grades:** ETC 3 Diamond **01332 513553** Mrs Dicken *bonehillfarm@ hotmail.com* **D:** £20.00–£25.00 **S:** £20.00–£25.00 **Beds:** 1F 1D 1T **Baths:** 2 En 2 Sh ➰ 🏱 (6) 🖭 ⊁ 🖤 🛲 ⚘

Middleton by Youlgreave

SK1963 🍺 *The Druids, George, Bowling Green*

Castle Farm, *Middleton by Youlgreave, Bakewell, Derbyshire, DE45 1LS.* Quiet, beautiful Peak District village. Excellent farmhouse breakfast. Warm welcome. **Open:** All year (not Xmas/New Year) **Grades:** ETC 3 Diamond **01629 636746** Mrs Butterworth **D:** £22.00 **S:** £35.00 **Beds:** 1F 1D **Baths:** 2 En ➰ 🏱 (6) ⚡ 🖭 ⊁ 🖤 🛲 ⚘

Millthorpe

SK3176

Carpenter House, *Millthorpe, Holmesfield, Dronfield, S18 7WH.* Ideal for Peak District and Tower alike. Local cricket within the grounds. **Open:** All year **0114 289 0307 Fax:** 0114 289 0551 *paddy@ mcghee44.freeserve.co.uk* **D:** £20.00–£22.50 **S:** £26.00–£28.00 **Beds:** 1F 1D **Baths:** 1 En 1 Pr ➰ 🏱 (20) 🖭 ⊁ 🖤 🛲 ⚘

Monyash

SK1566

Sheldon House, *Chapel Street, Monyash, Bakewell, Derbyshire, DE45 1JJ.* Recently renovated Grade II Listed house - a warm welcome awaits you. **Open:** All year (not Xmas) **01629 813067 (also fax)** Mr & Mrs Tyler *sheldonhouse@lineone.net* **D:** £20.00–£22.00 **S:** £30.00–£32.00 **Beds:** 3D **Baths:** 3 En ➰ (10) 🏱 (2) ⊁ ⚡ 🖭 🛲 ⚘

Rowson Farm, *Monyash, Bakewell, Derbyshire, DE45 1JH.* Clean and comfortable accommodation. Delicious Aga-cooked Breakfasts are served daily. **Open:** All year **01629 813521** Mr Mycock *gm@ rowson99.freeserve.co.uk* **D:** £20.00–£25.00 **S:** £15.00–£25.00 **Beds:** 5D/T **Baths:** 5 En ➰ 🏱 (10) ⊁ ⚡ 🏱 ⊁ × 🛲 ⚘

Morley

SK3940

Alambie, *189 Main Road, Morley, Ilkeston, Derbyshire, DE7 6DG.* Warm welcome. Good food. Comfy beds. Spotlessly clean. Ensuite rooms. **Open:** All year **01332 780349 (also fax)** Mrs Green-Armytage *alambie@beeb.net* www.alambieguesthouse.co.uk **D:** £20.00–£25.00 **Beds:** 1F 2D 1T **Baths:** 4 En ➰ 🏱 (5) ⊁ ⚡ × 🛲 ⚘

North Wingfield

SK4165

South View, *95 Church Lane, North Wingfield, Chesterfield, Derbyshire, S42 5HR.* Peaceful farmhouse, 3 miles from M1/j29; easy to find. **Open:** All year **01246 850091** Mrs Hopkinson **D:** £17.50 **S:** £17.00 **Beds:** 1D 1T 1S **Baths:** 1 Sh ➰ (10) 🏱 (4) ⊁ ⚡ 🛲 ⚘

Please respect a B&B's wishes regarding children, animals and smoking

Over Haddon

SK2066

Mandale House, *Haddon Grove, Over Haddon, Bakewell, Derbyshire, DE45 1JF.* Peaceful farmhouse near Lathkilldale. Good breakfasts, packed lunches available. **Open:** Feb to Nov **Grades:** ETC 4 Diamond **01629 812416** Mrs Finney *julia.finney@ virgin.net* www.mandalehouse.co.uk **D:** £20.00–£25.00 **S:** £25.00–£30.00 **Beds:** 2D 1T **Baths:** 3 En ➰ (5) 🏱 (4) ⊁ ⚡ 🖭 🛲 ⚘ ⚘

Padfield

SK0296

The Peels Arms, *Temple Street, Padfield, Hyde, Cheshire, SK14 7ET.* Country inn, oak beams, log fires, real ale, fine foods. Manchester/Sheffield 40 minutes. **Open:** All year **Grades:** ETC 3 Diamond **01457 852719** Mrs Murray **Fax:** 01457 850536 **D:** £20.00–£25.00 **S:** £25.00 **Beds:** 3D 2T **Baths:** 3 En 1 Sh ➰ 🏱 (20) 🖭 ⊁ × 🖤 🛲 ⚘ cc

Parwich

SK1854 🍺 *The Sycamore, Old Gate*

Flaxdale House, *Parwich, Ashbourne, Derbyshire, DE6 1QA.* **Open:** All year **Grades:** ETC 4 Diamond **01335 390252 & 07740 626804 (M)** Mr & Mrs Radcliffe **Fax:** 01335 390644 *b&b@ flaxdale.demon.co.uk* www.flaxdale.demon.co. uk **D:** £25.00 **S:** £30.00 **Beds:** 1T 1D **Baths:** 2 En ➰ 🏱 (3) ⊁ ⚡ 🖭 🛲 ⚘ Delightful Georgian farmhouse in centre of attractive, unspoilt village of Parwich. Ideally placed for Dovedale, Tissington and High Peak Trails, Carsington Water, Arbor Low, Minninglow and Roystone Grange and an abundance of public footpaths across glorious open countryside.

Peak Forest

SK1179 🍺 *The Devonshire Arms*

Dam Dale Farm, *Peak Forest, Buxton, Derbyshire, SK17 8EF.* Working farm, homely, comfortable atmosphere, wonderful views, hearty breakfast, secure parking. **Open:** All year (not Xmas/New Year) **01298 24104** Mrs Fletcher **D:** £20.00–£21.00 **S:** £25.00 **Beds:** 1T 1D **Baths:** 2 Sh ➰ (10) 🏱 (4) ⊁ ⚡ ⊁ 🖤 🛲

Pentrich

SK3952

Coney Grey Farm, *Chesterfield Road, Pentrich, Ripley, Derbyshire, DE5 3RF.* Beautiful farmhouse with panoramic views. Ripley, Alfreton and Crich nearby. **Open:** All year (not Xmas/New Year) **01773 833179** **D:** £14.00–£15.00 **S:** £15.00 **Beds:** 1T 1D **Baths:** 1 Sh ➰ (6) 🏱 (4) 🖭 🛲 ⚘

Riddings

SK4252

1 Peveril Drive, *Riddings, Alfreton, Derbyshire, DE55 4AP.* Self-contained bungalow accommodation with private bathroom, lounge and parking. **Open:** All year
01773 607712 Mrs Brown **D:** £15.00 **S:** £20.00 **Beds:** 1D **Baths:** 1 Pr ᗡ 🖵 (3) 🗺 🛉 🎟 ⚿ 🔒

Rowland

SK2172

Rowland Cottage, *Rowland, Great Longstone, Bakewell, Derbyshire, DE45 1NR.* Hamlet C17th cottage, near Chatsworth, traffic free, quiet, relaxing, comfortable.
Open: All year
01629 640365 (also fax) Mrs Scott *jgarde7@ aol.com* **D:** £17.50–£22.50 **S:** £20.00–£22.50 **Beds:** 1F 1T **Baths:** 1 Pr 1 Sh ᗡ 🖵 (3) ⚿ 🛉 ⚿ 🗺 🎟 ⚿ 🔒

Shatton

SK1982

The White House, *Shatton, Bamford, Hope Valley, S33 0BG.* Friendly, comfortable, private country house, lovely views, close to amenities. **Open:** All year (not Xmas)
01433 651487 (also fax) Mrs Middleton **D:** £17.50–£20.00 **S:** £17.50–£20.00 **Beds:** 1D 1T 2S **Baths:** 2 Sh ᗡ 🖵 (4) 🗺 🛉 🎟 🎟 🔒

Shirland

SK4058

Park Lane Farm, *Park Lane, Shirland, Alfreton, Derbyshire, DE55 6AX.* Early C18th farmhouse, situated on the borders of the Peak National Park. **Open:** All year
01773 831880 Mrs Davis **D:** £22.50–£25.00 **S:** £25.00 **Beds:** 2F 2D 2T ᗡ 🖵 (8) 🎟 🔒

Shirley

SK2141

Shirley Hall Farm, *Shirley, Brailsford, Ashbourne, Derbyshire, DE6 3AS.* Few minutes walk from Shirley Village. Superb breakfasts with home-made bread & preserves. **Open:** All year
01335 360346 (also fax) Mrs Foster *sylviafoster@shirleyhallfarm.com*
www.shirleyhallfarm.com **D:** £21.00–£25.00 **S:** £23.00–£27.00 **Beds:** 1F 1T 1D **Baths:** 2 En 1 Pr ᗡ (6) 🖵 (6) ⚿ 🎟 🔒

BEDROOMS

D = Double
T = Twin
S = Single
F = Family

RATES

D = Price range per person sharing in a double or twin room
S = Price range for a single room

Stanton by Bridge

SK3727

Ivy House Farm, *Stanton by Bridge, Derby, DE73 1HT.* **Open:** Mar to Oct
Grades: ETC 4 Diamond
01332 863152 Mrs Kidd *mary@ guesthouse.fsbusiness.co.uk*
www.ivy-house-farm.com **D:** £25.00–£45.00 **S:** £25.00 **Beds:** 4D 2T **Baths:** 6 En ᗡ 🖵 (9) ⚿ 🗺 🎟 🔒 ⚿3 🔒
These purpose-built B&B chalets are in this small quiet village, but close to lots of interesting things - Donington Park racing, Calke Abbey, Alton Towers, Twycross Zoo, Swadlincote ski slopes, the National Forest.

Taddington

SK1470

Ade House, *Taddington, Buxton, Derbyshire, SK17 9TY.* Find peace, home-baking, organic produce, good walks & a warm welcome. **Open:** All year (not Xmas)
01298 85203 Mrs Elkington **D:** £20.00 **S:** £20.00 **Beds:** 1F 1T 3S **Baths:** 2 Sh ᗡ 🖵 (4) ⚿ 🗺 🛉 ⚿ 🎟 🔒

Thorpe

SK1550   ⚓ *Coach & Horses*

Jasmine Cottage, *Thorpe, Ashbourne, Derbyshire, DE6 2AW.* Pretty stone cottage near Dovedale. Warm, peaceful, comfortable. Excellent food. **Open:** All year
01335 350465 Mrs Round **D:** £20.00–£25.00 **S:** £25.00–£35.00 **Beds:** 1D 1T 🖵 (4) ⚿ 🗺 ⚿ 🎟 🔒

The Old Orchard, *Thorpe, Ashbourne, Derbyshire, DE6 2AW.* Quietly situated limestone home with colourful gardens. Ample car parking. **Open:** Mar to Nov
01335 350410 (also fax) Mrs Challinor **D:** £20.00–£25.00 **S:** £25.00–£30.00 **Beds:** 2D 2S **Baths:** 2 En 1 Sh 🖵 (10) ⚿ 🛉 🎟 🔒

Tibshelf

SK4360

Rosvern House, *High Street, Tibshelf, Alfreton, Derbyshire, DE55 6AX.* Friendly, homely atmosphere. Comfortable rooms, convenient for business travellers/tourists.
Open: All year
01773 874800 Mrs Byard *byard.tibshelf@ lineone.net* **D:** £16.00–£18.00 **S:** £17.00–£18.00 **Beds:** 1F 1D ᗡ 🖵 (2) ⚿ 🗺 🎟 🔒

Tideswell

SK1575   ⚓ *The George, Star Inn, Horse & Jockey*

Poppies, *Bank Square, Tideswell, Buxton, Derbyshire, SK17 8LA.* Comfortable accommodation. Ideally located for Peak District activities and attractions. **Open:** All year (not Xmas/New Year) **Grades:** AA 3 Diamond
01298 871083 Mrs Pinnegar *poptidza@ dialstart.net* **D:** £18.00–£22.50 **S:** £18.00–£22.50 **Beds:** 1F 1T 1D **Baths:** 1 En ᗡ ⚿ 🗺 🛉 ⚿ 🎟 🔒 ⚿ cc

Uppertown

SK3264

Old School Farm, *Uppertown, Ashover, Chesterfield, Derbyshire, S45 0JF.* Spacious, comfortable, working farm, home from home, peaceful and friendly. **Open:** Easter to Oct **Grades:** ETC 4 Diamond, RAC 4 Diamond, Sparkling
01246 590813 Mrs Wooton **D:** £22.00 **S:** £22.00 **Beds:** 2F 1D 1T 1S **Baths:** 3 En 1 Pr 1 Sh ᗡ 🖵 (6) 🎟 🔒

Wessington

SK3757   ⚓ *Horse & Jockey, Plough Inn*

Crich Lane Farm, *Moorwood Moor Lane, Wessington, Alfreton, Derbyshire, DE55 6DU.* C17th farmhouse. Peaceful surroundings, friendly atmosphere. **Open:** All year (not Xmas) **Grades:** ETC 4 Diamond
01773 835186 & 07775 881423 (M) Mrs Green **D:** £20.00–£25.00 **S:** £20.00–£25.00 **Beds:** 2F 3D 2T 1S **Baths:** 5 En 1 Pr 1 Sh ᗡ 🖵 (8) ⚿ 🗺 🎟 🔒 ⚿

Oaktree Farm, *Matlock Road, Oakerthorpe, Wessington, Alfreton, Derbyshire, DE55 7NA.* Modern stone farmhouse. Coarse fishing free to residents. Sky TV. **Open:** All year (not Xmas/New Year)
01773 832957 Mrs Prince *oaktree_farm@ talk21.com* **D:** £21.00–£25.00 **S:** £23.00–£27.00 **Beds:** 2D 1T **Baths:** 3 En ᗡ 🖵 (10) ⚿ 🗺 🛉 ⚿ 🎟 🔒

Whatstandwell

SK3354   ⚓ *Holmesford Cottage, White Lion, Derwent Hotel*

Riverdale Guest House, *Middle Lane, Whatstandwell, Matlock, Derbyshire, DE4 5EG.* Enjoy panoramic views of Derwent Valley from our cul-de-sac house. **Open:** All year **Grades:** ETC 4 Diamond
01773 853905 (also fax) Mrs Durbridge **D:** £21.00–£26.00 **S:** £26.00 **Beds:** 1T 2D **Baths:** 1 Pr ᗡ (5) 🖵 (4) ⚿ 🗺 🛉 ⚿ 🎟 🔒 ⚿ 🔒

RATES

D = Price range per person sharing in a double or twin room

S = Price range for a single room

___

Meerbrook Farm, *Wirksworth Road, Whatstandwell, Matlock, Derbyshire, DE4 5HU.* Lovely old stone farmhouse set in the scenic Derbyshire Dales. **Open:** All year (not Xmas/New Year) **Grades:** ETC 3 Diamond
01629 824180 & 07713 769074 (M)
Mrs Johnson *jackie.johnson@tinyworld.co.uk*
D: £18.50 **S:** £20.00 **Beds:** 1F 1T **Baths:** 1 Sh
⌂ ⊞ (4) ⍑ ⊡ Ⓥ ▥ ♨

Youlgreave

SK2164   ◖ Bull's Head, George Hotel, Farmyard Inn

Bulls Head Hotel, *Fountain Square, Church Street, Youlgreave, Bakewell, Derbyshire, DE45 1UR.* **Open:** All year
01629 636307 Mrs Atkinson **D:** £15.00–£20.00 **S:** £20.00 **Beds:** 2F 2T 3D **Baths:** 1 En 1 Sh ⌂ (5) ⊞ ⊡ ✗ Ⓥ ▥ ♨ cc
A Grade II Listed building with lots of charm and a friendly welcome. Lying between two beautiful Dales, the Lathkill and Bradford. Great area for walking and touring the closeby Chatsworth house, Haddon Hall and market towns of Bakewell, Buxton, Chesterfield.

The Old Bakery, *Church Street, Youlgreave, Bakewell, Derbyshire, DE45 1UR.* Two bedroom guest wing or tasteful barn conversion for two. **Open:** All year **Grades:** ETC 3 Diamond, AA 3 Diamond, RAC 3 Diamond
01629 636887 Ms Croasdell *croasdell@oldbakeryyoulgrave.freeserve.co.uk* **D:** £16.00–£27.00 **S:** £22.00 **Beds:** 1D 2T **Baths:** 1 En 1 Sh ⌂ ⊞ (2) ⍑ ⊡ Ⓥ ▥ ❋ ♨

Fairview, *Bradford Road, Youlgreave, Bakewell, Derbyshire, DE45 1WG.* Small house with stunning views. Relaxed, friendly atmosphere. **Open:** All year
01629 636043 Mrs Bartlett **D:** £16.50 **S:** £18.00 **Beds:** 1F 1T 1D **Baths:** 1 Sh ⌂ (4) ⊞ (1) ⍑ Ⓥ ▥ ♨

Bankside Cottage, *Youlgreave, Bakewell, Derbyshire, DE45 1WD.* Large stone cottage, unique off-road position, terrace garden overlooks secluded Bradford Dale. **Open:** All year
01629 636689 Mr Blackburn **D:** £16.50 **S:** £16.50 **Beds:** 1D 1T **Baths:** 1 Sh ⌂ ⍑ ♞ Ⓥ ▥ ♨

Devon

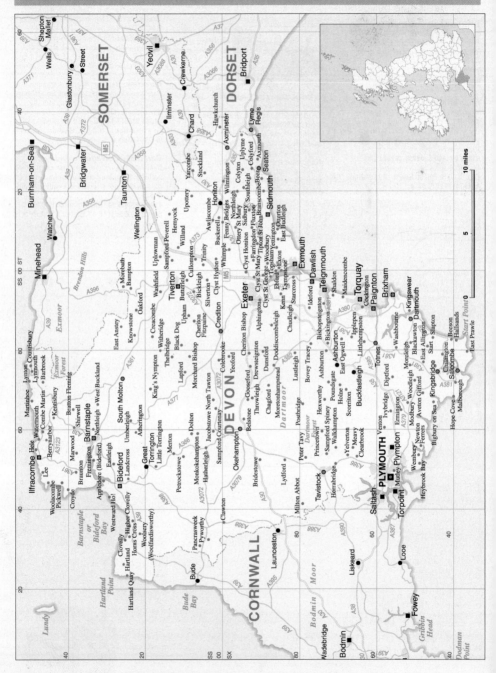

Alphington

SX9189

The Old Mill, Mill Lane, Alphington, Exeter, Devon, *EX2 8SG*. Historical premises in quiet area. Full farm breakfast. Recommended for 28 years. **Open:** All year **01392 259977** Mrs Marchant **D:** £10.50–£14.00 **S:** £10.50–£15.00 **Beds:** 2F 1D 1T 1S **Baths:** 1 Pr 1 Sh ⌂ 🖫 (8) ⊁ 🖵 🖻 & ♨

Appledore (Bideford)

SS4630

The Seagate Hotel, The Quay, Appledore, Bideford, Devon, *EX39 1QS*. C17th riverside inn. Quaint fishing village on Torridge Estuary. **Open:** All year **01237 472589 (also fax)** Mr & Mrs Gent **D:** £25.00–£35.00 **S:** £29.00–£35.00 **Beds:** 1F 5D 1T **Baths:** 7 Pr ⌂ 🖫 (10) 🖵 🏋 ✗ 🖵 🖻 ♨ cc

Ashburton

SX7570   ▨ Old Inn, Dart Bridge, Ruggle Stone Inn

Sladesdown Farm, Landscove, Ashburton, Newton Abbot, Devon, *TQ13 7ND*. Warm welcome, countryside views, farmhouse breakfast. Sea and moors nearby. **Open:** All year **Grades:** ETC 4 Diamond, Silver **01364 653973 (also fax)** sue@ sladesdownfarm.co.uk www.sladesdownfarm. co.uk **D:** £22.50–£25.00 **S:** £25.00–£30.00 **Beds:** 1F 2D **Baths:** 2 En 1 Pr ⌂ 🖫 (6) ⊁ 🖵 🖵 🖻 ♨

Rosary Mount House, Ashburton, Newton Abbot, Devon, *TQ13 7JL*. A luxuriously furnished country house (circa 1857) standing in its own landscaped gardens. **Open:** All year (not Xmas/New Year) **01364 653900** Mr Stone **Fax: 01364 653821** annette@rosarymount.co.uk www.roserymount. co.uk **D:** £17.50–£20.00 **S:** £25.00 **Beds:** 2D 1T **Baths:** 2 Sh ⌂ (8) 🖫 (6) ⊁ 🖵 🖻 ♨

Atherington

SS5922

The Village Shop and Tea Rooms, The Square, Atherington, Umberleigh, Devon, *EX37 9HY*.
C17th building in pretty North Devon village. Friendly comfortable atmosphere. **Open:** All year (not Xmas/New Year) **01769 560248** Mr & Mrs Hart **D:** £20.00 **S:** £20.00 **Beds:** 1T 1D **Baths:** 1 Sh ⌂ ⊁ 🖵 🏋 ✗ ♨

Planning a longer stay? Always ask for any special rates

Planning a longer stay? Always ask for any special rates

Aveton Gifford

SX6947

Marsh Mills, Aveton Gifford, Kingsbridge, Devon, *TQ7 4JW*. Mill house, pond, stream, gardens, orchard. Small farm, friendly animals. **Open:** All year (not Xmas/New Year) **01548 550549 (also fax)** Mrs Newsham newsham@marshmills.co.uk www.marshmills. co.uk **D:** £18.00–£22.00 **S:** £18.00–£22.00 **Beds:** 2T 2D 1S **Baths:** 2 En 1 Sh 1 Pr 🖫 (6) ⊁ 🖵 ♨

Awliscombe

ST1301   ▨ Awliscombe Inn, Otter Inn

Ridgeway Farm, Awliscombe, Honiton, Devon, *EX14 3PY*. **Open:** All year (not Xmas/ New Year) **01404 841331** Mrs Chamberlain susan.chamberlain@tesco.net www.smoothhound.co. uk/hotels/ridgewayfarm.html **D:** £20.00–£25.00 **S:** £22.00–£25.00 **Beds:** 1T 2D **Baths:** 2 En 1 Pr ⌂ (5) 🖫 (3) ⊁ 🖵 ✗ 🖵 🖻 ♨ C18th farmhouse, tucked away with country views, three miles North of Honiton. Tasteful decor and renovations have brought the accommodation up to a very high standard which is spotlessly clean. A superb English breakfast and a warm welcome await you.

Birds Farm, Awliscombe, Honiton, Devon, *EX14 0PU*. Comfortable C16th beamed farmhouse. Near coast and moors. Lovely countryside. **Open:** Mar to Oct **Grades:** ETC 2 Diamond **01404 841620** Mrs Manley **D:** £16.00–£17.00 **S:** £16.00–£17.00 **Beds:** 2D **Baths:** 1 Sh 🖫 (4) ⊁ 🖵 ♨

Wessington Farm, Awliscombe, Honiton, Devon, *EX14 3NU*. Elegant late Victorian stone farmhouse in designated AONB. **Open:** All year **Grades:** ETC 4 Diamond, Silver **01404 42280 & 07989 300392 (M)** Mrs Summers **Fax: 01404 45271** bandb@ eastdevon.com www.eastdevon. com/bedandbreakfast **D:** £20.00–£25.00 **S:** £20.00–£40.00 **Beds:** 1D 2T **Baths:** 2 En 1 Pr ⌂ 🖫 (10) ⊁ 🖵 🖵 🖻 ♨

Threshays, Awliscombe, Honiton, Devon, *EX14 3QB*. Warm, friendly, delightful views. Ideal for exploring glorious East Devon. **Open:** All year **01404 43551 (also fax)** Mrs Gillingham threshays@tesco.net **D:** £17.00 **S:** £17.00 **Beds:** 1F 1D **Baths:** 1 Sh ⌂ 🖫 (6) ⊁ 🖵 🖵 🖻

Axminster

SY2998   ▨ Tuckers Arms

Mount House, Lyme Road, Axminster, Devon, *EX13 5BL*. Large regency family house. Warm welcome, good food, lovely countryside. **Open:** All year **01297 34630** Mrs Morrison **D:** £17.00–£19.00 **S:** £17.00–£20.00 **Beds:** 2F 1D **Baths:** 2 En 1 Sh ⌂ 🖫 🖵 🏋 ✗ 🖵 🖻 ♨

Millbrook Farmhouse, Chard Road, Axminster, Devon, *EX13 5EG*. Millbrook Farmhouse is a Grade II Listed building in rural surroundings. **Open:** All year (not Xmas) **01297 35351** Ms Gay **Fax: 01297 35739** **D:** £20.00 **S:** £25.00 **Beds:** 1D 1T **Baths:** 1 En 1 Pr ⌂ 🖫 (3) ⊁ 🖵 ✗ 🖵 🖻 ♨

Coaxdon Farm, Smallridge, Coaxdon, Axminster, Devon, *EX13 7LP*. Peace and tranquillity set in 14 acres with indoor pool. **Open:** All year (not Xmas/New Year) **01297 35540** N & D Ray www.eclipse.co. uk/coaxdon **D:** £22.00–£34.00 **Beds:** 2F 1D **Baths:** 2 En ⌂ 🖫 (20) ⊁ 🖵 🖵 🖻 & ♨

Axmouth

SY2591   ▨ Ship Inn, Harbour Inn

Stepps House, Axmouth, Seaton, Devon, *EX12 4AR*. Thatched medieval 'hall' house - star listed. Beautiful village on Axe Estuary. **Open:** Easter to Oct **01297 20679 (also fax)** Mrs Trezise **D:** £20.00–£25.00 **S:** £25.00–£30.00 **Beds:** 1T 1D **Baths:** 1 Sh 🖫 (2) 🖵 ♨

Bampton

SS9522

Manor Mill House, Bampton, Devon, *EX16 9LP*. Welcoming C17th home in historic Bampton. Ideal base, close to Exmoor. **Open:** All year **01398 332211** Mrs Ayres **Fax: 01398 332009** stay@manormill.demon.co.uk www.manormill. demon.co.uk **D:** £21.00–£24.00 **Beds:** 2D 1T **Baths:** 3 En 🖫 (20) ⊁ 🖵 🖵 🖻 ♨

Please respect a B&B's wishes regarding children, animals and smoking

Barbrook

SS7147   ◀ *Beggars Roost Inn*

Manor Hotel, *Barbrook, Lynton, Devon, EX35 9BP.* **Open:** All year
01598 752404 Fax: 01598 753636
Beggars.Roost.Inn@tinyworld.co.uk
www.smoothhound.co.
uk/hotels/manorho1.html **D:** £25.00–
£30.00 **S:** £39.00 **Beds:** 2F 5D **Baths:** 7 En ⌂
🄿 (60) 🖤 🄩 🍴 ✕ 🄅 🛏 ⚹ 🖘 cc
A beautiful 300 year old manor house set in
magnificent countryside offering luxury
accommodation. Its own medieval-style
function room and C17th Inn serving
traditional home-cooked food, real ales,
open fire and oak beams makes it a special
place.

Barnstaple

SS5633   ◀ *The Bell, Rising Sun, Duke of York, Old
George, North Coutry Inn*

**Mount
Sandford,**
*Landkey Road,
Barnstaple,
Devon, EX32 0HL.*
Georgian house
set in beautiful
gardens, easy
reach of all resorts. **Open:** All year (not
Xmas/New Year)
01271 342354 (also fax) S White **D:** £20.00–
£25.00 **S:** £22.50–£25.00 **Beds:** 1F 1T 1D
Baths: 3 En 🄿 (3) ✕ 🛢 ▪

Crossways, *Braunton Road, Barnstaple,
Devon, EX31 1JY.* Detached house - town and
Tarka Trail 150 yards, bicycle hire. **Open:** All
year (not Xmas/New Year)
01271 379120 R F Tysn *xwaysbarnstaple@
netscapeonline.co.uk* **D:** £17.00–£20.00
S: £19.00–£23.00 **Beds:** 2F 2T 2D **Baths:** 2
En 2 Pr 1 Sh ⌂ 🄿 (7) ✕ 🄅 🛢 ▪

RATES

D = Price range per person
sharing in a double or twin
room
S = Price range for a single
room

Planning a longer stay? Always
ask for any special rates

Beer

SY2289   ◀ *Anchor Inn, Dolphin Hotel*

**Pamber
House,** *Clapps
Lane, Beer,
Seaton, Devon,
EX12 3HD.*
Open: All year
**01297 20722
(also fax)**
Mrs Cummins *pamber-beer-dgr-@amserve.net*
D: £21.00–£24.00 **S:** £28.00–£30.00 **Beds:** 1F
1D **Baths:** 3 Pr ⌂ (7) 🄿 (3) ✕ 🄅 🛢 ▪
Set in idyllic fishing village. Quiet position,
2 minutes walk from village and beach.
Stunning views, food cooked to order.
Winter rates, ideal base.

Garlands,
*Stovar Long
Lane, Beer,
Seaton, Devon,
EX12 3EA.*
Edwardian
character house
in an acre of ground - superb views sea and
Devon countryside. **Open:** All year (not
Xmas)
01297 20958 Ms Harding **Fax: 01297 23869**
nigelharding1@compuserve.com **D:** £20.00–
£23.00 **S:** £30.00–£33.00 **Beds:** 2F 2D 1T 1S
Baths: 6 En ⌂ 🄿 (10) 🄅 🍴 🛢 ▪ cc

Bay View Guest House, *Fore Street,
Beer, Seaton, Devon, EX12 3EE.* Seafront
location, coastal views, large comfortable
rooms and great breakfasts! **Open:** Easter
to Nov
01297 20489 Mr & Mrs Oswald **D:** £15.50
S: £15.50 **Beds:** 1F 1T 4D 2S **Baths:** 3 En 1
Pr 4 Sh ⌂ 🄅 🍴 🛢 ▪

Beeson

SX8140

Marybank House, *Beeson, Kingsbridge,
Devon, TQ7 2HW.* Beautifully located
Victorian country house. Have delicious
breakfast whilst enjoying sea views.
Open: All year
01548 580531 Mrs Honeywill **D:** £18.50–
£25.00 **S:** £18.50–£28.00 **Beds:** 1T 2D
Baths: 1 En 1 Pr ⌂ 🄿 ✕ 🄅 🍴 🛢 ▪

Belstone

SX6293

Moorlands House, *Belstone,
Okehampton, Devon, EX20 1QZ.* Beautifully
situated; edge of unspoilt Dartmoor village
with superb moorland views. **Open:** All year
01837 840549 Mr Weaver **D:** £18.00–£20.00
S: £20.00–£25.00 **Beds:** 2T 2D **Baths:** 1 En 1
Pr 1 Sh ⌂ 🄿 (6) 🄅 🍴 🛢 ▪

Berrynarbor

SS5646

Tower Cottage, *Berrynarbor, Ilfracombe,
Devon, EX34 9SE.* Charming cottage with
beautiful garden in 'Best Kept Village
Berrynarbor'. **Open:** All year (not Xmas/
New Year)
01271 883408 *tombartlettbooks@
berrynarbor.fsnet.co.uk* **D:** £18.00–£22.00
S: £25.00 **Beds:** 1F 1D **Baths:** 2 En ⌂ 🄿 ✕ 🄅
🛢 ▪

Bickington (Newton Abbot)

SX7972   ◀ *Halfway Inn, Toby Jug, Welcome
Stranger*

Chipley Farm, *Bickington, Newton
Abbot, Devon, TQ12 6JW.* Working dairy farm
in beautiful location. Highly recommended
by AA. **Open:** All year **Grades:** AA 4
Diamond
01626 821486 & 01626 821947 Mrs Westcott
Fax: 01626 821486 *louisa@
chipleyfarmholidays.co.uk*
www.chipleyfarmholidays.co.uk **D:** £20.00–
£25.00 **S:** £30.00 **Beds:** 1F 1T 1D 1S **Baths:** 1
En 1 Sh ⌂ 🄿 ✕ 🄅 ✕ 🄅 🛢 ▪

Rentor, *Bickington, Newton Abbot,
TQ12 6JW.* Refurbished former farmhouse,
country views, situated between Dartmoor
and Torbay. **Open:** Mar to Nov
01392 277443 Mr & Mrs Warren **D:** £17.50–
£19.00 **S:** £18.00–£19.50 **Beds:** 2D **Baths:** 2
En 🄿 (3) ✕ 🄅 🄅 🛢 ▪

Bickleigh (Tiverton)

SS9407   ◀ *The Mill, Trout Inn, Fishermans Cot*

Willow Grove House, *The Orchard,
Bickleigh, Tiverton, Devon, EX16 8RD.*
Situated in beautiful garden, walking
distance to thatched restaurants on river.
Open: All year
01884 855263 D M Lock *mjhowes@
bickleigh93freeserve.co.uk* **D:** £20.00–£25.00
S: £20.00–£25.00 **Beds:** 1T 1D 1S **Baths:** 1
En 2 Pr ⌂ (5) 🄿 (3) 🄅 🄅 🛢 ▪

The Old Post Office, *Bickleigh,
Tiverton, Devon, EX16 8RH.* Stay somewhere
special. Visit Exeter, Dartmoor, Exmoor,
coast, beautiful Dunster, Bickleigh Castle.
Open: All year
01884 855784 Mr Latchem **Fax: 0700
0783845** *bickleighpostoffice@asgardltd.co.uk*
D: £20.00–£25.00 **S:** £20.00 **Beds:** 1D 1T 1S
Baths: 2 En 1 Pr 1 Sh ⌂ 🄿 🄅 🍴 ✕ 🄅 🛢 ⚹ ▪

BEDROOMS

D = Double
T = Twin
S = Single
F = Family

Bideford

SS4526 🏨 *Commodore Hotel, Pig on the Hill*

The Mount Hotel, *Northdown Road, Bideford, Devon, EX39 3LP.* **Open:** Jan to Dec
01237 473748 Mr & Mrs Laugharne *andrew@themountbideford.fsnet.co.uk* **D:** £25.00–£27.00
S: £27.00–£33.00 **Beds:** 1F 3D 1T 2S
Baths: 7 En ⑤ 🖪 (4) ⚡ 🖵 🖿 ᪲ ♨ cc
Charming Georgian licensed guest house only 5 minutes' walk to town centre, private lounge for guests' use, all rooms ensuite, attractive garden, car parking for guests. Convenient for touring North Devon coastline, Clovelly, Lundy, Exmoor and Dartmoor. No smoking.

Corner House, *14 The Strand, Bideford, Devon, EX39 2ND.* Family-run, C18th building, clean, comfortable, close to amenities.
Open: All year
01237 473722 CandS Stone *ccornerhouse@aol.com* **D:** £19.00–£21.00 **S:** £20.00–£25.00
Beds: 1F 1D 1S **Baths:** 1 Sh ⑤ ⚡ 🖵 ᪲ × 🖵 🖿 ♨

Bigbury on Sea

SX6544 🏨 *Oysters, Pickwick Inn, Royal Oak, Dolphin, Pilchard, Journey's End*

Folly Foot, *Challaborough, Bigbury On Sea, Kingsbridge, Devon, TQ7 4JB.* 50m sandy beach/ South West Way. Warm welcome, bungalow. **Open:** Feb to Oct
01548 810036 *carolwalsh@freenet.co.uk*
D: £20.00–£26.00 **S:** £20.00–£25.00 **Beds:** 1F 2D 1S **Baths:** 2 En 1 Sh ⑤ (6) 🖪 (6) ⚡ 🖵 ♨

Bishopsteignton

SX9073

Cockhaven Manor, *Cockhaven Rd, Bishopsteignton, Teignmouth, Devon, TQ14 9RF.* Family-run freehouse for the best of West Country food. **Open:** All year
Grades: AA 2 Star
01626 775212 Fax: 01626 775572
cockhaven.manor@virgin.net **D:** £25.00–£30.00
S: £30.00–£40.00 **Beds:** 4T 7D 1S **Baths:** 12 En 🖪 (40) ⚡ 🖵 ᪲ × 🖵 🖿 ♨ cc

RATES

D = Price range per person sharing in a double or twin room
S = Price range for a single room

Black Dog

SS8009 🏨 *Thelbridge Cross Inn, Black Dog, London Inn, Mount Pleasant*

Lower Brownstone Farm, *Black Dog, Crediton, Devon, EX17 4QE.* Heart of Devon. Art gallery. Large lawn and fields. Painting holidays. **Open:** All year
01363 877256 H Wedlake **D:** £15.00–£19.00
S: £15.00–£19.00 **Beds:** 3D **Baths:** 2 Sh ⑤ 🖪 (10) 🖵 ᪲ × 🖵

Oaklands, *Black Dog, Crediton, Devon, EX17 4RQ.* Friendly accommodation in peaceful countryside, central for coast and moors. **Open:** All year
01884 860645 Mrs Bradford **Fax: 01884 861030 D:** £18.00–£20.00 **S:** £20.00–£22.00
Beds: 1F 1D 1T **Baths:** 2 En 1 Pr ⑤ 🖪 (6) 🖵 🖿 ♨

Blackawton

SX8050 🏨 *The Geoge, Start Bay, Old Inn*

Woodside Cottage BandB, *Blackawton, Totnes, Devon, TQ97BL.* **Open:** All year (not Xmas/ New Year)
Grades: ETC 4 Diamond, Silver
01803 712375 (also fax) T & S Adams
woodside-cottage@lineone.net
www.woodside-cottage-devon.co.uk
D: £25.00–£30.00 **S:** £30.00–£60.00 **Beds:** 1T 2D **Baths:** 3 En 🖪 (4) ⚡ 🖵 ᪲ × 🖵 🖿 ♨
C18th gamekeeper's lodge in peaceful valley with superb views from all rooms towards Start Point light. Short walk to village pubs, Dartmouth and the sea 4 miles. Beautifully furnished rooms, conservatory, fine terrace and lovely gardens.

Bovey Tracey

SX8178

Front House Lodge, *East Street, Bovey Tracey, Newton Abbot, Devon, TQ13 9EL.* Delightful C16th house, edge of Dartmoor. Antiques, atmosphere. Delicious breakfasts. **Open:** All year (not Xmas)
Grades: AA 5 Diamond
01626 832202 (also fax) Mr & Mrs Campbell
fronthouselodge@aol.com **D:** £22.50–£25.00
S: £27.50–£35.00 **Beds:** 1F 3D 2T 🖪 (6) ⚡ 🖵 × 🖵 🖿 ♨ cc

Whitstone Farm, *Bovey Tracey, TQ13 9NA.* Luxury accommodation, Gorgeous views overlooking Dartmoor. Excellent food. Warm welcome. **Open:** All year (not Xmas/ New Year)
01626 836494 (also fax) Mrs Bunn *kate@reynolds2000.co.uk* **D:** £25.00–£32.50
S: £40.00–£45.00 **Beds:** 1T 2D **Baths:** 3 En ⑤ (15) 🖪 (10) ⚡ 🖵 × 🖵 🖿 ♨

All details shown are as supplied by B&B owners in Autumn 2001

Branscombe

SY1988 🏨 *Masons' Arms*

Masons Arms, *Branscombe, Seaton, Devon, EX12 3DJ.* **Open:** All year **Grades:** AA 2 Star
01297 680300 Mr Inglis **Fax: 01297 680500**
reception@masonarms.co.uk www.masonarms.co.uk **D:** £22.00–£75.00 **S:** £22.00–£125.00
Beds: 6T 19D 3S **Baths:** 25 En 3 Pr ⑤ 🖪 (45) 🖵 ᪲ × 🖵 🖿 ❈ ♨ cc
Enchanting 600 year old inn and thatched cottages nestling in picturesque coastal village. Four poster beds, antiques and designer furnishings. ideal base for walks through stunning National Trust fields, along the Heritage Coastal Path or for touring Devon and Dorset.

Hole Mill, *Branscombe, Seaton, Devon, EX12 3BX.* **Open:** All year
01297 680314 Mr & Mrs Hart
www.users.globalnet.co.uk/~branscombe/hole1.htm **D:** £17.50–£21.00 **S:** £29.00–£37.00 **Beds:** 2D 1T
Baths: 2 Sh ⑤ (6) 🖪 (6) ⚡ 🖵 ᪲ 🖵 🖿 ♨
Old converted watermill providing comfortable accommodation in style of yesteryear. Beams, brass beds, inglenook lounge, garden, stream. No rush, no town noises - just peace/relaxation. Featured in 'Which? The Good Bed and Breakfast Guide' and 'Staying Off the Beaten Track'.

Bratton Fleming

SS6437 🏨 *White Hart Inn*

Haxton Down Farm, *Bratton Fleming, Barnstaple, Devon, EX32 7JL.* Peaceful, working farm in secluded but accessible setting. Good food. **Open:** Easter to Nov
Grades: ETC 3 Diamond
01598 710275 Mrs Burge *ron-steph@buckgrove.freeserve.co.uk* **D:** £18.00–£20.00
S: £20.00–£22.00 **Beds:** 1F 1D **Baths:** 2 En ⑤ 🖪 (3) ⚡ 🖵 ᪲ × 🖵 🖿 ♨

BEDROOMS

D = Double
T = Twin
S = Single
F = Family

Braunton

SS4936   🍴 *Agricultural Inn*

St Merryn, *Higher Park Road, Braunton, Devon, EX33 2LG.* **Open:** Jan to Dec **01271 813805** Mrs Bradford **Fax: 01271 812097** *ros@ st-merryn.co.uk* www.st-merryn.co.uk **D:** £20.00–£22.00 **S:** £20.00–£22.00 **Beds:** 1F 1T 1D **Baths:** 1 En 2 Pr 🛇 🄿 (5) 🛏 🖾 🍴 ✕ 🖾 🖩. 🚳

Beautiful home set in delightful large garden. Many suntraps with seating. Swimming pool, tranquil setting, excellent parking and within easy walking distance of village. Excellent beaches, golf courses, coastal path, Marwood Garden and RHS Rosemoor within short drive.

North Cottage, *14 North Street, Braunton, Devon, EX33 1AJ.* Well-situated for local beaches, golf course & South West Coastal Path. **Open:** All year **01271 812703** Mrs Watkins **D:** £17.50 **S:** £17.50 **Beds:** 1T 2D 1S **Baths:** 2 En 1 Sh 🛇 🄿 🖾 🍴 🖾 🖩. 🚳

Bridestowe

SX5189   🍴 *Fox & Hounds, White Hart, Dartmoor Inn, Castle Inn*

Knole Farm, *Bridestowe, Okehampton, Devon, EX20 4HA.* **Open:** All year (not Xmas/ New Year) **Grades:** ETC 4 Diamond, Silver **01837 861241** *beryl@corfton.freeserve.co.uk* **D:** £20.00–£22.00 **Beds:** 1T 2D **Baths:** 3 En 🛇 (10) 🖾 🍴 ✕ 🖾 🖩. 🚳

Knole farm 'West Devon' offers wonderful views, warm friendly atmosphere, brilliant farmhouse breakfast, evening meals optional. A perfect place for exploring the Dartmoor National Park. Local fishing, golfing, horseriding, National Trust properties. Easy to locate - 3 miles from A30.

The White Hart Inn, *Fore Street, Bridestowe, Okehampton, Devon, EX20 4EL.* C17th country inn, close to Dartmoor. Same owners for 39 years. **Open:** All year **01837 861318 (also fax)** Mr Owen *whihartinn@aol.com* members.aol. com/whihartinn/bridestowe.html **D:** £23.75 **S:** £29.95 **Beds:** 2D **Baths:** 2 En 🄿 (20) 🖾 ✕ 🖾 🚳 cc

Brixham

SX9255   🍴 *Quayside Hotel, Berry Head Hotel, Blue Anchor, Churston Court, Smugglers Inn*

Smugglers Haunt Hotel & Restaurant, *Church Hill, Brixham, Devon, TQ5 8HH.* **Open:** All year **Grades:** AA 1 Star, RAC 1 Star **01803 853050** Mr Hudson **Fax: 01803 858738** *enquiries@smugglershaunt-hotel-devon.co.uk* www.smugglershaunt-hotel-devon.co.uk **D:** £26.00–£29.00 **S:** £31.00–£34.00 **Beds:** 4F 7D 4T 1S **Baths:** 16 En 🛇 🖾 🍴 ✕ 🖾. 🌺 🚳 Friendly, private 300-year-old hotel. Up to 100 main course meals. Pets and children welcome.

Richmond House Hotel, *Higher Manor Road, Brixham, Devon, TQ5 8HA.* Comfortable Victorian house with spacious rooms and a homely atmosphere. **Open:** All year **Grades:** ETC 3 Diamond, AA 3 Diamond **01803 882391 (also fax)** Mrs Giblett **D:** £18.00–£24.00 **S:** £23.00–£29.00 **Beds:** 2F 3D 1T **Baths:** 5 En 1 Pr 🛇 🄿 (6) 🍴 🖾 🍴 🖩. 🚳 cc

Westbury, *51 New Road, Brixham, TQ5 8NL.* Charming Georgian house, short level walk from shops and harbour. **Open:** All year **01803 851684 (also fax)** *ann.burt@lineone.net* **D:** £16.00–£23.00 **S:** £16.00–£23.00 **Beds:** 4F 2D **Baths:** 4 En 1 Sh 🛇 (6) 🄿 ✕ 🖾 🖩. 🚳

Broadwoodwidger

SX4189

Rexon Cross Farm, *Broadwoodwidger, Lifton, Devon, PL16 0JJ.* Warm and friendly atmosphere on working farm in picturesque area **Open:** All year **01566 784295 (also fax)** Mrs Worden *johnworden@btclick.com* **D:** £20.00–£23.00 **S:** £25.00–£30.00 **Beds:** 1T 1D **Baths:** 1 Pr 1 Sh 🛇 (10) 🄿 (2) ✕ 🖾 🖩. 🚳

Buckerell

ST1200

Broadlands, *Buckerell, Honiton , Devon, EX14 3EP.* Charming house surrounded by country views, convenient for Exeter & South Coast. **Open:** All year **01404 850894** Mrs Pratt **D:** £20.00–£25.00 **S:** £25.00–£30.00 **Beds:** 2T 1D **Baths:** 2 En 1 Pr 🛇 🄿 (3) ✕ 🖾 🖩. 🚳

BATHROOMS
En = Ensuite
Pr = Private
Sh = Shared

Butterleigh

SS9708   🍴 *Butterleigh Inn*

Sunnyside Farmhouse, *Butterleigh, Cullompton, Devon, EX15 1PP.* Enjoy magnificent views, rolling hills and lush valleys of Devon. **Open:** All year (not Xmas) **01884 855322** B Hill **D:** £20.00–£22.00 **S:** £22.00 **Beds:** 1F 1T 2D **Baths:** 3 En 1 Pr 🛇 (5) 🄿 (4) 🖾 🍴 ✕ 🚳

Cadbury

SS9104   🍴 *Bell Inn, Thorverton Arms*

Beers Farm, *Cadbury, Exeter, Devon, EX5 5PY.* Comfortable farmhouse in beautiful countryside overlooking peaceful valley. Attractive gardens. **Open:** All year **01884 855426** Mrs Holmes *beersfarm@cs.com* **D:** £20.00 **S:** £20.00 **Beds:** 1F 1D **Baths:** 2 En 🛇 🄿 (6) ✕ 🖾. 🚳

Chagford

SX7087   🍴 *The Post*

Throwleigh Manor, *Throwleigh, Okehampton, Devon, EX20 2JF.* **Open:** All year **Grades:** ETC 4 Diamond **01647 231630 (also fax)** Mr & Mrs Smitheram *info@throwleighmanor.com* www.throwleighmanor.com **D:** £20.00– £26.00 **S:** £28.00–£38.00 **Beds:** 1F 1D 1S **Baths:** 1 En 2 Pr 🛇 (1) 🄿 (10) ✕ 🖾 🖩. 🚳 Beautiful country house set in 12 acres in idyllic, peaceful countryside of National Park. Tastefully decorated rooms, excellent breakfast and warm welcome. Heated swimming pool, games-room, woodland walk to private lake. Perfectly situated to explore whole of West Country.

St Johns West, *Chagford, Newton Abbot, Devon, TQ13 8HJ.* Tranquil setting, warm welcome, comfortable beds, sumptuous breakfasts. **Open:** All year **01647 432468** Mr & Mrs West *juwest@ ntlworld.com* **D:** £25.00 **S:** £30.00 **Beds:** 3T **Baths:** 3 En 🛇 (12) 🄿 (5) ✕ 🖾 🍴 ✕ 🖾 🖩. 🚳

Glendarah House, *Lower Street, Chagford, Newton Abbot, Devon, TQ13 8BZ.* Spacious Victorian house peaceful location. Five minutes' walk from village centre. **Open:** All year (not Xmas/New Year) **Grades:** ETC 4 Diamond, AA 4 Diamond
01647 433270 Mr & Mrs Croxen **Fax: 01647 433483** *enquiries@glendarah-house.co.uk* www.glendarah-house.co.uk **D:** £25.00–£32.00 **S:** £25.–£29.00 **Beds:** 3D 3T 1S **Baths:** 7 En (10) (7) cc

Cheriton Bishop

SX7793 *Drewe Arms*

Holly Farm, *Cheriton Bishop, Exeter, Devon, EX6 6JD.* Farm - edge of Dartmoor, stunning views, heated outdoor pool. **Open:** All year **Grades:** ETC 2 Diamond
01647 24616 *graham.sears@lineone.net* www.theaa.com/hotels/100359.html **D:** £20.00 **S:** £25.00–£30.00 **Beds:** 1T 2D **Baths:** 1 Pr (2) (8)

Cheriton Fitzpaine

SS8606

Jellicoe's, *Higher Holn, Upham, Cheriton Fitzpaine, Crediton, Devon, EX17 4HN.* Peaceful cottage and garden. Beautiful landscape. Convenient position. Exceptional food. **Open:** All year (not Xmas)
01363 866165 (also fax) Mr Jellicoe *jellicoes@higherholn.freeserve.co.uk* www.jellicoes.co.uk **D:** £22.00 **S:** £22.00 **Beds:** 2D 1T **Baths:** 3 En (4)

Chillington

SX7942 *Chillington Inn, Tradesman's Arms, Church Inn, Start Bay Inn, Open Arms, Mill Broook, Globe Inn*

Coleridge, *Chillington, Kingsbridge, Devon, TQ7 2JG.* Georgian farmhouse near Torcross and Slapton Nature Reserve, lovely beaches. **Open:** May to Oct
01548 580274 Mrs Darke **D:** £18.00 **S:** £18.00 **Beds:** 2T 1D **Baths:** 1 Pr 1 Sh (2)

Chudleigh

SX8679 *Old Coaching Inn, Bishop Lacey, Ship Inn, Highwayman's Haunt, Elizabethan Inn*

Huxbear Barton, *Teign Valley, Chudleigh, Newton Abbot, Devon, TQ13 0NY.* Spacious luxury barn conversion. Extensive grounds, pond, stream. Rural views. **Open:** All year (not Xmas)
01626 852670 Mrs Thomas **D:** £22.00–£24.50 **S:** £26.00–£30.00 **Beds:** 1T 1D 1S **Baths:** 1 En 1 Pr (12) (6)

Clawton

SX3599 *Molesworth Arms*

Claw House, *Clawton, Holsworthy, Devon, EX22 6QJ.* Georgian farmhouse in pretty village. Sea, moors nearby, every comfort. **Open:** All year
01409 253930 Mrs Wallis www.holsworthy.co.uk **D:** £17.00–£18.00 **S:** £18.00 **Beds:** 1F 1D 1S **Baths:** 1 En 1 Pr 1 Sh (6)

Court Barn Country Hotel, *Clawton, Holsworthy, Devon, EX22 6PS.* Charming country house, C17th origins, warm hospitality, log fires, food awards. **Open:** All year
01409 271219 Fax: 01409 271309 *courtbarnhotel@talk21.com* www.hotels-devon.com **D:** £25.00–£40.00 **S:** £35.00–£50.00 **Beds:** 1F 3T 3D 1S **Baths:** 8 En (16) cc

Clearbrook

SX5265

Sunbeam House, *Clearbrook, Yelverton, Devon, PL20 6JD.* Direct access to Dartmoor. Large double-fronted family house offering peace & tranquillity. **Open:** All year (not Xmas)
01822 853871 Ms Newberry **Fax: 01822 855672** *christine.newberry@lineone.net* **D:** £17.50 **S:** £20.00 **Beds:** 1D 1T **Baths:** 2 Sh (6)

Clovelly

SS3225 *Bell Inn*

Boat House Cottage, *148 Slerra Hill, Clovelly, Bideford, Devon, EX39 5ST.* Delightful C17th cottage. Sea views. Comfortable rooms, warm welcome **Open:** Jan to Dec
01237 431209 Mrs May **D:** £15.00–£16.00 **S:** £17.00–£18.00 **Beds:** 1F 1D 1T **Baths:** 1 En 1 Sh (3) (3)

The Old Smithy, *Slerra Hill, Clovelly, Bideford, Devon, EX39 5ST.* Cottage - converted C17th blacksmith's forge. Large rooms, warm welcome. **Open:** All year (not Xmas)
01237 431202 Mrs Vanstone **D:** £16.50–£20.50 **Beds:** 2F 1D **Baths:** 1 En 1 Pr 1 Sh (4)

Planning a longer stay? Always ask for any special rates

BATHROOMS
En = Ensuite
Pr = Private
Sh = Shared

Clyst Honiton

SX9893

Holbrook Farm, *Clyst Honiton, Exeter, Devon, EX5 2HR.* Delightful rooms with beautiful countryside views (own entrance, unrestricted access). Tasty breakfasts, fresh produce. **Open:** All year
01392 367000 Mrs Glanvill *heatherglanvill@holbrookfarm.co.uk* www.holbrookfarm.co.uk **D:** £19.00–£21.00 **S:** £18.00–£25.00 **Beds:** 1F 1D 1T **Baths:** 3 En (4)

Clyst Hydon

ST0301

Town Tenement Farm, *Clyst Hydon, Cullompton, Devon, EX15 2NB.* C16th farmhouse in quiet village, comfortable stop for good food. **Open:** All year (not Xmas)
01884 277230 Ms Coleman **D:** £16.00 **Beds:** 1D 1T 1F **Baths:** 1 En 1 Sh cc

Clyst St George

SX9888

Marianne Pool Farm, *Clyst St George, Exeter, Devon, EX3 0NZ.* Peaceful, thatched Devon longhouse overlooking countryside between Exeter and coast. **Open:** Mar to Nov
01392 874939 Mrs Bragg **D:** £18.00–£20.00 **S:** £18.00–£25.00 **Beds:** 1F 1T **Baths:** 1 En 1 Sh (2)

Clyst St Mary

SX9791 *Green Door*

Postlake Farm, *Clyst St Mary, Exeter, Devon, EX5 1AP.* Beautiful, individual rooms. Explore Exmouth, Exeter, Dartmoor. **Open:** All year
01395 232298 *postlake@lineone.net* **D:** £21.00–£25.00 **S:** £22.00–£27.00 **Beds:** 1F 1T 1D **Baths:** 3 En

Cockington

SX8963

Fairmount House Hotel, *Herbert Road, Cockington, Torquay, Devon, TQ2 6RW.* Unhurried English breakfast, quiet undisturbed nights. Small hotel in peaceful setting. **Open:** Mar to Oct
01803 605446 (also fax) Mr Richards **D:** £25.00–£35.50 **S:** £25.00–£35.50 **Beds:** 2F 2T 4D 2S **Baths:** 8 En (12) (9) cc

Colebrooke

SS7700

The Oyster, *Colebrooke, Crediton, Devon,*
EX17 5JQ. Peaceful, homely, modern,
spacious bungalow in beautiful mid-Devon.
Tea/coffee facilities & TV. **Open:** All year
01363 84576 Mrs Hockridge **D:** £17.00
S: £17.00 **Beds:** 2D 1T **Baths:** 1 En 2 Pr ⮕ 🖳
📺 🛏 🖭 🕭 🏖

Colyford

SY2592

Horriford Farm, *Holyford Lane, Colyford,*
Colyton, Devon, EX24 6HW. Attractive C16th
farmhouse in quiet valley, close to coast
near Devon/Dorset border. **Open:** All year
(not Xmas)
01297 552316 Mr & Mrs Pady *horriford@*
aol.com www.datacottage.com/horriford.htm
D: £20.00–£21.00 **S:** £18.00 **Beds:** 1D 1T 2S
Baths: 2 En 1 Pr ⮕ 🖳 (3) 🗶 📺 🖭 🕭

Colyton

SY2493

Bonehayne Farm, *Colyton, Devon,*
EX24 6SG. Clean/tidy working farm. Glorious
views, walks, fishing, coast 10 mins.
Open: All year
01404 871416 Mrs Gould *thisfarm33@*
netscapeonline.co.uk
members.netscapeonline.co.uk/thisfarm33
D: £16.00–£18.00 **S:** £18.00–£20.00 **Beds:** 1F
1D **Baths:** 1 Pr ⮕ 🖳 🗶 📺 🖭 🕭

Combe Martin

SS5846   🍺 *Dolphin Inn*

**Royal
Marine,**
*Seaside, Combe
Martin,
Ilfracombe,
EX34 0AW.* Award
winning pub
with five superbly appointed ensuite rooms,
home cooked food, sea views. **Open:** All
year
01271 882470 Mr Lethaby **Fax: 01271 889080**
www.combemartintouristinformation.com
D: £20.00–£25.00 **S:** £20.00–£25.00 **Beds:** 5F
Baths: 5 En ⮕ 🖳 📺 🖭 🕭 cc

Glendower, *King Street, Combe Martin,*
Ilfracombe, Devon, EX34 0AL. Small seaside
guest house near beach and Coastal Path.
Open: All year (not Xmas) and Coastal Path.
01271 883449 F J Barry *frankjbarry@*
netscapeonline.co.uk **D:** £18.00–£20.00
S: £20.00–£25.00 **Beds:** 3T 3D 3S **Baths:** 2
En 1 Sh ⮕ 🖳 (3) 🗶 📺 🛏 🗶 📺 🕭

Crimond, *King Street, Combe Martin,*
Ilfracombe, EX34 0BS. Friendly comfortable
Victorian house. Hearty English breakfast.
Close to sea. **Open:** All year (not Xmas)
01271 88234801271 882348
  Mr Parkes **Fax:**   **D:** £17.00 **S:** £17.00
Beds: 1F 1D 1T 1S **Baths:** 1 Sh 4 En ⮕ 🗶
📺 🛏 🖭 🕭

Cotleigh

ST2001

Barn Park Farm, *Stockland Hill,*
Stockland, Honiton, Devon, EX14 9JA.
Traditional old Devon dairy farm, excellent
walking country, abundance of wildlife.
Open: All year (not Xmas/New Year)
01404 861297 & 0800 3282605 (freephone)
Mrs Boyland **Fax: 01404 861297** *pab@*
barnparkfarm.co.uk **D:** £17.00–£20.00
S: £20.00 **Beds:** 1F 1T 1D 1S **Baths:** 2 En 1
Pr 1 Sh ⮕ 🖳 (10) 🗶 📺 🛏 🗶 📺 🕭

Countisbury

SS7449   🍺 *Rockford Inn, Staghunters Inn*

Coombe Farm, *Countisbury, Lynton,*
Devon, EX35 6NF. Homemade bread and
marmalade served in comfortable C17th
stone built farmhouse. **Open:** Mar to Nov
Grades: ETC 3 Diamond
01598 741236 (also fax) S Pile *coombefarm@*
freeuk.com **D:** £20.00–£25.00 **Beds:** 2F 1T 2D
Baths: 2 En 2 Sh ⮕ 🖳 (8) 🗶 📺 🛏 🖭 🕭 cc

Creacombe

SS8219

Creacombe Parsonage, *Parsonage*
Cross, Creacombe, Rackenford, Tiverton,
Devon, EX16 8EL. C17th farmhouse in open
countryside, views of Dartmoor. Ideal spot
to rest. **Open:** All year
01884 881441 Mrs Poole **Fax: 01884 881551**
creaky.parson@dial.pipex.com **D:** £18.00
S: £18.00 **Beds:** 1F 2T **Baths:** 1 Sh 1 En ⮕ 🖳
🗶 📺 🛏 🗶 📺 🖭 🕭 cc

Crediton

SS8300

Taw Vale, *2*
Taw Vale,
Crediton, Devon,
EX17 3BU.
Open: All year
01363 777879
(also fax)
Mrs Whitby **D:** £18.00–£20.00 **S:** £19.00–
£22.00 **Beds:** 1F 1D 1T **Baths:** 2 En 1 Pr ⮕
🖳 (3) 🗶 📺 🖭 🕭
Listed Georgian-style family home on edge
of Crediton. Ideal touring base for
Dartmoor, Exmoor and both coasts. Easy
access to Exeter and beyond, via bus and
train. 6 National Trust properties within 30
minutes. Choice of Aga cooked breakfasts.

Creedy Manor, *Long Barn, Crediton,*
Devon, EX17 4AB. Victorian farmhouse,
picturesque peaceful comfort. Town 0.5
mile. Also self-catering apartments.
Open: All year
01363 772684 (also fax) Mrs Turner
creedymanor@eclipse.co.uk **D:** £18.00–£25.00
S: £19.50 **Beds:** 1D 1T 1F **Baths:** 3 En ⮕
🖳 (6) 🗶 📺 📺 🖭 🕭 🕭

**Libbetts
Cottage,**
*Church Street,
Crediton, Devon,
EX17 2AQ.* A great
taste of Devon in
lovely olde
worlde cottage. **Open:** All year
01363 772709 Mrs Venn www.s-h-systems.co.
uk/hotels/libbetts **D:** £22.00 **S:** £30.00
Beds: 1D 1T **Baths:** 1 Pr ⮕ (6) 🖳 (2) 🗶 📺 🗶 📺
🖭 🌸 🕭

Croyde

SS4439   🍺 *Thatched Barn, Billy Budds*

Moorsands,
*Moor Lane,
Croyde Bay,
Braunton,
Devon, EX33 1NP.*
Open: All year
Grades: ETC 3
Diamond
01271 890781 Mr & Mrs Davis
www.croyde-bay.com/moorsands.htm
D: £20.00–£26.00 **S:** £20.00–£26.00 **Beds:** 1F
1T 2D **Baths:** 4 En ⮕ 🖳 (6) 🗶 📺 🖭 🕭
Originally a large Victorian coast guard
station with stunning views, Moorsands
offers short walks to beach, village and
local facilities. Surf, ride, cycle etc. or
simply relax with our comfortable ensuite
rooms, guest lounge, beautiful
surroundings, warm welcome and superb
breakfasts.

Vale Cottage, *Croyde, Braunton, Devon,*
EX33 1PL. One of the oldest Devon thatched
longhouses, with ensuite. **Open:** All year
(not Xmas)
01271 890804 Mrs Adey *mail@*
valecottage.co.uk www.valecottage.co.uk
D: £25.00–£30.00 **Beds:** 3D **Baths:** 3 En 🖳 (3)
🗶 📺 📺 🖭 🕭

Oamaru, *Down End, Croyde, Braunton,*
Devon, EX33 1QE. 400m from top surfing
beach and village. Relaxed friendly
atmosphere. **Open:** All year
01271 890765 Mr & Mrs Jenkins *philcroyde@*
hotmail.com **D:** £17.50–£25.00 **S:** £17.50–
£25.00 **Beds:** 1F 1D **Baths:** 1 En 1 Pr ⮕ 🖳 (6)
🗶 📺 📺 🖭 🕭 cc

Cullompton

ST0106

**Sunnyside
Farmhouse,**
*Butterleigh,
Cullompton,
Devon, EX15 1PP.*
Enjoy
magnificent
views, rolling
hills and lush valleys of Devon. **Open:** All
year (not Xmas)
01884 855322 B Hill **D:** £20.00–£22.00
S: £22.00 **Beds:** 1F 1T 2D **Baths:** 3 En 1 Pr
⮕ (5) 🖳 (4) 📺 🛏 🗶 🕭

Oburnford Farm, *Cullompton, Devon,*
EX15 1LZ. Georgian farmhouse. Within easy
reach of exploring main Devon attractions.
Open: All year
01884 32292 Mrs Chumbley **D:** £20.00
S: £23.00 **Beds:** 3F 4D 5S **Baths:** 3 En 1
Pr ⌂ ▣ (10) 📺 ⌁ ✕ Ⅴ 🍴 ⚓

Wishay, *Trinity, Cullompton, Devon,*
EX15 1PE. Spacious farmhouse in peaceful
countryside. Ideal touring base. **Open:** All
year (not Xmas/New Year) **Grades:** ETC 3
Diamond
01884 33223 (also fax) Mrs Baker **D:** £16.00–
£18.00 **Beds:** 2F **Baths:** 1 En 1 Sh ⌂ ▣ (2) 📺
🍴 ⚓

Dartmouth

SX8751 ⚓ *Queen's Arms, Tower Inn*

Greenswood Farm, *Greenswood Lane,*
Dartmouth, Devon, TQ6 0LY. **Open:** All year
01803 712100 Mrs Baron **D:** £20.00–£27.00
S: £25.00 **Beds:** 1F 1T 1D **Baths:** 3 En ⌂ (12)
▣ (8) 🍴 📺 ✕ 🍴 ⚓
A C15th Devon longhouse set in its own
secluded valley, with large sub-tropical
gardens. A haven for wildlife. Only 4 miles
to Dartmouth, Start Bay and Slapton Ley
nature reserve. 2 miles to Dartmouth golf
and country club.

**Browns
Norton Farm,**
Dartmouth,
Devon, TQ6 0ND.
Charming C17th
farmhouse with
sloping ceilings,
modern
bathroom
shower etc. **Open:** All year (not Xmas/New
Year)
01803 712321 Mrs Bond **D:** £15.00–£20.00
S: £12.50 **Beds:** 1T 1D 1S **Baths:** 1 Sh ▣ 🍴
📺 ⚓

The Cedars, *79 Victoria Road, Dartmouth,*
Devon, TQ6 9RX. The Cedars, level location,
near town centre, friendly welcome.
Open: All year (not Xmas)
01803 834421 Mrs Greeno **D:** £19.00–£20.00
S: £18.00–£20.00 **Beds:** 2F 1D 2T 1S
Baths: 1 Sh ⌂ 📺 ⌁ 🍴 ⚓

Planning a longer stay? Always
ask for any special rates

Valley House, *46 Victoria Road,*
Dartmouth, Devon, TQ6 9DZ. Comfortable,
small, friendly guest house. **Open:** Feb to
Dec
01803 834045 Mr & Mrs Ellis **D:** £21.00–
£25.00 **S:** £25.00–£30.00 **Beds:** 2D 2T
Baths: 4 En ▣ (4) 🍴 📺 🍴 ⚓

Sunnybanks, *1 Vicarage Hill, Dartmouth,*
Devon, TQ6 9EW. Friendly atmosphere.
Excellent breakfasts & just minutes from
the River Dart. **Open:** All year
01803 832766 (also fax) sue@sunnybanks.com
www.sunnybanks.com **D:** £21.00–£25.00
S: £20.00–£30.00 **Beds:** 2F 2T 5D 1S
Baths: 8 En 1 Pr 1 Sh ⌂ ▣ (2) 📺 ⌁ ✕ 🍴 ⚓

Dawlish

SX9676 ⚓ *Anchor Inn*

Ocean's Guest House, *9 Marine*
Parade, Dawlish, Devon, EX7 9DJ.
Open: Easter to Nov
01626 888139 **D:** £20.00–£30.00 **S:** £30.00–
£45.00 **Beds:** 3F 3T 9D 1S **Baths:** 16 En ⌂ ▣
🍴 📺 🍴 ⚓ ✕
Seafront location. Some sea views, all
ensuite, TV, tea/coffee making facilities,
balcony use overlooking sea. Full English
breakfast. Rooms on ground floor for
people with walking disabilities and ramp
for wheelchairs. Non-smoking.

Diptford

SX7256

Charford Manor, *Diptford, Totnes,*
Devon, TQ9 7LT. Friendly, family-run
restaurant with rooms in beautiful south
countryside. **Open:** All year (not Xmas/New
Year)
01364 73111 Mr & Mrs Trott **Fax:** 01364
72214 **D:** £17.50–£25.00 **S:** £30.00–£40.00
Beds: 1F 2D **Baths:** 2 En 1 Pr ⌂ ▣ 📺 ✕ ⚓
cc

Doddiscombsleigh

SX8586

**Whitemoor
Farm,**
Doddiscomb-
sleigh, Exeter,
Devon, EX6 7PU.
C16th thatched
farmhouse with
oak beams,
central heating, home produce. **Open:** All
year (not Xmas)
01647 252423 **D:** £18.50–£19.50 **S:** £19.50–
£20.00 **Beds:** 1D 1T 2S **Baths:** 1 Sh ⌂ ▣ (4)
🍴 📺 ⌁ ✕ 🍴 ⚓

Dolton

SS5712

Robin Cottage, *Church Street, Dolton,*
Winkleigh, Devon, EX19 8QE. Modernised
cottage situated near church in attractive
Devon village, near RHS Rosemoor Garden.
Open: All year
01805 804430 S Newman **D:** £18.00–£20.00
S: £18.00–£20.00 **Beds:** 1T 1S **Baths:** 1 En 1
Sh ⌂ (12) 🍴 📺 ⚓

Drewsteignton

SX7390 ⚓ *Old Inn, Drewe Arms, Anglers Rest.*

**The Old Inn Restaurant and Guest
House,** *The Square, Drewsteignton,*
Exeter, Devon, EX6 6QR. **Open:** All year
01647 281276 (also fax) Mr & Mrs Gribble
oldgribb@talk21.com www.smoothhound.co.
uk/hotels/oldinn.html **D:** £20.25–£27.50
S: £31.50–£40.00 **Beds:** 1F 1T 2D **Baths:** 2
En 1 Pr 1 Sh ⌂ ▣ (3) 📺 ⌁ ✕ 🍴 ⚓
Comfortable former C18th Inn in the village
square. One mile South of A30 and from
Castle Drogo and Fingle Bridge. Chagford 4
Miles, Okehampton 10 and Exeter 13.
Fishing and superb walks. Member
Dartmoor Tourist Association. Renowned
breakfasts. Three nights less 10%.

East Fingle Farm, *Drewsteignton,*
Exeter, Devon, EX6 6NJ. Devon farm
longhouse, beautiful views, friendly farm
animals, warm welcome, children half-
price. **Open:** All year
01647 281639 Mrs Cordy **D:** £18.00–£21.00
S: £18.00–£21.00 **Beds:** 3F 2T 1D **Baths:** 2
En 2 Pr ⌂ ▣ (10) 🍴 📺 ✕ Ⅴ ⚓

Puddicombe House,
Drewsteignton, Exeter, Devon, EX6 6RD. Converted apple store in Georgian house. Beautiful grounds. Dartmoor National Park. **Open:** All year (not Xmas/New Year) **01647 281206** Ms Hodge *judith.hodge@ virgin.net* **D:** £25.00 **S:** £30.00 **Beds:** 1D **Baths:** 1 En ⌂ ⊠ ✗ ⊠ ⌂ ✕ Ⓥ ▥ ♨

Dunsford

SX8189 ◀ *Bridford Inn, Artichoke, Ashton Manor, Royal Oak, Old Thatch Inn, Nobody Inn*

Oak Lodge, *The Court, Dunsford, Exeter, Devon, EX6 7DD.* **Open:** All year (not Xmas/New Year) **Grades:** ETC 4 Diamond, Silver **01647 252829** Ms Hodge *shirley.hodge@ virgin.net* www.oaklodge-devon.co.uk **D:** £18.00–£24.00 **S:** £25.00–£40.00 **Beds:** 1F 1T 1D **Baths:** 1 En 1 Pr ⌂ ⊠ (2) ✕ Ⓥ ⊠ ▥ ♨ Peacefully situated in picturesque Dartmoor village. Award winning breakfast. High quality accommodation with beautiful views. Ideal touring/walking area. Close to National Trust Properties. Eden Project one hour away. Exeter seven miles. Bargain breaks available. Telephone for brochure.

East Allington

SX7648

Tor Cottage, *The Mounts, East Allington, Totnes, Devon, TQ9 7QJ.* Warm welcome. Beautiful country views, central location, superb breakfasts. **Open:** All year **01548 521316 (also fax)** Mr Larner *john@ torcottage.freeserve.co.uk* www.torcottage. freeserve.co.uk **D:** £14.00–£19.00 **S:** £14.00– £19.00 **Beds:** 2F **Baths:** 2 En 1 Pr ⌂ (2) ⊠ (5) ✕ Ⓥ ⊠ ▥ ♨

The Fortescue Arms, *East Allington, Totnes, Devon, TQ9 7RA.* Delightful Devon inn with superb restaurant - CAMRA recommended real ales. **Open:** All year (not Xmas/New Year) **01548 521215** Mr Gledhill *steve_trish@ talk21.com* www.webmachine.co. uk/fortescue/ **D:** £17.50–£22.50 **S:** £22.50– £30.00 **Beds:** 3D 1T **Baths:** 2 En 2 Sh ⊠ (10) ✕ ⊠ ⌂ ✗ Ⓥ ▥ ♨ cc

East Anstey

SS8626

Threadneedle, *East Anstey, Tiverton, Devon, EX16 9JH.* Built in the style of a Devon Longhouse, set in 3 acres, close Dulverton. **Open:** All year **01398 341598** Mr & Mrs Webb **D:** £23.00– £25.00 **S:** £23.00–£25.00 **Beds:** 1D 1T **Baths:** 2 En ⌂ ⊠ (10) ✕ ⊠ ⌂ Ⓥ ▥ ♨

East Budleigh

SY0684

Wynards Farm, *East Budleigh, Budleigh Salterton, Devon, EX9 7DQ.* Farmhouse Bed & Breakfast on a working farm in heart of Raleigh country. **Open:** Easter to Oct **01395 443417 (also fax)** Mrs Smith *jsmith17@talk21.com* **D:** £18.00–£20.00 **S:** £20.00–£25.00 **Beds:** 1F 1D 1T **Baths:** 2 Sh ⌂ (1) ⊠ (3) ✕ ⊠ Ⓥ ▥ ♨

East Ogwell

SX8370

Milton Farm, *East Ogwell, Newton Abbot, Devon, TQ12 6AT.* Bungalow in picturesque village - 7 miles Torbay, golf 3 miles. **Open:** Mar to Nov **01626 354988** **D:** £16.50–£18.00 **S:** £18.00– £20.00 **Beds:** 1T 1D **Baths:** 1 Sh ⌂ ⊠ (3) ✕ ⊠ ▥

East Prawle

SX7836

Stures Court, *East Prawle, Kingsbridge, Devon, TQ7 2BY.* C17th thatched cottage with C21st comfort. Highly commended by guests. **Open:** All year **01548 511261** Miss Benson **D:** £18.00–£20.00 **S:** £19.00–£21.00 **Beds:** 2D 2S **Baths:** 1 Sh ⌂ (7) ✕ ⊠ Ⓥ ▥ ♨

Eastleigh

SS4927 ◀ *Crab Inn, Ale House*

Pillhead Farm, *Old Barnstaple Road, Bideford, Devon, EX39 4NF.* Extra special breakfasts in delightful, well-located period farmhouse. **Open:** All year **01237 479337** Mr & Mrs Hill *hill@ pillheadfarm.fsnet.co.uk* **D:** £17.00–£23.00 **S:** £20.00 **Beds:** 1F 1T 2D **Baths:** 2 En 2 Pr ⌂ ⊠ (8) ✕ ⊠ ✗ Ⓥ ▥ ♨

Ebford

SX9887

Ebford Court, *Ebford, Exeter, Devon, EX3 0RA.* C15th peaceful thatched farmhouse. Close to sea and moors. **Open:** All year (not Xmas) **01392 875353** Mrs Howard **Fax:** **01392 876776 D:** £17.00–£19.00 **S:** £17.00–£19.00 **Beds:** 1D 1T 1S **Baths:** 1 Sh ⌂ (8) ⊠ (7) ✕ ⊠ ✕ Ⓥ ▥ ♨

Little Holt, *Ebford Lane, Ebford, Exeter, Devon, EX3 0QX.* C18th coaching cottage, quiet hamlet, tranquil gardens: roses, honeysuckle, jasmine, pond & woodlands. **Open:** May to Oct **01392 876945 (also fax)** Ms Schoenburg **D:** £16.00–£20.00 **S:** £18.00–£22.00 **Beds:** 1D **Baths:** 1 En ✕ ⊠ ♨

Ermington

SX6453 ◀ *Rose & Crown*

Waye Farm, *The Grange, Ermington, Ivybridge, Devon, PL21 9NU.* Offering high standard accommodation and a hearty English breakfast. **Open:** Mar to Dec **01752 830427** Mr & Mrs Livermore *andrea@ livermore44.fsnet.co.uk* **D:** £20.00–£22.00 **S:** £28.00–£30.00 **Beds:** 1T 1D **Baths:** 2 En ⌂ ⊠ (2) ⊠ Ⓥ ▥ ♨

Exeter

SX9192 ◀ *Harry's*

The Grange,
Stoke Hill, Exeter, Devon, EX4 7JH. Country house in private grounds, wooded location overlooking Exeter, surrounding countryside. **Open:** All year **Grades:** ETC 3 Diamond **01392 259723** Mr Dudley *dudleythegrange@ aol.com* **D:** £18.00–£21.00 **S:** £26.00–£28.00 **Beds:** 4D **Baths:** 4 En ⌂ ⊠ (8) ✕ ⊠ ▥ ♨

Hotel Maurice,
5 Bystock Terrace, Exeter, Devon, EX4 4HY. Town house in quiet Georgian square in the heart of the city.
Open: All year (not Xmas) **01392 213079** Mr Wenley *hotel.maurice@ eclipse.co.uk* www.hotelmaurice.eclipse.co.uk **D:** £17.00–£19.00 **S:** £22.00 **Beds:** 1F 3D 2T 2S **Baths:** 8 En ⌂ (3) ⊠ (1) ✕ ⊠ ▥ ♨ cc

Marianne Pool Farm,
Clyst St George, Exeter, Devon, EX3 0NZ. Peaceful, thatched Devon longhouse overlooking countryside between Exeter and coast. **Open:** Mar to Nov **01392 874939** Mrs Bragg **D:** £18.00–£20.00 **S:** £18.00–£25.00 **Beds:** 1F 1T **Baths:** 1 En 1 Sh ⌂ ⊠ (2) ⊠ ⌂ Ⓥ ♨

Wood Barton, *Farringdon, Exeter, Devon, EX5 2HY.* Ensuite accommodation. 3 miles M5 junction 30. **Open:** All year **01395 233407** J D Bolt **Fax:** 01395 277226 *jackie_bolt@hotmail.com* **D:** £21.00–£25.00 **S:** £25.00–£30.00 **Beds:** 1F 1T 1D **Baths:** 3 En ⌂ ⊠ ✕ ⊠ ▥ ♨

Ebford Court, *Ebford, Exeter, Devon, EX3 0RA.* C15th peaceful thatched farmhouse. Close to sea and moors. **Open:** All year (not Xmas) **01392 875353** Mrs Howard **Fax: 01392 876776 D:** £17.00–£19.00 **S:** £17.00–£19.00 **Beds:** 1D 1T 1S **Baths:** 1 Sh ♥ (8) ⊕(7) ⊬ ⊙ ⊁ ⊻ ⊞ ⚓

Dunmore Hotel, *22 Blackall Road, Exeter, Devon, EX4 4HE.* Close to city centre, coach and railway stations and university. **Open:** All year **01392 431643** (also fax) Mr & Mrs Gilderthorp *dunmorehtl@aol.com* **D:** £18.00– £21.00 **S:** £20.00–£26.00 **Beds:** 3F 2D 1T 2S **Baths:** 5 En 3 Sh ♥ ⊙ ⊻ × ⊻ ⊞ ⚓ cc

St David's Guest House, *89 St David's Hill, Exeter, Devon, EX4 4DW.* Stations and city 10 mins walk. Good selection restaurants nearby. **Open:** All year **01392 434737** (also fax) Mr & Mrs Morris **D:** £15.00–£17.50 **S:** £15.00–£25.00 **Beds:** 1F 2D 2T 1S **Baths:** 4 En 1 Sh ♥ ⊕(4) ⊁ ⊁ ⊻ ⊞ ⚓

Crossmead, *Barley Lane, Dunsford Hill, Exeter, Devon, EX4 1TF.* Comfortable bedrooms within beautiful landscaped grounds of attractive Victorian house. **Open:** All year (not Xmas) **01392 273703** Mrs Snow **Fax: 01392 422594** *crossmead@exeter.ac.uk* **D:** £18.75–£27.50 **S:** £19.95–£32.50 **Beds:** 33D 15T 39S **Baths:** 52 En 30 Sh ♥ ⊕ ⊻ ⊻ ⊞ ⚓ cc

The Old Mill, *Mill Lane, Alphington, Exeter, Devon, EX2 8SG.* Historical premises in quiet area. Full farm breakfast. Recommended for 28 years. **Open:** All year **01392 259977** Mrs Marchant **D:** £10.50– £14.00 **S:** £10.50–£15.00 **Beds:** 2F 1D 1T 1S **Baths:** 1 Pr 1 Sh ♥ ⊕(8) ⊁ ⊻ ⊻ ⚓

Raffles Hotel, *11 Blackall Road, Exeter, Devon, EX4 4HD.* Centrally located Victorian townhouse, beautifully maintained with antique furniture. **Open:** All year **01392 270200** (also fax) *raffleshtl@ btinternet.com* raffles_exeter.co.uk **D:** £25.00 **S:** £34.00–£38.00 **Beds:** 1F 2T 2D 2S **Baths:** 7 En ♥ ⊕(6) ⊁ ⊻ ⊁ × ⊻ ⊞ ⚓ cc

Tanglewood, *Little Silver Lane, Matford, Exeter, Devon, EX2 8XZ.* Pleasantly situated bungalow in own grounds with rural views. Off-road parking. **Open:** Apr to Oct **01392 832556** Mrs Perks **D:** £15.00–£16.00 **S:** £16.00–£17.00 **Beds:** 1F 1D 1T **Baths:** 1 Sh ⊕(8) ⊙ × ⊻ ⊞ ⚓

2 Deanery Place, *Exeter, Devon, EX1 1HU.* Dating from C14th, looking out onto Cathedral, secluded from passing noise & traffic. **Open:** All year **01392 490081** Mrs Somers **D:** £26.50–£29.50 **S:** £23.00–£24.00 **Beds:** 2D 1S **Baths:** 2 En 1 Sh

Montgomery House, *144 Fore Street, Exeter, Devon, EX4 3AN.* Very large, well-furnished, quiet rooms in city centre, close cathedral, shops & quay. **Open:** All year **01392 424086** *0113@fsmail.net* **D:** £24.00– £28.00 **S:** £32.00–£38.00 **Beds:** 2T 2D **Baths:** 4 En ⊙ ⊞ ⚓ cc

Exmouth

SY0081 ⚓ *The Beach, Grove Inn*

The Swallows, *11 Carlton Hill, Exmouth, Devon, EX8 2AJ.* **Open:** All year **01395 263937 Fax: 01395 271040** *swallows@amserve.net* **D:** £20.00– £25.00 **S:** £30.00–£40.00 **Beds:** 1F 1T 2D **Baths:** 4 En 1 Pr ♥ ⊕(5) ⊁ ⊻ × ⊻ ⊞ ⚓ cc The Swallows Guest House is a late Georgian house tastefully converted and modernised whilst retaining its comfortable and peaceful atmosphere. Situated in attractive residential area close to the seafront and town centre.

Hope Cottage, *The Strand, Lympstone, Exmouth, Devon, EX8 5JS.* C15th cottage in beautiful village on Exe estuary (Mr & Mrs Clarke). **Open:** All year **01395 268349** Mr Clarke **D:** £17.50 **S:** £17.50 **Beds:** 3D 1T **Baths:** 1 En 1 Sh ⊕ ⊻ ⚓

Exton

SX9886

Chatfield, *Exmouth Road, Exton, Exeter, Devon, EX3 0PQ.* Edwardian house near Topsham, coast, motorway. Large garden. Comfortable rooms. **Open:** All year (not Xmas/New Year) **01392 874135** *chatfield@exton.freeserve.co.uk* **D:** £18.00–£22.00 **S:** £20.00–£25.00 **Beds:** 1F 1T 2D **Baths:** 2 En 1 Sh ♥ ⊕(8) ⊁ ⊻ ⊻ ⊞ ⚓

Farringdon

SY0191 ⚓ *White Horse*

Wood Barton, *Farringdon, Exeter, Devon, EX5 2HY.* Ensuite accommodation. 3 miles M5 junction 30. **Open:** All year **01395 233407** J D Bolt **Fax: 01395 277226** *jackie_bolt@hotmail.com* **D:** £21.00–£25.00 **S:** £25.00–£30.00 **Beds:** 1F 1T 1D **Baths:** 3 En ♥ ⊕ ⊁ ⊻ ⊞ ⚓

Fenny Bridges

SY1198

Little Ash Farm, *Fenny Bridges, Honiton, Devon, EX14 0BL.* Warm welcome at comfortable farmhouse. Large peaceful garden, mini golf. **Open:** All year (not Xmas) **01404 850271** Mrs Reid **D:** £14.00–£18.50 **S:** £14.00–£18.00 **Beds:** 1F 1T 1S **Baths:** 1 En ♥ ⊕(4) ⊁ ⊻ × ⊻ ⊞ ⚓

Fluxton

SY0892 ⚓ *Bowd Inn, Golden Lion, Fairmile Inn*

Fluxton Farm, *Fluxton, Ottery St Mary, Devon, EX11 1RJ.* Cat lovers paradise in lovely open countryside. Ideal touring area. **Open:** All year **Grades:** AA 2 Diamond **01404 812818** Mr & Mrs Forth **Fax: 01404 814843 D:** £25.00 **S:** £25.00 **Beds:** 1F 5T 3D 2S **Baths:** 11 En ♥ ⊕(15) ⊙ ⊁ × ⊻ ⊞ ⚓

Fremington

SS5132

Lower Yelland Farm, *Yelland Road, Fremington, Barnstaple, Devon, EX31 3EN.* North Devon Coast beautifully situated period house on Taw Estuary. **Open:** All year (not Xmas/New Year) **01271 860101** (also fax) Mr Day **D:** £20.00 **S:** £20.00 **Beds:** 1T 2D **Baths:** 3 En ♥ ⊕(6) ⊙ ⊁ ⊻ ⊞ ⚓

Gooseford

SX6791

Fairhaven Farm, *Gooseford, Whiddon Down, Okehampton, Devon, EX20 2QH.* Magnificent views of patchwork fields with rising hills of Dartmoor beyond. **Open:** All year (not Xmas/New Year) **01647 231261** Mrs Scott www.guestbeds.com **D:** £20.00–£24.00 **S:** £20.00–£24.00 **Beds:** 1F 1D **Baths:** 1 En 1 Sh ♥ ⊕(4) ⊙ ⊁ × ⚓

Hallsands

SX8138

Widget, *Hallsands, Kingsbridge, Devon, TQ7 2EX.* **Open:** All year (not Xmas) **01548 511110** Mrs Wolstenholme **D:** £20.00–£25.00 **S:** £20.00–£25.00 **Beds:** 2D 1T **Baths:** 1 En 1 Pr ♥ ⊕(4) ⊁ ⊻ ⊻ ⚓ A brand new bungalow 50 yards from the beach and coastal path in a wonderful peaceful area for relaxing or using as a base for the beautiful South Hams. A warm welcome, lovely accommodation and unbeatable breakfast await you.

Hartland

SS2624 ⚓ *Farmer's Arms*

Greenlake Farm, *Hartland, Bideford, Devon, EX39 6DN.* Warm welcome, old farmhouse on working farm in unspoilt countryside. **Open:** Easter to Nov **01237 441251** Mrs Heard **D:** £16.00–£18.00 **S:** £16.00–£18.00 **Beds:** 1F 1D **Baths:** 2 En ♥ ⊕ ⊻ ⊁ × ⚓

Hartland Quay
SS2224

Hartland Quay Hotel, *Hartland Quay, Hartland, Bideford, Devon, EX39 6DU.* An historic building on South West Coast Path. Fantastic views. **Open:** All year (not Xmas) **01237 441218** Mrs Johns **Fax: 01237 441371** *hartlandquayhotel@supanet.co.uk* www.harlandquayhotel.com **D:** £25.00–£27.00 **S:** £25.00–£27.00 **Beds:** 5F 4T 6D 2S **Baths:** 12 En 3 Pr 2 Sh ⚡🏠 (50) 📺 🛏 ✕ 📺 **cc**

Hatherleigh
SS5404

Pressland Country House Hotel, *Hatherleigh, Okehampton, Devon, EX20 3LW.* **Open:** Mar to Dec **Grades:** ETC 4 Diamond **01837 810871 Fax: 01837 810303** *accom@ presslandhouse.co.uk* www.presslandhouse.co. uk **D:** £25.00–£35.00 **S:** £33.00–£38.00 **Beds:** 2T 3D **Baths:** 4 En 1 Pr ⚡(12) 📼(6) ⚥ 📺 ✕ 📺 📺 🖬 ⚑ **cc** Delightful and spacious Victorian house set in 5 acres of landscaped garden, with glorious views of Dartmoor and surrounding countryside. The family-run hotel is licensed and there is a large, comfortable lounge, separate bar and a restaurant of growing repute.

Seldon Farm, *Monkokehampton, Winkleigh, Devon, EX19 8RY.* Charming C17th farmhouse in beautiful, tranquil, rural setting. **Open:** Easter to Oct **Grades:** ETC 2 Diamond **01837 810312** Mrs Case **D:** £20.00 **S:** £23.00 **Beds:** 1F 2D **Baths:** 1 Pr 1 En ⚡📼🏠🐾🛏⚑

Hawkchurch
ST3300

Castle House, *Hawkchurch, Axminster, Devon, EX13 5UA.* Comfortable Grade II Listed house set in 2 acres of beautiful gardens. **Open:** All year (not Xmas/New Year) **01297 678291** Mrs Lewis **D:** £18.00–£20.00 **S:** £18.00–£20.00 **Beds:** 1T 2D **Baths:** 1 En 1 Pr 1 Sh ⚡📼(4) ⚥ 📺 📺 ⚑

Please respect a B&B's wishes regarding children, animals and smoking

---

BEDROOMS
D = Double
T = Twin
S = Single
F = Family

Hele (Ilfracombe)
SS5347

Moles Farmhouse, *Old Berrynarbor Road, Hele, Ilfracombe, Devon, EX34 9RB.* Beautifully restored former farmhouse, situated in picturesque Hele Valley, near Ilfracombe. **Open:** All year **01271 862099 (also fax)** Ms Grindlay *wendy@ molesfarmhouse.freeserve.co.uk* www.molesfarmhouse.co.uk **D:** £17.00–£20.00 **Beds:** 1F 1T 1D **Baths:** 2 En 1 Sh ⚡📼(4) ⚥ 📺 📺 📺 ⚑

Hemyock
ST1313   🍺 *Catherine Wheel*

Orchard Lea, *78 Culmstock Road, Hemyock, Cullompton, Devon, EX15 3RN.* **Open:** All year (not Xmas/New Year) **01823 680057 (also fax)** Mrs Sworn **D:** £17.00 **S:** £17.00 **Beds:** 2T 1D **Baths:** 2 Sh ⚡📼(3) ⚥ 📺 ✕ 📺 📺 ⚑ Perfectly situated in the Blackdown Hills, ideally placed to explore Exmoor and Dartmoor and the thatched villages of Devon. Exclusive non-smoking accommodation is arranged on the ground floor and ideal for the elderly. Home cooking includes our own eggs.

Hexworthy
SX6572

The Forest Inn, *Hexworthy, Princetown, Devon, PL20 6SD.* Middle of Dartmoor, ideal for walking, fishing, riding, or just relaxing. **Open:** Feb to Dec **01364 631211** Mr Selwood **Fax: 01364 631515** *forestinn@hotmail.com* **D:** £20.00–£29.50 **S:** £25.00–£33.00 **Beds:** 5D 3T 2S **Baths:** 7 En 3 Pr 📠 (30) 📺 🛏 🖬 ⚑ **cc**

Heybrook Bay
SX4948   🍺 *Eddystone Inn, Mussel Inn*

Heybrook Bay Private Hotel, *Beach Road, Heybrook Bay, Plymouth, Devon, PL9 0BS.* Small family run hotel on Coastal Footpath, stunning sea views. **Open:** Mar to Nov **01752 862345** **D:** £17.50 **S:** £20.00–£22.00 **Beds:** 2T 4D 📺 📺 ⚑

Higher Clovelly
SS3124

Fuchsia Cottage, *Burscott Lane, Higher Clovelly, Bideford, Devon, EX39 5RR.* Situated in a quiet lane, beautiful coastal and countryside views. **Open:** All year (not Xmas/New Year) **Grades:** ETC 4 Diamond, AA 4 Diamond **01237 431398** Mrs Curtis *curtis@ fuchsiacottage.fslife.co.uk* www.clovelly-holidays.co.uk **D:** £20.00 **S:** £16.00 **Beds:** 1T 1D 1S **Baths:** 2 En 1 Sh ⚡📼(3) ⚥ 📺 📺 📺 ⚑

Holne
SX7069

Chase Gate Farm, *Holne, Newton Abbot, Devon, TQ13 7RX.* Comfortable, friendly farmhouse with lovely views and well-equipped rooms. **Open:** All year **01364 631261** Mr & Mrs Higman **D:** £19.00–£20.00 **S:** £19.00–£20.00 **Beds:** 2D 1T **Baths:** 1 En 1 Pr 1 Sh ⚡📼🏠🛏🖬⚑

Mill Leat Farm, *Holne, Ashburton, Newton Abbot, Devon, TQ13 7RZ.* C18th farmhouse offering great food, set off the beaten track. **Open:** All year (not Xmas) **01364 631283 (also fax)** Mrs Cleave **D:** £17.00–£19.00 **S:** £19.00–£20.00 **Beds:** 2F **Baths:** 1 En 1 Pr ⚡📼🛏✕📺⚑

Hazelwood, *Holne, Newton Abbot, Devon, TQ13 7SJ.* Friendly home from home welcome with panoramic views of Devon. **Open:** Easter to Oct **01364 631235** Mrs Mortimore **D:** £18.50–£19.00 **S:** £18.50–£19.00 **Beds:** 2D 1S ⚡📼(3) ⚥ 📺 🛏 ✕ 📺 🖬 ♿

Honiton
ST1600

Threshays, *Awliscombe, Honiton, Devon, EX14 3QB.* Warm, friendly, delightful views. Ideal for exploring glorious East Devon. **Open:** All year **01404 43551 (also fax)** Mrs Gillingham *threshays@tesco.net* **D:** £17.00 **S:** £17.00 **Beds:** 1F 1D **Baths:** 1 Sh ⚡📼(6) ⚥ 📺 📺 🖬

B&B owners may vary rates – be sure to check when booking

Wessington Farm, *Awliscombe, Honiton, Devon, EX14 3NU.* **Open:** All year **Grades:** ETC 4 Diamond, Silver **01404 42280 & 07989 300392 (M)** Mrs Summers **Fax:** 01404 45271 *bandb@ eastdevon.com* www.eastdevon. com/bedandbreakfast **D:** £20.00–£25.00 **S:** £20.00–£40.00 **Beds:** 1D 2T **Baths:** 2 En 1 Pr ⌂ 🅿 (10) ⌁ 📺 🆅 🛏 🎄 Elegant late Victorian stone farmhouse in designated AONB.

Hope Cove
SX6739

Hope Cove Hotel, *Hope Cove, Kingsbridge, Devon, TQ7 3HH.* On Coastal Path. Spectacular sea views to Eddystone Lighthouse. **Open:** Easter to Oct **01548 561233 (also fax)** Mr Clarke **D:** £23.50–£28.50 **S:** £33.50–£38.50 **Beds:** 2T 5D **Baths:** 7 En 🅿 (12) 📺 ✕ 🆅 🛏 🎄 cc

Horns Cross
SS3823

The Hoops Inn, *Horns Cross, Bideford, Devon, EX39 5DL.* Enjoy genuine hospitality at one of Devon's most famous inns. Camra, Which, AA Pick of pubs. **Open:** All year **01237 451222** G P Marriott **Fax:** 01237 451247 *reservations@hoopsinn.co.uk* www.hoopsinn.co.uk **D:** £70.00 **S:** £35.00–£73.00 **Beds:** 1F 6T 6D **Baths:** 12 En ⌂ (10) 🅿 📺 🛏 ✕ 🆅 🛏 🎄 cc

Horrabridge
SX5169 🍴 *Leaping Salmon, London Inn*

Overcombe Hotel, *Old Station Road, Horrabridge, Yelverton, Devon, PL20 7RA.* Homely, relaxed atmosphere. Comfortable ensuite bedrooms. Excellent food and wines. Beautiful views. **Open:** All year **Grades:** ETC 2 Star **01822 853501** JH & G Wright *enquiries@ overcombehotel.co. uk* **D:** £23.00–£25.00 **S:** £23.00–£28.00 **Beds:** 2F 2T 3D 1S **Baths:** 8 En ⌂ 🅿 (8) ⌁ ✕ 🛏 ♿ 🎄 cc

Ideford
SX8977

Higher Rixdale Farm, *Ideford, Newton Abbot, TQ13 0BW.* Situated near Teignmouth, secluded surroundings. Visitors can enjoy lovely walks around the farm. **Open:** Feb to Nov **01626 866232 D:** £15.00–£17.00 **S:** £15.00–£17.00 **Beds:** 1T 2D 1S **Baths:** 2 Sh ⌂ (2) 🅿 (8) 📺 🛏 🖳 🎄

Ilfracombe
SS5147

Strathmore Hotel, *57 St Brannock s Road, Ilfracombe, Devon, EX34 8EQ.* **Open:** All year **Grades:** ETC 4 Diamond, Silver Award, AA 4 Diamond, RAC 4 Diamond **01271 862248** Mrs Metaxas **Fax:** 01271 862243 *strathmore@ukhotels.com* www.strathmore.ukhotels.com **D:** £20.00–£29.00 **S:** £30.00–£39.00 **Beds:** 1F 5D 1T 1S **Baths:** 8 Pr ⌂ 🅿 (7) ⌁ 📺 🛏 ✕ 🆅 🖳 🎄 ♿ cc Delightful Victorian Hotel near to Ilfracombe town centre, Bicclescombe Park, Cairn Nature Reserve and glorious beaches. All rooms are ensuite with colour TV and hospitality trays. We offer varied and delicious menus. All meals are freshly prepared on the premises.

Seabreeze, *51 St Brannocks Road, Ilfracombe, Devon, EX34 8EQ.* Situated for exploring North Devon Moors, beaches. Warm, friendly establishment. **Open:** Mar to Nov **01271 863653 D:** £16.50–£20.00 **S:** £16.50–£20.00 **Beds:** 3F 2T **Baths:** 3 En 1 Sh ⌂ 🅿 (7) 📺 🖳 🎄

Planning a longer stay? Always ask for any special rates

Lyncott House, *56 St Brannock's Road, Ilfracombe, Devon, EX34 8EQ.* **Open:** All year **Grades:** ETC 4 Diamond **01271 862425 (also fax)** Mr & Mrs Holdsworth *david@ukhotels.com* www.lyncottdevon.com **D:** £19.00–£23.00 **S:** £20.00–£23.00 **Beds:** 2F 3D 1S **Baths:** 6 En ⌂ 🅿 (5) ⌁ 📺 🆅 🎄 Join David and Marianna in their charming, lovingly refurbished Victorian house pleasantly situated near lovely Bicclescombe Park. Relax in elegant, smoke free surroundings. Enjoy delightful, spacious, individually designed ensuite bedrooms and sample their delicious home-made breakfasts.

Varley House, *Chambercombe Park, Ilfracombe, Devon, EX34 9QW.* **Open:** All year (not Xmas/New Year) **Grades:** ETC 4 Diamond, AA 4 Diamond **01271 863927** Mrs O'Sullivan **Fax:** 01271 879299 *info@varleyhouse.freeserve.co.uk* www.varleyhouse.co.uk **D:** £25.00–£26.00 **S:** £30.00–£31.00 **Beds:** 2F 1T 4D 1S **Baths:** 7 En 1 Pr ⌂ (5) 🅿 (8) ⌁ 📺 🛏 ✕ 🆅 🖳 🎄 cc Built in the early 1900's to revitalise and refresh officers returning from the Boer War. Delightfully situated. All rooms have either sea or country views. Our aim is to offer a very friendly and personal atmosphere, combined with quality accommodation.

Combe Lodge Hotel, *Chambercombe Park, Ilfracombe, Devon, EX34 9QW.* Quiet position, overlooking harbour, ideal for walking, cycling, golf holidays. **Open:** All year (not Xmas) **01271 864518** Mr & Mrs Wileman **D:** £16.50–£18.50 **S:** £20.50–£22.50 **Beds:** 2F 4D 2S **Baths:** 4 En 1 Pr 1 Sh ⌂ (1) 🅿 (8) ⌁ 📺 🛏 ✕ 🆅 🖳 🎄 cc

Beechwood Hotel, *Torrs Park, Ilfracombe, Devon, EX34 8AZ.* Peacefully situated non-smoking Victorian mansion, own woods bordering spectacular NT lands, coast path. **Open:** Mar to Oct **01271 863800 (also fax)** P Burridge *info@beechwoodhotel.co.uk* www.beechwoodhotel.co.uk **D:** £22.00–£25.00 **S:** £22.00–£25.00 **Beds:** 2T 5D **Baths:** 7 En 🅿 (8) ⌁ 📺 🆅 🖳 🎄 cc

RATES

D = Price range per person sharing in a double or twin room

S = Price range for a single room

Cairn House Hotel, *43 St Brannocks Road, Ilfracombe, Devon, EX34 8EH.* Beautiful Victorian hotel delightfully situated in own grounds with extensive views. **Open:** All year (not Xmas/New Year)
01271 863911 (also fax) Mrs Tupper
D: £18.00–£21.50 **S:** £18.00–£21.50 **Beds:** 3F 6D 1S **Baths:** 10 En ♿ �🄿 �📺 ⬛ 🐾 ✕ 🖾 ⚲ **cc**

Harcourt Hotel, *Fore Street, Ilfracombe, Devon, EX34 9DS.* Small family run hotel - home from home. **Open:** All year
01271 862931 JM Doorbar **D:** £18.00–£24.00 **S:** £18.00–£24.00 **Beds:** 3F 1T 3D 1S **Baths:** 9 En ♿ �🄿 (4) 📺 🐾 ✕ 🖾 ☀ ⚲ **cc**

Ipplepen
SX8366

June Cottage, *Dornafield Road, Ipplepen, Newton Abbot, Devon, TQ12 5SH.* Very comfortable 250 year old cottage - Quiet, village edge location. **Open:** All year
01803 813081 Mr & Mrs Bell **D:** £19.00–£22.00 **S:** £19.00–£25.00 **Beds:** 1T 2D **Baths:** 1 En 1 Sh �🄿 (1) ✄ ✕ 🖾 ⬛ ⚲

Ivybridge
SX6356

The Toll House, *Exeter Road, Ivybridge, Devon, PL21 0DE.* 1850s house with attractive gardens overlooked by Dartmoor. **Open:** All year
01752 893522 Mrs Hancox *info@ thetollhouse.co.uk* www.thetollhouse.co.uk
D: £18.00 **S:** £25.00 **Beds:** 2T 1S **Baths:** 3 En ♿ �🄿 (5) ✄ 📺 🖾 ⚲

Jacobstowe
SS5801

Higher Cadham Farm, *Jacobstowe, Okehampton, Devon, EX20 3RB.* Superb farmhouse accommodation with country walks. Hearty farmhouse food. **Open:** All year (not Xmas)
01837 851647 Mrs King **Fax:** 01837 851410
www.highercadham.co.uk **D:** £20.00–£25.00 **S:** £20.00–£25.00 **Beds:** 3F 2D 3T 1S **Baths:** 5 En 1 Sh ♿ (1) �🄿 (10) 📺 🐾 ✕ 🖾 ⚲ **cc**

Kenn
SX9285 ⚓ Ley Arms

Bickham Farmhouse, *Kenn, Exeter, Devon, EX6 7XL.* Lovely country setting. Excellent touring base - Dartmoor National Park/ Devon Coastline. Warm welcome. **Open:** All year **Grades:** ETC 4 Diamond
01392 832206 (also fax) Mr & Mrs Lyne **D:** £19.00–£20.00 **S:** £20.00–£25.00 **Beds:** 1F 1D ♿ �🄿 📺 🐾 🖾 ⚲

Kentisbury
SS6243

Kentisbury Mill, *Kentisbury, Barnstaple, Devon, EX31 4NF.* Secluded house, 2 acre garden, close to sea and Exmoor. **Open:** All year (not Xmas/New Year)
01271 883545 Mr Denham *denham@ kenmill.fsnet.co.uk* **D:** £15.00 **S:** £17.50 **Beds:** 1T 3D �🄿 (4) 📺 🐾

King's Nympton
SS6819 ⚓ Grove Inn, Castle Inn, Exeter Inn, Bell Inn, Butcher's Arms

Sampson Barton Country Guest House, *King's Nympton, Umberleigh, Devon, EX37 9TG.* Perfect for exploring North Devon and Exmoor, delicious meals and a warm welcome. **Open:** All year
01769 572466 Mrs Hazelden *mail@ sampsonbarton.co.uk* www.sampsonbarton.co. uk **D:** £25.00 **S:** £30.00 **Beds:** 1F 1T 4D 1S **Baths:** 5 En 2 Pr ♿ �🄿 (6) ✄ ✕ 📺 ✕ 🖾 ☀ ⚲

Kingsbridge
SX7344

Ashleigh House, *Ashleigh Road, Kingsbridge, Devon, TQ7 1HB.* Licensed Victorian guest house. Spacious accommodation, good food in friendly atmosphere. **Open:** All year
01548 852893 *reception@ashleigh-house.co.uk* www.ashleigh-house.co.uk **D:** £19.00–£25.00 **S:** £24.00–£35.00 **Beds:** 1F 5D 2T **Baths:** 4 En 2 Sh ♿ �🄿 (3) ✄ 📺 🐾 ✕ 🖾 ⚲ **cc**

Kingswear
SX8851 ⚓ Ship Inn

Carlton House, *Higher Street, Kingswear, Dartmouth, Devon, TQ6 0AG.* Stunning views across the river Dart to Dartmouth. **Open:** All year
01803 752244 Mr & Mrs Congdon **D:** £15.00 **S:** £15.00 **Beds:** 1F 1T 2D 1S **Baths:** 2 Sh ♿ 📺 🐾 ⚲

Knowstone
SS8223 ⚓ Masons' Arms

West Bowden Farm, *Knowstone, South Molton, Devon, EX36 4RP.* West Bowden is a working farm quietly situated just north of the A361. **Open:** All year **Grades:** ETC 3 Diamond
01398 341224 Mrs Bray **D:** £19.00–£22.00 **S:** £19.00–£25.00 **Beds:** 2F 2T 4D 1S **Baths:** 5 En 1 Sh ♿ �🄿 📺 🐾 ✕ 🖾 & ⚲

West Cross Farm, *Knowstone, South Molton, Devon, EX36 4RT.* Period farmhouse with 66 acres in southern foothills of Exmoor. **Open:** All year (not Xmas/New Year)
01398 341288 Mr Begbie *enquiries@ devoncountryholidays.com* www.devoncountryholidays.com **D:** £15.00–£22.00 **S:** £21.00–£25.00 **Beds:** 1T 2D **Baths:** 2 En 1 Pr ♿ (3) ✄ 🖾 ⚲

Landcross
SS4623

Sunset Hotel, *Landcross, Bideford, Devon, EX39 5JA.* Small country hotel. Peaceful location overlooking spectacular scenery & Tarka Trail. **Open:** Easter to Nov
01237 472962 Mrs Lamb *bellcraig@ eidosnet.co.uk* **D:** £27.00–£30.00 **S:** £36.00–£40.00 **Beds:** 2F 2D 2T **Baths:** 4 En �🄿 (8) ✄ 📺 ✕ 🖾 ⚲ **cc**

Lapford
SS7308

Parsonage Farm, *Lapford, Crediton, Devon, EX17 6LX.* Working farm in mid-Devon. Central for visiting Devon. **Open:** All year
01363 83784 Mrs John **D:** £12.00–£18.00 **S:** £14.00–£20.00 **Beds:** 1F 1D ♿ (3) �🄿 ⚲

Lee
SS4846 ⚓ Lee Bay Hotel

Grampus Inn, *Old Farm, Lee, Ilfracombe, Devon, EX34 8LR.* Unspoilt coastal village. **Open:** All year (not Xmas/New Year)
01271 862906 Mrs Nustedt **D:** £17.50–£21.00 **Beds:** 1T 1D **Baths:** 2 En ♿ �🄿 ✄ 📺 🐾 ✕ ⚲

BATHROOMS
En = Ensuite
Pr = Private
Sh = Shared

Little Torrington

SS4916

Smytham Holiday Park, *Little Torrington, Torrington, Devon, EX38 8PU.* C17th manor house. Beautiful tranquil grounds. Outdoor heated pool. **Open:** All year (not Xmas/New Year)
01805 622110 Mr Bland **D:** £20.00–£30.00 **S:** £24.00–£36.00 **Beds:** 4D 3T **Baths:** 5 En 1 Sh ⭐🅿⛱📺🏠🛏✕▥🛍 ♿ cc

Littlehempston

SX8162

Post Cottage, *Littlehempston, Totnes, Devon, TQ9 6L.* Beams, thatch, books, friendly cats. 3 hours London, 2 from Eden Project. **Open:** All year (not Xmas/New Year)
01803 868192 Mr & Mrs Galton-Fenzi *hugh.gf@virgin.net* **D:** £20.00 **S:** £25.00 **Beds:** 1T 1D **Baths:** 1 Pr 🅿 (3) ⛱ ▥ ⓥ ♿

Luppitt

ST1606

Jacks House, *Luppitt, Honiton, Devon, EX14 4SR.* A charming stone house, surrounded by large gardens, in the Blackdown Hills. **Open:** All year (not Xmas/New Year)
01404 891341 Mrs Krestovnikoff **D:** £18.50–£25.00 **S:** £25.00 **Beds:** 1F 1T ⭐🅿⛱📺✕🛍 ♿

Lustleigh

SX7881

Brookside, *Lustleigh, Newton Abbot, Devon, TQ13 9TJ.* **Open:** All year (not Xmas/New Year)
01647 277310 (also fax) Judy Claxton **D:** £22.00 **S:** £25.00 **Beds:** 1T 2D **Baths:** 1 Sh ⭐ (10) 🅿⛱📺▥ⓥ🛍 ♿
Period granite property situated in picturesque Lustleigh within Dartmoor National Park. Its landscaped garden contains an old granite bridge and is raised up on what was once a railway embankment. Superb views across garden, river, village cricket field and countryside.

Lydford

SX5184

Moor View House, *Vale Down, Lydford, Okehampton, Devon, EX20 4BB.* Licensed Victorian country house, edge Dartmoor. Outskirts of Lydford, ideal touring Devon & Cornwall. **Open:** All year
01822 820220 (also fax) Mr Sharples **D:** £25.00–£36.00 **S:** £30.00–£45.00 **Beds:** 3D 1T **Baths:** 4 Pr ⭐ (12) 🅿⛱📺🏠✕▥🛍 ✳♿

Lympstone

SX9984 🍺 *Saddlers' Arms, Digger's Rest, White Hart*

Gulliford Farm, *Lympstone, Exmouth, Devon, EX8 5AQ.* Lovely C16th farmhouse. Garden, swimming pool, large rooms. **Open:** All year (not Xmas)
01392 873067 (also fax) Mrs Hallett **D:** £20.00–£25.00 **S:** £20.00–£25.00 **Beds:** 2F 1T 1S **Baths:** 1 En ⭐🅿 (6) ⛱📺▥🛍 ♿

Hope Cottage, *The Strand, Lympstone, Exmouth, Devon, EX8 5JS.* C15th cottage in beautiful village on Exe estuary (Mr & Mrs Clarke). **Open:** All year
01395 268349 Mr Clarke **D:** £17.50 **S:** £17.50 **Beds:** 3D 1T **Baths:** 1 En 1 Sh 🅿ⓥ♿

Lynmouth

SS7249 🍺 *Hunters Inn*

Tregonwell Riverside Guest House, *1 Tors Road, Lynmouth, Devon, EX35 6ET.* **Open:** All year (not Xmas)
01598 753369 Mrs Parker
www.smoothhound.co.uk/hotels/tregonwl. html **D:** £22.00–£27.00 **S:** £22.00–£25.00 **Beds:** 2F 5D 1T 1S **Baths:** 5 En 1 Pr 3 Sh ⭐🅿 (7) ⛱📺🏠🛍 ♿
Award-winning, romantic, elegant riverside (former sea captain's) stone-built house, snuggled amidst waterfalls, cascades, wooded valleys, soaring cliff tops, lonely beaches, enchanting harbourside 'Olde Worlde' smugglers' village. Shelley, Wordsworth, Coleridge stayed here. 'England's Switzerland'. Pretty bedrooms, dramatic views. Garaged parking.

Glenville House, *2 Tors Road, Lynmouth, Devon, EX35 6ET.* **Open:** Feb to Nov **Grades:** AA 4 Diamond
01598 752202
Mr & Mrs Francis *tricia@ glenvillelynmouth.co.uk*
www.glenvillelynmouth.co.uk **D:** £23.00–£27.00 **S:** £23.00–£30.00 **Beds:** 4D 1T 1S **Baths:** 3 En 1 Pr 2 Sh ⭐ (12) ⛱📺🛍 ♿
Idyllic riverside setting. Delightful Victorian house full of character and charm. Licensed. Tastefully decorated bedrooms. Picturesque harbour, village and unique Cliff Railway nestled amidst wooded valley. Magnificent Exmoor scenery, spectacular coastline and beautiful walks. Peaceful, tranquil, romantic - a very special place.

Lynton

SS7149 🍺 *George & Dragon, Globe, Dolphin, Fo'c's'le, Castle, Pack of Cards*

The North Cliff Hotel, *North Walk, Lynton, Devon, EX35 6HJ.* **Open:** Mar to Oct **Grades:** ETC 1 Star
01598 782357 Mr Hardy *holidays@ northcliffhotel.co.uk* www.northcliffhotel.co.uk **D:** £29.00–£34.00 **S:** £29.00–£34.00 **Beds:** 3F 2T 8D 1S **Baths:** 14 En ⭐ (8) 🅿 (12) ⛱📺🏠✕ ▥🛍 ♿ cc
Georgian Villa C1830, own grounds, magnificent Sea/Coastal views over Lynmouth Harbour and Countisbury Foreland Point. Ideal location for relaxing, comfortable stay in picturesque Lynton and for touring fascinating corners of Exmoors Lorna Doone Country. Golf, riding, tennis, fishing nearby.

Meadhaven, *12 Crossmead, Lynton, Devon, EX35 6DG.* Edwardian guest house. Traditional English cooking. Ideal ramblers/tourists. **Open:** All year **Grades:** ETC 2 Diamond
01598 753288 Ms Kirk **D:** £18.00–£19.00 **S:** £18.00–£19.00 **Beds:** 1T 2S **Baths:** 2 Sh ⛱🏠✕▥🛍 ♿

Planning a longer stay? Always ask for any special rates

The Denes Guest House,
Longmead, Lynton, Devon, *EX35 6DQ*. **Open:** All year **01598 753573** Mr McGowan *j.e.mcgowan@btinternet.com* www.thedenes.com **D:** £16.00–£22.50 **S:** £16.00–£22.50 **Beds:** 3F 2D **Baths:** 3 En 2 Sh ☎ 🖪 (5) ⊬ 🖾 ✕ ❂ ♨ ♦ cc
A warm friendly greeting awaits you at The Denes, with its Edwardian charm. Comfortable accommodation and home cooked food, evening meals served in our licensed dining room. Ideal base to explore Exmoor on the South West Coastal Path. An Exmoor Paths partner.

Woodlands, Lynbridge Road, Lynton, Devon, *EX35 6AX*. Ideal base for walkers. Beautiful views across Summerhouse Hill. **Open:** Mar to Nov **Grades:** ETC 4 Diamond **01598 752324** Mr & Mrs Kuczer **Fax: 01598 753828** *info@woodlandsguesthouse.co.uk* www.woodlandsguesthouse.co.uk **D:** £18.00–£25.00 **S:** £20.00–£25.00 **Beds:** 1T 5D 1S **Baths:** 6 En 1 Pr ☎ (12) 🖪 (8) ⊬ 🖾 ✕ ❂ ♨ ♦ cc

The Turret, 33 Lee Road, Lynton, Devon, *EX35 6BS*. Step back in time & experience old world hospitality. Cosy dining room. **Open:** All year **01598 753284 (also fax)** Mrs Wayman *nancy@theturret.fsbusiness.co.uk* www.exmoortourism.org/theturret.htm **D:** £18.00–£23.00 **S:** £25.00 **Beds:** 5D 1T **Baths:** 4 En ☎ (12) ⊬ 🖾 ✕ ❂ ♨ ♦ cc

Malborough
SX7039

Quill View, Well Hill Close, Malborough, Kingsbridge, Devon, *TQ7 3SS*. Very quiet village position with views and patios, super lounge. **Open:** All year (not Xmas) **01548 562085** *willwrite@tesco.net* **D:** £16.00–£20.00 **S:** £19.00–£23.00 **Beds:** 1D 1T **Baths:** 1 En 1 Pr ☎ (7) 🖪 (2) ⊬ 🖾 ❂ ♨ ♨.

Martinhoe
SS6648

Mannacott Farm, Martinhoe, Parracombe, Barnstaple, Devon, *EX31 4QS*. In area of outstanding natural scenery. Ideal for walkers, bird watchers. **Open:** Apr to Oct **01598 763227** Mrs Dallyn **D:** £15.00–£16.00 **S:** £16.00–£17.00 **Beds:** 1D 1T 1S **Baths:** 1 Sh 🖪 (2) ⊬ 🖾 ❂ ♨.

All details shown are as supplied by B&B owners in Autumn 2001

Marwood
SS5437

Lee House,
Marwood, Barnstaple, Devon, *EX31 4DZ*. **Open:** Apr to Oct **01271 374345** Mrs Darling **D:** £20.00–£22.00 **S:** £20.00–£22.00 **Beds:** 1T 2D **Baths:** 3 En ☎ (14) 🖪 (8) ⊬ 🖾 ❂ ♨ ♦
A stone built Elizabethan Manor house standing in own secluded grounds, magnificent views over rolling countryside. Family-run, friendly, relaxing atmosphere. Easy access to beaches, moor. Walking distance to local pub with excellent food. Marwood Hill Gardens one mile.

Meavy
SX5467   🍺 Rock Inn, Skylark, Burrator

Greenwell Farm, Meavy, Yelverton, Devon, *PL20 6PY*. Working away from home? Try our new do-it-yourself B & B. **Open:** All year **01822 853563 (also fax)** Mrs Cole *greenwellfarm@btconnect.com* **S:** £20.00–£30.00 **Beds:** 3S **Baths:** 3 En 🖪 (6) 🖾 ♨.

Merton
SS5212

Richmond House, New Road (A386), Merton, Okehampton, Devon, *EX20 3EG*. Country house within easy reach of beach, moors, gardens, Tarka Trail. **Open:** All year **01805 603258** Mrs Wickett **D:** £15.00 **S:** £15.00 **Beds:** 3F 1T 2D **Baths:** 1 Sh ☎ (5) 🖪 (4) 🐾 ❂ ✕ ♦ cc

Milton Abbot
SX4179   🍺 Royal Inn

Beera Farm, Milton Abbot, Tavistock, Devon, *PL19 8PL*. Come and relax on our working farm on the banks of the River Tamar. **Open:** All year **Grades:** ETC 4 Diamond, Silver **01822 870216 (also fax)** Mrs Tucker *robert.tucker@farming.co.uk* www.beera-farm.co.uk **D:** £20.00–£25.00 **S:** £25.00–£35.00 **Beds:** 1F 2D **Baths:** 3 En ☎ 🖪 (5) ⊬ 🖾 ✕ ❂ ♨ ♦ cc

Modbury
SX6551

Orchard Cottage, Palm Cross Green, Modbury, Ivybridge, Devon, *PL21 0QZ*. Double ensuite garden room in private cottage. Views over Modbury. **Open:** All year **01548 830633** Mrs Ewen **D:** £22.50 **S:** £27.50 **Beds:** 1D **Baths:** 1 En 🖪 ⊬ 🖾 ❂ ♨.

Monkokehampton
SS5805

Seldon Farm, Monkokehampton, Winkleigh, Devon, *EX19 8RY*. Charming C17th farmhouse in beautiful, tranquil, rural setting. **Open:** Easter to Oct **Grades:** ETC 2 Diamond **01837 810312** Mrs Case **D:** £20.00 **S:** £23.00 **Beds:** 1F 2D **Baths:** 1 Pr 1 En ☎ 🖪 🖾 ♦ ♨

Morchard Bishop
SS7607   🍺 London Inn, Thelbridge Cross, New Inn

Beech Hill House, Morchard Bishop, Crediton, Devon, *EX17 6RF*. Basic accommodation in rural community. Ideal for Two Moors Way. **Open:** All year (not Xmas/New Year) **01363 877228** www.beech-hill.org.uk **D:** £15.00 **S:** £15.00 **Beds:** 3F 1T **Baths:** 3 Sh

Oldborough Fishing Retreat, Morchard Bishop, Crediton, Devon, *EX17 6JQ*. Lakeside rural retreat. 40 minutes M5/j27. Nice place for Exeter city break. **Open:** All year (not Xmas/New Year) **01363 877437** Mrs Wilshaw *fishingretreat@eclipse.co.uk* **D:** £16.00–£17.00 **S:** £16.00–£17.00 **Beds:** 1F 1T **Baths:** 1 Sh ☎ 🖪 (10) ⊬ 🖾 ✕ ❂ ♨ ♦ cc

Morebath
SS9524   🍺 The Anchor

Lodfin Farm, Morebath, Bampton, Devon, *EX16 9DD*. Peaceful, welcoming farmhouse. Large gardens, hearty breakfast, ideal location for Exmoor. **Open:** All year (not Xmas/New Year) **Grades:** ETC 4 Diamond **01398 331400 (also fax)** Mrs Goodwin *lodfin.farm@eclipse.co.uk* **D:** £21.50–£23.50 **S:** £22.00–£25.00 **Beds:** 1F 1D 1S **Baths:** 1 En 1 Sh ☎ 🖪 (6) ⊬ 🖾 ❂ ♨ ♦ cc

Moreleigh
SX7652

Island Farm, Moreleigh, Totnes, Devon, *TQ9 7SH*. Situated in the heart of South Hams. Panoramic views of countryside. **Open:** All year (not Xmas/New Year) **01548 821441** Mrs Finch **D:** £20.00–£22.00 **S:** £20.00–£22.00 **Beds:** 1F 1T 2D **Baths:** 2 En 1 Pr ☎ 🖪 (4) 🖾 ✕ ❂ ♨.

Moretonhampstead
SX7586   🍺 White Hart, Plymouth Inn, Bell Inn, Ring of Bells

Great Wooston Farm, Moretonhampstead, Newton Abbot, Devon, *TQ13 8QA*. High above Teign Valley, a peaceful haven with views across the moors. **Open:** All year (not Xmas) **01647 440367 (also fax)** Mrs Cuming **D:** £20.00–£22.00 **S:** £20.00–£25.00 **Beds:** 2D 1T **Baths:** 2 En 1 Pr ☎ (8) 🖪 (3) ⊬ 🖾 ❂ ♨ ♦ cc

Moorcote Country Guest House,
*Chagford Cross, Moretonhampstead,
Newton Abbot, Devon, TQ13 8LS.* **Open:** Mar
to Oct **Grades:** ETC 4 Diamond, AA 4
Diamond
01647 440966 (also fax) Mr Lambert
moorcote@smartone.co.uk **D:** £19.00–£21.00
S: £25.00–£35.00 **Beds:** 2F 1T 2D **Baths:** 4
En 1 Pr ♿ (5) 🅿 (6) ✉ ⊠ 🏧 ⚡
Victorian house set well back from the road
in a mature garden, overlooking the town of
Moretonhampstead with stunning views of
Dartmoor and the surrounding countryside.
Ideal centre from which to explore
Dartmoor and beautiful Devon. Private
parking in grounds.

**Great
Sloncombe
Farm,**
*Moretonhamp-
stead, Newton
Abbot, Devon,
TQ13 8QF.*
Open: All year **Grades:** ETC 4 Diamond,
Silver, AA 4 Diamond
01647 440595 (also fax) Mrs Merchant
h.merchant@sloncombe.freeserve.co.uk
www.greatsloncombefarm.co.uk **D:** £23.00–
£24.00 **S:** £30.00 **Beds:** 2D 1T **Baths:** 3 En
♿ (8) 🅿 (3) ✉ ⊠ 🏧 ✕ ✉ ⊞ ⚡
C13th Dartmoor farmhouse, everything
provided for an enjoyable stay.

**Little
Wooston
Farm,**

*Moretonhampstead, Newton Abbot, Devon,
TQ13 8QA.* Working farm in beautiful
countryside. Ideally situated for walking.
Quiet location. **Open:** All year
01647 440551 & 07850 098789 (M)
Mrs Cuming **Fax:** 01647 440551 **D:** £16.00–
£17.00 **S:** £16.00–£17.00 **Beds:** 1F 1D 1S
Baths: 1 Sh ♿ 🅿 (4) ✕ ✉ 🏧 ✕ ✉ ⊞ ⚡

BEDROOMS

D = Double
T = Twin
S = Single
F = Family

Newton Ferrers

SX5448

Crown Yealm, *Bridgend Hill, Newton
Ferrers, Plymouth, Devon, PL8 1AW.* Beautiful
riverside country house. All guest rooms
overlook garden to water's edge. **Open:** All
year
01752 872365 (also fax) Mrs Johnson
D: £17.00–£22.00 **S:** £21.00–£30.00 **Beds:** 1F
1D 1T **Baths:** 2 En 1 Sh ♿ 🅿 (7) ✉ 🏧 ⊞ ⚡

North Tawton

SS6601

Kayden House Hotel, *High Street,
North Tawton, Devon, EX20 2HF.* Devon
heartland, ideal for moors and coasts.
Warm welcome assured. **Open:** All year
01837 82242 Ms Waldron **D:** £20.00 **S:** £26.00
Beds: 1F 2T 2D 2S **Baths:** 5 En 2 Pr ♿ 🏧
✕ ✉ ⊞ ⚡ **cc**

Northleigh (Honiton)

SY1996

Sunnyacre, *Rockerhayne Farm,
Northleigh, Colyton, Devon, EX24 6DA.*
Bungalow on working farm in beautiful
scenic countryside close to coast. **Open:** All
year (not Xmas)
01404 871422 N Rich **D:** £15.00–£20.00
S: £15.00–£20.00 **Beds:** 1F 1D 1T **Baths:** 1
Sh ♿ 🅿 (4) ✉ ✕ ✉ ⊞

Smallicombe Farm, *Northleigh,
Colyton, Devon, EX24 6BU.* Old world charm,
idyllic rural setting with only the sights &
sounds of the countryside. **Open:** All year
01404 831310 Mrs Todd **Fax:** 01404 831431
maggie_todd@yahoo.com www.smallicombe.
com **D:** £20.00–£23.50 **S:** £25.00 **Beds:** 1F 1D
1T **Baths:** 3 En ♿ 🅿 (10) ✕ ✉ ✕ ✉ ⊞ ♿3 ⚡

Oakford

SS9021

Harton Farm, *Oakford, Tiverton, Devon,
EX16 9HH.* Peaceful farmhouse. Home-grown
additive-free meat, vegetables. Friendly
animals. **Open:** All year (not Xmas/New
Year)
01398 351209 (also fax) Mrs Head *harton@
eclipse.co.uk* **D:** £16.00–£17.00 **S:** £16.00–
£17.00 **Beds:** 1F 1T **Baths:** 1 Sh ♿ (4) 🅿 (2)
✉ 🏧 ✕ ✉ ⚡

Okehampton

SX5895 ⬛ *The Tors, Crossways Inn, Dovecote,
Betty Cottles*

Southey Farm, *Sampford Courtenay,
Okehampton, Devon, EX20 2TE.* Comfortable
farmhouse within easy reach of many
attractions in Devon and Cornwall.
Open: All year (not Xmas/New Year)
01837 82446 Mr & Mrs Townsend Green *TG@
southeyfarm.freeserve.co.uk* **D:** £15.00 **S:** £15.00
Beds: 1T 1S/T **Baths:** 2 Pr ♿ 🅿 (4) ✉ ⊞ ⚡

Betty Cottles Inn, *Graddon Cross,
Okehampton, Devon, EX20 4LR.* **Open:** All
year
01837 55339 Mr & Mrs Wilson **Fax:** 01837
55191 *cottles@bell.co.uk* www.cottles.
eurobell.co.uk **D:** £18.50–£29.95 **S:** £20.00–
£37.50 **Beds:** 2F 1T 3D 2S **Baths:** 4 En 1 Sh
♿ 🅿 (50) ✉ 🏧 ✕ ✉ ⊞ ⚡ 🔥 ⚡ **cc**
Edge of Dartmoor National Park. Charming
country pub ideally placed for your holiday
base in West Devon. With the coast only 20
mins away, Dartmoor over the road and the
Eden Project within 50 mins' driving, there
is plenty to do and see.

**Heathfield
House,**
*Klondyke Road,
Okehampton,
Devon, EX20 1EW.*
Dartmoor,
views, fabulous
food, pottery with courses - Christmas
breaks. **Open:** Feb to Dec
01837 54211 & 07799 840989 (M) Mr & Mrs
Gibbins **Fax:** 01837 54211 *Tim@
tgibbins.freeserve.co.uk*
www.heathfieldhousehotel.co.uk **D:** £20.00–
£35.00 **S:** £35.00–£37.50 **Beds:** 1F 2D 1T
Baths: 4 En ♿ 🅿 (8) ✕ ✉ 🏧 ✕ ✉ ⊞ ❄ ⚡ **cc**

North Lake, *Exeter Road, Okehampton,
Devon, EX20 1QH.* Set in large grounds with
panoramic views across Dartmoor.
Tastefully furnished, good food. **Open:** All
year (not Xmas)
01837 53100 Mrs Jones **D:** £20.00 **S:** £23.00
Beds: 2D 1T **Baths:** 2 En 1 Pr ♿ (6) 🅿 (10) ✕
✉ 🏧 ✉ ⊞ ⚡

Otterton

SY0885 ⬛ *Sir Walter Raleigh, Kings Arms*

**Ropers
Cottage,**
*Ropers Lane,
Otterton,
Budleigh
Salterton,
Devon, EX9 7JF.*
C17th cottage in picturesque village, near
river and coastal path. **Open:** Easter to Oct
01395 568826 Mrs Earl **Fax:** 01395 568206
D: £18.00–£18.50 **S:** £18.00–£18.50 **Beds:** 1T
1S **Baths:** 2 En ♿ (1) 🅿 (2) ✕ ✉ ⊞ ⚡

Planning a longer stay? Always
ask for any special rates

Ottery St Mary

SY1095   *London Inn*

Fluxton Farm, Fluxton, Ottery St Mary, Devon, EX11 1RJ. Cat lovers paradise in lovely open countryside. Ideal touring area. **Open:** All year **Grades:** AA 2 Diamond **01404 812818** Mr & Mrs Forth **Fax:** 01404 814843 **D:** £25.00 **S:** £25.00 **Beds:** 1F 5T 3D 2S **Baths:** 11 En ⌂ (8) ⊡ (15) ⊡ ⊁ × ⊡ ▥ ⬮

Holly Ridge, West Hill, Ottery St Mary, Devon, EX11 1UX. Holly Ridge is on the edge of the peaceful village of West Hill. **Open:** All year **01404 812776 (also fax)** Mr Abel *HollyRidge@ aol.com* **D:** £18.00–£26.00 **S:** £18.00–£26.00 **Beds:** 1F 2D **Baths:** 1 En 1 Sh ⌂ (12) ⊡ (8) ⌁ ⊡ ⊁ × ⊡ ▥ & ⊛ ⬮

Paignton

SX8960

Greenford Lodge Hotel, 56 Dartmouth Road, Paignton, Devon, TQ4 5AN. Situated 5 mins from town centre/sea. Warm welcome. Ample Parking. **Open:** All year (not Xmas/New Year) **Grades:** ETC 3 Diamond **01803 553635** Mr & Mrs Nash **D:** £16.00–£24.00 **S:** £16.00–£18.00 **Beds:** 8F 2T 5D 1S **Baths:** 2 En 2 Pr 4 Sh ⌂ ⊡ ⊡ × ⊡ ▥ ⬮

Park View Guest House, 19 Garfield Road, Paignton, Devon, TQ4 6AX. Small friendly guest house - short level stroll town & sea front. **Open:** All year (not Xmas/New Year) **01803 528521** **D:** £13.00–£16.00 **S:** £13.00–£16.00 **Beds:** 3F 1D **Baths:** 1 Sh ⌂ ⊡ ⊡ ⌁ × ⊡ ▥ ⬮

South Sands Hotel, Alta Vista Road, Paignton, Devon, TQ4 6BZ. South-facing, licensed family-run hotel in peaceful location overlooking beach/park. **Open:** Mar to Oct **01803 557231 & 0500 432153 (ext 10)** Mr Cahill **D:** £20.00–£25.00 **S:** £20.00–£25.00 **Beds:** 7F 4D 6T 2S **Baths:** 17 En 2 Pr ⌂ ⊡ (17) ⊡ ⌁ × ⊡ ▥ & ⊛ ⬮ cc

Cherwood Hotel, 26 Garfield Road, Paignton, TQ4 6AX. All ensuite, licensed bar. Quality assured. Ideal position by central seafront/pier. **Open:** All year **01803 556515** J Alderson **Fax:** 01803 555126 *james-pauline@cherwood-hotel.co.uk* www.cherwood-hotel.co.uk **D:** £16.00–£20.00 **S:** £16.00–£20.00 **Beds:** 3F 3D 2T 1S **Baths:** 9 En ⌂ ⊡ (4) ⊡ ⌁ × ⊡ ▥ ⊛ ⬮ cc

Sundale Hotel, 10 Queens Road,

Paignton, Devon, TQ4 6AT. Quiet family run hotel, close to local amenities, highly recommended. **Open:** All year **01803 557431** Mr McDermott **D:** £14.50–£17.50 **S:** £14.50–£17.50 **Beds:** 2F 2T 3D 1S **Baths:** 4 En 1 Sh ⌂ ⌁ ⊡ ⌁ × ⊡ ▥ ⊛ ⬮

Hotel Fiesta, 2 Kernou Road, Paignton, TQ4 6BA. An attractive seaside property close to Paignton's clean beaches. **Open:** All year **01803 521862 (also fax)** Mr Hawker *hotelfiesta@alk21.com* **D:** £16.00–£20.00 **S:** £22.00–£26.00 **Beds:** 2F 5D 1T 2S **Baths:** 7 En 3 Sh ⌂ ⊡ ⊡ ▥ & ⊛ ⬮ cc

Bella Vista, 5 Berry Square, Paignton, TQ4 6AZ. On level adjacent to beach, town etc. Choice of menu. **Open:** Easter to Nov **01803 558122** *bellavista@berrysquare.co.uk* **D:** £14.00–£21.00 **S:** £14.00–£24.00 **Beds:** 2F 2T 3D 2S **Baths:** 4 En 2 Sh ⊡ (10) ⊡ × ⬮ cc

Pancrasweek

SS2906

The Barton, Pancrasweek, Holsworthy, Devon, EX22 7JT. Working farm. Peaceful position. Easy reach coast, moors, famous Clovelly. **Open:** Easter to Oct **01288 381315** Mrs Chant **D:** £20.00 **S:** £20.00 **Beds:** 2D 1T **Baths:** 3 En ⊡ ⌁ ⊡ × ⬮

Peter Tavy

SX5177   *Peter Tavy Inn, Elephant's Nest, Trout & Tipple*

Churchtown, Peter Tavy, Tavistock, Devon, PL19 9NP. Detached Victorian house standing in own large quiet garden. **Open:** All year (not Xmas) **01822 810477** Mrs Lane *lane@swcg.co.uk* **D:** £18.00–£19.00 **S:** £18.00–£19.00 **Beds:** 2D 1S **Baths:** 1 En 1 Sh ⌂ (10) ⊡ (6) ⊡ ⌁ ⊡ ▥ ⬮

Petrockstowe

SS5109

Aish Villa, Petrockstowe, Okehampton, Devon, EX20 3HL. Peaceful location, superb views, ideal for visiting Dartmoor, Exmoor, coast. **Open:** All year **01837 810581** Ms Gordon *gillandtonygordon@ hotmail.com* **D:** £17.00 **S:** £17.00 **Beds:** 1F 1T 1D **Baths:** 1 Sh ⌂ ⊡ (4) ⌁ ⊡ ⊡ ▥ & ⬮

Pickwell

SS4641

Meadow Cottage, Pickwell, Georgeham, Braunton, Devon, EX33 1LA. Tranquil setting of Pickwell. Off the beaten track with panoramic views. **Open:** All year **01271 890938 (also fax)** Mrs Holmes *rpholmes@talk21.com* members.aol.com/ SuzH2/MeadowCottageBedandBreakfast.htm **D:** £20.00 **S:** £20.00 **Beds:** 1D 1S **Baths:** 1 Pr ⊡ (3) ⌁ ⊡ ⊡ ▥

Plymouth

SX4756   *Langdon Court, Odd Wheel, Walrus Inn*

Smeaton's Tower Hotel, 40-42 Grand Parade, Plymouth, Devon, PL1 3DJ. **Open:** All year (not Xmas/New Year) **Grades:** ETC 4 Diamond **01752 221007** **Fax:** 01752 221664 *info@ smeatonstowehotel.co.uk* www.smeatonstowehotel.co.uk **D:** £22.50–£27.50 **S:** £30.00–£35.00 **Beds:** 4F 4D 2S **Baths:** 10 En ⌂ ⊡ ▥ ⬮ cc Smeaton's Tower Hotel is privately owned and operated, situated 20 yards from Plymouth Hoe foreshore, 15 minute walk from the famous Barbican and Mayflower steps, city centre shopping, Theatre Royal, Pavilions, Marine Aquarium, Brittany Ferry port. Ideal base to explore Dartmoor and Cornwall.

Mountbatten Hotel, 52 Exmouth Road, Stoke, Plymouth, Devon, PL1 4QH. **Open:** All year **Grades:** ETC 3 Diamond **01752 563843** Mr Hendy **Fax:** 01752 606014 **D:** £23.00–£25.00 **S:** £20.00–£27.00 **Beds:** 3F 6D 2T 4S **Baths:** 7 En 2 Sh ⌂ ⊡ (4) ⊡ ⌁ × ▥ ⬮ cc Small licensed Victorian hotel overlooking parkland with river views. Quiet cul de sac. Close city centre/ferryport. Good access Cornwall. Walking distance Naval base, Royal Fleet Club, FE College. Secure parking. Well appointed rooms. Tea/coffee, CTVs, telephones. Credit cards accepted.

Bay Cottage, 150 Church Road, Wembury, Plymouth, Devon, PL9 0HR. Victorian cottage by the sea, surrounded by National Trust land. **Open:** All year (not Xmas) **Grades:** ETC 3 Diamond **01752 862559 (also fax)** Mrs Farrington *TheFairies@aol.com* www.bay-cottage.com **D:** £27.00–£30.00 **S:** £27.00–£37.00 **Beds:** 2D 2T 1S **Baths:** 3 En 2 Sh ⌂ ⊡ (2) ⌁ ⊡ ⌁ ⊡ ▥ ⬮

The Old Pier Guest House, 20 Radford Road, West Hoe, Plymouth, Devon, PL1 3BY. Convenient for ferry, Barbican, city centre, sea front. Offers exceptional value. **Open:** All year (not Xmas/New Year) **Grades:** ETC 3 Diamond **01752 268468** Mrs Jones *enquiries@ oldpier.co.uk* www.oldpier.co.uk **D:** £16.00–£20.00 **S:** £16.00–£30.00 **Beds:** 1F 2T 3D 1S **Baths:** 1 En 2 Sh ⌁ ⊡ ⊡ ▥ ⬮ cc

Planning a longer stay? Always ask for any special rates

RATES

D = Price range per person sharing in a double or twin room

S = Price range for a single room

Cassandra Guest House, *13 Crescent Avenue, Plymouth, Devon, PL1 3AN.* Ideally situated for city centre, seafront, Barbican, Ferry Port, theatres, stations. **Open:** All year
01752 220715 (also fax) **D:** £17.00–£22.00 **S:** £17.00–£30.00 **Beds:** 3F 1T 1D 1S **Baths:** 2 En 1 Pr 1 Sh ♿ 🔥 🐾 🖥 ⛄ **cc**

Sunray Hotel, *3/5 Alfred Street, The Hoe, Plymouth, Devon, PL1 2RP.* Centrally located, convenient for theatre, shops, Barbican and National Aquarium. **Open:** All year (not Xmas/New Year)
01752 669113 Mr Thomas **Fax:** 01752 268969 **D:** £23.00–£26.00 **S:** £28.00–£35.00 **Beds:** 6F 4D 5T 3S **Baths:** 16 En 2 Pr 🅿 (6) 🔥 ⛄

Postbridge
SX6579

Hartyland, *Postbridge, Yelverton, Devon, PL20 6SZ.* Large, warm, comfortable Dartmoor house, direct access to open moorland. **Open:** All year (not Xmas)
01822 880210 Mr & Mrs Bishop **Fax:** 01822 880384 *andybishop@compuserve.com* **D:** £20.00–£25.00 **S:** £20.00–£25.00 **Beds:** 1F 3T 1S **Baths:** 2 Sh ♿ 🅿 (6) 🔥 🐾 ✗ 🖥 ⛄

Poundsgate
SX7072

New Cott Farm, *Poundsgate, Newton Abbot, Devon, TQ13 7PD.* Lovely walking in Dartmoor National Park. Good food, beds, welcoming & peaceful. **Open:** All year
01364 631421 Mrs Phipps *newcott@ ruralink.co.uk* **D:** £20.00–£22.00 **Beds:** 1F 2D 1T **Baths:** 3 En 1 Pr ♿ (5) 🅿 (4) ⛄ 🔥 ✗ 🖥 ⛄ ♿

Princetown
SX5873

Duchy House, *Tavistock Road, Princetown, Yelverton, Devon, PI20 6QF.* Warm welcome assured. Central base for exploring Dartmoor. Memorable breakfasts. **Open:** Dec to Oct
01822 890552 Mr Trimble *duchyhouse@aol.com* **D:** £18.00–£20.00 **S:** £18.00–£30.00 **Beds:** 1T 2D **Baths:** 1 En 1 Sh ♿ 🅿 (6) ⛄ 🔥 ⛄ **cc**

Pyworthy
SS3103 ◀ *Molesworth Arms, White Hart*

Leworthy Farm, *Pyworthy, Holsworthy, Devon, EX22 6SJ.* **Open:** All year **Grades:** ETC 4 Diamond, Silver, AA 4 Diamond
01409 259469 Mrs Jennings **D:** £22.00–£25.00 **S:** £25.00–£35.00 **Beds:** 1F 1T 2D **Baths:** 3 En 1 Pr ♿ 🅿 (8) ⛄ ✗ ⛄
North Cornish Coast 20 minutes. Georgian farmhouse in tranquil, unspoilt location. Lawned gardens, orchard, wildlife haven and fishing lake. Fresh flowers, pretty bone china, fresh milk, hearty breakfasts. Homely atmosphere. Peaceful lounge. Exquisitely decorated with pictures, plates and china throughout.

Salcombe
SX7339 ◀ *The Victoria, Fortescue, King's Arms*

Lyndhurst Hotel, *Bonaventure Road, Salcombe, Devon, TQ8 8BG.* Ideally located within 5 mins walk from harbour. Stunning views over estuary. Family run. **Open:** Easter to Oct
01548 842481 (also fax) Mrs Snelson **D:** £23.00–£30.00 **S:** £25.00–£35.00 **Beds:** 3F 5D **Baths:** 8 En ♿ (10) 🅿 (4) ⛄ 🖥 🐾 ⛄ ⛄

Motherhill Farm, *Salcombe, Devon, TQ8 8NB.* Peaceful and homely Victorian farmhouse on a mixed working farm. **Open:** Easter to Oct
01548 842552 (also fax) Mrs Weymouth *djw@dweymouth.fsnet.co.uk* **D:** £17.00–£19.00 **S:** £17.00–£19.00 **Beds:** 1F/D 1T 1S **Baths:** 1 Sh ♿ (7) 🅿 (6) ⛄ 🖥 ⛄

Sampford Courtenay
SS6301

Southey Farm, *Sampford Courtenay, Okehampton, Devon, EX20 2TE.* Comfortable farmhouse within easy reach of many attractions in Devon and Cornwall. **Open:** All year (not Xmas/New Year)
01837 82446 Mr & Mrs Townsend Green *TG@ southeyfarm.freeserve.co.uk* **D:** £15.00 **S:** £15.00 **Beds:** 1T 1S/T **Baths:** 2 Pr ♿ 🅿 (4) ⛄ 🔥 ⛄ ⛄

West Trecott Farm, *Sampford Courtenay, Okehampton, Devon, EX20 2TD.* Early C15th farmhouse in heart of Devon countryside close to Dartmoor National Park. **Open:** May to Oct
01837 82569 Mrs Horn **D:** £15.00 **S:** £15.00 **Beds:** 3D **Baths:** 2 En 1 Sh ♿ (2) 🅿 (6) ⛄ 🖥 🐾 ⛄

Sampford Peverell
ST0314 ◀ *Globe Inn, Herrimeade Hotel*

Challis, *12 Lower Town, Sampford Peverell, Tiverton, Devon, EX16 7BJ.* Centre of village with beautiful gardens leading to canal. **Open:** All year
01884 820620 Mrs Isaac **D:** £17.00–£20.00 **S:** £17.00 **Beds:** 1F 1T 1S 2D **Baths:** 1 En 1 Sh 🅿 (5) ⛄ 🖥 ⛄ ⛄

Sampford Spiney
SX5372

Withill Farm, *Sampford Spiney, Yelverton, Devon, PL20 6LN.* Dartmoor. Small secluded farm - beautiful setting, central for Devon, Cornwall. **Open:** All year
01822 853992 (also fax) Mrs Kitchen **D:** £19.00–£22.00 **S:** £20.00–£24.00 **Beds:** 2D 1T **Baths:** 1 En 1 Sh ♿ 🅿 (6) 🖥 🐾 ✗ 🖥 ⛄ ⛄

Scorriton
SX7068

The Tradesmans Arms, *Scorriton, Buckfastleigh, Devon, TQ11 0JB.* Warm friendly village pub. within Dartmoor National Park, set in beautiful Devon lanes. **Open:** All year (not Xmas/New Year)
01364 631206 Mr Lunday *john.lunday@ virgin.net* www.thetradesmansarms.com **D:** £25.00 **S:** £25.00 **Beds:** 2D **Baths:** 1 Sh 🅿 (20) ⛄ 🖥 🐾 ✗ ⛄ ⛄

Seaton
SY2490 ◀ *Harbour Inn, Ship Inn*

The Kettle Restaurant, *15 Fore Street, Seaton, Devon, EX12 2LE.* Close to shops, sea front. Comfortable, friendly and great food. **Open:** All year (not Xmas)
01297 20428 Mr Wallis *thekettleson@ seatondevon.freeserve.co.uk* www.thekettleson.com **D:** £17.00–£22.00 **S:** £19.00–£25.00 **Beds:** 1T 1D **Baths:** 2 En ♿ 🅿 (2) ⛄ 🖥 🐾 ✗ 🖥 ⛄ ⛄

Harbourside Guest House, *2 Trevelyan Road, Seaton, Devon, EX12.* Perfectly situated on the harbour and Southwest Coast Path. **Open:** Feb to Nov
01297 20085 **D:** £21.00–£23.00 **S:** £25.00–£28.00 **Beds:** 1T 1D **Baths:** 2 En ♿ (1) 🅿 (3) 🖥 ⛄ ⛄

The Harbour House, *1 Trevelyan Road, Seaton, Devon, EX12 2NL.* Spacious and comfortable harbourside house, directly on SW Coast Path. **Open:** Mar to Nov **01297 21797** Linda & Roger Sandbrook **D:** £20.00 **S:** £25.00 **Beds:** 1T 1D **Baths:** 2 En ⌂ 🅿 (5) 📺 🛋 ⚘

Shaldon

SX9372

Ringmore House, *Brook Lane, Shaldon, Teignmouth, Devon, TQ14 0AJ.* Beautiful old house & cottage set in ancient gardens full of exotic & unusual plants. **Open:** All year (not Xmas/New Year) **01626 873323** Mr & Mrs Scull **Fax: 01626 873353** *hscull@aol.com* **D:** £25.00–£35.00 **S:** £30.00–£40.00 **Beds:** 3D 1T **Baths:** 2 Pr 1 En ⌂ (9) 🅿 (10) ⌂ 📺 ✗ 🛋 ⚘

Virginia Cottage, *Brook Lane, Shaldon, Teignmouth, Devon, TQ14 0HL.* Early C17th house in one acre garden near sea. Ample parking. **Open:** All year **01626 872634 (also fax)** Mr & Mrs Britton **D:** £24.00–£25.00 **S:** £30.00–£35.00 **Beds:** 2D 1T **Baths:** 2 En 1 Pr 🅿 (4) ⌂ 📺 📺 🛋 ⚘

Shirwell

SS5937

Waytown Farm, *Shirwell, Barnstaple, Devon, EX31 4JN.* Comfortable C17th spacious farmhouse with superb views, 3 miles from Barnstaple. **Open:** All year (not Xmas) **01271 850396 (also fax)** Mrs Kingdon *hazel@waytown.enterprise-plc.com* www.waytownholidays.co.uk **D:** £20.00–£22.00 **S:** £18.50–£20.00 **Beds:** 2F 1T 1S **Baths:** 3 En 1 Sh ⌂ 🅿 (6) 📺 ✗ ⚘

Sidbury

SY1391   ⬤ Red Lion

Old Orchard Cottage, *Cotford Road, Sidbury, Sidmouth, Devon, EX10 0SQ.* **Open:** All year (not Xmas/New Year) **01395 597645** Ms Collings *collings.sidbury@btinternet.com* www.oldorchard.uk.com **D:** £20.00–£25.00 **S:** £20.00–£25.00 **Beds:** 1T 1D **Baths:** 1 En 1 Pr 🅿 (2) ⌂ 📺 🛋 ⚘ Set in a delightful Saxon Village. A haven for walkers & birdwatchers. The uniquely lovely coastal town of Sidmouth 3 miles away. Many places to visit. Breakfast on the terrace in fine weather overlooking the River Sid & orchard. A good local pub.

Planning a longer stay? Always ask for any special rates

Sidmouth

SY1287   ⬤ Tudor Rose

Barrington Villa Guest House, *Salcombe Road, Sidmouth, Devon, EX10 8PU.* **Open:** Jan to Nov **01395 514252** Mr & Mrs Carr **D:** £15.00–£24.00 **S:** £17.00–£24.00 **Beds:** 3D 2T 3S **Baths:** 4 En 4 Sh ⌂ 🅿 (10) 📺 ✗ ✗ 📺 🛋 ⚘ A charming Regency Gothic Villa, set in beautiful gardens on the bank of the River Sid in the heart of glorious East Devon.

Kyneton Lodge, *87 Alexandria Road, Sidmouth, Devon, EX10 9HG.* **Open:** All year (not Xmas/New Year) **Grades:** ETC 4 Diamond, Silver **01395 513213 (also fax)** Ms Wright *suawright@lineone.net* **D:** £24.00–£26.00 **S:** £24.00–£26.00 **Beds:** 1T 1D 1S **Baths:** 3 En ⌂ (5) 🅿 (6) ⌂ 📺 📺 🛋 ⚘ Perfectly situated for exploring the quaint nearby coastal towns and villages. Nice scenic walks. Full English breakfast. Approximately 1 mile walk to Sidmouth town centre and its lovely sea front. Bottled water, radio alarm clock and hairdryer in every room.

Bramley Lodge, *Vicarage Road, Sidmouth, Devon, EX10 8UQ.* 500 metres from sea. Garden overlooks river and Byes Parkland. **Open:** All year **01395 515710** Mr & Mrs Haslam *haslam@bramleylodge.fsnet.co.uk* **D:** £18.50–£25.00 **S:** £18.00–£25.00 **Beds:** 1F 1T 2D 3S **Baths:** 4 En 1 Sh ⌂ 🅿 (6) 📺 ✗ ✗ 📺 🛋 ⚘

Lynstead, *Lynstead Vicarage Road, Sidmouth, Devon, EX10 8UQ.* Cosy guest house backing onto The Byes NT park. **Open:** All year **Grades:** ETC 4 Diamond **01395 514635** Mr & Mrs Mair *lynstead@aol.com* **D:** £20.00–£22.00 **S:** £20.00–£30.00 **Beds:** 2F 2D 1T 1S **Baths:** 4 En 1 Sh ⌂ 🅿 (8) ⌂ 📺 📺 🛋 ⚘

Sidling Field, *105 Peaslands Road, Sidmouth, Devon, EX10 8XE.* Large bungalow on outskirts of town. Quiet location. Ample parking. **Open:** Jan to Nov **01395 513859** Mrs Shenfield *su1889@eclipse.co.uk* **D:** £18.00–£20.00 **S:** £25.00 **Beds:** 1D 1T **Baths:** 1 Sh ⌂ (8) 🅿 (3) 📺 ✗ 🛋 ⚘

Cheriton Guest House, *Vicarage Road, Sidmouth, Devon, EX10 8UQ.* Private garden for guests' use to banks of River Sid. **Open:** All year **01395 513810 (also fax)** Mrs Lee **D:** £18.00–£22.00 **S:** £18.00–£22.00 **Beds:** 2F 4D 2T 2S **Baths:** 10 En ⌂ 🅿 (10) ⌂ 📺 ✗ ✗ 📺 🛋 ⚘ ⚘

B&B owners may vary rates – be sure to check when booking

Avalon, *Vicarage Road, Sidmouth, Devon, EX10 8UQ.* Elegant town house, backing onto river and National Trust park. **Open:** All year (not Xmas) **01395 513443** Mrs Young *janetyoungavalon@aol.com* www.avalonsidmouth.co.uk **D:** £20.00–£27.50 **S:** £30.00–£40.00 **Beds:** 4D 1T **Baths:** 5 En 🅿 (5) ⌂ 📺 ✗ 📺 🛋 ⚘

Saltwynds Farm, *Saltwynds Lane, Bowd, Sidmouth, Devon, EX10 0NP.* The farmhouse is a hexagonal shape with large reception rooms. **Open:** All year (not Xmas/New Year) **01395 579441** C Edwards *carol27-53@aol.com* **D:** £20.00–£25.00 **S:** £20.00 **Beds:** 2F 2T 2D 2S **Baths:** 1Pr 1 Sh ⌂ 🅿 (8) ⌂ ✗ 📺 🛋 ⚘

Larkstone House, *22 Connaught Road, Sidmouth, Devon, EX10 8TT.* Detached, quiet surroundings yet adjacent shops. 1/3 mile beautiful Sidmouth seafront. **Open:** Easter to Nov **01395 514345** Mrs Lever **D:** £17.50–£19.50 **S:** £16.50–£18.00 **Beds:** 1F 1D 1S **Baths:** 1 En 1 Sh ⌂ 🅿 (3) ⌂ 📺 ✗ 🛋 ⚘

Higher Coombe Farm, *Tipton St John, Sidmouth, Devon, EX10 0AX.* Friendly welcome, comfortable rooms. Relaxed atmosphere. Working farm, sheep/cattle. **Open:** Mar to Dec **Grades:** ETC 3 Diamond **01404 813385 (also fax)** Mrs Farmer *kerstinfarmer@farming.co.uk* **D:** £18.00–£22.00 **S:** £18.00–£22.00 **Beds:** 1F 1T 1D 1S **Baths:** 1 En 1 Sh ⌂ 🅿 (4) ⌂ ✗ ⚘

Ryton Guest House, *52-54 Winslade Road, Sidmouth, Devon, EX10 9EX.* Attractive double-fronted house in central location 2 mins' walk from river. **Open:** Mar to Nov **01395 513981** Mr & Mrs Bradnam **D:** £20.00–£22.00 **S:** £20.00–£24.00 **Beds:** 4F 3D 1T 2S **Baths:** 8 En 2 Sh ⌂ 🅿 (6) 📺 ✗ ✗ 📺 🛋 ⚘

Woodlands Hotel, *Station Rd, Sidmouth, Devon, EX10 8HG.* C16th building. All modern conveniences in the heart of Sidmouth. **Open:** All year **01395 513120 (also fax)** *info@woodlands-hotel.com* **D:** £20.00–£44.00 **S:** £24.00–£42.00 **Beds:** 3F 8T 8D 5S **Baths:** 24 En ⌂ 🅿 (20) 📺 ✗ ✗ 📺 🛋 ⚘ ⚘ ⚘ cc

Silverton

SS9502

Hayne House, *Silverton, Exeter, Devon, EX5 4HE.* Georgian farmhouse, peacefully situated overlooking farm & woods. Relax in style. **Open:** Apr to Oct **01392 860725 (also fax)** Mrs Kelly *haynehouse@ukonline.co.uk* www.devonfarms.co.uk **D:** £16.00–£20.00 **S:** £16.00–£20.00 **Beds:** 1F 1T **Baths:** 2 Pr ⌂ 🅿 ✗ 📺 ⚘

Slapton

SX8245 🍺 *Queen's Arms, Tower Inn, King's Head*

Start House, *Start, Slapton, Kingsbridge, Devon, TQ7 2QD.* **Open:** All year (not Xmas) **Grades:** ETC 3 Diamond
01548 580254 Mrs Ashby **D:** £23.00 **S:** £21.00 **Beds:** 2D 1T 1S **Baths:** 2 Pr 1 Sh ⬧🅿(4)⚡ 📺🛏✕Ⓥ⊞ ♨
Comfortable Georgian house. Situated in quiet hamlet 1 mile from Slapton Ley. All bedrooms overlook a beautiful valley with Slapton and the sea at the end. Large interesting garden. Ideal for wildlife and walking. Traditional or vegetarian breakfast.

South Molton

SS7125 🍺 *Royal Oak, Poltimore Arms*

Stumbles Hotel & Restaurant, *131-134 East Street, South Molton, Devon, EX36 3BU.* **Open:** All year
01769 574145 M J Potter **Fax: 01769 572558**
info@stumbles.co.uk www.stumbles.co.uk
D: £22.50–£30.00 **S:** £35.00–£55.00 **Beds:** 1F 4T 5D **Baths:** 10 En ⬧🅿(15)📺🛏✕Ⓥ⊞♨ ♨ cc
On the edge of Exmoor, in historical market town. Highly acclaimed restaurant. Alfresco dining in pretty courtyard. Fishing on Mole and Taw rivers. Half-price golf on nearby spectacular 18 hole course with many leisure facilities. Fourth night free.

West Down Guest House, *Whitechapel, South Molton, Devon, EX36 3EQ.* Award-winning, outstanding 30 acres, beautiful gardens, spacious ensuite rooms. **Open:** All year **Grades:** ETC 4 Diamond
01769 550373 Mrs Savery **Fax: 01769 550839**
info@westdown.co.uk www.westdown.co.uk
D: £22.00–£24.00 **S:** £27.00–£29.00 **Beds:** 1F 1D 1T **Baths:** 3 En ⬧🅿(10)📺✕Ⓥ⊞ ♨

National Grid References given are for villages, towns and cities – not for individual houses

Southleigh

SY2093

South Bank, *Southleigh, Colyton, Devon, EX24 6JB.* Sunny house, beautiful garden, lovely views, relaxing walking/bird watching. **Open:** All year (not Xmas/New Year)
01404 871251 Mrs Connor **D:** £14.00–£15.00 **S:** £14.00–£15.00 **Beds:** 2D **Baths:** 2 Sh ⬧(10)🅿(4)⚡📺🛏✕Ⓥ⊞ ♨

Starcross

SX9781 🍺 *Courtenay Arms*

The Croft GuesHouse, *Cockwood Harbour, Starcross, Exeter, Devon, EX6 8QY.* **Open:** All year (not Xmas) **Grades:** ETC 3 Diamond
01626 890282 Mr Stewart **Fax: 01626 891768**
www.smoothhound.co.uk/hotels/croft/1. html **D:** £17.50–£23.00 **S:** £22.00–£28.00 **Beds:** 2F 3D 4T 1S **Baths:** 7 En ⬧(5)🅿(8)Ⓥ 🛏Ⓥ⊞♨ ♨
Set in an acre of secluded gardens overlooking Cockwood Harbour and River Exe. Convenient for Powderham Castle and Dawlish Warren Nature Reserve. 2 mins walk to two of Devon's finest seafood pub/restaurants, discount card for our guests.

Start

SX8044 🍺 *Fortescue Arms, Creeks End, Crabshell, Ashburton Arms, Globe Inn, Cricket Inn, Church House, California Cross*

Lamacraft House, *Start Point, Kingsbridge, Devon, TQ7 2NG.* **Open:** All year (not Xmas/New Year)
01548 511291 Mr & Mrs Sainthill **D:** £20.00 **S:** £21.00 **Beds:** 1T 2D **Baths:** 1 En 1 Sh🅿(6) 📺🛏Ⓥ
Beautiful secluded position overlooking Start Bay, midway Dartmouth/Salcombe. Unspoilt coast and countryside. One nights and singles welcome. Rooms with balcony overlooking gardens or overlooking sea. Morning and afternoon tea, transport for walkers to evening meals (four venues).

Stockland

ST2404

Barn Park Farm, *Stockland Hill, Stockland, Honiton, Devon, EX14 9JA.* Traditional old Devon dairy farm, excellent walking country, abundance of wildlife. **Open:** All year (not Xmas/New Year)
01404 861297 & 0800 3282605 (freephone)
Mrs Boyland **Fax: 01404 861297** *pab@ barnparkfarm.co.uk* **D:** £17.00–£20.00 **S:** £20.00 **Beds:** 1F 1T 1D 1S **Baths:** 2 En 1 Pr 1 Sh ⬧🅿(10)⚡📺🛏✕Ⓥ♨

The Kings Arms Inn, *Stockland, Honiton, Devon, EX14 9BS.* C16th inn set in beautiful Devon countryside. **Open:** All year (not Xmas)
01404 881361 Fax: 01404 881732 *reserve@ kingsarms.net* www.kingsarms.net **D:** £25.00 **S:** £30.00 **Beds:** 2D 1T **Baths:** 3 En ⬧🅿(40) 📺🛏✕Ⓥ⊞♨ ♨ cc

Tavistock

SX4874 🍺 *Mucky Duck, Dartmoor Inn*

Acorn Cottage, *Heathfield, Tavistock, Devon, PL19 0LQ.* **Open:** All year **Grades:** ETC 4 Diamond
01822 810038 Mrs Powell-Thomas *viv@ acorncot.fsnet.co.uk* www.geocities. com/acorncottage **D:** £15.00–£20.00 **S:** £20.00–£30.00 **Beds:** 1D 2T **Baths:** 3 En 1 Pr ⬧(6)🅿(20)⚡📺🛏Ⓥ⊞♨ ♨
C17th Grade II Listed, many original features retained. Peaceful, rural location, beautiful views, just 3 miles from Tavistock on the Chillaton road. Quality accommodation near Lydford Gorge and Brentor medieval church. Central to many activities. Also self catering accommodation available.

Beera Farm, *Milton Abbot, Tavistock, Devon, PL19 8PL.* **Open:** All year **Grades:** ETC 4 Diamond, Silver
01822 870216 (also fax)
Mrs Tucker *robert.tucker@farming.co.uk* www.beera-farm.co.uk **D:** £20.00–£25.00 **S:** £25.00–£35.00 **Beds:** 1F 2D **Baths:** 3 En ⬧🅿(5)⚡📺✕Ⓥ⊞♨ ♨ cc
Come and relax on our working farm on the banks of the River Tamar. Abundant wildlife. Beautiful location. Stay in spacious well-appointed rooms with attention to detail. Wonderful hospitality. Romantic four-poster bedroom. Delicious food. Warm friendly atmosphere.

Bracken B & B, *36 Plymouth Road, Tavistock, Devon, PL19 8BU.* Comfortable Victorian town house. Adjacent Dartmoor National Park. Warm welcome. **Open:** All year
01822 613914 Ms Spartley *niklin@ supanet.com* **D:** £16.00–£20.00 **S:** £20.00–£30.00 **Beds:** 1T 3D **Baths:** 1 En 1 Pr 1 Sh ⬧(5)🅿(4)⚡📺Ⓥ⊞♨ ♨

Bush Park, *Tavistock, Devon, PL19 0NE.* Stunning views. Next to Lydford Gorge and Forest. **Open:** All year
01822 820345 A S Hepworth *stay@ bushpark.co.uk* **D:** £18.00 **S:** £24.00 **Beds:** 1T 1D **Baths:** 1 Pr ⬧(3)🅿(4)⚡📺Ⓥ⊞♨ ♨

Kingfisher Cottage, *Mount Tavy Road,*
Tavistock, Devon, PL19 9JB. Riverside
accommodation in Characterful cottage.
Near beautiful Dartmoor. Weekly
discounts! **Open:** All year **Grades:** ETC 3
Diamond
01822 613801 M Toland **D:** £17.50–£22.00
S: £25.50–£40.00 **Beds:** 1F 1T 1D **Baths:** 2
En 1 Pr ॐ 🖬 (4) ⚡ 🖵 🛏 🖵 🛋 🛎

Teignmouth

SX9473   ◈ *Anchor Inn*

Leicester House, *2 Winterbourne Road,*
Teignmouth, Devon, TQ14 8JT. Imposing
towered Victoriana. Garden, parking and 5
mins to town and beach. **Open:** All year
(not Xmas/New Year) **Grades:** ETC 3
Diamond
01626 773043 S Pickup **D:** £18.00–£20.00
Beds: 1T 3D **Baths:** 4 En ॐ (6) 🖬 (3) ⚡ 🖵 🖵
🛋 🛎

Wytchwood, *West Buckeridge Road,*
Teignmouth, Devon, TQ14 8NF. Award-
winning excellence, lavish hospitality.
Beautiful garden. Homemade bread and
preserves. **Open:** All year (not Xmas/New
Year)
01626 773482 Mrs Richardson Brown
wytchwood@yahoo.com www.messages.
to/wytchwood **D:** £28.50–£35.00 **S:** £35.00–
£45.00 **Beds:** 1F 1T 1D **Baths:** 1 En 2 Pr 🖬 ⚡
🖵 ✕ 🛋 🛎 cc

The Bay Hotel, *Sea Front, Teignmouth,*
Devon, TQ14 8BL. Overlooking the sea,
previously summer house of Earl of Devon.
Open: All year
01626 774123 Mrs Dumont **Fax:** 01626
777794 **D:** £23.00–£26.00 **S:** £23.00–£26.00
Beds: 4F 6T 6D 2S **Baths:** 18 En ॐ 🖬 (14) 🖵
✕ 🖵 🛋 ❋ 🛎 cc

Thelbridge

SS7911   ◈ *Thelbridge Cross Inn*

Hele Barton, *Thelbridge Cross,*
Thelbridge, Black Dog, Crediton, Devon,
EX17 4QJ. Comfortable, friendly thatched
farmhouse accommodation. Ideal base for
exploring Devon. **Open:** Easter to Nov
Grades: ETC 3 Diamond
01884 860278 (also fax) Mrs Gillbard
gillbard@eclipse.co.uk www.eclipse.co.
uk/helebarton **D:** £16.00–£21.00 **Beds:** 2T
1D **Baths:** 1 En 1 Sh ॐ 🖬 🖵 🛎

RATES

D = Price range per person
sharing in a double or twin
room

S = Price range for a single
room

Planning a longer stay? Always
ask for any special rates

Throwleigh

SX6690

Well Farm,
Throwleigh,
Okehampton,
Devon, EX20 2JQ.
Open: All year
(not Xmas/New
Year)
01647 231294 Mrs Knox **Fax:** 01647 231561
D: £22.00 **Beds:** 1F 1T 1D **Baths:** 1 En 2 Pr ॐ
🖬 (6) ⚡ 🖵 🛏 ✕ 🖵 🛎
Grade II listed Devon longhouse in
Dartmoor National Park. Working family
farm with organic milking cows and own
pigs. Live as family with resident dogs and
cats in relaxed beautiful surroundings. Bed
& Breakfast, late evening meal, non-
smoking house.

Throwleigh Manor, *Throwleigh,*
Okehampton, Devon, EX20 2JF. Beautiful
country house set in 12 acres in idyllic,
peaceful countryside of National Park.
Tastefully decorated rooms, excellent
breakfast and warm welcome. Heated
swimming pool, games-room, woodland
walk to private lake. Perfectly situated to
explore whole of West Country. **Open:** All
year **Grades:** ETC 4 Diamond
01647 231630 (also fax) Mr & Mrs
Smitheram *info@throwleighmanor.com*
www.throwleighmanor.com **D:** £20.00–
£26.00 **S:** £28.00–£38.00 **Beds:** 1F 1D 1S
Baths: 1 En 2 Pr ॐ (1) 🖬 (10) ⚡ 🖵 🖵 🛋 🛎

Tipton St John

SY0991   ◈ *Golden Lion*

Higher Coombe Farm, *Tipton St John,*
Sidmouth, Devon, EX10 0AX. Friendly
welcome, comfortable rooms. Relaxed
atmosphere. Working farm, sheep/cattle.
Open: Mar to Dec **Grades:** ETC 3 Diamond
01404 813385 (also fax) Mrs Farmer
kerstinfarmer@farming.co.uk **D:** £18.00–£22.00
S: £18.00–£22.00 **Beds:** 1F 1T 1D 1S
Baths: 1 En 1 Sh ॐ 🖬 (4) ⚡ 🖵 🛎

Tiverton

SS9512

The Mill,
Lower Washfield,
Washfield,
Tiverton, Devon,
EX16 9PD. Relax,
unwind, enjoy
the peace and
tranquillity of our idyllic riverside location.
Open: All year
01884 255297 (also fax) Mrs Arnold
D: £19.00–£22.00 **S:** £20.00–£25.00 **Beds:** 1F
1T 2D **Baths:** 4 En ॐ 🖬 (8) 🖵 ✕ 🖵 ❋ 🛎

Angel Guest House, *13 St Peter Street,*
Tiverton, Devon, EX16 6NU. Town centre
Georgian house, large cycle shed, ideal
touring centre. **Open:** All year
01884 253392 Mr & Mrs Evans **Fax:** 01884
251154 *cerimar@globalnet.co.uk* **D:** £18.00–
£22.00 **S:** £18.00–£24.00 **Beds:** 2F 3D 1T 1S
Baths: 3 Pr 2 Sh ॐ 🖬 (4) 🖵 🖵 🛋 🛎

Hill Cottage, *Cove, Tiverton, Devon,*
EX16 7RN. Stress-free and calming
countryside location. The silence is
deafening. **Open:** All year (not Xmas)
01884 256978 Mrs Harris *bmbmbio@talk21.com*
D: £20.00 **S:** £20.00–£25.00 **Beds:** 1D 1T
Baths: 1 Sh 🖬 (4) ⚡ 🖵 ✕ 🛋 🛎

Topsham

SX9688   ◈ *The Passage, Lighter, Lord Nelson*

Broadway House, *33 High Street,*
Topsham, Exeter, Devon, EX3 0ED. Grade II*
listed Georgian property, on the High Street
of Topsham. **Open:** All year (not Xmas/New
Year)
01392 873465 H & G Knee **Fax:** 01392 666103
heather@broadwayhouse.com
www.broadwayhouse.com **D:** £22.00–£28.00
S: £22.00–£28.00 **Beds:** 1F 2T 3D 2S
Baths: 7 En 1 Sh 🖬 (6) ⚡ 🖵 🛏 🖵 🛋 cc

Torquay

SX9165   ◈ *Stumble Inn, Devon Arms, Hole in the*
Wall, Pit House, Hare & Hounds

Heathcliff
House Hotel,
16 Newton Road,
Torquay, TQ2 5BZ.
Open: All year
(not Xmas)
01803 211580
(also fax) Mr &
Mrs Sanders *hhhtorquay@btclick.com*
D: £17.00–£22.50 **S:** £20.00 **Beds:** 2F 8D
Baths: 10 En ॐ 🖬 (10) 🖵 ✕ 🛋 🛎 cc
Whether taking your main holiday, having a
weekend away, touring Devon, visiting
friends or on business, this family hotel
offers great value B&B. Built in 1860s, the
Heathcliff, once a vicarage, now features in
the official Torquay Agatha Christie trail.

Elmdene
Hotel,
Rathmore Road,
Torquay, Devon,
TQ2 6NZ.
Open: All year
Grades: ETC 4
Diamond
01803 294940 D: £20.00–£25.00 **S:** £25.00–
£30.00 **Beds:** 4F 1T 4D 2S **Baths:** 7 En 1 Sh
ॐ (8) 🖬 (10) ⚡ 🖵 ✕ 🖵 🛋 ❋ 🛎 cc
Situated on level ground close to sea front,
town and railway station. You are assured a
warm welcome, comfortable
accommodation and excellent food.
Licensed with own car park.

The Buckingham Lodge,
Falkland Road, Torquay, Devon, TQ2 5JP. **Open:** All year
01803 293538 Mr Lloyd *bookingbucklodge@aol.com* www.buckinghamlodge.co.uk
D: £18.50–£25.00 **S:** £20.00–£30.00 **Beds:** 1F 3T 3D 1S **Baths:** 7 En 1 Pr ✻ 🅿(8) 🅿(5) ⚷ 🖂 ✕ 🔟 🎟 ♨
A warm welcome awaits you at this small and comfortable accommodation. Walking distance to Riviera Conference Centre, Torre Abbey and seafront. Perfectly situated for exploring Torbay and surrounding areas. The beauty of Dartmoor is only a short drive away.

Clovelly Guest House,
91 Avenue Road, Torquay, Devon, TQ2 5LH. Level walk to seafront. Pets/children welcome. Full English breakfast. **Open:** ALl Year **Grades:** ETC 3 Diamond
01803 292286 (also fax) Mr & Mrs Frances *clovellytorquay@ntlworld.com* homepage.ntlworld.com/clovelly.
guesthouse **D:** £14.00–£20.00 **S:** £14.00–£16.00 **Beds:** 1F 1T 2D 2S **Baths:** 2 En 4 Sh ✻ 🅿(4) 🔟 🎟 🔟 🖂 ♨

Aries House,
1 Morgan Avenue, Torquay, Devon, TQ2 5RP. Central Victorian town house near bus/coach/train stations, shops, beaches, clubs. **Open:** All year (not Xmas/New Year)
01803 215655 & 01803 404926 Mr & Mrs Sherry **D:** £13.00–£20.00 **S:** £13.00–£18.00 **Beds:** 2F 2T 1D 1S **Baths:** 2 En 2 Sh ✻ (0) 🅿(1) ⚷ 🔟 ✕ 🔟 🖂 ♨

Chester Court Hotel,
30 Cleveland Road, Torquay, Devon, TQ2 5BE. Comfortable accommodation, quiet situation, level walk to seafront, good food. **Open:** All year **Grades:** ETC 3 Diamond
01803 294565 (also fax) Mrs Morris www.kpmorris.freeserve.co.uk/cch.htm
D: £17.50–£22.00 **S:** £17.50–£36.00 **Beds:** 3F 2T 4D 1S **Baths:** 9 En 1 Sh ✻ 🅿(10) ⚷ 🔟 🔟 🖂 ♨ cc

Planning a longer stay? Always ask for any special rates

All details shown are as supplied by B&B owners in Autumn 2001

Sandpiper Lodge Hotel,
96 Avenue Road, Torquay, TQ2 5LF. Guests keep returning, loving our homely atmosphere and hearty breakfasts. **Open:** All year
01803 293293 D: £15.00–£22.00 **S:** £13.00–£20.00 **Beds:** 2F 4D 1S **Baths:** 7 En ✻ 🅿(7) ⚷ 🔟 ✕ 🖂 ♨ cc

Palm Tree House,
93 Avenue Road, Torquay, Devon, TQ2 5LH. Small, friendly, relaxed guest house. Home from home. Good breakfast. **Open:** All year (not Xmas/New Year)
01803 299141 Mr & Mrs Brown **D:** £15.00–£17.00 **S:** £15.00–£17.00 **Beds:** 1F 1T 2D 1S **Baths:** 2 En 1 Sh ✻ 🅿(3) 🔟 🖂 ♨

Swiss Court,
68 Vane Hill Road, Torquay, Devon, TQ1 2BZ. Blissfully quiet location, sea views, yet near harbour and town. **Open:** All year (not Xmas)
01803 215564 Mr Davies **D:** £16.00–£20.00 **S:** £16.00–£20.00 **Beds:** 1F 2D 5S **Baths:** 6 En 1 Sh ✻ (6) 🅿(8) 🅿 🎟 🔟 ♿ ♨

Knowle Court Hotel,
Kents Road Wellswood, Torquay, TQ1 2NN. Peaceful location near beaches, town. Good bus service. **Open:** All year (not Xmas/New Year) **Grades:** ETC 4 Diamond
01803 297076 Mr Baderay **Fax: 01803 292980** www.knowle-court-hotel.co.uk
D: £22.00–£30.00 **S:** £22.00–£30.00 **Beds:** 3F 4D 1T 1S **Baths:** 9 En ✻ 🅿(5) ⚷ 🔟 🔟 🖂 ♨ cc

Brampton Court Hotel,
St Lukes Road South, Torquay, Devon, TQ2 2NZ. Panoramic views of Torbay, close to town, beach & conference centre. **Open:** All year
01803 294237 Mr & Mrs Markham **Fax: 01803 211842** *stay@bramptoncourt.co.uk* www.bramptoncourt.co.uk **D:** £22.00–£28.00 **S:** £27.00–£33.00 **Beds:** 6F 4T 8D 2S **Baths:** 20 En ✻ 🅿(14) ⚷ 🔟 🔟 🖂 ❋ cc

Treander Guest House,
10 Morgan Avenue, Torquay, Devon, TQ2 5RS. Stag and Hen parties welcome. Central all amenities. Access all times. **Open:** All year
01803 296906 B Hurren **D:** £13.50–£17.50 **S:** £13.50–£17.50 **Beds:** 3F 4T 4D 1S **Baths:** 2 En 1 Pr 2 Sh ✻ 🅿(4) 🔟 ✕ 🔟 🖂 ♨

Devon Court Hotel,
24 Croft Road, Torquay, Devon, TQ2 5UE. Family-run Victorian hotel in heart of Torquay. Few mins' walk beach. **Open:** All year
01803 293603 Fax: 01803 213660 *info@devoncourt.co.uk* www.devoncourt.co.uk
D: £15.00–£25.00 **S:** £22.50–£32.50 **Beds:** 4F 8D 2T **Baths:** 10 En 6 Pr ✻ 🅿(14) ⚷ 🔟 ✕ 🔟 ♨ ❋ cc

---

Totnes
SX8060 🍺 *Albert Inn, Church House , Smugglers' , Pig & Whistle*

The Old Forge at Totnes,
Seymour Place, Totnes, Devon, TQ9 5AY. Historic house, walled garden, whirlpool spa. Close town and river. **Open:** All year **Grades:** ETC 4 Diamond, Silver, AA 4 Diamond
01803 862174 Mrs Hillier and Mr D Miller **Fax: 01803 865385** *miller@supanet.com*
D: £27.00–£37.00 **S:** £17.00–£27.00 **Beds:** 2F 7D 1S **Baths:** 16 En ✻ (0) 🅿(10) ⚷ 🔟 ✕ 🔟 🖂 ♨ cc

Royal Seven Stars Hotel,
The Plains, Totnes, Devon, TQ9 5DD. 1660 town centre former coaching inn near River Dart, restaurant. **Open:** All year
01803 862125 R Baron **D:** £33.00–£37.00 **S:** £50.00–£60.00 **Beds:** 2F 10D 3T 1S **Baths:** 14 En 2 Pr ✻ 🅿(20) 🔟 ✕ 🔟 🖂 ♨ cc

Great Court Farm,
Weston Lane, Totnes, Devon, TQ9 6LB. Winner of 'South Hams For All Seasons Accommodation Award'. Totnes 1 mile. **Open:** All year **Grades:** ETC 4 Diamond, Silver
01803 862326 (also fax) J Hooper **D:** £18.50–£20.00 **S:** £20.00–£23.00 **Beds:** 1T 2D **Baths:** 1 Pr 1 Sh ✻ 🅿(5) 🅿(4) ⚷ 🔟 ✕ 🔟 🖂 ♨

Trinity
ST0207 🍺 *Weary Traveller, Merry Harriers*

Wishay,
Trinity, Cullompton, Devon, EX15 1PE. Spacious farmhouse in peaceful countryside. Ideal touring base. **Open:** All year (not Xmas/New Year) **Grades:** ETC 3 Diamond
01884 33223 (also fax) Mrs Baker **D:** £16.00–£18.00 **Beds:** 2F **Baths:** 1 En 1 Sh ✻ 🅿(2) 🔟 🖂 ♨

Umberleigh
SS6123

The Gables Guest House,
On-the-Bridge, Umberleigh, Devon, EX37 9AB. A warm & friendly personal service, situated in the picturesque Taw Valley. **Open:** Feb to Dec
01769 560461 Mr Pring **D:** £18.50–£22.50 **S:** £18.50–£22.50 **Beds:** 1T 1D 1S **Baths:** 3 En 🅿(4) 🔟 🔟 🖂 ♨

Upham
SS8808

Jellicoe's,
Higher Holn, Upham, Cheriton Fitzpaine, Crediton, Devon, EX17 4HN. Peaceful cottage and garden. Beautiful landscape. Convenient position. Exceptional food. **Open:** All year (not Xmas)
01363 866165 (also fax) Mr Jellicoe *jellicoes@higherholn.freeserve.co.uk* www.jellicoes.co.uk
D: £22.00 **S:** £22.00 **Beds:** 2D 1T **Baths:** 3 En ✻ 🅿(4) ⚷ 🔟 ✕ 🔟 🖂 ♨

Uplowman

ST0115

Hill Farm, *Uplowman, Tiverton, Devon, EX16 7PE.* C15th Devon longhouse quiet working farm. Tennis court games room. **Open:** All year
01884 820388 M Branton **D:** £17.00–£18.00
S: £17.00–£18.00 **Beds:** 3D 1S 🕑 🅿 (6) 📺 ☂
📷, ▣

Uplyme

SY3293

Lydwell House, *Lyme Road , Uplyme, Lyme Regis, Dorset, DT7 3TJ.* A pre-Victorian house set within 0.75 acre of Victorian gardens. **Open:** All year
01297 443522 Mr Brittain **D:** £23.00–£27.00
S: £23.00–£27.00 **Beds:** 2F 1D 1T 1S
Baths: 5 En 🕑 🅿 (7) ⊬ 📺 ✕ 📺 ▥, ▣ cc

Upottery

ST1907 ◨ *Sidmouth Arms*

Courtmoor Farm, *Upottery, Honiton, Devon, EX14 9QA.* **Open:** All year (not Xmas/ New Year)
01404 861565 R Buxton *courtmoor.farm@ btinternet.com www.btinternet. com/~courtmoor.farm* **D:** £20.00–£22.50
S: £23.50–£28.00 **Beds:** 1F 1T 1D **Baths:** 3 En 🕑 🅿 (20) ⊬ 📺 ✕ 📺 ▥, ▣ cc
Courtmoor Farm has spectacular views and is set in 17 acres. Rosalind and Bob Buxton offer a warm welcome and quality accommodation in peaceful surroundings. It is ideally situated for north and south coasts and moorland. The premises are licensed.

Venton (Sparkwell)

SX5956

Flora House, *Venton, Sparkwell, Plymouth, PL7 5DR.* Warm welcome, overlooking Dartmoor, home produce when available, morn/eve drinks. **Open:** All year (not Xmas/New Year)
01752 837239 Mrs Laid **D:** £17.50–£18.50
S: £17.50–£18.50 **Beds:** 1D 1T **Baths:** 1 Sh
🕑 🅿 (2) ⊬ 📺 ☂ ✕

Planning a longer stay? Always ask for any special rates

Walkhampton

SX5369

Town Farm, *Walkhampton, Yelverton, Devon, PL20 6JX.* Self-contained accommodation in recently refurbished Listed barn. Attractive courtyard location. **Open:** All year
01822 855145 Mr & Mrs Morley **Fax:** 01822 852180 *crmorley@town-farm.com*
www.town-farm.com **D:** £20.00 **S:** £25.00
Beds: 1T 1D **Baths:** 2 En 🕑 🅿 (2) ⊬ 📺 ✕ 📺 ▥, ▣

Washbourne

SX7954

Penny Rowden, *Washbourne, Dartmouth, Totnes, Devon, TQ9 7DN.* **Open:** All year (not Xmas) **Grades:** ETC 4 Diamond
01803 712485 (also fax) Mrs Parsons *ap@ pennyrowden.freeserve.co.uk* **D:** £20.00–£25.00
S: £20.00–£25.00 **Beds:** 1F 2D 1T 1S
Baths: 5 En 🕑 🅿 (10) 📺 ☂ ✕ 📺 ▥, ▣
200-year-old farmhouse nestling in a tranquil valley with 11 acres of conserved pastures and woods; e/m available, all meals served in beamed dining room with log fire. Ideally situated for spectacular South Devon coastline and moors.

Washfield

SS9315

The Mill, *Lower Washfield, Washfield, Tiverton, Devon, EX16 9PD.* Relax, unwind, enjoy the peace and tranquillity of our idyllic riverside location. **Open:** All year
01884 255297 (also fax) Mrs Arnold
D: £19.00–£22.00 **S:** £20.00–£25.00 **Beds:** 1F 1T 2D **Baths:** 4 En 🕑 🅿 (8) 📺 ✕ 📺 ☀ ▣

Watermouth

SS5547

The Old Sawmill Inn, *Watermouth, Ilfracombe, EX34 9SX.* Pub with stream through garden. Summer entertainment. **Open:** All year (not Xmas/New Year)
01271 882259 K Rudd **D:** £20.00 **S:** £20.00–£40.00 **Beds:** 4D **Baths:** 4 En 🕑 🅿 (30) 📺 ✕ 📺 ▥, ▣ cc

Wembury

SX5248

Bay Cottage, *150 Church Road, Wembury, Plymouth, Devon, PL9 0HR.* Victorian cottage by the sea, surrounded by National Trust land. **Open:** All year (not Xmas) **Grades:** ETC 3 Diamond
01752 862559 (also fax) Mrs Farrington
TheFairies@aol.com www.bay-cottage.com
D: £27.00–£30.00 **S:** £27.00–£37.00 **Beds:** 2D 2T 1S **Baths:** 3 En 2 Sh 🕑 🅿 (2) ⊬ 📺 ☂ 📺 ▣

West Anstey

SS8527

Jubilee House, *Highaton Farm, West Anstey, South Molton, Devon, EX36 3PJ.* **Open:** All year **Grades:** ETC 4 Diamond
01398 341312 Mrs Denton **Fax:** 01398 341323 *denton@exmoorholiday.co.uk*
www.exmoorholiday.co.uk **D:** £19.50–£25.00
S: £19.50 **Beds:** 2D 2S **Baths:** 2 En 1 Sh 🕑 🅿 (4) ⊬ 📺 ☂ ✕ 📺 ▥, ☀ ▣
Elegant farmhouse, close edge Exmoor National Park, situated on Two Moors Way. Peaceful surroundings, easily accessible, great atmosphere. Large lounge (with log fire), dining room available for guests, local produce/home preserves. Bill is an international chef. Patio/BBQ/badminton areas, therapeutic hot tub spa.

West Buckland

SS6531

Huxtable Farm, *West Buckland, Barnstaple, Devon, EX32 0SR.* Medieval farmhouse (1520) in secluded countryside. Tennis court and sauna. **Open:** Feb to Nov **Grades:** ETC 4 Diamond, Silver Award
01598 760254 (also fax) Mrs Payne
stilenquiries@huxtablefarm.co.uk
www.huxtablefarm.co.uk **D:** £25.00–£26.00
S: £35.00 **Beds:** 2F 3D 1T **Baths:** 5 En 1 Pr 🕑 🅿 (10) ⊬ 📺 ✕ 📺 ▥, ▣ cc

Westward Ho!

SS4329 ◨ *Country Cousins, Potwallopers*

Seadrift, *72 Atlantic Way, Westward Ho!, Bideford, Devon, EX39 1JG.* Comfortable family home. Hearty breakfast, lovely sea views, coastal walks. **Open:** All year
01237 421174 Mrs Shadbolt *chruth.shadalak@ zoom.co.uk* **D:** £17.50–£20.00 **S:** £20.00–£22.00 **Beds:** 2T 1D **Baths:** 3 En 🅿 ⊬ 📺 ▥, ▣

Brockenhurst, *11 Atlantic Way, Westward Ho!, Bideford, Devon, EX39 1HX.* Comfortable, detached house. Views of Lundy Island and vast beach. **Open:** All year (not Xmas)
01237 423346 (also fax) Mrs Snowball
D: £22.50–£25.00 **S:** £27.00–£30.00 **Beds:** 2D 1T **Baths:** 3 En 🅿 (4) 📺 ☂ 📺 ▥, ▣

Please respect a B&B's wishes regarding children, animals and smoking

Eversley, *1 Youngaton Road, Westward Ho!, Bideford, Devon, EX39 1HU.* Victorian gentleman's residence. Superb accommodation. Sea views, beach 2 mins. **Open:** All year **01237 471603** Mr Sharratt **D:** £18.00–£20.00 **S:** £24.00–£29.00 **Beds:** 1F 1D 1T **Baths:** 1 En 1 Sh ➜ 🄿 (3) 📺 🍴 Ⅴ ▥ 🏊

Whimple

SY0497   🍺 *Thirsty Farmer, Jack-in-the-Green*

Busy Bee, *Mellifera, Church Road, Whimple, Exeter, Devon, EX5 2TF.* Friendly, lovely views, bungalow. Ideal for coast, city or airport. **Open:** All year **01404 823019 (also fax)** Mr & Mrs Janaway *bandb.busybee@virgin.net www.whimple.swest.co.uk* **D:** £18.00–£19.00 **S:** £21.00–£22.00 **Beds:** 1T 2D **Baths:** 3 En ➜ (5) 🄿 (6) 📺 Ⅴ ▥ 🏊

The Jays, *The Square, Whimple, Exeter, Devon, EX5 2SL.* C16th village square cottage. Ideal for Dartmoor and coast. **Open:** All year (not Xmas/New Year) **01404 823614** J & J Discombe **Fax:** 01404 823629 *jaydiscombe@supanet.com* **D:** £17.50 **Beds:** 1T 2D 1S **Baths:** 2 Sh ⚹ 📺 ▥ 🏊

Holway Barton, *Whimple, Exeter, Devon, EX5 2QY.* Elegant country home. Attractive gardens surrounded by open farmland. **Open:** All year (not Xmas/New Year) **01404 822477** Mr Brown **D:** £20.00 **S:** £25.00 **Beds:** 1F 2T 2D **Baths:** 1 En 1 Pr 1 Sh ➜ 🄿 (6) ⚹ 📺 ▥ 🏊

Willand

ST0310

Pitfield House, *Willand Old Village, Cullompton, Devon, EX15 2RL.* Charming family home. Large secluded garden. Small outdoor swimming pool. **Open:** All year (not Xmas/New Year) **01884 32304** Mrs Armstrong **D:** £25.00–£30.00 **S:** £20.00–£25.00 **Beds:** 2T 1D **Baths:** 2 Sh ➜ 📺 🍴 ✗ Ⅴ ▥ 🏊

Wilmington

ST2000

The Crest Guest House, *Moorcox Lane, Wilmington, Honiton, Devon, EX14 9JU.* A modern chalet style house nestling in the picturesque Unborne valley. **Open:** All year **01404 831419** Mrs Kidwell **D:** £19.00–£21.00 **S:** £26.00–£27.00 **Beds:** 1F 1D 1T ➜ 🄿 (8) 📺 🍴 ✗ Ⅴ ▥ 🚻 🏊

Planning a longer stay? Always ask for any special rates

Witheridge

SS8014

Mitre Inn, *Two Moors Way, Witheridge, Tiverton, Devon, EX16 8AH.* Large Victorian coaching inn. **Open:** All year (not Xmas/New Year) **01884 861263** Mr & Mrs Parsons **D:** £18.00–£25.00 **S:** £20.00–£27.00 **Beds:** 3F 1D 5T **Baths:** 1 En 3 Sh ➜ 🄿 (5) ⚹ ✗ Ⅴ ▥ 🏊 cc

Woodbury

SY0187   🍺 *Digger's Rest*

Cottles Farm, *Woodbury, Exeter, Devon, EX5 1ED.* Wonderful views, ideally situated for coast and Exeter. Farmhouse breakfast. **Open:** All year (not Xmas/New Year) **01395 232547** Mrs Brown **D:** £20.00–£22.00 **S:** £23.00–£25.00 **Beds:** 1F 1T 1D **Baths:** 2 En 1 Pr ➜ 🄿 (3) ⚹ 📺 ▥ 🏊

Greenacre, *Couches Lane, Woodbury, Exeter, EX5 1HL.* Secluded, comfortable country accommodation near village. Large stream-bordered gardens. **Open:** All year (not Xmas) **01395 233574 (also fax)** Mrs Price **D:** £16.00–£19.00 **S:** £21.00–£24.00 **Beds:** 1D 2T **Baths:** 2 En 1 Pr ➜ 🄿 (5) 📺 🍴 ▥ 🏊

Rydon farm, *Woodbury, Exeter, Devon, EX5 1LB.* C16th Devon longhouse, dairy farm. Perfect retreat, highly recommended. **Open:** All year **01395 232341 (also fax)** Ms Glanvill *sallyglanvill@hotmail.com* **D:** £25.00–£28.00 **S:** £27.00–£30.00 **Beds:** 1F 1T 1D **Baths:** 2 En 1 Pr ➜ 📺 🍴 Ⅴ ▥ 🏊

Woodleigh

SX7448

Yeo Farm, *Topsham Bridge, Woodleigh, Kingsbridge, Devon, TQ7 4DR.* C14th farm house in 86 acres of woods & pasture. Mile of riverbank. **Open:** All year **01548 550586** Mrs Smith *yeomary@ appleonline.net* **D:** £20.00–£25.00 **S:** £20.00–£25.00 **Beds:** 1T **Baths:** 1 En 🄿 (2) ⚹ 📺 Ⅴ ▥ 🏊

Woolacombe

SS4543   🍺 *Rock Inn*

Clyst House, *Rockfield Road, Woolacombe, Devon, EX34 7DH.* Friendly, comfortable guest house close Blue Flag beach. Delicious English breakfast. Beautiful walking area. **Open:** Mar to Nov **01271 870220** Mrs Braund **D:** £20.00–£22.00 **S:** £20.00–£22.00 **Beds:** 1F 1D 1T **Baths:** 1 Sh ➜ (7) 🄿 ⚹ ✗ Ⅴ ▥ 🏊

Ossaborough House, *Woolacombe, Devon, EX34 7HJ.* **Open:** All year **Grades:** ETC 4 Diamond, AA 4 Diamond **01271 870297** Mr & Mrs Day *info@ ossaboroughhouse.co.uk* www.ossaboroughhouse.co.uk **D:** £23.00–£30.00 **S:** £23.00–£30.00 **Beds:** 2F 2T 2D **Baths:** 5 En 1 Pr ➜ 🄿 (8) ⚹ ✗ 🍴 ✗ Ⅴ ▥ 🏊 Escape to our lovely C17th country house originating in the days of Saxon England - rustic beams. Thick stone walls, inglenook fireplaces, candlelit dinners. All rooms sympathetically restored. Explore rolling hills, rugged cliffs, picturesque villages, stunning golden beaches and secluded coves.

Barton Lea, *Beach Road, Woolacombe, Devon, EX34 7BT.* Warm welcome, sea views, big breakfast menu, close to Coastal Foot Path. **Open:** Easter to Oct **01271 870928** Mrs Vickery **D:** £18.00–£20.00 **S:** £25.00 **Beds:** 1F 1D 1T **Baths:** 3 En ➜ 🄿 (7) ⚹ 📺 Ⅴ ▥ 🏊

Sunny Nook, *Beach Road, Woolacombe, Devon, EX34 7AA.* Delightful home in lovely situation, wonderful views and excellent breakfasts. **Open:** All year (not Xmas) **01271 870964** Mr Fenn **D:** £21.00–£23.00 **S:** £26.00–£30.00 **Beds:** 1F 1D 1T **Baths:** 3 En 🄿 (5) ⚹ 📺 ✗ Ⅴ ▥ 🏊

Camberley, *Beach Road, Woolacombe, Devon, EX34 7AA.* Large Victorian house with views to sea & NT land. Use of indoor pool. **Open:** All year (not Xmas) **01271 870231** Mr & Mrs Riley *camberley@ tesco.net* **D:** £20.00–£25.00 **S:** £19.00–£24.00 **Beds:** 3F 3D 1T **Baths:** 6 En 1 Pr ➜ 🄿 (6) 📺 ▥ 🏊 cc

Woolsery (Woolfardisworthy)

SS3321

Stroxworthy Farm, *Woolsery, Bideford, Devon, EX39 5QB.* Delightful farmhouse, working dairy farm, 4.5 miles from Clovelly. **Open:** Easter to Oct **01237 431333** Mrs Beck **D:** £20.00 **Beds:** 1F 2D **Baths:** 3 En ➜ 🄿 (10) 📺 🏊

# BEDROOMS
D = Double
T = Twin
S = Single
F = Family

Yarcombe

ST2408

The Belfry Country Hotel, *Yarcombe, Honiton, Devon, EX14 9BD.* Converted Victorian school, offering en-suite accommodation. Superb food. Fine wines. **Open:** All year **Grades:** ETC 2 Star **01404 861234** Mr Pierce **Fax: 01404 861579** *www.westcountryhotels.com* **D:** £36.00 **S:** £44.00 **Beds:** 2T 4D **Baths:** 1 En ☎ (12) �🅿 (10) ⌇ �📺 ⎌ ✕ Ⓥ ▥ ⅃ ♨ cc

Yelverton

SX5267

Overcombe Hotel, *Old Station Road, Horrabridge, Yelverton, Devon, PL20 7RA.* **Open:** All year **Grades:** ETC 2 Star **01822 853501** JH & G Wright *enquiries@ overcombehotel.co.uk* www.overcombehotel.co. uk **D:** £23.00–£25.00 **S:** £23.00–£28.00 **Beds:** 2F 2T 3D 1S **Baths:** 8 En ☎ �🅿 (8) ⌇ 📺 ✕ ▥ ⎌ ♨ cc
Homely, relaxed atmosphere. Comfortable ensuite bedrooms. Excellent food and wines. Beautiful views. Parking. Situated within Dartmoor National Park - walks from hotel. Buckland Abbey, The Garden House, Cotehele, historic Plymouth and Tavistock attractions are nearby. Totally non-smoking. No animals.

Rettery Bank, *Harrowbeer Lane, Yelverton, Devon, PL20 6EA.* Quiet house, central, wonderful views, pocket-sprung beds, jacuzzi, English breakfast. **Open:** All year (not Xmas)
01822 855088 (also fax) Ms Leavey *bandtleavey@aol.com* **D:** £18.00–£25.00 **S:** £16.00–£20.00 **Beds:** 1D 1T **Baths:** 1 En 1 Sh ☎ (5) �🅿 (2) 📺 ✕ Ⓥ ▥ ♨

Greenwell Farm, *Meavy, Yelverton, Devon, PL20 6PY.* Working away from home? Try our new do-it-yourself B & B. **Open:** All year
01822 853563 (also fax) Mrs Cole *greenwellfarm@btconnect.com* **S:** £20.00–£30.00 **Beds:** 3S **Baths:** 3 En �🅿 (6) ▥ ♨

The Rosemont Guest House, *Greenbank Terrace, Yelverton, Devon, PL20 6DR.* Overlooking moorland village green within the glorious Dartmoor National Park. **Open:** All year (not Xmas) **01822 852175** Mr & Mrs Eastaugh *b&b@ rosemontgh.fsnet.co.uk* **D:** £21.00–£22.00 **S:** £21.00–£32.00 **Beds:** 1F 3D 2T 1S **Baths:** 7 En ☎ �🅿 (5) ⌇ 📺 ✕ Ⓥ ▥ ♨ cc

Stokehill Farmhouse, *Yelverton, Devon, PL20 6EW.* Beautiful country house in lovely grounds in a quiet, rural setting. **Open:** All year (not Xmas/New Year) **01822 853791** Mrs Gozzard **D:** £22.50–£25.00 **S:** £27.00–£30.00 **Beds:** 1T 2D **Baths:** 1 En 1 Pr ☎ (10) ⅃ ⌇ 📺 Ⓥ ▥ ♨

Yeoford

SX7898

Warrens Farm, *The Village, Yeoford, Crediton, Devon, EX17 5JD.* C16th Devon longhouse. Antique furniture. Good meals. Prime touring position. **Open:** All year **01363 84304 (also fax)** W Brimacombe Nelissen **D:** £18.00 **S:** £20.00 **Beds:** 1F 2D **Baths:** 2 En ☎ ⅃ (4) 📺 ✕ Ⓥ ▥ ♨

Yettington

SY0585

Lufflands, *Yettington, Budleigh Salterton, Devon, EX9 7BP.* Comfortable C17th farmhouse in rural location. **Open:** All year **01395 568422** Mrs Goode **Fax: 01395 568810** *lufflands@compuserve.com* **D:** £20.00–£22.00 **S:** £20.00–£27.00 **Beds:** 1F 1D 1S **Baths:** 1 En 1 Pr ☎ ⅃ (10) ⌇ ⎌ ▥ ♨

Dorset

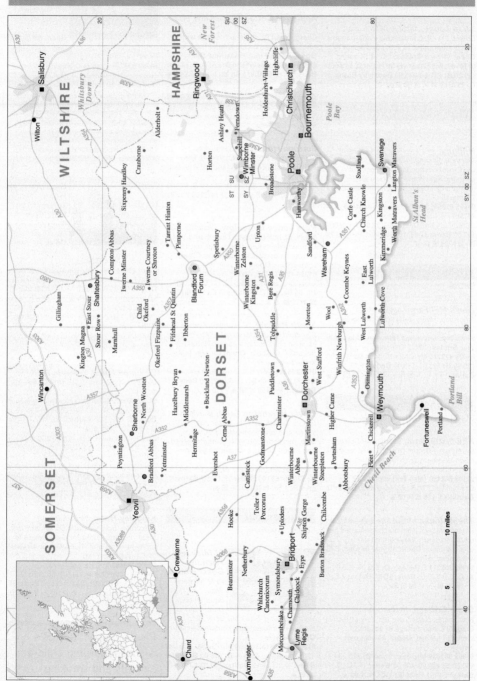

Abbotsbury

SY5785   ☜ *The Swan, Crown Inn, Manor House, Ilchester Arms, Elm Tree, Fir Tree*

Swan Lodge, Abbotsbury, Weymouth, Dorset, DT3 4JL. Comfortable modern rooms with tea and coffee facilities and colour TVs. **Open:** All year **Grades:** ETC 3 Diamond **01305 871249 (also fax)** Mr Roper **D:** £23.00–£29.00 **S:** £32.00–£45.00 **Beds:** 3D **Baths:** 3 En ⶸ🅿️📺🕈✕ⓋⅢ⚓cc

Alderholt

SU1212   ☜ *Churchill Arms*

Hillbury, 2 Fir Tree Hill, Camel Green, Alderholt, Fordingbridge, Hants, SP6 3AY. Large modern bungalow in peaceful surroundings. Warm welcome and comfortable. **Open:** All year **Grades:** ETC 3 Diamond **01425 652582** Mrs Sillence **Fax: 01425 657587** www.newforest.demon.co. uk/hillbury.htm **D:**£19.00–£22.00 **S:**£19.00–£22.00 **Beds:** 1F 1T 1S **Baths:** 1 Pr 1 Sh ⶸ 🅿️(4)⤨📺ⓋⅢ⚓

Ashley Heath

SU1205

Lion's Hill Farm, Ashley Heath, Ringwood, Hants, BH24 2EX. Traditional Victorian Farmhouse with uninterrupted views over forest and farmland. **Open:** All year **Grades:** ETC 2 Diamond **01425 472115** Mr & Mrs Hodges **D:** £20.00–£25.00 **S:** £25.00–£30.00 **Beds:** 1F 1T 1D **Baths:** 1 Pr 1 Sh ⶸ🅿️(6)📺🕈✕ⓋⅢ⚓⚓

Beaminster

ST4701   ☜ *The Greyhound, The Square.*

Kitwhistle Farm, Beaminster Down, Beaminster, Dorset, DT8 3SG. Quiet location, down land dairy farm. All facilities on ground floor. **Open:** Easter to Oct **01308 862458 (also fax)** Mrs Hasell **D:**£18.00–£22.00 **S:**£22.00–£25.00 **Beds:** 1F **Baths:** 1 En ⶸ🅿️⤨📺⚓

The Walnuts, 2 Prout Street, Beaminster, Dorset, DT8 3AY. Listed building situated just off town square. Very comfortable establishment. **Open:** All year **Grades:** ETC 4 Diamond, Silver **01308 862211** C Pieles'z **D:** £23.00–£25.00 **S:** £28.00–£35.00 **Beds:** 2D 1T **Baths:** 2 En 1 Pr ⶸ(8)🅿️(3)⤨📺ⓋⅢ⚓

Beam Cottage, 16 North Street, Beaminster, Dorset, DT8 3DZ. Very attractive Grade II Listed cottage in delightful secluded garden. **Open:** All year (not Xmas) **01308 863639** Mrs Standeven **D:** £25.00–£30.00 **S:** £30.00–£35.00 **Beds:** 1F 1D 2T **Baths:** 2 En 1 Pr ⶸ🅿️(3)📺🕈✕Ⅲ⚓

Bere Regis

SY8494

Appletree Cottage, 12 Sitterton, Bere Regis, Wareham, Dorset, BH20 7HU. Charming C17th thatched cottage with roses and honeysuckle around the door. **Open:** All year (not Xmas/New Year) **01929 471686** Mrs Wilson **D:** £20.00 **S:** £22.00 **Beds:** 1T 1D **Baths:** 1 Sh ⶸ(10)⤨📺ⓋⅢ⚓

Blandford Forum

ST8806   ☜ *The Greyhound, Milton Arms, Shire Horse, Hainbro Arms*

Fortune House, 19 Bayfran Way, Blandford Forum, Dorset, DT11 7RZ. Easy walking distance of town and local places of interest. **Open:** All year **01258 455154** Ms Billam **D:** £17.00 **S:** £17.00 **Beds:** 1D 2T 1S **Baths:** 2 Sh 🅿️(2)📺✕ⓋⅢ ❋

Park Lodge Bungalow, Whitecliff Mill Street, Blandford Forum, Dorset, DT11 7BN. Comfortable, refurbished bungalow, quiet surroundings, pleasant gardens. Close town centre. **Open:** All year **01258 452834** Mrs Atkins *jamesatkins@ ukonline.co.uk* **D:** £19.50–£22.50 **S:** £25.00–£30.00 **Beds:** 1D 1T **Baths:** 1 En 1 Pr 🅿️(2)⤨📺🕈ⓋⅢ⚓⚓

South Pasture, St Leonards Avenue, Blandford Forum, Dorset, DT11 7PD. Peaceful location close to town centre. Natural therapies available. **Open:** All year (not Xmas/New Year) **01258 452804** Mrs Busst *southpasture@aol.com* **D:** £20.00–£25.00 **S:** £20.00–£25.00 **Beds:** 1T **Baths:** 1 Pr 🅿️📺✕Ⅲ⚓

Lower Bryanston Farm, Blandford Forum, Dorset, DT11 0LS. Attractive farmhouse set in extensive grounds. Spacious bedrooms with comfortable beds and beautiful views. **Open:** All year (not Xmas) **01258 452009 (also fax)** **D:** £20.00–£25.00 **S:** £25.00–£30.00 **Beds:** 1F 1T 3D **Baths:** 1 En 1 Pr 1 Sh ⶸ🅿️(10)⤨📺⚓

Bournemouth

SZ0891   ☜ *Durley Inn*

St Michaels Friendly Guest House, 42 St Michaels Road, Westcliffe, Bournemouth, Dorset, BH2 5DY. Home cooking. Five minutes walk to town or sea and international conference centre. **Open:** All year **01202 557386 (also fax)** Mrs Davies *eileend@ 42stmichaels.fsworld.co.uk* **D:** £18.00 **S:** £20.00 **Beds:** 1F 2D 2T 1S **Baths:** 2 Sh ⶸ📺🕈✕Ⅴ Ⅲ⚓⚓

Whateley Hall Hotel, 7 Florence Road (off Sea Road), Bournemouth, BH5 1HH. **Open:** All year (not Xmas/New Year) **01202 397749 (also fax)** *whateleyhall.hotel@ virgin.net* **D:** £20.00–£25.00 **S:** £23.00–£28.00 **Beds:** 4F 2T 4D **Baths:** 10 En ⶸ(8)🅿️(7)⤨📺 ✕ⓋⅢ⚓
Small, friendly, family-run, non-smoking hotel with residential licence. The hotel is situated a few minutes' walk from either Boscombe's sandy beach, Blue Flag, or shopping centre. Traditional English cooking. Ideal base for excursions to the New Forest, Poole, Christchurch.

Cransley Hotel, 11 Knyveton Road, East Cliff, Bournemouth, Dorset, BH1 3QG. **Open:** All year **Grades:** ETC 4 Diamond, AA 4 Diamond **01202 290067** Mr Goodwin **Fax: 01202 292977** *info@cransley.com* www.cransley.co.uk **D:** £24.00–£28.00 **S:** £28.00–£48.00 **Beds:** 4T 5D 2S **Baths:** 10 En 1 Pr 🅿️(8)⤨📺✕Ⅲ⚓cc
A comfortable and elegant house for non smokers, set in a quiet pine avenue. Close to the town centre and beach. Conveniently placed for all major road and rail links. As seen on ITV's 'Dream Town'...

Chilterns Hotel, 44 Westby Road, Bournemouth, Dorset, BH5 1HD. **Open:** Apr to Sept **01202 396539 (also fax)** Mr Whitney *bwhit@ tinyworld.co.uk* **D:** £20.00–£25.00 **S:** £18.50 **Beds:** 3F 8D 4T 2S **Baths:** 9 En 1 Pr 7 Sh ⶸ 🅿️(10)📺✕Ⅲ⚓❋⚓
Excellent location. Few minutes to pier, glorious golden sandy beaches, wooded cliff top walks, shopping precinct, T/ Operators. Comfortable, welcoming. Highly recommended for short or long stay. Level walking, AMPLE PARKING. Parties welcome.

Kingsley Hotel, 20 Glen Road, Boscombe, Bournemouth, Dorset, BH5 1HR. Small, quality, smoke free hotel, close to sandy beaches and shops. **Open:** All year (not Xmas/New Year) **01202 398683** Mrs Barclay *enq@ kingsleyhotel.co.uk* www.kingsleyhotel.co.uk **D:** £20.00–£25.00 **S:** £20.00–£25.00 **Beds:** 4F 5D 2T 1S **Baths:** 11 En ⶸ(5)🅿️(6)⤨📺✕Ⅴ Ⅲ⚓cc

Please respect a B&B's wishes regarding children, animals and smoking

Shady Nook Guest House, 3 Upper Terrace Road, Bournemouth, Dorset, BH2 5NW. Town centre guest house near beach and entertainment. Excellent food and service. **Open:** All year (not Xmas)
01202 551557 Mr Holdaway *shady.nook@ btinternet.com* **D:** £19.00–£27.00 **S:** £22.00–£30.00 **Beds:** 2F 3D 2T 1S **Baths:** 5 En 1 Sh
⑤ ☐ (4) ⊠ 🛌 ✕ Ⅵ 🎟. ☕

Southernhay Hotel, 42 Alum Chine Road, Bournemouth, Dorset, BH4 8DX. Warm, homely and comfortable accommodation, perfectly situated for all amenities.
Open: All year **Grades:** ETC 3 Diamond
01202 761251 (also fax) Mrs Derby
D: £21.00–£24.00 **S:** £18.00–£25.00 **Beds:** 2F 1T 2D 1S **Baths:** 4 En 1 Sh ⑤ (1) ☐ (12) ⊠ 🛌 Ⅵ 🎟. ☕ ☕

Tenby House Hotel, 23 Pinecliffe, Southbourne, Bournemouth, Dorset, BH6 3PY. Delightful, Edwardian-style private hotel. Superbly located for shops, pubs, restaurant and beach. **Open:** Jan to Dec
01202 423696 Mrs Rudland **D:** £17.00–£22.00 **S:** £19.00–£24.00 **Beds:** 2F 3D 3T 2S
Baths: 4 En 3 Sh ⑤ (2) ☐ (5) ⊠ 🛌 ✕ Ⅵ 🎟. ☕

Audmore Hotel, 3 Cecil Road, Boscombe, Bournemouth, Dorset, BH5 1DU. Friendly family-run licensed hotel near beach/shop. Many ensuites. **Open:** All year (not Xmas/New Year) **Grades:** ETC 3 Diamond
01202 395166 Mrs Lane **D:** £18.00–£22.00 **S:** £18.00–£22.00 **Beds:** 5F 2D 1T 2S
Baths: 6 En 3 Sh ⑤ ☐ (4) ⅍ ✕ Ⅵ 🎟. ☕

West Cliff Sands Hotel, 9 Priory Road, West Cliff, Bournemouth, Dorset, BH2 5DF. Prime position on popular West Cliff. Two mins' walk pier, theatres, International Conference Centre. **Open:** All year
01202 557013 (also fax) Mr & Mrs Pannell www.westcliffsands.sageweb.co.uk **D:** £24.00–£35.00 **S:** £35.00–£45.00 **Beds:** 5F 11D
Baths: 16 En ⑤ ☐ (16) ⊠ 🛌 Ⅵ 🎟. ☕ cc

Mayfield Guest House, Knyveton Gardens, 46 Frances Road, Bournemouth, Dorset, BH1 3SA. Friendly guest house opposite Knyveton Gardens. Central sea, shops, rail, coach. **Open:** Jan to Nov
Grades: ETC 4 Diamond
01202 551839 (also fax) Mrs Barling *accom@ may-field.co.uk* www.may-field.co.uk
D: £18.00–£22.00 **S:** £18.00–£22.00 **Beds:** 1F 5D 1T 1S **Baths:** 7 En 1 Pr ⑤ (5) ☐ (5) ⊠ ✕ Ⅵ 🎟. ☕

Victoria, 120 Parkwood Road, Southbourne, Bournemouth, Dorset, BH5 2BN. A friendly, comfortable private house near beach, shops and buses.
Open: May to Oct
01202 423179 Mrs Rising **D:** £14.00–£14.50 **S:** £14.00 **Beds:** 1D 1T **Baths:** 1 Sh ⑤ (4)
☐ (2) ⊠ Ⅵ 🎟. ☕

Fircroft Hotel, Owls Road, Boscombe, Bournemouth, BH5 1AE. Friendly family hotel close sea and shops (cycle friendly). Free entry to health club. **Open:** All year
Grades: ETC 2 Star, AA 2 Star, RAC 2 Star
01202 309771 Fax: 01202 395644 D: £22.00–£30.00 **S:** £22.00–£30.00 **Beds:** 14F 12D 18T 6S ⑤ ☐ ☐ 🛌 ✕ Ⅵ 🎟. ☀ ☕ cc

Redlands Hotel, 79 St Michaels Road, Bournemouth, Dorset, BH2 5DR. Family run hotel near town centre and sea, private parking. **Open:** All year
01202 553714 Mr & Mrs Wood *enquiries@ redlandhotels.co.uk* www.redlandshotel.co.uk
D: £20.00–£28.00 **S:** £20.00–£28.00 **Beds:** 3F 1T 6D 2S **Baths:** 10 En 2 Sh ⑤ ☐ (10) ⊠ 🎟. ☕ cc

Rivers Reach, 4 Broadlands Avenue, Bournemouth, Dorset, BH6 4HQ. Quiet residential house. Ideally situated New Forest, Christchurch and Bournemouth.
Open: All year
01202 429042 Mrs Gibbs **D:** £20.00–£25.00 **S:** £20.00–£35.00 **Beds:** 2D 1S **Baths:** 1 En 1 Sh ⑤ ☐ (1) ⅍ ⊠ 🎟. ☕

Wrenwood Hotel, 11 Florence Road, Bournemouth, Dorset, BH5 1HH. Small Victorian family hotel. Close to sea, shops and transport. **Open:** All year **Grades:** ETC 3 Diamond
01202 395086 Mr Masson *bookings@ wrenwood.co.uk* www.wrenhood.co.uk
D: £18.00–£25.00 **S:** £23.00–£35.00 **Beds:** 5F 1T 5D **Baths:** 11 En ⑤ ☐ (8) ⅍ ⊠ 🛌 ✕ Ⅵ 🎟. ☕ cc

Chelsea Hotel, 32 St Swithuns Road, Bournemouth, Dorset, BH1 3RH. Popular family run hotel. Great atmosphere. Near train/coach station. **Open:** Easter to Oct
01202 290111 (also fax) Mr & Mrs Beere *info@chelseahotel32.co.uk* www.chelseahotel32. co.uk **D:** £20.00–£25.00 **S:** £20.00–£25.00 **Beds:** 5F 2T 2D 1S **Baths:** 7 En 2 Pr ⑤ ⊠ 🛌 ✕ 🎟. ☕ cc

Avonwood Hotel, 20 Owls Road, Bournemouth, Dorset, BH5 1AF. A friendly, family-run hotel close to sandy beach, pier, shops and gardens. **Open:** All year
01202 394704 Mr & Mrs Hutchinson *avonwood.hotel@tinyworld.co.net* **D:** £19.00–£26.00 **S:** £19.00–£26.00 **Beds:** 4F 3T 8D 1S **Baths:** 11 En ⑤ ☐ (14) ⊠ ✕ Ⅵ 🎟. ☕ cc

West Cliff Hall Hotel, 14 Priory Road, West Cliff, Bournemouth, BH2 5DN. Superb central location, beautiful Westcliff. Close beaches and shops, entertainment.
Open: All year
01202 299715 *info@bournehall.co.uk* www.bournehall.co.uk **D:** £25.00–£39.00 **S:** £30.00–£49.00 **Beds:** 7F 15T 9S **Baths:** 48 En ⑤ ☐ (35) ⊠ 🛌 ✕ Ⅵ 🎟. ☀ ☕ cc

Sirena Hotel, 20 Knole Road, Bournemouth, Dorset, BH1 4DQ. Small family hotel, near Boscombe gardens few mins from sea/shops. **Open:** All year
01202 394877 Miss Williams **D:** £16.00–£20.00 **S:** £14.00–£16.00 **Beds:** 2F 3D 2T 2S **Baths:** 2 En 2 Sh ⑤ (5) ☐ ⅍ ⊠ 🛌 Ⅵ ☕

Alum Chine Hotel, 33 Studland Road, Bournemouth, Dorset, BH4 8HZ. Comfortable, friendly licensed hotel, offering delicious home-cooked food, facing wooded Alum Chine. **Open:** All year
01202 761193 Mr & Mrs Lait *alum.chine.hotel@ ukgateway.net* **D:** £18.00–£22.00 **S:** £18.00–£22.00 **Beds:** 4F 2D 1T 2S **Baths:** 6 En 1 Sh ⑤ ☐ (4) ⅍ ⊠ ✕ Ⅵ 🎟. ☕ cc

Balincourt Hotel, 58 Christchurch Road, Bournemouth, Dorset, BH1 3PF. Elegant Victorian residence, luxury spacious rooms. Close to sea front, town centre. **Open:** All year
01202 552962 Mr & Mrs Gandolfi **D:** £25.00–£30.00 **S:** £30.00–£45.00 **Beds:** 5D 5T 2S **Baths:** 12 En 1 Sh ☐ (11) ⅍ ⊠ ✕ Ⅵ 🎟. ☀ ☕ cc

Ardene Hotel, 12 Glen Road, Boscombe, Bournemouth, Dorset, BH5 1HR. Friendly hotel situated close to beach and nightlife.
Open: Easter to Sept
01202 394928 (also fax) Miss Griffiths *ardenehotel@talk21.com* **D:** £17.50–£24.00 **S:** £17.50–£21.50 **Beds:** 3F 2D 4T 4S **Baths:** 6 En 3 Sh ⑤ ☐ (5) ⊠ 🛌 ✕ 🎟. ☕

Highclere Hotel, 15 Burnaby Road, Bournemouth, Dorset, BH4 8JF. Edwardian house hotel only 4 minutes from safe sandy beaches. **Open:** Easter to Oct
01202 761350 Mr & Mrs Baldwin **Fax: 01202 767110** *daveril@highclerehotel.freeserve.co.uk* www.he.a.a.co.uk/hotels **D:** £22.00–£25.00 **S:** £22.00–£25.00 **Beds:** 4F 1T 4D **Baths:** 9 En ⑤ (3) ☐ (5) ⊠ 🛌 🎟. ☕ cc

Cremona Hotel, 61 St Michaels Road, West Cliff, Bournemouth, Dorset, BH2 5DP. A small family-run hotel in the town centre and near sea. **Open:** All year
01202 290035 P Littlewort **Fax: 01202 297177** *Enquiries@cremona.co.uk* www.cremona.co.uk **D:** £16.00–£25.00 **S:** £20.00–£35.00 **Beds:** 3F 2T 4D **Baths:** 7 En 2 Sh ⑤ ☐ 🛌 Ⅵ 🎟. ☕ cc

Shoreline Hotel, 7 Pinecliffe Avenue, Southbourne, Bournemouth, BH6 3PY. Close to new Forest, Beaulieu Motor Museum, Salisbury Wilton House. **Open:** Easter to Dec
01202 429654 (also fax) **D:** £13.00–£21.00 **S:** £13.00–£24.00 **Beds:** 2F 4D 2T 2S **Baths:** 5 En 2 Sh ⑤ (5) ☐ (5) ⊠ 🛌 Ⅵ 🎟. ☀ ☕

Bradford Abbas
ST5814

Heartsease Cottage, North Street, Bradford Abbas, Sherborne, Dorset, DT9 6SA. Delightful Dorset village cottage. Idyllic garden, conservatory, themed bedrooms.
Open: All year
01935 475480 (also fax) Mr & Mrs Dann **D:** £20.00–£27.00 **S:** £20.00–£29.00 **Beds:** 1D 2T **Baths:** 1 En 1 Pr ⑤ (8) ☐ (4) ⊠ ✕ Ⅵ 🎟. ☕

Bridport

SY4693   🍺 *Marquis of Lorne, Three Horseshoes*

Britmead House, *West Bay Road, Bridport, Dorset, DT6 4EG.* **Open:** All year **Grades:** ETC 4 Diamond, AA 4 Diamond
01308 422941 Mr Hardy **Fax: 01308 422516**
britmead@talk21.com www.britmeadhouse.co.uk **D:** £22.00–£31.00 **S:** £26.00–£40.00 **Beds:** 2F 3D 2T **Baths:** 7 En ⏳🅿(12)🐾🛏📷, 🔥 cc
An elegant Edwardian house situated between Bridport and West Bay Harbour, with its beaches, golf course and the Dorset Coast Path, all just a short walk away. We offer comfortable ensuite rooms with many thoughtful extras and a warm welcome. Non-smoking.

The Old Dairy House, *Walditch, Bridport, Dorset, DT6 4LB.* **Open:** All year **01308 458021** Mrs Long **D:** £20.00 **S:** £20.00 **Beds:** 1D 1T **Baths:** 1 Sh 🅿(4)🖤📺📷, 🔥
A friendly welcome to relax in this peaceful corner of West Dorset. Enjoy full English breakfast. Guests' TV lounge with log fire. Gardens, abundant wildlife. Rural/coastal walks. 18-hole golf 2 miles. Good selection country pubs nearby. Adults only.

Green Lane House, *Bridport, Dorset, DT6 4LH.* Welcoming, spacious home in own grounds. 1.5 miles from coast. **Open:** All year (not Xmas/New Year)
01308 422619 (also fax) Mrs Prideaux
D: £20.00 **S:** £20.00 **Beds:** 1S 1T 1D **Baths:** 2 En 1 Sh ⏳🅿(5)🖤📺🛏✕📷, 🔥

Saxlingham House, *West Road, Symondsbury, Bridport, Dorset, DT6 6AA.* Extensive country views many local attractions warm friendly welcome. **Open:** Easter to Sept
01308 423629 Mr & Mrs Nicholls **D:** £18.00 **S:** £18.00 **Beds:** 1T 2D **Baths:** 3 En 🅿🖤📺, 🔥

Broadstone

SZ0095

Ashdell, *85 Dunyeats Road, Broadstone, Poole, Dorset, BH18 8AF.* Central, comfortable, secluded. Breakfast/EM choice. Historic countryside/beaches, short breaks. **Open:** All year (not Xmas) **Grades:** ETC 2 Diamond
01202 692032 Mrs Critchley *ian@ashdell.fsnet.co.uk* www.ashdell.co.uk
D: £16.00–£19.00 **S:** £19.00–£22.00 **Beds:** 1F 1D 1T 1S **Baths:** 1 Sh ⏳(5)🅿(3)🖤🛏✕📷,

All details shown are as supplied by B&B owners in Autumn 2001

Buckland Newton

ST6805

Holyleas House, *Buckland Newton, Dorchester, Dorset, DT2 7DP.* **Open:** All year (not Xmas/New Year) **Grades:** ETC 4 Diamond, Silver
01300 345214 Mrs Bunkall **Fax: 01305 264488** *tiabunkall@holyleas.fsnet.co.uk*
D: £22.50–£27.00 **S:** £25.00–£35.00 **Beds:** 1T 1D 1S **Baths:** 2 En 1 Pr ⏳🅿(6)🖤🐾🛏📺📷,
The family Labrador will welcome you to this typical period country house set in 1/2 acre lovely garden. Rooms are beautifully decorated with antique furniture and enjoy fine views. Relax in the guests sitting room with log fire burning in winter.

Rew Cottage, *Buckland Newton, Dorchester, DT2 7DN.* Lovely views, good walking, easy reach Dorchester, Sherborne and sea. **Open:** Jan to Dec **Grades:** ETC 4 Diamond
01300 345467 (also fax) Mrs McCarthy **D:** £22.50–£27.00 **S:** £29.00–£35.00 **Beds:** 1D 1T 1S **Baths:** 2 Pr ⏳🅿(6)📺🛏📺📷, 🔥

Whiteways Farmhouse Accommodation, *Bookham Farm, Buckland Newton, Dorchester, Dorset, DT2 7RP.* Warm welcome awaits at hamstone and flint farmhouse. Head of Blackmore Vale. **Open:** All year (not Xmas/New Year)
01300 345511 (also fax) *bookhamfarm@netscapeonline.co.uk* **D:** £20.00–£25.00 **S:** £20.00–£25.00 **Beds:** 1F 1S **Baths:** 1 En 1 Pr ⏳🅿(3)🖤📷, 🔥

Burton Bradstock

SY4889

Burton Cliff Hotel, *Cliff Road, Burton Bradstock, Bridport, Dorset, DT6 4RB.* On cliff top, superb sea views, surrounded by NT countryside. Many rooms overlook beach. **Open:** All year
01308 897205 Mr Hoare **Fax: 01308 898111**
D: £21.00–£39.00 **S:** £24.50–£36.00 **Beds:** 8T 7D 3S **Baths:** 12 En 12 Pr 3 Sh ⏳🅿(40)🖤📺 🛏✕📺📷, 🚿, 🔥 cc

Cattistock

SY5999

Sandhills Cottage, *Sandhills, Cattistock, Dorchester, DT2 0HQ.* Rural hamlet. Superb scenery, good walking. Some of Dorset's finest beaches easy driving distance. **Open:** All year
01300 321146 Mr & Mrs Roca **Fax: 01300 321 146** *m.vroca@lineone.net* **D:** £22.00–£24.00 **S:** £25.00–£28.00 **Beds:** 2T 1D **Baths:** 3 En ⏳(12)🅿(8)🖤📺📷, 🔥

Cerne Abbas

ST6601

Cowden House, *Frys Lane, Godmanstone, Dorchester, Dorset, DT2 7AG.* Vegetarian B&B. Spacious, peaceful house surrounded by beautiful downland. **Open:** All year (not Xmas)
01300 341377 Mr Mills www.cowdenhouse.co.uk **D:** £22.00–£25.00 **S:** £26.00–£30.00 **Beds:** 1D 1F 1T 1D **Baths:** 1 En 1 Sh ⏳🅿(2)🖤🐾🛏✕📺📷, 🔥

Charminster

SY6892

Slades Farm, *North Street, Charminster, Dorchester, Dorset, DT2 9QZ.* Superb accommodation and every comfort in recently converted barn. **Open:** All year **Grades:** ETC 4 Diamond
01305 265614 (also fax) Mr & Mrs Woods **D:** £23.00–£25.00 **S:** £30.00–£35.00 **Beds:** 1F 2D **Baths:** 3 En ⏳🅿(8)🖤📺🛏📷, 🔥

Charmouth

SY3693   🍺 *George Inn, Royal Oak*

Clifton, *Five Acres, Charmouth, Bridport, Dorset, DT6 6BE.* Views over beach and bay. Excellent food. Easy walk to beach. **Open:** All year
01297 560574 (also fax) Mrs Dedman
D: £22.50–£25.00 **S:** £27.50–£30.00 **Beds:** 1F 1T 1D **Baths:** 3 En ⏳🅿(2)🖤✕📺📷, 🚿🔥

Chickerell

SY6480

Stonebank, *14 West Street, Chickerell, Weymouth, Dorset, DT3 4DY.* Charming C17th former farmhouse ideally situated for exploring coast and country. **Open:** Apr to Sept **Grades:** ETC 5 Diamond, Gold
01305 760120 Mrs Westcott **Fax: 01305 760871** *stw@stonebank-chickerell.co.uk* www.stonebank-chickerell.co.uk **D:** £22.50–£25.00 **S:** £35.00–£40.00 **Beds:** 2D **Baths:** 2 En 🅿(2)🖤📺📷, 🔥 cc

Chideock

SY4292 🍺 *Royal Oak, New Inn, George Inn, Clockhouse, Anchor Inn*

Chideock House Hotel, Main St, Chideock, Bridport, *DT6 6JN.* **Open:** Feb to Jan **Grades:** ETC 2 Star, AA 2 Star, 1 Rosette
01297 489242 Mr Dunn **Fax: 01297 489184**
still@chideockhousehotel.com
www.chideockhousehotel.com **D:** £30.00–£42.50 **S:** £50.00–£80.00 **Beds:** 9D **Baths:** 8 En 1 Pr ⌂ 🖭 ✟ ✕ ♉ ▥ ✻ ♿ cc
10-min walk to the sea and coastal path with stunning scenery. 'Harbour Lights' filmed locally. Abbots Swannery, Mapperton Gardens and Athelhampton House all nearby. Stunning food in candle lit restaurant. Close to Lyme Regis and Charmouth. Weymouth 20 mins.

Frogmore Farm, Chideock, Bridport, Dorset, *DT6 6HT.* C17th farmhouse overlooking Lyme Bay. Adjoining South West Coast Path.
Open: All year
01308 456159 Mrs Norman **D:** £16.00–£20.00 **S:** £20.00–£23.00 **Beds:** 1F 1D 1T 1S **Baths:** 2 En 2 Pr ⌂ (8) 🅿 (6) ⌷ 🖭 ✟ ✕ ♉ ▥ ✻ ♿

Chimneys Guest House, Main Street, Chideock, Bridport, Dorset, *DT6 6JH.* Warm welcome, comfortable bedrooms, guest lounge and dining room. Private parking.
Open: All year (not Xmas)
01297 489368 D Backhouse & J M Backhouse **D:** £22.50–£25.00 **S:** £25.00 **Beds:** 1F 1T 3D **Baths:** 4 En ⌂ 🅿 (5) ✕ 🖭 ✟ ▥ ♿

Betchworth House, Chideock, Bridport, Dorset, *DT6 6JW.* Very friendly C17th guest house has been refurbished to a very high standard. **Open:** All year
01297 489478 Jill & John Lodge **Fax: 01297 489932 D:** £22.00–£25.00 **S:** £27.00–£30.00 **Beds:** 1F 2D 2T **Baths:** 3 En 2 Pr ⌂ (10) 🅿 (6) ✕ 🖭 ▥ ♿ cc

Chilcombe

SY5291

Rudge Farm, Chilcombe, Bridport, Dorset, *DT6 4NF.* Peacefully situated in beautiful Bride Valley, overlooking lakes in wild flower meadow. **Open:** All year (not Xmas)
01308 482630 Ms Diment **Fax: 01308 482635**
sue@rudgefarm.co.uk www.rudgefarm.co.uk
D: £25.00–£27.00 **S:** £24.00–£26.00 **Beds:** 1F 2D 1T **Baths:** 4 En ⌂ 🅿 (4) ✕ 🖭 ▥ ♿ cc

Child Okeford

ST8312

Bartley House, Upper Street, Child Okeford, Blandford Forum, Dorset, *DT11 8EF.* Beautiful, spacious Victorian house in quiet village location. Great breakfasts! **Open:** All year
01258 860420 Mrs Langley *rmw@ukf.net*
www.scalelink.co.uk **D:** £17.50–£25.00 **S:** £20.00–£25.00 **Beds:** 2F 1D 1T **Baths:** 2 En 1 Pr ⌂ 🅿 (6) ⌷ ✟ ✕ ♉ ▥ ♿

Christchurch

SZ1693

Ashbourne Guest House, 47 Stour Road, Christchurch, Dorset, *BH23 1LN.* Perfectly situated for exploring Christchurch. Warm welcome, delicious breakfast. **Open:** All year
01202 475574 Ms Hamilton **Fax: 01202 482905** *ashcroft@hotmail.com* **D:** £20.00–£28.00 **S:** £20.00–£40.00 **Beds:** 2F 2T 3D 0S **Baths:** 4 En 1 Pr 2 Sh ⌂ 🅿 🖭 ♉ ▥ ♿

Beverly Glen, 1 Stuart Road, Highcliffe, Christchurch, Dorset, *BH23 5JS.* 5 mins walk to seafront, shops, restaurants, etc. 10 mins car to New Forest.
Open: All year (not Xmas) **Grades:** ETC 4 Diamond
01425 273811 Mr Welch **D:** £20.00–£30.00 **S:** £22.00–£30.00 **Beds:** 1F 3D 1T 1S **Baths:** 6 En ⌂ (6) 🅿 ⌷ ♉ ▥ ♿ cc

Lyndhurst Lodge Guest House, Lyndhurst Road, Christchurch, Dorset, *BH23 4SD.* Perfectly situated for beaches, forest, leisure activities and business parks.
Open: All year (not Xmas/New Year)
01425 276796 Mrs Green **Fax: 01425 276499**
lynlodge1@aol.com www.lyndhurstlodge.co.uk
D: £18.00–£26.00 **S:** £19.00–£25.00 **Beds:** 1F 1T 3D 2S **Baths:** 4 En 3 Sh ⌂ 🅿 (8) ✕ ✕ ▥ ♿

Bure Farmhouse, 107 Bure Lane, Friar's Cliff, Christchurch, Dorset, *BH23 4DN.* Edwardian farmhouse, beautiful, peaceful surroundings, sea and New Forest.
Open: All year
01425 275498 Mrs Erhardt **D:** £18.00–£23.00 **S:** £20.00–£25.00 **Beds:** 2D 1T **Baths:** 3 En ⌂ (4) 🅿 (4) ✕ 🖭 ▥ ♿

BATHROOMS
En = Ensuite
Pr = Private
Sh = Shared

Church Knowle

SY9381

Bradle Farmhouse, Church Knowle, Corfe Castle, Wareham, Dorset, *BH20 5NU.* Relax and unwind in our picturesque farmhouse in the heart of Purbeck.
Open: All year (not Xmas) **Grades:** ETC 4 Diamond, Silver
01929 480712 Mrs Hole **Fax: 01929 481144**
bradlefarmhouse@farmersweekly.net
www.smoothhound.co.uk/hotels/bradle.
html **D:** £23.00–£26.00 **S:** £25.00–£42.00 **Beds:** 2D 1T **Baths:** 3 En ⌂ (5) 🅿 (3) 🖭 ▥ ♿

Compton Abbas

ST8617 🍺 *The Cricketers*

The Old Forge, Fanners Yard, Chapel Hill, Compton Abbas, Shaftesbury, Dorset, *SP7 0NQ.* **Open:** All year
01747 811881 (also fax) Mrs Kerridge
theoldforge@hotmail.com www.smoothhound.
co.uk/oldforge **D:** £22.50–£27.50 **S:** £40.00 **Beds:** 1F 1D 1S **Baths:** 1 En 1 Pr ⌂ (8) 🅿 (3) ✕ 🖭 ♿
Charming converted C18th wheelwright's with views to National Trust downland. Ideal for relaxing, walking, wildlife etc. Guests have their own private sitting/dining room. A traditional farmhouse breakfast is served using local organic produce. We offer a warm welcome all year round.

Coombe Keynes

SY8484 🍺 *Weld Arms*

West Coombe Farmhouse, West Farm, Coombe Keynes, Wool, Wareham, Dorset, *BH20 5PS.* **Open:** All year (not Xmas/New Year)
01929 462889 Mr & Mrs Brachi **Fax: 01929 405863** *west.coombe.farmhouse@barclays.net*
www.westcoombefarmhouse.com
D: £20.00–£27.50 **S:** £20.00–£35.00 **Beds:** 1T 1D 1S **Baths:** 1 En 1 Pr 1 Sh ⌂ (12) 🅿 (7) ✕ 🖭 ▥ ♿
Relax in our period farmhouse situated in a quiet village close to Lulworth Cove. Spectacular walking or borrow our bikes, central to all Dorset has to offer. Private sitting room with log fires in winter, excellent selection of local pubs.

Corfe Castle

SY9682 🍷 *Scott Arms, Greyhound, New Inn, Half Way Inn*

Knitson Old Farm House, Corfe Castle, Wareham, Dorset, BH20 5JB. **Open:** All year **01929 422836** Mrs Helfer *mark@knitson.freeserve.co.uk* **D:** £20.00–£22.00 **S:** £20.00–£22.00 **Beds:** 1F 1D 1S **Baths:** 2 Sh ⬆ 🅿 (6) 📺 ✕ 🖽 🛲 C16th farmhouse, 3 miles from Corfe, 1 from Swanage. Ridgeway and footpaths in all directions. Plantsman's garden, long views, whole food in season, wood stove, carpeted comfortable rooms, traditional breakfasts, years of experience, featured in the Best of British.

Lower Lynch House, Kingston Hill, Corfe Castle, Wareham, Dorset, BH20 5LG. Comfortable country house, quiet location in the heart of Purbeck. **Open:** All year (not Xmas/New Year) **01929 480089** Mrs Burt **D:** £22.50–£25.00 **Beds:** 1T 1D **Baths:** 1 En 1 Pr🅿(6)🛏🖽🛲

Bradle Farmhouse, Church Knowle, Corfe Castle, Wareham, Dorset, BH20 5NU. Relax and unwind in our picturesque farmhouse in the heart of Purbeck. **Open:** All year (not Xmas) **Grades:** ETC 4 Diamond, Silver **01929 480712** Mrs Hole **Fax:** 01929 481144 *bradlefarmhouse@farmersweekly.net* www.smoothhound.co.uk/hotels/bradle. html **D:** £23.00–£26.00 **S:** £25.00–£42.00 **Beds:** 2D 1T **Baths:** 3 En ⬆ (5) 🅿 (3) 📺 🖽 🛲 🛲

Cranborne

SU0513

La Fosse Restaurant, London House, The Square, Cranborne, Wimborne, Dorset, BH21 5PR. Small, family run restaurant with rooms, super food, comfortable accommodation. **Open:** All year **01725 517604** Mr La Fosse **Fax:** 01725 517778 **D:** £32.50–£35.00 **S:** £35.00–£37.50 **Beds:** 2D 1T **Baths:** 3 En ⬆(10)✕🖽📺🛲 🛲 cc

Planning a longer stay? Always ask for any special rates

Please respect a B&B's wishes regarding children, animals and smoking

Dorchester

SY6890 🍷 *Cornwall Hotel*

Maiden Castle Farm, Dorchester, Dorset, DT2 9PR. **Open:** All year **Grades:** ETC 4 Diamond, SIlver **01305 262356** Mrs Hoskin **Fax:** 01305 251085 *maidencastlefarm@euphony.net* www.maidencastlefarm.co.uk **D:** £25.00 **S:** £25.00 **Beds:** 1F 2D 1T 2S **Baths:** 3 En 1 Pr ⬆ 🅿 (10) 📺 🛏 📺 🖽 🛲 Nestling beneath the famous prehistoric earthworms, from which we take our name, in the heart of Hardy country, 1m Dorchester, 7m Weymouth. Museums, fossil hunting, beaches, Abbotsbury Swannery all within a few miles.

Churchview Guest House, Winterbourne Abbas, Dorchester, Dorset, DT2 9LS. **Open:** All year (not Xmas) **Grades:** ETC 3 Diamond **01305 889296 (also fax)** Mr Deller *stay@churchview.co.uk* www.churchview.co.uk **D:** £24.00–£30.00 **S:** £27.00–£35.00 **Beds:** 1F 4D 3T 1S **Baths:** 8 En 1 Pr ⬆ (5) 🅿 (10) ✕ 📺 🛏 ✕ 🖽 🛲 cc Delightful C17th village guest house near Dorchester offers comfort, delicious breakfasts.

Slades Farm, North Street, Charminster, Dorchester, Dorset, DT2 9QZ. Superb accommodation and every comfort in recently converted barn. **Open:** All year **Grades:** ETC 4 Diamond **01305 265614 (also fax)** Mr & Mrs Woods **D:** £23.00–£25.00 **S:** £30.00–£35.00 **Beds:** 1F 2D **Baths:** 3 En ⬆ 🅿 (8) ✕ 🛏 🖽 🛲

Maumbury Cottage, 9 Maumbury Road, Dorchester, Dorset, DT1 1QW. Homely accommodation, Thomas Hardy country, local produce, 8 mins town centre, museums, transport. **Open:** All year **01305 266726 D:** £18.00 **S:** £18.00–£25.00 **Beds:** 1D 1T 1S **Baths:** 1 Sh 🅿 (3) ✕ 📺 🖽 🛲

Higher Came Farmhouse, Higher Came, Dorchester, DT2 8NR. **Open:** All year **Grades:** ETC 4 Diamond **01305 268908 (also fax)** Mrs Bowden *highercame@eurolink.ltd.net* **D:** £25.00–£30.00 **S:** £28.00–£32.00 **Beds:** 1F 2D **Baths:** 1 En 2 Pr ⬆ 🅿 (4) 📺 🛏 📺 🖽 ✸ 🛲 cc Beautiful C17th farmhouse nestling at the foot of the Ridgeway in the heart of Hardy country. Spacious rooms, lovely gardens, great breakfast, relaxing atmosphere. Close to Maiden Castle, Dorchester and the spectacular Dorset coastline - discover and explore.

The Old Rectory, Winterbourne Steepleton, Dorchester, Dorset, DT2 9LG. Quiet hamlet in Hardy country. Peaceful night's sleep, copious English, vegetarian or continental breakfast. **Open:** All year (not Xmas/New Year) **Grades:** ETC 4 Diamond, Silver **01305 889468** M Tree **Fax:** 01305 889737 *trees@eurobell.co.uk* www.trees.eurobell.co.uk **D:** £25.00–£55.00 **Beds:** 3T **Baths:** 3 En ⬆ 🅿 (6) ✕ 📺 📺 🖽 🛲

Joan's B&B, 119 Bridport Road, Dorchester, Dorset, DT1 2NH. Comfortable relaxed atmosphere. Excellent breakfast, beautiful wildlife garden. **Open:** All year (not Xmas/New Year) **Grades:** ETC 3 Diamond **01305 267145 (also fax)** J Cox *b_and_b@joancox.freeserve.co.uk* **D:** £20.00–£22.00 **S:** £20.00–£24.00 **Beds:** 1T 1D 1S **Baths:** 2 Sh 🅿 (3) ✕ 📺 🛏 📺 🖽 🛲

Long Barn House, 1 Barton Mews, West Stafford, Dorchester, Dorset, DT2 8UB. Converted byre/granary between pub and church in tranquil ancient village. **Open:** All year **01305 266899** *pessame@amserve.net* **D:** £20.00–£27.00 **S:** £25.00–£32.00 **Beds:** 1T 1D 1S **Baths:** 1 En 1 Pr ⬆ (10) 🅿 (2) ✕ 📺 🛏 📺 🖽 🛲 cc

---

BATHROOMS

En = Ensuite
Pr = Private
Sh = Shared

Yellowham Farmhouse,
Yellowham Wood, Dorchester, Dorset, DT2 8RW. Situated in the heart of Hardy country on the edge of idyllic Yellowham Wood. **Open:** All year **Grades:** ETC 4 Diamond, Silver, AA 4 Diamond, RAC 4 Diamond, Sparkling **01305 262892** *b+b@yellowham.freeserve.co.uk* www.yellowham.freeserve.co.uk **D:** £25.00–£30.00 **S:** £30.00–£40.00 **Beds:** 1F 1T 2D 1S **Baths:** 4 En ♿ 🅿 (8) ⤳ 📺 ⭐ ✕ Ⅴ 🛏 ♨

East Lulworth
SY8682

Botany Farm House, *East Lulworth, Wareham, Dorset, BH20 5QH.* Ancient, atmospheric, tranquil. Fresh, robust, simple food. Birds, wildlife & "Mrs Tiggywinkle" garden. **Open:** All year (not Xmas/New Year) **01929 400427** Mrs Hemsley *hemsleys@ lineone.net* www.botany-farmhouse.com **D:** £20.00–£25.00 **S:** £25.00 **Beds:** 1T 2D **Baths:** 2 En ♿ 🅿 ⤳ ⭐ ✕ Ⅴ 🛏 ♨

East Stour
ST7922

Aysgarth, *Back Street, East Stour, Gillingham, Dorset, SP8 5JY.* Ground floor accommodation. Good touring centre. Discount 3 night stay. **Open:** All year (not Xmas) **01747 838351** Mrs Dowding *aysgarth@ lineone.net* **D:** £17.50–£19.00 **S:** £20.00–£22.00 **Beds:** 1T 2D **Baths:** 2 En 1 Pr ♿ 🅿 (3) ⤳ 📺 🛏 ♨

Evershot
ST5704   ⚑ *The Acorn, Fox Inn*

West Woods Farm,
Evershot, Dorchester, Dorset, DT2 0PG. Charming converted barn accommodation on working farm amid beautiful countryside. **Open:** All year (not Xmas/New Year) **Grades:** ETC 4 Diamond **01935 83351 & 07970 052785 (M) D:** £25.00–£30.00 **S:** £30.00 **Beds:** 1T 2D **Baths:** 3 En 🅿 (4) ⤳ 📺 Ⅴ 🛏 ♨

Eype
SY4491

Eypes Mouth Country Hotel, *Eype, Bridport, Dorset, DT6 6AL.* In a secret spot down a leafy lane, 5-min walk from the sea. **Open:** All year **01308 423300** Ms Tye **Fax:** 01308 420033 **D:** £29.50–£38.00 **S:** £29.50–£38.00 **Beds:** 18F 3T 13D 2S **Baths:** 18 En 🅿 📺 ⭐ ✕ Ⅴ 🛏 ✿ ♨ cc

Ferndown
SU0700

Pennington Copse, *11 Denewood Road, West Moors, Ferndown, Dorset, BH22 0LX.* Quiet Edwardian house, 5 min walk to village pubs and restaurants. **Open:** All year (not Xmas) **01202 894667** Mrs Hedley **D:** £18.00–£20.00 **S:** £25.00–£30.00 **Beds:** 2D **Baths:** 1 Sh 🅿 ⤳ 📺 🛏 ♨

Fifehead St Quintin
ST7710   ⚑ *Crown Inn*

Lower Fifehead Farm, *Fifehead St Quintin, Sturminster Newton, Dorset, DT10 2AP.* Beautiful listed farmhouse situated countryside, warm welcome. **Open:** All year **01258 817335 (also fax)** Mrs Miller **D:** £17.50–£25.00 **S:** £20.00–£25.00 **Beds:** 1T 1D **Baths:** 1 En 1 Pr ♿ 🅿 📺 Ⅴ 🛏 ♨

Fleet
SY6380

Highfield, *Fleet, Weymouth, Dorset, DT3 4EB.* Ideal location, beautiful countryside, excellent accommodation, wonderful walks, relaxation. **Open:** All year (not Xmas) **01305 776822** Mrs Weeden *highfield.fleet@ lineone.net* **D:** £22.00–£25.00 **Beds:** 1F 1D 1T **Baths:** 3 En ♿ 🅿 (4) ⤳ 📺 Ⅴ 🛏 ♨

Gillingham
ST8026

Bugley Court Farm,
Gillingham, Dorset, SP8 5RA. Peaceful location with wonderful views in comfortable family home. **Open:** All year **01747 823242** Mrs Lewis **D:** £18.00 **Beds:** 1D 1T **Baths:** 1 Pr 🅿 (2) ⤳ 📺 🛏 ♨

Godmanstone
SY6696   ⚑ *Smiths Arms*

Cowden House, *Frys Lane, Godmanstone, Dorchester, Dorset, DT2 7AG.* Vegetarian B&B. Spacious, peaceful house surrounded by beautiful downland. **Open:** All year (not Xmas) **01300 341377** Mr Mills www.cowdenhouse. co.uk **D:** £22.00–£25.00 **S:** £26.00–£30.00 **Beds:** 1D 1F 1T 1D **Baths:** 1 En 1 Sh ♿ 🅿 (2) ⤳ 📺 ⭐ ✕ Ⅴ 🛏 ♨

Planning a longer stay? Always ask for any special rates

Hamworthy
SY9991   ⚑ *Yachtsman Inn*

Seashells, *4 Lake Road, Hamworthy, Poole, Dorset, BH15 4LH.* Perfectly situated for Dorset coastline, countryside. Poole Quay, beautiful beaches. Warm welcome. **Open:** All year (not Xmas/New Year) **Grades:** ETC 3 Diamond **01202 671921** Mrs Hockey **D:** £16.00–£20.00 **S:** £25.00–£30.00 **Beds:** 1T 2D **Baths:** 1 En 1 Pr 1 Sh ♿ (5) 🅿 (3) ⤳ 📺 Ⅴ 🛏 ♨

Individual Touristik Poole, *53 Branksea Avenue, Hamworthy, Poole, Dorset, BH15 4DP.* Select accommodation for those seeking something special, facing Poole Harbour, Brownsea Island. **Open:** All year **Grades:** ETC 4 Diamond **01202 673419** Renate Wadham **Fax:** 01202 667260 *johnrenate@lineone.net* **D:** £28.00–£32.00 **S:** £32.00–£40.00 **Beds:** 2D/T **Baths:** 2 En ♿ (9) 🅿 (3) ⤳ 📺 Ⅴ 🛏 ♨

Hazelbury Bryan
ST7408

The Old Malthouse, *Droop, Hazelbury Bryan, Sturminster Newton, Dorset, DT10 2ED.* C17th malt house renowned for its peaceful rural location and traditional hospitality. **Open:** All year **01258 817735** Mr Bleathman **D:** £18.00–£20.00 **S:** £20.00–£25.00 **Beds:** 1F 2D **Baths:** 1 En

Hermitage
ST6406   ⚑ *Rose & Crown*

Almshouse Farm, *Hermitage, Sherborne, Dorset, DT9 6HA.* Listed farmhouse, retaining age and beauty with every modern convenience. **Open:** Feb to Dec **01963 210296 (also fax)** Mrs Mayo **D:** £22.00–£26.00 **S:** £30.00 **Beds:** 1T 2D **Baths:** 2 En 1 Pr ♿ (10) 🅿 (6) 📺 🛏 ♨

Highcliffe
SZ2094

The White House, *428 Lymington Road, Highcliffe, Christchurch, Dorset, BH23 5HF.* Beautiful Victorian house. 5 min walk beach, shops, restaurants. Short drive New Forest. **Open:** All year (not Xmas/New Year) **01425 271279** F G White **Fax:** 01425 276900 *thewhitehouse@themail.co.uk* www.thewhite-house.co.uk **D:** £22.00–£25.00 **S:** £25.00–£35.00 **Beds:** 6F 2T 3D 1S **Baths:** 5 En 5 Pr 1 Sh ♿ 🅿 ⤳ 📺 🛏 ♨ cc

Higher Came

SY6987

Higher Came Farmhouse, *Higher Came, Dorchester, DT2 8NR.* Beautiful C17th farmhouse, foot of the Ridgeway, heart of Hardy country. **Open:** All year **Grades:** ETC 4 Diamond
01305 268908 (also fax) Mrs Bowden *highercame@eurolink.ltd.net* **D:** £25.00–£30.00 **S:** £28.00–£32.00 **Beds:** 1F 2D **Baths:** 1 En 2 Pr ⌂ ⛉ ☑ (4) ☑ ⊁ ☑ ▥ ❋ ▮ **cc**

Holdenhurst Village

SZ1395

Magdalen Cottage, *17 Holdenhurst Village, Holdenhurst, Bournemouth, Dorset, BH8 0EE.* Charming C17th Grade II Listed thatched cottage with wealth of character, beams, inglenook. **Open:** All year (not Xmas)
01202 395582 Mrs Bowring **D:** £18.00–£22.00 **S:** £20.00–£25.00 **Beds:** 2T **Baths:** 1 Sh ⛉ (2) ☑ ⊁ ▥ ▮

Hooke

ST5300

Watermeadow House, *Bridge Farm, Hooke, Beaminster, Dorset, DT8 3PD.* Part of a working dairy farm, large Georgian-style house on edge of small village.
Open: Easter to Oct **Grades:** ETC 4 Diamond, Silver, AA 4 Diamond
01308 862619 (also fax) Mrs Wallbridge *enquiries@watermeadowhouse.co.uk* www.watermeadowhouse.co.uk **D:** £22.00–£24.00 **S:** £24.00–£28.00 **Beds:** 1F 1D **Baths:** 1 En 1 Pr ⌂ ⛉ (4) ⊁ ☑ ▥ ▮

Horton

SU0307

Treetops, *Wigbeth, Horton, Wimborne, Dorset, BH21 7JH.* Rural, light airy rooms, large garden, ideally situated for touring. **Open:** All year
01258 840147 Mr Purchase *treetops.bandb@virgin.net* **D:** £18.00 **S:** £20.00 **Beds:** 1T 1D **Baths:** 2 En ⌂ ⛉ (3) ⊁ ☑ ⊁ ▥ ▮

Ibberton

ST7807

Manor House Farm, *Ibberton, Blandford Forum, Dorset, DT11 0EN.* C16th comfortable farmhouse. Also working dairy and sheep farm. **Open:** All year
01258 817349 Mrs Old **D:** £16.00–£18.00 **S:** £17.00–£20.00 **Beds:** 2D 1T **Baths:** 2 En 1 Sh ⌂ ⛉ (3) ⊁ ☑ ⊁ ▥ ▮

Planning a longer stay? Always ask for any special rates

Iwerne Courtney or Shroton

ST8512

Lattemere, *Frog Lane, Iwerne Courtney or Shroton, Blandford Forum, Dorset, DT11 8QL.* Comfortable welcoming home in quiet picturesque village. Outstanding countryside walks. **Open:** All year
01258 860115 (also fax) Mrs Wright **D:** £20.00–£22.00 **S:** £20.00–£25.00 **Beds:** 1D 1T **Baths:** 1 En 1 Pr ⌂ ⛉ (3) ⊁ ☑ ▥ ▮

Foxhangers, *4 Old Mill Cottages, Iwerne Courtney or Shroton, Blandford Forum, Dorset, DT11 8TW.* Modern cottage in quiet and peaceful village. Excellent breakfast. **Open:** All year (not Xmas)
01258 861049 Mrs Moss **Fax: 01258 860785** *jane_moss@talk21.com* **D:** £20.00 **S:** £25.00 **Beds:** 1D **Baths:** 1 En ⛉ ⊁ ☑ ✕ ▥ ▮

Iwerne Minster

ST8614

The Talbot Hotel, *Blandford Road, Iwerne Minster, Blandford Forum, Dorset, DT11 8QN.* Country Inn offering comfortable rooms, good food, ale, affordable prices. **Open:** All year
01747 811269 Mr & Mrs Richardson **D:** £13.75–£19.25 **S:** £15.00–£35.00 **Beds:** 2F 2D 1T 1S **Baths:** 2 En 2 Sh ⌂ ⛉ (30) ☑ ✕ ☑ ▥

Kimmeridge

SY9179

Kimmeridge Farmhouse, *Kimmeridge, Wareham, Dorset, BH20 5PE.* Picturesque farmhouse with views of Kimmeridge Bay - spacious and attractively furnished ensuite bedrooms. **Open:** All year (not Xmas)
01929 480990 Mrs Hole **D:** £22.00–£23.00 **S:** £25.00–£35.00 **Beds:** 2D 1T **Baths:** 3 En ⌂ (10) ⛉ (3) ⊁ ☑ ✕ ☑ ▥ ▮

RATES

D = Price range per person sharing in a double or twin room

S = Price range for a single room

Kingston (Swanage)

SY9579

Kingston Country Courtyard, *Greystone Court, Kingston (Corfe Castle), Wareham, Dorset, BH20 5LR.* **Open:** All year (not Xmas/New Year) **Grades:** ETC 4 Diamond
01929 481066 Mrs Fry **Fax: 01929 481256** *annfry@kingstoncountrycourtyard.co.uk* www.kingstoncountrycourtyard.co.uk **D:** £24.00–£35.00 **S:** £26.00–£35.00 **Beds:** 1T 4D 2S **Baths:** 7 En ⛉ (20) ⊁ ☑ ☑ ↕2 ▮ Character guest rooms in a courtyard setting. Magnificent views of Corfe Castle from our gardens where peacocks roam. Close to coastal path for walkers or ideal base for touring Dorset. Beaches or shops and theatres within easy reach by car.

Kington Magna

ST7623

Kington Manor Farm, *Church Hill, Kington Magna, Gillingham, Dorset, SP8 5EG.* Attractive farmhouse. Peaceful, pretty village overlooking Blackmore Vale. Heated pool. **Open:** All year (not Xmas)
01747 838371 (also fax) Mrs Gosney **D:** £22.00 **S:** £24.00 **Beds:** 1F 1D 1T **Baths:** 3 Pr ⌂ ⛉ ⊁ ☑ ⊁ ▥ ▮

Langton Matravers

SY9978   ⚓ *Ship Inn, King's Arms*

Maycroft, *Old Malthouse Lane, Langton Matravers, Swanage, Dorset, BH19 3JA.* Quiet position with lovely views. Close to sea and coastal path. Recommended by 'Which?' **Open:** Feb to Nov
01929 424305 (also fax) Mrs Bjorkstrand *janet.bjorkstrand@btinternet.com* **D:** £17.50–£20.00 **S:** £25.00 **Beds:** 1D 1T **Baths:** 1 Sh ⌂ (3) ⛉ (4) ☑ ☑ ▥ ▮

Seacombe, *54 High Street, Langton Matravers, Swanage, Dorset, BH19 3HB.* Comfortable, friendly, stone cottage in beautiful countryside. 2 miles Swanage. **Open:** All year (not Xmas/New Year)
01929 426066 *stella@utal.demon.co.uk* **D:** £16.00 **Beds:** 1F 1T 1D **Baths:** 1 Sh ⌂ ⛉ ⊁ ☑ ▥ ▮

BEDROOMS

D = Double
T = Twin
S = Single
F = Family

Lulworth Cove

SY8279

Shirley Hotel, *West Lulworth, Wareham, Dorset, BH20 5RL.* Comfortable bedrooms, delicious food. Super indoor pool. Magnificent coastal walks. **Open:** Feb to Nov **Grades:** ETC 2 Star, AA 2 Star
01929 400358 Mr Williams **Fax: 01929 400167** *durdle@aol.com* www.shirleyhotel.co.uk **D:** £36.00–£45.50 **S:** £36.00–£37.00 **Beds:** 1F 4T 9D 1S **Baths:** 15 En �🅱(22) 📺 ⽊✕⺉ 🎵 ⚓ cc

Botany Farm House, *East Lulworth, Wareham, Dorset, BH20 5QH.* Ancient, atmospheric, tranquil. Fresh, robust, simple food. Birds, wildlife & Mrs Tiggywinkle garden. **Open:** All year (not Xmas/New Year)
01929 400427 Mrs Hemsley *hemsleys@ lineone.net* www.botany-farmhouse.com **D:** £20.00–£25.00 **S:** £25.00 **Beds:** 1T 2D **Baths:** 2 En ⊱🅿⽊✕⺉ 🎵 ⚓

Mill House Hotel, *Lulworth Cove, West Lulworth, Wareham, Dorset, BH20 5RQ.* 9-bedroom country house-style hotel in heart of Lulworth Cove, 150 yards water's edge. **Open:** Feb to Dec
01929 400404 & 01929 400261 Mr Payne **Fax: 01929 400508** *dukepayne@hotmail.com* millhousehotel.tripod.com **D:** £25.00–£40.00 **S:** £35.00–£40.00 **Beds:** 2F 6D 1T **Baths:** 9 En ⊱🅿(9) 📺 🎵 ⚓ cc

Lyme Regis

SY3392

Charnwood Guest House, *21 Woodmead Road, Lyme Regis, Dorset, DT7 3AD.* **Open:** All year **Grades:** ETC 4 Diamond
01297 445281 Mr Bradbury *charnwood@ lymeregis62.freeserve.co.uk* www.lymeregisaccommodation.com **D:** £21.00–£25.00 **S:** £21.00–£25.00 **Beds:** 1F 4D 2T 1S **Baths:** 7 En 1 Pr ⊱(5) 🅿(7) ⽡ 📺 📺 🎵 ⚓ cc
Edwardian house modernised inside to a high standard of comfort. Close to restaurants, shops and pubs etc. Quiet, safe area with onsite parking. Walk, fossil and enjoy the beach/coast/history. Midweek discounts. Hearty English breakfast/vegetarian. Ideal touring base.

The Old Monmouth Hotel, *12 Church Street, Lyme Regis, Dorset, DT7 3BS.* C17th building, centrally situated for beaches, harbour and all amenities. **Open:** All year (not Xmas) **Grades:** AA 3 Diamond
01297 442456 (also fax) Mr & Mrs Brown *enquiries@lyme-regis-hotel.co.uk* www.lyme-regis-hotel.co.uk **D:** £22.00–£25.00 **S:** £30.00–£34.00 **Beds:** 2F 4D 1T **Baths:** 5 En 1 Sh ⊱⽡ 📺 ✕ 🎵 ⚓ cc

Mayflower Cottage, *39 Sherborne Lane, Lyme Regis, Dorset, DT7 3NY.* Quiet, traffic-free. Secluded garden. Town centre free parking nearby. **Open:** All year (not Xmas)
01297 445930 & 01297 442452 Mr Snowsill **D:** £20.00–£25.00 **S:** £25.00 **Beds:** 1F 1D 1T **Baths:** 3 En ⊱🅿(3) 📺 ⽊ 🎵 ⚓

Tudor House Hotel, *3/5 Church Street, Lyme Regis, Dorset, DT7 3BS.* An historic Elizabethan house, c1580, 1 min's level walk to sea. **Open:** All year (not Xmas/New Year)
01297 442472 Mr Ray www.thetudorhousehotel.co.uk **D:** £24.00–£49.00 **S:** £28.00–£38.00 **Beds:** 9F 5D 1T 1S **Baths:** 14 En 2 Pr ⊱🅿(15) ⽡ 📺 🎵 ⚓

Hillsett, *Haye Lane, Lyme Regis, Dorset, DT7 3NG.* Lovely modern family home set in beautiful surroundings overlooking Lym valley. **Open:** All year (not Xmas/New Year)
01297 445 259 (also fax) Mr Thompson *pat.thompson@bigfoot.com* **D:** £20.00–£25.00 **S:** £20.00–£25.00 **Beds:** 1F 1D **Baths:** 1 En 1 Sh ⊱(8) 🅿(7) 📺 🎵 ⚓

Marnhull

ST7718 🍺 *Blackmore Vale*

Moorcourt Farm, *Moorside, Marnhull, Sturminster Newton, Dorset, DT10 1HH.* Friendly, welcoming, happy farmhouse. Central touring. Ginormous breakfast menu. **Open:** Easter to Oct
01258 820271 (also fax) Mrs Martin **D:** £18.00–£20.00 **S:** £18.00–£20.00 **Beds:** 2D 1T **Baths:** 2 Sh ⊱(10) 🅿(6) 📺 ⚓

Martinstown

SY6488

The Old Post Office, *Martinstown, Dorchester, Dorset, DT2 9LF.* Good rural base in small village. **Open:** All year
01305 889254 (also fax) Mrs Rootham **D:** £17.50–£25.00 **S:** £25.00 **Beds:** 1D 2T **Baths:** 1 Sh ⊱🅿(3) ⽊ 📺 🎵 ⚓

RATES

D = Price range per person sharing in a double or twin room

S = Price range for a single room

Middlemarsh

ST6706 🍺 *White Horse, Royal Oak*

White Horse Farm, *Middlemarsh, Sherborne, Dorset, DT9 5QN.* In beautiful Thomas Hardy country, within easy reach of the south coast. **Open:** All year (not Xmas/New Year) **Grades:** ETC 3 Diamond
01963 210222 (also fax) Mr & Mrs Wilding *enquiries@whitehorsefarm.co.uk* www.whitehorsefarm.co.uk **D:** £20.00–£29.00 **S:** £25.00–£30.00 **Beds:** 1S 2D **Baths:** 3 En 🅿(10) 📺 🎵 ⚓

Morcombelake

SY3994 🍺 *Ship Inn, Five Bells*

Wisteria Cottage, *Taylors Lane, Morcombelake, Bridport, Dorset, DT6 6ED.* Country cottage, panoramic views in area of outstanding natural beauty. **Open:** All year (not Xmas/New Year) **Grades:** ETC 3 Diamond
01297 489019 Mrs Ellis **D:** £20.00–£25.00 **S:** £30.00–£35.00 **Beds:** 1T 1D **Baths:** 2 En 🅿(3) ⽡ 📺 📺 🎵 ⚓

Moreton

SY8089

Frampton Arms, *Moreton, Dorchester, Dorset, DT2 8BB.* Traditional country pub with two bars, two restaurants and function room. **Open:** All year (not Xmas)
01305 852253 Mr Paulson **Fax: 01305 854586** *john_paulson@framptonarms.fsnet.co.uk* **D:** £20.00–£27.50 **S:** £30.00–£35.00 **Beds:** 1F 2D **Baths:** 2 En 1 Sh ⊱🅿(40) ⽡ 📺 📺 🎵 ⚓ cc

Netherbury

SY4699

Southview, *Whitecross, Netherbury, Bridport, Dorset, DT6 5NH.* Detached country cottage, lovely views and gardens in picturesque village. **Open:** All year **Grades:** ETC 3 Diamond
01308 488471 Mr Kennedy website.lineone.net/~southviewbb **D:** £22.50–£25.00 **S:** £25.00 **Beds:** 1F 1T 1D **Baths:** 1 En 1 Sh ⊱(5) 🅿(4) ⽡ 📺 ⽊ ✕ 🎵 ⚓

North Wootton

ST6514

Stoneleigh Barn, North Wootton, Sherborne, Dorset, DT9 5JW. Beautiful stone barn close to Sherborne. A special place. **Open:** All year (not Xmas/New Year) **01935 815964** Mrs Chant *stoneleigh@ic24.net* **D:** £23.00–£25.00 **S:** £30.00–£37.50 **Beds:** 1F 1D **Baths:** 1 En 1 Pr ⛴ (6) ▣ (4) ⵁ ⵁ ▥ ⵁ

Okeford Fitzpaine

ST8010

Etheridge Farm, Darknoll Lane, Okeford Fitzpaine, Blandford Forum, Dorset, DT11 0RP. In the heart of the Blackmore Vale, close to Lulworth. **Open:** Feb to Dec **01258 860037** Ms Thorne **D:** £17.00 **Beds:** 1F 1T 1D **Baths:** 2 Sh ⛴ ▣ ⵁ ⵁ

Osmington

SY7283

Rosedale, Church Lane, Osmington, Weymouth, Dorset, DT3 6EW. Very attractive cottage. Large, comfortable rooms, warm friendly atmosphere. **Open:** Mar to Oct **01305 832056** Mrs Legg **D:** £18.00–£20.00 **S:** £18.00–£19.00 **Beds:** 1D 1T **Baths:** 1 En 1 Pr ⛴ (5) ▣ (3) ⵁ ⵁ ⵁ

Rosthwaite, Church Lane, Osmington, Weymouth, Dorset, DT3 6EW. Bungalow set in picturesque village, comfortable beds and excellent breakfasts. **Open:** All year **01305 833621** Ms Leigh **D:** £15.00–£17.00 **S:** £15.00–£20.00 **Beds:** 1D 1T **Baths:** 1 Sh ⛴ ▣ (2) ⵁ ⵁ ⵁ ⵁ ⵁ

Pimperne

ST9008

The Old Bakery, Church Road, Pimperne, Blandford Forum, Dorset, DT11 8UB. A warm welcome awaits, in this former shop and bakery. **Open:** All year **01258 455173** P J Tanner **D:** £12.50–£15.00 **S:** £15.00–£20.00 **Beds:** 1T 1D 1S **Baths:** 2 Sh ⛴ (3) ▣ (2) ⵁ ⵁ × ⵁ

Poole

SZ0191   ⛴ Salterns Hotel, Yachtsman, Red Lion

Southern Comfort Guest House, 192 Bournemouth Road, Poole, Dorset, BH14 9HZ. Midway Poole-Bournemouth, main A35. Clean, family run, most rooms ensuite. Guests' patio. **Open:** All year **01202 722250 (also fax)** Mrs Richmond *pam@scomfort.co.uk* **D:** £20.00–£25.00 **S:** £35.00–£45.00 **Beds:** 1F 3D 1T 1S **Baths:** 4 Pr 1 Sh ⛴ ▣ (6) ⵁ ⵁ × ⵁ ⵁ ⵁ cc

Individual Touristik Poole, 53 Branksea Avenue, Hamworthy, Poole, Dorset, BH15 4DP. **Open:** All year **Grades:** ETC 4 Diamond **01202 673419** Renate Wadham **Fax: 01202 667260** *johnrenate@lineone.net* **D:** £28.00–£32.00 **S:** £32.00–£40.00 **Beds:** 2D/T **Baths:** 2 En ⛴ (9) ▣ (3) ⵁ ⵁ ⵁ ⵁ Select accommodation for those seeking something special. Luxury double/twin bed suite, facing Poole Harbour, Brownsea Island, Purbeck Hills, Park Beach. Own balcony, optional kitchen/diner or twin/double room facing pretty garden. Baths/separate showers. Walking distance Quay/Town.

Harbour Lea, 1 Whitecliff Road, Poole, Dorset, BH14 8DU. Harbour views, ideal French/Jersey ferries and blue flag beaches. **Open:** All year (not Xmas/New Year) **Grades:** ETC 3 Diamond **01202 744346 Fax: 01202 268930** *harbourlea@easicom.com* **D:** £20.00–£23.00 **S:** £25.00 **Beds:** 1F 1T 1D **Baths:** 2 En 1 Pr ⛴ ▣ (3) ⵁ ⵁ ⵁ ⵁ ⵁ ⵁ

Melbury Guest House, 101 Parkstone Road, Poole, Dorset, BH15 2NZ. Comfortable Edwardian home opposite Poole Park, near beaches, ferries, town. **Open:** All year **01202 749015** Mrs Lloyd **D:** £16.00–£20.00 **S:** £16.00–£20.00 **Beds:** 1F 1D 1T 1S **Baths:** 2 Sh ⛴ (5) ▣ (4) ⵁ ⵁ ⵁ ⵁ

Shalimar, 14 Burngate, Hamworthy, Poole, Dorset, BH15 4HS. Stair lift available. Quiet cul-de-sac. Homely atmosphere. Lovely Dorset coastline. Continental breakfast. **Open:** All year (not Xmas/New Year) **01202 680070** Mrs Batten **D:** £15.00 **S:** £15.00 **Beds:** 1T 1D 1S **Baths:** 1 Sh ⛴ ▣ (2) ⵁ × ⵁ ⵁ ⵁ

Please respect a B&B's wishes regarding children, animals and smoking

Sarnia Cherie, 375 Blandford Road, Hamworthy, Poole, Dorset, BH15 4JL. A warm welcome offering excellent B&B only 5 mins to town centre. **Open:** All year (not Xmas) **01202 679470 & 01585 319931** C Collier **Fax: 01202 679470 D:** £20.00–£22.50 **S:** £25.00–£30.00 **Beds:** 2D 1T **Baths:** 3 En ⛴ ▣ (3) ⵁ ⵁ ⵁ ⵁ ⵁ

Highways Bed & Breakfast, 29 Fernside Road, Poole, Dorset, BH15 2QU. 1920's house, very comfortable. Fire hygiene certificate, all ensuite & parking. **Open:** All year **01202 677060** Mr & Mrs Bailey **D:** £20.00–£22.50 **S:** £20.00–£25.00 **Beds:** 4D 1T **Baths:** 5 En ⛴ ▣ (6) ⵁ × ⵁ ⵁ ⵁ

Ashdell, 85 Dunyeats Road, Broadstone, Poole, Dorset, BH18 8AF. Central, comfortable, secluded. Breakfast/EM choice. Historic countryside/beaches, short breaks. **Open:** All year (not Xmas) **Grades:** ETC 2 Diamond **01202 692032** Mrs Critchley *ian@ashdell.fsnet.co.uk* www.ashdell.co.uk **D:** £16.00–£19.00 **S:** £19.00–£22.00 **Beds:** 1F 1D 1T 1S **Baths:** 1 Sh ⛴ (5) ▣ (3) ⵁ ⵁ × ⵁ ⵁ ⵁ

Portesham

SY6085   ⛴ King's Arms

Manor Farm House, Portesham, Weymouth, Dorset, DT3 4ET. **Open:** All year (not Xmas/New Year) **01305 871025** Mr Gargrave **Fax: 01305 871031** *bbportesham@yahoo.co.uk* **D:** £25.00 **S:** £25.00–£35.00 **Beds:** 2D 1S **Baths:** 1 Sh ▣ (4) ⵁ ⵁ ⵁ Beautiful Georgian farmhouse, superb location close to the spectacular Chesil Beach. Ideally situated for Dorchester, Weymouth and the historic village of Abbotsbury. Spacious south-facing accommodation. Relaxed, informal atmosphere in a quiet village setting. Private drive and parking.

Lavender Cottage, 9 Malthouse Meadow, Portesham, Weymouth, Dorset, DT3 4NS. Lovely scenery, quiet location, birdwatchers and walkers paradise, hearty breakfast. **Open:** All year (not Xmas) **01305 871924** Mrs Haine **D:** £17.50 **S:** £17.50 **Beds:** 1D 1T **Baths:** 1 Sh ⵁ ⵁ ⵁ ⵁ

All details shown are as supplied by B&B owners in Autumn 2001

Corfe Gate House, 2 Coryates, Portesham, Weymouth, Dorset, *DT3 4HW.* Victorian house peacefully situated in Waddon Valley near beautiful West Dorset coastline. **Open:** Easter to Oct **01305 871483** Mrs Adams **Fax: 01305 264024** *adams@corfegatehouse.co.uk* www.corfegatehouse.co.uk **D:** £20.00–£25.00 **S:** £35.00 **Beds:** 1F 1T 1D **Baths:** 3 En ♿ (4) 🅿 (3) ⌿ 📺 🛏 ♨

Portland

SY6874 🍺 *Mermaid Inn, Pulpit Inn*

The Old Vicarage, Grove Road, Portland, Dorset, *DT5 1DB.* Substantial Victorian vicarage. Spacious, comfortable rooms, good food, friendly atmosphere. **Open:** All year (not Xmas/New Year) **01305 824117** Carolyn Robb *mccormicksmith@ oldvicarage.fsnet.co.uk* **D:** £22.00–£25.00 **S:** £25.00–£30.00 **Beds:** 1F 1T 1D **Baths:** 3 En 🅿 (3) 📺 🛏 📺 🛏 ♨

Poyntington

ST6420

Welgoer, Poyntington, Sherborne, Dorset, *DT9 4LF.* Comfortable accommodation in quiet village near Sherborne. Ideal touring base. **Open:** All year **01963 220737** Mrs Neville **D:** £20.00–£25.00 **S:** £20.00–£25.00 **Beds:** 1T 1D **Baths:** 1 En 1 Pr ♿ (5) 🅿 (2) ⌿ 📺 📺 ♨

Puddletown

SY7594 🍺 *Blue Vinny, Prince of Wales, Martyrs Inn*

Zoar House, Puddletown, Dorchester, Dorset, *DT2 8SR.* Victorian house. Garden, orchard, paddocks, Hardy's Cottage, Athelhampton, Forest nearby. **Open:** All year **01305 848498** Mrs Stephens **D:** £15.00– £19.00 **S:** £16.00–£20.00 **Beds:** 1F 1D 1T **Baths:** 1 En 1 Sh ♿ 🅿 (6) ⌿ 📺 🛏 📺 ♨

Sandford

SY9289

Foresters, 14 Keysworth Drive, Sandford, Wareham, Dorset, *BH20 7BD.* Modern spacious bungalow. Peaceful location. Wildlife garden, private off-road parking. Large breakfasts. **Open:** All year (not Xmas/ New Year) **01929 556090** Mrs Harris *foresters@ keysworth14.freeserve.co.uk* www.keysworth14. freeserve.co.uk **D:** £16.50–£20.00 **S:** £16.50– £22.50 **Beds:** 1T 1D 1S 🅿 (5) ⌿ 📺 📺 ♨

Shaftesbury

ST8622

Charnwood Cottage, Charlton, Shaftesbury, Dorset, *SP7 9LZ.* C17th thatched cottage with lovely garden. Good base for touring. **Open:** All year (not Xmas/New Year) **01747 828310 (also fax)** Mr & Mrs Morgan **D:** £19.00 **Beds:** 1T 1D **Baths:** 1 Sh 🅿 (2) 📺 🛏

Maple Lodge, Christys Lane, Shaftesbury, Dorset, *SP7 8DL.* Within 5 mins walk of shops, restaurants and famous Gold Hill. **Open:** All year (not Xmas/New Year) **01747 853945** Mr & Mrs Jameson *maplelodge@tesco.net* www.maplelodgebb.com **D:** £18.00–£22.00 **S:** £20.00–£25.00 **Beds:** 1F 1T 1D **Baths:** 2 En 1 Pr ♿ 🅿 (8) ⌿ 📺 📺 ♨

Sherborne

ST6316

Britannia Inn, Sherborne, Dorset, *DT9 3EH.* Listed building, town centre, 300 years old. **Open:** All year **01935 813300** Mr Blackmore www.thebritanniainn.co.uk **D:** £20.00–£35.00 **S:** £20.00–£35.00 **Beds:** 2F 1D 2T 2S **Baths:** 1 En 3 Sh ♿ 🅿 (6) ⌿ 📺 🛏 × 📺 ♨ cc

Clatcombe Grange, Bristol Road, Sherborne, Dorset, *DT9 4RH.* Charming Listed converted barn. Spacious accommodation/ garden. Ample parking. Warm welcome. Peaceful and friendly. **Open:** All year **Grades:** ETC 4 Diamond **01935 814355 & 07773 969145 (M)** Hellyar **D:** £26.00 **S:** £36.00 **Beds:** 1T 1D 1S **Baths:** 2 En 1 Pr ♿ 🅿 ⌿ 📺 × 📺 ♨

Bridleways, Oborne Road, Sherborne, Dorset, *DT9 3RX.* Comfortable house overlooking castle, 10 mins' walk to historic town centre. **Open:** All year (not Xmas) **01935 814716 (also fax)** Mr & Mrs Dimond **D:** £18.00–£22.00 **S:** £20.00–£22.00 **Beds:** 1D 2T **Baths:** 1 En 1 Pr ♿ 🅿 (5) 📺 🛏 📺 ♨

Shipton Gorge

SY4991

Cairnhill, Shipton Gorge, Bridport, *DT6 4LL.* Beautiful countryside, warm welcome. Comfortable, spacious rooms, heated indoor pool. **Open:** Easter to Oct **01308 898203 (also fax)** R W Waite *cairnhill@talk21.com* **D:** £25.00 **S:** £25.00– £30.00 **Beds:** 1D 1T 1S **Baths:** 2 En 1 Pr ♿ (7) 🅿 ⌿ 📺 × 📺 ♨

Planning a longer stay? Always ask for any special rates

B&B owners may vary rates – be sure to check when booking

Sixpenny Handley

ST9918

Town Farm Bungalow, Sixpenny Handley, Salisbury, Wilts., *SP5 5NT.* Excellent friendly accommodation. Magnificent views and peaceful surrounding. Superb breakfasts. **Open:** All year **01725 552319 (also fax)** Mrs Inglis **D:** £17.50–£20.00 **S:** £22.50–£35.00 **Beds:** 1T 2D **Baths:** 1 En 1 Sh ♿ 🅿 (6) 📺 🛏 × 📺 ♨

Stapehill

SU0500 🍺 *Old Thatch*

Pear Tree Cottage, 248 Wimborne Road West, Stapehill, Wimborne, Dorset, *BH21 2DZ.* Charming thatched cottage, large, secluded gardens. Easy access to A31. **Open:** All year (not Xmas/New Year) **01202 890174 D:** £25.00 **S:** £35.00 **Beds:** 1T 1D 1S **Baths:** 1 Pr 2 Sh 🅿 (3) ⌿ 📺 📺 ♨

Stour Row

ST8221 🍺 *King's Arms, Crown Inn*

Beechmead, Stour Row, Shaftesbury, Dorset, *SP7 0QF.* Bungalow in a tiny village - surrounded by fields **Open:** All year **01747 838405** Mrs Slingerland **D:** £15.00– £17.00 **S:** £17.00–£19.00 **Beds:** 1T 1D **Baths:** 1 Pr 1 Sh 🅿 (3) ⌿ 📺 ♨ ♿ ♨

Studland

SZ0382 🍺 *Manor House Hotel, Bankes Arms, Village Inn*

Bankers Arms Hotel, Manor Road, Studland, Swanage, Dorset, *BH19 3AU.* **Open:** All year **01929 450225 D:** £27.00–£36.00 **S:** £27.00– £36.00 **Beds:** 1F 2T 4D 1S **Baths:** 6 En 1 Sh ♿ (4) 🅿 (10) 📺 🛏 × ♨ cc Lovely old country inn overlooking the sea in beautiful NT area. Log fires, ensuite accommodation, extensive homemade bar menu. AA fish & seafood recommended. CAMRA joint Pub of the Year for Dorset, real ale award, also outright winner for autumn CAMRA Pub of the Season.

Swanage

SZ0278   *The Galley, King's Arms, Purbeck Inn, Royal Oak, Ship Inn, White Swan*

Plum Tree Cottage, 60 Bell Street, Swanage, Dorset, *BH19 2SB*. Comfortable rooms, generous breakfasts, in area of outstanding natural beauty. **Open:** All year
01929 421601 & 07971 552082 (M) Mr & Mrs Howells **Fax: 01929 421601 D:** £22.50–£30.00 **S:** £30.00–£40.00 **Beds:** 3D **Baths:** 1 En 2 Pr ⚑ (2) ⌇ ⧖ ⧖ ✕ ⧖ ⧖, ⚡

Glenlee Hotel, 6 Cauldon Avenue, Swanage, Dorset, *BH19 1PQ*. Friendly family run hotel in delightful position close to beach.
Open: Mar to Oct **Grades:** ETC 4 Diamond **01929 425794** Mr Jones **Fax: 01929 421530** *info@glenleehotel.co.uk* www.glenleehotel.co. uk **D:** £22.50–£27.50 **S:** £35.00–£40.00 **Beds:** 2F 2T 3D **Baths:** 7 En ⧖ (3) ⚑ (7) ⧖ ✕ ⧖, ⚡ cc

Perfick Piece, Springfield Road, Swanage, Dorset, *BH19 1HD*. Small family guest house in quiet cul-de-sac near shops, beach and steam railway. **Open:** All year **01929 423178 Fax: 01929 423558** *perfick-piece@supanet.com* perfick-piece.supanet.com **D:** £15.00–£20.00 **S:** £16.00–£20.00 **Beds:** 1F 1T 1D 1S **Baths:** 1 En 1 Pr 1 Sh ⧖ ⚑ (3) ⧖ ⧖ ✕ ⧖ ⧖ ❋ ⚡

Hermitage Guest House, 1 Manor Road, Swanage, Dorset, *BH19 2BH*. Quiet central location, relaxed atmosphere, bay views. 2 mins beach, Coastal Path.
Open: Easter to Nov **01929 423014** Mrs Pickering **D:** £18.50–£19.50 **S:** £20.00 **Beds:** 4F 2D 1T **Baths:** 2 Sh ⧖ (5) ⚑ (7) ⚑ ⧖ ⧖ ⧖ ⧖, ⚡

Sydling St Nicholas

SY6399

Lamperts Cottage, Sydling St Nicholas, Dorchester, Dorset, *DT2 9NU*. Traditional C16th thatched cottage, stream at front, beams, inglenook, flagstones. **Open:** All year **Grades:** ETC 3 Diamond **01300 341659** Mr Wills **Fax: 01300 341699** *nickywillis@tesco.net* **D:** £21.00–£22.00 **S:** £25.00 **Beds:** 1F 1D 1T **Baths:** 2 Sh ⧖ (8) ⚑ (3) ⧖ ⧖ ⧖ ⧖, ⚡ cc

---

Planning a longer stay? Always ask for any special rates

Magiston Farm, Sydling St Nicholas, Dorchester, Dorset, *DT2 9NR*. C16th farmhouse, 400 acre working farm, large garden. Very peaceful. **Open:** All year (not Xmas)
01300 320295 Mrs Barraclough **D:** £18.50 **S:** £18.50 **Beds:** 1D 3T 1S **Baths:** 1 Pr 1 Sh ⧖ (10) ⚑ (12) ⧖ ✕ ⧖ ⧖, ⧖ ⚡

City Cottage, Sydling St Nicholas, Dorchester, Dorset, *DT2 9NX*. Country cottage, comfortable and a warm welcome assured. **Open:** All year (not Xmas) **01300 341300** Mrs Wareham **D:** £18.00 **S:** £18.00 **Beds:** 1D 1S **Baths:** 1 Sh ⧖ (12) ⚑ (2) ⧖ ⧖

Symondsbury

SY4493   *Ilchester Arms*

Saxlingham House, West Road, Symondsbury, Bridport, Dorset, *DT6 6AA*. Extensive country views many local attractions warm friendly welcome. **Open:** Easter to Sept **01308 423629** Mr & Mrs Nicholls **D:** £18.00 **S:** £18.00 **Beds:** 1T 2D **Baths:** 3 En ⚑ ⚑ ⧖ ⚡

Tarrant Hinton

ST9311

Meadow House, Tarrant Hinton, Blandford Forum, Dorset, *DT11 8JG*. Quiet farm house over looking countryside, excellent tourist base, home-produced breakfast. **Open:** All year (not Xmas) **01258 830498 (also fax)** Ms Webster *rose.web@virgin.net* **D:** £19.00–£25.00 **S:** £19.00–£25.00 **Beds:** 1F 1D 1S **Baths:** 2 Sh ⧖ ⚑ (6) ⚑ ⧖ ⧖, ⚡

Toller Porcorum

SY5698

Colesmoor Farm, Toller Porcorum, Dorchester, Dorset, *DT2 0DU*. Small family farm in quiet setting with excellent views. **Open:** May to Feb **01300 320812** Mrs Geddes **Fax: 01300 321402** *geddes.colesmoor@eclipse.co.uk* **D:** £20.00 **S:** £25.00 **Beds:** 1D 1T **Baths:** 2 En ⧖ ⚑ (4) ⚑ ⧖ ⧖ ⧖3 ⚡

RATES
D = Price range per person sharing in a double or twin room
S = Price range for a single room

Tolpuddle

SY7994   *Greyhound, Martyrs*

Lawrences Farm, Southover, Tolpuddle, Dorchester, *DT2 7HF*.
Open: All year (not Xmas/New Year)
01305 848460 Mrs Slocock *sally.slocock@ virgin.net* www.goflyfishing.co.uk **D:** £22.00 **S:** £22.00 **Beds:** 1F 1T 1D **Baths:** 2 En 1 Pr ⧖ (8) ⚑ (6) ⚑ ⧖ ⧖
Lawrences farm nestles in Dorset's famous Piddle Valley. In the 1830s the Tolpuddle Martyrs ensured worldwide fame for the village. Explore other Piddle and Puddle villages and Thomas Hardy countryside. Marvellous bird watching. Our own lake and river trout fishing.

Uploders

SY5093   *Loders Arms*

Uploders Farm, Uploders, Bridport, Dorset, *DT6 4NZ*. Quiet position. Ideal for touring. Beautiful countryside. Good English breakfast. **Open:** Easter to Oct **Grades:** ETC 3 Diamond **01308 423380 D:** £18.00–£20.00 **Beds:** 1F 1D **Baths:** 2 En ⧖ (7) ⚑ (3) ⚑ ⧖ ⧖, ⚡

Upton (Poole)

SY9793

Tideway, Beach Road, Upton, Poole, Dorset, *BH16 5NA*. Please look at our website for further detail & pictures - www.maidinwessex.com/tideway. **Open:** All year (not Xmas) **01202 621293 (also fax)** Mr & Mrs Yates *tidewaybb@aol.com* www.maidinwessex. com/tideway **D:** £20.00–£25.00 **S:** £23.00–£25.00 **Beds:** 1D 1T **Baths:** 1 Sh ⧖ ⚑ (3) ⚑ ⧖ ✕ ⧖, ⧖

Wareham

SY9287

Ashcroft Bed & Breakfast, 64 Furzebrook Road, Wareham, Dorset, *BH20 5AX*. Friendly, comfortable, good food. Convenient for bird watching and walking. **Open:** All year (not Xmas) **01929 552392** Mrs Cake **Fax: 01929 552422** *cake@ashcroft-b-and-b.freeserve.co.uk* www.ashcroft-b-and-b.freeserve.co.uk **D:** £18.00–£25.00 **S:** £18.00–£30.00 **Beds:** 1F 1D 1T **Baths:** 2 En 2 Pr ⧖ (3) ⚑ (6) ⚑ ⧖ ⧖ ✕ ⧖ ⧖, ⚡

Planning a longer stay? Always ask for any special rates

West Lulworth

SY8280 🍺 *Castle Inn*

The Copse, School Lane, West Lulworth, Wareham, Dorset, *BH20 5SA.* **Open:** All year (not Xmas)
01929 400581 (also fax) Mr & Mrs Johari *ulla.johari@tesco.net* **D:** £15.00–£17.50 **S:** £15.00–£17.50 **Beds:** 1D 1T 1S **Baths:** 1 Sh ⭘ 🄿 (3) 📺 🖳 🐾
Detached house in picturesque coastal village. Quiet location off main road overlooking field in area of outstanding natural beauty. Close to Lulworth Cove and beaches. Coastal walks, restaurants and village pub. Generous continental breakfast.

Graybank Bed & Breakfast, Main Road, West Lulworth, Wareham, Dorset, *BH20 5RL.* Victorian house, peaceful location, warm welcome plus excellent breakfast. **Open:** Feb to Nov **Grades:** ETC 3 Diamond
01929 400256 Mr & Mrs Burrill **D:** £17.00–£20.00 **S:** £17.00–£20.00 **Beds:** 2F 3D 1T 1S **Baths:** 3 Sh ⭘ (4) 🄿 (7) ⤬ 📺 📺 🖳 🐾

West Down Farm, West Lulworth, Wareham, Dorset, *BH20 5RY.* Beautiful coastal area. Outstanding views. Ideal riding, cycling and walking. **Open:** All year
01929 400308 (also fax) Ms Weld *westdownfarm@saqnet.co.uk* **D:** £18.00–£20.00 **S:** £25.00–£30.00 **Beds:** 1T 1D **Baths:** 1 Sh ⭘ 🄿 📺 🐾 📺 🖳 🐾

Gatton House, West Lulworth, Wareham, Dorset, *BH20 5RU.* Picturesque guest house with spectacular views, near Lulworth Cove and coastal path. **Open:** Mar to Oct **Grades:** ETC 4 Diamond
01929 400252 (also fax) Mr Dale *mike@ gattonhouse.co.uk* www.gattonhouse.co.uk **D:** £23.00–£35.00 **S:** £33.00–£45.00 **Beds:** 1F 1T 6D **Baths:** 8 En ⭘ 🄿 (9) ⤬ 📺 🐾 📺 🖳 🐾 cc

Tewkesbury Cottage, 28 Main Road, West Lulworth, Wareham, Dorset, *BH20 5RL.* C1600 thatched cottage 8 minutes walk to beach, coastal paths. Full English breakfast. **Open:** All year
01929 400561 (also fax) Mrs Laing **D:** £18.00–£20.00 **S:** £20.00–£25.00 **Beds:** 2D 1T 1S **Baths:** 1 En 2 Sh ⭘ (12) 🄿 (6) 🐾 📺 🐾

Rose Cottage, Main Road, West Lulworth, Wareham, Dorset, *BH20 5RJ.* Beautiful thatched cottage situated 2 mins walk from Lulworth Cove. **Open:** All year (not Xmas/New Year)
01929 400150 B Clarke *barbara@ rosecottage.fsworld.co.uk* www.rosecottage. fsworld.co.uk **D:** £20.00–£25.00 **S:** £20.00–£22.00 **Beds:** 1T 2D 1S **Baths:** 1 En 1 Sh ⭘ 🄿 (3) ⤬ 📺 🐾 📺 🖳 🐾

West Stafford

SY7289 🍺 *Wise Man*

Long Barn House, 1 Barton Mews, West Stafford, Dorchester, Dorset, *DT2 8UB.* Converted byre/granary between pub and church in tranquil ancient village. **Open:** All year
01305 266899 *pessame@amserve.net* **D:** £20.00–£27.00 **S:** £25.00–£32.00 **Beds:** 1T 1D 1S **Baths:** 1 En 1 Pr ⭘ (10) 🄿 (2) ⤬ 📺 🐾 📺 🖳 🐾 cc

Weymouth

SY6779 🍺 *The Lodmoor, Ferrybridge, Wyke Smugglers*

Mar Jun Guest House, 32 Lennox Street, Weymouth, Dorset, *DT4 7HD.* Pretty guest house, two minutes Weymouth Bay, good home cooking. **Open:** All year
01305 761320 Mr & Mrs Edmondson
D: £18.00–£20.00 **Beds:** 1F 1T 4D **Baths:** 6 En ⭘ (5) ⤬ 📺 ⤬ 🖳 🐾 🐾

Morven Hotel, 2 Westerhall Road, Weymouth, Dorset, *DT4 7SZ.* Family hotel. 150 yards from sea and beautiful green hill gardens. **Open:** Easter to Oct **Grades:** ETC 3 Diamond
01305 785075 Mr Lambley **D:** £20.00–£22.00 **S:** £20.00–£25.00 **Beds:** 2T 7D 1S **Baths:** 7 En 3 Sh ⭘ (10) 📺 🖳 🐾

Kings Acre Hotel, 140 The Esplanade, Weymouth, Dorset, *DT4 7NH.* Lovely, privately run hotel in a grand Victorian terrace, offering friendly, courteous service, good food. **Open:** Feb to Nov
01305 782534 Mrs Mears **Fax: 01305 732354** **D:** £25.00–£35.00 **S:** £32.50–£40.00 **Beds:** 2F 7D 2T **Baths:** 10 En 1 Pr ⭘ 🄿 (9) ⤬ 📺 ⤬ 📺 🐾 cc

Seaways, 5 Turton Street, Weymouth, Dorset, *DT4 7DU.* Victorian Building close to all amenities, beach, town and station. **Open:** All year (not Xmas/New Year)
01305 771646 Mr & Mrs Seward *seasw@ supanet.com* **D:** £16.00 **S:** £16.00 **Beds:** 5D 1T 1S **Baths:** 2 Sh ⭘ ⤬ 📺 📺 🖳 🐾

Esplanade Hotel, 141 The Esplanade, Weymouth, Dorset, *DT4 7NJ.* Sea front 1835 Georgian terrace hotel. Superior ensuite accommodation with car parking. **Open:** Easter to Oct
01305 783129 Mr & Mrs Paul **D:** £25.00–£35.00 **S:** £32.00–£35.00 **Beds:** 1F 7D 2T 1S **Baths:** 11 En ⭘ (6) 🄿 (9) ⤬ 📺 📺 🖳 🐾

Greenlands Guest House, 8 Waterloo Place, The Esplanade, Weymouth, Dorset, *DT4 7PR.* Family run guest house, on the sea front. Good wholesome breakfast. **Open:** All year (not Xmas)
01305 776368 (also fax) Mr & Mrs Turbett *greenlands@kevandjackie.demon.co.uk* **D:** £15.00–£20.00 **Beds:** 2F 5D ⭘ 🄿 (7) 📺 📺 🖳 🐾 cc

Birchfields Hotel, 22 Abbotsbury Road, Weymouth, Dorset, *DT4 0AE.* Close to beach and town, short breaks welcome, ideal touring base. **Open:** Easter to Oct **Grades:** RAC 3 Diamond, Sparkling
01305 773255 (also fax) Mr & Mrs Dutton *birchfieldshotel@lineone.net* www.smoothhound.co. uk/hotels/birchfields.html **D:** £20.00–£25.00 **S:** £16.00–£25.00 **Beds:** 2F 3D 2T 2S **Baths:** 3 En 7 Sh ⭘ 🄿 (3) ⤬ 📺 🖳 🐾 cc

Whitchurch Canonicorum

SY3995

Cardsmill Farm, Whitchurch Canonicorum, Bridport, Dorset, *DT6 6RP.* Comfortable farmhouse on working family farm 3 miles from coast. **Open:** All year (not Xmas)
01297 489375 (also fax) Mrs Johnson *cardsmill@aol.com* **D:** £18.00–£24.00 **S:** £19.00–£23.00 **Beds:** 1F 1D 1S **Baths:** 2 En ⭘ 🄿 (6) 📺 🐾 📺 🖳 🐾

Wimborne Minster

SU0100 🍺 *Willett Arms*

Peacehaven, 282 Sopwith Crescent Merley, Wimborne Minster, Dorset, *BH21 1XL.* **Open:** All year
01202 880281 Mr & Mrs Justice **D:** £20.00–£22.50 **S:** £22.50–£25.00 **Beds:** 2D **Baths:** 1 Sh ⭘ 🄿 ⤬ 📺 ⤬ 📺 📺 🖳 🐾 🐾
Perfectly situated with bus stops outside for Poole, Wimborne and Bournemouth. In easy reach of Dorset coast, New Forest, health clubs, fishing, golf, and many places of historical interest, museums, houses and gardens to visit, churches. All rooms on ground floor.

Please respect a B&B's wishes regarding children, animals and smoking

Heatherlands, 13 *Wimborne Road, Colehill, Wimborne Minster, Dorset, BH21 2RS.* A large Victorian house where guests are treated as friends. **Open:** All year (not Xmas/New Year)
01202 882032 Mrs Gibbs **D:** £18.00 **S:** £18.00
Beds: 2F 1D **Baths:** 1 Sh ⌂ 🅿 ⌀ 🅅 🛏 🆅 🏬 ♨

Turi, 21 *Grove Road, Wimborne Minster, Dorset, BH21 1BN.* Victorian house with garden, off main road between Minster and market. **Open:** All year
01202 884818 Mrs Joyner *joyturi@care4free.net*
D: £14.00–£16.00 **S:** £14.00–£16.00 **Beds:** 1F 1T **Baths:** 2 Sh ⌂ ⌀ 🅅 🆅 🏬 ♨

Sunnysides, 18 *Victoria Road, Wimborne Minster, Dorset, BH21 1EW.* Warm, friendly, good touring centre close to town centre and eating places. **Open:** All year
01202 884963 Mrs Randall **D:** £16.00
S: £16.00 **Beds:** 1D 1T **Baths:** 1 Sh 🅿 (2) ⌀ 🅅 🆅 🏬 ♨

Crab Apple Corner, 40 *Lacy Drive, Wimborne, Dorset, BH21 1DG.* Situated close to town centre. Warm welcome. Full English breakfast. **Open:** All year (not Xmas/New Year)
01202 840993 Mrs Curry *Andrew.Curry@virgin.net* **D:** £20.00–£22.00 **S:** £22.00
Beds: 1D **Baths:** 1 Sh ⌂ 🅿 (1) ⌀ 🅅 🆅 🏬 ♨

Moor Allerton, *Holtwood, Wimborne Minster, Dorset, BH21 7DU.* Tranquillity amidst glorious countryside, beaches, New Forest. Warmest Christian welcome. **Open:** All year (not Xmas/New Year)
01258 840845 (also fax) Mrs Oliver
martinoliver1@talk21.com **D:** £18.00–£23.00
S: £20.00–£24.00 **Beds:** 1T 1D 1S **Baths:** 2 Pr ⌂ 🅿 ⌀ 🛏 ✕ 🆅 🏬 ♨ ♨

Winfrith Newburgh

SY8084 🍴 *Sailor's Return, Weld Arms, Countryman*

The Manor House, *Winfrith Newburgh, Dorchester, Dorset, DT2 8JR.* Historic manor house with luxury rooms near Lulworth Cove. **Open:** All year (not Xmas)
01305 854987 Mr & Mrs Smith **Fax: 01305 854988** *jennie@dorsetcoastalcottages.com*
D: £23.00–£25.00 **Beds:** 1D 1T **Baths:** 1 En 1 Pr ⌂ ⌀ 🅅 🆅 🏬 ♨

Marleywood House, *Winfrith Newburgh, Dorchester, Dorset, DT2 8UQ.* Converted downland barn, one mile from sea, cliffs and country walks. **Open:** All year
01929 400582 Mr & Mrs Wintrip *info@marleywoodhouse.com* www.marleywoodhouse.com **D:** £20.00 **S:** £27.50 **Beds:** 1T 3D
Baths: 1 En 2 Sh ⌂ 🅿 (20) ⌀ 🅅 🛏 ✕ 🆅 🏬 ♨ ✻ ♨

Winterborne Kingston

SY8697

West Acres, *West Street, Winterborne Kingston, Blandford Forum, Dorset, DT11 9AT.* Quiet spacious rural bungalow, large garden, excellent walking/riding paths. **Open:** All year
01929 471293 Mrs Jenkins **D:** £20.00
S: £23.00 **Beds:** 1F 1T 1D **Baths:** 1 En 1 Sh ⌂ (10) 🅿 (8) ⌀ 🅅 ✕ 🏬 ♨ ♨

Winterborne Zelston

SY8997

Brook Farm, *Winterborne Zelston, Blandford Forum, Dorset, DT11 9EU.* In quiet pretty hamlet, comfortable farmhouse accommodation, river and farmland views. Numerous country inns. **Open:** All year (not Xmas)
01929 459267 (also fax) Mrs Kerley
D: £17.00–£22.00 **S:** £22.00–£25.00 **Beds:** 2D 1T **Baths:** 2 En 1 Pr ⌂ (10) 🅿 ⌀ 🅅 🆅 🏬 ♨

Winterbourne Abbas

SY6190

Churchview Guest House, *Winterbourne Abbas, Dorchester, Dorset, DT2 9LS.* Delightful C17th village guest house near Dorchester offers comfort, delicious breakfasts. **Open:** All year (not Xmas)
Grades: ETC 3 Diamond
01305 889296 (also fax) Mr Deller *stay@churchview.co.uk* www.churchview.co.uk
D: £24.00–£30.00 **S:** £27.00–£35.00 **Beds:** 1F 4D 3T 1S **Baths:** 8 En 1 Pr ⌂ (5) 🅿 (10) ⌀ 🅅 🛏 ✕ 🆅 🏬 ♨ cc

---

Please respect a B&B's wishes regarding children, animals and smoking

Winterbourne Steepleton

SY6289

The Old Rectory, *Winterbourne Steepleton, Dorchester, Dorset, DT2 9LG.* Quiet hamlet in Hardy country. Peaceful night's sleep, copious English, vegetarian or continental breakfast. **Open:** All year (not Xmas/New Year) **Grades:** ETC 4 Diamond, Silver
01305 889468 M Tree **Fax: 01305 889737** *trees@eurobell.co.uk* www.trees.eurobell.co.uk
D: £25.00–£55.00 **Beds:** 3T **Baths:** 3 En ⌂ 🅿 (6) ⌀ 🅅 🆅 🏬 ♨

Wool

SY8486

Fingle Bridge, *Duck Street, Wool, Wareham, Dorset, BH20 6DE.* Warm welcome. Close Monkey World, Tank Museum, coast and countryside. **Open:** All year
01929 462739 Mrs Baker **D:** £20.00–£25.00
S: £20.00 **Beds:** 1F 1T 1D **Baths:** 1 En 1 Sh ⌂ 🅿 (3) ⌀ 🅅 🆅 🏬 ♨

East Burton House, *East Burton, Wool, Wareham, Dorset, BH20 6HE.* Relax and enjoy real food in our peaceful country house.
Open: All year
01929 463857 Mr Francis **Fax: 01929 463026**
mikefr@ntlworld.com **D:** £22.00–£23.00
S: £32.00–£36.00 **Beds:** 2D 1T **Baths:** 2 Sh ⌂ 🅿 (6) ⌀ 🅅 🆅 🏬 ♨

Worth Matravers

SY9777

The Haven, *Worth Matravers, Swanage, Dorset, BH19 3LF.* Friendly welcome to comfortable modern house with pleasant sea views. **Open:** All year
01929 439388 & 01929 439388 Mr & Mrs Taylor **D:** £20.00–£25.00 **S:** £20.00–£25.00
Beds: 1D 1T **Baths:** 1 En 1 Pr ⌂ ⌀ 🅅 🛏 ✕ 🏬 ♨

Yetminster

ST5910

Manor Farm House, *High Street, Yetminster, Sherborne, Dorset, DT9 6LF.* Interesting manor farmhouse rebuilt in C17th, with many architectural features.
Open: All year (not Xmas)
01935 872247 & 0800 0566761 Mr & Mrs Partridge **Fax: 01935 872247** www.nsl.co.uk/shogun/manor/manpics.htm **D:** £30.00–£35.00 **S:** £35.00 **Beds:** 2T 1D 1S **Baths:** 4 En 🅿 (20) ⌀ 🅅 ✕ 🆅 🏬 ♨ cc

County Durham

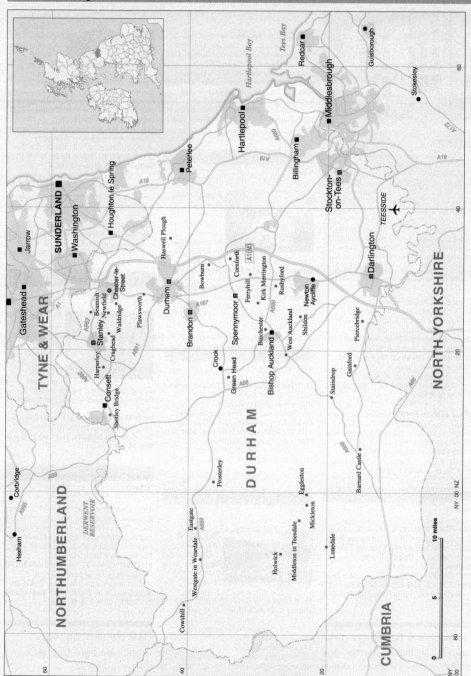

Barnard Castle

NZ0516 🍴 *Kirk Inn*

Old Well Inn, 21 The Bank, Barnard Castle, Co Durham, *DL12 8PH.* **Open:** All year **Grades:** ETC 3 Diamond **01833 690130** Mrs Rabley **Fax: 01833 690140** *reservations@oldwellinn.co.uk* www.oldwellinn. co.uk **D:** £30.00–£35.00 **S:** £48.00–£57.00 **Beds:** 2F 6D 2T **Baths:** 10 En ⅖ 🛏 ☑ 🛏 ✕ ☑ 🎇 ₺ ₴ cc
Recommended by the Times and Sunday Telegraph, this C17th tavern in Teesdale boasts spacious ensuite rooms, freshly prepared local produce, antique shops, museums, castles. Beautiful scenery, wonderful walks, river and reservoir fishing and riding.

Cloud High, Eggleston, Barnard Castle, Co Durham, *DL12 0AU.* Luxurious accommodation and hospitality, gourmet breakfasts, a delight. Sheer indulgence! **Open:** All year (not Xmas/New Year) **Grades:** ETC 4 Diamond, Gold **01833 650644 (also fax)** Mr & Mrs Bell *cloudhigh@btinternet.com* www.cloudhigh-teesdale.co.uk **D:** £23.00– £25.00 **S:** £30.00 **Beds:** 2D 1T **Baths:** 3 En 🖫 (4) ⅍ ☑ ☑ 🎇 ₴

West Roods Farm, Boldron, Barnard Castle, Co Durham, *DL12 9SW.* Geordie welcome, kettle on the boil on arrival 5pm (1700 hrs). **Open:** May to Oct **01833 690116** Mrs Lowson **D:** £20.00 **S:** £20.00–£25.00 **Beds:** 1F 1D 1S **Baths:** 2 En 1 Sh ⅖ (5) 🖫 (6) ⅍ 🎇 ₴

Beamish

NZ2253

No Place House, Beamish, Stanley, Co Durham, *DH9 0QH.* Converted co-operative store, close to Beamish Museum. Friendly warm welcome. **Open:** All year **Grades:** ETC 2 Diamond **0191 370 0891** Mrs Wood www.noplace.co.uk **D:** £18.50–£21.00 **S:** £22.00–£25.00 **Beds:** 2D 1T **Baths:** 2 En 1 Sh ⅖ (3) 🖫 (5) ☑ 🛏 ☑ 🎇 ✱ ₴

National Grid References given are for villages, towns and cities – not for individual houses

---

Planning a longer stay? Always ask for any special rates

The Coach House, High Urpeth, Beamish, Stanley, Co Durham, *DH9 0SE.* Country hamlet location, near Durham City, Beamish, Metro Centre and A1(M). **Open:** All year **Grades:** ETC 4 Diamond **0191 370 0309** Kim Foreman **Fax: 0191 370 0046** *coachhouse@foreman25.freeserve.co.uk* www.coachhousebeamish.ntb.org.uk **D:** £20.00–£22.50 **S:** £25.00–£30.00 **Beds:** 1F 1T 1D **Baths:** 1 En 2 Pr ⅖ 🖫 (6) ☑ 🛏 ✕ ☑ 🎇 ₺ cc

Binchester

NZ2031

Five Gables, Binchester, Bishop Auckland, *DL14 8AT.* Recommended by Which? Good B&B Guide. 15 mins from Durham. **Open:** All year (not Xmas/New Year) **Grades:** ETC 3 Diamond **01388 608204** P.M.I Weston **Fax: 01388 663092** *book.in@fivegables.co.uk* www.fivegables.co.uk **D:** £24.00–£25.00 **S:** £28.00–£30.00 **Beds:** 1T 2D 1S **Baths:** 3 En 1 Pr 🖫 (2) ⅍ ☑ 🛏 ☑ 🎇 ₴ cc

Bowburn

NZ3038

Hillrise Guest House, 13 Durham Road West, Bowburn, Durham, *DH6 5AU.* Recommended standard of accommodation in large ensuite rooms. **Open:** All year **Grades:** AA 4 Diamond **0191 377 0302** G B Webster **Fax: 0191 377 0898** *hillrise.guesthouse@btinternet.com* www.hill-rise.com **D:** £25.00 **S:** £30.00 **Beds:** 3F 2D **Baths:** 5 En ⅖ 🖫 (4) ⅍ ☑ 🎇 ₴ cc

Brandon

NZ2439

Bay Horse Inn, Brandon, Durham, *DH7 8ST.* **Open:** All year **0191 378 0498** Mr & Mrs Maddock **D:** £25.00–£30.00 **S:** £40.00 **Beds:** 1F 6T 3D **Baths:** 10 En ⅖ 🖫 🛏 ✕ ☑ 🎇 ₺ cc
Situated in the quaint village of Brandon only 3 miles from the historical city of Durham. The Inn offers comfortable and friendly accommodation for the business person or the holiday maker. Nearby attractions include countryside walks, cathedral, museums and castles.

Chester-le-Street

NZ2751 🍴 *Chester Moor*

Waldridge Fell Guest House, Waldridge Lane, Waldridge, Chester-le-Street, Co Durham, *DH2 3RY.* Three minutes from Chester-le-Street Centre. Panoramic views. Friendly, relaxed atmosphere. **Open:** All year (not Xmas/New Year) **Grades:** ETC 4 Diamond, AA 4 Diamond **0191 389 1908** Mrs Sharratt *bbchesterlestreet@ btinternet.com* www.smoothhound.co. uk/hotels/waldridgefell.html **D:** £23.00– £24.00 **S:** £27.00–£28.00 **Beds:** 3F 2D 1S **Baths:** 6 En ⅖ 🖫 (8) ⅍ ☑ 🎇 ₴

Hollycroft, 11 The Parade, Chester-le-street, County Durham, *DH3 3LR.* Ideally located: A1(m), Country cricket, Beamish museum, Lumley Castle, Durham. **Open:** All year (not Xmas/New Year) **0191 388 7088 & 07932 675069 (M)** Mr Cutter *cutter@hollycroft11.freeserve.co.uk* **D:** £22.50 **S:** £27.00 **Beds:** 1T 2D 🖫 (2) ⅍ ☑ ☑ 🎇 ₴

Cornforth

NZ3134 🍴 *Poacher's Pocket*

Ash House, 24 The Green, Cornforth, Co Durham, *DL17 9JH.* On village green, tastefully decorated, carved four-posters, adjacent A1M (motorway). **Open:** All year (not Xmas/New Year) **01740 654654 & 07711 133574 (M)** Mrs Slack *delden@easicom.com* **D:** £20.00–£22.50 **S:** £25.00–£30.00 **Beds:** 1F 1T 1D ⅖ 🖫 ⅍ ☑ 🛏 ☑ 🎇 ₴

Cowshill

NY8540

Low Cornriggs Farm, Cowshill, Bishop Auckland, Co Durham, *DL13 1AQ.* Magnificent views, excellent location, quality accommodation, good farmhouse breakfast. Riding school. **Open:** All year **Grades:** AA 4 Diamond **01388 537600** Mrs Elliott **Fax: 01388 537777** *enquiries@lowcornriggsfarm.fsnet.co.uk* britnett.com/lowcornriggsfarm **D:** £22.00 **S:** £28.00–£30.00 **Beds:** 1T 2D **Baths:** 4 Pr ⅖ (5) 🖫 (6) ☑ 🛏 ✕ ☑ 🎇 ₴ cc

---

B&B owners may vary rates – be sure to check when booking

Planning a longer stay? Always ask for any special rates

Craghead

NZ2151

The Punch Bowl, Craghead, Stanley, *County Durham, DH9 6EF.* Village public house. Near Beamish Museum and Durham City. **Open:** All year (not Xmas/ New Year) **Grades:** ETC 2 Diamond **01207 232917 D:** £15.00–£20.00 **S:** £15.00– £20.00 **Beds:** 1T 1D **Baths:** 1 Sh ⌂ 🄿 (15) ⊬ 🅥 ✕ 🅥 🕮. ☀

Darlington

NZ2814

Aberlady Guest Hotel, 51 Corporation Road, Darlington, Co Durham, DL3 6AD. Victorian house close to town centre, Railway Museum, cinema and restaurants. **Open:** All year (not Xmas) **01325 461449** Mrs Chaplin **D:** £15.00–£20.00 **S:** £15.00–£20.00 **Beds:** 2F 3T 2S **Baths:** 2 Sh ⌂ 🄿 (2) 🅥 ♁ 🅥 🕮. ☀

Balmoral Guest House, 63 Woodland Road, Darlington, Co Durham, DL3 7BQ. Victorian Town house with individually decorated bedrooms close to centre. **Open:** All year (not Xmas/New Year) **01325 461908** Mr Hawke **D:** £18.00–£23.00 **S:** £22.00–£35.00 **Beds:** 3F 1D 1T 4S **Baths:** 4 Pr 2 Sh ⌂ ⊬ 🅥 🕮. ☀

Durham

NZ2742

The Anchorage, 25 Langley Road, Newton Hall, Durham, DH15LR. Spacious, detached, comfortable family-run home in historic city. Wonderful breakfasts. **Open:** All year **Grades:** ETC 3 Diamond **0191 386 2323 (also fax)** S E Percival *anchorageb@aol.com* **D:** £22.50 **S:** £25.00 **Beds:** 1F 1T **Baths:** 1 En 1 Pr ⌂ 🄿 (2) ⊬ 🅥 🕮. ✻ ☀

14 Gilesgate, Durham, DH1 1QW. Central, spacious C18th town house with four-poster beds and antiques. **Open:** All year (not Xmas/New Year) **Grades:** ETC 2 Diamond **0191 384 6485** Mr Nimmins **Fax: 0191 386 5173** *bb@nimmins.co.uk* www.nimmins.co.uk **D:** £20.00 **S:** £20.00 **Beds:** 1F 1D 1T 1S **Baths:** 2 Sh ⌂ 🄿 (1) 🅥 ♁ 🅥 🕮. ☀

The Pink House, 16 Gilesgate, Durham, DH1 1QW. Small Georgian house. Homely, central. **Open:** All year **0191 386 7039** Mrs Miles **D:** £16.00 **S:** £20.00 **Beds:** 1F 1D **Baths:** 1 Sh ⌂ 🄿 🅥 ♁ 🅥 🕮. ♿ ☀

Castle View Guest House, 4 Crossgate, Durham, DH1 4PS. City centre Georgian guest house, close to castle and cathedral. **Open:** All year (not Xmas) **0191 386 8852 (also fax)** Mrs Williams *castle_view@hotmail.com* **D:** £29.00 **S:** £45.00 **Beds:** 3D 2T 1S **Baths:** 6 En ⌂ (2) ⊬ 🅥 🅥 🕮. ☀ cc

Green Grove, 99 Gilesgate, Durham, DH1 1JA. Large Victorian town house 12 min walk from city centre. **Open:** All year (not Xmas) **0191 384 4361** Mr Dockery *bill-dockery@ guesthouse.fsnet.co.uk* **D:** £20.00–£35.00 **S:** £20.00–£35.00 **Beds:** 1F 2D 2T 2S **Baths:** 4 En 1 Sh ⌂ 🄿 (8) 🅥 🅥 🕮. ☀

Hillrise Guest House, 13 Durham Road West, Bowburn, Durham, DH6 5AU. Recommended standard of accommodation in large ensuite rooms. **Open:** All year **Grades:** AA 4 Diamond **0191 377 0302** G B Webster **Fax: 0191 377 0898** *hillrise.guesthouse@btinternet.com* www.hill-rise.com **D:** £25.00 **S:** £30.00 **Beds:** 3F 2D **Baths:** 5 En ⌂ 🄿 (4) ⊬ 🅥 🕮. cc

26 St Johns Road, Nevilles Cross, Durham, DH1 4NU. Late Victorian house. Good food, friendly welcome, quiet residential area. **Open:** All year (not Xmas) **0191 384 8329** Mrs Burton **D:** £18.00 **S:** £21.00 **Beds:** 1D 1T **Baths:** 1 Sh 🅥 🅥 🕮. ☀

Queens Head Hotel, 2-6 Sherburn Road, Gilesgate Moor, Durham, DH1 2JR. Comfortable, clean, friendly. Full breakfast. English, Cantonese food. 2 minutes A1. **Open:** All year **0191 386 5649** P Collins **Fax: 0191 386 7451 D:** £17.50–£27.50 **S:** £22.00 **Beds:** 2F 1D 2T 2S **Baths:** 2 Sh ⌂ 🄿 (7) 🅥 ✕ 🅥 🕮. ☀ cc

The Gilesgate Moor Hotel, Teasdale Terrace, Gilesgate, Durham, DH1 2RN. Friendly family run pub offering attractive high quality accommodation. **Open:** All year (not Xmas) **0191 386 6453** R Sutton **D:** £18.00 **S:** £18.00 **Beds:** 1F 5T 1S **Baths:** 3 En 2 Sh ⌂ 🄿 (7) 🅥 ♁ 🕮. ☀

9 Leazes Place, Claypath, Durham, DH1 1RE. Situated in charming period cul-de-sac. Short walk from market place. **Open:** Easter to Oct **0191 386 8479** Miss Thomas **D:** £15.00 **S:** £15.00 **Beds:** 2T **Baths:** 1 Sh ⌂ (3) 🄿 (1) ⊬ 🅥 🅥 🕮. ☀

BEDROOMS
D = Double
T = Twin
S = Single
F = Family

Eastgate

NY9539

Rose Hill Farm, Eastgate, Bishop Auckland, County Durham, DL13 2LB. **Open:** All year **Grades:** ETC 4 Diamond **01388 517209 & 07808 402425 (M)** Ms Wearmouth **Fax: 01388 517209** *june@ rosehillfarm.fsnet.co.uk* www.rosehillfarmholidays.co.uk **D:** £22.50– £25.00 **S:** £30.00 **Beds:** 2F 1T 2D **Baths:** 5 En ⌂ 🄿 (5) ⊬ 🅥 🅥 🕮. ☀ Spacious barn conversion on working hill farm offering a warm welcome together with a high standard of accommodation. Panoramic views of Weardale from the large enclosed garden. Ideal base for visiting Durham, Beamish, Hexham, Barnard Castle. Ground floor rooms available.

Eggleston

NZ0023

Moorcock Inn, Hill Top, Gordon Bank, Eggleston, Co Durham, DL12 0AU. Country inn with scenic views over Teesdale ideal for walking. Cosy ensuite bedrooms. **Open:** All year **01833 650395** Mr & Mrs Zacharias **Fax: 01833 650052 D:** £32.00–£37.00 **S:** £20.00– £25.00 **Beds:** 6D 6S **Baths:** 4 En 3 Sh ⌂ 🄿 (30) ⊬ 🅥 ♁ ✕ 🅥 🕮. ☀ cc

Ferryhill

NZ2832

Elm Garth, Mainsforth, Ferryhill, Co Durham, DL17 9AA. Fine accommodation in superb countryside. C17th house, very quiet location. Brochure available. **Open:** All year (not Xmas) **01740 652676** Mr & Mrs Dobbing *elmgarth_bedandbreakfast@yahoo.com* www.elmgarth.ntb.org.uk **D:** £18.00–£20.00 **S:** £20.00–£22.00 **Beds:** 1F 1D **Baths:** 1 En 1 Pr ⌂ 🄿 (3) ⊬ 🅥 🕮. ☀

Frosterley

NZ0237

High Laithe, Hill End, Frosterley, Bishop Auckland, County Durham, DL13 2SX. Small working farm. Peacefully situated. Splendid views. Ideal touring, walking. **Open:** All year (not Xmas) **01388 526421** Mr Moss **D:** £18.00 **S:** £18.00 **Beds:** 1D 1S **Baths:** 1 Pr ⌂ (5) 🄿 (2) ⊬ 🅥 ♁ ✕ 🕮. ☀

Gainford

NZ1617

Queens Head Hotel, 11 Main Road, Gainford, Darlington, DL2 3DZ. Inn/restaurant/bar meals. A67 between Darlington and Barnard Castle. **Open:** All year
01325 730958 Mrs Batty **D:** £22.50 **S:** £35.00 **Beds:** 2F 1T 2D **Baths:** 5 En ⛥🅿(30)🅲🅗✕ 🆅▦🟊 cc

Green Head

NZ1434   *The Victoria, Duke of York, Helm Park, Fir Tree*

Greenhead Country Caravan Park, Fir Tree, Crook, Co Durham, DL15 8BL. Private hotel with all en-suite bedrooms restricted to resident guests. **Open:** All year
Grades: AA 4 Diamond, Sparkling, RAC 4 Diamond
01388 763143 (also fax) Mr Birkbeck *info@ thegreenheadhotel.co.uk*
www.thegreenheadhotel.co.uk **D:** £30.00–£35.00 **S:** £45.00–£55.00 **Beds:** 2T 4D 2S **Baths:** 8 En ⛥(14) 🅿✕🆅▦🟊 cc

Harperley

NZ1753

Bushblades Farm, Harperley, Stanley, County Durham, DH9 9UA. Georgian farmhouse, rural setting. Close Beamish Museum and Durham City. **Open:** All year (not Xmas) **Grades:** ETC 3 Diamond
01207 232722 Mrs Gibson **D:** £18.50–£21.00 **S:** £25.00–£30.00 **Beds:** 2D 1T **Baths:** 1 En 2 Sh ⛥(12) 🅿(4)🆅▦🟊🟊

Haswell Plough

NZ3742

The Gables Hotel, Haswell Plough, Durham, DH6 2EW. Small family run hotel 5 miles east of Durham city on the B1283. **Open:** All year
0191 526 2982 (also fax) Mr Milner *johngables@aol.com* www.powow. com/thegables/index.htm. **D:** £17.50–£28.00 **S:** £19.00–£30.00 **Beds:** 1F 2D 2T **Baths:** 2 Sh 3 En ⛥🅿(30)✕🅲▦🟊🟊🟊

Holwick

NY9027

The Strathmore Arms, Holwick, Middleton-in-Teesdale, Barnard Castle, Co Durham, DL12 0NJ. Idyllic C17th Teesdale Inn, near High Force Waterfalls on the Pennine Way. **Open:** All year
01833 640362 (also fax) *hojo@supanet.com*
D: £22.50–£25.00 **S:** £30.00–£35.00 **Beds:** 1F 1T 2D **Baths:** 4 En ⛥🅿✕🅲🅗✕🆅▦🟊

Kirk Merrington

NZ2631

Highview Country House, Kirk Merrington, Spennymoor, DL16 7JT. Set in one acre panoramic countryside, good pubs, safe parking, peaceful. **Open:** All year
01388 811006 (also fax) *highview house@ genie.co.uk* **D:** £23.00 **S:** £25.00 **Beds:** 1F 1T 4D 1S **Baths:** 7 En ⛥🅿✕🅲🅗✕🆅▦🟊🟊

Lunedale

NY9221

Wemmergill Hall Farm, Lunedale, Middleton in Teesdale, Barnard Castle, County Durham, DL12 0PA. Traditional farmhouse, views over moorland and reservoir. Walkers/ birdwatchers paradise! **Open:** Jan to Nov
01833 640379 (also fax) Mrs Stoddart **D:** £18.00–£20.00 **S:** £20.00–£25.00 **Beds:** 1F 1D ⛥(4) 🅿(2)✕✕🟊

Mickleton

NY9623

Pine Grove, Lowside, Mickleton, Barnard Castle, Co Durham, DL12 0JQ. Situated on quiet back road with fine views of Teesdale. **Open:** All year (not Xmas)
01833 640886 Mr & Mrs Gillings *chris@ cgillings.freeserve.co.uk* **D:** £16.00–£18.00 **S:** £17.00–£19.00 **Beds:** 1F 1D 1T **Baths:** 1 Sh ⛥🅿(4)✕🅲🅗✕🆅▦🟊

Middleton in Teesdale

NY9425   *Teesdale Hotel*

Brunswick House, 55 Market Place, Middleton in Teesdale, Barnard Castle, Co Durham, DL12 0QH. Charming C18th guest house, excellent food. Many beautiful walks. **Open:** All year
01833 640393 (also fax) Mr & Mrs Milnes *enquiries@brunswickhouse.net*
www.brunswickhouse.net **D:** £20.00–£24.00 **S:** £24.00–£32.00 **Beds:** 3D 2T **Baths:** 5 En ⛥🅿(5)✕🅲✕🆅▦🟊 cc

Belvedere House, 54 Market Place, Middleton-in-Teesdale, Barnard Castle, Co Durham, DL12 0QA. Enjoy a warm welcome, English breakfast and explore Teesdale's beautiful countryside. **Open:** All year
Grades: ETC 4 Diamond
01833 640884 (also fax) Mrs Finn *belvedere@ thecoachhouse.net* www.thecoachhouse.net
D: £17.00 **S:** £18.00 **Beds:** 1T 2D **Baths:** 3 En ⛥🅿(3)✕🅲🅗✕🆅▦🟊

Ivy House, Stanhope Road, Middleton in Teesdale, Barnard Castle, Co Durham, DL12 0RT. Victorian house overlooking lovely countryside. Friendly welcome to all guests. **Open:** Apr to Oct **Grades:** ETC 3 Diamond
01833 640603 M Ebdon **D:** £17.00–£18.00 **S:** £18.00–£20.00 **Beds:** 1T 1D **Baths:** 1 En 1 Pr ⛥(5) 🅿(2)🆅▦🟊

Planning a longer stay? Always ask for any special rates

Bluebell House, Market Place, Middleton in Teesdale, Barnard Castle, Co Durham, DL12 0GG. Former inn, beautiful walks, good food, friendly family atmosphere guaranteed. **Open:** All year (not Xmas)
01833 640584 Ms Northey **D:** £16.00–£17.00 **S:** £21.00–£25.00 **Beds:** 2D 2T **Baths:** 3 En 1 Pr ⛥🅿(2)✕🅲🅗✕🆅▦🟊

Newfield

NZ2452

Malling House, 1 Oakdale Terrace, Newfield, Chester-le-Street, County Durham, DH2 2SU. Heather, your host, has extensive knowledge of area and attractions. **Open:** All year
0191 370 2571 Ms Rippon **Fax:** 0191 370 1391
www.mallingguesthouse.freeserve.co.uk
D: £36.00–£46.00 **S:** £20.00–£26.00 **Beds:** 1F 1T 1S ⛥🅿(3)🅲🆅▦🟊

Piercebridge

NZ2015

Holme House, Piercebridge, Darlington, Co Durham, DL2 3SY. Attractive C18th farmhouse surrounded by beautiful countryside, spacious comfortable accommodation. **Open:** All year (not Xmas) **Grades:** ETC 3 Diamond
01325 374280 (also fax) Mrs Graham *graham@holmehouse22.freeserve.co.uk*
D: £22.50–£25.00 **S:** £22.50–£30.00 **Beds:** 1F 1T **Baths:** 2 En ⛥🅿(4)🅲🆅▦🟊

Plawsworth

NZ2647

Lilac Cottage, Wheatley Well Lane, Plawsworth, Chester-le-Street, Co Durham, DH2 3LD. Stone built Georgian cottage just off A167. Very conveniently situated for Durham city. **Open:** All year (not Xmas)
0191 371 2969 Mrs Prizeman **D:** £17.50
S: £17.50 **Beds:** 1D 1T 1S **Baths:** 2 Sh 🅿(2)✕🅲🆅▦🟊

Rushyford

NZ2829

Garden House, Windlestone Park, Windlestone, Rushyford, Ferryhill, County Durham, DL17 0LZ. House with stunning walled garden. Haven of peace and tranquillity. **Open:** All year
01388 720217 & 07979 297374 (M) Ms Cattell
D: £20.00–£22.00 **S:** £25.00–£28.00 **Beds:** 1T 2D **Baths:** 2 En 1 Pr ⛥🅿✕🅲✕🆅▦🟊

Shildon

NZ2227

101 Main Street, *Shildon, Co Durham, DL4 1AW.* 8 miles from A1(m). Ample parking. Georgian mid terrace. **Open:** All year (not Xmas/New Year)
01388 772646 Mr Walton **D:** £17.00 **S:** £17.00
Beds: 1F 1T 1D ⌛ 🅿 (18) 📺 ▥ ♠

Shotley Bridge

NZ0852

Crown & Crossed Swords Hotel, *Shotley Bridge, Consett, Co Durham, DH8 0NH.* Historic country hotel. Meals all day 12-9.30 Mon-Sat. Sunday lunch 12-3. **Open:** All year
01207 502006 Mrs Suddick **D:** £18.00–£23.00 **S:** £20.00–£25.00 **Beds:** 2F 4D 3T 1S
Baths: 4 En 2 Sh ⌛ 🅿 (40) 📺 ♔ ✕ ▥ ♠ cc

Spennymoor

NZ2533 🎵 *Bobby Shaftoes, Top House*

The Gables, *10 South View, Middlestone Moor, Spennymoor, Co Durham, DL16 7DF.* Ideal touring base for North East. Ground floor ensuite rooms. **Open:** All year (not Xmas/New Year) **Grades:** ETC 3 Diamond
01388 817544 V Atkinson **Fax: 01388 812533**
thegablesghouse@aol.com www.thegables.ntb. org.uk **D:** £19.00–£22.50 **S:** £20.00–£45.00
Beds: 4T 2D 1S **Baths:** 3 En 1 Sh ⌛ 🅿 (6) ⌖ 📺 ♔ ▥ ♠ cc

Idsley House, *4 Green Lane, Spennymoor, Co Durham, DL16 6HD.* Warm welcome assured. Local knowledge. Close to Durham A167/A688 Junction. **Open:** All year **Grades:** ETC 4 Diamond
01833 814237 Mrs Dartnall **D:** £24.00 **S:** £35.00–£38.00 **Beds:** 1F 2D 2T 1S
Baths: 4 En 1 Pr ⌛ (5) 🅿 (8) ⌖ 📺 ♔ ▥ ♠ cc

Staindrop

NZ1220

Malvern House, *7 Front Street, Staindrop, Darlington, Co Durham, DL2 3LZ.* Georgian town house, overlooking the green in conservation village. **Open:** All year
01833 660846 Mrs Young **D:** £18.00 **S:** £18.00
Beds: 2T **Baths:** 1 Sh ⌛ 📺 ♔ ▥ ♠

Stanley

NZ1952

Bushblades Farm, *Harperley, Stanley, County Durham, DH9 9UA.* Georgian farmhouse, rural setting. Close Beamish Museum and Durham City. **Open:** All year (not Xmas) **Grades:** ETC 3 Diamond
01207 232722 Mrs Gibson **D:** £18.50–£21.00 **S:** £25.00–£30.00 **Beds:** 2D 1T **Baths:** 1 En 2 Sh ⌛ (12) 🅿 (4) 📺 ▥ ♿ ♠

Waldridge

NZ2550

Waldridge Fell Guest House, *Waldridge Lane, Waldridge, Chester-le-Street, Co Durham, DH2 3RY.* Three minutes from Chester-le-Street Centre. Panoramic views. Friendly, relaxed atmosphere. **Open:** All year (not Xmas/New Year) **Grades:** ETC 4 Diamond, AA 4 Diamond
0191 389 1908 Mrs Sharratt *bbchesterlestreet@ btinternet.com* www.smoothhound.co. uk/hotels/waldridgefell.html **D:** £23.00– £24.00 **S:** £27.00–£28.00 **Beds:** 3F 2D 1S
Baths: 6 En ⌛ 🅿 (8) ⌖ 📺 ▥ ♠

West Auckland

NZ1726

Country Style, *Etherley Bank, West Auckland, Bishop Auckland, Co Durham, DL14 0LG.* All rooms are ground floor, each with separate entry from off-road car park. **Open:** All year
01388 832679 Ms Walton **D:** £18.50–£20.00 **S:** £20.00–£22.00 **Beds:** 1F 1D 1T 1S
Baths: 4 En ⌛ (1) 🅿 (8) 📺 ♔ ♠

Westgate in Weardale

NY9038 🎵 *Hare & Hounds, Cross Keys*

Lands Farm, *Westgate in Weardale, Bishop Auckland, Co Durham, DL13 1SN.* Peaceful location, ideal for exploring Durham and the Pennines. **Open:** All year **Grades:** ETC 4 Diamond, Silver
01388 517210 Mrs Reed **D:** £22.50–£23.00 **S:** £27.00 **Beds:** 1F 1D **Baths:** 2 En ⌛ 🅿 (4) 📺 📺 ▥

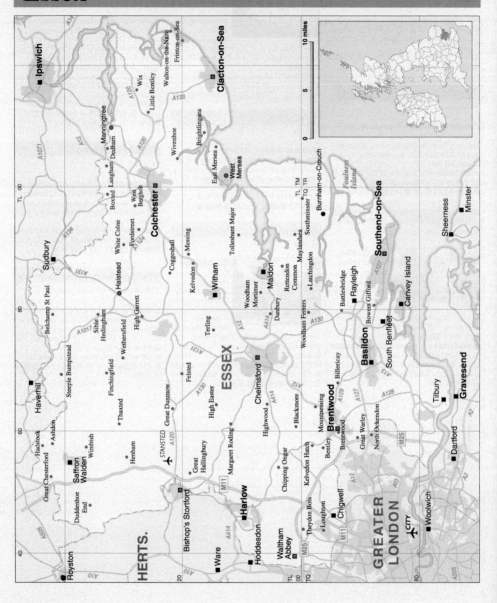

Ashdon

TL5842

Cobblers, *Bartow Road, Ashdon, Saffron Walden, Essex, CB10 2HR.* Peaceful place, warm welcome, relaxing rooms, bountiful breakfasts, great garden! **Open:** All year (not Xmas)
01799 584666 Mrs Slater *cobblers@ashdon2000.freeserve.co.uk* **D:** £20.00 **S:** £20.00–£25.00 **Beds:** 2D **Baths:** 1 En 1 Pr (3) (4)

Battlesbridge

TQ7794

The Cottages Guest House, *Beeches Road, Battlesbridge, Wickford, Essex, SS11 8TJ.* Rural, cosy, licensed guest house. Easy reach Southend, Chelmsford, Basildon. Licensed bar. **Open:** All year (not Xmas)
01702 232105 Miss Carr *cottages2000@totalise.co.uk* www.yell.co.uk/sites/cottages-guest-house/ **D:** £20.00–£25.00 **S:** £20.00–£29.00 **Beds:** 3D 3T 1S **Baths:** 2 En 1 Sh (10)

Belchamp St Paul

TL7942

The Plough, *Belchamp St Paul, Sudbury, Suffolk, CO10 7BT.* Charming former pub. Peaceful village. Comfortable friendly atmosphere. Centrally located. **Open:** All year **Grades:** ETC 4 Diamond
01787 278882 Mrs Stormont *info@theplough-belchamp.co.uk* www.theplough-belchamp.co.uk **D:** £20.00–£25.00 **S:** £25.00–£35.00 **Beds:** 1T 1D **Baths:** 2 En (6) (6)

Bentley

TQ5696

The Coach House, *Mores Lane, Bentley, Brentwood, Essex, CM14 5PZ.* 200 year old coaching house in 1 acre grounds. **Open:** All year (not Xmas/New Year)
01277 375015 S Mead **Fax: 01277 372954** *sheilaghandroger@aol.com* **D:** £22.00–£25.00 **S:** £22.00–£25.00

Billericay

TQ6794 *Kings Head*

Badgers' Rest, *2 Mount View, Billericay, Essex, CM11 1HB.* 'Badgers Rest' is in a pleasant, select area of Billericay. **Open:** All year **Grades:** ETC 4 Diamond
01277 625384 & 07778 444169 (M) C J Parker **Fax: 01277 633912** **D:** £23.00–£25.00 **S:** £23.00–£25.00 **Beds:** 3S 1D **Baths:** 2 Sh 1 En (10) (6)

Blackmore

TL6001

Little Lampetts, *Hay Green Lane, Blackmore, Ingatestone, Essex, CM4 0QE.* Secluded period house. Easy access to M25 mainline stations towns. **Open:** All year
01277 822030 Mrs Porter *littlelampetts@hotmail.com* **D:** £22.50–£25.00 **S:** £25.00–£27.50 **Beds:** 2T **Baths:** 1 Pr (5)

Bowers Gifford

TQ7588

38 Kelly Road, *Bowers Gifford, Basildon, Essex, SS13 2HL.* Self contained apartment. Train to London 45 minutes. Country setting and views. **Open:** All year
01268 726701 Ms Jenkinson *patricia.jenkinson@tesco.net* **D:** £28.00–£40.00 **S:** £22.00–£25.00 **Beds:** 2D (8)

Boxted

TL9933

Round Hill House, *Parsonage Hill, Boxted, Colchester, Essex, CO4 5ST.* In Constable Country on the edge of the Dedham Vale. **Open:** All year
01206 272392 (also fax) Mrs Carter *jermar@appleonline.net* **D:** £22.50–£26.00 **S:** £30.00–£35.00 **Beds:** 1F 1D 1T **Baths:** 2 En 1 Pr (6)

Brentwood

TQ6093

77 Rose Valley, *Brentwood, Essex, CM14 4HJ.* Family run, recently refurbished. Close town centre/station. 25 mins London, 1m M25. **Open:** All year
01277 262713 Mr & Mrs Corbo **Fax: 01277 211146** **D:** £35.00–£40.00 **S:** £40.00–£60.00 **Beds:** 4F 2T 2D 1S **Baths:** 8 En 2 Pr cc

Brightlingsea

TM0817 *Cherry Tree, Red Lion*

Paxton Dene, *Church Road, Brightlingsea, Essex, CO7 0QT.* Attractive spacious cottage-style accommodation set in 1/2 acre grounds **Open:** All year
01206 304560 Mr & Mrs Reynolds **Fax: 01206 302877** *nora@paxtondene.freeserve.co.uk* **D:** £20.00–£22.50 **S:** £30.00–£40.00 **Beds:** 3F **Baths:** 3 Pr (4)

Chelmsford

TL7006 *Black Bull*

Aarandale, *9 Roxwell Road, Chelmsford, Essex, CM1 2LY.* Charming friendly B&B in large Victorian House, close town centre. **Open:** All year (not Xmas/New Year)
01245 251713 (also fax) M Perera *aarandaleuk@aol.com* **D:** £22.00 **S:** £25.00–£35.00 **Beds:** 1F 1T 4S **Baths:** 1 En 1 Pr 1 Sh (6)

Clacton-on-Sea

TM1715

The Hamelin Hotel, *20 Penfold Road, Clacton-on-Sea, Essex, CO15 1JN.* A Christian family-run hotel close to sea and shops. **Open:** All year (not Xmas)
01255 474456 Mrs Baker **Fax: 01255 428053** *healingch@aol.com* **D:** £16.00–£24.00 **S:** £20.00–£28.00 **Beds:** 3F 2D 2T 1S **Baths:** 3 En 1 Sh (3) cc

Coggeshall

TL8522

White Heather Guest House, *19 Colchester Road, Coggeshall, Colchester, Essex, CO6 1RP.* Modern, family-run guest house, overlooking farmland. **Open:** All year (not Xmas)
01376 563004 Mrs Shaw **D:** £22.00–£22.50 **S:** £22.00–£25.00 **Beds:** 2D 2S **Baths:** 2 En 1 Sh (8)

Colchester

TL9925 *Rovers Tye*

Salisbury Hotel, *112 Butt Road, Colchester, Essex, CO3 3DL.* **Open:** All year **Grades:** AA 3 Diamond
01206 508508 **Fax: 01206 797265** www.thesalisburyhotel.co.uk **D:** £25.00–£35.00 **S:** £30.00–£40.00 **Beds:** 2F 4T 3D 3S **Baths:** 12 En cc
Situated in the historical garrison town of Colchester and within easy reach of 3 cathedral cities. Despite being in the centre of town this pub has a relaxed and informal atmosphere. The in-house bar and restaurant serve delicious and innovative meals

BEDROOMS
D = Double
T = Twin
S = Single
F = Family

RATES

D = Price range per person sharing in a double or twin room

S = Price range for a single room

Globe Hotel, *71 North Station Road, Colchester, Essex, CO1 1RQ.* Close to main railway station, A12 and town centre. **Open:** All year **Grades:** ETC 2 Diamond
01206 502502 J Higgins **Fax: 01206 506506**
www.theglobehotel.co.uk **D:** £25.00–£30.00
S: £40.00 **Beds:** 4F 2T 3D 3S **Baths:** 12 En ♋
⊡ (18) 🅃 ✕ 🆅 🎟 💺 cc

Mill View House, *8 Guildford Road, Colchester, Essex, CO1 2YL.* Detached house convenient town, sports. Healthy breakfasts. Parking. Company rates. **Open:** All year
01206 512303 Ms Harris **Fax: 01206 870260**
appleblossom.harris@virgin.net **D:** £18.00–£20.00 **S:** £20.00–£24.00 **Beds:** 1D 1S
Baths: 2 En ⊡ (4) ⊱ 🅃 🆅 🎟 💺

St John's Guest House, *330 Ipswich Road, Colchester, Essex, CO4 4ET.* Well-situated close to town, convenient to A12 and A120 Harwich. **Open:** All year
01206 852288 E Knight **D:** £20.00–£30.00
S: £30.00–£50.00 **Beds:** 2F 2T 2D 1S
Baths: 6 En 1 Sh ♋ ⊡ ⊁ 🅃 🆅 🎟 💺

Danbury
TL7705

Southways, *Copt Hill, Danbury, Chelmsford, Essex, CM3 4NN.* House with large attractive garden adjoining National Trust common land. **Open:** All year
01245 223428 Mrs Deavin **D:** £19.00–£20.00
S: £20.00 **Beds:** 2T **Baths:** 1 Sh ♋ ⊡ (2) 🅃 🎟
🆅 🎟 💺

Wych Elm, *Mayers Lane, Danbury, Chelmsford, Essex, CM3 4NJ.* Welcoming, convenient central village location, quiet aspect. Extensive woods nearby **Open:** All year
01245 222674 Mrs Axon *aconwychelm@tinyworld.co.uk* **D:** £20.00–£23.00 **S:** £23.00–£26.00 **Beds:** 2T 1D 1S **Baths:** 1 En 1 Sh ⊡ (6)
⊁ 🅃 🎟 🆅 🎟 💺

Dedham
TM0533

Mays Barn Farm, *Mays Lane, Dedham, Colchester, Essex, CO7 6EW.* A Comfortable well-furnished old house with wonderful views of Dedham Vale. **Open:** All year **Grades:** ETC 4 Diamond
01206 323191 Mrs Freeman *maysbarn@talk21.com* www.mays.barn.btinternet.co.uk
D: £20.00–£23.00 **S:** £25.00–£30.00 **Beds:** 1D
1T **Baths:** 1 En 1 Pr ♋ (10) ⊡ (3) ⊁ 🅃 🆅 🎟 💺

Duddenhoe End
TL4636

Rockells Farm, *Duddenhoe End, Saffron Walden, Essex, CB11 4UY.* Georgian farmhouse with lake view. **Open:** All year (not Xmas/New Year)
01763 838053 Mrs Westerhuis **D:** £20.00–£25.00 **S:** £20.00–£25.00 **Beds:** 1F 1T 1S
Baths: 3 En ♋ ⊡ (4) 🅃 🎟 💺

East Mersea
TM0514

Bromans Farm, *East Mersea, Colchester, Essex, CO5 8UE.* Grade II Listed C14th farmhouse, 5 minutes from sea & 9 miles Colchester. **Open:** All year **Grades:** ETC 4 Diamond
01206 383235 (also fax) Mrs Dence
D: £20.00–£25.00 **S:** £25.00–£30.00 **Beds:** 1D
1T 1S **Baths:** 2 Pr ♋ ⊡ (3) 🅃 🎟 🆅 🎟 💺

Felsted
TL6720

Yarrow, *Felsted, Great Dunmow, Essex, CM6 3HD.* Please see website www.yarrow.ic24.net. **Open:** All year
01371 820878 (also fax) Mr & Mrs Bellingham Smith *yarrow@ic24.net*
www.yarrow.ic24.net **D:** £18.00 **S:** £19.00
Beds: 1D 1T 1S **Baths:** 1 En 1 Sh ♋ ⊡ (6) ⊁
🅃 🎟 💺

BEDROOMS
D = Double
T = Twin
S = Single
F = Family

Fordstreet
TL9226

Old House, *Fordstreet, Aldham, Colchester, Essex, CO6 3PH.* Fascinating Grade II Listed C14th hall house - oak beams, log fires, large garden. **Open:** All year **Grades:** ETC 3 Diamond
01206 240456 (also fax) Mrs Mitchell
D: £22.50–£27.50 **S:** £27.50–£35.00 **Beds:** 1F
1T 1S **Baths:** 1 En 2 Pr ♋ ⊡ (6) 🅃 🎟 💺 cc

Frinton-on-Sea
TM2318

Russell Lodge, *47 Hadleigh Road, Frinton-on-Sea, Essex, CO13 9HQ.* Home comfort and Edwardian elegance near seafront and town centre.
Open: All year
01255 675935 J M Russell
www.russell-lodgefsnet.co.uk **D:** £20.00
S: £20.00 **Beds:** 1T 1D 1S **Baths:** 1 En 1 Sh
♋ ⊡ ⊁ 🅃 🎟 🐾 🎟 💺

Uplands Guest House, *41 Hadleigh Road, Frinton-on-Sea, Essex, CO13 9HQ.* Quiet and comfortable. Just three minutes sea, shops. Ample parking. **Open:** All year (not Xmas) **Grades:** ETC 3 Diamond, AA 3 Diamond
01255 674889 Mrs Fitzgerald **D:** £22.00–£28.00 **S:** £22.00–£28.00 **Beds:** 1D 3S 2T
Baths: 4 En 2 Sh ⊡ (5) ⊁ 🎟 💺

Great Chesterford
TL5042

White Gates, *School Street, Great Chesterford, Saffron Walden, Essex, CB10 1PH.* C18th timber framed cottage in heart of historic village. **Open:** All year
01799 530249 Mrs Mortimer **D:** £19.00–£25.00 **S:** £23.00–£25.00 **Beds:** 1F 1T 1S
Baths: 1 En 1 Sh ♋ ⊡ (3) ⊁ 🅃 🎟 💺

Great Dunmow
TL6221

Homelye Farm, *Homelye Chase, Braintree Road, Great Dunmow, Essex, CM6 3AW.* Good quality motel-style accommodation close to Stansted Airport. **Open:** All year **Grades:** ETC 4 Diamond, AA 4 Diamond
01371 872127 Mrs Pickford **Fax: 01371 876428** *homelye@supanet.com*
www.homelyefarm.co.uk **D:** £25.00 **S:** £30.00
Beds: 1F 3D 2T 3S **Baths:** 9 En ♋ ⊡ (9) ⊁ 🅃
🎟 💺 cc

RATES

D = Price range per person sharing in a double or twin room

S = Price range for a single room

Great Hallingbury

TL5019

Yew Tree Farmhouse, *Tilekiln Green, Great Hallingbury, Bishops Stortford, Herts, CM22 7TQ.* Family-run C17th farmhouse in 2 acres, close M11 & Stansted Airport. **Open:** All year (not Xmas) **01279 758875 (also fax) D:** £27.50–£45.00 **S:** £45.00–£65.00 **Beds:** 1F 1D 1T 1S **Baths:** 4 Pr ⛱ (5) 🅿 (10) ⊬ 📺 📹 🕮 ♨

Great Warley

TQ5890 🍺 *Thatcher's Arms*

Chestnut Tree Cottage, *Great Warley Street, Great Warley, Brentwood, Essex, CM13 3JF.* Attractive country cottage. Conveniently located M25, A127, A12. 1 mile to London. **Open:** All year **Grades:** ETC 3 Diamond **01277 221727** Mrs Malyon **D:** £25.00–£28.00 **S:** £25.00–£35.00 **Beds:** 1F 1T 1D **Baths:** 3 En ⛱ 🅿 (31) ⊬ 📺 📹 🕮 ♨

Hadstock

TL5544

Yardleys, *Orchard Pightle, Hadstock, Cambridge, CB1 6PQ.* Peace and quiet in pretty village only 20 mins Cambridge, 10 mins Saffron Walden. **Open:** All year (not Xmas/New Year) **01223 891822 (also fax)** Mrs Ludgate *yardleys@waitrose.com* **D:** £22.00–£25.00 **S:** £25.00–£32.00 **Beds:** 2T 1D **Baths:** 1 En 2 Pr ⛱ 🅿 (5) ⊬ 📺 × 📹 🕮 ♨ cc

Halstead

TL8130

Mill House, *The Causeway, Halstead, Essex, CO9 1ET.* Listed town house in the market town, private parking, Brochure available. **Open:** All year (not Xmas) **01787 474451** Mr & Mrs Stuckey **Fax: 01787 473893** *stuckey@townsford.freeserve.co.uk* **D:** £24.00–£25.00 **S:** £30.00–£48.00 ⛱ (12) 🅿 (18) ⊬ 📺 📹 🕮 ♨ cc

Please respect a B&B's wishes regarding children, animals and smoking

Henham

TL5428

Pleasant Cottage, *Woodend Green, Henham, Bishops Stortford, Essex, CM22 6AZ.* **Open:** All year **Grades:** ETC 4 Diamond **01279 850792 (also fax)** Mr & Mrs Griffiths **D:** £25.00–£30.00 **S:** £34.00–£38.00 **Beds:** 1T 2D **Baths:** 3 En ⛱ (10) ⊬ 📺 📹 🕮 ♨
Grade II listed thatched cottage on village green, excellent accommodation with warm welcome. Well positioned for Cambridge, London and Stansted Airport only 5 miles. Plus charming countryside with many delightful villages and market towns of Thaxted and Saffron Walden.

Roblin, *Carters Lane, Henham, Bishop's Stortford, Herts, CM22 6AQ.* Family home, picturesque village. 4 miles Stansted Airport, M11 **Open:** Apr to Oct **01279 850370 (also fax)** Mrs Burgess **D:** £20.00 **S:** £22.50 **Beds:** 1D 1T **Baths:** 1 Sh ⛱ (8) ⊬ 📺 🕮 ♨

High Easter

TL6214

The Cock & Bell, *The Street, High Easter, Chelmsford, Essex, CM1 4QW.* C14th former coaching inn, operating as charming Guest House. **Open:** All year (not Xmas/New Year) **01245 231296** A Steel **D:** £19.50–£24.50 **S:** £22.50–£27.50 **Beds:** 2D 1F 1S **Baths:** 2 En 1 Sh 🅿 📹 × 📹 🕮 ♨

High Garrett

TL7726

Hare & Hounds, *High Garrett, Braintree, Essex, CM7 5NT.* A friendly welcome and hearty breakfast awaits all that stay. **Open:** All year **01376 324430** J Bowyer **D:** £22.00–£50.00 **S:** £22.00–£50.00 **Beds:** 1F 1D 2T 1S **Baths:** 3 En 1 Sh ⛱ 🅿 (20) 📺 🕮 × 📹 ♨ cc

Highwood

TL6404

Wards Farm, *Loves Green, Highwood Road, Highwood, Chelmsford, Essex, CM1 3QJ.* Traditional oak beamed C16th farmhouse, moated grounds, log fires. **Open:** Mar to Dec **01245 248812** Mrs Barton **D:** £22.50 **S:** £23.00–£25.00 **Beds:** 1T 1D ⛱ (101) 🅿 (8) 📺 × 📹 🕮 ♨

Kelvedon

TL8518

Highfields Farm, *Kelvedon, Colchester, Essex, CO5 9BJ.* Farmhouse in quiet countryside location, convenient for A12 and London. **Open:** All year **Grades:** ETC 3 Diamond **01376 570334 (also fax)** Mrs Bunting *highfieldsfarm@farmersweekly.net* **D:** £20.00 **S:** £24.00–£26.00 **Beds:** 1D 2T **Baths:** 2 En 1 Pr ⛱ 🅿 (4) ⊬ 📺 🕆 📹 🕮 ♨

Kelvedon Hatch

TQ5799

57 Great Fox Meadow, *Kelvedon Hatch, Brentwood, Essex, CM15 0AX.* Homely, friendly, clean, comfortable. Overlooking farmlands. 4 miles from Brentwood and Ongar. **Open:** All year (not Xmas) **01277 37465** Mrs Maguire **D:** £16.00–£21.00 **S:** £16.00–£21.00 **Beds:** 1D 1S **Baths:** 1 Sh ⛱ (3) 🅿 (2) ⊬ 📺 🕮 ♨

Langham

TM0233

Oak Apple Farm, *Greyhound Hill, Langham, Colchester, Essex, CO4 5QF.* Comfortable farmhouse tastefully decorated with large attractive garden. **Open:** All year (not Xmas) **01206 272234** Mrs Helliwell *rosie@oakapplefarm.fsnet.co.uk* **D:** £22.00 **S:** £22.00 **Beds:** 2T 1S **Baths:** 1 Sh ⛱ 🅿 (6) 📺 🕮 ♨

Latchingdon

TL8800

Neptune Cafe Motel, *Burnham Road, Latchingdon, Chelmsford, Essex, CM3 6EX.* **Open:** All year **Grades:** ETC 2 Diamond **01621 740770** Mr Lloyd **D:** £17.50 **S:** £25.00 **Beds:** 4F 4D 2T 10S **Baths:** 10 En 2 Pr 1 Sh ⛱ 🅿 (40) ⊬ 📺 🕆 📹 🕮 ♨1 ♨
Cafe motel, luxury chalets adjoining. Close to boating and fishing areas, golfing and horse riding close by. Lovely rural setting with grand views.

Planning a longer stay? Always ask for any special rates

Little Bentley

TM1125

Bentley Manor, *Little Bentley, Colchester, Essex, CO7 8SE.* C15th manor house, close to Colchester, 15 mins port of Harwich. **Open:** All year
01206 250622 Mrs Dyson **Fax: 01206 251820** *ngd@freenet.co.uk* www.dysontextiles. com/bentleymanor.html **D:** £20.00–£22.00 **S:** £24.00–£26.00 **Beds:** 1F 1S 1T **Baths:** 2 En ⛺ 🏠 ⊬ 🏧 ▥ 🛁

Loughton

TQ4396

Forest Edge, *61 York Hill, Loughton, Essex, IG10 1HZ.* Quiet location. Off-street parking. Convenient for Central Line. **Open:** All year (not Xmas/New Year)
020 8508 9834 E Catterall **Fax: 020 8281 1894** *arthur@catterallarthur.fsnet.co.uk* **D:** £19.00–£20.00 **S:** £22.25–£25.00 **Beds:** 2T 1S

Manningtree

TM1031

Dairy House Farm, *Bradfield Road, Wix, Manningtree, Essex, CO11 2SR.* Spacious, quality, rural accommodation. A really relaxing place to stay. **Open:** All year (not Xmas) **Grades:** ETC 5 Diamond, Silver **01255 870322** Mrs Whitworth **Fax: 01255 870186** *bridgetwhitworth@hotmail.com* **D:** £20.00–£22.00 **S:** £26.00–£28.00 **Beds:** 1D 1T **Baths:** 2 En ⛺ (12) 🏧 (4) ▥ 🏧 ▥ 🛁

Margaret Roding

TL5912

Greys, *Ongar Road, Margaret Roding, Great Dunmow, Essex, CM6 1QR.* Old beamed cottage, surrounded by our farmland, tiny village. Good B&B. **Open:** All year (not Xmas) **Grades:** ETC 3 Diamond, AA 3 Diamond
01245 231509 Mrs Matthews **D:** £22.50 **S:** £25.00 **Beds:** 2D 1T **Baths:** 1 Sh 🏧 (3) ⊬ ▥ 🏧

Maylandsea

TL9002

25 West Avenue, *Maylandsea, Chelmsford, Essex, CM3 6AE.* Modern detached private residence, country views, few minutes to sailing facilities. **Open:** All year (not Xmas/New Year)
01621 740972 Mrs Clark **Fax: 01621 740945** **D:** £17.00–£19.00 **S:** £17.00–£19.00 **Beds:** 1D 1T **Baths:** 1 Pr 🏧 (5) ⊬ ▥ 🏧 🛁

Messing

TL8918

Crispin's, *The Street, Messing, Colchester, CO5 9TR.* Elizabethan building with garden in pretty village. Close to Constable country. **Open:** All year **Grades:** ETC 4 Diamond
01621 815868 **D:** £27.00 **S:** £35.00–£40.00 **Beds:** 2F 1T 2S **Baths:** 2 En ⛺ (5) ⊬ ▥ ✕ ▥ 🛁 ❄ 🛁 cc

North Ockendon

TQ5984 ⬛ *Old White Horse*

Corner Farm, *Fen Lane, North Ockendon, Upminster, Essex, RM14 3RB.* Detached bungalow in rural setting. 4 Miles Upminster station. Breakfast served in conservatory. **Open:** All year (not Xmas/New Year) **Grades:** ETC 3 Diamond
01708 851310 **Fax: 01708 852025** *corner.farm@virgin.net* **D:** £17.50–£18.75 **S:** £25.00–£35.00 **Beds:** 1F 1T 2S **Baths:** 1 En 1 Sh 🏧 (8) ⊬ ▥ 🏧 🛁 cc

Saffron Walden

TL5438

80 High Street, *Saffron Walden, Essex, CB10 1EE.* Excellent central location. Historic Saffron town. C18th Georgian town house. **Open:** All year
01799 516418 Mrs Brown **D:** £32.50–£40.00 **S:** £40.00–£60.00 **Beds:** 1D **Baths:** 1 Sh ⊬ ▥ 🏧 🛁

Rowley Hill Lodge, *Little Walden Road, Saffron Walden, Essex, CB10 1UZ.* C19th farm lodge thoughtfully enlarged. Both bedrooms with baths & power showers. **Open:** All year (not Xmas)
01799 525975 Mr &rs Haslam **Fax: 01799 516622** *eh@clara.net* **D:** £24.00 **S:** £28.00 **Beds:** 1D 1T **Baths:** 2 Pr ⛺ 🏧 (4) ▥ ▥ 🛁

Archway Guest House, *Church Street, Saffron Walden, Essex, CB10 1JW.* Unique house decorated with antiques, toys and rock & pop memorabilia. **Open:** All year
01799 501500 F Miles **D:** £25.00–£30.00 **S:** £30.00–£40.00 **Beds:** 1F 2D 2T 1S **Baths:** 3 En 1 Pr 1 Sh ⛺ 🏧 (3) ▥ ▥ 🏧 🛁

Sible Hedingham

TL7734

Hedingham Antiques, *100 Swan Street, Sible Hedingham, Halstead, Essex, CO9 3HP.* Victorian house and shop combined in centre of busy village. **Open:** All year (not Xmas) **Grades:** ETC 3 Diamond
01787 460360 Mrs Patterson **Fax: 01787 469109** *patriciapatterson@totalise.co.uk* **D:** £22.50 **S:** £25.00 **Beds:** 1D 1T 1S **Baths:** 3 En ⛺ 🏧 (4) ▥ ▥ 🏧 🛁

Southend-on-Sea

TQ8786

Darnley Guest House, *103-107 York Road, Southend-on-Sea, Essex, SS1 2DL.* 400 yards sea front, 400 yards shopping. Family atmosphere. **Open:** All year
01702 468800 Mrs Riel **Fax: 01702 468431** *pathenstock@cs.com* **D:** £35.00 **S:** £20.00–£30.00 **Beds:** 5F 5T 6S **Baths:** 5 En 2 Sh ⛺ 🏧 (9) ▥ ✕ 🏧 🛁

Retreat Guest House, *12 Canewdon Road, Westcliff-on-Sea, Southend-on-Sea, Essex, SS0 7NE.* **Open:** All year
Grades: ETC 3 Diamond
01702 348217 & 01702 337413 Mr & Mrs Bartholomew **Fax: 01702 391179** *retreatguesthouse.co.uk@tinyworld.co.uk* www.retreatguesthouse.co.uk **D:** £25.00–£27.50 **S:** £27.50–£40.00 **Beds:** 1F 5D 3T 4S **Baths:** 6 En 1 Pr 2 Sh ⛺ 🏧 (7) 🏧 🛏 ▥ 🏧 🛁 Quality accommodation, ideally situated. Close to the Cliff's Pavillion, Westcliff Station and near to the seafront leading to Southend's main attractions. Most rooms ensuite. Some on ground floor. Some bedrooms available with ensuite bathrooms and own kitchen. Private secure parking.

Regency Hotel, *18 Royal Terrace, Southend-on-Sea, Essex, SS1 1DU.* Very clean/secure. Convenient everywhere. Friendly/polite/comfortable. Visa/ Mastercard. **Open:** Jan to Sept
01702 340747 (also fax) R Fidgeon **D:** £15.00–£35.00 **S:** £20.00–£50.00 **Beds:** 5F 8T 10D 2S ⛺ ▥ 🛁 cc

Southminster

TQ9599

Saxegate Guest House, *44 North Street, Southminster, Essex, CM0 7DG.* Victorian home within easy reach of Maldon and Burnham-on-Crouch. **Open:** All year **Grades:** ETC 3 Diamond
01621 773180 Mrs Battson **Fax: 01621 774116** **D:** £18.00–£25.00 **S:** £18.00–£25.00 **Beds:** 1F 2T 1D **Baths:** 2 En 1 Sh ⛺ 🏧 (7) ▥ ✕ 🏧 🛁 🛁

Steeple Bumpstead

TL6841

Yew Tree House, *15 Chapel Street, Steeple Bumpstead, Haverhill, Suffolk, CB9 7DQ.* Victorian home offering superior accommodation, breakfast menu. Centre of village. **Open:** All year (not Xmas/New Year)
01440 730364 (also fax) Mrs Stirling *yewtreehouse@btinternet.com* www.haverhill-uk. com/yewtree **D:** £22.00 **S:** £27.00 **Beds:** 1D 1T **Baths:** 2 En ⛺ (3) 🏧 (2) ⊬ ✕ ▥ 🏧 🛁

Terling

TL7614

Old Bakery, *Waltham Road, Terling, Chelmsford, Essex, CM3 2QR.* Converted bakery in quiet unspoilt village on the Essex Way. **Open:** All year
01245 233363 Mrs Lewis **D:** £22.50–£25.00 **S:** £22.50–£25.00 **Beds:** 1T 1D **Baths:** 2 En ⏀ (10) 🅿 (2) ⏀ ⏀ ⏀ ⏀ ⏀

Thaxted

TL6131 🍺 *Swan Inn, Star Inn, Rose & Crown*

Crossways Guest House, *32 Town Street, Thaxted, Dunmow, Essex, CM6 2LA.* Elegant C16th house in centre old historic Thaxted. **Open:** All year **Grades:** ETC 4 Diamond, Silver
01371 830348 Mr Millett and Mr Dominguez-Soult **D:** £27.50–£29.00 **S:** £37.00–£40.00 **Beds:** 1T 1D **Baths:** 2 En ⏀ ⏀ ⏀ ⏀ ⏀

Theydon Bois

TQ4499 🍺 *Bull Inn, Railway Arms, Queen Victoria*

Glenfield, *26 Hill Road, Theydon Bois, Epping, Essex, CM16.* Detached family house furnished to a high standard, adjacent forest, underground and M25. **Open:** All year
01992 812541 (also fax) Mr & Mrs Day **D:** £22.00–£26.00 **S:** £22.00–£55.00 **Beds:** 3T 1S **Baths:** 1 Sh ⏀ 🅿 (4) ⏀ ⏀ ⏀

Tolleshunt Major

TL9011

Wicks Manor Farm, *Witham Road, Tolleshunt Major, Maldon, Essex, CM9 8JU.* Comfortable moated farmhouse with large garden near Blackwater Estuary. Working farm. **Open:** All year (not Xmas/New Year)
01621 860629 (also fax) Mrs Howie **D:** £18.00 **S:** £20.00 **Beds:** 1D **Baths:** 1 Pr ⏀ 🅿 ⏀ ⏀ ⏀ ⏀ ⏀ ⏀

Waltham Abbey

TL3800

Ivydene Cottage, *Woodgreen Road, Waltham Abbey, EN9 3SD.* Historic town and surroundings, canals and local interests. **Open:** All year (not Xmas)
01992 716082 (also fax) Mrs Oatham **D:** £20.00–£35.00 **S:** £25.00 **Beds:** 2T 1D **Baths:** 2 En 2 Sh 🅿 (5) ⏀ ⏀ × ⏀ ⏀ ⏀

All details shown are as supplied by B&B owners in Autumn 2001

Walton-on-the-Naze

TM2521 🍺 *The Victory*

Bufo Villae, *31 Beatrice Road, Walton-on-the-Naze, Essex, CO14 8HJ.* Two rooms have sea views. **Open:** All year
01255 672644 Miss Hodges & Mrs J King **D:** £17.50–£19.50 **S:** £17.50–£19.50 **Beds:** 1T 1D 1S **Baths:** 3 En ⏀ 🅿 ⏀ ⏀ ⏀ ⏀ ⏀ 🄰1 ⏀

West Bergholt

TL9627

The Old Post House, *10 Colchester Road, West Bergholt, Colchester, Essex, CO6 3JG.* Large Victorian private house, warm welcome, quiet secluded garden. **Open:** All year **Grades:** ETC 3 Diamond
01206 240379 & 01206 243301 Mrs Brown **Fax: 01206 243301 D:** £20.00–£25.00 **S:** £20.00 **Beds:** 1D 2T **Baths:** 1 En 1 Sh ⏀ (1) 🅿 (3) ⏀ ⏀ ⏀

West Mersea

TM0112

Hazel Oak, *28 Seaview Avenue, West Mersea, Colchester, Essex, CO5 8HE.* A quiet residential family home, situated in tree-lined avenue leading to waterfront. **Open:** All year (not Xmas)
01206 383030 (also fax) Mrs Blackmore *ann.blackmore@btinternet.com* www.btinternet. com/~dave.blackmore **D:** £22.00–£25.00 **S:** £25.00–£30.00 **Beds:** 1D 1T **Baths:** 1 En 1 Pr ⏀ 🅿 (2) ⏀ ⏀ ⏀ ⏀

Wethersfield

TL7131

Spicers Farm, *Rotten End, Wethersfield, Braintree, Essex, CM7 4AL.* Attractive farmhouse in tranquil surroundings, lovely views. Rooms ensuite. **Open:** All year (not Xmas)
01371 851021 (also fax) Mrs Douse *spicers.farm@talk21.com* **D:** £18.50–£19.50 **S:** £26.00–£30.00 **Beds:** 1D 2T **Baths:** 3 Pr ⏀ 🅿 (6) ⏀ ⏀ ⏀ ⏀ ⏀

White Colne

TL8729

Larkswood, *32 Colchester Road, White Colne, Colchester, Essex, CO6 2PN.* Pretty chalet bungalow in Colne Valley west of Colchester. **Open:** All year
01787 224362 Mr Fewster **D:** £17.50–£19.00 **S:** £25.00 **Beds:** 1T **Baths:** 1 En 🅿 (2) ⏀ ⏀ ⏀

Wimbish

TL5837

Newdegate House, *Howlett End, Wimbish, Saffron Walden, Essex, CB10 2XW.* Warm welcome, convenient for Duxford War Museum, Cambridge, Stansted Airport. **Open:** All year (not Xmas)
01799 599748 (also fax) Mr & Mrs Haigh **D:** £17.00–£20.00 **S:** £24.00–£29.50 **Beds:** 1D 1T **Baths:** 1 En 1 Pr ⏀ (10) 🅿 (10) ⏀ ⏀ ⏀ ⏀ ⏀

Wivenhoe

TM0421

2 Alma Street, *Wivenhoe, Colchester, Essex, CO7 9DL.* Grade II Listed early Victorian house, close to River Colne. **Open:** All year (not Xmas)
01206 823100 & 07976 246082 (M) Mrs Tritton **D:** £23.00–£25.00 **S:** £23.00–£25.00 **Beds:** 1T 1S **Baths:** 1 Sh ⏀ × ⏀ ⏀ ⏀

Wix

TM1628

Dairy House Farm, *Bradfield Road, Wix, Manningtree, Essex, CO11 2SR.* Spacious, quality, rural accommodation. A really relaxing place to stay. **Open:** All year (not Xmas) **Grades:** ETC 5 Diamond, Silver
01255 870322 Mrs Whitworth **Fax: 01255 870186** *bridgetwhitworth@hotmail.com* **D:** £20.00–£22.00 **S:** £26.00–£28.00 **Beds:** 1D 1T **Baths:** 2 En ⏀ (12) 🅿 (4) ⏀ ⏀ ⏀ ⏀

Woodham Mortimer

TL8104

Little Owls, *Post Office Road, Woodham Mortimer, Maldon, Essex, CM9 6ST.* Panoramic views over surrounding countryside. Private indoor swimming pool. **Open:** All year
01245 224355 (also fax) Mrs Bush *the.bushes@virgin.net* **D:** £20.00–£25.00 **S:** £25.00–£30.00 **Beds:** 1F 1T 1D **Baths:** 2 Sh ⏀ 🅿 (10) ⏀ ⏀ ⏀ × ⏀ ⏀ ⏀

Gloucestershire

Alderley

ST7690

Hillesley Mill, *Alderley, Wotton-under-Edge, Glos, GL12 7QT.* Converted mill with lake in undulating fields and prolific woodland. **Open:** All year (not Xmas/New Year) **Grades:** ETC 3 Diamond **01453 843258** Mrs James **D:** £20.00–£23.00 **S:** £22.00–£24.00 **Beds:** 1F 1D 1T **Baths:** 1 En 1 Sh ⚘ 🅿 (8) 📺 🏕 ☑ 💷 🏊

Amberley

SO8501 ● *Black Horse*

High Tumps, *St. Chloe Green, Amberley, Stroud, Glos, GL5 5AR.* Modest secluded family home offers bed and breakfast accommodation in self contained annexe. **Open:** All year **Grades:** ETC 4 Diamond **01453 873584 Fax: 01453 873587** *dakavic@ high-tumps.freeserve.co.uk* **D:** £15.00–£17.00 **S:** £15.00–£17.00 **Beds:** 1T **Baths:** 1 En 📺 💷 🏊

Arlingham

SO7010 ● *Red Lion*

Horseshoe View, *Overton Lane, Arlingham, Gloucester, GL2 7JJ.* A new house, with lovely views across Severn and Forest of Dean. **Open:** All year **01452 740293** D Turrell **D:** £15.00 **S:** £13.50 **Beds:** 3F 1T 1D 1S **Baths:** 2 En 1 Pr 1 Sh 🅿 (5) ☒ 📺 🏕 ☑ 💷

RATES

D = Price range per person sharing in a double or twin room

S = Price range for a single room

Aston Magna
SP1935

Bran Mill Cottage, *Aston Magna, Moreton in Marsh, Glos, GL56 9QP.* Small traditional B&B in peaceful Cotswold cottage. Friendly, welcoming, homely. **Open:** All year (not Xmas) **Grades:** ETC 3 Diamond
01386 593517 Mr & Mrs Baggaley *enquiries@ branmillcottage.co.uk* www.branmillcottage.co.uk **D:** £17.00–£20.00 **S:** £19.00–£25.00 **Beds:** 1D 1T 1S **Baths:** 1 Pr 1 Sh ♿ (14) ⊞ (3) ⊬ 🖾 🖳 ♨

Aston on Carrant
SO9434

Wistaria Cottage, *Aston on Carrant, Tewkesbury, Glos, GL20 8HL.* Pretty rural hamlet, traditional country breakfast, excellent walking/touring area.
Open: Easter to Oct
01684 772357 Mrs Allen **D:** £18.00–£20.00 **S:** £22.00–£25.00 **Beds:** 1D 1T **Baths:** 1 En 1 Pr ♿ ⊞ (3) ⊬ 🖾 ♨ ♨

Aylburton
SO6101

Lynwood, *97 High Street, Aylburton, Lydney, Glos, GL15 6DZ* **Open:** Feb to Oct
01594 843366 Mrs Stilwell *lynwood@ amserve.net* **D:** £18.00–£20.00 **S:** £18.00–£20.00 **Beds:** 2D 1S **Baths:** 3 En ♿ ⊞ (4) ⊬ 🖾 × 🖳
Situated in a pleasant village on the A48 with easy access to the Royal Forest of Dean and Wye Valley. Beautiful views to the River Severn and two inns within short walking distance. Comfortably furnished accommodation and friendly atmosphere.

Baunton
SP0204

Windrush, *Baunton, Cirencester, Glos, GL7 7BA.* Detached house in large gardens. Beautiful views over Cotswold countryside. **Open:** All year (not Xmas)
01285 655942 (also fax) S J Rees **D:** £20.00–£25.00 **S:** £20.00–£30.00 **Beds:** 1F 1D 1T **Baths:** 1 En 1 Pr 1 Sh ♿ ⊞ (4) ⊬ 🖾 🖸 🖳 ♨

Berkeley
ST6899

The Old Swan, *High Street, Berkeley, Glos, GL13 9BJ.* Beautiful town house very close to Berkeley Castle & Jenner Museum **Open:** All year (not Xmas/New Year)
01453 810273 Mr & Mrs Stump **D:** £12.50–£40.00 **S:** £15.00–£20.00 **Beds:** 1F 2D 1S **Baths:** 1 Sh ♿ 🖾 🖳 ♨

Berry Hill
SO5712

Westlands House, *20 Grove Road, Berry Hill, Coleford, Glos, GL16 8QY.* Cottage close to forest walks, historic sites, outdoor pursuits. **Open:** All year (not Xmas)
01594 837143 Mrs Atherley **D:** £15.00 **S:** £15.00 **Beds:** 1D 1T **Baths:** 1 Sh ♿ ⊞ (2) ⊬ 🖐 🖳 ♨

Birdlip
SO9214

Beechmount, *Birdlip, Gloucester, GL4 8JH.* **Open:** All year **Grades:** ETC 3 Diamond
01452 862262 **(also fax)** Mrs Carter *thebeechmount@ breathemail.net* www.beechmount.co.uk
D: £17.00–£22.00 **S:** £16.00–£32.00 **Beds:** 2F 2D 2T **Baths:** 2 En 3 Sh ♿ ⊞ (7) ⊬ 🖾 🖐 × 🖾 🖳 ♨ cc
Warm hospitality. Personal attention. Family-run guest house. Ideal centre for exploring Cotswolds. All bedrooms individually decorated having many extras including hairdryers and welcome pack of toiletries etc. Large choice of menu for breakfast. Unrestricted access. Minutes from M5. Highly recommended.

BATHROOMS

En = Ensuite

Pr = Private

Sh = Shared

BEDROOMS

D = Double

T = Twin

S = Single

F = Family

Birdwood
SO7418

Birdwood Villa Farm, *Main Road, Birdwood, Huntley, Gloucester, GL19 3EQ.* A warm welcome awaits you at our 60-acre arable farm. **Open:** All year
01452 750451 M King **D:** £20.00–£25.00 **S:** £21.00–£26.00 **Beds:** 1F 1D **Baths:** 2 En ♿ ⊞ (8) ⊬ 🖾 🖐 🖾 🖳 ♨ cc

Blakeney
SO6706 🍺 *Red Hart*

Viney Hill Country Guesthouse, *Blakeney, Glos, GL15 4LT.* A period house set in the quiet Gloucestershire countryside. **Open:** All year (not Xmas/New Year)
01594 516000 Mr Parsons **Fax:** **01594 516018** *info@vineyhill.com* www.vineyhill.com
D: £26.00–£32.00 **S:** £35.00 **Beds:** 3D 1T **Baths:** 4 En ♿ ⊞ (4) ⊬ 🖾 × 🖳 ♨ cc

Blockley
SP1634 🍺 *Crown Inn, Bakers' Arms, Great Western Arms*

Park Farm, *Blockley, Moreton in Marsh, Glos, GL56 9TA.* Beautiful old farmhouse; idyllic location, easy walk village. Warm welcome. **Open:** All year
01386 700266 Mr & Mrs Dee **D:** £17.00 **S:** £17.00 **Beds:** 1D 1T 2S **Baths:** 1 Sh ♿ ⊞ (6) ⊬ 🖾 🖐 🖾 ♨

Tudor House, *High Street, Blockley, Moreton in Marsh, Glos, GL56 9EX.* Excellent walking, gardens to visit. Warm welcome. Own sitting room. **Open:** All year (not Xmas)
01386 700356 Mrs Thompson **D:** £25.00–£30.00 **S:** £25.00–£30.00 **Beds:** 1D 1T **Baths:** 1 Sh ♿ (10) ⊞ (2) ⊬ 🖾 🖳 ♨

The Malins, 21 Station Road, Blockley, Moreton In Marsh, Glos, *GL56 9ED*. Attractive Cotswold stone house, many facilities, friendly hosts. **Open:** All year
01386 700402 (also fax) Mrs Malin **D:** £18.00 **S:** £25.00 **Beds:** 1D 2T **Baths:** 3 Pr ⌂ 🅿 (5) ⌀ 📺 Ⓥ 🏠. ✱ ☂

Arreton Guest House, Station Road, Blockley, Moreton-in-Marsh, Glos, *GL56 6DT*. Arreton is situated in the north Cotswold in the village of Blockley. **Open:** All year
01386 701077 (also fax) *bandb@ arreton.demon.co.uk www.arreton.demon.co. uk* **D:** £20.00–£22.00 **S:** £28.00–£30.00 **Beds:** 1F 1D 1T **Baths:** 3 En ⌂ 🅿 ⌀ 📺 Ⓥ 🏠. ✱ ☂

Bourton-on-the-Water

SP1620 🍺 *Mousetrap, New Inn, Duke of Wellington, Painted House, Kingsbridge, Inn for All Seasons, Coach & Horses*

6 Moore Road, Bourton-on-the-Water, Cheltenham, Glos, *GL54 2AZ*. Cotswold stone house, quiet road, yards to village, peaceful garden. **Open:** Feb to Dec
01451 820767 Mrs Mustoe **D:** £19.00–£21.00 **S:** £20.00–£25.00 **Beds:** 1D 1T **Baths:** 1 En 1 Pr ⌂ (5) 🅿 (3) ⌀ 📺 🐾 Ⓥ 🏠. ☂

Lansdowne House, Lansdowne, Bourton-on-the-Water, Cheltenham, Glos, *GL54 2AT*. Tastefully furnished ensuite accommodation. Combination of old and antique furniture. **Open:** All year (not Xmas)
01451 820812 Mrs Garwood **Fax:** 01451 822484 *stilwell@lansdownehouse.co.uk www.lansdownehouse.co.uk* **D:** £17.50– £20.00 **S:** £30.00–£35.00 **Beds:** 1F 2D **Baths:** 3 En ⌂ 🅿 (4) 📺 Ⓥ 🏠. ☂

Breadstone

SO7100

Green Acres Farm Guest House, Breadstone, Berkeley, Glos, *GL13 9HF*. Tranquil setting in large garden overlooking Welsh Hills and Cotswolds. Full English breakfast. **Open:** All year
01453 810348 Ms Evans **Fax:** 01453 810799 *barbara@greenacresfarm.co.uk* **D:** £23.50– £26.00 **S:** £24.50–£26.50 **Beds:** 2T 2D 2S **Baths:** 6 En 🅿 ⌀ ⌂ 🐾 🏠. ☂ cc

Brimscombe

SO8702 🍺 *Ship Inn, Ram Inn*

Brandon Quarhouse, Brimscombe, Chalford, Stroud, Glos, *GL5 2RS*. Cotswold hillside house, pretty/productive garden, exquisite walks, warm welcome. **Open:** All year (not Xmas/New Year)
01453 883664 Mrs Clapham **D:** £19.00 **S:** £16.00–£19.00 **Beds:** 1T 1S **Baths:** 1 En 1 Sh ⌂ (8) 🅿 (4) ⌀ 🐴 ✕ Ⓥ 🏠. ☂

The Yew Tree, Walls Quarry, Brimscombe, Stroud, Glos, *GL5 2PA*. C17th Cotswold stone house overlooks the Golden Valley. **Open:** All year **Grades:** ETC 4 Diamond
01453 883428 (also fax) Mrs Peters **D:** £20.00–£30.00 **S:** £20.00–£30.00 **Beds:** 1F 1T 1D **Baths:** 1 En 1 Pr ⌀ 📺 Ⓥ 🏠. ☂

Broad Campden

SP1537

Marnic House, Broad Campden, Chipping Campden, Glos, *GL55 6UR*. Comfortable, friendly and well furnished family home. Peacefully situated, scenic views. **Open:** All year (not Xmas/New Year) **Grades:** ETC 4 Diamond, Gold, AA 4 Diamond
01386 840014 Mrs Rawlings **Fax:** 01386 840441 *marnic@zoom.co.uk* **D:** £24.00–£25.00 **S:** £38.00–£40.00 **Beds:** 2D 1T **Baths:** 2 En 1 Pr ⌂ (10) 🅿 (4) 📺 Ⓥ 🏠. ☂

Brookthorpe

SO8312

Brookthorpe Lodge, Stroud Road, Brookthorpe, Gloucester, Glos, *GL4 0UQ*.
Open: All year
01452 812645 Mr Bailey *enq@ brookthorpelodge.demon.co.uk* **D:** £20.00–£25.00 **S:** £31.00–£35.00 **Beds:** 2F 2D 3T 3S **Baths:** 6 En 2 Pr 1 Sh ⌂ 🅿 (15) 📺 🐾 ✕ Ⓥ 🏠. ⚕ ✱ ☂
Licensed family-run three storey Georgian house in lovely countryside at foot of Cotswold escarpment, 4 miles from Gloucester. Close to ski slope, horse riding and golfing. Good walking country - ideal base for Cotswolds, Gloucester docks and cathedral. Separate smoking area.

Chalford

SO8902

Beechcroft, Brownshill, Chalford, Stroud, Glos, *GL6 8AG*. Quietly situated Edwardian house. Home made bread and preserves. Good walking. **Open:** All year **Grades:** ETC 3 Diamond
01453 883422 Mrs Salt **D:** £20.00–£25.00 **S:** £24.00–£30.00 **Beds:** 1T 1D ⌂ 🅿 (2) ⌀ 📺 ✕ Ⓥ 🏠. ☂

BATHROOMS
En = Ensuite
Pr = Private
Sh = Shared

Charfield

ST7191

Falcon Cottage, 15 Station Road, Charfield, Wotton-under-Edge, Glos, *GL12 8SY*. Convenient for M5, Bath, Bristol, Cheltenham, Cotswolds, Cotswold Way. **Open:** All year (not Xmas) **Grades:** ETC 4 Diamond
01453 843528 Mrs Haddrell **D:** £20.00 **S:** £20.00 **Beds:** 1T 1D **Baths:** 1 Sh ⌂ 🅿 (2) ⌀ 📺 Ⓥ 🏠. ☂

Charlton Kings

SO9620 🍺 *Waterside*

Langett, London Road, Cheltenham, Glos, *GL54 4HG*. Perfect stop for walkers on the Cotswold Way. **Open:** Easter to Oct
01242 820192 (also fax) Mr Cox *cox.langett@ btopenworld.com* **D:** £20.00–£25.00 **S:** £25.00 **Beds:** 1T 1D **Baths:** 1 Pr ⌂ 🅿 ⌀ 📺 Ⓥ 🏠. ☂

Cheltenham

SO9422 🍺 *Green Dragon, Air Balloon Inn*

Clun House, 4 The Oaks, Up Hatherley, Cheltenham, Glos, *GL51 5TS*. Spacious, attractive, quiet house; lounge available, easy access M5. **Open:** All year (not Xmas)
01242 523255 & 07703 798230 (M) Mrs Hyde **D:** £17.00 **S:** £17.00 **Beds:** 1D 2S **Baths:** 1 Pr 1 Sh 🅿 (5) ⌀ 📺 Ⓥ 🏠. ☂

Heron Haye, Cleeve Hill, Cheltenham, Glos, *GL52 3PW*. Quiet location, 1/4 mile Cotswold Way. Comfortable home. Full English breakfast. Superb views. **Open:** All year
01242 672516 Mr Saunders *dick.whittamore@ virgin.net* **D:** £22.50–£30.00 **S:** £25.00–£30.00 **Beds:** 2D 1S **Baths:** 1 Sh 🅿 (4) ⌀ 🐾 🏠.

Parkview, 4 Pittville Crescent, Cheltenham, Glos, *GL52 2QZ*. Regency house in Cheltenham - nicest area. Cotswolds, Sudeley Castle, Stratford are nearby. **Open:** All year
01242 575567 Mrs Sparrey *jospa@ tr250.freeserve.co.uk* **D:** £20.00–£25.00 **S:** £20.00–£25.00 **Beds:** 1F 1S **Baths:** 2 En 2 Sh ⌂ ⌀ 🐾 🏠. ☂

Crossways Guest House, Oriel Place, 57 Bath Road, Cheltenham, Glos, *GL53 7LH*. Fine Regency house in the centre of Cheltenham. **Open:** All year
01242 527683 Mr Lynch **Fax:** 01242 577226 *cross.ways@btinternet.com www.cross.ways. btinternet.co.uk* **D:** £22.00–£25.00 **Beds:** 3F 1T 1D 1S **Baths:** 3 En 1 Sh ⌂ ⌀ ⌀ Ⓥ 🏠. ☂ cc

Beaumont House Hotel, Shurdington Road, Cheltenham, Glos, *GL53 0JE*. Relaxed, friendly, peaceful, comfortable, totally non-smoking. Four poster rooms. Garden. **Open:** All year (not Xmas/New Year)
01242 245986 Fax: 01242 520044 *rocking.horse@virgin.net* **D:** £30.00–£40.00 **S:** £42.00–£56.00 **Beds:** 1F 3T 10D 2S **Baths:** 16 En ⌂ (10) 🅿 (16) ⌀ 📺 Ⓥ 🏠. ☂ cc

Central Hotel, *7-9 Portland Street, Cheltenham, Glos, GL52 2NZ.* Grade II Listed building in town centre, one block from shops and Regent Arcade. **Open:** All year **01242 582172** Mr Rouse **D:** £22.00–£28.50 **S:** £27.00–£37.00 **Beds:** 2F 3D 5T 4S **Baths:** 6 En 2 Sh ➳ 🅿 (8) ⚲ 🅣 ✕ 🆅 ♿ cc

Chipping Campden

SP1539 🍺 *Eight Bells, Lygon Arms*

Holly House, *Ebrington, Chipping Campden, Glos, GL55 6NL.* **Open:** All year (not Xmas) **Grades:** AA 4 Diamond **01386 593213** Mrs Hutsby **Fax: 01386 593181** *hutsby@talk21.com* www.stratford-upon-avon.co.uk/hollyhouse.htm **D:** £21.00–£24.00 **S:** £35.00–£46.00 **Beds:** 3F/D/T **Baths:** 3 En ➳ 🅿 (5) ⚲ 🅣 🆅 ▦ ♿ Situated in centre of picturesque Cotswold village, 2 miles Chipping Campden and Hidcote Gardens, 11 miles Stratford, 20 miles Warwick. All rooms spaciously appointed with ensuite facilities. Lovely garden room at guests' disposition. Private parking. Local pub serves meals.

Marnic House, *Broad Campden, Chipping Campden, Glos, GL55 6UR.* Comfortable, friendly and well furnished family home. Peacefully situated, scenic views. **Open:** All year (not Xmas/New Year) **Grades:** ETC 4 Diamond, Gold, AA 4 Diamond **01386 840014** Mrs Rawlings **Fax: 01386 840441** *marnic@zoom.co.uk* **D:** £24.00–£25.00 **S:** £38.00–£40.00 **Beds:** 2D 1T **Baths:** 2 En 1 Pr ➳ (10) 🅿 (4) 🅣 🆅 ▦ ♿

The Guest House, *Lower High Street, Chipping Campden, Glos, GL55 6DZ.* Period Cotswold stone cottage, easy walking to local beauty spots and shops. **Open:** Easter to Nov **01386 840163** Mrs Benfield **D:** £19.00–£22.00 **S:** £25.00 **Beds:** 1D 1T **Baths:** 2 En 🅣 ♙ ▦ ♿

Old Barn House, *Mill Lane, Mickleton, Chipping Campden, Glos, GL55 6RT.* Quiet location. Heart of conservation area. Ground floor, twin room. **Open:** All year (not Xmas/New Year) **Grades:** ETC 3 Diamond **01386 438668 (also fax)** J Lodge **D:** £23.00 **S:** £35.00–£40.00 **Beds:** 1T 1D **Baths:** 2 Pr ➳ (10) 🅿 (3) 🅣 🆅 ▦ ♿

All details shown are as supplied by B&B owners in Autumn 2001

Churcham

SO7618

Edgewood House, *Churcham, Gloucester, GL2 8AA.* Large country house overlooking secluded gardens. Comfortable rooms, generous breakfasts. **Open:** All year (not Xmas) **Grades:** AA 4 Diamond **01452 750232** **D:** £23.00–£27.00 **S:** £25.00–£35.00 **Beds:** 1F 1D 1T **Baths:** 2 En 1 Pr ➳ (10) 🅿 (6) ⚲ 🅣 🆅 ▦ ♿

Cirencester

SP0202 🍺 *Wild Duck, Bakers' Arms, Bear Inn, Bathurst Arms, Hare & Hounds*

Sunset, *Baunton Lane, Cirencester, Glos, GL7 2NQ.* Quiet, small family house conveniently situated for touring the Cotswolds. **Open:** Easter to Oct **Grades:** ETC 3 Diamond **01285 654822** Mrs Castle **D:** £16.00–£17.00 **S:** £16.00–£17.00 **Beds:** 1T 2S **Baths:** 1 Sh ➳ (5) 🅿 (5) ⚲ 🅣 🆅 ▦ ♿

Chesil Rocks, *Baunton Lane, Cirencester, Glos, GL7 2LL.* Pleasant friendly home, quiet lane. Access town and country walks. **Open:** All year (not Xmas) **Grades:** ETC 3 Diamond **01285 655031** Mrs Clayton **D:** £20.00 **S:** £20.00 **Beds:** 1T 2S **Baths:** 1 Sh ➳ (2) 🅿 (2) ⚲ 🅣 🆅 ▦ ♿

Sprucewood, *Elf Meadow, Poulton, Cirencester, Glos, GL7 5HQ.* Quiet, homely, comfortable. Open views. Warm, friendly welcome awaits you. **Open:** All year (not Xmas) **Grades:** ETC 4 Diamond **01285 851351 (also fax)** Mr & Mrs Walker **D:** £16.00–£20.00 **S:** £22.00–£25.00 **Beds:** 1D 1T 1S **Baths:** 1 Sh ➳ 🅿 (4) ⚲ 🅣 🆅 ▦ ♿

Clapton-on-the-Hill

SP1617

Farncombe, *Clapton-on-the-Hill, Bourton-on-the-Water, Cheltenham, Glos, GL54 2LG.* Come and share our peace and tranquillity with superb views. **Open:** All year (not Xmas) **01451 820120 & 07714 703142 (M)** Mrs Wright **Fax: 01451 820120** *jwrightbb@aol.com* www.farncombecotswolds.com **D:** £20.00–£23.00 **S:** £25.00–£30.00 **Beds:** 2D 1T **Baths:** 1 En 2 Sh ➳ 🅿 (4) ⚲ 🅣 🆅 ▦ ♿

Cleeve Hill

SO9826

Heron Haye, *Cleeve Hill, Cheltenham, Glos, GL52 3PW.* Quiet location, 1/4 mile Cotswold Way. Comfortable home. Full English breakfast. Superb views. **Open:** All year **01242 672516** Mr Saunders *dick.whittamore@virgin.net* **D:** £22.50–£30.00 **S:** £25.00–£30.00 **Beds:** 2D 1S **Baths:** 1 Sh 🅿 (4) ⚲ ♀ ▦

Coleford

SO5710 🍺 *The Crown, Angel Hotel, Tudor Farmhouse*

Marefold, *Gorsty Knoll, Milkwall, Coleford, Glos, GL16 7LR.* Edge Forest nature reserve. Walkers, cyclists, birdwatchers paradise. Village half a mile. **Open:** All year (not Xmas) **01594 833969** Mrs Webb **D:** £18.00–£20.00 **S:** £18.00–£20.00 **Beds:** 1T 1S **Baths:** 1 Pr 1 Sh ➳ 🅿 (2) 🅣 ♀ 🆅 ▦ ♿

Perouges, *31 Newland Street, Coleford, Glos, GL16 8AJ.* Several nearby children and adult attractions. Central location. Comfortable, modern. **Open:** All year (not Xmas/New Year) **Grades:** ETC 3 Diamond **01594 834287** **D:** £14.00–£17.00 **Beds:** 1T 1D **Baths:** 1 Pr ➳ 🅿 (1) ⚲ 🅣 🆅 ▦ ♿

Coopers Hill

SO8914 🍺 *Royal William, Air Balloon, 12 Bells*

The Haven Tea Garden, *Coopers Hill, Brockworth, Gloucester, GL3 4SB.* Green wooden bungalow. Country garden. Wonderful walks - woodland or fields. **Open:** Easter to Sept **01452 863213** R Hellerman **D:** £20.00 **Beds:** 1F 1T **Baths:** 1 Sh ➳ 🅿 (2) 🅣 ✕ 🆅

Corse

SO7826

Kilmorie, *Gloucester Ro, GL19 3RQ.* Quality all ground floor accommodation, tea trays, toiletries, TVs all rooms, mainly ensuite. **Open:** All year (not Xmas) **01452 840224** Ms Barnfield **D:** £17.00–£20.00 **S:** £18.00–£20.00 **Beds:** 1F 2D 1T 1S **Baths:** 3 En 1 Pr 1 Sh ➳ (5) 🅿 (8) 🅣 ✕ 🆅 ▦ ♿

Cranham

SO8913

Pound Cottage, *Cranham, Gloucester, GL4 8HP.* Old Cotswold cottage. Quiet village - good walkin beechwoods and grassland. **Open:** All year (not Xmas/New Year) **01452 812581** Ms Dann **Fax: 01452 814380** *ddann@globalnet.co.uk* **D:** £20.00 **S:** £25.00 **Beds:** 1T 1D **Baths:** 1 Sh ➳ (2) ⚲ 🅣 🆅 ▦ ♿

Down Hatherley

SO8622

Frog Furlong Cottage, *Frog Furlong Lane, Down Hatherley, Gloucester, GL2 9QE.* In the Green Belt, standing quietly alone, surrounded by fields. **Open:** All year (not Xmas/New Year)
01452 730430 (also fax) Mrs Rooke
D: £20.00–£22.00 **S:** £19.00–£27.00 **Beds:** 1D 1T **Baths:** 1 En (3)

Dumbleton

SP0136

Raymeadow Farm, *Dumbleton, Evesham, Worcs, WR11 7TR.* Peaceful farmhouse nestling within the Cotswolds between Stratford/ Cheltenham and Worcester. **Open:** Mar to Oct
01242 621215 Ms Alvis **D:** £20.00–£25.00 **S:** £20.00–£25.00 **Beds:** 1F 1T 1S **Baths:** 1 Sh

Dursley

ST7698

Drakestone House, *Stinchcombe, Dursley, Glos, GL11 6AS.* An Arts and Crafts building with a large garden from the same period. **Open:** Feb to Nov
01453 542140 (also fax) Mr & Mrs St John Mildmay **D:** £31.50–£36.50 **S:** £36.50
Beds: 1D 2T **Baths:** 1 Pr 1 Sh (4)

Eastcombe

SO8804

Pretoria Villa, *Wells Road, Eastcombe, Stroud, Glos, GL6 7EE.* Enjoy luxurious bed and breakfast in relaxed family country house. **Open:** All year (not Xmas)
Grades: ETC 4 Diamond
01452 770435 Mrs Solomon **D:** £22.00
S: £25.00 **Beds:** 1D 1T 1S **Baths:** 2 En 1 Pr (3)

Ebrington

SP1840

Holly House, *Ebrington, Chipping Campden, Glos, GL55 6NL.* Situated in centre of picturesque Cotswold village, 2 miles Chipping Campden and Hidcote Gardens. **Open:** All year (not Xmas) **Grades:** AA 4 Diamond
01386 593213 Mrs Hutsby **Fax: 01386 593181**
hutsby@talk21.com www.stratford-upon-avon.co.uk/hollyhouse.htm **D:** £21.00–£24.00
S: £35.00–£46.00 **Beds:** 3F/D/T **Baths:** 3 En (5)

English Bicknor

SO5815

Dryslade Farm, *English Bicknor, Coleford, Glos, GL16 7PA.* Daphne and Philip ensure a relaxed, friendly atmosphere at their C17th farmhouse. **Open:** All year **Grades:** ETC 4 Diamond
01594 860259 (also fax) Mrs Gwilliam
dryslade@agriplus.net www.fweb.org.uk./dryslade **D:** £20.00–£22.00 **S:** £23.00–£25.00
Beds: 1F 1T 1D **Baths:** 2 En 1 Pr (6)

Fairford

SP1500 *Bull Inn*

Waiten Hill Farm, *Mill Lane, Fairford, Glos, GL7 4JG.* Imposing C19th farmhouse overlooking River Coln and famous church.
Open: All year **Grades:** ETC 2 Diamond
01285 712652 (also fax) Mrs Rymer
D: £17.50–£20.00 **S:** £20.00–£25.00 **Beds:** 1F 1D 1T **Baths:** 2 En

Milton Farm, *Fairford, Glos, GL7 4HZ.* Impressive Georgian farmhouse with large bedrooms. Quiet pleasant outlook.
Open: All year (not Xmas/New Year)
Grades: ETC 3 Diamond
01285 712205 Mrs Paton **Fax: 01285 711349**
milton@farmersweekly.net **D:** £20.00–£25.00
S: £25.00–£30.00 **Beds:** 2T 1D **Baths:** 3 En

Frampton Mansell

SO9202

Crown Inn and Hotel, *Frampton Mansell, Stroud, Glos, GL6 8JG.* Picturesque Inn. Ideally situated. Walks, real ales, log wood. Hot meals. **Open:** All year
01285 760601 D: £64.00–£72.00 **S:** £44.00–£52.00 **Beds:** 1F 7T 4D **Baths:** 12 En cc

Gloucester

SO8318

Alston Field Guest House, *88 Stroud Road, Gloucester, GL1 5AJ.* Well located for city and countryside. Short breaks. Brochure available. **Open:** All year (not Xmas/New Year)
01452 529170 & 01452 526625 D: £18.00–£25.00 **S:** £18.00–£28.00 **Beds:** 1F 1T 1S
Baths: 2 En 1 Sh cc

Georgian Guest House, *85 Bristol Road, Gloucester, GL1 5SN.* Part-Georgian terraced house, 15 minutes walk city centre.
Open: All year
01452 413286 (also fax) J W Nash **D:** £15.00–£16.50 **S:** £15.00 **Beds:** 4F 3T 2S **Baths:** 5 En 1 Sh (3)

Gotherington

SO9629

Moat Farm, *Malleson Road, Gotherington, Cheltenham, Glos, GL52 4ET.* Situated in the heart of the Cotswolds between Cheltenham and Tewkesbury.
Open: All year (not Xmas)
01242 672055 & 01242 676807 Mr & Mrs Tilley **Fax: 07050 665639 D:** £18.00–£19.00
S: £18.00–£19.00 **Beds:** 2D 2T

Pardon Hill Farm, *Prescott, Gotherington, Cheltenham, Glos, GL52 4RD.* Modern, comfortable farmhouse, lovely views. **Open:** All year
01242 672468 (also fax) Mrs Newman
janet@pardonhillfarm.freeserve.co.uk www.margintrip co.uk/pardonhill.shtml
D: £22.00–£50.00 **S:** £27.00–£35.00 **Beds:** 1D 1T 1S **Baths:** 3 En (6)

Great Rissington

SP1917 *Lamb Inn*

Lower Farmhouse, *Great Rissington, Bourton on the Water, Cheltenham, Glos, GL54 2LH.* Listed Georgian house with guest annexe in Cotswold barn conversion.
Open: All year **Grades:** ETC 3 Diamond
01451 810163 Mr & Mrs Fleming **Fax: 01451 810187** *kathryn@lowerfarmhouse.co.uk* www.lowerfarmhouse.co.uk **D:** £18.00–£22.00 **S:** £18.00–£30.00 **Beds:** 1D 1S
Baths: 1 Sh

Haresfield

SO8110

Lower Green Farmhouse, *Haresfield, Stonehouse, Glos, GL10 3DS.* C18th Listed Cotswold stone farmhouse with countryside views. **Open:** All year (not Xmas/New Year)
01452 728264 (also fax) Mrs Reed
lowergreen@lineone.net **D:** £18.50 **S:** £20.00
Beds: 1F 1T **Baths:** 2 Sh (6)

Hawkesbury

ST7686

Ivy Cottage, *Inglestone Common, Hawkesbury, Badminton, GL9 1BX.* Comfortable cottage surrounded by ancient woodland on edge of Cotswolds.
Open: All year (not Xmas/New Year)
01454 294237 Mrs Canner **D:** £19.00–£20.00
S: £22.00–£25.00 **Beds:** 1F 1D 1T 1S
Baths: 2 Sh (3)

Huntley

SO7219

Forest Gate, Huntley, Gloucester, GL19 3EU. Spacious Victorian rectory ideal for visiting Royal Forest of Dean, great breakfasts, also camping. **Open:** All year (not Xmas) **Grades:** ETC 3 Diamond
01452 831192 (also fax) Mr Blakemore
forest.gate@huntley-glos.demon.co.uk
www.huntley-glos.demon.co.uk **D:** £23.00–£26.00 **S:** £23.00–£26.00 **Beds:** 1F 1D 1S
Baths: 1 En 1 Sh ☎ ▣ (6) ⚡ ⊡ ⓥ ▥ ♨ cc

Kemble

ST9897

Smerrill Barns, Kemble, Cirencester, Glos, GL7 6BW. C18th converted barn, guest lounge with log fires in winter, drinks licence. **Open:** All year (not Xmas)
01285 770907 Mrs Sopher **Fax: 01285 770706 D:** £27.50 **S:** £45.00 **Beds:** 1F 5D 1T
Baths: 7 En 1 Sh ☎ ▣ (8) ⚡ ⊡ ▥ ♨

Kilcot

SO6925

Cherry Grove B&B, Mill Lane, Kilcot, Newent, Glos, GL18 1NY. Peaceful rural situation near Wye Valley, good cycling and walking. **Open:** All year (not Xmas)
01989 720126 Mr & Mrs Inwood **D:** £15.00–£17.00 **S:** £16.00–£18.00 **Beds:** 1F 1D
Baths: 1 Pr 1 Sh ☎ (5) ▣ (6) ⚡ ⊡ ⓥ ▥ ♨

Kings Stanley

SO8103

Old Chapel House, Broad Street, Kings Stanley, Stonehouse, Glos, GL10 3PN. Converted chapel on Cotswold Way overlooking escarpment. **Open:** All year (not Xmas)
01453 826289 Mrs Richards Hanna
jeanhannaoldchapelhouse@hotmail.com
D: £21.50 **S:** £20.00 **Beds:** 1F 1D 2T 1S
Baths: 2 En 1 Sh ☎ (5) ▣ (4) ⊡ ✕ ▥ ♨

BATHROOMS

En = Ensuite
Pr = Private
Sh = Shared

RATES

D = Price range per person sharing in a double or twin room
S = Price range for a single room

Knockdown

ST8388

Avenue Farm, Knockdown, Tetbury, Glos, GL8 8QY. 300-year-old farmhouse in farm adjoining Westonbirt Arboretum. Bath, Bristol, Gloucester easy reach. **Open:** All year
01454 238207 Mrs King **Fax: 01454 238033**
sonjames@breathemail.net **D:** £20.00–£25.00
S: £25.00 **Beds:** 1F 1D 2T **Baths:** 2 En 1 Sh ☎ ▣ (6) ⚡ ⊡ ⓥ ▥ ♨

Laverton

SP0735

Gunners Orchard, Laverton, Broadway, Glos, WR12 7NA. Comfortable private house in quiet and beautiful setting personal attention. **Open:** All year (not Xmas/New Year)
01386 584213 Mrs Stephenson **D:** £18.00–£20.00 **S:** £25.00–£30.00 **Beds:** 1D 1T
Baths: 1 Sh ▣ (6) ⚡ ⊡ ⓥ ▥ ♨

Lechlade

SU2199

The New Inn Hotel, Market Square, Lechlade On Thames, Glos, GL7 3AB. C17th fully modernised coaching inn on River Thames in the Cotswold. **Open:** All year
01367 252296 Mr Sandhu **Fax: 01367 252315**
info@newinnhotel.co.uk www.members.aol.com/newinnlech **D:** £20.00–£32.50
S: £40.00–£55.00 **Beds:** 2F 10D 10T 4S
Baths: 26 En ▣ (40) ⚡ ⊡ ✕ ⓥ ▥ ❋ ♨

Cambrai Lodge Guest House, Oak Street, Lechlade On Thames, Glos, GL7 3AY. Modern comfortable house off the road. Ideal for touring Cotswolds. **Open:** All year
01367 253173 & 07860 150467 (M)
Mr Titchener **D:** £23.50–£29.50 **S:** £29.00–£39.00 **Beds:** 1F 1D 1T 2S **Baths:** 2 En 1 Pr 1 Sh ☎ ▣ (9) ⚡ ⊡ ★ ▥ ♨

BEDROOMS

D = Double
T = Twin
S = Single
F = Family

Longhope

SO6818 🍺 Farmer's Boy, Nag's Head, Moody Cow

The Old Farm, Barrell Lane, Longhope, Glos, GL17 0LR. **Open:** All year **Grades:** ETC 4 Diamond
01452 830252 Mrs Rodger **Fax: 01452 830255** *lucy@the-old-farm.co.uk*
www.the-old-farm.co.uk **D:** £20.00–£26.00
S: £29.00 **Beds:** 2D 1T **Baths:** 3 En ☎ (12) ▣ (6) ⚡ ⊡ ★ ⓥ ▥ ♨ cc
Charming C16th farmhouse full of character, beams and fireplaces. Set in an idyllic rural location, within easy reach of the Cotswolds, Oxford, Cheltenham and Stratford. Royal Forest of Dean nearby. Excellent walking/cycling from the farm. Or just come to relax!

Lower Slaughter

SP1623

Seymour House Farm, Fosseway, Lower Slaughter, Bourton-on-the-Water, Cheltenham, Glos, GL54 2HW. Traditional Cotswold house on working small holding. Excellent touring centre. **Open:** All year
01451 820132 (also fax) Mr & Mrs Hedges
D: £17.50–£20.00 **Beds:** 1F 1D ▣ (6) ⚡ ⊡ ★ ▥ ♨

Marshfield

ST7773 🍺 Catherine Wheel, Crown Inn, Lord Nelson

Knowle Hill Farm, Beeks Lane, Marshfield, Chippenham, Wilts, SN14 8BB. Modern farmhouse accommodation on outskirts of Marshfield. Peaceful location. **Open:** All year
01225 891503 C Bond **D:** £20.00–£24.00
S: £20.00–£24.00 **Beds:** 1F 1T 1D **Baths:** 1 En 1 Sh ☎ ▣ (4) ⊡ ★ ✕ ▥ ♨

Meysey Hampton

SU1199

The Masons Arms, High Street, Meysey Hampton, Cirencester, Glos, GL7 5JT. Origins date C17th beside village green in award-winning village. **Open:** All year
01285 850164 (also fax) Mr O'Dell *jane@themasonsarms.freeserve.co.uk* **D:** £28.00–£32.00
S: £38.00–£42.00 **Beds:** 1F 5D 2T 1S
Baths: 9 En ☎ (3) ▣ (4) ⊡ ★ ✕ ⓥ ▥ ♨ cc

Mickleton

SP1643   *Threeways Hotel, King's Arms, Butcher's Arms*

Nineveh Farm, Campden Road, Mickleton, Chipping Campden, Glos, *GL55 6PS.* Award winning Cotswold B&B, convenient for Stratford-upon-Avon/ Warwick. **Open:** All year **Grades:** ETC 4 Diamond
01386 438923 *stay@ninevehfarm.co.uk* www.ninevehfarm.co.uk **D:** £25.00–£27.50 **S:** £40.00–£42.50 **Beds:** 1F 2T 3D **Baths:** 5 En 1 Pr ☎ (5) ₱ (6) ⊬ ▥ ▦ ♨ cc

Old Barn House, Mill Lane, Mickleton, Chipping Campden, Glos, *GL55 6RT.* Quiet location. Heart of conservation area. Ground floor, twin room. **Open:** All year (not Xmas/New Year) **Grades:** ETC 3 Diamond
01386 438668 (also fax) J Lodge **D:** £23.00 **S:** £35.00–£40.00 **Beds:** 1T 1D **Baths:** 2 Pr ☎ (10) ₱ (3) ⊬ ▥ ▦ ♨

Middle Duntisbourne

SO9806

Manor Farm, Middle Duntisbourne, Cirencester, Glos, *GL7 7AR.* Farmhouse set in beautiful Duntisbourne. **Open:** All year (not Xmas/New Year)
01285 658145 Mrs Barton **Fax: 01285 641504** *tina.barton@farming.co.uk* **D:** £20.00–£25.00 **S:** £40.00–£45.00 **Beds:** 1D 1T **Baths:** 1 En 1 Pr ☎ ₱ (8) ⊬ ▥ ♨

Minchinhampton

SO8600

Hyde Crest, Cirencester Road, Minchin-hampton, Stroud, Glos, *GL6 8PE.* Beautiful country house. All bedrooms have own patio into gardens. **Open:** All year **Grades:** ETC 4 Diamond
01453 731631 Mrs Rhoton *hydecrest@ compuserve.com.com* www.hydecrest.co.uk **D:** £22.50 **S:** £30.00 **Beds:** 2D 1T **Baths:** 3 En ☎ (7) ₱ (6) ⊬ ▥ ≒ ▥ ▦ ♿ ♨

Burleigh Farm, Minchinhampton, Stroud, Glos, *GL5 2PF.* Attractive Cotswold stone farmhouse in 38 acres of parkland. Breathtaking views. **Open:** All year (not Xmas)
01453 883112 (also fax) Mr & Mrs Vines **D:** £24.00–£28.50 **S:** £39.00 **Beds:** 2D 1T **Baths:** 2 En 1 Pr ☎ (10) ₱ (5) ⊬ ▥ ✕ ▦ ♨

Mitcheldean

SO6618   *Fox & Hounds, Red Lion, Horse & Groom*

Gunn Mill House, Lower Spout Lane, Mitcheldean, Glos, *GL17 0EA.* **Open:** All year **Grades:** ETC 4 Diamond, Silver
01594 827577 (also fax) *info@ gunnmillhouse.co.uk* www.gunnmillhouse.co. uk **D:** £25.00–£40.00 **S:** £30.00–£45.00 **Beds:** 1F 5D 2T **Baths:** 8 En ☎ ▥ (14) ⊬ ▥ ✕ ▥ ▦ ♨ cc
The Andersons offer great hospitality and food in their Georgian home set in the 27000 acres of the Royal Forest of Dean. Enjoy trips to Tintern Abbey, Gloucester and Hereford Cathedrals or walking, cycling, pony trekking through the Forest.

Moreton-in-Marsh

SP2032

Bran Mill Cottage, Aston Magna, Moreton in Marsh, Glos, *GL56 9QP.* Small traditional B&B in peaceful Cotswold cottage. Friendly, welcoming, homely. **Open:** All year (not Xmas) **Grades:** ETC 3 Diamond
01386 593517 Mr & Mrs Baggaley *enquiries@ branmillcottage.co.uk* www.branmillcottage.co. uk **D:** £17.00–£20.00 **S:** £19.00–£25.00 **Beds:** 1D 1T 1S **Baths:** 1 Pr 1 Sh ☎ (14) ₱ (3) ⊬ ▥ ▥ ▦ ♨

Warwick House, London Road, Moreton-in-Marsh, Glos, *GL56 0HH.* A perfect touring base for the Cotswolds. Facilities include washing/ironing, VCR, phone. **Open:** All year
01608 650773 (also fax) Mr & Mrs Grant *charlie@warwickhousebnb.demon.co.uk* www.snoozeandsizzle.com **D:** £17.50–£20.00 **S:** £20.00–£25.00 **Beds:** 1T 2D **Baths:** 2 En 1 Pr ₱ (3) ⊬ ▥ ▥ ▦ ✾ ♨

Fourshires, Great Wolford Road, Moreton-in-Marsh, Glos, *GL56 0PE.* Beautiful country house set in 3 acres of garden, 1 mile from Moreton-in-Marsh. **Open:** All year (not Xmas)
01608 651412 & 01608 652069 Mrs Affron **Fax: 01608 651412** *m1aff@aol.com* www.fourshires.com **D:** £20.00–£22.00 **S:** £25.00–£30.00 **Beds:** 2D 1T **Baths:** 2 En 1 Pr ☎ (10) ₱ (6) ⊬ ▥ ▦ ♨

National Grid References given are for villages, towns and cities – not for individual houses

---

Planning a longer stay? Always ask for any special rates

Nailsworth

ST8499

Aaron Farm, Nympsfield Road, Nailsworth, Stroud, Glos, *GL6 0ET.* Panoramic views. Ideal for touring Cotswolds. Warm welcome. **Open:** All year **Grades:** ETC 4 Diamond
01453 833598 (also fax) Mrs Mulligan *aaronfarm@compuserve.com* **D:** £21.00–£22.00 **S:** £30.00 **Beds:** 2T 1D **Baths:** 3 En ☎ ₱ (5) ⊬ ▥ ≒ ✕ ♨

The Vicarage, Nailsworth, Stroud, Glos, *GL6 0BS.* Large, comfortable, quiet Victorian vicarage. Beautiful garden. Good breakfast. **Open:** All year
01453 832181 Mrs Strong **D:** £23.00 **S:** £22.00 **Beds:** 1T 3S **Baths:** 1 Pr 1 Sh ₱ (4) ⊬ ▥ ≒ ▦ ♨

Newent

SO7225

Merton House, 7 Birches Lane, Newent, Gloucestershire, *GL18 1DN.* Quiet rural location, good views, excellent walking, touring, local attractions. **Open:** All year
01531 820608 **D:** £17.00–£18.00 **S:** £22.00–£24.00 **Beds:** 2D **Baths:** 1 Sh ₱ (4) ⊬ ▥ ▥ ▦ ♨

The Old Winery, Welsh House Lane, Newent, Gloucestershire, *GL18 1LR.* Comfortable, very attractive former winery, overlooking pretty countryside and vineyards. **Open:** All year (not Xmas)
01531 890824 Mr & Mrs Kingham **Fax: 01594 890824** **D:** £28.00–£32.00 **S:** £28.00–£32.00 **Beds:** 1T **Baths:** 1 En ☎ ₱ (20) ⊬ ▥ ✕ ▥ ▦ ♨

Newnham-on-Severn

SO6911   *Railway Inn, White Hart*

Swan House, High Street, Newnham-on-Severn, Glos, *GL14 1BY.* **Open:** All year (not Xmas/New Year) **Grades:** ETC 4 Diamond, AA 4 Diamond
01594 516504 **Fax: 01594 516177** *prsheldrake@cs.com* **D:** £25.00–£35.00 **S:** £30.00–£40.00 **Beds:** 1F 1T 4D **Baths:** 6 En ☎ ₱ (4) ▥ ≒ ✕ ▥ ▦ ♿ ♨ cc
A warm welcome to our family guest house, C17th merchant's house which is tastefully furnished, all rooms individually decorated and carefully tended garden. Picturesque village and nearby beautiful Forest of Dean offers much, especially for those who enjoy the outdoors.

North Nibley

ST7395

Nibley House, North Nibley, Dursley, Glos, GL11 6DL. Magnificent Georgian manor house, centrepiece of 200 acre farm. **Open:** All year (not Xmas) **01453 543108** Mrs Eley **D:** £22.00–£25.00 **S:** £22.00–£25.00 **Beds:** 1F 1D 1T **Baths:** 2 En 1 Pr ⌅ 🅿 (12) ⊬ 🖵 ⑂ ✕ ▼ ▥ ⚓

Old Sodbury

ST7581   🍺 Bell Inn, Dog Inn

Dornden Guest House, Church Lane, Old Sodbury, Bristol, BS37 6NB. Former vicarage, quietly situated, views to Welsh hills. **Open:** All year (not Xmas) **01454 313325** Mrs Paz **Fax: 01454 312263** dorndenguesthouse@tinyworld.co.uk **D:** £29.00–£32.00 **S:** £29.00–£42.00 **Beds:** 5F 2T 2S **Baths:** 6 En 2 Sh ⌅ 🅿 (15) ⊬ 🖵 ⑂ ✕ ▼ ▥ ⚓

Elmgrove, Badminton Road, Old Sodbury, Bristol, BS17 6LR. Large airy rooms. Homely, friendly accommodation. Lovely gardens. **Open:** All year **01454 313276** E V Arney **D:** £16.00 **S:** £16.00 **Beds:** 2T 2S **Baths:** 1 Sh 🅿 (4) 🖵 ▥ ⚓

1 The Green, Old Sodbury, Bristol, BS37 6LY. Close M4, M5. Ideal location for Cotswold Way, Bath and Bristol. **Open:** All year (not Xmas) **01454 314688** Mr & Mrs Rees **D:** £22.00–£26.00 **S:** £22.00–£26.00 **Beds:** 2D 1T 3S **Baths:** 1 En 2 Sh 🅿 (4) ⊬ 🖵 ▥ ⚓

Painswick

SO8609   🍺 Falcon, Butchers' Arms

Thorne, Friday Street, Painswick, Stroud, Glos, GL6 6QJ. **Open:** Easter to Nov **Grades:** ETC 3 Diamond **01452 812476 (also fax)** **D:** £25.00–£27.00 **S:** £25.00–£30.00 **Beds:** 2T **Baths:** 2 Pr 🅿 🖵 ▥ ⚓
Tudor merchants house with market hall pillars 'in situ' on Cotswold Way.

Planning a longer stay? Always ask for any special rates

Wheatleys, Cotswold Mead, Painswick, Stroud, Glos, GL6 6XB. **Open:** All year (not Xmas) **Grades:** ETC 5 Diamond, Gold **01452 812167** Mrs Burgess **Fax: 01452 814270** wheatleys@dial.pipex.com www.wheatleys-b-and-b.co.uk **D:** £25.00 **S:** £35.00 **Beds:** 1D 1T **Baths:** 2 En ⌅ (10) 🅿 (4) ⊬ 🖵 ▥ ⚓
Set in a beautiful Cotswold village, Wheatley's offers a relaxing base to unwind. A particularly well-appointed suite with connecting sitting room. Guests have full use of the pleasant secluded garden (with croquet), and breakfast can be served on the terrace.

Upper Doreys Mill, Edge, Painswick, Stroud, Glos, GL6 6NF. Rural, peaceful streamside idyll. Log fires, good walking, lovely garden! **Open:** All year **Grades:** ETC 3 Diamond **01452 812459** S Marden **Fax: 01452 814756** sylvia@painswick.co.uk www.doreys.co.uk **D:** £25.00 **S:** £30.00–£35.00 **Beds:** 1T 2D **Baths:** 3 En ⌅ 🅿 (4) ⊬ 🖵 ⚓ cc

Cardynham House, The Cross, Painswick, Glos, GL6 6XA. Charming C16th house. All rooms have 4-poster beds. **Open:** All year **Grades:** ETC 4 Diamond **01452 814006** Ms Keyes **Fax: 01 452 812321** iijo@cardynham.co.uk www.cardynham.co.uk **D:** £30.00–£60.00 **S:** £47.00–£64.00 **Beds:** 3F 6D **Baths:** 3 En 1 Pr ⌅ 🖵 ✕ ▥ ⚓ cc

Pitchcombe

SO8508

Gable End, Pitchcombe, Stroud, Glos, GL6 6LN. C16th - C17th house commands an elevated position overlooking Painswick Valley. **Open:** All year (not Xmas/New Year) **01452 812166** Mrs Partridge **Fax: 01452 812719** **D:** £22.50 **S:** £30.00 **Beds:** 2D **Baths:** 2 En ⌅ (5) 🅿 (4) ▥ ⚓

Poulton

SP1001

Sprucewood, Elf Meadow, Poulton, Cirencester, Glos, GL7 5HQ. Quiet, homely, comfortable. Open views. Warm, friendly welcome awaits you. **Open:** All year (not Xmas) **Grades:** ETC 4 Diamond **01285 851351 (also fax)** Mr & Mrs Walker **D:** £16.00–£20.00 **S:** £22.00–£25.00 **Beds:** 1D 1T 1S **Baths:** 1 Sh ⌅ 🅿 (4) ⊬ 🖵 ▼ ▥ ⚓

Prestbury Park

SO9524

Hunters Lodge, Cheltenham Race Course, Prestbury Park, Cheltenham, Glos, GL50 4SH. Hunters lodge is a friendly hotel situated within the grounds of Cheltenham Racecourse. **Open:** May to Sept **01242 513345** Ms Clark **Fax: 01242 527306** **D:** £18.50 **S:** £21.00 **Beds:** 31F 31T 51S **Baths:** 18 Sh ⌅ 🅿 🖵 ⑂ ✕ ▥ ⚓ cc

Redbrook

SO5310

Tresco, Redbrook, Monmouth, NP5 4LY. Beautiful Wye Valley riverside house, fishing, pony trekking, walking, canoeing. **Open:** All year **01600 712325** Mrs Evans **D:** £16.50 **S:** £16.50 **Beds:** 1F 1D 1T 2S **Baths:** 2 Sh ⌅ 🅿 🖵 ⑂ ✕ ▼ ▥ ⚓ ✳ ⚓

Sherborne

SP1714   🍺 The Fox

The Mead House, Sherborne, Cheltenham, Gloucs, GL54 3DR. Welcoming, comfortable, peaceful old house. Charming garden, views. Exceptional breakfast. **Open:** Mar to Oct **01451 844239** Mrs Medill **D:** £20.00–£25.00 **S:** £25.00 **Beds:** 1T 1D 1S **Baths:** 1 Pr ⌅ (10) 🅿 (1) ⊬ 🖵 ⑂ ▥ ⚓

Siddington

SU0399

Coleen B&B, Ashton Road, Siddington, Cirencester, Glos, GL7 6HR. Choice accommodation in the Cotswolds. Pub with character 50 metres. **Open:** All year **01285 642203** Mrs Proctor proprietor@coleen.co.uk www.coleen.co.uk **D:** £20.00–£25.00 **S:** £30.00–£40.00 **Beds:** 2D 1T **Baths:** 1 En 1 Pr 🅿 (4) ⊬ 🖵 ▼ ▥ ⚓

St Briavels

SO5604

Offas Mead, The Fence, St Briavels, Lydney, Glos, GL15 6QG. Large country home on Offa's Dyke Path. Ensuite available. **Open:** Easter to Oct **01594 530229 (also fax)** Mrs Lacey **D:** £18.00–£20.00 **S:** £18.00–£20.00 **Beds:** 1D 2T **Baths:** 21 En 1 Pr ⌅ (10) 🅿 (6) ⊬ 🖵 ▼ ▥ ⚓

Stanton

SP0634   🍺 Mount Inn

Shenberrow Hill, Stanton, Broadway, Worcs, WR12 7NE. Charming house and cottage accommodation in beautiful unspoilt village. Unforgettable. **Open:** All year (not Xmas) **Grades:** ETC 4 Diamond **01386 584468 (also fax)** Mrs Neilan **D:** £25.00–£27.50 **S:** £30.00 **Beds:** 1F 1D 1T **Baths:** 2 En 1 Pr ⌅ (5) 🅿 (5) 🖵 ⑂ ✕ ▥ ⚓

Staunton (Coleford)

SO5412

Graygill, Staunton, Coleford, Glos, *GL16 8PD.* Quietly situated off A4136. Ideal for Forest of Dean, Wye Valley. **Open:** All year (not Xmas)
01600 712536 Mrs Bond **D:** £17.50 **S:** £17.50 **Beds:** 1D 1T **Baths:** 2 En ⌂ ▣ (4) ▥ ⅏ ▦.

Staunton (Gloucester)

SO7829

Kilmorie, Gloucester Road, Corse, Staunton, Gloucester, *GL19 3RQ.*
Open: All year (not Xmas)
01452 840224 Ms Barnfield **D:** £17.00–£20.00 **S:** £18.00–£20.00 **Beds:** 1F 2D 1T 1S **Baths:** 3 En 1 Pr 1 Sh ⌂ ▣ (8) ▥ ⅏ ▦. Grade II Listed (c1848) smallholding. Quality all ground floor accommodation, tea trays, toiletries, TVs all rooms, mainly ensuite. Rural location, large garden to relax - watch birds, butterflies, wildlife we encourage, meet our pony, free-range hens. Ramble countryside footpaths, safe parking.

Staverton

SO8823

Hope Orchard, Gloucester Road, Staverton, Cheltenham, Glos, *GL51 0TF.* Attractive rooms overlooking old orchard and paddock. Picnic area available. **Open:** All year (not Xmas/New Year)
01452 855556 Mrs Parker **Fax:** 01452 530037 *info@hopeorchard.com* www.hopeorchard.com **D:** £20.00–£45.00 **S:** £25.00–£30.00 **Beds:** 3F 2T 3D **Baths:** 8 En ⌂ ▣ (12) ▥ ⅏ ▦ & ♦ cc

Stonehouse

SO8005

Tiled House Farm, Oxlynch, Stonehouse, Glos, *GL10 3DF.* C16th black and white half-timbered farmhouse, with oak beams and inglenook fireplace. **Open:** All year (not Xmas)
01453 822363 Mrs Jeffrey *nigel.jeffery@ukgateway.net* **D:** £19.00–£21.00 **S:** £19.00–£20.00 **Beds:** 1D 1T 1S **Baths:** 1 Pr 1 Sh ⌂ (10) ▣ ⅄ ▥ ▦.

Stow-on-the-Wold

SP1826 ⊲ The Fox, Talbot, Horse & Groom, Eagle & Child, King's Arms

The Limes, Evesham Road, Stow-on-the-Wold, Cheltenham, Glos, *GL54 1EN.* Large Victorian house, attractive garden. 4 minute walk to town, comfortable. **Open:** All year (not Xmas)
01451 830034 Mr Keyte **D:** £21.50–£22.00 **S:** £25.00–£42.00 **Beds:** 1F 4D 2T **Baths:** 4 En 1 Pr ⌂ ▣ (5) ▥ ⅏ ▥ ▦.

South Hill Farmhouse, Fosseway, Stow-on-the-Wold, Cheltenham, Glos, *GL54 1JU.* Listed Cotswold farmhouse. Warm welcome. Ideal for walking or touring. **Open:** All year **Grades:** ETC 3 Diamond
01451 831888 Mr & Mrs Cassie **Fax:** 01451 832255 *info@southhill.co.uk* www.southhill.co. uk **D:** £24.00 **S:** £35.00 **Beds:** 1F 2D 2T 1S **Baths:** 1 Pr 5 En ▣ (10) ⅄ ▥ ▦. ♦ cc

Fifield Cottage, Fosse Lane, Stow-on-the-Wold, Cheltenham, Glos, *GL54 1EH.* Cottage on private road, peaceful situation. Close to town. Attractive garden. **Open:** All year (not Xmas)
01451 831056 Mrs Keyte **D:** £21.00–£22.00 **S:** £25.00 **Beds:** 1F 1D 1T **Baths:** 2 En 1 Pr ⌂ ▣ (4) ▥ ⅏ ▥ ▦. ♦

Corsham Field Farmhouse, Bledington Road, Stow-on-the-Wold, Cheltenham, Glos, *GL54 1JH.* Homely farmhouse with breathtaking views. Ideally situated for exploring Cotswolds. **Open:** All year **Grades:** ETC 3 Diamond, AA 3 Diamond
01451 831750 Mr Smith **D:** £20.00–£25.00 **S:** £25.00 **Beds:** 3F 2D 2T **Baths:** 5 En 1 Sh ⌂ ▣ (10) ▥ ⅏ ▥ ▦. ♦

Stroud

SO8405

The Downfield Hotel, Cainscross Road, Stroud, Glos, *GL5 4HN.* Stunning views of the hills and valleys. An unforgettable holiday. **Open:** All year **Grades:** ETC 3 Star
01453 764496 **Fax:** 01453 753150 *messenger@downfieldotel.demon.co.uk* **D:** £20.00–£29.50 **S:** £30.00–£45.00 **Beds:** 2F 9D 6T 4S **Baths:** 11 En 10 Sh ⌂ ▣ (25) ⅄ ▥ ⅏ × ▥ ▦. cc

Fir Tree House, Rodborough Common, Stroud, Glos, *GL5 5BJ.* Be warm and comfortable, have fabulous views, explore The Cotswolds. **Open:** All year (not Xmas/New Year)
01453 762591 (also fax) Mrs Peters *cip@virgin.net* **D:** £20.00 **S:** £20.00 **Beds:** 1T **Baths:** 1 En ▣ ⅄ ▥ × ▥ ▦. ♦

Beechcroft, Brownshill, Chalford, Stroud, Glos, *GL6 8AG.* Quietly situated Edwardian house. Home made bread and preserves. Good walking. **Open:** All year **Grades:** ETC 3 Diamond
01453 883422 Mrs Salt **D:** £20.00–£25.00 **S:** £24.00–£30.00 **Beds:** 1T 1D ⌂ ▣ (2) ⅄ ▥ × ▥ ▦. ♦

Clothiers Arms, Bath Road, Stroud, Glos, *GL5 3JJ.* Within walking distance of Stroud town centre, trains and bus station. **Open:** All year
01453 763801 Mrs Close **Fax:** 01453 757161 *luciano@clothiersarms.demon.co.uk* www.clothiersarms.co.uk **D:** £20.00–£33.00 **S:** £23.00–£35.00 **Beds:** 7F 3D 2T **Baths:** 6 En 1 Pr ⌂ ▣ (50) ⅄ ▥ ⅏ × ▥ ▦. ♦ cc

Swineford

ST6969

Crofton Cottage, Bath Road, Swineford, Bitton, Bristol, *BS30 6LW.* Pretty 1800s cottage, recently refurbished, on the banks of the River Avon. **Open:** All year
0117 932 3671 Mr & Mrs Marsh *crofton.cott@virgin.net* **D:** £20.00–£25.00 **S:** £30.00–£35.00 **Beds:** 1T 1D **Baths:** 2 En ▣ (6) ⅏ ▥ ▦. ♦

Tewkesbury

SO8933 ⊲ Fleet Inn, Crown Inn, Bell Inn, Royal Hop Pole

Carrant Brook House, Rope Walk, Tewkesbury, Glos, *GL20 5DS.* Warm welcome, great breakfast. Quiet location, 3 minutes from amenities. **Open:** All year **Grades:** ETC 3 Diamond
01684 290355 Mrs Bishop *lorraine@carrantbrookhouse.co.uk* **D:** £25.00–£55.00 **S:** £27.50–£35.00 **Beds:** 1D 1T 1S **Baths:** 3 En ⌂ ▣ (4) ⅄ ▥ × ▥ ▦. ✿ ♦

Barton House Guesthouse, 5 Barton Road, Tewkesbury, Glos, *GL20 5QG.* Regency house close to town centre, Abbey, rivers and M5. **Open:** All year
01684 292049 M J Green **D:** £18.00–£25.00 **S:** £25.00–£30.00 **Beds:** 2F 1T 1D **Baths:** 1 En 1 Sh ⌂ ▣ (4) ▥ ♦

Hoo Farm, Gloucester Road, Tewkesbury, Glos, *GL20 7DD.* Superior hospitality in beautiful farmhouse, six acre grounds in glorious countryside. **Open:** All year
01684 292185 & 07801 506083 (M) Mrs Mitchell **Fax:** 01684 292185 *hoofarm@ukonline.co.uk* **D:** £20.00–£25.00 **S:** £25.00 **Beds:** 2T 1S **Baths:** 1 Pr 1 Sh ⌂ ▣ (10) ⅄ ▥ ⅏ × ▥ ▦. ♦

Two, Back of Avon, Riverside Walk, Tewkesbury, Glos, *GL20 5BA.* Lovely Queen Anne house, Grade II Listed, overlooking river. **Open:** All year
01684 298935 Mr & Mrs Leach **D:** £19.00–£22.00 **S:** £22.00–£25.00 **Beds:** 1F 1D 1T **Baths:** 2 En ⌂ ▣ ⅄ ▥ ⅏ × ▥ ▦. ♦

All details shown are as supplied by B&B owners in Autumn 2001

Todenham

SP2336

Roosters, Todenham, Moreton-in-Marsh, Glos, GL56 9PA. Beautifully situated for exploring Cotswolds. Lovely C17th stone house. Lovely gardens. **Open:** All year (not Xmas)
01608 650645 (also fax) Ms Longmore www.touristnet.uk.com/wm/roosters
D: £23.00–£25.00 **S:** £25.00–£30.00 **Beds:** 1D 2T **Baths:** 2 En 1 Pr ⊃ 🄿 (8) ⠂ 🄫 ⌖ ✕ 🄥 🎬, ♨

Tormarton

ST7678

Chestnut Farm, Tormarton, Badminton, GL9 1HS. Small Georgian farmhouse. **Open:** All year
01454 218563 (also fax) Ms Cadei www.chestnut.farm.co.uk **D:** £30.00–£45.00 **S:** £30.00–£45.00 **Beds:** 1F 4D 2T **Baths:** 7 Pr ⊃ 🄿 (8) 🄫 ⌖ ✕ 🄥 🎬, ✿ ♨

The Portcullis, Tormarton, Badminton, GL9 1HZ. Traditional ivy-clad inn and restaurant in pretty Cotswold village. **Open:** All year (not Xmas)
01454 218263 Fax: 01454 218094 D: £20.00–£25.00 **S:** £28.00–£30.00 **Beds:** 1F 2D 4T **Baths:** 7 En ⊃ (6) 🄿 (40) 🄥 ✕ 🄥 🎬, ♨ cc

Tredington

SO9029

Gothic Farm, Tredington, Tewkesbury, Glos, GL20 7BS. Friendly, comfortable, character farmhouse with wonderful views of the Cotswolds. **Open:** All year (not Xmas)
01684 293360 Mr Coleman molliecoleman@ aol.com **D:** £18.00–£25.00 **S:** £20.00–£30.00 **Beds:** 1D 1T **Baths:** 1 Pr 2 Sh ⊃ (2) 🄿 (10) ⠂ 🄫 🄫 ⌖ ✕ 🄥 🎬, ♨ cc

Uley

ST7898   ◭ King's Head, Crown Inn

Hill House, Crawley Hill, Uley, Dursley, Glos, GL11 5BH. Very warm welcome. Cotswold stone house, beautiful views, quiet location. **Open:** All year (not Xmas)
01453 860267 Mrs V Coates **D:** £18.50–£22.00 **S:** £17.00–£30.00 **Beds:** 1F 1D 1T 1S **Baths:** 2 En 1 Sh ⊃ 🄿 (5) ⠂ 🄫 ✕ 🄥 🎬, ♨

Upton St Leonards

SO8614   ◭ King's Head, Four Mile House, Royal William, Black Horse

Bullens Manor Farm, Portway, Upton St Leonards, Gloucester, GL4 8DL. Beautiful views. Lovely walks. **Open:** All year (not Xmas/New Year) **Grades:** ETC 4 Diamond
01452 616463 Mrs Warner **D:** £21.00–£22.00 **S:** £23.00–£25.00 **Beds:** 2T 3D 3S **Baths:** 3 En 🄿 (6) ⠂ 🄫 🄥 ♨

Westonbirt

ST8589

Avenue Farm, Knockdown, Tetbury, Glos, GL8 8QY. 300-year-old farmhouse in farm adjoining Westonbirt Arboretum. Bath, Bristol, Gloucester easy reach. **Open:** All year
01454 238207 Mrs King **Fax: 01454 238033** sonjames@breathemail.net **D:** £20.00–£25.00 **S:** £25.00 **Beds:** 1F 1D 2T **Baths:** 2 En 1 Sh ⊃ 🄿 (6) ⠂ 🄫 🄥 🎬, ♨

Whittington

SP0021   ◭ Craven Arms

Whittington Lodge Farm, Whittington, Cheltenham, Glos, GL54 4HB. Beautiful Cotswold stone farmhouse. Perfect for relaxing, walking, town, racecourse. **Open:** All year (not Xmas/New Year) **Grades:** ETC 4 Diamond, Silver
01242 820603 & 07976 691589 (M) C Boyd **Fax: 01242 820603** cathy@ whittlodgefarm.fslife.co.uk **D:** £23.00–£25.00 **S:** £30.00 **Beds:** 2T 1D **Baths:** 1 En 1 Pr 1 Sh ⊃ (12) 🄿 (4) ⠂ 🄫 🄥 🎬, ♨

Winchcombe

SP0228   ◭ White Hart, White Lion, Corner Cupboard, Plaisterers' Arms

Manor Farm, Winchcombe, Cheltenham, Glos, GL54 5BJ. Luxurious Cotswold manor on family farm. Camping and caravan space on farm with facilities. **Open:** All year (not Xmas)
01242 602423 (also fax) Mr & Mrs Day janet@ dickandjanet.fsnet.co.uk **D:** £25.00–£30.00 **S:** £30.00 **Beds:** 2D 1T **Baths:** 3 En ⊃ 🄿 (20) 🄥 🄥 ♨

Ireley Farm, Ireley Road, Winchcombe, Cheltenham, Glos, GL54 5PA. C18th Cotswold stone character farmhouse. Relaxed. Excellent breakfasts. **Open:** Jan to Nov
01242 602445 Mrs Warmington warmingtonmaggot@aol.com **D:** £20.00–£25.00 **S:** £20.00–£25.00 **Beds:** 1F 1D 1T **Baths:** 2 En 1 Pr ⊃ 🄿 🄥 ✕ 🄥 ♨

Gower House

Gower House, 16 North Street, Winchcombe, Cheltenham, Glos, GL54 5LH. Ideally situated for exploring Cotswolds. Close to shops, pubs, restaurants. **Open:** All year (not Xmas)
01242 602616 Mrs Simmonds **D:** £22.50–£24.00 **S:** £30.00–£40.00 **Beds:** 1D 2T **Baths:** 3 En ⊃ 🄿 (3) 🄥 🄥 🎬, ♨

Blair House, 41 Gretton Road, Winchcombe, Cheltenham, Glos, GL54 5EG. Georgian house in historic town. Warm friendly welcome, excellent breakfasts. **Open:** All year **Grades:** ETC 4 Diamond
01242 603626 Mrs Chisholm **Fax: 01242 604214** chisssurv@aol.com **D:** £22.50 **S:** £25.00–£30.00 **Beds:** 1D 1T 2S **Baths:** 1 En 1 Sh ⊃ 🄿 (1) ⠂ 🄫 🄥 🎬, ♨

Sudeley Hill Farm, Winchcombe, Cheltenham, Glos, GL54 5JB. Comfortably furnished C15th farmhouse. **Open:** All year (not Xmas)
01242 602344 (also fax) Mrs Scudamore **D:** £22.00–£25.00 **S:** £30.00–£32.00 **Beds:** 1F 1D 1T **Baths:** 3 En ⊃ 🄿 (10) 🄥 🄥 🎬, ♨

Ireley Grounds, Barnhouse, Broadway Road, Winchcombe, Cheltenham, Glos, GL54 5NY. Stunning Cotswold house in 6 acres of attractive gardens, magnificent views of the countryside. **Open:** All year (not Xmas)
01242 603736 Mr Wright **D:** £22.50–£32.50 **S:** £22.50–£32.50 **Beds:** 1F 3D **Baths:** 4 En ⊃ 🄿 (20) ⠂ 🄫 🄥 🎬, ♨

Wotton-under-Edge

ST7692

Wotton Guest House, 31a Long Street, Wotton-under-Edge, Glos, GL12 7BX. C17th Manor house. Superb food in adjoining coffee shop. **Open:** All year
01453 843158 Mrs Nixon **Fax: 01453 842410 D:** £24.00 **S:** £30.00 **Beds:** 1F 2D 2T 2S **Baths:** 7 En ⊃ 🄿 (12) ⠂ 🄫 🄫 🎬, ♨

Under-the-Hill-House, Adeys Lane, Wotton-under-Edge, Glos, GL12 7LY. C18th listed period house overlooking National Trust land. **Open:** Mar to Oct
01453 842557 Mrs Forster **D:** £20.00–£22.00 **S:** £20.00–£22.00 **Beds:** 1T 1D **Baths:** 1 Sh ⊃ (13) 🄿 (2) ⠂ 🄫 🄥 🎬, ♨

Greater Manchester & Merseyside

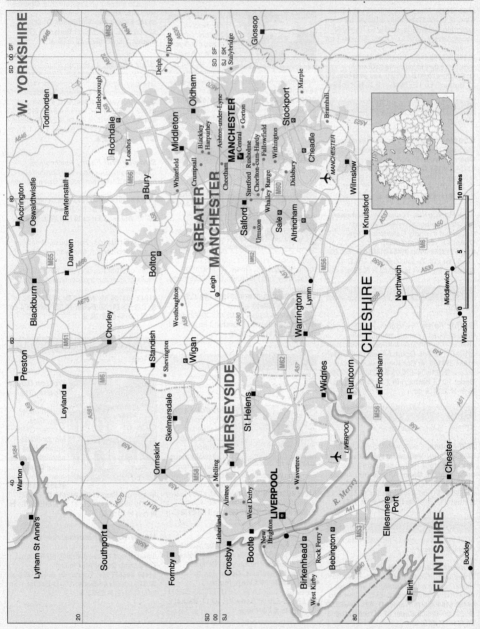

Altrincham

SJ7687

Oasis Hotel, *46-48 Barrington Road, Altrincham, Cheshire, WA14 1HN.* With warm and friendly welcome, ideally located in South Manchester and Manchester airport. **Open:** All year
0161 928 4523 D: £20.00–£24.00 **S:** £30.00–£36.00 **Beds:** 4F 9T 10D 10S **Baths:** 33 En cc

Belvedere Guest House, *58 Barrington Road, Altrincham, Cheshire, WA14 1HY.* Close to tram, restaurants, pubs. Manchester Airport 12 minutes away. **Open:** All year
0161 941 5996 Mr Kelly **Fax: 0161 929 6450 D:** £18.00 **S:** £20.00 **Beds:** 2F 1T **Baths:** 4 Pr (5) 1

Acorn Of Oakmere, *6 Wingate Drive Timperley, Altrincham, Greater Manchester, WA15 7PX.* Warm comfortable family home, attractive walled garden. Relax with sunken spa bath. **Open:** All year
0161 980 8391 Mrs Moore *oakmere6@cwctv.net* **D:** £25.00–£30.00 **S:** £25.00–£30.00 **Beds:** 1T 1S **Baths:** 1 En 1 Sh (2)

Ashton-under-Lyne

SJ9399

Lynwood Hotel, *3 Richmond Street, Ashton-under-Lyne, Greater Manchester, OL6 7TX.* **Open:** All year **Grades:** ETC 3 Diamond
0161 330 5358 (also fax) Mrs Lindsay **D:** £20.00–£24.00 **S:** £20.00–£24.00 **Beds:** 1F 1T 2S **Baths:** 2 En 1 Sh
A friendly family-run hotel in a quiet location, 5 mins from Ashton and Portland Basin. Manchester Airport 20 mins, convenient to motorways, Manchester, Gmex, Arena, Lowry centre, Velodrome and Trafford Centre, also for Commonwealth Games. Pubs and restaurants close by. A warm welcome guaranteed.

King William IV Hotel, *Stamford Street West, Ashton-under-Lyne, Lancashire, OL6 7QU.* Mainly for commercial traveller seeking good clean accommodation at reasonable rates. **Open:** All year (not Xmas/ New Year)
0161 339 6016 D: £15.00 **S:** £15.00 **Beds:** 5T 2D 1S **Baths:** 5 Pr cc

Bebington

SJ3383

Bebington Hotel, *24 Town Lane, Bebington, Wirral, Merseyside, L63 5JG.* All rooms of high standard, tastefully decorated, home from home comforts. Well lit car park. **Open:** All year (not Xmas)
0151 645 0608 (also fax) Mrs Vaghena **D:** £20.00–£22.50 **S:** £25.00 **Beds:** 1F 5D 1T 8S **Baths:** 15 En (12)

Birkenhead

SJ3088

Ashgrove Guest House, *14 Ashville Road, Claughton, Prenton, Birkenhead, Merseyside, CH43 8SA.* **Open:** All year
0151 653 3794 Mr Lupton *briory@barclays.net* **D:** £20.00–£24.00 **S:** £20.00–£24.00 **Beds:** 1F 2D 2T 2S **Baths:** 1 En 3 Sh (6)
Friendly family-run establishment with musical ties, overlooking parkland. Main shopping area 1 mile . Mileage Liverpool 4, Chester 17, Southport 23, Blackpool 80. Games room. Self catering from £15 per night/ £75 per week, per person.

Bolton

SD7108

Glengarry Guest House, *79 Bradford Street, Bolton, Lancs, BL2 1JY.* Small, established, family run. 5 mins motorway and town centre. **Open:** All year (not Xmas)
01204 534299 Mrs Hope *sue@glengarry.info* **D:** £17.00–£18.00 **S:** £17.00–£18.00 **Beds:** 1F 1D 4T 1S **Baths:** 3 Sh

Heyesleigh, *98 Castle Street, Bolton, Lancs, BL2 1JL.* Situated off main A58. Bury Bolton Road. 7 minute walk town centre. **Open:** All year (not Xmas)
01204 523647 (also fax) Mrs Daley **D:** £16.00–£18.00 **S:** £17.00–£22.00 **Beds:** 3F 2D 1T 3S **Baths:** 5 En 1 Sh

Bramhall

SJ8984 *Ladybrook*

280 Bramhall Lane South, *Bramhall, Stockport, Cheshire, SK7 3DJ.* Close to South Manchester. Luxury accommodation. Warm, friendly. English breakfast. **Open:** All year
0161 439 5600 Mrs Hurd *guests@brookfieldguesthouse.co.uk* www.brookfieldguesthouse.co.uk **D:** £19.00–£24.00 **S:** £28.00–£30.00 **Beds:** 1F 1T 2D 1S **Baths:** 2 En 2 Sh cc

Bury

SD8010 *Pack Horse, Game Cock, George Inn*

Ashbury Guest House, *235 Rochdale Road, Bury, Greater Manchester, BL9 7BX.* **Open:** All year
0161 762 9623 G Woodall **Fax: 0161 763 3887 D:** £20.00–£22.00 **S:** £20.00–£25.00 **Beds:** 1D 1T 2S **Baths:** 1 En 1 Sh
Relax in a warm friendly family-run guest house. All rooms have TV/radio alarm. Tea/ coffee, en-suite rooms available. Direct access to Manchester via metro approximately 20 mins situated main road position directly off M66 motorway Junction 2.

Cheadle Hulme

SJ8786

Spring Cottage, *60 Hulme Hall Road, Cheadle Hulme, Cheadle, Cheshire, SK8 6JZ.* Beautiful Victorian house adjacent to the C17th Hulme Hall. **Open:** All year **Grades:** ETC 3 Diamond
0161 485 1037 (also fax) Mr & Mrs Buckley **D:** £30.00–£42.00 **S:** £23.00–£28.00 **Beds:** 2T 1S 1F **Baths:** 3 Pr 1 Sh (6) cc

Delph

SD9807 *Great Western*

Globe Farm Guest House, *Huddersfield Road, Delph, Oldham, Lancashire, OL3 5LU.* Former coaching house converted into comfortable ensuite bed & breakfast. **Open:** All year (not Xmas/New Year)
01457 873040 (also fax) *globefarm@amserve.com* www.globefarm.co.uk **D:** £22.50 **S:** £25.00 **Beds:** 1F 4T 5D 4S **Baths:** 14 En (30) cc

Diggle

SE0008

New Barn, *Harrop Green Farm, Diggle, Oldham, Lancs, OL3 5LW.* Working farm, lovely views over Saddleworth villages. Close to Standedge Canal Tunnel. **Open:** All year (not Xmas)
01457 873937 & 07979 598232 (M) Mr Rhodes **Fax: 01457 873937 D:** £17.00–£18.00 **S:** £17.00–£18.00 **Beds:** 1F 1D 1T 1S **Baths:** 1 Pr 1 Sh (10)

Sunfield, *Diglea, Diggle, Saddleworth, Oldham, Lancs, OL3 5LA.* Scenic Saddleworth Canal towpaths, walking, cycling, horse riding - it's all here. **Open:** All year
01457 874030 Mr & Mrs Francis **Fax: 01457 810488 D:** £15.00–£18.00 **S:** £20.00–£25.00 **Beds:** 1F 3D 2T 1S **Baths:** 7 En (8)

Leigh

SD6500

Three Crowns, *188 Chapel Street, Leigh, Lancashire, WN7 2DW.* Three Crowns, Leigh, pub/restaurant open all year round. **Open:** All year
01942 673552 D: £15.00 **S:** £15.00 **Beds:** 1T 1S cc

Planning a longer stay? Always ask for any special rates

Litherland

SJ3498

Litherland Park, *34 Litherland Park, Litherland, Bootle, L21 9HP.* Victorian detached house, spacious lounge, three bedrooms. Warm welcome assured. **Open:** All year (not Xmas/New Year)
0151 928 1085 B Harper **D:** £19.00 **S:** £20.00
Beds: 2D 1S **Baths:** 2 Sh ▣ (4) ⊠ ✕ 皿 ♨

Littleborough

SD9316

Hollingworth Lake B&B, *164 Smithybridge Road, Hollingworth Lake, Littleborough, Lancashire,*
OL15 0DB. 5 Diamond Gold Award Winner 2001 at Hollingworth Lake Country Park.
Open: All year
01706 376583 Ms Wood **D:** £15.00–£22.50
S: £25.00–£30.00 **Beds:** 1F 2D 1T 1S
Baths: 5 En ⊱ ▣ (5) ⊬ ⊠ ⊁ ⊠ 皿 ♨⅃ ♨ ⚊ cc

Swing Cottage Guest House, *31 Lakebank, Hollingworth Lake Country Park, Littleborough, Greater Manchester, OL15 0DQ.* 'North West Best B&B' winner 2000 - beautiful countryside. **Open:** All year
01706 379094 C Dean **Fax: 01706 379091**
swingcottage@aol.com www.hollingworthlake.
com **D:** £22.50 **S:** £35.00 **Beds:** 2F 1T
Baths: 3 En ⊱ ⊠ ⊬ ⊠ ✕ 皿 ♨ ⚊ cc

LIVERPOOL   Central

SJ3490

Embassie Youth Hostel, *1 Falkner Square, Liverpool, L8 7NU.* Town house in beautiful Georgian Falkner Square. Head towards Anglican cathedral, up Canning St.
Open: All year
0151 707 1089 Mr Murphy **D:** £12.50
S: £9.50–£11.50 **Beds:** 20S **Baths:** 5 Sh
⊱ (12) ▣ ⊠ 皿.

LIVERPOOL   Wavertree

SJ3889

Holmeleigh Guest House, *93 Woodcroft Road, Wavertree, Liverpool, L15 2HG.* Family-run, continental breakfast, only 2.5 miles from city centre. **Open:** All year
0151 734 2216 (day) & 0151 726 9980
Mrs Bridge **Fax: 0151 728 9521** *bridges01@ cableinet.co.uk* **D:** £15.00–£25.00 **S:** £15.00–£30.00 **Beds:** 4T 2D 4S **Baths:** 6 En 1 Sh ⊱
⊠ 皿 ♨

Planning a longer stay? Always ask for any special rates

LIVERPOOL   West Derby

SJ3993

Parkland Bed & Breakfast, *38 Coachman's Drive, Croxteth Park, Liverpool, L12 0HX.* Quiet residential house in country park. 5 miles from city centre. **Open:** All year (not Xmas/New Year)
0151 259 1417 R Todd **D:** £20.00 **S:** £20.00
Beds: 1T 1D **Baths:** 1 Sh ▣ (2) ⊬ ⊠ 皿 ♨

MANCHESTER   Blackley

SD8602

New White Lion, *7 Middleton Old Road, Blackley, Manchester, M9 3DS.* Pleasant location, 7 mins city centre, 4 mins Commonwealth Stadium. Licensed bar on site. **Open:** All year
0161 720 7218 **D:** £13.00–£15.00 **S:** £13.00–£15.00 **Beds:** 2F 3T 1D **Baths:** 6 En ⊱ ⊠ ✕
皿 ♨

Bentley Guest House, *64 Hill Lane, Blackley, Manchester, M6 0PF.* A private homely semi-detached house, personal service, comfortable quality accommodation. **Open:** All year
0161 795 1115 R Kerassites **D:** £15.00–£20.00
S: £18.00–£20.00 **Beds:** 2D 1S **Baths:** 1 En 1
Sh ⊱ (9) ▣ (3) ⊬ ⊠ 皿 ♨

MANCHESTER   Central

SJ8397

Monroes Hotel, *38 London Road, Manchester, M1 1PE.* Small family hotel in city centre opposite Piccadilly Station. Showers in most rooms. **Open:** All year (not Xmas/New Year)
0161 236 0564 Mr Ryan **D:** £16.00 **S:** £16.00
Beds: 4T 1D 2S **Baths:** 2 Sh ⊱ ⊠ ✕ ⊠ 皿 ♨

MANCHESTER   Cheetham

SD8400

New Central Hotel, *144-146 Heywood Street, Cheetham, Manchester, M8 7PD.* Small, comfortable, friendly hotel.
Open: All year
0161 205 2169 (also fax) Mrs Greenwood
newcentral@talk21.com **D:** £16.50–£17.50
S: £18.50–£21.50 **Beds:** 1F 1D 2T 7S
Baths: 5 Pr 2 Sh ⊱ (2) ▣ (7) ⊠ ⊁ ✕ ⊠ 皿 ♨

MANCHESTER   Chorlton-cum-Hardy

SJ8193

Abbey Lodge Hotel, *501 Wilbraham Road, Chorlton-cum-Hardy, Manchester, M21 0UJ.* Elegant Edwardian house. Large, comfortable ensuite rooms. Centrally located. Breakfast served. **Open:** All year (not Xmas/New Year) **Grades:** ETC 3 Star
0161 862 9266 **D:** £25.00–£40.00 **S:** £30.00–£50.00 **Beds:** 1T 3D **Baths:** 4 En ⊱ ▣ ⊬ ⊠ ✕
皿 ♨

Kempton House Hotel, *400 Wilbraham Road, Chorlton-cum-Hardy, Manchester, M21 0UH.* Friendly, family run hotel, comfortable, good food and children very welcome. **Open:** All year (not Xmas/New Year)
0161 881 8766 Mr Paterson *kempton.house@ virgin.net* **D:** £20.00–£25.00 **S:** £20.00–£25.00
Beds: 1F 1T 5D 3S **Baths:** 5 En 2 Sh ⊱ ▣ (6)
⊠ ✕ ⊠ 皿 ♨ ⚊ cc

MANCHESTER   Crumpsall

SD8402

Cleveland Lodge, *117 Cleveland Road, Crumpsall, Manchester, M8 4GX.* Nearby Metrolink station, serves city centre and places of interest. **Open:** All year
0161 795 0007 (also fax) A Musgrove
D: £17.00 **S:** £25.00 **Beds:** 2D 1S ⊱ ⊬ ⊠ ⊠
皿 ♨

MANCHESTER   Didsbury

SJ8491

Palatine Hotel, *88 Palatine Road, West Didsbury, Manchester, M20 3JW.* Conveniently situated in best suburb. Warm, friendly, clean. Detached period dwelling. **Open:** All year **Grades:** ETC 3 Diamond
0161 446 2222 **D:** £20.00–£23.00 **S:** £25.00–£32.00 **Beds:** 3F 13T 10D 10S **Baths:** 2 En 17
Pr 7 Sh ⊱ ▣ (16) ⊠ ⊠ 皿 ♨ ⚊ cc

MANCHESTER   Fallowfield

SJ8593

Wilmslow Hotel, *356 Wilmslow Road, Fallowfield, Manchester, M14 6AB.* Family run, helpful staff, pubs and restaurants 5 minutes walk. **Open:** All year
0161 225 3030 Fax: 0161 257 2854 D: £15.32–£20.62 **S:** £19.95–£25.95 **Beds:** 4F 6T 9D 9S
Baths: 14 En 3 Sh ⊱ ▣ (10) ⊠ 皿 ♨ cc

MANCHESTER   Gorton

SJ8896

Clyde Mount Guest House, *866 Hyde Road Debdale Park, Gorton, Manchester, M18 7LH.* Large Victorian house overlooking park, friendly, comfortable, convenient city centre. **Open:** All year
0161 231 1515 *clydemount.sw@amserve.net*
D: £18.00 **S:** £18.00 **Beds:** 1F 3D 3T 3S
Baths: 3 Sh ⊱ ▣ (8) ⊠ 皿 ♨ cc

BATHROOMS
En = Ensuite
Pr = Private
Sh = Shared

MANCHESTER
Harpurhey
SD8601

Harpers Hotel, *745 Rochdale Road, Harpurhey, Manchester, M9 5SB.* Rooms ensuite. 2 miles city centre, Manchester Arena, Velodrome, 2002 Stadium. **Open:** All year
0161 203 5475 (also fax) D: £22.00–£30.00 **S:** £32.00–£40.00 **Beds:** 13F **Baths:** 13 En ☎ 🖂 ▥ ♿

MANCHESTER
Rusholme
SJ8695

Luther King House, *Brighton Grove, Manchester, M14 5JP.* Comfortable and value for money, overnight and short stay accommodation. **Open:** All year (not Xmas/New Year)
0161 224 6404 Fax: 0161 248 9201
accomodation@lkh.co.uk www.lkh.co.uk
D: £17.75–£19.75 **S:** £24.50 **Beds:** 3F 8T 3D 35S **Baths:** 25 En 12 Sh ☎ 🖻 (46) ⅟✓ ▥ ✝ ✕ ▣ ▥ ♿ ☕ cc

Elton Bank Hotel, *62 Platt Lane, Rusholme, Manchester, M14 5NE.* Peaceful parkside setting. Fast access to Manchester city centre. **Open:** All year (not Xmas/New Year)
0161 224 6449 *eltonbank@dial.pipex.com*
D: £39.00–£43.00 **S:** £28.00–£33.00 **Beds:** 3T 3S **Baths:** 1 En 1 Pr 1 Sh 🖻 (6) ▥ ▣ ☕ cc

MANCHESTER   Stretford
SJ8095

Greatstone Hotel, *843-845 Chester Road, Gorse Hill, Stretford, Manchester, M32 0RN.* Family-run. Five minute walk Manchester Utd football ground. **Open:** All year
0161 865 1640 Mr Sill **D:** £18.00–£20.00 **S:** £20.00–£22.00 **Beds:** 1F 5T 6D 12S
Baths: 2 En 4 Pr 3 Sh ☎ 🖻 (50) ▥ ▣ ▥ cc

MANCHESTER
Whalley Range
SJ8294

Polex Hotel, *70-78 Dudley Road, off Withington Road, Whalley Range, Manchester, M16 8DE.* 2m city centre, 1.5m Old Trafford, 3m airport. Continental breakfast, CH, 4 languages spoken. **Open:** All year
0161 881 4038 Mr Klocek **Fax: 0161 881 1567**
D: £26.00–£30.00 **S:** £25.00 **Beds:** 2F 10D 24S **Baths:** 38 En ☎ (6) 🖻 (24) ▥ ▣ ☕ cc

MANCHESTER
Withington
SJ8592

The Drop Inn Hotel, *393 Wilmslow Road, Withington, Manchester, M20 4WA.* Pub/hotel separate buildings. Satellite television. Pool room. Very warm and cosy. **Open:** All year
0161 286 1919 G Wood **Fax: 0161 286 8880**
thedropinn@maileaseynet.co.uk
www.maileaseynet.co.uk **D:** £25.00–£45.00
Beds: 15F 23T 7D 1S ☎ 🖻 (50) ▥ ✝ ✕ ▣ ▥ ✳ ☕ cc

Marple
SJ9588

Sinclair Lodge, *84 Strines Road, Marple, Stockport, SK6 7DU.* Modern bungalow, countryside setting, yet convenient for town and airport. **Open:** All year (not Xmas)
0161 449 9435 (also fax) M Scott *mscott144@aol.com* www.members.aol.com/mscott144
D: £20.00–£28.00 **S:** £20.00–£25.00 **Beds:** 1D 1S **Baths:** 1 En ☎ 🖻 (6) ⅟✓ ▥ ▣ ☕

New Brighton
SJ3093

Sherwood Guest House, *55 Wellington Road, New Brighton, Wallasey, Wirral, CH45 2ND.* Family run guest house close to train/bus station/ motorway. **Open:** All year (not Xmas/New Year) **Grades:** ETC 3 Diamond
0151 639 5198 Mrs Brereton *frankbreo@btinternet.com* **D:** £15.00–£18.00 **S:** £18.00–£20.00 **Beds:** 2F 3T 1S **Baths:** 3 En 3 Sh ☎ ▥ ✝ ✕ ▥ ▣ ☕

Wellington House Hotel, *65 Wellington Road, New Brighton, Wirral, Merseyside, CH45 2NE.* Sea views, ground floor rooms available, bar, enclosed car park, CCTV. **Open:** All year (not Xmas/New Year) **Grades:** ETC 3 Diamond
0151 639 6594 (also fax) L Edwards
www.wellington-hotel.freeserve.co.uk
D: £20.00–£22.50 **S:** £22.00–£25.00 **Beds:** 4F 3T 2D 2S **Baths:** 8 En 2 Sh ☎ 🖻 (14) ▥ ✝ ✕ ▣ ♿ ☕ cc

Rochdale
SD8913   🍺 *Egerton Arms, Owd Bets*

Harridge End Homestay, *Shawclough Road, Rochdale, Lancs, OL12 7HL.* Large, comfortable, friendly and quiet house, private parking. **Open:** All year
01706 645272 M Whiteley **D:** £22.50–£25.00 **S:** £25.00 **Beds:** 1F 1T **Baths:** 2 Sh ☎ 🖻 (6) ⅟✓ ▥ ✕ ▥ ▣ ☕

B&B owners may vary rates – be sure to check when booking

Planning a longer stay? Always ask for any special rates

Leaches Farm, *Ashworth Valley, Rochdale, Lancs, OL11 5UN.* C17th Pennine farm. Wonderful views. Home from home. **Open:** All year (not Xmas/New Year)
01706 641116 & 01706 641117 Mrs Neave
Fax: 01706 228520 D: £20.00 **S:** £22.00–£28.00 **Beds:** 1T 1S **Baths:** 1 Sh ☎ (8) 🖻 (6) ⅟✓ ▥ ✝ ▥ ▣

Britannia Inn, *4 Lomax Street, Rochdale, Lancs, OL12 0DN.* Friendly local public house serving real ale, CAMRA listed. **Open:** All year
01706 646391 Mr Ainsworth **D:** £13.00–£15.00 **S:** £15.00 **Beds:** 3T **Baths:** 1 Sh ▥ ✕ ▣ ☕

Sale
SJ7891

Corner-stones, *230 Washway Road, Sale, M33 4PA.* **Open:** All year (not Xmas/New Year)
Grades: ETC 4 Diamond
0161 283 6909 (also fax) Mrs Casry *toncasey@aol.com* www.cornerstoneshotel.com
D: £25.00–£29.12 **S:** £25.00–£41.12 **Beds:** 3F 3T 3D **Baths:** 7 En 1 Pr 1 Sh ☎ ⅟✓ ▥ ▣ ▥ ☕ cc
Located on the main A56 road into the city and 5 mins away from Brooklands Metro Station. This fine Victorian building built by Sir William Canfitt Brooks was totally restored in 1985 reproducing the splendour of the Victorian era.

Brooklands Luxury Lodge, *208 Marsland Road, Sale, Cheshire, M33 3NE.* Convenient for all major venues including the fabulous Trafford Centre. **Open:** All year
0161 973 3283 Mr Bowker **Fax: 0161 282 0524 D:** £24.00–£29.00 **S:** £27.00–£33.00 **Beds:** 2F 2D 1T 4S **Baths:** 5 En 2 Sh ☎ (1) 🖻 (7) ⅟✓ ▥ ✕ ▣ ☕ cc

Shevington
SD5408

Wilden, *11a Miles Lane, Shevington, Wigan, Lancashire, WN6 8EB.* Large bungalow. Secluded large gardens. 1 mile M6. Off road parking. **Open:** All year (not Xmas/New Year)
01257 251516 D Axon **D:** £17.50–£20.00 **S:** £17.50–£20.00 **Beds:** 1T 2D **Baths:** 1 En 1 Sh 🖻 (5) ⅟✓ ▥ ✕ ▥ ♿ ☕ cc

National Grid References given are for villages, towns and cities – not for individual houses

Southport

SD3317

Rosedale Hotel, *11 Talbot Street, Southport, Merseyside, PR8 1HP.* Friendly family run hotel close to all Southport's main attractions. **Open:** All year (not Xmas/New Year) **Grades:** ETC 4 Diamond, AA 4 Diamond, RAC 4 Diamond **01704 530604 (also fax)** Mr & Mrs Beer *info@ rosedalehotelsouthport.co.uk* www.rosedalehotelsouthport.co.uk **D:** £25.00 **S:** £25.00 **Beds:** 2F 2T 2D 3S **Baths:** 8 En 1 Pr ⓢ 🅿 (6) 📺 🎞 ♨ cc

The Sidbrook Hotel, *14 Talbot Street, Southport, Lancashire, PR8 1HP.* Family run hotel close to town centre and amenities. **Open:** All year (not Xmas) **Grades:** ETC 3 Diamond, AA 3 Diamond **01704 530608 (also fax)** Mrs Barker *sidbrookhotel@tesco.net* www.thesidbrooksouthport.co.uk **D:** £19.50– £26.50 **S:** £28.50 **Beds:** 1F 5D 2T **Baths:** 8 En ⓢ 🅿 (8) 📺 🎞 ♨ cc

The White Lodge, *12 Talbot Street, Southport, PR8 1HP.* Small select hotel offering high standards in food, cleanliness and service. **Open:** All year (not Xmas) **Grades:** AA 3 Diamond, RAC 3 Diamond **01704 536320 (also fax)** Mr McKee **D:** £25.00–£30.00 **S:** £25.00–£40.00 **Beds:** 2F 2D 1T 2S **Baths:** 6 En 1 Sh ⓢ 🅿 (6) ⏣ 📺 ✕ 📶 🎞 ♨

Aaron Hotel, *18 Bath Street, Southport, Lancashire, PR9 0DA.* Family run hotel located in the centre of Southport. **Open:** All year **Grades:** ETC 3 Diamond **01704 530283** Mr Urbanowski **Fax: 01704 501055** *info@aaronhotel.co.uk* www.aaronhotel. co.uk **D:** £23.00–£28.00 **S:** £28.00–£35.00 **Beds:** 2F 2T 2D 2S **Baths:** 8 En ⓢ (2) 🅿 (6) 📺 ✕ 📶 🎞 ♨ cc

Stalybridge

SJ9698

The Wharf Tavern, *Staley Wharf, Stalybridge, SK15 1PD.* Canal mooring facilities, family run. Warm welcome. Explore Cheshire countryside. **Open:** All year (not Xmas/New Year) **0161 338 2662 D:** £45.00 **S:** £25.00 **Beds:** 3T 1S **Baths:** 4 En 📺 🐾 ✕ 📶 🎞 ♨

Stockport

SJ8990

Northumbria House, *35 Corbar Road, Stockport, Cheshire, SK2 6EP.* Edwardian house, quiet location, beautiful garden, Heartbeat Award, Northumbrian hospitality. **Open:** All year (not Xmas) **0161 483 4000** Mrs Kennington **D:** £18.00– £21.00 **S:** £20.00–£23.00 **Beds:** 1D 1T **Baths:** 1 Sh 🅿 (2) ⏣ 📺 🎞 ♨

Urmston

SJ7594

Beech Cottage, *80 Bent Lanes, Davyhulme, Urmston, Manchester, M41 8WY.* C16th black and white cottage, large gardens with natural pond and orchard. **Open:** All year (not Xmas) **0161 748 4649** Mr & Mrs Pollington **D:** £18.00 **S:** £20.00 **Beds:** 1D **Baths:** 1 Pr 🅿 (1) ⏣ 📺 ♨

West Kirby

SJ2086

Maconachie Guest House, *1 Victoria Road, West Kirby, Wirral, Merseyside, CH48 3HJ.* Victorian house overlooking the Dee estuary. Manx kippers a breakfast speciality. **Open:** All year **Grades:** ETC 3 Diamond **0151 625 1915** Mrs Hicks **D:** £22.50 **S:** £25.00 **Beds:** 1D 1T **Baths:** 2 Pr ⓢ 🅿 (1) 📺 🎞 ♨

Please respect a B&B's wishes regarding children, animals and smoking

Caldy Warren Cottage, *42 Caldy Road, West Kirby, Wirral, Merseyside, CH48 2HQ.* Spectacular river views. Exceptional accommodation, close to Chester, Liverpool. **Open:** All year **0151 625 8740** Mrs Graves **Fax: 0151 625 4115** *sue@warrencott.demon.co.uk* www.warrencott.demon.co.uk **D:** £20.00– £30.00 **S:** £25.00–£35.00 **Beds:** 1D 1F 1S **Baths:** 2 En 1 Sh ⓢ 🅿 (2) ⏣ 📺 📶 🎞 ♨

120 Frankby Road, *West Kirby, Wirral, Merseyside, CH48 9UX.* Perfectly situated for Wirral Pennisula. Farmhouse breakfast. Very warm welcome. **Open:** All year **0151 625 6215** Mrs Halliwell **D:** £25.00– £30.00 **S:** £25.00–£30.00 **Beds:** 1S 2F **Baths:** 1 Sh ⓢ 🅿 (2) ⏣ 📺 📶 🎞 ♨

Westhoughton

SD6506

Daisy Hill Hotel, *3 Lower Leigh Road, Daisy Hill, Westhoughton, Bolton, BL5 2JP.* Village pub close to motorway and train station, rooms, separate building to pub. **Open:** All year **01942 812096** J Nuttal *daisy.hill@cwcom.net* www.daisyhillhotel.co.uk **D:** £17.50–£20.00 **S:** £25.00–£27.50 **Beds:** 2 T 2S **Baths:** 4 Pr ⓢ 🅿 📺 🐾 🎞 ♨ cc

Whitefield

SD8106   ♨ *Sir Robert Peel*

122 Radcliffe New Road, *Whitefield, Manchester, M45 7RW.* Ideally situated for Manchester and exploring Lancashire towns and countryside. **Open:** All year (not Xmas/New Year) **0161 766 5161** A P Burke **D:** £16.00 **S:** £16.00 **Beds:** 1T 1D 1S **Baths:** 2 Sh 📺 🐾 🎞 ♨

Wigan

SD5805

Hotel Bel-Air, *236 Wigan Lane, Wigan, Lancs, WN1 2NU.* Family run hotel and restaurant close to Wigan centre and M6 motorway J27. **Open:** All year **Grades:** AA 2 Star, RAC 2 Star **01942 241410** Mr Lacaille **Fax: 01942 243967** *belair@hotelwigan.freeserve.co.uk* www.belairhotel.co.uk **D:** £22.50–£24.75 **S:** £35.00–£39.50 **Beds:** 11F **Baths:** 11 En ⓢ 🅿 (12) 📺 ✕ 📶 🎞 ♨

Hampshire

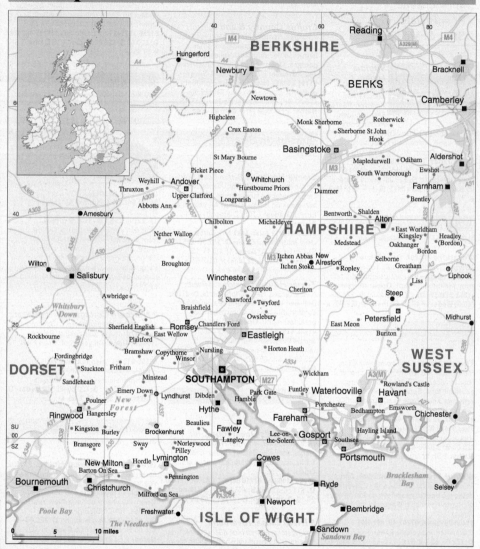

Abbotts Ann

SU3243

Carinya Farm, Cattle Lane, Abbotts Ann, Andover, Hampshire, SP11 7DR. Working stock farm, modern farmhouse with traditional values. Wildlife pond, large patio and conservatory. **Open:** All year **01264 710269** D W Fergusson *carinya.farm@ virgin.net* carinyafarm.co.uk **D:** £20.00 **S:** £25.00 **Beds:** 1T 1D **Baths:** 2 En 🅿 (4) ⤙ 📺 📺 🛏, ♨

RATES

D = Price range per person sharing in a double or twin room

S = Price range for a single room

BEDROOMS

D = Double

T = Twin

S = Single

F = Family

BATHROOMS
En = Ensuite
Pr = Private
Sh = Shared

Virginia Lodge, *Salisbury Road, Abbotts Ann, Andover, Hants, SP11 7NX.* Ideal Portsmouth, Winchester, Salisbury, Oxford, Stonehenge, welcome tray, excellent breakfasts. **Open:** All year (not Xmas/New Year) **Grades:** ETC 3 Diamond **01264 710713** Mrs Stuart *b-stuart@talk21.com* **D:** £20.00–£23.00 **S:** £25.00–£35.00 **Beds:** 2T 1D **Baths:** 1 En 1 Sh ⓢ (5) ℗ (6) ⊁ �📺 ▥ & ⚓

Aldershot

SU8750 ◁ *The Goose, Railway Tavern*

Alexandra Hotel, *Barrack Road, Aldershot, Hants, GU11 3NP.* Town centre, close to bars, restaurants, nightclubs and army military museum. **Open:** All year **01252 312550 D:** £20.00–£30.00 **S:** £25.00–£40.00 **Beds:** 1F 4T 2D **Baths:** 2 Sh ℗ ▥ ⚓

Alton

SU7139

The Vicarage, *East Worldham, Alton, Hants, GU34 3AS.* Warm, friendly peaceful country vicarage. Pub nearby serving excellent food. Separate toilet. **Open:** All year (not Xmas/New Year) **Grades:** ETC 3 Diamond **01420 82392 & 03788 00804** Mrs Bradford **Fax: 01420 82367** *wenrose@bigfoot.com* www.altonbedandbreakfast.co.uk **D:** £20.00–£23.00 **S:** £20.00–£23.00 **Beds:** 1D 1S/T 1F **Baths:** 2 Sh ⓢ (10) ℗ (5) ⊁ 📺 ⓣ ▥ ⚓

Walnut Tree Barn, *Bentworth, Alton, Hampshire, GU34 5JT.* Recently converted detached barn in peaceful location on edge of charming village. **Open:** All year (not Xmas) **01420 561281 & 07767 497482 (M)** J Crawford *jackiecrawfor25@hotmail.com* **D:** £22.00–£25.00 **S:** £25.00–£30.00 **Beds:** 1D 1T **Baths:** 1 En 1 Pr ℗ (4) ⊁ 📺 ▥ ⚓

Andover

SU3645

Salisbury Road Bed & Breakfast, *99 Salisbury Road, Andover, Hants, SP10 2LN.* Virtually self-contained ground floor with access to beautiful garden. **Open:** All year (not Xmas) **01264 362638** Mrs Targett **D:** £20.00–£25.00 **S:** £20.00–£30.00 **Beds:** 1F **Baths:** 1 Pr ⓢ ℗ (2) ⊁ 📺 ▥ ⚓

Awbridge

SU3324 ◁ *Bear & Ragged Staff, Malthouse, Mill Arms, Star Inn*

Crofton Country B and B, *Kents Oak, Awbridge, Romsey, Hants, SP51 0HH.* Luxury, hotel-quality accommodation, small hamlet in beautiful Test Valley. 2 acres of gardens. **Open:** All year (not Xmas/New Year) **Grades:** ETC 4 Diamond, Silver **01794 340333 (also fax)** Mrs Lightfoot *pauline@crofton-ca.fsnet.co.uk* **D:** £22.50–£25.00 **S:** £25.00–£30.00 **Beds:** 1F 1T 1S **Baths:** 3 En ⓢ ℗ (3) ⊁ 📺 ▥ ⚓ cc

Barton on Sea

SZ2393

Cleeve House, *58 Barton Court Avenue, Barton on Sea, New Milton, Hants, BH25 7HG.* Large character family home, close to sea, non-smoking house. **Open:** All year (not Xmas) **Grades:** ETC 4 Diamond, AA 4 Diamond **01425 615211 (also fax)** Mrs Carter *cleeve.house@btinternet.com* **D:** £22.50–£25.00 **S:** £25.00–£50.00 **Beds:** 1F 1D 1T 1S **Baths:** 2 En 1 Sh ⓢ ℗ (8) ⊁ 📺 ▥ ⚓

Tower House, *Christchurch Road, Barton on Sea, New Milton, Hants, DH25 6QQ.* Between New Forest and sea, spacious comfortable rooms. Comprehensive breakfast menu. **Open:** All year (not Xmas) **01425 629508 (also fax)** Mrs Steenhuis *bandb@towerhouse-newforest.co.uk* www.towerhouse-newforest.co.uk **D:** £20.00–£25.00 **S:** £20.00–£25.00 **Beds:** 2D 1T **Baths:** 3 En ⓢ (7) ℗ (7) ⊁ 📺 ▥ ⚓

Basingstoke

SU6352

The Carroll's Guesthouse, *104 Gershwin Road, Brighton Hill, Basingstoke, Hants, RG22 4HJ.* Basing House; Cromwell battle, many other historical places around. **Open:** All year **01256 410024 & 07710 649077 (M)** Mr Carroll **D:** £17.50–£18.50 **S:** £15.50–£17.50 **Beds:** 1F 2T 1S **Baths:** 1 Sh ⓢ (5) ℗ (4) 📺 ▥ ⚓

3 Irwell Close, Riverdene, *Basingstoke, Hampshire, RG21 4DG.* Informal theatrical atmosphere, short walk to town, restaurants, theatres. **Open:** All year **01256 325610 (also fax)** Mr Bye *graham@ozuk.demon.co.uk* www.ozuk.demon.co.uk **S:** £15.00–£18.00 **Beds:** 1S **Baths:** 1 Sh ℗ (1) ⊁ 📺 ▥ ⚓

Please respect a B&B's wishes regarding children, animals and smoking

---

Mrs Broad's Rowan B&B, *3 Roding Close, Riverdene, Basingstoke, Hampshire, RG21 4DU.* Private house. Clean, comfortable. 10 mins walk town. Monday - Friday. No Cards/cheques accepted. **Open:** All year (not Xmas/New Year) **01256 321143** Mrs Broad **Fax: 01256 420828** **D:** £20.00 **S:** £25.00 **Beds:** 1T 1S **Baths:** 1 Sh ⊁ 📺 ▥ ⚓

Beaulieu

SU3802 ◁ *Montagu Arms, Red Lion, East End Arms*

Leygreem Farm House, *Lyndhurst Road, Beaulieu, Brockenhurst, Hants, SO42 7YP.* **Open:** All year (not Xmas) **Grades:** ETC 3 Diamond **01590 612355 (also fax)** Mr Helyer **D:** £21.00–£24.00 **S:** £25.00–£30.00 **Beds:** 2D 1T **Baths:** 3 En ℗ (6) ⊁ 📺 ▥ ⚓ Victorian farmhouse in rural setting 1 mile from Beaulieu village ideal for Motor Museum, Buckler's Yard, New Forest and Exbury Gardens. Mountain bikes available for guests' use. Off-road private parking. Discounts 3 days or more. A warm welcome assured.

2 Northern Cottages, *Beaulieu, Hants, SO42 7YE.* Lovingly restored C18th cottage, centre of village overlooking 'Palace House'. **Open:** All year (not Xmas/New Year) **01590 612127 (also fax)** Mrs Hills *christine.hills@btinternet.com* www.beaulieu-newforest-bandb.co.uk **D:** £22.50–£25.00 **S:** £22.50–£25.00 **Beds:** 1D 1T **Baths:** 1 Sh ⊁ 📺 ▥ ⚓

Bedhampton

SU7006 ◁ *Belmont Inn*

Green Cottage Guest House, *23 Park Lane, Bedhampton, Havant, Hampshire, PO9 3HG.* Organic ingredients used where possible in breakfasts and dinners. **Open:** All year (not Xmas/New Year) **Grades:** RAC 3 Diamond **023 9247 5670** Mrs Henning **D:** £22.50–£25.00 **S:** £25.00–£30.00 **Beds:** 1T 1D **Baths:** 2 En ⓢ ℗ (2) ⊁ ✕ 📺 ▥ ⚓

Bentley

SU7844

Pittersfield, *Hole Lane, Bentley, Farnham, Surrey, GU10 5LT.* Period courtyard annexe in peaceful rural surroundings. **Open:** All year **01420 22414 (also fax)** Mrs Coulton **D:** £25.00–£30.00 **S:** £25.00–£30.00 **Beds:** 3F 1T 1D 1S **Baths:** 2 En 2 Pr 1 Sh ⓢ ℗ (3) ⊁ 📺 ▥ ⚓

Bentworth

SU6640

Newmans Cottage, *Drury Lane, Bentworth, Alton, Hampshire, GU34 5RJ.* C17th cottage of great character in lovely gardens overlooking countryside. **Open:** All year (not Xmas/New Year)
01420 563707 *AdmiralD@aol.com* **D:** £20.00–£22.50 **S:** £25.00–£30.00 **Beds:** 1D **Baths:** 1 Pr ▣ (2) ⌇ ⊡ ⊻ 🏛 ⚲

Bordon

SU7935 🍺 *Robin Hood*

Bunga Raya, *36 Forest Road, Bordon, Hants, GU35 0PT.* Bungalow. Suitable for less abled. Situated close to main A3 trunk road. **Open:** All year (not Xmas/New Year)
01420 473835 & 01420 474191 Mrs Morrish **D:** £30.00 **S:** £15.00 **Beds:** 2F 2T 2D 1S **Baths:** 3 Sh ⌇ (3) ⊻ 🏛 ⚲ ⚲

30 Churchfields, *Kingsley, Bordon, Hants, GU35 9PJ.* Modern village house adjoining commonland. Close Selborne, Chawton, Watercress Line. **Open:** All year (not Xmas/New Year)
01420 472271 Mrs Clack **D:** £20.00–£22.50 **S:** £22.50–£25.00 **Beds:** 1D 1S **Baths:** 1 Pr ▣ (2) ⊡ 🏛 ⚲

Braishfield

SU3725 🍺 *Moathouse, Duke's Head, Wheatsheaf, Dog & Crook*

Cranford Farm, *Rudd Lane, Braishfield, Romsey, Hants, SO51 0PY.*
Open: All year
Grades: AA 4 Diamond
01794 368216 (also fax) Mr Brooks **D:** £22.50–£32.50 **S:** £35.00 **Beds:** 3F 1T 2D **Baths:** 6 En ⊡ ⚲
Cranford Farm is a large secluded farmhouse set in 3 acres of farmland in the beautiful Test Valley. Just off A3057 between Braishfield and Michelmersh. All rooms are comfortably furnished with colour TV, tea and coffee. All ensuite.

Springwood, *Crook Hill, Braishfield, Romsey, Hants, SO51 0QB.* Opposite Hillier gardens/arboretum. 2.5 acres includes copse. French spoken. **Open:** All year
01794 368134 Mrs Dickens **D:** £18.00 **S:** £20.00 **Beds:** 1D **Baths:** 1 Pr ▣ (4) ⌇ ⊡ ✕ 🏛 ⚲

BEDROOMS
D = Double
T = Twin
S = Single
F = Family

Bramshaw

SU2716

Forge Cottage, *Stocks Cross, Bramshaw, Lyndhurst, SO43 7JB.* Private rooms situated within the beautiful gardens of Listed cottage. **Open:** All year (not Xmas/New Year)
023 8081 3873 Mr & Mrs Davies *idavies1@cs.com* www.newforest-uk.com/forgecottage.htm **D:** £20.00–£25.00 **S:** £40.00 **Beds:** 2D ▣ (3) ⌇ ⊡ 🏛 ⚲

Bransgore

SZ1998

The Corner House, *Betsy Lane, Bransgore, Christchurch, Hants., BH23 8AQ.* Family house, edge of village, close to forest and pubs. **Open:** All year (not Xmas/New Year) **Grades:** ETC 4 Diamond
01425 673201 J Staniland **D:** £20.00 **S:** £22.00 **Beds:** 1F 1T **Baths:** 2 En ⌇ ▣ (3) ⌇ ⊡ 🏛 ⚲

Brockenhurst

SU2902 🍺 *Filly Inn, Hobler Inn, New Forest, Snakecatcher, Foresters*

Little Heathers, *13 Whitemoor Road, Brockenhurst, Hants, SO42 7QG.* Friendly comfortable spacious bungalow, quiet location, 3 - 7 days special breaks. **Open:** All year **Grades:** ETC 4 Diamond, Silver
01590 623512 Mrs Harris **Fax:** 01590 624255 *little_heathers@hotmail.com* www.newforest.demon.co.uk/littleheathers.htm **D:** £23.00–£28.00 **Beds:** 1T 1D **Baths:** 2 En ⌇ ▣ (5) ⌇ ⊡ ⊻ 🏛 ⚲

Seraya Guest House, *8 Grigg Lane, Brockenhurst, Hants, SO42 7RE.* Family-run B&B in heart of New Forest. Easy reach Portsmouth, Stonehenge, Bournemouth, IOW. **Open:** All year
01590 622426 Mrs Ward *edwin.ward@btinternet.com* **D:** £19.00–£25.00 **S:** £22.00 **Beds:** 2D 1T **Baths:** 1 Sh 1 En ⌇ ▣ (4) ⌇ ⊡ 🐾 ⊻ 🏛 ⚲

Crossings, *Lyndhurst Road, Brockenhurst, Hampshire, SO42 7RL.* Comfortable family home near railway, shops, forest. Good hearty breakfast. **Open:** All year **Grades:** AA 2 Diamond
01590 622478 Mrs Ferguson **D:** £20.00–£23.00 **S:** £25.00–£30.00 **Beds:** 1T 2D **Baths:** 1 Sh ▣ (2) ⌇ ⊡ 🏛 ⚲

Hilden, *Southampton Road, Boldre, Brockenhurst, Hampshire, SO41 8PT.* Large, comfortable Edwardian house 50 yards open New Forest, 2.5m sea. **Open:** All year **Grades:** ETC 3 Diamond
01590 623682 Mrs Arnold-Brown **Fax:** 01590 624444 www.newforestbandb-hilden.co.uk **D:** £20.00–£25.00 **S:** £20.00–£35.00 **Beds:** 3F **Baths:** 3 En ⌇ ▣ (6) ⊡ 🐾 🏛 ⚲ ⚲

Golden Hayes, *9 Chestnut Road, Brockenhurst, Hants, SO42 7RF.* Owner-occupied home in central but quiet situation, large garden. **Open:** All year
01590 623743 B Curtis **D:** £15.00–£18.00 **S:** £15.00–£20.00 **Beds:** 1F 1S **Baths:** 1 Sh ⌇ ▣ ⌇ ⊡ 🐾 ⊻ 🏛 ⚲

Brookside Cottage, *Collyers Road, Brockenhurst, Hants, SO42 7SE.* Picturesque cottage, secluded area. Golf, riding, famous gardens nearby. **Open:** All year (not Xmas) **Grades:** ETC 3 Diamond
01590 623973 Mrs Branfoot **D:** £27.00–£28.00 **S:** £27.00–£28.00 **Beds:** 1T 1S **Baths:** 1 Pr ⌇ ▣ (2) ⌇ ⊻ 🏛 ⚲

Briardale, *11 Noel Close, Brockenhurst, Hants., SO42 7RP.* Friendly comfortable home - quiet yet close to village & forest. **Open:** Feb to Dec
01590 623946 (also fax) Mrs Parkin **D:** £22.50–£27.00 **S:** £32.00–£40.00 **Beds:** 2D **Baths:** 2 En ▣ (3) ⌇ ⊡ ✕ ⊻ 🏛 ⚲

Thatched Cottage Hotel, *16 Brookley Road, Brockenhurst, Hampshire, SO42 7RR.* 400 year old cottage with double deluxe bedrooms. Superlative cuisine. **Open:** Feb to Dec **Grades:** ETC 5 Diamond
01590 623090 *sales@thatchedcottage.co.uk* www.thatchedcottage.co.uk **D:** £45.00–£85.00 **S:** £70.00–£90.00 **Beds:** 5D **Baths:** 5 En ⌇ (12) ▣ (12) ⌇ ⊡ 🐾 ✕ ⊻ 🏛 ⚲ ⚲ cc

Porthilly House, *Armstrong Road, Brockenhurst, Hants, SO42 7TA.* Luxurious king size suites in lovely, spacious 1920s house in heart of New Forest. **Open:** All year
01590 623182 Mrs Brown **Fax:** 01590 622178 *sue@bandbnewforest.co.uk* www.bandbnewforest.co.uk **D:** £29.00–£32.00 **S:** £40.00–£50.00 **Beds:** 2D **Baths:** 2 En ⌇ (8) ▣ (4) ⌇ ⊡ ⊻ 🏛 ⚲

Broughton

SU3133

Kings, *Salisbury Road, Broughton, Stockbridge, SO20 8BY.* Standing in half acre of garden, surrounded by open countryside. **Open:** All year (not Xmas/New Year)
01794 301458 Mrs Heather **D:** £18.00 **S:** £18.00 **Beds:** 1T 1S **Baths:** 1 Pr ▣ (3) ✕ ⊡ 🏛 ⚲

The Old Plough, *High Street, Broughton, Stockbridge, Hampshire, SO20 8AE.* Charming listed cottage idyllic village between Winchester and Salisbury. **Open:** All year (not Xmas)
01794 301598 Mrs Paul *paul_family@broughton26.fre* **D:** £20.00 **S:** £25.00 **Beds:** 1D **Baths:** 1 Pr ⌇ ▣ (1) ⌇ ⊡ 🐾 ⊻ 🏛 ⚲

Buriton

SU7320

Nursted Farm, *Buriton, Petersfield, Hants, GU31 5RW.* Relax in the atmosphere of our 300 year old farmhouse. **Open:** May to Feb **01730 264278** Mrs Bray **D:** £20.00 **S:** £20.00 **Beds:** 3T **Baths:** 1 Pr 1 Sh ⌂ ☐ 🖪 ☑ Ⓥ ▥.

Burley

SU2103   🍺 *White Buck, Queen's Head, Burley Manor*

Charlwood, *Longmead Road, Burley, Ringwood, Hants, BH24 4BY.* Country house. Lovely gardens, views, quiet. Rural - off main road. **Open:** Feb to Nov **01425 403242** Mrs Russell **D:** £24.00–£26.00 **S:** £28.00–£30.00 **Beds:** 1D 1T **Baths:** 1 Sh 🖪 (3) ⅄ ☑ 🐾 Ⓥ ▥.

Holmans, *Bisterne Close, Burley, Ringwood, Hants, BH24 4AZ.* Charming country house, perfectly situated in the heart of the N Forest. **Open:** All year (not Xmas) **01425 402307** (also fax) R Ford **D:** £27.50–£32.00 **S:** £32.00–£35.00 **Beds:** 1T 2D **Baths:** 3 En ⌂ 🖪 ⅄ ☑ ▥.

Bay Tree House, *1 Clough Lane, Burley, Ringwood, Hants, BH24 4AE.* Large garden, lovely walks, cycle hire, riding, fishing nearby. Good English breakfast, home produce. **Open:** Mar to Oct **Grades:** ETC 3 Diamond **01425 403215** (also fax) Mrs Allen *baytreehousebandb@burleyhants.freeserve.co.uk* www.smoothhound.co.uk/hotels/baytree **D:** £23.00–£26.00 **S:** £23.00–£26.00 **Beds:** 1F 1S **Baths:** 1 Sh ⌂ 🖪 (4) ⅄ ☑ Ⓥ ▥.

Great Wells House, *Beechwood Lane, Burley, Ringwood, Hants, BH24 4AS.* Beautiful period property in the heart of the New Forest. **Open:** Feb to Nov **Grades:** ETC 5 Diamond, Gold **01425 402302** (also fax) Mrs Stewart *chrisstewart@compuserve.com* www.smoothhound.co.uk/hotels/greatwel. html **D:** £25.00–£37.50 **S:** £35.00–£60.00 **Beds:** 3D **Baths:** 3 En 🖪 (10) ⅄ ☑ Ⓥ ▥.

Toad Hall, *The Cross, Burley, Ringwood, Hampshire, BH24 4AB.* Spectacularly at the heart of the new forest. **Open:** All year **01425 403448 Fax: 01425 402058 D:** £23.00–£45.00 **S:** £40.00–£50.00 **Beds:** 2T 6D 2S **Baths:** 10 En ⅄ ☑ ✕ ▥. ♨ cc

Chandlers Ford

SU4320

133 Bournemouth Road, *Chandlers Ford, Eastleigh, Hants, SO53 3HA.* Comfortable accommodation, choice of breakfast. Easy access to M3/M27. **Open:** All year **023 8025 4801** (also fax) Mr Lanham **D:** £20.00–£21.00 **S:** £20.00–£21.00 **Beds:** 1F 1S **Baths:** 1 Sh ⌂ ⅄ ☑ ▥.

Blackbird Hill, *24 Ashbride Rise, Chandlers Ford, Eastleigh, Hampshire, SO53 1SA.* Detached bungalow in quiet residential area. Easy access to M3 and M27. **Open:** All year (not Xmas) **023 8026 0398 D:** £20.00–£22.00 **S:** £20.00–£22.00 **Beds:** 1D 1S **Baths:** 1 Sh ⌂ (5) 🖪 (1) ⅄ 🐾 ✕ ▥.

Cheriton

SU5828

Flower Pots Inn, *Cheriton, Alresford, Hants, SO24 0QQ.* C19th Former farmhouse with microbrewery, situated in central Hampshire village. **Open:** All year (not Xmas/New Year) **01962 771318** (also fax) **Beds:** 3T 2D **Baths:** 5 En ⌂ (12) 🖪 (30) ☑ 🐾 ▥.

The Garden House, *Cheriton, Alresford, Hampshire, SO24 0QQ.* Edge of pretty village. Tennis court. Near Cheriton Battle Field. Personal tour by arrangement. **Open:** All year **01962 771352 & 01962 771666** Mrs Verney **Fax: 01962 771667** *verney@standrewsball.co.uk* **D:** £20.00–£24.00 **S:** £20.00–£24.00 **Beds:** 2T 1D **Baths:** 1 Pr 1 Sh ⌂ 🖪 (4) ⅄ ✕ Ⓥ ▥. ♨

Chilbolton

SU3940

Uplands, *Drove Road, Chilbolton, Stockbridge, Hants, SO20 6AD.* Lovely Test Valley, south of Andover. Bungalow, large garden, very quiet. **Open:** All year (not Xmas) **01264 860650** (also fax) Mrs Hayman-Joyce *june@haymanjoyce.freeserve.co.uk* www.haymanjoyce.freeserve.co.uk **D:** £22.50 **S:** £26.00 **Beds:** 1S 1D **Baths:** 1 En 1 Sh ⌂ 🖪 (5) ⅄ ☑ Ⓥ ▥. ♨

The Rectory, *Chilbolton, Stockbridge, SO20 6BA.* Large bungalow situated centrally near pub in beautiful village. **Open:** All year **01264 860258** (also fax) Mrs Williams *errolw@compuserve.com* **D:** £20.00 **S:** £20.00–£25.00 **Beds:** 1F 1S **Baths:** 1 En 1 Pr ⌂ 🖪 🐾 Ⓥ ▥. ♨

Compton

SU4625   🍺 *The Otter*

Wood Ridge, *Field Close, Compton Down, Compton, Winchester, Hampshire, SO21 2AP.* Rural area, convenient for Winchester, New Forest and South Coast. **Open:** All year (not Xmas/New Year) **01962 711226** *woodridge@hotmail.com* **D:** £20.00–£25.00 **S:** £20.00–£30.00 **Beds:** 1T 2S **Baths:** 1 En 1 Sh 🖪 (3) ⅄ ☑ ✕ Ⓥ ▥. ♨

Copythorne

SU3115

The Old Well Restaurant, *Romsey Road, Copythorne, Southampton, SO40 2PE.* Beautiful rest/hotel on the edge of the New Forest. **Open:** All year **023 8081 2321** Mrs Thompson **Fax: 023 8081 2158 D:** £22.50–£30.00 **S:** £26.00–£35.00 **Beds:** 2F 5D **Baths:** 4 En 3 Sh ⌂ 🖪 ⅄ ☑ 🐾 ✕ Ⓥ ▥. ♿ ✳ ♨ cc

Crux Easton

SU4256

Manor House, *Crux Easton, Newbury, Hants, RG20 9QF.* Historic farmhouse in quiet village, lovely views, near Highclere Castle. **Open:** All year **01635 254314** Mrs O'Shaughnessy **Fax: 01635 254246 D:** £22.50–£25.00 **S:** £22.50–£25.00 **Beds:** 3T **Baths:** 2 Sh ⌂ 🖪 (8) ☑ 🐾 ✕ Ⓥ ▥. ♨

Dibden

SU4008

Dale Farm Guest House, *Manor Road, Applemore Hill, Dibden, Southampton, SO45 5TJ.* Olde world farmhouse with direct access to the New Forest, horse riding next door. **Open:** All year **Grades:** ETC 3 Diamond **023 8084 9632** Mrs Archdeacon **Fax: 023 8084 0285** *info@dalefarmhouse.co.uk* www.dalefarmhouse.co.uk **D:** £19.50 **S:** £25.50 **Beds:** 1F 1T 3D 1S **Baths:** 4 Pr 2 Sh ⌂ 🖪 ☑ ✕ Ⓥ ▥. ✳ ♨

Dummer

SU5845

Oakdown Farm, *Dummer, Basingstoke, Hants, RG23 7LR.* Secluded modern farm bungalow next to M3 J7 on Wayfarers walk. **Open:** All year **Grades:** ETC 3 Diamond **01256 397218** Mrs Hutton **D:** £17.50 **S:** £20.00 **Beds:** 1D 2T **Baths:** 1 Sh ⌂ (12) 🖪 (4) ⅄ ☑ Ⓥ ▥. ♨

East Meon

SU6822 ⚓ *Old George Inn, Isaac Walton*

Drayton Cottage, *East Meon, Petersfield, Hants, GU32 1PW.* Luxury accommodation in beamed cottage with superb views. Excellent beds. **Open:** All year
01730 823472 J Rockett *draytoncottage@ btinternet.com* **D:** £22.00–£25.00 **S:** £30.00 **Beds:** 1T 1D **Baths:** 1 En 1 Pr 🅿(3)⚡📺📹🗻

Coombe Cross House and Stables, *Coombe Road, East Meon, Petersfield, Hants, GU32 1HQ.* Early Georgian House. 1.5 miles from East Meon on South Downs Way. **Open:** All year (not Xmas/New Year)
01730 823298 Mrs Bulmer **Fax:** 01730 823515 *investor.focus@btinternet.com***D:** £30.00–£35.00 **S:** £30.00–£35.00 **Beds:** 1T 1D **Baths:** 1 En 🅿(6)⚡📺🗻

East Wellow

SU3020

Roselea, *Hamdown Crescent, East Wellow, Romsey, Hampshire, SO51 6BJ.* Quiet mainly ground floor accommodation, near New Forest and M27. **Open:** All year (not Xmas) **Grades:** ETC 4 Diamond
01794 323262 (also fax) Mr & Mrs Cossburn *pennyc@tcp.co.uk* **D:** £17.50–£20.00 **S:** £20.00–£25.00 **Beds:** 1D 1T 1S **Baths:** 2 En 1 Sh ⏰(8)🅿(2)⚡📺🐾🗻

East Worldham

SU7438

The Vicarage, *East Worldham, Alton, Hants, GU34 3AS.* Warm, friendly peaceful country vicarage. Pub nearby serving excellent food. Separate toilet. **Open:** All year (not Xmas/New Year) **Grades:** ETC 3 Diamond
01420 82392 & 03788 00804 Mrs Bradford **Fax:** 01420 82367 *wenrose@bigfoot.com* www.altonbedandbreakfast.co.uk **D:** £20.00–£23.00 **S:** £20.00–£23.00 **Beds:** 1D 1S/T 1F **Baths:** 2 Sh ⏰(10)🅿(5)⚡📺🐾📹🗻

Eastleigh

SU4519

Twyford Lodge, *104-106 Twyford Road, Eastleigh, Hants, SO50 4HN.* Family-run, good food, good local amenities. Southampton Airport 10 mins. **Open:** All year (not Xmas)
023 8061 2245 **D:** £20.00 **S:** £20.00–£30.00 **Beds:** 2F 1D 6T 4S **Baths:** 1 Pr 3 Sh ⏰🅿(15)📺🐾📹🗻

Emery Down

SU2808

Stable End Guest House, *Mill Lane, Emery Down, Lyndhurst, Hants, SO43 7FJ.* Lovely forest views and usually ponies outside the gate. **Open:** All year
023 8028 2504 (also fax) Mrs Dibben *dibbenfam@aol.com* **D:** £25.00–£30.00 **S:** £25.00–£30.00 **Beds:** 1D 1T **Baths:** 2 En 🅿(4)⚡📺📹🗻

Emsworth

SU7406 ⚓ *Bluebell Inn, Kings Arms, Royal Oak, Coal Exchange, Sussex Brewery*

33 Far Meadow Way, *Emsworth, Hants, PO10 7PA.* Detached house in quiet cul de sac, south of A259. **Open:** All year (not Xmas/New Year)
01243 378047 Mr & Mrs Jacobs **D:** £14.00–£15.00 **Beds:** 1T 1D **Baths:** 1 Sh ⏰(5)🅿(2)⚡📺🗻

Bunbury Lodge, *10 West Road, Emsworth, Hampshire, PO10 7JT.* Perfect location 250 yards from Emsworth Harbour Foreshore. Superb breakfast. **Open:** Jan to Dec **Grades:** ETC 4 Diamond
01243 432030 Mr & Mrs Knight *bunbury.lodge@breathemail.net* **D:** £25.00–£30.00 **S:** £35.00–£40.00 **Beds:** 2D/T **Baths:** 1 En 1 Pr ⏰(10)🅿(4)⚡📺📹🗻✳🗻

Ewshot

SU8149

The Oast House, *Ewshot, Farnham, Hampshire, GU10 5BP.* Charming oast house c1850, peaceful rural village, 10 mins M3. **Open:** All year
01252 850474 (also fax) Mrs Morgan **D:** £20.00–£25.00 **S:** £25.00–£30.00 **Beds:** 1F 1T 1D 1S **Baths:** 1 En 1 Sh ⏰🅿(6)⚡📺✕📹🗻

Fareham

SU5606 ⚓ *Birds in Hand, Castle*

Beaulieu, *67 Portchester Road, Fareham, Hants, PO16 8AP.* Detached house, pleasant gardens, non-smoking, near golf club. M27 (J11) one mile. **Open:** All year
01329 232461 (also fax) Mrs Wycherley **D:** £20.00 **S:** £20.00–£30.00 **Beds:** 1D 1T 1S **Baths:** 1 Sh ⏰🅿(3)⚡📺📹🗻

Irish Shebeen, *63 Laburnum Road, Fareham, Hants, PO16 0SN.* Friendly house near HMS Collingwood, Fort Fareham. Football golf, bowling. **Open:** All year
01329 232643 Mrs McGuinness **D:** £15.00–£17.00 **S:** £15.00–£17.00 **Beds:** 3F 1T 1D 2S **Baths:** 1 En 1 Pr ⏰🅿⚡📺📹🗻🗻

Fawley

SU4603

Walcot House, *Blackfield Road, Fawley, Southampton, SO45 1ED.* Home from home. Good location for touring the area. **Open:** All year
023 8089 1344 Fax: 023 8089 0748 D: £18.50–£20.00 **S:** £19.00–£22.00 **Beds:** 1T 1D 5S **Baths:** 1 En 1 Sh ⏰🅿(13)⚡📺📹🗻🗻cc

Fordingbridge

SU1414

Hillbury, *2 Fir Tree Hill, Camel Green, Alderholt, Fordingbridge, Hants, SP6 3AY.* Large modern bungalow in peaceful surroundings. Warm welcome and comfortable. **Open:** All year **Grades:** ETC 3 Diamond
01425 652582 Mrs Sillence **Fax:** 01425 657587 www.newforest.demon.co. uk/hillbury.htm **D:** £19.00–£22.00 **S:** £19.00–£22.00 **Beds:** 1F 1T 1S **Baths:** 1 Pr 1 Sh ⏰🅿(4)⚡📺📹🗻

Fritham

SU2314

Amberwood Cottage, *Fritham, Lyndhurst, Hants, SO43 7HL.* Self-contained. Off no through road, direct access into forest. **Open:** Mar to Oct **Grades:** ETC 3 Diamond
023 8081 2359 A Borrelli **D:** £21.00 **Beds:** 1D **Baths:** 1 En 🅿⚡📺🐾🗻🗻

Primrose Cottage, *Fritham, Lyndhurst, Hants, SO43 7HH.* Victorian cottage, forest access. Your own lounge and bathroom. Garage. **Open:** Mar to Nov
023 8081 2272 Mr & Mrs Penfound www.smoothhound.co.uk/hotels/primrose. html **D:** £19.00–£21.00 **S:** £24.00–£26.00 **Beds:** 1D/T **Baths:** 1 Pr ⏰(8)🅿(1)⚡📺📹🗻🗻

Funtley

SU5608

17 Lakeside, Funtley, Fareham, Hants, *PO17 5EP.* Lakeside location. Modern family house. Fishing, walking, horseriding all nearby. **Open:** All year (not Xmas/New Year)
01329 236128 L Moore **D:** £17.00–£20.00 **S:** £17.00–£20.00 **Beds:** 1T 2S **Baths:** 1 Sh
🅿 (3) 📺 🛶 ♨

Gosport

SU5900   🥢 North Star, Bridgemary Manor Hotel

Raysal, 90a Fareham Road, Gosport, Hants, *PO13 0AG.* Family run guest house, large landscaped garden and sun lounge. **Open:** All year
01329 280093 Mrs Rolls **D:** £19.00–£24.00 **S:** £20.00–£25.00 ⅍ (5) 🅿 (6) ⅍ 📺 📺 🛶 ♨

Greatham

SU7831

The Silver Birch Inn, Petersfield Road (A325), Greatham, Liss, Hampshire, *GU33 6AS.* Village Inn on three counties borders - Hampshire, Surrey, W Sussex. **Open:** All year
01420 538262 (also fax) *michelle@ thesilverbirch.co.uk* **D:** £24.00–£35.00 **S:** £25.00–£29.50 **Beds:** 2F 2T 2D 2S **Baths:** 2 Pr 1 Sh ⅍ 🅿 (20) 📺 ✕ 📺 🛶 ♨ cc

Hamble

SU4706

Honeysuckle, Flowers Close, Hamble, Southampton, Hants, *SO31 4LU.* Bed and breakfast close to Hamble River, Marinas, pubs, yacht clubs. **Open:** All year (not Xmas)
023 8045 3209 (also fax) **D:** £18.00–£20.00 **S:** £20.00–£25.00 **Beds:** 2D **Baths:** 1 Sh ⅍ (10) 🅿 (2) ⅍ 📺 📺 🛶 ♨

Hangersley

SU1706

Dunain Farm, Hangersley, Ringwood, Hants, *BH24 3JN.* Secluded bungalow, situated on high ground, 1.5 miles from Ringwood. **Open:** Mar to Oct
01425 472611 Mrs Griffin *dunain@aol.com* **D:** £19.00–£20.00 **S:** £22.00–£24.00 **Beds:** 1F 1T 1D **Baths:** 1 Sh ⅍ 🅿 (8) 📺 🛶 ♨

Havant

SU7107

Church View, 107 West Street, Havant, Hampshire, *PO9 1LE.* Close town centre. Friendly welcome. Suit holiday/business visitors. Families accommodated. Full English breakfast. **Open:** Feb to Nov
023 9247 2405 Mrs Bryant **D:** £20.00 **S:** £25.00 **Beds:** 1D **Baths:** 1 Pr ⅍ (5) 🅿 (1) ⅍ 📺 📺 🛶 ♨

Planning a longer stay? Always ask for any special rates

Hayling Island

SU7201   🥢 Olive Leaf

Ravensdale, 19 St Catherines Road, Hayling Island, Hampshire, *PO11 0HF.* Friendly welcome, quiet location, close to beach, excellent home cooking. **Open:** All year
023 9246 3203 & 07802 188259 (M) Mr & Mrs Taylor **Fax:** 023 9246 3203 **D:** £20.00–£24.00 **S:** £28.00–£32.00 **Beds:** 1F 3D **Baths:** 2 En ⅍ (8) 🅿 (6) ⅍ 📺 ✕ 📺 🛶 ♨

The Old Vine, 67 Havant R, *PO11 0PT.* Easy access, beach, country, windsurfing, marinas, peaceful gardens. Warm welcome. **Open:** All year
023 9246 2543 Mrs Panagiotidis *gpanag67@ aol.com* **D:** £18.00–£21.00 **S:** £20.00–£25.00 **Beds:** 1F 1T 1D **Baths:** 2 Pr ⅍ 🅿 (8) ⅍ 🛏 ♀ ✕ 🛶 ♨

Maidlings, 55 Staunton Avenue, Hayling Island, Hants, *PO11 0EW.* Delightful family home close to beach with a great breakfast. **Open:** All year (not Xmas/New Year)
023 9246 6357 Mrs Harper **D:** £20.00–£25.00 **S:** £25.00 **Beds:** 2D 1T ⅍ 🅿 (3) ⅍ 📺 🛶

Anns Cottage, 45 St Andrews Road, Hayling Island, Hants, *PO11 9JN.* Quiet location opposite open parkland. Good English breakfast, 60 yards seafront. **Open:** All year
023 9246 7048 Mrs Jay *Ann.Jay@virgin.net* **D:** £20.00–£25.00 **S:** £20.00–£25.00 **Beds:** 1F 1D 1T **Baths:** 1 Sh ⅍ 🅿 (3) ⅍ 📺 📺 🛶 ♨

Redwalls, 66 Staunton Avenue, Hayling Island, Hampshire, *PO11 0EW.* Non-smoking superior, quiet accommodation close to the sea. Extensive breakfasts. **Open:** All year (not Xmas/New Year) **Grades:** RAC 3 Diamond
023 9246 6109 Mr & Mrs Grover *daphne@ redwalls66.co.uk* www.redwalls.co.uk **D:** £20.00£22.50 **S:** £25.00–£30.00 **Beds:** 2T 1D **Baths:** 2 En 1 Pr 🅿 (4) ⅍ 📺 🛶 ♨

Farmhouse, 23 Sandy Point Road, Hayling Island, Hampshire, *PO11 9RP.* 1900's farmhouse close to beach and sailing club. Warm welcome. **Open:** All year (not Xmas/New Year)
023 9246 9287 *penny-bennet@madasafish.com* **D:** £13.00–£19.00 **S:** £18.00–£24.00 **Beds:** 2T 1D **Baths:** 1 Sh ⅍ 🅿 (4) 📺 🛶

Tide Reach, 214 Southwood Road, Hayling Island, Hants, *PO11 9QQ.* Right on the beach! Sailors, surfers and anglers particularly welcome, landlubbers too. Which? Recommended. **Open:** All year
0800 970 1670 & 023 9246 7828 Colin & Guoying Huggins **Fax:** 023 9246 7828 **D:** £15.00–£23.00 **S:** £15.00–£23.00 **Beds:** 1D 1T **Baths:** 1 Pr 1 Sh ⅍ (12) 🅿 (5) ⅍ 📺 📺 🛶 ♨

Headley (Bordon)

SU8236

Heather Bank, May Close, Headley, Bordon, Hants, *GU35 8LR.* Family house in quiet private lane surrounded by National Trust land. **Open:** All year
01428 712666 Mrs McBeath **D:** £17.50–£20.00 **S:** £18.00–£20.00 **Beds:** 1D 2T **Baths:** 1 Sh ⅍ 🅿 (6) ⅍ 📺 🛏 ✕ 📺 🛶 ♨

Highclere

SU4360

Westridge Open Centre, Andover Road, Highclere, Newbury, Berks, *RG20 9PJ.* Venue for recitals. Limited accommodation, light breakfast is included. **Open:** All year (not Xmas/New Year)
01635 253322 D R Gribble **D:** £15.00 **S:** £15.00 **Beds:** 1T **Baths:** 1 Sh 🅿 (2) ⅍ 📺 🛶 ♨

Highclere Farm, Highclere, Newbury, Hampshire, *RG20 9PY.* Situated in designated Area of Outstanding Natural Beauty. Close to Highclere Castle & Newbury Racecourse. **Open:** All year (not Xmas/New Year)
01635 255013 Mrs Walsh *walshhighclere@ newburyweb.com* **D:** £25.00 **S:** £40.00 **Beds:** 1F 1D **Baths:** 1 En ⅍ 🅿 📺 📺 🛶 ♨

Hook

SU7254

Cherry Lodge, Reading Road, Hook (Basingstoke), Basingstoke, Hants, *RG27 9DB.* Friendly family-run guest house in country surroundings. **Open:** All year (not Xmas/New Year)
01256 762532 (also fax) Mrs Phillips **D:** £32.00–£35.00 **S:** £32.00–£35.00 **Beds:** 2F 5T 4D 3S **Baths:** 14 En ⅍ (4) 🅿 (35) 📺 🛶 ♨ & ♨ cc

---

BEDROOMS
D = Double
T = Twin
S = Single
F = Family

Hordle

SZ2795

Spinney Cottage, *219 Everton Road, Hordle, Lymington, Hants, SO41 0HE.* Welcome, charming, New Forest Home. Rural setting, superb breakfasts. **Open:** Jan to Oct
01590 644555 (also fax) Mrs Blackwell *spinneycottage@aol.com* www.spinneycottage.co.uk **D:** £22.00–£25.00 **S:** £22.00–£26.00 **Beds:** 2D 1S **Baths:** 2 Pr (3)

Horton Heath

SU4916

Sandelwood, *Knowle Lane, Horton Heath, Eastleigh, Hants, SO50 7DZ.* Quiet country house, extensive rural views. Friendly. Comfortable attractive rooms. **Open:** All year
023 8069 3726 Mrs Phipp **D:** £44.00–£48.00 **S:** £22.00–£26.00 **Beds:** 1F 1D **Baths:** 2 En (3)

Hurstbourne Priors

SU4346

The Hurstbourne, *Hurstbourne Priors, Whitchurch, Hants, RG28 7SE.* Public house, offering good food and quality ales. **Open:** All year
01256 892000 Mr & Mrs Essen **Fax: 01256 895351 D:** £20.00–£25.00 **S:** £25.00 **Beds:** 3F 2D 1T **Baths:** 1 Sh cc

Itchen Abbas

SU5332

The Trout, *Itchen Abbas, Winchester, Hampshire, SO21 1BQ.* **Open:** All year **Grades:** ETC 4 Di
01962 779537 Emma Howe **Fax: 01962 791046** *thetroutinn@freeuk.com* **D:** £35.00 **S:** £40.00 **Beds:** 2T 3D **Baths:** 5 En cc
Set in the heart of the Itchen Valley, a stone's throw away from the beautiful River Itchen. Ideal for the keen fisherman. We have a superb non-smoking restaurant with excellent food, real ales and wines of the world.

Itchen Stoke

SU5532

The Parsonage, *Itchen Stoke, Alresford, Hants, SO24 0QU.* Modern house, quiet rural setting, very central for touring. **Open:** All year (not Xmas)
01962 732123 Mrs Pitt **D:** £20.00 **S:** £20.00 **Beds:** 1T **Baths:** 1 Sh (20) cc

Kingsley

SU7838 Cricketers

30 Churchfields, *Kingsley, Bordon, Hants, GU35 9PJ.* Modern village house adjoining commonland. Close Selborne, Chawton, Watercress Line. **Open:** All year (not Xmas/New Year)
01420 472271 Mrs Clack **D:** £20.00–£22.50 **S:** £22.50–£25.00 **Beds:** 1D 1S **Baths:** 1 Pr (2)

Kingston

SU1402

Greenacres Farmhouse, *Christchurch Road, Kingston, Ringwood, Hants, BH24 3BJ.* Comfortable Victorian family home near New Forest and River Avon. **Open:** All year (not Xmas)
01425 480945 Mrs Armstrong **D:** £18.00 **S:** £20.00 **Beds:** 1D 2T **Baths:** 1 En 1 Sh (5)

Langley

SU4400

Langley Village Restaurant & Guest House, *Lepe Road, Langley, Southampton, SO45 1XR.* Close to Motor Museum, Beaulieu, Exbury Gardens and Calshot Castle. **Open:** All year (not Xmas)
023 8089 1667 Mrs McEvoy *alexismcevoy@tinyworld.co.uk* www.langley-hampshire.co.uk **D:** £21.00 **S:** £21.00 **Beds:** 1D 1T 2S **Baths:** 1 Sh (12) (8)

Lee-on-the-Solent

SU5600

Chester Lodge, *20 Chester Crescent, Lee-on-the-Solent, Gosport, Hampshire, PO13 9BH.* Family-run, quiet location, convenient for exploring the Solent area. **Open:** All year (not Xmas/New Year) **Grades:** ETC 3 Diamond
023 9255 0894 Mrs Jeffery **Fax: 023 9255 6291 D:** £19.00 **S:** £25.00 **Beds:** 1D 1F 1S **Baths:** 2 Sh (6)

Liphook

SU8431

The Bailiffs Cottage, *Hollycombe, Liphook, Hants, GU30 7LR.* C18th cottage. 25 miles Chichester, Guildford, Portsmouth. 55 mins train to London **Open:** All year **Grades:** ETC 3 Diamond
01428 722171 Mrs Jenner **Fax: 01428 729394** *jenner@bailiffs.fsnet.co.uk* **D:** £21.00–£23.00 **S:** £21.00–£23.00 **Beds:** 1T 1S **Baths:** 1 Sh (3)

Liss

SU7827

Glendale, *Hatch Lane, Rake, Liss, Hampshire, GU33 7NJ.* Large family house in 4.5 acres, garden with tennis court set in country woodland. **Open:** All year (not Xmas)
01730 893451 Mrs Browse **Fax: 01730 892626** *carol@cbrowse.fsnet.co.uk* **D:** £22.50–£25.00 **S:** £25.00–£30.00 **Beds:** 1D 1T 1S **Baths:** 1 En 1 Pr

Longparish

SU4344

Yew Cottage, *Longparish, Andover, Hampshire, SP11 6QE.* Cosy thatched cottage in beautiful village on the River Test. **Open:** All year
01264 720325 Mr & Mrs Lowry *yewcottage@ukgateway.net* **D:** £20.00–£25.00 **S:** £22.50–£27.50 **Beds:** 2T 1S **Baths:** 1 En 1 Sh (3)

Lymington

SZ3295 *Chequers, Red Lion, Mayflower, Ship Inn, Musketeers*

Jevington, *47 Waterford Lane, Lymington, Hants, SO41 3PT.* Comfortable family-run B&B, in quiet lane yet only few minutes walk to town. **Open:** All year **Grades:** ETC 4 Diamond
01590 672148 (also fax) Mr & Mrs Carruthers *jevingtonbb@lineone.net* www.caruthers.co.uk **D:** £22.00–£25.00 **S:** £22.00–£35.00 **Beds:** 1F 1D 1T **Baths:** 3 En (4) (4)

Admiral House, *3 Stanley Road, Lymington, Hants, SO41 3SJ.* Comfortable accommodation near pubs, shops, coastal walk, marinas and forest. **Open:** All year
01590 674339 Mrs Wild *bill@wild27.freeserve.co.uk* **D:** £12.00–£14.00 **S:** £12.00–£14.00 **Beds:** 2F 1T **Baths:** 1 Sh

The Rowans, *76 Southampton Road, Lymington, Hants, SO41 9GZ.* Delightful detached period house, 5 mins' walk to High Street. **Open:** All year
01590 672276 & 07860 630361 (M) Mrs Baddock **Fax: 01590 688610 D:** £20.00–£25.00 **S:** £20.00–£27.00 **Beds:** 3F 3D 3T **Baths:** 3 En (5) (6)

Monks Pool, *Waterford Lane, Lymington, Hants, SO41 3PS.* Unique spacious home. Centre Lymington. Large, sunny garden, private lake. **Open:** Jan to Dec
01590 678850 (also fax) M C Otten *cam@monkspool.swinternet.co.uk* **D:** £20.00–£30.00 **S:** £25.00–£35.00 **Beds:** 2D 1T **Baths:** 2 En 1 Sh (4)

Lyndhurst

SU2908 🍺 *Fox & Hounds, Crown, Mailman's Arms, Oak Inn, Waterloo Arms, Mill House, Crown Stirrup*

The Penny Farthing Hotel, *Romsey Road, LYNDHURST, Hampshire, SO43 7AA.* **Open:** All year (not Xmas) **Grades:** ETC 4 Diamond
023 8028 4422 Mr & Mrs Saqui **Fax: 023 8028 4488** *stay@pennyfarthinghotel.co.uk* www.pennyfarthinghotel.co.uk **D:** £29.50–£45.00 **S:** £35.00–£45.00 **Beds:** 2F 9D 3T 1S **Baths:** 15 En 2 Sh ⛲ 🅿 (15) ☑ ⊀ 📺 🎢 ⓥ 🕮 ♨
Welcome to our cheerful hotel, ideally situated in Lyndhurst village centre. We offer a variety of rooms that are all ensuite with colour TV, tea/coffee tray and telephones. There is a large car park and secure bike store. New Forest Visitor Centre 5 mins walk.

Lyndhurst House, *35 Romsey Road, Lyndhurst, Hants, SO43 7AR.* **Open:** All year (not Xmas) **Grades:** ETC 4 Diamond, Sparkling, RAC 4 Star, Silver
023 8028 2230 Mrs Sullivan **Fax: 023 8028 3190** *lyndhursthouse@aol.com* www.lyndhursthousebandb.co.uk **D:** £24.00–£26.00 **S:** £30.00 **Beds:** 1F 4D **Baths:** 5 En ⛲ 🅿 (5) ⊁ ☑ 🕮 ♨
In the heart of New Forest and conveniently situated for a complete range of activities. Lyndhurst House offers a comfortable and relaxed homely atmosphere. All ensuite and well equipped bedrooms, some with four posters. Excellent English or vegetarian breakfast.

Forest Cottage, *High Street, Lyndhurst, Hants, SO43 7BH.* Delightful 300-year-old cottage. Warm, comfortable and friendly. **Open:** All year **Grades:** ETC 4 Diamond, Silver
023 8028 3461 Mrs Rowland
www.forestcottage.i12.com **D:** £22.00–£24.00 **S:** £22.00–£24.00 **Beds:** 1D 1T 1S **Baths:** 2 Sh ⛲ (14) 🅿 (3) ⊁ ☑ ⓥ 🕮 ♨

The Laurels, *9 Wellands Road, Lyndhurst, Hants, SO43 7AB.* Excellent accommodation, quiet, central, New Forest location. Warm welcome guaranteed. **Open:** All year (not Xmas)
023 8028 2545 Mrs Kennard *kennard.laurels@ virgin.net* www.smoothhound.co.uk/hotels/laur.html **D:** £19.00–£20.00 **S:** £20.00 **Beds:** 1D/T **Baths:** 1 Pr ⛲ (8) 🅿 (1) ⊀ 📺 🕮 ♨

Rose Cottage, *Chapel Lane, Lyndhurst, Hants, SO43 7FG.* Charming cottage set in beautiful, peaceful garden, close to forest and village. **Open:** All year **Grades:** ETC 4 Diamond
023 8028 3413 (also fax) Mrs Dawson *cindy@ rosecottageb-b.freeserve.co.uk* www.rosecottageb-b.freeserve.co.uk/ **D:** £22.00–£25.00 **S:** £25.00–£30.00 **Beds:** 1F 2D **Baths:** 1 En 1 Sh ⛲ 🅿 (6) ⊁ ☑ 🎢 ⊀ ⓥ 🕮 ♨

Whitemoor House Hotel, *Southampton Road, Lyndhurst, Hants, SO43 7BU.* Award-winning food. Log fires in winter. Beautiful gardens in summer. **Open:** All year (not Xmas)
023 8028 2186 Mr Barron **D:** £20.00–£30.00 **S:** £20.00–£40.00 **Beds:** 2F 4D 2T **Baths:** 8 En ⛲ 🅿 (12) ⊁ ☑ 🎢 ⊀ ⓥ 🕮 ♨ cc

Clarendon Villa, *Gosport Lane, Lyndhurst, Hants, SO43 7BL.* Victorian family house, village centre, breakfast served in your room. **Open:** All year (not Xmas)
023 8028 2803 M Preston **Fax: 023 8028 4303** *clarendonvilla@i12.com* www.clarendonvilla.i12.com **D:** £22.50–£30.00 **S:** £25.00–£35.00 **Beds:** 1F 2D **Baths:** 3 En ⛲ 🅿 (4) ⊁ ☑ ⓥ 🕮 ♨ cc

Owl Cottage, *Clayhill, Lyndhurst, Hants, SO43 7DE.* Off beaten track, direct access to forest - escape for a while. **Open:** All year
023 8028 3800 Mr & Mrs Lowe **D:** £20.00 **Beds:** 1D 1S **Baths:** 1 En 🅿 (6) ⊁ ☑ ⓥ 🕮 ♨

Mapledurwell

SU6951

Eastside Coach House, *Frog Lane, Mapledurwell, Basingstoke, Hants, RG25 2LP.* A unique very attractive property sitting in the bed of the Basingstoke Canal. **Open:** All year
01256 465559 & 01256 363311 Mr & Mrs Cashmore **Fax: 01256 465559** *eastside@ breathmail.net* **D:** £20.00–£25.00 **S:** £25.00–£30.00 **Beds:** 2F 1D 4T 2S **Baths:** 3 En 1 Pr 2 Sh ⛲ 🅿 (12) ⊁ ☑ 🎢 ⊀ ⓥ 🕮 ♨ ♨

Medstead

SU6537

Orchard View, *High Street, Medstead, Alton, Hants., GU34 5LN.* Modern bungalow secluded ample parking central for touring bus route. **Open:** All year (not Xmas)
01420 562480 Mrs Westbrook **D:** £16.00–£18.00 **S:** £16.00–£20.00 **Beds:** 1D 1T **Baths:** 1 En 1 Sh

---

Micheldever

SU5139

Orchard Close, *The Highways, Micheldever, Winchester, Hampshire, SO21 3BP.* Quiet spacious accommodation overlooking lawns and garden. Private off-road parking. 6m city centre. **Open:** Easter to Dec
01962 774470 & 07885 482654 (M) Mrs Holmes **D:** £18.00–£20.00 **S:** £25.00–£30.00 **Beds:** 1T 2D **Baths:** 1 En 1 Sh ⛲ 🅿 ☑ ⓥ 🕮 ♿ ♨

Milford on Sea

SZ2891 🍺 *Smugglers, Red Lion*

Compton Hotel, *59 Keyhaven Road, Milford on Sea, Lymington, Hants, SO41 0QX.* Small private hotel with ensuite rooms and TV. Outdoor swimming pool. **Open:** All year (not Xmas/New Year)
01590 643117 Mr Emberson **D:** £21.00–£24.00 **S:** £30.00–£32.00 **Beds:** 1F 1T 4D 2S **Baths:** 4 En 1 Sh ⛲ 🅿 (8) ☑ 🎢 ⊀ ⓥ 🕮 ♨

Cherry Trees, *Lymington Road, Milford on Sea, Lymington, Hants, SO41 0QL.* Warm welcome assured at this lovely character retreat. Pretty rooms, delightful garden. **Open:** All year
01590 643746 & 07976 382828 (M) S Gadd *cherrytrees@beeb.net* **D:** £20.00–£25.00 **S:** £22.00–£35.00 **Beds:** 1F 1T 1D **Baths:** 2 En 1 Pr ⛲ 🅿 ⊁ ☑ 🎢 ⊀ ⓥ 🕮 ♿ ♨

Minstead

SU2811

Grove House, *Minstead, Lyndhurst, Hants, SO43 7GG.* New Forest small holding. Excellent comfort, varied breakfast, superb walking/riding. **Open:** All year
023 8081 3211 Mrs Dixon **D:** £22.00–£25.00 **Beds:** 1T **Baths:** 1 Pr ⛲ 🅿 ⊁ ☑ 🎢 🕮 ♨

Monk Sherborne

SU6056

Manor Farm, *Monk Sherborne, Basingstoke, Hants, RG26 5HW.* Traditional old farmhouse in a rural setting. **Open:** All year (not Xmas/New Year)
01256 850889 Mrs Dalgarno **D:** £16.00 **S:** £20.00–£22.00 **Beds:** 1D 1F **Baths:** 1 Sh 🅿 (6) ⊁ ☑ 🕮 ♨

Nether Wallop

SU3036 🍺 *Five Bells, George Inn*

York Lodge, *Nether Wallop, Stockbridge, Hants, SO20 8HE.* **Open:** All year **Grades:** ETC 4 Diamond, AA 4 Diamond
01264 781313 Mrs Bradley *bradley@ yorklodge.fslife.com.uk* **D:** £22.50–£25.00
S: £27.00–£30.00 **Beds:** 2T **Baths:** 2 En ⥾ (8)
⥾ ⊡ ⟡ ✕ ⊡ ▥ ⚓
Comfortable, self-contained accommodation in peaceful garden in picturesque village used as setting for Agatha Christie's 'Miss Marples' series. Ideal base for exploring Southern England (easy reach Winchester, Salisbury, Stonehenge). Excellent stopover for West Country. Adjacent A343/A30, 10 Minutes A303.

Halcyon, *Church Hill, Nether Wallop, Stockbridge, Hants, SO20 8EY.* Extensive modern bungalow in quiet country lane with delightful views. **Open:** All year **01264 781348** Mrs Ayers **D:** £22.00–£23.00 **S:** £28.00–£30.00 **Beds:** 1F 1T 1S **Baths:** 1 En 1 Sh ⥾ ⊡ (6) ⥾ ⊡ ⟡ ⊡ ▥ ⚓

New Milton

SZ2395

Willy's Well, *Bashley Common Road, New Milton, Hants, BH25 5SF.* **Open:** All year **Grades:** ETC 3 Diamond **01425 616834** *moyramac2@hotmail.com* **D:** £22.50–£25.00 **S:** £25.00–£30.00 **Beds:** 1T 1D **Baths:** 1 En 1 Pr ⊡ ⊡ ⟡ ⊡ ▥ ⚓
A warm welcome awaits you at our mid C18th thatched cottage. We are ideally situated for exploring the New Forest and coastal towns in the area. The cottage is set in 7 acres with 1 acre of garden.

Saint Ursula, *30 Hobart Road, New Milton, Hants, BH25 6EG.* Ideal for New Forest/coast. Large comfortable house. Central. Disabled facilities. **Open:** All year **01425 613515** Mrs Pearce **D:** £20.00 **S:** £20.00 **Beds:** 1F 1D 2T 2S **Baths:** 3 En 2 Pr 1 Sh ⥾ ⊡ (4) ⥾ ⊡ ⟡ ⊡ ▥ ♿3 ✳ ⚓

Newtown (Newbury)

SU4763

White Cottage, *Newtown, Newbury, Berks, RG20 9AP.* Delightful semi-rural cottage on the edge of Watership Down. **Open:** All year (not Xmas) **01635 43097 (also fax)** Mrs Meiklejohn *ellie@ p-p-ifsnet.co.uk* **D:** £22.00–£25.00 **S:** £25.00–£30.00 **Beds:** 1D 1T 1S **Baths:** 1 Sh ⥾ (3) ⊡ ⥾ ⊡ ⟡ ⊡ ▥ ⚓

Norleywood

SZ3698 🍺 *Waggon & Horses*

Carters Farm, *Norleywood, Lymington, Hampshire, SO41 5RR.* C14th farmhouse between Beaulieu and Lymington. Scenic and peaceful. **Open:** All year **01590 626630 (also fax)** Mrs Silvester **D:** £20.00 **S:** £20.00 **Beds:** 2D **Baths:** 2 Pr ⥾ ⊡ ⊡ ✕ ⊡ ⚓

Nursling

SU3716

Conifers, *6 Nursling Street Cottages, Nursling, Southampton, Hants, SO16 0XH.* Attractive 1930s cottage. Comfortable beds. Family Garden. Country pubs nearby. **Open:** All year **Grades:** ETC 3 Diamond **023 8034 9491 (also fax)** Mrs Hinton **D:** £18.00–£25.00 **S:** £18.00–£28.00 **Beds:** 1F 1D 1S **Baths:** 1 En ⥾ ⊡ (2) ⥾ ⊡ ⟡ ✕ ⊡ ▥ ⚓

Oakhanger

SU7635

Ivanhoe, *Oakhanger, Bordon, Hants., GU35 9JG.* Comfortable accommodation with rural views. Small village central for walking. **Open:** All year (not Xmas/New Year) **01420 473464** Mrs Britton **D:** £18.00 **S:** £25.00 **Beds:** 1T **Baths:** 1 Pr ⥾ ⊡ (1) ⥾ ⊡ ⊡ ▥ ⚓

Odiham

SU7451

Newlands Farm, *Odiham, Hook, Hampshire, RG29 1JD.* Period farmhouse, businessmen welcome. Quiet. Basins rooms, home made bread, marmalade. **Open:** All year (not Xmas) **01256 702373 (also fax)** Mrs Saunders *mary.saunders@farming.co.uk* **D:** £15.00–£16.00 **S:** £15.00–£16.00 **Beds:** 2S 1D **Baths:** 2 Sh ⊡ (3) ⥾ ⊡ ▥ ⚓

BATHROOMS

En = Ensuite

Pr = Private

Sh = Shared

Owslebury

SU5123

Mays Farmhouse, *Longwood Dean, Owslebury, Winchester, Hants, SO21 1JS.* Lovely C16th farmhouse, beautiful countryside; peaceful with good walks. **Open:** All year **01962 777486** Mrs Ashby **Fax: 01962 777747** *rosalieashhby@maysfarm.fsnet.co.uk* **D:** £22.50–£25.00 **S:** £25.00–£30.00 **Beds:** 1F 1D 1T **Baths:** 3 Pr ⥾ (7) ⊡ (5) ⥾ ⊡ ⟡ ⊡ ▥ ♿ ⚓

Park Gate

SU5108

60 Southampton Road, *Park Gate, Southampton, Hants., SO31 6AF.* Quiet peaceful situation in lovely garden convenient to motorway. **Open:** All year (not Xmas/New Year) **01489 573994** Mrs White **D:** £18.00–£20.00 **S:** £18.00–£20.00 **Beds:** 1F 1S **Baths:** 1 Sh ⥾ ⊡ (5) ⥾ ⊡ ▥ ⚓

Pennington

SZ3194 🍺 *Hare & Hounds, Gordleton Mill*

Restormel, *Sway Road, Pennington, Lymington, Hants, SO41 8LJ.* Picturesque cottage, adjoining family farm. Varied breakfasts. Forest, coast nearby. **Open:** All year **Grades:** ETC 4 Diamond **01590 673875 (also fax)** Mrs Morgan *judy@ restormel-newforest.co.uk* *www.restormel-newforest.co.uk* **D:** £20.00–£25.00 **S:** £25.00–£30.00 **Beds:** 1F 1D **Baths:** 1 En 1 Pr ⥾ ⊡ (4) ⥾ ⊡ ⟡ ▥ ⚓

Our Bench Guest House, *9 Lodge Road, Pennington, Lymington, Hants, SO41 8HH.* Large non-smoking bungalow between the forest and coast. Garden with heated indoor pool. **Open:** All year (not Xmas) **01590 673141 (also fax)** Mrs Lewis *ourbench@newforest.demon.co.uk* *www.ourbench.co.uk* **D:** £22.00–£27.50 **S:** £22.00–£30.00 **Beds:** 1D 1T 1S **Baths:** 3 En ⥾ (14) ⊡ (6) ⥾ ⊡ ✕ ⊡ ▥ ♿3 ⚓ cc

Petersfield

SU7423 🍺 *White Hart*

Heath Farmhouse, *Sussex Road, Petersfield, Hants, GU31 4HU.* Georgian farmhouse, lovely views, large garden, quiet surroundings, near town. **Open:** All year **Grades:** ETC 3 Diamond **01730 264709** Mrs Scurfield *bandb@ heathfarmhouse.co.uk* www.heathfarmhouse. co.uk **D:** £18.00–£20.00 **S:** £20.00–£25.00 **Beds:** 1F 1D 1T **Baths:** 1 En 1 Sh ⥾ ⊡ (5) ⥾ ⊡ ▥ ⚓

Beaumont, *22 Stafford Road, Petersfield, Hampshire, GU32 2JG.* Warm welcome, comfortable beds, excellent breakfasts with home-made preserves. **Open:** All year (not Xmas) **Grades:** ETC 3 Diamond **01730 264744 (also fax)** Mrs Bewes *david.bewes@btinternet.com* **D:** £20.00–£25.00 **S:** £20.00–£25.00 **Beds:** 2T 1S **Baths:** 1 Sh ॐ (12) ▣ (2) ⠇ 📺 Ⅴ 🏠

The Causeway Guest House, *64a The Causeway, Petersfield, Hants, GU31 4JS.* Modern, centrally situated. Close to sporting activities. English/continental breakfast. **Open:** All year **01730 262924** Mrs Fell *eileen.fell@talk21.com* **D:** £18.00–£20.00 **S:** £20.00–£35.00 **Beds:** 1F 1T 1D 1S **Baths:** 1 Sh ▣ (6) ⠇📺 ⍒ 🏠 ☀ ⤶

Ridgefield, *Station Road, Petersfield, Hants, GU32 3DE.* Friendly family atmosphere, near town & station. Portsmouth ferries 20 mins drive. **Open:** All year (not Xmas) **01730 261402 & 01730 260028** Mrs West *ymcokw@hants.gov.uk* **D:** £20.00 **S:** £25.00–£30.00 **Beds:** 1D 2T **Baths:** 2 Sh ▣ (4) ⠇📺 Ⅴ 🏠 ⅋

Picket Piece

SU3947

Cherry Trees, *Picket Piece, Andover, Hampshire, SP11 6LY.* Perfectly situated for business or pleasure. Warm welcome. Large garden. **Open:** All year **Grades:** ETC 3 Diamond **01264 334891 (also fax)** S Barnett **D:** £22.00–£27.50 **S:** £22.00–£27.50 **Beds:** 1F 1T 1S **Baths:** 1 Sh ▣ (6) ⠇📺 ⍒

Pilley

SZ3499

Mistletoe Cottage, *3 Jordans Lane, Pilley Bailey, Pilley, Lymington, Hampshire, SO41 5QW.* Quiet New Forest hamlet. Convenient for Beaulieu and the coast. **Open:** All year **01590 676361** **D:** £18.00–£25.00 **S:** £25.00–£35.00 **Beds:** 2D **Baths:** 2 En ▣ (4) ⠇📺 Ⅴ 🏠 ⍒

Plaitford

SU2719

Southernwood, *Plaitford Common, Salisbury Road, Plaitford, Romsey, Hants, SO51 6EE.* Family home, edge of New Forest, ferries, Stonehenge, Romsey, Salisbury. **Open:** All year **01794 323255** Mrs Hocking **D:** £35.00–£40.00 **S:** £35.00–£40.00 **Beds:** 1F 3D 1T **Baths:** 1 Pr 1 Sh ॐ ▣ (4) ⠇📺 ⍒ 🏠 ⍒

Pyesmead Farm, *Salisbury Road, Plaitford, Romsey, Hants, SO51 6EE.* Farmhouse on family stock farm. **Open:** All year (not Xmas/New Year) **01794 323386 (also fax)** Mrs Pybus *pyesmead@talk21.com* **D:** £17.00–£20.00 **S:** £20.00–£25.00 **Beds:** 2D 1T **Baths:** 1 En 1 Pr ॐ ▣ (10) ⠇📺 ⍒

Portchester

SU6105

Appletrees, *144 Castle Street, Portchester, Fareham, Hants, PO16 9QH.* Near Portchester Castle, Port Solent Marina, Portsmouth ferries/maritime attractions. **Open:** All year **023 9237 0376** Mrs Jones **D:** £18.00–£22.00 **S:** £20.00–£25.00 **Beds:** 1T 1S **Baths:** 1 Pr 1 Sh ▣ (2) ⠇📺 🏠 ⍒

Portsmouth

SU6501

Hamilton House, *95 Victoria Road North, Southsea, Portsmouth, Hants, PO5 1PS.* **Open:** All year **023 9282 3502 (also fax)** Graham & Sandra Tubb *sandra@hamiltonhouse.co.uk* www.hamiltonhouse.co.uk **D:** £21.00–£25.00 **S:** £25.00–£45.00 **Beds:** 3F 3D 2T 1S **Baths:** 5 En 2 Sh ॐ ⠇📺 Ⅴ 🏠 ⍒ cc Delightful Victorian Townhouse B&B. Bright, modern rooms, many original features. Centrally located 5 mins by car from Historic Ships Museum, University, City Centres/Stations, Guildhall, Continent/ I.O.W Ferry-ports and Gunwharf Quays. Breakfast served from 6.15am for early travellers.

Bembell Court Hotel, *69 Festing Road, Southsea, Portsmouth, Hants, PO4 0NQ.* **Open:** All year **Grades:** ETC 3 Diamond, AA 3 Diamond **023 9273 5915** Mr Irwin **Fax: 023 9275 6497** *keith@bembell.freeserve.co.uk* www.bembell.com **D:** £26.00–£28.00 **S:** £38.00–£42.00 **Beds:** 2F 4D 4T 3S **Baths:** 13 En ॐ ▣ (10) 📺 Ⅴ 🏠 ⍒ cc A friendly, family run hotel, ideally situated in Portsmouth's prime holiday area. Nearby you'll find an excellent selection of shops, pubs and restaurants. Also canoe lake, The Rose Gardens, bowling greens, South Parade Pier and one of the finest promenades.

The Elms Guest House, *48 Victoria Road South, Southsea, Hants, PO5 2BT.* Close to Naval Heritage Complex. Within walking distance of restaurants and seafront. **Open:** All year **Grades:** ETC 3 Diamond, AA 3 Diamond **023 9282 3924 (also fax)** Mrs Erskine *theelmsgh@aol.com* **D:** £21.00–£24.00 **S:** £35.00–£48.00 **Beds:** 2F 1D 2T **Baths:** 5 En ॐ (4) ▣ (2) ⠇📺 🏠 ⍒ cc

Hillside Lodge, *1 Blake Road, Farlington, Portsmouth, Hants, PO6 1ET.* House on hill slopes above Portsmouth. Business personnel always welcome. **Open:** All year **023 9237 2687** Mrs Wood **D:** £18.00–£22.00 **S:** £18.00 **Beds:** 1D 1T 1S **Baths:** 1 En 1 Sh ॐ ▣ 📺 🏠 ⍒

The Festing Grove Guest House, *8 Festing Grove, Southsea, Hants, PO4 9QA.* Situated in quieter area of Southsea yet within 3 mins walking of sea front. **Open:** All year **023 9273 5239** Mr Newton **D:** £16.00–£20.00 **S:** £19.00–£28.00 **Beds:** 3F 2T 1D **Baths:** 1 En 3 Sh ⠇📺 Ⅴ 🏠 ⍒ cc

Poulner

SU1606

The Old Cottage, *Cowpitts Lane, Poulner, Ringwood, Hants, BH24 3JX.* Stunning views over the forest from our secluded C17th thatched and beamed cottage. **Open:** Jan to Nov **Grades:** AA 4 Diamond **01425 477956 (also fax)** Mr Theobald *forestgatewines@btinternet.com* **D:** £22.00–£28.00 **Beds:** 1F 1D 1T **Baths:** 3 En ॐ (8) ▣ (4) ⠇📺 Ⅴ 🏠 ⍒

Ringwood

SU1505 🍺 *Elm Tree*

Lion's Hill Farm, *Ashley Heath, Ringwood, Hants, BH24 2EX.* **Open:** All year **Grades:** ETC 2 Diamond **01425 472115** Mr & Mrs Hodges **D:** £20.00–£25.00 **S:** £25.00–£30.00 **Beds:** 1F 1T 1D **Baths:** 1 Pr 1 Sh ॐ ▣ (6) ⍒ ✕ 🏠 ☀ ⍒ Traditional Victorian Farmhouse with uninterrupted views over forest and farmland. Direct access to forest trail way for cycling horse riding, walking. Stabling for horses and other pets welcome. Guests' heated swimming pool. Close to country park, Bournemouth and New Forest. Aga cooked breakfasts.

The Old Cottage, *Cowpitts Lane, Poulner, Ringwood, Hants, BH24 3JX.* **Open:** Jan to Nov **Grades:** AA 4 Diamond **01425 477956 (also fax)** Mr Theobald *forestgatewines@btinternet.com* **D:** £22.00–£28.00 **Beds:** 1F 1D 1T **Baths:** 3 En ॐ (8) ▣ (4) ⠇📺 Ⅴ 🏠 ⍒ Stunning views over the forest from our secluded C17th thatched and beamed cottage.

Planning a longer stay? Always ask for any special rates

Fraser House, *Salisbury Road, Blashford, Ringwood, Hants, BH24 3PB.* Very comfortable accommodation. Easy access to New Forest and South Coast. **Open:** All year **Grades:** ETC 3 Diamond **01425 473958 (also fax)** *fraserhouse@ b.t.internet.com* **D:** £23.00 **S:** £30.00 **Beds:** 2T 2D **Baths:** 4 En ⬛ (6) ⌇ ⧖ ⬛ ⧖ ⬛ ⬛ . ⬛ cc

The Nest, *10 Middle Lane, off School Lane, Ringwood, Hants, BH24 1LE.* Lovely Victorian family home, recommended, quiet, convenient town centre position, parking. **Open:** All year **Grades:** AA 4 Diamond **01425 476724 & 07813 539138 (M) Fax:** **01425 467724** *ynixonuk@yahoo.com* **D:** £21.00– £25.00 **S:** £25.00–£30.00 **Beds:** 2D 1T 1S **Baths:** 2 Sh ⬛ ⬛ (6) ⌇ ⬛ ⬛ ⬛ .

Old Stacks, *154 Hightown Road, Ringwood, Hants, BH24 1NP.* Warm welcome. Home from home hospitality. Excellent breakfasts. Near country inn. **Open:** All year (not Xmas/New Year) **Grades:** ETC 4 Diamond **01425 473840 (also fax)** Mrs Peck *oldstacksband@aol.com* **D:** £21.00–£23.00 **S:** £30.00 **Beds:** 1T 1D **Baths:** 1 En 1 Pr

Beau Cottage, *1 Hiltom Road, Ringwood, Hants, BH24 1PW.* Quiet, old, modernised cottage. Comfortable and friendly. Good English breakfast. **Open:** All year (not Xmas) **01425 461274** Mrs Willis **D:** £17.00–£22.00 **S:** £17.00–£24.00 **Beds:** 1T 1D 1S **Baths:** 3 En ⬛ (12) ⬛ ⌇ ⬛ ⬛ ⬛ .

Rockbourne

SU1118

Shearings, *Rockbourne, Fordingbridge, Hants, SP6 3NA.* C16th stunning timberland thatched cottage set in a delightful garden in a pretty village. **Open:** Feb to Dec **01725 518256** Mr Watts **Fax: 01725 518255** **D:** £26.00–£30.00 **S:** £26.00–£30.00 **Beds:** 1D 1T 1S **Baths:** 3 Pr ⬛ (12) ⬛ (5) ⌇ ⬛ ⬛ .

Romsey

SU3521

Ranvilles Farm House, *Pauncefoot Hill, Romsey, Hants, SO51 6AA.* C16th rural farmhouse - king beds, antiques, pretty garden, farmhouse breakfast. **Open:** All year (not Xmas) **023 8081 4481** Mrs Hughes **D:** £25.00–£35.00 **S:** £30.00–£40.00 **Beds:** 1F 1D 1T **Baths:** 3 En ⬛ ⬛ (8) ⌇ ⬛ ⧖ ⬛ ⬛ .

Crofton Country B and B, *Kents Oak, Awbridge, Romsey, Hants, SP51 0HH.* **Open:** All year (not Xmas/New Year) **Grades:** ETC 4 Diamond, Silver **01794 340333 (also fax)** Mrs Lightfoot *pauline@crofton-ca.fsnet.co.uk* **D:** £22.50– £25.00 **S:** £25.00–£30.00 **Beds:** 1F 1T 1S **Baths:** 3 En ⬛ ⬛ (3) ⌇ ⬛ ⬛ ⬛ . ⬛ cc Nestled in 2 acres of gardens including a vineyard, Crofton offers luxury, hotel-quality accommodation within the tranquil setting of a small hamlet in the beautiful Test Valley, 4 miles north of Romsey.

Woodlands Guest House, *Bunny Lane, Sherfield English, Romsey, Hants, SO51 6FT.* Woodlands - overlooking farmland, situated in quiet country lane. Friendly accommodation. **Open:** All year **01794 884840** Mrs Hayter **D:** £15.00–£18.00 **S:** £15.00–£20.00 **Beds:** 1F 1D 1T **Baths:** 2 En 1 Sh ⬛ ⬛ (4) ⌇ ⬛ ⬛ ⬛ .

Chalet Guest House, *105 Botley Road, Romsey, Hants, SO51 5RQ.* Small family run B&B approximately 1 mile from Romsey Centre. **Open:** All year **01794 517299** Mrs Male *b-and-b@ the-chalet.freeserve.co.uk* **D:** £20.00 **S:** £25.00 **Beds:** 2F 1D **Baths:** 2 En 1 Sh ⬛ ⬛ (4) ⌇ ⬛ ⬛ .

Ropley

SU6431

Thickets, *Swelling Hill, Ropley, Alresford, Hants, SO24 0DA.* Comfortable house with two acre garden in Jane Austen Country. **Open:** All year (not Xmas) **01962 772467** Mr & Mrs Lloyd-Evans **D:** £22.00 **S:** £24.00 **Beds:** 2T **Baths:** 2 Pr ⬛ (10) ⬛ (2) ⌇ ⬛ ⬛ .

Rotherwick

SU7156

Tylney Hall Hotel, *Tylney Hall, Rotherwick, Hook, Hampshire, RG27 9AZ.* 4 red star country house hotel set within 66 acres. **Open:** All year **Grades:** ETC 4 Star **01256 764881** **D:** £82.00–£215.00 **S:** £130.00–£400.00 **Beds:** 1F 8T 101D **Baths:** 110 En ⬛ ⬛ (120) ⬛ ⧖ ⬛ ⬛ . ⬛ cc

---

Rowland's Castle

SU7310

Cripple Creek Guest House, *86 Whichers Gate Road, Rowland's Castle, Hampshire, PO9 6BB.* In countryside, pub 7 minute walk, 2 miles M27. **Open:** All year **023 9241 2468 (also fax)** Mr & Mrs Harrod **D:** £18.00–£24.00 **S:** £18.00–£24.00 **Beds:** 2D 1T **Baths:** 3 En ⬛ ⬛ (6) ⌇ ⬛ ⬛ ⬛ . ⬛ .

Sandleheath

SU1215

Sandleheath Post Office, *Sandleheath, Fordingbridge, Hants, SP6 1PP.* Perfect stop. Close Salisbury, New Forest and South Coast. **Open:** All year **Grades:** ETC 3 Diamond **01425 652230 (also fax)** Mr & Mrs Champion *sue@sandleheath.com* *www.sandleheath.com/* **D:** £22.00–£25.00 **S:** £25.00–£35.00 **Beds:** 1F 1T 1D 1S **Baths:** 1 En 1 Sh ⬛ ⬛ (4) ⌇ ⬛ ⧖ ⬛ ⬛ . ⬛ cc

Selborne

SU7433

The Queens and The Limes, *High Street, Selborne, Hants, GU34 3JH.* Country Inn set in Gilbert White's famous village. **Open:** All year **Grades:** ETC 3 Diamond **01420 511454** Mr Paton **Fax: 01420 511272** *enquiries@queens-selborne.co.uk* **D:** £24.00– £36.00 **S:** £37.00–£52.00 **Beds:** 1F 5T 3D 1S **Baths:** 5 En 1 Pr 2 Sh ⬛ ⬛ (30) ⬛ ⧖ ⬛ ⬛ . ⬛ cc

Shalden

SU6941

Sunacres Farm, *Shalden, Alton, Hampshire, GU34 4DU.* Comfortable farmhouse with views over own land. Excellent walking, cycling. **Open:** All year (not Xmas/New Year) **01420 88635** Mrs Saponaro **Fax: 01420 89734** **D:** £22.00–£25.00 **S:** £20.00–£30.00 **Beds:** 1T 1D 1S **Baths:** 1 En 1 Pr 1 Sh ⬛ ⬛ (10) ⬛ ⧖ ⬛ ⬛ .

Shawford

SU4624 ⬛ *Captain Barnard, Old Forge*

Greenmead Cottage, *Fairfield Road, Shawfield, Winchester, Hants, SO21 2DA.* Superior accommodation in delightful cottage. One acre gardens. Delicious breakfasts. **Open:** All year **01962 713172** Ms Tice **Fax: 01962 711903** *junetice@amserve.net* *www.greenmeadcottage. com* **D:** £30.00 **S:** £30.00 **Beds:** 1T 2D **Baths:** 1 En 1 Pr 1 Sh ⬛ (2) ⌇ ⬛ ⬛ .

Sherborne St John

SU6254

Cranes Farmhouse, *Sherborne St John, Basingstoke, Hants, RG24 9LJ.* C15th spacious farmhouse set in beautiful gardens with pond. **Open:** All year (not Xmas/New Year)
01256 850126 T J & L D Bell **Fax: 01256 851714 D:** £25.00–£30.00 **S:** £22.00–£25.00 **Beds:** 1T 1D 1S **Baths:** 2 Pr ⅏ (8) 🖳 (4) ⅄ 🖵 🖵 ▥ ♨

Sherfield English

SU2922

Woodlands Guest House, *Bunny Lane, Sherfield English, Romsey, Hants, SO51 6FT.* Woodlands - overlooking farmland, situated in quiet country lane. Friendly accommodation. **Open:** All year
01794 884840 Mrs Hayter **D:** £15.00–£18.00 **S:** £15.00–£20.00 **Beds:** 1F 1D 1T **Baths:** 2 En 1 Sh ⅏ 🖳 (4) ⅄ 🖵 × 🖵 ▥ ♨

South Warnborough

SU7247

Street Farm House, *The Street, South Warnborough, Basingstoke, Hants, RG29 1RS.* Charming Jacobean farmhouse in village setting restored to offer extremely comfortable accommodation. **Open:** All year
01256 862225 (also fax) Mrs Turner *wendy@ streetfarmhouse.co.uk* **D:** £17.00–£25.00 **Beds:** 1F 2T **Baths:** 1 Pr 1 Sh ⅏ 🖳 (9) ⅄ 🖵 🖵 ▥ ♨

Southampton

SU4212

Fenland Guest House, *79 Hill Lane, Southampton, SO15 5AD.* **Open:** All year (not Xmas/New Year) **Grades:** ETC 3 Diamond
023 8022 0360 S P Denham **Fax: 023 8022 6574** *SDE5999756@aol.com* **D:** £22.00–£24.00 **S:** £23.00–£30.00 **Beds:** 1F 2T 2D 1S **Baths:** 3 En 1 Sh 🖳 (6) ⅄ 🖵 🖵 ▥ ♨ Quality non-smoking accommodation, well situated for all amenities.

Ashelee Lodge, *36 Atherley Road, Shirley, Southampton, SO15 5DQ.* **Open:** All year (not Xmas)
023 8022 2095 (also fax) Mrs Ward **D:** £18.00–£23.00 **S:** £20.00 **Beds:** 1F 1D 1T 1S **Baths:** 1 En 1 Sh ⅏ (4) 🖳 (3) ⅄ 🖵 🖵 ▥ ♨ cc
Homely guest house. Dip pool, garden, cable TV lounge, home-cooking. Base for historic areas Salisbury, Stonehenge, New Forest. Easy reach Southampton Docks, universities, station. 0.5 mile city. Pat Ward proprietor.

Madeleine Guest House, *55 The Polygon, Southampton, SO15 2BP.* Family-run, city centre, close to rail, coach, station, docks. **Open:** All year (not Xmas)
023 8033 3331 Mrs Gilligan **D:** £17.00 **S:** £17.00 **Beds:** 2F 1D 1T 2S **Baths:** 1 Sh ⅏ 🖳 (4) 🖵 ♛ × 🖵 ♨

Conifers, *6 Nursling Street Cottages, Nursling, Southampton, Hants, SO16 0XH.* Attractive 1930s cottage. Comfortable beds. Family Garden. Country pubs nearby. **Open:** All year **Grades:** ETC 3 Diamond
023 8034 9491 (also fax) Mrs Hinton **D:** £18.00–£25.00 **S:** £18.00–£28.00 **Beds:** 1F 1D 1S **Baths:** 1 En ⅏ 🖳 (2) ⅄ ♛ ♛ × 🖵 ▥ ♨

Pages Place Guest House, *14 Porchester Road, Southampton, SO19 2LD.* Friendly, quiet, yet near town. **Open:** All year
023 8042 1275 (also fax) Mrs Smith **D:** £15.00–£17.00 **S:** £22.00–£24.00 **Beds:** 1D 1T 1S **Baths:** 1 Sh ⅏ ⅄ 🖵 × 🖵 ▥ ♨

Banister House Hotel, *Banister Road, Southampton, SO15 2JJ.* A friendly welcome assured in this central family-run hotel. **Open:** All year (not Xmas/New Year)
023 8022 1279 & 023 8022 5753 Mr Ridley **Fax: 023 8022 6551** *banisterhouse@lineone.net* **D:** £22.00–£24.00 **S:** £26.00–£30.00 **Beds:** 2F 4T 4D 12S **Baths:** 13 En 4 Sh ⅏ 🖳 (9) 🖵 ♛ × 🖵 ▥ ♨ cc

Aavon Pennywell Guest House, *12 Howard Road, Southampton, Hants, SO15 5BP.* Clean, friendly. Situated close to central Southampton and train station. **Open:** All year (not Xmas)
023 8033 3886 Mrs Augar **D:** £20.00–£22.00 **S:** £21.00–£23.00 **Beds:** 1F 2T 2D 5S **Baths:** 1 En 2 Sh ⅏ (0) 🖳 (9) 🖵 🖵 ▥ ♨ cc

Villa Capri, *50-52 Archers Road, Southampton, SO15 2LU.* Two Victorian houses joint converted to a guest house near the cricket ground. **Open:** All year
023 8063 2800 Mr Fantini & Mrs Tordo **Tel: 023 8063 0100 D:** £25.00–£27.00 **S:** £27.00–£30.00 **Beds:** 17F 1T 7D 6S **Baths:** 17 En 2 Sh ⅏ (10) 🖳 (14) 🖵 ♛ × ▥ ♨ cc

BATHROOMS
En = Ensuite
Pr = Private
Sh = Shared

Southsea

SZ6598   🍺 *Eastney Tavern*

Amberly Guest House, *37 Castle Road, Southsea, Hants, PO5 3DE.* **Open:** All year (not Xmas/New Year)
023 9283 0563 Mr Pullen **Fax: 023 9287 6389** *info@aigh.co.uk* www.aigh.co.uk **D:** £20.00–£39.00 **S:** £20.00–£30.00 **Beds:** 3F 3T 1S **Baths:** 5 En 4 Pr ⅏ ⅄ 🖵 ♛ × 🖵 ▥ ♨ cc
Centrally situated for arrival and departure terminals. Most tourist attractions within walking distance, including Gun Wharf, Historic Ships, Pyramids Leisure Centre, Guildhall, Naval Base, Museums, South Parade Pier, Clarance Pier, Old Portsmouth.

Hamilton House, *95 Victoria Road North, Southsea, Portsmouth, Hants, PO5 1PS.* Delightful Victorian Townhouse B&B. Bright, modern rooms, many original features. **Open:** All year
023 9282 3502 (also fax) Graham & Sandra Tubb *sandra@hamiltonhouse.co.uk* www.hamiltonhouse.co.uk **D:** £21.00–£25.00 **S:** £25.00–£45.00 **Beds:** 3F 3D 2T 1S **Baths:** 5 En 2 Sh ⅏ ⅄ 🖵 🖵 ▥ ♨ cc

Bembell Court Hotel, *69 Festing Road, Southsea, Portsmouth, Hants, PO4 0NQ.* A friendly, family run hotel, ideally situated in Portsmouth's prime holiday area. **Open:** All year **Grades:** ETC 3 Diamond, AA 3 Diamond
023 9273 5915 Mr Irwin **Fax: 023 9275 6497** *keith@bembell.freeserve.co.uk* www.bembell.com **D:** £26.00–£28.00 **S:** £38.00–£42.00 **Beds:** 2F 4D 4T 3S **Baths:** 13 En ⅏ 🖳 (10) 🖵 🖵 ▥ ♨ cc

The Elms Guest House, *48 Victoria Road South, Southsea, Hants, PO5 2BT.* Close to Naval Heritage Complex. Within walking distance of restaurants and seafront. **Open:** All year **Grades:** ETC 3 Diamond, AA 3 Diamond
023 9282 3924 (also fax) Mrs Erskine *theelmsgh@aol.com* **D:** £21.00–£24.00 **S:** £35.00–£48.00 **Beds:** 2F 1D 2T **Baths:** 5 En ⅏ (4) 🖳 (2) ⅄ 🖵 ▥ ♨ cc

White House Hotel, *26 South Parade, Southsea, Hants, PO5 2JF.* Overlooking the Solent, most rooms seaview, residents bar. **Open:** All year
023 9282 3709 L Keast **Fax: 023 9273 2759 D:** £20.00–£25.00 **S:** £25.00–£35.00 **Beds:** 5F 5T 8D 1S **Baths:** 19 En ⅏ 🖵 × 🖵 ▥ ♨ cc

RATES
D = Price range per person sharing in a double or twin room
S = Price range for a single room

Oakleigh Guest House, *48 Festing Grove, Southsea, Hants, PO4 9QD.* Family run guest house, 10 minutes from seafront attractions. **Open:** All year (not Xmas/New Year) **Grades:** ETC 3 Diamond **023 9281 2276** Mr Willett *dwillet@cwru.net* www.oakleighguesthouse.co.uk **D:** £18.00–£36.00 **S:** £15.00–£25.00 **Beds:** 1F 1T 2D 2S **Baths:** 3 En ⓑ (2) ⏣ �📺 🖾 ⚓

Pembroke Park Hotel, *1 Bellevue Terrace, Southsea, Hants, PO5 3AT.* Ideally situated close to sea front. Attractions, walking distance. **Open:** All year **Grades:** ETC 3 Diamond · **023 9229 6817** *pembrokepark@ntlworld.com* **D:** £18.00–£24.00 **S:** £17.00–£46.00 **Beds:** 1F 2T 2D 2S **Baths:** 3 En 📺 📹 🖾 ⚓

Norfolk Hotel, *25 Granada Road, Southsea, Hants, PO4 0RD.* Small friendly family-run. Close to seafront, convenient for ferries and local attractions. **Open:** All year (not Xmas) **023 9282 4162** Mr Pilkington **D:** £17.00–£21.00 **S:** £25.00 **Beds:** 2F 5D 2T 4S **Baths:** 12 En 1 Pr ⓑ 🅿 (9) 📺 ✕ 📹 🖾 ⚓ cc

Victoria Court, *29 Victoria Road North, Southsea, Hants, PO5 1PL.* Central Portsmouth. Near main attractions and ferries. Motorway access and railways nearby. **Open:** All year **023 9282 277** Mr Johnson *stay@ victoriacourt.co.uk* www.victoriacourt.co.uk **D:** £17.00–£25.00 **S:** £20.00–£40.00 **Beds:** 2F 3T 1D **Baths:** 6 En 📺 📹 🖾 ⚓

St Ma Bourne

SU4250

Coronation Arms, *St Mary Bourne, Andover, Hants, SP11 6AR.* Traditional country pub in the heart of the beautiful Bourne Valley. **Open:** All year **01264 738432** *davidpeartpeat32@supanet.com* **D:** £22.00 **S:** £22.00 **Beds:** 1F 1T 1D **Baths:** 1 En 1 Sh ⓑ 🅿 (20) 📺 🍴 ✕ 📹 🖾 ⚓ cc

Stuckton

SU1613

The Old Posthouse, *Stuckton Road, Stuckton, Fordingbridge, Hants, SP6 2HE.* Comfortable detached house in New Forest village. Half hour from Salisbury and Bournemouth. **Open:** All year **01425 657477** Mrs Troy **Fax:** 01425 657963 **D:** £18.00 **S:** £18.00 **Beds:** 1D 1T **Baths:** 2 Sh ⓑ 🅿 📺 🍴 📹 🖾 ⚓

Sway

SZ2798

Squirrels, *Broadmead, Sway, Lymington, Hants, SO41 6DH.* Secluded modern home. Tranquil setting. Forest, coast and Lymington town nearby. **Open:** Mar to Dec **01590 683163** Mrs Kilford www.newforest. demon.co.uk/squirrels.htm **D:** £19.00–£21.00 **S:** £25.00–£30.00 **Beds:** 1F 1D 1T 1S **Baths:** 1 En 1 Sh ⓑ (8) 🅿 (8) ⏣ 📺 🍴 📹 🖾 ⚓ cc

Thruxton

SU2946

May Cottage, *Thruxton, Andover, Hampshire, SP11 8LZ.* Dating back to 1740, situated in heart of picturesque tranquil village of Thruxton. **Open:** All year **01264 771241 & 07768 242166 (M)** Tom & Fiona Biddolph **Fax:** 01264 771770 **D:** £25.00–£30.00 **Beds:** 1D 2T **Baths:** 2 En 1 Pr ⓑ (8) 🅿 (4) ⏣ 📺 📹 🖾 ⚓

Twyford

SU4824

Twyford House, *Main Road, Twyford, Winchester, Hampshire, SO21 1NJ.* Family home in Queen Anne House, large grounds, country walks. **Open:** All year (not Xmas/New Year) **01962 713114** Mrs Hawkes **D:** £20.00 **S:** £25.00 **Beds:** 1F 1D **Baths:** 1 Pr 1 Sh ⓑ 🅿 (3) ⏣ 📺 🍴 🖾 ⚓

Upper Clatford

SU3543   🍽 *Crook & Shears*

Malt Cottage, *Upper Clatford, Andover, Hants, SP11 7QL.* Beautiful old country house with modern facilities in idyllic setting. **Open:** All year (not Xmas/New Year) **01264 323469** Mrs Mason **Fax:** 01264 334100 *info@maltcottage.co.uk* www.maltcottage.co.uk **D:** £30.00–£35.00 **S:** £35.00–£45.00 **Beds:** 1T 2D **Baths:** 3 En ⓑ 🅿 ⏣ 📺 ✕ 📹 🖾 ⚓

Waterlooville

SU6809   🍽 *George Inn, Hampshire Rose*

Corner House Hotel, *9 London Road, Waterlooville, Hants, PO8 8HH.* **Open:** All year **023 9237 4079** *thebar@fishjuice.net* www.corner_house.net **D:** £20.00–£25.00 **S:** £20.00–£25.00 **Beds:** 1T 2D 3S **Baths:** 2 Sh ⓑ 🅿 ⏣ 📺 📹 🖾 ⚓ Craig and Lesley assure you of a warm welcome to our family run establishment. Near the top of Portsdown Hill with its fabulous views over Portsmouth and surrounding areas. Close to Portsmouth with its maritime heritage. Short walk to rolling heathland. Bus stop outside.

Weyhill

SU3146

Juglans, *Red Post Lane, Weyhill, Andover, Hampshire, SP11 0PY.* Large cottage garden, food/ale, 5 minutes Thruxton Circuit Close. **Open:** All year **Grades:** ETC 4 Diamond **01264 772651 & 07808 369464 (M)** Mrs Rotherham **D:** £22.00–£27.00 **S:** £22.00–£27.00 **Beds:** 1D 1S **Baths:** 1 Sh ⓑ (12) 🅿 (4) ⏣ 📺 📹 🖾 ⚓

Whitchurch

SU4647

Long Barrow House, *Cole Henley, Whitchurch, Hants, RG28 7QJ.* **Open:** All year **Grades:** ETC 4 Diamond **01256 895980** Mrs Stevens *info@ longbarrowhouse.co.uk* www.longbarrowhouse. co.uk **D:** £20.00–£25.00 **S:** £25.00–£30.00 **Beds:** 1D 1T **Baths:** 2 En ⓑ 🅿 (20) ⏣ 📺 🖾 ⚓ Come and relax in our peaceful, comfortable farmhouse on our dairy farm, nestled in glorious unspoilt countryside yet only 2 miles from A34. Charming ensuite bedrooms with lovely views. Ample parking. Very tranquil. Many repeat bookings.

Wickham

SU5711

Wickhaven, *23 School Road, Wickham, Fareham, Hants, PO17 5AA.* Quality B&B in peaceful, friendly, comfortable house. Free tea/coffee. **Open:** All year (not Xmas) **01329 832457** Mrs Toogood **D:** £18.00 **S:** £18.00 **Beds:** 1F 1D 1T 1S **Baths:** 1 Sh ⓑ (12) 🅿 (2) ⏣ 📺 🍴

The Willows, *Fareham Road, Wickham, Fareham, Hampshire, PO17 5BY.* Close to twelve golf courses, sea and main cities/attractions. **Open:** All year (not Xmas) **01329 833742 & 07879 298103 (M)** Mr Barnatt **Fax:** 01329 833742 **D:** £17.50–£20.00 **S:** £17.50 **Beds:** 1F 3D 1S **Baths:** 2 Sh ⓑ (6) 🅿 (10) ⏣ 📺 🖾 ⚓

Winchester

SU4829   🍽 *Roebuck, Willow Tree, Cart & Horses*

Giffard House Hotel, *50 Christchurch Road, Winchester, Hants, SO23 9SU.* **Open:** All year (not Xmas/New Year) **01962 852628** **Fax:** 01962 856722 **D:** £27.50–£42.50 **S:** £45.00–£55.00 **Beds:** 1F 2T 6D 4S **Baths:** 12 En ⓑ (12) 🅿 (12) ⏣ 📺 🖾 ⚓ cc Recently restored to a very high standard, to recreate the atmosphere of a prosperous Victorian home. Situated in a leafy part of the city, just 10 minutes walk from the centre. The Cathedral, Winchester College and Watermeadows are nearby.

Langhouse BandB, *27 Chilbolton Avenue, Winchester, Hampshire, SO22 5HE.*
Open: All year (not Xmas/New Year)
01962 860620 (also fax) Mrs Hooper *sheila@langhouse0.demon.co.uk* **D:** £25.00–£30.00
S: £40.00–£50.00 **Beds:** 1T 3D **Baths:** 3 En 1 Pr **P** (10) ⊬ ⊡ ⊻ ▥ ⚲
Spacious, elegant family home, set in 1 acre, overlooking Royal Winchester Golf Course. Extremely comfortable quality accommodation with splendid breakfasts. Perfectly situated for exploring historic Winchester and surrounding Hampshire countryside. 15 mins walk or 5 min drive to city centre.

The Farrells,
5 Ranelagh Road, Winchester, Hants, SO23 9TA.
Open: All year (not Xmas)
Grades: ETC 3 Diamond
01962 869555 (also fax) Mr Farrell
thefarrells@easicom.com **D:** £20.00–£25.00
S: £22.00 **Beds:** 1F 1D 1T 1S **Baths:** 1 En 1 Pr 2 Sh ⊱ (5) ⊬ ⊡ ▥ ⚲
Turn-of-the-20th-Century Victorian villa, furnished in that style. We are close to the Cathedral and local inns which provide excellent meals. It is our pleasure to help our visitors to enjoy Winchester.

Planning a longer stay? Always ask for any special rates

8 Salters Acres, *Winchester, Hants, SO22 5JW.* Detached family home in large gardens. Easy access to city's historic attractions.
Open: All year (not Xmas/New Year)
01962 856112 Mr & Mrs Cater
accommodation@8salters.freeserve.co.uk
D: £20.00–£24.00 **S:** £22.50–£27.50 **Beds:** 1T 1D 1S **Baths:** 1 Pr 1 Sh ⊱ (8) **P** (8) ⊬ ⊡ ⊻ ▥ ⚲

85 Christchurch Road, *Winchester, Hants, SO23 9QY.* Comfortable detached Victorian family house. Convenient base for Hampshire sightseeing. **Open:** All year **Grades:** ETC 4 Diamond, Silver
01962 868661 (also fax) Mrs Fetherston-Dilke *dilke@waitrose.com* **D:** £25.00–£26.00
S: £25.00–£32.00 **Beds:** 1D 1T 1S **Baths:** 2 En 1 Sh ⊱ **P** (3) ⊬ ⊡ ▥ ⚲

Rocquaine, *19 Downside Road, Winchester, SO22 5LT.* Spacious welcoming detached family home in quiet residential area. **Open:** All year (not Xmas)
01962 861426 Mrs Quick **D:** £18.00–£19.00
S: £20.00–£25.00 **Beds:** 1D 1T 1S **Baths:** 1 Sh ⊱ (8) **P** (4) ⊬ ⊡ ▥ ⚲

Sycamores, *4 Bereweeke Close, Winchester, Hants, SO22 6AR.* Well-maintained, peaceful, easily accessible. Approximately, 2km/1m north-west of city centre. **Open:** All year **Grades:** ETC 4 Diamond
01962 867242 Mrs Edwards **Fax: 01962 620300** *sycamores.b-and-b@virgin.net* **D:** £20.00–£22.50 **Beds:** 2D 1T **Baths:** 3 Pr **P** (3) ⊬ ⊡ ⊻ ▥ ⚲

BATHROOMS
En = Ensuite
Pr = Private
Sh = Shared

St Margaret's, *3 St Michael's Road, Winchester, Hampshire, SO23 9JE.* Comfortable rooms in Victorian house, close to cathedral and colleges. **Open:** All year (not Xmas) **Grades:** ETC 3 Diamond
01962 861450 & 07802 478926 (M) Mrs Brett
Brigid.brett@amserve.net
www.winchesterbandb.com **D:** £21.00–£22.00
S: £30.00–£35.00 **Beds:** 1D 1T 2S **Baths:** 2 Sh ⊱ (4) **P** (1) ⊬ ⊡ ⊻ ▥ ⚲

Wood Ridge, *Field Close, Compton Down, Compton, Winchester, Hampshire, SO21 2AP.* Rural area, convenient for Winchester, New Forest and South Coast.
Open: All year (not Xmas/New Year)
01962 711226 *woodridge@hotmail.com*
D: £20.00–£25.00 **S:** £20.00–£30.00 **Beds:** 1T 2S **Baths:** 1 En 1 Sh ⊱ (3) ⊬ ⊡ ✕ ▥ ⚲

The Lilacs, *1 Harestock Close, off Andover Road North, Winchester, Hants, SO22 6NP.* Attractive Georgian style family home. Clean, comfortable, friendly. Excellent cooking. **Open:** All year (not Xmas/New Year)
01962 884122 & 01962 622387 Mrs Pell **Fax: 01962 884122** *susan@pbpell.freeserve.co.uk*
www.smoothhound.co.uk/hotels/lilacs.html
D: £19.00–£20.00 **S:** £26.00–£28.00 **Beds:** 1F 1T **Baths:** 1 Sh ⊱ **P** (2) ⊬ ⊡ ⊻ ▥ ⚲

Winsor
SU3114

Bushfriers, *Winsor Road, Winsor, Southampton, SO40 2HF.* Forest cottage, peaceful surroundings, New Forest heritage area, highly rated breakfasts.
Open: All year (not Xmas)
023 8081 2552 Mr & Mrs Wright **D:** £19.00–£21.00 **S:** £23.00–£25.00 **Beds:** 1F **Baths:** 1 Pr ⊱ **P** (2) ⊬ ⊡ ⇞ ⊻ ▥ ⚲

Herefordshire

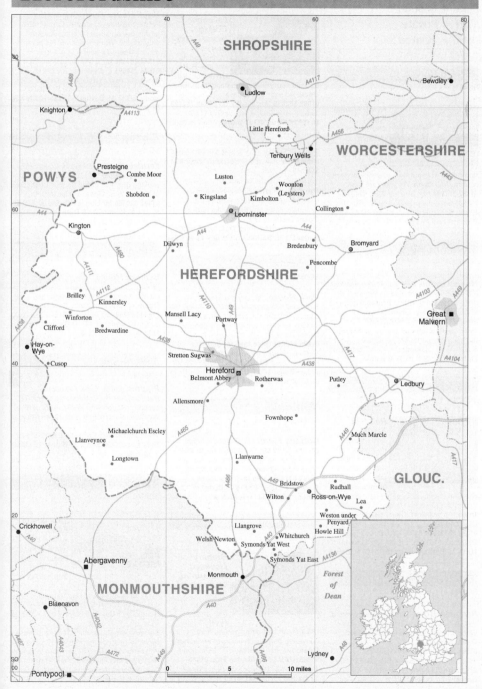

BATHROOMS
En = Ensuite
Pr = Private
Sh = Shared

Allensmore
SO4635

Holly House Farm, *Allensmore, Hereford, HR2 9BH.* Delightful family country farmhouse in beautiful and peaceful open countryside. **Open:** All year (not Xmas) 01432 277294 Mrs Sinclair **Fax:** 01432 261285 *hollyhousefarm@aol.com* **D:** £20.00–£25.00 **S:** £20.00–£25.00 **Beds:** 1D 2T 1S **Baths:** 1 En 2 Pr 1 Sh ♿ 🅿 (30) 📺 🐾 📹 💷 👶

Belmont Abbey
SO4838

Hedley Lodge, *Belmont Abbey, Hereford, HR2 9RZ.* Superbly located on the edge of historic Hereford, within beautiful grounds of Belmont Abbey. **Open:** All year 01432 277475 **Fax:** 01432 277597 *hedleylodge@aol.com* www.belmontabbey.org.uk/hedley.shtml **D:** £24.50–£26.00 **S:** £29.50–£31.50 **Beds:** 1F 4D 12T **Baths:** 17 En ♿ 🅿 (200) 📺 ✗ 📹 💷 ❀ ☕ cc

Bredenbury
SO6056

Red Hill Farm, *Bredenbury, Bromyard, Herefordshire, HR7 4SY.* C17th comfortable farmhouse, peaceful countryside, panoramic views. Central for Malvern, Hereford, Worcester. **Open:** All year (not Xmas) **Grades:** ETC 2 Diamond 01885 483255 & 01885 483535 Mrs Evans **D:** £16.00–£18.00 **S:** £18.00–£20.00 **Beds:** 1F 1D 1T 1S **Baths:** 1 Sh ♿ 🅿 (10) 📺 🐾 📹 💷 👶

Bredwardine
SO3344

Red Lion Hotel, *Bredwardine, Hereford, HR3 6BU.* C17th inn in heart of Wye Valley. Warm friendly atmosphere, good food. **Open:** All year 01981 500303 **Fax:** 01981 500400 www.hay-on-wye.co.uk/redlion **D:** £20.00–£29.50 **S:** £28.00–£40.00 **Beds:** 2F 5T 2D **Baths:** 9 En ♿ 🅿 (15) 📺 🐾 ✗ 📹 💷 ☕ cc

Bridstow
SO5824

Lavender Cottage, *Bridstow, Ross-on-Wye, Herefordshire, HR9 6QB.* Part C17th house in tranquil countryside with delightful views. **Open:** All year (not Xmas) 01989 562836 Mrs Nash **Fax:** 01989 762129 *barbara_lavender@yahoo.co.uk* **D:** £17.50 **S:** £25.00 **Beds:** 1D 2T **Baths:** 2 En 1 Pr ♿ (8) 🅿 (3) ⚲ 📺 ✗ 📹 💷 👶

Brilley
SO2649

Pentwyn Farm, *Brilley, Hereford, HR3 6HW.* Victorian stone farmhouse. Fantastic views on Offa's Dyke path. **Open:** Easter to Oct 01497 831337 Mrs Price **D:** £16.00 **S:** £16.00 **Beds:** 2D 2S **Baths:** 1 Sh ♿ 🅿 ⚲ 📺 🐾 ✗ 💷

Bromyard
SO6554

Park House, *28 Sherford Street, Bromyard, Herefordshire, HR7 4DL.* Enjoy the country without the crowds. Great walks, superb pubs and really friendly people. **Open:** All year 01885 482294 (also fax) Mr Gardiner *parkhouse@callnetuk.com* www.bromyard.co.uk/parkhouse **D:** £20.00–£25.00 **S:** £22.50–£30.00 **Beds:** 1F 1T 2D **Baths:** 3 En 1 Pr ♿ 🅿 (6) 📺 🐾 ✗ 📹 💷 👶 ❀ ☕

Clifford
SO2445

Cottage Farm, *Middlewood, Clifford, Hereford, HR3 5SX.* Quiet location, birds, walking, working farm, families welcome, good value. **Open:** All year (not Xmas) 01497 831496 (also fax) Mrs Jones **D:** £17.00–£18.00 **S:** £18.00 **Beds:** 1F 1T **Baths:** 1 Sh ♿ 🅿 (4) ✗ 💷 👶 ☕

Collington
SO6460

Granary Licensed Restaurant, *Church House Farm, Collington, Bromyard, Herefordshire, HR7 4NA.* All bedrooms ground floor in converted barns with licensed restaurant. **Open:** All year **Grades:** ETC 3 Diamond 01885 410345 Mrs Maiden **Fax:** 01885 410555 **D:** £22.50–£25.00 **S:** £22.50 **Beds:** 1D 4T **Baths:** 5 Pr ♿ 🅿 (40) 📺 🐾 ✗ 📹 💷 👶 ☕ cc

Combe Moor
SO3663

Brick House Farm, *Combe Moor, Presteigne, Powys, LD8 2HY.* Comfortable farmhouse on small holding. Beautiful countryside. Warm welcome. Memorable meals. **Open:** All year 01544 267306 Mr & Mrs Johnstone **Fax:** 01544 260601 *dmfj@johnstone.kc3.co.uk* www.kc3.co.uk/chamber/brickhouse/index.html **D:** £17.50–£20.00 **S:** £20.00 **Beds:** 3D 1T 1S **Baths:** 2 Sh 🅿 (4) 📺 🐾 ✗ 📹 💷 👶

Cusop
SO2341

Fernleigh, *Hardwick Road, Cusop, Hay-on-Wye, Hereford, HR3 5QX.* Quiet location walking distance of the famous book town of Hay-on-Wye. **Open:** Easter to Oct 01497 820459 Mr Hughes **D:** £16.00–£20.00 **S:** £19.00 **Beds:** 2D 1S **Baths:** 1 En 1 Sh ♿ 🅿 (4) ⚲ 📺 ✗ 📹 💷 👶

Dilwyn
SO4154

Bedford House, *Dilwyn, Hereford, HR4 8JJ.* Small friendly farm offering excellent accommodation, peace and quiet. **Open:** All year (not Xmas/New Year) 01544 388260 Mrs Anthony **D:** £18.00–£20.00 **S:** £20.00 **Beds:** 1F 1T 1D **Baths:** 1 En 1 Sh ♿ 🅿 (4) 📺 🐾 ✗ 📹 💷 👶

Fownhope
SO5834

Pippins, *Capler Lane, Fownhope, Hereford, HR1 4PJ.* Comfortable spacious accommodation with lovely views of River Wye and rolling countryside. **Open:** All year (not Xmas/New Year) 01432 860677 Mrs Corby **D:** £20.00–£22.00 **S:** £23.00–£25.00 **Beds:** 2T **Baths:** 1 Pr 🅿 (4) ⚲ 📺 📹 💷 👶

Hereford
SO5140

Sink Green Farm, *Rotherwas, Hereford, HR2 6LE.* **Open:** All year (not Xmas) **Grades:** AA 4 Diamond 01432 870223 Mr Jones *sinkgreenfarm@msn.com* **D:** £21.00–£27.00 **S:** £22.00–£27.00 **Beds:** 2D 1T **Baths:** 3 En ♿ 🅿 (10) ⚲ 📺 🐾 📹 💷

We welcome you to our C16th farmhouse set in the picturesque Wye Valley, yet only 3 miles from Hereford. Relax in our tastefully decorated ensuite rooms, one 4 poster, all having tea/coffee facilities, colour TV and central heating.

Cedar Guest House, *123 White Cross Road, Hereford, HR4 0LS.* Family-run former Victorian gentleman's residence, many original features. Spacious centrally-heated accommodation. **Open:** All year **Grades:** ETC 3 Diamond **01432 267235 (also fax)** Mr & Mrs Williams www.cedarguesthouse.com **D:** £18.00–£20.00 **S:** £25.00–£35.00 **Beds:** 2F 1T 2D **Baths:** 1 En 1 Sh ⌂ 🅿 (8) 🔟 ✕ 🏛 🌣

Howle Hill
SO6020

Old Kilns, *Howle Hill, Ross-on-Wye, Herefordshire, HR9 5SP.* Stay as our guests at our privately owned country house. **Open:** All year **Grades:** AA 4 Diamond, RAC 4 Diamond, Sparkling **01989 562051 (also fax)** Mrs Smith **D:** £15.00–£30.00 **Beds:** 1F 1T 2D **Baths:** 1 En 1 Pr 1 Sh ⌂ 🅿 (8) 🔟 ⋔ ✕ 🔟 🏛 ☕ ✿ 🌣

Kimbolton
SO5261   🍺 *Stockton Cross Inn, Roebuck*

The Fieldhouse Farm, *Bache Hill, Kimbolton, Leominster, Herefordshire, HR6 0EP.* A warm welcome awaits you in our traditional farmhouse with oak beams, log fires, stunning views and delicious breakfasts. **Open:** Apr to Nov **01568 614789** Mrs Franks **D:** £20.00–£23.00 **S:** £22.00–£24.00 **Beds:** 1T **Baths:** 1 Pr ⌂ 🅿 (4) 🌣 🔟 ⋔ ✕ 🔟 🌣

Kingsland
SO4461

Holgate Farm, *Kingsland, Leominster, Herefordshire, HR6 9QS.* Attractive farmhouse. Delicious breakfasts. Near Leominster, Ludlow and Welsh Marches. **Open:** All year (not Xmas/New Year) **01568 708275** Mrs Davies **D:** £18.00 **S:** £20.00 **Beds:** 1F 1T **Baths:** 1 Sh ⌂ 🅿 (3) 🌣 🔟 🔟 🏛 🌣

Kington
SO2956   🍺 *Stag Inn*

Cambridge Cottage, *19 Church Street, Kington, Herefordshire, HR5 3BE.* C17th Cottage, tea-tray welcome, many return visits, comfortable beds, camping. **Open:** All year (not Xmas/New Year) **01544 231300** Hooton gerry@ kington.softnet.co.uk **D:** £17.50 **S:** £17.50 **Beds:** 1F 1S **Baths:** 1 En 1 Sh ⌂ (3) 🅿 (2) 🌣 🔟 ⋔ 🔟 🏛 🌣

Bredward Farm, *Kington, Herefordshire, HR5 3HP.* **Open:** All year (not Xmas/New Year) **01544 231462** Mrs Wright **D:** £16.00 **S:** £16.00 **Beds:** 1D 1S **Baths:** 1 Sh ⌂ (2) 🅿 (4) 🌣 🔟 ✕ 🏛 🌣 Bredward Farm dates back to C16th. Tastefully decorated sitting room, dining room, two bedrooms, shower room/WC. Car parking. Lovely garden. 1 mile from Offa's Dyke. Farmhouse breakfast and evening meal provided 3 miles from the Welsh Border.

Dunfield Cottage, *Kington, Herefordshire, HR5 3NN.* Friendly, relaxed; lovely views;large garden; log fires; H&C in bedrooms. **Open:** All year **01544 230632 (also fax)** Ms Green robann@ dunfieldcottage.kc3.co.uk **D:** £16.00–£18.00 **S:** £16.00–£18.00 **Beds:** 1T 1D 1S **Baths:** 1 Sh ⌂ (10) 🅿 (6) 🌣 🔟 ✕ 🔟 🏛 🌣

Church House, *Church Road, Kington, Herefordshire, HR5 3AG.* Large rooms with fine views in elegant Georgian family home. **Open:** All year (not Xmas) **01544 230534** Mrs Darwin **Fax:** **01544 231100** darwin@kc3.co.uk www.churchhouse. kington.co.uk **D:** £25.00 **S:** £30.00–£40.00 **Beds:** 1D 1T **Baths:** 1 Sh ⌂ 🅿 (2) 🌣 ⋔ 🔟 🏛 🌣

Southbourne, *Newton Lane, Kington, Herefordshire, HR5 3NF.* Warm welcome by well travelled couple. Walking/mountain bike guide. **Open:** All year **01544 231706** Mr & Mrs Cooper **D:** £16.00–£18.00 **S:** £16.00–£18.00 **Beds:** 1F 1T 1S **Baths:** 2 Sh 🅿 (5) 🌣 🔟 ✕ 🔟 🏛 🌣

Bollingham House, *Kington, Herefordshire, HR5 3LE.* Period residence with glorious views. Gracious rooms. Delightful English garden. **Open:** All year **01544 327326** Mrs Grant **Fax:** **01544 327880** bollhouse@bigfoot.com **D:** £25.00–£28.50 **S:** £27.50 **Beds:** 2D 1T 1S **Baths:** 2 Pr ⌂ 🅿 (10) 🌣 🔟 ⋔ ✕ 🔟 🏛 🌣

Kinnersley
SO3449

Upper Newton Farmhouse, *Kinnersley, Hereford, HR3 6QB.* C17th award-winning timbered farmhouse on working farm. Always a warm welcome. **Open:** All year **01544 327727 (also fax)** Mrs Taylor enquiries@bordertrails.u-net.com www.uppernewton.hereford.com **D:** £25.00–£30.00 **Beds:** 2D 1T **Baths:** 3 Pr ⌂ 🅿 (6) 🌣 🔟 ✕ 🔟 🏛 🌣

Lea
SO6521   🍺 *Penny Farthing*

Forest Edge, *4 Noden Drive, Lea, Ross-on-Wye, HR9 7NB.* Situated in a quiet rural area with beautiful views from garden. **Open:** All year (not Xmas/New Year) **Grades:** ETC 4 Diamond, Gold **01989 750682** Mr & Mrs Wood don@ wood11.freeserve.co.uk www.wood11.freeserve. co.uk **D:** £21.00–£25.00 **S:** £31.00–£35.00 **Beds:** 1T 1D **Baths:** 2 En ⌂ (10) 🅿 (4) 🌣 🔟 🔟 🏛 🌣

Ledbury
SO7137

Leadon House Hotel, *Ross Road, Ledbury, Herefordshire, HR8 2LP.* **Open:** All year **Grades:** ETC 2 Star, Silver **01531 631199** M H J Williams **Fax:** **01531 631476** leadon.house@amserve.net www.leadonhouse.co.uk **D:** £27.00–£34.00 **S:** £35.00–£55.00 **Beds:** 2F 1T 2D 1S **Baths:** 6 En ⌂ 🅿 (8) 🔟 🔟 🏛 ☕ 🌣 cc Elegant Edwardian house in picturesque setting, approx. 1 mile from historic Ledbury convenient to Malvern Hills, Wye Valley and Herefordshire's renowned black and white villages. Refurbished in period style with comfortable accommodation, attractive gardens. Good home cooked food. Non smoking.

The Royal Oak Hotel, *The South End, Ledbury, Herefordshire, HR8 2EY.* Situated 15 miles equidistant from Hereford, Gloucester, Worcester. Real beer. Real breakfasts. **Open:** All year **01531 632110** Mr Barron royaloak@ ukonline.co.uk **D:** £30.00 **S:** £30.00 **Beds:** 3F 3T 9D 3S **Baths:** 7 En 1 Sh ⌂ 🅿 🌣 🔟 ⋔ ✕ 🔟 🏛 🌣 cc

Leominster
SO4959   🍺 *The Fountain*

Highfield, *Newtown Ivington Road, Leominster, Herefordshire, HR6 8QD.* Comfortable Edwardian house, pleasant rural location, delicious home prepared food. **Open:** Mar to Oct **Grades:** ETC 4 Diamond **01568 613216** M & C Fothergill info@ stay-at-highfield.co.uk www.stay-at-highfield.co. uk **D:** £19.00–£25.00 **Beds:** 2T 1D **Baths:** 1 En 2 Pr ⌂ (3) 🔟 ✕ 🔟 🏛 🌣

Planning a longer stay? Always ask for any special rates

Woonton Court Farm,
Woonton, Leysters, Leominster, Hereford, HR6 0HL. Comfortable Tudor farmhouse, own produce. Freedom to walk and enjoy wildlife. Rural peace. **Open:** All year (not Xmas)
01568 750232 (also fax) Mrs Thomas
thomas.woontoncourt@farmersweekly.net
D: £20.00–£24.00 **S:** £22.00–£25.00 **Beds:** 1F 1D 1T **Baths:** 3 En ℁ ▣ (3) 📺 📺 ▥ ▥ ⚓

Rossendale Guest House, 46 Broad
Street, Leominster, Herefordshire, HR6 8BS. Friendly traditional town centre establishment welcoming tourists and business visitors. **Open:** All year
01568 612464 Mr Hosegood **D:** £20.00–£25.00 **S:** £20.00 **Beds:** 3D 2T 6S **Baths:** 1 En 1 Sh ▣ (10) 📺 ✕ ▥ ⚓

Copper Hall, South Street, Leominster,
Herefordshire, HR6 8JN. An attractive and comfortable C17th house with a warm welcome. **Open:** All year
01568 611622 Mr & Mrs Crick *SCCrick@copperhall.freeserve.co.uk* **D:** £20.00–£22.00 **S:** £20.00–£25.00 **Beds:** 2D 2T **Baths:** 3 En 1 Pr ℁ ▣ (4) 📺 ✲ ▥ ▥ ⚓

Little Hereford
SO5568

Haynall Villa, Haynall Lane, Little
Hereford, Ludlow, Shropshire, SY8 4BG. 1820s farmhouse with original features, attractive garden in peaceful location. **Open:** All year (not Xmas/New Year)
01584 711589 (also fax) Mrs Edwards
D: £18.00–£24.00 **S:** £18.00–£28.00 **Beds:** 1F 1D 1T **Baths:** 1 En 1 Sh ℁ (6) ▣ (3) ✕ 📺 ✲ ✕ ▥ ▥ ⚓

Llangrove
SO5219 ⚔ Royal Arms

Thatch Close, Llangrove, Ross-on-Wye,
Herefordshire, HR9 6EL. Secluded, quiet Georgian farmhouse, set in panoramic countryside, sympathetically modernised. **Open:** All year
01989 770300 Mrs Drzymalski *thatch.close@virgin.net* **D:** £19.00–£21.00 **S:** £24.00–£26.00 **Beds:** 2D 1T **Baths:** 2 En 1 Pr ℁ ▣ (8) ✕ 📺 ✲ ✕ ▥ ▥ ⚓

Llanveynoe
SO3031

Olchon Court, Llanveynoe, Hereford,
HR2 0NL. Romantic medieval farmhouse in beautiful secluded valley. **Open:** All year (not Xmas/New Year) **Grades:** ETC 4 Star
01873 860356 (also fax) Mrs Carter
D: £25.00–£27.00 **S:** £30.00–£32.00 **Beds:** 2T 2D **Baths:** 2 En ℁ (12) ▣ (15) ✕ 📺 ✲ ✕ ▥ ▥ ⚓

Llanwarne
SO5028

The Lawns, Llanwarne, Hereford, HR2 8EN.
Far from the madding crowd. **Open:** All year (not Xmas/New Year)
01981 540351 R B Howard **Fax: 01981 540273** *elrah@breathemail.com*
www.the-lawns-bed-and-breakfast.co.uk
D: £24.00–£30.00 **S:** £24.00–£30.00 **Beds:** 1T 2D **Baths:** 2 En 1 Pr ℁ (12) ▣ ✕ 📺 ▥ ⚓

Longtown
SO3228

Olchon Cottage Farm, Turnant Road,
Longtown, Hereford, HR2 0NS. Warm welcome to explore Herefordshire and Marches. Farmhouse breakfasts. **Open:** All year **Grades:** ETC 3 Diamond
01873 860233 (also fax) Mrs Pritchard
www.golden-valley.co.uk/olchon **D:** £21.00–£22.00 **S:** £21.00–£22.00 **Beds:** 2F **Baths:** 2 En ℁ ▣ (6) 📺 ✲ ✕ ▥ ▥ ⚓

Luston
SO4863

Little Bury Farm, Luston, Leominster,
Herefordshire, HR6 0EB. Secluded country cottage in seven acres of gardens and paddocks. **Open:** Apr to Oct **Grades:** ETC 3 Diamond
01568 611575 Mrs Field **D:** £20.00–£22.00 **S:** £22.00–£24.00 **Beds:** 2D **Baths:** 1 Pr ▣ (4) ✕ 📺

Ladymeadow Farm, Luston,
Leominster, Herefordshire, HR6 0AS. Large, friendly, comfortable C17th farmhouse near two NT properties. **Open:** Easter to Nov
01568 780262 Mrs Ruell **D:** £19.00–£22.00 **S:** £19.00–£22.00 **Beds:** 1F 1D 1S **Baths:** 1 En 1 Sh ℁ ▣ (20) ✕ 📺 ▥ ▥ ⚓

Mansell Lacy
SO4245

Apple Tree Cottage, Mansell Lacy,
Hereford, HR4 7HH. C15th cottage in a peaceful situation surrounded by fields. **Open:** All year
01981 590688 Mrs Barker *monica.barker@tesco.net* **D:** £17.00–£20.00 **S:** £17.00–£20.00 **Beds:** 2T 1S **Baths:** 1 Pr ℁ (14) ▣ (4) ✕ 📺 ▥ ▥ ⚓

Michaelchurch Escley
SO3134

Grove Farm, Michaelchurch Escley,
Hereford, Herefordshire, HR2 0PT. Situated near Black Mountains. Lovely and peaceful, warm welcome, farmhouse breakfasts. **Open:** All year (not Xmas/New Year) **Grades:** ETC 4 Diamond
01981 510229 (also fax) Mrs Lloyd **D:** £20.00 **S:** £18.00 **Beds:** 1F 1D 1S **Baths:** 1 En 1 Pr ℁ ▣ (6) 📺 ✕ ▥ ▥ ⚓

Much Marcle
SO6532

New House Farm, Much Marcle,
Ledbury, Herefordshire, HR8 2PH. Comfortable farmhouse and cottage, log fire, swimming pool, good food. **Open:** All year
01531 660604 A Jordan **D:** £18.00–£20.00 **S:** £18.00–£20.00 **Beds:** 1F 1T 1D **Baths:** 1 En 1 Sh ℁ ▣ (6) 📺 ✲ ✕ ▥ ▥ ⚓

Pencombe
SO5952

Hennerwood Farm, Pencombe,
Bromyard, Herefordshire, HR7 4SL. Traditional dairy farm, quiet position. Panoramic views of beautiful Herefordshire. **Open:** Easter to Oct
01885 400245 (also fax) Mrs Thomas
hennerwood@farming.co.uk **D:** £20.00 **S:** £20.00 **Beds:** 1F 1D ℁ (2) ▣ ✕ 📺 ▥ ⚓

Portway
SO4845

Heron House, Canon Pyon Road,
Portway, Hereford, HR4 8NG. Relaxing house, near Hereford City, with spacious rooms and country views. **Open:** All year
01432 761111 R F Huckle **Fax: 01432 760603** *bb.hereford@tesco.net* homepages.tesco.net/~bb.hereford/heron.htm **D:** £19.00–£21.00 **S:** £16.00–£17.50 **Beds:** 1F 1D **Baths:** 1 En 1 Sh ℁ (10) ▣ (4) ✕ 📺 ✕ ▥ ▥ ✲ ⚓

Putley
SO6337

The Coach House, Putley, Ledbury,
Herefordshire, HR8 2QP. The Coach House is an C18th coaching stable set in gorgeous Herefordshire. **Open:** All year
01531 670684 (also fax) Mrs Born
wendyborn@putley-coachhouse.co.uk
www.putley-coachhouse.co.uk **D:** £16.00–£17.50 **S:** £22.00–£25.00 **Beds:** 1T 2D 1S ▣ ✕ 📺 ▥ ⚓

Ross-on-Wye
SO6024

Sunnymount Hotel, Ryefield
Road, Ross-on-Wye, Herefordshire, HR9 5LU. Small family-run hotel, quiet, comfortable, excellent home-cooked meals. **Open:** All year
01989 563880 Mr & Mrs Robertson **Fax: 01989 566251** *sunnymount@tinyworld.co.uk*
D: £23.00–£26.00 **S:** £23.00–£28.00 **Beds:** 4D 2T **Baths:** 2 En 1 Sh ℁ (6) 📺 ✕ ▥ ▥ ⚓ **cc**

BATHROOMS
En = Ensuite
Pr = Private
Sh = Shared

Forest Edge, *4 Noden Drive, Lea, Ross-on-Wye, HR9 7NB.* **Open:** All year (not Xmas/New Year) **Grades:** ETC 4 Diamond, Gold **01989 750682** Mr & Mrs Wood *don@wood11.freeserve.co.uk* www.wood11.freeserve.co.uk **D:** £21.00–£25.00 **S:** £31.00–£35.00 **Beds:** 1T 1D **Baths:** 2 En ⛥ (10) 🅿 (4) ⊬ 🆅 ▥, ⚲
A friendly welcome awaits you at our modern home. Situated in a quiet rural area with beautiful views from garden. Rooms furnished and equipped to a high standard. Quality breakfasts. Ideal base for picturesque Wye Valley and Forest of Dean.

Thatch Close, *Llangrove, Ross-on-Wye, Herefordshire, HR9 6EL.* Secluded, quiet Georgian farmhouse, set in panoramic countryside, sympathetically modernised. **Open:** All year **01989 770300** Mrs Drzymalski *thatch.close@virgin.net* **D:** £19.00–£21.00 **S:** £24.00–£26.00 **Beds:** 2D 1T **Baths:** 2 En 1 Pr ⛥ 🅿 (8) ⊬ 🆅 × 🆅 ▥, ⚲

Rowan Lea, *Ponts Hill, Ross-on-Wye, Herefordshire, HR9 5SY.* Friendly, peaceful, detached dormer bungalow. Lovely views, gardens, big breakfast. **Open:** All year **01989 750693** Ms Griffiths **D:** £15.00–£16.00 **S:** £15.00–£16.00 **Beds:** 1F 1D **Baths:** 1 Sh 🅿 (2) ⊬ 🆅 ▥, ⚲

Rotherwas
SO5338

Sink Green Farm, *Rotherwas, Hereford, HR2 6LE.* We welcome you to our C16th farmhouse set in the picturesque Wye Valley. **Open:** All year (not Xmas) **Grades:** AA 4 Diamond **01432 870223** Mr Jones *sinkgreenfarm@msn.com* **D:** £21.00–£27.00 **S:** £22.00–£27.00 **Beds:** 2D 1T **Baths:** 3 En ⛥ 🅿 (10) ⊬ 🆅 ⤬ ▥, ⚲

Rudhall
SO6225

Rudhall Farm, *Rudhall, Ross-on-Wye, Herefordshire, HR9 7TL.* Elegant country house. Warm welcome. Aga cooked breakfasts. Highly recommended by guests. **Open:** All year (not Xmas) **01989 780240** Mrs Gammond **D:** £25.00–£50.00 **S:** £25.00–£30.00 **Beds:** 2D **Baths:** 1 Pr 1 Sh 🅿 (10) ⊬ 🆅 🆅 ▥, ⚲

Shobdon
SO3961

The Paddock, *Shobdon, Leominster, Herefordshire, HR6 9NQ.* **Open:** All year (not Xmas) **Grades:** ETC 4 Diamond, Gold, AA 4 Diamond **01568 708176** Mrs Womersley **Fax:** 01568 708829 *thepaddock@talk21.com* **D:** £22.00–£24.00 **S:** £32.00–£34.00 **Beds:** 4D 1T **Baths:** 5 En ⛥ 🅿 (5) ⊬ 🆅 ⤬ 🆅 ▥, ♨3 ⚲
Delightful ground floor ensuite accommodation, situated in the beautiful border region between England and Wales. Large garden and patio, delicious home cooked food. Popular walking area, local National Trust attractions.

Stretton Sugwas
SO4642

New Priory Hotel, *Stretton Sugwas, Hereford, HR4 7AR.* A comfortable, friendly, family run hotel on the edge of Hereford. **Open:** All year **Grades:** ETC 1 Star **01432 760264** Mr Benjamin **Fax:** 01432 761809 *newprioryhotel@ukonline.co.uk* www.newprioryhotel.co.uk **D:** £27.50–£40.00 **S:** £35.00–£65.00 **Beds:** 1F 1T 4D 1S **Baths:** 7 En ⛥ 🅿 🆅 ⤬ 🆅 ▥, ⚲ cc

Symonds Yat East
SO5616

Rose Cottage, *Symonds Yat East, Ross-on-Wye, Herefordshire, HR9 6JL.* Comfortable riverside accommodation with a touch of luxury. **Open:** All year **Grades:** ETC 3 Diamond **01600 890514** Mrs Whyberd **Fax:** 01600 890498 www.smoothhound.co.uk/hotels/rose2.html **D:** £17.50–£25.00 **S:** £30.00–£35.00 **Beds:** 3D **Baths:** 2 En 1 Pr 🅿 (3) ⊬ 🆅 ⤬ 🆅 ▥, ⚲

Symonds Yat West
SO5516

Riversdale Lodge Hotel, *Symonds Yat West, Ross-on-Wye, Herefordshire, HR9 6BL.* Family run country house hotel, Riverside setting overlooking Wye Rapids. **Open:** Feb to Dec **01600 890445** Mr & Mrs Armsden **Fax:** 01600 890443 *info@riversdale.uk.com* **D:** £35.00 **S:** £50.00 **Beds:** 1F 1T 3D **Baths:** 5 En ⛥ (1) 🅿 (11) 🆅 ⤬ ▥, ⚲ cc

Welsh Newton
SO5017 ⚘ *Royal Arms*

The Lower Cwm, *Welsh Newton, Monmouth, NP25 5RW.* **Open:** All year (not Xmas/New Year) **Grades:** ETC 2 Star **01600 713040** (also fax) Mrs Kelly **D:** £20.00 **S:** £25.00 **Beds:** 1F 1D **Baths:** 2 Pr ⛥ 🅿 (3) 🆅 ⤬ 🆅 ▥, ⚲
Stone farmhouse with terrace and vine-shaded conservatory, unusual garden, great views. Golf, fishing, canoeing and river swimming nearby. Ideal for exploring mountains and castles of Wales and towns of Hereford, Gloucester, Ross-on-Wye and Forest of Dean.

Weston under Penyard
SO6223

Wharton Farm, *Weston under Penyard, Ross-on-Wye, Herefordshire, HR9 5SX.* C17th and C19th farmhouse, near the forest of Dean and Wye Valley. **Open:** All year (not Xmas) **Grades:** ETC 4 Diamond **01989 750255** (also fax) Mrs Savidge *je.savage@breathemail.net* **D:** £20.00–£23.00 **S:** £20.00–£25.00 **Beds:** 2D 1T **Baths:** 1 En 2 Pr ⛥ 🅿 (5) 🆅 🆅 ▥, ⚲

RATES
D = Price range per person sharing in a double or twin room
S = Price range for a single room

Whitchurch

SO5417

Norton House, *Whitchurch, Ross-on-Wye, Herefordshire, HR9 6DJ.* **Open:** All year **Grades:** ETC 4 Diamond, Gold, AA 4 Diamond
01600 890046 Mr & Mrs Jackson **Fax: 01600 890045** *nort@osconwhi.source.co.uk*
www.Norton-House.com **D:** £22.00–£24.00 **S:** £28.00–£32.00 **Beds:** 1T 2D **Baths:** 3 En
ち (12) ❒ ⊬ ⊡ ★ ✕ Ⓥ ▥ ●
C17th listed building, with a wealth of character, and all the modern comforts our guests could wish for. Freshly prepared, locally produced food, cooked on the Aga and served in the beautiful oak-beamed dining room. River Wye and Symonds Yat nearby.

Wilton

SO5824

Benhall House, *Wilton, Ross-on-Wye, Herefordshire, HR9 6AG.* Down a quiet cul-de-sac road on the edge of Ross-on-Wye.
Open: All year (not Xmas)
01989 567420 (also fax) Mrs Beddows
D: £20.00 **S:** £25.00 **Beds:** 1F **Baths:** 1 En ち
❒ (10) Ⓥ ★ Ⓥ ▥ ●

Winforton

SO2947   🍺 *Sun Inn*

Winforton Court, *Winforton, Hereford, HR3 6EA.* Romantic C16th manor. King size, 4-posters. Log fires. Gardens. Relax and be pampered. **Open:** All year (not Xmas)
01544 328498 (also fax) J Kingdon
D: £27.00–£36.00 **S:** £42.00–£52.00 **Beds:** 3D
Baths: 3 En ち (10) ❒ (10) ⊬ Ⓥ ★ Ⓥ ●

Woonton (Leysters)

SO5462

Woonton Court Farm, *Woonton, Leysters, Leominster, Hereford, HR6 0HL.* Comfortable Tudor farmhouse, own produce. Freedom to walk and enjoy wildlife. Rural peace. **Open:** All year (not Xmas)
01568 750232 (also fax) Mrs Thomas
thomas.woontoncourt@farmersweekly.net
D: £20.00–£24.00 **S:** £22.00–£25.00 **Beds:** 1F 1D 1T **Baths:** 3 En ち ❒ (3) Ⓥ Ⓥ ▥ ●

Hertfordshire

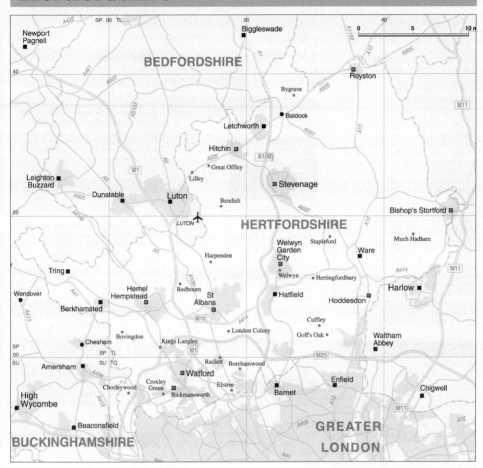

Bendish

TL1621

Bendish House, Bendish, Hitchin, Hertfordshire, SG4 8JA. Hilltop location, stunning views overlooking Mimram valley. **Open:** All year (not Xmas) **01438 871519 Fax: 01438 871499 D:** £20.00–£25.00 **S:** £20.00–£25.00 **Beds:** 1D 1T 1S ⌂ ⊞ (6) ⚡ 📺 ▥ ♿

Bishop's Stortford

TL4921

Pearse House Conference & Trng Centre, Parsonage Lane, Bishop's Stortford, Herts, CM23 5BQ. Victorian mansion housing excellent conference facilities and ensuite bedrooms. **Open:** All year (not Xmas/New Year) **01279 757400** D Doyle **Fax: 01279 506591** pearsehouse@route56.co.uk www.pearsehouse.co.uk **D:** £35.00–£40.00 **S:** £60.00–£70.00 **Beds:** 2F 5T 7D 23S **Baths:** 35 En 2 Pr ⌂ ⊞ ⚡ 📺 ✕ 📺 ▥ ♿ ♿ **cc**

Broadleaf Guest House, 38 Broadleaf Avenue, Bishop's Stortford, Herts, CM23 4JY. Close to Stansted Airport; fast trains into London and Cambridge. **Open:** All year (not Xmas) **01279 835467** Mrs Cannon paula@broadleaf63.freeserve.co.uk **D:** £25.00 **S:** £25.00–£30.00 **Beds:** 1F 1D 1T **Baths:** 1 Pr ⌂ ⊞ ⚡ (2) ⚡ 📺 🐾 📺 ▥ ♿

Borehamwood
TQ1996

84 Stevenage Crescent, *Borehamwood, Herts, WD6 4NS.* Luxury, modern private house. **Open:** All year **020 8207 3320** M Feehily *miriamfeehily@ aol.com* **D:** £25.00 **S:** £30.00 **Beds:** 3T **Baths:** 1 Sh ⛌ 🅿 (4) 📺 🐾 🏛 ✻ ♨

Bovingdon
TL0103

Rose Farm, *Water Lane, Bovingdon, Hemel Hempstead, Herts, HP3 0NA.* Country situated, newly-built farmhouse convenient M1, M25, trains, London. **Open:** All year (not Xmas) **01442 834529** Mrs Mills **D:** £30.00 **S:** £40.00 **Beds:** 6T **Baths:** 5 En 1 Pr ⛌ (3) 🅿 (10) 📺 📺 🏛 ♿ ♨

Bygrave
TL2636

Bygrave B&B, *59 Ashwell Road, Bygrave, Baldock, Hertfordshire, SG7 5DY.* Friendly family home, rural location. Guests' room, use of garden. **Open:** All year (not Xmas) **01462 894749** Mrs Spaul **D:** £22.00–£25.00 **S:** £22.00–£25.00 **Beds:** 2D 2T 1S **Baths:** 2 En 1 Sh ⛌ 🅿 (5) ⚡ 📺 🏛 ♨

Chorleywood
TQ0296

Kennels Cottage, *Common Road, Chorleywood, Herts, WD3 5LW.* A quiet oasis. A mellow brick cottage. A warm welcome. **Open:** All year (not Xmas) **01923 282927** Mrs Smethurst **D:** £22.50 **S:** £25.00 **Beds:** 2F 2S **Baths:** 1 Sh ⛌ 🅿 (4) ⚡ 📺 📺 🏛 ♨

Croxley Green
TQ0695

Farthings, *Copthorne Road, Croxley Green, Rickmansworth, Hertfordshire, WD3 4AE.* Situated in private road. Close to station and M25 Motorway. **Open:** All year (not Xmas/New Year) **01923 771431** Mrs Saunders *bazmau@ barclays.net* **D:** £22.50 **S:** £22.50 **Beds:** 1T 2S **Baths:** 1 Sh ⛌ (6) 🅿 (6) ⚡ 📺 🏛 ♨

All details shown are as supplied by B&B owners in Autumn 2001

RATES
D = Price range per person sharing in a double or twin room
S = Price range for a single room

Cuffley
TL3003

Wutherings, *43 Colesdale, Cuffley, Potters Bar, Herts, EN6 4LQ.* Unusual split-level bungalow, near London yet overlooking open country. **Open:** All year (not Xmas) **01707 874545** Mrs Pettit **D:** £20.00–£26.00 **S:** £20.00–£26.00 **Beds:** 1D 1S **Baths:** 1 Sh 🅿 (2) ⚡ 📺 📺 🏛 ♨

Elstree
TQ1795

North Medburn Farm, *Watlin Street, Elstree, Herts, WD6 3AA.* Easy access to London. **Open:** All year (not Xmas) **020 8953 1522** Mrs Williams **D:** £20.00–£25.00 **S:** £20.00–£25.00 **Beds:** 1F 3T 1S **Baths:** 1 En 1 Sh 🅿 (4) ⚡ 🏛

Goff's Oak
TL3203

329 Goffs Lane, *Goff's Oak, Cheshunt, Herts, EN7 5QH.* Detached house close to countryside, walks drives, country pubs. **Open:** All year **01992 628524 (also fax)** Mrs Morgan **D:** £30.00–£32.00 **S:** £28.00–£30.00 **Beds:** 2F 3D 1T **Baths:** 6 En ⛌ 🅿 (5) 📺 ✕ 📺 🏛 ✻ ♨

Great Offley
TL1426

Church View, *Kings Walden Road, Great Offley, Hitchin, Herts, SG5 3DU.* **Open:** All year (not Xmas) **01462 768719** Mrs Maybury **D:** £22.50–£25.00 **S:** £30.00–£35.00 **Beds:** 1D 1T **Baths:** 1 En 1 Pr ⛌ (10) 🅿 (2) ⚡ 📺 🏛 ♨ Ideally situated between Luton (M1) and Hitchin (A1(M)) Airport 3 miles. You are assured of a warm welcome with well-equipped and comfortable accommodation. Full English breakfast. The village includes two pubs and a restaurant. Good surrounding country walks.

All details shown are as supplied by B&B owners in Autumn 2001

Harpenden
TL1314

The Old Cottage, *417 Luton Road, Harpenden, Herts, AL5 3QE.* Comfortable C18th cottage, convenient London and airports, warm welcome. **Open:** All year (not Xmas) **01582 762257** Mr & Mrs Horn **D:** £20.00 **S:** £20.00–£30.00 **Beds:** 1F 1D 1S **Baths:** 1 En 1 Sh ⛌ 🅿 (3) 📺 ♨

Hemel Hempstead
TL0607

Southville Private Hotel, *9 Charles Street, Hemel Hempstead, Herts, HP1 1JH.* Detached small hotel, near town centre. Car park. Near M1 and M25. **Open:** All year **01442 251387** Mr Davis **D:** £20.56 **S:** £29.38 **Beds:** 2F 1D 6T 10S **Baths:** 6 Sh ⛌ 🅿 (7) 📺 🐾 📺 🏛 ♨ cc

Hertingfordbury
TL3011   🍺 *Cowpers' Arms*

Orchard Cottage, *East End Green, Hertingfordbury, Hertford, SG14 2PD.* Cosy country cottage, rural setting, 5 mins' drive Hertford, Hatfield, Welwyn Garden City. **Open:** All year (not Xmas/New Year) **01992 583494 (also fax)** Mrs Adms **D:** £25.00–£30.00 **Beds:** 3T **Baths:** 2 Sh ⛌ 🅿 ⚡ 📺 🏛 ♨

Hitchin
TL1828

Firs Hotel, *83 Bedford Road, Hitchin, Herts, SG5 2TY.* Comfortable hotel with relaxed informal atmosphere. Excellent rail/road links and car parking. **Open:** All year **Grades:** ETC 2 Star, AA 2 Star, RAC 2 Star **01462 422322** M Girgenti **Fax:** **01462 432051** *info@firshotel.co.uk* www.firshotel.co.uk **D:** £31.00 **S:** £52.00 **Beds:** 3F 3D 8T 16S **Baths:** 30 En ⛌ 🅿 (30) ⚡ ✕ 📺 🏛 ♨ cc

---

BEDROOMS
D = Double
T = Twin
S = Single
F = Family

Hoddesdon
TL3708

The Bell Inn, *Burford Street, Hoddesdon, Herts, EN11.* Close to M25 and A10. Contractors welcome. Entertainment weekends. **Open:** All year
01992 463552 Mr & Mrs Corrigan **Fax:** 01992 450400 welcome.to/thebellinn **D:** £17.00–£22.00 **S:** £21.00–£26.00 **Beds:** 5F 5T 4S **Baths:** 2 En ⓢ ⓣⓥ ✠ ✕ Ⓥ ▥ ⚓ cc

Kings Langley
TL0702

71 Hempstead Road, *Kings Langley, Herts, WD4 8BS.* Ideally situated M1, M25 near Watford, Hemel Hempstead, St Albans. Village centre within walking distance. **Open:** All year (not Xmas/New Year)
01923 270925 Mrs Fulton **D:** £22.50–£25.00 **S:** £22.50–£25.00 **Beds:** 1D **Baths:** 1 Sh ✠ ⓣⓥ ▥ ⚓

Woodcote House, *7 The Grove, Chipperfield Road, Kings Langley, Herts, WD4 9JF.* Detached timber-framed house in acre of gardens. **Open:** All year (not Xmas) **Grades:** ETC 4 Diamond
01923 262077 Mr & Mrs Leveridge **Fax:** 01923 266198 *leveridge@btinternet.com* **D:** £22.00–£26.00 **S:** £24.00–£28.00 **Beds:** 1D 1T 2S **Baths:** 4 En ⓢ (1) Ⓟ (6) ✠ ✕ Ⓥ ▥ ⚓

Lilley
TL1126

Lilley Arms, *West Street, Lilley, Luton, Beds, LU2 8LN.* Early C18th coaching inn. **Open:** All year
01462 768371 Mrs Brown **D:** £20.00–£30.00 **Beds:** 1F 1D 3T **Baths:** 3 En 1 Sh ⓢ Ⓟ ✠ ✕ Ⓥ ▥ ⚓ cc

London Colney
TL1804

The Conifers, *42 Thamesdale, London Colney, St Albans, Herts, AL2 1TL.* Modern detached house. Historic city St Albans 3 miles. Easy access motorway network. **Open:** All year **Grades:** ETC 3 Diamond
01727 823622 D: £22.00–£26.00 **S:** £22.00–£26.00 **Beds:** 1D 1T 1S **Baths:** 1 Sh ⓢ (12) Ⓟ ✠ ⓣⓥ ▥ ⚓

Please respect a B&B's wishes regarding children, animals and smoking

---

B&B owners may vary rates – be sure to check when booking

Much Hadham
TL4219

Sidehill House, *Perry Green, Much Hadham, Herts, SG10 6DS.* C17th house, 4 acres of garden and wood in pretty village. **Open:** All year
01279 843167 Mrs Stephens **D:** £23.00–£26.00 **S:** £25.00–£48.00 **Beds:** 2T **Baths:** 1 Pr 1 En ⓢ Ⓟ ⓣⓥ ▥ ⚓

Radlett
TL1600   ◗ *Red Lion*

The Turners, *43 Craigweil Avenue, Radlett, Hertfordshire, WD7 7ET.* Warm welcome. Ideally situated for Herts, Beds and Bucks. 20 mins to London. **Open:** All year
01923 469245 & 07776 132416 (M) Mrs Turner **D:** £20.00–£22.50 **S:** £20.00–£25.00 **Beds:** 1T 1S **Baths:** 1 En 1 Sh ⓢ Ⓟ (4) ✠ ⓣⓥ ✠ ▥ ⚓

Redbourn
TL1012

20 Cumberland Drive, *Redbourn, Herts, AL3 7PG.* Comfortable quiet home in village; easy access to M1/M25, London. **Open:** All year (not Xmas)
01582 794283 Mrs Tompkins **D:** £22.00 **S:** £22.00 **Beds:** 1T 1S **Baths:** 1 Pr 1 Sh ⓢ (10) Ⓟ ✠ ⓣⓥ ▥ ⚓

Rickmansworth
TQ0494

The Millwards Guest House, *30 Hazelwood Road, Croxley Green, Rickmansworth, Herts, WD3 3EB.* Family run, pleasant canalside location. Convenient motorways, trains, airport, business parks. **Open:** All year (not Xmas/New Year)
01923 226666 & 07881 658870 (M) Mrs Millward **Fax:** 01923 252874 *bandb@ millwards.com* **D:** £40.00–£45.00 **S:** £25.00–£30.00 **Beds:** 3T **Baths:** 2 Sh ⓢ (2) Ⓟ (2) ✠ ⓣⓥ ✠ Ⓥ ▥ ⚓

Tall Trees, *6 Swallow Close, Nightingale Road, Rickmansworth, Herts, WD3 2DZ.* Situated in quiet cul-de-sac near underground station. Home-made bread and preserves. **Open:** All year
01923 720069 Mrs Childerhouse **D:** £25.00–£28.00 **S:** £25.00–£28.00 **Beds:** 1D 3S **Baths:** 1 Sh ⓢ (10) Ⓟ (4) ✠ ⓣⓥ ▥ ⚓

Royston
TL3541

Jockey Inn, *31-33 Baldock Street, Royston, Herts, SG8 5BD.* Traditional public house, real ales. Comfortable rooms - ensuite/cable TV. Hearty breakfast. **Open:** All year
01763 243377 D: £26.50–£28.50 **S:** £29.95–£34.00 **Beds:** 3T 1F **Baths:** 5 En Ⓟ (5) ⓣⓥ ▥ ⚓

St Davids
TL1507

2 The Limes, Spencer Gate, *St Albans, Herts, AL1 4AT.* A modern, comfortable home, quiet cul de sac, 10 mins town centre. Home-baked bread. **Open:** All year **Grades:** ETC 3 Diamond
01727 831080 Mrs Mitchell *hunter.mitchell@ virgin.net* **D:** £18.00 **S:** £18.00–£25.00 **Beds:** 1T 1S **Baths:** 1 Sh ⓢ (3) Ⓟ (2) ✠ ⓣⓥ ▥ ⚓

7 Marlborough Gate, *St Albans, Herts, AL1 3TX.* Detached house close to station. **Open:** All year (not Xmas/New Year)
01727 865498 Mrs Jameson **Fax:** 01727 812966 *michael.jameson@btinternet.com* **D:** £20.00–£24.00 **S:** £20.00–£24.00 **Beds:** 1T 2S Ⓟ (3) ⓣⓥ Ⓥ ▥ ⚓

76 Clarence Road, *St Albans, Herts, AL1 4NG.* Spacious Edwardian house opposite park. Easy walking to trains (London). **Open:** All year (not Xmas/New Year)
01727 864880 (also fax) Mr & Mrs Leggatt *pat.leggatt@talk21.com www.twistedsilicon.co. uk/76/index.htm* **D:** £23.00–£25.00 **S:** £26.00–£30.00 **Beds:** 1T 1S **Baths:** 1 Sh Ⓟ (2) ✠ ⓣⓥ Ⓥ ▥ ⚓

Stapleford
TL3116

Little Pipers, *1 Church Lane, Stapleford, Hertford, Herts, SG14 3NB.* Quiet riverside village location. Good transportation links to London. **Open:** All year
01992 589085 Mrs Lewis **D:** £18.00–£25.00 **S:** £20.00–£30.00 **Beds:** 4D **Baths:** 1 En 1 Sh Ⓟ (6) ✠ ⓣⓥ ✠ ▥ ⚓ & ⚓

Stevenage
TL2424

Abbington Hotel, *23 Hitchin Road, Stevenage, Herts, SG1 3BJ.* Old town location. All ensuite, telephone, remote CTV, hairdryer etc. **Open:** All year (not Xmas/New Year)
01438 315241 Fax: 01438 745043 *bookings@ abbingtonhotel.co.uk www.abbingtonhotel.co. uk* **D:** £22.50–£29.50 **S:** £35.00–£54.00 **Beds:** 1F 2T 10D 7S **Baths:** 20 En ⓢ Ⓟ (24) ✠ ⓣⓥ ✕ Ⓥ ▥ ⚓ cc

Watford

TQ1097

33 Courtlands Drive, *Watford, Herts,*
WD1 3HU. Detached house, warm and
friendly. Convenient London, Canal,
motorways M1, M25. **Open:** All year (not
Xmas)
01923 220531 A Troughton **D:** £20.00–£22.50
S: £25.00 **Beds:** 2T 1S **Baths:** 1 Sh ⛱ (2)
🅿 (6) ⸝ 📺 🗡 ▥ ☘

Applecrust BandB, *52 Rickmansworth*
Road, Watford, Herts, WD1 7HT. Friendly,
comfortable, centrally located
accommodation with high quality home
cooking. **Open:** All year
01923 223125 Mrs Spicer **Fax: 01923 211652**
D: £22.50–£27.50 **S:** £30.00–£40.00 **Beds:** 1F
1T 1D **Baths:** 1 En 1 Sh 🅿 (4) 📺 ✗ ▥ ▥ ☘

National Grid References given
are for villages, towns and
cities – not for individual houses

BATHROOMS
En = Ensuite
Pr = Private
Sh = Shared

Grey s Bed & Breakfast, *1 Wellington*
Road, Watford, Herts, WD1 1QU. Ideally
located for railway station, town centre and
business parks. **Open:** Jan to Dec
07990 956260 (M) M-L Grey **Fax: 01923**
492446 *greysbnb@bigfoot.com* www.users.
globalnet.co.uk/~outpost/bnb/home.html
D: £22.50 **S:** £25.00 **Beds:** 2T 1S **Baths:** 2 Sh
🅿 (4) ⸝ 📺 ☘

The Millwards Guest House, *30*
Hazelwood Road, Croxley Green,
Rickmansworth, Herts, WD3 3EB. Family run,
pleasant canalside location. Convenient
motorways, trains, airport, business parks.
Open: All year (not Xmas/New Year)
01923 226666 & 07881 658870 (M)
Mrs Millward **Fax: 01923 252874** *bandb@*
millwards.com **D:** £40.00–£45.00 **S:** £25.00–
£30.00 **Beds:** 3T **Baths:** 2 Sh ⛱ (2) 🅿 (2) ⸝ 📺
🗡 ▥ ▥ ☘

Welwyn

TL2316

Christmas Cottage, *3 Ayot Green,*
Welwyn, Herts, AL6 9AB. **Open:** All year
01707 321489 Mr & Mrs Sherriff **Fax: 01707**
392659 *janesherriff@tesco.net* **D:** £30.00
S: £55.00 **Beds:** 1D 1T 1S **Baths:** 2 En 1 Pr
⛱ 🅿 (10) ⸝ 📺 🗡 ▥ ▥ ☘
Charming 300-year-old cottage on village
green, comfortable bedrooms overlooking
garden and swimming pool, close to
Hatfield and Welwyn Garden City stations.
Rich local interest including cathedral city
of St Albans and Hatfield House.

Welwyn Garden City

TL2413

The Seven Bees, *76 Longcroft Lane,*
Welwyn Garden City, Herts, AL8 6EF. Peaceful
detached house, beautiful garden, short
walk to town centre. **Open:** All year (not
Xmas)
01707 333602 Mrs Bunyan **D:** £25.00
S: £25.00 **Beds:** 1T 1S **Baths:** 1 Sh 🅿 (1) ⸝ 📺
▥ ▥ ☘

Isle of Wight

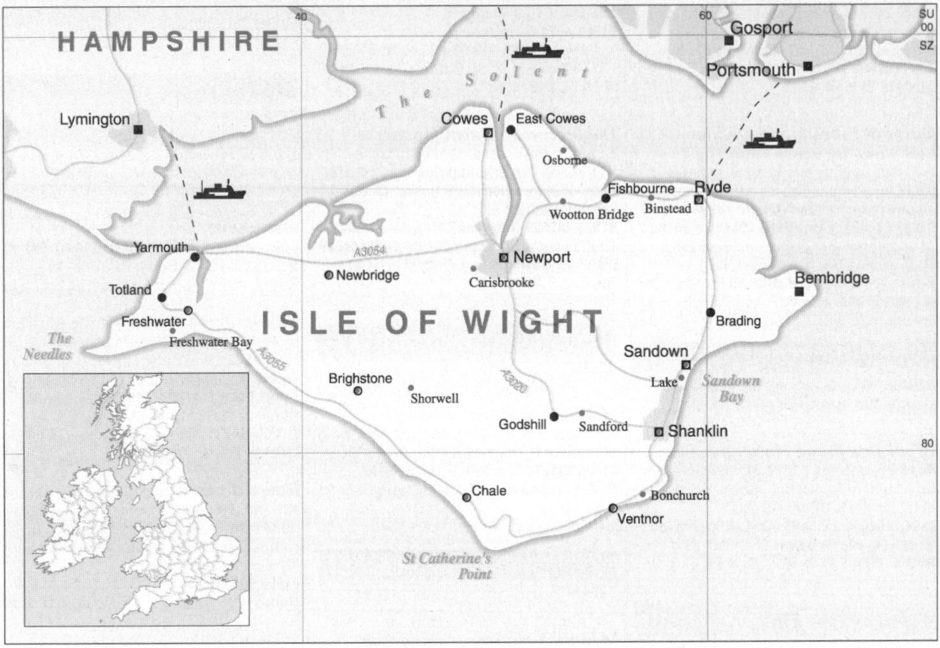

Binstead

SZ5791 *Fishbourne Inn*

Elm Close Cottage, *Ladies Walk, Binstead, Isle of Wight, PO33 3SY.* Converted stables to C18th mansion. Tranquil coastal footpath setting. **Open:** All year (not Xmas/New Year) **Grades:** ETC 4 Diamond, Silver
01983 567161 *elm-cottage@hotmail.com*
D: £20.00–£25.00 **S:** £22.50–£25.00 **Beds:** 1T 2D **Baths:** 3 En (3)

Bonchurch

SZ5777

The Lake Hotel, *Shore Road, Bonchurch, Ventnor, Isle of Wight, PO38 1LF.* Country house hotel, 2-acre garden in Bonchurch seaside village. **Open:** Mar to Nov
Grades: ETC 4 Diamond, AA 4 Diamond, RAC 4 Diamond
01983 852613 (also fax) Mr Wyatt *richard@lakehotel.co.uk* www.lakehotel.co.uk **D:** £26.00–£30.00 **Beds:** 3F 8T 8D 1S **Baths:** 20 En (3) (20)

Planning a longer stay? Always ask for any special rates

Brighstone

SZ4382 *Three Bishops, Countryman, Crown Inn, Wight Mouse*

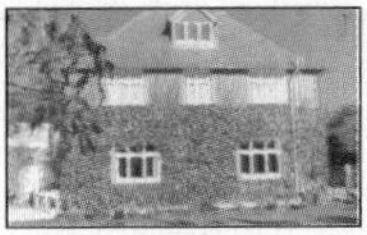

Buddlebrook Guest House, *Moortown Lane, Brighstone, Newport, Isle of Wight, PO30 4AN.* Peaceful country guest house. Adults only. Non-smokers. Super breakfast. **Open:** All year
01983 740381 (also fax) Mr & Mrs Woodford *patanddavid@onetel.net.uk*
www.buddlebrookguesthouse.co.uk
D: £20.00–£25.00 **S:** £22.00–£25.00 **Beds:** 2D 1T **Baths:** 3 En (3)

Carisbrooke

SZ4888 *Eight Bells*

The Mount, *1 Calbourne Road, Carisbrooke, Newport, Isle of Wight, PO30 5AP.* Large Victorian private house in the beautiful village of Carisbrooke.
Open: Easter to Oct
01983 522173 & 01983 524359 Mrs Skeats
D: £16.00–£17.00 **S:** £16.00–£17.00 **Beds:** 1T 1D **Baths:** 1 Sh (2)

Chale

SZ4877

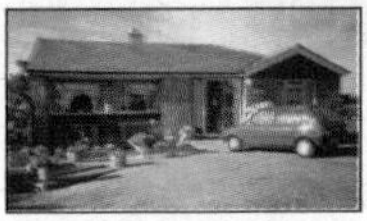

Cortina, *Gotten Lane, Chale, Ventnor, Isle of Wight, PO38 2HQ.* Modern comfortable bungalow. **Open:** All year (not Xmas)
01983 551292 Mrs Whittington **D:** £17.00 **S:** £20.00 **Beds:** 1D 1T **Baths:** 1 Sh (6)

Cowes

SZ4996 *Duke of York, Anchor Inn, Union Inn, Pier View, Harbour Lights*

Royal Standard Antiques, *70-72 Park Road, Cowes, Isle of Wight, PO31 7LY.* Converted Victorian pub; lovingly restored; warm, friendly atmosphere. Delightful scenery. **Open:** All year
01983 281672 Ms Bradbury *caroline@royalstandardantiques.fsbusines.co.uk*
royalstandardantiques.fsbusiness.co.uk
D: £21.00–£26.00 **S:** £24.00–£29.00 **Beds:** 1T 1D 1S **Baths:** 1 Pr 1 Sh (2) cc

Halcyone Villa, *Grove Road, off Mill Hill Road, Cowes, Isle of Wight, PO31 7JP.* Small friendly Victorian guest house situated near marinas and town. **Open:** All year **01983 291334** Miss Fussell *sandra@ halcyone.freeserve.co.uk* www.halcyonevilla. freeuk.com **D:** £17.50–£35.00 **S:** £17.50–£35.00 **Beds:** 1F 2D 2T 1S **Baths:** 1 En 1 Pr 1 Sh ❦ ☎ ▣ ☑ ⛵ Ⅲ. ♿

Gurnard Pines Holiday Village, *Cockleton Lane, Cowes, Isle of Wight, PO31 8QE.* Countryside location close to yachting haven of Cowes. Luxury pine lodges or bungalows. **Open:** All year **01983 292395 Fax: 01983 299415** *mail@ pines.tcp.co.uk* www.gurnardpines.co.uk **D:** £25.00–£40.00 **S:** £35.00–£50.00 **Beds:** 20F 30T 30D **Baths:** 40 En 40 Pr ❦ ▣ (200) ☑ × ☑ ♿ ♨ cc

Freshwater

SZ3486 ◗ *Colwell Bay Inn, Red Lion, Royal Standard, Vine, Wheatsheaf*

Brookside Forge Hotel, *Brookside Road, Freshwater, Isle of Wight, PO40 9ER.* Small family-run hotel. Centre of village, yet quiet location. **Open:** All year **01983 754644** J Chettle **D:** £24.00–£26.00 **S:** £26.00–£28.00 **Beds:** 2F 2T 2D 1S **Baths:** 6 En 1 Pr ❦ ▣ (7) ☑ × Ⅲ. ♨ cc

Freshwater Bay

SZ3485

Wight Haven, *Aston Road, Freshwater Bay, Freshwater, Isle of Wight, PO40 9TT.* Ideal for walking/cycling holidays, 400 yards from Bay. **Open:** All year (not Xmas/New Year) **Grades:** ETC 4 Diamond **01983 753184** Mr & Mrs Searle *wighthaven@ btinternet.com* **D:** £25.00 **S:** £35.00 **Beds:** 1T 2D **Baths:** 3 En ▣ ⅙ ☑ ⛵ Ⅲ. ♨

Lake

SZ5883

Cliff Lodge, *13 Cliff Path, Lake, Isle of Wight, PO36 8PL.* Edwardian house. Gardens access coastal path. Warm welcome. English breakfast. **Open:** Feb to Nov **Grades:** ETC 3 Diamond **01983 402963** Mrs Grinstead **D:** £18.00–£21.00 **S:** £18.00–£21.00 **Beds:** 2F 6D 1S **Baths:** 8 En ❦ (2) ▣ (8) ☑ ☑ Ⅲ. ♨

Osterley Lodge, *62 Sandown Road, Lake, Sandown, Isle of Wight, PO36 9JX.* Between Sandown/Shanklin. Close to all amenities/transport/beach. **Open:** All year **Grades:** ETC 3 Diamond **01983 402017** Horton *osterleylodge@ netguides.co.uk* **D:** £16.00–£25.00 **S:** £16.00–£25.00 **Beds:** 1F 1T 5D **Baths:** 6 En 1 Pr ❦ (5) ▣ (7) ☑ × Ⅲ. ♨ cc

Pebblecombe Guest House, *48 Sandown Road, Lake, Sandown, Isle of Wight, PO36 9JT.* Five minutes from coastal path, station, village and buses. **Open:** All year (not Xmas) **01983 402609 (also fax)** Mr & Mrs Hallett **D:** £13.00–£16.00 **S:** £13.00–£16.00 **Beds:** 2F 2D 1T 1S **Baths:** 3 En 2 Pr ❦ ▣ (6) ⅙ ☑ × ☑ Ⅲ. ♨

Newbridge

SZ4187

Homestead Farm, *Newbridge, Yarmouth, Isle of Wight, PO41 0TZ.* New wing of modern farmhouse. **Open:** Jan to Dec **01983 531270** Mrs Priddle **D:** £20.00 **S:** £25.00 **Beds:** 1F 1T 1D 1S **Baths:** 2 En ❦ ▣ ☑ ☑ & ♨

Newport

SZ5089

Magnolia House, *6 Cypress Road, Newport, Isle of Wight, PO30 1EY.* Picturesque character house, secluded garden, large rooms, convenient for town. **Open:** All year **01983 529489** Mrs Brooks *magnoliaiw@ aol.com* **D:** £19.00–£21.00 **S:** £22.00–£25.00 **Beds:** 1D 1S **Baths:** 2 En ▣ (2) ⅙ ☑ ☑ Ⅲ. ♨ cc

Osborne

SZ5194

The Doghouse, *Crossways Road, Osborne, East Cowes, Isle of Wight, PO32 6LJ.* Somewhere special. Popular friendly comfortable ensuite rooms near Osborne House. **Open:** All year **01983 293677 D:** £20.00–£30.00 **S:** £30.00–£35.00 **Beds:** 1T 1D **Baths:** 2 En ▣ (3) ⅙ ☑ ⛵ Ⅲ. ♨

RATES

D = Price range per person sharing in a double or twin room

S = Price range for a single room

B&B owners may vary rates – be sure to check when booking

Ryde

SZ5992 ◗ *Thatcher's*

Dorset Hotel, *Dover Street, Ryde, Isle of Wight, PO33 2BW.* Centrally located, close to the beach. **Open:** All year (not Xmas/New Year) **Grades:** ETC 3 Diamond **01983 564327** *hoteldorset@aol.com* www.thedorsethotel.co.uk **D:** £19.00–£21.00 **S:** £25.00–£28.00 **Beds:** 2F 8T 8D 4S **Baths:** 18 En 4 Sh ❦ (3) ▣ (16) ☑ ⛵ Ⅲ. ♨ cc

Seaward, *14 & 16 George Street, Ryde, Isle of Wight, PO332EW.* Close to beach, ferry terminals, town centre and local amenities. **Open:** All year **01983 563168 & 0800 9152966** *seaward@ fsbdial.co.uk* **D:** £15.00–£22.00 **S:** £18.00–£24.00 **Beds:** 2F 1T 3D 1S **Baths:** 2 En 4 Sh ❦ ☑ × ☑ & ♨

Rowantrees, *63 Spencer Road, Ryde, Isle of Wight, PO33 3AF.* Modern detached house, quiet rural setting, minutes from town centre & sea front. **Open:** All year (not Xmas/New Year) **01983 568081 D:** £15.00–£16.00 **S:** £16.00 **Beds:** 1D/F 2S **Baths:** 1 Sh ❦ ▣ (4) ☑ ⛵ Ⅲ. ♨

Sandford

SZ5481 ◗ *Cask & Taverners, Griffin, White Horse*

The Barn, *Pound Farm, Shanklin Road, Sandford, Isle of Wight, PO38 3AW.* 1816 converted barn in 6 acres - golf, cycling. Farmhouse breakfast. **Open:** All year **Grades:** ETC 4 Diamond **01983 840047 (also fax)** Mr & Mrs Squire *barnpoundfarm@free-online.co.uk* **D:** £20.00 **S:** £25.00 **Beds:** 1F 1T 1D **Baths:** 3 En ❦ ▣ ⅙ ☑ ☑ ♨

Sandown

SZ5984

The Iona Private Hotel, *44 Sandown Road, Sandown, Isle of Wight, PO36 9JT.* 9-room guest house, few mins' walk from beautiful cliff path and sandy beach. **Open:** All year **01983 402741 (also fax)** Mr Joy & Nora Dempsey *lionahotel@netscapeonline.co.uk* **D:** £15.00–£19.00 **S:** £15.00–£19.00 **Beds:** 3F 4D 2T 3S **Baths:** 4 Pr 2 Sh ❦ ▣ (6) ☑ × ☑ ✳ ♨ cc

Mount Brocas Guest House, *15 Beachfield Road, Sandown, Isle of Wight, PO36 8LT.* Beach, pier, shops, buses, coastal walks. 2 mins from Mount Brocas. **Open:** All year (not Xmas) **01983 406276** Mrs King *brocas@netguides.co.uk* **D:** £15.00–£20.00 **S:** £16.00–£22.00 **Beds:** 2F 3D 2T 1S **Baths:** 4 En 2 Pr ❦ ⅙ ☑ ⛵ ☑ Ⅲ. ♨

Willow Dene Guest House, *110 Station Avenue, Sandown, Isle of Wight, PO36 8HD.* Near all amenities, home cooking, friendly atmosphere. **Open:** Feb to Oct **01983 403100** S Ratcliffe **D:** £16.00–£18.00 **Beds:** 3T 1D 1S **Baths:** 1 Sh ⊠ �🛏 ✕ Ⅴ ▥ ♨

Hazelwood Hotel, *19 Carter Street, Sandown, Isle of Wight, PO36 8BL.* Victorian hotel. near sea and nightclub. Home cooking, relaxed family atmosphere. **Open:** All year **01983 402536** Mrs Wright **D:** £18.00–£24.00 **S:** £20.00 **Beds:** 3F 1T 1D **Baths:** 1 Sh ♒ ₽ (8) ⊠ 🛏 ✕ Ⅴ ❋ ♨

Montpelier Hotel, *Pier Street, Sandown, Isle of Wight, PO36 8JR.* Situated in one of the finest positions in Sandown. **Open:** All year **01983 403964** S Birks **Fax:** 0709 2212734 www.montpelier-hotel.co.uk **D:** £18.00–£25.00 **S:** £18.00–£25.00 **Beds:** 2F 1T 3D 1S **Baths:** 5 En 1 Pr ♒ ⊠ ♨ **cc**

Shanklin

SZ5881 ◁ *Village Inn, Crab Inn, Longshoreman, Steamer Inn*

Culham Lodge Hotel, *31 Landguard Manor Road, Shanklin, Isle of Wight, PO37 7HZ.* **Open:** Feb to Dec **Grades:** ETC 4 Diamond **01983 862880 (also fax)** Mr Metcalf *metcalf@culham99.freeserve.co.uk* **D:** £24.00–£25.00 **S:** £24.00–£25.00 **Beds:** 4D 5T 1S **Baths:** 10 En ♒ (12) ₽ (8) ⊠ ✕ Ⅴ ▥ ♨ **cc** This delightful small hotel perfect for breaks is well known for good value, with lovely gardens, heated swimming pool, conservatory. All rooms ensuite, satellite TV, hairdryers, teamakers. Ferry-inclusive packages available. We can book your ferry and save you money.

Planning a longer stay? Always ask for any special rates

The Hazelwood, *14 Clarence Road, Shanklin, Isle of Wight, PO37 7BH.* Friendly hotel, own grounds close to cliff path, station, town. **Open:** All year (not Xmas) **Grades:** ETC 3 Diamond **01983 862824 (also fax)** Mr & Mrs Tubbs *barbara.tubbs@thehazelwood.free-online.co.uk* www.thehazelwood.free-online.co.uk **D:** £19.00–£21.00 **S:** £19.00–£21.00 **Beds:** 2F 3D 2T 1S **Baths:** 8 En ♒ (5) ₽ (3) ⊠ 🛏 ✕ Ⅴ ▥ ♨ **cc**

Knight's Rest, *20 Queens Road, Shanklin, Isle of Wight, PO37 6AW.* **Open:** All year **01983 862727 (also fax)** Mrs Groves www.knightsrest.co.uk **D:** £20.00–£25.00 **S:** £20.00–£25.00 **Beds:** 1T 5D 1S **Baths:** 6 En 1 Pr ₽ (8) ⊠ Ⅴ ▥ ♨ **cc** Knight's Rest was built in the 1830s. Ideally situated in the islands favourite seaside town, offering a blend of sandy beaches combined with old world charm. Recently refurbished tastefully by the new owners, ideal relaxing holiday for adults only.

Overstrand Hotel, *Howard Road, Shanklin, Isle of Wight, PO37 6HD.* **Open:** Easter to Oct **Grades:** ETC 4 Diamond **01983 862100** Mr & Mrs Vale *stillwell@overstrand-hotel.co.uk* www.overstrand-hotel.co.uk **D:** £29.00–£34.00 **S:** £29.00–£39.00 **Beds:** 6F 3D 2T 2S **Baths:** 12 En 1 Pr ♒ ₽ (20) ⊠ Ⅴ ▥ ⬥ ♨ **cc** Beautiful character building with fantastic sea and coastal views. New heated swimming pool (85 deg F) Huge 3 acre garden. Children most welcome. Free parking guaranteed. Free use of local leisure centre. Resident proprietors in 28th year. Bedrooms and dining room No Smoking.

BATHROOMS
En = Ensuite
Pr = Private
Sh = Shared

B&B owners may vary rates – be sure to check when booking

St Georges House Hotel, *St Georges Road, Shanklin, Isle of Wight, PO37 6BA.* 2 minutes from glorious beaches and the 'old village'. **Open:** Mar to Dec **Grades:** ETC 3 Diamond **01983 863691 Fax:** 01983 861597 **D:** £22.00–£27.00 **S:** £25.00–£30.00 **Beds:** 3F 2T 3D **Baths:** 7 En 1 Pr ♒ ₽ ✂ ⊠ ✕ Ⅴ ▥ ♨ **cc**

Ryedale Private Hotel, *3 Atherley Road, Shanklin, Isle of Wight, PO37 7AT.* Small and friendly. Near station and beach, children welcome. **Open:** Easter to Oct **01983 862375 & 07831 413233 (M)** Mrs Carney **Fax:** 01983 862375 *ryedale@dottydots.co.uk* www.smoothhound.co.uk/hotels/ryedale **D:** £18.00–£23.00 **S:** £18.00–£23.00 **Beds:** 4F 1T 2D 2S **Baths:** 5 En 1 Pr 1 Sh ♒ ⊠ 🛏 Ⅴ ▥ ♨ **cc**

Hambledon Hotel, *Queens Road, Shanklin, Isle of Wight, PO37 6AW.* Family licensed hotel offers genuine personal service. All bedrooms ensuite and tastefully decorated. **Open:** All year **01983 862403** Mr Sewell www.hambledon-hotel.co.uk **D:** £23.00–£26.00 **S:** £25.00 **Beds:** 4F 4D 1T 1S **Baths:** 10 En ♒ ₽ (8) ⊠ ✕ Ⅴ ♨

Shorwell

SZ4682 ◁ *Crown Inn*

Northcourt, *Shorwell, Newport, Isle of Wight, PO30 3JG.* Historic manor house in outstanding 15-acre garden. **Open:** All year **01983 740415 Fax:** 01983 740409 *john@north-court.demon.co.uk* www.wightfarmholidays.co.uk/northcourt **D:** £24.00–£30.00 **S:** £34.00–£40.00 **Beds:** 3T 3D 1S **Baths:** 6 En ♒ ₽ ✂ ⊠ ✕ ▥ ♨

Ventnor

SZ5677 ◁ *Tavern, Mill Bay, Spyglass, Blenheim*

Picardie Hotel, *Esplanade, Ventnor, Isle of Wight, PO38 1JX.* Welcoming small family hotel on sea front with fine walking, cycling. **Open:** All year **01983 852647 (also fax) D:** £25.00–£35.00 **S:** £30.00–£35.00 **Beds:** 3F 1T 4D 1S **Baths:** 5 En 4 Pr ♒ ⊠ ✕ Ⅴ ⬥ ❋ ♨

Cornerways Hotel, *39 Medeira Road, Ventnor, Isle of Wight, PO38 1QS.* Quiet location with magnificent views over sea and Downs. **Open:** Mar to Oct **Grades:** ETC 3 Diamond **01983 852323** Mr Malcolm www.cornerwaysventnor.co.uk **D:** £20.00–£25.00 **S:** £20.00–£39.00 **Beds:** 2F 3D 1T **Baths:** 6 En ⛄ 🅿 (4) ⅍ �📺 ≛ cc

Wootton Bridge

SZ5491

Briddlesford Lodge Farm, *Wootton Bridge, Ryde, Isle of Wight, PO33 4RY.* Friendly family farm with 150 Guernsey Dairy herd. Good breakfasts. **Open:** All year (not Xmas/New Year) **01983 882239** Mrs Griffin **D:** £20.00–£22.00 **S:** £20.00–£22.00 **Beds:** 1F 1D 1T **Baths:** 1 En 1 Sh ⛄ 🅿 (3) 📺 🏲 �📺 🛏 ≛

Isles of Scilly

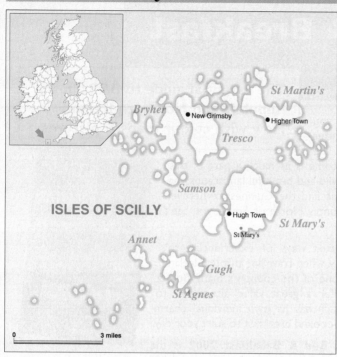

ISLES OF SCILLY

St Martin's

Bryher
New Grimsby
Higher Town

Tresco

Samson

Hugh Town
St Mary's
St Mary's

Annet

Gugh

St Agnes

0   3 miles

Bryher

SV8715

Soleil d'Or, *Bryher, Isles of Scilly, TR23 0PR.*
Soleil d'Or, the perfect base to enjoy the
tranquillity of Bryher. **Open:** Easter to Oct
01720 422003 Mrs Street **D:** £22.00–£26.00
S: £22.00–£40.00 **Beds:** 2D 1T **Baths:** 3 En
⮛ (3) ⊞ Ⅴ ▥ ♨

St Agnes

SV8807

Covean
Cottage, *St*
Agnes, Isles of
Scilly, TR22 0PL.
Attractive
granite cottage
set in
subtropical garden. Highly recommended.
Open: Easter to Nov **Grades:** ETC 4
Diamond
01720 422620 (also fax) Mrs Sewell
D: £26.00–£32.50 **S:** £30.00–£35.00 **Beds:** 2D
2T **Baths:** 3 En 1 Sh ⮛ (9) ⊞ ♒ ✕ Ⅴ ♨

St Mary's

SV9010   ⬗ *Bishop & Wolf, Atlantic, Mermaid*

Lyonnesse House, *The Strand, St*
Mary's, Isles of Scilly, TR21 0PT. Magnificent
sea views and imaginative Aga cooked
cuisine, great hospitality. **Open:** Mar to Oct
01720 422458 Mrs Woodcock **D:** £26.00
S: £26.00 **Beds:** 1F 3D 3T 2S **Baths:** 5 Sh
⮛ (5) ⅋ ⊞ Ⅴ ✕ ▥ ♨

Marine House, *Church Street, Hugh*
Town, St Mary's, Isles of Scilly, TR21 0JT. A
very comfortable guest house, near
harbour, beaches and shops. **Open:** Easter
to Sept
01720 422966 Mrs Rowe *peggy@*
rowe55.freeserve.co.uk **D:** £22.00–£25.00
S: £22.00–£25.00 **Beds:** 1D 1T 1S **Baths:** 1
En ⮛ (9) ℙ ⅋ ⊞ Ⅴ ♨

Ireland: Bed & Breakfast 2002

The essential guide to B&Bs in the Republic and Northern Ireland
Now with colour maps & pictures

Think of Ireland and you think of that famous Irish hospitality. The warmth of the welcome is as much a part of this great island as the wild and beautiful landscapes, the traditional folk music and the Guinness. Wherever you go, town or country, North or South, you can't escape it.

There are few better ways of experiencing this renowned hospitality, when travelling through Ireland, than by staying at one of the country's many Bed & Breakfasts. They offer a great value alternative to expensive hotels, each has its own individual charm and you get a home-cooked breakfast to start your day.

Stilwell's Ireland: Bed & Breakfast 2002 is the most comprehensive guide of its kind, with over 1,000 entries listed by county and location in the Republic and Northern Ireland. Each entry includes room rates, facilities, Tourist Board grades, local maps and a description of the B&B, its location and surroundings.

Treat yourself to some Irish hospitality with **Stilwell's Ireland: Bed & Breakfast 2002**.

Private Houses, Country Halls, Farms, Cottages, Inns, Small Hotels and Guest Houses

£7.95 from all good bookstores (ISBN 1-900861-30-5) or £8.95 (inc p&p) from Stilwell Publishing, 59 Charlotte Road, London EC2A 3QW (020 7739 7179)

- Over 1,000 entries
- Average price £18 per person per night
- All official grades shown
- Local maps
- Pubs serving hot evening meals shown
- Tourist Information Offices listed
- Handy size for easy packing

Kent

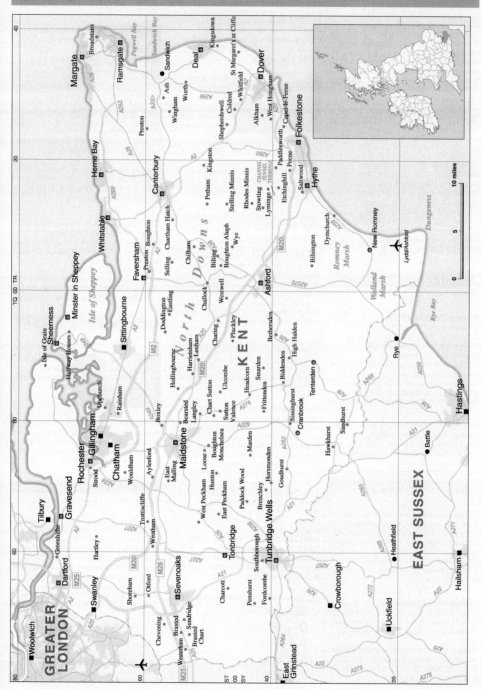

Alkham

TR2542

Owler Lodge, *Alkham Valley Road, Alkham, Dover, Kent, CT15 7DF.* Lovely house in beautiful village for touring East Kent. **Open:** All year (not Xmas) 01304 826375 Mrs Owler **Fax:** 01304 829372 *owlerlodge@aol.com* **D:** £21.00–£25.00 **S:** £35.00–£38.00 **Beds:** 1F 1D 1T **Baths:** 3 En ⌷ (5) ▣ (3) ⅋ ▣ Ⅲ. ♨

Ash (Sandwich)

TR2758   ◆ *Lion Inn, Chequers*

55 Guilton, *Ash, Canterbury, Kent, CT3 2HR.* **Open:** All year (not Xmas) 01304 812809 Mrs Smith **D:** £17.00 **S:** £20.00 **Beds:** 2D **Baths:** 1 En ▣ (2) ⅋ ▣ ♨ Between Canterbury and Sandwich, Victorian cottage, log fires, Victorian type dining room with original features, cottage garden, ideal touring Kent nature reserves, wildlife park, historic buildings, wine trails, Dover ferries, Manston airport and coast within easy reach.

Ashford

TR0042

Warren Cottage Hotel, *136 The Street, Willesborough, Ashford, Kent, TN24 0NB.* C17th hotel. M20 J10. Close to Channel Tunnel. Car Park. **Open:** All year **Grades:** ETC 3 Diamond 01233 621905 Mrs Jones **Fax:** 01233 623400 *general@warrencottage.co.uk* www.warrencottage.co.uk **D:** £25.00–£35.00 **S:** £20.00–£45.00 **Beds:** 1F 3D 1T 1S **Baths:** 6 En ⌷ ▣ (20) ⅋ ⩩ ⋔ ✕ Ⅲ. ♨ cc

Mayflower House, *61 Magazine Road, Ashford, Kent, TN24 8NH.* Friendly atmosphere, large garden. Close to town centre, international station. **Open:** All year (not Xmas) 01233 621959 (also fax) Mrs Simmons **D:** £16.50–£17.50 **S:** £18.00–£20.00 **Beds:** 1D 2S **Baths:** 1 Sh ⌷ ▣ ✕ Ⅴ Ⅲ. ♨

Glenmoor, *Maidstone Road, Ashford, Kent, TN25 4NP.* Victorian gamekeeper's cottage close to international station and motorway. **Open:** All year (not Xmas/New Year) 01233 634767 Mrs Rowlands **D:** £17.00 **S:** £20.00 **Beds:** 2D 1T **Baths:** 1 Sh ⌷ (5) ▣ (3) ⅋ ▣ Ⅲ. ♨

Vickys Guest House, *38 Park Road North, Ashford, Kent, TN24 8LY.* Town centre, close to international station, Canterbury, Folkestone and Dover nearby. **Open:** All year 01233 631061 Mrs Ford **Fax:** 01233 640420 *vicky@ford27.freeserve.co.uk* **D:** £21.00–£25.00 **S:** £25.00 **Beds:** 1F 1D 1S **Baths:** 2 Pr 1 Sh ⌷ ▣ ▣ ⩩ ✕ Ⅴ Ⅲ. ♨ cc

Heather House, *40 Burton Road, Kennington, Ashford, Kent, TN24 9DS.* Heather House offers a warm, friendly welcome in quiet residential area. Near Eurostar. **Open:** All year (not Xmas/New Year) 01233 661826 Mrs Blackwell **Fax:** 01233 635183 **D:** £20.00 **S:** £20.00 **Beds:** 1T 1D 1S **Baths:** 2 Sh ▣ ▣ ♨

Quantock House, *Quantock Drive, Ashford, Kent, TN24 8QH.* Quiet residential area. Easy walk to town centre. Comfortable and welcoming. **Open:** All year (not Xmas) **Grades:** ETC 3 Diamond 01233 638921 Mr & Mrs Tucker *tucker100@ madasafish.com* **D:** £20.00–£22.00 **S:** £22.00–£25.00 **Beds:** 1F 1D 1T 1S **Baths:** 3 En ⌷ (5) ▣ (3) ⅋ Ⅴ Ⅲ. ♨

Aylesford

TQ7258   ◆ *Chequers*

Wickham Lodge, *The Quay, High Street, Aylesford, Kent, ME20 7AY.* **Open:** All year **Grades:** ETC 4 Diamond 01622 717267 Mrs Bourne **Fax:** 01622 792855 *wickhamlodge@aol.com* www.wickhamlodge.com **D:** £25.00–£30.00 **S:** £30.00 **Beds:** 1F 1D 1S **Baths:** 2 En 1 Pr ⌷ ▣ (4) ⅋ ▣ ⋔ Ⅴ Ⅲ. ♨ cc Historic Georgian/Tudor house in Aylesford Village on bank of the River Medway, close to the old bridge. Recently terraced and landscaped walled garden at rear. Individually furnished accommodation to a high standard. Self-catering stable cottage also available.

Court Farm, *High Street, Aylesford, Maidstone, Kent, ME20 7AZ.* Beams, four poster, spa, antiques, drawing room. Sorry, no children. **Open:** All year 01622 717293 (also fax) Mrs Tucker *enquiries@courtfarm.co.uk* www.courtfarm.co. uk **D:** £25.00 **S:** £25.00 **Beds:** 2D 1T 1S **Baths:** 3 En 1 Pr ▣ (6) ⅋ ▣ ⋔ ✕ Ⅴ Ⅲ. ♨ cc

The Guest House, *The Friars, Aylesford Priory, Aylesford, Kent, ME20 7BX.* Picturesque priory home to a community of Carmelite friars, founded in 1242. **Open:** All year (not Xmas/New Year) 01622 717272 M Larcombe **Fax:** 01622 715575 *friarsreception@hotmail.com* www.carmelite.org **D:** £19.00–£24.00 **S:** £19.00–£24.00 **Beds:** 2F 1D **Baths:** 2 Pr ⌷ ▣ (50) ⅋ ✕ Ⅴ Ⅲ. cc

---

BEDROOMS
D = Double
T = Twin
S = Single
F = Family

Bearsted

TQ7955   ◆ *The Bell, White Horse, Black Horse, Windmill*

Tollgate House, *Ashford Road, Bearsted, Maidstone, Kent, ME14 4NS.* **Open:** All year (not Xmas/New Year) **Grades:** ETC 3 Diamond 01622 738428 Mrs Wise **D:** £20.00–£25.00 **S:** £25.00–£30.00 **Beds:** 1F 1T **Baths:** 2 En ⌷ ▣ (3) ⅋ ▣ Ⅴ Ⅲ. ♨ Detached house with friendly atmosphere and large garden. Situated on A20 convenient for Leeds Castle, M20 J8, Channel Tunnel and Dover Ferries. Rooms have ensuite bathrooms, TV and tea and coffee making facilities. Guests' sitting room and off-street parking.

The Hazels, *13 Yeoman Way, Bearsted, Maidstone, Kent, ME15 8PQ.* Large, comfortable family home in quiet location, easy access M20 and A20. **Open:** All year **Grades:** ETC 4 Diamond 01622 737943 Mr & Mrs Buse *dbuse@ totalise.co.uk* www.aspwebspace. com/thehazels **D:** £21.00–£23.00 **S:** £24.00–£25.00 **Beds:** 1T **Baths:** 1 En ▣ (2) ⅋ ▣ Ⅲ. ♨

Bethersden

TQ9240

The Coach House, *Oakmead Farm, Bethersden, Ashford, Kent, TN26 0NB.* Rural, well back off road in 5 acres gardens and paddocks. **Open:** Mar to Oct **Grades:** ETC 3 Diamond 01233 820583 (also fax) B Broad **D:** £20.00 **S:** £25.00 **Beds:** 1F 1D 1T **Baths:** 2 En 1 Pr ⌷ ▣ (10) ▣ Ⅴ Ⅲ. ♨

Biddenden

TQ8438   ◆ *Three Chimneys, Red Lion*

Frogshole Oast, *Sissinghurst Road, Biddenden, Ashford, Kent, TN27 8LW.* Attractively located C18th oasthouse, 1.5 acre garden, adjacent Sissinghurst Castle. **Open:** Easter to Oct 01580 291935 (also fax) D Hartley *hartley@ frogsholeoast.freeserve.co.uk* www.geocities. com/frogsholeoast/sissinghurst.html **D:** £23.00–£26.00 **S:** £30.00–£40.00 **Beds:** 2T 1D **Baths:** 1 En 1 Sh ⌷ (9) ▣ (4) ⅋ ▣ Ⅴ Ⅲ. ♨

Drayton House Farm, *Stede Quarter, Biddenden, Ashford, Kent, TN27 8JQ.* Small working farm within easy reach of many tourist attractions. **Open:** Apr to Oct 01580 291931 (also fax) Mrs Lidgett **D:** £13.00–£18.00 **Beds:** 2T **Baths:** 2 Sh ⌷ ▣ (3) ⅋ ▣ Ⅲ.

Bilsington

TR0434

Willow Farm, Stone Cross, Bilsington, Ashford, Kent, TN25 7JJ. Organic smallholding in rural setting. Home-made bread but no chintz. **Open:** All year (not Xmas) **01233 721700** Mrs Hopper *renee@ willow-farm.freeserve.co.uk* **D:** £18.50–£20.00 **S:** £20.00–£25.00 **Beds:** 1F 1D 1T 1S **Baths:** 1 Pr 1 Sh ⌂ 🖭 (6) ⊬ 🖭 ✕ 🖭 🖦

Bilting

TR0449

The Old Farm House, Soakham Farm, White Hill, Bilting, Ashford, Kent, TN25 4HB. Beautiful rolling countryside on North Downs Way, working farm ideal for walking, touring. **Open:** All year (not Xmas) **01233 813509** Mrs Feakins **D:** £16.00–£19.00 **S:** £18.00–£25.00 **Beds:** 1F 1D 1T ⌂ 🖭⊬🖭🖭 🖦

Boughton

TR0659

Tenterden House, 209 The Street, Boughton, Faversham, Kent, ME13 9BL. Half-acre garden in historic village with two pubs. **Open:** All year **01227 751593** Mrs Latham **D:** £20.00–£22.00 **S:** £30.00–£35.00 **Beds:** 1D 1T **Baths:** 2 En ⌂ 🖭 (4) 🖭 🖦

Boughton Aluph

TR0348 🍴 Flying Horse, Chequers, Half Way House

Warren Cottage, Boughton Aluph, Ashford, Kent, TN25 4HS. Quiet cottage with garden, fantastic view! **Open:** All year **01233 740483** B K Fearne **D:** £20.00 **S:** £20.00 **Beds:** 1T 1D ⌂ (5) 🖭 (4) ⊬ 🖭 ✈ 🖦 🖦

Boughton Monchelsea

TQ7651

Hideaway, Heath Road, Boughton Monchelsea, Maidstone, Kent, ME17 4HN. Chalet bungalow edge of village. Pub meals 1-minute walk. **Open:** Jan to Dec **01622 747453** (also fax) Mrs Knight **D:** £16.00 **S:** £20.00 **Beds:** 1D **Baths:** 1 Pr 🖭 (2) 🖭 ✈ 🖭 🖦 🖦

Boxley

TQ7757 🍴 Kings Arms, Chiltern Hundreds

Barn Cottage, Harbourland, Boxley, Maidstone, Kent, ME14 3DN. Converted C16th barn, convenient for M2, M20 and Channel. **Open:** All year (not Xmas/New Year) **01622 675891** (also fax) Mrs Munson **D:** £18.00–£20.00 **S:** £18.00–£20.00 **Beds:** 1T 1D 1S **Baths:** 2 En 1 Pr ⌂ (5) 🖭 (6) ⊬ 🖭 🖦

Brasted

TQ4755

Holmesdale House, High Street, Brasted, Westerham, Kent, TN16 1HS. Delightful Victorian house (part C17th). Chartwell, Hever, Knole and mainline station. **Open:** All year **01959 564834** (also fax) Mr Jinks **D:** £20.00–£29.00 **S:** £32.00–£45.00 **Beds:** 1F 3D 1T **Baths:** 3 En 1 Sh ⌂ 🖭 (7) 🖭 🖭 🖦 🖦 🖦

Brasted Chart

TQ4653

The Orchard House, Brasted Chart, Westerham, Kent, TN16 1LR. Family home, quiet, rural surroundings, near Chartwell, Hever, Knole, Gatwick. **Open:** All year (not Xmas) **Grades:** ETC 3 Diamond **01959 563702** Mrs Godsal David.Godsal@ tesco.net **D:** £22.50 **S:** £25.00 **Beds:** 2T 1S **Baths:** 2 Sh ⌂ 🖭 (4) ⊬ 🖭 🖦 🖦

Brenchley

TQ6741

Hononton Cottage, Palmers Green Lane, Brenchley, Tonbridge, Kent, TN12 7BJ. Delightfully situated Listed home amidst close to Tunbridge Wells. **Open:** All year (not Xmas/New Year) **01892 722483** Mrs Marston **D:** £23.00–£24.00 **S:** £30.00 **Beds:** 1T **Baths:** 1 Pr ⌂ 🖭 (2) 🖭 ✈ 🖭 🖦 🖦 🖦

Broadstairs

TR3967 🍴 Charles Dickens, Tartar Frigate

Goodwin Sands Guest House, 15 Wrotham Road, Broadstairs, Kent, CT10 1QG. Close to amenities and sea front. Substantial breakfast. Warm, friendly atmosphere. **Open:** Feb to Dec **01843 862309** Mr & Mrs Hills **D:** £19.00–£21.00 **S:** £23.00–£28.00 **Beds:** 3F 3D 2S **Baths:** 5 En 1 Sh ⌂ 🖭 (2) 🖭 🖭 🖦 🖦

Devonhurst Hotel, Eastern Esplanade, Broadstairs, Kent, CT10 1DR. Overlooking sandy beach and English Channel. Residential licensed family-run. **Open:** All year **01843 863010** Mr & Mrs Payne **Fax:** 01843 868940 info@devonhurst.co.uk www.devonhurst.co.uk **D:** £26.50–£29.50 **S:** £29.50 **Beds:** 1F 7D 1T **Baths:** 9 En ⌂ (5) 🖭 ✕ 🖭 🖦 ☀ 🖦 cc

Keston Court Hotel, 14 Ramsgate Road, Broadstairs, Kent, CT10 1PS. Pleasant hotel with hospitality to match, five mins' walk to town, beach, most amenities. **Open:** All year **01843 862401** Mr & Mrs McVicker **D:** £16.00–£19.00 **S:** £16.00–£19.00 **Beds:** 5D 2T 1S **Baths:** 3 En 2 Sh 🖭 (8) 🖭 ✕ 🖭 🖦 🖦

Canterbury

TR151560

Clare Ellen Guest House, 9 Victoria Road, Canterbury, Kent, CT1 3SG. **Open:** All year **Grades:** ETC 4 Diamond, Silver, AA 4 Diamond **01227 760205** Mrs Williams **Fax:** 01227 784482 loraine.williams@ clareellenguesthouse.co.uk www.clareellenguesthouse.co.uk **D:** £24.50–£28.00 **S:** £27.00–£35.00 **Beds:** 1F 2D 2T 1S **Baths:** 6 En ⌂ 🖭 (8) 🖭 🖭 🖦
Large elegant ensuite rooms with TV, hairdryer, clock/radio and tea/coffee facilities. Full English breakfast. Vegetarian and special diets catered for on request. Six minutes walk to town centre, bus and train station. Parking/garage available. Credit cards accepted.

Chaucer Lodge, 62 New Dover Road, Canterbury, Kent, CT1 3DT. **Open:** All year **Grades:** ETC 4 Diamond, AA 4 Diamond **01227 459141** (also fax) Mr Wilson wchaucerldg@aol.com www.thechaucerlodge. co.uk **D:** £21.00–£25.00 **S:** £25.00–£35.00 **Beds:** 2F 2T 3D 2S **Baths:** 9 En ⌂ 🖭 (10) ⊬ 🖭 ✕ 🖭 🖦 ☀ 🖦
Family-run friendly guest house close to City Centre. Cathedral, Cricket Club and Hospitals. Fridges in all rooms and telephone. Breakfast menu. High standard of cleanliness and service provided in a relaxed atmosphere. Secure off-road parking. Ideal base for visiting Canterbury and touring Kent.

Little Courtney Guest House, 5 Whitstable Road, St Dunstans, Canterbury, Kent, CT2 8DG. **Open:** All year **01227 454207** Mrs Mercer **D:** £17.50–£20.00 **S:** £20.00–£25.00 **Beds:** 2T 1S **Baths:** 1 Sh 🖭 (1) 🖭 ✈ 🖦 🖦
A warm welcome awaits you at our small family run guest house, we are close to the town centre of Canterbury, University and railway station. Ideal for destinations with the coast only a short drive away.

Cathedral Gate Hotel, 36 Burgate, Canterbury, Kent, CT1 2HA. Family-run medieval hotel next to Canterbury Cathedral. Warm welcome. **Open:** All year **Grades:** ETC 3 Diamond, AA 3 Diamond **01227 464381** Mrs Jubber **Fax:** 01227 462800 cgate@cgate.demon.co.uk **D:** £23.50–£41.75 **S:** £23.50–£55.50 **Beds:** 5F 9D 7T 6S **Baths:** 12 En 3 Sh ⌂ 🖭 ✈ ✕ 🖭 🖦 🖦 cc

Ashton House, *129 Whitstable Road, Canterbury, Kent, CT2 8EQ.* Beautifully refurbished Edwardian house. Warm, relaxed ambience. Superb breakfast, excellent location. Individual requirements our priority. **Open:** All year **01227 455064** Mrs Nimmons *ashtonbnb@ hotmail.com* **D:** £20.00–£22.50 **S:** £25.00–£30.00 **Beds:** 1T 1D **Baths:** 2 En 🅿 (2) ⚥ 📺 📺 ▥ ♨

Abberley House, *115 Whitstable Road, Canterbury, Kent, CT2 8EF.* Comfortable B&B in residential area close to centre. Warm welcome. **Open:** All year (not Xmas) **Grades:** ETC 3 Diamond **01227 450265** Mr Allcorn **Fax: 01227 478626** **D:** £21.00–£24.00 **S:** £25.00–£28.00 **Beds:** 2D 1T **Baths:** 1 En 1 Sh 🅿 (3) ⚥ 📺 ▥ ♨

Abbey Lodge Guest House, *8 New Dover Road, Canterbury, Kent, CT1 3AP.* Cathedral city centre 10 mins' walk, Dover 20 mins ride. **Open:** All year **01227 462878** Mrs Gardner **D:** £17.00–£20.00 **S:** £20.00–£25.00 **Beds:** 1F 1T 1S **Baths:** 2 En 1 Sh ⏰ 🅴 (16) ⚥ 📺 🐾 📺 ▥

London Guest House, *14 London Road, Canterbury, Kent, CT2 8LR.* Recommended by Let's Go and Which? Good B&B guides. **Open:** All year **Grades:** ETC 3 Diamond **01227 765860** Mrs Cabrini **Fax: 01227 456721** *londonguesthousecabnkz@supanet.com* **D:** £20.00–£25.00 **S:** £20.00–£40.00 **Beds:** 1F 1D 2T 2S **Baths:** 2 Sh ⏰ 📺 ▥ ♨

Maynard Cottage, *106 Wincheap, Canterbury, Kent, CT1 3RS.* Newly refurbished luxury accommodation. Ensuite. Hearty breakfasts and evening meals. **Open:** All year (not Xmas/New Year) **07951 496836 (M)** Mrs Ely *fionaely@ onetel.co.uk* **D:** £20.00–£27.50 **S:** £25.00–£55.00 **Beds:** 1T 1D ⏰ 🅿 📺 ✕ 📺 ▥ ♨ cc

Castle Court Guest House, *8 Castle Street, Canterbury, Kent, CT1 2QF.* Friendly family house offering comfortable and clean accommodation. 2 mins' walk shops, buses, trains. **Open:** All year **01227 463441 (also fax)** Mr Turner *guesthouse@castlecourt.fsnet.co.uk* **D:** £21.00–£26.00 **S:** £21.00–£24.00 **Beds:** 3F 2D 3T 1S **Baths:** 4 En 3 Sh ⏰ 🅿 (3) 📺 🐾 ▥ ♨ cc

Capel-le-Ferne

TR2538 ⚓ *Lighthouse, Valiant Sailor*

Xaipe, *18 Alexandra Road, Capel-le-Ferne, Folkestone, Kent, CT18 7LD.* Comfortable, detached bungalow. **Open:** All year (not Xmas/New Year) **01303 257956** D Strutt **D:** £18.00 **S:** £18.00 **Beds:** 1T 1D 🅿 (2) ⚥ 📺 🐾 ▥

Please respect a B&B's wishes regarding children, animals and smoking

RATES

D = Price range per person sharing in a double or twin room

S = Price range for a single room

Challock

TR0150

Hegdale Farm House, *Hegdale Lane, Challock, Ashford, Kent, TN25 4BE.* C16th farmhouse, good food, relaxing atmosphere. Comfortable lounge and peaceful garden. **Open:** All year (not Xmas) **01233 740224** Mrs Baxter **D:** £20.00–£22.50 **S:** £22.50 **Beds:** 1F 1D 1T **Baths:** 1 En 2 Sh ⏰ 🅿 (8) ⚥ 📺 ▥ ♨

Charcott

TQ5247

Charcott Farmhouse, *Charcott, Leigh, Tonbridge, Kent, TN11 8LG.* Family home in glorious rural setting. Home-made bread. Free-range eggs. Guests' lounge. **Open:** All year (not Xmas/New Year) **01892 870024** Mr & Mrs Morris **Fax: 01892 870158** *nicholasmorris@charcott.freeserve.co.uk* **D:** £45.00 **S:** £30.00 **Beds:** 3T **Baths:** 2 En 1 Pr ⏰ (5) 🅿 (4) ⚥ 📺 ▥ ♨

Charing

TQ9549 ⚓ *Royal Oak*

23 The Moat, *Charing, Ashford, Kent, TN27 0JH.* On North Downs Way. Shops, buses, trains, London, Canterbury, Eurostar. **Open:** Apr to Sept **01233 713141** Mrs Micklewright **D:** £20.00 **S:** £25.00 **Beds:** 1T **Baths:** 1 En 🅿 (1) ⚥ 📺 ▥ ♨

Timber Lodge, *Charing Hill, Charing, Ashford, Kent, TN27 0NG.* Unusual upside down house. Tea/coffee on terrace. Ensuite. Near Pilgrim's Way. **Open:** All year (not Xmas/New Year) **Grades:** ETC 4 Star **01233 712822 (also fax)** Mrs Bigwood **D:** £20.00–£25.00 **S:** £20.00–£35.00 **Beds:** 1F 1T 1S **Baths:** 2 En ⏰ 🅿 (8) ⚥ 📺 ✕ 📺 ▥ ♨

Barnfield, *Charing, Ashford, Kent, TN27 0BN.* Charming C15th farmhouse in superb location, overlooking lake and garden. **Open:** All year (not Xmas) **01233 712421 (also fax)** Mrs Pym **D:** £22.00–£24.00 **S:** £24.00–£28.00 **Beds:** 2D 1T 3S **Baths:** 1 Sh ⏰ 🅿 (99) ⚥ 📺 ▥ ♨

Chart Sutton

TQ8049

White House Farm, *Green Lane, Chart Sutton, Maidstone, Kent, ME17 3ES.* C15th farmhouse, good home-cooking, near Leeds and Sissinghurst Castles and M20. **Open:** All year (not Xmas) **Grades:** ETC 3 Diamond **01622 842490 (also fax)** Mrs Spain *sue.spain@totalise.co.uk* **D:** £20.00–£25.00 **S:** £25.00–£30.00 **Beds:** 2D 1T **Baths:** 1 En 2 Pr ⏰ (8) 🅿 (4) ⚥ 📺 📺 ▥ ♨

Chartham Hatch

TR1056

The Willows, *Howfield Lane, Chartham Hatch, Canterbury, Kent, CT4 7HG.* Quiet country lane - garden for enthusiasts, 2 miles Canterbury. **Open:** All year **01227 738442 (also fax)** Mrs Gough *thegoughs@hotmail.com* **D:** £23.00–£27.00 **Beds:** 1D 1T **Baths:** 2 Pr ⏰ (5) 🅿 ⚥ 📺 📺 ▥ ♿ ♨

Chevening

TQ4857

Crossways House, *Chevening Road, Chevening, Sevenoaks, Kent, TN14 6HF.* Beautiful Kentish Ragstone c1760 in 5 acres. Conferences welcome. **Open:** All year (not Xmas/New Year) **01732 456334** Mrs Weavers **Fax: 01732 452334** **D:** £25.00 **S:** £25.00 **Beds:** 4D **Baths:** 3 En 1 Pr ⏰ 🅿 (4) ⚥ 📺 ▥ ♨

Chilham

TR0653

Maynard Cottage, *106 Wincheap, Canterbury, Kent, CT1 3RS.* Newly refurbished luxury accommodation. Ensuite. Hearty breakfasts and evening meals. **Open:** All year (not Xmas/New Year) **07951 496836 (M)** Mrs Ely *onetel.co.uk* **D:** £20.00–£27.50 **S:** £25.00–£55.00 **Beds:** 1T 1D ⏰ 🅿 📺 ✕ 📺 ▥ ♨ cc

BEDROOMS

D = Double

T = Twin

S = Single

F = Family

Coldred

TR2746

Colret House, *The Green, Coldred, Dover, Kent, CT15 5AP.* **Open:** All year **Grades:** ETC 4 Diamond
01304 830388 Mrs White **Fax: 01304 830348**
D: £25.00–£30.00 **S:** £25.00–£30.00 **Beds:** 2F
Baths: 2 En 🛏 🅿 (6) ⌂ 📺 🔥 ✕ 🞐 🕭 ♨
Garden rooms in grounds of detached Edwardian property facing the village green of Coldred - twice recently voted the best kept village in Kent. Easy access from A2 - Canterbury/Sandwich/Dover all within 15 mins' drive. Ideal overnight stop for ferries/shuttle.

Cranbrook

TQ7736

The Hollies, *Old Angley Road, Cranbrook, Kent, TN17 2PN.* Well-appointed comfortable bungalow, delightful garden, close to town centre and Sissinghurst Gardens. **Open:** All year (not Xmas)
01580 713106 Mrs Waddoup **D:** £22.50
S: £22.50 **Beds:** 1F 1T 1S **Baths:** 1 En 1 Pr 🛏
🅿 (2) ⌂ 📺 🔥 ✕ 🞐 🕭1 ♨

Cordons, *Round Green Lane, Colliers Green, Cranbrook, Kent, TN17 2NB.* House in lovely garden off quiet wooded lane. Close to Sissinghurst. **Open:** All year
01580 211633 Mrs Johnstone **D:** £18.00–£20.00 **S:** £20.00–£22.00 **Beds:** 1D 1T 1S
Baths: 2 Pr 🅿 (4) ⌂ 📺 🔥 📺 🞐 ♨

Dartford

TQ5273

Royal Victoria and Bull Hotel, *1 High Street, Dartford, Kent, DA1 1DU.* An C18th inn. Easy access to town centre and motorways. **Open:** All year
01322 224415 **Fax: 01322 289474 D:** £27.00
S: £54.00 **Beds:** 2F 5D 9T 8S **Baths:** 25 En 📺
✕ 📺 🞐 cc

Deal

TR3752   🍴 *King's Head, Three Compasses, New Inn, Hole in the Roof, Rising Sun*

The Roast House Lodge, *224 London Road, Deal, Kent, CT14 9PW.* Lodge accommodation, garden and sunbathing patio. 1 mile Deal seafront, golf courses nearby. **Open:** All year **Grades:** ETC 3 Diamond
01304 380824 M Stokes **D:** £20.00–£25.00
S: £30.00–£35.00 **Beds:** 2F 1D 1T 1S
Baths: 5 En 🛏 🅿 📺 🔥 🞐 🕭 ♨ cc

Sondes Lodge, *14 Sondes Road, Deal, Kent, CT14 7BW.* Close to seafront, town, castles, golf courses. Warm welcome. **Open:** All year **Grades:** ETC 4 Diamond, AA 4 Diamond
01304 368741 (also fax) J Hulme **D:** £25.00–£28.00 **S:** £35.00–£40.00 **Beds:** 2D 1T
Baths: 3 En 📺 🞐 ♨ cc

Doddington

TQ9357   🍴 *Red Lion, George*

Palace Farmhouse, *Chequers Hill, Doddington, Sittingbourne, Kent, ME9 0AU.* C19th farmhouse. Comfortably furnished, pleasant gardens. Well situated. Warm welcome. **Open:** All year
01795 886820 Leake **D:** £18.00–£22.00
S: £15.00–£25.00 **Beds:** 1F 1T 2S **Baths:** 1 En 2 Sh 🛏 🅿 (6) ⌂ 📺 🔥 ✕ 📺 🞐 🕭 ♨

Dover

TR3141   🍴 *Park Inn*

Bleriot's, Belper House, *47 Park Avenue, Dover, Kent, CT16 1HE.* One night 'stopovers' and 'mini-breaks'. Ensuite rooms, off-road parking. **Open:** All year (not Xmas)
01304 211394 Mrs Casey **D:** £18.00–£23.00
S: £20.00–£46.00 **Beds:** 2F 3D 2T 1S
Baths: 6 En 2 Sh 🛏 🅿 (8) 📺 🞐 ♨ cc

Valjoy Guest House, *237 Folkestone Road, Dover, Kent, CT17 9SL.* Victorian family house situated near rail, ferry and tunnel terminals. **Open:** All year (not Xmas)
01304 212160 Mr Bowes **D:** £15.00–£20.00
S: £15.00–£20.00 **Beds:** 3F 1S **Baths:** 1 Sh 🛏 🅿 (5) 📺 ✕ 🞐 ♨

Hubert House, *9 Castle Hill Road, Dover, Kent, CT16 1QW.* Comfortable Georgian house with parking; ideally situated for local attractions and ferries. **Open:** Nov to Sept
01304 202253 Mr Hoynes *huberthouse@btinternet.com* www.huberthouse.co.uk
D: £20.00–£25.00 **S:** £30.00–£34.00 **Beds:** 2F 2D 2T 1S **Baths:** 7 En 🅿 (6) 📺 🞐 ♨ cc

Owler Lodge, *Alkham Valley Road, Alkham, Dover, Kent, CT15 7DF.* Lovely house in beautiful village for touring East Kent. **Open:** All year (not Xmas)
01304 826375 Mrs Owler **Fax: 01304 829372**
owlerlodge@aol.com **D:** £21.00–£25.00
S: £35.00–£38.00 **Beds:** 1F 1D 1T **Baths:** 3 En 🛏 (5) 🅿 (3) ⌂ 📺 🞐 ♨

Tower Guest House, *98 Priory Hill, Dover, Kent, CT17 0AD.* Old water tower now fully modernised into high standard accommodation. **Open:** All year
Grades: RAC 4 Diamond
01304 208212 (also fax) D Wraight
enquiries@towerhouse.net www.towerhouse.net
D: £20.00–£25.00 **Beds:** 1F 1D **Baths:** 2 En 🛏 🅿 (2) ⌂ 📺 🞐 ♨

Number One Guest House, *1 Castle Street, Dover, Kent, CT16 1QH.* Georgian town house. All rooms ensuite. GARAGE PARKING. Port nearby **Open:** All year
01304 202007 Ms Reidy **Fax: 01304 214078**
res@number1guesthouse.co.uk
www.number1guesthouse.co.uk **D:** £20.00–£25.00 **S:** £25.00–£30.00 **Beds:** 1F 2D 2T
Baths: 5 En 🛏 🅿 (4) 📺 📺 🞐 ♨

Beulah House, *94 Crabble Hill, Dover, Kent, CT17 0SA.* Welcome to this imposing award-winning guest house in 1 acre of magnificent topariad gardens. **Open:** All year
01304 824615 Mrs Owen **Fax: 01304 828850**
owen@beulahhouse94.freeserve.co.uk **D:** £22.00–£25.00 **S:** £30.00–£35.00 **Beds:** 2F 4D 3T
Baths: 9 En 🛏 🅿 🅿 ⌂ 📺 📺 🞐 ♨ cc

Dymchurch

TR1029

Dr Syn's Restaurant and Guest House, *24 Mill Road, Dymchurch, Romney Marsh, Kent, TN29 0NY.* **Open:** All year
01303 873159 Mr Low **Fax: 01303 870080**
www.drsyns.co.uk **D:** £22.50 **S:** £45.00
Beds: 1T 2D **Baths:** 2 Sh 🛏 🅿 (6) ⌂ 📺 ✕ 🞐 ♨ cc
Just 2 mins' walk to the beach, Dr Syn's has a licensed bar and restaurant, car parking, conservatory and large garden. A short drive to Rye or steam train ride to Hythe, Dungeness and New Romney. The legend lives on.

The Ship Inn, *118 High Street, Dymchurch, Romney Marsh, Kent, TN29 0LD.* Family-run C15th inn on the South Coast of Kent. **Open:** All year
01303 872122 Mr Sharp *stilwells@theshipinn.co.uk* www.theshipinn.co.uk
D: £19.00–£21.00 **S:** £19.00–£31.00 **Beds:** 4F 2D 2S **Baths:** 2 Sh 🛏 🅿 📺 ✕ 📺 🞐 ♨

RATES
D = Price range per person sharing in a double or twin room
S = Price range for a single room

Waterside Guest House,
15 Hythe Road, Dymchurch, Romney Marsh, Kent, TN29 0LN.
Open: All year
Grades: ETC 4 Diamond, AA 4 Diamond, RAC 4 Diamond
01303 872253 Mrs Tinklin *info@ watersideguesthouse.co.uk*
www.watersideguesthouse.co.uk **D:** £20.00–£22.50 **S:** £25.00–£30.00 **Beds:** 1F 2D 2T **Baths:** 5 En ⌂ 🅿 (7) 📺 ✕ 📺 📖 ☀ ♨
Cottage-style house offering comfortable rooms, attractive gardens. Ideally situated for Channel crossings and exploring Kent and E Sussex. Experience the R H & D railway or stroll along nearby sandy beaches, finally enjoying a drink or meal chosen from our varied menu.

East Malling
TQ7057

Hawthorn Cottage, *Easterfields, East Malling, West Malling, ME19 6BE.* Quiet country setting ideally situated for touring Kent, 3 miles M20 J5. **Open:** All year (not Xmas)
01732 843805 (also fax) Mrs Horvath *easterfields@talk21.com* www.easterfields.co.uk **D:** £18.00 **S:** £18.00 **Beds:** 1T 1S **Baths:** 1 Pr ⌂ 🅿 (3) ✑ 📺 📖 ♨

East Peckham
TQ6648

Roydon Hall, *off Seven Mile Lane, East Peckham, Tonbridge, Kent, TN12 5NH.*
Open: All year (not Easter or Xmas/New Year) **Grades:** ETC 3 Diamond
01622 812121 Mrs Bence **Fax: 01622 813959** *roydonhall@btinternet.com*
www.southeastengland.uk.com **D:** £22.50–£32.50 **S:** £30.00–£50.00 **Beds:** 1F 3D 5T 1S **Baths:** 7 En 1 Pr 2 Sh ⌂ 🅿 ✑ ✕ 📺 📖 ♨ cc
Very attractive C16th manor in 10 acres of woodlands and gardens. Peaceful atmosphere, magnificent views. Comfortable rooms. Organic meals available. Less than one hour from central London, Dover and south coast. Perfect for exploring historic towns and beautiful houses and gardens of Kent and Sussex.

Eastling
TQ9656

The Carpenters' Arms, *The Street, Eastling, Faversham, Kent, ME13 0AZ.* C14th inn, candlelit restaurant, adjoining lodge, 30 mins Channel Ports. **Open:** All year (not Xmas/New Year)
01795 890234 Mrs O'Regan **Fax: 01795 890654** www.swale.gov.uk **D:** £24.75–£26.00 **S:** £41.50 **Beds:** 3D **Baths:** 3 En ⌂ (12) 🅿 (20) 📺 ✕ 📺 📖 ♨ cc

Etchinghill
TR1639

One Step Beyond,
Westfield Lane, Etchinghill, Folkestone, Kent, CT18 8BT.
Quiet village location. Nearby walks. 4 mins from Channel Tunnel **Open:** All year (not Xmas/New Year)
01303 862637 (also fax) J Holden *johnosb@ rdplus.net* **D:** £17.50–£20.00 **S:** £20.00–£22.00 **Beds:** 1D **Baths:** 1 En ✑ 📺 📺 📖 ♨

Faversham
TR0161

Preston Lea,
Canterbury Road, Faversham, Kent, ME13 8XA.
Open: All year **Grades:** ETC 4 Diamond, Silver, AA 4 Diamond
01795 535266 Mr Turner **Fax: 01795 533388** *preston.lea@which.net* homepages.which. net/~alan.turner10 **D:** £28.00–£30.00 **S:** £40.00 **Beds:** 1T 2D **Baths:** 2 En 1 Pr ⌂ 🅿 (10) ✑ 📺 📖 ♨ cc
A warm welcome in this large elegant house with unique architectural features set in beautiful secluded gardens. The sunny, spacious bedrooms furnished with antiques offer every comfort. Afternoon tea on arrival and delicious breakfast grilled in the Aga, to order.

Owens Court Farm, *Selling, Faversham, Kent, ME13 9QN.* A lovely traditional Georgian farmhouse, pretty garden, peace and quiet! **Open:** All year (not Xmas) **Grades:** ETC 3 Diamond
01227 752247 (also fax) Mrs Higgs **D:** £20.00–£25.00 **S:** £25.00–£30.00 **Beds:** 1F 1T 1S **Baths:** 1 En 1 Sh ⌂ 🅿 (5) 📺 📺 📖 ♨

Tanners Cottage, *37 Tanner Street, Faversham, Kent, ME13 7JP.* Attractive old cottage in quiet area of lovely old market town. **Open:** All year (not Xmas)
01795 536698 M Jameson **D:** £15.00 **S:** £15.00 **Beds:** 1D 1T **Baths:** 1 Sh ⌂ (5) ✑ 📺 📖 ♨ cc

BEDROOMS
D = Double
T = Twin
S = Single
F = Family

Folkestone
TR2136 ⌖ Wetherspoons

Wycliffe Hotel, *63 Bouverie Road West, Folkestone, Kent, CT20 2RN.*
Clean, comfortable, affordable accommodation near shuttle, Seacat, 15 mins Dover Port.
Open: All year
01303 252186 (also fax) Mr & Mrs Shorland *shorland@wycliffehotel.freeserve.co.uk* www.visitus.co.uk/bnbhtm/wycliffe.htm **D:** £19.00–£22.00 **S:** £19.00–£22.00 **Beds:** 2F 5D 4T 1S **Baths:** 1 Pr 2 Sh ⌂ 🅿 (8) 🛎 ✕ 📺 ☀ ♨ cc

Banque Hotel, *4 Castle Hill Avenue, Folkestone, Kent, CT20 2QT.* Small comfortable hotel. Near town centre, Channel Tunnel. Breakfast served.
Open: All year **Grades:** ETC 3 Diamond
01303 253797 *banquehotel4@hotmail.com* www.banquehotel.com **D:** £20.00–£25.00 **S:** £25.00–£30.00 **Beds:** 3F 3T 3D 3S **Baths:** 12 En ⌂ 🅿 (2) ✑ 📺 🛎 📺 📖 ♨ cc

Folkestone Kentmere Guest House, *76 Cheriton Road, Folkestone, Kent, CT20 1DG.* Situated near Channel Tunnel terminal. Close to town centre and sea front. **Open:** All year
01303 259661 *kentmere.guesthouse@ ntlworld.com* www.smoothhound.co. uk/hotels/kentmere **D:** £18.00–£25.00 **S:** £18.00–£25.00 **Beds:** 4T 1D 2S **Baths:** 3 En 4 Sh ⌂ (2) ✑ 📺 📺 📖 ♨ cc

Frittenden
TQ8141

Tolehurst Barn, *Knoxbridge, Cranbrook Road, Frittenden, Cranbrook, Kent, TN17 2BP.* Quiet, rural environment, near to many fine houses, castles & gardens. **Open:** All year (not Xmas/New Year)
01580 714385 (also fax) Mrs Tresilian **D:** £20.00 **S:** £25.00 **Beds:** 1F 1T 1D **Baths:** 2 En 1 Pr ⌂ 🅿 (4) ✑ 📺 🛎 ✕ 📺 📖 ♨

Gillingham
TQ7767

Mayfield Guest House,
34 Kingswood Road, Gillingham, Kent, ME7 1DZ.
Victorian house with modern extension. Established for 18 years.
Open: All year (not Xmas) **Grades:** ETC 2 Diamond
01634 852606 Mrs Sumner **D:** £17.50 **S:** £20.00 **Beds:** 2F 2D 5T 1S **Baths:** 5 En 2 Sh ⌂ 🅿 (5) 📺 📺 📖 ♨ cc

4 The Rise, *Gillingham, Kent, ME7 3SF.*
Open: All year **Grades:** ETC 3 Diamond
01634 388156 Mrs Haddow **D:** £18.00
S: £18.00 **Beds:** 1F 1T 1S **Baths:** 1 En 1 Pr
Close to Exit 4 Gillingham M2. Coach stop to
London and coast. Shopping centre close
by. Friendly and welcoming household.
Rural location ideal for ramblers. Transport
to/from railway station if required.
Rochester Dickens Experience nearby.

178 Bredhurst Road, *Wigmore,*
Gillingham, Kent, ME8 0QX. Large chalet
bungalow 4 minutes M2. **Open:** All year
01634 233267 Mrs Penn **D:** £16.00–£20.00
S: £16.00–£20.00 **Beds:** 1F 1T **Baths:** 2 En ⊱
🅿 (2) 🗹 🖳 ⚲

Abigails, *17 The Maltings, Rainham,*
Gillingham, Kent, ME8 8JL. Friendly service,
family establishment, central location, rural
views, water garden. **Open:** All year
01634 365427 Ms Penfold **D:** £15.00 **S:** £15.00
Beds: 1F 1D 1S **Baths:** 2 En ⊱ 🅿 (4) 🗹 🗹 🖳
⚲

Ramsey House, *228a Barnsole Road,*
Gillingham, Kent, ME7 4JB. Established 15
years. Friendly atmosphere, close A2, M2,
maritime museums, Kent. **Open:** All year
01634 854193 Mrs Larssen **D:** £16.00–£18.00
S: £20.00–£25.00 **Beds:** 1S 2T **Baths:** 1 En 1
Sh ⊱ (3) 🅿 (2) ⊬ 🗹 🗹 🖳 ⚲

King Charles Hotel, *Brompton Road,*
Gillingham, Kent, ME7 5QT. Modern, family-
run hotel, set in the heart of maritime Kent.
Open: All year
01634 830303 Mr DeGiorgio **Fax:** 01634
829430 *enquiries@kingcharleshotel.co.uk*
D: £20.00 **S:** £34.00 **Beds:** 20F 30T 30D 1S
Baths: 81 En ⊱ 🅿 ⊬ 🗹 🟙 🗙 🗹 🖳 ⚹ ⚲ cc

Goudhurst
TQ7237

West Winchet, *Winchet Hill, Goudhurst,*
Cranbrook, Kent, TN17 1JX. Victorian
mansion in parkland with 2 beautifully
decorated rooms on ground floor. **Open:** All
year
01580 212024 Mrs Parker **D:** £25.00–£35.00
S: £35.00–£40.00 **Beds:** 1D 1T **Baths:** 1 En 1
Pr ⊱ (5) 🅿 (5) ⊬ 🗹 🟙 🗹 🖳 ⚲ ⚲

Gravesend
TQ6574

48 Clipper Crescent, Riverview
Park, *Gravesend, Kent, DA12 4NN.*
Comfortable bedrooms. Close to A2/M2
frequent trains to London. **Open:** All year
(not Xmas)
01474 365360 Mrs Jeeves **D:** £17.00–£17.50
S: £17.50 **Beds:** 1T 1S **Baths:** 1 Sh ⊱ (3)
🅿 (1) ⊬ 🗹 🖳 ⚲

Planning a longer stay? Always
ask for any special rates

Greenhithe
TQ5874

Metraro
Hotel, *Cobham*
Terrace,
Greenhithe,
Kent, DA9 9JB.
Open: All year
01322 383767
Fax: 01322
380834 **D:** £21.00–£26.00 **S:** £33.00–£46.00
Beds: 3F 1T 3D 2S **Baths:** 7 En 2 Sh ⊱ (3)
🅿 (15) 🗹 🟙 🗙 🗹 🖳 ⚲ cc
Well-restored Victorian hotel, run and
owned by same family for 20 years. Edge of
riverside conservation village, 300 metres
from Bluewater entrance. Close to A2 and
M25, few miles Kent gardens and orchards.
Historic Rochester 8 miles.

Halfway Houses
TQ9373 ⚓ *Lady Hamilton*

Kingsferry Guest House, *247*
Queenborough Road, Halfway Houses,
Sheerness, Kent, ME12 3EW. Warm welcome.
Full English breakfast. Near RSPB
sanctuary. New management. **Open:** All
year (not Xmas/New Year)
01795 663606 Mrs Ellis **D:** £20.00–£25.00
S: £25.00 **Beds:** 2F 3S **Baths:** 2 Sh ⊱ 🅿 (7) ⊬
🗹 ⚲

Harrietsham
TQ8752

Homestay, *14 Chippendayle Drive,*
Harrietsham, Maidstone, Kent, ME17 1AD.
Close to Leeds Castle and ideally situated
for exploring Kent. **Open:** All year (not
Xmas/New Year)
01622 858698 (also fax) Ms Beveridge
johnbtaylor@homestay14.freeserve.co.uk
www.skybusiness.com/jonba **D:** £18.00–
£20.00 **S:** £23.00–£24.00 **Beds:** 2T ⊬ 🗹 🗙 🖳
⚲

Hartley (Meopham)
TQ6067

Dartford Kaye Cottage, *18 Old Downs,*
Hartley, Longfield, Kent, DA3 7AA. **Open:** All
year (not Xmas) **Grades:** ETC 4 Diamond
01474 702384 (also fax) Mrs Smith *b-b@*
kaye-cottage.freeserve.co.uk **D:** £22.50–£35.00
S: £25.00–£30.00 **Beds:** 1F 2D 1T 1S
Baths: 2 En 2 Sh ⊱ 🅿 (5) ⊬ 🗹 🖳 ⚲
Picturesque cottage. Excellent location A2,
A20, M20, M25 Dartford crossing.
Gravesend 5 minutes Brands Hatch.
London golf club, Bluewater shopping
complex and Dartford crossing, BR Victoria
40 minutes. Friendly Accommodation. All
rooms to high standard. Lovely gardens.
Tennis court. quiet location.

Hawkhurst
TQ7630 ⚓ *The Curlew*

The Wren's Nest, *Hasting Road,*
Hawkhurst, Cranbrook, Kent, TN18 4RT.
Open: All year
01580 754919 (also fax) Mrs Rodger
D: £27.50–£29.50 **S:** £45.00–£49.00 **Beds:** 3D
Baths: 3 En ⊱ (10) 🅿 (10) ⊬ 🗹 🖳 ⚲ ⚲
Spacious, beautifully appointed hotel-style
suites, with character, comfortable lounge
area in all rooms. Peaceful, delightful
views, safe private parking. Ideal base for
Sissinghurst, Great Dixter, Batemans,
Bodiam Castle and many more places of
interest. Perfect accommodation for longer
stays.

Southgate Little Fowlers, *Rye Road,*
Hawkhurst, Kent, TN18 5DA. C17th country
house Kent/Sussex border. Amidst many
NT properties and gardens. **Open:** Easter to
Nov
01580 752526 (also fax) Mrs Woodard
susan.woodard@btinternet.com www.southgate.
uk.net/ **D:** £24.00–£30.00 **S:** £30.00–£40.00
Beds: 1T 1D **Baths:** 2 En ⊱ (10) 🅿 (4) ⊬ 🗹 🗹
🖳 ⚲

Headcorn
TQ8344

Four Oaks,
Four Oaks Road,
Headcorn,
Ashford, Kent,
TN27 9PB.
Restored 500-
year-old
farmhouse. Quiet location. Close Leeds
Castle, Sissinghurst, Eurolink. **Open:** All
year **Grades:** ETC 3 Diamond, RAC 3
Diamond
01622 891224 Mrs Thick **Fax:** 01622 890630
info@fouroaks.uk.com www.fouroaks.uk.com
D: £19.00–£21.00 **S:** £20.00–£25.00 **Beds:** 2F
1T **Baths:** 1 En 1 Sh ⊱ 🅿 (4) ⊬ 🗹 🟙 🗙 🗹 🖳 ⚲
cc

Waterkant Guest House, *Moat Road,*
Headcorn, Ashford, Kent, TN27 9NT.
Detached house in beautiful landscaped
gardens of Old Wealden village. **Open:** All
year
01622 890154 & 07779 487519 (M)
Dorothy Burbridge **D:** £18.00–£23.00
S: £25.00 **Beds:** 2D 1S **Baths:** 1 En 1 Sh ⊱
🅿 (6) ⊬ 🗹 🗹 🖳 ⚲

RATES
**D = Price range per person
sharing in a double or twin
room
S = Price range for a single
room**

Herne Bay

TR1768

'Hobbit Hole', *41a Pigeon Lane, Herne Bay, Kent, CT6 7ES.* **Open:** All year (not Xmas)
01227 368155 (also fax) Mrs Herwin *hobhole@aol.com* **D:** £20.00–£22.00 **S:** £20.00–£26.00 **Beds:** 1F 1T 1D **Baths:** 1 En 1 Pr 🅿 (7) 📺 Ⓥ 🗻 🌲

Dream with abandonment on transcendental beds; enjoy 'Bilbo Baggins' breakfasts. Taverns? Short gallop away! Most sports! Early or late arrival? Not problematical! Nearby: coastline (Saxon Shore Way), Canterbury (Cathedral), Ashford (International 'Chunnel' station and Business Centre), Sandwich (golf), Leeds Castle (spectacular entertainment).

High Halden

TQ8937   🍺 *Chequers, Royal Standard*

Draylands, *High Halden, Ashford, Kent, TN23 3JG.* Secluded location in Garden of England. Bedrooms with extensive views over open farmland. **Open:** All year (not Xmas/New Year)
01233 850048 (also fax) Mrs Russell *sallyrussell30@hotmail.com* **D:** £23.00–£25.00 **S:** £27.00–£30.00 **Beds:** 2D **Baths:** 2 En 🅿 (3) 🍴 📺 🗻 🌲

Bachelors Cottage, *High Halden, Ashford, Kent, TN26 3JD.* Comfortable converted oasthouse; secluded home near village. Garden, guests' sitting room. **Open:** All year (not Xmas/New Year) **Grades:** ETC 4 Diamond
01233 850280 Mrs Kenyon-Slaney **D:** £23.00–£25.00 **S:** £25.00–£28.00 **Beds:** 1T **Baths:** 1 En 🅿 (4) 🍴 📺 🗻 🌲

11 The Martins, *High Halden, Ashford, Kent, TN26 3LD.* Quiet rural modern house. Safe parking. Good food. Homely atmosphere. **Open:** Mar to Nov
01233 850013 Mr & Mrs Thorowgood **Fax:** **01233 850549** *bobandsandy@ thorowgood.fsnet.co.uk* **D:** £22.50–£25.00 **S:** £27.50 **Beds:** 1F 1D 1T **Baths:** 1 En 1 Pr 1 Sh 🅿 (4) 🍴 📺 🗻 🌲

Hollingbourne

TQ8455

Woodhouses, *49 Eyhorne Street, Hollingbourne, Maidstone, Kent, ME17 1TR.* C17th interconnected cottages close to village pubs and Leeds Castle. **Open:** All year **Grades:** ETC 4 Diamond
01622 880594 (also fax) Mr & Mrs Woodhouse *woodhouses@supanet.com* **D:** £21.00–£22.00 **S:** £22.00–£24.00 **Beds:** 3T **Baths:** 3 En 🅿 (3) 🍴 📺 Ⓥ 🗻 🌲

The Limes, *53 Eyhorne Street, Hollingbourne, Maidstone, Kent, ME17 1TS.* Wonderful C18th home, large walled garden and conservatory; nearby village pubs, Leeds Castle, M20. **Open:** Feb to Dec **Grades:** ETC 4 Diamond
01622 880554 Mrs Reed **Fax: 01622 880063** *thelimes@btinternet.com* **D:** £20.00–£22.50 **S:** £25.00–£30.00 **Beds:** 1D 2S **Baths:** 1 Pr 1 Sh 🌅 (10) 🅿 (5) 🍴 📺 🗻 🌲

Horsmonden

TQ7040

Forge House, *Brenchley Road, Horsmonden, Tonbridge, Kent, TN12 8DN.* Friendly house, ideal touring base, washbasins in all bedrooms. **Open:** All year **01892 723584** Mrs Brett **D:** £16.00–£17.00 **S:** £16.00–£17.00 **Beds:** 1D 1T 1S **Baths:** 1 Sh 🌅 🅿 (5) 🍴 📺 Ⓥ 🗻 🌲

Hunton

TQ7149

The Woolhouse, *Grove Lane, Hunton, Maidstone, Kent, ME15 0SE.* **Open:** All year (not Xmas/New Year)
01622 820778 A Wetton **Fax:** 01622 820645 **D:** £30.00 **S:** £30.00 **Beds:** 1T 1D 2S **Baths:** 4 En 🌅 (10) 🅿 (10) 📺 🍴 🗻 🌲
Lovely 300-year-old Grade II listed brick barn conversion, in quiet country lane in conservation area. Exposed beams, open fireplace, farmhouse kitchen, conservatory, comfortable and pretty bedrooms with private bathrooms. TV lounge for guest use only. Friendly atmosphere.

Hythe

TR1634

Hill View, *4south Road, Hythe, Kent, CT21 6AR.* Late Victorian house close to sea swimming pool and town. **Open:** All year (not Xmas)
01303 269783 Mrs Warbuton *beewarb@ tesco.net* **D:** £16.00–£18.00 **S:** £18.00–£20.00 **Beds:** 1F 1T **Baths:** 1 Sh 🌅 (5) 📺 🗻 🌲

Maccassil, *50 Marine Parade, Hythe, Kent, CT21 6AW.* A warm and friendly B&B in an idyllic peaceful location. **Open:** All year **01303 261867** **D:** £18.00–£21.00 **S:** £20.00–£25.00 **Beds:** 1F 1D 1T **Baths:** 2 En 1 Sh 🌅 🅿 (3) 🍴 📺 🗻 👶 🌲

Isle of Grain

TQ8875   🍺 *Hogarth Inn*

Grayne Lodge, *Chapel Road, Isle of Grain, Rochester, Kent, ME3 0BZ.* Near the sea, close to London and the Channel Ports. **Open:** All year (not Xmas/New Year)
01634 271576 **D:** £16.00–£18.00 **S:** £19.00–£22.00 **Beds:** 4T 2D 6S **Baths:** 1 En 3 Sh 🌅 🅿 (10) 📺 Ⓥ 🗻 👶 🌲

Kingsdown

TR3648   🍺 *Zetland Arms*

Sparrow Court, *Chalk Hill Road, Kingsdown, Deal, Kent, CT14 8DP.* Quiet seaside village between Deal and Dover. Bathing, walking, golf. **Open:** All year **Grades:** ETC 3 Diamond
01304 389253 The Hon Mrs Maude **Fax:** **01304 389016** *www.farmstaykent.com* **D:** £25.00–£30.00 **S:** £25.00–£30.00 **Beds:** 1T 1D **Baths:** 2 Pr 🌅 🅿 🍴 🐾 🗻 🌲

Kingston

TR1851   🍺 *Black Robin, Duke of Cumberland*

Oast Cottage, *13 The Street, Kingston, Canterbury, Kent, CT4 6JB.* **Open:** All year **01227 830929** Mrs Simpson *oastcotts@aol.com* oastcottage-bedandbreakfast.co.uk
D: £17.50–£22.50 **Beds:** 1F 1T 1S **Baths:** 1 En 1 Sh 🌅 (0) 🅿 (4) 🍴 📺 Ⓥ 🗻
Comfortable, clean, quiet, attractive and tastefully furnished period cottage situated in a pretty village near Canterbury. Amenities close by include castles, gardens and countryside walks plus easy access to the continent. Enjoy a relaxing stay in the heart of Kent.

Langley

TQ8051

Langley Oast, Langley Park, Langley, Maidstone, Kent, *ME17 3NQ.* Luxuriously converted oast off A274 south of Maidstone in open countryside overlooking a lake. **Open:** All year (not Xmas) **Grades:** AA 4 Diamond
01622 863523 (also fax) Mrs Clifford *margaret@langleyoast.freeserve.co.uk* **D:** £22.50–£35.00 **S:** £28.00–£50.00 **Beds:** 1F 1D 2T 1S **Baths:** 2 En 1 Sh ♿ (2) 🅿 (5) ⚡ 📺 Ⅴ 🛏 ♨

Lenham

TQ8951   🍺 Dog & Bear, Harrow, Red Lion

East Lenham Farm, Lenham, Maidstone, Kent, *ME17 2DP.* Superb country views. Sitting room, garden and tennis court. 5 miles Leeds Castle. **Open:** Mar to Jan **Grades:** ETC 4 Diamond, Silver
01622 858686 Mrs Barr **Fax: 01622 859474** *eastlenham@farmline.com* members.farmline.com/abarr **D:** £27.50–£32.50 **S:** £45.00–£50.00 **Beds:** 1D **Baths:** 1 En 🅿 (3) ⚡ 📺 🛏 ♨

Loose

TQ7551

Vale House, Old Loose Hill, Loose, Maidstone, Kent, *ME15 0BH.* Vale House stands in a secluded garden in the pretty historic village of Loose. **Open:** All year (not Xmas) **Grades:** ETC 3 Diamond
01622 743339 Mrs Gethin **Fax: 01622 743103** **D:** £25.00–£27.50 **S:** £26.00–£30.00 **Beds:** 2D 2T 1S **Baths:** 1 Pr 1 Sh ♿ 🅿 ⚡ 📺 🛏 ♨

Lyminge

TR1541

Southfields, Farthing Common, Lyminge, Folkestone, Kent, *CT18 8DH.* **Open:** Mar to Oct
01303 862391 Ms Wadie **D:** £18.00 **S:** £18.00 **Beds:** 1F 1T **Baths:** 1 Sh ♿ 🅿 (6) ⚡ 📺 ✕ Ⅴ 🛏 ♨

A peaceful home on the North Downs with a spectacular sea view. Ideal walking country dotted with village pubs. Central by car to Kent's many places of historic interest and France, through the Tunnel barely an hour away. Cyclists welcome.

Planning a longer stay? Always ask for any special rates

Maidstone

TQ7655   🍺 Bull Inn, White Horse

172 Tonbridge Road, Maidstone, Kent, *ME16 8SR.* **Open:** All year (not Xmas/New Year)
01622 720427 Mr Tindle *metindle@dialstart.net* **D:** £19.00–£22.00 **S:** £19.00–£22.00 **Beds:** 2T 1D 1S **Baths:** 2 Sh 🅿 (5) ⚡ 📺 Ⅴ 🛏 ♨
Perfectly situated for exploring the 'Garden of England' and yet within easy walking distance of Maidstone town centre. Easy access from the M20 Motorway and good rail links to London. Comfortable accommodation and a warm welcome await all our guests.

Aylesbury Hotel, 56-58 London Road, Maidstone, Kent, *ME16 8QL.* **Open:** All year (not Xmas/New Year) **Grades:** ETC 3 Diamond, AA 3 Diamond
01622 762100 *aylesbury@onetel.net.uk* **D:** £23.00–£26.00 **S:** £42.00 **Beds:** 4T 4D 2S **Baths:** 6 En 1 Sh ♿ 🅿 (8) ⚡ 📺 Ⅴ 🛏 ♨ cc
Built in 1861, the house has 8 individually decorated bedrooms. Walking distance to town centre and stations. Ideal touring base for the beautiful South East. Close to Leeds Castle. French and German spoken.

Langley Oast, Langley Park, Langley, Maidstone, Kent, *ME17 3NQ.* **Open:** All year (not Xmas)
Grades: AA 4 Diamond
01622 863523 (also fax) Mrs Clifford *margaret@langleyoast.freeserve.co.uk* **D:** £22.50–£35.00 **S:** £28.00–£50.00 **Beds:** 1F 1D 2T 1S **Baths:** 2 En 1 Sh ♿ (2) 🅿 (5) ⚡ 📺 Ⅴ 🛏 ♨
Luxuriously converted oast off A274 south of Maidstone in open countryside overlooking a lake.

Court Farm, High Street, Aylesford, Maidstone, Kent, *ME20 7AZ.* Beams, four poster, spa, antiques, drawing room. Sorry, no children. **Open:** All year
01622 717293 (also fax) Mrs Tucker *enquiries@courtfarm.co.uk* www.courtfarm.co.uk **D:** £25.00 **S:** £25.00 **Beds:** 2D 1T 1S **Baths:** 3 En 1 Pr 🅿 (6) ⚡ 📺 🛏 ✕ Ⅴ 🛏 ♨ cc

10 Fant Lane, Maidstone, Kent, *ME16 8NL.* A character cottage with beams, quiet area, friendly accommodation. **Open:** All year **Grades:** ETC 3 Diamond
01622 729883 Mrs Layton **D:** £20.00–£30.00 **S:** £16.00–£25.00 **Beds:** 1F 1S **Baths:** 1 Sh ♿ (4) 🅿 (1) ⚡ 📺 ✕ Ⅴ 🛏 ♨

Grove House, Grove Green Road, Weavering, Maidstone, Kent, *ME14 5JT.* Attractive front garden for guests to enjoy quiet peaceful surroundings. **Open:** All year
01622 738441 S Costella **D:** £22.50–£25.00 **S:** £25.00–£35.00 **Beds:** 1T 2D **Baths:** 1 En 1 Sh 🅿 (6) ⚡ 📺 🛏 ♨ cc

Marden

TQ7444   🍺 West End Tavern

Tanner House, Tanner Farm, Goudhurst Road, Marden, Tonbridge, Kent, *TN12 9ND.* **Open:** All year (not Xmas) **Grades:** ETC 4 Diamond
01622 831214 Mrs Mannington **Fax: 01622 832472** *tannerhouse@cs.com* www.tannerfarmpark.co.uk **D:** £22.50–£25.00 **S:** £30.00 **Beds:** 1D 2T **Baths:** 3 En ♿ (5) 🅿 ⚡ 📺 Ⅴ 🛏 ♨ cc
Comfortable surroundings await you at Tanner House set in the midst of 150-acre family farm. Ideal for a break, stopover or holiday, quality cuisine using local produce and our own jams and preserves. Quality touring caravan park also available.

Margate

TR3570

Vienna Guest House, 28 Canterbury Road, Margate, Kent, *CT9 5BN.* 300 yards to seafront. 17 miles to the city of Canterbury. **Open:** All year
01843 224522 Mr & Mrs Mullin **D:** £16.00–£25.00 **S:** £16.00–£25.00 **Beds:** 4F 3T 10D 4S **Baths:** 17 En ♿ 🅿 (16) ⚡ 📺 ✕ Ⅴ 🛏 ♨ cc

Fulwood Hotel, 2-4 Surrey Road, Margate, Kent, *CT9 2LA.* Situated in Margate - a leisure destination. Easy access to Margate beaches. **Open:** All year **Grades:** ETC 2 Diamond
01843 293977 Mr Haiwad *haiwad_a@hotmail.com* www.fulwoodhotel.co.uk **D:** £40.00–£50.00 **S:** £20.00–£25.00 **Beds:** 1F 9T 6D 6S **Baths:** 8 En 9 Pr 10 Sh ♿ 🅿 ⚡ 📺 🛏 ✕ Ⅴ 🛏 ♿ ♨ cc

The Happy Dolphin, 11 Buenos Ayres, Margate, Kent, *CT9 5AE.* Victorian private guest house overlooking beach. CTV, radio/cassette, fridge, phone, iron, hairdryer. **Open:** All year
01843 296473 (also fax) Ms Stratford **D:** £15.00–£35.00 **S:** £20.00–£35.00 **Beds:** 4F 1D 1T 2S **Baths:** 6 En 2 Pr 📺 🛏 ✕ Ⅴ 🛏 ♨ cc

Malvern Hotel, *Eastern Esplanade, Cliftonville, Margate, Kent, CT9 2HL.* Small, seafront hotel, close to indoor bowls, Winter Gardens, amenities etc. **Open:** All year
01843 290192 (also fax) **D:** £20.00–£22.50 **S:** £22.50–£30.00 **Beds:** 2F 5D 2T 1S **Baths:** 8 En 1 Sh ⓣ 📺 🛋 ♨ cc

Somerville Hotel, *9 Canterbury Road, Margate, Kent, CT9 5AQ.* Family-run hotel overlooking sea close to all amenities. **Open:** All year (not New Year)
01843 224401 Mr Hubbard **D:** £15.00–£20.00 **S:** £20.00–£25.00 **Beds:** 1F 5D 2T **Baths:** 2 En 2 Sh ⓣ 📺 ✕ 📺 🛋 ✳ ♨

Minster in Sheppey
TQ9573

Mia Crieff, *Mill Hill, Chequers Road, Minster in Sheppey, Sheerness, ME12 3QL.* Detached house with large garden. Comfortable accommodation and full breakfast. **Open:** All year (not Xmas)
01795 870620 Mrs White **D:** £19.00–£20.00 **S:** £23.00–£25.00 **Beds:** 3D **Baths:** 3 En ⓣ 📶 (5) 📺 📺 🛋 ♨

Otford
TQ5159 🍺 *Bull Inn, Kings Arms*

9 Warham Road, *Otford, Sevenoaks, Kent, TN14 5PF.* Modern detached house in centre of village. London 35 mins. **Open:** All year (not Xmas/New Year) **Grades:** ETC 2 Diamond
01959 523596 Mrs Smith **D:** £20.00 **S:** £20.00 **Beds:** 1T 1D 1S **Baths:** 1 Sh ⓣ ✕ 📺 🛏 🛋 ♨

Darenth Dene, *Shoreham Road, Otford, Sevenoaks, Kent, TN14 5RP.* Quiet location. Half mile from Otford. Reduced rates 4 nights plus. **Open:** All year (not Xmas/New Year) **Grades:** ETC 4 Diamond
01959 522293 Mrs Reid **D:** £25.00–£30.00 **S:** £25.00–£30.00 **Beds:** 1T 2S **Baths:** 1 En 1 Sh 📶 📺 🛋

Paddlesworth
TR1940

Pigeonwood House, *Arpinge, Folkestone, Kent, CT18 8AQ.* Ancient homely farmhouse in beautiful downland spectacular views, rural tranquillity. **Open:** Apr to Oct
01303 891111 Mr & Mrs Martin **Fax:** 01303 891019 *samandmary@aol.com* www.arpinge. com **D:** £20.00–£25.00 **S:** £25.00–£35.00 **Beds:** 1F 1D 1T **Baths:** 2 En 1 Pr ⓣ (5) 📶 (5) ✕ 📺 🛋 ♨

Paddock Wood
TQ6744

Little Fowle Hall Oast, *Lucks Lane, Paddock Wood, Tonbridge, Kent, TN12 6PA.* London: train 1 hour. **Open:** All year (not Xmas)
01892 832602 Mr Lumley **D:** £20.00 **S:** £20.00 **Beds:** 1F 2T **Baths:** 1 En 1 Sh ⓣ 📶 (8) ✕ 🛏 🛋 ♨

Peene
TR1837

West Lodge, *Peene, Folkestone, Kent, CT18 8BA.* Grade II Listed property set in 3 acres in quiet village. **Open:** All year (not Xmas)
01303 274762 *john@gredley.freeserve.co.uk* **D:** £17.50 **S:** £25.00 **Beds:** 2F **Baths:** 1 Sh ⓣ 📶 (3) 📺 🛏 🛋 ♨

Penshurst
TQ5243 🍺 *Leicester Arms, Spotted Dog, Bottle House*

Well Place Farm, *Penshurst, Tonbridge, Kent, TN11 8BY.* Comfortable, secluded Victorian farmhouse with stunning views over Penshurst. **Open:** All year
01892 870894 Mrs Scott *scottswpf@aol.com* **D:** £22.50 **S:** £22.50 **Beds:** 1T 1D **Baths:** 1 Pr 1 Sh 📶 📶 ✕ 📺 🛋 ♨

Petham
TR1351 🍺 *Compasses Inn*

South Wootton House, *Capel Lane, Petham, Canterbury, Kent, CT4 5RG.* A beautiful farmhouse with conservatory set in extensive gardens, surrounded by fields and woodland. **Open:** All year (not Xmas/New Year) **Grades:** ETC 3 Diamond
01227 700643 F Mount **Fax:** 01227 700613 **D:** £40.00–£45.00 **S:** £25.00–£30.00 **Beds:** 1F 1T **Baths:** 1 Pr ⓣ 📶 ✕ 📺 🛋 ♨

Upper Ansdore, *Duckpit Lane, Petham, Canterbury, Kent, CT4 5QB.* Medieval house overlooking nature reserve, very secluded views. Canterbury 15 mins. **Open:** All year (not Xmas/New Year)
01227 700672 R Linch **Fax:** 01227 700840 www.smoothhound.co.uk/hotels/upperans. html **D:** £21.00–£22.50 **S:** £30.00–£38.00 **Beds:** 1F 1T 3D **Baths:** 3 En ⓣ (5) 📶 (5) ✕ 🛏 📺 🛋 ♨ cc

RATES

D = Price range per person sharing in a double or twin room

S = Price range for a single room

Pluckley
TQ9245 🍺 *Rose & Crown, Swan Inn, Dering Arms*

Glebelands Bed and Breakfast, *Station Road, Pluckley, Ashford, Kent, TN27 0QU.*

Open: All year
01233 840089 (also fax) Mrs MacDonald *enquiries@glebelands-bedandbreakfast.co.uk* www.glebelands-bedandbreakfast.co.uk **D:** £22.50–£25.00 **S:** £30.00–£35.00 **Beds:** 1T 1D 1S **Baths:** 1 Sh ⓣ 📶 (3) ✕ 📺 🛏 📺 🛋 ♨ A warm, friendly welcome awaits you. Enjoy a Kentish breakfast with our own eggs and fresh local produce. Situated near the Greensand Way in the heart of 'Darling Buds of May' countryside, with easy access to Ashford International Station and the channel crossings.

Preston (Faversham)
TR0261

The Windmill Inn, *Canterbury Road, Preston, Faversham, ME13 8LT.* Typical English pub, two bars, dining area, warm friendly welcome. **Open:** All year
01795 536505 **D:** £22.00–£36.00 **S:** £18.00 **Beds:** 2T 2S **Baths:** 1 Sh ⓣ 📶 (8) ✕ 📺 🛋 ♨

Preston (Wingham)
TR2561

Forstal House, *The Forstal, Preston, Canterbury, Kent, CT3 1DT.* Secluded C18th country house near river and orchards. Beautiful walled garden. **Open:** All year (not Xmas)
01227 722282 Mrs Scott **Fax:** 01227 722295 **D:** £20.00 **S:** £22.00 **Beds:** 1D 1T **Baths:** 1 En 1 Pr ⓣ 📶 (4) ✕ 📺 📺 ♿ ♨

Rainham
TQ8165

Irwin Grange, *Meresborough Road, Rainham, Gillingham, Kent, ME8 8PN.* Farm house set in 13 acres, good view of River Medway. **Open:** All year (not Xmas)
01634 232801 Mrs Knight **D:** £17.50 **S:** £20.00 **Beds:** 1F 2T **Baths:** 2 Sh ⓣ 📶 (10) 📺 🛋 ♨

Ramsgate
TR3864 🍺 *Prince Harry*

Ramsgate Abbeygail Guest House, *17 Penshurst Road, Ramsgate, Kent, CT11 8EG.* 10 mins from award-winning sandy beach. **Open:** All year **Grades:** ETC 3 Diamond
01843 594154 **D:** £18.00–£25.00 **S:** £18.00 **Beds:** 3F 2T 2D 1S **Baths:** 3 En 2 Sh ⓣ 📶 📺 📺 🛋 ♨

The Regency Hotel and School Of English, *Royal Crescent, Ramsgate, Kent, CT11 9PE.* Facing English Channel on west cliffs of Ramsgate. Glorious sea views. **Open:** All year
01843 591212 Fax: 01843 850035
regency.school@btinternet.com **D:** £17.00–£19.00 **S:** £24.00–£34.00 **Beds:** 3F 58T 26S **Baths:** 16 En 11 Sh ❂ (3) ✕ ☑ Ⅷ. **cc**

The Royale Guest House, *7 Royal Road, Ramsgate, Kent, CT11 9LE.* Friendly, family-run guest house; close to all amenities. **Open:** All year **Grades:** ETC 3 Diamond
01843 594712 (also fax) Mrs Barry
theroyalguesthouse@talk21.com **D:** £17.00–£20.00 **S:** £17.00–£20.00 **Beds:** 1F 2D 2T 4S **Baths:** 3 En 2 Sh ❂ (2) ☑ ★ Ⅷ. ♨

Glendevon Guest House, *8 Truro Road, Ramsgate, Kent, CT11 8BD.* Comfortable ensuite rooms with own well equipped kitchen/eating areas. **Open:** All year **Grades:** ETC 3 Diamond
01843 570909 (also fax) S & A Everix
glendevon@currantbun.com **D:** £16.00–£20.00 **S:** £20.00–£24.00 **Beds:** 1F 2T 3D **Baths:** 6 En ❂ (5) ☑ Ⅷ. ♨ **cc**

Rhodes Minnis
TR1443

Monsoon Lodge, *Rhodes Minnis, Canterbury, Kent, CT4 6XX.* Family home, quiet, relaxing. Rural location near Channel Tunnel and Canterbury. **Open:** All year (not Xmas/New Year) **Grades:** ETC 3 Diamond
01303 863272 (also fax) Mrs Mills *jm@farmersweekly.net* www.monsoonlodge.co.uk
D: £20.00–£25.00 **S:** £20.00–£25.00 **Beds:** 1F 1T 1D **Baths:** 3 En ❂ ❒ (4) ⌫ ☑ ☑ Ⅷ. ♨ **cc**

Rochester
TQ7468

11 Ethelbert Road, *Rochester, Kent, ME1 3EU.* Large family home 10 mins' walk from historic city centre. **Open:** All year (not Xmas)
01634 403740 Mrs Jenkinson **D:** £18.00–£20.00 **S:** £20.00 **Beds:** 1D 1T ⌫ ☑ Ⅷ. ♨

255 High Street, *Rochester, Kent, ME1 1HQ.* Victorian family house near station. Antique 4-poster bed. **Open:** All year (not Xmas)
01634 842737 Mrs Thomas **D:** £14.00–£16.00 **S:** £16.00–£25.00 **Beds:** 1F 1D 1T **Baths:** 1 Pr 1 Sh ❂ ☑ ♨

52 Borstal Street, *Rochester, Kent, ME1 3HL.* Comfortable Victorian Terraced house. Suitable for cat lovers. Smokers welcome. **Open:** All year
01634 812347 Ms Walker **D:** £12.50 **S:** £20.00 **Beds:** 1D **Baths:** 1 Sh ❒ ☑ Ⅷ. ♨

St Martin, *104 Borstal Road, Rochester, Kent, ME1 3BD.* Comfortable Victorian home overlooking river, easy walk to city centre. **Open:** All year (not Xmas) **Grades:** ETC 3 Diamond
01634 848192 Mrs Colvin *icolvin@stmartin.freeserve.co.uk* **D:** £18.00 **S:** £18.00 **Beds:** 1D 2T **Baths:** 2 Sh ❂ ☑ ★ ✕ ☑ Ⅷ. ♨

Wouldham Court Farmhouse, *246 High Street, Wouldham, Rochester, Kent, ME1 3TY.* Beamed Grade II Listed farmhouse, inglenook fireplace, overlooking River Medway. **Open:** All year (not Xmas) **Grades:** ETC 3 Diamond
01634 683271 (also fax) Ms Parnell
wouldham.b-b@virgin.net **D:** £22.00 **S:** £18.00–£22.00 **Beds:** 1F 1D 1S **Baths:** 2 Sh ❂ ❒ (1) ⌫ ☑ ★ ✕ ☑ Ⅷ. ♨ **cc**

St Ouen, *98 Borstal Road, Rochester, Kent, ME1 3BD.* Victorian house with comfortable rooms overlooking River Medway. Amenities close by. **Open:** All year (not Xmas)
01634 843528 Mrs Beggs *m.s.beggs@98borstal.freeserve.co.uk* **D:** £16.00–£20.00 **S:** £18.00–£20.00 **Beds:** 1D 1T 1S **Baths:** 1 Sh ❂ ⌫ ☑ ★ Ⅷ. ♨

Saltwood
TR1536 ⚓ Castle Hotel

The Shrubsoles, *62 Brockhill Road, Saltwood, Hythe, Kent, CT21 4AG.* Victorian home in village setting, 5m Channel Tunnel entrance. **Open:** Nov to Sept
01303 238832 Mrs Shrubsole
marion_shrubsole@lineone.net **D:** £20.00–£25.00 **S:** £22.00–£35.00 **Beds:** 1T 1D **Baths:** 1 En 1 Pr ❂ ❒ (2) ⌫ ☑ Ⅷ. ♨

Sandhurst
TQ7928 ⚓ Bull Inn

Hoads Farm, *Crouch Lane, Sandhurst, Cranbrook, Kent, TN18 5PA.* Comfortable C16th farmhouse on working farm. **Open:** All year
01580 850296 (also fax) A Nicholas
canicholas@btinternet.com **D:** £20.00 **S:** £20.00–£25.00 **Beds:** 3T **Baths:** 2 Sh ❂ ❒ (10) ☑ ✕ ☑ Ⅷ. ♨ **cc**

Planning a longer stay? Always ask for any special rates

Selling
TR0456

Owens Court Farm, *Selling, Faversham, Kent, ME13 9QN.* A lovely traditional Georgian farmhouse, pretty garden, peace and quiet! **Open:** All year (not Xmas) **Grades:** ETC 3 Diamond
01227 752247 (also fax) Mrs Higgs
D: £20.00–£25.00 **S:** £25.00–£30.00 **Beds:** 1F 1T 1S **Baths:** 1 En 1 Sh ❂ ❒ (5) ☑ ☑ Ⅷ. ♨

Sevenoaks
TQ5255 ⚓ Blacksmith's Arms

Green Tiles, *46 The Rise, Sevenoaks, Kent, TN13 1RJ.* Quiet annexe in lovely garden, own entrance, for 1-5 guests. **Open:** All year
01732 451522 (also fax) Mrs Knoops **D:** £20.00–£22.00 **S:** £30.00 **Beds:** 1F **Baths:** 1 En ❂ ❒ (2) ☑ Ⅷ. ♨

40 Robyns Way, *Sevenoaks, Kent, TN13 3EB.* Quiet location, station 10 mins' walk. French spoken, self catering available. **Open:** All year **Grades:** ETC 3 Diamond
01732 452401 Mrs Ingram *valerie.ingram@centrenet.co.uk* **D:** £25.00–£28.00 **S:** £27.00–£30.00 **Beds:** 1D 1T 1S **Baths:** 1 En 1 Sh ❂ ❒ (3) ⌫ ☑ Ⅷ. ♨ ♨

56 The Drive, *Sevenoaks, Kent, TN13 3AF.* Lovely Edwardian house and garden close to station and town. Peaceful. **Open:** All year (not Xmas)
01732 453236 Mrs Lloyd *jwlloydsks@aol.com* **D:** £19.00–£24.50 **S:** £22.00–£28.00 **Beds:** 2T 2S **Baths:** 2 Sh ❒ (4) ☑ ♨

Sheerness
TQ9175

Sheppey Guest House, *214 Queenborough Road, Sheerness, Kent, ME12 3DF.* Friendly family guest house, which has served the public for 26 years. **Open:** All year
01795 665950 Ms Allen **Fax: 01795 661200**
D: £15.00 **S:** £20.00 **Beds:** 5F 1T 2D 1S **Baths:** 9 En ❂ ❒ ☑ ★ ✕ ☑ Ⅷ. ♨2 ♨

The Whitehouse, *The Leas, Sheerness, Isle of Sheppey, ME12 2TE.* Small, friendly B&B with restaurant. All rooms with river views. **Open:** All year
01795 872266 & 0800 9230158 Fax: 01708 404508 *pat@leas.co.uk* www.leas.co.uk
D: £23.00–£29.00 **S:** £25.00–£28.00 **Beds:** 4D 1S **Baths:** 1 Sh ❂ ❒ (15) ☑ ✕ ☑ Ⅷ. ♨ **cc**

Shepherdswell

TR2547

Sunshine Cottage, *The Green, Mill Lane, Shepherdswell, Dover, Kent, CT15 7LQ.* C17th cottage on village green, beautifully restored. Pretty garden/courtyard. **Open:** All year **Grades:** ETC 4 Diamond, Silver
01304 831359 & 01304 831218 Mrs Popple
sunshinecottage@sheperdswell.fsnet.co.uk
www.sunshine-cottage.co.uk **D:** £24.00–£29.00 **S:** £25.00–£35.00 **Beds:** 1F 4D 1T **Baths:** 2 Pr 2 Sh ⌦ ⊡ ⊡ ▥ ♨ cc

Shoreham

TQ5261

Church House, *Church Street, Shoreham, Sevenoaks, Kent, TN14 7SB.* Georgian house; large garden and tennis court in picturesque village. **Open:** All year (not Xmas/New Year)
01959 522241 (also fax) Mrs Howie
katehowie@compuserve.com www.heartofkent.
org.uk **D:** £22.00–£28.00 **S:** £30.00–£35.00 ⊡ ⊡ ▥ ♿ ♨

Sissinghurst

TQ7937

Frogshole Oast, *Sissinghurst Road, Biddenden, Ashford, Kent, TN27 8LW.* Attractively located C18th oasthouse, 1.5 acre garden, adjacent Sissinghurst Castle. **Open:** Easter to Oct
01580 291935 (also fax) D Hartley *hartley@ frogsholeoast.freeserve.co.uk* www.geocities. com/frogsholeoast/sissinghurst.html
D: £23.00–£26.00 **S:** £30.00–£40.00 **Beds:** 2T 1D **Baths:** 1 En 1 Sh ⌦ (9) ⊡ (4) ⌦ ⊡ ⊡ ▥ ♨

Hillview Cottage, *Starvenden Lane, Sissinghurst, Cranbrook, Kent, TN17 2AN.* Total peace. Attractive, comfortable house close NT properties. **Open:** All year
01580 712823 & 07850 909838 (M) Mrs Lloyd Jones *rmlj@starlaine.freeserve.co.uk* **D:** £20.00–£30.00 **S:** £20.00–£30.00 **Beds:** 1D 1T **Baths:** 2 En 1 Pr ⊡ ⊡ ⌁ ✕ ▥ ♨

Smarden

TQ8842

Chequers Inn, *Smarden, Ashford, Kent, TN27 8QA.* C14th village inn. Renowned for good food and ambience. **Open:** All year (not Xmas)
01233 770217 Fax: 01233 770623 D: £25.00 **S:** £26.00 **Beds:** 1F 2T 2D 1S **Baths:** 3 En 2 Pr ⌦ ⊡ (18) ⊡ ⌁ ✕ ⊡ ♨

Gate Cottage, *Maltmans Hill, Smarden, Ashford, Kent, TN27 8RD.* C17th tollhouse. Superb food. Ideal touring Kent/Sussex/Channel crossings. **Open:** All year (not Xmas/New Year)
01233 770226 (also fax) Mr & Mrs Ralph
D: £25.00–£27.50 **S:** £35.00–£37.50 **Beds:** 2D **Baths:** 2 En ⌦ (12) ⊡ (4) ⌦ ⊡ ✕ ⊡ ▥ ♨

Southborough

TQ5842

10 Modest Corner, *Southborough, Tunbridge Wells, Kent, TN4 0LS.* You will experience a warm welcome in this very comfortable, tastefully decorated B&B. **Open:** All year (not Xmas/New Year)
01892 522450 (also fax) Mr Leemhuis
modestanneke@lineone.net **D:** £22.50–£25.00 **S:** £30.00–£35.00 **Beds:** 2T 1D **Baths:** 1 Pr 1 Sh ⌦ ⊡ (2) ⊡ ⌁ ✕ ▥ ♨

St Margaret's at Cliffe

TR3644

Wallets Court Manor, *West Cliffe, St Margaret's at Cliffe, Dover, Kent, CT15 6EW.* C17th hotel. Restaurant and spa in White Cliffs country. **Open:** All year **Grades:** ETC 3 Star
01304 852424 Mr Oakley *stay@ wallettscourt.com* www.wallettscourt.com
D: £45.00–£75.00 **S:** £75.00 **Beds:** 1F 3T 12D **Baths:** 16 En ⌦ ⊡ (50) ⊡ ✕ ⊡ ▥ ♨ cc

Stelling Minnis

TR1346

Bower Farm House, *Bossingham Road, Stelling Minnis, Canterbury, Kent, CT4 6BB.* **Open:** All year (not Xmas/New Year)
01227 709430 *book@bowerbb.freeserve.co.uk*
D: £22.00–£25.00 **S:** £28.00–£30.00 **Beds:** 1T 1D **Baths:** 1 En 1 Pr ⌦ ⊡ (5) ⊡ ⌁ ⊡ ▥ ♨ Breakfast on fresh bread and new laid eggs in a charming heavily beamed C17th Kentish farmhouse on the edge of a medieval common. Visit historic Canterbury, walk in the beautiful countryside or see Dover castle and the white cliffs.

National Grid References given are for villages, towns and cities – not for individual houses

---

BEDROOMS
D = Double
T = Twin
S = Single
F = Family

Stowting

TR1241   🍺 *Tiger Inn, Five Bells, Black Horse*

Water Farm, *Stowting, Ashford, Kent, TN25 6BA.* Lakeside farm; homely and comfortable, beautiful scenery, trout fishing. **Open:** All year (not Xmas/New Year)
01303 862401 C Cole **D:** £21.00 **S:** £21.00 **Beds:** 1T 1D **Baths:** 1 En 1 Pr ⌦ (12) ⊡ (2) ⌦ ⊡ ▥ ♨

Strood

TQ7268

3 Hillside Avenue, Frindsbury, *Strood, Rochester, ME2 3DB.* Friendly family Victorian home in quiet road, close to amenities. **Open:** All year
01634 713642 Mrs Firmin **D:** £15.00–£18.00 **S:** £15.00–£18.00 **Beds:** 1F 1T 1S **Baths:** 2 Sh ⌦ ⌦ ⊡ ⌁ ✕ ⊡ ▥ ♨

Sundridge

TQ4855

The Red House, *Church Road, Sundridge, Sevenoaks, Kent, TN14 6EA.* Queen Anne House in Beautiful gardens near Hever, Chartwell, London. **Open:** All year (not Xmas/New Year)
01959 565444 Mrs Belle **Fax: 01732 452312** *balles@waitrose.com* **D:** £25.00 **S:** £25.00 **Beds:** 3D **Baths:** 1 En 1 Sh ⊡ (4) ⌦ ⊡ ▥ ♨

Sutton Valence

TQ8149   🍺 *King's Head*

West Belringham, *Chart Road, Sutton Valence, Maidstone, Kent, ME17 3AW.* Spacious bungalows, panoramic views. Breakfast. Complementary tea/coffee with home-made cakes. **Open:** All year (not Xmas/New Year) **Grades:** ETC 3 Diamond
01622 843995 (also fax) Mrs King
west.belringham@tesco.net **D:** £21.00 **S:** £27.00 **Beds:** 2T **Baths:** 1 Pr ⌦ (7) ⊡ (5) ⌦ ⊡ ⊡ ▥ ♨

The Queens Head, *High Street, Sutton Valence, Maidstone, Kent, ME17 3AG.* Spectacular countryside views of Weald of Kent. Excellent home cooked food in countryside style. **Open:** All year
01622 843225 J Pilcher **Fax: 01622 842651 D:** £22.50–£25.00 **S:** £22.50–£25.00 **Beds:** 2F 1T 1D **Baths:** 1 Sh ⌦ ⊡ ⊡ ⌦ ⊡ ▥ ♨ cc

Planning a longer stay? Always ask for any special rates

Tenterden

TQ8833 🍺 *William Caxton, Vine Inn, Eight Bells*

The White Cottage, London Beach, Tenterden, Kent, *TN30 6SR.* 2 miles north of Tenterden on A28 road, rural position. **Open:** All year **Grades:** ETC 3 Diamond **01233 850583** Mrs Matthews www.smoothhound.co.uk/shs.html **D:** £16.50–£18.50 **S:** £20.00–£25.00 **Beds:** 2D 1T **Baths:** 1 En 2 Sh 🛇 🄿 (3) ⌨ 📺 🌡

Old Burren, 25 Ashford Road, Tenterden, Kent, *TN30 6LL.* C17th home where a warm friendly welcome awaits you. **Open:** All year **Grades:** ETC 3 Diamond **01580 764442** *poo@burren.fsbusiness.co.uk* www.oldburren.co.uk **D:** £20.00–£25.00 **S:** £25.00–£45.00 **Beds:** 2D 1S **Baths:** 1 En 1 Pr 🄿 (2) ⌨ 🐾 🌮 ▦ ✿ 🌡

Tonbridge

TQ5946

Starvecrow Place, Starvecrow Hill, Shipbourne Road, Tonbridge, Kent, *TN11 9NL.* Relaxed luxury accommodation set in delightful woodlands. Heated outdoor swimming pool. **Open:** All year (not Xmas) **01732 356863** Mrs Batson **D:** £19.00–£22.00 **S:** £30.00 **Beds:** 2D 1T **Baths:** 2 En 1 Pr 🛇 (13) 🄿 (6) ⌨ 📺 ▦ 🌡

Trottiscliffe

TQ6460

Bramble Park, Church Lane, Trottiscliffe, West Malling, Kent, *ME19 5E.* Secluded tranquil Victorian rectory in beautiful private parkland. Spacious comfortable. **Open:** All year **01732 822397** Mrs Towler **D:** £25.00 **S:** £25.00 **Beds:** 1F 1D 1S **Baths:** 1 Pr 2 Sh 🛇 🄿 (6) ⌨ ▦

Tunbridge Wells

TQ5839 🍺 *Weatherspoons, Opera House*

Ash Tree Co, Eden Road, Tunbridge Wells, Kent, *TN1 1TS.* Delightful cottage-style house, short walk to the famous Pantiles. **Open:** All year (not Xmas/New Year) **01892 541317** Mrs Rogers **Fax:** 01892 616770 **D:** £22.50–£25.00 **S:** £35.00–£42.00 **Beds:** 1D 1T **Baths:** 2 En 🛇 (9) 🄿 (4) ⌨ 📺 📺 ▦ ⚬ 🌡

10 Modest Corner, Southborough, Tunbridge Wells, Kent, *TN4 0LS.* **Open:** All year (not Xmas/New Year) **01892 522450 (also fax)** Mr Leemhuis *modestanneke@lineone.net* **D:** £22.50–£25.00 **S:** £30.00–£35.00 **Beds:** 2T 1D **Baths:** 1 Pr 1 Sh 🛇 🄿 (2) ⌨ 🌮 ⨯ ▦ 🌡 You will experience a warm welcome in this very comfortable, tastefully decorated B&B situated on the outer edge of Tunbridge Wells in a little hamlet away from noisy traffic. Easy access M25 and main line station.

Blundeston, Eden Road, Tunbridge Wells, Kent, *TN1 1TS.* **Open:** All year (not Xmas/New Year) **Grades:** ETC 4 Diamond **01892 513030** Mrs Day **Fax:** 01892 540255 **D:** £23.00–£26.00 **S:** £23.00–£26.00 **Beds:** 1T 1D **Baths:** 2 En 🄿 ⌨ 📺 📺 ▦ 🌡 Beautiful period house in quiet secluded part of the old village area of Tunbridge Wells. Within five minutes walk of many restaurants the old High Street, Pantiles and railway station.

Vale Royal Hotel, 54-57 London Road, Tunbridge Wells, Kent, *TN1 1DS.* **Open:** All year **01892 525580** V Constantine *reservations@valeroyalhotel.co.uk* www.valeroyalhotel.co.uk **D:** £32.50–£34.50 **S:** £45.00–£48.00 **Beds:** 2F 6D 6T 6S **Baths:** 20 En 🛇 🄿 (3) ⌨ 🌮 ⨯ 📺 ▦ 🌡 cc Situated in the lovely Spa Town, overlooking the common. All rooms undergone recent refurbishment and include direct dial telephones. Relax in the countryside, visit stately homes, formal gardens, close to M25 and Gatwick Airport.

66 Tunnel Road, Tunbridge Wells, Kent, *TN1 2BX.* Comfortable, modest accommodation. Centre beautiful town. Many interesting places nearby. **Open:** All year (not Xmas/New Year) **01892 529125** Mrs Harrison **D:** £16.00–£18.00 **S:** £17.00–£19.00 **Beds:** 1D **Baths:** 1 Sh ⌨ 📺 ▦

Ford Cottage, Linden Park Road, Tunbridge Wells, Kent, *TN2 5QL.* Picturesque and charming Victorian cottage, 3 mins' walk to Pantiles. **Open:** Feb to Nov **01892 531419** Mrs Cusdin *FordCottage@tinyworld.co.uk* **D:** £21.00–£25.00 **Beds:** 3T **Baths:** 2 En 1 Pr 🛇 (5) 🄿 (5) ⌨ 📺 📺 ▦ ⚬ 🌡

Ulcombe

TQ8448

Bramley Knowle Farm, Eastwood Road, Ulcombe, Maidstone, Kent, *ME17 1ET.* Modern farmhouse, 10 mins M20 J8, near Leeds castle. **Open:** All year (not Xmas) **01622 858878** D Leat **Fax:** 01622 851121 www.bramleyknowlefarm.co.uk **D:** £19.00–£22.50 **S:** £20.00–£25.00 **Beds:** 2D 1S **Baths:** 1 En 1 Sh 🛇 (3) 🄿 (6) ⌨ 📺 📺 ▦ 🌡

Upchurch

TQ8467

Suffield House, The Street, Upchurch, Sittingbourne, Kent, *ME9 7EU.* **Open:** All year (not Xmas) **Grades:** ETC 4 Diamond **01634 230409 & 07715 691683 (M)** Mr & Mrs Newbery **D:** £24.00 **S:** £24.00 **Beds:** 2D 1T 🛇 (10) 🄿 (10) ⌨ 📺 ⨯ 📺 ▦ 🌡 Suffield House - a Victorian house set in the rural village of Upchurch, between Rainham and Sittingbourne. Easy access to historic Faversham, Rochester and the Saxon Shore Way. Village pub and golf course. Warm and friendly welcome and a superb breakfast.

West Hougham

TR2540 🍺 *Marquis of Gramby*

Bramble Hill Cottage, Meggett Lane, West Hougham, Dover, Kent, *CT15 7BS.* Warm welcome, beautiful rural setting, 15 mins tunnel and ferries. **Open:** Mar to Nov **01303 253180** **D:** £18.00–£20.00 **Beds:** 1T 2D **Baths:** 2 En 1 Pr 🛇 🄿 📺 ▦ 🌡

West Peckham

TQ6452

Adams Well Cottage, Forge Lane, Gover Hill, West Peckham, Maidstone, Kent, *ME18 5JR.* Victorian county cottage, rural location, surrounded by half acre mature garden. **Open:** All year (not Xmas) **01732 851729 (also fax)** Mr & Mrs Higgs *adamswell@msn.com* **D:** £20.00 **S:** £23.00–£28.00 **Beds:** 2D 1S **Baths:** 1 Sh 🛇 (8) 🄿 (3) ⌨ 📺 🌡

National Grid References given are for villages, towns and cities – not for individual houses

Westerham

TQ4454

The Orchard House, Brasted Chart, Westerham, Kent, TN16 1LR. Family home, quiet, rural surroundings, near Chartwell, Hever, Knole, Gatwick. **Open:** All year (not Xmas) **Grades:** ETC 3 Diamond **01959 563702** Mrs Godsal *David.Godsal@ tesco.net* **D:** £22.50 **S:** £25.00 **Beds:** 2T 1S **Baths:** 2 Sh ☎ �🄿 (4) ⥶ ⊡ 🎟 ⚘

Holmesdale House, High Street, Brasted, Westerham, Kent, TN16 1HS. Delightful Victorian house (part C17th). Chartwell, Hever, Knole and mainline station. **Open:** All year **01959 564834 (also fax)** Mr Jinks **D:** £20.00– £29.00 **S:** £32.00–£45.00 **Beds:** 1F 3D 1T **Baths:** 3 En 1 Sh ☎ �🄿 (7) ⊡ ⒱ 🎟 ⚘ ⚘

Corner Cottage, Toys Hill, Westerham, Kent, TN16 1PY. Attractive self-contained accommodation in Laura Ashley fabrics. Spectacular panoramic views. **Open:** All year **01732 750362** Mrs Olszowska **Fax: 01959 561911** *olszowskiathome@jshmanco.com* **D:** £45.00–£50.00 **S:** £30.00–£35.00 **Beds:** 1F ☎ �🄿 (1) ⥶ ⊡ ⒱ 🎟 ⚘

Westwell

TQ9847

Dean Court Farm, Challock Lane, Westwell, Ashford, Kent, TN25 4NH. Period rural farmhouse, central for channel ports and touring Kent. **Open:** All year (not Xmas) **Grades:** ETC 3 Diamond **01233 712924** Mrs Lister **D:** £20.00–£25.00 **S:** £20.00–£25.00 **Beds:** 1D 2T **Baths:** 1 Sh ☎ �🄿 (3) ⊡ 🎟 ⚘

Whitfield

TR2945

Rolles Court, Church Whitfield Road, Whitfield, Dover, Kent, CT16 3HY. Country home 3 miles Dover. Picturesque gardens. Very friendly atmosphere. **Open:** All year **01304 827487** Mrs Montgomery **Fax: 01304 827877** *rollescourt@tesco.net* **D:** £25.00–£30.00 **S:** £25.00–£30.00 **Beds:** 1F 1T 1D 1S **Baths:** 4 En ☎ �🄿 ⥶ ⊡ ✕ ⒱ 🎟 ⚘

Whitstable

TR1066 🐦 Rose in Bloom

Alliston House, 1 Joy Lane, Whitstable, Kent, CT5 4LS. **Open:** All year **Grades:** ETC 3 Diamond **01227 779066** **D:** £22.50–£27.50 **S:** £35.00– £45.00 **Beds:** 3T 1D **Baths:** 1 En 1 Pr 2 Sh ☎ (14) �🄿 (4) ⥶ ⊡ ⒱ 🎟 ⚘ Whitstable, a pretty harbour town on the Saxon Shore. Famous for seafood restaurants and oysters. Your comfort is our priority. Tastefully decorated, pretty bedrooms and an excellent breakfast menu. Private parking. Special rates, 1st Nov - 1st April 2002 for 3-day stay or more, excluding Xmas.

Wingham

TR2357

Twitham Court Farm, Staple Road, Wingham, Canterbury, Kent, CT3 1LP. Enjoy our friendly, peaceful, comfortable farmhouse, organic breakfasts and beautiful gardens. **Open:** All year **01227 720265** M Duck & D Bowden **Fax: 01227 722177** *flower@twitham.fsnet.co.uk* **D:** £17.50–£30.00 **S:** £20.00–£35.00 **Beds:** 1F 2D 1T **Baths:** 2 En 1 Sh ☎ �🄿 (8) ⥶ ⊡ ⒱ 🎟 ⚘

The Dog Inn, Canterbury Road, Wingham, Canterbury, Kent, CT3 1BB. Quaint C13th village inn near historic Canterbury. Warm welcome. **Open:** All year **01227 720339 (also fax)** **D:** £25.00 **S:** £30.00 **Beds:** 2F 1T 3D **Baths:** 6 En ☎ �🄿 ⊡ ✕ 🎟 ⚘ cc

B&B owners may vary rates – be sure to check when booking

Planning a longer stay? Always ask for any special rates

Worth

TR3355

Ilex Cottage, Temple Way, Worth, Deal, Kent, CT14 0DA. Lovely, secluded C18th village house, guest conservatory, pretty rural views. **Open:** All year (not Xmas/New Year) **Grades:** ETC 4 Diamond **01304 617026** Mrs Stobie **Fax: 01304 620890** *info@ilexcottage.com* www.ilexcottage.com **D:** £20.00–£27.50 **S:** £30.00–£35.00 **Beds:** 1F 1T 1D **Baths:** 3 En ☎ �🄿 ⥶ ⊡ ✕ ⒱ 🎟 ⚘ ⚘ cc

Wouldham

TQ7164

Wouldham Court Farmhouse, 246 High Street, Wouldham, Rochester, Kent, ME1 3TY. Beamed Grade II Listed farmhouse, inglenook fireplace, overlooking River Medway. **Open:** All year (not Xmas) **Grades:** ETC 3 Diamond **01634 683271 (also fax)** Ms Parnell *wouldham.b-b@virgin.net* **D:** £22.00 **S:** £18.00– £22.00 **Beds:** 1F 1D 1S **Baths:** 2 Sh ☎ �🄿 (1) ⥶ ⊡ ✕ ⒱ 🎟 ⚘ cc

Wrotham

TQ6059 🐦 Rose & Crown, George & Dragon

Hillside House, Gravesend Road, Wrotham, Sevenoaks, Kent, TN15 7JH. Ideally situated for touring, Channel Ports, M20, M25, Gatwick, London. **Open:** All year (not Xmas/New Year) **Grades:** ETC 3 Diamond **01732 822564** J Thomas *clive@ broteham.freeserve.co.uk* **D:** £20.00–£22.00 **S:** £20.00–£25.00 **Beds:** 1T 1D 1S **Baths:** 1 Sh �🄿 (3) ⊡ 🎟 ⚘

Wye

TR0546

Mistral, 3 Oxenturn Road, Wye, Ashford, Kent, TN25 5BH. Comfortable and well appointed house, mature garden, secluded but readily accessible to Wye village. **Open:** Jan to Dec **01233 813011** Mr & Mrs Chapman **Fax: 01233813011** *geoff@chapman.invictanet.co.uk* www.wye.org **D:** £25.00 **S:** £25.00 **Beds:** 1T 1S **Baths:** 1 Sh ☎ �🄿 (2) ⥶ ⊡ 🎟 ⚘

Lancashire

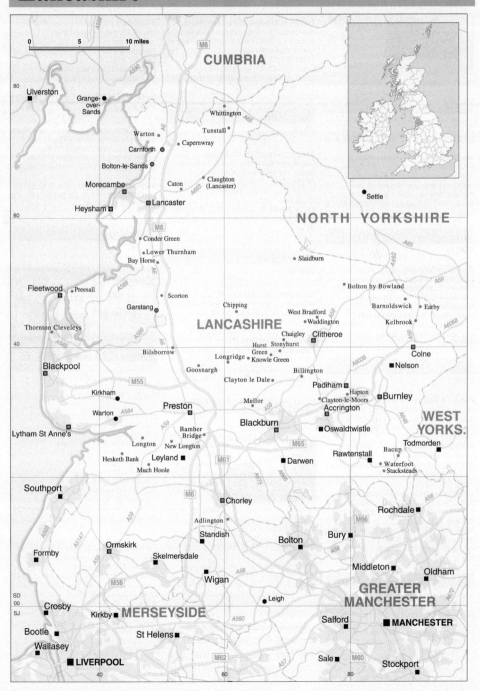

CUMBRIA

NORTH YORKSHIRE

LANCASHIRE

WEST
YORKS.

GREATER
MANCHESTER

MERSEYSIDE

0   5   10 miles

M6

80
Ulverston

Grange-
over-
Sands

Whittington

Warton   Tunstall
Carnforth   Capernwray

Bolton-le-Sands

Morecambe   Caton   Claughton
(Lancaster)

Heysham   Lancaster

Settle

60

M6

Conder Green

Lower Thurnham
Bay Horse

Slaidburn

Fleetwood   Preesall

Bolton by Bowland

Scorton

Garstang

Chipping

Barnoldswick   Earby

West Bradford
Waddington

Kelbrook

Thornton Cleveleys

LANCASHIRE

40

Chaigley   Clitheroe

Bilsborrow

Hurst   Stonyhurst
Green

Longridge   Knowle Green

Colne

Blackpool

Goosnargh

Billington

Nelson

Clayton le Dale

M55

Kirkham

Padiham
Hapton

Burnley

Clayton-le-Moors

Mellor

Accrington

Warton   A584

Preston

Blackburn

Oswaldtwistle

Lytham St Anne's

Longton   Bamber
Bridge   New Longton

Hesketh Bank   Leyland

Much Hoole

M65

Rawtenstall

Bacup

Todmorden

Darwen

Waterfoot
Stacksteads

M61

Southport

M6

Chorley

Rochdale

Adlington

M66

Standish

Bolton

Bury

Ormskirk

Formby

Skelmersdale

Middleton

Oldham

Wigan

M58

GREATER
MANCHESTER

SD
00
SJ

Crosby

Leigh

Kirkby   MERSEYSIDE

Salford

MANCHESTER

Bootle

Wallasey

St Helens

LIVERPOOL

M62

Sale   M60

Stockport

Accrington

SD7528

Maple Lodge Hotel, 70 Blackburn Road, Clayton-le-moors, Accrington, BB5 5JH. Friendly family-run licensed hotel off M65 J7. Home cooking. **Open:** All year **Grades:** ETC 3 Diamond
01254 301284 Fax: 01254 388152 maplelod@aol.com www.maplelodgehotel.co.uk
D: £25.00–£27.00 **S:** £35.00–£39.00 **Beds:** 2T 6D **Baths:** 8 En ⛻ 🖘 🅿 (8) ⊬ ⊠ ✕ ⊠ ▥ ♿ 🐾 cc

Wendys B&B, 139 Whalley Road, Accrington, Lancs, BB5 1BX. Friendly welcome; close to town centre and motorway networks. **Open:** All year
01254 871060 Mrs Walsh **D:** £18.00 **S:** £18.00 **Beds:** 2F 1T 1S **Baths:** 1 En 1 Sh ⛻ 🖘 🅿 ⊠ ✕ ⊠ ▥ 🐾

Adlington

SD6013

Briarfield House, Bolton Road, Anderton, Adlington, Chorley, Lancs, PR6 9HW. In own grounds, beautiful views over open countryside. Private parking. **Open:** All year
01257 480105 & 07831 651704 (M) Mrs Baldwin briarfieldhouse@aol.com **D:** £18.50 **S:** £22.50 **Beds:** 1D 2T **Baths:** 2 En 1 Pr ⛻ ⊬ ⊠ ⊠ ▥ 🐾

Bacup

SD8622

Pasture Bottom Farm, Bacup, Lancs, OL13 0UZ. Comfortable farmhouse B&B in a quiet rural area on a working beef farm. **Open:** All year (not Xmas) **Grades:** ETC 3 Diamond
01706 873790 (also fax) A Isherwood ha.isherwood@zen.co.uk **D:** £17.00–£18.00 **S:** £17.00–£18.00 **Beds:** 1D 2T **Baths:** 2 En 1 Pr 1 Sh ⛻ 🖘 🅿 (4) ⊬ ⊠ 🐾 ✕ ▥ 🐾

Oakenclough Farm, Oakenclough Road, Bacup, Lancashire, OL13 9ET. Peaceful farmhouse. Cast iron fires. **Open:** All year **Grades:** ETC 3 Star
01706 879319 & 07973 314489 (M) Mr & Mrs Worswick **Fax: 01706 879319** wharflenwickle@aol.com **D:** £29.00–£46.00 ⛻ 🖘 🅿 (4) ⊠ 🐾 ✕ ⊠ ▥ ✳ 🐾

Bamber Bridge

SD5626

Anvil Guest House, 321 Station Road, Bamber Bridge, Preston, Lancs, PR5 6EE. Comfortable, friendly, near junct M6, M61, M65. Central heating, TV lounge. **Open:** All year (not Xmas)
01772 339022 J C Arkwright **D:** £13.50 **S:** £15.00 **Beds:** 2F 4D 3T **Baths:** 2 Sh ⛻ ⊠ ▥ 🐾

Barnoldswick

SD8746

Foster's House, 203 Gisburn Road, Barnoldswick, Lancs, BB18 5JU. A warm welcome awaits at our beautiful home from home. **Open:** All year
01282 850718 Mr & Mrs Edwards www.hotpots.com/fostershouse.htm **D:** £20.00 **S:** £20.00 **Beds:** 2D 2T **Baths:** 3 En 1 Sh ⛻ 🖘 🅿 (4) ⊠ ⊠ ▥ 🐾

Bay Horse

SD4953

Stanley Lodge Farmhouse, Cockerham Road, Bay Horse, Lancaster, Lancs., LA2 0HE. Rural area, Lancaster canal nearby. Lakes, Yorkshire Dales, golfing, horse riding nearby. **Open:** All year (not Xmas/New Year)
01524 791863 **D:** £18.00–£20.00 **S:** £18.00–£20.00 **Beds:** 1F 2D **Baths:** 1 Sh ⛻ 🅿 (4) ⊠ ⊠ ▥ 🐾

Billington

SD7235

Rosebury, 51 Pasturelands Drive, Billington, Clitheroe, Lancs, BB7 9LW. Quality family accommodation, guest rooms overlook the beautiful Ribble Valley. **Open:** All year (not Xmas/New Year) **Grades:** ETC 3 Diamond
01254 822658 C P Hamer enquiries_rosebury@yahoo.co.uk www.rosebury-guest-house.co.uk **D:** £20.00–£22.50 **S:** £20.00–£22.50 **Beds:** 1F 1T **Baths:** 2 Sh ⛻ 🅿 ⊬ ⊠ 🐾 ⊠ ▥ 🐾

Bilsborrow

SD5139 🍺 Roebuck

Olde Duncombe House, Garstang Road, Bilsborrow, Preston, Lancs, PR3 0RE. **Open:** All year
Grades: ETC 3 Diamond
01995 640336 (also fax) Mr Bolton oldedunc@aol.com **D:** £22.50–£25.00 **S:** £35.00–£37.50 **Beds:** 1F 2T 5D 1S **Baths:** 9 En ⛻ 🅿 ⊠ ▥ 🐾 cc
An attractive, traditional, cottage style, family run bed and breakfast. It is believed to date back to the 1500s and that some of Bonnie Prince Charlie's men slept in the attached barn on the way back from the Battle of Preston.

National Grid References given are for villages, towns and cities – not for individual houses

Blackburn

SD6827

Shalom, 531b Livesey Branch Road, Blackburn, BB2 5DF. Luxurious accommodation in uniquely styled home. Hospitality second to none. **Open:** All year **Grades:** ETC 4 Diamond
01254 209032 (also fax) Mr Schofield paul@shalomblackburn.co.uk www.shalomblackburn. co.uk **D:** £22.00–£25.00 **S:** £22.00–£35.00 **Beds:** 1D 1T 1S **Baths:** 3 En ⛻ 🅿 (4) ⊬ ⊠ 🐾 ⊠ ▥ 🐾

The Chimneys, 139 Preston New Road, Blackburn, Lancs, BB2 6BJ. Family-run Victorian property, central location, comfortable accommodation, friendly service. **Open:** All year (not Xmas/New Year)
01254 665026 **D:** £18.00–£20.00 **S:** £18.00–£25.00 **Beds:** 2F 4T 3D 2S **Baths:** 2 En 3 Sh ⛻ 🅿 (8) ⊠ 🐾 ✕ ⊠ ▥ 🐾

Blackpool

SD3136

Raffles Hotel, 73-75 Hornby Road, Blackpool, Lancashire, FY1 4QJ. **Open:** All year **Grades:** ETC 3 Diamond
01253 294713 Fax: 01253 294240 www.raffleshotelblackpool.co.uk **D:** £21.00–£28.00 **S:** £27.00–£34.00 **Beds:** 2F 3T 11D 1S **Baths:** 17 En ⛻ 🅿 (6) ⊠ 🐾 ✕ ⊠ ▥ ♿ 🐾 cc
5 mins Winter Gardens, Theatre, Tower. ETC 3 Diamonds, licensed, parking, fully ensuite with colour TV, tea/coffee facilities, daily housekeeper. Imaginative choice menus. Full entry in the Good Hotel Guide 2000-2002. As featured on BBC's 'Summer Holiday'.

Fairway Hotel, 34/36 Hull Road, Blackpool, Lancs, FY1 4QB. **Open:** All year **Grades:** ETC 3 Diamond
01253 623777 Mr Hodges **Fax: 01253 753455** bookings@fairway.gb.com www.come.to/fairway **D:** £20.00–£25.00 **S:** £31.00–£33.00 **Beds:** 10F 8D **Baths:** 18 En ⛻ ⊠ ⊠ ▥ 🐾 cc
Family-run licensed hotel, close to Tower, Winter Gardens, shops and night life. No hidden extras. Deposit refundable if not satisfied on arrival. New Year breaks a speciality.

The Arncliffe Hotel, 24 *Osborne Road, South Shore, Blackpool, Lancs, FY4 1HJ.* **Open:** Mar to Jan **Grades:** ETC 3 Diamond **01253 345209 (also fax)** Mrs Wood *arncliffe.hotel@virgin.net* www.blackpool-internet.co. uk/HOMEarncliffe.html **D:** £14.00–£25.00 **S:** £14.00–£20.00 **Beds:** 1F 5D 1T 1S **Baths:** 5 En 1 Sh ⚡ 🅿 (3) 📺 ✕ 🆅 🖩 ❋ 🚲 **cc** Voted 'Hotel of the Year 2000' in Blackpool Tourism Awards. Small licensed, family-run hotel, catering for couples and families only. Close to Pleasure Beach, Promenade and all road/rail/air links. Discounted tickets available for Pleasure Beach, Tower and Zoo.

Pembroke Private Hotel, 11 *King Edward Avenue, Blackpool, Lancashire, FY2 9TD.* **Open:** Mar to Nov **Grades:** ETC 4 Diamond **01253 351306 (also fax)** *stay@ pembrokehotel.com* www.pembrokehotel.co **D:** £19.00–£25.00 **S:** £22.00–£28.00 **Beds:** 1F 2T 5D 3S **Baths:** 11 En 🅿 (6) 📺 ✕ 🆅 🖩 ❋ 🚲 **cc**
One of the very best small hotels in Blackpool, providing quality ensuite accommodation. Situated in a select area of North Shore, just off the Queen's Promenade and close to Gynn Gardens and North Shore Golf Course.

St Ives Hotel, 10 King George Avenue, North Shore, Blackpool, Lancs, FY2 9SN. **Open:** All year **01253 352122 (also fax)** Mrs Dempsey *june@ stiveshotel-blackpool.co.uk* **D:** £16.00–£22.00 **Beds:** 3F 4D 2T **Baths:** 5 En 4 Sh ⚡ (2) 🅿 (2) ✍ 📺 ✕ 🆅 🖩 ❋ 🚲 **cc**
A highly recommended hotel situated just off Queen's Promenade, within easy reach of all amenities, including golf course. Most rooms ensuite with tea/coffee making facilities and full central heating throughout. Excellent food and a high standard of cleanliness.

The Carlis Private Hotel, 34 Charnley Road, Blackpool, Lancs, FY1 4PF. **Open:** All year **01253 622586 (also fax)** Mrs Boyd *alan.boyd5@btinternet.com* www.carlis-hotel.co. uk **D:** £13.00–£25.00 **S:** £16.00–£30.00 **Beds:** 5F 9D 3T 2S **Baths:** 12 En 7 Sh ⚡ 📺 ✕ 🆅 🖩 🚲 **cc**
Licensed, good food and cleanliness assured. Central to beach, shops, shows, Tower and winter gardens. TV lounge, pool table. Hygiene certificate. Weekly rates from £69 B&B, e/s extra. All rooms have tea/coffee making facilities, central heating, TV.

May Dene Private Hotel, 10 Dean Street, Blackpool, Lancs, FY4 1AU. Clean, comfortable, 50 yards off Promenade. Close to entertainments and attractions. **Open:** All year **Grades:** ETC 3 Diamond **01253 343464** *may_dene_hotel@hotmail.com* www.blackpoolhotelmaydene.co.uk **D:** £21.00–£35.00 **S:** £25.00–£60.00 **Beds:** 14F 1T 4D **Baths:** 10 En 8 Pr 1 Sh ⚡ (0) 🅿 (8) 📺 🍴 ✕ 🆅 🖩 ❋ 🚲 **cc**

Wescoe Private Hotel, 14 Dean Street, Blackpool, Lancs, FY4 1AU. Quality hotel near to sea front. Friendly welcome and cleanliness assured. **Open:** All year **01253 342772** Ms McClelland *wescoe@ amserve.net* www.wescoehotel.co.uk **D:** £15.00–£26.00 **S:** £15.00–£26.00 **Beds:** 4F 1T 5D **Baths:** 8 En 1 Sh ⚡ 🅿 (4) 📺 🍴 ✕ 🆅 🖩 🚲 **cc**

Westcliffe Private Hotel, 46 King Edward Avenue, Blackpool, Lancs, FY2 9TA. Homely hotel in select area adjacent Queen's Promenade; comfort assured. **Open:** All year (not Xmas) **01253 352943** Mr Carter **D:** £18.00–£22.00 **S:** £18.00–£22.00 **Beds:** 2D 2T 3S **Baths:** 8 Pr ⚡ (7) 📺 ✕ 🆅 🖩 🚲

The Beverley Hotel, 25 Dean Street, Blackpool, Lancashire, FY4 1AU. Near Promenade, South Pier, Pleasure Beach, Sandcastle/Casino Leisure Complex. **Open:** All year **Grades:** ETC 3 Diamond **01253 344426** Mrs Yarnell *beverley.hotel@ virgin.net* beverleyhotel-blackpool.co.uk **D:** £17.00–£27.00 **S:** £20.00–£80.00 **Beds:** 1S 1T 5D 4F **Baths:** 11 En ⚡ 📺 ✕ 🆅 🖩 🚲 **cc**

Clarron House, 22 Leopold Grove, Blackpool, Lancs, FY1 4LD. Welcome Host Bronze graded. Adjacent Winter Gardens, theatres, shops, piers. **Open:** All year **01253 623748** Mr & Mrs O'Donnell **D:** £14.00–£21.00 **S:** £17.00–£24.00 **Beds:** 3F 4D 1T **Baths:** 6 En 1 Sh ⚡ 📺 ✕ 🆅 🖩 ❋ 🚲 **cc**

Trevine Hotel, 4 *Havelock Stret, Blackpool, FY1 4BN.* Perfectly situated for theatres, clubs, shopping and all main attractions. **Open:** All year **01253 620897** Mrs Ainsworth *trevine@btinternet.com* **D:** £16.00–£20.00 **S:** £18.00–£22.00 **Beds:** 4F 1T 4D 1S **Baths:** 10 En 10 Pr ⚡ 📺 ✕ 🆅 🖩 ❋ 🚲 **cc**

Langworthy House Hotel, 5 Lonsdale Road, Blackpool, Lancs, FY1 6EE. Family-run guest house. Children welcome. Licensed bar, centrally situated. **Open:** All year **01253 345914** Roger & Maggie Holdoway **D:** £12.00–£25.00 **S:** £12.00–£25.00 **Beds:** 5F 1T 4D **Baths:** 4 En 3 Sh ⚡ 🚲 🖩 🚲

Astoria Hotel, 118-120 Albert Road, Blackpool, Lancs, FY1 4PN. Excellent food & accommodation, all ensuite with satellite TV. Adjacent Winter Gardens, shops & theatres. **Open:** All year **01253 621321** Ann Brown **Fax: 01253 293203** *astoria.hotel@cableinet.co.uk* **D:** £19.00–£29.00 **S:** £19.00–£29.00 **Beds:** 12F 13D 1T 2S **Baths:** 28 En ⚡ 🅿 (4) 📺 ✕ 🆅 🖩 ❋ 🚲 **cc**

Wilmar, 42 Osborne Road, Blackpool, Lancs, FY4 1HQ. Situated close to Promenade and all Blackpool's amenities. Cleanliness Award. **Open:** All year (not Xmas/New Year) **Grades:** AA 3 Diamond, RAC 3 Diamond **01253 346229** Mrs Hyde **D:** £17.50–£25.00 **S:** £25.00–£35.00 **Beds:** 1F 1T 4D 1S **Baths:** 6 En 1 Sh 📺 ✕ 🆅 🖩 🚲

Grasmere Hotel, 51 Palatine Road, Blackpool, FY1 4BX. Friendly, family-run hotel. Good food and a warm welcome. **Open:** All year **01253 294887** *dave.jill@ukonline.co.uk* **D:** £15.00–£22.00 **S:** £15.00–£22.00 **Beds:** 4F 2T 2D **Baths:** 2 En 3 Sh ⚡ 🚲 ✕ 🖩 🚲

Cresta Hotel, 85 Whithnell Road, Blackpool, FY4 1HE. Family-run, all ensuite hotel adjacent to the pleasure beach. **Open:** All year **Grades:** ETC 3 Diamond **0800 0745584 (also fax)** J Snelson *john@ snelly.co.uk* www.snelly.co.uk **D:** £14.00–£25.00 **S:** £16.00–£25.00 **Beds:** 1F 4D 3S **Baths:** 8 En ⚡ 🅿 (3) 📺 ✕ 🆅 🖩 🚲 **cc**

Thistledome Guest House, 67 Alexandra Road, Blackpool, FY1 6HW. Small, friendly. 2 mins promenade between Central and South Piers. **Open:** Easter to Nov **01253 408787** Mrs Jackson **D:** £13.00–£15.00 **S:** £14.00 **Beds:** 2F 4D 2S **Baths:** 2 En 2 Sh ⚡ 📺 🆅 🚲

Dale House, *16 Dale Street, Blackpool, FY1 6EE.* Friendly house. Central location near sea front. Home cooked food, personal service. **Open:** All year
01253 620548 (also fax) D: £15.00–£18.00 **S:** £15.00–£18.00 **Beds:** 2F 3D 1T **Baths:** 3 En 1 Pr 1 Sh ⛟ ▣ (3) 📺 ➤ ✕ 📺 ▥ ✱ ♨

Summerville Guest House, *132 Albert Road, Blackpool, FY1 4PN.* A guest house in the centre of town. Free brochure! **Open:** All year (not Xmas)
01253 621300 Mr & Mrs Nichol *avril@ summerville132.freeserve.co.uk*
www.summerville132.freeserve.co.uk
D: £13.00–£19.00 **S:** £13.00–£19.00 **Beds:** 3F 3D 1T 1S **Baths:** 1 En 1 Sh ⛟ ▣ (2) 📺 ✕ 📺 ▥

Beachcomber Hotel, *78 Reads Avenue, Blackpool, FY1 4DE.* Comfortable centrally situated hotel; all rooms ensuite, off-road parking. **Open:** All year **Grades:** ETC 3 Diamond
01253 621622 Mr & Mrs Mcphail **Fax:** 01253 299254 *beachcomber@euphony.net* **D:** £18.00– £24.00 **S:** £18.00–£24.00 **Beds:** 2F 4D 3T 1S **Baths:** 10 En ⛟ ▣ (10) 📺 ➤ ✕ 📺 ▥ ♨ **cc**

The Hatton, *10 Banks Street, Blackpool, Lancs, FY1 1RN.* Ideally situated 3 doors from Promenade adjacent North Pier. **Open:** All year
01253 624944 (also fax) Mrs Bliss
www.hattonhotel.com **D:** £16.00–£30.00 **S:** £20.00–£35.00 **Beds:** 4F 2T 6D **Baths:** 12 En ⛟ 📺 ✕ 📺 ♨

Lynton House, *24 St Bedes Avenue, Blackpool, Lancs, FY4 1AQ.* Family guest house, close to all amenities, Piers, shops, Promenade. **Open:** All year
01253 345784 D Halloran **D:** £10.00–£20.00 **S:** £10.00–£20.00 **Beds:** 6F 2T 5D 1S **Baths:** 2 En 2 Sh ⛟ 📺 ✕ 📺 ▥ ♨ **cc**

Kingsway Hotel, *68 Charnley Road, Blackpool, Lancs, FY1 4PF.* Small family-run hotel. **Open:** All year
01253 627696 Mr Armstrong **D:** £20.00– £40.00 **S:** £30.00–£50.00 **Beds:** 4F 2T 10D **Baths:** 16 En ⛟ (1) ▣ (10) 📺 ➤ ✕ 📺 ♨ **cc**

The Belgrave Hotel, *313-315 South Promenade, Blackpool, Lancs, FY1 6AN.* Rooms with sea views. Late bar. Winter cabarets. Xmas/New Year parties. Breakfast upto 10am. **Open:** All year
01253 346581 Mr Woolley **D:** £22.00–£30.00 **S:** £25.00–£32.00 **Beds:** 5F 5T 28T 1S **Baths:** 40 En ⛟ ▣ (27) 📺 ➤ ✕ 📺 ▥ ✱ ♨ **cc**

Robin Hood Hotel, *100 Queens Promenade, Blackpool, Lancs, FY2 9NS.* A quality no smoking hotel overlooking the Irish Sea. **Open:** Easter to Nov **Grades:** ETC 3 Diamond
01253 351599 www.robinhoodhotel.co.uk
D: £18.50–£26.50 **S:** £20.50–£28.50 **Beds:** 3F 1T 6D **Baths:** 10 Pr ✓ ✕ 📺 ▥ ♨ **cc**

Berwick Hotel, *23 King Edward Avenue, Blackpool, Lancs, FY2 9TA.* Small, friendly. No smoking. Home cooking, choice breakfast. Adjacent promenade. **Open:** All year **Grades:** ETC 3 Diamond
01253 351496 *chris@berwickhotel.fsnet.co.uk*
D: £17.00–£21.00 **S:** £20.00–£24.00 **Beds:** 1F 2T 5D **Baths:** 8 En ⛟ ▣ (4) ✓ 📺 ✕ 📺 ▥ ♨ ✱ **cc**

Sandylands Guest House, *47 Banks Street, North Shore, Blackpool, Lancashire, FY1 2BE.* Clean, comfortable, good food, friendly. Ideal for over 40s. **Open:** Mar to Nov
01253 294670 D: £13.00–£15.00 **S:** £13.00– £15.00 **Beds:** 1F 5D 2S **Baths:** 1 Sh ⛟ (8) 📺 ✕ ♨

Ashcroft Hotel, *42 King Edward Avenue, Blackpool, Lancashire, FY2 9TA.* Select North Shore area. 2 mins from Queen's Promenade tram stops. **Open:** All year (not Xmas/New Year) **Grades:** ETC 3 Diamond
01253 351538 *dave@ ashcroftblackpool.freeserve.co.uk*
www.smoothhound.co.uk/hotels/ashcroft. html **D:** £19.00–£23.00 **S:** £19.00–£23.00 **Beds:** 2F 1T 4D 3S **Baths:** 7 En 2 Sh ⛟ 📺 ✕ ▥

Sheron House, *21 Gynn Avenue, Blackpool, Lancs, FY1 2LD.* In a word - 'Quality'. Good food, good company, comfortable bed! **Open:** Feb to Dec
01253 354614 D. Atkinson & S. Fellows
sheronhouse@amserve.net
www.usefulblackpool.com/ghouses/sheron
D: £16.50–£22.00 **S:** £16.50–£27.00 **Beds:** 2F 1T 3D **Baths:** 6 En ⛟ 📺 ✕ 📺 ▥ ✱ ♨ **cc**

Regency Hotel, *50 Charnley Road, Blackpool, Lancs, FY1 4PE.* Family-run hotel ideally situated in heart of Blackpool. Near shops, Tower, Winter Gardens, Promenade. **Open:** All year (not Xmas/New Year)
01253 625186 (also fax) Mr Wyers
regency.hotel@talk21.com **D:** £14.00–£35.00 **S:** £20.00–£45.00 **Beds:** 8F 9D **Beds:** 14 En 2 Sh ⛟ (1) ▣ (3) 📺 ✕ 📺 ♨ **cc**

Cherry Blossom Hotel, *2 Warley Road Corner, North Promemade, Blackpool, FY1 2JU.* Large Victorian house, overlooking Irish sea, 15-bedroom hotel with large public bar. **Open:** All year
01253 355533 Fax: 01253 355534 **D:** £17.00– £30.00 **S:** £17.00–£30.00 **Beds:** 4F 4D 6T 1S **Baths:** 15 En ⛟ ▣ (14) 📺 ▥ ♨ **cc**

The Blue Royale, *11 Charles Street, Blackpool, FY1 3HD.* Small friendly guest house caters for all. **Open:** All year
01253 628107 D: £13.00–£20.00 **S:** £13.00– £20.00 **Beds:** 3F 4D 3T 1S **Baths:** 4 En 1 Pr ⛟ 📺 ➤ ✕ 📺 ♨

Granville Hotel, *12 Station Road, Blackpool, Lancashire, FY4 1BE.* Close to pleasure beach, South Pier, and all amenities etc. **Open:** Easter to Nov
01253 343012 Mr Taylor **Fax:** 01253 408594 *wilft@thegranvillehotel.co.uk* **D:** £18.00–£26.00 **S:** £19.00–£26.00 **Beds:** 5F 5D 2S **Baths:** 11 En 1 Pr ⛟ ▣ (2) 📺 ✕ 📺 ▥ ♨ **cc**

Bolton by Bowland

SD7849   🍺 *Duke of York, Coach & Horses*

Middle Flass Lodge, *Settle Road, Bolton by Bowland, Clitheroe, Lancashire, BB7 4NY.* Idyllic countryside location. Chef prepared cuisine. Cosy rooms. Friendly welcome. **Open:** All year **Grades:** ETC 4 Diamond, AA 4 Diamond
01200 447259 Mrs Simpson **Fax:** 01200 447300 *info@middleflasslodge.fsnet.co.uk*
mflodge.freeservers.com **D:** £22.00–£30.00 **S:** £28.00–£36.00 **Beds:** 1F 2D 2T **Baths:** En ⛟ ▣ (24) ✓ 📺 ✕ 📺 ▥ ♨ **cc**

Burnley

SD8332

Eaves Barn Farm, *Hapton, Burnley, Lancs, BB12 7LP.* Luxuriously furnished farmhouse, individually styled deluxe bedrooms. Excellent breakfast. **Open:** All year (not Xmas/New Year) **Grades:** AA 4 Diamond
01282 771591 (also fax) Butler **D:** £22.50– £25.00 **S:** £26.00–£30.00 **Beds:** 1T 1D 1S **Baths:** 3 En ⛟ (10) ▣ (8) ✓ 📺 ✕ 📺 ♨

Windsor House, *71 Church Street, Padiham, Burnley, Lancs, BB12 8JH.* Large family-run Victorian house, with a huge Lancashire welcome. **Open:** All year (not Xmas)
01282 773271 Mrs Stinton **D:** £18.00 **S:** £18.00 **Beds:** 1D 3T 3S **Baths:** 1 Pr 3 Sh ⛟ (10) ▣ (8) ✓ 📺 ✕ 📺 ▥ ♨

Capernwray

SD5371

Capernwray House, *Capernwray, Carnforth, Lancs, LA6 1AE.* Beautiful country house. Panoramic views. Tastefully decorated throughout. Close Lakes, Dales, Lancaster. **Open:** All year (not Xmas) **Grades:** ETC 4 Diamond, Silver
01524 732363 (also fax) Mrs Smith
thesmiths@capernwrayhouse.com **D:** £22.00– £24.00 **S:** £22.00–£30.00 **Beds:** 2D 1T 1S **Baths:** 3 En 1 Sh ⛟ (5) ▣ (8) ✓ ✕ 📺 ▥ ♨ **cc**

Carnforth

SD4970   🍺 *Wheatsheaf Hotel, Craven Heifer*

Galley Hall Farm, *Shore Road, Carnforth, Lancashire, LA5 9HZ.* C17th farm house, lovely coastal and Lakeland views and friendly welcome. **Open:** All year (not Xmas/New Year) **Grades:** ETC 4 Diamond
01524 732544 V Casson **D:** £18.00 **S:** £18.00 **Beds:** 1T 1D 1S **Baths:** 1 Sh ✓ 📺 ➤ 📺 ▥ ♨

High Bank, Hawk Street, Carnforth, Lancs., *LA5 9LA.* Charming Victorian house. Panoramic views. Convenient for M6. RSPB lakes. **Open:** All year **Grades:** ETC 4 Diamond **01524 733827 D:** £19.00 **S:** £19.00–£22.00 **Beds:** 1F 2T 1D **Baths:** 2 Sh ⌁ ▤ (4) ⌁ ⊡ ▥ ⌁

Capernwray House, Capernwray, Carnforth, Lancs, *LA6 1AE.* Beautiful country house. Panoramic views. Tastefully decorated throughout. Close Lakes, Dales, Lancaster. **Open:** All year (not Xmas) **Grades:** ETC 4 Diamond, Silver **01524 732363 (also fax)** Mrs Smith *thesmiths@capernwrayhouse.com* www.capernwrayhouse.com **D:** £22.00–£24.00 **S:** £22.00–£30.00 **Beds:** 2D 1T 1S **Baths:** 3 En 1 Sh ⌁ (5) ▤ (8) ⌁ ⊡ × ▥ ⌁ cc

26 Victoria Street, Carnforth, Lancs, *LA5 9ED.* Small, homely B&B adjacent canal walk. 6 miles Lancaster or Morecambe. **Open:** All year (not Xmas/New Year) **01524 732520** D Dickinson **D:** £15.00 **S:** £16.00 **Beds:** 1F 1T **Baths:** 1 Sh ⌁ ▤ (2) ⊡ ▥ ▥ ⌁

Caton
SD5364

Kilcredan, 14 Brookhouse Road, Caton, Lancaster, Lancashire, *LA2 9QT.* Friendly welcome set in the Lune Valley. Ideal for walking. **Open:** All year **01524 770271** Miss Beattie **D:** £18.00 **S:** £18.00 **Beds:** 1F 1D 1T 1S **Baths:** 1 En 1 Sh ⌁ ▤ (3) ⊡ ⌁ ▥ ⌁

Chaigley
SD6941

Rakefoot Farm, Chaigley, Clitheroe, Lancs, *BB7 3LY.* Peacefully situated, ideal touring (motorway 8 miles). Holiday/business. Farmhouse meals. **Open:** All year **Grades:** ETC 4 Diamond **01995 61332** P Gifford **Fax:** 01995 61296 **D:** £16.50–£20.50 **S:** £16.50–£25.00 **Beds:** 3F 2T 4D 1S **Baths:** 6 En 2 Pr 1 Sh ⌁ ▤ (10) ⊡ ⌁ × ▥ ⌁

Chipping
SD6243

Carrside Farm, Chipping, Preston, Lancs, *PR3 2TS.* Working sheep farm with hill views in the forest of Bowland. **Open:** All year **01995 61590** J Cowgill **D:** £25.00–£30.00 **S:** £25.00–£30.00 **Beds:** 1D 1F 1S **Baths:** 2 En 1 Pr 1 Sh ⌁ (5) ▤ (8) ⌁ ⊡ ⌁ ▥ ⌁

Chorley
SD5817

Crowtress Cottage Guest House, 190 Preston Road, Chorley, Lancashire, *PR6 7AZ.* C18th country cottage complemented by Lancashire hospitality. **Open:** All year **01257 269380** J Wrenall **D:** £20.00–£30.00 **S:** £25.00 **Beds:** 1D 1T 1S **Baths:** 1 En 1 Sh

Claughton (Lancaster)
SD5666

Low House Farm, Claughton, Lancaster, Lancs., *LA2 9LA.* Working mixed dairy farm in the heart of the picturesque Lune Valley. **Open:** All year (not Xmas/New Year) **015242 21260** Mrs Harvey *shirley@lunevalley.freeserve.co.uk* **D:** £20.00 **S:** £20.00–£25.00 **Beds:** 1F 1D 1S **Baths:** 1 En 1 Pr 1 Sh ⌁ ▤ (4) ⌁ ⊡ ⌁ ▥ ⌁

Clayton Le Dale
SD6733

2 Rose Cottage, Longsight Road, Clayton le Dale, Blackburn, Lancs, *BB1 9EX.* Picturesque cottage, gateway to Ribble Valley. Comfortable, fully equipped rooms. **Open:** All year **01254 813223** M Adderley **Fax:** 01254 813831 *bbrose.cott@talk21.com* www.smoothhound.co.uk/hotels/rosecott.html **D:** £20.00 **S:** £24.00 **Beds:** 2D 1T **Baths:** 3 En 1 Pr ▤ (4) ⊡ ⌁ ▥ ⌁ cc

Clayton-le-Moors
SD7431

Maple Lodge Hotel, 70 Blackburn Road, Clayton-le-moors, Accrington, *BB5 5JH.* Friendly family-run licensed hotel off M65 J7. Home cooking. **Open:** All year **Grades:** ETC 3 Diamond **01254 301284 Fax:** 01254 388152 *maplelod@aol.com* www.maplelodgehotel.co.uk **D:** £25.00–£27.00 **S:** £35.00–£39.00 **Beds:** 2T 6D **Baths:** 8 En ⌁ ▤ (8) ⌁ × ▥ ⌁ & ⌁ cc

Clitheroe
SD7441

Brooklands, 9 Pendle Road, Clitheroe, Lancs, *BB7 1JQ.* Breakfasts cooked the way you like them. Town centre nearby, A59 half mile. **Open:** All year **Grades:** ETC 3 Diamond **01200 422797 & 07713 021505 (M)** J Lord **Fax:** 01200 422797 *kenandjean@tesco.net* www.s-h-systems.co.uk/hotels/brookland.html **D:** £18.00–£20.00 **S:** £20.00–£25.00 **Beds:** 1D 2T **Baths:** 2 En 1 Sh ⌁ ▤ (5) ⊡ ⌁ ▥ ⌁

Selborne House, Back Commons, Kirkmoor Road, Clitheroe, Lancs, *BB7 2DX.* Detached house on quiet lane giving peace and tranquillity. Excellent for walking, birdwatching, fishing. **Open:** All year **Grades:** ETC 3 Diamond **01200 423571 & 01200 422236** J V Barnes **Fax:** 01200 423571 *judithv.barnes@lineone.net* ribblevalleyguesthouse.com **D:** £20.00 **S:** £22.50 **Beds:** 3D 1T **Baths:** 4 En ⌁ (1) ▤ (4) ⊡ ⌁ ▥ ⌁

Colne
SD8940

Wickets, 148 Keighley Road, Colne, Lancs, *BB8 0PJ.* Edwardian family home overlooking open countryside, comfortable and attractive bedrooms. **Open:** All year (not Xmas) **01282 862002** Mrs Etherington **Fax:** 01282 859675 *wickets@colne148.fsnet.co.uk* **D:** £18.00–£21.00 **S:** £18.00–£22.00 **Beds:** 1D 1T 1S **Baths:** 1 En 1 Pr 1 Sh ⌁ (11) ▤ (1) ⌁ ⊡ ▥ ⌁

Conder Green
SD4656

Stork Hotel, Conder Green, Lancaster, Lancashire, *LA2 0AN.* Traditional country inn 3 miles from Lancaster and close to Glasson Dock. **Open:** All year **01524 751234** A Cragg **D:** £20.00 **S:** £24.50 **Beds:** 1F 3D 3T 2S **Baths:** 9 Pr ⌁ ▤ (20) ⊡ ⌁ × ▥ ⌁

Earby
SD9046 ⬧ *Punch Bowl*

Grange Fell, Skipton Road, Earby, Colne, Lancs, *BB8 6JL.* Edwardian family home, split-level accommodation, private and comfortable rooms. **Open:** Easter to Sept **01282 843621** I Eden **Fax:** 01282 842193 **D:** £18.00 **Beds:** 1F **Baths:** 1 Pr ⌁ ▤ ⌁ ⊡ ▥ ⌁

Fleetwood
SD3247

Chavock Guest House, 116 London Street, Fleetwood, Lancs, *FY7 6EU.* Licensed guest house. **Open:** All year (not Xmas/New Year) **01253 771196 (also fax)** Mr McEvoy *suemcevoy@justtalk21.com* **D:** £14.00–£19.00 **S:** £15.00–£20.00 **Beds:** 1F 2D 1S 1T **Baths:** 1 En ⌁ ▤ ⊡ ⌁ × ▥ ⌁

Please respect a B&B's wishes regarding children, animals and smoking

B&B owners may vary rates – be sure to check when booking

Garstang
SD4945

Guys Thatched Hamlet, *Canal Side, Garstang, Preston, Lancs, PR3 0RS.* Picturesque thatched hamlet complex with country-style tavern and continental restaurant. **Open:** All year (not Xmas) **01995 640010** R Wilkinson **Fax: 01995 640141** *guyshamlet@aol.com* www.guysthatchedhamlet.co.uk **D:** £21.00–£24.00 **S:** £42.50–£52.00 **Beds:** 8F 10T 50D **Baths:** 68 En ♿ ⊞ (200) ⊡ ⊁ ⅹ ♥ ⊞ ৬ ♨ cc

Sandbriggs, *Lancaster Road, Garstang, Preston, Lancs, PR3 1JA.* Comfortable, convenient, secluded private house and gardens with secure parking. **Open:** All year **01995 603080 (also fax)** Mr Wilkinson **D:** £15.00–£18.00 **S:** £15.00 **Beds:** 1D 2T **Baths:** 1 Pr 2 Sh ♿ (4) ⊞ (10) ⊡ ♥ ⊞ ♨

Goosnargh
SD5536

Isles Field Barn, *Syke House Lane, Goosnargh, Preston, Lancs, PR3 2EN.* Spacious accommodation surrounded by beautiful countryside. Hearty breakfast, friendly welcome. **Open:** All year **01995 640398** Mr McHugh **D:** £20.00 **S:** £20.00 **Beds:** 1F 1D 1T **Baths:** 3 En ♿ ⊞ (6) ⊡ ♥ ⊞ ♨

Hapton
SD7931

Eaves Barn Farm, *Hapton, Burnley, Lancs, BB12 7LP.* Luxuriously furnished farmhouse, individually styled deluxe bedrooms. Excellent breakfast. **Open:** All year (not Xmas/New Year) **Grades:** AA 4 Diamond **01282 771591 (also fax)** Butler **D:** £22.50–£25.00 **S:** £26.00–£30.00 **Beds:** 1T 1D 1S **Baths:** 3 En ♿ (10) ⊞ (8) ⊁ ⊡ ⅹ ⊞ ♨

Hesketh Bank
SD4423

The Becconsall Hotel, *25 Station Road, Hesketh Bank, Preston, PR4 6SP.* Friendly local pub/restaurant in semi-rural location. **Open:** All year **01772 815313 D:** £17.50 **S:** £22.50 **Beds:** 3D ⊞ (20) ⊡ ⅹ ♥ ⊞ ♨ cc

Heysham
SD4161

It'll Do, *15 Oxcliffe Road, Heysham, Morecambe, Lancs., LA3 1PR.* Ideal for touring Lake District, Heysham Port. Lancaster M6. **Open:** Jan to Dec **01524 850763** Mrs Peter **D:** £14.00 **S:** £15.00 **Beds:** 1T 1D **Baths:** 1 Sh ♿ ⊞ (4) ⊡ ♥ ⊞ ♨

Hurst Green
SD6838

Shireburn Arms Hotel, *Whalley Road, Hurst Green, Clitheroe, Lancs, BB6 9QJ.* A warm friendly welcome, excellent inn and restaurant, unrivalled views. **Open:** All year **01254 826518** S J Alcock **Fax: 01254 826208** *sales@shireburnarms.fsnet.co.uk* www.shireburn-hotel.co.uk **D:** £32.50–£42.50 **S:** £45.00–£65.00 **Beds:** 1S 2F 12D 3T **Baths:** 18 En ♿ ⊞ (50) ⊁ ⊡ ♥ ⅹ ♥ ⊞ ✿ ♨ cc

Knowle Green
SD6338   ⊟ *New Drop Inn*

Oak Lea, *Clitheroe Road, Knowle Green, Longridge, Preston, Lancs, PR3 2YS.* Ribble Valley Victorian country house, gardens, views, welcoming family atmosphere. **Open:** All year (not Xmas/New Year) **Grades:** ETC 4 Diamond **01254 878486 (also fax)** Mrs Mellor **D:** £21.00–£24.00 **S:** £21.00–£26.00 **Beds:** 2T 1D 1S **Baths:** 2 En 1 Pr ♿ ⊞ (4) ⊁ ⊡ ♥ ♨

Lancaster
SD4761

Lancaster Town House, *11/12 Newton Terrace, Caton Road, Lancaster, Lancashire, LA1 3PB.* Award-winning guest house, close to city centre, minutes from M6 J34. **Open:** All year **01524 65527** Mrs Hedge-Holmes *hedge-holmes@talk21.com* www.lancastertownhouse.co.uk **D:** £20.00–£25.00 **S:** £25.00 **Beds:** 1F 3D 1T 3S **Baths:** 8 En ♿ ⊞ ⊡ ♥ ⊞ ♨ cc

Longridge
SD6037

14 Whittingham Road, *Longridge, Preston, Lancs, PR3 2AA.* Homely, hearty breakfasts, scenic area, walking, sports, shopping, motorway accessibility. **Open:** All year **01772 783992** D Morley **D:** £18.00 **S:** £18.00 **Beds:** 1F 1T 1S **Baths:** 1 Sh ♿ ⊞ (4) ⊡ ♥ ⊞ ♨

Please respect a B&B's wishes regarding children, animals and smoking

Planning a longer stay? Always ask for any special rates

Longton
SD4726   ⊟ *Fish Inn, Midge Hall*

Willow Cottage, *Longton Bypass, Longton, Preston, Lancs, PR4 4RA.* Old cottage set in beautiful gardens and countryside with its own horse stud farm. **Open:** All year (not Xmas/New Year) **01772 617570** Caunce *info@lancashirebedandbreakfast.co.uk* www.lancashirebedandbreakfast.co.uk **D:** £23.00–£24.00 **S:** £24.00–£25.00 **Beds:** 2T 3D 4S **Baths:** 1 En 1 Sh ♿ (14) ⊞ (8) ⊁ ⊡ ♥ ⊞ ♨

Lower Thurnham
SD4655

Thurnham Mill Hotel, *Thurnham, Lancaster, LA2 0BD.* Located in the heart of a picturesque and historical area close to Lancaster. **Open:** All year **01524 752852 Fax: 01524 752477 D:** £27.25 **S:** £39.50 **Beds:** 6F 3T 8D **Baths:** 17 En ♿ ⊞ (80) ⊁ ⊡ ♥ ⅹ ♥ ⊞ ৬ ♨ ♨ cc

Lytham St Annes
SD3327

Monarch Hotel, *29 St Annes Road East, Lytham St Annes, Lancs, FY8 1TA.* Clean, comfortable hotel with great food, licensed. Aromatherapy, reflexology available. **Open:** All year (not Xmas) **Grades:** ETC 3 Diamond **01253 720464** Mr Churchill *churchill@monarch91.freeserve.co.uk* www.monarch-st-annes.co.uk **D:** £21.00–£27.00 **S:** £21.00–£27.00 **Beds:** 2F 2D 3T 3S **Baths:** 7 En 1 Pr ♿ ⊞ (8) ⊡ ⅹ ♥ ⊞ ♨

Sea Croft Hotel, *5 Eastbank Road, Lytham St Annes, Lancs, FY8 1ND.* A warm welcome in friendly, family-run licensed hotel adjacent to promenade and town centre. **Open:** All year (not Xmas) **01253 721806 (also fax)** Mrs Bradshaw *seacrofthotel@aol.com* www.sea-croft.co.uk **D:** £20.00–£21.00 **S:** £15.00–£22.00 **Beds:** 5F 1D 1T 2S **Baths:** 8 En 1 Sh ♿ ⊞ (5) ⊡ ⅹ ♥ ⊞ ♨

Harcourt, *21 Richmond Road, Lytham St Annes, Lancs, FY8 1PE.* Small private family hotel, town centre. 200 yds to beach and attractions. **Open:** All year **01253 722299 D:** £16.00–£19.00 **S:** £16.00–£18.00 **Beds:** 3F 3D 1T 3S **Baths:** 5 En 5 Sh ♿ ⊞ (6) ⊡ ♥ ⊞ ♨

Mellor

SD6531

2 Rose Cottage, *Longsight Road, Clayton le Dale, Blackburn, Lancs, BB1 9EX.* Picturesque cottage, gateway to Ribble Valley. Comfortable, fully equipped rooms. **Open:** All year **01254 813223** M Adderley **Fax: 01254 813831** *bbrose.cott@talk21.com* www.smoothhound.co.uk/hotels/rosecott.html **D:** £20.00 **S:** £24.00 **Beds:** 2D 1T **Baths:** 3 En 1 Pr ♥ 🏠(4) 📺 ✿ 📺 ⬛, ♨ cc

Morecambe

SD4364

Harwood House Hotel, *1 Chatsworth Road, Westminster Road, Morecambe, Lancs, LA4 4JG.* Central for Lakes, Lune Valley. 2 mins' walk from sea front, licensed. **Open:** All year **01524 412845** J R Whitworth **Fax: 01524 409138** *hhhotel@supanet.com* www.harwoodhousehotel.co.uk **D:** £15.00–£22.00 **S:** £15.00–£22.00 **Beds:** 1F 2T 6D 4S **Baths:** 2 En 1 Pr 2 Sh ♥ (4) 📺 ✿ ✕ 📺 ⬛, ♨

The Trevelyan, *27 Seaview Parade, West End Road, Morecambe, Lancs, LA4 4DJ.* Comfortable guest house. Glorious Morecambe Bay. Ideal touring base. **Open:** All year **Grades:** ETC 3 Diamond **01524 412013** G Catterall *thetrevelyan@supanet.com* www.thetrevelyan.freeserve.co.uk **D:** £15.00–£17.50 **S:** £15.00 **Beds:** 2F 1T 4D 4S **Baths:** 1 En 4 Sh ♥ 🏠 📺 ✕ 📺 ⬛, ♨

Roxbury, *78 Thornton Road, Morecambe, Lancashire, LA4 5PJ.* Small, friendly family hotel, quiet but close to all amenities. **Open:** All year **01524 410561** Ms Gerrard **Fax: 01524 420286** *ritall@bigfoot.com* **D:** £18.00–£19.00 **S:** £17.00–£19.00 **Beds:** 1F 1T 2D 3S **Baths:** 6 En 1 Sh ♥ (0) 📺 ✿ ✕ 📺 ⬛, ♨

Westleigh Licensed Hotel, *9 Marine Road, Morecambe, Lancs, LA3 1BS.* Overlooks Morecambe Bay and Lakeland **Open:** All year (not Xmas/New Year) **Grades:** ETC 3 Diamond **01524 418352** Mr & Mrs Harrison **D:** £17.00 **S:** £17.00 **Beds:** 7T 4D 3S **Baths:** 14 En 📺 ✿ ✕ 📺 ⬛, ♨

The Channings, *455-456 Marine Road East, Morecambe, Lancs, LA4 6AD.* Victorian building, tastefully modernised. Situated on Promenade. Leisure centres adjacent. **Open:** All year **Grades:** ETC 2 Diamond **01524 417925** *channings.hotel@ukgateway.net* www.channingshotel.co.uk **D:** £19.00–£23.00 **S:** £21.00–£25.00 **Beds:** 4F 2T 9D 4S **Baths:** 17 En 2 Sh ♥ 🏠 📺 ✿ ✕ 📺 ⬛ cc

Warwick Hotel,

394 Marine Road East, Morecambe, Lancs, LA4 5AN. Non-smoking hotel overlooking bay and South Lakeland Hills. Victorian terraced property on the promenade. **Open:** All year (not Xmas/New Year) **01524 418151** A & A Leach **Fax: 01524 427235 D:** £23.00–£27.00 **S:** £25.00–£30.00 **Beds:** 3T 7D 3S **Baths:** 13 Pr 🏠 ✂ 📺 ⬛, ♨

Much Hoole

SD4723

The Barn Guest House, *204 Liverpool Old Road, Much Hoole, Preston, Lancs., PR4 4QB.* Semi rural location off the A59 between Preston and Southport. **Open:** All year (not Xmas/New Year) **Grades:** ETC 3 Diamond **01772 612654** L Gabbott **D:** £20.00–£22.50 **S:** £25.00–£27.50 **Beds:** 1F 1T 1S **Baths:** 2 Sh ♥ 🏠 (3) 📺 ✿ ⬛, ♨

New Longt

SD5125 🍺 *Farmers' Arms, Midge Hall*

Pleasant View, *Long Moss Lane, New Longton, Preston, Lancs, PR4 4XN.* Warm welcome, quiet area, close motorways, overlooking fields/gardens. **Open:** All year (not Xmas/New Year) **01772 615863** *sarah@dalgleish615.freeserve.co.uk* **D:** £23.00–£26.00 **S:** £30.00–£35.00 **Beds:** 2T **Baths:** 2 Pr 🏠 (3) ✂ 📺 📺 ⬛, ♨

Ormskirk

SD4108

The Meadows, New Sutch Farm, *Sutch Lane, Ormskirk, Lancashire, L40 4BU.* Beautiful C17th farmhouse. Ground floor guest rooms. Excellent breakfasts. **Open:** All year (not Xmas) **01704 894048 D:** £19.50 **S:** £22.00 **Beds:** 2D 1S **Baths:** 2 En 1 Pr 📺 📺 ⬛, ♿ ♨

Padiham

SD7933

Windsor House, *71 Church Street, Padiham, Burnley, Lancs, BB12 8JH.* Large family-run Victorian house, with a huge Lancashire welcome. **Open:** All year (not Xmas) **01282 773271** Mrs Stinton **D:** £18.00 **S:** £18.00 **Beds:** 1D 3T 3S **Baths:** 1 Pr 3 Sh ♥ (10) 🏠 (8) ✂ 📺 ✕ 📺 ⬛, ♨

Preesall

SD3647

Townfoot Cottage, *Back Lane, Preesall, Poulton le Fylde, Lancs, FY6 0NG.* Country cottage, comfortable accommodation, good food, picturesque setting, relaxing break. **Open:** All year (not Xmas/New Year) **01253 812681** C Richards **D:** £17.00–£19.00 **S:** £20.00–£25.00 **Beds:** 1F 1D **Baths:** 1 Sh ♥ (3) ✂ 📺 ⬛, ♨

Preston

SD5329

Stanley Guest House, *7 Stanley Terrace, Preston, PR1 8JE.* 5 mins' walk to town centre, overlooking quiet bowling area. **Open:** All year **01772 253366 Fax: 01772 252802** *stanley.guest.house@prestonlancs.freeserve.co.uk* www.prestonlancs.freeserve.co.uk **D:** £16.00–£18.00 **S:** £20.00–£25.00 **Beds:** 3F 2D 2S **Baths:** 2 En 1 Sh ♥ 🏠 (5) 📺 ✿ ✕ 📺 ⬛, ♨ cc

Scorton

SD5049

Woodacre Hall Farm, *Scorton, Preston, Lancs., PR3 1BN.* Working farm built in the late 1600s, comfortable and friendly. **Open:** Easter to Nov **01995 602253 (also fax)** Ms Whitaker **D:** £17.00–£19.00 **S:** £22.00–£22.00 **Beds:** 2D 1T **Baths:** 2 En 1 Pr 🏠 (4) 📺 ✿ ✕ ♨

Slaidburn

SD7152 🍺 *Hark to Bounty*

Pages Farm, *Woodhouse Lane, Slaidburn, Clitheroe, Lancs, BB7 3AH.* A friendly welcome in the beautiful Bowland countryside. **Open:** All year (not Xmas) **Grades:** ETC 3 Diamond **01200 446205** M Cowking *pagesfarm@freeuk.com* **D:** £18.50–£20.00 **S:** £20.00 **Beds:** 1F 1T 1D **Baths:** 3 En ♥ 🏠 📺 ✕ 📺 ⬛, ♨

Stacksteads

SD8421

Glen Heights, *190 Booth Road, Stacksteads, Bacup, Lancs, OL13 0TH.* Warm welcome. Near motorways, Ski Rossendale, steam railways, hillwalking. **Open:** All year (not Xmas/New Year) **01706 875459** D Graham **D:** £16.00 **S:** £19.50 **Beds:** 1T 1D 1S **Baths:** 1 Sh ♥ (3) 🏠 (3) 📺 ✿ ✕ 📺 ⬛, ♨

Stonyhurst

SD6939

Alden Cottage, *Kemple End, Birdy Brow, Stonyhurst, Clitheroe, Lancashire, BB7 9QY.* Luxury accommodation in an idyllic C17th beamed cottage. **Open:** All year (not Xmas/New Year) **01254 826468** Mrs Carpenter *carpenter@aldencottage.f9.co.uk* **D:** £24.50 **S:** £25.50 **Beds:** 1T 2D **Baths:** 1 En 2 Pr 🏠 (3) ✂ 📺 📺 ⬛, ♨

Thornton Cleveleys
SD3442

Beacholme Guest House, *38 Beach Road, Thornton Cleveleys, Lancs, FY5 1EQ.* Small, friendly, non-smoking guest house, close to tramline and seashore. **Open:** All year
01253 855350 *beach_holme@hotmail.com*
D: £15.00 **S:** £15.00 **Beds:** 2D 1T 2S **Baths:** 1 En 1 Sh �� (2) ⌇ 🕾 ✗ 🅅 ▥ ⅋ ❄ ♨

Esperance Villa Guest House, *30 Ellerbeck Road, Thornton-Cleveleys, Lancs, FY5 1DH.* Family-run hotel, close to shops, Blackpool and Fleetwood bingo and clubs.
Open: All year (not Xmas/New Year)
01253 853513 Mrs Duckett **D:** £15.00–£17.00 **S:** £15.00–£17.00 **Beds:** 1F 4D 1T 1S **Baths:** 2 Sh ⌁ ⓟ (3) 🕾 ✗ 🅅 ▥ ♨

Tunstall
SD6073   🍴 *Lunesdale Arms*

Barnfield Farm, *Tunstall, Kirkby Lonsdale, Carnforth, Lancs, LA6 2QP.* 1702 family farmhouse on a 200-acre working farm. **Open:** All year (not Xmas/New Year)
015242 74284 (also fax) J Stephenson
D: £17.00–£17.50 **S:** £17.50–£20.00 **Beds:** 1F 1D **Baths:** 1 Sh ⌁ ⓟ (2) ⌇ 🕾 🅅 ▥ ♨

Waddington
SD7243   🍴 *Duke of York, Moorcock*

Peter Barn Country House, *Cross Lane, Waddington, Clitheroe, Lancs, BB7 3JH.* Explore Ribble Valley then sink into sumptuous sofas! Home-made jams.
Open: All year (not Xmas/New Year)
Grades: ETC 4 Diamond
01200 428585 Mrs Smith *jean@ peterbarn.fsnet.co.uk* **D:** £25.00–£26.00 **S:** £29.00 **Beds:** 1T 2D **Baths:** 2 En 1 Pr ⌁ (12) ⓟ (6) ⌇ 🕾 🅅 ▥ ♨

Backfold Cottage, *The Square, Waddington, Clitheroe, Lancs, BB7 3JA.* Luxury mini country hotel. **Open:** All year
01200 422367 D Forbes **D:** £21.00–£23.00 **S:** £21.00–£31.00 **Beds:** 1T 1D 1S **Baths:** 3 En ⌁ (5) ⓟ (4) 🕾 🍴 ✗ 🅅 ▥

Moorcock Inn, *Slaidburn Road, Waddington, Clitheroe, Lancs, BB7 3AA.* A warm welcome awaits at this friendly country inn. **Open:** All year
01200 422333 F M Fillary **D:** £30.00–£35.00 **S:** £38.00–£42.00 **Beds:** 3D 8T **Baths:** 11 Pr ⌁ ⓟ (150) 🕾 🍴 ✗ 🅅 ▥ ♨ cc

Warton
SD5072

Cotestone Farm, *Sand Lane, Warton, Carnforth, Lancs, LA5 9NH.* Near Leighton Moss RSPB Reserve, Lancaster/ Morecambe, Lakes & Dales. **Open:** All year (not Xmas)
01524 732418 G Close **D:** £16.00 **S:** £17.00 **Beds:** 1F 1D 1T 1S **Baths:** 2 Sh ⌁ ⓟ (4) 🕾 🍴 🅅 ▥ ♨

Waterfoot
SD8322

729 Bacup Road, *Waterfoot, Rossendale, Lancs, BB4 7EU.* In the heart of the picturesque Rossendale Valley. Food everyday. **Open:** All year
01706 214493 P Stannard **Fax: 01706 215371** *info@theroyal-hotel.co.uk* www.theroyal-hotel. co.uk **D:** £23.50–£30.00 **S:** £25.00–£35.00 **Beds:** 1F 5D 2T 5S **Baths:** 13 En ⌁ ⓟ (10) 🅅 🍴 ✗ 🅅 ▥ ♨ cc

West Bradford
SD7444   🍴 *Buck Inn, Duke of York*

Old Hall, *Back Lane, West Bradford, Clitheroe, Lancs, BB7 4SN.* Elegant friendly family home in own grounds near Ribble Way. **Open:** All year (not Xmas/New Year)
01200 423282 E H Gretton *argettm@aol.com* **D:** £19.00–£20.00 **S:** £20.00–£22.00 **Beds:** 2T 1S **Baths:** 1 Sh ⌁ ⓟ (4) ⌇ 🅅 🍴 ▥ ♨

Whittington
SD6076

The Dragon's Head, *Main Street, Whittington, Carnforth, LA6 2NY.* Small country pub in Lune Valley 2 miles west of Kirkby Lonsdale, B6254. **Open:** All year
015242 72383 **D:** £20.00–£25.00 **S:** £20.00–£25.00 **Beds:** 1F 1D 1S **Baths:** 1 Sh ⌁ (5) ⓟ (10) 🕾 🍴 ✗ ▥ ♨

Leicestershire

Planning a longer stay? Always ask for any special rates

Ab Kettleby
SK7222

White Lodge Farm, Nottingham Road, *Ab Kettleby, Melton Mowbray, Leicestershire, LE14 3JB.* Farm buildings tastefully converted into self-contained rooms overlooking garden. **Open:** All year **01664 822286** Mrs Spencer **D:** £19.00 **S:** £22.00 **Beds:** 1F 1D 1T **Baths:** 3 En ⌕ (9) ▣ (4) ⌖ ⊡ ▥ ☆

Appleby Magna
SK3110

Ferne Cottage, 5 Black Horse Hill, *Appleby Magna, Swadlincote, Derbyshire, DE12 7AQ.* C18th beamed cottage in Appleby Magna, quiet historic village. Lace making tuition by arrangement. **Open:** All year (not Xmas) **01530 271772** G A Bird **Fax: 01530 270652** **D:** £17.00–£25.00 **S:** £17.00–£25.00 **Beds:** 1F 1D 1T 1S **Baths:** 1 En 1 Sh ⌕ ▣ (5) ⊡ ⌖ ⊻ ▥ ☆

Appleby Parva
SK3109

Elms Farm, Atherstone Road, Appleby *Parva, Swadlincote, Leicestershire, DE12 7AG.* Pleasant farmhouse in rural position within 1.5 miles of M42. **Open:** All year (not Xmas) **01530 270450** Ms Frisby **D:** £20.00–£22.00 **S:** £20.00–£22.00 **Beds:** 1D 1T 1S **Baths:** 2 En 1 Pr ⌕ (4) ▣ (4) ⊡ ▥ ☆

Asfordby
SK7019   ⬤ Blue Bell, Crown Inn

Amberley, 4 Church Lane, Asfordby, *Melton Mowbray, Leics, LE14 3RU.* Beautiful riverside bungalow. Idyllic floodlit lawns/ gardens. Enjoy breakfast in garden room. **Open:** All year **Grades:** ETC 4 Diamond **01664 812314** B P Brotherhood **Fax: 01664 813740** doris@amberleygardens.net www.amberleygardens.net **D:** £19.00–£25.00 **S:** £20.00–£25.00 **Beds:** 1T 1D 1S **Baths:** 3 En ⌕ (14) ▣ ⌖ ⊡ ▥ ⬤ ☆

Barkestone-le-Vale
SK7834   ⬤ Windmill Inn

Little Orchard, Chapel Street, *Barkestone-le-Vale, Nottingham, NG13 0HE.* Pretty village bungalow near Belvoir Castle, Nottingham, Metro and Motorway. **Open:** All year (not Xmas/New Year) **01949 842698** M A Fisher **D:** £18.00 **S:** £18.00 **Beds:** 1T 1D **Baths:** 1 Pr ⌕ ▣ (3) ⊡ ⊻ ▥ ⬤ ☆

Belton
SK4420

George Hotel, 17 Market Place, Belton, *Loughborough, Leics, LE12 9UH.* Old C18th coaching inn. **Open:** All year (not Xmas/ New Year) **01530 222426** thegeorgehotelbelton@hotmail.com www.thegeorgehotelbelton.com **D:** £50.00– £60.00 **S:** £30.00–£45.00 **Beds:** 2F 8T 8D 4S **Baths:** 15 En 7 Sh ⌕ ▣ ⊡ ✕ ⊻ ▥ ⬤ ☆ cc

Coalville
SK4214

Church Lane Farm House, Ravenstone, Coalville, Leicester, LE67 2AE. Queen Anne farmhouse. Interior designer and artist's home, antique furnishings throughout. **Open:** All year (not Xmas) **Grades:** ETC 4 Diamond, AA 4 Diamond **01530 810536 & 01530 811299** Mrs Thorne annthorne@ravenstone-guesthouse.co.uk www.ravenstone-guesthouse.co.uk **D:** £27.50– £31.50 **S:** £29.50–£35.00 **Beds:** 2D 2T **Baths:** 4 En ▣ (6) ⌖ ⊡ ⌖ ✕ ⊻ ☆

Cosby
SP5494

The Vineries, Cosby, Leicester, LE9 1UL. Lovely period house in 1.5 acre gardens. All rooms tastefully furnished, overlooking gardens, countryside. **Open:** All year (not Xmas/New Year) **01162 2750817** Mrs Warren **D:** £25.00–£27.50 **S:** £35.00 **Beds:** 2D 1S **Baths:** 3 En ⌕ (16) ▣ (8) ⌖ ✕ ⊻ ▥ ☆

Foxton
SP7089

The Old Manse, Swingbridge Street, *Foxton, Market Harborough, Leics, LE16 7RH.* Period house in conservation village. Canals, locks, local inns nearby. **Open:** All year (not Xmas) **Grades:** ETC 4 Diamond, Silver **01858 545456** Mrs Pickering **D:** £23.00 **S:** £32.00 **Beds:** 3T/D **Baths:** 3 En ⌕ ▣ (6) ⌖ ⊡ ⊻ ▥ ☆

RATES

D = Price range per person sharing in a double or twin room

S = Price range for a single room

Goadby
SP7598

The Hollies, Goadby, Leicester, LE7 9EE. Beautiful Listed house in quiet village in pretty Leicestershire countryside. **Open:** All year (not Xmas) **Grades:** ETC 3 Diamond **0116 259 8301** Mrs Parr **Fax: 0116 259 8491** j.parr@btinternet.com **D:** £22.50 **S:** £25.00 **Beds:** 1F 1D 1S **Baths:** 1 En 1 Sh ⌕ (5) ▣ (3) ⌖ ⊡ ⌖ ▥ ☆

Great Dalby
SK7414

Dairy Farm, 8 Burrough End, Great Dalby, *Melton Mowbray, Leics, LE14 2EW.* Working dairy farm 30 minutes from Leicester, Nottingham, 5 mins Melton. **Open:** All year **01664 562783** Mrs Parker **D:** £18.00–£20.00 **S:** £20.00 **Beds:** 2D 1T **Baths:** 2 En 1 Pr ⌕ ▣ (5) ⊡ ⌖ ⊻ ▥ ☆

Grimston
SK6821

Gorse House, Main Street, Grimston, *Melton Mowbray, Leicestershire, LE14 3BZ.* Extended C17th cottage, well furnished attractive garden, in quiet conservation village. **Open:** All year **01664 813537 (also fax)** Mr & Mrs Cowdell cowdell@gorsehouse.co.uk www.gorsehouse.co. uk **D:** £20.00–£25.00 **S:** £20.00–£25.00 **Beds:** 1F 1T 1D **Baths:** 2 En 1 Sh ⌕ (12) ▣ (4) ⌖ ⊡ ⊻ ▥ ☆

Hathern
SK5022

Leys Guest House, Loughborough Road, Hathern, Loughborough, Leics, *LE12 5JB.* Situated in small village. Close to Derbyshire, Leicestershire and Nottinghamshire. **Open:** All year **01509 844373 (also fax)** Mrs Hudson leysab3@mail.com.uk **D:** £17.00–£19.00 **S:** £17.00–£19.00 **Beds:** 2F 2T 2S **Baths:** 2 En 2 Sh ⌕ ▣ (8) ⊡ ⌖ ✕ ⊻ ▥ ⬤ ☆ cc

Hinckley
SP4294

The Guest House, 45 Priesthills Road, *Hinckley, Leics, LE10 1AQ.* Edwardian period house set in quiet pleasant area of Hinckley. **Open:** All year (not Xmas) **01455 619720 & 01455 446602** S Farmer priest@hills45.freeserve.co.uk **D:** £20.00 **S:** £22.00 **Beds:** 3T 1S **Baths:** 2 Sh 1 En ⌖ ⊡ ▥ ☆

Kirby Muxloe

SK5104

Faith Cottage, *400 Ratby Lane, Kirby Muxloe, Leicester, Leics, LE9 9AQ.* Quaint spotlessly clean cottage type accommodation, easy access to M1. **Open:** All year (not Xmas) **0116 238 7435** Mrs Saunders *faithcottage@ netscapeonline.co.uk* www.faithcottage.co.uk **D:** £22.00 **S:** £22.00 **Beds:** 2T 1S **Baths:** 1 En 1 Pr ⛤ (7) ▣ (6) ⚡ ☑ ▥ ♨

Kirkby Bellars

SK7117

Tole Cottage, *10 Main Street, Kirby Bellars, Melton Mowbray, Leicestershire, LE14 2EA.* Charming early C19th cottage, inspirational garden, rooms containing unique decorative effects. Picturesque Wreake Valley. **Open:** All year **01664 812932 & 07748 924617 (M)** *michael@ handjean.freeserve.co.uk* **D:** £20.00–£21.00 **S:** £25.00 **Beds:** 1F 1D 1S **Baths:** 1 En 1 Sh ⛤ (7) ▣ (3) ⚡ ☑ ✕ ☑ ▥ ♨

Leicester

SK5804   🍴 *Merry Monarch, Old Horse, Varsity*

Cumbria Guest House, *16 Westcotes Drive, Leicester, LE3 0QR.* Friendly accommodation. One mile city centre, two miles from M1 and M69. **Open:** All year (not Xmas/New Year) **0116 254 8459** Mrs Ball **D:** £15.00–£17.00 **S:** £18.00–£20.00 **Beds:** 4T 4S **Baths:** 1 Sh ⛤ ▣ (1) ☞ ☑ ▥ ♨

The Craft Hotel, *3 Stanley Road, Leicester, LE2 1RF.* Situated close to the city centre, Leicester University and De Montfort Hall. **Open:** All year **0116 270 3220** *crofthotel@hotmail.com* **D:** £17.50–£22.50 **S:** £25.00–£35.00 **Beds:** 3F 6T 2D 1S **Baths:** 7 En 4 Sh ▣ (18) ☑ ☞ ✕ ▥ ❄ ♨ cc

Craigleigh Hotel, *17-19 Westleigh Road, Leicester, LE3 0HH.* Victorian house, pleasant location, close to city and sports venues. **Open:** All year (not Xmas) **0116 254 6875 (also fax)** S T Pattison **D:** £19.00–£22.00 **S:** £18.00–£28.00 **Beds:** 4D 3T 4S **Baths:** 8 En 2 Sh ☑ ☑ ▥ ♨ cc

Long Clawson

SK7227

Elms Farm, *52 East End, Long Clawson, Melton Mowbray, Leics, LE14 4NG.* Warm comfortable old farmhouse village setting in Vale of Belvoir. **Open:** All year (not Xmas) **01664 822395** Mrs Whittard **Fax: 01664 823399** *jwhittard@ukonline.co.uk* **D:** £17.00–£21.00 **S:** £18.00–£26.00 **Beds:** 1F 1D 1S **Baths:** 1 En 1 Sh ⛤ ▣ (4) ⚡ ☑ ✕ ☑ ▥ ♨

Loughborough

SK5319

Peachnook Guest House, *154 Ashby Road, Loughborough, Leics, LE11 3AG.* Ideally situated 5 miles from all amenities. Good breakfast, vegetarian/ vegan catered for. **Open:** All year **Grades:** ETC 2 Diamond **01509 264300 & 01509 217525** Ms Wood www.smoothhound.co.uk/hotels/peachno. html **D:** £19.00–£22.50 **S:** £15.00–£30.00 **Beds:** 2F 2D 2T 1S ⛤ (5) ☑ ♨

New Life Guest House, *121 Ashby Road, Loughborough, Leics, LE11 3AB.* Family-run Victorian villa. 5 minutes centre, university, M1. Parking outside house. **Open:** All year **Grades:** ETC 3 Diamond **01509 216699** Mrs Burnard **Fax: 01509 210020** *jean-of-newlife@assureweb.com* **D:** £23.00–£25.00 **S:** £18.00–£25.00 **Beds:** 1F 1T 2S **Baths:** 2 En 1 Sh ⛤ ⚡ ☑ ☑ ▥ ❄ ♨

Charnwood Lodge Guest House, *136 Leicester Road, Loughborough, Leics, LE11 2AQ.* Spacious Victorian licensed guest house in quiet surroundings, 5 mins town centre. **Open:** All year (not Xmas) **Grades:** ETC 3 Diamond **01509 211120** Mrs Charwat **Fax: 01509 211121** *charnwoodlodge@charwat.freeserve.co.uk* www.charnwoodlodge.com **D:** £20.00–£35.00 **S:** £30.00–£45.00 **Beds:** 2F 1T 4D 1S **Baths:** 6 En ⛤ ▣ (8) ☑ ☞ ✕ ☑ ▥ & ♨ cc

Measham

SK3312

Laurels Guest House, *17 Ashby Road, Measham, Swadlincote, Derbyshire, DE12 7JR.* High class accommodation. Rural surroundings. Orchard, pond. Parking. Motorway access. **Open:** All year **01530 272567 (also fax)** Mrs Evans *evanslaurels@onetel.net.uk* www.thelaurelsguesthouse.com **D:** £22.00–£25.00 **S:** £22.00–£25.00 **Beds:** 1D 2T **Baths:** 2 En 1 Pr ⛤ (1) ▣ (8) ☑ ☑ ▥ ♨

Measham House Farm, *Gallows Lane, Measham, Swadlincote, Derbyshire, DE12 7HD.* Large Georgian farmhouse on working farm close to heart of the National Forest. **Open:** All year (not Xmas) **01530 270465 (also fax)** Mr Lovett **D:** £21.00 **S:** £21.00 **Beds:** 1F 2T **Baths:** 3 En 1 Pr ⛤ ▣ (20) ⚡ ☑ ☞ ☑ ▥ ♨

Planning a longer stay? Always ask for any special rates

Please respect a B&B's wishes regarding children, animals and smoking

Medbourne

SP7993

Medbourne Grange, *Nevill Holt, Market Harborough, Leics, LE16 8EF.* Comfortable farmhouse with breathtaking views; quiet location and heated pool. **Open:** All year (not Xmas) **01858 565249** Mrs Beaty **Fax: 01858 565257** **D:** £20.00–£22.00 **S:** £20.00–£25.00 **Beds:** 2D 1T **Baths:** 1 Sh 2 En ⛤ ▣ (6) ⚡ ☑ ✕ ▥ ♨

Melton Mowbray

SK7519

Shoby Lodge Farm, *Shoby, Melton Mowbray, Leics, LE14 3PF.* **Open:** All year (not Xmas/New Year) **Grades:** ETC 4 Diamond **01664 812156** Mrs Lomas **D:** £20.00–£22.00 **S:** £25.00 **Beds:** 1T 2D **Baths:** 2 En 1 Pr ▣ (6) ⚡ ☑ ☑ ▥ ♨

Assured a warm welcome. Relax in the comfortable lounge with open log fire. Enjoy the garden and unspoilt countryside beyond from the conservatory. Ideally situated for Ragdale Hall, Six Hills Golf, Jet-Ski, Prestwold Hall for the Ferrari experience.

Amberley, *4 Church Lane, Asfordby, Melton Mowbray, Leics, LE14 3RU.* Beautiful riverside bungalow. Idyllic floodlit lawns/gardens. Enjoy breakfast in garden room. **Open:** All year **Grades:** ETC 4 Diamond **01664 812314** B P Brotherhood **Fax: 01664 813740** *doris@amberleygardens.net* www.amberleygardens.net **D:** £19.00–£25.00 **S:** £20.00–£25.00 **Beds:** 1T 1D 1S **Baths:** 3 En ⛤ (14) ▣ ⚡ ☑ ▥ & ♨

Kirmel Guesthouse, *23 Mill Street, Melton Mowbray, Leics, LE13 1AY.* Competitively priced first class accommodation situated close to all amenities. **Open:** All year **01664 564374** Mrs Hardy **D:** £19.00–£25.00 **S:** £20.00 **Beds:** 1T 1S 1F 1D **Baths:** 1 Sh 1 En ⛤ ▣ ⚡ ☑ ☞ ☑ ▥ ❄ ♨

The Noel Arms, *31 Burton Street, Melton Mowbray, Leics, LE13 1AE.* Ensuite B&B. Real ale. Clean, friendly atmosphere. **Open:** All year **01664 562363** Mrs Ling **D:** £17.50 **S:** £17.50 **Beds:** 2F 2T 2S **Baths:** 4 En ⛤ ▣ ☑ ☞ ▥ ♨

Mountsorrel

SK5814

Barley Loft Guest House, *33a Hawcliffe Road, Mountsorrel, Loughborough, Leics, LE12 7AQ.*
Open: All year
01509 413514 Mrs Pegg **D:** £19.00–£20.00 **S:** £19.00–£23.00 **Beds:** 2F 1D 1T 2S **Baths:** 2 Sh ⬧ 🖪 (12) 📺 ⛤ 📺 📖 & ⚲
Spacious bungalow close A6 Leicester/ Loughborough, 10 mins M1. Quiet location, riverside walks, historical attractions. Comfortable working base: guests' fridge, microwave, toaster, with 24-hour use of dining area. Excellent nearby takeaways, supermarket, pubs, restaurants. Traditional hearty breakfast from 7am.

Nailstone

SK4107

Glebe Farm, *Rectory Lane, Nailstone, Nuneaton, Warks, CV13 0QQ.* Comfortable farmhouse on working farm near Bosworth Battlefield and Mallory Park. **Open:** All year (not Xmas)
01530 260318 Mrs Payne **D:** £16.00 **S:** £16.00 **Beds:** 1D 1T 1S **Baths:** 2 Sh ⬧ 🖪 (5) ⚲ 📺 📺 📖.

Oaks in Charnwood

SK4716

St Josephs, *Abbey Road, Oaks in Charnwood, Coalville, Leics, LE67 4UA.* Old country house where hosts welcome you to their home. **Open:** Apr to Oct
01509 503943 Mrs Havers *m.havers@virgin.net* **D:** £20.00 **S:** £20.00 **Beds:** 2T 1S **Baths:** 1 Sh ⬧ 🖪 (3) ⚲ 📺 📺 📖.

Lubcloud Farm, *Charley Road, Oaks in Charnwood, Loughborough, Leics, LE12 9YA.* Organic working dairy farm. Peaceful rural location on Charnwood Forest. **Open:** All year
01509 503204 Mr & Mrs Newcombe **Fax:** 01509 651267 www.lubcloudbednbreakfast. co.uk **D:** £20.00–£22.00 **S:** £22.50–£25.00 **Beds:** 1F 2D **Baths:** 3 En ⬧ 🖪 (10) ⚲ 📺 📖. ⚲

Osgathorpe

SK4219

The Royal Oak Guest House, *20 Main Street, Osgathorpe, Loughborough, Leicestershire, LE12 9TA.* High standard picturesque countryside. Secured parking, close M1, M42, EM Airport. **Open:** All year
01530 222443 V A Jacobs **D:** £20.00–£22.50 **S:** £30.00–£35.00 **Beds:** 2T 1D **Baths:** 3 En ⬧ 🖪 (50) ⚲ 📺 ✕ 📺 📖 & ⚲

Queniborough

SK6412 ⬧ *Britannia Inn, Horse & Groom*

Three Ways Farm, *Melton Road, Queniborough, Leicester, Leics, LE7 3FN.* Comfortable and attractive bungalow surrounded by fields. Good food and beds. **Open:** All year (not Xmas/New Year) **Grades:** ETC 3 Diamond
0116 260 0472 J S Clarke **D:** £19.00–£20.00 **S:** £19.00–£20.00 **Beds:** 1F 1T 1D 1S **Baths:** 1 Sh ⬧ (5) 🖪 (6) 📺 ⛤ 📺 📖 & ⚲

Ratcliffe Culey

SP3299

Manor Farm, *Ratcliffe Culey, Atherstone, Warks, CV9 3NY.* Victorian house located in small quiet friendly village in beautiful countryside. **Open:** All year
01827 712269 Mrs Trivett *jane@ousbey.com* **D:** £17.00–£18.00 **S:** £20.00 **Beds:** 3D **Baths:** 2 Sh ⬧ 🖪 (3) ⚲ 📺 ⛤ ✕ 📖. ⚲ cc

Ravenstone

SK4013

Church Lane Farm House, *Ravenstone, Coalville, Leicester, LE67 2AE.* Queen Anne farmhouse. Interior designer and artist's home, antique furnishings throughout. **Open:** All year (not Xmas) **Grades:** ETC 4 Diamond, AA 4 Diamond
01530 810536 & 01530 811299 Mrs Thorne *annthorne@ravenstone-guesthouse.co.uk* www.ravenstone-guesthouse.co.uk **D:** £27.50–£31.50 **S:** £29.50–£35.00 **Beds:** 2D 2T **Baths:** 4 En 🖪 (6) ⚲ 📺 ⛤ ✕ 📺 ⚲

Saddington

SP6591 ⬧ *Queen's Head*

Breach Farm, *Shearsby Road, Saddington, Leicester, Leics, LE8 0QU.* Modern comfortable farmhouse. Panoramic views. Breakfast served in large conservatory. **Open:** All year
0116 240 2539 Mrs Thornton **D:** £18.00–£20.00 **S:** £20.00 **Beds:** 1T 2D **Baths:** 1 Sh ⬧ 🖪 ⚲ 📺 📺 📖. ⚲

Shearsby

SP6290

The Greenway, *Knaptoft House Farm, Bruntingthorpe Road, Shearsby, Lutterworth, Leics, LE17 6PR.* Farmhouse B&B at its best. Set deep in Leicestershire countryside. **Open:** All year (not Xmas/New Year)
0116 247 8388 (also fax) Mr Hutchinson *info@knaptoft.com* www.knaptoft.com **D:** £21.00–£24.00 **S:** £27.00–£38.00 **Beds:** 2D 1T **Baths:** 2 Pr 1 Sh ⬧ (5) 🖪 (5) ⚲ 📺 📺 📖. ⚲ cc

Sheepy Magna

SK3201

Elmsdale, *Ratcliffe Lane, Sheepy Magna, Atherstone, Leicestershire, CV9 3QY.* **Open:** All year (not Xmas)
01827 718810 & 07973 506979 (M) Mrs Calcott *sue@elmsdalehouse.fsnet.co.uk* **D:** £18.00 **S:** £18.00 **Beds:** 1F 2S **Baths:** 1 Sh ⬧ 🖪 (5) ⚲ 📺 ⛤ 📺 📖. ⚲
Modern family farmhouse set in 200 acres of farmland. River and pool fishing, clay pigeon shooting (by arrangement) country paths. A warm welcome awaits you. Well equipped rooms with extras.

Shoby

SK6820 ⬧ *Crown Inn, Bell Inn, Black Horse*

Shoby Lodge Farm, *Shoby, Melton Mowbray, Leics, LE14 3PF.* Assured a warm welcome. Relax in the comfortable lounge with open log fire. **Open:** All year (not Xmas/New Year) **Grades:** ETC 4 Diamond
01664 812156 Mrs Lomas **D:** £20.00–£22.00 **S:** £25.00 **Beds:** 1T 2D **Baths:** 2 En 1 Pr 🖪 (6) ⚲ 📺 📺 📖. ⚲

Swannington

SK4115 ⬧ *Robin Hood*

Hillfield House, *52 Station Hill, Swannington, Coalville, Leicestershire, LE67 8RH.* **Open:** All year
01530 837414
Ms Nicholls **Fax:** 01530 458233 *molly@hillfieldhouse.co.uk* www.hillfieldhouse.co.uk **D:** £20.00 **S:** £25.00 **Beds:** 3T **Baths:** 2 En 1 Pr ⬧ 🖪 (5) ⚲ 📺 📺 📖. ⚲
Perfectly located to explore National Forest/Middle England. In easy reach of EMA/Birmingham Airports and motorway network. Family home purposely extended with spacious and tastefully decorated rooms. Large, pleasant garden for the enjoyment of guests. Warm welcome. Hearty breakfasts.

Tilton on the Hill

SK7405

Knebworth House, *Loddington Lane, Launde, Tilton on the Hill, Leicester, Leics, LE7 9DE.* Comfortable accommodation in secluded countryside. **Open:** All year (not Xmas)
0116 259 7257 Mrs Setaycor **D:** £15.00 **S:** £15.00 **Beds:** 1F 1T 1S **Baths:** 1 Sh 🖪 (10) 📺 📖. ⚲

Planning a longer stay? Always ask for any special rates

Ullesthorpe
SP5087

Forge House, *College Street, Ullesthorpe, Lutterworth, Leics, LE17 5BU.* Quiet village accommodation. Ideal for business and pleasure. Restaurants nearby. **Open:** All year *s.silvester@virgin.net*
01455 202454 (also fax)
D: £20.00–£22.50 **S:** £20.00–£25.00 **Beds:** 1D 1T **Baths:** 1 En 1 Sh ⌂ (10) ▣ (3) ⌀ ⊡ Ⅲ ⊾

Upton
SP3699

Sparkenhoe Farm, *Upton, Nuneaton, Warks, CV13 6JX.* Beautiful Georgian farmhouse, fabulous countryside views. Large comfortable rooms recently refurbished to high standard. **Open:** All year
01455 213203 Mrs Clarke **D:** £25.00 **S:** £25.00–£30.00 **Beds:** 1D 2T **Baths:** 2 En 1 Pr ⌂ ▣ (10) ⌀ ⊡ ⌁ Ⅴ Ⅲ ⊾

Waltham on the Wolds
SK8025

Bryn Barn, *38 High Street, Waltham on the Wolds, Melton Mowbray, Leics, LE14 4AH.* Charmingly converted stables & barn, original timber beams, picturesque conservation village in Vale of Belvoir.
Open: All year (not Xmas)
01664 464783 Mr & Mrs Rowlands **D:** £19.00–£21.00 **S:** £25.00–£28.00 **Beds:** 1F 2D 1T **Baths:** 2 En 2 Sh ⌂ ▣ (4) ⌀ ⊡ ⌁ Ⅲ ⊾

Lincolnshire

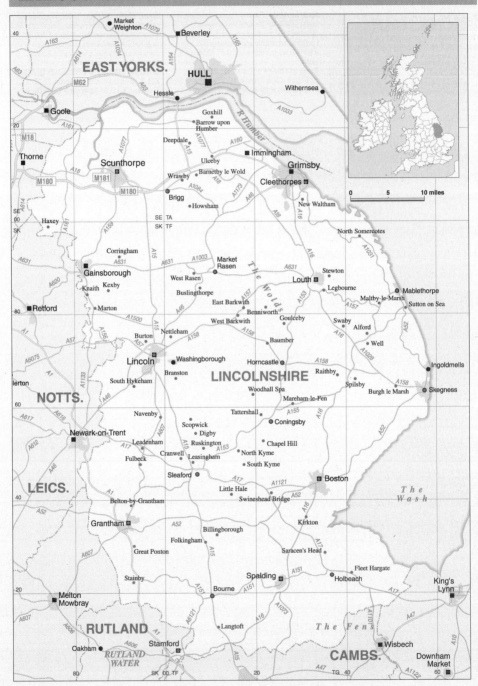

Please respect a B&B's wishes regarding children, animals and smoking

Alford

TF4575 ◀ *Woodthorpe Country Inn*

Halton House, 50 East Street, Alford, Lincs, LN13 9EH. Comfortable relaxing accommodation. **Open:** All year (not Xmas) 01507 462058 Mrs Mackey **D:** £18.00 **S:** £19.00 **Beds:** 1D 1T **Baths:** 1 Sh ▣ (3) ✠ ▣ ▥ ▪

Barnetby le Wold

TA0509

Holcombe Guest House, 34 Victoria Road, Barnetby le Wold, Lincs, DN38 6JR. First class accommodation and a warm welcome await you. **Open:** All year 01652 680655 & 07850 764002 **(M)** Mrs Vora **Fax:** 01652 680841 *holcombe.house@virgin.net* www.holcombeguesthouse.co.uk **D:** £16.25–£20.00 **S:** £20.00 **Beds:** 2F 1T 5S **Baths:** 4 Pr 2 Sh ▧ ▣ (7) ▥ ▶ ✕ ▣ ▥ ☖ ▪ cc

Barrow upon Humber

TA0720

Glengarth, South End, Goxhill, Barrow-upon-Humber, Lincs, DN19 7LZ. Comfortable, modernised farmhouse, open fires, quiet location in beautiful countryside, warm welcome. **Open:** All year **Grades:** ETC 3 Diamond 01469 530991 (also fax) Mrs Monro *monroracing@onetel.net.uk* **D:** £16.00–£17.50 **S:** £16.00–£17.50 **Beds:** 1D 1T **Baths:** 1 Pr 1 Sh ▧ ▣ (8) ✠ ▥ ▶ ✕ ▣ ▥ ❋ ▪

Glebe Farm, Cross Street, Barrow upon Humber, Lincolnshire, DN19 7AL. Spacious accommodation in village location. Superb for walking, cycling, sightseeing. **Open:** All year (not Xmas/New Year) 01469 531548 Mrs Styles **Fax:** 01469 530034 *glebe_farm@lineone.net* **D:** £19.00–£20.00 **S:** £16.00–£20.00 **Beds:** 1D 1S **Baths:** 1 Pr ▧ (5) ▣ (2) ✠ ▥ ▪

Baumber

TF2274

Baumber Park, Baumber, Horncastle, Lincs, LN9 5NE. Period farmhouse; bedrooms with fine views; gardens, walking, cycling, golf. **Open:** All year (not Xmas) 01507 578235 & 01507 578352 Mrs Harrison **Fax:** 01507 578417 **D:** £20.00–£25.00 **S:** £20.00–£30.00 **Beds:** 1D 1T **Baths:** 1 En 1 Pr ▧ ▣ (4) ▥ ▶ ✕ ▥ ▪

Belton-by-Grantham

SK9239 ◀ *The Stag*

Coach House, Belton-by-Grantham, Grantham, Lincs, NG32 2LS. Centre of Belton NT village. Extensive gardens, private parking. **Open:** All year (not Xmas/New Year) 01476 573636 (also fax) Mrs Norton *coachhousebandb@yahoo.co.uk* www.smoothhound.co. uk/hotels/coachhouse **D:** £22.00–£23.00 **S:** £30.00–£35.00 **Beds:** 1F 2D **Baths:** 3 En ▣ (10) ✠ ▥ ▥ ▥ ▪

Benniworth

TF2081

Glebe Farm, Church Lane, Benniworth, Market Rasen, Lincolnshire, LN8 6JP. C18th Listed farmhouse in Lincolnshire Wolds. **Open:** All year 01507 313231 (also fax) Mrs Selby **D:** £22.50–£27.00 **S:** £25.00–£27.00 **Beds:** 1D 2T **Baths:** 2 En 1 Pr ▣ (6) ✠ ▥ ✕ ▥ ▥ ❋ ▪ ▪

Billingborough

TF1134 ◀ *Fortesque Arms, Plough Inn*

Tiffany House, 2a Station Road, Billingborough, Sleaford, NG34 0NR. Warm welcome awaits, friendly atmosphere, light airy rooms, pine furnishings. **Open:** All year 01529 240543 Mrs Abbott **D:** £20.00–£24.00 **S:** £22.00–£24.00 **Beds:** 1T 1D 1S **Baths:** 2 Sh ▧ (2) ▣ (2) ✠ ▥ ▶ ▥ ▪

Boston

TF3344

Lochiel Guest House, 69 Horncastle Road, Boston, Lincs, PE21 9HY. Comfortable, friendly, picturesque waterside setting. Large garden. Working windmill view. **Open:** All year 01205 363628 Mr & Mrs Lynch **D:** £18.00 **S:** £20.00 **Beds:** 1D 1T 1S **Baths:** 1 Sh ▧ ▣ (3) ✠ ▥ ▥ ▪

Bourne

TF0920

The Old Mill, 16 Victoria Place, Bourne, Lincs, PE10 9LJ. Spacious family home where a warm and friendly welcome awaits. **Open:** All year (not Xmas/New Year) 01778 394893 Mr Davison *oldmill@ bourne1.screaming.net* **D:** £15.00 **S:** £15.00 **Beds:** 2T **Baths:** 1 Sh ▧ ▣ ✠ ▥ ▶ ▥ ▥

Branston

TF0267

73 Station Road, Branston, Lincoln, Lincs., LN4 1LG. Modern house, ground floor bedrooms. Attractive gardens. Quiet location, easy to find. Wonderful breakfasts. **Open:** All year 01522 828658 M A Buckingham **D:** £40.00 **S:** £25.00 **Beds:** 1T 1D **Baths:** 1 En 1 Pr ▧ (5) ▣ (4) ✠ ▥ ▶ ▥ ▥ ▪

Brigg

TA0007

Hamsden Garth, Cadney Road, Howsham, Market Rasen, Lincolnshire, LN7 6LA. **Open:** All year (not Xmas) **Grades:** AA 3 Diamond 01652 678703 Mrs Robinson *reservations@ hamsden.co.uk* www.hamsden.co.uk **D:** £16.50 **S:** £18.00 **Beds:** 1T 2S **Baths:** 1 Sh ▧ ▣ (10) ✠ ▥ ▶ ▥ ▥ ▪ Warm friendly welcome, substantial English breakfast and very comfortable accommodation, in pleasant rural setting. Convenient for Humberside Airport, M18/M180 and Humber Bank industries. Enjoy Market Rasen Races, Forest Pines/Elsham Golf Courses, Viking Way long distance footpath, Eastern Cycle Route.

The Woolpack Hotel, Market Place, Brigg, Lincs., DN20 8HA. A Grade II Listed building and a fully licensed public house, with comfortable accommodation. **Open:** All year (not Xmas) 01652 655649 (also fax) *harry@ woolpack488.freeserve.co.uk* **D:** £15.00–£20.00 **S:** £18.00–£25.00 **Beds:** 2F 3T 1S **Baths:** 2 En 1 Pr 1 Sh ▧ ▣ (20) ✠ ▥ ✕ ▥ ▥ ▪

Burgh le Marsh

TF5064

The Old Mill, West End, Burgh le Marsh, Skegness, Lincs, PE24 5EA. Tastefully converted windmill set in lovely countryside, near the coast. **Open:** All year (not Xmas) 01754 810081 (also fax) Mr & Mrs Southward *oldmillburgh@talk21.com* www.skegness-resort.co.uk/oldmillburgh **D:** £16.00–£26.00 **S:** £25.00–£30.00 **Beds:** 1F 1D 1T **Baths:** 2 En 1 Sh ▧ ▣ (6) ✠ ▥ ▥ ▪

Burton

SK9674

New Farm, Burton, Lincoln, Lincs, LN1 2RD. 328-acre working farm, open countryside, Lincoln Cathedral nearby. **Open:** Easter to Nov 01522 527326 Mrs Russon **D:** £19.00 **S:** £22.50 **Beds:** 2T **Baths:** 1 Pr 1 Sh ▧ (5) ▣ (3) ✠ ▥ ✕ ▥ ▥ ☖ ▪ ▪

Buslingthorpe

TF0885   White Hart

East Farm House, *Middle Rasen Road, Buslingthorpe, Market Rasen, Lincs, LN3 5AQ.* Oak-beamed farmhouse, built 1750. Peaceful location 2 miles south of Middle Rasen. **Open:** All year (not Xmas/New Year) **01673 842283** Mrs Grant **D:** £23.00–£24.50 **S:** £28.00 **Beds:** 1T 1D **Baths:** 1 En 1 Pr (10)

Chapel Hill

TF2054

The Crown Lodge, *Chapel Hill, Tattershall, Lincoln, LN4 4PX.* Ensuite rooms,varied menu, walks, fishing, boating, real ale, entertainment. **Open:** All year **01526 342262 (also fax)** Mr Harrington *barryharrington@hotmail.com* **D:** £20.00 **S:** £20.00 **Beds:** 1F 2T 1S (15)

Cleethorpes

TA3008

Hotel 77, *77 Kingsway, Cleethorpes, Lincs, DN35 0AB.* Situated near the leisure centre, boating lake and leisure park. **Open:** All year (not Xmas/New Year) **Grades:** ETC 3 Diamond **01472 692035 (also fax)** Mr & Mrs Knox *hotel77@knox24.fsbusiness.com.uk* **D:** £19.50 **S:** £25.00 **Beds:** 3F 3T 4D 4S **Baths:** 14 En cc

Gladson Guest House, *43 Isaacs Hill, Cleethorpes, Lincs, DN35 8JT.* Licensed family guest house, personal attention. Close to seafront. **Open:** All year **Grades:** ETC 3 Diamond **01472 694858 & 01472 239642** Mrs Pearce **Fax: 01472 239642** *enquiries@ gladsonguesthouse.co.uk* www.gladsonguesthouse.co.uk **D:** £15.00– £16.00 **S:** £17.00–£18.00 **Beds:** 2F 1D 2S (3)

Lindenthorpe Guest House, *19 Grant Street, Cleethorpes, Lincs, DN35 8AT.* Comfortable accommodation, 5 mins to rail station, sea front, attractions. **Open:** All year **01472 313005 & 01472 312070** Mrs Richardson **Fax: 01472 312070** *lindenthorpe@fsbdial.co.uk* www.lindenthorpe. co.uk **D:** £25.00–£28.00 **S:** £14.00 **Beds:** 1F 2T 2S **Baths:** 1 Sh

Alpine Guest House, *55 Clee Road, Cleethorpes, Lincs., DN35 8AD.* Welcoming comfortable accommodation at realistic prices. **Open:** All year (not Xmas) **01472 690804 (also fax)** W M Sanderson *w.sanderson@ntlworld.com* **D:** £13.00–£15.00 **S:** £15.00–£16.00 **Beds:** 2F 1T 2S **Baths:** 2 Sh (2) (3)

Abbeydale Guest House, *39 Isaacs Hill, Cleethorpes, NE Lincs, DN35 8JT.* Clean comfortable accommodation. Excellent base for touring. Friendly welcome. **Open:** All year **Grades:** ETC 3 Diamond **01472 692248 & 01472 311088** Mr Inskip **Fax: 01472 311088** *enquiries@ abbeydaleguesthouse.co.uk* www.abbeydaleguesthouse.co.uk **D:** £14.00– £15.00 **S:** £16.00–£22.00 **Beds:** 2F 1D 2S **Baths:** 2 Sh cc

Holmhirst Hotel, *3 Alexandra Road, Cleethorpes, Lincs, DN35 8LQ.* Family-run seafront hotel. Good food a speciality. **Open:** All year (not Xmas) **01472 692656 (also fax)** Mr Barrs *holmhirst@ aol.com* **D:** £20.00 **S:** £18.00–£25.00 **Beds:** 1D 2T 5S **Baths:** 5 En 1 Sh (3) cc

Pelham View Guest House, *12 Isaacs Hill, Cleethorpes, Lincs, DN35 8JS.* A warm welcome awaits all guests to Pelham View Guest House. **Open:** All year (not Xmas) **01472 690781** Mr Sharpe **D:** £13.00–£16.00 **S:** £14.00 **Beds:** 3F 1D 1T **Baths:** 1 Pr

Adelaide Hotel, *41 Isaacs Hill, Cleethorpes, Lincs, DN35 8JT.* Small delightful family-run hotel. Superb accommodation, friendliness, cleanliness home quality cooked food. **Open:** All year **01472 693594 Fax: 01472 329717** *robert.callison@dtn.ntl.com* **D:** £15.00–£18.50 **S:** £16.00–£25.00 **Beds:** 2F 5T 4D 2S **Baths:** 3 En 2 Sh (3) (4)

Coningsby

TF2258

The White Bull, *High Street, Coningsby, Lincoln, Lincs, LN4 4RB.* Friendly pub, real ale, riverside beer garden, large children's playground. Traditional home-made meals everyday. **Open:** All year **01526 342439** Mr & Mrs Gordon **Fax: 01526 342818** *thewhitebullconingsby@tinyworld.co.uk* www.thewhitebull.co.uk **D:** £15.00–£19.00 **S:** £15.00–£20.00 **Beds:** 2F **Baths:** 2 En (35)

Corringham

SK8791

The Beckett Arms, *25 High Street, Corringham, Gainsborough, Lincolnshire, DN21 5QP.* Centrally located accommodation offering a warm welcome and home-cooked meals. **Open:** All year **01427 838201** **D:** £17.00–£20.00 **S:** £20.00–£24.00 **Beds:** 2F 1T 1D **Baths:** 4 En (30) cc

Cranwell

TF0349

Byards Leap Cottage, *Cranwell, Sleaford, Lincs, NG34 8EY.* Comfortable country cottage, beautiful garden, home cooking with home-grown produce. **Open:** All year (not Xmas) **Grades:** ETC 3 Diamond **01400 261537** Mrs Wood *lustacottage@ supanet.com* **D:** £20.00 **S:** £20.00 **Beds:** 1D 1T **Baths:** 1 Sh (6)

Deepdale

TA0418

West Wold Farmhouse, *Deepdale, Barton-upon-Humber, Lincs., DN18 6ED.* Welcoming, friendly farmhouse. Home cooking. Peaceful surroundings, near historic Barton. **Open:** All year **01652 633293 (also fax)** P Atkin **D:** £17.50–£19.50 **S:** £17.50–£19.50 **Beds:** 1T 1D **Baths:** 1 Sh

Digby

TF0855   Red Lion

The Shepherd's Cottage, *40 North Street, Digby, Lincoln, Lincs., LN4 3LY.* Traditional cottage in delightful village. Short walk to local pub. **Open:** All year (not Xmas/New Year) **01526 323151** **D:** £16.00–£20.00 **S:** £22.00–£25.00 **Beds:** 1D 1S **Baths:** 1 Pr (2)

East Barkwith

TF1681

The Grange, *Torrington Lane, East Barkwith, Market Rasen, Lincs, LN8 5RY.* A beautiful Georgian farmhouse offering everything for a perfect break. **Open:** All year (not Xmas) **01673 858670** *sarahstamp@farmersweekly.net* **D:** £22.00 **S:** £25.00–£28.00 **Beds:** 2D **Baths:** 2 En

Fleet Hargate

TF3925

Willow Tea Rooms And B&b, *Old Main Road, Fleet Hargate, Spalding, Lincs, PE12 8LL.* Pretty English tea rooms renowned for good food. Comfortable accommodation. **Open:** All year **01406 423112** **D:** £16.00–£18.00 **S:** £20.00–£22.00 **Beds:** 2F 3D 1T **Baths:** 5 En 1 Pr (6)

Folkingham

TF0733 🍺 *Fortesque Arms, Red Lion, Three Kings*

6 Sleaford Road, *Folkingham, Sleaford, Lincs, NG34 0SB.* Comfortable family home with pleasant meadow views in conservation village. **Open:** All year (not Xmas/New Year)
01529 497277 W H Lack **D:** £16.00–£18.00 **S:** £18.00–£20.00 **Beds:** 3T **Baths:** 1 Sh ⶾ
🄿 (3) 📺 🍴 ✕ 📺 ⅲ,

Fulbeck

SK9450

Hare & Hounds, *The Green, Fulbeck, Grantham, Lincs, NG32 3JJ.* C17th inn. Real ales, food all week. Patio garden. 10 mins A1. **Open:** All year
01400 272090 A Nicholas **Fax:** 01400 273663 **D:** £20.00–£27.50 **S:** £30.00–£40.00 **Beds:** 4D 2T 2F **Baths:** 8 En ⶾ 🄿 ✂ 📺 🍴 ✕ 📺 ▲ cc

Goulceby

TF2579

Holly House, *Watery Lane, Goulceby, Louth, Lincs, LN11 9UR.* Quiet village location in Lincolnshire Wolds. Comfortable cottage set in large garden. **Open:** All year (not Xmas)
01507 343729 Mrs Lester **D:** £15.00–£16.00 **S:** £15.00–£16.00 **Beds:** 1D 1T **Baths:** 1 Sh
🄿 (2) 📺 ✕ 📺 ⅲ,

Goxhill

TA1021

Glengarth, *South End, Goxhill, Barrow-upon-Humber, Lincs, DN19 7LZ.* Comfortable, modernised farmhouse, open fires, quiet location in beautiful countryside, warm welcome. **Open:** All year **Grades:** ETC 3 Diamond
01469 530991 (also fax) Mrs Monro *monroracing@onetel.net.uk* **D:** £16.00–£17.50 **S:** £16.00–£17.50 **Beds:** 1D 1T **Baths:** 1 Pr 1 Sh ⶾ 🄿 (8) ✂ 📺 🍴 ✕ 📺 ⅲ, ✿ ▲

Grantham

SK9136

The Roost Guest House, *82 Harrowby Road, Grantham, Lincs, NG31 9DS.* Large Victorian private house, close to town centre. **Open:** All year (not Xmas/New Year) **Grades:** AA 3 Diamond
01476 560719 Mr & Mrs Stobbs **Fax:** 01476 563303 *stobbs@theroost.fsnet.co.uk* **D:** £17.50–£22.50 **S:** £20.00–£30.00 **Beds:** 2T 1D **Baths:** 2 En 1 Sh 🄿 (3) 📺 ⅲ, ▲

Church View, *12 North Parade, Grantham, Lincs, NG31 8AN.* A well appointed Listed Georgian town house. Town centre location. **Open:** All year
01476 560815 Mr & Mrs Waldren *churchview@excite.com* **D:** £15.00–£18.00 **S:** £20.00–£22.00 **Beds:** 1D 1T 1F **Baths:** 2 En 1 Sh 🄿 ✂ 📺 📺
ⅲ, ▲

Park Lodge Guest House, *87*

Harrowby Road, Grantham, Lincolnshire, NG31 9ED. A Victorian town house decorated in the William Morris style. **Open:** All year (not Xmas)
01476 567330 (also fax) Mr & Mrs Parkes *kath@parkes.org* www.parklodge.co.uk **D:** £20.00 **S:** £24.00 **Beds:** 2D 1T 1S **Baths:** 2 En 1 Pr 🄿 (12) 🄿 (7) ✂ 📺 🍴 📺 ⅲ, ▲

Great Ponton

SK9230 🍺 *Welby Arms*

The Mews House, *Great Ponton, Grantham, Lincs., NG33 5AG.* C19th Mews, walled garden, access for country walks/cycling. **Open:** All year (not Xmas/New Year)
01476 530311 & 07980 598328 (M) Fax: 01476 530311 *Accommodation@ themewshouse.freeserve.co.uk* **D:** £20.00–£25.00 **S:** £25.00–£30.00 **Beds:** 2D **Baths:** 2 En 🄿 (12) ✂ 📺 ⅲ, ♿ ▲

Haxey

SK7799

Duke William, *Church Street, Haxey, Doncaster, South Yorkshire, DN9 2HY.* C18th inn refurbished to provide accommodation in a warm and friendly atmosphere **Open:** All year
01427 752210 (also fax) D: £22.50 **S:** £32.00 **Beds:** 2T 4D ⶾ 🄿 (36) 📺 ⅲ, ♿ ▲ cc

Holbeach

TF3625

Elloe Lodge, *37 Barrington Gate, Holbeach, Spalding, Lincs, PE12 7LB.* Spacious house, old market town, close pubs and restaurants. Drawing room, delightful gardens. **Open:** All year (not Xmas) **Grades:** AA 4 Diamond
01406 423207 (also fax) Mrs Vasey *bandbholbeach@lineone.net* **D:** £19.00 **S:** £25.00 **Beds:** 1F 1D 1T **Baths:** 1 En 1 Pr ⶾ 🄿 (10) ✂ 📺 📺 ⅲ, ▲

Horncastle

TF2669

Milestone Cottage, *42 North Street, Horncastle, Lincs, LN9 5DX.* Comfortable, self contained accommodation in Georgian town cottage. Self-catering option available. **Open:** All year
01507 522238 D: £20.00 **S:** £20.00 **Beds:** 1T **Baths:** 1 En ⶾ 🄿 (2) 📺 🍴 📺 ⅲ, ▲

Howsham

TA0403

Hamsden Garth, *Cadney Road, Howsham, Market Rasen, Lincolnshire, LN7 6LA.* Warm friendly welcome, substantial English breakfast and very comfortable accommodation. **Open:** All year (not Xmas) **Grades:** AA 3 Diamond
01652 678703 Mrs Robinson *reservations@ hamsden.co.uk* www.hamsden.co.uk **D:** £16.50 **S:** £18.00 **Beds:** 1T 2S **Baths:** 1 Sh ⶾ 🄿 (10) ✂ 📺 🍴 📺 ⅲ, ▲

Kexby

SK8785 🍺 *Red Lion*

Kexby Grange, *Kexby, Gainsborough, Lincs, DN21 5PJ.* Victorian farmhouse in pleasant countryside, convenient for Hemswell antiques, Lincoln and Wolds. **Open:** All year (not Xmas) **Grades:** ETC 3 Diamond
01427 788265 Mrs Edwardson **D:** £17.00 **S:** £17.00 **Beds:** 1D 1S **Baths:** 1 Pr 1 Sh 🄿 (4) ✂ 📺 ✕ 📺 ⅲ, ▲

Kirton

TF3038

Westfield House, *31 Willington Road, Kirton, Boston, Lincs, PE20 1EP.* Victorian house in large village, 4 miles from historic Boston. **Open:** All year
01205 722221 Mrs Duff **D:** £15.00 **S:** £15.00 **Beds:** 1F 1D 1S **Baths:** 1 Sh ⶾ 🄿 (5) 📺 🍴 📺 ⅲ, ▲

Langtoft

TF1212

Courtyard Cottage, *2 West End, Langtoft, Peterborough, PE6 9LS.* A tastefully refurbished C18th stone cottage providing a warm welcome. **Open:** All year
01778 348354 (also fax) *david_tinegate@ ic24.net* **D:** £22.50–£30.00 **S:** £30.00–£50.00 **Beds:** 1F 1D 1T **Baths:** 2 En 1 Pr ⶾ ✂ 📺 🍴 ✕ 📺 ⅲ, ♿ ▲

RATES

D = Price range per person sharing in a double or twin room

S = Price range for a single room

Planning a longer stay? Always ask for any special rates

Leadenham

SK9552

George Hotel, *High Street, Leadenham, Lincoln, Lincs, LN5 0P4.* **Open:** All year **Grades:** ETC 3 Diamond **01400 272251** Mr Willgoose **Fax: 01400 272091 D:** £15.00–£21.00 **S:** £25.00–£32.00 **Beds:** 1F 2D 2T 1S **Baths:** 6 En ⇄ 🗗 🖾 🔭 ⊁ 🖾 🕮 ₺1 ≗ cc
The George at Leadenham is a small country hotel just off the A17 midway between Newark, Sleaford, Grantham, Lincoln. Its homely atmosphere and reputation for fine food makes it a haven for the weary tourist and accessible stopping place for businessmen.

Leasingham

TF0548

Manor Farm, *Leasingham, Sleaford, Lincs, NG34 8JN.* Two pleasant rooms overlooking large garden on working farm. Peaceful. **Open:** All year **Grades:** ETC 2 Diamond **01529 302671** Mrs Franks **Fax: 01529 414946** *j.h.franks@amserve.net* **D:** £15.00–£17.50 **S:** £20.00 **Beds:** 2F **Baths:** 1 Sh ⇄ 🗗 🖾 🔭 🖾 🕮 ≗

Legbourne

TF3684

Boothby House, *Legbourne, Louth, Lincolnshire, LN11 8LH.* Situated at the edge of the picturesque Lincolnshire Wolds. **Open:** All year (not Xmas) **01507 601516 (also fax)** Mrs Wilson *boothbyhouse@freeuk.com* www.boothbyhouse. freeuk.com **D:** £18.00–£21.00 **S:** £18.00 **Beds:** 1D 1T 1S **Baths:** 1 En 1 Sh ⇄ 🗗 🖾 ⊁ ≗

Lincoln

SK9771   🍺 *Dambusters Inn, Inn on the Green.*

Edward King House, *The Old Palace, Minster Yard, Lincoln, LN2 1PU.* **Open:** All year (not Xmas) **Grades:** AA 2 Diamond **01522 528778** Rev Adkins **Fax: 01522 527308** *enjoy@ekhs.org.uk* www.ekhs.org.uk **D:** £18.50– £20.50 **S:** £19.00–£21.00 **Beds:** 1F 11T 5S **Baths:** 8 Sh ⇄ 🗗 (12) ⊬ 🖾 🔭 🖾 🕮 ≗ cc
A former residence of the Bishops of Lincoln at the historic heart of the city and next to the Cathedral and medieval Bishops' Palace. We offer a peaceful haven with a secluded garden and superb views.

Admiral Guest House, *16/18 Nelson Street, Lincoln, LN1 1PJ.* **Open:** All year (not Xmas) **Grades:** RAC 3 Diamond **01522 544467 (also fax)** Mr Major *tony@ admiral63.freeserve.co.uk* **D:** £18.00–£20.00 **S:** £22.00–£25.00 **Beds:** 1F 3D 2T 3S **Baths:** 7 En 2 Pr ⇄ 🗗 🖳 (12) 🖾 🔭 ⊁ 🖾 🕮 ₺ ≗ cc
Admiral Guest House, also known as Nelsons Cottages, situated just off main A57 close to city centre and Lincoln University, offering large floodlit car park, also close to Brayford pool, cathedral and castle and all amenities. All rooms ensuite and private bath.

South Park Guest House, *11 South Park, Lincoln, LN5 8EN.* **Open:** All year (not Xmas/New Year) **01522 528243** Mr Bull **Fax: 01522 524603** www.southpark-lincoln.co.uk **D:** £20.00 **S:** £22.00–£25.00 **Beds:** 1F 2T 2D 1S **Baths:** 6 En ⇄ (1) 🖳 (6) 🖾 ✕ 🖾 🕮 ≗
Fine Victorian detached house, recently refurbished to provide excellent quality accommodation, while maintaining many original features and character. Situated overlooking the South Common, only a short walk to shops, pubs, restaurants, city centre and tourist attractions. Ensuite rooms. Private parking.

The Old Rectory, *19 Newport, Lincoln, LN1 3DQ.* Large Edwardian home near cathedral, castle, pubs and restaurants. **Open:** All year (not Xmas) **01522 514774** Mr Downes **D:** £20.00 **S:** £20.00–£25.00 **Beds:** 2F 4D 1T 1S **Baths:** 6 En 1 Sh ⇄ 🖳 (8) ⊁ 🖾 🖾 🕮 ≗

Ridgeways Guest House, *243 Burton Road, Lincoln, LN1 3UB.* Uphill Lincoln, ten minutes walk to lawn visitors centre and castle. **Open:** All year **Grades:** ETC 3 Diamond **01522 546878 (also fax)** D M Barnes *ridgeways@talk21.com* **D:** £20.00–£25.00 **S:** £20.00–£25.00 **Beds:** 2F 1T 1D **Baths:** 3 En 1 Pr 🖳 (4) ⊁ 🖾 🔭 🖾 🕮 ≗ cc

B&B owners may vary rates – be sure to check when booking

Please respect a B&B's wishes regarding children, animals and smoking

Newport Guest House, *26-28 Newport, Lincoln, LN1 3DF.* A high standard establishment 500 metres from historic city centre. **Open:** All year (not Xmas) **Grades:** ETC 3 Diamond, AA 3 Diamond **01522 528590** Mr Clarke **Fax: 01522 542868** *info@newportguesthouse.co.uk* www.newportguesthouse.co.uk **D:** £16.00– £20.00 **S:** £16.00–£28.00 **Beds:** 3D 4T 1S **Baths:** 7 En 2 Sh ⇄ (6) 🖳 (5) ⊬ 🖾 🔭 🖾 🕮 ₺ ≗

The Old Bakery Guest House, *26-28 Burton Road, Lincoln, LN1 3LB.* Converted Victorian bakery. Two mins from Lincoln Cathedral and Castle. **Open:** All year **Grades:** ETC 3 Diamond **01522 576057 (also fax)** Mr Pearson **D:** £20.00–£25.00 **S:** £30.00–£35.00 **Beds:** 1F 2D 1T **Baths:** 3 En 1 Pr ⇄ ⊁ 🖾 🕮 ≗ cc

Hamiltons Hotel, *2 Hamilton Road, St Catherines, Lincoln, LN5 8ED.* Friendly family-run hotel in a detached former Victorian home. **Open:** All year **01522 528243** June Bull **Fax: 01522 524603** www.hamiltonhotel.co.uk **D:** £18.00–£20.00 **S:** £18.00–£25.00 **Beds:** 1F 3T 2D 3S **Baths:** 4 En 5 Sh ⇄ 🖳 (9) 🖾 🔭 ⊁ 🖾 🕮 ✳ ≗

Carline Guest House, *3 Carline Road, Lincoln, LN1 1HL.* Perfectly situated for castle, cathedral, town centre. Individually decorated bedrooms. **Open:** All year (not Xmas/New Year) **01522 530422 D:** £21.00–£22.00 **S:** £30.00– £35.00 **Beds:** 2T 6S **Baths:** 8 En ⇄ (2) 🖳 (6) ⊬ 🖾 🕮 ≗

Westlyn House, *67 Carholme Road, Lincoln, LN1 1RT.* Late Georgian house close to university, marina, cathedral, castle, city centre. **Open:** All year (not Xmas) **01522 537468 (also fax)** Mrs Shelton *westlyn.bblincoln@easicom.com* **D:** £17.50– £20.00 **S:** £20.00–£25.00 **Beds:** 1F 1T 2D 1S **Baths:** 5 En ⇄ (3) 🖳 (4) ⊁ 🖾 🔭 🖾 🕮 ≗

A B C Charisma Guest House, *126 Yarborough Road, Lincoln, LN1 1HP.* Beautiful views overlooking Trent valley 10 mins' walk to tourist area. **Open:** All year **01522 543560 (also fax) D:** £20.00–£22.50 **S:** £20.00–£25.00 **Beds:** 1F 2T 6D 2S **Baths:** 3 En 4 Sh ⇄ (10) 🖳 (10) ⊬ 🖾 🖾 🕮 ≗

Little Hale

TF1441

Bywell, *20 Chapel Lane, Little Hale, Sleaford, Lincs, NG34 9BE.* Bungalow backing onto farmland. Heckington Windmill & tea-room 1.5 miles. **Open:** All year **01529 460206** Mrs Downes **D:** £17.50 **Beds:** 1D 1T **Baths:** 1 En 1 Sh ⇄ (5) 🖳 (3) ≗ 🖾 ✕ 🕮 ₺

Louth

TF3387

Boothby House, *Legbourne, Louth, Lincolnshire, LN11 8LH.* Situated at the edge of the picturesque Lincolnshire Wolds. **Open:** All year (not Xmas) **01507 601516 (also fax)** Mrs Wilson *boothbyhouse@freeuk.com* www.boothbyhouse. freeuk.com **D:** £18.00–£21.00 **S:** £18.00 **Beds:** 1D 1T 1S **Baths:** 1 En 1 Sh ♿🅿🗹✕♨

Mablethorpe

TF5085

Park View Guest House, *48 Gibralter Road, Mablethorpe, Lincs, LN12 2AT.* **Open:** All year **01507 477267 (also fax)** Mr Dodds **D:** £14.00–£16.00 **S:** £14.00–£16.00 **Beds:** 2F 1T 2D **Baths:** 1 En 2 Sh ♿🅿(6)🗹🏋✕♨🍴 ♿❊♨
Clean and comfortable licensed guest house with some ground floor bedrooms. Beside sandy beach and Queens Park, with lake, boating, bowling, crazy golf, children's play land and funfair. Free private parking, good home cooked food and optional evening meals.

Maltby-le-Marsh

TF4681 🍺 *Turk's Head*

Old Mill Restaurant and Guest House, *Main Road, Maltby-le-Marsh, Alford, Lincs, LN13 0JP.* Excellent village location. Peaceful, good food. Comfortable. Warm welcome. **Open:** All year **01507 450504** *ros-harris@lineone.net* www.maltbymill.co.uk **D:** £20.00–£23.00 **S:** £25.00–£30.00 **Beds:** 1F 2D **Baths:** 2 En 1 Sh ♿🅿(20)🗹🗹🏋✕♨🍴 ♨

Mareham le Fen

TF2761

Barn Croft, *Main Street, Mareham le Fen, Boston, Lincs, PE22 7QJ.* Ensuite facilities in rural setting. Ideal for coast, Lincoln, Boston. **Open:** All year **01507 568264** Mrs Shaw **D:** £17.50 **S:** £25.00 **Beds:** 2D 1T **Baths:** 2 En 1 Pr 🅿(4)🗹🗹♨ ♨

Market Rasen

TF1089

Waveney Cottage Guest House, *Willingham Road, Market Rasen, Lincs, LN8 3DN.* Recommended for its warm, friendly welcome and delicious food. **Open:** All year **Grades:** ETC 4 Diamond **01673 843236** Mrs Bridger www.waveneycottage.co.uk **D:** £18.00–£20.00 **S:** £21.00–£23.00 **Beds:** 1D 2T **Baths:** 3 En ♿🅿(6)✕✕♨🗹♨

East Farm House, *Middle Rasen Road, Buslingthorpe, Market Rasen, Lincs, LN3 5AQ.* Oak-beamed farmhouse, built 1750. Peaceful location 2 miles south of Middle Rasen. **Open:** All year (not Xmas/New Year) **01673 842283** Mrs Grant **D:** £23.00–£24.50 **S:** £28.00 **Beds:** 1T 1D **Baths:** 1 En 1 Pr 🅿(10)✕🗹🗹♨♨

Marton

SK8482

The Black Swan Guest House, *High St, Marton, Gainsborough, Lincolnshire, DN21 5AH.* **Open:** All year **Grades:** AA 4 Diamond **01427 718878 (also fax)** A & V Ball *info@ blackswan-marton.co.uk* www.blackswan-marton.co.uk **D:** £25.00–£30.00 **S:** £30.00 **Beds:** 2F 4D 1T 1S **Baths:** 8 En ♿🅿(8)✕🗹🗹♨♿♨ 🚭 **cc**
A beautifully restored C18th coaching inn offering high quality ensuite accommodation. Much favoured stop for business travellers, British and international tourists and family groups. Excellent breakfasts in house, and superb choice of dinners only 5 minutes away. booking advisable.

Navenby

SK9858

The Barn, *North Lane, Navenby, Lincoln, LN5 0EH.* Beautiful home adjacent walking. Convenient Air field - Trails, Lincoln, Grantham, Newark. **Open:** All year (not Xmas/New Year) **01522 810318 (also fax)** Mr & Mrs Gill *peter.sheila@thebarnnavenby.freeserve.co.uk* **D:** £17.00–£19.00 **S:** £25.00 **Beds:** 1F 1T **Baths:** 1 En 1 Pr ♿(7)🅿(6)🗹🗹♨

Nettleham

TF0075 🍺 *Black Horse*

The Old Vicarage, *25 East Street, Nettleham, Lincoln, LN2 2SL.* **Open:** All year **01522 750819** Mrs Downs *susan@oldvic.net*
D: £20.00 **S:** £24.50 **Beds:** 1T 1D **Baths:** 1 En 1 Pr 🅿(2)✕🗹♨♨
Welcome to our listed Georgian farmhouse near the centre of an attractive village with traditional 'village green' and 'beck'. A warm welcome, tastefully furnished rooms and excellent location make us an ideal base when visiting historic Lincoln and surrounding counties.

Planning a longer stay? Always ask for any special rates

Haymans Ghyll, *9 Church Street, Nettleham, Lincoln, LN2 2PD.* C18th cottage situated centre village, private lounge. Lincoln 10 mins. **Open:** All year (not Xmas/ New Year) **01522 751812 (also fax)** Mr Dawkins *dawkins_net@talk21.com* **D:** £20.00–£22.00 **S:** £25.00–£30.00 **Beds:** 2D **Baths:** 1 En 1 Pr ✕🗹🗹♨♨

New Waltham

TA2904

Peaks Top Farm, *Hewitts Avenue, New Waltham, Grimsby, DN36 4RS.* Our converted barns offer stylish, comfortable accommodation, farmhouse breakfasts. **Open:** Mar to Dec **01472 812941** *lmclayton@tinyworld.co.uk* **D:** £18.00 **S:** £18.00–£25.00 **Beds:** 2F 1D 2S **Baths:** 5 En 🅿(6)✕🗹♨♿♨

North Kyme

TF1552

Old Coach House Tea Rooms & Cafe, *Church Lane, North Kyme, Lincoln, LN4 4DJ.* Beautifully refurbished old Georgian house offering warm and friendly welcome. **Open:** All year **01526 861465** Mr & Mrs Grice **Fax:** 01526 861659 **D:** £18.00–£22.00 **Beds:** 3D 3T 1S **Baths:** 3 En ♿🅿🗹✕✕🗹♨❊♨

North Somercotes

TF4296

Pigeon Cottage, *Conisholme Road, North Somercotes, Louth, Lincolnshire, LN11 7PS.* Fishing lake on site, craft studio, pets area, 4 acres of playing field together. **Open:** All year **01507 359063** Ms Hill **D:** £20.00–£22.00 **S:** £20.00–£22.00 **Beds:** 3F 1T 1D 1S **Baths:** 6 En ♿🅿(6)🗹🏋✕🗹♨♿♨

Raithby (Spilsby)

TF3767

Red Lion Inn, *Raithby, Spilsby, Lincs, PE23 4DS.* **Open:** All year **01790 753727** Mrs Smith *alcaprawn@aol.com* **D:** £18.50–£20.00 **S:** £27.00–£30.00 **Beds:** 2D 1T **Baths:** 3 En ♿🅿(20)🗹🏋✕🗹♨♨ **cc**
Old world inn in centre of pretty Wolds village. Real ales, log fires in the winter, char gril

Ruskington

TF0851

Sunnyside Farm, *Leasingham Lane, Ruskington, Sleaford, Lincolnshire, NG34 9AH.* Perfectly located base for historic centres, golf, walking, cycling. Horse riding. **Open:** All year
01526 833010 D A Luke **D:** £20.00–£22.00 **S:** £20.00–£22.00 **Beds:** 1F 1T **Baths:** 2 En ⌂
🄿 📺 ⼞ ✕ 🛏️ ♨

Saracen's Head

TF3427

Pipwell Manor, *Washaway Road, Saracen's Head, Holbeach, Spalding, Lincs, PE12 8AL.* Tastefully furnishedooms. Beautiful grounds featuring a miniature railway. Free use of cycles. **Open:** All year (not Xmas/New Year)
01406 423119 (also fax) Mrs Honnor **D:** £44.00–£46.00 **S:** £30.00–£32.00 **Beds:** 2D 1T 1S **Baths:** 3 En 1 Pr 🄿 (6) ⼞ 📺 🛏️ ♨

Scopwick

TF0658

The Millhouse, *Heath Road, Scopwick, Lincoln, Lincs, LN4 3JB.* Fine Georgian stone house set in beautiful gardens amidst open countryside. **Open:** All year
01526 321716 (also fax) Ms Gale *shirley.gale@farming.co.uk* www.millhousebandb.co.uk
D: £20.00–£25.00 **S:** £25.00–£28.00 **Beds:** 1T 2D **Baths:** 3 En ⌂ 🄿 (6) ⼞ 📺 🛏️ 🛏️ ♨

Scunthorpe

SE8910

Lindsey Hotel, *26-28 Normanby Road, Scunthorpe, Lincs, DN15 6AL.* Central family-run hotel on route between Lincoln and York. **Open:** All year
01724 844706 (also fax) **D:** £14.00–£17.00 **S:** £17.00–£24.00 **Beds:** 2F 2D 3T 4S **Baths:** 3 En 3 Sh ⌂ (1) 🄿 (10) 📺 🛏️ ⼞ 📺 ♨

Skegness

TF5663   🚢 *Ship Hotel, Welcome Inn*

The Tudor Lodge Licensed Guest House, *61 Drummond Road, Skegness, Lincolnshire, PE25 3BB.* Close to all amenities. B&B and eve meals, col TV, tea/coff machines. **Open:** All year
01754 766487 M Lowe **D:** £15.00–£20.00 **S:** £18.00–£20.00 **Beds:** 3F 2D 3T 1S ⌂ 🄿 (12) 📺 🛏️ ✕ ⼞ 📺 ♿ ✳ 🅲🅲

The Carlton Hotel and Holiday Flats, *70 Drummond Road, Skegness, Lincs, PE25 3BR.* Family hotel and flats near to sea front and town centre. **Open:** All year (not Xmas)
01754 765340 Mr & Mrs Parker **Fax:** 0870 1115700 *carltonhotel@yahoo.co.uk*
www.carltonpp.freeserve.co.uk **D:** £14.00–£19.00 **S:** £28.00–£38.00 **Beds:** 3F 4D 2T **Baths:** 4 En 4 Sh ⌂ (2) 🄿 (9) 📺 ♨ 🅲🅲

National Grid References given are for villages, towns and cities – not for individual houses

Glynvale Hotel, *101 Drummond Road, Skegness, Lincs, PE25 3EH.* Small family-run hotel, close to beach and all amenities. **Open:** All year
01754 767190 Mrs Wood **D:** £14.00–£20.00 **Beds:** 4F 3T 2D **Baths:** 3 Sh ⌂ 🄿 (5) ✕ ⼞ ♨

Merlewood Hotel, *61 Park Avenue, Skegness, PE25 1BL.* Situated on tree lined avenue. Walking distance from beaches, town centre. **Open:** All year
01754 762942 **D:** £18.00–£20.00 **S:** £23.00–£25.00 **Beds:** 3F 6D **Baths:** 9 En ⌂ 🄿 (6) ⼞ 📺 ✕ ⼞ 📺 ✳ ♨

Craigside Hotel, *26 Scarborough Avenue, Skegness, Lincs, PE25 2SY.* Family run hotel, close to sea front, theatre and town centre. **Open:** Easter to Sept
01754 763307 (also fax) Mrs Milner *kenanddeb@craigside69.freeserve.co.uk* www.skegness-resort.co.uk/craigside **D:** £20.00–£22.00 **S:** £20.00–£22.00 **Beds:** 5F 5D 3T 3S **Baths:** 12 En 1 Sh ⌂ 🄿 (10) 📺 ✕ ⼞ 📺 ✳ ♨ 🅲🅲

Mayfair Hotel, *10 Saxby Avenue, Skegness, PE25 3JZ.* The Mayfair is well situated in quiet location close to sea front/town centre. **Open:** All year (not Xmas/New Year)
01754 764687 **D:** £14.00–£20.00 **S:** £14.00–£20.00 **Beds:** 1F 5T 2D **Baths:** 8 En ⌂ 🄿 (5) ⼞ 📺 🛏️ ✕ ⼞ 📺 ♿ ♨ ♨

Sleaford

TF0645

Anna Farmhouse, *Holdingham, Sleaford, Lincs, NG34 8NR.* **Open:** All year (not Xmas)
01529 307292 Mrs Wiles **D:** £18.00–£19.00 **S:** £22.00 **Beds:** 1F 1D 1T **Baths:** 2 Sh ⌂ 🄿 (6) ⼞ 📺
Friendly atmosphere in C16/17th farmhouse. Ideal stop London airports to York and Edinburgh also Scotland and the North to Norfolk Broads and Gt Yarmouth. Ample parking, large English breakfast served after 7.30, continental earlier. Quiet position close to A15/17.

The Mallards Hotel, *6 Eastgate, Sleaford, Lincolnshire, NG34 7DJ.* 10 rooms, family hotel, riverside location, central Sleaford. **Open:** All year (not Xmas)
01529 413758 Mr & Mrs Smith **D:** £25.00–£40.00 **S:** £25.00 **Beds:** 6T 2D 2S **Baths:** 10 En ⌂ 🄿 📺 🛏️ ✕ ⼞ 📺 ♨ 🅲🅲

South Hykeham

SK9364

The Hall, *Meadow Lane, South Hykeham, Lincoln, Lincs, LN6 9PF.* Quiet rural setting close to Lincoln. Breakfasts prepared using local produce. **Open:** All year
01522 686432 Mrs Phillips **Fax:** 01522 696496 **D:** £22.00–£25.00 **S:** £22.00–£25.00 **Beds:** 1F 2D **Baths:** 1 En ⌂ 🄿 ⼞ ⼞ 🛏️ ✕ ♨

South Kyme

TF1749

Hume Arms Hotel, *High Street, South Kyme, Lincoln, LN4 4AD.* Home cooked food and traditional beers. Fishing lake. Caravans welcome. **Open:** All year
01526 861004 Mr Leggat **D:** £15.00–£16.00 **S:** £20.00 **Beds:** 1D 1T **Baths:** 1 En 1 Sh ⌂ 🄿 (20) 📺 ✕ ♨

Spalding

TF2422   🚩 *Red Lion*

88 Winsover Road, *Spalding, Lincs, PE11 1HA.* Victorian family house; very good area for fishing. **Open:** All year
01775 714465 Mrs Rae **D:** £15.00 **S:** £15.00 **Beds:** 2T 1S **Baths:** 1 Sh ⌂ 📺 🛏️ ⼞ ♨

High Bridge House, *9 London Road, Spalding, Lincs, PE11 2TA.* Georgian House situated along riverside next to town centre. Friendly. **Open:** All year (not Xmas/New Year)
01775 725810 Mrs Marshall **D:** £38.00–£40.00 **S:** £19.00–£25.00 **Beds:** 2T 4S 6F **Baths:** 3 Sh ⌂ (10) 📺 ♨

Spilsby

TF4066

Hethersett House, *3 The Terrace, Spilsby, Lincolnshire, PE23 5JR.* Listed Georgian townhouse in small market town, antiques, log fires, walled garden, home-cooked food. **Open:** All year
01790 752666 C M Morgan **D:** £17.50 **S:** £17.50 **Beds:** 1T 2D **Baths:** 1 Sh ⌂ (10) 🄿 ⼞ 📺 ✕ ⼞ 📺 ♨

Stainby

SK9022

The Old Blue Dog, *Colsterworth Road, Stainby, Grantham, Lincs, NG33 5QT.* Beautiful stone residence in lovely rural countryside. Leicestershire/Lincolnshire border. **Open:** All year
01476 861010 Mrs Jones **Fax:** 01476 861645 *fiona@thinkingstyles.co.uk* **D:** £25.00 **S:** £25.00 **Beds:** 1F 1D ⌂ 🄿 (7) ⼞ 📺 ✕ ⼞ 📺 ♨

Stamford
TF0207

High Trees, North Street, Stamford, Lincs., PE9 1EE. Comfortable, friendly accommodation only 2 mins' walk to town centre. **Open:** All year **01780 754842** Mrs Bennet **D:** £25.00 **S:** £25.00–£35.00 **Beds:** 2T 2D **Baths:** 1 Pr 1 Sh ⛄ ▣ (4) ⚡ 📺 🛇 ♨

Birch House, 4 Lonsdale Road, Stamford, Stamford, Lincs, PE9 2RW. Established, well presented large comfortable house on outskirts of Stamford. **Open:** All year (not Xmas/New Year) **01780 754876 (also fax)** J Headland birch_house@faxvia.net **D:** £20.00–£25.00 **S:** £20.00–£25.00 **Beds:** 1T 1D 2S **Baths:** 1 Sh ⛄ (5) ▣ (3) ⚡ 📺 🛇 ♨

Stewton
TF3586

The Old Rectory, Stewton, Louth, Lincs, LN11 8SF. An old rectory in peaceful garden. Come and see! **Open:** All year **01507 328063** ajp100@postmaster.co.uk **D:** £22.50 **S:** £25.00 **Beds:** 2T 2D **Baths:** 3 En 1 Pr ⛄ ▣ (6) 📺 🐾 📺 🛇 ♨

Sutton on Sea
TF5281 ⚓ Bacchus Hotel

Walnut End, 53a Alford Road, Sutton on Sea, Mablethorpe, Lincs, LN12 2HQ. Modern bungalow. Quiet location. Close to shops and Blue Flag Beach. **Open:** All year (not Xmas/New Year) **01507 443451 (also fax)** Mrs Smith **D:** £20.00–£24.00 **S:** £24.00–£28.00 **Beds:** 3D ▣ (4) ⚡ 📺 🛇 ♨

Swaby
TF3876

Jasmine Cottage, Church Lane, Swaby, Alford, Lincolnshire, LN13 0BQ. Peaceful village, excellent accommodation in an Area of Outstanding Natural Beauty. **Open:** All year (not Xmas/New Year) **01507 480283 (also fax)** P Fieldsend fieldsend@btinternet.com **D:** £19.00–£20.00 **S:** £24.00–£25.00 **Beds:** 1T 2D **Baths:** 2 En ▣ (2) ⚡ 📺 🛇 ♨

Planning a longer stay? Always ask for any special rates

Swineshead Bridge
TF2242

Boston Lodge, Browns Drove, Swineshead Bridge, Boston, Lincs, PE20 3PX. Ideally situated for touring the Fens and South Lincolnshire. **Open:** All year (not Xmas) **01205 820983** S Humphreys **Fax:** 01205 820512 info@bostonlodge.co.uk www.bostonlodge.co.uk **D:** £18.00 **S:** £22.00 **Beds:** 2F 3D 2T 2S **Baths:** 9 En ⛄ ▣ (12) ⚡ 📺 🐾 📺 🛇 ♨2 ♨

Tattershall
TF2158

Lodge House, Market Place, Tattershall, Lincoln, Lincs, LN4 4LQ. Clean comfortable accommodation. Close RAF Coningsby. Walking, Cycling, Angling, Golf. Light breakfast in own room. **Open:** All year **01526 342575 (also fax)** Mr Palethorpe **D:** £14.00–£16.00 **S:** £14.00–£16.00 **Beds:** 1D 1T 2S **Baths:** 2 En 2 Sh ⛄ (1) ▣ (3) ⚡ 📺 🛇 ♨

Ulceby (Immingham)
TA1014

Gillingham Court, Spruce Lane, Ulceby, Lincolnshire, DN39 6UL. Quiet extremely comfortable high class guest house situated 4 miles from Humberside International Airport. **Open:** All year (not Xmas) **Grades:** ETC 4 Diamond **01469 588427** Ms Connole www.awentsbury.co.uk **D:** £20.00 **S:** £23.00 **Beds:** 2T 2S **Baths:** 2 En 2 Pr ⛄ ▣ (12) 📺 🛇 ♨

Well
TF4474

The Old Paddock, High Lane, Well, Alford, Lincs., LN13 0ET. **Open:** All year (not Xmas/New Year) **01507 463726 D:** £25.00 **S:** £35.00 **Beds:** 1T 1D **Baths:** 1 Sh ⛄ (12) ▣ (2) ⚡ 📺 🐾 📺 🛇 ♨. 'Well' is a tranquil hamlet on the edge of the Wolds, ideal for touring historic Lincolnshire. We offer sole occupancy of a self contained bungalow annex, consisting of two bedrooms, lounge and bathroom (shower). Full English breakfast is provided.

West Barkwith
TF1580

The Manor House, West Barkwith, Market Rasen, Lincs., LN8 5LF. Beautiful C18th manor house overlooking extensive landscaped gardens and lake. **Open:** All year (not Xmas/New Year) **01673 858253 (also fax)** J A HObbins **D:** £22.50 **S:** £25.00–£28.00 **Beds:** 1T 1D **Baths:** 2 En

West Rasen
TF0689

Chuck Hatch, Kingerby Road, West Rasen, Market Rasen, Lincs, LN8 3NB. Superb facilities, hospitality, quiet country lakeside garden location, coarse fishing. **Open:** All year **Grades:** AA 4 Diamond **01673 842947 (also fax)** chuck.hatch@btinternet.com **D:** £22.50–£27.50 **S:** £32.50–£40.00 **Beds:** 2D 2T **Baths:** 4 En ▣ (4) ⚡ 📺 🛇 ♨

Woodhall Spa
TF1963 ⚓ Kings Arms, Mall Hotel Abbey Lodge

Claremont Guest House, 9-11 Witham Road, Woodhall Spa, Lincs, LN1 6RW. Friendly personal service in a traditional unspoilt Victorian guest house. **Open:** All year **Grades:** AA 2 Diamond **01526 352000** Mrs Brennan **D:** £15.00–£20.00 **S:** £15.00–£20.00 **Beds:** 4F 2D 1T 3S **Baths:** 4 En 2 Sh ⛄ ▣ (4) 📺 🐾 📺 ♨

Newlands Guest House, 56 Woodland Drive, Woodhall Spa, Lincs, LN10 6YG. Luxury accommodation in quiet tree-lined lane. Very convenient for village and international golf courses. **Open:** All year (not Xmas) **Grades:** ETC 4 Diamond **01526 352881 D:** £20.00 **S:** £25.00 **Beds:** 1D 2T **Baths:** 2 En 1 Pr ⛄ ▣ (8) ⚡ 📺 🛇 ♨

Wrawby
TA0308

Wish-u-well Guest House, Brigg Road, Wrawby, Brigg, Lincolnshire, DN20 8RH. Modern bungalow in extensive private grounds. Country pub short walk. **Open:** All year **01652 652301 (also fax)** Mrs Jobson wishwell@talk21.com **D:** £17.00–£25.00 **S:** £18.00–£25.00 **Beds:** 2S 3D 2F 1T **Baths:** 8 En ⛄ ▣ (6) ⚡ 📺 ✕ 🛇 ♨ ✳ ♨

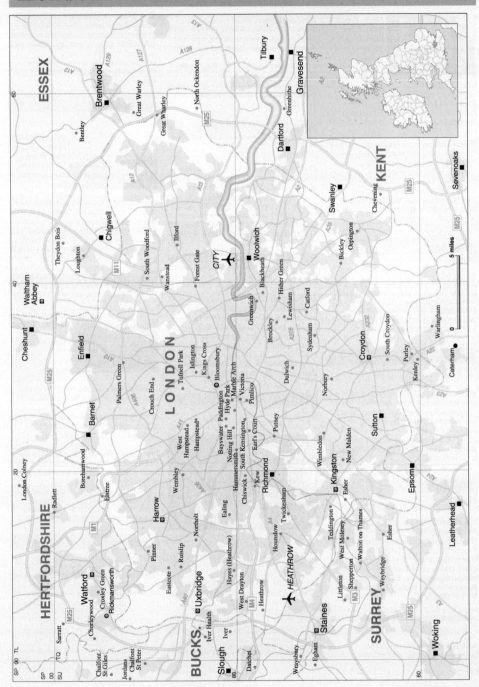

B&B owners may vary rates – be sure to check when booking

CENTRAL LONDON
Bayswater
TQ2580

Prince William Hotel, *42-44 Gloucester Terrace, Bayswater, London, W2 3DA.* Newly refurbished hotel, central location, close Hyde Park and shopping centres, cinemas, Soho. **Open:** All year
020 7724 7414 **Fax: 020 7706 2411**
theprincewilliamhotel@hotmail.com **D:** £27.50–£37.50 **S:** £35.00–£55.00 **Beds:** 4F 15T 15D 13S **Baths:** 13 En 🛏 ♨ cc

---

CENTRAL LONDON
Bloomsbury
TQ3082

Garth Hotel, *69 Gower Street, Bloomsbury, London, WC1E 6HJ.* **Open:** All year
020 7636 5761 Mr Hoare *garth.hotel@virgin.net*
www.garthhotel-london.com **D:** £25.00–£40.00 **S:** £35.00–£48.00 **Beds:** 5F 5T 4D 3S **Baths:** 8 En 4 Sh 🛏 🅿 🗙 📺 🖳 ✳ ♨ cc
The hotel, in the heart of London, has a friendly, peaceful atmosphere with clean comfortable rooms. All seventeen rooms have central heating, colour TV, tea/coffee facilities and direct-dial telephones. It has recently been refurbished to a very high standard.

Acorns Hotel, *42 Tavistock Place, Bloomsbury, London, WC1H 9RE.* Listed building near Russell Square, Euston Square. **Open:** All year
020 7837 3077 Mr Grover **D:** £22.00–£26.00 **S:** £30.00–£38.00 **Beds:** 1F 6D 4T 1S **Baths:** 4 Sh 📺 🖳 ✳

Mentone Hotel, *54-55 Cartwright Gardens, Bloomsbury, London, WC1H 9EL.* Long a popular choice with tourists, due to pleasant surrounding and central location.
Open: All year
020 7387 3927 Mr Tyner **Fax: 020 7388 4671**
mentonehotel@compuserve.com
www.mentonehotel.com **D:** £74.00–£79.00 **S:** £74.00–£79.00 **Beds:** 10F 10D 10T 10S **Baths:** 40 En 🛏 📺 🖳 ♿ ♨ cc

---

RATES
D = Price range per person sharing in a double or twin room
S = Price range for a single room

CENTRAL LONDON
Earl's Court
TQ2578

Merlyn Court Hotel, *2 Barkston Gardens, Earl's Court, London, SW5 0EN.*
Open: All year
Grades: ETC 2 Diamond, RAC 2 Diamond
020 7370 1640 **Fax: 020 7370 4986** *london@merlyncourt.demon.co.uk* www.smoothhound.co.uk/hotels/merlyn.html **D:** £28.00–£40.00 **S:** £30.00–£60.00 **Beds:** 5F 4D 6T 4S **Baths:** 10 En 2 Pr 🛏 ⅍ 🛏 🖳 ♨ cc
This is a clean, friendly, good value hotel in a quiet garden square in Kensington. Family rooms are also available, very central with easy connections to all motorways and trains - direct links to Heathrow and Gatwick airports.

Rasool Court Hotel, *19-21 Penywern Road, Earl's Court, London, SW5 9TT.*
Open: All year
Grades: ETC 2 Diamond
020 7373 8900 Mr Younis **Fax: 020 7244 6835**
rasool@rasool.demon.co.uk
www.rasoolcourthotel.com **D:** £24.00–£28.00 **S:** £33.00–£45.00 **Beds:** 8F 16D 8T 25S **Baths:** 38 En 🛏 📺 🖳 cc
The hotel is ideally located in fashionable Kensington close to the heart of the city. The tourist attractions of Buckingham Palace, the Tower of London and the museums are easily accessible. The immediate area itself has a variety of restaurants and shops for your convenience.

Ramsees Hotel, *32-36 Hogarth Road, Earl's Court, London, SW5 0PU.*
Open: All year
Grades: ETC 2 Diamond
020 7370 1445
Mr Younis **Fax: 020 7244 6835** *ramsees@rasool.demon.co.uk* www.ramseeshotel.com **D:** £24.00–£27.00 **S:** £33.00–£42.00 **Beds:** 14F 26D 11T 15S **Baths:** 56 En 🛏 📺 🖳 cc
The hotel is ideally located in fashionable Kensington close to the heart of the city. Within one minute's walk from Earls Court station which makes most major shopping areas of Knightsbridge, Oxford Street and Kensington within easy reach.

Planning a longer stay? Always ask for any special rates

Windsor House, *12 Penywern Road, Earl's Court, London, SW5 9ST.* **Open:** All year
020 7373 9087 J Wardle **Fax: 020 7385 2417**
bookings@windsor-house-hotel.com
www.windsor-house-hotel.com **D:** £20.00–£30.00 **S:** £28.00–£46.00 **Beds:** 6F 5D 5T 2S **Baths:** 12 En 5 Pr 1 Sh 🛏 📺 🛏 🖳 ♨
Central London: friendly, family-run B&B. Walk to Olympia/Earls Court. Super-comfortable, super-affordable! Use of hotel kitchen for own meals! Single rooms £29–£46, Doubles £36–£65, 3/4/5 family studios £16–£26pppn. Good breakfast/VAT included. Great reductions for families with children. Group discounts.

Oliver Plaza Hotel, *33 Trebovir Road, Earl's Court, London, SW5 0LR.* **Open:** All year
020 7373 7183 **Fax: 020 7244 6021**
oliverplaza@capricornhotels.co.uk
www.capricornhotels.co.uk **D:** £20.00–£35.00 **S:** £15.00–£25.00 **Beds:** 6F 20T 10D 2S **Baths:** 38 En 🅿 (3) 📺 🖳 ♨ cc
A nice value for money property in the heart of London. Good access to all public transport facilities and helpful staff to make your stay an enjoyable experience. Family run with emphasis on comfort.

Lord Jim Hotel, *23-25 Penywern Road, Earl's Court, London, SW5 9TT.* Attractive, well-appointed, moderately priced hotel close to city, airports, Earl's Court, Olympia. **Open:** All year
020 7370 6071 Mr Tayeb **Fax: 020 7373 8919**
ljh@lgh-hotels.com www.lgh-hotels.com
D: £15.00–£30.00 **S:** £25.00–£50.00
Beds: 12F 10D 4T 8S **Baths:** 30 En 22 Sh 🛏 ⅍ 📺 🖳 ♨ cc

Mowbray Court Hotel, *28-32 Penywern Road, Earl's Court, London, SW5 9SU.* Centrally located B&B hotel, 60% ensuite rooms, bar, lift, satellite TV. **Open:** All year
020 7370 2316 & 020 7370 3690 **Fax: 020 7370 5693** *mowbraycrthot@hotmail.com*
www.m-c-hotel.mcmail.com **D:** £28.00–£34.00 **S:** £23.00–£26.00 **Beds:** 15F 18T 18D 25S **Baths:** 30 En 20 Pr 26 Sh 🛏 ⅍ 📺 🛏 🖳 cc

---

CENTRAL LONDON
Hyde Park
TQ2780

Classic Hotel, *92 Sussex Gardens, Hyde Park, London, W2 1UY.* Beautifully decorated, ideal for business, shopping, leisure. Paddington station close by. **Open:** All year
020 7706 7776 Mrs Hassan *classichotel@compuserve.com* **D:** £30.00–£36.00 **S:** £45.00–£52.00 **Beds:** 3F 3D 4T 2S 🛏 🅿 (2) 📺 🖳 ♨ cc

CENTRAL LONDON
Islington
TQ3184

Kandara Guest House, *68 Ockendon Road, Islington, London, N1 3NW.* **Open:** All year **Grades:** ETC 3 Diamond, AA 3 Diamond
020 7226 5721 Mrs Harmon **Fax: 020 7226 3379** *admin@kandara.co.uk* www.kandara.co.uk **D:** £25.50–£29.00 **S:** £39.00–£45.00 **Beds:** 3F 3D 1T 4S **Baths:** 5 Sh ⅄ ✏ ⻌ ▥ ♨ cc
Small family-run guest house near the Angel, Islington. Excellent public transport to the West End and City. All our bedrooms and bathrooms have recently been decorated and refitted to a high standard. Rooms are quiet, clean and comfortable.

CENTRAL LONDON
Kings Cross
TQ3083

A Fairway Hotel, *13-15 Argyle Street, Kings Cross, London, WC1H 8EJ.* Comfortable family run B&B close to all major tourist attractions and shopping centres. **Open:** All year
020 7278 8682 (also fax) Mrs Caruana *fairway@cyberlobby.com* www.cyberlobby.com **D:** £19.00–£22.00 **S:** £28.00–£35.00 **Beds:** 7F 10T 10D 6S **Baths:** 3 En 8 Sh ⅀ ▥ ⻌ ♨ ✦ cc

CENTRAL LONDON
Marble Arch
TQ2881 ◀ *Masons Arms*

Lincoln House Hotel, *33 Gloucester Place, Marylebone, London, W1U 8HY.* Built in days of George III, Georgian charms & character. Ensuite rooms with modern comforts. **Open:** All year
020 7486 7630 Mr Shariff **Fax: 020 7486 0166** *reservations@lincoln-house-hotel.co.uk* www.lincoln-house-hotel.co.uk **D:** £39.50–£44.50 **S:** £65.00–£79.00 **Beds:** 3F 7D 3T 9S **Baths:** 22 En ⅀ ▥ ♨ cc

Marble Arch Inn, *49-50 Upper Berkeley Street, Marble Arch, London, W1H 7PN.* Small, friendly, clean, comfortable hotel near Oxford Street and Hyde Park. **Open:** All year **Grades:** ETC 2 Diamond
020 7723 7888 Fax: 020 7723 6060 *sales@marblearch-inn.co.uk* www.marblearch-inn.co.uk **D:** £32.50–£37.50 **S:** £45.00–£75.00 **Beds:** 9F 7T 13D 2S **Baths:** 26 En 3 Sh ⅀ ▥ ⻌ ♨ cc

BATHROOMS
En = Ensuite
Pr = Private
Sh = Shared

CENTRAL LONDON
Notting Hill
TQ2480

Manor Court Hotel, *7 Clanricarde Gardens, Notting Hill Gate, London, W2 4JJ.* Only a few minutes away from Kensington and Hyde Park. **Open:** All year **Grades:** ETC 1 Diamond
020 7727 5407 & 020 7792 3361 Mr Zaidi **Fax: 020 7229 2875 D:** £25.00–£30.00 **S:** £35.00–£45.00 **Beds:** 3F 9D 3T 5S **Baths:** 17 En 3 Sh ⅀ ▥ ♨ cc

CENTRAL LONDON
Paddington
TQ2681

Barry House Hotel, *12 Sussex Place, Paddington, London, W2 2TP.* **Open:** All year **Grades:** ETC 2 Diamond, RAC 2 Diamond
020 7723 7340 R S Bhasin **Fax: 020 7723 9775** *bh-hotel@bigfoot.com* Barryhouse.co.uk **D:** £39.00–£43.00 **S:** £38.00–£45.00 **Beds:** 4F 6T 4D 4S **Baths:** 14 En ⅀ ▥ ♨ cc
Family-run B&B offering warm and friendly welcome. Ensuite rooms with phones, TV, hairdryers, tea/coffee facilities. Convenient Madame Tussaud's, Buckingham Palace, Oxford St, Hyde Park and other sightseeing places. Paddington Station 5 mins' walk. Heathrow Airport 15 mins by train.

Albro House Hotel, *155 Sussex Gardens, Paddington, London, W2 2RY.* Near Hyde Park, public transport. Ideal location. Comfortable rooms, all with TV. **Open:** All year
020 7724 2931 G A Caruso **Fax: 020 7262 2278** *joe@albrohotel.freeserve.co.uk* **D:** £28.00–£36.00 **S:** £38.00–£56.00 **Beds:** 4F 6D 6T 2S **Baths:** 18 En ⅀ (4) ▣ (1) ⅄ ▥ ♨

Ruddimans Hotel, *160 Sussex Gardens, Paddington, London, W2 1UD.* A warm and friendly atmosphere with a bit of a difference. **Open:** All year **Grades:** ETC 2 Diamond
020 7723 1026 Mr Charalambols **Fax: 020 7262 2983** *reservations@ruddimonshotel.co.uk* www.ruddimonshotel.co.uk **D:** £25.00–£32.00 **S:** £35.00–£48.00 **Beds:** 15F 15D 6T 5S **Baths:** 32 Pr 3 Sh ⅀ ▣ ▥ ⻌ cc

CENTRAL LONDON
Pimlico
TQ2978

Elizabeth House Hotel, *118 Warwick Way, Pimlico, London, SW1 4JB.* B&B close Victoria Station. Underground, BR, coach station. 24 hour reception. **Open:** All year
020 7630 0741 Mr Hussain **Fax: 020 7630 0740 D:** £25.00–£30.00 **S:** £30.00–£35.00 **Beds:** 8F 13T 3D 11S **Baths:** 10 En ▥ ⻌ cc

CENTRAL LONDON
South Kensington
TQ2678

Swiss House Hotel, *171 Old Brompton Road, South Kensington, London, SW5 0AN.* The hotel knows guests' priorities and aims to meet them all. **Open:** All year
020 7373 2769 Mr Vincenti **Fax: 020 7373 4983** *recep@swiss-hh.demon.co.uk* www.swiss-hh.demon.co.uk **D:** £42.50–£49.50 **S:** £48.00–£68.00 **Beds:** 8F 11D 10T 4S **Baths:** 1 Sh ⅀ ⅄ ▥ ⑂ ⻌ cc

CENTRAL LONDON
Victoria
TQ2878 ◀ *Marquis of Westminster, The Constitution*

Edward House B&B, *5 St George's Drive, Victoria, London, SW1V 4DP.* **Open:** All year
020 7834 5207 Fax: 020 7976 5428 *enquiry@edwardhouse.co.uk* **D:** £30.00–£35.00 **S:** £37.50–£50.00 **Beds:** 21F 4D 8T **Baths:** 15 En 3 Pr 4 Sh ⅀ ▣ ▥ ⻌ ♨
Conveniently situated, walking distance famous landmarks - Buckingham Palace, Westminster Abbey, Houses of Parliament, Trafalgar Square, Piccadilly Circus, Leicester Square, many more. Victoria rail, bus, tube and Victoria Coach Station, serving London and the whole country, just a few minutes away.

BEDROOMS
D = Double
T = Twin
S = Single
F = Family

All details shown are as supplied by B&B owners in Autumn 2001

Stanley House Hotel, 19-21 Belgrave Road, Victoria, London, SW1V1RB. **Open:** All year **020 7834 5042** Mr Shah **Fax: 020 7834 8439** *cmahotel@aol.com* www.affordablehotel.com **D:** £25.00–£31.00 **S:** £42.00–£52.00 **Beds:** 11F 25D 8T **Baths:** 11 En 26 Pr 6 Sh ♥ 🖸 🖾 🖾 cc Stanley House Hotel, central location in elegant Belgravia, 4/5 minutes walk from Victoria Transport complex for easy access to all famous sights and West End shopping and theatre. Spacious bedrooms having ensuite facilities. Prices inclusive of full English breakfast. Tea/coffee available 24 hours.

St George's Hotel, 25 Belgrave Road, Victoria, London, SW1V 1RB. **Open:** All year **020 7828 2061 & 020 7828 3605** Mr Zaidi **Fax: 020 7834 8439** *cmahotel@aol.com* www.londonbudgethotels. co.uk **D:** £25.00–£30.00 **S:** £30.00–£45.00 **Beds:** 4D 4T 2F 1S **Baths:** 3 En 8 Pr ♥ 🖾 🖾. Comfortable, clean, spacious bright rooms. Handy for Gatwick and Heathrow. Great central location.

Holly House Hotel, 20 Hugh Street, Victoria, London, SW1V 1RP. **Open:** All year **020 7834 5671** Mr Jessa **Fax: 020 7233 5154** *hhhotel@ukgateway.net* www.hollyhousehotel. co.uk **D:** £40.00–£50.00 **S:** £30.00–£45.00 **Beds:** 2F 10D 7T 6S **Baths:** 11 En 7 Sh ♥ 🖾 🖾. cc Bed and breakfast in the heart of London. Affordable accommodation perfectly situated.

Marne Hotel, 34 Belgrave Road, Victoria, London, SW1V 1RG. Comfortable family-run B&B in the heart of London. **Open:** All year **020 7834 5195 & 07771 950095 (M)** Mr Montagnani **Fax: 020 7976 6180** www.freepages.co.uk/marne_hotel/ **D:** £21.00–£35.00 **S:** £35.00–£55.00 **Beds:** 3F 5D 1T 3S **Baths:** 8 En 1 Sh ♥ 🖾 🖾. cc

Dover Hotel, 44 Belgrave Road, Victoria, London, SW1V 1RG. Small, friendly, clean, comfortable hotel near Buckingham Palace, Gatwick Express. **Open:** All year **Grades:** ETC 2 Diamond **020 7821 9085 Fax: 020 7834 6425** *reception@ dover-hotel.co.uk* www.dover-hotel.co.uk **D:** £32.50–£37.50 **S:** £55.00–£65.00 **Beds:** 8F 7T 14D 4S **Baths:** 29 En 4 Sh ♥ 🖾 🖾. ♣ cc

Melita House Hotel, 35 Charlwood Street, Victoria, London, SW1V 2DU. Excellent location and value, extensive facilities for category, recommended. **Open:** All year **Grades:** ETC 3 Diamond **020 7828 0471** Mr Gabrielle **Fax: 020 7932 0988** *reserve@melita.co.uk* www.melitahotel. com **D:** £42.50–£50.00 **S:** £55.00–£70.00 **Beds:** 4F 6T 10D **Baths:** 22 En ♥ ⅜ 🖾 🖾. ❋ cc

Alexander Hotel, 13 Belgrave Road, Victoria, London, SW1V 1RB. Clean, comfortable, affordable family-run B&B situated in the centre of London. **Open:** All year (not Xmas) **020 7834 9738** Mr Montagnani **Fax: 020 7630 9630** www.alexanderhotel.co.uk **D:** £22.50–£65.00 **S:** £30.00–£60.00 **Beds:** 3F 7D 2T 1S **Baths:** 13 En ♥ 🖸 🖾 🖾. cc

Collin House, 104 Ebury Street, Victoria, London, SW1W 9QD. Centrally located providing an ideal base for visiting London's many attractions. **Open:** All year (not Xmas/New Year) **020 7730 8031 (also fax)** Mr Thomas **D:** £32.50–£40.00 **S:** £52.00–£60.00 **Beds:** 1F 5D 4T 3S **Baths:** 8 En 3 Sh ♥ ⅜

Grangewood Lodge Hotel, 104 Clova Road, Forest Gate, London, E7 9AF. 5 minute walk Forest Gate station for easy access central London & Docklands. **Open:** All year **Grades:** ETC 1 Diamond **020 8534 0637** Mr Downing **Fax: 020 8503 0941** *grangewoodlodgehotel@talk21.com* www.grangewoodlodgehotel.co.uk **D:** £17.50–£22.00 **S:** £22.00–£40.00 **Beds:** 4F 1D 4T 9S **Baths:** 2 En 4 Sh ♥ (10) 🖸 (2) 🖾 🖾. ♣ cc

Woodville Guest House, 10/12 Argyle Road, Ilford, Essex, IG1 3BQ. Private family-run business for 25 years. Extremely friendly, minutes from shops and trains. **Open:** All year (not Xmas/New Year) **020 8478 3779** Mrs Murray **Fax: 020 8478 6282** www.cassewoodville-guesthouse.co.uk **D:** £20.00–£30.00 **S:** £30.00–£45.00 **Beds:** 3F 6T 4D 3S **Baths:** 5 En 2 Pr 5 Sh ♥ 🖸 (12) 🖾 🖾. ♣

Grove Hill Hotel, Grove Hill, South Woodford, London, E18 2JG. Quiet, central location. Good breakfast. **Open:** All year (not Xmas/New Year) **020 8989 3344** Mr Mamelok **Fax: 0208 530 5286 D:** £53.00–£61.00 **S:** £33.00–£45.00 **Beds:** 3F 4T 13D 8S **Baths:** 11 En 11 Pr 3 Sh ♥ 🖸 (12) 🖾 ⇟ 🖾 🖾. ♣ cc

Sunningdale Guest House, 35 Lonsdale Road, Wanstead, London, E11 2PH. Friendly, family-run hotel. Close Green Belt. Five mins' walk direct line to central London. **Open:** All year **020 8989 3435** I A Novlis *irenenovlis@ lineone.net* **D:** £17.50–£20.00 **S:** £23.00–£25.00 **Beds:** 2F 1T 6D 3S ♥ 🖸 (4) 🖾 🖾 🖾. ♣ ♣

The Fosters, 71 Grosvenor Road, Wanstead, London, E11 2ES. Excellent accommodation, quiet, welcoming, comfortable. Close to tube. Unrestricted parking. **Open:** All year (not Xmas) **020 8530 6970 (also fax)** Mrs Foster *b&b@ the-fosters71.freeserve.co.uk* **D:** £22.00–£25.00 **S:** £37.50–£45.00 **Beds:** 1F 1D 1T **Baths:** 2 En 1 Sh ♥ ⅜ 🖾 🖾. ♣ cc

22 Trinder Road, (off Shaftesbury Road), Crouch Hill, London, N19 4QU. Quiet, rustic, terraced house near lively bars, cafes, leafy area. Longer stays negotiated. **Open:** All year **020 7686 4073** Ms Shrive **D:** £17.50–£20.00 **S:** £20.00–£25.00 **Beds:** 2D 1S **Baths:** 2 Sh 🖸 🖾 🖾. ♣

Dillons Hotel, 21 Belsize Park, Hampstead, London, NW3 4DU. Handy for central London - budget B&B close Hampstead and Camden. **Open:** All year **Grades:** ETC 1 Diamond **020 7794 3360** Mr Dillon **Fax: 020 7431 7900** *desk@dillonshotel.com* www.dillonshotel.com **D:** £24.00–£30.00 **S:** £32.00–£44.00 **Beds:** 3F 5D 4T 1S **Baths:** 8 En 3 Sh ♥ 🖾 🖾. cc

71 Berkshire Gardens, Palmers Green, London, N13 6AA. Private house with garden. **Open:** All year **020 8888 5573** Mr Clark **D:** £18.00–£22.00 **S:** £18.00–£22.00 **Beds:** 1T 1D **Baths:** 1 Sh

BATHROOMS
En = Ensuite
Pr = Private
Sh = Shared

NORTH LONDON
Tufnell Park
TQ2986

Five Kings Guest House, 59 Anson Road, Tufnell Park, London, N7 0AR. **Open:** All year **020 7607 3996** Mr Poulacheris **Fax: 020 7609 5554 D:** £19.00 **S:** £24.00–£28.00 **Beds:** 4F 3D 3T 6S **Baths:** 16 En 7 Pr 3 Sh ➣ (4) ⊠ 📺 ♨ cc
Five Kings is a family-run guest house in a quiet residential area. Only 15 minutes to Central London and tourist attractions. Camden Lock, London Zoo, Kings Cross, St Pancras station are only 2 miles away. No parking restrictions in Anson Road.

NORTH LONDON
West Hampstead
TQ2585

Charlotte Guest House, 195-197 Sumatra Road, West Hampstead, London, NW6 1PF. Central London. Accessible transport. Free London travel card for 7 nights' stay. **Open:** All year **020 7794 6476** L Koch **Fax: 020 7431 3584** *enquiries@charlotteguesthouse.co.uk* www.charlotteguesthouse.co.uk **D:** £23.00–£28.00 **S:** £35.00–£45.00 **Beds:** 2F 12T 12D 12S **Baths:** 20 En 6 Sh ➣ ⊠ 📺 ♨ cc

OUTER LONDON
Bentley
TQ5696

The Coach House, Mores Lane, Bentley, Brentwood, Essex, CM14 5PZ. 200 year old coaching house in 1 acre grounds. **Open:** All year (not Xmas/New Year) **01277 375015** S Mead **Fax: 01277 372954** *sheilaghandroger@aol.com* **D:** £22.00–£25.00 **S:** £22.00–£25.00 ⊱ ⊠ 📺 🖾 ♨

OUTER LONDON
Borehamwood
TQ1996

84 Stevenage Crescent, Borehamwood, Herts, WD6 4NS. Luxury, modern private house. **Open:** All year **020 8207 3320** M Feehily *miriamfeehily@aol.com* **D:** £25.00 **S:** £30.00 **Beds:** 3T **Baths:** 1 Sh ➣ 🄿 (4) ⊠ ⊁ 🖾 ✸ ♨

OUTER LONDON
Chalfont St Giles
SU9893

Gorelands Corner, Gorelands Lane, Chalfont St Giles, Bucks, HP8 4HQ. Family house set in large garden. Easy access to motorways. **Open:** All year **Grades:** ETC 3 Diamond **01494 872689 (also fax)** Mrs Bickford *bickfordcsg@compuserve.com* **D:** £27.50 **S:** £22.50 **Beds:** 1D 1S **Baths:** 1 En 1 Pr ➣ 🄿 (3) ⊁ ⊠ 📺 🖾 ♨

OUTER LONDON
Chevening
TQ4857

Crossways House, Chevening Road, Chevening, Sevenoaks, Kent, TN14 6HF. Beautiful Kentish Ragstone c1760 in 5 acres. Conferences welcome. **Open:** All year (not Xmas/New Year) **01732 456334** Mrs Weavers **Fax: 01732 452334 D:** £25.00 **S:** £25.00 **Beds:** 4D **Baths:** 3 En 1 Pr ➣ 🄿 (4) ⊁ ⊠ 🖾 ♨

OUTER LONDON
Chorleywood
TQ0296

Kennels Cottage, Common Road, Chorleywood, Herts, WD3 5LW. A quiet oasis. A mellow brick cottage. A warm welcome. **Open:** All year (not Xmas) **01923 282927** Mrs Smethurst **D:** £22.50 **S:** £25.00 **Beds:** 2F 2S **Baths:** 1 Sh ➣ 🄿 (4) ⊁ ⊠ 📺 🖾 ♨

OUTER LONDON
Croxley Green
TQ0695

Farthings, Copthorne Road, Croxley Green, Rickmansworth, Hertfordshire, WD3 4AE. Situated in private road. Close to station and M25 Motorway. **Open:** All year (not Xmas/New Year) **01923 771431** Mrs Saunders *bazmau@barclays.net* **D:** £22.50 **S:** £22.50 **Beds:** 1T 2S **Baths:** 1 Sh ➣ (6) 🄿 (6) ⊁ ⊠ 🖾 ♨

OUTER LONDON
Dartford
TQ5273

Royal Victoria and Bull Hotel, 1 High Street, Dartford, Kent, DA1 1DU. An C18th inn. Easy access to town centre and motorways. **Open:** All year **01322 224415 Fax: 01322 289474 D:** £27.00 **S:** £54.00 **Beds:** 2F 5D 9T 8S **Baths:** 25 En ⊠ ⊁ 🖾 ♨ cc

OUTER LONDON   Elstree
TQ1795

North Medburn Farm, Watling Street, Elstree, Herts, WD6 3AA. Easy access to London. **Open:** All year (not Xmas) **020 8953 1522** Mrs Williams **D:** £20.00–£25.00 **S:** £20.00–£25.00 **Beds:** 1F 3T 1S **Baths:** 1 En 1 Sh 🄿 (4) ⊁ 🖾

OUTER LONDON   Esher
TQ1464

Lilac Cottage, 14 Greenways, Hinchley Wood, Esher, Surrey, KT10 0QD. Luxury friendly family home convenient London, Hampton Court, Wisley, Sandown. **Open:** All year (not Xmas) **020 8398 7546 (also fax)** Mrs Evans *evans@greenways.demon.co.uk* **D:** £30.00 **S:** £35.00 **Beds:** 1D 1T **Baths:** 2 En ⊁ ⊠ 🖾 ♨ cc

OUTER LONDON
Great Warley
TQ5890   🍺 Thatcher's Arms

Chestnut Tree Cottage, Great Warley Street, Great Warley, Brentwood, Essex, CM13 3JF. Attractive country cottage. Conveniently located M25, A127, A12. 1 mile to London. **Open:** All year **Grades:** ETC 3 Diamond **01277 221727** Mrs Malyon **D:** £25.00–£28.00 **S:** £25.00–£35.00 **Beds:** 1F 1T 1D **Baths:** 3 En ➣ 🄿 (31) ⊁ ⊠ 📺 🖾 ♨

OUTER LONDON
Greenhithe
TQ5874

Metraro Hotel, Cobham Terrace, Greenhithe, Kent, DA9 9JB. **Open:** All year **01322 383767 Fax: 01322 380834 D:** £21.00–£26.00 **S:** £33.00–£46.00 **Beds:** 3F 1T 3D 2S **Baths:** 7 En 2 Sh ➣ (3) 🄿 (15) ⊠ ➤ ⊁ ⊠ 🖾 ♨ cc
Well-restored Victorian hotel, run and owned by same family for 20 years. Edge of riverside conservation village, 300 metres from Bluewater entrance. Close to A2 and M25, few miles Kent gardens and orchards. Historic Rochester 8 miles.

BEDROOMS
D = Double
T = Twin
S = Single
F = Family

OUTER LONDON
Iver Heath
TQ0282

Oaklands, *Bangors Road South, Iver Heath, Slough, Bucks, SL10 0BB.* Large family house convenient for Heathrow, Windsor, Uxbridge and Slough. **Open:** All year (not Xmas)
01753 653005 Mrs Fowler **Fax:** 01753 653003
D: £20.00 **S:** £20.00–£25.00 **Beds:** 1F 1D 2T 1S **Baths:** 1 En 2 Sh ⊞ (4) 𝌆 ⊡ ▥ ♨

OUTER LONDON
Jordans
SU9791

Old Jordans, *Jordans Lane, Jordans, Beaconsfield, Buckinghamshire, HP9 2SW.* Historic venue in large grounds. Traditional food and excellent hospitality. **Open:** All year **Grades:** ETC 3 Diamond
01494 874586 Fax: 01494 875657 *reception@ oldjordans.org.uk* oldjordans.org.uk
D: £25.00–£31.00 **S:** £31.00–£49.00 **Beds:** 1F 3T 9D 11S **Baths:** 15 En 4 Sh ➳⊞✕⊡▥♿✸ ♨ cc

OUTER LONDON
Littleton
TQ0668

Old Manor House, *Squires Bridge Road, Littleton, Shepperton, Middx, TW17 0QG.* Listed building dating from reign of Henry VII, set in 5 acres of garden. **Open:** All year
01932 571293 Mrs Bouwens *victor@ oldmanorhouse.demon.co.uk*
www.oldmanorhouse.demon.co.uk
D: £25.00–£27.50 **S:** £30.00 **Beds:** 1D 1T 1S **Baths:** 1 En 1 Sh ➳ (10) ⊞ (6) ☒ ⍩ ▥ ♨

OUTER LONDON
London Colney
TL1804

The Conifers, *42 Thamesdale, London Colney, St Albans, Herts, AL2 1TL.* Modern detached house. Historic city St Albans 3 miles. Easy access motorway network. **Open:** All year **Grades:** ETC 3 Diamond
01727 823622 D: £22.00–£26.00 **S:** £22.00–£26.00 **Beds:** 1D 1T 1S **Baths:** 1 Sh ➳ (12) ⊞ 𝌆 ⊡ ▥ ♨

All details shown are as supplied by B&B owners in Autumn 2001

OUTER LONDON
Loughton
TQ4396

Forest Edge, *61 York Hill, Loughton, Essex, IG10 1HZ.* Quiet location. Off-street parking. Convenient for Central Line. **Open:** All year (not Xmas/New Year)
020 8508 9834 E Catterall **Fax:** 020 8281 1894
arthur@catterallarthur.fsnet.co.uk **D:** £19.00–£20.00 **S:** £22.25–£25.00 **Beds:** 2T 1S

OUTER LONDON
North Ockendon
TQ5984 ⌘ *Old White Horse*

Corner Farm, *Fen Lane, North Ockendon, Upminster, Essex, RM14 3RB.* Detached bungalow in rural setting. 4 Miles Upminster station. Breakfast served in conservatory. **Open:** All year (not Xmas/ New Year) **Grades:** ETC 3 Diamond
01708 851310 Fax: 01708 852025
corner.farm@virgin.net **D:** £17.50–£18.75 **S:** £25.00–£35.00 **Beds:** 1F 1T 2S **Baths:** 1 En 1 Sh ⊞ (8) 𝌆 ⊡ ▥ ♨ cc

OUTER LONDON Radlett
TL1600 ⌘ *Red Lion*

The Turners, *43 Craigweil Avenue, Radlett, Hertfordshire, WD7 7ET.* Warm welcome. Ideally situated for Herts, Beds and Bucks. 20 mins to London. **Open:** All year
01923 469245 & 07776 132416 (M)
Mrs Turner **D:** £20.00–£22.50 **S:** £20.00–£25.00 **Beds:** 1T 1S **Baths:** 1 En 1 Sh ➳⊞ (4) 𝌆 ⊡ ☒ ▥ ♨

OUTER LONDON
Rickmansworth
TQ0494

The Millwards Guest House, *30 Hazelwood Road, Croxley Green, Rickmansworth, Herts, WD3 3EB.* Family run, pleasant canalside location. Convenient motorways, trains, airport, business parks. **Open:** All year (not Xmas/New Year)
01923 226666 & 07881 658870 (M)
Mrs Millward **Fax:** 01923 252874 *bandb@ millwards.com* **D:** £40.00–£45.00 **S:** £25.00–£30.00 **Beds:** 3T **Baths:** 2 Sh ➳ (2) ⊞ (2) 𝌆 ☒ ☒ ⊡ ▥ ♨

Tall Trees, *6 Swallow Close, Nightingale Road, Rickmansworth, Herts, WD3 2DZ.* Situated in quiet cul-de-sac near underground station. Home-made bread and preserves. **Open:** All year
01923 720069 Mrs Childerhouse **D:** £25.00–£28.00 **S:** £25.00–£28.00 **Beds:** 1D 3S **Baths:** 1 Sh ➳ (10) ⊞ (4) 𝌆 ⊡ ▥ ♨

OUTER LONDON
Shepperton
TQ0767 ⌘ *The Kingfisher, Thames Court Hotel*

The Bull Inn, *152 Laleham Road, Shepperton, TW17 0DB.* Perfect for visiting all main attractions in Surrey. Friendly Atmosphere. **Open:** All year
01932 221667 D: £21.00 **S:** £16.00 **Beds:** 3T 1S **Baths:** 3 En 1 Sh ⊞ (20) ⊡ ▥ ♨ cc

Splash Cottage, *91 Watersplash Road, Shepperton, TW17 0EE.* Olde worlde cottage with pretty bedrooms and old fashioned hospitality. **Open:** All year **Grades:** ETC 3 Diamond
01932 229987 (also fax) Mr Shaw
www.lazy-river.co.uk **D:** £20.00–£25.00 **S:** £27.00–£35.00 **Beds:** 2D 1T ➳ 𝌆 ⊡ ▥ ♨

OUTER LONDON Staines
TQ0471

The Penton, *39 Penton Road, Staines, TW18 2JL.* Homely character cottage close to River Thames, access to scenic walks and historic surroundings. **Open:** All year
01784 458787 D: £20.00–£25.00 **S:** £20.00–£26.00 **Beds:** 4F 1D 1T 1S **Baths:** 2 En 1 Sh ➳ ⊞ (2) 𝌆 ⊡ ☒ ▥ ✸ ♨

OUTER LONDON
Theydon Bois
TQ4499 ⌘ *Bull Inn, Railway Arms, Queen Victoria*

Glenfield, *26 Hill Road, Theydon Bois, Epping, Essex, CM16.* Detached family house furnished to a high standard, adjacent forest, underground and M25. **Open:** All year
01992 812541 (also fax) Mr & Mrs Day
D: £22.00–£26.00 **S:** £22.00–£55.00 **Beds:** 3T 1S **Baths:** 1 Sh ➳ ⊞ (4) 𝌆 ⊡ ▥ ♨

OUTER LONDON
Waltham Abbey
TL3800

Ivydene Cottage, *Woodgreen Road, Waltham Abbey, EN9 3SD.* Historic town and surroundings, canals and local interests. **Open:** All year (not Xmas)
01992 716082 (also fax) Mrs Oatham
D: £20.00–£35.00 **S:** £25.00 **Beds:** 2T 1D **Baths:** 2 En 2 Sh ⊞ (5) 𝌆 ⊡ ✕ ⊡ ▥ ♨

OUTER LONDON
Walton-on-Thames

TQ1066 🏮 *Badgers Rest*

Beech Tree Lodge, 7 Rydens Avenue, Walton-on-Thames, Surrey, KT12 3JB. In quiet avenue, close BR station, local shops. Foreign languages spoken. **Open:** All year **Grades:** ETC 3 Diamond
01932 242738 & 01932 886667 Mrs Spiteri
joanspiteri@aol.com **D:** £20.00–£21.00
S: £22.00–£36.00 **Beds:** 1F 1T 1S **Baths:** 2 Sh ☞ 🅿 (8) ⊁ 🅥 ⊁ 🆅 📖 ⚲

OUTER LONDON
Warlingham

TQ3558

Glenmore, Southview Road, Warlingham, Surrey, CR6 9JE. Victorian House in the large grounds close to the countryside and London. **Open:** All year
01883 624530 Fax: 01883 624199 **D:** £17.50
S: £22.00 **Beds:** 2F 1T 2D **Baths:** 1 En 2 Sh ☞ 🅿 (6) ⊁ 🆅 📖 ⚲

OUTER LONDON
Watford

TQ1097

33 Courtlands Drive, Watford, Herts, WD1 3HU. Detached house, warm and friendly. Convenient London, Canal, motorways M1, M25. **Open:** All year (not Xmas)
01923 220531 A Troughton **D:** £20.00–£22.50
S: £25.00 **Beds:** 2T 1S **Baths:** 1 Sh ☞ (2) 🅿 (6) ⊁ 🆅 ⊁ 📖 ⚲

Applecrust B&B, 52 Rickmansworth Road, Watford, Herts, WD1 7HT. Friendly, comfortable, centrally located accommodation with high quality home cooking. **Open:** All year
01923 223125 Mrs Spicer **Fax:** 01923 211652
D: £22.50–£27.50 **S:** £30.00–£40.00 **Beds:** 1F 1T 1D **Baths:** 1 En 1 Sh 🅿 (4) 🆅 ⊁ 🆅 📖 ⚲

Grey's Bed & Breakfast, 1 Wellington Road, Watford, Herts, WD1 1QU. Ideally located for railway station, town centre and business parks. **Open:** Jan to Dec
07990 956260 (M) M-L Grey **Fax:** 01923 492446 *greysbnb@bigfoot.com* www.users. globalnet.co.uk/~outpost/bnb/home.html
D: £22.50 **S:** £25.00 **Beds:** 2T 1S **Baths:** 2 Sh 🅿 (4) ⊁ 🆅 ⚲

OUTER LONDON
West Molesey

TQ1268

Pilgrim's Retreat, 43 Grange Road, West Molesey, Surrey, KT8 2PR. Friendly, family home, one mile from Hampton Court. Continental breakfast. **Open:** All year (not Xmas/New Year)
020 8224 2460 Ms Vaughan-Spruce
vaughan_spruce@hotmail.com **D:** £16.50
S: £22.00 **Beds:** 1T 1S **Baths:** 1 Sh 🅿 (1) ⊁ 🆅 📖 ⚲

OUTER LONDON
Wraysbury

TQ0073

Honeysuckle Cottage, 61 Fairfield Approach, Wraysbury, Staines, TW19 5DR. Picturesque cottage in the historic Thames-side village of Wraysbury. Excellent country pubs. **Open:** All year (not Xmas)
01784 482519 Mrs Vogel **Fax:** 01784 482305
B&B@berks.force9.co.uk www.berks.force9.co. uk **D:** £22.50–£27.50 **S:** £30.00–£40.00
Beds: 2F 1D 1T 1S **Baths:** 4 En 1 Pr ☞ (3) 🅿 (8) ⊁ 🆅 🆅 📖 ⚲ ⚲ cc

SOUTH LONDON
Bickley

TQ4269

Glendevon House Hotel, 80 Southborough Road, Bickley, Bromley, Kent, BR1 2EN. 3 Crown hotel near Bromley town centre. All rooms ensuite. **Open:** All year
020 8467 2183 **D:** £34.00 **S:** £35.00–£46.00
Beds: 4T 4D 2S 2F **Baths:** 12 En 1 Pr ☞ (2) 🅿 (8) ⊁ 🆅 ✕ 🆅 📖 ⚹ ⚲ cc

SOUTH LONDON
Blackheath

TQ3976

Numbernine Blackheath Ltd., 9 Charlton Road, Blackheath, London, SE3 7EU.
Open: All year **Grades:** ETC 4 Diamond
020 8858 4175 & 020 8293 0351 Fax: 020 8858 4175 *derek@numbernineblackheath.com* www.numbernineblackheath.com **D:** £37.50
S: £45.00 **Beds:** 1F 4D **Baths:** 5 Pr ☞ (5) 🅿 (4) ⊁ 🆅 ✕ 🆅 📖 ⚲ cc
Number Nine is a friendly, non-smoking guest house located at The Royal Standard, within twenty minutes walking distance of the historic town of Greenwich. This recently fully refurbished Victorian guest house provides warm, comfortable, safe, fully Fire Certificated surroundings. Individual Sky TV. Free video library.

29 Tellson Avenue, Blackheath, London, SE18 4PD. Situated in quiet tree lined avenue opposite bus stop. Leisure and shopping centres nearby. **Open:** All year (not Xmas/New Year) **Grades:** ETC 2 Diamond
020 8856 9213 P T Nagalingham
ptndedicatedservices@compuserve.com **S:** £21.00
Beds: 2S **Baths:** 1 Sh 🅿 (3) ⊁ 🆅 📖 ⚲

SOUTH LONDON
Brockley

TQ3674

Geoffrey Road B & B, 66 Geoffrey Road, Brockley, London, SE4 1NT. Friendly and relaxed Victorian family home in Brockley conservation area. **Open:** All year
020 8691 3887 (also fax) Ms Dechamps
b&bgeoffrey@woodin.u-net.com **D:** £20.00–
£22.50 **S:** £20.00–£25.00 **Beds:** 1T **Baths:** 1 Sh ☞ 🆅 🆅 📖 ⚲

SOUTH LONDON
Catford

TQ3873

Hazeldene Bed & Breakfast, 75 Brownhill Road (South Circular Road), Catford, London, SE6 2HF. Traditional English B&B, Victorian house. Greenwich 3 miles/Zone 3. **Open:** All year
020 8697 2436 Fax: 020 8473 9601 *hazeldene@ zoo.co.uk* **D:** £19.00–£22.50 **S:** £20.00–£35.00
Beds: 1F 1D 2T 2S **Baths:** 1 En 2 Sh ☞ (8) 🅿 (1) 🆅 🆅 📖 ⚲

SOUTH LONDON
Croydon

TQ3265

Croydon Friendly Guest House, 16 St Peters Road, Croydon, CR0 1HD. Large character full detached house enjoying a warm friendly atmosphere. **Open:** All year
020 8680 4428 Mr Hasan **D:** £20.00–£30.00
S: £25.00–£30.00 **Beds:** 1T 5S **Baths:** 2 En 2 Sh ☞ (1) 🅿 (6) ⊁ 🆅 ✕ 🆅 📖 ⚲

SOUTH LONDON
Dulwich

TQ3472

Diana Hotel, 88 Thurlow Park Road, West Dulwich, London, SE21 8HY. Comfortable hotel near Dulwich Village, a pleasant London suburb. **Open:** All year
020 8670 3250 Fax: 020 8761 8300 *dihotel@ aol.com* www.dianahotel.com **D:** £25.00–
£30.00 **S:** £30.00–£60.00 **Beds:** 1F 5T 5D 2S **Baths:** 4 En 2 Sh ☞ 🅿 📖 ⚲

SOUTH LONDON
Greenwich

TQ3977

78 Vanbrugh Park, Blackheath, Greenwich, London, SE3 7JQ. **Open:** All year
020 8858 0338 Mrs Mattey **Fax:** 020 8244 6690 **D:** £20.00–£25.00 **S:** £25.00–£30.00
Beds: 1F 2T **Baths:** 1 En 1 Pr ☞ 🅿 (3) 🆅 📖 ⚲
Lovely Victorian house near Greenwich Park and Heath. Close to Blackwall tunnel and buses. Suit holidaymakers, weekly workers and weekenders. Rooms organised as flats with living-kitchen areas with cooker/fridge. Bedrooms overlook beautiful south-facing garden.

Greenwich Parkhouse Hotel, 1 & 2 Nevada Street, Greenwich, London, SE10 9JL. Small hotel, beautifully situated within World Heritage site by gates of Royal Greenwich Park. **Open:** All year
020 8305 1478 Mrs Bryan **D:** £20.00–£25.00
S: £33.00 **Beds:** 21F **Baths:** 2 En 1 Pr 2 Sh ☞ 🅿 (8) ⊁ 🆅 📖 ⚲

Planning a longer stay? Always ask for any special rates

Dover House, 155 Shooters Hill, Greenwich, London, SE18 3HP. Victorian family house opposite famous Oxleas Wood, 8 miles Central London. Warm welcome awaits. **Open:** All year (not Xmas) 020 8856 9892 (also fax) Mrs Araniello *joan.araniello@lineone.net* **D:** £20.00–£25.00 **S:** £25.00 **Beds:** 2F 2T 2S **Baths:** 1 Sh ☎ 🖭 ⚡ 🗁 🖵 🏧 ⚡

SOUTH LONDON
Hither Green
TQ3974

51 Manor Park, Hither Green, London, SE13 5RA. Generous friendly Victorian house. 20 mins central London. Own kitchen. **Open:** All year 020 8318 6474 Mr McMurray **Fax:** 020 8244 6690 *mcmurray@dircon.co.uk* **D:** £20.00 **S:** £20.00 **Beds:** 2T 1S **Baths:** 2 Sh ☎ (10) 🖵 (2) 🖭 🏧 ⚡

Hither Green
TQ3974

13 Wellmeadow Road, Hither Green, London, SE13 6SY. 3 mins BR Station, 6 mins A2 to Dover or M25. **Open:** All year 020 8697 1398 Mrs Noonan **Fax:** 020 8 697 1398 **D:** £20.00 **S:** £18.00 **Beds:** 2F 2D **Baths:** 2 Sh ☎ 🖵 (2) ⚡ 🖭 ✕ 🏧

SOUTH LONDON Kenley
TQ3259

Appledore, 6 Betula Close, Kenley, Surrey, CR8 5ET. Comfortable detached house in quiet wooded location. Near M25, Gatwick. **Open:** All year 020 8668 4631 (also fax) Mrs Wilmshurst **D:** £22.00–£24.00 **S:** £25.00 **Beds:** 1D 1T 1S **Baths:** 1 Sh ☎ (12) 🖵 (2) ⚡ 🖭 🏧 ⚡

SOUTH LONDON
Kingston
TQ1869

40 The Bittoms, Kingston, KT1 2AP. Very close to town centre & River Thames. Quiet location. **Open:** All year 020 8541 3171 Mrs Lefebvre **D:** £22.50–£27.50 **S:** £25.00–£35.00 **Beds:** 1T 1D 1S **Baths:** 1 Sh ☎ (4) 🖭 ✕ 🖵 🏧 ⚡

SOUTH LONDON
Lewisham
TQ3875 ◖ Brockley Jack

Family Stay, 2 Crofton Gateway, Lewisham, London, SE4 2DL. Easy transport access. South East London, connected train. Buses accessible. **Open:** All year **Grades:** ETC 2 Diamond 020 8694 0011 **D:** £15.00 **S:** £15.00 **Beds:** 1D 1S **Baths:** 1 Sh ☎ 🖵 (3) 🖭 🏧 &

8 Yeats Close, Eliot Park, Lewisham, London, SE13 7ET. **Open:** All year **Grades:** ETC 2 Diamond 020 8318 3421 (also fax) Ms Hutton **D:** £22.50–£25.00 **S:** £25.00 **Beds:** 1D 1T 1S **Baths:** 1 Sh ☎ ⚡ 🖭 🏧 ⚡ Homely base in quiet tree-lined road convenient for Greenwich, Docklands and Central London, yet only 5 mins from the Heath. East access to all bus, train and DLR connections so you can be in Central London in 15 mins.

SOUTH LONDON
New Malden
TQ2167

30 Presburg Road, New Malden, Surrey, KT3 5AH. Easy 20-min rail journey Central London or Hampton Court; 10 mins Kingston-upon-Thames, Wimbledon. **Open:** All year (not Xmas) 020 8949 4910 Mr & Mrs Evans **D:** £22.50–£25.00 **S:** £25.00–£30.00 **Beds:** 1F 1D 1S **Baths:** 2 Sh ☎ (6) 🖵 (1) ⚡ 🖭 ✕ 🖵 🏧 ⚡

SOUTH LONDON
Norbury
TQ3169

The Konyots, 95 Pollards Hill South, Norbury, London, SW16 4LS. Located in a quiet residential area with a park nearby. **Open:** All year 020 8764 0075 Mrs Konyot **D:** £15.00 **S:** £15.00 **Beds:** 1F 1S **Baths:** 1 Sh ☎ 🖵 (1) 🖭 ⌂ 🖭 🏧 ⚡

SOUTH LONDON
Orpington
TQ4565

20 The Avenue, St Pauls Cray, Orpington, Kent, BR5 3DL. Detached family house in cul-de-sac. Excellent full English breakfast. Good road and rail connections. **Open:** All year (not Xmas/New Year) 020 8300 1040 (also fax) Mrs Tomkins *tomkinsbandb@20theavenue.freeserve.co.uk* **D:** £21.00 **S:** £21.00–£25.00 **Beds:** 1D 1T 1S **Baths:** 1 Sh ☎ 🖵 (1) ⚡ 🖭 ⌂ 🖭 🏧 ⚡

SOUTH LONDON Purley
TQ3161

The Nook, 12 Grasmere Road, Purley, Surrey, CR8 1DU. Edwardian house, near to Purley station, small house with personal attention. **Open:** Jan to Dec 020 8660 1742 Mrs Andrews **D:** £18.00–£20.00 **S:** £18.00–£20.00 **Beds:** 1D 2S **Baths:** 1 Sh ☎ (5) ⚡ 🖭 ⌂ 🏧 ⚡

SOUTH LONDON Putney
TQ2374

The Grange, One Fanthorpe Street, Putney, London, SW15 1DZ. **Open:** All year (not Xmas) 020 8785 7609 Mr & Mrs Taylor **Fax:** 020 8789 5584 *bbputney@btinternet.com* www.bbputney. btinternet.co.uk **D:** £27.50 **S:** £35.00 **Beds:** 1D 1T **Baths:** 1 En 1 Sh ☎ ⚡ ✕ 🖭 🏧 A warm welcome awaits you to our comfortable family home, which is close to Thames, and convenient for bus, Underground and BR Mainline. No smoking. Evening meals by arrangement. Bed and excellent continental breakfast £27.50–£35 per person per night.

SOUTH LONDON
South Croydon
TQ3263

Owlets, 112 Arundel Avenue, Selsdon, Croydon, Surrey, CR2 8BH. Situated within easy reach of Croydon, Purley, London, Gatwick Airport. **Open:** All year (not Xmas/New Year) **Grades:** ETC 3 Diamond 020 8657 5213 & 07946 282562 (M) **Fax:** 020 8657 5213 *owlets@talk21.com* **D:** £20.00–£25.00 **S:** £25.00–£30.00 **Beds:** 3T **Baths:** 1 Sh ☎ ⚡ 🖭 🏧 ⚡

SOUTH LONDON
Sydenham
TQ3471

97 Wiverton Road, Sydenham, London, SE26 5JB. We offer bed and breakfast accommodation in our charming Victorian home in South-East London. **Open:** All year (not Xmas/New Year) 020 8778 8101 Dr & Mrs Tegner *henrytegner@sydenham2.demon.co.uk* www.sydenham2. demon.co.uk/b-and-b.htm **D:** £30.00–£40.00 **S:** £30.00–£40.00 **Beds:** 2T **Baths:** 1 Pr 1 Sh ☎ ⚡ 🖭 ✕ 🖭 🏧 ⚡

SOUTH LONDON
Wimbledon
TQ2471

22 Mayfield Road, Wimbledon, London, SW19 3NF. Artist's detached house. Warm welcome. Near BR, Underground, A3 and M25. **Open:** All year 020 8543 2607 (also fax) Mr & Mrs Daglish **D:** £25.00–£28.00 **S:** £25.00–£29.00 **Beds:** 1D 1T **Baths:** 1 En 1 Pr 🖵 (2) ⚡ 🖭 🖭 🏧 ⚡

Planning a longer stay? Always ask for any special rates

WEST LONDON
Chiswick
TQ2078

Fouberts Hotel, *162-166 Chiswick High Road, Chiswick, London, W4 1PR.* Family-run hotel, continental atmosphere. **Open:** All year
020 8994 5202 & 020 8995 6743 Mr Lodico
D: £35.00–£40.00 **S:** £25.00–£27.50 **Beds:** 6F 6D 4T 16S **Baths:** 32 Pr ⓈＰ✔♥×♥囲. cc

WEST LONDON   Ealing
TQ1780

4 Carlton Gardens, *Ealing, London, W5 2AN.* Lovely Victorian house, quiet conservation area. Easy access central London, theatres, tourist attractions. **Open:** All year (not Xmas/New Year)
020 8997 7712 Mrs Lynch **Fax: 020 8998 2590**
acc@bblondon.demon.co.uk **D:** £22.50 **S:** £35.00
Beds: 1T 2D **Baths:** 2 Pr 1 Sh Ⓢ (10)✔♥♥囲.

Abbey Lodge Hotel, *51 Grange Park, Ealing, London, W5 3PR.* Halfway between Heathrow and Central London. Home from home atmosphere. **Open:** All year (not Xmas) **Grades:** ETC 2 Diamond, AA 2 Diamond
020 8567 7914 Mrs Grindrod **Fax: 020 8579 5350** *enquiries@londonlodgehotels.com*
www.londonlodgehotels.com **D:** £28.50
S: £45.00 **Beds:** 3F 3D 1T 9S **Baths:** 16 En Ⓢ ♥★囲.♣cc

Grange Lodge Hotel, *48/50 Grange Road, Ealing, London, W5 5BX.* Home away from home - close to 3 tube stations and lines. **Open:** All year (not Xmas)
Grades: ETC 3 Diamond, AA 3 Diamond
020 8567 1049 Fax: 020 8579 5360 *enquiries@ londonlodgehotels.com*
www.londonlodgehotels.com **D:** £24.00–
£28.50 **S:** £35.00–£45.00 **Beds:** 2F 3D 2T 7S **Baths:** 9 En 5 Sh Ⓢ Ｐ (7) ♥ ★囲.♣cc

68 Cleveland Road, *Ealing, London, W13 8AJ.* Large luxury house overlooking parkland, 30 mins to central London or Heathrow. **Open:** All year
020 8991 5142 Mrs McHugh **Fax: 020 8998 2872 D:** £26.00–£28.00 **S:** £28.00–£30.00
Beds: 2F 1D 1T 1S **Baths:** 1 En 2 Pr 1 Sh Ⓢ (4)Ｐ (4)✔♥囲.♣

WEST LONDON Eastcote
TQ1088

7 Eastfields, *Eastcote, Pinner, HA5 2SR.* Access to places of interest, many excellent restaurants, transport nearby. **Open:** All year (not Xmas)
020 8429 1746 Mrs Mash **D:** £23.00 **S:** £23.00 **Beds:** 2T **Baths:** 1 Sh✔♥囲.♣

WEST LONDON
Hammersmith
TQ2279

67 Rannoch Road, *Hammersmith, London, W6 9SS.*
Open: All year
020 7385 4904
Mr & Mrs Armanios **Fax: 020 7610 3235**
D: £24.00 **S:** £34.00 **Beds:** 1F 1D 1T **Baths:** 1 Sh Ⓢ✔♥♥囲.♣
Comfortable, central, Edwardian family home. Quiet, close river, pubs, restaurants. Great base for sightseeing/courses/ business. Excellent transport facilities. Direct lines to theatres, shopping, Harrods, museums, Albert Hall, Earls Court/Olympia Exhibitions; Heathrow, Gatwick (Victoria), Eurostar. Children's reductions. Continental Breakfast.

WEST LONDON   Harrow
TQ1488

Crescent Hotel, *58-60 Welldon Crescent, Harrow, Middx, HA1 1QR.*
Open: All year
020 8863 5491
Mr Jivraj **Fax: 020 8427 5965** *ferndalebandb@ aol.com* www.fort-william.net/ferndale
D: £27.50–£32.50 **S:** £40.00–£50.00 **Beds:** 2F 2D 4T 13S **Baths:** 18 En 3 Sh Ⓢ Ｐ (7) ♥♥囲.♣cc
Modern, friendly hotel in quiet crescent in heart of Harrow, yet only a short drive to Wembley and the West End with Heathrow easily accessible. 21 rooms all ensuite, comfortable and well furnished, with colour TV, satellite, fridge, telephone and tea/ coffee making facilities.

Harrow Guest House, *48 Butler Road, Harrow, Middx, HA1 4DR.* Small town centre B&B near all travel facilities, pubs, restaurants, shops, hospitals and Harrow School. In quiet residential road. Non-smoking. **Open:** All year
020 8621 9090 Mrs Chaplin **D:** £18.50
S: £25.00 **Beds:** 1T 1D 2S **Baths:** 2 Sh Ⓢ (6) ✔♥♥囲.♣

WEST LONDON
Hayes (Heathrow)
TQ0880   ♣ Grapes, Crown

Balmoral Guest House, *262 Balmoral Drive, Hayes, Middx, UB4 8DQ.* Newly decorated family home, 10 mins from Heathrow. Use of kitchen. **Open:** All year
020 8848 3882 & 07973 875312 (M)
Ms Dodder *mdodder@hotmail.com* **D:** £35.00–
£40.00 **S:** £20.00–£30.00 **Beds:** 2T 2D 2S **Baths:** 1 En Ⓢ Ｐ (4) ♥★囲.♣

WEST LONDON
Heathrow
TQ0980

Shepiston Lodge, *31 Shepiston Lane, Heathrow, Middx, UB3 1LJ.* Character house near Heathrow. **Open:** All year
020 8573 0266 Mr Dhawan **Fax: 020 8569 2536** *shepiston@aol.com* **D:** £30.00 **S:** £45.00
Beds: 2F 11T 3D 6S **Baths:** 22 En Ⓢ Ｐ♥×♥囲.♣♣cc

WEST LONDON
Hounslow
TQ1475

Lampton Guest House, *47 Lampton Road, Hounslow, Middx, TW3 1JG.* Ideal for Heathrow airport and central London, stopover, superbly located. **Open:** All year
020 8570 0056 Fax: 020 8570 1220 D: £25.00–£30.00 **S:** £45.00–£60.00 **Beds:** 4F 4D 4T 8S **Baths:** 20 En 1 Pr 1 Sh Ⓢ (3)Ｐ (10)♥囲.♣cc

WEST LONDON   Kew
TQ1876   ♣ Coach & Horses

34 Forest Road, *Kew, Richmond, Surrey, TW9 3BZ.* **Open:** All year
020 8332 6289 (also fax) Mrs Royle
ShirleyRoyle2@activemail.co.uk **D:** £20.00–
£23.00 **S:** £25.00–£30.00 **Beds:** 1F 1D 1T Ⓢ (12)✔♥囲.♣
A comfortable Edwardian era family home. 5 mins' walk from Kew Gardens station, 35 mins to Westminster. 5 mins to Richmond, Kew Botanical Gardens and Public Records Office. Pleasant walks along Thames river bank. Good selection of pubs and restaurants nearby.

Melbury, *33 Marksbury Avenue, Kew, Richmond, Surrey, TW9 4JE.* Friendly and welcoming, refurbished private home, close to Richmond and Kew Gardens Underground.
Open: All year
020 8876 3930 (also fax) Mrs Allen
D: £25.00–£35.00 **S:** £30.00 **Beds:** 1T 1D 1F 1S **Baths:** 2 En 1 Sh Ⓢ (2)Ｐ (1)✔♥囲.♣

1 Chelwood Gardens, *Kew, Richmond, Surrey, TW9 4JG.* Situated in quiet cul-de-sac. Friendly house near Kew Gardens Station. **Open:** All year
Grades: ETC 3 Diamond
020 8876 8733 L J Gray **Fax: 020 8255 0171**
MrsLJGray@aol.com **D:** £30.00–£32.00
S: £34.00–£36.00 **Beds:** 2F 2T 2S **Baths:** 2 Sh Ⓢ (5)Ｐ (6)✔♥囲.♣

BATHROOMS
En = Ensuite
Pr = Private
Sh = Shared

179 Mortlake Road, *Kew, Richmond, Surrey, TW9 4AW.* Georgian house close to Kew Gardens, PRO and Underground. **Open:** All year **Grades:** ETC 3 Diamond **020 8876 0584 (also fax)** Mrs Butt **D:** £25.00 **S:** £35.00 **Beds:** 1T **Baths:** 1 En 🖭 (5) 🖭 ⛺ 🏧. ♨

WEST LONDON Northolt
TQ1283 🍺 *Crown Inn*

5 Doncaster Drive, *Northolt, Middx., UB5 4AS.* **Open:** All year **Grades:** ETC 3 Diamond **020 8423 5072** Mr & Mrs Wooster **D:** £25.00–£30.00 **S:** £25.00–£30.00 **Beds:** 1T 1S **Baths:** 1 Pr 1 Sh 🖭 (2) 🗡 🖭 🏧. ♨
Leafy suburban Northolt - 15 mins Heathrow, 25 mins Central London. Ideal base for Stratford, Brighton, Oxford etc. All these destinations available on a daytrip basis. Our local knowledge will save you money and ensure that you get the mostest for the leastest.

WEST LONDON Pinner
TQ1189

Goodmans, *11 Meadow Road, Pinner, Middx, HA5 1EB.* Modern family house, 2 twin rooms, open all year, from £15 pppn. **Open:** All year **020 8868 1074** S Goodman **D:** £15.00 **Beds:** 2T **Baths:** 2 Sh 🖭. ♨

WEST LONDON Ruislip
TQ0987

2 Cornwall Road, *Ruislip, Middx, HA4 6RS.* Small friendly private house. Short walk underground stations. Near M40/M25. **Open:** All year **01895 636676 (also fax)** Mrs Glanvill **D:** £20.00 **S:** £25.00 **Beds:** 1D 2S **Baths:** 1 Sh 🗡 🖭 🖭 🏧. ♨

WEST LONDON Teddington
TQ1670

93 Langham Road, *Teddington, Middx, TW11 9HG.* Sympathetically restored Edwardian house with original features and brass beds. **Open:** All year (not Xmas) **020 8977 6962** Mrs Norris *lesleyanorris@ aol.com* **D:** £22.50–£25.00 **S:** £30.00–£45.00 **Beds:** 1D 1T **Baths:** 1 Sh 🗡 🖭 🖭.

WEST LONDON Twickenham
TQ1573

11 Spencer Road, *Strawberry Hill, Twickenham, Middx, TW2 5TH.* Stylish Edwardian house near Richmond and Hampton Court. Excellent transport, easy parking. **Open:** All year **020 8894 5271** Mrs Duff **D:** £20.00–£25.00 **S:** £20.00–£25.00 **Beds:** 2D 1T **Baths:** 1 En 1 Sh 🗡 🖭 🖭.

WEST LONDON Uxbridge
TQ0583

Spackman Guest House, *14 Hillingdon Road, Uxbridge, Middx, UB10 0AD.* Listed house near town centre, Heathrow, M4, M40. English breakfast. **Open:** All year (not Xmas) **01895 237994** Mrs Spackman **Fax:** 01895 234953 **D:** £20.00–£25.00 **S:** £25.00 **Beds:** 1D 1T 1S **Baths:** 1 Sh 🖭 🖭 (3) 🖭 🗡 🖭 🖭. ♨

Cleveland Hotel, *4 Cleveland Road, Uxbridge, Middx, UB8 2DW.* Early Victorian detached property with modern extension. Convenient for central London and Heathrow. **Open:** All year **01895 257618** Mrs Tindale **Fax:** 01895 239710 **D:** £20.00–£22.00 **S:** £29.00–£36.00 **Beds:** 5F 3D 1T 5S **Baths:** 9 En 3 Sh 🖭 🖭 (10) 🖭 🖭. ♨ cc

Hillbenn House, *235 Park Road, Uxbridge, Middx, UB8 1NS.* 10 mins from Heathrow Airport. 10 mins' walk to tube station. **Open:** All year **01895 850787 Fax:** 01895 814909 *hillbenn.house@btinternet.com* **D:** £22.50–£25.00 **S:** £35.00–£40.00 **Beds:** 1F 3T 1S **Baths:** 5 En 🖭 (4) 🗡 🖭 🖭. ♨

WEST LONDON Wembley
TQ1785

Elm Hotel, *1-7 Elm Road, Wembley, Middx, HA9 7JA.* **Open:** All year (not Xmas) **Grades:** ETC 3 Diamond, RAC 3 Diamond **020 8902 1764** Mr Gosden **Fax:** 020 8903 8365 *info@elmhotel.co.uk* www.elmhotel.co.uk **D:** £32.50–£36.00 **S:** £48.00 **Beds:** 9F 7D 11T 6S **Baths:** 33 En 🖭 🖭 (7) 🖭 🗡 🖭. ♨ cc
Wembley Stadium, area and conference centre 1200 yds. Wembley central (main line and underground) 150 yards. M1 2.5 miles, Heathrow Airport 8 miles. Comfortable family run 33 bedroom hotel. Get into hot water with your wife, some double rooms have Jacuzzi jet spa baths.

RATES
D = Price range per person sharing in a double or twin room
S = Price range for a single room

Aaron, Wembley Park Hotel, *8 Forty Lane, Wembley, Middx, HA9 9EB.* **Open:** All year **020 8904 6329** Mr Patel **Fax:** 020 8385 0472 *enquiries@aaronhotel.com* www.aaronhotel.com **D:** £22.50–£35.00 **S:** £29.00–£49.00 **Beds:** 6F 2D 1T 1S **Baths:** 9 En 1 Sh 🖭 🖭 (11) 🖭 🗡 🖭 🖭. ♨ ♨
We are a small family-run hotel. We are within easy reach of the Wembley Stadium Arena, Conference Centre and exhibition halls. Park Royal, Harrow are close by. Wembley Park Tube Station is 10 minutes walk away, West End 20 minutes by tube. Visit www.aaronhotel.com

Adelphi Hotel, *4 Forty Lane, Wembley, Middx, HA9 9EB.* Close to Wembley complex. Warm, friendly atmosphere. Free car park. **Open:** All year **Grades:** ETC 3 Diamond, AA 3 Diamond, RAC 3 Diamond **020 8904 5629** Mr Bajaj **Fax:** 020 8904 5314 *enquiry@adelphihotel.co.uk* www.hoteladelphi.co.uk **D:** £22.50–£27.50 **S:** £35.00–£49.00 **Beds:** 2F 3T 5D 3S **Baths:** 11 En 9 Pr 2 Sh 🖭 🖭 🖭. ♨ cc

WEST LONDON West Drayton
TQ0679 🍺 *Six Bells*

Oakwood Guest House, *121-123 Station Road, West Drayton, Middx, UB7 7DA.* Excellent location for Heathrow airport, motorways and London. English breakfast. **Open:** All year **01895 466554 & 07720 074800 (M)** *oakwood121@yahoo.co.uk* www.oakwood121. co.uk **D:** £20.00–£30.00 **S:** £30.00–£43.00 **Beds:** 1F 4T 2D 6S **Baths:** 13 En 2 Sh 🖭 🖭 🗡 🖭 🏧. ♨ cc

BEDROOMS
D = Double
T = Twin
S = Single
F = Family

Norfolk

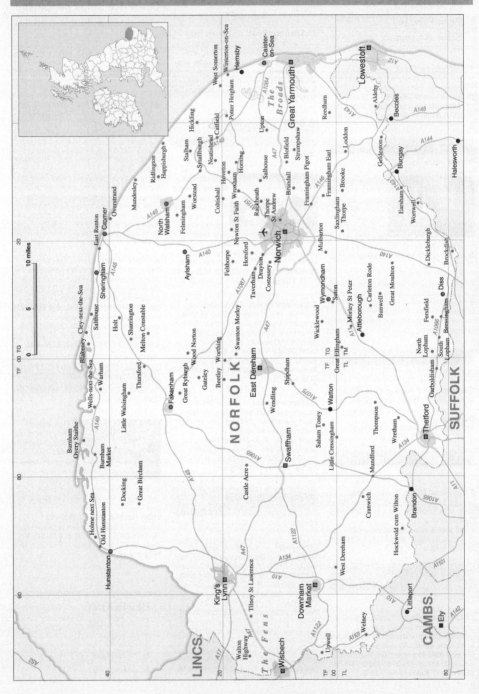

Aldeby

TM4493

The Old Vicarage, *Rectory Road, Aldeby, Beccles, Suffolk, NR34 0BJ.* Spacious old vicarage, tranquil 3 acre garden within open countryside. **Open:** All year (not Xmas) **Grades:** ETC 3 Diamond **01502 678229** Mrs Butler **D:** £17.00–£18.00 **S:** £18.00 **Beds:** 3T **Baths:** 1 En 2 Pr ⌂ ▣ (3) ⅍ ▨ ⊞ ♨

Aylsham

TG1927 🍺 *Crown Inn*

The Old Pump House, *Holman Road, Aylsham, Norwich, NR11 6BY.* **Open:** All year (not Xmas) **Grades:** ETC 4 Diamond **01263 733789 (also fax)** Mr & Mrs Richardson **D:** £20.00–£24.00 **S:** £20.00–£30.00 **Beds:** 1F 2D 2T 1S **Baths:** 4 En 1 Sh ⌂ ▣ (6) ⅍ ▨ ✕ ▨ ⊞ ♨ Warm, welcoming Georgian farmhouse full of character and near to the Broads, Norwich, stately houses (Blickling Hall 1 mile) and the coast. Breakfasts freshly cooked to order in the pine-shuttered Red Room overlooking the peaceful garden.

Birchdale House, *Blickling Road, Aylsham, Norwich, NR11 6ND.* Charming house in conservation area, attractive gardens, close town centre. **Open:** All year **01263 734531** Mrs Blake *jillmblake@hotmail.com* **D:** £22.00–£24.00 **S:** £22.00–£24.00 **Beds:** 1T 1D 1S **Baths:** 1 En 1 Sh ▣ (5) ⅍ ▨ ⊞ ♨

Beetley

TF9718 🍺 *New Inn, Brisley Bell*

Peacock House, *Peacock Lane, Beetley, Dereham, Norfolk, NR20 4DG.* Beautifully restored farmhouse, lovely views. Perfect location for exploring Norfolk. **Open:** All year **Grades:** ETC 4 Diamond, Gold **01362 860371** Mrs Bell *PeacockH@aol.com* www.smoothhound.co.uk/hotels/peacockh. html **D:** £22.00–£24.00 **S:** £28.00–£30.00 **Beds:** 1F 1T 1D **Baths:** 3 En ⌂ ▣ (4) ⅍ ▨ ⊁ ▨ ⊞ ♨

Blakeney

TG0243 🍺 *White Horse, Manor Hotel, Blakeney Hotel, King's Arms, George Inn, Bell Inn*

White Barn, *Back Lane, Blakeney, Norfolk, NR25 7NP.* Delightful ensuite annexe with individual access near Blakeney Quay. **Open:** All year (not Xmas) **01263 741359 (also fax)** Mr & Mrs Millard *millard@clara.co.uk* members.tripod.co. uk/raymillard **D:** £20.00–£25.00 **S:** £25.00–£35.00 **Beds:** 1D 1D/T **Baths:** 2 En ▣ (5) ⅍ ▨ ▨ ⊞ ♨

Dallinga, *71 Morston Road, Blakeney, Holt, Norfolk, NR25 7BD.* 4-5 minutes walk to Blakeney Quay. Excellent breakfast menu from local produce. **Open:** All year **01263 740943** Mr & Mrs Ward **D:** £18.75–£21.25 **Beds:** 1D 1T **Baths:** 2 En ⌂ (12) ▣ (6) ▨ ▨ ⊞ ♨

Blofield

TG3309

Aldwin, *Woodbastwick Road, Blofield, Norwich, NR13 4QH.* Large detached bungalow convenient for Norwich and Broads. Norwich 7 miles. **Open:** Easter to Oct **01603 713059** Mr Key **D:** £15.00–£20.00 **S:** £16.00–£20.00 **Beds:** 1D 1T **Baths:** 1 Sh ▣ (3) ⊞

Bressingham

TM0780

Poplar Farm, *Fersfield Road, Bressingham, Diss, Norfolk, IP22 2AP.* Quiet countryside, close Bloom's Gardens and steam museums, Norwich, Ipswich and coast. **Open:** All year (not Xmas) **01379 687261** Mrs Soar **D:** £18.20–£20.00 **S:** £18.20–£20.00 **Beds:** 1D 1T 2S **Baths:** 1 En 2 Sh ▣ (10) ▨ ⊞ ♨

Brockdish

TM2079

Grove Thorpe, *Grove Road, Brockdish, Diss, IP21 4JE.* Country house built 1610 nestling in 9 acres private fishing lake. **Open:** Jan to Dec **01379 668305** Mr & Mrs Morrish **Fax:** 01379 688305 **D:** £25.00–£32.00 **S:** £40.00 **Beds:** 1T 2D ⌂ (12) ▣ (20) ⅍ ▨ ✕ ▨ ⊞ ♿ ♨

RATES

D = Price range per person sharing in a double or twin room

S = Price range for a single room

Brooke

TM2899

The Old Vicarage, *48 The Street, Brooke, Norwich, Norfolk, NR15 1JU.* Beautiful house, beautiful garden, totally secluded, peace perfect peace. **Open:** All year (not Xmas/New Year) **Grades:** ETC 4 Diamond, AA 4 Diamond **01508 558329** **D:** £21.00 **Beds:** 2D **Baths:** 2 En ▣ (3) ⅍ ▨ ✕ ▨ ⊞ ♨

Brundall

TG3208

Braydeston House, *The Street, Brundall, Norwich, NR13 5JY.* Elegant house in wooded gardens only 10 minutes from Norwich. **Open:** All year (not Xmas/New Year) **Grades:** ETC 3 Diamond **01603 713123** Mrs Knox *ann@ braydeston.freeserve.co.uk* **D:** £22.50–£25.00 **S:** £25.00–£28.00 **Beds:** 2T **Baths:** 1 Pr 1 Sh ⌂ ▣ (2) ▨ ▨ ⊞ ♨

Bunwell

TM1293

The Cottage, *Rectory Lane, Bunwell, Norwich, Norfolk, NR16 1QU.* Picturesque C18th thatched cottage set in peaceful country gardens. **Open:** All year **01953 789226 & 07719 596070 (M)** P M Jenkins **D:** £17.00–£20.00 **S:** £28.00–£30.00 **Beds:** 1F 2D **Baths:** 3 En ⌂ ▣ (4) ⅍ ▨ ✕ ▨ ⊞ ♿ ♨

Burnham Market

TF8342

Wood Lodge, *Millwood, Herrings Lane, Burnham Market, King's Lynn, Norfolk, PE31 8DP.* Peaceful, luxurious coastal lodge. **Open:** All year (not Xmas) **01328 730152** Mrs Leftley **Fax:** 01328 730158 **D:** £27.50–£30.00 **S:** £35.00–£45.00 **Beds:** 1D 1T ⌂ (8) ▣ ⅍ ▨ ⊞ ♨

Burnham Overy Staithe

TF8444 🍺 *Hoste Arms, Lord Nelson, Fishers, The Hero*

Domville Guest House, *Glebe Lane, Burnham Overy Staithe, Kings Lynn, Norfolk, PE31 8JQ.* Quietly situated family-run B&B. **Open:** All year (not Xmas) **Grades:** ETC 3 Diamond **01328 738298 (also fax)** Mrs Smith **D:** £22.00–£25.00 **S:** £22.00–£25.00 **Beds:** 1T 2D 1S **Baths:** 4 En ▣ (10) ⅍ ▨ ✕ ▨ ♨

Caister-on-Sea

TG5112

Old Hall, *High Street, Caister-on-Sea, Great Yarmouth, Norfolk, NR30 5JL.* **Open:** All year (not Xmas/New Year)
01493 720400 *oldhall@rjt.co.uk* www.oldhall. net **D:** £25.00–£27.50 **S:** £35.00–£40.00 **Beds:** 1T 4D **Baths:** 5 En 🅿 ⊁ 🖵 ✕ 🖵 ▦ 🛎 cc
Warm welcome and extremely comfortable accommodation situated in the world famous lifeboat village. Ideal base for touring and exploring the bright lights of Great Yarmouth, the serene splendour of the Norfolk Broads and coastline and the majestic city of Norwich.

Carleton Rode

TM1193

Upgate Farm, *Carleton Rode, Norwich, NR16 1NJ.* Friendly homely accommodation offered in comfortable farmhouse set in rural location. **Open:** All year (not Xmas) **01953 860300 (also fax)** Mr Wright **D:** £17.00–£18.00 **S:** £17.00–£18.00 **Beds:** 1D 1T **Baths:** 1 Sh ☺ 🅿 (2) ⊁ 🖵 ▦ 🛎

Castle Acre

TF8115   🍺 *The Ostrich*

Willow Cottage Tea Rooms & B&B, *Stocks Green, Castle Acre, Kings Lynn, Norfolk, PE32 2AE.* **Open:** All year (not Xmas) **01760 755551** Mr Moister **Fax: 01760 755799** *willowcottage@webwise.fm* **D:** £35.00 **S:** £20.00 **Beds:** 2D 2T **Baths:** 1 Sh ☺ 🅿(4)⊁ 🖵 🖵 ▦ 🛎
Attractive beamed tea rooms and guest bedrooms, delicious home-cooked cakes, soups and puddings. Warm friendly welcome. Within walking distance of Cluniac Priory, Castle and River Nar. Ideal base for visiting local attractions in North and West Norfolk.

Gemini House, *Pyes Lane, Castle Acre, Kings Lynn, Norfolk, PE32 2XB.* Well-situated for all Norfolk sights. **Open:** All year **01760 755375** Mrs Clark **D:** £15.00–£17.50 **S:** £15.00 **Beds:** 2D 2T **Baths:** 1 En 1 Sh ☺ 🅿 (4) 🖵 🛏 ▦ 🛎

Catfield

TG3821   🍺 *Crown Inn*

Grebe Cottage, *New Road, Catfield, Great Yarmouth, Norfolk, NR29 5DQ.* Between Hickling and Barton Broads. Ideal for sailing, fishing, walking. **Open:** All year (not Xmas/New Year) **01692 584179** Mrs Wickens *jill@ wickens61.freeserve.net* **D:** £18.00–£20.00 **S:** £16.00–£18.00 **Beds:** 1T 2D **Baths:** 1 En 1 Sh ☺ 🅿 (3) ⊁ 🖵 🛏 ▦ 🛎

Cley-next-the-Sea

TG0443   🍺 *George & Dragon, Three Swallows*

Cley Windmill, *Cley-next-the-Sea, Holt, Norfolk, NR25 7NN.* Historic windmill overlooking beautiful unspoilt Norfolk coastal marshes. Wonderfully atmospheric. **Open:** All year **01263 740209 (also fax)** Mr Bolam **D:** £35.00–£54.00 **S:** £70.00 **Beds:** 4D 3T **Baths:** 7 Pr ☺ 🅿 (12) 🖵 🛏 ✕ 🖵 & 🛎 cc

Marshlands, *High Street, Cley-next-the-Sea, Holt, Norfolk, NR25 7RB.* Victorian old town hall house, with warm and friendly atmosphere. **Open:** All year (not Xmas/New Year) **01263 740284** Mr & Mrs Kinsella www.broadland.com/marshland **D:** £16.00 **S:** £28.00 **Beds:** 1D 2T **Baths:** 2 En 1 Pr ☺ (12) ⊁ 🖵 🛏 🖵 ▦ 🛎

Coltishall

TG2720

Broadgates, *1 Wroxham Road, Coltishall, Norwich, NR12 7DU.* Comfortable accommodation in Broadland village. **Open:** All year (not Xmas) **01603 737598** Mrs Dack *broad1gates@tesco.net* www.norfolkbroads.com/broadgates **D:** £21.00 **S:** £21.00 **Beds:** 1F 1T **Baths:** 1 En 1 Pr ☺ 🅿 (8) ⊁ 🖵 🖵 ▦ 🛎

Costessey

TG1711   🍺 *Red Lion*

St Edmundsbury, *146 The Street, Costessey, Norwich, NR8 5DG.* **Open:** All year **01603 745959 (also fax)** *smiths@ stedmundsbury.co.uk* www.stedmundsbury.co. uk **D:** £20.00–£25.00 **S:** £25.00–£28.50 **Beds:** 1F 2T 3D 2S **Baths:** 3 En 1 Pr 3 Sh 🅿 (8) ⊁ 🖵 🖵 ▦ & 🛎 cc
Surrounded by 8 golf courses, close to the Royal Norwich Showground, St Edmundsbury stands in a large attractive garden with ample on-site parking. Situated within easy reach of historic city of Norwich. Most rooms are ground floor and extremely comfortably furnished.

Cranwich

TL7794

Old Bottle House, *Cranwich, Mundford, Thetford, Norfolk, IP26 5JL.* 275-year-old former coaching inn, edge of Thetford Forest. Dining room with inglenook fireplace. **Open:** All year **01842 878012** Mrs Ford **D:** £20.00–£22.00 **S:** £20.00–£22.00 **Beds:** 1F 2T 1D **Baths:** 1 Sh ☺ (5) 🅿 (10) ⊁ 🖵 ✕ 🖵 ▦ 🛎

Cromer

TG2142   🍺 *Red Lion, White Horse, Albion, Suffield Arms, Dolphin Inn*

Cambridge House, *Sea Front, East Cliff, Cromer, Norfolk, NR27 9HD.* Superb, uninterrupted sea views above the promenade and beach. Good touring base. **Open:** All year (not Xmas/New Year) **Grades:** ETC 3 Diamond **01263 512085** Mrs Wass www.broadland. com/cambridgehouse **D:** £18.00–£25.00 **S:** £18.00–£25.00 **Beds:** 3F 1D 1S **Baths:** 3 En 1 Pr 1 Sh ☺ 🅿 (5) ⊁ 🖵 🛏 ✕ 🖵 🛎

The Grove Guest House, *95 Overstrand Road, Cromer, Norfolk, NR27 0DS.* Ideal for North Norfolk. Beautiful, spacious, C18th guest house. **Open:** Easter to Sept **Grades:** ETC 3 Diamond **01263 512412** Mrs Graveling **Fax: 01263 513416 D:** £26.00 **S:** £26.00 **Beds:** 2F 2T 4D 1S **Baths:** 9 En ☺ 🅿 ⊁ 🖵 ✕ 🖵 ▦ 🛎

Please respect a B&B's wishes regarding children, animals and smoking

Beachcomber Guest House, *17 Macdonald Road, Cromer, Norfolk, NR27 9AP.* Visiting North Norfolk? Excellent accommodation, well-placed for exploring entire area **Open:** All year (not Xmas/New Year) **Grades:** AA 4 Diamond **01263 516698** Mrs Weinle www.beachcomber-guesthouse.co.uk **D:** £19.00–£25.00 **S:** £19.00–£38.00 **Beds:** 1F 1T 4D **Baths:** 5 En 1 Sh ⌕ (6) ⊞ ⊡ ▥ ♨

Dickleburgh

TM1682 🍺 *Half Moon*

Blacksmiths Cottage, *Langmere, Dickleburgh, Diss, Norfolk, IP21 4AQ.* Detached country cottage. Close to A140. Friendly environment. **Open:** Easter to Oct **01379 740982** J A Potterton **Fax:** 01379 741917 *pottertonj@aol.com* **D:** £17.00 **S:** £17.00 **Beds:** 1D 1S **Baths:** 1 Sh ⊡ (4) ⊞ × ▥ ♨

Diss

TM1180

Strenneth, *Airfield Road, Fersfield, Diss, Norfolk, IP22 2B.* Close to Bressingham Gardens and Snetterton Circuit. C17th courtyard wing. **Open:** All year **Grades:** ETC 4 Diamond *pdavey@strenneth.co.uk* www.strenneth.co.uk **D:** £25.00–£35.00 **S:** £28.00–£50.00 **Beds:** 4D 2T 1S **Baths:** 7 En ⌕ ⊡ (9) ⊬ ⊞ ⊁ ▥ & ♨ cc

Park Hotel, *29 Denmark Street, Diss, IP22 4LE.* Friendly run market town hotel, ideal for touring Norfolk and Suffolk. **Open:** All year **01379 642244** R Twigge **Fax:** 01379 644218 *park.hotel@btinternet.com* **D:** £27.50–£40.00 **S:** £25.00–£30.00 **Beds:** 2F 8D 4T 2S ⌕ ⊡ ⊬ ⊞ ⊁ × ⊡ ▥ & ✽ ♨ cc

Docking

TF7637 🍺 *Pilgrim's Reach, Railway Inn, Crown Inn.*

Jubilee Lodge, *Station Road, Docking, King's Lynn, Norfolk, PE31 8LS.* Comfortable Tudor-style house. Pleasant village between Fakenham and the seaside resort of Hunstanton. **Open:** Dec to Oct **Grades:** ETC 3 Diamond **01485 518473 (also fax)** Mrs Howard *eghoward62@hotmail.com* www.jubilee-lodge. co.uk **D:** £20.00 **S:** £25.00 **Beds:** 2D 1T **Baths:** 3 En ⊡ (3) ⊬ ⊞ × ⊡ ▥ ♨

Downham Market

TF6103

The Dial House, *12 Railway Road, Downham Market, Norfolk, PE38 9EB.* lovely old C18th family home. Good food ad home-made bread. **Open:** All year **01366 388358** Mrs Murray *bookings@ thedialhouse.co.uk* www.thedialhouse.co.uk **D:** £17.50–£22.50 **S:** £25.00–£33.00 **Bds:** 1D 2T **Baths:** 2 En 1 Pr ⊡ (6) ⊬ ⊞ × ▥ ♨

Drayton

TG1813 🍺 *Red Lion, Cock*

The Chestnuts, *27 Fakenhar Road, Drayton, Norwich, NR8 6PS.* Bungalow accommodation, central for touring Norfolk/coastal areas. **Open:** All year **01603 868860** M Howard **D:** £18.00–£19.00 **S:** £20.00–£25.00 **Beds:** 1T 2/ **Baths:** 1 En 1 Sh ⌕ (3) ⊡ (10) ⊬ ⊞ ▥ ♨

Earsham

TM3289

Park Farm, *Harlesto Road, Earsham, Bungay, Norfolk, NR35 AQ.* Spacious farmhouse, unique hnd decoration, fantastic views with very comfort. **Open:** All year **01986 892180** Mrs Vatchorn **Fax:** 01986 894796 *watchorn_s@reenet.co.uk* **D:** £23.00–£35.00 **S:** £32.00–£46.00 **Beds:** 2D 1T **Baths:** 3 En ⌕ ⊡ 10) ⊬ ⊞ ⊁ ⊡ ▥ ♨ cc

Fakenham

TF9230 🍺 *Henry IV*

Highfield Farm, *Great Ryburgh, Fakenham, Norfolk, NR21 7AL.* Elegant farmhouse, welcoming hosts, comfortable rooms, peaceful and quiet. **Open:** All year (not Xmas/New Year) **Grades** ETC 4 Diamond **01328 829249** Mrs Savory **Fax:** 01328 829422 *jeghshighfield@onet.co.uk* www.broadland. com/lighfield **D:** £20.00–£25.00 **S:** £25.00–£35.00 **Beds:** 2T 1D **Baths:** 1 En 1 Sh ⊡ (8) ⊬ ⊡ ▥ ♨

Yew Tree House, *2 East View, Hempton, Fakenham, Norfolk, NR21 7LW.* Open spaces, birdwatching area. Close to Sandringham, North Norfolk Coast. **Open:** All year **01328 851450** Mr Beales **D:** £15.00–£18.00 **S:** £15.00–£18.00 **Beds:** 1F 1D 1T 1S **Baths:** 1 Sh ⌕ (1) ⊡ (5) ⊬ ⊞ ⊁ × ⊡ ♨

Planning a longer stay? Always ask for any special rates

Felmingham

TG2529

Larks Rise, *North Walsham Road, Felmingham, North Walsham, Norfolk, NR28 0JU.* **Open:** Jan to Nov **Grades:** ETC 2 Diamond **01692 403173** Mrs Rudd www.broadland. com/larksrise **D:** £16.00–£20.00 **S:** £18.00–£22.00 **Beds:** 1F 1D 1T **Baths:** 1 En 1 Sh ⊡ (2) ⊡ ▥ ♨ Traditionally-built family home with half acre secluded gardens in quiet rural area full of wildlife and historical interest. Superb centre for exploring North Norfolk and the Broads. Close to Weavers Way and Norfolk Coastal footpaths. Riding and fishing nearby.

Felthorpe

TG1618

Spinney Ridge, *Hall Lane, Felthorpe, Norwich, NR10 4BX.* **Open:** All year (not Xmas) **01603 754833** Mr & Mrs Thompson **D:** £20.00–£22.00 **S:** £20.00–£22.00 **Beds:** 2D 2T 1S **Baths:** 2 En 1 Sh ⌕ (1) ⊡ (6) ⊬ ⊡ ⊡ ▥ ♨ Characterful quiet house in a wooded rural setting with a warm and friendly welcome and service 6 miles North of Norwich off the A1149. Centre for North Norfolk and the Broads, convenient for recommended restaurants. No smoking, no dogs, please.

Lodge Farmhouse, *89 The Street, Felthorpe, Norwich, NR10 4BY.* Comfortable friendly family house, edge of village location, good breakfast. **Open:** All year (not Xmas) **01603 754896** Mrs Howe **D:** £17.00 **S:** £17.00 **Beds:** 1D 1T 1S **Baths:** 1 Sh ⌕ ⊡ (4) ⊬ ⊡ ⊡ ▥ ♨

Fersfield

TM0683

Strenneth, *Airfield Road, Fersfield, Diss, Norfolk, IP22 2B.* Close to Bressingham Gardens and Snetterton Circuit. C17th courtyard wing. **Open:** All year **Grades:** ETC 4 Diamond **01379 688182** K Webb **Fax:** 01379 688260 *pdavey@strenneth.co.uk* www.strenneth.co.uk **D:** £25.00–£35.00 **S:** £28.00–£50.00 **Beds:** 4D 2T 1S **Baths:** 7 En ⌕ ⊡ (9) ⊬ ⊞ ⊁ ▥ & ♨ cc

Flint Barn, Fenners Farm, Fersfield,
Diss, IP22 2AW. Converted barn in rural setting of 2 acres. NT properties, Norfolk Broads. **Open:** All year (not Xmas/New Year)
01379 687794 Mr & Mrs Green *Joan.Green@tesco.net* **D:** £18.00–£19.00 **S:** £18.00–£20.00 **Beds:** 1F 1S **Baths:** 1 Sh ♨ (10) ▣ (4) ⌁ ▣ ▥ 🕭

Framingham Earl
TG2702

The Old Rectory, Hall Road,
Framingham Earl, Norwich, NR14 7SB. Beautifully restored period family house in large country garden. **Open:** All year (not Xmas)
01508 493590 Mr & Mrs Wellings **Fax: 01508 495110** *brucewellings@drivedevice.freeserve.co.uk* **D:** £21.00–£25.00 **S:** £25.00–£28.00 **Beds:** 1D 1T **Baths:** 1 Sh ♨ 🛏 (4) ⌁ ▣ ▥ 🕭 🛁

Framingham Pigot
TG2703

The Old Rectory, Rectory Lane,
Framingham Pigot, Norwich, NR14 7QQ. Friendly Victorian rectory. Large garden. 10 mins Norwich centre. **Open:** All year (not Xmas)
01508 493082 Mrs Thurman **D:** £22.00 **S:** £22.00 **Beds:** 1F 1D 1T **Baths:** 2 En 1 Sh ♨ 🛏 (6) ⌁ ▣ ▥ 🕭

Garboldisham
TM0081

Ingleneuk Lodge, Hopton Road,
Garboldisham, Diss, Norfolk, IP22 2RQ. Pretty rural location with all rooms overlooking partly wooded grounds. **Open:** All year **Grades:** ETC 4 Diamond
01953 681541 & 01953 681138 Mr & Mrs Stone **Fax: 01953 681638** *info@ingleneuklodge.co.uk* **D:** £27.50 **S:** £33.00 **Beds:** 3D 3T 1S 1F **Baths:** 8 En ♨ 🛏 (15) ▣ 🛏 🕭 & 🐾 cc

Gateley
TF9624

Centre Farm, Gateley, Fakenham,
Norfolk, NR20 5EF. Beautiful Georgian farm house set in quiet country village. **Open:** All year
01328 829618 (also fax) Mrs Savory *gillsavory@savoryfarm.co.uk* www.savoryfarm.co.uk **D:** £20.00–£25.00 **Beds:** 3T **Baths:** 2 Pr ♨ (8) ▣ 🛁

Geldeston
TM3992

Archway Cottage, Geldeston, Beccles,
Suffolk, NR34 0LB. Clean comfortable cottage with a warm welcome to all our guests. **Open:** All year
01508 518056 Mrs Dean *archwaycottage@btinternet.com* www.archwaycottage.co.uk **D:** £20.00 **S:** £25.00–£28.00 **Beds:** 2D **Baths:** 1 Sh ▣ (2) ⌁ ▣ ▥ 🕭 🛁

Great Bircham
TF762

Kings Head Hotel, Great
Bircham, Kings Lynn, Norfolk, PE31 6RJ. **Open:** All year **01485 578265**
I Verrando
D: £29.9–£35.00 **S:** £39.00 **Beds:** 1F 2T 2D 1S **Bath:** 6 En ♨ (1) ▣ (40) ▣ 🛏 ✕ ▥ 🕭 🛁 cc
Friendly village inn and restaurant close to Sandringham, King's Lynn and the coast, Italian restaurant. Fresh Norfolk seafood and produce. Six ensuite rooms with colour TV, tea/coffee making facilities. English and Italian cuisine. Breaks available, for two nights and over.

Great Ellingham
TM0197

Cannells Farm, Bow Street, Great
Ellingham, Attleborough, Norfolk, NR17 1JA. C18th traditional Norfolk farmhouse overlooking open countryside. Quiet location. **Open:** All year (not Xmas/New Year)
01953 454133 (also fax) Mrs Thomas **D:** £18.00–£20.00 **S:** £18.00–£20.00 **Beds:** 1T 1D 1S **Baths:** 1 Sh ♨ (8 ▣ (8) ⌁ ▣ ▥ ✕ ▥ 🕭 🛁

Home Cottage Farm, Penhill Road,
Great Ellingham, Attleborough, Norfolk, NR17 1LS. Spacious self-contained B&B accommodation at period farmhouse in rural seclusion. **Open:** All year
01953 483734 M Jacobs *roya@maureen@mail.com* **D:** £18.00–£20.00 **S:** £18.00–£20.00 **Beds:** 2T 1D 1S **Baths:** 1 Pr 1Sh ♨ 🛏 (4) ⌁ ▣ ▥ 🕭 🛁

Great Moulton
TM1690

Oakbrook, Frith Way, Great
Moulton, Norwich, NR15 2HE. **Open:** All year **01379 677359**
Mr Hawes
www.norfolkbroads.com/oakbrook/
D: £19.00–£22.00 **S:** £19.00–£22.00 **Beds:** 1F 1T 2S ♨ 🛏 (8) ⌁ ▣ 🛏 ✕ ▥ 🕭 🛁 & 🛁 🐾
Very friendly reception. Food excellent, just like staying with old friends: Doris, Ted and Jackie Salisbury. Very hospitable, helpful and friendly. Good location to get away from the busy city life, nice to get a good taste of beautiful Norfolk.

Planning a longer stay? Always ask for any special rates

Great Ryburgh
TF9527

Highfield Farm, Great Ryburgh,
Fakenham, Norfolk, NR21 7AL. Elegant farmhouse, welcoming hosts, comfortable rooms, peaceful and quiet. **Open:** All year (not Xmas/New Year) **Grades:** ETC 4 Diamond
01328 829249 Mrs Savory **Fax: 01328 829422** *jegshighfield@onet.co.uk* www.broadland.com/highfield **D:** £20.00–£25.00 **S:** £25.00–£35.00 **Beds:** 2T 1D **Baths:** 1 En 1 Sh ▣ (8) ⌁ ▣ ▥ 🕭 🛁

Great Yarmouth
TG5207   ◈ Numerous

The Collingwood Hotel, 25/26 Princes
Road, Great Yarmouth, NR30 2DG. **Open:** Mar to Nov **Grades:** RAC 3 Diamond
01493 844398 (also fax) Mr & Mrs Mills www.smoothhound.co.uk/hotels/collingwood.html **D:** £19.00–£25.00 **S:** £18.00–£22.00 **Beds:** 2F 9D 2T 6S **Baths:** 10 En 9 Sh ⌁ ▣ ▥ 🕭 🛁 cc
Princes Road is the best road for hotels. We are at the seafront and 100 yds from Britannia Pier and all the shows and amusements. Walking distance from main shops at the heart of the Norfolk Broads - no hills to walk up. Guest lounge, licensed bar.

Lynden House, 102
Wellesley Road, Great Yarmouth, Norfolk, NR30 2AR. Assured a warm welcome 3 mins from beach and shops. **Open:** All year (not Xmas/New Year)
01493 844693 Mrs Hinkley **D:** £12.00–£18.00 **S:** £12.00–£18.00 **Beds:** 3F 1S **Baths:** 2 En 1 Sh ♨ ▣ 🛏 ▥ 🕭 🛁

Sliverstone House, 29
Wellesley Road, Great Yarmouth, NR30 1EU. All rooms ensuite, residential bar, close to all amenities. **Open:** All year (not Xmas) **Grades:** ETC 3 Diamond
01493 844862 Mr Parker **D:** £15.00–£17.50 **S:** £15.00–£17.50 **Beds:** 5F 5D **Baths:** 10 En ♨ ▣ ▥ 🕭 🛁 cc

Holland House, 13 Apsley Road, Great
Yarmouth, Norfolk, NR30 2HG. Friendly family run guest house, one minute from sea. **Open:** All year (not Xmas/New Year)
01493 859534 Mr & Mrs Simmons **D:** £12.00–£15.00 **S:** £12.00–£15.00 **Beds:** 2F 4D 1S ♨ ▣ ✕ ▥ 🕭 🛁

Britannia Guest House, *119 Wellesley Road, Great Yarmouth, NR30 2AP.* Comfortable rooms, good breakfasts, close to beach, shops, restaurants, amusements. **Open:** All year
01493 856488 (also fax) D: £14.00–£17.00 **S:** £14.00–£17.00 **Beds:** 1F 3D 1T 2S **Baths:** 1 En 1 Sh ⌂ (3) ⊬ ⚑ ⚥ ▥

Senglea Lodge, *7 Euston Road, Great Yarmouth, Norfolk, NR30 1DX.* Family run. Voted to be best guest house by Which? magazine. **Open:** All year (not Xmas/New Year) **Grades:** ETC 3 Diamond
01493 859632 Mrs Formosa *info@ senglealodge.freeserve.co.uk* **D:** £14.00–£17.00 **S:** £5.00–£20.00 **Beds:** 2F 2T 2D 1S **Baths:** 4 En 1 Sh ⌂ ⚥ ▥ cc

Armani Hotel, *14-15 Sandown Road, Great Yarmouth, Norfolk, NR30 1EY.* 50 yards from the beach. Licensed bar, car park. **Open:** All year **Grades:** ETC 3 Diamond
01493 843870 (also fax) R Boon *armani-hotel@faxvia.net* www.armanihotel.co. uk **D:** £25.00–£30.00 **S:** £25.00–£35.00 **Beds:** 10F 6T 2D 4S **Baths:** 22 En ⌂ (3) ⚑ (50) ⚥ ✕ ⚥ ▥, ✻ ⚐

Siesta Lodge, *53/54 York Road, Great Yarmouth, Norfolk, NR30 2NE.* Small family run guest house. Close to amenities. **Open:** All year **Grades:** ETC 3 Diamond
01493 843207 Mrs Brown *siestalodge@aol.com* www.siestalodge.co.uk **D:** £1520.00 **S:** £15.00–£20.00 **Beds:** 3F 3T 3D 2S **Baths:** 1 En 2 Sh ⊬ ⚥ ✕ ▥,

Seamore Guest House, *116 Wellesley Road, Great Yarmouth, NR30 2AR.* Family guest house. One minute from beach, five minutes from shops. **Open:** All year (not Xmas/New Year)
01493 857389 D: £13.00–£18.00 **S:** £13.00–£18.00 **Beds:** 2F 2T 3D 1S **Baths:** 2 Sh ⌂ (4) ⚥ ▥, ⚐

Strathclyde Guest House, *6 Paget Road, Great Yarmouth, NR30 2DN.* 24 hour bar/games room. 100 yards from sea front. **Open:** All year
01493 851596 Zoe Cook *strathclyde-yarmouth@ hotmail. com* **D:** £13.00–£17.00 **S:** £12.00–£16.00 **Beds:** 2F 2T 2D 1S **Baths:** 1 En, 3 Sh ⌂ ✕ ✕ ▥, ⚐

Barnard House, *2 Barnard Crescent, Great Yarmouth, Norfolk, NR30 4DR.* Delightful family home. Bedrooms overlooking gardens. Excellent Aga cooked breakfast. **Open:** All year (not Xmas/New Year)
01493 855139 J Norris **Fax: 01493 843143** *barnardhouse@btinternet.com* www.barnardhouse.com **D:** £22.00–£24.00 **S:** £25.00–£30.00 **Beds:** 1F 2D **Baths:** 2 En 1 Pr ⌂ ⚑ (3) ⊬ ⚥ ⚑ ✕ ⚥ ▥, ⚐

National Grid References given are for villages, towns and cities – not for individual houses

Happisburgh
TG3731

Manor Farmhouse, *Happisburgh, Norwich, NR12 0SA.* **Open:** All year (not Xmas/New Year)
01692 651262 Mr & Mrs Eldridge **Fax: 01692 650220** www.northnorfolk.co.uk/manorbarn **D:** £20.00–£25.00 **S:** £25.00 **Beds:** 1T/D 2D **Baths:** 3 En ⌂ (7) ⚑ (4) ⊬ ⚑ ✕ ⚥ ▥, The best of both worlds - C21st luxury in a stunningly converted thatched C16th barn. Hearty Norfolk breakfasts, warm welcome, rural location. 5 mins sea, 5 miles Broads, yet only 1/2 hour Norwich - the perfect rural retreat.

Cliff House Guest House, *And Tea Shop, Beach Road, Happisburgh, Norwich, NR12 0PP.* Comfortable Edwardian guest house and teashop on cliff top in attractive village. **Open:** All year (not Xmas)
01692 650775 Ms Wrightson **D:** £18.00 **S:** £18.00 **Beds:** 1D 1T 2S **Baths:** 2 Sh ⌂ ⚑ (4) ⊬ ⚥ ⚥ ▥, ⚐

Hickling
TG4123 🍺 *Greyhound, Pleasure Boat*

Paddock Cottage, *Staithe Road, Hickling, Norwich, NR12 0YJ.* Comfortable modern cottage, quiet location, close nature reserve, sailing, fishing. **Open:** Mar to Oct **Grades:** ETC 3 Diamond
01692 598259 Mrs Froggatt **D:** £20.00–£25.00 **S:** £25.00–£30.00 **Beds:** 1F 1D 1T **Baths:** 1 En 2 Pr ⌂ ⚑ (4) ⊬ ⚥ ▥, ⚐

Hockwold cum Wilton
TL7388

Junipers, *18 South Street, Hockwold cum Wilton, Thetford, Norfolk, IP26 4JG.* Village near Mildenhall, Thetford. Forest, fishing, touring, historic sites. **Open:** All year
01842 827370 Mrs Waddington **D:** £20.00 **S:** £20.00 **Beds:** 2T 1S **Baths:** 2 Sh ⚑ (4) ⊬ ⚥ ⚑ ▥,

Holme next Sea
TF7043 🍺 *White Horse, Lifeboat*

Orchard House, *1 Kirkgate Street, Thornham, Hunstanton, Norfolk, PE36 6LY.* Delightful cottage in conservation village. Ideal for all rural pursuits. **Open:** All year (not Xmas)
01485 525695 Mrs Rutland **D:** £25.00–£35.00 **S:** £35.00–£45.00 **Beds:** 1F/D 1T **Baths:** 2 En ⌂ (8) ⚑ ⊬ ⚥ ⚥ ▥, ⚐

Holt
TG0739 🍺 *Three Pigs, Saracen's Head, Wheatsheaf, King's Head, Feathers*

50 Grove Lane, *Holt, Norfolk, NR25 6ED.* Well situated for exploring lovely North Norfolk, 1/2 mile town centre. **Open:** All year (not Xmas/New Year)
01263 712554 Mrs Cuthbert *bridgetnigel@ aol.com* **D:** £17.00–£18.00 **S:** £19.00–£20.00 **Beds:** 1T 2S **Baths:** 1 Sh ⌂ (8) ⚑ (3) ⊬ ⚥ ▥, ⚐

Horning
TG3417

Keppelgate, *Upper Street, Horning, Norwich, NR12 8NG.* Delightful rural Broadland views. Boating, fishing, windmills. Convenient for coast. **Open:** All year (not Xmas/New Year)
01692 630610 Mrs Freeman **D:** £17.00–£18.00 **S:** £20.00 **Beds:** 1F 1D 1T **Baths:** 1 En 1 Sh ⌂ (2) ⚑ (3) ⚥ ▥, ⚐

Horsford
TG1916

Church Farm Guest House, *Church Street, Horsford, Norwich, NR10 3DB.* Modern comfortable farmhouse, large garden. **Open:** All year
01603 898020 Mrs Hinchley **Fax: 01603 891649 D:** £25.00–£30.00 **S:** £25.00–£30.00 **Beds:** 2F 2D 2T **Baths:** 6 Pr 6 En 1 Sh ⌂ ⚑ (20) ⚥ ⚥ ▥, ⚐ cc

Hoveton
TG3018

The Vineries, *72 Stalham Road, Hoveton, Norwich, NR12 8DU.* Self-contained granny annexe, 1/2 mile from shops and Broads. **Open:** All year
01603 782514 S Meacock **D:** £25.00–£30.00 **S:** £25.00–£30.00 **Beds:** 1D **Baths:** 1 En ⚑ (2) ⊬ ⚥ ▥, ⚐

The Beehive, *Riverside Road, Hoveton, Norwich, NR12 8UD.* Beautiful thatched riverside cottage overlooking River Bure and the Broads. **Open:** All year (not Xmas/New Year)
01603 784107 R J Wendrop **D:** £20.00–£22.00 **S:** £25.00–£30.00 **Beds:** 1F 1T 2D **Baths:** 1 En 1 Sh ⌂ (15) ⚑ (7) ⊬ ⚥ ✕ ⚥ ▥, ⚐ cc

BEDROOMS
D = Double
T = Twin
S = Single
F = Family

Hunstanton

TF6740

Kiama Cottage, *23 Austin Street, Hunstanton, Norfolk, PE36 6AN.* **Open:** All year (not Xmas) **Grades:** ETC 3 Diamond
01485 533615 Mr & Mrs Gardiner **D:** £18.00–£25.00 **S:** £20.00–£25.00 **Beds:** 2F 2D **Baths:** 3 En 1 Pr
A warm welcome awaits you at our Victorian-style cottage located in a quiet residential area and ideally situated for visiting Hunstanton attractions and West Norfolk generally. Hosts Neville and Beverley are well travelled and are sensitive to your needs.

Rosamaly Guest House, *14 Glebe Avenue, Hunstanton, Norfolk, PE36 6BS.* Cosy ensuite bedrooms, ground floor/four poster available. Traditional hearty breakfasts, candlelit evening meals. **Open:** All year (not Xmas) **Grades:** ETC 3 Diamond
01485 534187 Mrs Duff Dick *rosamaly@supanet.com* **D:** £20.00–£25.00 **S:** £22.00–£30.00 **Beds:** 1F 3D 1T 1S **Baths:** 5 En

Peacock House, *28 Park Road, Hunstanton, Norfolk, PE36 5BY.* A large warm and comfortable Victorian house serving memorable breakfasts. **Open:** All year **Grades:** ETC 4 Diamond
01485 534551 Mrs Sandercock *peacockhouse@onetel.net.uk* www.web.onetel.net.uk/~peacockhouse/ **D:** £20.50–£27.00 **S:** £24.00–£30.00 **Beds:** 1F 1T 1D **Baths:** 3 En (5)

The Gables, *28 Aus, PE36 6AW.* Recently refurbished attractive Edwardian home retaining many original features. **Open:** All year
01485 532514 Mrs Bamfield *bbathegables@aol.com* **D:** £17.00–£25.00 **Beds:** 5F 1D 1T **Baths:** 5 En cc

King's Lynn

TF6120

Twinson Lee, *109 Tennyson Road, King's Lynn, Norfolk, PE30 5PA.* Friendly family run guest house, within walking distance of town centre. **Open:** All year (not Xmas/New Year)
01553 762900 Ms Thomas **Fax: 01553 769944 D:** £25.00 **S:** £20.00–£25.00 **Beds:** 1F 1T 1S **Baths:** 1 En 1 Sh (3)

Maranatha Havana Guestouse, *115 Gaywood Road, King's Lynn, Norfolk, PE30 2PU.* Friendly family run. Special rates for children, groups catered for. **Open:** All year
01553 774596 Mr Bastone **D:** £15.00–£20.00 **S:** £20.00 **Beds:** 2F 2D 3T 2S **Baths:** 4 En 2 Sh (9)

The Old Rectory, *33 Goodwins Road, King's Lynn, Norfolk, PE30 5QX.* Well-appointed, high quality ensuite accommodation. Quietly situated, near centre of historic market town. **Open:** All year
01553 768544 C Faulkner **D:** £21.00 **S:** £32.00 **Beds:** 2F 2T **Baths:** 4 En (5)

Little Cressingham

TF8700

Sycamore House, *Little Cressingham, Thetford, Norfolk, IP25 6NE.* Large country home, tranquil village, luxurious jacuzzi bathroom, numerous attractions. **Open:** All year
01953 881887 (also fax) Mr Wittridge **D:** £22.00 **S:** £22.00 **Beds:** 2D 1T 1S **Baths:** 1 En 1 Sh (10)

Little Walsingham

TF9337

St Davids House, *Friday Market, Little Walsingham, Walsingham, Norfolk, NR22 6BY.* Tudor house in medieval village; five miles from coast. **Open:** All year **Grades:** ETC 2 Diamond
01328 820633 Mrs Renshaw **D:** £22.00–£25.00 **Beds:** 2F 1D 2T **Baths:** 2 En 2 Sh

Loddon

TM3698

Poplar Farm, *Sisland, Loddon, Norwich, NR14 6EF.* Working farm pigs, cows. Quiet, rural setting near Broads. **Open:** All year (not Xmas)
01508 520706 Mrs Hemmant *milly@hemmant.myhome.org.uk* **D:** £17.00–£25.00 **S:** £18.00–£25.00 **Beds:** 1F 1D 1T **Baths:** 1 En 1 Pr

Melton Constable

TG0433

Burgh Parva Hall, *Melton Constable, Norfolk, NR24 2PU.* Listed C16th farmhouse with country views, near coast, large bedrooms. **Open:** All year
01263 862569 (also fax) Mrs Heal *judyheal@talk21.com* **D:** £18.00 **S:** £20.00 **Beds:** 1D 1T **Baths:** 1 Sh (4)

Morley St Peter

TM0697

Home Farm, *Morley St Peter, Wymondham, Norfolk, NR18 9SU.* Set in 4 acres of secluded grounds, 3 miles from 2 towns. **Open:** All year (not Xmas)
01953 602581 Mrs Morter **D:** £18.00–£20.00 **S:** £18.00–£20.00 **Beds:** 1T 1D 1S **Baths:** 1 Sh (5) (5)

Mulbarton

TG1901

Richmond Lodge, *The Common, Mulbarton, Norwich, Norfolk, NR14 8JW.* Beautiful setting, games room, outdoor heated swimming pool, palm trees, barbecue area. **Open:** All year (not Xmas/New Year)
01508 570449 Mrs Freeman **Fax: 01508 570372** *gillandpaul.freeman@ukgateway.net* **D:** £39.50–£41.00 **S:** £23.50–£25.00 **Beds:** 1F 3D 1S **Baths:** 2 En 2 Sh (20)

Mundford

TL7993

Treetops, *6 Swaffham Road, Mundford, Thetford, Norfolk, IP26 5HR.* Comfortable bungalow on A1065. Guests own entrance, sitting/dining room. **Open:** All year (not Xmas/New Year)
01842 878557 Mrs Edmunds **Fax: 01842 879078 D:** £18.00 **S:** £18.00 **Beds:** 1T 1D **Baths:** 1 En 1 Pr (8)

Neatishead

TG3420 *White Horse*

Ramblers, *School Lane, Neatishead, Norwich, Norfolk, NR12 8XW.* **Open:** All year **Grades:** ETC 3 Diamond
01692 630864 Ms Griffiths **D:** £18.50 **S:** £22.00 **Beds:** 1D 1S **Baths:** 1 Sh (10) (2)
Country bed and breakfast in 200-year-old cottage in the heart of the spectacular Norfolk Broads. Ramblers is a perfect base for exploring this beautiful and historic region within easy reach of Norwich/coast and Georgian market town of Holt.

The Barton Angler Country Inn, *Instead Road, Neatishead, Norwich, NR12 8XP.* Once a rectory from which Nelson sailed as a boy, adjacent to Barton Broad. **Open:** All year (not Xmas/New Year)
01692 630740 Fax: 01692 631122 D: £30.00 **S:** £25.00 **Beds:** 4D 3S **Baths:** 5 En 2 Sh (40) cc

Allens Farmhouse, *Three Hammer Common, Neatishead, Norwich, NR12 8XW.* **Open:** All year
01692 630080 Mr & Mrs Smerdon **D:** £16.00–£20.00 **Beds:** 2D 1T **Baths:** 1 En 1 Sh ♿ 🅿 (3) ⚲ 📺 ♒ 📷 ⬛, ♨

Allens Farmhouse, built in early 1700s, was a working farm until early 1980s when it was extensively modernised. Large walled garden, landscaped to create a beautiful lawn surrounded by flower beds with the added attraction of a well, fish pond and orchard.

Newton St Faith

TG2117

Elm Farm Country House, *Horsham St Faith, Norwich, NR10 3HH.* Country house in village of Horsham St Faith, 4 miles from Norwich. **Open:** All year
01603 898366 Fax: 01603 897129 D: £26.00–£29.00 **S:** £31.00–£38.00 **Beds:** 2F 5T 4D 3S **Baths:** 14 En ♿ 🅿 (20) 📺 📷 ⬛, ♨ cc

North Lopham

TM0382

Belgate, *The Street, North Lopham, Diss, Norfolk, IP22 2LR.* Peaceful bungalow. Large secluded garden, benefit of own front door. **Open:** All year
01379 687346 Mrs Hogg **Fax: 01379 688439 D:** £18.00 **S:** £18.00 **Beds:** 1T **Baths:** 1 En ♿ (16) 🅿 (2) ⚲ 📺 📷 ⬛, ♨

North Walsham

TG2830

Green Ridges, *104 Cromer Road, North Walsham, Norfolk, NR28 0HE.* Excellent ensuite accommodation in attractive setting, walking distance town centre. **Open:** All year
01692 402448 & 07748 542964 (M) Mrs Mitchell **D:** £20.00–£30.00 **S:** £20.00–£35.00 **Beds:** 1F 1T 1D **Baths:** 2 En 1 Pr ♿ 🅿 (5) 📺 📷 ♒ 📷 ⬛, ♨

Toll Barn, *Heath Rd, Norwich Road, North Walsham, Norfolk, NR28 0JB.* Private lodges in a quiet rural setting, adjacent to grazing farmland with horses & sheep. **Open:** All year (not Xmas)
01692 403638 Fax: 01692 500993 nola@toll-barn.fsbusiness.co.uk **D:** £18.00–£25.00 **S:** £25.00 **Beds:** 1F 1D 1T 1S **Baths:** 4 En ♿ 🅿 (6) ⚲ 📺 ⬛, ♨

Pine Trees, *45 Happisburgh Road, North Walsham, Norfolk, NR28 9HB.* Lovely house, guest bedrooms overlooking garden with grass tennis court. **Open:** All year (not Xmas/New Year)
01692 404213 (also fax) Mrs Blaxell **D:** £20.00 **S:** £20.00 **Beds:** 1T 1D **Baths:** 2 Sh ♿ (10) 🅿 (2) ⚲ 📺 ⬛, ♨

Norwich

TG2308 ⬛ The Eagle, York Tavern

Earlham Guest House, *147 Earlham Road, Norwich, NR2 3RG.* **Open:** All year (not Xmas)
Grades: ETC 4 Diamond, AA 4 Diamond
01603 454169 (also fax) Mr & Mrs Wright earlhamgh@hotmail.com **D:** £22.00–£25.00 **S:** £23.00–£26.00 **Beds:** 1F 3D 1T 3S **Baths:** 2 En 2 Sh ♿ (10) ⚲ 📺 📷 ⬛, ♨

Susan and Derek Wright offer welcoming and friendly hospitality with comfortable modern facilities, close historic Norwich, University and Norfolk Broads. Vegetarian choices, personal keys. Short break rates available 1 Oct - 31 Mar. No smoking throughout

Rosedale, *145 Earlham Road, Norwich, NR2 3RG.* Comfortable, family-run guest house. Easy access to city, coast and university. **Open:** All year (not Xmas)
01603 453743 Mrs Curtis **Fax: 01603 259887** drcbac@aol.com members.aol.com/drcbac **D:** £19.00–£40.00 **S:** £19.00–£25.00 **Beds:** 2F 2T 2S **Baths:** 2 Sh ♿ (4) ⚲ 📺 ⬛, ♨ cc

EdMar Lodge, *64 Earlham Road, Norwich, NR2 3DF.* Family run guest house. Ten minutes walk from city centre. **Open:** All year
01603 615599 Mr & Mrs Lovatt **Fax: 01603 495599** edmar@cwcom.net **D:** £20.00–£24.00 **S:** £28.00–£34.00 **Beds:** 1F 1T 3D **Baths:** 5 En 🅿 (8) ⚲ 📺 📷 ⬛, ♨ cc

Aylwyne House, *59 Aylsham Road, Norwich, NR3 2HF.* Quiet, spacious modern house, walking distance city and cathedral. **Open:** All year
01603 665798 Mrs Adams **D:** £19.00–£21.00 **S:** £22.00–£26.00 **Beds:** 1F 1D 1S **Baths:** 2 En 1 Pr ♿ (3) 🅿 (3) ⚲ 📺 ✕ ⬛, ♨

Wedgewood House, *42 St Stephens Road, Norwich, NR1 3RE.* Comfortable city centre house. Close to Norwich's shops and attractions. **Open:** All year (not Xmas/New Year)
01603 625730 stay@wedgewoodhouse.co.uk www.wedgewoodhouse.co.uk **D:** £24.00–£26.00 **S:** £34.00–£36.00 **Beds:** 3F 2T 5D 2S **Baths:** 9 En ♿ 🅿 (7) 📺 📷 ⬛, ♨ cc

Trebeigh House, *16 Brabazon Road, Hellesdon, Norwich, NR6 6SY.* Warm welcome to quiet friendly house, convenient city, country, airport. **Open:** All year (not Xmas)
01603 429056 Mrs Jope **Fax: 01603 414247** christine@trebeigh.madasafish.com **D:** £18.00–£19.00 **S:** £18.00–£20.00 **Beds:** 1D 1T **Baths:** 1 Sh ♿ 🅿 (3) ⚲ 📺 📷 ⬛, ♨

Arbor Linden Lodge, *Linden House, 557 Earlham Road, Norwich, NR4 7HW.* Family run for quality and warmth of welcome. Free parking near city centre. **Open:** All year
01603 451303 Mr Betts **Fax: 01603 250641** info@guesthouses.uk.com www.guesthouses.uk.com **D:** £20.00–£25.00 **S:** £26.00–£35.00 **Beds:** 1F 1T 3D 1S **Baths:** 6 En ♿ 🅿 (10) ⚲ 📺 📷 ⬛, ♨ cc

Beaufort Lodge, *62 Earlham Road, Norwich, NR2 3DF.* Spacious Victorian house with ample parking. Within easy walking distance of city centre. **Open:** All year (not Xmas/New Year)
01603 627928 (also fax) Mr Dobbins **D:** £25.00 **S:** £35.00–£40.00 **Beds:** 3D 1S **Baths:** 3 En 1 Pr 🅿 ⚲ 📺 ♨

Pine Lodge, *518 Earlham Road, Norwich, NR4 7HR.* Distinctive, cheerful and comfortable accommodation between university and the city centre. **Open:** All year
01603 504834 Mr & Mrs Tovell tovell@tovell.fsnet.co.uk **D:** £18.00–£20.00 **S:** £25.00 🅿 📺 📷 ⬛, ♨

Old Hunstanton

TF6842 ⬛ Neptune, Marine Hotel

Cobblers Cottage, *3 Wodehouse Road, Old Hunstanton, Hunstanton, Norfolk, PE36 6JD.* Quietly situated 500 yards to sea, coastal path, pubs. Fantastic breakfasts. **Open:** Mar to Oct **Grades:** ETC 3 Diamond
01485 534036 Ms Poore lesley.cobblerscottage@btinternet.com **D:** £23.00–£28.00 **S:** £28.00–£32.00 **Beds:** 2T 1D **Baths:** 3 En 🅿 (8) 📺 📷 ♒ 📷 ⬛, ♨

Overstrand

TG2440 ⬛ Saracen's Head, Walpole Arms, Sea Marge Hotel, White Horse

Cliif Cottage, *18 High Street, Overstand, Cromer, Norfolk, NR27 0AB.* C18th cottage. Two minutes from sandy beach. **Open:** All year **Grades:** ETC 3 Diamond
01263 578179 R & M Cooper roymin@btinternet.com **D:** £18.00–£22.00 **S:** £23.00–£27.00 **Beds:** 1T **Baths:** 2 En 🅿 (2) ⚲ 📺 📷 ⬛, ♨

Potter Heigham

TG4119

Hazelden, *Bridge Road, Potter Heigham, Great Yarmouth, NR29 5JB.* Ideal for coast, Broads, nature reserve, walking, boating, cycling, fishing. **Open:** All year (not Xmas) **01692 670511** Mr & Mrs Girling **D:** £18.00–£20.00 **S:** £21.00–£25.00 **Beds:** 1D/F **Baths:** 1 En ⌂ ▣ (2) ⊬ ⊠ ⊁ �v ▥.

Rackheath

TG2813

Manor Barn House, *Back Lane, Rackheath, Norwich, NR13 6NN.* Traditional C17th Norfolk barn, exposed beams and cottage in garden. **Open:** All year **01603 783543** Mrs Lebbell www.manorbarnhouse.co.uk **D:** £22.00–£25.00 **S:** £23.00–£29.00 **Beds:** 3D 2T 1S **Baths:** 4 En 1 Pr ⌂ (5) ▣ (6) ⊬ ⊠ ⊁ ▣ ▥.

Barn Court, *Back Lane, Rackheath, Norwich, NR13 6NN.* Spacious accommodation built around a courtyard. Ideal for exploring Norfolk. **Open:** All year (not Xmas) **01603 782536 (also fax)** Mrs Simpson **D:** £18.00–£21.00 **S:** £20.00–£25.00 **Beds:** 2D 1T **Baths:** 1 En 2 Sh ⌂ ▣ (3) ⊬ ⊠ ⊁ ▣ ▥ & ‗.

Reedham

TG4201   *Ferry Inn, Ship Inn*

The Railway Tavern, *17 The Havaker, Reedham, Norwich, NR13 3HG.* A slice of rural heaven, close to the Norfolk Broads. **Open:** All year **01493 700340** I SwanCuders *thetophouse@aol.com* www.reedham.net **D:** £25.00–£30.00 **S:** £30.00 **Beds:** 1F 1T 1D **Baths:** 3 En ⌂ ▣ ⊠ ⊁ × ▣ ▥ & ‗ cc

The Pyghtie, *26A The Hills, Reedham, Norwich, NR13 3AR.* Perfectly situated for exploring Norwich and Norfolk countryside. Superb accommodation. **Open:** All year **Grades:** ETC 4 Diamond **01493 701262** M M Blanche **Fax:** 01493 701635 *Blanches@Reedham.co.uk* **D:** £22.50–£25.00 **S:** £30.00–£35.00 **Beds:** 1D **Baths:** 1 En ▣ (6) ▣ ▥ ‗.

BATHROOMS
En = Ensuite
Pr = Private
Sh = Shared

Ridlington

TG3431   *Butchers' Arms*

The Old Rectory, *Ridlington, North Walsham, Norfolk, NR28 9NZ.* Perfectly situated; ideal for exploring Norfolk. Home-made breakfast. Tennis court. **Open:** All year **01692 650247** Mr Black *blacks7@email.com* **D:** £20.00–£25.00 **S:** £25.00–£30.00 **Beds:** 1D **Baths:** 1 En ⊬ × ▣ ▥ ‗.

Saham Toney

TF8902

The Croft, *69 Hills Road, Saham Toney, Thetford, Norfolk, IP25 7EW.* Beautiful creeper covered Victorian farmhouse. Delightful garden, quiet position. **Open:** All year **01953 881372** Mrs Baldwin **D:** £20.00–£22.00 **S:** £22.00–£24.00 **Beds:** 1T 1D **Baths:** 1 En 1 Sh ⌂ (12) ▣ (4) ⊬ ⊠ ▣ ▥ ‗.

Salhouse

TG3114

Brooksbank, *Lower Street, Salhouse, Norwich, NR13 6RW.* C18th house Broadland village within easy reach of Norfolk coast. **Open:** All year (not Xmas) **01603 720420 (also fax)** Mr & Mrs Coe *ray@brooksbanks.freeserve.co.uk* **D:** £18.00–£20.00 **S:** £25.00–£28.00 **Beds:** 2D 1T **Baths:** 3 En ▣ (4) ⊬ ⊠ ⊁ ▥ ‗.

Salthouse

TG0843   *Dun Cow*

Cumfus Bottom, *Purdy St, Salthouse, Holt, Norfolk, NR25 7XA.* Rooms set in country garden, only minutes away from the beach and Heath Lane. **Open:** All year **01263 741118 (also fax)** Mrs Holman **D:** £20.00–£22.50 **S:** £20.00–£30.00 **Beds:** 1D 1T **Baths:** 2 En ⌂ ▣ ▣ ⊠ ⊁ ▥ ‗.

Saxlingham Thorpe

TM2197

Foxhole Farm, *Windy Lane, Foxhole, Saxlingham Thorpe, Norwich, NR15 1UG.* Friendly welcome. Spacious farmhouse. Comfortable bedrooms. Generous English breakfasts. **Open:** All year (not Xmas) **Grades:** ETC 4 Diamond, AA 4 Diamond **01508 499226 (also fax)** *foxholefarm@hotmail.com* **D:** £20.00–£21.00 **S:** £25.00 **Beds:** 1D 1T **Baths:** 2 En ⌂ (14) ▣ (8) ⊬ × ▣ ▥ ‗.

Sharrington

TG0336

Daubeney Hall, *Sharrington, Melton Constable, Norfolk, NR24 2PQ.* Attractive Listed farmhouse in quiet village. Splendid breakfast. Warm welcome. **Open:** Easter to Oct **Grades:** RAC 4 Diamond **01263 861412** N Ogier *ninaogier@hotmail.com* **D:** £20.00 **S:** £20.00–£25.00 **Beds:** 1T 2D **Baths:** 2 En 1 Pr ⊬ ▣ ⊁ ▣ ‗.

Sheringham

TG1543   *Dunstable Arms*

Sheringham Lodge, *50 Cromer Road, Sheringham, Norfolk, NR26 8RS.* **Open:** All year **01263 821954** Mr & Mrs Hare *mikewalker19@hotmail.com* **D:** £22.00–£24.00 **S:** £22.00–£24.00 **Beds:** 1F 2D 1T 1S **Baths:** 1 Sh ⌂ (5) ▣ (6) ⊬ ⊠ × ▥ ‗. Sheringham Lodge, run by Mike and Maggie Walker, is an attractive Edwardian house offering a warm welcome and accommodation with ensuite facilities to most rooms. We are a few minutes walk from the centre of Sheringham and the sea front.

Canton House, *14 Cliff Road, Sheringham, Norfolk, NR26 8BJ.* Warm welcome. Comfortable surroundings. Excellent breakfast. Home made bread. **Open:** All year (not Xmas/New Year) **01263 824861** Ms Rayment *chrissy@tooment.freeserve.co.uk* **D:** £20.50–£21.00 **S:** £20.50–£21.00 **Beds:** 1F 1T 1D **Baths:** 2 En 2 Sh ⌂ (1) ▣ ⊁ ▣ ▥ ‗.

The Bay-Leaf Guest House, *10 St Peters Road, Sheringham, Norfolk, NR26 8QY.* Charming Victorian licensed guest house, nestled between steam railway and sea. **Open:** All year **01263 823779** Mr Pigott **Fax:** 01263 820041 **D:** £22.00–£25.00 **S:** £25.00 **Beds:** 2F 3D 2T **Baths:** 7 En ⌂ ▣ (4) ▣ ▥ & ‗.

Highfield Guest House, *5 Montague Road, Sheringham, Norfolk, NR26 8LN.* Peaceful residence of character and quality. Luxury ensuites. Choice menus. **Open:** All year **Grades:** AA 4 Diamond **01263 825524** Mr & Mrs Caldwell **D:** £18.00–£25.00 **Beds:** 2F 2T 3D **Baths:** 6 En 1 Sh ⌂ (7) ▣ (2) ⊬ ▣ ▥ ‗.

Holly Cottage, *14a The Rise, Sheringham, Norfolk, NR26 8QB.* Traditionally-built beamed cottage. Warm Christian welcome. Suit less abled. **Open:** All year **Grades:** ETC 4 Diamond **01263 822807** Mrs Perkins *hollyperks@aol.com* www.sheringham-network.co.uk **D:** £15.00–£25.00 **S:** £25.00–£34.00 **Beds:** 1T 1D **Baths:** 2 En ⌂ ▣ ⊁ ▣ ▥ & ‗.

All details shown are as supplied by B&B owners in Autumn 2001

The Birches, *27 Holway Road, Sheringham, Norfolk, NR26 8HW.* Small guest house conveniently situated for town and sea front. **Open:** Apr to Oct
01263 823550 Ms Pearce www.broadland. com/thebirches **D:** £20.00–£25.00 **S:** £25.00 **Beds:** 1D 1T **Baths:** 2 En ॐ (12) 🖪 (2) ⊬ 🗹 ✕ 🗹 ▥, ≜

Whelk Coppers, *Westcliff, Sheringham, Norfolk, NR26 8LD.* Traditional English tea rooms panelled in Indian teak from old sailing ship. **Open:** All year (not Xmas/New Year)
01263 825771 S & P Foster *peter.foster@ ic24.net* **D:** £17.00–£20.00 **S:** £17.00–£20.00 **Beds:** 1F 1D **Baths:** 1 En 1 Pr ॐ 🗹 ≜

Shipdham
TF9507

Pound Green Hotel, *Pound Green Lane, Shipham, Thetford, Norfolk, IP2S 7LS.* An acre of own grounds. Peaceful rural setting. **Open:** All year
01362 820940 Mr Hales & Ms S Woods **Fax:** 01362 821253 *poundgreen@aol.com* www.poundgreen.co.uk **D:** £22.50–£25.00 **S:** £25.00–£35.00 **Beds:** 1F 8D 1S **Baths:** 8 En 2 Pr ॐ 🖪 (50) ⊬ 🗹 ✕ 🗹 ▥, ♣ ❅ ≜ cc

Smallburgh
TG3324

Bramble House, *Catts Common, Smallburgh, Norfolk, NR12 9NS.* Friendliness and comfort guaranteed in our large country house, in 1.5 acres **Open:** All year (not Xmas)
01692 535069 (also fax) S Ross *bramblehouse@tesco.com* **D:** £22.00–£24.00 **S:** £30.00 **Beds:** 1F 1T 1D 1S **Baths:** 4 En ॐ 🖪 (4) ⊬ 🗹 ✕ 🗹 ▥, ≜

South Lopham
TM0481

Malting Farm, *Blo Norton Road, South Lopham, Diss, Norfolk, IP22 2HT.* Elizabethan timber-framed farmhouse on working farm. Patchwork and quilting. **Open:** Jan to Dec **Grades:** ETC 3 Diamond
01379 687201 Mrs Huggins www.farmstayangela.co.uk **D:** £21.00–£25.00 **S:** £25.00–£30.00 **Beds:** 1D 1T **Baths:** 1 En 1 Sh ॐ 🖪 🗹 ⊬ 🗹 🗹 ▥, ≜

Stalham
TG3725   🐟 *Kingfisher, Swan Inn*

The White House, *Wayford Bridge, Stalham, Norwich, Norfolk, NR12 9LH.* Comfortable detached family home close to the Broads **Open:** Easter to Oct
01692 583316 Mr Blowers **D:** £16.00 **S:** £18.00 **Beds:** 1D 2T 🖪 🗹 ⊬ 🗹 ▥,

Strumpshaw
TG3407   🐟 *Shoulder of Mutton, Huntsman*

Carr House, *Low Road, Strumpshaw, Norwich, Norfolk, NR13 4HT.* Overlooking RSPB reserve. Close to Norwich Broads Coast. 2 acre garden/lake. **Open:** All year **Grades:** ETC 4 Diamond
01603 713041   *margotdunham@supanet.com* **D:** £20.00–£25.00 **S:** £25.00–£35.00 **Beds:** 1T 2D **Baths:** 2 En 1 Pr ॐ (2) 🖪 (4) 🗹 ⊬ 🗹 ▥, ≜

Suton
TM0999

Avalon Farm, *Suton, Wymondham, Norfolk, NR18 9JQ.* Traditional farmhouse, quiet country location, few mins A11. All rooms decorated to high standard. **Open:** All year
01953 602339 Mrs Reynolds **D:** £20.00–£25.00 **S:** £20.00–£25.00 **Beds:** 1F 1T 3D 1S **Baths:** 1 En 2 Sh ॐ 🖪 (8) ⊬ 🗹 ✕ 🗹 ▥, ≜

Swaffham
TF8109

Purbeck House, *Whitsands Road, Swaffham, Norfolk, PE37 7BJ.* Friendly family house, warm welcome. Full breakfast, large garden. **Open:** All year
01760 721805 & 01760 725345 Mrs Webster **D:** £18.00–£20.00 **S:** £20.00 **Beds:** 2F 2T 2S **Baths:** 1 En 2 Sh ॐ 🖪 (3) 🗹 ⊬ 🗹 ▥, ≜

Swanton Morley
TG0217   🐟 *Darby's, Angel Inn*

Kesmark House, *Gooseberry Hill, Swanton Morley, Dereham, Norfolk, NR20 4PP.* Beautiful listed house. Aga breakfasts. Breckland, Coast, Norwich. Also cottage. **Open:** All year (not Xmas/New Year)
01362 637663 Mr & Mrs Willis **Fax:** 01362 637800 *kesmark@netcomuk.co.uk* www.northnorfolk.co.uk/kesmark/ **D:** £20.00–£25.00 **S:** £29.00–£40.00 **Beds:** 1F 1T 2D **Baths:** 1 En 2 Pr ॐ 🖪 (3) ⊬ 🗹 ✕ 🗹 ▥, ≜

Taverham
TG1514

Taverham Mill, *Costessey Road, Taverham, Norwich, Norfolk, NR8 6TA.* Quiet riverside location, fishing available. Private entrance, bathroom, sitting room with TV. **Open:** All year
01603 869495 & 01603 868200 Mr Watts **Fax:** 01603 869495 **D:** £22.50 **S:** £30.00 **Beds:** 1D **Baths:** 1 Pr ॐ 🖪 🗹 ▥, ≜ cc

Thetford
TL8783

43 Magdalen Street, *Thetford, Thetford, Norfolk, IP24 2BP.* House built in 1575 close to town centre. **Open:** All year (not Xmas/New Year)
01842 764564 Mrs Findlay **D:** £36.00 **S:** £18.00 **Beds:** 2T 1S **Baths:** 1 Sh ॐ 🖪 (1) 🗹 🗹 ▥, ≜

Thompson
TL9196

The Thatched House, *Pockthorpe Corner, Thompson, Thetford, Norfolk, IP24 1PJ.* C16th, delightful village on the edge of the Brecklands. **Open:** All year
01953 483577 Mrs Mills **D:** £20.00 **S:** £25.00 **Beds:** 1D 2T **Baths:** 2 Sh 1 Pr ॐ (6) 🖪 (4) ⊬ 🗹 ✕ 🗹 ▥, ≜

College Farm, *Thompson, Thetford, Norfolk, IP24 1QG.* Converted C14th college of priests; 3 acre garden, wonderful breakfasts. **Open:** All year
01953 483318 (also fax) Mrs Garnier **D:** £22.50–£25.00 **S:** £22.50–£25.00 **Beds:** 2D 1T **Baths:** 1 Pr 1 Sh 2 En ॐ (7) 🖪 (10) 🗹 ▥,

Thorpe St Andrew
TG2609

Raeburn, *83 Yarmouth Road, Thorpe St Andrew, Norwich, NR7 0HE.* 2 miles Norwich centre, on bus route, opposite River Tare. **Open:** All year (not Xmas/New Year)
01603 439177 Mrs Hawkins **D:** £20.00–£22.00 **S:** £20.00 **Beds:** 1D 1T 1S **Baths:** 1 Sh 🖪 (4) 🗹 🗹 ▥, ≜

Norwood House, *14 Stanmore Road, Thorpe St Andrew, Norwich, Norfolk, NR7 0HB.* Detached house with attractive garden in peaceful cul-de-sac, 2 miles from historic Norwich. **Open:** All year (not Xmas)
01603 433500 Mrs Simpson **D:** £20.00–£22.50 **S:** £20.00–£22.50 **Beds:** 2D 1S **Baths:** 2 Sh ॐ (10) 🖪 (4) ⊬ 🗹 ▥, ≜

Thursford

TF9734

Old Coach House, *Thursford, Fakenham, Norfolk, NR21 0BD.* Peaceful farmhouse. 8m beautiful coastline. Suit birdwatchers and country lovers. **Open:** All year (not Xmas/New Year)
01328 878273 Mrs Green **D:** £20.00–£28.00 **S:** £24.00–£28.00 **Beds:** 3T 1D **Baths:** 2 En 1 Sh ⌂ 🅿 (6) 📺 ☰ 🛉 ⚲

Tilney St Lawrence

TF5514

The Garden House, *27 Magdalen Road, Tilney St Lawrence, King's Lynn, Norfolk, PE34 4QX.* Open countryside, fishing, Sandringham House and Historic Lynn nearby. **Open:** Easter to Oct
01945 880610 Mr & Mrs Swain **D:** £16.00 **S:** £20.00 **Beds:** 1T 1D **Baths:** 1 En 1 Sh ⌂ 🅿 (8) ⅍ 📺 🛉 ☰ ⚲

Upton

TG3912   ⚐ *White Horse*

Cherry Tree Cottage, *Marsh Road, Upton, Norwich, NR13 6BS.* Comfortably converted cottage, close broads. Coasts: Norwich and Yarmouth. **Open:** All year (not Xmas/New Year)
01493 750509 **D:** £23.00 **S:** £23.00 **Beds:** 1T 1S **Baths:** 1 Pr ⌂ 🅿 (3) ⅍ 📺 ☑ ☰ ⚲

Upwell

TF5002

Five Bells Inn, *1 New Road, Upwell, Wisbech, Cambs, PE14 9AA.* Attractive riverside village inn, comfortable rooms and award-winning restaurant. **Open:** All year
01945 772222 Fax: 01945 774433 D: £20.00–£25.00 **S:** £25.00–£30.00 **Beds:** 1F 3D 3T **Baths:** 7 En ⌂ 🅿 (20) ⅍ 📺 🛉 ✕ ☑ ☰ ⚲ cc

Walton Highway

TF4912

Homeleigh Guest House, *Lynn Road, Walton Highway, Wisbech, Cambs, PE14 7DE.* Homeleigh guest house built 1880s. All rooms ensuite. **Open:** All year
01945 582356 Mrs Wiseman **Fax: 01945 587006 D:** £20.00 **S:** £20.00 **Beds:** 2D 2T 2S **Baths:** 6 En 🅿 (6) 📺 ✕ ☑ ☰ & ✽ ⚲ cc

Warham

TF9441

The Three Horseshoes / The Old Post Office, *69 Bridge Street, Warham, Wells-next-the-Sea, Norfolk, NR23 1NL.* Dream country cottage adjoining award-winning village pub. **Open:** All year (not Xmas)
01328 710547 Mr Salmon **D:** £24.00–£26.00 **S:** £24.00 **Beds:** 3D 1S **Baths:** 1 En 1 Sh 🅿 (10) ⅍ 📺 🛉 ✕ ☑ ☰ ⚲

Wells-next-the-Sea

TF9143   ⚐ *Ark Royal, Bowling Green, Crown Inn, Corner House*

Wingate, *Two Furlong Hill, Wells-next-the-Sea, Norfolk, NR23 1HQ.*
Open: All year
01328 711814
Ms Stocker **D:** £25.00–£28.00 **S:** £40.00–£43.00 **Beds:** 1T 2D **Baths:** 2 En 1 Pr ⌂ (10) ⅍ 📺 🛉 ☑ ☰ ⚲
Built for artist Frank Southgate, this lovely house offers excellent accommodation in a peaceful location, a few minutes from the delightful town centre and quay. Renowned for a warm welcome, delicious breakfasts and friendly service. A home from home.

East House, *East Quay, Wells-next-the-Sea, Norfolk, NR23 1LE.* Old house overlooking marsh, creeks and boats to distant sea. **Open:** All year (not Xmas)
01328 710408 Mrs Scott **D:** £22.50 **S:** £26.00 **Beds:** 2T **Baths:** 2 En ⌂ (7) 🅿 (2) 📺 ☑ ☰ ⚲

Greengates, *Stiffkey Road, Wells-next-the-Sea, Norfolk, NR23 1QB.* C18th cottage with views over salt marsh to sea. **Open:** All year (not Xmas)
01328 711040 Mrs Jarvis **D:** £20.00–£25.00 **S:** £25.00–£30.00 **Beds:** 1D 1T **Baths:** 1 En 1 Pr 1 Sh 🅿 (2) ⅍ 📺 ☑ ☰ ⚲

St Heliers Guest House, *Station Road, Wells-next-the-Sea, Norfolk, NR23 1EA.* Central Georgian family house in secluded gardens with excellent breakfasts. **Open:** All year
01328 710361 (also fax) Mrs Kerr *bookings@ st-heliers.co.uk* st-heliers.co.uk **D:** £17.00–£25.00 **S:** £18.00–£30.00 **Beds:** 1D 1T 1S **Baths:** 2 Sh 1 En 🅿 (4) ⅍ 📺 ☑ ☰ ⚲

Hideaway, *Red Lion Yard, Wells-next-the-Sea, Norfolk, NR23 1AX.* Evening meals supplied on special out of season weekends. **Open:** All year (not Xmas/New Year) **Grades:** ETC 3 Diamond
01328 710524 Miss Higgs *hideaway.wells@ btinternet.com* **D:** £21.00–£22.50 **S:** £25.00–£35.00 **Beds:** 2T 1D **Baths:** 3 En 🅿 ☑ 🛉 ☰ ⚲

Brambledene, *Warham Road, Wells-next-the-Sea, Norfolk, NR23 1NE.* Homely bungalow near the Wells and Washington miniature railway. **Open:** Easter to Sept
01328 711143 Mr & Mrs Bramley **D:** £16.00 **S:** £16.00 **Beds:** 1F **Baths:** 1 Sh ⌂ 🅿 (2) ⅍ ☰ & ⚲

Welney

TL5294   ⚐ *Lamb & Flag*

Stockyard Farm, *Wisbech Road, Welney, Wisbech, Cambs, PE14 9RQ.* Comfortable former Fenland farmhouse, rurally situated between Ely and Wisbech. **Open:** All year (not Xmas/New Year)
01354 610433 Mrs Bennett **D:** £18.00 **S:** £23.00–£25.00 **Beds:** 1T 1D **Baths:** 1 Sh ⌂ (5) 🅿 (2) ⅍ 📺 🛉 ☑ ☰ ⚲

Wendling

TF9213

Greenbanks Country Hotel, *Wendling, Dereham, Norfolk, NR19 2AR.* Central touring, NT properties, private fishing, 5 ground floor suites. Meadow gardens. **Open:** All year
01362 687742 *greenbanks@skynow.com*
D: £28.00–£36.00 **S:** £36.00–£50.00 **Beds:** 3F 3T 2D **Baths:** 8 En ⌂ 🅿 📺 🛉 ✕ ☑ ☰ & ✽ ⚲ cc

West Dereham

TF6500

Bell Barn, *Lime Kiln Road, West Dereham, King's Lynn, PE33 9RT.* Quality accommodation with rustic charm, quiet rural setting. **Open:** All year (not Xmas) **Grades:** ETC 4 Diamond
01366 500762 (also fax) Mrs Wood *chris@ woodbarn.freeserve.co.uk* **D:** £20.00 **S:** £25.00 **Beds:** 1F 1D **Baths:** 1 En 1 Pr ⌂ 🅿 (4) 📺 ☑ ☰ ⚲

West Somerton

TG4620

The White House Farm, *The Street, West Somerton, Great Yarmouth, Norfolk, NR29 4EA.*
Open: All year (not Xmas)
Grades: ETC 4 Diamond
01493 393991 Mr Dobinson *whitehousefarm@ connectfree.co.uk* **D:** £18.00–£20.00 **S:** £25.00 **Beds:** 2D 1T **Baths:** 1 En 1 Sh ⌂ 🅿 (4) ⅍ ☰ ⚲
Welcoming, peaceful old farmhouse close to Broads (rowing dinghy) and lovely beach. Enjoyable walks and bike rides. Substantial breakfasts. Private/ensuite shower/bath rooms. Comfortable bedrooms overlooking sunny walled garden. Guest lounge and conservatory for space and relaxation.

Wicklewood

TG0702

Witch Hazel, Church Lane, Wicklewood, *Wymondham, NR18 9QH.* Peter and Eileen welcome you to Witch Hazel - a spacious detached house. **Open:** All year **01953 602247 (also fax)** Mr & Mrs Blake **D:** £20.00 **S:** £26.00 **Beds:** 3D **Baths:** 3 En ☼ (15) 🅿 (3) ⊁ 🖾 ✕ 🖾 🖩 🛧

Winterton-on-Sea

TG4919 ⚓ Fisherman's Return

Tower Cottage, Black Street, Winterton-on-Sea, Great Yarmouth, *Norfolk, NR29 4AP.* Pretty flint cottage. Excellent breakfast. Peaceful village with sandy beach. **Open:** All year (not Xmas) **01493 394053** Mr Webster *towercott@ aladdinscave.net* **D:** £19.00–£21.00 **S:** £24.00 **Beds:** 2D 1T **Baths:** 1 En 2 Pr 🅿 (3) 🖾 🖩 🛧

Wood Norton

TG0127

Manor Farm, Wood Norton, Dereham, *Norfolk, NR20 5BE.* A warm welcome awaits you at large Grade II Listed farmhouse. **Open:** All year (not Xmas/New Year) **01362 683231** Mrs Crowe **D:** £20.00–£25.00 **Beds:** 1T 2D **Baths:** 2 En 1 Pr ☼ (10) 🅿 (4) ⊁ 🖾 ✕ 🖾 🖩 🛧

Worstead

TG3026 ⚓ New Inn

Geoffrey The Dyer House, Church Plain, Worstead, North Walsham, Norfolk, *NR28 9AL.* C17th Listed building. Centre conservation village **Open:** All year **01692 536562** Mrs O'Hara *vacarie@bun.com* **D:** £25.00 **S:** £25.00–£28.00 **Beds:** 1F 1T 1D 1S **Baths:** 4 En ☼ 🅿 (4) 🖾 🛧 ✕ 🖾 🖩 🛧

Worthing

TG0019

Tannery House, Church Road, Worthing, Dereham, Norfolk, *NR20 5HR.* **Open:** All year (not Xmas/New Year) **01362 668202** Mr & Mrs Eve *georgebelindaeve@ tesco.net* **D:** £22.00–£26.00 **S:** £24.00–£28.00 **Beds:** 2T 2D **Baths:** 2 En 1 Sh ⊁ 🖾 🖩 🛧 Quietly situated C18th house in the heart of rural Norfolk. In unspoilt hamlet convenient to the coast, Broads, Norwich and Sandringham. The beautiful 4 acre garden with riverside setting includes a swimming pool and well-stocked fishing lake and water.

Wortwell

TM2784

Rose Cottage, 62 High Road, Wortwell, Harleston, *IP20 0EF.* Friendly proprietor, Otter Trust close by, 45 minutes from coast. **Open:** All year **01986 788174** Mrs Gaffney **D:** £19.00–£22.00 **S:** £20.00–£25.00 **Beds:** 1D 1T **Baths:** 1 Sh ☼ 🅿 (6) ⊁ 🖾 🛧 🖩 🛧

BEDROOMS
D = Double
T = Twin
S = Single
F = Family

Wretham

TL9190

Dog and Partridge, Watton Road, Wretham, Thetford, *Norfolk, IP24 1QS.* Perfectly situated for exploring Peddars Way. Friendly traditional pub. **Open:** All year **01953 498245** Mr Ashman *dogman@ dog&partridge.freeserve.co.uk* **D:** £17.00–£20.00 **S:** £20.00–£23.00 **Beds:** 1F 4T **Baths:** 2 Sh ☼ (5) 🅿 (10) 🖾 🛧 ✕ 🖾 🖩 🛧 **cc**

Wroxham

TG3017

Wroxham Park Lodge, 142 Norwich Road, Wroxham, Norwich, *NR12 8SA.* Victorian house with garden, ideal touring Norfolk and the Broads. **Open:** All year **Grades:** ETC 4 Diamond **01603 782991** K Jackman **D:** £20.00–£24.00 **S:** £20.00–£28.00 **Beds:** 1F 1T 2D **Baths:** 4 En ☼ 🅿 (4) 🖾 🛧 🖩 🛧

Wymondham

TG1101

Home Farm, Morley St Peter, Wymondham, *Norfolk, NR18 9SU.* Set in 4 acres of secluded grounds, 3 miles from 2 towns. **Open:** All year (not Xmas) **01953 602581** Mrs Morter **D:** £18.00–£20.00 **S:** £18.00–£20.00 **Beds:** 1T 1D 1S **Baths:** 1 Sh ☼ (5) 🅿 (5) ⊁ 🖾 🖩 🛧

Turret House, 27 Middleton Street, Wymondham, Norfolk, *NR18 0AB.* Victorian town house of considerable character - close to historic abbey. **Open:** All year (not Xmas) **01953 603462 (also fax)** Mrs Morgan **D:** £20.00 **S:** £20.00 **Beds:** 1F 1T 1S **Baths:** 1 Sh ☼ 🅿 (2) ⊁ 🖾 🛧 🖾 🖩 🛧 **cc**

Northamptonshire

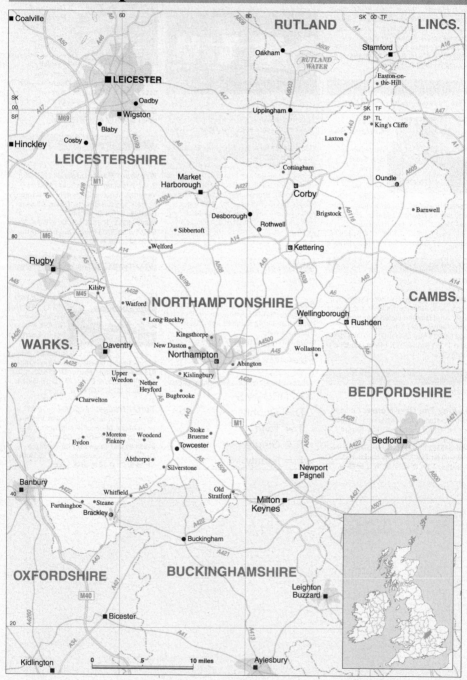

B&B owners may vary rates – be sure to check when booking

Abington
SP7761

Pembroke House, *36 Garrick Road, Abington, Northampton, NN1 5ND.* Beautiful Victorian property, all facilities, near park, town and M1. **Open:** Jan to Nov **01604 621858** Mr Thomas **D:** £17.00–£19.00 **S:** £17.50–£19.50 **Beds:** 1D 1T 1S **Baths:** 1 Sh ☒ ⊬ ⊠ ⊁ ▥ ⚊

Abthorpe
SP6446 ⬛ *Crown Inn, The New Inn*

Hilltop House, *Wappewham Road, Helmdow, Brackley, Northants, NN13 5QA.* Modern stone house convenient to Silverstone, Oxford Cotswolds and M40. **Open:** All year **01295 760560** Mrs Brodie **Fax: 01295 760 485** **D:** £30.00–£35.00 **S:** £30.00–£35.00 **Beds:** 2T **Baths:** 1 En 1 Pr ⊠ (4) ⊠ ▥ ⚊

Barnwell
TL0484

Lilford Lodge Farm, *Barnwell, Oundle, Peterborough, Cambridgeshire, PE8 5SA.* C19th farmhouse and adjoining barn recently converted. Set in the Nene Valley. **Open:** All year (not Xmas) **01832 272230 (also fax)** Mrs Dijksterhuis *trudy@lilford-lodge.demon.co.uk* www.lilford-lodge.demon.co.uk **D:** £18.00–£21.00 **S:** £18.00–£21.00 **Beds:** 1F 1D 1T 2S **Baths:** 5 En ☒ ⊠ (20) ⊬ ⊠ ▥ ⚊

Brackley
SP5837

Walltree House Farm, *Steane, Brackley, Northants, NN13 5NS.* Central touring base. Comfortable warm converted stables. Ground floor bedrooms and cottages. Laundry. **Open:** All year (not Xmas) **01295 811235** Mrs Harrison **Fax: 01295 811147 D:** £27.50–£37.50 **S:** £37.50–£40.00 **Beds:** 2F 2D 2T **Baths:** 5 En 1 Pr ☒ ⊠ (15) ⊬ ⊠ ▥ ⚊ cc

Brigstock
SP9485

Bridge House, *3 Grafton Road, Brigstock, Kettering, Northants, NN14 3EY.* Quiet modern home in pretty village. Warm welcome. Full breakfast. **Open:** All year (not Xmas) **01536 373297 D:** £16.50–£18.00 **S:** £16.50–£18.00 **Beds:** 1T 1S **Baths:** 1 Sh ☒ ⊠ (3) ⊬ ⊠ ✕ ▥ ⚊

Bugbrooke
SP6757

Cherry Tree Cottage, *26a Camphill, Bugbrooke, Northampton, NN7 3PH.* Cleanliness, warm hospitality, hearty breakfast and pleasant surrounding are our speciality. **Open:** All year **01604 830929** Mrs Corben **D:** £20.00–£25.00 **S:** £20.00–£25.00 **Beds:** 1T 1D **Baths:** 1 Sh ☒ (2) ⊠ (5) ⊬ ⊠ ⊠ ▥ ⚊

Charwelton
SP5356 ⬛ *Fox & Hounds*

Foxhall Farmhouse, *Charwelton, Daventry, Northants, NN11 6YY.* Self contained comfort, easily located, family run old traditional farmhouse. **Open:** All year **01327 261817 Fax: 01327 264445** *drawit@ globalnet.co.uk* **D:** £20.00 **S:** £25.00 **Beds:** 1T 1S **Baths:** 1 Pr ☒ ⊠ (6) ⊬ ⊠ ▥ ⚊

Corby
SP8889

16 Dixon Walk, *Corby, Northants, NN17 1UR.* Near Rockingham Castle, Indy race track (opening Sept 2001). **Open:** All year **01536 402649** Mrs MacLeod **D:** £15.00–£18.00 **S:** £15.00–£18.00 **Beds:** 2S 1T ⊠ ▥ ⚊

The Raven Hotel, *Rockingham Road, Corby, Northants, NN17 1UG.* The quality of a travel lodge plus that extra personal touch **Open:** All year **01536 202313 Fax: 01536 203159** *ravenhotel@ hotmail.com* www.mrbip.com **D:** £21.50–£26.50 **S:** £34.00–£44.00 **Beds:** 3F 12T 2D **Baths:** 5 En ☒ ⊠ ⊬ ⊠ ✕ ▥ ⚊ cc

Cottingham
SP8490

Bancroft House, *34 Bancroft Road, Cottingham, Market Harborough, Leics, LE16 8XA.* Friendly atmosphere. Quiet location. Basins in all bedrooms. Huge breakfast if required. **Open:** All year (not Xmas/New Year) **01536 770799** Mrs Evans *judy@ bancroft88.fsnet.co.uk* **D:** £20.00 **S:** £20.00 **Beds:** 1D 2S **Baths:** 1 Sh ☒ (0) ⊠ (6) ⊬ ⊠ ⊠ ▥ ⚊

Please respect a B&B's wishes regarding children, animals and smoking

Easton-on-the-Hill
TF0004

Hillcroft House, *25 High Street, Easton-on-the-Hill, Stamford, Lincs, PE9 3LN.* Converted stone farmhouse, spacious grounds, quiet position in conservation village. **Open:** All year (not Xmas) **01780 755598** Mrs McCallum **D:** £17.50–£20.00 **S:** £20.00–£22.50 **Beds:** 1D 2T **Baths:** 1 Pr 1 Sh ☒ ⊠ (4) ⊬ ⊠ ⊁ ⊠ ▥ ⚊

Eydon
SP5450

Crockwell Farm, *Eydon, Daventry, Northants, NN11 3QA.* Individually furnished accommodation in beautiful C17th barns. All bedrooms views over open countryside. **Open:** All year **01327 361358 & 07850 050716 (M)** J B Harper **Fax: 01327 361573** *info@ crockwellfarm.co.uk* www.crockwellfarm.co.uk **D:** £25.00–£30.00 **S:** £30.00 **Beds:** 2F 2T 1D **Baths:** 4 En 1 Pr ☒ ⊠ (6) ⊠ ⊁ ▥ ⚊ cc

Farthinghoe
SP5339

Greenfield, *Baker Street, Farthinghoe, Brackley, Northants, NN13 5PH.* Post office, C16th church and pub are near our comfortable modern home. **Open:** All year (not Xmas) **01295 712380** V Webb **Fax: 01295 710557** *vivwebb@aol.com* www.webb52.freeserve.co.uk **D:** £20.00–£25.00 **S:** £20.00–£25.00 **Beds:** 1D 1T **Baths:** 1 Pr ☒ (8) ⊠ (2) ⊬ ⊠ ⊠ ▥ ⚊

Kettering
SP8778

Hawthorn House Private Hotel, *2 Hawthorn Road, Kettering, Northants, NN15 7HS.* Victorian town house private hotel. Short drive J9 A14 **Open:** All year **Grades:** ETC 3 Diamond **01536 482513** Mrs McQuade **Fax: 01536 513121 D:** £25.00 **S:** £30.00 **Beds:** 1D 4T **Baths:** 3 En 2 Pr ☒ ⊠ (4) ⊠ ✕ ▥ ⚊

Pennels Guest House, *175 Beatrice Road, Kettering, Northants, NN16 9QR.* Quality accommodation, well-maintained, some ground room bedrooms overlooking private garden, quiet area. **Open:** All year **01536 481940** Mrs Green **Fax: 01536 410798** *pennelsgh@aol.com* www.members.aol. com/pennelsgh **D:** £20.00–£22.00 **S:** £22.50–£25.00 **Beds:** 1D 3T 3S **Baths:** 5 En 1 Sh ☒ ⊠ (6) ⊬ ⊠ ⊁ ✕ ⊠ ▥ ⚊ ⚊ cc

All details shown are as
supplied by B&B owners in
Autumn 2001

Kilsby

SP5570

The Hollies Farmhouse, *Main Road,
Kilsby, Rugby, CV23 8XR.* Comfortable
farmhouse, conveniently central for leisure
or business activities. **Open:** All year
01788 822629 Mrs Liddington **D:** £20.00–
£25.00 **S:** £25.00–£35.00 **Beds:** 2D 1T
Baths: 1 En 1 Sh ⛄ ⚑ (8) ⌫ ⌸ ⏠ ▦ ♨

King's Cliffe

TL0097

***19 West
Street,*** *King's
Cliffe,
Peterborough,
Northampton-
shire, PE8 6XB.*
Grade II Listed
500-year-old house, beautiful walled
garden, a King John hunting lodge.
Open: All year (not Xmas) **Grades:** ETC 4
Diamond
01780 470365 J Dixon **Fax:** 01780 470623
100537.156@compuserve.com **D:** £20.00–
£25.00 **S:** £25.00–£30.00 **Beds:** 1S 1D 1T
Baths: 3 Pr ⚑ (2) ⌫ ⌸ ✕ ⌸ ▦ ♨

Freestone Lodge, *Bridge Street, King's
Cliffe, Peterborough, PE8 6XH.* Traditional
stone house in countryside. Rooms
overlook garden and stables. **Open:** All year
01780 470213 (also fax) Mr & Mrs Blunt
freesto@aol.com **D:** £20.00–£25.00 **S:** £20.00–
£25.00 **Beds:** 1F 2T **Baths:** 1 Sh ⛄ ⚑ (6)
⌫ ⏠ ▦ ♨

Kingsthorpe

SP7563

The Old Church Institute,
Kingsthorpe Village, Northampton, NN2 6QB.
Tastefully converted detached Edwardian
property, attractive gardens. Close pubs/
shops etc. **Open:** All year
01604 715500 (also fax) E Bergin **D:** £20.00–
£25.00 **S:** £20.00–£25.00 **Beds:** 2D 2T
Baths: 2 En 1 Sh ⌐ ▦ ♨

Kislingbury

SP6959

The Elms, *Kislingbury, Northampton,
NN7 4AH.* Victorian house overlooking our
farm land. Close to Nene Way Walk.
Open: All year
01604 830326 Mrs Sanders **D:** £19.00
S: £19.00 **Beds:** 1D 1T 1S 3F **Baths:** 1 Sh ⛄
⚑ (4) ⌫ ⏠ ✕ ⌸ ▦ ♨

Laxton

SP9496 ◀ *Queen's Head*

The Old Vicarage, *Laxton, Corby,
Northants, NN17 3AT.* Beautiful, C19th old-
fashioned family home. Animals, art and
lots more. **Open:** All year
01780 450248 Mrs Hill-Brookes **Fax:** 01780
450398 *susan@marthahill.co.uk* **D:** £21.00
S: £21.00 ⛄ ⚑ (5) ⌫ ⏠ ▦ ♨ cc

Long Buckby

SP6267 ◀ *Globe Hotel, Stag's Head, Pytchley
Hotel*

Murcott Mill, *Murcott, Long Buckby,
Northampton, NN6 7QR.* Brilliant location for
visiting Northamptonshire. Luxurious
farmhouse accommodation. Friendly hosts.
Open: All year
01327 842236 Mrs Hart **Fax: 01327 844524**
bhart6@compuserve.com www.farmhohdap.co.
uk **D:** £22.00–£25.00 **S:** £25.00–£30.00
Beds: 1F 2T **Baths:** 3 En ⛄ ⚑ (12) ⌐ ⌫ ⏠ ⌸
▦ ♨

Moreton Pinkney

SP5749

The Old Vicarage, *Moreton Pinkney,
Daventry, Northants, NN11 3SQ.*
Comfortable, pretty C18th house with
walled garden in rural village. **Open:** All
year (not Xmas)
01295 760057 (also fax) Col & Mrs
Eastwood *tim@tandjeastwood.fsnet.co.uk*
www.tandjeastwood.co.uk **D:** £27.50–
£30.00 **S:** £30.00–£35.00 **Beds:** 1D 1T
Baths: 1 En 1 Pr ⛄ (7) ⚑ (3) ⌫ ⏠ ✕ ▦ ♨

Nether Heyford

SP6658

Heyford B&B, *27 Church Street, Nether
Heyford, Northampton, NN7 3LH.* Lovely
village, 1.5 miles M1 J16. Quiet, friendly and
comfortable. **Open:** All year
01327 340872 Mrs Clements **D:** £16.00–
£20.00 **S:** £20.00–£25.00 **Beds:** 3T 2S
Baths: 2 En 1 Sh ⛄ ⚑ (8) ⌫ ▦ ♨

Northampton

SP7561

Rowena, *569 Harlestone Road, New
Duston, Northampton, NN5 6NX.* Full of
Victorian charm and character, close to city
centre and Althorp. **Open:** All year
Grades: ETC 4 Diamond
01604 755889 P Adcock *pat&bob@
rowenabb.co.uk* www.rowenabb.co.uk
D: £22.50–£25.00 **S:** £22.50–£25.00 **Beds:** 1D
1T 1S **Baths:** 1 Sh ⚑ (3) ⌐ ⌫ ▦ ♨

Castilian House, *34 Park Avenue North,
Northampton, NN3 2JE.* Family-run, easy
access to main routes, town centre
amenities. **Open:** All year (not Xmas)
01604 712863 (also fax) Mrs Smith **D:** £21.00
S: £21.00 **Beds:** 1D 1S 1T ⌫ ⏠ ▦ ♨

Abington Town House, *Ardington
Road, Abington Park, Northampton, NN15LP.*
A traditional Edwardian house with a
typically English atmosphere, adjacent to
delightful Abington Park. **Open:** All year
(not Xmas/New Year)
01604 633128 & 07889 747240 (M) Ms Brown
www.abingtontownhouse.co.uk **D:** £20.00–
£22.50 **S:** £20.00–£30.00 **Beds:** 2D 2T 2S
Baths: 3 En 1 Sh ⌐ ⌫ ⌸ ▦ ♨

Old Stratford

SP7741

Furtho Manor Farm, *Old Stratford,
Milton Keynes, Bucks, MK19 6BA.* Dairy and
arable farm, 10 mins to central Milton
Keynes. **Open:** All year (not Xmas)
01908 542139 (also fax) Mrs Sansome
D: £20.00–£22.00 **S:** £20.00–£25.00 **Beds:** 1D
2T **Baths:** 2 Sh ⛄ ⚑ (6) ⌫ ⌸ ▦ ♨ ♨

Oundle

TL0487

***Ashworth
House,*** *75 West
Street, Oundle,
Peterborough,
Northampton-
shire, PE8 4EJ.*
Open: All year
Grades: ETC 4
Diamond
01832 275312 (also fax) Mrs Crick
D: £20.00–£25.00 **S:** £25.00–£30.00 **Beds:** 1D
1T **Baths:** 2 En ⛄ (1) ⌐ ⌫ ⌸ ▦ ♨
Grade II Listed town house with attractive
walled gardens, in historic Oundle, close to
the town centre and amenities, country
park and the famous public school. Very
comfortable ensuite accommodation with
colour TV. Imaginative, traditional Aga
cooking.

***Lilford Lodge
Farm,*** *Barnwell,
Oundle,
Peterborough,
Cambridgeshire,
PE85SA.* **Open:** All
year (not Xmas)
01832 272230 (also fax) Mrs Dijksterhuis
trudy@lilford-lodge.demon.co.uk
www.lilford-lodge.demon.co.uk **D:** £18.00–
£21.00 **S:** £18.00–£21.00 **Beds:** 1F 1D 1T 2S
Baths: 5 En ⛄ ⚑ (20) ⌐ ⌫ ⌸ ▦ ♨
C19th farmhouse and adjoining barn
recently converted. Set in the Nene Valley, 3
miles south of Oundle, 5 miles north of A14.
Peterborough, Stamford, Kettering,
Wellingborough and Corby are within easy
reach. Coarse fishing available. Quiet, rural
location.

Planning a longer stay? Always
ask for any special rates

Rothwell

SP8180

Rothwell House Hotel, *Bridge Street, Rothwell, Kettering, Northants, NN14 6JW.* A family run establishment offering a warm welcome. All rooms are ensuite with TV. **Open:** All year
01536 713000 Mr Cleary **Fax: 01536 713888** *rothwell.house@virgin.net* www.smoothhound. co.uk/hotels/rothwell.html **D:** £25.00–£30.00 **S:** £37.00–£49.50 **Beds:** 1F 5D 3T 11S **Baths:** 20 En ⑤ ⊞ (10) ⊬ ⊡ ⌗ ✕ Ⅵ 🖿 ♨ cc

Rushden

SP9666

The Old Rectory, *45 Rushden Road, Wymington, Rushden, Northants, NN10 9LN.* A Victorian rectory set in 5.5 acres of private grounds. A warm welcome guaranteed. **Open:** All year
01933 314486 Mrs Denton **Fax: 01933 411266** *oldrectory.wymington@btinternet.com* **D:** £20.00–£21.00 **S:** £22.00–£24.00 **Beds:** 1F 4D 3T 1S **Baths:** 8 En ⑤ ⊡ (20) ⊬ ⊡ ✕ Ⅵ 🖿 ⚓ ♨

Sibbertoft

SP6882 🍺 *Red Lion*

The Wrongs, *Welford Road, Sibbertoft, Market Harborough, Leics, LE16 9UJ.* Modern bungalow in open countryside. Carp fishing lake, working farm. **Open:** All year
01858 880886 Mrs Hart **Fax: 01858 880485** *maryhart@farming.co.uk* **D:** £18.00 **S:** £18.00 **Beds:** 1D 1S **Baths:** 1 Sh ⑤ ⊡ ⊬ ⌗ Ⅵ 🖿 ♨ cc

Silverstone

SP6644

Silverthorpe Farm, *Abthorpe Road, Silverstone, Towcester, Northants, NN12 8TW.*
Spacious, family-run, rural bungalow, 1.5 miles Silverstone Circuit. **Open:** All year (not Xmas) **Grades:** AA 3 Diamond
01327 858020 Mrs Branch **D:** £25.00 **S:** £25.00–£30.00 **Beds:** 1F 1D 1T 1S **Baths:** 2 Sh ⑤ ⊡ (8) ⊬ ⊡ Ⅵ 🖿 ♨

BATHROOMS
En = Ensuite
Pr = Private
Sh = Shared

Steane

SP5539

Walltree House Farm, *Steane, Brackley, Northants, NN13 5NS.* Central touring base. Comfortable warm converted stables. Ground floor bedrooms and cottages. Laundry. **Open:** All year (not Xmas)
01295 811235 Mrs Harrison **Fax: 01295 811147 D:** £27.50–£37.50 **S:** £37.50–£40.00 **Beds:** 2F 2D 2T **Baths:** 5 En 1 Pr ⑤ ⊡ (15) ⊬ Ⅵ 🖿 ♨ cc

Stoke Bruerne

SP7449 🚤 *Boat Inn*

Waterways Cottage, *Stoke Bruerne, Towcester, Northants, NN12 7RZ.* Modernised and extended thatched cottage in centre of lively canalside village. **Open:** All year (not Xmas)
01604 863865 (also fax) Mrs Cox **D:** £15.00 **S:** £18.00–£20.00 **Beds:** 1D 2T **Baths:** 1 En 1 Sh ⑤ ⊡ (6) ⊡ ⌗ 🖿 ♨

Beam End, *Stoke Park, Stoke Bruerne, Towcester, Northants, NN12 7RZ.* Converted Victorian stable/barn with log fires, acre gardens. Mile-long private road. **Open:** All year (not Xmas)
01604 864802 Ms Hart **Fax: 01604 864637** *beamend@bun.com* **D:** £25.00–£30.00 **S:** £25.00–£30.00 **Beds:** 2D 1T **Baths:** 1 En 1 Sh ⑤ ⊡ (5) ⊬ ✕ Ⅵ 🖿 ♨

Upper Weedon

SP6258

Mullions, *9 Oak Street, Upper Weedon, Northampton, NN7 4RQ.* C17th stone cottage, quiet location. Fields view from back garden. **Open:** All year (not Xmas)
01327 341439 (also fax) Mrs Piercey **D:** £19.50 **S:** £19.50 **Beds:** 1D **Baths:** 1 Pr ⊡ (2) ⊬ ⊡ ✕ 🖿 ♨

Watford

SP6068

Pandock Cottage, *Watford, Northampton, NN6 7UE.* Close to M1 (J18), spacious and traditionally furnished, rural - car essential. **Open:** All year (not Xmas)
01788 823615 D: £20.00–£30.00 **S:** £20.00–£25.00 **Beds:** 3F 1D 1T 1S **Baths:** 2 En ⊡ (3) ⊬ ⊡ 🖿 ♨

Welford

SP6480

West End Farm, *5 West End, Welford, Northampton, NN6 6HJ.* Comfortable 1848 farmhouse. Quiet village street. 2 miles A14/J1.
Open: All year **Grades:** ETC 4 Diamond
01858 575226 Mrs Bevin *bevin@uklynx.net* **D:** £18.00–£20.00 **S:** £18.00–£24.00 **Beds:** 1D 1T **Baths:** 1 Sh ⑤ ⊡ (2) ⊬ ⊡ Ⅵ ♨

Wellingborough

SP8967

Duckmire, *1 Duck End, Wollaston, Wellingborough, Northants, NN29 7SH.* Old stone house full of character, accessible for Wellingborough, Northampton, Milton Keynes. **Open:** All year (not Xmas) **Grades:** ETC 4 Diamond
01933 664249 (also fax) Mrs Woodrow *kerry@foreverengland.freeserve.co.uk* **D:** £22.00 **S:** £22.00 **Beds:** 1T **Baths:** 1 Pr ⊡ (2) ⊬ ⊡ ✕ 🖿 ♨

High View Hotel, *156 Midland Road, Wellingborough, Northants, NN8 1NG.* Large detached brick building near town centre and railway station. **Open:** All year (not Xmas/New Year) **Grades:** ETC 2 Star, AA 2 Star
01933 278733 Fax: 01933 225948 *hotelhighview@hotmail.com* **D:** £22.50–£29.50 **S:** £29.95–£45.00 **Beds:** 2F 3T 4D 5S **Baths:** 14 En ⑤ (3) ⊡ (10) ⊬ ⊡ ✕ 🖿 ♨ cc

Euro-Hotel, *90-92 Midland Road, Wellingborough, Northamptonshire, NN8 1BN.* Modernised new hotel **Open:** All year
01933 228761 D: £15.00–£18.00 **S:** £20.00–£28.00 **Beds:** 2F 3T 6D 5S **Baths:** 6 En 3 Sh ⑤ ⊡ (15) ⊬ ⊡ ✕ Ⅵ 🖿 ♨ ⚓ cc

Whitfield

SP6039 🚤 *Sun Inn*

The Thatches, *Whitfield, Brackley, Northants, NN13 5TQ.* Close to Silverstone NT Gardens, Sulgrave Manor, overlooking beautiful countryside. **Open:** All year (not Xmas/New Year) **Grades:** ETC 3 Diamond
01280 850358 Field **D:** £20.00–£22.50 **S:** £20.00–£25.00 **Beds:** 1F 1T 1D **Baths:** 1 Sh ⑤ ⊡ (2) ⊬ ⊡ 🖿 ♨

Wollaston

SP9162

45 Eastfield Road, *Wollaston, Wellingborough, Northamptonshire, NN29 7RS.* Friendly, helpful accommodation offering quality rooms and excellent breakfasts. **Open:** All year
01933 665266 Mr & Mrs Childs *eastfield.wollaston@talk21.com* **D:** £20.00–£25.00 **S:** £25.00–£30.00 **Beds:** 1F 1T **Baths:** 1 En 1 Pr ⊬ ⊡ Ⅵ 🖿 ♨

Woodend

SP6149

Christacorn House, *Main Street, Woodend, Towcester, Oxon, NN12 8RX.* Period house in rural village. Parking. 5 Miles from Silverstone. **Open:** All year (not Xmas/New Year)
01327 860968 Ms Manners **Fax: 01327 860452** *mannersfam@ntlworld.com* **D:** £22.50–£25.00 **S:** £22.50–£25.00 **Beds:** 1S 2D 1T **Baths:** 2 Sh ⑤ ⊡ (6) ⊬ ⊡ ⌗ Ⅵ 🖿 ♨

Northumberland

Acomb

NY9366

Mariner's Cottage Hotel, *Fallowfield Dene Road, Acomb, Hexham, Northd, NE46 4RP.* **Open:** All year **01434 603666** Mrs Darling **D:** £18.00–£20.00 **S:** £18.00–£20.00 **Beds:** 1F 1D 1T 2S **Baths:** 3 Pr 2 Sh ⌂ (5) ▣ (60) ⊡ ⊁ ✕ ⊠ ▥ ﹐ Hotel set in country, 3 miles from market town of Hexham and within easy reach of Hadrian's Wall, Kielder Water, Beamish Museum, Metro Shopping Centre.

Allendale

NY8355

Thornley House, *Allendale, Hexham, Northd, NE47 9NH.* Beautiful country house in spacious grounds near Hadrian's Wall. **Open:** All year **01434 683255** Mr Finn *e.finn@ukonline.co.uk* **D:** £18.50–£19.50 **S:** £18.50–£19.50 **Beds:** 2D 1T **Baths:** 2 En 1 Pr ⌂ (9) ▣ (4) ⊡ ⊁ ✕ ⊠ ▥ ✻ ﹐

Alnmouth

NU2410 ⚑ *Red Lion, Saddle, Hope & Anchor, Schooner*

4 Diamond
01665 830206 (also fax) Ms Tulip **D:** £24.00–£30.00 **S:** £24.00–£30.00 **Beds:** 2D 1T **Baths:** 3 En ▣ ⊁ ⊠ ▥ ﹐ Large Georgian farmhouse, centrally located on heritage coast line, superb views over Aln Estuary. Ideally situated for golfers, walkers and bird watchers. Northumberland National Park offers a wonderful opportunity for those wishing to walk and explore also Farne Islands famous for colonies of seals and seabirds.

Beaches B&B, *56 Northumberland Street, Alnmouth, Northd, NE66 2RJ.* Cosy oak-beamed farmer granary, bright spacious bedrooms above popular BYO restaurant. **Open:** All year **01665 830443** Mrs Hall **D:** £18.00–£25.00 **S:** £18.00–£30.00 **Beds:** 1D 1T **Baths:** 2 En ⌂ ⊠ ⊁ ✕ ⊠ ▥﹒

Alnwick

NU1813 ⚑ *Plough, White Swan, Dun Bull, Royal Oak, Topsy Turvy, Schooner*

Aydon House, *South Road, Alnwick, Northd, NE66 2NT.* Comfortable and clean accommodation offered. Large private car park. **Open:** Easter to Oct **Grades:** ETC 3 Diamond **01665 602218** Mr Carroll **D:** £17.00–£22.00 **S:** £17.00–£22.00 **Beds:** 2F 2D 2T 2S **Baths:** 8 En ⌂ ▣ (9) ⊠ ▥﹒ ﹐

Swarland Old Hall, *Swarland, Morpeth, Northumberland, NE65 9HU.* **Open:** All year (not Xmas/New Year) **Grades:** ETC 4 Diamond, Silver Award **01670 787642 & 07801 688153 (M)** Mrs Proctor *proctor@ swarlandoldhall.fsnet.co.uk* www.swarlandoldhall.com **D:** £22.00 **S:** £30.00 **Beds:** 1F 1T 1D **Baths:** 2 En 1 Pr ⌂ (3) ▣ (8) ⊠ ▥﹒ ﹐ Grade 2 listed Georgian farmhouse, situated on the banks of the river Coquet, with breathtaking views over the Northumberland countryside. An ideal base for touring, walking and golfing and also to explore the magnificent coast, castles and countryside. Full colour brochure available on request.

Charlton House, *2 Aydon Gardens, Alnwick, Northd, NE66 2NT.* Enjoy Northumberland Coast and Castles from our delightful Victorian house. **Open:** All year (not Xmas/New Year) **Grades:** ETC 4 Diamond **01665 605185** K & R J Bateman **D:** £20.00–£23.00 **S:** £25.00–£30.00 **Beds:** 1T 3D 1S **Baths:** 5 En ▣ (4) ⊁ ⊠ ⊠ ▥﹒ ﹐

Rooftops, *14 Blakelaw Road, Alnwick, Northd, NE66 1AZ.* Spacious accommodation panoramic views. Friendly, hospitality tray with home baking, fresh fruit. **Open:** Jan to Nov **Grades:** ETC 4 Diamond, Silver **01665 604201** Mrs Blair *rooftops.alnwick@ talk21.com* www.rooftops.ntb.org.uk **D:** £18.00–£19.00 **Beds:** 1D **Baths:** 1 En ⌂ ▣ (1) ⊁ ⊠ ⊠ ▥﹒ ﹐

The Georgian Guest House, *Hotspur Street, Alnwick, Northd, NE66 1QE.* Friendly, family-run stone guest house only yards from C14th Hotspur Tower. **Open:** All year **01665 602398 (also fax)** Mr Gibb *georgianguesthouse@eggconnect.net* **D:** £15.00–£20.00 **S:** £20.00–£25.00 **Beds:** 2T 2D **Baths:** 4 En ⌂ ▣ (3) ⊁ ⊠ ⊁ ⊠ ▥﹒ ﹐

National Grid References given are for villages, towns and cities – not for individual houses

Bamburgh

NU1734 ⚑ *Victoria Hotel, Lord Crewe Arms, Greenhouse, Castle, Warenford Lodge, Apple Inn, Blue Bell Hotel*

Greengates, *34 Front Street, Bamburgh, Northumberland, NE69 7BJ.* Castle views (100m away). Free range breakfast cycle hire. **Open:** All year **01668 214535** Claire Sundin *bamburgh.sunset@talk21.com* **D:** £19.50–£35.00 **S:** £25.00–£45.00 **Beds:** 2T 1D **Baths:** 2 En 1 Pr ⌂ ▣ ⊁ ⊠ ⊁ ⊠ ▥﹒ ﹐

Broome, *22 Ingram Road, Bamburgh, Northumberland, NE69 7BT.* Peaceful location on edge of village - 5 mins walk to beach/castle. **Open:** All year (not Xmas/New Year) **Grades:** ETC 4 Diamond **01668 214287** Ms Dixon *MDixon4394@aol.com* **D:** £25.00–£28.00 **S:** £30.00 **Beds:** 1T 1D **Baths:** 1 Sh ⌂ (12) ▣ (2) ⊁ ⊠ ✕ ⊠ ▥﹒ ⚬ ﹐

Bardon Mill

NY7865 ⚑ *Milecastle Inn*

The Craws Nest, *East Twice Brewed Farm, Bardon Mill, Hexham, Northd, NE47 7AL.* Converted farmhouse with spectacular views **Open:** All year (not Xmas/New Year) **01434 344348** Mrs Wanless **D:** £20.00 **S:** £20.00 **Beds:** 2F 1T **Baths:** 2 Sh ⊁ ⊠ ▥﹒ ﹐

Carrsgate East, *Bardon Mill, Hexham, Northumberland, NE47 7EX.* Relaxing, comfortable C17th home. Great views, good exploration base. **Open:** Feb to Nov **01434 344376 & 07710 981533 (M)** Mrs Armstrong **Fax:** 01434 344011 *lesley@ armstrongrl.freeserve.co.uk* **D:** £23.00–£27.00 **S:** £25.00–£27.00 **Beds:** 2D **Baths:** 2 En ▣ (6) ⊁ ⊠ ▥﹒ ﹐

Beadnell

NU2329 ⚑ *Craster Arms, Victoria Hotel*

Beach Court, *Harbour Road, Beadnell, Northd, NE67 5BJ.* Magnificent turreted beachside home offering an atmosphere of timeless tranquillity. **Open:** All year **Grades:** ETC 5 Diamond, Silver **01665 720225** Mrs Field **Fax:** 01665 721499 *info@beachcourt.com* www.beachcourt.com **D:** £29.50–£49.50 **S:** £44.50–£64.50 **Beds:** 2D 1T **Baths:** 3 Pr ▣ (4) ⊁ ⊠ ⊁ ⊠ ▥﹒ ﹐

Beadnell Bay

NU2327

Low Dover, *Harbour Road, Beadnell Bay, Chathill, Northd, NE67 5BJ.* Relax in comfort, ground floor suites, beautiful gardens, beach 50 metres. **Open:** All year (not Xmas) **01665 720291 & 07971 444070 (M)** Mrs Thompson **Fax:** 01665 720291 *kathandbob@lowdover.co.uk* www.lowdover.co. uk **D:** £26.00–£29.00 **Beds:** 1D 1T **Baths:** 2 En ⌂ (12) ▣ (2) ⊁ ⊠ ⊠ ▥﹒ ⚬ ﹐

Beal

NU0643

Brock Mill Farmhouse, *Brock Mill, Beal, Berwick-upon-Tweed, Northumberland, TD15 2PB.*
Quality accommodation opposite Lindisfarne. Perfect for discovering Northumbria and Borders. **Open:** Feb to Mar **Grades:** ETC 3 Diamond
01289 381283 (also fax) Ms Rogerson
D: £20.00–£25.00 **S:** £20.00–£30.00 **Beds:** 1F 1T 1D 1S **Baths:** 2 Sh ♨ ▣ (6) ⊬ ⊡ ⊁ ⊻ ♨ cc

Bedlington

NZ2582

Woodside, *Hartford Bridge Farm, Hartford Bridge, Bedlington, Northumberland, NE22 6AL.* Centrally situated for rural or urban businesses. Guests' comfort our main aim. **Open:** All year (not Xmas/New Year) **Grades:** ETC 4 Diamond
01670 822035 Mrs Hoskins **D:** £20.00–£22.00 **S:** £18.00–£25.00 **Beds:** 1T 1S **Baths:** 1 En 1 Pr ♨ ▣ (5) ⊬ ⊡ ⊁ ▥ ♨

Belford

NU1033 ◗ *Apple Inn, Black Swan, Bluebell Hotel, Warenford Lodge*

The Farmhouse Guest House, *24 West Street, Belford, Northumberland, NE70 7QE.* Central village location quiet comfortable accommodation home cooking speciality. **Open:** All year (not Xmas)
01668 213083 Mr & Mrs Wood **D:** £18.00–£23.00 **S:** £23.00–£28.00 **Beds:** 1F 2D **Baths:** 2 En 1 Pr ♨ ▣ (1) ⊬ ⊡ × ⊻ ▥ ♨

Rosebank, *5 Cragside Avenue, Belford, Northd, NE70 7NA.* Warm welcome to comfortable Dutch bungalow. Private parking and large garden. **Open:** Easter to Oct
01668 213762 (also fax) Mrs Godtschalk
D: £19.00–£23.00 **S:** £21.00–£25.00 **Beds:** 1F 1T **Baths:** 1 Sh ♨ ▣ (2) ⊬ ⊡ × ⊻ ♨

Oakwood House, *3 Cragside Avenue, Belford, Northumberland, NE70 7NA.* A quality country-style home with panoramic views over open countryside. **Open:** All year
01668 213303 Ms Allan **D:** £21.00–£23.00 **S:** £26.00–£28.00 **Beds:** 2D 1T **Baths:** 2 En 1 Pr ▣ (3) ⊬ ⊡ ⊁ ▥ ♨

Please respect a B&B's wishes regarding children, animals and smoking

Bellingham

NY8383 ◗ *Cheviot Hotel, Rose & Crown, Riverdale Hall Hotel*

Lyndale Guest House, *Bellingham, Hexham, Northd, NE48 2AW.* **Open:** All year (not Xmas)
01434 220361 & 07778 925479 (M) Mrs Gaskin **Fax: 01434 220361** *joy@lyndalegh.fsnet.co.uk* www.s-h-systems.co.uk/hotels/lyndalehtm/ **D:** £23.50–£25.00 **S:** £25.00–£30.00 **Beds:** 1F 2D 1T 1S **Baths:** 2 En 1 Pr 1 Sh ♨ ▣ (5) ⊬ ⊡ × ⊻ ▥ ♿ ♨ cc
Explore Borderlands and Nature Trails and Hadrian's Wall, Pennine Way, Kielder Water or Cycleways including 'Reivers' Route. Enjoy a welcome break. Relax in our walled garden. Sun lounge. Panoramic views. Excellent dinners. Superb Breakfasts. Quality ground-floor ensuites.

Belsay

NZ1078 ◗ *Highlander*

Bounder House, *Belsay, Newcastle-upon-Tyne, NE20 0JR.* Comfortable B&B. Newcastle Airport nearby. Convenient for exploring Northumberland. **Open:** All year
01661 881267 Mrs Fearns **Fax: 01661 881266** *k.fearns@bigfoot.com* **D:** £20.00 **S:** £25.00 **Beds:** 1F 1T 1D **Baths:** 2 En 1 Pr ♨ ▣ ⊬ ⊡ ⊁ ▥ ♨ cc

Berwick-upon-Tweed

NT9953 ◗ *Brewers' Arms, Canty's Brig, Leaping Salmon, Plough Inn, Salutation*

40 Ravensdowne, *Berwick-upon-Tweed, Northumberland, TD15 1DQ.* **Open:** All year (not Xmas) **Grades:** ETC 4 Diamond, Silver, RAC 4 Diamond, Sparkling
01289 306992 Mrs Muckle **Fax: 01289 331606** *petedot@dmuckle.freeserve.co.uk* www.secretkingdom.com/40/ **D:** £22.50–£27.50 **Beds:** 1F 2D 1T **Baths:** 4 En ♨ ⊬ ⊡ ▥
A warm welcome awaits you, 3 luxury ensuite rooms furnished to a very high standard. Hearty breakfast with fresh local produce and real coffee. 1 minute to Elizabethan walls. 2 minutes to town centre. Resident parking tickets supplied. No smoking.

Rob Roy Pub and Restaurant, *Dock Road, Tweedmouth, Berwick-upon-Tweed, Northumberland, TD15 2BQ.* **Open:** All year (not Xmas) **Grades:** ETC 4 Diamond
01289 306428 Mr Wilson **Fax: 01289 303629** *therobroy@btinternet.com* www.therobroy.co.uk
D: £24.00 **S:** £30.00 **Beds:** 1D 1T **Baths:** 2 En ⊡ × ⊻ ▥ ♨
Stone-built cosy riverside pub with open coal fire. Bar/restaurant menus offer fresh Northumbrian salmon and seafood, lobster, crab, oysters etc. 2 mins Berwick centre or sea front. Excellent situation to explore Northumberland. Celebrating 21 years this year with the Wilsons.

The Old Vicarage Guest House, *Church Road, Tweedmouth, Berwick-upon-Tweed, Northumberland, TD15 2AN.* Attractive C19th detached house, refurbished to highest standards. 10 minutes walk from town centre. **Open:** All year (not Xmas) **Grades:** ETC 4 Diamond, AA 4 Diamond
01289 306909 Mrs Richardson **Fax: 01289 309052** *stay@oldvicarageberwick.co.uk* www.oldvicarageberwick.co.uk **D:** £17.00–£27.00 **S:** £17.00–£18.00 **Beds:** 1F 4D 1T 1S **Baths:** 4 En 1 Sh ♨ ▣ (5) ⊡ ⊁ ⊻ ▥ ♨

Heron's Lee, *Thornton, Berwick-upon-Tweed, Northumberland, TD15 2LP.* Peaceful countryside, panoramic views. Northumbrian coastline. Genuine care and welcome. **Open:** All year (not Xmas/New Year) **Grades:** ETC 4 Diamond, Silver Award
01289 382000 (also fax) Mrs Burton *john_burton@btconnect.com* **D:** £23.00–£29.00 **S:** £23.00–£34.00 **Beds:** 1T 1D **Baths:** 1 En 1 Pr ▣ (3) ⊬ ⊡ ⊻ ▥ ♨

Bridge View, *14 Tweed Street, Berwick-upon-Tweed, Northumberland, TD15 1NG.* Centrally situated 200-year-old house, three minutes from town centre and railway station. **Open:** All year **Grades:** ETC 4 Diamond
01289 308098 Mrs Weatherley **D:** £20.00–£25.00 **S:** £25.00–£28.00 **Beds:** 1F 1S **Baths:** 1 En 1 Sh ♨ ▣ ⊁ ⊡ ⊻ ▥ ♨

National Grid References given are for villages, towns and cities – not for individual houses

Dervaig Guest House, 1 North Road, Berwick-upon-Tweed, TD15 1PW. Large Victorian guest house, close railway station/town centre ample private parking. **Open:** All year **Grades:** ETC 4 Diamond, AA 4 Diamond **01289 307378** Mrs Tait **Fax: 01289 332321** *dervaig@talk21.com* www.dervaig-guesthouse. co.uk **D:** £20.00–£27.00 **S:** £25.00–£45.00 **Beds:** 1F 2D 2T **Baths:** 5 En 🅿 (8) 📺 📺 🛏 ♨

West Sunnyside House, Tweedmouth, Berwick-upon-Tweed, Northd, TD15 2QN. C19th farmhouse, adjacent to Swan Leisure Centre on the A1167. **Open:** All year **01289 305387** Ms Jamieson **D:** £20.00–£25.00 **S:** £25.00–£30.00 **Beds:** 1T 2D **Baths:** 2 En 1 Pr ⊬ 📺 🛏 ♨

Cobbled Yard Hotel, 40 Walkergate, Berwick-upon-Tweed, Northumberland, TD15 1DJ. Surrounded by Berwick's Elizabethan walls, 2 mins' walk town centre. Food for all tastes. **Open:** All year **Grades:** ETC 3 Diamond **01289 308407** Ms Miller **Fax: 01289 330623** *cobbledyardhotel@berwicks35.fsnet.co.uk* www.cobbledyardhotel.com **D:** £25.00 **S:** £30.00 **Beds:** 3F 2D **Baths:** 5 En 🛏 🅿 📺 🛏 ✕ 📺 ♨ ♨ cc

51 Church Street, Berwick-upon-Tweed, Northumberland, TD15 1EE. Situated within town walls, near shops and amenities. **Open:** All year **01289 306666** Mr Silvester *silprops@aol.com* **D:** £18.00–£22.00 **S:** £20.00–£25.00 **Beds:** 1T 1D **Baths:** 2 En 🛏 📺 🛏 ♨

Hillend, 4 The Crescent, Berwick-upon-Tweed, TD15 1RT. Victorian family home over looking sea. Lindisfarne/Holy Island nearby. **Open:** Easter to Oct **01289 304454** Ms Law **D:** £17.00–£20.00 **Beds:** 1T 1D **Baths:** 1 Pr 1 Sh 🅿 (2) ⊬ 📺 🛏 ♨

Queens Head Hotel, 6 Sandgate, Berwick-upon-Tweed, TD15 1EP. Family-run hotel, situated in town centre near historic town walls. **Open:** All year **01289 307852** Mr Kerr **Fax: 01289 307858** **D:** £35.00–£40.00 **S:** £35.00–£40.00 **Beds:** 2F 1D 2T 1S **Baths:** 6 En 🛏 ⊬ 🅿 🛏 ✕ 📺 ♨ ♨ cc

6 North Road, Berwick-upon-Tweed, Northumberland, TD15 1PL. Beautiful Edwardian house; spacious, comfortable rooms near town centre, railway station. **Open:** All year (not Xmas) **01289 308949 (also fax)** Ms Booth **D:** £17.00–£19.00 **Beds:** 1F 1D **Baths:** 1 Sh 🛏 🅿 ⊬ 📺 📺 ♨

The Friendly Hound, Ford Common, Berwick-upon-Tweed, Northumberland, TD15 2QD. Sympathetically restored to create a welcoming home, comfortable accommodation, good food, super views. **Open:** All year **01289 388554** Mrs Maycock *friendlyhound.b.b@talk21.com* **D:** £21.50–£23.00 **S:** £21.50–£23.00 **Beds:** 1F 2D **Baths:** 3 En 🛏 🅿 (5) ⊬ ✕ 📺 ♨ ♨

Blacka Burn
NY8278

Hetherington Farm, Blacka Burn, Wark, Hexham, Northd, NE48 3DR. Comfortable farmhouse on Pennine Way. Friendly atmosphere. Ideal walking, cycling. **Open:** All year (not Xmas/New Year) **01434 230260 (also fax)** Mrs Nichol *a-nichol@hotmail.com* **D:** £20.00–£26.00 **S:** £22.00–£26.00 **Beds:** 3F 1T 1D 2S **Baths:** 2 En 1 Sh 🛏 (8) 🅿 (2) 📺 🛏 ♨ ♨

Boulmer
NU2614

21 Boulmer Village, Alnwick, Northumberland, NE66 3BS. Charming fisherman's cottage. Log fire. Beautiful views overlooking the sea. **Open:** Mar to Nov **Grades:** ETC 4 Diamond **01665 577262** M H Campbell **D:** £20.00–£25.00 **S:** £20.00–£27.00 **Beds:** 2D **Baths:** 2 En 1 Pr 🛏 🅿 (5) ⊬ 📺 📺 ♨ 🔥 ♨

Byrness
NT7602

Low Byrness Farm, Byrness, Otterburn, Newcastle-upon-Tyne, Northumberland, NE19 1TF. 150-year-old house in the Northumberland national Park. **Open:** All year (not Xmas/New Year) **01830 520648** Mrs Cranston **Fax: 01830 520733** *pdq@globalnet.co.uk* **D:** £9.00–£10.00 **S:** £22.00–£28.00 **Beds:** 1F 3D **Baths:** 2 En 1 Sh 🛏 (12) 🅿 (8) 📺 🛏 ✕ 📺 ♨

Chatton
NU0528

The Old Manse, New Road, Chatton, Alnwick, Northumberland, NE66 5PU. Beautiful Victorian Manse, NTB B&B of Year 1999 & 2000. **Open:** All year **01668 215343** C Brown *chattonbb@aol.com* www.oldmansechatton.ntb.org.uk **D:** £25.00–£30.00 **S:** £25.00–£45.00 **Beds:** 1T 1D **Baths:** 2 En 🛏 (10) 🅿 (4) ⊬ 📺 🛏 📺 ♨ ♨ ♨

Cheswick
NU0246

The Cat Inn, Cheswick, Berwick-upon-Tweed, TD15 2RL. Ideally situated for Lindisfarne golf, fishing, beaches and castles. **Open:** All year (not Xmas/New Year) **01289 387251 (also fax)** **D:** £18.00–£20.00 **S:** £18.00–£25.00 **Beds:** 2F 5T **Baths:** 4 En 3 Sh 🛏 🅿 (20) 📺 ✕ 📺 ♨ ♨

Ladythorne House, Cheswick, Berwick-upon-Tweed, TD15 2RU. Beautiful Georgian country house, wonderful views, central rural location, unspoilt beaches. **Open:** All year **Grades:** ETC 3 Diamond **01289 387382** Mrs Parker **Fax: 01289 387073** *valparker@ladythorneguesthouse.freeserve.co.uk* www.ladythorneguesthouse.freeserve.co.uk **D:** £17.00–£18.00 **S:** £17.00–£18.00 **Beds:** 2F 2T 1D 1S **Baths:** 3 Sh 🛏 🅿 (8) ⊬ ♨

Chollerford
NY9170

Brunton Water Mill, Chollerford, Hexham, Northd, NE46 4EL. Beautifully converted water mill on the doorstep of Brunton Turrett. **Open:** All year **01434 681002** Mrs Pesarra *pessara@bruntonmill.freeserve.co.uk* **D:** £24.00–£26.00 **S:** £40.00 **Beds:** 1D 1T **Baths:** 2 En 1 Sh 🅿 (8) ⊬ 📺 📺 ♨ ♨

Corbridge
NY9964 🍴 Black Bull, Angel

The Hayes Guest House, Newcastle Road, Corbridge, Northd, NE45 5LP. Family run. Ideal for exploring historical and scenic attractions of Northumbria. **Open:** All year (not Xmas/New Year) **Grades:** ETC 3 Diamond **01434 632010** Mrs Matthews *mjct@mmatthews.fsbusiness.co.uk* www.hayes-corbridge.co.uk **D:** £20.00–£25.00 **S:** £20.00–£30.00 **Beds:** 2F 1T 1S **Baths:** 2 En 1 Sh 🛏 🅿 (12) 📺 ♨ ♨

Clive House, Appletree Lane, Corbridge, Northumberland, NE45 5DN. Converted Victorian schoolhouse with beamed breakfast room. Central village location. **Open:** All year (not Xmas/New Year) **Grades:** ETC 4 Diamond **01434 632617 & 07949 766143 (M)** Mrs Hodgson *atclive@supanet.com* **D:** £28.00 **S:** £36.00 **Beds:** 3D 1S **Baths:** 4 En 🅿 (2) ⊬ 📺 ♨ ♨

Dilston Mill, Dilston, Corbridge, Northumberland, NE45 5QZ. Historic converted mill. Private suite: sleeps 2-6. Beautiful riverside setting. **Open:** All year **01434 633493** Mrs Ketelaar **Fax: 01434 633513** *susan@dilstonmill.com* www.dilstonmill.com **D:** £25.00–£28.00 **S:** £35.00–£40.00 **Beds:** 1F 1T 1D **Baths:** 1 Pr 🛏 🅿 (3) ⊬ 📺 ♨ ♨

All details shown are as supplied by B&B owners in Autumn 2001

Priorfield, *Hippingstones Lane, Corbridge, Northd, NE45 5JP.* Elegantly furnished family house. Peaceful location. Whirlpool bath in double room. **Open:** All year
01434 633179 (also fax) Mrs Steenberg **D:** £18.00–£25.00 **S:** £25.00–£32.00 **Beds:** 1D 1T **Baths:** 2 En ⅁ (5) 🅿 (2) ⚥ ⊡ ▦ ⚲

Cottonshopeburnfoot
NT7801

Border Forest Caravan Park, *Cottonshopeburnfoot, Otterburn, Newcastle-upon-Tyne, NE19 1TF.* Attractive motel, chalet rooms situated in picturesque Kielder Forest Park. **Open:** All year (not Xmas)
01830 520259 Mr & Mrs Bell **D:** £19.00 **S:** £21.00 **Beds:** 2F **Baths:** 2 En ⅁ (1) 🅿 (10) ⚥ ⊡ ⼎ ⊡ ▦ ♿ ⚲

Craster
NU2519 ⚓ *Dunstanburgh Castle, Cottage Inn*

Howick Scar Farm House, *Craster, Alnwick, Northd, NE66 3SU.* Comfortable farmhouse with views towards the sea. Explore coast, castles.
Open: Easter to Nov **Grades:** ETC 3 Diamond
01665 576666 (also fax) Mrs Curry *howickscar@lineone.net* **D:** £17.50–£18.00 **S:** £25.00–£28.00 **Beds:** 2D **Baths:** 1 Sh 🅿 (3) ⚥ ⊡ ⊡ ▦ ⚲

Stonecroft, Dunstan, *Craster, Alnwick, Northd, NE66 3SZ.* Friendly family home. Spacious comfortable. Rural. Hearty breakfasts. Wonderful coastline. **Open:** All year (not Xmas/New Year) **Grades:** ETC 4 Diamond, Silver
01665 576433 Mrs Stafford **Fax:** 01665 576311 *sally@stonestaff.freeserve.co.uk* www.stonecroft.ntb.org.uk **D:** £20.00 **Beds:** 2D **Baths:** 2 En ⅁ (1) 🅿 (4) ⚥ ⊡ ⊡ ▦ ⚲

Cresswell
NZ2993 ⚓ *Plough Inn*

Cresswell House, *Cresswell, Morpeth, Northumberland, NE61 5LA.* Hearty breakfast. Welcoming-overlooking 7 miles of golden beach. **Open:** All year **Grades:** ETC 4 Diamond
01670 861302 Ms Murdy **D:** £18.00–£19.50 **S:** £18.00 **Beds:** 2D 2S **Baths:** 1 En 1 Pr 1 Sh ⅁ (8) ⊡ ⼎ ✕ ⊡ ▦ ⚲

Crookham
NT9138

The Coach House, *Crookham, Cornhill-on-Tweed, Northd, TD12 4TD.* Spacious warm accommodation, excellent fresh food. Free afternoon tea. **Open:** Easter to Oct **Grades:** ETC 4 Diamond
01890 820293 Mrs Anderson **Fax:** 01890 820284 *stay@coachhousecrookham.com* www.coachhousecrookham.com **D:** £25.00–£43.00 **S:** £25.00–£39.00 **Beds:** 2D 5T 2S **Baths:** 7 En ⅁ 🅿 (15) ⊡ ⼎ ✕ ⊡ ▦ ♿ ⚲ **cc**

Dilston
NY9862

Dilston Mill, *Dilston, Corbridge, Northumberland, NE45 5QZ.* Historic converted mill. Private suite: sleeps 2-6. Beautiful riverside setting. **Open:** All year
01434 633493 Mrs Ketelaar **Fax:** 01434 633513 *susan@dilstonmill.com* www.dilstonmill.com **D:** £25.00–£28.00 **S:** £35.00–£40.00 **Beds:** 1F 1T 1D **Baths:** 1 Pr ⅁ 🅿 (3) ⚥ ⊡ ▦ ⚲

Eachwick
NZ1171

Hazel Cottage, *Eachwick, Newcastle-upon-Tyne, NE18 0BE.* Traditional Northumbrian farmhouse in pretty rural area. Easy access Newcastle. **Open:** All year
01661 852415 Fax: 01661 854797 *hazelcottage@eastwick.fsbusiness.co.uk* **D:** £20.00 **S:** £25.00 **Beds:** 1T 1D 🅿 (4) ⚥ ⊡ ✕ ⊡ ▦ ⚲ **cc**

Eglingham
NU1019

Ash Tree House, *The Terrace, Eglingham, Alnwick, Northd, NE66 2UA.* Warm Northumbrian welcome in our lovely home between hills and coast. **Open:** All year
01665 578533 Mrs Marks www.secretkingdom.com/ashtree/house.htm **D:** £22.00 **S:** £27.00 **Beds:** 1D 1T **Baths:** 1 Sh 🅿 (3) ⚥ ⊡ ✕ ⊡ ▦

Ellington
NZ2791

Hagg Farmhouse, *Ellington, Ashington, Northd, NE61 5JW.* Old farmhouse, open aspect coast and country. **Open:** All year (not Xmas/New Year)
01670 860514 Mrs Nixon **D:** £15.00–£18.00 **S:** £16.00–£20.00 **Beds:** 1F 1D 1T 1S **Baths:** 1 En 1 Pr 2 Sh ⅁ 🅿 (6) ⚥ ⊡ ⼎ ▦ ⚲

Planning a longer stay? Always ask for any special rates

Gilsland
NY6366

The Hill on the Wall, *Gilsland, Brampton, Cumbria, CA8 7DA.* Fascinating Listed C16th 'fortified farmhouse' overlooking Hadrian's Wall. **Open:** All year
016977 47214 (also fax) Mr Swan *thehill@ hadrians-wall.demon.co.uk* www.hadrians-wall.demon.co.uk **D:** £20.00–£22.00 **S:** £25.00–£27.00 **Beds:** 2D 1T **Baths:** 3 En 🅿 ⚥ ⊡ ⼎ ▦

Great Tosson
NU0200

Tosson Tower Farm, *Great Tosson, Rothbury, Morpeth, Northd, NE65 7NW.* Spacious, warm, wonderful views, good food, friendly welcome. Free fishing. **Open:** All year (not Xmas/New Year)
01669 620228 (also fax) Mrs Foggin *ann@ tossontowerfarm.com* www.tossontowerfarm.com **D:** £22.00–£22.50 **S:** £30.00–£35.00 **Beds:** 1F 1D 1T **Baths:** 3 En ⅁ 🅿 (4) ⼎ ⊡ ▦ ⚲

Greenhead
NY6665 ⚓ *Greenhead Hotel*

Holmhead Licensed Guest House, *Thirlwall Castle Farm, Hadrian's Wall, Greenhead, Brampton, Cumbria, CA8 7HY.* Enjoy fine food and hospitality with a personal touch. **Open:** All year (not Xmas) **Grades:** ETC 4 Diamond, AA 4 Diamond
016977 47402 (also fax) Mr & Mrs Staff *Holmhead@hadrianswall.freeserve.co.uk* www.bandbhadrianswall.com **D:** £29.00–£30.00 **S:** £34.00–£38.00 **Beds:** 1F 1D 2T **Baths:** 4 En ⅁ 🅿 (4) ⚥ ⊡ ✕ ⊡ ▦ ❄ ⚲ **cc**

Braeside, *Banktop, Greenhead, Brampton, CA8 7HA.* Perfect location on Hadrian's Wall. Extensive views from spacious bedroom. **Open:** Easter to Nov
016977 47443 Mrs Potts *smpotts@talk21.com* **D:** £22.00–£24.00 **S:** £30.00 **Beds:** 1F **Baths:** 1 En ⅁ (4) 🅿 (2) ⚥ ⊡ ▦ ⚲

Haltwhistle
NY7064 ⚓ *Milecastle, Spotted Cow, Manor House, Wallace Arms, Centre of Britain Hotel*

Hall Meadows, *Main Street, Haltwhistle, Northd, NE49 0AZ.* Large comfortable C19th private house, central for Hadrian's Wall. **Open:** All year (not Xmas)
01434 321021 (also fax) Mrs Humes **D:** £17.00–£22.50 **S:** £18.00 **Beds:** 2D 1T **Baths:** 2 En 1 Sh ⅁ 🅿 (3) ⊡ ▦ ⚲

Broomshaw Hill Farm, *Willia Road, Haltwhistle, Northd, NE49 9NP.* **Open:** Mar to Nov
01434 320866 Mrs Brown *stay@ broomshaw.co.uk* www.broomshaw.co.uk
D: £23.00–£24.00 **Beds:** 1T 2D **Baths:** 2 En 1
Pr ⛅ (6) ⊬ 🗹 Ⅲ ♨
C18th farmhouse, enlarged and modernised to very high standards. Set on the side of a wooded valley through which runs the Haltwhistle Burn. It stands on the conjunction of a footpath and bridleway, both leading to Hadrian's Wall.

Oakey Knowe Farm, *Haltwhistle, Northd, NE49 0NB.* **Open:** All year **Grades:** ETC 3 Diamond **01434 320648**
(also fax) Mrs Murray **D:** £18.00–£20.00
S: £20.00–£25.00 **Beds:** 1F 1T 1D **Baths:** 1
Pr 1 Sh ⛅ 🄿 (6) 🗹 🕇 Ⅲ ♨
Oakey Knowe Farm/Equitation smallholding of 18 acres is situated within walking distance of Haltwhistle and Roman Wall. Has panoramic views over the Tyne Valley, comfortable, friendly atmosphere for both yourself and horse if required.

Riverway House, *4 Wydon Avenue, Haltwhistle, Northd, NE49 0AS.* Roman wall area. Free packed lunch. Spa back facility. **Open:** All year (not Xmas/New Year)
01434 320378 Mrs Dawson **D:** £15.00–£17.00
S: £15.00–£17.00 **Beds:** 1D 1S **Baths:** 1 Sh
⛅ (10) 🄿 (1) ⊬ 🗹 Ⅲ ♨

Manor House Hotel, *Main Street, Haltwhistle, Northd, NE49 0BS.* Small hotel with busy public bar serving good selection of real ales, wines & spirits. **Open:** All year **01434 322588** R Nicholson **D:** £15.00–£22.00
S: £20.00–£25.00 **Beds:** 1F 1D 4T **Baths:** 3 En 3 Sh ⛅ 🄿 (4) 🗹 ✕ Ⅴ Ⅲ ♨ cc

Harbottle
NT9304

The Byre Vegetarian B&B, *Harbottle, Morpeth, Northumberland, NE65 7DG.* Central for coast and Cheviots. Beautiful Walks. Historic village. **Open:** All year **Grades:** ETC 4 Diamond
01669 650476 Mrs Srinivasan *rosemary@ the-byre.co.uk* www.the-byre.co.uk **D:** £18.00–£24.00 **S:** £18.00–£29.00 **Beds:** 1T 1D
Baths: 1 En 1 Pr ⛅ 🄿 (2) ⊬ 🗹 ✕ Ⅴ Ⅲ ♨

Haydon Bridge
NY8464 🍴 *General Havelock, Anchor Hotel, Haydon Hotel*

Hadrain Lodge Country Hotel, *Hindshield Moss, North Road, Haydon Bridge, Hexham, Northumberland, NE47 6NF.* In tranquil rural location, set in open pasture near Hadrian's Wall. **Open:** All year **Grades:** ETC 3 Diamond
01434 688688 Mrs Murray **Fax: 01434 684867**
hadrianlodge@hadrianswall.co.uk
www.hadrianswall.co.uk **D:** £19.50–£24.50
S: £26.00 **Beds:** 3F 4D 1T 1S **Baths:** 8 En 1
Pr ⛅ 🄿 🗹 ✕ Ⅴ ♿ ♨ cc

Hexham
NY9364 🍴 *Dipton Mill, Rose & Crown, Travellers Rest*

Woodley Field, *Allendale Road, Hexham, Northumberland, NE46 2NB.* **Open:** All year (not Xmas/New Year) **Grades:** ETC 3 Diamond
01434 601600 Mrs Charlton **D:** £27.50–£40.00 **S:** £35.00–£45.00 **Beds:** 1F 1D
Baths: 2 En ⛅ 🄿 (10) ⊬ 🗹 🕇 ✕ Ⅴ Ⅲ ♨
Large stone-built Victorian family house situated south-western outskirts of Hexham. Set in 2 acres of mature gardens with ample off-road parking. The bedrooms have recently been upgraded to ensuites, but remain very spacious with delightful views.

RATES
D = Price range per person sharing in a double or twin room
S = Price range for a single room

Topsy Turvy,

9 Leazes Lane, Hexham, Northd, NE46 3BA. Situated in market town near Hadrian's Wall.
Comfortable, colourful, friendly and peaceful. **Open:** All year **Grades:** ETC 4 Diamond
01434 603152 M McCormick *topsy.turvy@ ukonline.co.uk* **D:** £20.00 **Beds:** 2D **Baths:** 1 En 1 Pr ⛅ ⊬ 🗹 Ⅲ ♨

Rose & Crown Inn,

Slaley, Hexham, Northd, NE47 0AA. Warm, friendly family-run inn, with good wholesome home cooking. Meals served daily. **Open:** All year
01434 673263 Mr & Mrs Pascoe **Fax: 01434 673305** *rosecrowninn@supanet.com* **D:** £22.50–£25.00 **S:** £27.50–£32.50 **Beds:** 2T 1S
Baths: 3 En 3 Pr ⛅ (5) 🄿 (35) ⊬ 🗹 ✕ Ⅴ Ⅲ ♨ cc

Burncrest Guest House, *Burnland Terrace, Hexham, Northd, NE46 3JT.* Spacious terraced house, home from home, private car park. **Open:** All year
01434 605163 (also fax) Mr Ellery **D:** £20.00–£25.00 **S:** £20.00–£25.00 **Beds:** 3D **Baths:** 2 Sh 🄿 (3) ⊬ 🗹 Ⅲ ♨

Dene House, *Juniper, Hexham, Hexham, Northd, NE46 1SJ.* Northumbria, near Hadrian's Wall and breakfast. **Open:** All year (not Xmas/New Year) **Grades:** ETC 4 Diamond
01434 673413 (also fax) Mrs Massey *margaret@dene-house.hexham.co.uk*
www.denehouse-hexham.co.uk **D:** £22.00
S: £25.00 **Beds:** 1T 1S **Baths:** 2 En ⛅ 🄿 (4) ⊬ 🗹 🕇 Ⅴ Ⅲ ♨ cc

Old Red House Farm, *Dipton Mill, Hexham, NE46 1XY.* Superbly appointed C19th private stone cottage in lovely rural location. **Open:** Feb to Oct
01434 604463 Mrs Bradley *susan.bradley@ ukonline.co.uk* **D:** £23.00–£25.00 **S:** £30.00
Beds: 1T **Baths:** 1 Pr 🄿 (2) ⊬ 🗹 🕇 Ⅲ ♨

Horsley (Newcastle-upon-Tyne)
NZ0965

Belvedere,

Harlow Hill, Horsley, Newcastle-upon-Tyne, NE15 0QD. Stone built 1830's house on Hadrian's Wall, lovely rural views.
Open: Easter to Nov **Grades:** ETC 4 Diamond
01661 853689 Mrs Carr *pat.carr@btinternet.com*
www.belvederehouse.co.uk **D:** £19.00
S: £21.00 **Beds:** 1T 1D **Baths:** 2 En 🄿 (3) ⊬ 🗹 🕇 Ⅴ Ⅲ ♨ ♿

Housesteads
NY7868

Crindledykes Farm, Housesteads, Bardon Mill, Hexham, Northd, *NE47 7AF.* Well-maintained C17th farmhouse, good food and a warm welcome. **Open:** Easter to Nov **01434 344316** Mrs Davidson **D:** £17.00–£20.00 **S:** £20.00 **Beds:** 1D 1T **Baths:** 1 Sh ⌘ 🄿 ⅍ 📺 ✕ 🖾 ▣

Juniper
NY9358

Peth Head Cottage, Juniper, Hexham, Northd, *NE47 0LA.* **Open:** All year **Grades:** ETC 4 Diamond, AA 4 Diamond **01434 673286** Mrs Liddle **Fax: 01434 673038** *tedliddle@compuserve.com* www.peth-head-cottage.co.uk **D:** £20.00 **S:** £20.00 **Beds:** 2D **Baths:** 2 En ⌘ 🄿 (2) ⅍ 📺 🖾, ✻ cc
Pretty rose-covered cottage dating from 1825 in very peaceful location. Ideal for Hadrian's Wall, Northumbria's wonderful coast and castles, the beautiful heather-covered North Pennines. Easy access for Bamburgh, Beamish, Alnwick, Durham, Metro Centre and Newcastle.

Kirkwhelpington
NY9984

Cornhills, Klrkwhelpington, Northumberland, *NE19 2RE.* Large Victorian farmhouse. Working farm, outstanding views in peaceful surroundings. **Open:** All year (not Xmas) **01830 540232** Ms Thornton **Fax: 01830 540388** *cornhills@farming.co.uk* northumberlandfarmhouse.co.uk **D:** £21.00–£23.00 **S:** £25.00–£30.00 **Beds:** 1D 2T **Baths:** 2 En 1 Pr ⌘ 🄿 (10) ⅍ 📺 🖾, ▣

Lanehead
NY7985

Ivy Cottage, Lanehead, Tarset, Hexham, Northumberland, *NE48 1NT.* 200-year-old cottage with stunning views over open countryside. **Open:** All year **01434 240337 (also fax)** Mrs Holland *john.holland@compag.com* **D:** £18.00–£20.00 **S:** £18.00–£20.00 **Beds:** 1T 1D **Baths:** 1 En 1 Sh ⌘ 🄿 📺 🖾, ▣

Lesbury
NU2312   ⍟ Saddle Grill Hotel

Hawkhill Farmhouse, Lesbury, Alnwick, Northumberland, *NE66 3PG.* **Open:** All year (not Xmas) **01665 830380** Mrs Vickers **Fax: 01665 830093 D:** £23.00–£25.00 **S:** £25.00–£30.00 **Beds:** 2T 1D **Baths:** 3 En ⌘ (10) 🄿 (10) 📺 🖾
Large traditional farmhouse set in extensive, secluded gardens, with magnificent views of the Aln valley mid way Alnwick/ Alnmouth. Ideal for beaches, castles and places of interest, walking, golf and bird watching. Warm welcome and very peaceful.

Longframlington
NU1300

The Lee Farm, Longframlington, Morpeth, Northd, *NE65 8JQ.* Ideal Northumberland's many attractions. Pride of Northumbria - winner B&B of the Year 2001. **Open:** All year (not Xmas/New Year) **Grades:** ETC 4 Diamond, Gold **01665 570257 (also fax)** S Aynsley *enqs@ leefarm.co.uk* www.leefarm.co.uk **D:** £22.50–£23.00 **S:** £30.00 **Beds:** 1F 1T 1D **Baths:** 2 En 1 Pr ⌘ (2) 🄿 (4) ⅍ 📺 ⼉ 🖾, ▣

Morpeth
NZ2085   ⍟ Dyke Neuk

Elder Cottage, High Church, Morpeth, Northd, *NE61 2QT.* C18th cottage with garden and sun room; easy access from A1. **Open:** All year (not Xmas) **Grades:** ETC 4 Diamond, Silver **01670 517664** Mrs Cook **Fax: 01670 517644** *cook@eldercot.freeserve.co.uk* www.eldercottage. co.uk **D:** £17.50 **S:** £20.00–£25.00 **Beds:** 2D 1T **Baths:** 1 Sh ⌘ 🄿 (3) ⅍ 📺 ✕ 🖾 ▣

Newton
NZ0364

Crookhill Farm, Newton, Stocksfield, Northd, *NE43 7UX.* Comfortable welcoming farmhouse ideal for exploring Hadrian's Wall Beamish and NT Properties. **Open:** All year **Grades:** ETC 3 Diamond **01661 843117** Mrs Leech **Fax: 01661 844702 D:** £20.00 **S:** £20.00–£22.50 **Beds:** 1F 1T 1S **Baths:** 1 Sh ⌘ 🄿 (4) ⅍ 📺 ✕ 📺 🖾, ▣

Ninebanks
NY7853

Taylor Burn, Ninebanks, Hexham, Northd, *NE47 8DE.* Large, comfortable farmhouse, excellent food, warm welcome, wonderful scenery. **Open:** All year **01434 345343** Mrs Ostler *mavis@ taylorburn.freeserve.co.uk* **S:** £18.00 **Beds:** 1D 1S 1T **Baths:** 1 Pr ⌘ (7) 🄿 (5) ⅍ 📺 ⼉ ✕ 📺 🖾, ▣

Norham
NT9047

Todlaw, 58 Castle Street, Norham, Berwick-upon-Tweed, *TD15 2LQ.* Lovely old village on Tweed; ideal for touring and fishing. **Open:** All year (not Xmas) **01289 382447** Mr Brown **D:** £18.00–£20.00 **S:** £20.00–£22.00 **Beds:** 1D 1T **Baths:** 1 En 1 Sh ⌘ (7) 🄿 (3) ⅍ 📺 ⼉ ✕ 🖾, ▣

North Charlton
NU1623

North Charlton Farmhouse, North Charlton, Chathill, Northumberland, *NE66 5HP.* A warm welcome awaits you in our newly restored, beautifully furnished farmhouse. **Open:** All year **01665 579443** Ms Armstrong **Fax: 01665 579407** *glenc99@aol.com* **D:** £25.00–£30.00 **S:** £35.00 **Beds:** 1T 2D **Baths:** 2 En 1 Pr ⌘ (12) 🄿 (10) 📺 📺 🖾,

Otterburn
NY8893   ⍟ Percy Arms, Bird & Bush

Brown Rigg Cottage, Troughend, Otterburn, Newcastle-upon-Tyne, *NE19 1LG.* Wind and solar powered 200-year-old cottage. Excellent meals. **Open:** All year **01830 520541** A D Boon **Fax: 01830 520999** *davidn.boon@btinternet.com* **D:** £25.00 **S:** £25.00 **Beds:** 1T 1D **Baths:** 1 Sh 🄿 (6) ⅍ 📺 ⼉ ✕ 📺 🖾,

---

Planning a longer stay? Always ask for any special rates

Dunns Houses, Otterburn, Newcastle-upon-Tyne, *NE19 1LB.* **Open:** All year **Grades:** ETC 4 Diamond **01830 520677** Ms Findlay *dunnshouses@ hotmail.com* www.dunnshouses.freeserve.co. uk **D:** £20.00–£30.00 **S:** £25.00–£30.00 **Beds:** 1F 1D **Baths:** 2 En ⌚ 🅿 (10) ⅟ ⬜ ♒ ✕ ⓥ ▥. ⚘
Warm, friendly welcome to this Victorian farmhouse with spacious ensuite bedrooms, lounge, traditional English breakfast made from local produce. Magnificent countryside views, activities, onsite fishing, birdwatching and stables. Kielder, Hadrian's Wall and historical houses and towns. Expect serene tranquillity.

The Butterchurn Guest House, Main Street, Otterburn, Newcastle-upon-Tyne,
Northumberland, NE19 1NP. **Open:** All year **01830 520585** Val Anderson **Fax: 01830 520874** *keith@butterchurn.freeserve.co.uk* www.butterchurn.freeserve.co.uk **D:** £20.00–£25.00 **S:** £25.00–£30.00 **Beds:** 1F 2T 3D 1S **Baths:** 7 En ⌚ 🅿 (10) ✕ ⬜ ♒ ▥. ⅋ ⚘ **cc**
Excellent ensuite quality accommodation in rural Northumberland. Ideally situated in Northumberland National Park to explore 'The Land of Far Horizons'. Jewels include, Kielder Water and forest, Hadrian's Wall, The Cheviot Hills, Castles and Coastline.

Ponteland

NZ1673 ⬛ *The Badger, Blackbird*

7 Collingwood Cottages, Limestone Lane, Ponteland, Newcastle-upon-Tyne, *NE20 0DD.* Open views over countryside fields. 2.5 miles from Newcastle airport. **Open:** All year (not Xmas/New Year) **01661 825967** Mrs Baxter **D:** £18.00–£20.00 **S:** £25.00 **Beds:** 1F 1D **Baths:** 1 Sh ⌚ 🅿 (4) ⅟ ⬜ ♒ ▥. ⚘

BATHROOMS
En = Ensuite
Pr = Private
Sh = Shared

BEDROOMS
D = Double
T = Twin
S = Single
F = Family

Stone Cottage, Prestwick Road, Ponteland, Newcastle-upon-Tyne, NE20 9BX. **Open:** All year
Grades: ETC 3 Diamond **01661 823957** (also fax) *stay@ stonecottageguesthouse.com* www.stonecottageguesthouse.com **D:** £20.00–£22.50 **S:** £25.00–£28.00 **Beds:** 1F 1T 1D **Baths:** 1 En 1 Sh ⌚ 🅿 (10) ⅟ ⬜ ♒ ▥. ⚘
160-year-old stone cottage, extensively modernised and upgraded. Large, well kept gardens with secure parking. Situated 8 miles from Newcastle City Centre on the edge of Ponteland Village with its historic inns and ancient church. 5 mins walk Newcastle Airport.

Riding Mill

NZ0161

Low Fotherley Farm, Riding Mill, Northumberland, NE44 6BB. **Open:** All year
(not Xmas/New Year) **Grades:** ETC 4 Diamond **01434 682277** (also fax) Mrs Adamson *hugh@lowfotherleyfsnet.co.uk* www.westfarm. freeserve.co.uk **D:** £20.00 **S:** £20.00–£25.00 **Beds:** 1T 1D **Baths:** 1 En 1 Pr ⌚ 🅿 ⅟ ⬜ ⓥ ▥. ⚘
Low Fotherley is an impressive Victorian farmhouse built around 1895 in the beautiful Northumbrian countryside. Close to Hexham, Corbridge, Hadrian's Wall, Scottish Borders. Spacious accommodation with open fires and beams. Aga farmhouse breakfast with home-made marmalade and jams. Families welcome.

Broomley Fell Farm, Riding Mill, Northumberland, NE44 6AY. Warm welcome in cosy separate annexe, beams and log fire. **Open:** All year **Grades:** ETC3 Diamond **01434 682682** Ms Davies **Fax: 01434 682728** *enquiries@broomleyfell.com* www.broomleyfell. co.uk **D:** £20.00 **S:** £20.00–£25.00 **Beds:** 1F 1S **Baths:** 1 En 1 Pr ⌚ 🅿 (6) ⬜ ✕ ▥. ⚘ **cc**

Planning a longer stay? Always ask for any special rates

Rochester

NY8398

Redesdale Arms Hotel, Rochester, Otterburn, Newcastle-upon-Tyne, NE19 1TA. Friendly,
comfortable country inn. Home cooking, ring for special bargain breaks. **Open:** All year **Grades:** ETC 4 Diamond **01830 520668** Mrs Wright **Fax: 01830 520063** *redesdalehotel@hotmail.com* www.redesdale-hotel.co.uk **D:** £30.00–£35.00 **S:** £38.00–£43.00 **Beds:** 3F 3T 4D **Baths:** 10 En ⌚ 🅿 (40) ⬜ ♒ ✕ ⬜ ▥. ⚘ **cc**

Rothbury

NU0501 ⬛ Queen's Head, Newcastle House, Linden Hall, Anglers' Arms

Katerina's Guest House, Sun Buildings, High Street, Rothbury, Morpeth, Northumberland, NE65 7TQ.
Open: All year **Grades:** ETC 4 Diamond, Silver, RAC 4 Diamond, Sparkling **01669 620691 & 07977 555692 (M)** *cath@ katerinasguesthouse.co.uk* www.katerinasguesthouse.co.uk **D:** £22.00–£23.00 **S:** £30.00 **Beds:** 3D **Baths:** 3 En ⌚ ⅟ ⬜ ✕ ⓥ ⚘
Charming old building with beautiful 4-poster bedrooms, all ensuite, TV etc. Perfect situation close to all village amenities. Ideal central location for hills, coastline, castles, Hadrian's Wall, Scottish Borders. Extensive menus for breakfasts and (if required) evening meals. No smoking.

Orchard Guest House, High Street, Rothbury, Morpeth, Northd, NE65 7TL. **Open:** All year (not Xmas/New Year) **Grades:** ETC 4 Diamond, AA 4 Diamond **01669 620684** Mrs Pickard *email@ orchardguesthouse.co.uk* www.orchardguesthouse.co.uk **D:** £23.00–£25.00 **S:** £25.00–£30.00 **Beds:** 1F 2T 3D **Baths:** 3 En 3 Pr ⌚ ⅟ ⬜ ⓥ ▥. ⚘
A warm welcome and quality accommodation is offered in this comfortable Georgian home. Guest lounge with books and information. Excellent freshly cooked breakfasts. Rothbury is the ideal location for exploring beautiful Northumberland with its countryside, coast, castles, NT and Hadrian's Wall.

Silverton House, Rothbury, Morpeth, Northumberland, NE65 7RJ. Built in 1901 as a work house, now a comfortable home. **Open:** All year (not Xmas) **01669 621395** Mrs Wallace *maggie.wallace1@ virgin.net* **D:** £18.00–£19.00 **S:** £25.00–£38.00 **Beds:** 1D 1T ⌚ 🅿 (2) ⅟ ⬜ ♒ ✕ ⓥ ▥. ⚘

The Lee Farm, *Longfram-lington, Morpeth, Northd, NE65 8JQ.* Ideal Northumberland's many attractions. Pride of Northumbria - winner B&B of the Year 2001. **Open:** All year (not Xmas/New Year) **Grades:** ETC 4 Diamond, Gold **01665 570257 (also fax)** S Aynsley *enqs@leefarm.co.uk* www.leefarm.co.uk **D:** £22.50–£23.00 **S:** £30.00 **Beds:** 1F 1T 1D **Baths:** 2 En 1 Pr ⌂ (2) 🅿 (4) ⌇ 📺 👤 📺 🏠 ♨

Wagtail Farm, *Rothbury, Morpeth, Northumberland, NE65 7PL.* Comfortable bedrooms, good breakfasts, in a beautiful location. **Open:** May to Oct **01669 620367** Mrs Taylor *wagtail@tinyworld.co.uk* **D:** £19.00 **S:** £24.50 **Beds:** 2D **Baths:** 1 En 1 Pr ⌂ (12) 🅿 (2) ⌇ 📺 👤 🏠 ♨

Seahouses

NU2032 🍺 *Bamburgh Castle, Lodge Inn, Olde Ship*

Leeholme, *93 Main Street, Seahouses, Northd, NE68 7TS.* Perfectly situated for exploring Northumbria. Warm welcome. Hearty breakfast assured! **Open:** Mar to Oct **Grades:** ETC 3 Diamond **01665 720230** Mr & Mrs Wood **D:** £18.00–£25.00 **S:** £20.00–£25.00 **Beds:** 2T 1D **Baths:** 1 En 2 Sh ⌂ 🅿 (2) ⌇ 📺 👤 🏠 ♨

Wyndgrove House, *156 Main Street, Seahouses, Northumberland, NE68 7HA.* Family-run guest house. Ideal base for countryside, coast and Farne Islands. **Open:** All year **Grades:** ETC 3 Diamond **01665 720658** Mr & Mrs Haile **D:** £20.00–£25.00 **S:** £20.00–£25.00 **Beds:** 4F 2T 1D **Baths:** 2 En 3 Sh ⌂ 📺 🐾 🏠 ♨ cc

Seaton Sluice

NZ3376

The Waterford Arms, *Collywell Bay Road, Seaton Sluice, Whitley Bay, NE26 4QZ.* Very famous fish restaurant in a busy tourist area. **Open:** All year **0191 237 0450** **D:** £22.95–£24.95 **S:** £30.00 **Beds:** 1F 2T 2D **Baths:** 5 En 2 Pr ⌂ 🅿 (30) ⌇ 📺 🐾 ✕ 📺 🏠 ♨ ♨2 ♨ cc

Slaley

NY9757

Rose & Crown Inn, *Slaley, Hexham, Northd, NE47 0AA.* Warm, friendly family-run inn, with good wholesome home cooking. Meals served daily. **Open:** All year **01434 673263** Mr & Mrs Pascoe **Fax:** 01434 673305 *rosecrowninn@supanet.com* **D:** £22.50–£25.00 **S:** £27.50–£32.50 **Beds:** 2T 1S **Baths:** 3 En 3 Pr ⌂ (5) 🅿 (35) ⌇ 📺 ✕ 📺 🏠 ♨ cc

---

BATHROOMS
En = Ensuite
Pr = Private
Sh = Shared

Rye Hill Farm, *Slaley, Hexham, Northd, NE47 0AH.* **Open:** All year **Grades:** AA 4 Diamond **01434 673259 (also fax)** Mrs Courage *enquiries@consult-courage.co.uk* www.ryehillfarm.co.uk **D:** £22.50 **S:** £28.00 **Beds:** 2F 3D 1T **Baths:** 6 En ⌂ 🅿 (6) 📺 🐾 ✕ 📺 🏠 ♨ cc Small livestock farm. Gorgeous views all round. Pretty ensuite rooms in converted barn. We are noted for tasty evening meals (home cooked), friendly atmosphere and large bath towels. 5 miles south of Hexham.

Steel

NY9363

Dukesfield Hall Farm, *Steel, Hexham, Northumberland, NE46 1SH.* Charming Grade II farmhouse. warm and friendly. Excellent facilities. **Open:** All year **01434 673634** Mrs Swallow *cath@dukesfield.supanet.com* **D:** £22.50 **S:** £20.00 **Beds:** 1T 2D **Baths:** 3 En ⌂ 🅿 (4) ⌇ 📺 🐾 📺 🏠 ♨

Stocksfield

NZ0561

Old Ridley Hall, *Stocksfield, Northd, NE43 7RU.* Large private house. Listed. Quiet. Near Metro centre, Durham, Beamish. **Open:** All year (not Xmas) **01661 842816** Mrs Aldridge *oldridleyhall@talk21.com* **D:** £19.50–£25.00 **S:** £19.50–£25.00 **Beds:** 1F 2T 1S **Baths:** 1 Pr 2 Sh ⌂ 🅿 (14) ⌇ 📺 🐾 ✕ 📺 🏠 ♨

Swarland

NU1603 🍺 *Cook and Barker, Granby Inn, Anglers Arms*

Swarland Old Hall, *Swarland, Morpeth, Northumberland, NE65 9HU.* Grade 2 listed Georgian farmhouse, situated on the banks of the river Coquet. **Open:** All year (not Xmas/New Year) **Grades:** ETC 4 Diamond, Silver Award **01670 787642 & 07801 688153 (M)** Mrs Proctor *proctor@swarlandoldhall.fsnet.co.uk* www.swarlandoldhall.com **D:** £22.00 **S:** £30.00 **Beds:** 1F 1T 1D **Baths:** 2 En 1 Pr ⌂ (3) 🅿 (8) 📺 📺 🏠 ♨

Planning a longer stay? Always ask for any special rates

Thornton

NT9447 🍺 *Plough Inn, Salutation Inn*

Heron's Lee, *Thornton, Berwick-upon-Tweed, Northumberland, TD15 2LP.* Peaceful countryside, panoramic views. Northumbrian coastline. Genuine care and welcome. **Open:** All year (not Xmas/New Year) **Grades:** ETC 4 Diamond, Silver Award **01289 382000 (also fax)** Mrs Burton *john_burton@btconnect.com* **D:** £23.00–£29.00 **S:** £23.00–£34.00 **Beds:** 1T 1D **Baths:** 1 En 1 Pr 🅿 (3) ⌇ 📺 📺 🏠 ♨

Thropton

NU0202 🍺 *Three Wheat Heads*

Lorbottle, *West Steads, Thropton, Morpeth, Northd, NE65 7JT.* **Open:** May to Nov **Grades:** ETC 3 Diamond **01665 574672 (also fax)** Mrs Farr *helen.farr@farming.co.uk* www.destination-england.co.uk/lorbottle.html **D:** £19.00–£20.00 **S:** £18.00–£25.00 **Beds:** 1D 1T 1S **Baths:** 1 Sh ⌂ 🅿 (3) ⌇ 📺 📺 🏠 ♨ Spacious farmhouse overlooking the Simonside Hills, Coquet Valley, Cheviot Hills. Rothbury 5 miles.

Farm Cottage Guest House, *Thropton, Morpeth, Northumberland, NE65 7NA.* Olde worlde cottage with pretty country gardens, exceptional evening meals. **Open:** All year (not Xmas) **Grades:** ETC 4 Diamond, Silver **01669 620831 (also fax)** Mrs Telford *joan@farmcottageguesthouse.co.uk* www.farmcottageguesthouse.com **D:** £21.00–£23.00 **S:** £31.00–£33.00 **Beds:** 3D 1T **Baths:** 4 En 🅿 (4) ⌇ 📺 ✕ 📺 🏠 ♨ cc

Troughend

NY8692

Brown Rigg Cottage, *Troughend, Otterburn, Newcastle-upon-Tyne, NE19 1LQ.* Wind and solar powered 200-year-old cottage. Excellent meals. **Open:** All year **01830 520541** A D Boon **Fax:** 01830 520999 *davidn.boon@btinternet.com* **D:** £25.00 **S:** £25.00 **Beds:** 1T 1D **Baths:** 1 Sh 🅿 (6) ⌇ 📺 🐾 ✕ 📺 🏠

RATES

D = Price range per person sharing in a double or twin room

S = Price range for a single room

Twice Brewed

NY7567

Saughy Rigg Farm, *Twice Brewed, Haltwhistle, Northumberland, NE49 9PT.* Near Hadrian's Wall, delicious food, comfortable accommodation, children & pets welcome. **Open:** All year **01434 344746** Ms McNulty *kathandbrad@aol.com* www. northumberlandaccommodation.co.uk **D:** £15.00 **S:** £15.00 **Beds:** 1F 1T **Baths:** 1 En 1 Pr ➤ ⊟ ☑ ★ ✕ ☑ Ⅲ ✻ ♨

Warkworth

NU2405 ◖ *Sun Inn, Masons' Arms, Hermitage, Topsy Turvey, Green Room*

Bide A While, *4 Beal Croft, Warkworth, Morpeth, Northd, NE65 0XL.* **Open:** All year **Grades:** ETC 3 Diamond **01665 711753** D M Graham **D:** £18.00–£20.00 **S:** £20.00–£24.00 **Beds:** 1F 2D **Baths:** 1 En 1 Sh ➤ ⊟ (3) ✔ ☑ ★ ☑ Ⅲ ♨ Bungalow in historic village of Warkworth, which has a castle, ancient church and hermitage. Good base for touring Northumberland, bird watching, etc. On cycle route, and within a mile of the beach and sea.

North Cottage, *Birling, Warkworth, Morpeth, Northd, NE65 0XS.* Centrally situated to explore Northumbria. Comfortable ensuite ground floor bedrooms. **Open:** All year (not Xmas/New Year) **Grades:** ETC 4 Diamond **01665 711263** Mrs Howliston *edithandjohn@another.com* www.accta.co.uk/north **D:** £22.00–£24.00 **S:** £25.00–£30.00 **Beds:** 1T 2D 1S **Baths:** 3 En 1 Sh ⊟ (4) ✔ ☑ Ⅲ ♨

Hermitage Inn, *23 Castle St, Warkworth, Morpeth, Northumberland, NE65 0UL.* Perfectly situated for exploring Northumberland coast. Warm welcome. Excellent food. **Open:** All year **01665 711258** **D:** £20.00–£25.00 **S:** £20.00–£25.00 **Beds:** 2F 2D 1S **Baths:** 3 En 2 Pr ➤ ☑ ★ ✕ Ⅲ ♨ cc

West Woodburn

NY8887

Yellow House Farm, *West Woodburn, Hexham, Northumberland, NE48 2SB.* Old farmhouse with all modern conveniences, half hour from Hadrian's Wall, Kielder Water. **Open:** All year **01434 270070** Mrs Walton **D:** £15.00–£19.00 **S:** £15.00–£20.00 **Beds:** 1F 1T 1D **Baths:** 3 En ➤ ⊟ (6) ✔ ☑ ★ Ⅲ ♨

Plevna House, *West Woodburn, Hexham, Northumberland, NE48 2RA.* Centre for Borders, Hadrian's Wall, Kielder and coast. Warm welcome. **Open:** All year (not Xmas/New Year) **Grades:** ETC 4 Diamond **01434 270369** Mr Pickford *plevnaho@aol.com* **D:** £18.00–£20.00 **S:** £25.00 **Beds:** 2D **Baths:** 2 En ➤ ⊟ (4) ✔ ☑ ✕ ☑ Ⅲ ♨

Whitton

NU0500

Whitton Farmhouse Hotel, *Whitton, Rothbury, Morpeth, Northd, NE65 7RL.* **Open:** Easter to Oct **Grades:** ETC 4 Diamond **01669 620811 (also fax)** *whittonfarmhotel@supanet.com* www.smoothhound.co.uk/hotels/whitton **D:** £25.00–£29.00 **S:** £25.00–£29.00 **Beds:** 1F 1T 1D **Baths:** 3 En ➤ (0) ⊟ (10) ✔ ☑ ★ ✕ ☑ Ⅲ & ♨ Charming unusual converted farmhouse and buildings on edge of National Park, overlooking Coquet Valley. Convenient for coast and country with many historic houses and castles nearby. Separate residents lounge with bar and delightful dining room. Excellent reputation for food.

Wooler

NT9928 ◖ *Anchor, Black Bull, Blue Bell, Red Lion, Tankerville Arms, Wheatsheaf Hotel*

St Hilliers, *6 Church Street, Wooler, Northd, NE71 6DA.* Stone-built village house, quiet side of town. Homely, excellent breakfast **Open:** All year **Grades:** ETC 3 Diamond **01668 281340** Mrs Hugall **D:** £18.00–£20.00 **S:** £22.00–£25.00 **Beds:** 2T 1D **Baths:** 1 Sh ➤ ⊟ ✔ ☑ ★ ☑ Ⅲ ♨

Winton House, *39 Glendale Road, Wooler, Northumberland, NE71 6DL.* Edwardian house, quiet position, comfortable, spacious rooms. Walkers/cyclists welcome. **Open:** Mar to Oct **Grades:** ETC 3 Diamond **01668 281362 (also fax)** Mr Gilbert *winton.house@virgin.net* www.wintonhouse.ntb.org.uk **D:** £19.00–£22.00 **S:** £25.00–£28.00 **Beds:** 1T 2D **Baths:** 2 En 1 Sh ➤ (4) ✔ ☑ Ⅲ ♨

Wylam

NZ1164

Wormald House, *Main Street, Wylam, Northd, NE41 8DN.* Very welcoming, pleasant country home in attractive Tyne Valley village. **Open:** All year (not Xmas) **Grades:** ETC 4 Diamond **01661 852529 (also fax)** Mr & Mrs Craven *john.craven3@btinternet.com* **D:** £20.00–£22.00 **S:** £20.00–£22.00 **Beds:** 1D 1T **Baths:** 2 En ➤ ⊟ (3) ✔ ☑ ☑ Ⅲ ♨ cc

Nottinghamshire

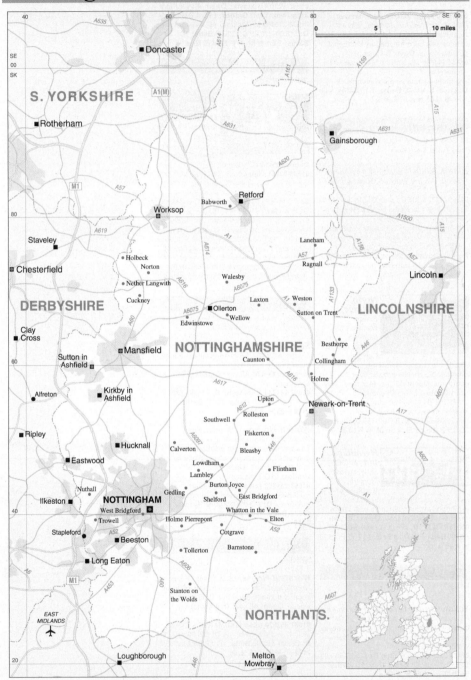

Babworth

SK6880

The Barns Country Guest House,
Morton Farm, Babworth, Retford, Notts,
DN22 8HA. Rural setting close to A1 on
pilgrim fathers trail. **Open:** All year (not
Xmas)
01777 706336 H R R Kay **Fax: 01777 709773**
harry@thebarns.co.uk www.thebarns.co.uk
D: £22.00–£26.00 **S:** £30.00–£33.00 **Beds:** 1F
5D **Baths:** 6 En ⌂ 🄿 (6) ⌽ 📺 📖 ♨ cc

Barnstone

SK7335

Barnstone Olde House, Barnstone,
Nottingham, NG13 9JP. Central for Newark,
Grantham, Nottingham. Landscaped
garden, rustic charm, beautiful view.
Open: All year (not Xmas)
01949 860456 (also fax) Mrs Baker
D: £20.00–£25.00 **S:** £22.50–£30.00 **Beds:** 2D
1T **Baths:** 2 En ⌂ 🄿 (4) ⌽ 📺 🐾 ✕ 📺 📖 ♨

Besthorpe

SK8265

Lord Nelson Inn, Main Road, Besthorpe,
Newark, Nottinghamshire, NG23 7HR. C18th
former coaching inn with excellent food
reputation. **Open:** All year (not Xmas/New
Year)
01636 892265 D: £20.00 **S:** £25.00 **Beds:** 2T
1D 1S **Baths:** 1 En 1 Sh 🄿 (20) ⌽ ✕ 📺 📖 ♨ cc

Bleasby

SK7149

Little Rudsey Farm, Bleasby,
Nottingham, NG14 7FR. Traditional
farmhouse, rural setting. Robin Hood
country. Newark/Nottingham/Lincoln/
Southwell easy reach. **Open:** All year (not
Xmas/New Year)
01636 830249 Mrs Norman **D:** £16.00
S: £16.00 **Beds:** 1F 1T **Baths:** 1 Sh ⌂ (4)
🄿 (3) 📺 🐾 📺 📖 ♨

Burton Joyce

SK6443

Willow House, 12 Willow Wong, Burton
Joyce, Nottingham, NG14 5FD. 1850s house
with Victorian charm. Beautiful riverbanks
2 minutes walk. **Open:** All year
0115 931 2070 Mrs Baker **D:** £19.00
S: £16.00–£20.00 **Beds:** 1F 1D 1T **Baths:** 2
Sh ⌂ 🄿 📺 🐾 📺 📖 ♨

B&B owners may vary
rates – be sure to check
when booking

Calverton

SK6149

Patchings Farm Arts Centre, Oxton
Road, Calverton, Nottingham, NG14 6NU.
Part of 60-acre art centre. Private garden.
Open: All year
0115 965 3479 Fax: 0115 9655308 *admin@*
patchingsartcentre.co.uk
www.patchingsartcentre.co.uk **D:** £20.00
S: £25.00 **Beds:** 3T **Baths:** 3 En ⌂ 🄿 ⌽ 📺 🐾
✕ 📺 ♿ ♨ cc

Caunton

SK7460

Knapthorpe Lodge, Hockerton Road,
Caunton, Newark, Notts, NG23 6AZ. Large
farmhouse overlooking beautiful
countryside. Comfortable & friendly.
Open: All year
01636 636262 Fax: 01636 636415 D: £20.00–
£25.00 **S:** £25.00–£30.00 **Beds:** 1F 1D
Baths: 1 En 1 Pr ⌂ 🄿 (6) 📺 ✕ 📺 📖 ♨

Collingham

SK8361

**Lime Tree
Farm,** Lunn
Lane,
Collingham,
Newark, Notts,
NG23 7LP.
Attractive,
converted barn
in quiet conservation area of village.
Open: All year
01636 892044 Mrs Glenny **D:** £18.00–£20.00
S: £20.00–£25.00 **Beds:** 1D 2T **Baths:** 2 En 1
Pr ⌂ 🄿 (6) 📺 📺 📖 ♨

Cotgrave

SK6435

Marl Pit Cottage, 28 Main Road,
Cotgrave, Nottingham, NG12 3HN. Quality
cottage accommodation, semi-rural
location, very comfortable and friendly.
Open: All year (not Xmas)
0115 989 4805 (also fax) Mrs Prescott *mp1@*
nascr.net **D:** £20.00 **Beds:** 2D **Baths:** 1 Sh ⌂
🄿 (2) ⌽ 📺 🐾 📺 📖 ♨

Cuckney

SK5670

The Greendale Oak, High Croft,
Cuckney, Mansfield, Notts, NG20 9NQ. 300-
year-old pub/restaurant near Sherwood
Forest & the Dureries. **Open:** All year
01623 844441 & 01623 844237 D: £37.00
S: £18.50 **Beds:** 1F 1T 1D 2S **Baths:** 2 Sh ⌂
🄿 (4) ⌽ 📺 🐾 ✕ 📺 📖 ♨ cc

East Bridgford

SK6943 🛎 *Reindeer Inn*

Barn Farm Cottage, Kneeton Road,
East Bridgford, Nottingham, NG13 8PH.
Lovely cottage overlooking fields and Trent
Valley. Delicious organic breakfast.
Open: All year
01949 20196 Mrs Shouls **D:** £20.00 **S:** £20.00
Beds: 2F 2T 1S **Baths:** 1 En ⌂ 🄿 (6) ⌽ 📺 📺 ♨

Edwinstowe

SK6266

Marion's Manor, Ollerton Road,
Edwinstowe, Mansfield, Nottinghamshire,
NG21 9QG. Enjoy a break in the heart of
Sherwood Forest staying with a real
Marion. **Open:** All year
01623 822135 D: £18.00–£25.00 **S:** £22.00–
£25.00 **Beds:** 1F 1D 1T **Baths:** 3 En ⌂ 🄿 (4) ⌽
📺 🐾 📺 ♨

Robin Hood Farm, Rufford Road,
Edwinstowe, Mansfield, Notts, NG21 9HX.
Olde farmhouse in Robin Hood's village in
Sherwood Forest. Close Clumber & Rufford
Country Parks. **Open:** All year
01623 824367 *robinhoodfarm@aol.com*
D: £17.50–£20.00 **S:** £17.50–£20.00 **Beds:** 1F
1D 1T **Baths:** 1 Sh ⌂ 🄿 (6) ⌽ 📺 🐾 📺 📖 ♨

Elton

SK7738

Grange Farm, Sutton Lane, Elton, Notts,
NG13 9LA. Splendid views over open
countryside. Belvoir Castle and market
towns nearby. **Open:** All year (not Xmas/
New Year)
01949 850357 (also fax) Mrs Tomlinson
D: £20.00 **Beds:** 1D **Baths:** 1 Pr 🄿 (4) ⌽ 📺 📖
♨

Fiskerton

SK7351

The Three Firs, 21 Marlock Close,
Fiskerton, Southwell, Notts, NG25 0UB.
Modern detached corner residence in quiet
cul-de-sac with secluded garden. **Open:** All
year (not Xmas)
01636 830060 (also fax) Mr & Mrs Jakeman
three-firs@bushinternet.com **D:** £17.50–£21.50
S: £19.00–£24.00 **Beds:** 2D 2S **Baths:** 1 En 1
Pr 1 Sh ⌂ (5) 🄿 (4) ⌽ 📺 📺 📖 ♨

Flintham

SK7445

The Boot & Shoe Inn, Main Street,
Flintham, Newark, Notts, NG23 5LA. Recently
renovated family run pub in quiet village.
Open: All year (not Xmas/New Year)
Grades: ETC 4 Diamond
01636 525246 K M Butler **D:** £24.00 **S:** £32.00
Beds: 1F 1T 2D 1S **Baths:** 5 En ⌂ 🄿 (5) ⌽ 📺
🐾 ✕ 📺 📖 ♨ cc

Planning a longer stay? Always ask for any special rates

Holbeck

SK5473   🍺 *Greendale Oak, Elm Tree*

The Old Orchard Cottage, *Holbeck, Worksop, Notts, S80 3NF*. Winner of four tourism awards **Open:** All year (not Xmas/New Year) **Grades:** ETC 5 Diamond, Silver, AA 5 Diamond
01909 720659 Mrs Brown **D:** £23.00–£30.00 **S:** £38.00–£40.00 **Beds:** 1T 2D **Baths:** 3 En ▣ (3) ⅏ 🖵 📺 🛋 ♨

Holme

SK8059

Gothic Farmhouse, *Main Street, Holme, Newark, Nottinghamshire, NG23 7RZ*. Old farmhouse near old church close to Trent River. **Open:** All year (not Xmas/New Year)
01636 640656 Mr & Mrs Oxford **D:** £25.00–£50.00 **S:** £25.00 **Beds:** 2T **Baths:** 1 En 1 Sh ▣ 🖵 📺 🛋 ♨

Holme Pierrepont

SK6339

Holme Grange Cottage, *Adbolton Lane, Holme Pierrepont, Nottingham, NG12 2LU*. Victorian cottage, 3 miles city, close to National Water Sports Centre. **Open:** All year (not Xmas)
0115 981 0413 *jean.colinwightman@talk21.com* **D:** £18.00–£20.00 **S:** £18.00–£20.00 **Beds:** 1F 1D 1T **Baths:** 1 En 1 Sh ▣ (6) ⅏ 🖵 🛏 📺 🛋 ♨

Lambley

SK6345

Magnolia Guest House, *22 Spring Lane, Lambley, Nottingham, NG4 4PH*. Close to Sherwood Forest, Robin Hood Country and Nottingham Castle. **Open:** All year **Grades:** ETC 4 Diamond
0115 931 4404 Fax: 0115 9314582 *magnoliahouse@lineone.net* **D:** £20.00 **S:** £20.00–£25.00 **Beds:** 1F 1T 1D 1S **Baths:** 3 En ▨ ▣ (6) ⅏ 🖵 📺 🛋 ♿ ♨

Laneham

SK8076

The Old Cottage, *Laneham, Retford, Notts, DN22 0NA*. Quiet location, close to River Trent, Sherwood Forest, Lincoln, Newark. **Open:** All year
01777 228555 Mrs Hardman **Fax:** 01777 228900 **D:** £20.00 **S:** £25.00 **Beds:** 1F 1T 2S **Baths:** 3 En 1 Pr ▨ (10) ▣ (6) ⅏ 📺 🛋 ♨

Laxton

SK7267

Lilac Farm, *Laxton, Newark, Notts, NG22 0NX*. Laxton: last remaining open field village. Heritage museum adjacent to Lilac Farm. **Open:** All year (not Xmas/New Year) **Grades:** ETC 3 Diamond
01777 870376 (also fax) Mrs Rose **D:** £18.00–£20.00 **S:** £20.00 **Beds:** 1F 2D **Baths:** 1 Sh ▨ ▣ (6) 📺 🛏 📺 🛋 ♨

Manor Farm, *Moorhouse Road, Laxton, Newark, Notts, NG22 0NU*. Old comfortable farmhouse in medieval village near to Sherwood Forest. **Open:** All year (not Xmas)
01777 870417 Mrs Haigh **D:** £16.00–£17.00 **S:** £17.00–£18.00 **Beds:** 2F 1D **Baths:** 1 Sh ▨ ▣ (3) 📺 🛏 📺 ♨

Lowdham

SK6746

Old School Mews, *64a Main Street, Lowdham, Nottingham, NG14 7BE*. Spacious, interesting, historic converted school house in Robin Hood country. **Open:** All year (not Xmas/New Year)
0115 966 4838 & 07885 497536 (M) J A McLaughlin *robert@turnell75.freeserve.co.uk* **D:** £22.50 **S:** £30.00 **Beds:** 2T 1D **Baths:** 1 En 1 Pr ▣ ⅏ 🖵 📺 🛋 ♨

Mansfield

SK5361

Parkhurst Guest House, *28 Woodhouse Road, Mansfield, Notts, NG18 2AF*. Friendly family-run guest house, walking distance to Mansfield centre. **Open:** All year
01623 627324 Fax: 01623 621855 *philfletcher@parkhurst28.freeserve.co.uk* www.parkhurst.guesthouse.co.uk **D:** £17.50–£25.00 **Beds:** 3F 4D 2T 3S **Baths:** 5 En 1 Sh ▨ ▣ (10) 🖵 📺 🛋 ❊ ♨

Bridleways Guest House, *Newlands Farm Lane, Mansfield, Notts, NG19 0HU*. Bridgeways - originally 2 late-C18th farm cottages, retains many period features inside. **Open:** Jan to Dec
01623 635725 D: £20.00–£25.00 **S:** £22.50–£25.00 **Beds:** 1F 2D 2T 1S **Baths:** 6 En ▨ ▣ (20) ⅏ 🖵 📺 🛋 ♿ ♨

BATHROOMS
En = Ensuite
Pr = Private
Sh = Shared

Please respect a B&B's wishes regarding children, animals and smoking

Nether Langwith

SK5370

Boon Hills Farm, *Nether Langwith, Mansfield, Notts, NG20 9JQ*. Comfortable stone farmhouse with large garden on working farm. **Open:** Mar to Oct
01623 743862 Mrs Palmer *michael.palmer3@virgin.net* **D:** £17.00 **S:** £18.00 **Beds:** 2D 1T **Baths:** 1 En 1 Sh ▨ ▣ (4) ⅏ 📺 🛋 ♨

Newark

SK7953

The Boot & Shoe Inn, *Main Street, Flintham, Newark, Notts, NG23 5LA*. Recently renovated family run pub in quiet village. **Open:** All year (not Xmas/New Year) **Grades:** ETC 4 Diamond
01636 525246 K M Butler **D:** £24.00 **S:** £32.00 **Beds:** 1F 1T 2D 1S **Baths:** 5 En ▨ ▣ (5) ⅏ 📺 🛏 ✕ 📺 🛋 ♨ cc

Rutland Arms, *13-15 Barnbygate, Newark, Nottinghamshire, NG24 1PX*. Central location. Old coaching inn. **Open:** All year
01636 703399 D: £20.00 **S:** £35.00 **Beds:** 2F 2T 2D 4S **Baths:** 10 En ▨ ⅏ ✕ 📺 🛋 ♨ cc

Norton

SK5772

Norton Grange Farm, *Norton, Cuckney, Mansfield, Notts, NG20 9LP*. Situated in beautiful village on edge of Sherwood Forest. **Open:** All year (not Xmas)
01623 842666 Mr Palmer **D:** £18.00–£20.00 **S:** £20.00–£22.00 **Beds:** 1F 1D 1T **Baths:** 1 Sh ▨ ▣ (4) 🛏 ♨

Nottingham

SK5641

Croft Hotel, *6-8 North Road, West Bridgford, Nottingham, NG2 7NH*. Charming, quiet Victorian B&B, 1.5 miles from Nottingham city centre. **Open:** All year (not Xmas/New Year)
0115 981 2744 (also fax) Kennedy *croft.hotel.wb@talk21.com* www.smoothhound.co.uk/hotels/crofth **D:** £18.00–£20.00 **S:** £20.00–£25.00 **Beds:** 2F 3T 2D 7S **Baths:** 5 Sh ▨ ▣ (12) 📺 🛏 📺 🛋 ♨

Talbot House Hotel, *18-20 Bridgford Road, West Bridgford, Nottingham, NG2 6AB.* **Open:** All year **0115 981 1123 & 0115 982 1814** Mr Brown **Fax: 0115 981 3545** *jkta1bot@onetel.net.uk* **D:** £25.00–£40.00 **S:** £25.00–£40.00 **Beds:** 6F 6D 6T 6S **Baths:** 20 En 4 Sh ➤ 🅿 (30) 📺 🕇 ✕ 📺 🚿, ♿ cc
Central position. 1 mile Nottingham City Centre, national Ice Centre. Holme Pierrepont National Water Sports Centre and central TV studios. One minute walk Notts Forest and Notts County football grounds. Opposite Trent Bridge Cricket Ground. Half mile rail/bus station.

Gallery Hotel, *8-10 Radcliffe Road, West Bridgford, Nottingham, NG2 5FW.* Old Victorian house family hotel. 12 years by Mr and Mrs Don Masson. **Open:** All year **Grades:** ETC 3 Diamond, AA 3 Diamond **0115 981 3651** Mr & Mrs Masson **Fax: 0115 981 3732** www.yell.com. uk/sites/gallery-hotel/ **D:** £25.00 **S:** £29.00–£35.00 **Beds:** 3F 5D 4T 3S **Baths:** 15 En ➤ (1) 🅿 (50) ⸆ 📺 📺

Adams' Castle View Guest House, *85 Castle Boulevard, Nottingham, NG7 1FE.* Comfortable city guest house, close to bus/railway stations, activities. **Open:** All year **Grades:** ETC 3 Diamond **0115 950 0022** Mr Adams **D:** £22.50–£25.00 **S:** £22.50–£25.00 **Beds:** 1D 1T 2S **Baths:** 4 En ⸆ 📺 📺 🚿

The Willows, Tophouse Farm, *Lamin's Lane, Arnold, Nottingham, NG5 8PH.* Working farm near Sherwood Forest. Excellent neighbouring bar and restaurant. **Open:** All year (not Xmas/New Year) **0115 967 0089** A Lamin *lamin.tophousefarm@btinternet.com* **D:** £19.00–£20.00 **S:** £22.00–£25.00 **Beds:** 1T **Baths:** 1 En ➤ (20) ⸆ 📺 📺 🚿

Nuthall
SK5144

Camelot, *22 Watnall Road, Nuthall, Nottingham, NG16 1DU.* J(26), M1, Spacious family bungalow. Large pleasant gardens. Guest lounge. **Open:** All year **0115 938 2597 (also fax)** Mr & Mrs Cains **D:** £20.00–£22.00 **S:** £22.00–£24.00 **Beds:** 1F 1D **Baths:** 1 En 1 Sh ➤ 🅿 (2) ⸆ 📺 📺 🚿 ♿ 🚿

National Grid References given are for villages, towns and cities – not for individual houses

Ragnall
SK8073

Ragnall House, *Ragnall, Newark, Notts, NG22 0UR.* Period residence in large grounds. Lincoln and Sherwood Forest nearby. **Open:** All year **Grades:** ETC 3 Diamond **01777 228575 (also fax)** Mrs Hatfield *ragnallhouse@gofornet.co.uk* **D:** £17.00–£20.00 **S:** £17.00–£20.00 **Beds:** 1F 1D 2T 1S **Baths:** 1 En 2 Pr 1 Sh ➤ 🅿 (7) 📺 📺 🚿

Rolleston
SK7452

Racecourse Farm, *Station Road, Rolleston, Newark, Notts, NG23 5SE.* 200-year-old cottage facing the village church. **Open:** All year **01636 812176** Mrs Lee **D:** £22.00–£23.00 **S:** £25.00 **Beds:** 1T 1D **Baths:** 1 En 1 Sh ➤ (14) 🅿 (4) ⸆ 📺 ✕ 📺 📺 🚿

Shelford
SK6642

Fox Cottage, *Main Street, Shelford, Nottingham, NG12 1ED.* Beautiful cottage in delightful gardens with country views, quiet village **Open:** All year **0115 933 5741 & 07976 705066 (M)** Mrs Lewis **Fax: 0115 933 5741** **D:** £20.00 **S:** £25.00 **Beds:** 3D **Baths:** 3 En ➤ 🅿 (8) ⸆ 📺 🕇 📺 📺 ♿ 🚿

Southwell
SK7053 🍺 *Admiral Rodney, Bramley Apple, Crown Hotel, Wheatsheaf*

Church Street Bed & Breakfast, *56 Church Street, Southwell, Nottinghamshire, NG25 0HG.* **Open:** All year **Grades:** ETC 4 Diamond **01636 812004** Mr Wright *ian.wright5@btinternet.com* www.southwell-online.co.uk **D:** £20.00–£25.00 **S:** £25.00–£35.00 **Beds:** 1T 2D **Baths:** 1 En 1 Sh ➤ 🅿 (2) ⸆ 📺 🕇 📺 📺 🚿
Breakfast our speciality! Beautifully restored Georgian Grade II town house offering a friendly relaxed atmosphere. Town centre 5 mins, Southwell Minster pubs and restaurants. Historic Newark 6 miles, Nottingham City 12 miles. 'Shop till you drop'. Robin Hood Country 10 miles.

Barn Lodge, *Duckers Cottage, Brinkley, Southwell, Notts, NG25 0TP.* Converted barn in open countryside. . Railway station, race course, Southwell Minster nearby. **Open:** All year (not Xmas/New Year) **01636 813435** Mrs Hanbury *barnlodge@hotmail.com* **D:** £20.00 **S:** £25.00 **Beds:** 1F 1D 1T **Baths:** 3 En ➤ 🅿 (3) 📺 🕇 📺 📺 🚿

Stanton-on-the-Wolds
SK6330 🍺 *Pullman Inn*

Laurel Farm, *Browns Lane, Stanton-on-the-Wolds, Keyworth, Nottingham, NG12 5BL.* Lovely old farmhouse, NGS garden. Spacious rooms, convenient attractions. **Open:** All year **Grades:** ETC 3 Diamond **0115 937 3488** Mrs Moffat **Fax: 0115 937 6490** *laurelfarm@yahoo.com* www.s-h-systems.co.uk/hotels/laurelfa.html **D:** £22.50 **S:** £35.00 **Beds:** 2D 1T **Baths:** 2 En 1 Pr ➤ 🅿 (8) ⸆ 📺 📺 🚿 ♿ cc

Sutton in Ashfield
SK4958

Dalestorth Guest House, *Skegby Lane, Skegby, Sutton in Ashfield, Notts, NG17 3DH.* Grade II Georgian Listed building. Clean, friendly accommodation hotel standards. **Open:** All year **01623 551110** Mr Jordan **Fax: 01623 442241** **D:** £15.00–£17.50 **S:** £16.00–£18.00 **Beds:** 2F 3D 3T 5S **Baths:** 8 Sh ➤ 🅿 (50) 📺 📺 ♿ 🚿

Sutton on Trent
SK7965

Woodbine Farmhouse, *1 Church Street, Sutton on Trent, Newark, Notts, NG23 6PD.* Heavily beamed farmhouse. Quiet, yet near A1. Aga cooking. **Open:** All year (not Xmas) **01636 822549** Mrs Searle **Fax: 01636 821716** *woodbinefmhouse@cs.com* **D:** £18.00–£21.00 **S:** £20.00 **Beds:** 3D 1T 1S 1F **Baths:** 1 En 3 Sh ➤ 🅿 (5) ⸆ ✕ 📺 📺 🚿

Tollerton
SK6134

Cherry Tree, *13 Lothain Road, Tollerton, Nottingham, NG12 4EH.* Peaceful and friendly family home in quiet cul-de-sac in village south east of Nottingham. **Open:** All year **0115 937 5076** Ms Gaskell **D:** £18.00–£19.00 **S:** £18.00–£20.00 **Beds:** 1T 1D 1S **Baths:** 2 Sh ➤ 🅿 (4) ⸆ 📺 🕇 📺 📺 ♿ 🚿

Trowell
SK4839 🍺 *Broad Oak, Festival Inn, Admiral Rodney*

Church Farm Guest House, *1 Nottingham Road, Trowell, Nottingham, NG9 3PA.* C17th former farmhouse. **Open:** All year (not Xmas) **0115 930 1637** **Fax: 0115 930 6991** **D:** £20.00 **S:** £20.00 **Beds:** 1F 3D 2T 2S **Baths:** 2 Sh ➤ 🅿 ⸆ 📺 📺 🚿

Orchard Cottage Superior BandB,
Moor Cottages, Trowell Moor, Trowell, Nottingham, NG9 3PQ. **Open:** All year **Grades:** ETC 4 Diamond **0115 9280933 (also fax)** Mr Woodland *orchardcottage.bandb@virgin.net* www.orchardcottages.com **D:** £22.50–£30.00 **S:** £35.00–£48.00 **Beds:** 2T 1D **Baths:** 3 En ▯ (6) ⅍ ▯ ▯ ▯ ⅋ ⌖ cc
Orchard Cottage is a totally refurbished wing of a workhouse built 1817 and situated in a tranquil greenbelt location, surrounded by open farmland and orchards. Close to J25 and J26 (M1). Short distance from several pubs serving excellent evening meals.

Upton (Southwell)
SK7354

The Wheelhouse, *Mill Lane, Upton,*
Newark, Notts, NG23 5SZ. Mill situated over river, views over all elevations, overlooks racecourse. **Open:** All year (not Xmas) **01636 813572** Mrs Scothern **D:** £20.00 **S:** £20.00 **Beds:** 1F 1D 1S **Baths:** 1 En ▯ ▯ (6) ⅍ ▯

Walesby
SK6870

13 New Hill, *Walesby, Newark, Notts,*
NG22 9PB. 1950 semi-detached house with large garden in a small village. **Open:** All year (not Xmas)
01623 863834 Mrs Marsh **D:** £15.00 **S:** £15.00 **Beds:** 2D **Baths:** 1 Sh ▯ (0) ▯ (3) ⅍ ▯ ▯ ▯ ▯, ⌖

West Bridgford
SK5836   ◀ *Stratford Haven*

Acorn Hotel, *4 Radcliffe Road, West*
Bridgford, Nottingham, NG2 5FW. **Open:** All year **Grades:** ETC 3 Diamond, AA 3 Diamond
0115 981 1297 Mr Palley **Fax: 0115 981 7654** **D:** £22.00–£32.00 **S:** £35.00 **Beds:** 2F 7T 2D 1S **Baths:** 12 En ▯ ▯ (12) ⅍ ▯ ▯, ⌖ cc
Comfortable family-run hotel, 300 yards from Trent Bridge and 1.5 miles from the city centre. Convenient for all Nottingham's sporting attractions. All ensuite bedrooms are tastefully decorated with TV and tea making facilities.

Gallery Hotel, *8-10 Radcliffe Road, West*
Bridgford, Nottingham, NG2 5FW. Old Victorian house family hotel. 12 years by Mr and Mrs Don Masson. **Open:** All year **Grades:** ETC 3 Diamond, AA 3 Diamond **0115 981 3651** Mr & Mrs Masson **Fax: 0115 981 3732** www.yell.com. uk/sites/gallery-hotel/ **D:** £25.00 **S:** £29.00–£35.00 **Beds:** 3F 5D 4T 3S **Baths:** 15 En ▯ (1) ▯ (50) ⅍ ▯ ▯

Croft Hotel, *6-8 North Road, West*
Bridgford, Nottingham, NG2 7NH. Charming, quiet Victorian B&B, 1.5 miles from Nottingham city centre. **Open:** All year (not Xmas/New Year)
0115 981 2744 (also fax)
Kennedy *croft.hotel.wb@talk21.com* www.smoothhound.co.uk/hotels/crofth **D:** £18.00–£20.00 **S:** £20.00–£25.00 **Beds:** 2F 3T 2D 7S **Baths:** 5 Sh ▯ ▯ (12) ▯ ▯ ▯ ▯, ⌖

Weston
SK7767

The Boot and Shoe Hotel, *Great North*
Road, Weston, Newark, Notts, NG23 6SY. Excellent food and beers. Off A1. Close to power stations. **Open:** All year
01636 821257 **D:** £20.00 **S:** £20.00 **Beds:** 2F 1D **Baths:** 1 Sh ▯ ▯ ▯ ▯ ⌖ × ▯ ▯, ⌖ cc

Whatton in the Vale
SK7439

The Dell, *Church Street, Whatton in the*
Vale, Nottingham, Notts., NG13 9EL. Conservation area residence. Guests private sitting rooms, swimming pool, snooker. **Open:** All year
01949 850832 Mrs Fraser **D:** £17.50–£19.50 **S:** £25.00–£27.50 **Beds:** 1F 1T 1D **Baths:** 1 En 1 Pr ▯ ▯ (3) ⅍ ▯ ▯ ▯, ⌖

Worksop
SK5879   ◀ *Newcastle Arms*

Sherwood Guest House, *57 Carlton*
Road, Worksop, Notts, S80 1PP. Comfortable/ friendly accommodation near railway station, Clumber Park, A1/M1. **Open:** All year **Grades:** ETC 3 Diamond
01909 474209 Mr Wilkinson **Fax: 01909 476470** *cherwould@aol.com* **D:** £21.00–£23.50 **S:** £21.00–£26.00 **Beds:** 1F 1D 3T 1S **Baths:** 2 En 2 Sh ▯ ▯ (2) ▯ ▯ ▯ ▯, ⅋ ⌖

Riseholme Guest House, *215 Carlton*
Road, Worksop, Nottinghamshire, S81 7HN. Very comfortable,detached Victorian house. 10 minutes from town centre. **Open:** All year
01909 481506 *riseholme215@aol.com* **D:** £20.00 **S:** £21.00 **Beds:** 1T 2D **Baths:** 2 Sh ▯ (8) ▯ (3) ⅍ ▯ ▯ ▯, ⌖

Dukeries LIcensed Guest House, *29*
Park Street, Worksop, Notts, S80 1HW. Small and friendly with quality accommodation. Licensed lounge/bar. Close A1/M1. **Open:** All year
01909 476674 *www.dukeries@supanet.com* **D:** £22.50–£25.00 **S:** £30.00–£35.00 **Beds:** 2T 2D 2S **Baths:** 6 En ▯ ▯ ▯ × ▯ ▯, ⌖ cc

Oxfordshire

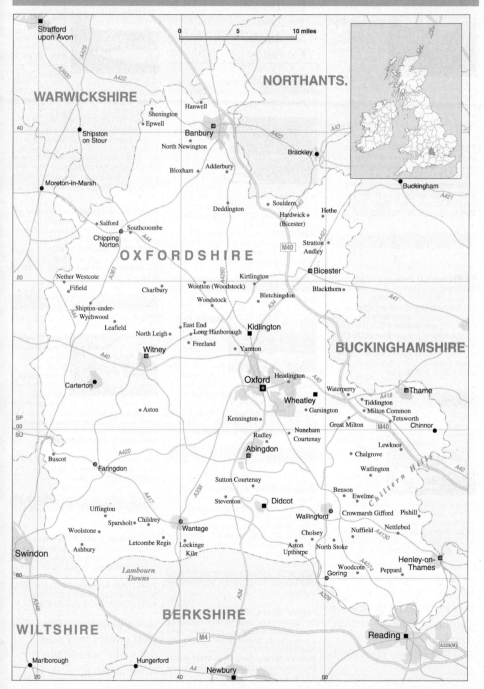

0   5   10 miles

Stratford upon Avon

NORTHANTS.

WARWICKSHIRE

Hanwell
Shenington
Epwell
Banbury
North Newington
Shipston on Stour
Bloxham   Adderbury
Brackley
Moreton-in-Marsh
Buckingham
Deddington   Souldern
Hardwick   Hethe
(Bicester)
Salford   Southcoombe
Chipping Norton
Stratton
Audley
OXFORDSHIRE
M40
Nether Westcote   Kirtlington
Fifield   Charlbury   Wootton (Woodstock)   Blackthorn
Bicester
Bletchingdon
Woodstock
Shipton-under-Wychwood
Leafield   East End   **Kidlington**
North Leigh   Long Hanborough
Witney   Freeland
Yarnton
BUCKINGHAMSHIRE
Carterton
Headington
Oxford   Waterperry   **Thame**
Aston   **Wheatley**   Tiddington
Garsington   Milton Common
Kennington   Tetsworth
Great Milton   M40   Chinnor
Nuneham
Radley   Courtenay
Abingdon   Lewknor
Chalgrove
Buscot   Watlington
Faringdon
Sutton Courtenay   Benson
Ewelme
Uffington   Steventon   **Didcot**   Crowmarsh Gifford   Pishill
Sparsholt   Childrey   **Wallingford**   Nuffield   Nettlebed
Woolstone   Cholsey
Ashbury   Letcombe Regis   **Wantage**   Aston   North Stoke   **Henley-on-Thames**
Swindon   Lockinge   Upthorpe
Kiln   Woodcote   Peppard
Lambourn Downs   Goring
BERKSHIRE
WILTSHIRE   M4
Reading
Marlborough   Hungerford   A329(M)
Newbury

Abingdon

SU4997

Barrows End, *3 The Copse, Abingdon, Oxon, OX14 3YW.* Modern chalet bungalow, peaceful setting. Easy access Oxford/Abingdon. **Open:** All year (not Xmas)
01235 523541 Mrs Harmsworth *DSHarm@ tesco.net* **D:** £24.00–£25.00 **S:** £26.00–£27.00 **Beds:** 3T **Baths:** 1 En 2 Pr ▣ (3) ⊬ ⊠ �▥ ⚤

22 East St Helen Street, *Abingdon, Oxon, OX14 5EB.* Friendly elegant Georgian town house on river. **Open:** All year (not Easter or Xmas/New Year)
01235 550979 Mrs Howard **Fax: 01235 533278** *srhoward@talk21.com* **D:** £30.00–£35.00 **S:** £32.00–£40.00 **Beds:** 1T 1D 2S **Baths:** 1 En 2 Sh ⌖ ⊬ ⊠ ⊠ ▥ ⚤ ⚤

Adderbury

SP4735

Le Restaurant Francais at Morgans Orchard, *9 Twyford Gardens, Adderbury, Banbury, Oxon, OX17 3JA.* North Oxfordshire's premier award-winning French restaurant with family hospitality. **Open:** All year **Grades:** ETC 3 Diamond **01295 812047** C Morgan **Fax: 01295 812341** *morgarest@aol.com* www.banbury-cross.co. uk/morgans **D:** £20.00–£25.00 **S:** £25.00–£40.00 **Beds:** 2T 1D 1S **Baths:** 2 En 2 Sh ⌖ ▣ (4) ⊬ ⊠ ⅋ ⚤ × ▥ ⚤ cc

Ashbury

SU2685

The Village Stores, *Ashbury, Swindon, Wiltshire, SN6 8NA.* Thatched cottage in pretty downland village, 5 minutes from Ridgeway. **Open:** All year (not Xmas/New Year)
01793 710262 (also fax) Mr & Mrs Schiff **D:** £20.00–£25.00 **S:** £20.00–£25.00 **Beds:** 1F 1T 1D **Baths:** 1 Pr ⌖ ▣ ⊬ × ⊠

RATES

D = Price range per person sharing in a double or twin room
S = Price range for a single room

BEDROOMS

D = Double
T = Twin
S = Single
F = Family

Aston

SP3303   ⚘ *The Trout*

Chimney Farmhouse, *Chimney-on-Thames, Aston, Bampton, Oxon, OX18 2EH.* Peaceful farmhouse offers warm welcome and comfortable accommodation. Ideal for exploring Oxfordshire and Cotswolds. **Open:** Feb to Nov **Grades:** ETC 4 Diamond **01367 870279** www.country-accom.co. uk/chimneyfarmhouse **D:** £22.50–£30.00 **S:** £25.00–£30.00 **Beds:** 1T 1D 1S **Baths:** 3 En ⌖ (10) ▣ (6) ⊬ ⊠ ⊠ ▥ ⚤

Aston Upthorpe

SU5585

Middle Fell, *Moreton Road, Aston Upthorpe, Didcot, Oxon, OX11 9ER.* Georgian village house, tastefully appointed. Secluded garden bordering Aston Stud. **Open:** All year (not Xmas) **Grades:** ETC 4 Diamond **01235 850207 (also fax)** C Millin **D:** £22.50–£25.00 **S:** £25.00–£35.00 **Beds:** 1F 1D 1T **Baths:** 3 En ⌖ (10) ▣ (4) ⊬ ⊠ ▥ ⚤

Banbury

SP4540

Belmont Guest House, *34 Crouch Street, Banbury, Oxon, OX16 9PR.* Family run guest house, close to all town amenities. **Open:** All year (not Xmas)
01295 262308 Mr Raby **Fax: 01295 275982 D:** £21.00–£22.50 **S:** £25.00–£35.00 **Beds:** 1F 2D 2T 3S **Baths:** 5 Pr 1 Sh ⌖ (10) ▣ (6) ⊬ ⊠ × ⊠ ▥ ⚤ ⚤ cc

Benson

SU6191

Fyfield Manor, *Brook Street, Benson, Wallingford, Oxon, OX10 6HA.* Medieval dining room. Beautiful water gardens. Essentially a family house. **Open:** All year (not Xmas/New Year)
01491 835184 Mrs Brown **Fax: 01491 825635 D:** £25.00 **S:** £30.00 **Beds:** 1D 1T **Baths:** 2 En 1 Pr ⌖ (10) ▣ (6) ⊬ ⊠ ⊠ ▥ ⚤

Bicester

SP5822

The Old School, *Stratton Audley, Bicester, Oxon, OX6 9BJ.* **Open:** All year **Grades:** ETC 3 Diamond **01869 277371** Mrs Wertheimer *sawertheimer@ euphony.com* www.old-school.co.uk **D:** £30.00–£35.00 **S:** £30.00–£35.00 **Beds:** 3T 1S **Baths:** 2 Sh ⌖ ▣ (6) ⊠ ⅋ ⊠ ▥. Interesting C17th house in pretty village. Pleasant garden with tennis court and croquet. Guests' own drawing room. Tea and home-made cakes on arrival. Village has charming thatched pub serving excellent meals. Very comfortable beds. Everyone sleeps well - so peaceful.

Home Farm House, *Middle Aston, Bicester, Oxon, OX25 5PX.* Peaceful C17th farmhouse with stunning views and lovely garden. **Open:** All year **01869 340666 Fax: 01869 347789** *cparsons@ telinco.co.uk* **D:** £25.00–£28.00 **S:** £25.00–£35.00 **Beds:** 1T 1D **Baths:** 1 En 1 Pr ⌖ (12) ▣ (4) ⊬ ⊠ ▥ ⚤

Blackthorn

SP6218   ⚘ *Greyhound*

Lime Trees Farm, *Lower Road, Blackthorn, Bicester, Oxon, OX6 0TG.* Relaxed, comfortable accommodation providing a perfect springboard for Oxford and Cotswolds. **Open:** All year **Grades:** ETC 4 Diamond **01869 248435 Fax: 01869 325843** *limetreesfarm@hotmail.com* limetreesfarm.freeserve.co.uk **D:** £25.00–£30.00 **S:** £30.00 **Beds:** 1T 1D **Baths:** 1 En 1 Pr ⌖ ▣ ⊬ ⊠ ⅋ × ⊠ ▥ ⚤

Bletchingdon

SP5018

Stonehouse Farm, *Weston Road, Bletchingdon, Kidlington, Oxon, OX5 3EA.* C17th farmhouse set in 560 acres, 15 mins from Oxford. **Open:** All year (not Xmas/New Year)
01869 350585 Mrs Hedges **D:** £18.00–£22.00 **S:** £20.00–£24.00 **Beds:** 1F 1D 1T 1S **Baths:** 2 Sh ⌖ (12) ▣ (6) ⊬ ⊠ ⊠ ⚤

B&B owners may vary rates – be sure to check when booking

Bloxham

SP4236

Brook Cottage, *Little Bridge Road, Bloxham, Banbury, Oxon, OX15 4PU.* Warm welcome to C17th thatched cottage. Personal management by owner. **Open:** All year
01295 721089 D: £18.50 **S:** £18.50 **Beds:** 1D 1T 1S **Baths:** 1 En 1 Pr 🅿 (4) ⊬ 📺 🎞 ♨

Buscot

SU2397

Apple Tree House, *Buscot, Faringdon, Oxon, SN7 8DA.* Old property in National Trust village, 5 mins' walk River Thames, one acre garden. **Open:** All year (not Xmas)
01367 252592 Mrs Reay *emreay@aol.com*
D: £18.00–£22.00 **S:** £23.00–£28.00 **Beds:** 2D 1T **Baths:** 1 En 2 Pr ⭐ 🅿 (10) ⊬ 📺 🎞 ♨

Chalgrove

SU6396

Cornerstones, *1 Cromwell Close, Chalgrove, Oxford, OX44 7SE.* Pretty detached bungalow, situated just off B480 in charming Oxfordshire village. **Open:** All year
01865 890298 D: £14.50 **S:** £23.00 **Beds:** 2T **Baths:** 1 Sh ⭐ (5) 🅿 (2) ⊬ 📺 🎞 ♨

Charlbury

SP3619

Cotswold View Caravan & Camping Site, *Banbury Hill Farm, Enstone Road, Charlbury, Chipping Norton, Oxon, OX7 3JH.* Situated on eastern edge of Cotswolds, overlooking the Evenlode Valley. **Open:** All year (not Xmas)
01608 810314 Mrs Widdows **Fax: 01608 811891 D:** £18.00–£25.00 **S:** £20.00–£35.00 **Beds:** 7F 2D 3T 1S **Baths:** 11 En 1 Sh ⭐ 🅿 (10) ⊬ 📺 🎞 ♿ ♨ cc

Childrey

SU3587   ⚞ *Star Inn*

Ridgeway House, *West Street, Childrey, Wantage, Oxon, OX12 9UL.* Award winning bed and breakfast. All ensuite, quiet and wonderful views. **Open:** All year
Grades: ETC 4 Diamond, Silver
01235 751538 (also fax) Mrs Roberts *robertsfamily@compuserve.com* **D:** £25.00–£29.00 **S:** £29.00–£39.00 **Beds:** 2F 2T 2D 2S
Baths: 2 En ⭐ 🅿 (5) ⊬ 📺 📹 🎞 ♨

BATHROOMS
En = Ensuite
Pr = Private
Sh = Shared

All details shown are as supplied by B&B owners in Autumn 2001

Chipping Norton

SP3126

The Old Bakehouse, *50 West Street, Chipping Norton, Oxon, OX7 5ER.* An old bakehouse, warm & friendly atmosphere, near town centre. **Open:** All year (not Xmas/New Year)
01608 643441 Mr & Mrs Cashmore
D: £22.50–£25.00 **S:** £35.00 **Beds:** 1F 1D **Baths:** 2 En ⭐ (8) 🅿 (2) ⊬ 📺 🎞 ♨

Cholsey

SU5886

The Well Cottage, *Caps Lane, Cholsey, Wallingford, Oxon, OX10 9HQ.* Delightful cottage with ensuite bedrooms in secluded garden flat. **Open:** All year
01491 651959 & 07887 958920 (M)
J Alexander **Fax: 01491 651675**
thewellcottage@talk21.com **D:** £15.00–£25.00 **S:** £20.00–£30.00 **Beds:** 2T 1D **Baths:** 2 En 1 Pr

Deddington

SP4631

Hill Barn, *Milton Gated Road, Deddington, Banbury, Oxon, OX15 0TS.* Converted barn in open countryside, convenient for Oxford, Cotswolds, Warwick, Stratford. **Open:** All year (not Xmas) **Grades:** ETC 2 Diamond
01869 338631 Mrs White *hillbarn-bb@supanet.com* **D:** £20.00–£25.00 **S:** £25.00–£30.00 **Beds:** 1F 1D 2T **Baths:** 1 En 1 Sh ⭐ 🅿 (6) 📺 🎞 ♨

Stonecrop Guest House, *Hempton Road, Deddington, Banbury, Oxon, OX15 0QH.* Detached house close to places of interest. A warm welcome. **Open:** All year
01869 338335 Fax: 01869 338505 D: £16.00–£19.00 **S:** £16.00–£19.00 **Beds:** 1F 1D 1T 1S **Baths:** 2 Sh ⭐ (10) 🅿 (6) 📺 🎞 ♨

East End

SP3914   ⚞ *Woodman*

Forge Cottage, *East End, North Leigh, Witney, Oxon, OX8 6PZ.* Old cottage. Organic home grown food. Hot toast available. **Open:** Aug to July
01993 881120 Mrs French *jillfrench@talk21.com* **D:** £22.00–£23.00 **Beds:** 1D **Baths:** 1 En ⭐ 🅿 (2) ⊬ 📺 🎞 📹 🎞 ♨

Epwell

SP3441

Yarnhill Farm, *Shenington Road, Epwell, Banbury, Oxon, OX15 6JA.* Peaceful farmhouse; ideally situated for Cotswolds, Stratford-upon-Avon, Oxford. **Open:** All year (not Xmas)
01295 780250 D: £18.00–£25.00 **S:** £18.00–£25.00 **Beds:** 1D 1T 1S **Baths:** 1 Pr 1 Sh ⭐ (8) 🅿 (6) ⊬ 📺 🎞 ♨

Ewelme

SU6491

May's Farm, *Turner's Court, Ewelme, Wallingford, Oxon, OX10 6QF.* Friendly farmhouse and bungalow - wonderful views. Working stock farm. peaceful. **Open:** All year
01491 641294 & 01491 642056 Mrs Passmore **Fax: 01491 641697** *apister.v@virgin.net*
D: £20.00–£25.00 **S:** £22.50–£35.00 **Beds:** 1F 1T 1S **Baths:** 1 En 1 Sh ⭐ 🅿 (6) ⊬ 📺 🎞 📹 🎞 ♿ ♨

Dormer Cottage, *High Street, Ewelme, Wallingford, Oxon, OX10 6HQ.* Old cottage in pretty historic village, warm welcome, friendly atmosphere. **Open:** All year (not Xmas)
01491 833987 Mrs Standbridge **D:** £17.00–£19.00 **S:** £20.00–£22.00 **Beds:** 1T 1D **Baths:** 1 Sh 🅿 (2) ⊬ 📺 ♨

Fords Farm, *Ewelme, Wallingford, Oxon, OX10 6HU.* Picturesque setting in historic village. Warm, friendly atmosphere. Good views. **Open:** All year
01491 839272 Miss Edwards **D:** £24.00–£25.00 **S:** £30.00–£35.00 **Beds:** 1D 2T **Baths:** 1 Pr 1 Sh 🅿 (8) ⊬ 📺 🎞 ♨

Faringdon

SU2895

Faringdon Hotel, *1 Market Place, Faringdon, Oxon, SN7 7HL.* **Open:** All year **Grades:** ETC 3 Diamond, AA 2 Star, RAC 2 Star
01367 240536 Fax: 01367 243250 D: £30.00–£35.00 **S:** £45.00–£60.00 **Beds:** 3F 14D 1T 3S **Baths:** 20 En ⭐ 📺 🎞 ✕ 🎞 ♨ Situated near C12th parish church, on site of palace of Alfred the Great.

Portwell House Hotel, *Market Place, Faringdon, Oxon, SN7 7HU.* Relax in the ancient market town of Faringdon within reach of the Cotswolds. **Open:** All year
01367 240197 Mr Pakeman **Fax: 01367 244330 D:** £25.00 **S:** £40.00 **Beds:** 2F 3D 2T 1S **Baths:** 8 En ⭐ (2) 🅿 (4) ⊬ 📺 ✕ 🎞 ♿ ❋ ♨ cc

Fifield

SP2319 🍺 *Merrymouth Inn*

Merryfield, High Street, Fifield, Chipping Norton, Oxon, *OX7 6HL.* Quiet and peaceful, an ideal centre for touring the Cotswolds. **Open:** All year (not Xmas) **Grades:** ETC 3 Diamond **01993 830517** Mrs Palmer *jpmgtd@freeuk.com* merryfieldbandb.co.uk **D:** £25.00 **S:** £25.00–£30.00 **Beds:** 2T **Baths:** 1 En 1 Pr 🅿(4) 🚭 📺 🛋 🛉

Freeland

SP4112

Shepherds Hall Inn, Witney Road, Freeland, Witney, Oxon, *OX29 8HQ.* **Open:** All year **Grades:** ETC 3 Diamond **01993 881256** Mr Fyson **Fax:** 01993 883455 **D:** £24.00–£27.50 **S:** £25.00–£35.00 **Beds:** 1F 1D 2T 1S **Baths:** 5 En 🍴 🅿(50) 📺 🛏 🛋 🛉 ♿ cc Attractive inn with excellent well-appointed accommodation. Wide selection of appetising meals available lunch times and evenings. Ideally situated for Oxford, Woodstock - Blenheim Palace - and Cotswolds. On A4095 Woodstock-Witney Road.

Garsington

SP5801 🍺 *Three Horseshoes*

Hill Copse Cottage, Wheatley Road, Garsington, Oxford, Oxfordshire, *OX44 9DT.* **Open:** All year (not Xmas/New Year) **Grades:** ETC 3 Diamond **01865 361478 & 07778 776209 (M)** Mrs Winstone **Fax:** 01865 361478 **D:** £30.00 **S:** £30.00–£40.00 **Beds:** 1F 2D 1S **Baths:** 4 En 🅿(5) 🚭 📺 🛋 🛉 Detached house surrounded by farmland with lovely views. Secure parking in own grounds. 4 miles from J8/8a M40. Easy access to Oxford, Cotswolds, Chilterns, London and Heathrow. Visit the Norman Church and view C17th Manor House.

BATHROOMS
En = Ensuite
Pr = Private
Sh = Shared

Goring

SU6081 🍺 *Catherine Wheel, John Barleycorn*

The Catherine Wheel, Station Road, Goring, Reading, Berks, *RG8 9HB.* Accommodation in a Victorian cottage in riverside village. **Open:** All year **01491 872379** Mrs Kerr **D:** £20.00 **S:** £25.00 **Beds:** 2D 1T **Baths:** 2 Sh 🍴🚭 📺 ✕ 📺 🛋 🛉 cc

Northview House, Farm Road, Goring-on-Thames, Reading, Oxon, *RG8 0AA.* Five minutes from Ridgeway. Close to pubs, river and stations. **Open:** All year (not Xmas/New Year) **01491 872184** Mr & Mrs Sheppard *hi@goring-on-thames.freeserve.co.uk* **D:** £18.00 **Beds:** 2D 1T **Baths:** 1 Sh 🍴🅿(3) 🚭 📺 🛋 🛉

Great Milton

SP6302

Colletts View, Great Milton, Oxford, Oxfordshire, *OX44 7NY.* Set in lovely gardens, ground floor rooms, Oxford, Chilterns close. **Open:** All year (not Xmas/New Year) **01844 278824** Mrs Hayes *sputnik@ukgateway.net* **D:** £18.00–£20.00 **S:** £20.00–£22.00 **Beds:** 2F 2T **Baths:** 1 Sh 🍴(15) 🅿(2) 🚭 🛋 🛉

Hanwell

SP4344

The Coach House, Hanwell Castle, Hanwell, Banbury, Oxon, *OX17 1HN.* Part of C15th castle in 20 acre garden undergoing restoration. **Open:** Apr to Oct **01295 730764** Mrs Taylor **D:** £18.00–£25.00 **S:** £18.00–£25.00 **Beds:** 1F 1D 1T **Baths:** 3 En 🍴(1) 🅿(6) 📺 🛏 🛋 ♿ 🛉

Hardwick (Bicester)

SP5729

Sycamore House, Church Lane, Hardwick, Bicester, Oxon, *OX6 6SS.* Newly built farmhouse in a secluded area in a small village. **Open:** All year (not Xmas/New Year) **01869 277984** Ms Curtis **D:** £20.00–£25.00 **S:** £20.00–£25.00 **Beds:** 1T 1D 1S **Baths:** 1 Sh 🍴(3) 🅿(6) 🚭 📺 📺 🛋 🛉

Henley-on-Thames

SU7682 🍺 *Sacarens Head*

Ledard, Rotherfield Road, Henley-on-Thames, Oxon, *RG9 1NN.* Elegant Victorian house and garden within easy reach of Henley. **Open:** All year (not Xmas) **01491 575611** Mrs Howard *alan.howard@iee.org* **D:** £20.00 **S:** £20.00 **Beds:** 1F 1D 1T **Baths:** 2 Pr 🍴🅿(4) 🚭 📺 📺 🛋 🛉

Planning a longer stay? Always ask for any special rates

Orchard Dene Cottage, Lower Assenden, Henley-on-Thames, Oxon, *RG9 6AG.* **Open:** All year **01491 575490 (also fax)** Ms Batchelor Smith *orcharddene@freeuk.com* www.orcharddene.freeuk.com **D:** £20.00–£25.00 **S:** £25.00 **Beds:** 1D 1S **Baths:** 1 Sh 🍴 🅿 🚭 📺 🛏 📺 🛋 🛉 Two miles from Henley, in beautiful walking country (Chilterns, Thames Path, Oxfordshire Way) and within easy reach of Oxford and Windsor by rail or road. Enjoy an interesting garden, comfortable rooms, a relaxed atmosphere and a delicious full English breakfast.

Alftrudis, 8 Norman Avenue, Henley-on-Thames, Oxon, *RG9 1SG.* Victorian home, quiet cul-de-sac two minutes town centre station, river. **Open:** All year **Grades:** ETC 4 Diamond **01491 573099 & 07802 408643 (M)** Mrs Lambert **Fax:** 01491 411747 *b&b@alftrudis.fsnet.co.uk* **D:** £27.50–£30.00 **S:** £45.00–£50.00 **Beds:** 2D 1T **Baths:** 2 En 1 Pr 🍴(8) 🅿(2) 🚭 📺 🛋 🛉

Pennyford House, Peppard, Henley-on-Thames, Oxon, *RG9 5JE.* Family home with dogs. Happy atmosphere. Nice garden. Local interests. **Open:** All year **01491 628272 (also fax)** Mrs Howden-Ferme **D:** £25.00–£35.00 **S:** £30.00–£35.00 **Beds:** 1T 3D 1S **Baths:** 4 En 1 Pr 🅿(10) 🚭 📺 🛏 🛋 🛉

The Laurels, 107 St Marks Road, Henley-on-Thames, Oxon, *RG9 1LP.* Walking distance to town, river and station. Quiet, clean, comfortable. **Open:** All year **Grades:** ETC 3 Diamond **01491 572982** Mrs Bridekirk **D:** £28.00–£30.00 **S:** £38.00–£48.00 **Beds:** 1T 1D 1S **Baths:** 2 En 1 Pr 🍴(10) 🅿(3) 🚭 📺 ✕ 🛉

Vine Cottage, 53 Northfield End, Henley-on-Thames, Oxon, *RG9 2JJ.* Victorian cottage with pretty garden, 5 mins walk from town centre. **Open:** All year (not Xmas/New Year) **01491 410707 D:** £25.00 **S:** £25.00 **Beds:** 1T 2S **Baths:** 1 Sh 🍴(10) 🅿(3) 🚭 📺 🛋 🛉

New Lodge, Henley Park, Henley-on-Thames, Oxon, *RG9 6HU.* Victorian lodge in tranquil park settings. Minimum two nights stay. **Open:** All year **Grades:** ETC 3 Diamond **01491 576340 (also fax)** Mrs Warner *newlodge@mail.com* **D:** £23.00–£25.00 **S:** £30.00–£32.00 **Beds:** 1F 2D 1S **Baths:** 1 En 1 Pr 🍴🅿(4) 🚭 📺 📺 🛋 ♿ 🛉

BEDROOMS

D = Double
T = Twin
S = Single
F = Family

Hethe
SP5829

Manor Farm, *Hethe, Bicester, Oxfordshire, OX6 9ES.* Between Oxford and Stratford. Charming stone manor house in lovely village. **Open:** All year **01869 277602 Fax: 01869 278376 D:** £25.00–£30.00 **S:** £30.00–£35.00 **Beds:** 2D **Baths:** 1 En 1 Pr 🛇 🖬 (2) 🗶 🗹 ✕ 🗹 🛍, 🛋

Kennington
SP5201 🍺 *Tandem Pub*

Ambleside, *94 The Avenue, Kennington, Oxford, Oxfordshire, OX1 5RJ.* Comfortable and friendly accommodation, convenient to A34 Oxford and Abingdon. **Open:** All year **01865 735463** Mrs Bowles *phil_bowles@ lineone.net* www.geocities.com/ambleside **D:** £18.00–£20.00 **S:** £24.00–£28.00 **Beds:** 1T 2D **Baths:** 1 Sh 🛇 (5) 🖬 (3) 🗶 🗹 🗹 🛍, 🛋

Kirtlington
SP4919

Two Turnpike Cottages, *Kirtlington, Oxford, OX5 3HB.* Cotswold stone cottage with pretty gardens in village setting. **Open:** All year **01869 350706** Mrs Jones *margarethjones@ hotmail.com* **D:** £21.00–£25.00 **S:** £30.00 **Beds:** 2D **Baths:** 1 Sh 🛇 🖬 (2) 🗶 🗹 🕈 🛍, 🛋

Leafield
SP3115

Langley Farm, *Leafield, Witney, Oxon, OX8 5QD.* Working farm set in open country 3 miles from Burford. **Open:** May to Oct **01993 878686** Mrs Greves *gwengreves@ farmline.com* **D:** £17.50–£20.00 **Beds:** 2D 1T **Baths:** 1 Pr 2 Sh 🖬 (8) 🕈 🛍, 🛋

Letcombe Regis
SU3886

Quince Cottage, *Letcombe Regis, Wantage, Oxon, OX12 9JP.* Large thatched cottage, exposed beams, near Ridgeway, warm family atmosphere. **Open:** All year **01235 763652** Mrs Boden **D:** £21.00–£25.00 **S:** £25.00 **Beds:** 1T 1S **Baths:** 1 Pr 🛇 (1) 🛋 (2) 🗶 🗹 🛍, 🛋

Lewknor
SU7197

Moorcourt Cottage, *Weston Road, Lewknor, Watlington, Oxfordshire, OX9 5RU.* **Open:** All year (not Xmas/New Year) **Grades:** ETC 4 Diamond **01844 351419 (also fax)** Mrs Hodgson *p.hodgson@freeuk.com* **D:** £25.00 **S:** £35.00 **Beds:** 1T 1D **Baths:** 1 En 1 Pr 🛋 (4) 🗹 🗹 🛍, 🛋 Beautiful C15th cottage. views of Chiltern Hills and farmland. Quiet, friendly and very comfortable. traditional English breakfast. Ideal touring centre for Oxford, Henley on Thames, Cotswolds. Frequent bus service to London from Lewknor. Many walks, cycleways, public golf courses nearby.

Lockinge Kiln
SU4283

Lockinge Kiln Farm, *The Ridgeway, Lockinge, Wantage, Oxon, OX12 8PA.* Quiet comfortable farmhouse, working farm. Ideal walking, riding, cycling country. **Open:** All year (not Xmas) **01235 763308 (also fax)** Mrs Cowan *stellacowan@hotmail.com* **D:** £20.00 **S:** £25.00 **Beds:** 1D 2T **Baths:** 3 Sh 🛇 (10) 🖬 (3) 🗶 🛍, 🛋

Long Hanborough
SP4114

Wynford House, *79 Main Road, Long Hanborough, Witney, Oxon, OX8 8BX.* Comfortable warm family house in village. Good walks, local pubs. **Open:** All year (not Xmas) **01993 881402** Mrs Ellis **Fax: 01993 883661 D:** £21.00–£23.00 **S:** £25.00–£40.00 **Beds:** 1F 1D 1T **Baths:** 1 En 1 Sh 🛇 🖬 🗶 🗹 🕈 🗹 🛍, 🛋

Milton Common
SP6503

Byways, *Old London Road, Milton Common, Thame, Oxon, OX9 2JR.* A spacious bungalow, comfortable and cosy, good views, with large garden. **Open:** All year **01844 279386 D:** £23.00 **S:** £25.00 **Beds:** 2T **Baths:** 1 En 1 Pr 🖬 (3) 🗶 🗹 🛍, 🛋

National Grid References given are for villages, towns and cities – not for individual houses

---

RATES

D = Price range per person sharing in a double or twin room
S = Price range for a single room

Nether Westcote
SP2220

Cotswold View Guest House, *Nether Westcote, Chipping Norton, Oxon, OX7 6SD.* Cotswold view guest house, built on site of my family's farmyard. **Open:** All year (not Xmas/New Year) **01993 830699** Mr Gibson *info@ cotswoldview-guesthouse.co.uk* www.cotswoldview-guesthouse.co.uk **D:** £20.00–£25.00 **S:** £25.00–£30.00 **Beds:** 2D 2T 1S 2F **Baths:** 5 En 2 Pr 🛇 🖬 (8) 🗶 🗹 🕈 🛍, 🛋 **cc**

Nettlebed
SU6986

Park Corner Farm House, *Nettlebed, Henley-on-Thames, Oxon, RG9 6DX.* Queen Anne farmhouse in AONB between Henley-on-Thames and Oxford. **Open:** All year (not Xmas/New Year) **01491 641450** Mrs Rutter **D:** £22.50 **S:** £25.00 **Beds:** 2T 1S **Baths:** 1 Sh 1 Pr 🛇 🖬 (6) 🗶 🕈 🛍, 🛋

North Leigh
SP3812

Gorselands Hall, *Boddington Lane, North Leigh, Witney, Oxon, OX29 6PU.* Lovely old Cotswold stone farmhouse, oak beams, flagstone floors in delightful rural setting. **Open:** All year **Grades:** ETC 4 Diamond, RAC 4 Diamond **01993 882292** Mr & Mrs Hamilton **Fax: 01993 883629** *hamilton@gorselandshall.com* www.gorselandshall.com **D:** £22.50–£25.00 **S:** £30.00–£35.00 **Beds:** 4D 1T 1F **Baths:** 6 En 🛇 🖬 (6) 🗶 🗹 🕈 🛍, 🛋 **cc**

Elbie House, *East End, North Leigh, Witney, Oxon, OX8 6PZ.* C16th home, edge of Cotswolds close to Blenheim Palace. Banquet Breakfast! **Open:** All year **Grades:** ETC 4 Diamond, Silver **01993 880166** Mrs Buck *buck@ elbiehouse.freeserve.co.uk* **D:** £25.00–£27.50 **S:** £30.00–£38.00 **Beds:** 2F **Baths:** 2 En 🛇 (7) 🖬 (10) 🗶 🗹 🗹 🛍, 🛋

North Leigh Guest House, *28 Common Road, North Leigh, Witney, Oxon, OX8 6RA.* Clean friendly family home, guest own suite. Evening meal available. **Open:** All year **01993 881622** Mrs Perry **D:** £22.50 **S:** £22.50 **Beds:** 1F 1T **Baths:** 2 En 🛇 🖬 (5) 🗶 🗹 ✕ 🗹 🛍, 🛋

B&B owners may vary
rates – be sure to check
when booking

North Newington

SP4239

Broughton Grounds Farm, *North Newington, Banbury, Oxon, OX15 6AW.*
Open: All year (not Xmas)
01295 730315 Margaret Taylor
broughtongrounds@hotmail.com
www.broughtongrounds.co.uk **D:** £18.00–£20.00 **S:** £18.00–£20.00 **Beds:** 1D 1T 1S
Baths: 1 Sh 🛁 (2) 🅿 (3) 🗝 🖾 🌣
Enjoy warm hospitality and peaceful surroundings at our C17th stone farmhouse. A working family farm situated on the Broughton Castle estate with beautiful views and walks. Very comfortable spacious accommodation, log fire in dining room, delicious breakfast with home produce.

North Stoke

SU6186

Footpath Cottage, *The Street, North Stoke, Wallingford, Oxon, OX10 6BJ.*
Lovely old cottage, peaceful river village. Warm welcome, excellent food. **Open:** All year
01491 839763 Mrs Tanner **D:** £19.00–£20.00 **S:** £20.00 **Beds:** 1D 1S **Baths:** 1 Sh 🛁 🖾 🌣 ✕ 🖾 🌣

Nuffield

SU6687

The Rectory, *Nuffield, Henley-on-Thames, Oxon, RG9 5SN.* Working Rectory on the Ridgeway path at 700 feet; Aga breakfasts **Open:** All year
01491 641305 (also fax) Mr Shearer
D: £15.00–£18.00 **S:** £18.00–£20.00 **Beds:** 1D 1T 1S **Baths:** 1 Pr 🛁 🅿 (4) 🌣 ✕ 🖾 🖾

Nuneham Courtenay

SU5598

The Old Bakery, *Nuneham Courtenay, Oxford, OX44 9NX.* Beautifully renovated large Listed C18th country cottage, 5m Oxford centre. **Open:** All year
01865 343585 *maggie.howard@virgin.net*
skybusiness.com/mage11 **D:** £25.00–£30.00
S: £30.00–£40.00 **Beds:** 1F 2T 1D **Baths:** 4 En 🛁 🅿 (10) 🌣 🖾 🌣 ✕ 🖾 🌣 ♣ ✿ ♣ cc

---

Oxford

SP5106   🍴 *Bullingdon Arms, The Trout, Red Lion, The Perch, King's Arms, Turf Tavern, Royal Oak, Eagle & Child*

The Bungalow, *Cherwell Farm, Mill Lane, Old Marston, Oxford, OX3 0QF.*
Open: Mar to Oct **Grades:** ETC 3 Diamond
01865 557171 Mrs Burdon **D:** £22.00–£26.00
S: £25.00–£35.00 **Beds:** 2D 2T **Baths:** 2 En 1 Sh 🛁 (7) 🅿 (6) 🌣 🖾 🖾 🌣
Delightful small, family-run modern bungalow in five acres open countryside, no bus route. 3 miles to city centre. Excellent location. Non-smoking.

Green Gables, *326 Abingdon Road, Oxford, OX1 4TE.* **Open:** All year (not Xmas/New Year)
01865 725870 Mr & Mrs Bhella **Fax: 01865 723115** *green.gables@virgin.net*
freespace.virgin.net/narinder.bhella
D: £27.00–£33.00 **S:** £35.00–£52.00 **Beds:** 3F 4D 1T 1S **Baths:** 9 En 🛁 🅿 (9) 🖾 🖾 🌣 ♣ cc
Characterful detached Edwardian house shielded by trees. Bright spacious rooms with TV and beverage facilities. Ensuite rooms. 1.25 miles to city centre, on bus routes. Ample off-street parking. Direct line phones in rooms and disabled room available.

Arden Lodge, *34 Sunderland Avenue, Oxford, OX2 8DX.* Perfectly situated for Oxford city centre. Touring, Cotswolds, Stratford, London. **Open:** All year (not Xmas/New Year)
01865 552076 (also fax) Mr & Mrs Price
D: £23.00–£25.00 **S:** £28.00–£35.00 **Beds:** 1F 1D 1S **Baths:** 1 En 2 Pr 🛁 (5) 🅿 (4) 🌣 🖾 🖾 🌣

Sportsview Guest House, *106-110 Abingdon Road, Oxford, OX1 4PX.* South of city centre. Few mins' walk towpath for very pleasant walk to city. **Open:** All year (not Xmas)
Grades: ETC 3 Diamond
01865 244268 Mrs Saini **Fax: 01865 249270**
stay@sportsview-guest-house.freeserve.co.uk
www.smoothhound.co.uk/hotelssportsvi.
html **D:** £27.00–£33.00 **S:** £30.00–£50.00
Beds: 5F 6T 3D 6S **Baths:** 12 En 12 Pr 2 Sh 🛁 (4) 🅿 (11) 🌣 🖾 🖾 🌣 ♣ cc

---

Planning a longer stay? Always ask for any special rates

BATHROOMS
En = Ensuite
Pr = Private
Sh = Shared

Highfield West, *188 Cumnor Hill, Oxford, OX2 9PJ.* Comfortable home in residential area, heated outdoor pool in season.
Open: All year (not Xmas) **Grades:** ETC 3 Diamond
01865 863007 Mr & Mrs Mitchell
highfieldwest@email.msn.com **D:** £24.50–£29.50
S: £27.00–£30.00 **Beds:** 1F 1D 1T 2S
Baths: 3 En 1 Sh 🛁 🅿 (5) 🌣 🖾 🌣 🖾 🖾 🌣 ♣

All Seasons Guest House, *63 Windmill Road, Headington, Oxford, Oxfordshire, OX3 7BP.* Comfortable guest house, non-smoking, parking, convenient airports and Brookes University. **Open:** All year
01865 742215 Mr & Mrs Melbye **Fax: 01865 432691** *admin@allseasonsguesthouse.com*
www.allseasonsguesthouse.com **D:** £25.00–£32.50 **S:** £30.00–£50.00 **Beds:** 1T 3D 2S
Baths: 4 En 1 Sh 🛁 (6) 🅿 (6) 🌣 🖾 🖾 🌣 ♣ cc

58 St John Street, *Oxford, OX1 2QR.* Tall Victorian house central to all colleges, museums and theatres. **Open:** All year
01865 515454 Mrs Old **D:** £18.00–£20.00
S: £18.00–£20.00 **Beds:** 1F 1T 1S **Baths:** 2 En 🛁 (1) 🌣 🖾 ♣

Acorn Guest House, *260 Iffley Road, Oxford, Oxfordshire, OX4 1SE.* Modern comfort in Victorian house convenient for all local attractions. **Open:** All year (not Xmas/New Year)
01865 247998 Mrs Lewis **D:** £24.00–£26.00
S: £29.00 **Beds:** 2F 4D 2T 4S **Baths:** 1 En 4 Sh 🛁 (9) 🅿 (11) 🖾 🖾 🌣 ♣ cc

Nanford Guest House, *Iffley Road, Oxford, OX4 1EJ.* Period guest house located 5 minutes on foot from Oxford University.
Open: All year
01865 244743 Mr Cronin **Fax: 01865 249596**
B.Cronin@btinternet.com www.comestaywithus.
com **D:** £17.50–£20.00 **S:** £28.00–£38.00
Beds: 10F 10T 10D 5S **Baths:** 35 En 🛁 (1) 🅿 🌣 🖾 🌣 🖾 🌣 ♣ ✿ ♣ cc

Gables Guest House, *6 Cumnor Hill, Oxford, Oxfordshire, OX2 9HA.* Award winning detached house with beautiful garden. Close to city. **Open:** All year (not Xmas)
01865 862153 Mrs Tompkins **Fax: 01865 864054** *stay@gables-oxford.co.uk*
www.oxfordcity.co.uk/accom/gables
D: £22.00 **S:** £26.00 **Beds:** 2S 2D 2T **Baths:** 6 En 🛁 🅿 (6) 🌣 🖾 🖾 🌣 ♣

Pine Castle Hotel, *290 Iffley Road, Oxford, OX4 4AE.* Close to shops, launderette, post office. Frequent buses. River walks nearby. **Open:** All year (not Xmas)
01865 241497 & 01865 728887 Mrs Trkulja
Fax: 01685 727230 *stay@pinecastle.co.uk*
D: £32.50–£37.00 **S:** £55.00–£60.00 **Beds:** 1F 5D 2T **Baths:** 8 En 🛁 🅿 (4) 🖾 🖾 🖾 🌣

RATES
D = Price range per person sharing in a double or twin room

S = Price range for a single room

Peppard
SU7081

Pennyford House, *Peppard, Henley-on-Thames, Oxon, RG9 5JE.* Family home with dogs. Happy atmosphere. Nice garden. Local interests. **Open:** All year
01491 628272 (also fax) Mrs Howden-Ferme **D:** £25.00–£35.00 **S:** £30.00–£35.00 **Beds:** 1T 3D 1S **Baths:** 4 En 1 Pr ▣ (10) ⅍ 🗹 🛏 🖳 ♨

Slaters Farm, *Peppard, Henley-on-Thames, Oxon, RG9 5JL.* Quiet, friendly country house with lovely garden and tennis court. **Open:** All year (not Xmas)
01491 628675 (also fax) Mrs Howden **D:** £24.00 **S:** £28.00 **Beds:** 1D 2T **Baths:** 1 Pr 1 Sh ᗌ ▣ (6) ⅍ 🗹 ✕ 🗹 🖳

Pishill
SU7289

Bank Farm, *Pishill, Henley-on-Thames, Oxon, RG9 6HS.* Quiet comfortable farmhouse, beautiful countryside. Convenient Oxford, London, Windsor. **Open:** All year (not Xmas) **Grades:** ETC 2 Diamond
01491 638601 Mrs Lakey *bankfarm@btinternet.com* **D:** £24.00 **S:** £20.00–£24.00 **Beds:** 1F 1D **Baths:** 1 En 1 Sh ᗌ ▣ (5) ⅍ 🗹 🛏 🖳 ♨

Orchard House, *Pishill, Henley-on-Thames, Oxfordshire, RG9 6HJ.* Quiet, comfortable house, large grounds, in Chilterns. Surrounded by woodland. **Open:** All year (not Xmas/New Year) **Grades:** ETC 3 Diamond
01491 638351 (also fax) Mrs Connolly **D:** £25.00 **S:** £30.00 **Beds:** 2F 1D 1T **Baths:** 3 En 1 Pr ᗌ ▣ (10) ⅍ 🗹 🛏 ✕ 🖳 ♨

Radley
SU5298

Hollies, *8 New Road, Radley, Abingdon, Oxon, OX14 3AP.* Rural small and friendly family B&B, convenient for all attractions. **Open:** All year
01235 529552 D: £25.00 **S:** £25.00 **Beds:** 2T **Baths:** 1 Sh ᗌ ▣ ⅍ 🗹 🛏 ✕ 🗹 🖳 ♨

Salford
SP2828   🍷 *Red Lion*

1 Lower Barns, *Salford, Chipping Norton, Oxon, OX7 5YP.* Traditionally furnished, well situated for Cotswolds, Oxford, Stratford. Homely welcome. **Open:** All year (not Xmas/New Year)
01608 643276 Mrs Barnard **D:** £16.00–£17.00 **S:** £16.00–£17.00 **Beds:** 1T **Baths:** 1 En ᗌ ▣ (2) 🛏 🖳 ♨

Shenington
SP3742

Top Farm House, *Shenington, Banbury, Oxfordshire, OX15 6LZ.* C17th Hornton stone farmhouse set on the edge of village green. **Open:** All year (not Xmas/New Year)
01295 670226 Fax: 01295 678170 *m.coles2@ntlworld.com* www.topfarmhouse.co.uk **D:** £20.00–£25.00 **S:** £25.00–£30.00 **Beds:** 1T 2D **Baths:** 1 En 1 Sh ᗌ ▣ (4) ⅍ 🗹 🖳 ♨

Shipton-under-Wychwood
SP2717

Garden Cottage, *Fiddlers Hill, Shipton-under-Wychwood, Chipping Norton, Oxon, OX7 6DR.* Attractive stone cottage, country views, quiet, ideal for exploring Cotswolds. **Open:** All year (not Xmas)
01993 830640 C Worker **D:** £15.00–£25.00 **S:** £25.00–£35.00 **Beds:** 1D 1T **Baths:** 2 En ᗌ (8) ▣ (2) ⅍ 🗹 🖳 ♨

Souldern
SP5231   🍷 *Fox Inn*

The Fox Inn, *Souldern, Bicester, Oxon, OX6 9JN.* Stone inn, beautiful village convenient for Oxford, Woodstock, Stratford and Warwick. Bar/restaurant. **Open:** All year (not Xmas)
01869 345284 Mr MacKay **Fax:** 01869 345667 **D:** £22.50–£27.50 **S:** £32.00–£38.00 **Beds:** 3D 1T **Baths:** 2 En 1 Sh ᗌ ▣ (6) 🗹 🛏 ✕ 🗹 🖳 ♨ cc

Towerfields, *Tusmore Road, Souldern, Bicester, Oxon, OX6 9HY.* Comfortable ensuite rooms, easy access to Oxford and Stratford. Beautiful views. **Open:** All year **Grades:** ETC 3 Diamond
01869 346554 C Hamilton Gould **Fax:** 01869 345157 *hgould@souldern.powernet.co.uk* **D:** £26.00–£28.00 **S:** £30.00–£32.00 **Beds:** 1F 1T 1D 1S **Baths:** 4 En ᗌ (10) ▣ (20) ⅍ 🗹 🛏 🖳 ♿ ♨

National Grid References given are for villages, towns and cities – not for individual houses

Southcoombe
SP3327   🍷 *Blue Boar*

Southcoombe Lodge Guest House, *Southcoombe, Chipping Norton, Oxon, OX7 5QH.* Southcombe Lodge - next door to Chipping Norton golf club **Open:** All year **Grades:** ETC 3 Diamond
01608 643068 Mrs Findlay **D:** £23.00–£26.00 **S:** £26.00–£35.00 **Beds:** 1F 2T 3D **Baths:** 4 En 2 Sh ᗌ ▣ (10) ⅍ 🗹 🗹 🖳 ♨

Sparsholt
SU3487   🍷 *The Star Inn*

Westcot Lodge, *Westcot, Sparsholt, Wantage, Oxon, OX12 9QA.* Comfortable country house. Peaceful hamlet. Magnificent views to Ridgeway, one mile. **Open:** All year (not Xmas/New Year)
01235 751251 Mrs Upton **D:** £30.00 **S:** £30.00 **Beds:** 1T 1D 1S **Baths:** 1 Pr 1 Sh ᗌ ▣ (2) ⅍ 🗹 🗹 🖳 ♨

Steventon
SU4691

Tethers End, *Abingdon Road, Steventon, Abingdon, Oxon, OX13 6RW.* **Open:** All year
01235 834015 Ms Miller **Fax:** 01235 862990 *peterdmiller@btinternet.com* **D:** £22.00–£25.00 **S:** £25.00–£28.00 **Beds:** 1F 1D **Baths:** 2 En ᗌ ▣ ⅍ 🗹 🗹 🖳 ♨

Comfortable ground floor accommodation, situated on the edge of a peaceful village green. Ideally placed for visiting Oxford, Abingdon, Wantage, historic Ridgeway, Blenheim Palace and Didcot Railway Centre. Caroline and Peter Miller offer you a warm welcome.

Stratton Audley
SP6026   🍷 *Red Lion*

West Farm, *Stratton Audley, Bicester, Oxfordshire, OX6 9BW.* **Open:** All year **Grades:** ETC 4 Diamond
01869 278344 (also fax) Ms Howson *sara.westfarmbb@vigin.net* www.westfarmbb.co.uk **D:** £25.00–£30.00 **S:** £25.00–£30.00 **Beds:** 1T 1D **Baths:** 2 Pr ᗌ ▣ (7) ⅍ 🗹 🛏 ✕ 🖳 ♨

C17th farmhouse offering a high standard of accommodation situated in an attractive peaceful village. Convenient base for Bicester village, Silverstone, Oxford and the Cotswolds. Good local pub offering great food and even better wine!

Planning a longer stay? Always ask for any special rates

The Old School, *Stratton Audley, Bicester, Oxon, OX6 9BJ.* Interesting C17th house in pretty village. Pleasant garden with tennis court and croquet. **Open:** All year **Grades:** ETC 3 Diamond **01869 277371** Mrs Wertheimer *sawertheimer@ euphony.com* www.old-school.co.uk **D:** £30.00– £35.00 **S:** £30.00–£35.00 **Beds:** 3T 1S **Baths:** 2 Sh ♦ ♦ (6) 📺 ♦ 📺 🍴

Sutton Courtenay
SU5093

Bekynton House, *7 The Green, Sutton Courtenay, Abingdon, Oxon, OX14 4AE.* Courthouse overlooking village green. Thames and 3 pubs - 5 minutes. **Open:** All year (not Xmas) **01235 848630 & 01235 848888** Ms Cornwall **Fax: 01235 848436** *suecornwall@aol.com* **D:** £28.00 **S:** £28.00 **Beds:** 1D 2T 1S **Baths:** 2 Sh ♦ ♦ 📺 📺 🍴

Tetsworth
SP6802

Little Acre, *4 High Street, Tetsworth, Thame, Oxon, OX7 7AT.* Warm welcome-every comfort. Near Chilterns, Oxford, Cotswolds, Heathrow Airport **Open:** All year **01844 281423 (also fax)** Ms Tanner **D:** £18.00–£22.50 **S:** £25.00–£35.00 **Beds:** 1F 2D 2T **Baths:** 3 En 2 Sh ♦ ♦ (5) 📺 ♦ 🍴 ♦ ♦

Thame
SP7005

Vine Cottage, *Moreton, Thame, Oxon, OX9 2HX.* Novelist's enchanting thatched cottage in tranquil hamlet. Perfect touring base. **Open:** All year (not Xmas/New Year) **01844 216910** Ms Blumenthal **D:** £23.00– £26.00 **S:** £26.00 **Beds:** 1D 1S **Baths:** 1 Sh ♦ (10) 📺 (4) ♦ 📺 🍴 ♦

Oakfield, *Thame Park Road, Thame, Oxon, OX9 3PL.* Lovely farmhouse home, 25 acres grounds - part of larger 400-acre mixed farm. **Open:** All year (not Xmas) **01844 213709 & 07785 764447 (M) D:** £20.00– £25.00 **S:** £27.50 **Beds:** 1D 2T **Baths:** 1 En 1 Sh ♦ (8) 📺 (6) ♦ 📺 ♦ 🍴 ♦ ♦

Tiddington
SP6504

Albury Farm, *Draycott, Tiddington, Thame, Oxon, OX9 2LX.* Peaceful open views in quiet location, clean, tidy, friendly. **Open:** All year **01844 339848 (also fax)** Mrs Ilbery **D:** £20.00 **S:** £20.00 **Beds:** 1D 1T **Baths:** 1 Pr 1 Sh 📺 (4) ♦ 📺 ✕ 📺 🍴 ♦

Uffington
SU3089

Norton House, *Broad Street, Uffington, Faringdon, Oxon, SN7 7RA.* Friendly C18th family home in centre of quiet, pretty village. **Open:** All year (not Xmas) **01367 820230 (also fax)** Mrs Oberman *106436.145@compuserve.com* **D:** £20.00– £21.00 **S:** £23.00–£26.00 **Beds:** 1F 1D 1S **Baths:** 2 Pr ♦ 📺 (3) ♦ 📺 ♦ 📺 🍴 ♦

Wallingford
SU6089   🍺 *Six Bells*

Little Gables, *166 Crowmarsh Hill, Wallingford, Oxford, OX10 8BG.* Delightfully large private house where a warm welcome awaits you. **Open:** All year **Grades:** ETC 3 Diamond **01491 837834** Mrs Reeves **Fax: 01491 834426** *jill@stayingaway.com* www.stayingaway. com **D:** £25.00–£35.00 **S:** £35.00–£40.00 **Beds:** 2F 2D 3T 1S **Baths:** 2 En 1 Pr ♦ 📺 ♦ 📺 📺 🍴 ♦ ♦

52 Blackstone Road, *Wallingford, Oxon, OX10 8JL.* Small friendly house, 1/2 mile from R.Thames. 10 min walk from town. **Open:** All year (not Xmas/New Year) **01491 201917** Mrs Barnard *enid.barnard@ ebarnard.fsnet.co.uk* **D:** £20.00–£35.00 **S:** £17.50 **Beds:** 1D 1S 📺 (1) 📺 ♦

North Farm, *Shillingford Hill, Wallingford, Oxon, OX10 8NB.* Generous farmhouse breakfast after a peaceful night. Explore Oxfordshire countryside. **Open:** All year (not Xmas/New Year) **01865 858406** Mrs Warburton **Fax: 01865 858519** *northfarm@compuserve.com* www.country-accom.co.uk/north-farm **D:** £25.00–£30.00 **S:** £30.00–£45.00 **Beds:** 1T 2D **Baths:** 1 En 2 Pr ♦ (10) 📺 (6) ♦ 📺 📺 🍴 ♦

Wantage
SU4087

The Bell Inn, *38 Market Place, Wantage, Oxon, OX12 8AH.* C16th market town inn serving good food in a warm and friendly atmosphere. **Open:** All year **01235 763718 (also fax)** Mrs Williams **D:** £25.00–£35.00 **S:** £45.00–£55.00 **Beds:** 7F 2T 2D 5S **Baths:** 10 En ♦ 📺 ♦ ✕ 📺 🍴 ♦

Waterperry
SP6205

Holbeach, *Worminghall Road, Waterperry, Oxford, OX33 1LF.* Private country home, good food, comfortable beds and friendly service. **Open:** All year (not Xmas) **01844 339623 D:** £20.00 **S:** £20.00–£25.00 **Beds:** 1F 2D 1S **Baths:** 1 En 1 Pr 1 Sh ♦ 📺 (6) 📺 🍴 ✕ 📺 🍴 ♦

Watlington
SU6894

Woodgate Orchard Cottage, *Howe Road, Watlington, Oxon, OX9 5EL.* Warm welcome, countryside location, comfortable rooms, home-cooking, restful gardens, red kites gliding above. **Open:** All year **01491 612675 (also fax)** R Roberts *mailbox@ wochr.freeserve.co.uk* **D:** £25.00–£35.00 **S:** £30.00 **Beds:** 1F 1T 1D **Baths:** 1 En 1 Pr ♦ 📺 (8) ♦ 📺 ✕ 📺 🍴 ♦

Witney
SP3509   🍺 *Three Horseshoes*

Springhill Farm, *Cogges, Witney, Oxon, OX8 6UL.* **Open:** All year (not Xmas/New Year)

Grades: ETC 3 Diamond **01993 704919** Mrs Strainge **D:** £20.00–£22.50 **S:** £20.00–£25.00 **Beds:** 1F 1D 1T **Baths:** 3 En ♦ (4) ♦ 📺 📺 🍴 ♦ Working farm overlooking the Windrush Valley. We offer a warm welcome in our old Cotswold stone farmhouse, with lovely views from comfortable ensuite rooms. Ensuite disabled friendly twin/double room available from April 2002, good centre for Oxford, Cotswolds, Blenheim.

The Witney Hotel, *7 Church Green, Witney, Oxon, OX8 6AZ.* Family-run B&B, Listed building overlooking historic Church Green, few mins' walk local amenities. **Open:** All year (not Xmas/New Year) **01993 702137** Mrs McDermott **Fax: 01993 705337** *reservations@thewitneyhotel.co.uk* **D:** £52.00 **S:** £30.00–£36.00 **Beds:** 2F 5D 2T 1S **Baths:** 10 En ♦ 📺 📺 🍴 ♦ ♦ **cc**

Windrush House, *55 Crawley Road, Witney, Oxon, OX28 1HX.* Comfortable home with indoor pool, ideally situated for the Cotswolds. **Open:** All year **01993 774454** Mr & Mrs Curtis **Fax: 01993 709877** *heraldic@compuserve.com* www.simplybedandbreakfast.com/windrush **D:** £25.00–£26.00 **S:** £28.00–£32.00 **Beds:** 1D 1T **Baths:** 2 Pr 📺 (6) ♦ 📺 🍴 ♦

BATHROOMS
En = Ensuite
Pr = Private
Sh = Shared

Quarrydene, *Dene Rise, Witney, Oxon,*
OX8 5LU. Friendly B&B, quiet location, only a
few minutes walk from town centre.
Open: All year (not Xmas/New Year)
01993 772152 & 07850 054786 (M)
Mrs Marshall **Fax: 01993 772152**
jeanniemarshall@quarrydene.fsworld.co.uk
www.fsworld.co.uk **D:** £25.00 **S:** £25.00–
£30.00 **Beds:** 1T 1D 2S **Baths:** 1 En 2 Sh ▣(2)
⊬✕▦♨

Woodcote
SU6481

The Hedges, *South Stoke Road,*
Woodcote, Reading, Berks, RG8 0PL. Peaceful,
rural situation, historic Area of Outstanding
Natural Beauty. **Open:** All year (not Xmas)
Grades: ETC 3 Diamond
01491 680461 Mrs Howard-Allen **D:** £17.00–
£19.00 **S:** £17.00–£19.00 **Beds:** 2T 2S
Baths: 1 Pr 1 Sh ⊱▣(4) 🖵🛏▦♨

Woodstock
SP4416

The Lawns, *2 Flemings Road, Woodstock,*
Oxon, OX20 1NA. **Open:** All year **Grades:** ETC
2 Diamond
01993 812599 (also fax) Mr & Mrs Farrant
thelawns@amserve.net **D:** £19.00–£20.00
S: £25.00–£30.00 **Beds:** 1F 1T 1D 1S
Baths: 1 Pr 1 Sh ⊱▣⊬🖵🛏▦♨cc
Lovely homely accommodation. All guests
welcomed as family. Attractive garden
surroundings, real old English (eccentric)
welcome. Just see the garden items
(unusual). 5 minutes walk to town centre
and Blenheim Palace Gates - probably one
of the best (value for money) B&B
accommodation in England. Free car
wash+laundry+taxi-cab collection service.

RATES

D = Price range per person
sharing in a double or twin
room
S = Price range for a single
room

Planning a longer stay? Always
ask for any special rates

The Townhouse, *16 High Street,*
Woodstock, Oxon, OX20 1TE. Listed building,
centrally located. Ideal for Blenheim
Palace, Oxford, Cotswolds. **Open:** All year
Grades: ETC 4 Diamond
01993 810843 (also fax) Ms Edsor *info@*
woodstock-townhouse.com
www.woodstock-townhouse.com **D:** £32.50–
£37.50 **S:** £45.00–£50.00 **Beds:** 1F 1T 3D
Baths: 5 En ⊱⊬🖵Ⓥ▦♨cc

Elbie House,
East End, North
Leigh, Witney,
Oxon, OX8 6PZ.
C16th home,
edge of
Cotswolds close
to Blenheim Palace. Banquet Breakfast!
Open: All year **Grades:** ETC 4 Diamond,
Silver
01993 880166 Mrs Buck *buck@*
elbiehouse.freeserve.co.uk **D:** £25.00–£27.50
S: £30.00–£38.00 **Beds:** 2F **Baths:** 2 En ⊱(7)
▣(10) ⊬🖵Ⓥ▦♨

Plane Tree
House B&B,
48 Oxford Street,
Woodstock,
Oxon, OX20 1TT.
Open: All year
(not Xmas)
Grades: ETC 4
Diamond, Silver
01993 813075
Mrs Clark
D: £25.00–£35.00 **S:** £45.00–£70.00 **Beds:** 2D
1T **Baths:** 2 En 1 Pr ⊱⊬🖵Ⓥ▦♨
A recently renovated Listed Cotswold stone
house with exposed beams and open fires
in Woodstock's historic town centre. Only
minutes walk from Blenheim Palace and
excellent shops and restaurants. An ideal
base for touring Oxford and the Cotswolds.

Gorselands
Hall,
Boddington
Lane, North
Leigh, Witney,
Oxon, OX29 6PU.
Open: All year
Grades: ETC 4 Diamond, RAC 4 Diamond
01993 882292 Mr & Mrs Hamilton **Fax: 01993**
883629 *hamilton@gorselandshall.com*
www.gorselandshall.com **D:** £22.50–£25.00
S: £30.00–£35.00 **Beds:** 4D 1T 1F **Baths:** 6
En ⊱▣(6) ⊬🖵🛏▦♨cc
Lovely old Cotswold stone farmhouse with
oak beams and flagstone floors in
delightful rural setting. Large garden with
tennis-court. Ideal for Blenheim Palace,
Cotswolds and Oxford. Comfortable,
attractively furnished bedrooms (one
ground-floor) with views of the garden or
surrounding countryside.

Hamilton House, *43 Hill Rise, Old*
Woodstock, Woodstock, Oxon, OX20 1AB.
Open: All year
01993 812206 & 07778 705568 (M)
Mrs Bradford **Fax: 01993 812206**
www.smoothhound.co.
uk/hotels/hamiltonh.html **D:** £22.00–
£25.00 **S:** £30.00–£35.00 **Beds:** 1T 2D
Baths: 3 En ⊱▣🖵Ⓥ▦♨cc
Very widely acclaimed B&B. Offering
unbeatable standards of cleanliness,
service and hospitality. Almost every
amenity available. Excellent location for
beginning and ending your tour. Constantly
revisited due unquestionably to the
helpfulness and friendliness of Kay - your
hostess.

Woolstone
SU2988

Hickory
House,
Woolstone,
Faringdon, Oxon,
SN7 7QL.
Open: All year
(not Xmas)
01367 820303 Mr & Mrs Grist **Fax: 01367**
820958 *rlg@hickoryhouse.freeserve.co.uk*
D: £19.00–£25.00 **S:** £21.00–£25.00 **Beds:** 2T
Baths: 2 En ▣(2) ⊬🖵▦♨
Situated in a delightful village beneath the
White Horse Hill near the Ridgeway,
Hickory House offers comfortable,
spacious accommodation in a recently built
self-contained extension. Pub serving food
is a minutes walk. Oxford, Bath and the
Cotswolds are within easy driving distance.

Wootton (Woodstock)
SP4319 ⚜ *Killingworth Castle*

8 Manor Court, *Wootton, Woodstock,*
Oxon, OX20 1EU. Ideal centre for exploring
Cotswolds and Oxford. Friendly village
home. **Open:** All year (not Xmas/New Year)
01993 811186 Mrs Fletcher **D:** £20.00
S: £20.00 **Beds:** 1T 1S ⊱(12)▣(2)⊬🖵Ⓥ▦
♨

Yarnton
SP4712

Kings Bridge Guest House,
Woodstock Road, Yarnton, Kidlington, Oxon,
OX5 1PH. Ideally situated for Oxford and
Blenheim Palace in Woodstock. **Open:** All
year (not Xmas/New Year)
01865 841748 Ms Shaw **Fax: 01865 370215**
kings.bridge@talk21.com **D:** £22.50–£30.00
S: £35.00–£50.00 **Beds:** 1F 2D 1T **Baths:** 4
En ⊱▣(6) ⊬🖵▦♨cc

Independent Holiday Cottages 2002

The Essential Guide to Independent Holiday Cottages

1,500 colour pictures

Did you know that you can rent a first-class holiday property without paying an inflated agency price? You can when you choose an independent holiday cottage. By booking direct with the owner, you cut out the middle man and save money! Up to one third off the price of comparable, agency-managed properties.

Stilwell's Independent Holiday Cottages 2002 contains detailed listings of over 5,000 first-class independent holiday properties throughout Britain and Ireland, arranged by country, county and location. Each entry includes weekly rates, sleeping capacities, Tourist Board grades, local maps, a description of the cottage and its surroundings and whether or not 'short breaks' are accepted. Stilwell's has a quick-reference location index and lists of properties with swimming pools and sleeping capacities of 10 or more.

Whether you're looking for a quiet and cosy cottage for two or for accommodation for an adventurous party of 20, **Stilwell's Independent Holiday Cottages 2002** is the directory for you.

**Cottages • Apartments • Houses
Bungalows • Chalets • Long Lets
Short Breaks**

For a free copy, telephone

01271 336028

**Clear local maps
All official grades shown
Pubs serving hot evening meals shown
Over 1,500 colour photos
Quick-reference Location Index
List of properties with swimming pools
List of properties sleeping over 10 persons
List of No Smoking properties**

Rutland

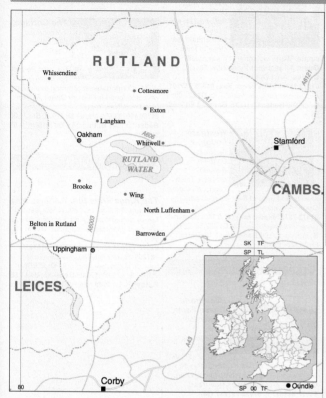

Belton in Rutland

SK8101 🍺 Bewicke Arms, Plough, White Hart, The Vaults, Coach & Horses, The Cuckoo

The Old Rectory, 4 New Road, Belton in Rutland, Oakham, Rutland, LE15 9LE. **Open:** All year
Grades: RAC 3 Diamond
01572 717279 Mr Peach *bb@iepuk.com*
www.rutnet.co.uk/orb **D:** £20.00–£25.00
S: £25.00–£35.00 **Beds:** 1F 2D 3T 1S
Baths: 4 En 1 Sh 🛏 🅿 (10) 🗲 🗹 🏠 🛏 ♨ cc
Large country house and guest annexe in conservation village overlooking Eyebrook valley and rolling Rutland countryside. Comfortable/ varied selection of rooms, mostly ensuite, direct outside access. Real farmhouse or continental breakfast. Public house 100 yds. 10 minutes Rutland Water.

Brooke

SK8505

The Old Rectory, Brooke, Oakham, Rutland, LE15 8DE. Stone thatched cottage in quiet hamlet. Large garden, good walking area. **Open:** All year
01572 770558 (also fax) Mrs Clemence
D: £20.00–£25.00 **S:** £20.00–£25.00 **Beds:** 1F 1T 1S **Baths:** 3 En 🛏 🅿 (6) 🗲 🏠 🏚 ♨

Cottesmore

SK9013

The Tithe Barn, Clatterpot Lane, Cottesmore, Oakham, Rutland, LE15 7DW. Comfortable, spacious, ensuite rooms with a wealth of original features. **Open:** All year
01572 813591 D: £18.00–£24.00 **S:** £20.00–£35.00 **Beds:** 2F 1D 1T **Baths:** 3 En 1 Pr 🛏 (1) 🅿 (6) 🗲 🗹 🏠 🏚 ❄ ♨ cc

Exton

SK9211

Fox & Hounds, Exton, Oakham, Rutland, LE15 8AP. Country inn overlooking village green. 2 miles Rutland Water, half mile Bransdale Gardens. **Open:** All year (not Xmas/New Year)
01572 812403 D Hillier **D:** £20.00–£22.00 **S:** £22.00–£24.00 **Beds:** 1D 1T 1S 🅿 (20) 🏠 ✕ 🗹 🏚

Hall Farm, Cottesmore Road, Exton, Oakham, Rutland, LE15 8AN. Close to Rutland Water and Geoff Hamilton's Barnsdale TV gardens. **Open:** All year (not Xmas)
01572 812271 Mr & Mrs Williamson
D: £17.50–£22.00 **S:** £20.00–£24.50 **Beds:** 1F 1D 1T **Baths:** 1 En 2 Sh 🛏 🅿 (6) 🗲 🗹 🏠 🏚 ♨

Barrowden

SK9500

Exeter Arms, Barrowden, Oakham, Rutland, LE15 8EQ. C17th village inn with C21st accommodation, overlooking Welland Valley. **Open:** All year (not Xmas/New Year)
01572 747247 Mr & Mrs Blencowe **Fax:** **info@exeterarms.co.uk** www.exeterarms.co.uk **D:** £25.00–£35.00 **S:** £30.00–£35.00
Beds: 2T 1D **Baths:** 3 En 🅿 🗲 🗹 ✕ 🏚 ♨ cc

Ashleigh House, 2 Wakerley Road, Barrowden, Oakham, Rutland, LE15 8EP. Stunning views of Welland Valley, Rockingham Forest. Barrowden is a beautiful Rutland village. **Open:** All year (not Xmas/New Year)
01572 747398 Mrs Kennedy **Fax:** 01572 747117 *ashleighhouse@cwcom.net* **D:** £18.50–£25.00 **S:** £20.00–£35.00 **Beds:** 1T 2D
Baths: 1 En 1 Pr 1 Sh 🛏 🅿 (4) 🗲 🗹 🏠 🏚 ♨

31 Wakerley Road, Barrowden, Oakham, Rutland, LE15 8EP. Rutland Water, Welland Valley. Bungalow, garden, attractive conservation village. **Open:** All year (not Xmas/New Year)
01572 747455 Mr & Mrs Hennessy **D:** £18.00–£20.00 **S:** £18.00–£28.00 **Beds:** 1F 1T 1D 1S **Baths:** 1 En 1 Sh 🛏 🅿 (8) 🗲 🗹 🏠 🗹 🏚 ♿ ♨

RATES

D = Price range per person sharing in a double or twin room

S = Price range for a single room

Langham

SK8410

Keighwood House, *The Range, Langham, Oakham, Rutland, LE15 7EB.* Large, modern, detached house. 0.33 acre nature and gardens, picturesque village. **Open:** All year (not Xmas)
01572 755924 Mr McMorran **D:** £25.00
S: £25.00 **Beds:** 1D 1T 2S **Baths:** 1 Sh ▣ (3)
⚞ 📺 ▥ 🕭

North Luffenham

SK9303   ⚓ *Horse & Panniers*

Pinfold House, *6 Pinfold Lane, North Luffenham, Oakham, Rutland, LE15 8LE.* C18th cottage with large garden, attractive village near Rutland Water. **Open:** All year (not Xmas/New Year)
01780 720175 Mrs Cook *dcook@fish.co.uk*
D: £16.00–£17.00 **S:** £20.00 **Beds:** 1T 2D ⚞ ▣
⚞ 📺 ▣ ▥ 🕭

Oakham

SK8508   ⚓ *Horseshoe, Sun Inn*

Angel House, *20 Northgate, Oakham, Rutland, LE15 6QS.* Unique Victorian house. Converted outbuildings. Secluded courtyard. Lounge, patio, fridge/freezer, microwave. **Open:** All year
01572 756153 Mrs Weight **D:** £11.00–£17.00
S: £22.00–£34.00 **Beds:** 1D 2T **Baths:** 3 En
⚞ ▣ 📺 ▣ 🕭

Dial House, *18 Uppingham Road, Oakham, LE15 6JD.* **Open:** All year (not Xmas/New Year)
01572 771685
Mrs Davis *virginia@ oakham2000.freeserve.co.uk* **D:** £22.50–£25.00
S: £25.00–£35.00 **Beds:** 2T 1D 1S **Baths:** 4
En ⚞ ▣ (4) ⚞ 📺 ⚓ ✕ ▣ ▥.
Traditional English home, within walking distance of attractive and historic town centre. Rutland Water is nearby, offering bird watching, cycling, fishing and woodland walks, short drives take you to beautiful stately homes and gardens. Good local pubs and restaurants.

Kirkee House, *35 Welland Way, Oakham, Rutland, LE15 6SL.* In quiet residential area close to town centre. Warm welcome is guaranteed.
Open: All year (not Xmas/New Year)
Grades: AA 4 Diamond
01572 757401 Mrs Beech **Fax: 01572 757301**
carolbeech@kirkeehouse.demon.co.uk **D:** £22.00
S: £22.00 **Beds:** 1T 1D 1S **Baths:** 3 En ⚞ 📺
▥, 🕭

Westgate Lodge, *9 Westgate, Oakham, Rutland, LE15 6BH.* Town centre, all rooms ensuite and ground floor off-road parking.
Open: All year (not Xmas/New Year)
01572 757370 (also fax) Mr & Mrs Garwood
westgatelodge@gofornet.co.uk **D:** £22.50–£25.00
S: £35.00–£50.00 **Beds:** 1F 1T 1D **Baths:** 3
En ⚞ ▣ ⚞ 📺 ▥, 🕭 🕭

Uppingham

SP8699   ⚓ *The Vaults*

Beaumont Chase Farm, *Stockerston Road, Uppingham, Oakham, Rutland, LE15 9HJ.*
Old farmhouse in beautiful countryside. Good walking, birdwatching and cycling.
Open: All year (not Xmas/New Year)
01572 823677 & 07980 567237 (M)
Mrs Nourish *beaumontchase@farming.co.uk*
D: £21.00–£24.00 **S:** £25.00–£30.00 **Beds:** 1F 1D **Baths:** 2 En ⚞ (2) ▣ (4) ⚞ 📺 ▥, 🕭

Boundary Farm B&B, *Glaston Road, Uppingham, Oakham, Rutland, LE15 9PX.*
Modern farmhouse in countryside. 5 mins easy walk into Uppingham. **Open:** Easter to Dec **Grades:** ETC 4 Diamond
01572 822354 (also fax) Mrs Scott **D:** £21.00
S: £22.00 **Beds:** 1T 1D **Baths:** 2 En ⚞ ▣ (3)
⚞ 📺 ▥, 🕭

Whitwell

SK9208

The Cottage, *9 Main Road, Whitwell, Oakham, Rutland, LE15 8BW.* Perfect for Rutland Water. Comfortable accommodation, warm welcome, good breakfast. **Open:** All year (not Xmas/New Year)
01780 460793 Mrs Maher **D:** £20.00 **S:** £24.00
Beds: 1D 1D/T **Baths:** 2 En ⚞ (10) ▣ (6) ⚞ 📺
▣ ▥,

Wing

SK8903

The Kings Arms Inn, *Top Street, Wing, Oakham, Rutland, LE15 8SE.* A 350-year-old family owned country inn. Peaceful village, plenty of character throughout. **Open:** All year
01572 737634 Mr Hornsey **Fax: 01572 737255** *enquiries@thekingsarms-wing.co.uk*
www.thekingsarms-wing.co.uk **D:** £25.00–£50.00 **S:** £35.00–£70.00 **Beds:** 4F 4D 4T 8S
Baths: 20 En ⚞ (40) ⚞ 📺 ✕ ▣ ▥, ✳ 🕭 cc

Britain & Ireland Hostels & Camping 2002

The essential guide to good-value and group accommodation in Britain & Ireland
With colour maps & pictures

It's the secret all budget travellers know: if you're travelling on a shoestring, organising sleeping arrangements for a party of 20 or just escaping to the great outdoors, hostels and camping sites can provide the ideal solution to your accommodation needs.

Stilwell's Britain & Ireland: Hostels & Camping 2002 is the only directory to list hostels, camping sites, bunkhouses and camping barns together in one easy-to-carry book. With over 3,500 entries arranged by country, county and location, it's perfect for finding the right accommodation at the right price in city, town, countryside or seaside. Each entry includes rates, facilities, official grades, local maps and a description of the venue and its surroundings.

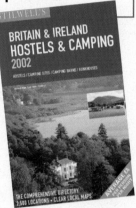

If you're travelling on a limited budget, alone or in a group, **Stilwell's Britain & Ireland: Hostels & Camping 2002** is the book for you.

Hostels • Camping Sites • Bunkhouses • Camping Barns City • Town • Countryside • Seaside

£6.95 from all good bookstores (ISBN 1-900861-20-8) or £7.95 (inc p&p) from Stilwell Publishing, 59 Charlotte Road, London EC2A 3QW (020 7739 7179)

Over 3,500 entries

Average price £8 per person per night

Official grades shown

Local maps

Quick-reference location index

Handy size for easy packing

Shropshire

RATES

D = Price range per person sharing in a double or twin room

S = Price range for a single room

Abdon

SO5786

Earnstrey Hill House, Abdon, Craven Arms, Shropshire, SY7 9HU. **Open:** All year (not Xmas) **Grades:** ETC 4 Diamond 01746 712579 Mrs Scurfield **Fax:** 01746 712631 **D:** £25.00 **S:** £20.00 **Beds:** 1D 2T **Baths:** 1 En 2 Sh ⌨ 🅿 ⊬ ✕ 🛏️ 🖳 ⚓ Comfortable, warm, spacious family house 1200 ft up Brown Clee Hill. Superb views westwards towards Long Mynd and Wales. We keep horses, sheep, dogs, free-range hens on our 11 acres. Wonderful walking and riding. Experienced walking hosts will help plan/guide.

Acton Scott

SO4589   🍺 *Station Inn, Plough Inn*

Acton Scott Farm, Acton Scott, Church Stretton, Shropshire, SY6 6QN. Lovely C17th farmhouse in peaceful hamlet. Good walking area. **Open:** Mar to Oct **Grades:** ETC 3 Diamond 01694 781260 Mrs Jones **D:** £19.00–£22.00 **S:** £20.00–£40.00 **Beds:** 1F 1T 1D **Baths:** 2 En 1 Pr 🅿 (6) ⊬ 🛏️ ✕ 🖳 ⚓

All Stretton

SO4595

Stretton Hall Hotel, All Stretton, Church Stretton, Shropshire, SY6 6HG. Outstanding country manor hotel. Warm, comfortable and excellent value. **Open:** All year 01694 723224 Mr & Mrs Parry *enquiries@ strettonhall.co.uk* www.strettonhall.co.uk **D:** £30.00–£55.00 **S:** £40.00–£65.00 **Beds:** 1F 1T 9D 1S **Baths:** 12 En ⌨ 🅿 (50) 📺 🛏️ ✕ 🖳 ⚓ cc

BATHROOMS

En = Ensuite
Pr = Private
Sh = Shared

Alveley

SO7684   🍺 *Red Lion, Royal Oak*

Arnside, Kidderminster Road, Alveley, Bridgnorth, Shropshire, WV15 6LL. **Open:** All year (not Xmas) **Grades:** ETC 4 Diamond, Silver 01746 780007 (also fax) Mr Haynes *arnside@ ptah.freeserve.co.uk* www.virtual-shropshire.co. uk/arnside **D:** £20.00–£35.00 **S:** £30.00– £35.00 **Beds:** 1F 1T 1D **Baths:** 3 En ⌨ 🅿 (6) ⊬ 📺 🖳 ⚓ Luxurious bungalow in acre of lawned gardens. Beautifully furnished ensuite rooms. Pubs/shops in walking distance. Perfectly situated for visiting historic Bridgnorth, Ironbridge, Shrewsbury and exploring rural delights of Shropshire and Worcestershire. Convenient for Kidderminster, Worcester and Black Country.

Aston on Clun

SO3881

Millstream Cottage, Aston on Clun, Craven Arms, Shropshire, SY7 8EP. Grade II Listed cottage, 6 acres private fields/ woodland. Comfortable beds, good breakfast. AONB. **Open:** All year 01588 660699 & 07977 922572 (M) Miss Reeves **D:** £24.00–£26.00 **S:** £24.00– £26.00 **Beds:** 1D 1T **Baths:** 1 Sh ⌨ 🅿 (2) 📺 🛏️ 🖳 ⚓

Bishop's Castle

SO3288   🍺 *Three Tuns, Castle Hotel, Boar's Head, Kings Head*

Lower Broughton Farm, Bishop's Castle, Shropshire, SY15 6SZ. Originally a medieval hall house, now a spacious and comfortable farmhouse. **Open:** Feb to Dec **Grades:** ETC 3 Diamond 01588 638393 Mr & Mrs Bason **Fax:** 01588 638153 **D:** £18.00–£20.00 **S:** £20.00–£25.00 **Beds:** 1T 2D **Baths:** 1 En 1 Sh ⌨ 🅿 (6) ⊬ 📺 🛏️ 🖳 ⚓

Old Brick Guest House, 7 Church Street, Bishop's Castle, Shropshire, SY9 5AA. C17th house in conservation area. Log fires. Beautiful garden. **Open:** All year (not Xmas/New Year) 01588 638471 P Hutton *oldbrick@beeb.net* www.oldbrick.co.uk **D:** £25.00 **S:** £29.00 **Beds:** 1F 1T 2D **Baths:** 4 En ⌨ 🅿 📺 🛏️ 🖳 ⚓ cc

Planning a longer stay? Always ask for any special rates

Please respect a B&B's wishes regarding children, animals and smoking

Bridgnorth

SO7193   🍺 *Bailey's*

St Leonards Gate, 6 Church Street, Bridgnorth, Shropshire, WV16 4EQ. Grade II Listed family home, located in picturesque church cul-de-sac. **Open:** All year 01746 766647 Mr & Mrs Buchanan **D:** £36.00–£46.00 **S:** £20.00–£26.00 **Beds:** 1F 1T 1D 1S **Baths:** 1 En ⌨ 📺 🛏️ 🖳 ⚓

Bearwood Lodge Hotel, 10 Kidderminster Road, Bridgnorth, Shropshire, WV15 6BW. Family guest house. Large private car park. Conservatory gardens **Open:** All year **Grades:** ETC 3 Diamond 01746 762159 Mr Lloyd *bearwoodlodge@ bridgnorth3.freeserve.co.uk* **D:** £20.00–£23.00 **S:** £25.00–£35.00 **Beds:** 3T 3D **Baths:** 6 En ⌨ (5) 🅿 (9) ⊬ 📺 🖳 ⚓ ♿ ⚓

Pen-Y-Ghent, 7 Sabrina Road, Bridgnorth, Shropshire, WV15 6DQ. Riverside family house within walking distance of Bridgnorth. **Open:** All year (not Xmas/New Year) **Grades:** ETC 3 Diamond 01746 762880 Mrs Firman **D:** £19.00 **S:** £25.00 **Beds:** 2D 2S **Baths:** 2 En 1 Pr 1 Sh ⌨ (8) 🅿 📺 📺 🖳 ⚓

Wyndene Guest House, 57 Innage Lane, Bridgnorth, Shropshire, WV16 4HS. Near to Severn Valley Railway, Ironbridge and Much Wenlock. **Open:** All year 01746 764369 & 07977 943074 (M) Mrs Morse *wyndene@bridgnorth2000.freeserve.co.uk* **D:** £20.00–£22.00 **S:** £20.00–£21.00 **Beds:** 1D 1T 2S **Baths:** 1 En 1 Sh ⌨ 🅿 (3) ⊬ 📺 ✕ 🖳 ⚓

Brockton (Much Wenlock)

SO5793

Old Quarry Cottage, Brockton, Much Wenlock, Shropshire, TF13 6JR. Lovely stone cottage set in the countryside. Close to Ironbridge, Wenlock Edge and Ludlow. **Open:** All year (not Xmas/New Year) 01746 785596 Mrs Thorpe *nan@ brockton.fsbusiness.co.uk* **D:** £20.00–£21.00 **S:** £30.00 **Beds:** 1T 1D **Baths:** 2 En 🅿 (2) ⊬ 📺 📺 🖳 ⚓

Burlton

SJ4526

The Grove, Burlton, Shrewsbury, SY4 5SZ. Tucked away in Brother Cadfael country 9m north of Shrewsbury. Imposing 'foursquare' sandstone farmhouse. **Open:** All year 01939 270310 Mrs Martin **D:** £17.00–£19.00 **S:** £20.00 **Beds:** 1T 1D **Baths:** 2 En ⌨ 🅿 (4) ⊬ 📺 🖳 ⚓

Cardington

SO5095

Grove Farm, Cardington, Church Stretton, Shropshire, SY6 7JZ. Central to many places of interest, good home cooking. Recommended. **Open:** All year **01694 771451** Mrs Pennington **D:** £16.00–£18.00 **S:** £18.00–£20.00 **Beds:** 1F 1T **Baths:** 1 Sh ⛌ ♿ 🅿 (10) ⚡ 📺 ♒

Chapel Lawn

SO3176   ⛽ Baron of Beef

The Quern, Chapel Lawn, Bucknell, SY7 0BW. C16th cottage, self-contained, wood stove, good walking, bike track.
Open: All year **01547 530344 Fax: 01547 530844** davequern@ aol.com **D:** £17.50 **S:** £17.50 **Beds:** 1D **Baths:** 1 Pr 🅿 (2) 🐾 📺 ♒ ♿

Chetwynd

SJ7321

Lane End Farm, Chester Road, Chetwynd, Newport, Shropshire, TF10 8BN. Friendly farmhouse in wonderful countryside. Large comfortable rooms. Delicious breakfasts. **Open:** All year **Grades:** ETC 4 Diamond **01952 550337 (also fax)** Mrs Park www.virtual-shropshire.co.uk/lef **D:** £20.00–£25.00 **S:** £25.00–£30.00 **Beds:** 2D 1T **Baths:** 2 En 1 Pr ⛌ 🅿 (5) 📺 🐾 ✗ 📺 ♒ ❀ ♿

Church Stretton

SO4593   ⛽ Royal Oak, Longville Arms

Woolston Farm, Brereton, Church Stretton, Shropshire, SY6 6QD. Victorian farmhouse, outstanding views and very peaceful location. Large bedrooms.
Open: Mar to Nov **Grades:** ETC 3 Diamond **01694 781201** Mrs Brereton joanna@ breretonhouse.f9.co.uk **D:** £21.00 **S:** £26.00 **Beds:** 1T 2D **Baths:** 3 En ⚡ 📺 ♒ ♿

Gilberries Farm Cottage, Wall-under-Heywood, Church Stretton, Shropshire, SY6 7HZ. A haven of peace and tranquillity with views of the famous Wenlock Edge. **Open:** Easter to Nov **01694 771400 (also fax)** Mrs Griffiths **D:** £20.00–£22.00 **S:** £22.00–£25.00 **Beds:** 1D 1T **Baths:** 1 En 1 Pr ⛌ (3) 🅿 (10) 📺 📺 ♒ ♿

Old Rectory House, Burway Road, Church Stretton, Shropshire, SY6 6DW. Georgian house-lovely garden- great view-convenient town and hills. **Open:** All year **01694 724462** Mr Smith **Fax: 01694 724799** Smamos@btinternet.com www.oldrectoryhouse. co.uk **D:** £18.00–£25.00 **S:** £20.00–£25.00 **Beds:** 2D 1T **Baths:** 1 En 1 Sh ⛌ 🅿 (4) 📺 ✗ 📺 ♒ ♿

Belvedere Guest House, Burway Road, Church Stretton, Shropshire, SY6 6DP. Beautiful rural surroundings, on the edge of 6,000 acres of National Trust hill country. **Open:** All year (not Xmas) **01694 722232 (also fax)** Mr Rogers belv@ bigfoot.com www.s-h-systems.co. uk/hotels/belveder **D:** £25.00–£27.00 **S:** £25.00–£30.00 **Beds:** 3F 4D 2T 3S **Baths:** 6 En 3 Sh ⛌ 🅿 (8) 🐾 ♒ ♿ ≋ cc

Cleobury Mortimer

SO6775

Woodview, Mawley Oak, Cleobury Mortimer, Kidderminster, Shropshire, DY14 9BA. Villa-style country residence in five acres, with indoor heated swimming pool. **Open:** All year **01299 271422** Mrs Hale **D:** £25.00 **Beds:** 1T 1D **Baths:** 2 En 🅿 (2) ⚡ 📺 ♒

Clun

SO3080   ⛽ Sun Inn, White Horse, Crown Inn, Hundred House

The Old Stables And Saddlery, Crown House, Church Street, Clun, Craven Arms, Shropshire, SY7 8JW. Superb self-contained Georgian stable conversion in lovely courtyard garden. **Open:** All year (not Xmas) **Grades:** ETC 4 Diamond **D:** £20.00–£23.00 **S:** £22.00–£25.00 **Beds:** 1T 1S **Baths:** 1 En 1 Pr 1 Sh ⛌ (8) 🅿 (2) ⚡ 📺 🐾 📺 ♒ ♿

New House Farm, Mainstone, Clun, Craven Arms, Shropshire, SY7 8NJ. Peaceful C18th farmhouse. Set high - Clun Hills. Ring for brochure. **Open:** Easter to Oct **Grades:** ETC 5 Diamond, Gold **01588 638314** Mrs Ellison sarah@ bishopscastle.co.uk www.new-house-clun.co.uk **D:** £25.00–£27.50 **S:** £27.50–£30.00 **Beds:** 1F 1T **Baths:** 1 En 1 Pr ⛌ (10) 🅿 (6) ⚡ 🐾 ♒ ♿

Llanhedric Farm, Clun, Craven Arms, Shropshire, SY7 8NG. Tranquil country retreat - rooms overlooking beautiful views of Clun Valley. **Open:** Easter to Nov **Grades:** ETC 3 Diamond **01588 640203 (also fax)** M Jones llanhedric@ talk21.com **D:** £19.00–£22.00 **S:** £20.00–£25.00 **Beds:** 1F 1T 1D **Baths:** 1 En 1 Sh ⛌ 🅿 ⚡ 📺 ✗ 📺 ♒ ♿

Planning a longer stay? Always ask for any special rates

Clungunford

SO3978   ⛽ Engine & Tender, Hundred House

North Barn, Abcott Manor, Clungunford, Craven Arms, Shropshire, SY7 0PX. Peacefully situated in south Shropshire Hills. Ideal for walking, touring. **Open:** All year (not Xmas/ New Year) **01588 660596** P Mattison **D:** £19.00–£20.00 **S:** £21.00–£22.00 **Beds:** 1D 1S **Baths:** 1 Sh ⛌ (5) 🅿 (4) ⚡ 📺 🐾 ✗ ♒ ♿

Clunton

SO3381   ⛽ Sun Inn

Hurst Mill Farm, Clunton, Craven Arms, Shropshire, SY7 0JA. Riverside farm in beautiful Clun Valley. Winner of 'Breakfast Challenge'. **Open:** All year (not Xmas) **Grades:** AA 3 Diamond, RAC 3 Diamond **01588 640224 (also fax)** Mrs Williams **D:** £23.00 **S:** £25.00 **Beds:** 2T 1D **Baths:** 1 En 1 Sh ⛌ (2) 🅿 (6) 📺 🐾 ✗ 📺 ♒ ♿

Coalport

SJ6902

Thorpe House, Coalport, Telford, Shropshire, TF8 7HP. Riverside country house in beautiful Ironbridge Gorge, close to museums. **Open:** All year **Grades:** ETC 3 Diamond **01952 586789 (also fax)** Mr Richards **D:** £18.00–£25.00 **S:** £18.00–£35.00 **Beds:** 1F 2D 1S **Baths:** 2 En 1 Sh ⛌ 🅿 (6) 📺 🐾 📺 ♒ ♿

Craignant

SJ2535

The Quarry, Craignant, Selattyn, Oswestry, Shropshire, SY11 4LT. Attractive farmhouse. Offa's Dyke path 0.1 miles. **Open:** Easter to Oct **01691 658674** Mrs Tomley **D:** £16.00 **S:** £16.00 **Beds:** 1D 2S 3F **Baths:** 1 Sh ⛌ 🅿 📺 🐾 ✗ 📺 ♒ ♿

Ellesmere

SJ3934

The Grange, Grange Road, Ellesmere, Shropshire, SY12 9DE. Peaceful Georgian country house in ten acres. Characterful and spacious. **Open:** All year (not Xmas) **Grades:** ETC 3 Diamond **01691 623495** Mrs Ward-Allen **Fax: 01691 623227** rosie@thegrange.uk.com www.thegrange.uk.com **D:** £28.50–£32.00 **S:** £29.00 **Beds:** 2F 4D 3T 5S **Baths:** 11 En 3 Sh ⛌ 🅿 (15) ⚡ 📺 ♿ ♒ ♿

Hordley Hall, Hordley, Ellesmere, Shropshire, *SY12 9BB.* Georgian house, large garden, very peaceful, rural location, home cooking. **Open:** All year
01691 622772 Mrs Rodenhurst **D:** £20.00–£25.00 **S:** £20.00–£25.00 **Beds:** 2D 1T 1S
Baths: 2 En 1 Sh ⌂ 🅿 (6) ⅙ 📺 ✕ 🆅 🛏 ⚲

Mereside Farm, Ellesmere, Shropshire, *SY12 0PA.* Happy friendly atmosphere in C18th farmhouse situated between the mere and canal. **Open:** All year (not Xmas)
01691 622404 (also fax) Mrs Stokes *nicky@ mereside.free-online.co.uk* www.ellesmere.co.uk/mereside **D:** £20.00 **S:** £20.00–£25.00
Beds: 1D 1T **Baths:** 1 En 1 Pr ⌂ 🅿 (7) ⅙ 📺 🛏 🆅 🛏 ⚲

Ford
SJ4113

Cardeston Park Farm, Ford, Shrewsbury, Shropshire, *SY5 9NH.* Large farm house set in peaceful countryside close to Welsh border. **Open:** All year (not Xmas)
01743 884265 (also fax) Mrs Edwards **D:** £20.00–£40.00 **S:** £20.00–£40.00 **Beds:** 2D 1T **Baths:** 2 En 1 Pr 🅿 (4) 🛏 🆅

Frodesley
SJ5101

Meadow-lands, Lodge Lane, Frodesley, Dorrington, Shrewsbury, Shropshire, *SY5 7HD.*
Open: All year **Grades:** ETC 3 Diamond
01694 731350 (also fax) Ron & Jennie Repath *meadowlands@talk21.com* **D:** £20.00–£25.00 **S:** £20.00–£27.50 **Beds:** 2D 1T
Baths: 2 En 1 Pr 🅿 (4) ⅙ 📺 ✕ 🆅 🛏 ⚲
Comfortable modern house set in eight acres of accessible gardens, woodland and paddocks. Quiet location in delightful hamlet with panoramic views of Stretton Hills. Large residents' lounge, silent fridge in guest rooms, brochure available, maps and guides for loan.

Halfway House
SJ3411

Brambleberry, Halfway House, Shrewsbury, Shropshire, *SY5 9DD.* Tastefully furnished house, lovely garden, rooms overlooking beautiful Shropshire countryside. **Open:** All year (not Xmas)
01743 884762 Mrs Astbury **D:** £15.00–£25.00 **S:** £17.00–£25.00 **Beds:** 1D 1T 1S **Baths:** 1 Sh ⌂ (8) 🅿 (6) ⅙ 📺 ✕ 🆅 🛏 ⚲

Harley
SJ5901 🍺 Plume of Feathers

Rowley Farm, Harley, Shrewsbury, Shropshire, *SY5 6LX.* Clean comfortable Georgian farm house. **Open:** Easter to Oct **Grades:** ETC 3 Star
01952 727348 Ms Munslow **D:** £18.00–£20.00 **S:** £22.00–£25.00 ⌂ (2) 🅿 ⅙ 📺 🛏 ⚲

High Ercall
SJ5917

The Mill House, Shrewsbury Road, High Ercall, Telford, Shropshire, *TF6 6BE.* Grade II converted watermill on working small holding and family home. **Open:** All year (not Xmas/New Year) **Grades:** ETC 4 Diamond
01952 770394 Mrs Yates *mill-house@ talk21.com* www.virtualshropshire.co.uk/millhouse **D:** £15.00–£20.00 **S:** £25.00–£30.00 **Beds:** 1F 1T 1S **Baths:** 1 En 1 Pr ⌂ 🅿 (4) ⅙ 📺 🛏 🆅 🛏 ⚲

Hope Bagot
SO5874

Croft Cottage, Cumberley Lane, Hope Bagot, Ludlow, Shropshire, *SY8 3LJ.* Peace and quiet - brook, gardens, badgers, honey, dogs and ducks! **Open:** All year (not Xmas)
01584 890664 (also fax) Mrs Hatchell *croft.cottage@virgin.net* freespace.virgin.net/david-elizabeth.hatchell **D:** £20.00–£21.00 **S:** £20.00–£23.00 **Beds:** 1D 1T **Baths:** 1 En 1 Pr ⌂ 🅿 (4) ⅙ 📺 🛏 ✕ 🆅 🛏 ♿ ⚲

Hordley
SJ3830

Hordley Hall, Hordley, Ellesmere, Shropshire, *SY12 9BB.* Georgian house, large garden, very peaceful, rural location, home cooking. **Open:** All year
01691 622772 Mrs Rodenhurst **D:** £20.00–£25.00 **S:** £20.00–£25.00 **Beds:** 2D 1T 1S
Baths: 2 En 1 Sh ⌂ 🅿 (6) ⅙ 📺 ✕ 🆅 🛏 ⚲

Ironbridge
SJ6703

Golden Ball Inn, 1 Newbridge Road, Ironbridge, Telford, Shropshire, *TF8 7BA.* Ironbridge's oldest and finest inn and restaurant. Relaxed atmosphere. **Open:** All year (not Xmas/New Year)
01952 432179 Fax: 01952 433123 *matrowland@hotmail.com* www.goldenballinn.co.uk **D:** £24.00–£58.00 **S:** £38.00–£48.00 **Beds:** 1T 2D **Baths:** 3 En 🅿 (40) ⅙ 📺 🆅 🛏 ⚲ cc

---

Planning a longer stay? Always ask for any special rates

Post Office House, 6 The Square, Ironbridge, Telford, Shropshire, *TF8 7AQ.* **Open:** All year **Grades:** ETC 3 Diamond
01952 433201 Mrs Hunter **Fax: 01952 433582** *hunter@pohouse-ironbridge.fsnet.co.uk* www.pohouse-ironbridge.fsnet.co.uk **D:** £21.00–£22.00 **S:** £32.00–£34.00 **Beds:** 1F/T 1D/T 1D **Baths:** 2 En 1 Pr ⌂ 🆅 🛏 🛏 ⚲
Comfortable C18th house. Grade II Listed. In the square overlooking Iron Bridge and beautiful wooded Ironbridge Gorge, whilst centrally located for museums. Within easy reach of Bridgnorth, Much Wenlock, Shrewsbury, Weston Park, Cosford Aerospace Museum and Telford International Centre.

Knockin
SJ3222

Top Farm House, Knockin, Oswestry, Shropshire, *SY10 8HN.* Lovely half timbered C16th house in attractive village. Comfortable and pretty ensuite bedrooms. **Open:** All year
01691 682582 P Morrissey **Fax: 01691 682070** *p.a.m@knockin.freeserve.co.uk* **D:** £22.50–£25.00 **S:** £27.50–£30.00 **Beds:** 1F 1T 1D **Baths:** 3 En ⌂ (12) 🅿 (6) 📺 🛏 🆅 🛏 ⚲

Leaton
SJ4618

The Old Vicarage, Leaton, Shrewsbury, Shropshire, *SY4 3AP.* Set in acres of grounds in beautiful open countryside 4 miles from medieval Shrewsbury. **Open:** All year
01939 290989 (also fax) Ms Mansell Jones *m-j@oldvicleaton.freeserve.co.uk* **D:** £20.00 **S:** £25.00 **Beds:** 1T 1D **Baths:** 2 En 🅿 (6) ⅙ 📺 🆅 🛏 ⚲

Leighton
SJ6105

Eye Manor, Leighton, Ironbridge, Shrewsbury, Shropshire, *SY5 6SQ.* Manor house listed in Domesday Book, close to Ironbridge. **Open:** All year (not Xmas/New Year)
01952 510066 Mrs Chillcott **Fax: 01952 610066 D:** £20.00–£25.00 **S:** £20.00–£30.00 **Beds:** 1T **Baths:** 1 Pr ⅙ 🆅 🛏 ⚲

Little Wenlock

SJ6406   🍴 *Huntsman Inn*

Wenboro Cottage, *Church Lane, Little Wenlock, Telford, Shrops, TF6 5BB.* Pretty cottage set in peaceful village near Ironbridge and Telford centre. **Open:** All year (not Xmas)
01952 505573 Mrs Carter *rcarter@ wenboro.freeserve.co.uk* **D:** £20.00–£22.50 **S:** £25.00 **Beds:** 1D 1T **Baths:** 1 En 1 Pr ⌂ 🄿 (2) 📺 🛏. 🕭

Llanfair Waterdine

SO2476

The Mill, *Lloyney, Llanfair Waterdine, Knighton, Powys, LD7 1RG.* Wonderful countryside in the Teme Valley, home cooking. **Open:** All year (not Xmas/New Year)
01547 528049 (also fax) Mr & Mrs Davies **D:** £20.00 **S:** £20.00 **Beds:** 2D 2T 1S **Baths:** 1 En 2 Pr 2 Sh ⌂ 🄿 (6) 🛏 📺 🛏 ✕ 📺 🛏. ♨2 🕭

Llanforda

SJ2528

The Old Mill Inn, *Candy, Llanforda, Oswestry, Shropshire, SY10 9AZ.* On Offa's Dyke path. Excellent, superb food and welcome. **Open:** All year
01691 657058 (also fax) Mrs Atkinson *theoldmill.inn@virgin.net* **D:** £20.00 **S:** £20.00–£35.00 **Beds:** 2T 1D 2S **Baths:** 2 Sh ⌂ 🄿 (50) 🛏 📺 ✕ 📺 🛏. 🕭 cc

Llynclys

SJ2823

Bridge House, *Llynclys, Oswestry, SY10 8AE.* Lovely rooms. Beautiful views. Superb breakfasts. Comfort, quality and value. **Open:** All year (not Xmas/New Year)
01691 830496 (also fax) Mr & Mrs Taylor *jenny@llynclys.freeserve.co.uk* **D:** £18.50–£22.00 **S:** £20.00–£25.00 **Beds:** 1T 1D **Baths:** 2 En ⌂ (5) 🄿 (4) 🛏 📺 🛏 📺 🛏. 🕭

Longdon upon Tern

SJ6215

Red House Farm, *Longdon upon Tern, Wellington, Telford, Shropshire, TF6 6LE.* Late Victorian farmhouse with comfortable well furnished rooms. Excellent breakfasts. **Open:** All year
01952 770245 Mrs Jones *rhf@ virtual-shropshire.co.uk* www.virtual-shropshire.co. uk/redhouse-farm **D:** £18.00–£25.00 **S:** £20.00–£25.00 **Beds:** 1F 1T 1D 1S **Baths:** 2 En 1 Sh ⌂ 🄿 (4) 📺 🛏 ♨ 🕭

Ludlow

SO5174

Henwick House, *Gravel Hill, Ludlow, Shropshire, SY8 1QU.*
Open: Apr to Dec
01584 873338
Mrs Cecil-Jones **D:** £22.00 **S:** £22.00
Beds: 1D 2T 1S **Baths:** 2 En ⌂ 🄿 (3) 🛏 📺 🛏 📺. 🕭

Warm, comfortable Georgian coach house with private parking. Friendly, informal atmosphere, good traditional English breakfast. Ensuite bedrooms, comfortable beds, TV, tea/coffee facilities and much more. Easy walking distances from town centre and local inns.

Arran House, *42 Gravel Hill, Ludlow, Shropshire, SY8 1QR.* Comfortable Victorian house. 5 minutes walk town centre, railway station. **Open:** All year
01584 873764 Mrs Bowen **D:** £17.00–£19.00 **S:** £17.00–£19.00 **Beds:** 1T 1D 2S **Baths:** 1 Sh ⌂ (5) 🄿 (4) 🛏 ✕ 📺 🛏. 🕭

Maesbury

SJ3026

Ashfield Farmhouse, *Maesbury, Oswestry, Shrops, SY10 8JH.* Most enchanting C16th Welsh Border coaching/farmhouse. 1 mile Oswestry, A5, A483. **Open:** All year
Grades: ETC 4 Diamond, Silver
01691 653589 & 07989 477414 (M) Mrs Jones
Fax: 01691 653589 *marg@ ashfieldfarmhouse.co.uk*
www.ashfieldfarmhouse.co.uk **D:** £20.00 **S:** £25.00 **Beds:** 1F 1T 1D **Baths:** 2 En 1 Pr ⌂ 🄿 (8) 📺 🛏 📺 🛏. 🕭 cc

Mainstone

SO2787   🏰 *Castle Hotel*

New House Farm, *Mainstone, Clun, Craven Arms, Shropshire, SY7 8NJ.* Peaceful C18th farmhouse. Set high - Clun Hills. Ring for brochure. **Open:** Easter to Oct
Grades: ETC 5 Diamond, Gold
01588 638314 Mrs Ellison *sarah@ bishopscastle.co.uk* www.new-house-clun.co.uk **D:** £25.00–£27.50 **S:** £27.50–£30.00 **Beds:** 1F 1T **Baths:** 1 En 1 Pr ⌂ (10) 🄿 (6) 🛏 🛏 🛏. 🕭

Market Drayton

SJ6734

80 Rowan Road, *Market Drayton, Shropshire, TF9 1RR.* Peaceful, hospitable. Home form home. Short walk to town centre. **Open:** All year (not Xmas/New Year)
01630 655484 (also fax) Mrs Russell **D:** £19.00–£21.00 **S:** £20.00–£22.00 **Beds:** 1T **Baths:** 1 Pr 🄿 (1) 📺 🛏. 🕭

Melverley

SJ3316

Church House, *Melverley, Oswestry, Shropshire, SY10 8PJ.* Beautiful setting next to River Vyrnwy by historic Melverley church. **Open:** All year (not Xmas)
01691 682754 Mr & Mrs Sprackling *melverley@aol.com* members.aol. com/melverley **D:** £17.00–£20.00 **S:** £20.00 **Beds:** 1F 1D 1T **Baths:** 2 Pr ⌂ 🄿 (3) 🛏 📺 🛏 📺. 🕭

Middleton (Ludlow)

SO5377   🍴 *The Unicorn*

Middleton Court, *Middleton, Ludlow, Shropshire, SY8 2DZ.* Only 2 miles from Ludlow. Gourmet breakfast. Stunning 1864. **Open:** All year (not Xmas/New Year)
01584 872842 Miss O'Meara **D:** £25.00–£27.50 **S:** £30.00 **Beds:** 2D **Baths:** 1 Pr 1 Sh ⌂ 🄿 (10) 🛏 🛏 🛏.

Minsterley

SJ3705

Cricklewood Cottage, *Plox Green, Minsterley, Shrewsbury, Shropshire, SY5 0HT.* Delightful C18th cottage in unspoilt Shropshire countryside. Beautiful cottage garden. **Open:** All year (not Xmas)
01743 791229 Costello *paul.crickcott@ bushinternet.com* **D:** £23.50–£26.00 **S:** £23.50–£35.00 **Beds:** 1T 2D **Baths:** 3 En ⌂ (8) 🄿 (3) 🛏 📺 🛏 🛏. 🕭

Newport

SJ7418

Lane End Farm, *Chester Road, Chetwynd, Newport, Shropshire, TF10 8BN.* Friendly farmhouse in wonderful countryside. Large comfortable rooms. Delicious breakfasts. **Open:** All year
Grades: ETC 4 Diamond
01952 550337 (also fax) Mrs Park www.virtual-shropshire.co.uk/lef **D:** £20.00–£25.00 **S:** £25.00–£30.00 **Beds:** 2D 1T **Baths:** 2 En 1 Pr ⌂ 🄿 (5) 📺 🛏 ✕ 📺 🛏. ♣ 🕭

Sambrook Manor, *Sambrook, Newport, Shropshire, TF10 8AL.* 200-acre mixed farm. Old manor farmhouse built in 1702. Beautiful gardens. **Open:** All year (not Xmas)
Grades: ETC 3 Diamond
01952 550256 Mrs Mitchell **D:** £18.00–£25.00 **S:** £18.00–£25.00 **Beds:** 2D 1T **Baths:** 2 En ⌂ 🄿 (5) 🛏 📺 ✕ 🛏. 🕭

Nobold
SJ4710

The Day House, *Nobold, Shrewsbury, Shropshire, SY5 8NL.* Delightful period farmhouse, extensive gardens, abundant wildlife, easy access Shrewsbury. **Open:** All year (not Xmas/New Year) **01743 860212 (also fax)** Mrs Roberts **D:** £23.00–£26.00 **S:** £25.00–£27.00 **Beds:** 1F 1T 1D **Baths:** 3 En ⌂ 🖻 ✠ 📺 ⚡ 📺 ▥ ⚓

Norbury
SO3592

Suttocks Wood, *Norbury, Bishops Castle, Shropshire, SY9 5EA.* Scandinavian house in a woodland setting near Long Mynd and Stiperstones. **Open:** All year **01588 650433** Mrs Williams **Fax: 01588 650492** *shuttockswood@baclays.net* www.go2.co. uk/suttockswood/index.html **D:** £20.00–£26.00 **S:** £25.00–£28.00 **Beds:** 1D 2T **Baths:** 3 En ⌂ (12) 🖻 (8) ✠ 📺 ✕ 📺 ▥ ⚓ cc

Nordley
SO6996

The Albynes, *Nordley, Bridgnorth, Shropshire, WV16 4SX.* Beautiful country house peacefully set in Parkland. Guest rooms overlook gardens. **Open:** All year (not Xmas/New Year) **01746 762261** Mrs Woolley **D:** £20.00–£25.00 **S:** £25.00–£30.00 **Beds:** 1D 1T 1S **Baths:** 2 En 1 Pr 🖻 (10) ✠ 📺 📺 ▥ ⚓

Norton (Craven Arms)
SO4581

The Firs, *Norton, Craven Arms, Shropshire, SY7 9LS.* **Open:** All year **Grades:** ETC 4 Diamond **01588 672511 (also fax)** Mrs Bebbington *thefirs@go2.co.uk* www.go2.co.uk/firs **D:** £20.00–£25.00 **S:** £20.00–£25.00 **Beds:** 1F 2D **Baths:** 2 En 1 Pr 🖻 (5) ✠ 📺 📺 ▥ ⚓ Victorian stone farmhouse standing in large garden with ample parking, magnificent views in Area of Outstanding Natural Beauty. Walking distance of Stokesay Castle, 6 miles to historic Ludlow, with its abundance of Michelin star restaurants. Horse and pony stabling available.

BATHROOMS
En = Ensuite
Pr = Private
Sh = Shared

Please respect a B&B's wishes regarding children, animals and smoking

---

Oakengates
SJ7011

Sunnymede Guest House, *Leonard Street, Oakengates, Telford, Shropshire, TF2 6EU.* Close to Telford amenities, 5 mins from M54, junction 5. **Open:** All year (not Xmas/New Year) **01952 612980** Mrs Hume **D:** £20.00 **S:** £20.00 **Beds:** 1T 1D 2S **Baths:** 2 Sh 🖻 (6) 📺 ✕ 📺 ▥ cc

Oswestry
SJ2929

Ashfield Farmhouse, *Maesbury, Oswestry, Shrops, SY10 8JH.* Most enchanting C16th Welsh Border coaching/farmhouse. 1 mile Oswestry, A5, A483. **Open:** All year **Grades:** ETC 4 Diamond, Silver **01691 653589 & 07989 477414 (M)** Mrs Jones **Fax: 01691 653589** *marg@ ashfieldfarmhouse.co.uk* www.ashfieldfarmhouse.co.uk **D:** £20.00 **S:** £25.00 **Beds:** 1F 1T 1D **Baths:** 2 En 1 Pr ⌂ 🖻 (8) 📺 ✠ 📺 ▥ ⚓ cc

Ash Court, *Weston Lane, Oswestry, Shropshire, SY11 2BB.* Beautiful C18th house with country style bedrooms overlooking Gardens and countryside. **Open:** All year **01691 662921** J Edwards *edwards.ashcourt@ virgin.net* www.virtualshropshire.co. uk/ashcourt **D:** £18.00–£20.00 **S:** £20.00–£23.00 **Beds:** 1T 1D **Baths:** 1 Sh ⌂ 🖻 (2) ✠ 📺 📺 ▥ ⚓

Pant
SJ2722

Three Firs, *Pant, Oswestry, Shropshire, SY10 8LB.* Quiet homely countryside accommodation adjoining golf course, Welsh/English border. **Open:** All year **01691 831375** *three.firs@lineone.net* **D:** £18.00–£25.00 **S:** £18.00–£25.00 **Beds:** 2F 1D **Baths:** 2 En 1 Sh ⌂ 🖻 (6) 📺 ✠ ✕ 📺 ▥ ⚓ ⚡

Rowton (Telford)
SJ6119 ⬛ *Seven Stars*

Church Farm, *Rowton (Wellington), Wellington, Telford, Shropshire, TF6 6QY.* Superb breakfast. Spacious rooms. Relaxing spa bath. **Open:** All year (not Xmas/New Year) **Grades:** ETC 3 Diamond **01952 770381** Mrs Evans *church.farm@ pipemedia.co.uk* **D:** £20.00–£22.00 **S:** £25.00–£35.00 **Beds:** 3F 1T 2D **Baths:** 2 En ⌂ (10) 📺 ✠ 📺 ▥ ⚓

Rushbury
SO5191

The Coates, *Rushbury, Church Stretton, Shropshire, SY6 7DZ.* C15th family farmhouse with tennis court, in beautiful peaceful countryside. **Open:** Feb to Nov **Grades:** ETC 2 Diamond **01694 771330 (also fax)** Mrs Madeley **D:** £19.00–£22.00 **S:** £22.00–£25.00 **Beds:** 2T **Baths:** 1 En 1 Sh ⌂ ✠ 📺 📺 ⚓

Ruyton-XI-Towns
SJ3922

Brownhill House, *Brownhill, Ruyton-XI-Towns, Shrewsbury, SY4 1LR.* Old world standards, modern facilities and relaxed atmosphere. All rooms ensuite. **Open:** All year **Grades:** AA 3 Diamond **01939 261121** Yoland & Roger Brown **Fax: 01939 260626** *brownhill@eleventowns.co.uk* www.eleventowns.co.uk **D:** £17.50–£23.00 **S:** £20.50–£26.00 **Beds:** 1D 1T 1S **Baths:** 3 En ⌂ 🖻 (5) 📺 ✕ 📺 ▥ ⚓ cc

Sambrook
SJ7024

Sambrook Manor, *Sambrook, Newport, Shropshire, TF10 8AL.* 200-acre mixed farm. Old manor farmhouse built in 1702. Beautiful gardens. **Open:** All year (not Xmas) **Grades:** ETC 3 Diamond **01952 550256** Mrs Mitchell **D:** £18.00–£25.00 **S:** £18.00–£25.00 **Beds:** 2D 1T **Baths:** 2 En ⌂ 🖻 (5) ✠ 📺 ✕ ▥ ⚓

Shifnal
SJ7407

Tree Tops, *The Hem, Shifnal, Shropshire, TF11 9PS.* C18th cottage with friendly atmosphere, near Ironbridge, Cosford, Weston Park. **Open:** All year **01952 460566** Mrs Bell *julia@treetops.enta.net* **D:** £18.00–£22.00 **S:** £20.00–£25.00 **Beds:** 1D 1T 1S **Baths:** 1 Pr 1 Sh 🖻 (3) ✠ 📺 ✠ ▥

Shrewsbury
SJ4912 ⬛ *Coach & Horses, Corn House*

The Stiperstones, *18 Coton Crescent, Coton Hill, Shrewsbury, SY1 2NZ.* Very comfortable, quality accommodation. High standard of cleanliness. Extensive facilities. **Open:** All year **01743 246720 & 01743 350303** Judy MacLeod **Fax: 01743 350303** *thestiperstones@aol.com* www.thestiperstones.com **D:** £19.00–£21.00 **S:** £22.50 **Beds:** 1F 2D 2T 1S **Baths:** 4 Sh ⌂ 🖻 (6) 📺 📺 ▥ ⚓

Merevale House, *66 Ellesmere Road, Shrewsbury, SY1 2QP.* **Open:** All year (not Xmas)
01743 243677 J Spooner **D:** £18.00 **Beds:** 3D **Baths:** 1 Sh 🅿 (3) 📺 🛍 👗
Lovely Victorian house with private parking and pretty garden. 10 minutes walk to town and railway and bus stations. Very attractive bedrooms with drinks, biscuits, television and many extra home comforts. Good breakfasts with vegetarians also catered for.

Brownhill House, *Brownhill, Ruyton-XI-Towns, Shrewsbury, SY4 1LR.* **Open:** All year **Grades:** AA 3 Diamond
01939 261121 Yoland & Roger Brown **Fax: 01939 260626** *brownhill@eleventowns.co.uk* www.eleventowns.co.uk **D:** £17.50–£23.00 **S:** £20.50–£26.00 **Beds:** 1D 1T 1S **Baths:** 3 En 🔁 🅿 (5) 🍴 × 📺 🛍 👗 **cc**
Old world standards, modern facilities and relaxed atmosphere. All rooms ensuite. Local/home grown produce. Ground floor room. Computers, fax, e-mail. Easy access, Chester to Ludlow, Snowdonia to Ironbridge. Unique 2 acre garden, the icing on the cake!

Avonlea, *33 Coton Crescent, Coton Hill, Shrewsbury, Shropshire, SY1 2NZ.* **Open:** Jan to Dec **Grades:** ETC 2 Diamond
01743 359398 Mrs O'Keefe **D:** £17.00–£19.00 **S:** £18.00–£20.00 **Beds:** 2T 1S **Baths:** 1 En 1 Sh 🔁 (11) 📺 🛍 👗
Comfortable, attractive Edwardian town house. Ten minute walk from town centre, Railway, Bus stations, records and research library. Shrewsbury Castle, 'Brother Cadfael' trail. Town centre attractions of historical Shrewsbury. Quarry park, Dingle agricultural show ground. Venue for flower show.

Sandford House Hotel, *St. Julians Friars, Shrewsbury, SY1 1XL.* Georgian town house close to river. **Open:** All year **Grades:** ETC 3 Diamond
01743 343829 (also fax) *sandfordhouse@lineone.net* **D:** £25.00–£27.00 **S:** £40.00 **Beds:** 4F 2T 2D 2S **Baths:** 10 En 🔁 🅿 📺 🛍 👗 🛍 👗 **cc**

Severn Cottage, *Coton Hill, Shrewsbury, Shropshire, SY1 2DZ.* Spectacular views of river and countryside. Town centre - 500 metres.
Open: Mar to Oct **Grades:** ETC 4 Diamond
01743 358467 Mr Tudor **Fax: 01743 340254** *david.tudor@virgin.net* www.shrewsbury.com **D:** £25.00–£27.50 **S:** £30.00–£35.00 **Beds:** 2D **Baths:** 2 Pr 🔁 (10) 🅿 (3) 🍴 📺 🛍 🛍 👗

The Bancroft, *17 Coton Crescent, Shrewsbury, Shropshire, SY1 2NY.* Warm welcome and comfortable accommodation. Close to railway/bus station. **Open:** All year (not Xmas) **Grades:** ETC 3 Diamond
01743 231746 (also fax) Mrs Oldham-Malcolm *bancroft01@aol.com* **D:** £17.00–£21.00 **S:** £18.00–£24.00 **Beds:** 1D 1T 2S **Baths:** 2 Sh 🔁 🅿 (4) 🍴 📺 🛍 👗 **cc**

2 Lythwood Hall, Bayston Hill, *Shrewsbury, Shropshire, SY3 0AD.* Quality accommodation in a comfortable spacious Georgian house. **Open:** All year
01743 874747 & 07074 874747 (M) Mr & Mrs Bottomley **Fax: 01743 874747** *lythwoodhall@amserve.net* **D:** £20.00 **S:** £20.00–£25.00 **Beds:** 1D 1T **Baths:** 1 Pr 1 Sh 🔁 🅿 (2) 🍴 🛍 × 📺 🛍 👗

Castlecote Guest House, *77 Monkmoor Road, Shrewsbury, Shropshire, SY2 5AT.* Family-run, comfortable Victorian house, close to all amenities. **Open:** All year (not Xmas)
01743 245473 Mrs Tench **D:** £17.50–£22.00 **S:** £17.50–£22.00 **Beds:** 2F 4D 2T 0S **Baths:** 1 En 2 Sh 🔁 🅿 (4) 📺 🛍 🛍 👗

Meole Brace Hall, *Meole Brace, Shrewsbury, Shropshire, SY3 9HF.* Beautiful house set in 3 acres yet close to town.
Open: All year (not Xmas/New Year)
01743 235566 & 07710 644696 (M) Mrs Hathaway **Fax: 01743 236886** *enquiries@meolebracehall.co.uk* **D:** £24.50–£28.00 **S:** £39.00–£46.00 **Beds:** 1T 2D **Baths:** 2 En 1 Pr 🔁 (12) 🅿 (12) 🍴 📺 🛍 × 📺 🛍 👗

Snailbeach

SJ3702

Sycamore Cottage, *5 Perkins Beach, Snailbeach, Stiperstones, Shrewsbury, Shropshire, SY5 0PE.* Perfect location on Stiperstones Hills for exploring beautiful South Shropshire. very comfortable accommodation. **Open:** All year (not Xmas/New Year)
01743 790914 Mrs Barrett **D:** £21.00 **S:** £25.00 **Beds:** 1T **Baths:** 1 En 🅿 (2) 📺 🛍 × 🛍 👗

St George's

SJ7010

Grove House, *1 Stafford Street, St Georges, Telford, Shropshire, TF2 9JW.* Ideally situated for all of Shropshire attractions. Home from home. **Open:** All year (not Xmas/New Year) **Grades:** ETC 3 Diamond
01952 616140 (also fax) Mr & Mrs Woodhall **D:** £19.00 **S:** £22.00–£28.00 **Beds:** 1F 2T 3D 2S **Baths:** 7 En 1 Pr 🔁 (5) 🅿 (8) 🍴 📺 🛍 👗

Stokesay

SO4381   🏰 *Stokesay Castle*

Castle View B&B, *Stokesay, Craven Arms, Shropshire, SY7 9AL.* Large Victorian stone house opposite Stokesay Castle. Extensive gardens.
Open: All year **Grades:** ETC 4 Diamond
01588 673712 Mrs Grizzell www.southshropshire.org.uk/castleview **D:** £20.00–£22.50 **S:** £25.00 **Beds:** 1T 1D 1S **Baths:** 1 En 2 Pr 🔁 (3) 🅿 (6) 📺 🛍 🛍 👗

Stottesdon

SO6682

Cox's Barn, *Bagginswood, Stottesdon, Kidderminster, Worcs, DY14 8LS.* Rural setting, perfectly situated for exploring Ludlow, Bridgnorth, Bewdley, Worcester. **Open:** All year **Grades:** ETC 4 Diamond
01746 718415 Mr & Mrs Thompson **D:** £20.00–£25.00 **Beds:** 3D **Baths:** 3 En 🔁 🅿 (4) 🍴 📺 🛍 × 📺 🛍 👗

Strefford

SO4385

Strefford Hall, *Strefford, Craven Arms, Shropshire, SY7 8DE.* Spacious farmhouse in peaceful setting with panoramic views of Wenlock Edge. **Open:** All year (not Xmas/New Year) **Grades:** ETC 4 Diamond
01588 672383 Mrs Morgan **Fax: 01588 673855** *strefford@orange.net* **D:** £23.00 **S:** £25.00–£28.00 **Beds:** 1T 2D **Baths:** 3 En 🔁 🅿 🍴 📺 🛍 👗

Telford

SJ6909   🏰 *Station Inn*

Sunnymede Guest House, *Leonard Street, Oakengates, Telford, Shropshire, TF2 6EU.* Close to Telford amenities, 5 mins from M54, junction 5. **Open:** All year (not Xmas/New Year)
01952 612980 Mrs Hume **D:** £20.00 **S:** £20.00 **Beds:** 1T 1D 2S **Baths:** 2 Sh 🅿 (6) 📺 × 🛍 👗 **cc**

All details shown are as supplied by B&B owners in Autumn 2001

Church Farm, Wrockwardine, Wellington, Telford, Shropshire, TF6 5DG. Down a lime-tree avenue lies our superb situated C18th village farmhouse. **Open:** All year **Grades:** AA 4 Diamond
01952 244917 (also fax) J Savage *jo@ churchillfarm.freeserve.co.uk*
www.churchfarmshropshire.co.uk **D:** £24.00– £28.00 **S:** £26.00–£36.00 **Beds:** 3T 3D **Baths:** 3 Pr 1 Sh 🅿 🅣 🖳 🔥 cc

The Old Rectory, Stirchley, Telford, Shropshire, TF3 1DY. Quiet location, secluded garden, convenient Telford Town Centre and Ironbridge. **Open:** All year (not Xmas/New Year) **Grades:** ETC 4 Diamond
01952 596308 (also fax) Mrs Miller *hazelmiller@waitrose.com* **D:** £20.00–£22.00 **S:** £26.00–£27.00 **Beds:** 1F 2T 1D 2S **Baths:** 4 En 2 Pr 🅢 🅿 (6) ⅙ 🅣 🅥 🖳 🔥1 🔥

Wenboro Cottage, Church Lane, Little Wenlock, Telford, Shrops, TF6 5BB. Pretty cottage set in peaceful village near Ironbridge and Telford centre. **Open:** All year (not Xmas)
01952 505573 Mrs Carter *rcarter@ wenboro.freeserve.co.uk* **D:** £20.00–£22.50 **S:** £25.00 **Beds:** 1D 1T **Baths:** 1 En 1 Pr 🅢 🅿 (2) 🅣 🖳 🔥

Stone House, Shifnal Road, Priorslee, Telford, Shropshire, TF2 9NN. A warm, friendly guest house with a large walled garden. **Open:** All year
01952 290119 (also fax) Mrs Silcock *dave@ stonehouseguesthouse.freeserve.co.uk* **D:** £20.00– £21.00 **S:** £26.00–£27.00 **Beds:** 1F 2D 2T **Baths:** 5 En 🅢 🅿 (4) ⅙ 🅣 ✕ 🅥 🖳 🔥

Trefonen
SJ2526

The Pentre, Trefonen, Oswestry, Shropshire, SY10 9EE. Rural bliss, C16th farmhouse, stunning views, dinner specialities. **Open:** All year (not Xmas/New Year)
01691 653952 Mr Gilbert *thepentre@ micro-plus-web.net* **D:** £21.00 **S:** £29.00 **Beds:** 2F **Baths:** 2 En 🅢 🅿 (10) ⅙ 🔥 ✕ 🅥 🖳 🔥

Upper Affcot
SO4486

Travellers Rest Inn, Upper Affcot, Church Stretton, Shropshire, SY6 6RL. Traditional inn with good food, real ale, good company. **Open:** All year (not Xmas)
01694 781275 Mr Allison **Fax:** 01694 781555 *reception@travellersrestinn.co.uk*
www.travellersrestinn.co.uk **D:** £25.00 **S:** £30.00 **Beds:** 5D 2T 1S **Baths:** 8 En 🅢 🅿 (30) 🅣 🔥 ✕ 🅥 🖳 🔥 cc

Walcot (Shrewsbury)
SJ5911

Alscott Inn, Walcot, Wellington, Telford, Shropshire, TF6 5EQ. Friendly, family run country inn. Home cooking, Beer garden. **Open:** All year (not Xmas/New Year)
01952 248484 Ms Young *alscottinn@ yahoo.co.uk* **D:** £16.00–£20.00 **S:** £20.00– £25.00 **Beds:** 2D 2T **Baths:** 2 En 1 Sh 🅢 🅿 (40) 🅣 🔥 ✕ 🅥 🖳 🔥 cc

Wall-under-Heywood
SO5192

Gilberries Farm Cottage, Wall-under-Heywood, Church Stretton, Shropshire, SY6 7HZ. A haven of peace and tranquillity with views of the famous Wenlock Edge. **Open:** Easter to Nov
01694 771400 (also fax) Mrs Griffiths **D:** £20.00–£22.00 **S:** £22.00–£25.00 **Beds:** 1D 1T **Baths:** 1 En 1 Pr 🅢 (3) 🅿 (10) 🅣 🅥 🖳 🔥

Wellington
SJ6411

Lord Nelson Hotel, 11-13 Park Street, Wellington, Telford, Shropshire, TF1 3AE. Relaxed atmosphere in comfortable surroundings. Central to Shropshire's tourist attractions. **Open:** All Year
01952 223498 **D:** £18.50–£25.00 **S:** £45.00 **Beds:** 2D 2T 8F **Baths:** 12 En 🅢 🅿 ⅙ 🅣 🔥 ✕ 🅥 🖳 🔥 cc

Wem
SJ5129 🍺 Raven Inn

Forncet, Soulton Road, Wem, Shrewsbury, Shropshire, SY4 5HR. Warm welcome at spacious Victorian house. Ideal for touring, good home cooking. **Open:** All year (not Xmas) **Grades:** ETC 3 Diamond
01939 232996 Mr & Mrs James **D:** £19.00 **S:** £20.00 **Beds:** 1D 1T 1S **Baths:** 2 Sh 🅢 🅿 (6) ⅙ 🅣 ✕ 🅥 🖳 🔥

Foxleigh House, Foxleigh Drive, Wem, Shrewsbury, Shropshire, SY4 5BP. Comfort assured in Georgian/Victorian home near Shropshire Way. **Open:** All year (not Xmas/New Year)
01939 233528 (also fax) B L Barnes *foxleigh01@aol.com* **D:** £20.00–£24.00 **S:** £24.00–£25.00 **Beds:** 4T **Baths:** 1 Pr 1 Sh 🅢 (8) 🅿 (6) ⅙ 🅣 🔥 ✕ 🖳 🔥

Greenfields, 55 Roden Grove, Wem, Shrewsbury, SY4 5HJ. Comfortable, relaxing atmosphere within 10 minutes walk of town centre. **Open:** All year
01939 232850 Mrs Johnson **D:** £18.00 **S:** £18.50 **Beds:** 2D 1S **Baths:** 1 Sh 🅿 (2) ⅙ 🅣 🖳 🔥

Weston-under-Redcastle
SJ5628

Windmill Cottage Guest House, Weston-under-Redcastle, Shrewsbury, Shropshire, SY4 5UX. Next to Hawkstone golf follies. Ideal walkers, golfers, countryside lovers. **Open:** Feb to Dec
01939 200219 (also fax) Mr & Mrs Trasatti *gh@windmillcottage.co.uk*
www.windmillcottage.co.uk **D:** £20.00 **S:** £30.00 **Beds:** 4T **Baths:** 4 En 🅢 (9) 🅿 (8) ⅙ 🅣 🅥 🖳 🔥 🔥

Whitchurch
SJ5441

Stoneleigh, 16 Sedgeford, Whitchurch, Shropshire, SY13 1EX. Home from home, comfortable beds, good breakfast, beautiful garden. **Open:** All year (not Xmas)
01948 664618 Mrs Gibson **D:** £15.00 **S:** £15.00 **Beds:** 1D 1T 1S **Baths:** 2 Sh 🅢 🅿 (3) 🅣 🖳 🔥

Roden View, Dobson's Bridge, Whixall, Whitchurch, Shropshire, SY13 2QL. Make yourselves at home and enjoy the comfort of our C17th country cottage. **Open:** Feb to Dec **Grades:** ETC 4 Diamond, RAC 4 Diamond
01948 710320 (also fax) J James *rodenview@ talk21.com* **D:** £20.00 **S:** £20.00 **Beds:** 1D/F 1D 2T **Baths:** 4 En 🅢 🅿 (8) 🅣 🔥 ✕ 🅥 🖳 🔥

Hamner Arms Village Hotel, Hamner, Whitchurch, Shropshire, SY13 3DE. A return to the values of yesteryear. Service and hospitality. **Open:** All year
01948 830532 **Fax:** 01948 830740 *enquiries@ thehamnerarms.freeserve.co.uk*
www.thehamnersarms.freeserve.co.uk **D:** £25.00–£37.50 **S:** £35.00–£47.50 **Beds:** 4F 24D **Baths:** 28 En 🅢 🅿 (80) 🅣 🔥 ✕ 🅥 🖳 🔥 🔥 cc

Planning a longer stay? Always ask for any special rates

Whixall
SJ5134

Roden View, Dobson's Bridge, Whixall, Whitchurch, Shropshire, SY13 2QL. Make yourselves at home and enjoy the comfort of our C17th country cottage. **Open:** Feb to Dec **Grades:** ETC 4 Diamond, RAC 4 Diamond
01948 710320 (also fax) J James *rodenview@ talk21.com* **D:** £20.00 **S:** £20.00 **Beds:** 1D/F 1D 2T **Baths:** 4 En ⌂ ⊡ (8) ⊙ ⊁ ✕ ⊻ ▥ ⚓

BEDROOMS

D = Double

T = Twin

S = Single

F = Family

Wistanstow
SO4285

Leacroft, Leamoor Common, Wistanstow, Craven Arms, Shropshre, SY7 8DN. Beautiful country home, between Wenlock Edge and the Long Mynd. **Open:** All year
01694 781556 (also fax) Mr & Mrs Maddock *sue@maddock.enta.net* **D:** £20.00–£22.50 **S:** £22.50–£25.00 **Beds:** 1T 1D **Baths:** 1 En 1 Pr ⊡ ⊁ ⊙ ⊁ ▥ ⚓

Withington
SJ5712

Garden Cottage, Withington, Shrewsbury, Shropshire, SY4 4QA. Delightful Grade II Listed country house, great charm and character, quiet village setting. **Open:** All year (not Xmas)
01743 709511 (also fax) Mrs Hopper *silvia.hopper@garden-cottage.fsnet.co.uk* **D:** £20.00–£22.00 **S:** £19.00–£30.00 **Beds:** 1D 1T 1S **Baths:** 1 En 1 Sh ⊡ (6) ⊁ ⊙ ⊻ ▥ ⚓

Woofferton
SO5268 ⊜ *The Boot*

Ravenscourt Manor, Woofferton, Ludlow, Shropshire, SY8 4AL. Ancient manor close to Ludlow, superb ensuite rooms. **Open:** Mar to Jan
01584 711905 & 07855 797845 (M) Mrs Purnell **Fax: 01584 711905 D:** £27.50–£30.00 **S:** £35.00–£40.00 **Beds:** 1F 1T 1D **Baths:** 3 En ⌂ ⊡ ⊙ ⊻ ▥ ⚓

Wrockwardine
SJ6211

Church Farm, Wrockwardine, Wellington, Telford, Shropshire, TF6 5DG. Down a lime-tree avenue lies our superb situated C18th village farmhouse. **Open:** All year **Grades:** AA 4 Diamond
01952 244917 (also fax) J Savage *jo@ churchillfarm.freeserve.co.uk* www.churchfarmshropshire.co.uk **D:** £24.00–£28.00 **S:** £26.00–£36.00 **Beds:** 3T 3D **Baths:** 3 Pr 1 Sh ⊡ ⊙ ⊁ ▥ ⚓ cc

Somerset

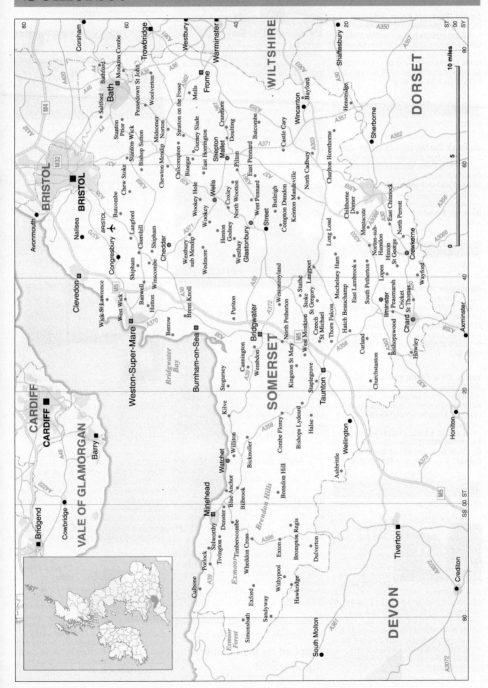

Ashbrittle

ST0521

Lower Westcott Farm, *Ashbrittle, Wellington, Somerset, TA21 0HZ.* Devon/Somerset borders family farm, ideal Moors/Coasts. Picturesque countryside. **Open:** All year (not Xmas)
01398 361296 Mrs Heard **D:** £18.00–£20.00
S: £18.00–£20.00 **Beds:** 1F 1T **Baths:** 1 En 1
Pr ♿ 🅿 (4) ⚡ 📺 ✕ Ⓥ 🛏 ♨

Banwell

ST3959

Banwell Castle, *Banwell, Weston-super-Mare, Somerset, BS29 6NX.* Victorian castle, outstanding views, still a family home.
Open: All year
01934 822263 Mr Parsons **Fax: 01934 823946**
BanwellCastle@supanet.com
www.BanwellCastle.co.uk **D:** £25.00 **S:** £25.00
Beds: 4D **Baths:** 4 En ♿ 🅿 (40) 📺 🛏 ✕ Ⓥ 🛏
♨ cc

Batcombe

ST6837

Batcombe Vale, *Batcombe, Shepton Mallet, Somerset, BA4 6BW.* Own secluded valley of lakes and wild gardens. Wells-Longleat. **Open:** Mar to Nov
01749 830246 (also fax) Mrs Sage
donaldsage@compuserve.com **D:** £18.00–£20.00
S: £20.00–£22.00 **Beds:** 1F 1T 1D ♿ 🅿 (6) ⚡
📺 🛏 ♨

Valley View Farm, *Batcombe, Shepton Mallet, Somerset, BA4 6AJ.* Bungalow residence, extensive gardens, secluded, overlooking a picturesque valley. **Open:** All year (not Xmas/New Year) **Grades:** ETC 3 Diamond
01749 850302 & 07813 679020 (M) Mrs Mead
Fax: 01749 850302 *valleyviewfarm@lineone.net*
D: £20.00 **S:** £22.00–£25.00 **Beds:** 1T 1D
Baths: 1 En 1 Sh ♿ 🅿 ⚡ 📺 🛏 Ⓥ 🛏 ♨

Bath

ST7464 🍺 *Royal Oak*

Crofton Cottage, *Bath Road, Swineford, Bitton, Bristol, BS30 6LW.*
Open: All year
0117 932 3671
Mr & Mrs Marsh *crofton.cott@virgin.net*
D: £20.00–£25.00 **S:** £30.00–£35.00 **Beds:** 1T
1D **Baths:** 2 En 🅿 (6) 📺 🛏 Ⓥ 🛏 ♨
4 miles from Bath and 6 miles from Bristol on the A431. This pretty 1800s cottage, recently refurbished, on the banks of the River Avon, with private fishing and moorings. Offering bed and breakfast to a high standard.

Cranleigh, *159 Newbridge Hill, Bath, BA1 3PX.*
Open: All year (not Xmas)
Grades: AA 4 Diamond
01225 310197 Mr Poole **Fax: 01225 423143**
cranleigh@btinternet.com
www.cranleighguesthouse.com **D:** £33.00–£43.00 **S:** £45.00–£55.00 **Beds:** 2F 2T 4D
Baths: 8 En ♿ (5) 🅿 (5) ⚡ 📺 🛏 ♨ cc
Charming Victorian house a short distance from the city centre. Spacious bedrooms, most with country views, offer comfort and quality. Imaginative breakfasts served in elegant dining room include fresh fruit salad and scrambled eggs with smoked salmon.

Wentworth House Hotel, *106 Bloomfield Road, Bath, BA2 2AP.* **Open:** All year **Grades:** AA 2 Star, RAC 4 Diamond
01225 339193 Mrs Boyle **Fax: 01225 310460**
stay@wentworthhouse.co.uk
www.wentworthhouse.co.uk **D:** £26.00–£50.00 **S:** £40.00–£70.00 **Beds:** 2F 12D 2T 2S
Baths: 17 En 1 Pr ♿ (5) 🅿 (20) 📺 ✕ Ⓥ 🛏 ♨ cc
A Victorian mansion 15 minutes walk from the city. Quiet location with large garden and car park. Heated swimming pool, licensed restaurant and cocktail bar. Golf and walks nearby. Lovely rooms, some with four-poster beds and conservatories.

The Albany Guest House, *24 Crescent Gardens, Bath, BA1 2NB.* **Open:** All year (not Xmas/New Year) **Grades:** ETC 4 Diamond, Silver
01225 313339 Mrs Wotley *the_albany@lineone.net* www.bath.org/hotel/albany.htm
D: £18.00–£25.00 **S:** £25.00–£35.00 **Beds:** 2D
1T 1S **Baths:** 1 En 1 Sh ♿ (5) 🅿 (3) ⚡ 📺 Ⓥ 🛏
♨
Jan and Bryan assure you of a warm welcome to their Victorian home. Only five minutes walk to the city centre - Roman Baths, Abbey, Royal Crescent etc. Delicious English or vegetarian breakfast. Imaginatively decorated rooms and first class service.

All details shown are as supplied by B&B owners in Autumn 2001

Planning a longer stay? Always ask for any special rates

Pantiles, *Bathway, Chewton Mendip, Bath, Somerset, BA3 4Ns.* **Open:** All year (not Xmas) **Grades:** ETC 4 Diamond
01761 241519 Ms Hellard **Fax: 01761 241598**
D: £19.00–£20.00 **S:** £21.00–£22.00 **Beds:** 1F
2T **Baths:** 2 En 1 Pr ♿ 🅿 (20) ⚡ 📺 🛏 Ⓥ 🛏 ♨
Delightful family home set in 2 acres of garden and paddock, offering 2 ensuite bedrooms with colour TV and hospitality trays. Pretty garden with summer house where guests can sit and relax. Traditional English breakfasts. 15 miles Bath/Bristol. 5: Wells, 8: Cheddar.

Marlborough House, *1 Marlborough Lane, Bath, BA1 2NQ.* **Open:** All year
Grades: ETC 4 Diamond
01225 318175 L Dunlop **Fax: 01225 466127**
mars@manque.dircon.co.uk
www.marlborough-house.net **D:** £32.50–£47.50 **S:** £45.00–£75.00 **Beds:** 2F 1T 3D 1S
Baths: 7 En ♿ 🅿 ⚡ 📺 🛏 ✕ Ⓥ 🛏 ❄ ♨ cc
An enchanting Victorian small hotel in the heart of Georgian Bath, exquisitely furnished, but run in a friendly and informal style. Specialising in organic vegetarian world cuisine. Our central location, gorgeous rooms, and unique menu make Marlborough House truly special.

Cherry Tree Villa, *7 Newbridge Hill, Bath, Somerset, BA1 3PW.* Small friendly Victorian home 1 mile from city centre. **Open:** All year (not Xmas/New Year) **Grades:** ETC 3 Diamond
01225 331671 Ms Goddard **D:** £18.00–£24.00
S: £20.00–£30.00 **Beds:** 1F/T 1D 1S **Baths:** 1
Sh ♿ (4) 🅿 📺 Ⓥ 🛏 ♨

Bailbrook Lodge, *35-37 London Road West, Bath, BA1 7HZ.* **Open:** All year **Grades:** ETC 3 Diamond, AA 3 Diamond
01225 859090 Mrs Sexton **Fax: 01225 852299** *hotel@bailbrooklodge.co.uk* www.bailbrooklodge.co.uk **D:** £25.00–£40.00 **S:** £39.00–£50.00 **Beds:** 4F 4D 4T **Baths:** 12 En ☎ ⚲ (14) ⎗ 📺 ✕ 📶 ▥ 🚲 **cc**
Bailbrook Lodge is an imposing Georgian House set it its own gardens. The elegant period bedrooms (some four posters) offer ensuite facilities, TV and hospitality trays, bar and restaurant overlook each other. Private parking. 1.5 miles from Bath centre. Close to M4.

Dorset Villa, *14 Newbridge Road, Bath, BA1 3JZ.* Walking distance from centre and amenities. Quality surroundings. Cooked breakfast. **Open:** All year (not Xmas/New Year)
01225 425975 (also fax) *reception@ dorsetvilla-bath.activehotels.com* www.dorsetvilla.co.uk **D:** £19.00–£30.00 **S:** £20.00–£34.00 **Beds:** 2F 2T 4D 1S **Baths:** 8 En 1 Sh ☎ 🅿 (9) ⎗ 📺 📶 ▥ 🚲 ♿ **cc**

Grove Lodge, *11 Lambridge, Bath, BA1 6BJ.* Grade II listed Georgian villa, large rooms with views. **Open:** All year (not Xmas/New Year)
01225 310860 I Miles **Fax: 01225 429630** *grovelodge@bath24.fsnet.co.uk* **D:** £25.00– £32.50 **S:** £30.00–£45.00 **Beds:** 1F 2T 3D **Baths:** 3 En 2 Pr ☎ (6) ⎗ 📺 ▥ 🚲

Dene Villa, *5 Newbridge Hill, Bath, BA1 3PW.* Victorian family-run guest house, a warm welcome is assured. **Open:** All year
01225 427676 Mrs Surry **Fax: 01225 482684** *denevilla@yahoo.co.uk* **D:** £20.00–£22.50 **S:** £20.00–£23.00 **Beds:** 1F 1D 1T 1S **Baths:** 3 En ☎ (3) 🅿 (4) 📺 📶 🚲

Flaxley Villa, *9 Newbridge Hill, Bath, BA1 3PW.* Comfortable Victorian house near Royal Crescent. 15 minute walk to centre. **Open:** All year **Grades:** ETC 3 Diamond
01225 313237 Mrs Cooper **D:** £20.00–£30.00 **S:** £18.00–£36.00 **Beds:** 3D 1T 1S **Baths:** 3 En ☎ (5) 📺 📶 🚲

Koryu B&B, *7 Pulteney Gardens, Bath, Somerset, BA2 4HG.* Completely renovated Victorian home, extremely clean, beautiful linens. Delicious breakfasts with wide menu. **Open:** All year **Grades:** AA 3 Diamond
01225 337642 (also fax) Mrs Shimizu **D:** £24.00–£25.00 **S:** £28.00–£30.00 **Beds:** 1F 2D 2T 2S **Baths:** 5 En 2 Sh ☎ 🅿 (2) ⎗ 📺 ✕ 📶 🚲

Lindisfarne, *41a Warminster Road, Bath, Somerset, BA2.* Friendly and comfortable with great breakfasts. Handy for historic Bath. **Open:** All year **Grades:** ETC 4 Diamond
01225 466342 *lindisfarne-bath@talk21.com* **D:** £20.00–£30.00 **S:** £35.00–£38.00 **Beds:** 1F 1T 2D **Baths:** 4 En ☎ (8) 🅿 (6) ⎗ 📺 📶 ▥ 🚲 **cc**

14 Raby Place, *Bathwick Hill, Bath, Somerset, BA2 4EH.* Charming Georgian terraced house with beautiful interior rooms. **Open:** All year **Grades:** ETC 4 Diamond
01225 465120 Mrs Guy **Fax: 01225 465283** **D:** £22.50–£28.00 **S:** £25.00–£35.00 **Beds:** 1F 2D 1T 1S **Baths:** 3 En 2 Pr ☎ ⎗ 📺 📶 ▥ 🚲

Georgian Guest House, *34 Henrietta Street, Bath, BA2 6LR.* Situated just 2 mins walk to city centre in a peaceful location. **Open:** All year (not Xmas)
01225 424103 Mr Kingwell **Fax: 01225 425279** *georgian@georgian-house.co.uk* www.georgian-house.co.uk **D:** £30.00–£35.00 **S:** £30.00–£50.00 **Beds:** 7D 2T 2S **Baths:** 7 En 1 Sh ☎ ⎗ 📺 📶 ▥ 🚲 **cc**

Wellsway Guest House, *51 Wellsway, Bath, BA2 4RS.* Edwardian house near Alexandra Park. Easy walks to city centre. **Open:** All year **Grades:** ETC 2 Diamond
01225 423434 Mrs Strong **D:** £18.00–£20.00 **S:** £20.00–£25.00 **Beds:** 1F 1D 1T 1S **Baths:** 4 Sh ☎ 🅿 (4) 📺 📹 📶 🚲

The Old Red House, *37 Newbridge Road, Bath, BA1 3HE.* A romantic Victorian gingerbread house with stained glass windows, comfortable bedrooms, superbly cooked breakfasts. **Open:** Mar to Dec
01225 330464 Fax: 01225 331661 *oldredhouse@amserve.net* www.oldredhouse.co. uk **D:** £22.00–£33.00 **S:** £30.00–£45.00 **Beds:** 1F 4D 1T 1S **Baths:** 3 En 1 Pr 1 Sh ☎ (4) 🅿 (4) ⎗ 📺 📹 📶 🚲 **cc**

Brookfields, *29 London Road West, Bath, Somerset, BA1 7HZ.* One mile from Bath centre. Easy from M4. Parking. All facilities **Open:** All year
01225 859090 D: £20.00–£27.50 **S:** £25.00– £40.00 **Beds:** 3D **Beds:** 2 En 1 Pr ☎ 🅿 (14) 📺 ✕ 📶 🚲 **cc**

Royal Park Guest House, *16 Crescent Gardens, Bath, Somerset, BA1 2NA.* Close to Bath's centre Roman Baths, Royal Crescent and circus. **Open:** All year (not Xmas) **Grades:** ETC 2 Diamond
01225 317651 Fax: 01225 483950 *royal@ park6-6.freeserve.co.uk* **D:** £21.00–£25.00 **S:** £50.00–£30.00 **Beds:** 1F 1T 1D 1S **Baths:** 3 En 1 Pr ☎ (5) 🅿 (3) ⎗ 📶 🚲

Membland Guest House, *7 Pulteney Terrace Pulteney Road, Bath, BA2 4HJ.* Comfortable Victorian guest house close to Roman Baths, Abbey, train/coach stations. **Open:** All year (not Xmas)
01225 336712 & 07958 599572 (M) Mr Moore *prmoore@wimpey.co.uk* www.accommodation-bath.com **D:** £20.00– £24.00 **S:** £30.00–£35.00 **Beds:** 1F 1T 1D 🅿 📺 📶 🚲

No 2 Crescent Gardens, *Upper Bristol Road, Bath, BA1 2NA.* Beautiful B&B in the heart of Bath. Warm welcome. **Open:** All year (not Xmas/New Year)
01225 331186 Mr Bez **D:** £19.00–£25.00 **S:** £19.00–£25.00 **Beds:** 1F 3T 3D **Baths:** 3 En 1 Sh ⎗ 📺 📶 🚲

Sarnia, *19 Combe Park, Weston, Bath, BA1 3NR.* Superb B&B in large Victorian home, easy reach of town centre. **Open:** All year (not Xmas/New Year)
01225 424159 Mr & Mrs Fradley **Fax: 01225 337689 D:** £25.00–£32.50 **S:** £30.00–£40.00 **Beds:** 1F 1D 1T **Baths:** 2 En 1 Pr ☎ (3) ⎗ 📺 📶 🚲 **cc**

Forres House, *172 Newbridge Road, Bath, BA1 3LE.* A warm welcome, comfortable bed and big breakfast awaits you. **Open:** All year
01225 427698 J Jones *clive.sampson@eke.co.uk* **D:** £20.00–£25.00 **S:** £30.00–£35.00 **Beds:** 2F 1T 2D **Baths:** 5 En ☎ 🅿 (5) ⎗ 📺 📶 🚲 **cc**

Blairgowrie House, *55 Wellsway, Bath, BA2 4RT.* Fine late Victorian residence operating as a privately owned family-run guest house. **Open:** All year
01225 332266 Mr Roberts **Fax: 01225 484535** *blairgowrie.bath@ukgateway.net* **D:** £27.50– £30.00 **Beds:** 1T 2D **Baths:** 2 En 1 Pr ☎ 🅿 ⎗ 📺 📶 🚲

3 Thomas Street, *Walcot, Bath, Somerset, BA1 5NW.* Charming Georgian house convenient to all city amenities and shops. **Open:** All year (not Xmas)
01225 789540 Ms Saunders **D:** £20.00– £22.50 **S:** £20.00–£22.50 **Beds:** 2T **Baths:** 1 En 1 Sh ⎗ 📺 📶 🚲

The Glade, *Shaft Road, Combe Down, Bath, Somerset, BA2 7HP.* Secluded sylvan retreat. Comfortable, spacious accommodation in half acre natural woodland garden. **Open:** All year
01225 833172 L Markham *theglade@uk2.net* www.thegladebath.co.uk **D:** £18.00–£27.50 **S:** £20.00–£30.00 **Beds:** 1F 1D **Beds:** ☎ 🅿 (4) ⎗ 📺 📶 🚲 ♿ 🚲

Bathford

ST7966   ⚓ *Crown Inn, Swan Inn, Avondale*

Bridge Cottage, *Northfield End, Ashley Road, Bathford, Bath, BA1 7TT.* Idyllic cottage in award-winning gardens, village location adjoining Bath. **Open:** Easter to Oct
01225 852399 Mrs Mackay *daphne@ bridge-cottages.co.uk* **D:** £25.00–£27.50 **S:** £35.00–£37.50 **Beds:** 1T 2D **Baths:** 3 En ☎ 🅿 (2) ⎗ 📺 📶 🚲 ♿ 🚲

BEDROOMS
D = Double
T = Twin
S = Single
F = Family

Garston Cottage, Ashley Road, Bathford, Bath, N E Somerset, BA1 7TT. 3 miles from Bath, walled garden, spa pool, pool room. **Open:** All year
01225 852510 Ms Smart **Fax: 01225 852793**
garstoncot@aol.com **D:** £25.00–£30.00
S: £25.00–£35.00 **Beds:** 1F 1T 1D **Baths:** 3 En 1 Sh ➏ ☐ (1) ⟋ ☒ ⌁ ☒ ▦ cc

Bayford
ST7228

The Unicorn Inn, Bayford, Wincanton, Somerset, BA9 9NL. Bordering three counties warm welcome, excellent food-real ale. **Open:** All year
01963 32324 Mrs Waite **D:** £22.00–£26.00
S: £30.00 **Beds:** 1T 2D 1S **Baths:** 4 En ☐ (20) ☒ ✕ ☒ ▦ ⅏ cc

Berrow
ST2952

Martins Hill Farmhouse, Red Road, Berrow, Burnham-on-Sea, Somerset, TA8 2RW. Quiet farmhouse overlooking countryside. Golf course, sandy beach 1 mile. **Open:** Mar to Oct
01278 751726 Mrs Davies **Fax: 01278 751230**
D: £20.00–£22.50 **Beds:** 1F 1D 1T **Baths:** 1 En 1 Pr 1 Sh ➏ ☐ (6) ⟋ ☒ ▦ ⅏ cc

Bicknoller
ST1139

Quantock Moor Farm Cottage, Bicknoller, Taunton, Somerset, TA4 4ER. Peaceful surroundings, on Greenway path around Quantock Hills - Ideal walking.
Open: All year (not Xmas)
01984 656626 Mrs Seamons *quantock@ operamail.com* **D:** £17.00 **S:** £17.00 **Beds:** 1D 1T 1S **Baths:** 1 Pr ➏ ☐ (3) ☒ ⌁ ✕ ☒ ▦ ⅏

Bilbrook
ST0240

Steps Farmhouse, Bilbrook, Minehead, Somerset, TA24 6HE. Traditional C16th former farmhouse situated near Dunster, offering ensuite B&B accommodation. **Open:** Feb to Nov
01984 640974 Mr & Mrs James
stepsfarmhouse@fsbdial.co.uk **D:** £20.00–£22.00
S: £22.00–£25.00 **Beds:** 1F 1D 1T **Baths:** 3 En ➏ ☐ (6) ⟋ ☒ ☒ ▦ ⅏

Please respect a B&B's wishes regarding children, animals and smoking

---

BATHROOMS
En = Ensuite
Pr = Private
Sh = Shared

Binegar
ST6149

Mansefield House, Old Rectory Garden, Binegar, Bath, Somerset, BA3 4UG. Spacious detached house, edge of Mendip Hills. Quiet village location. Good food local inns.
Open: All year (not Xmas/New Year)
01749 840568 Ms Anstey **Fax: 01749 840572**
mansfieldhouse@aol.com **D:** £25.00 **S:** £30.00
Beds: 2T 1D **Baths:** 2 En 1 Pr ☐ (4) ⟋ ☒ ▦ ⅏

Bishop Sutton
ST5859

Centaur, Ham Lane, Bishop Sutton, Bristol, BS39 5TZ. Comfortable house, peaceful location, within easy reach Bath, Bristol, Wells, Cheddar. **Open:** Mar to Oct
Grades: ETC 3 Diamond
01275 332321 Mrs Warden **D:** £18.50–£20.00
S: £17.00–£22.00 **Beds:** 1F 1T 1S **Baths:** 1 En 2 Sh ➏ ☐ (4) ☒ ☒ ⅏

Bishops Lydeard
ST1629

West View, Minehead Road, Bishops Lydeard, Taunton, Somerset, TA4 3BS. Delightful listed Victorian house in village near the West Somerset Steam Railway. **Open:** All year
01823 432223 (also fax) Mrs Pattemore
D: £20.00–£25.00 **S:** £20.00–£30.00 **Beds:** 2T 1D **Baths:** 2 En ➏ (10) ☐ ⟋ ☒ ⌁ ☒ ▦ ⅏

The Mount, 32 Mount Street, Bishops Lydeard, Taunton, Somerset, TA4 3AN. Comfortable Georgian period residence in picturesque village at foot of Quantock Hills. **Open:** All year (not Xmas)
01823 432208 Mr & Mrs Hinton *d.hinton@ talk21.com* **D:** £20.00 **S:** £20.00–£25.00
Beds: 1D 3T **Baths:** 2 Sh ➏ (2) ☐ (4) ⟋ ☒ ▦ ⅏

Bishopswood
ST2512   🕯 Candelight Inn

Hawthorne House, Bishopswood, Chard, Somerset, TA20 3RS. Comfortable C19th house situated in the Blackdown Hills (AONB) 1 mile off the A303. **Open:** All year **Grades:** ETC 3 Diamond
01460 234482 & 07710 255059 (M) R & S Newman-Coburn **Fax: 01460 234482** *info@ roger-sarah.co.uk* www.roger-sarh.co.uk
D: £22.00 **S:** £30.00 **Beds:** 1T 2D **Baths:** 2 En 1 Pr ➏ (12) ☐ ⟋ ☒ ⌁ ☒ ▦ ⅏

B&B owners may vary rates – be sure to check when booking

Blagdon
ST4958

Butcombe Farm, Aldwick Lane, Butcombe, Bristol, BS40 7UW. **Open:** All year (not Xmas/New Year)
01761 462380 Mr Harvey **Fax: 01761 462300**
info@butcombe-farm.demon.co.uk
www.butcombe-farm.demon.co.uk
D: £20.00–£27.00 **S:** £30.00–£39.00 **Beds:** 2T 3D **Baths:** 5 En ➏ ☐ ⟋ ☒ ✕ ☒ ▦ ⅏ cc
Converted C14th manor house with character accommodation nestled at foot of Mendip Hills. Glorious countryside. ideal for walking cycling, horse riding,golf, clay pigeon and fishing nearby at Blagdon Lake. Close to Bristol, Bath, Cheddar, Wells, Glastonbury and Exmoor.

Blue Anchor
ST0343

Langbury Hotel, Blue Anchor, Minehead, Somerset, TA24 6LB. Small hotel. Sea views. 4 miles Minehead, in quiet village. **Open:** All year (not Xmas) **Grades:** ETC 3 Diamond, AA 3 Diamond
01643 821375 Fax: 01643 822012 *enquiries@ langbury.co.uk*www.langbury.co.uk **D:** £22.00–£25.00 **S:** £22.00–£45.00 **Beds:** 1F 2D 2T **Baths:** 5 En ➏ ☐ (5) ☒ ⌁ ☒ ▦ �👤 ⅏ cc

---

RATES
D = Price range per person sharing in a double or twin room
S = Price range for a single room

Brendon Hill

ST0234

Raleigh Cross Inn, *Brendon Hill, Watchet, Somerset, TA23 0LN.* **Open:** All year **01984 640343** Mrs Brinkley *ruth@raleghs@ aol.com* **D:** £20.00–£35.00 **S:** £30.00–£45.00 **Beds:** 4F 5T 8D **Baths:** 17 En ⌕ (0) 🅿 🗲 📺 ✝ ✕ 📺 ⬛ ♨ ♿ **cc**
Reputedly a C16th coaching inn, situated in the beautiful Brendon Hills. All food is freshly prepared and home cooked. Daily and weekend specials. We're famous locally for our farmer's carvery. 'An ideal base for discovering Exmoor, the Quantocks and the varied and interesting coastline'.

Brent Knoll

ST3250

Woodlands Country House Hotel, *Hill Lane, Brent Knoll, Highbridge, Somerset, TA9 4DF.* Quiet rural setting, lovely views, five minutes J22 M5. Warm welcome, comfortable accommodation. **Open:** All year **Grades:** AA 2 Star **01278 760362 & 01278 760232 Fax:** 01278 769090 *info@woodlands-hotel.co.uk* www.woodlands-hotel.co.uk **D:** £30.00 **S:** £30.00 **Beds:** 1F 1T 6D **Baths:** 8 En ⌕ 🅿 (16) 🗲 📺 ✕ 📺 ⬛ ♨ **cc**

Bridgwater

ST3037

Ash-Wembdon Farm, *Hollow Lane, Wembledon, Bridgewater, Somerset, TA5 2BD.* Enjoy a refreshing and memorable stay at our elegant yet homely farmhouse. **Open:** All year (not Xmas) **Grades:** ETC 4 Diamond, Silver **01278 453097** Mr Rowe **Fax:** 01278 445856 *mary.rowe@btinternet.com* www.farmaccommodation.co.uk **D:** £22.00–£25.00 **S:** £25.00–£30.00 **Beds:** 2D 1T **Baths:** 2 En 1 Pr ⌕ (10) 🅿 (4) 🗲 📺 📺 ⬛ ♨ **cc**

The Acorns, *61 Taunton Road, Bridgwater, Somerset, TA6 3LP.* Jill & Ken offer welcoming and friendly hospitality with modern facilities, good breakfast, guest lounge. **Open:** All year (not Xmas) **01278 445577 & 07767 892703 (M)** *jillgraham@theacorns.fsbusiness.co.uk* **D:** £17.50–£20.00 **S:** £17.50–£20.00 **Beds:** 3F 2D 5T 3S **Baths:** 5 En 3 Sh ⌕ 🅿 (15) 📺 ✝ ⬛ ♨

Brompton Regis

SS9431

Bruneton House, *Brompton Regis, Dulverton, Somerset, TA22 9NN.* Spacious C17th house with beautiful garden overlooking the Pulham Valley. **Open:** All year (not Xmas) **01398 371224** J Stringer *brunetonhouse@ hotmail.com* **D:** £18.00–£20.00 **S:** £18.00–£20.00 **Beds:** 2D 1T **Baths:** 1 En 2 Pr ⌕ 🅿 (3) 📺 ✕ 📺 ⬛ ♨

Burnham-on-Sea

ST3049 *White Horse*

Priorsmead, *23 Rectory Road, Burnham-on-Sea, Somerset, TA8 2BZ.* Edwardian family home, peaceful gardens, swimming, quality accommodation. Reduction three nights. **Open:** All year (not Xmas) **01278 782116 & 07990 595585 (M)** Mrs Alexander **Fax:** 01278 782116 *PriorsMead@aol.com* www.smoothhound.co.uk/hotels/priors.html **D:** £17.00–£20.00 **S:** £20.00–£25.00 **Beds:** 1D 2T **Baths:** 2 En 1 Pr ⌕ (12) 🅿 (3) 🗲 📺 ✝ 📺 ⬛ ♨

Somewhere House, *68 Berrow Road, Burnham-on-Sea, Somerset, TA8 2EZ.* Victorian property within easy reach of town centre, near golf course. **Open:** All year (not Xmas/New Year) **Grades:** ETC 3 Diamond **01278 795236** Mr & Mrs Fellingham *di@ somewherehouse.com* www.somewherehouse.com **D:** £20.00 **S:** £26.00 **Beds:** 2F 2T 1D **Baths:** 5 En 🅿 (6) 🗲 📺 📺 ⬛ ♨

Butleigh

ST5233

Court Lodge, *Butleigh, Glastonbury, Somerset, BA6 8SA.* Attractive modernised 1850 lodge. In picturesque garden, edge of Butleigh. 3m Glastonbury, Street. **Open:** All year (not Xmas) **01458 850575** Mrs Atkinson **D:** £15.50 **S:** £15.50 **Beds:** 1D 1T 2S **Baths:** 2 En ⌕ 🅿 🗲 📺 ✝ ✕ 📺 ⬛

Cannington

ST2539 *Kings Head, Friendly Spirit, Malt Shovel, Globe*

Gurney Manor Mill, *Gurney Street, Cannington, Bridgwater, Somerset, TA5 2HW.* **Open:** All year **Grades:** ETC 4 Diamond **01278 653582** Mr & Mrs Sutton **Fax:** 01278 653993 *gurneymill@yahoo.co.uk* www.gurneymill.freeserve.co.uk **D:** £20.00–£25.00 **S:** £25.00–£30.00 **Beds:** 2F 1T 1D **Baths:** 4 En ⌕ 🅿 (15) 🗲 📺 ✝ 📺 ⬛ ♨ ♿ **cc**
Old watermill and barn conversion alongside a stream with waterfall and wildlife in picturesque village, private fishing, golf, rambling, and heritage gardens nearby. Ideal location for touring South West, Devon, Dorset, Wiltshire. The gateway to Quantock Hills.

Castle Cary

ST6332 *Pilgrim's Rest, George Hotel, Manor Inn*

Orchard Farm, *Castle Cary, Somerset, BA7 7NY.* Comfortable farmhouse in large gardens and quiet countryside. **Open:** All year **01963 350418 (also fax)** Mr & Mrs Boyer *boyeroj@talk21.com.uk* **D:** £20.00–£24.00 **S:** £22.00–£24.00 **Beds:** 1F 1D **Baths:** 2 Pr ⌕ 🅿 (4) 📺 ✝ ⬛ ♨

Clanville Manor, *Castle Cary, Somerset, BA7 7PJ.* C18th elegance. C21st comfort. **Open:** All year (not Xmas/New Year) **Grades:** ETC 4 Diamond **01963 350124 & 07966 512732 (M)** Mrs Snook **Fax:** 01963 350313 *info@clanvillemanor.co.uk* www.clanvillemanor.co.uk **D:** £25.00–£30.00 **S:** £25.00–£45.00 **Beds:** 1F 1T 1D 1S **Baths:** 3 En ⌕ 🅿 (6) 🗲 📺 📺 ⬛ ♨ **cc**

Chard

ST3208

The Firs, *Crewkerne Road, Cricket St Thomas, Chard, Somerset, TA20 4BU.* Warm and friendly, 'Home from Home' with beautiful countryside views. **Open:** All year **01460 65646 (also fax)** S Bright **D:** £20.00 **S:** £25.00 **Beds:** 1T 2D **Baths:** 1 En 2 Pr ⌕ 🅿 🗲 📺 📺 ⬛ ♨

Please respect a B&B's wishes regarding children, animals and smoking

Yew Tree Cottage, Hornsbury Hill, Chard, Somerset, *TA20 3DB.* Equipped to a high standard with large ensuite bathrooms, large mature gardens, excellent position. **Open:** All year (not Xmas/New Year)
01460 64735 Viv & Phillip Hopkins **Fax:** 01460 66163 *ytcottage@aol.com* yewtreecottage.org.uk **D:** £22.50 **S:** £30.00–£35.00 **Beds:** 1T 2D **Baths:** 3 En ☺ (10) ▣ (4)
⊬ ⊡ Ⅴ ▥ ᵻ

Charlton Horethorne

ST6623 ⦚ *The Mitre, Queens Arms, Kings Head*

Beech Farm, Sigwells, Charlton Horethorne, Sherborne, Dorset, *DT9 4LN.*
Open: All year (not Xmas/New Year)
01963 220524 (also fax) Mrs Stretton
D: £16.00 **S:** £16.00 **Beds:** 1T 1D 1S **Baths:** 1 En 1 Sh ☺ ▣ (6) ⊡ ⋔ ▥ ᵻ
Comfortable, spacious farmhouse with relaxed atmosphere on dairy farm with horses. Wonderful views from Corton Beacon. Six miles from Wincanton, 4 miles from historic abbey town of Sherborne. Just 2 miles off A303. Less 10% for 3 nights or more.

Ashclose Farm, Charlton Horethorne, Sherborne, Dorset, *DT9 4PG.* Comfortable farmhouse, peaceful countryside, friendly welcome and relaxed atmosphere.
Open: All year (not Xmas)
01963 220360 Mr & Mrs Gooding *gooding@ ashclosefarm.freeserve.co.uk* **D:** £18.00–£22.00
S: £18.00–£22.00 **Beds:** 1D 1T 1S **Baths:** 1 En 1 Sh ☺ ▣ (5) ⊡ ⋔ Ⅴ ▥ ᵻ

Cheddar

ST4553 ⦚ *Gardeners' Arms*

Tor Farm Guest House, Nyland, Cheddar, Somerset, *BS27 3UD.* High quality farmhouse accommodation close to Bath, Wells, Glastonbury and Cheddar. **Open:** All year (not Xmas) **Grades:** ETC 4 Diamond
01934 743710 Mrs Ladd *bcjbkj@aol.com*
D: £17.50–£24.00 **S:** £25.00–£30.00 **Beds:** 1F 3D 2T 1S **Baths:** 5 En 2 Sh ☺ ▣ (10) ⊬ ⊡ ▥ ᵻ cc

Southland House, Upper New Road, Cheddar, Somerset, *BS27 3DW.* Excellent ensuite accommodation, outskirts of Cheddar Village, ideal touring centre.
Open: All year (not Xmas)
01934 742189 Mrs Biggin *bb@ southlandhouse.freeserve.co.uk* **D:** £20.00–£22.00 **S:** £25.00 **Beds:** 1F 1T **Baths:** 2 En ☺ (1) ▣ (4) ⊬ ⊡ Ⅴ ▥ ᵻ

Constantine, Lower New Road, Cheddar, Somerset, *BS27 3DY.* Beautiful views of Cheddar Gorge and Mendips. Good breakfast.
Open: All year (not Xmas) **Grades:** ETC 3 Diamond
01934 741339 Mr & Mrs Mitchell **D:** £18.00–£20.00 **S:** £18.00–£20.00 **Beds:** 1F 2D 1S **Baths:** 1 Sh ☺ ▣ (5) ⊬ ⊡ ⋔ ✕ Ⅴ ▥ ᵻ

Chew Stoke

ST5561

Orchard House, Bristol Road, Chew Stoke, Bristol, *BS40 8UB.* Family-run, 'home from home'. **Open:** All year
01275 333143 Mrs Hollomon **Fax:** 01275 333754 *orchardhse@ukgateway.net*
www.orchardhse.ukgateway.net **D:** £20.00–£25.00 **S:** £22.00–£27.00 **Beds:** 1F 2D 3T 1S **Baths:** 5 En 1 Pr 1 Sh ☺ ▣ (8) ⊡ ✕ Ⅴ ▥ ᵻ cc

Chewton Mendip

ST5953

Franklyns Farm, Chewton Mendip, Bath, Somerset, *BA3 4NB.* Cosy farmhouse in heart of Mendip Hills. Superb views, peaceful setting. Large garden, tennis. **Open:** All year **Grades:** ETC 3 Diamond
01761 241372 (also fax) Mrs Clothier
D: £20.00 **S:** £22.50 **Beds:** 2T 1D **Baths:** 2 En 1 Pr ☺ ▣ ⊬ ⊡ ⋔ Ⅴ ▥ ✳ ᵻ

Pantiles, Bathway, Chewton Mendip, Bath, Somerset, *BA3 4Ns.* Delightful family home set in 2 acres of garden and paddock. Traditional English breakfasts. **Open:** All year (not Xmas) **Grades:** ETC 4 Diamond
01761 241519 Ms Hellard **Fax:** 01761 241598
D: £19.00–£20.00 **S:** £21.00–£22.00 **Beds:** 1F 2T **Baths:** 2 En 1 Pr ☺ ▣ (20) ⊬ ⊡ ⋔ Ⅴ ▥ ᵻ

Chilcompton

ST6452

Pipers Pool, Wells Road, Chilcompton, Bath, Somerset, *BA3 4ET.* Friendly welcome, indoor pool, great food, near Bath, Cheddar, Wells. **Open:** All year (not Xmas/New Year)
01761 233803 Mrs Sawyer **D:** £20.00–£25.00 **S:** £25.00–£30.00 **Beds:** 1T 2D **Baths:** 1 En ☺ ▣ (6) ⊬ ⊡ ✕ Ⅴ ▥ ᵻ

Chilthorne Domer

ST5219

Jessops, Vagg Lane, Chilthorne Domer, Yeovil, *BA22 8RY.* New bungalow, Jessops, with panoramic views,set in open countryside, one ensuite with four-poster.
Open: All year (not Xmas/New Year)
01935 841097 (also fax) Mr & Mrs White
D: £40.00–£48.00 **S:** £20.00–£25.00 **Beds:** 1T 1D 1S **Baths:** 1 En 1 Sh ☺ ▣ ⊬ ⊡ ⋔ Ⅴ ▥ ᵻ

Churchill

ST4359

Clumber Lodge, New Road, Churchill, Winscombe, Somerset, *BS25 5NW.* Bungalow with pretty garden, situated at the foot of Mendip Hills (AONB). **Open:** All year
01934 852078 (also fax) **D:** £15.00–£17.00 **S:** £16.00–£18.00 **Beds:** 2T **Baths:** 1 Sh ☺ ▣ (3) ⊬ ⊡ Ⅴ ▥ ᵻ

Churchstanton

ST1914

Pear Tree Cottage, Stapley, Churchstanton, Taunton, Somerset, *TA3 7QA.*
Open: All year **Grades:** ETC 2 Diamond
01823 601224 (also fax) Mrs Parry
colvin.parry@virgin.net **D:** £15.00–£17.00
S: £24.00 **Beds:** 1F 1D 1S **Baths:** 1 En 1 Pr ☺ ▣ (4) ⊬ ⊡ ⋔ ✕ Ⅴ ▥ ᵻ
Picturesque thatched cottage. Traditional garden, croquet lawn plus 2.5 acres arboretum. Idyllic tranquillity in beautiful AONB countryside. Central for touring north/south coasts, Exmoor, Dartmoor, Bath, Wells, Cheddar etc. Encircled by many famous private/National Trust Gardens. Stress-free paradise.

Combe Florey

ST1531

Redlands House, *Trebles Holford, Combe Florey, Taunton, Somerset,* TA4 3HA. **Open:** All year (not Xmas) **Grades:** ETC 4 Diamond, AA 4 Diamond
01823 433159 B L Totman *redlandshouse@ hotmail.com* www.escapetothecountry.co.uk
D: £26.50 **S:** £28.00 **Beds:** 1D 1T **Baths:** 2 En ⑤ ▣ (3) ⊬ ⊡ ☩ ▥ ▥, ♿ ☂
A warm welcome awaits you at this peaceful spot by the Quantock Hills. Good location for touring, walking, cycling or just enjoying the local scenery and wildlife. Close to the restored West Somerset Railway. Downstairs courtyard room suitable for disabled.

Compton Dundon

ST4933

Rickham House, *Compton Dundon, Somerton, Somerset,* TA11 6QA.
Fantastic views, filling farmhouse breakfasts. Close to Clarks village/ Glastonbury. **Open:** All year **Grades:** ETC 4 Diamond
01458 445056 Ms Rood *rickham.house@ talk21.com* **D:** £20.00–£25.00 **S:** £25.00– £30.00 **Beds:** 2D **Baths:** 2 En ⑤ ⊬ ⊡ ▥ ▥, ☂

Coxley

ST5343

Tynings House, *Harters Hill Lane, Coxley, Wells, Somerset,* BA5 1RF. **Open:** All year (not Xmas/ New Year)
Grades: AA 4 Diamond
01749 675368 (also fax) Mrs Parsons *b+b@ tynings.co.uk* www.tynings.co.uk **D:** £25.00– £35.00 **S:** £35.00–£45.00 **Beds:** 1T 2D
Baths: 3 En 3 Pr ▣ (10) ⊬ ⊡ ☓ ▥ ▥, ☂
Tynings House lies on the edge of a small village in the heart of Somerset. It is surrounded by 8 acres of Garden and Meadow with beautiful views over unspoilt countryside

Cranmore

ST6643

Burnt House Farm, *Waterlip, Cranmore, Shepton Mallet, Somerset,* BA4 4RN. Amazing breakfasts in happy cottage-style period farmhouse. Wine for multiple night stays. **Open:** All year **Grades:** ETC 4 Diamond, Silver
01749 880280 Mr Hoddinott **Fax: 01749 880004 D:** £22.00–£25.00 **S:** £25.00–£30.00 **Beds:** 1F 1D 1T **Baths:** 1 En 2 Pr ⑤ (4) ▣ (10) ⊬ ⊡ ▥ ▥, ☂

BATHROOMS
En = Ensuite
Pr = Private
Sh = Shared

Lynfield, *Frome Road, Cranmore, Shepton Mallet, Somerset,* BA4 4QQ. Country house in large garden, close Bath and West show ground. **Open:** All year (not Xmas)
01749 880600 Mrs Gilderthorp *rsgildo@ aol.com* **D:** £20.00 **S:** £25.00 **Beds:** 1D 1T 1S **Baths:** 2 En 1 Sh ⑤ ▣ (3) ⊬ ⊡ ▥ ▥, ♿ ☂

Creech St Michael

ST2625

Creechbarn, *Vicarage Lane, Creech St Michael, Taunton,* TA3 5PP. Converted longbarn in rural location. Quiet. 3 mins M5 J25. **Open:** All year (not Xmas/New Year)
01823 443955 H M Humphreys **Fax: 01823 443509** *mick@somersite.co.uk* www.somersite. co.uk **D:** £20.00–£22.00 **S:** £20.00–£29.00 **Beds:** 1T 2D **Baths:** 1 En ⑤ ▣ (4) ⊡ ☩ ☓ ▥ ▥, ☂

Crewkerne

ST4409

Manor Farm, *Wayford, Crewkerne, Somerset,* TA18 8QL. Beautiful Victorian home in a peaceful location with undulating views. **Open:** All year **Grades:** AA 4 Diamond
01460 78865 & 07767 620031 (M) Mr Emery www.manorfarm.com **D:** £22.00–£25.00 **S:** £22.00–£25.00 **Beds:** 3F 1T **Baths:** 4 En ⑤ ▣ (50) ⊬ ⊡ ▥ ▥, ☂

Cricket St Thomas

ST3708

The Firs, *Crewkerne Road, Cricket St Thomas, Chard, Somerset,* TA20 4BU. Warm and friendly, 'Home from Home' with beautiful countryside views. **Open:** All year **01460 65646 (also fax)** S Bright **D:** £20.00 **S:** £25.00 **Beds:** 1T 2D **Baths:** 1 En 2 Pr ⑤ ▣ ⊬ ⊡ ▥ ▥, ☂

Culbone

SS8448

Silcombe Farm, *Culbone, Porlock, Minehead, Somerset,* TA24 8JN. Comfortable secluded Exmoor farmhouse overlooking sea in beautiful walking country. **Open:** All year (not Xmas)
01643 862248 Mrs Richards **D:** £18.00– £20.00 **S:** £20.00 **Beds:** 1D 2T 1S **Baths:** 1 En 1 Sh ⑤ (4) ▣ (6) ▣ ☩ ☓ ⊡ ▥ ▥, ☂

Curland

ST2717

The Spinney, *Curland, Taunton, Somerset,* TA3 5SE. Quality ensuite B&B with excellent evening meals (recommended). Convenient from M5 and A303. **Open:** All year
01460 234362 (also fax) Mr & Mrs Bartlett *bartlett.spinney@zetnet.co.uk* www.somerweb. co.uk/ spinney-bb **D:** £22.00–£24.00 **S:** £30.00 **Beds:** 1F 1D 1T **Baths:** 3 En ⑤ ▣ (6) ⊬ ⊡ ☓ ▥ ▥, ☂

Doulting

ST6443

Temple House Farm, *Doulting, Shepton Mallet, Somerset,* BA4 4RQ. Listed farmhouse, warm welcome, close to East Somerset Railway and many other attractions. **Open:** All year
01749 880294 Mrs Reakes **D:** £42.00 **S:** £25.00 **Beds:** 1T 1D ⑤ (5) ▣ (4) ⊬ ⊡ ☓ ▥ ▥, ☂

Dulverton

SS9128

Winsbere House, *64 Battleton, Dulverton, Somerset,* TA22 9HU. Delightful private House. Lovely country views. Excellent location touring Exmoor. **Open:** All year (not Xmas/New Year) **Grades:** ETC 3 Diamond
01398 323278 Mrs Rawle www.exmoor.tv **D:** £17.00–£22.50 **S:** £20.00 **Beds:** 1T 2D **Baths:** 2 En 1 Sh ⑤ (8) ▣ (3) ⊬ ⊡ ▥ ▥, ☂

Springfield Farm, *Ashwick Lane, Dulverton, Somerset,* TA22 9QD. Ensuite accommodation with delicious meals. Ideal location for walking/touring Exmoor and North Devon. **Open:** Easter to Nov **Grades:** ETC 4 Diamond
01398 323722 Mrs Vellacott *info@ springfieldfarms.co.uk* www.springfieldfarms. co.uk **D:** £20.00–£23.50 **S:** £25.00–£35.00 **Beds:** 1D 1T/F **Baths:** 2 En 1 Pr ⑤ (3) ▣ (3) ⊬ ⊡ ☩ ☓ ▥ ☂

Highercombe Farm, *Dulverton, Somerset,* TA22 9PT. On the very edge of expansive moorland, you will find our welcoming farmhouse home. **Open:** Mar to Nov
01398 323616 (also fax) Mrs Humphrey *abgail@highercombe.demon.co.uk* www.highercombe.demon.co.uk **D:** £20.00 **S:** £28.00 **Beds:** 2D 1T **Baths:** 3 En ⑤ (6) ▣ ⊡ ☩ ☓ ⊡ ▥ ▥, ☂

Planning a longer stay? Always ask for any special rates

Town Mills, *Dulverton, Somerset, TA22 9HB.* Enjoy English breakfast served in your spacious comfortable bedroom. Relax. **Open:** All year
01398 323124 J Buckingham *townmills@ onetel.co.uk* **D:** £20.00–£27.00 **S:** £25.00–£42.00 **Beds:** 1T 4D **Baths:** 3 En 2 Sh ☜ ⴲ(5) ⵣⵣⵣ ⵣ

Dunster

SS9943 ⬛ *Dunster Hotel, Foresters' Arms, Hathways, The Stables*

Spears Cross Hotel, *1 West Street, Dunster, Minehead, Somerset, TA24 6SN.* Listed C15th family-run hotel situated in the picturesque medieval village of Dunster. **Open:** Feb to Dec **Grades:** ETC 4 Diamond **01643 821439 (also fax)** Mr & Mrs Capel *mjcapel@aol.com* www.smoothhound.co. uk/hotels/spearsx.html **D:** £24.00–£27.50 **S:** £30.00–£35.00 **Beds:** 2F 1T 1D **Baths:** 4 En ☜ ⴲ(5) ⵋ ⵣ ⵣ ✕ ⵣ ⵣ ⴲ cc

Buttercross, *St Georges Street, Dunster, Minehead, Somerset, TA24 6RS.* Quiet location, close to village centre. Spacious period home. **Open:** All year (not Xmas/ New Year) **Grades:** AA 4 Diamond **01643 821413** S M Buck *megabucks@ buttercross39.freeserve.co.uk* **D:** £20.00–£25.00 **S:** £20.00–£25.00 **Beds:** 1F 1D **Baths:** 1 En 1 Sh ☜ (10) ⵋ ⵣ ⵣ ⵣ ⵣ

East Chinnock

ST4913

The Gables Guest House, *High Street, East Chinnock, Yeovil, Somerset, BA22 9DR.* 300-year-old cottage on A30 between Yeovil and Crewkerne. Cream teas and home cooking. **Open:** All year (not Xmas/New Year) **01935 862237 (also fax)** L W J Jones **D:** £18.00–£20.00 **S:** £18.00–£20.00 **Beds:** 1F 2T 2D **Baths:** 3 En ☜ ⴲ(6) ⵋ ⵣ ⵣ

East Horrington

ST5746

Manor Farm, *Old Frome Road, East Horrington, Wells, BA5 3DP.* Guaranteed warm welcome to our stunning C15th Listed farmhouse. Abundant period features. **Open:** All year **01749 679832 & 07774 733702 (M)** Mrs Fridd **Fax:** 01749 679849 *fridd@ fridd-wells.freeserve.co.uk* **D:** £25.00 **S:** £30.00 **Beds:** 2T **Baths:** 1 En 1 Pr ☜ ⴲ(3) ⵣ ⵣ ⵣ ⵣ ⵣ

BEDROOMS

D = Double
T = Twin
S = Single
F = Family

National Grid References given are for villages, towns and cities – not for individual houses

---

East Lambrook

ST4318 ⬛ *Rose & Crown*

East Lambrook Farm, *East Lambrook, South Petherton, Somerset, TA13 5HH.* C17th thatched farmhouse. Quiet, comfortable, excellent breakfasts, large garden, tennis. **Open:** All year (not Xmas) **01460 240064** Mrs Eeles **D:** £23.00–£25.00 **S:** £23.00–£25.00 **Beds:** 2D 1T **Baths:** 2 Pr ☜ (3) ⴲ(3) ⵋ ⵣ ✕ ⵣ ⵣ

East Pennard

ST5937

Pennard Hill Farm, *Stickleball Hill, East Pennard, Shepton Mallet, Somerset, BA4 6UG.* Total luxury and tranquillity. Breathtaking views. Ravishing outdoor pool. **Open:** All year **01749 890221** Mrs Judah **Fax:** 01749 890665 *phebejudah@aol.com* **D:** £50.00–£80.00 **S:** £70.00–£140.00 **Beds:** 1T 4D 3S **Baths:** 3 En 2 Pr 3 Sh ☜ ⴲ ⵣ ✕ ⵣ

Exford

SS8538 ⬛ *Crown Inn, White Horse*

Edgcott House, *Exford, Minehead, Somerset, TA24 7QG.* Old country house, peacefully situated in heart of Exmoor National Park. **Open:** All year (not Xmas/ New Year) **Grades:** ETC 3 Diamond **01643 831495 (also fax)** G Lamble **D:** £20.00–£23.00 **S:** £20.00–£23.00 **Beds:** 1T 2D **Baths:** 1 En 2 Pr ⴲ(6) ⵣ ⵣ ⵣ ⵣ ⵣ

Court Farm, *Exford, Minehead, Somerset, TA24 7LY.* In the heart of Exmoor. **Open:** All year (not Xmas/New Year) **01643 831207 (also fax)** Mr & Mrs Horstmann *beth@courtfarm.co.uk* www.courtfarm.co.uk **D:** £18.00 **S:** £18.00 **Beds:** 1T 1D **Baths:** 1 Sh ☜ ⴲ(15) ⵋ ⵣ ⵣ ⵣ ⵣ ⵣ cc

Exton

SS9233

Exton House Hotel, *Exton, Dulverton, Somerset, TA22 9JT.* A small family-run hotel set amidst wonderful scenery on the side of Exton valley. **Open:** All year **01643 851365** Mr & Mrs Glaister **Fax:** 01643 851213 **D:** £25.00–£32.50 **S:** £32.50 **Beds:** 3F 4D 1T 1S **Baths:** 8 En 1 Pr ☜ ⴲ(9) ⵋ ⵣ ⵣ ⵣ ⵣ ⵣ ✳ ⵣ cc

---

Frome

ST7747

Wadbury House, *Mells, Frome, Somerset, BA11 3PA.* Historic house, quiet surroundings, close to many places of interest. **Open:** All year **Grades:** ETC 3 Diamond **01373 812359** Mrs Brinkmann *sbrinkman@ btinternet.com* **D:** £28.00–£36.00 **S:** £28.00–£36.00 **Beds:** 1F 3T 1D **Baths:** 3 En 1 Pr ☜ ⴲ(10) ⵣ ⵣ ✕ ⵣ ⵣ ⵣ

Kensington Lodge Hotel, *The Butts, Frome, Somerset, BA11 4AA.* Comfortable hotel fitness and leisure facilities near Bath, Longleat, Cheddar Caves. **Open:** All year **01373 463935** Mr Aryan **Fax:** 01373 303570 *irajaryan@aol.com* **D:** £25.00 **S:** £30.00–£40.00 **Beds:** 1F 2D 3T 1S **Baths:** 6 En ☜ ⴲ(40) ⵣ ⵣ ⵣ ⵣ

Glastonbury

ST5039 ⬛ *The Appletree*

Meadow Barn, *Middlewick Farm, Wick Lane, Glastonbury, Somerset, BA6 8JW.* **Open:** All year (not Xmas) **Grades:** ETC 3 Diamond **01458 832351 (also fax)** Mrs Coles www.s. -h-systems.co.uk/212436 **D:** £22.00–£24.00 **S:** £26.00–£30.00 **Beds:** 1F/T 2D **Baths:** 3 En ☜ ⴲ ⵣ ✕ ⵣ ⵣ ⵣ ⵣ
Tastefully converted barn, ground floor ensuite accommodation with olde worlde charm and country-style decor. Set in award-winning cottage gardens, apple orchards and meadows. Beautiful tranquil countryside. Meadow Barn has a luxury indoor heated swimming pool.

Lottisham Manor, *Glastonbury, Somerset, BA6 8PF.* C16th manor house. Lovely garden. Hard tennis court. Perfect peace and comfort. **Open:** All year **01458 850205** Mrs Barker-Harland **D:** £17.50–£20.00 **S:** £17.50–£20.00 **Beds:** 1D 1T 1S **Baths:** 2 Sh ☜ ⴲ(8) ⵋ ⵣ ⵣ ⵣ ⵣ

Court Lodge, *Butleigh, Glastonbury, Somerset, BA6 8SA.* Attractive modernised 1850 lodge. In picturesque garden, edge of Butleigh. 3m Glastonbury, Street. **Open:** All year (not Xmas) **01458 850575** Mrs Atkinson **D:** £15.50 **S:** £15.50 **Beds:** 1D 1T 2S **Baths:** 2 En ☜ ⵋ ⵣ ⵣ ✕ ⵣ ⵣ

Pippin, *4 Ridgeway Gardens, Glastonbury, Somerset, BA6 8ER.* Every comfort in peaceful home opposite Chalice Hill. Short walk Tor/town. **Open:** All year **Grades:** ETC 3 Diamond
01458 834262 Mrs Slater *daphneslater@ talk21.com* www.smoothhound.co. uk/hotels/pippin.html **D:** £16.50–£18.50 **S:** £18.00–£22.00 **Beds:** 1D 1T **Baths:** 1 Sh
🄿 (2) 📺 ⌨ 📺 🛏, ♨

Hillclose, *Street Road, Glastonbury, Somerset, BA6 9EG.* Warm friendly atmosphere, clean rooms, comfortable beds, full English breakfast. **Open:** All year (not Xmas)
01458 831040 (also fax) Mr & Mrs Riddle **D:** £16.00–£20.00 **S:** £25.00–£35.00 **Beds:** 1F 2D 1T **Baths:** 2 Sh 🄿 (4) 📺 🛏, ♨

Divine Light, *16a Magdelene Street, Glastonbury, Somerset, BA6 9EH.* Central. Listed. Guest kitchen, lounge, terraced garden. Healing and massage. **Open:** All year **Grades:** ETC 3 Diamond
01458 835909 Mr & Mrs Flanagan *info@ glastonburyrose.co.uk* www.divinelightcentre. co.uk **D:** £20.00–£25.00 **S:** £30.00–£35.00 **Beds:** 1T 1D **Baths:** 1 Sh 🄿🛏⌨📺🛏, ✼ ♨

Shambhala Healing Centre, *Coursing Batch, Glastonbury, Somerset, BA6 8BH.* Beautiful house, sacred site on side of the Tor. Healing, massage, great vegetarian food. **Open:** All year **Grades:** ETC 2 Diamond
01458 833081 & 01458 831797 Mrs Nixon **Fax: 01458 831797** *isisandargon@ shambhala.co.uk* **D:** £64.00 **S:** £35.00 **Beds:** 2T 2D 1S **Baths:** 2 En 2 Sh 🛏, ♨ cc

Blake House, *3 Bove Town, Glastonbury, Somerset, BA6 8JE.* Listed stone house, close to town centre and all attractions. **Open:** All year (not Xmas/New Year) **Grades:** AA 3 Diamond
01458 831680 S Hankins *dshankins@ ukonline.co.uk* www.blake-house.co.uk **D:** £20.00–£22.00 **S:** £25.00–£30.00 **Beds:** 1T 2D **Baths:** 3 En 🄿 (2) ⌨ 📺 🛏, ♨

1 The Gables, *Street Road, Glastonbury, Somerset, BA6 9EG.* One minute from town centre. Good English breakfast. **Open:** All year (not Xmas/New Year)
01458 832519 Mrs Stott **D:** £17.00 **S:** £17.00 **Beds:** 1F 1T 2D **Baths:** 1 Sh 🄿⌨📺📺🛏, ♨

Southtown House, *Southtown, West Pennard, Glastonbury, Somerset, BA6 8NS.* Traditional farmhouse, superb views. Enthusiastic welcome. Breakfast provided. **Open:** Feb to Nov **Grades:** ETC 3 Diamond
01458 834552 Mr Trelawny **Fax: 01458 834494** *trelawny@tesco.net* **D:** £20.00–£25.00 **S:** £25.00–£30.00 **Beds:** 1T 1D **Baths:** 1 Sh 🄿 (8) 🄿 (5) ⌨ 📺 🛏 📺 🛏,

Little Orchard, *Ashwell Lane, Glastonbury, Somerset, BA6 8BG.* Glastonbury, famous for historic Tor, King Arthur, abbey ruins and alternative centre. **Open:** All year
01458 831620 Mrs Gifford **D:** £16.50–£21.00 **S:** £17.00–£22.00 **Beds:** 1F 1D 1T 2S **Baths:** 2 Sh 🛏 🄿⌨📺🛏 📺🛏, ♨

Godney

ST4842 🍺 *Sheppey Inn*

Double Gate Farm, *Godney, Wells, Somerset, BA5 1RX.* Comfortable, friendly, award-winning accommodation. Wonderful breakfasts - lots to see and do. **Open:** All year (not Xmas/New Year) **Grades:** ETC 4 Diamond, Gold, AA 4 Diamond, RAC 4 Diamond, Sparkling
01458 832217 Mrs Millard **Fax: 01458 835612** *hilary@doublegate.demon.co.uk* www.doublegatefarm.com **D:** £22.50 **S:** £30.00 **Beds:** 1F 3D 2T **Baths:** 6 En 🛏 🄿 (8) ⌨ 📺 📺 🛏, ♨

The Sheppey Inn, *Godney, Wells, Somerset, BA5 1RX.* Country pub, good pub grub. Live music Fri, Sat, Sun. **Open:** All year
01458 832917 **D:** £17.50 **S:** £17.50 **Beds:** 1F 1T 1S **Baths:** 1 Sh 🛏 🄿 (20) 📺 ✕ 📺 🛏, ♨ cc

Gurney Slade

ST6249

Lilac Cottage, *Gurney Slade, Bath, BA3 4TT.* Charming C18th house in village location between Bath and Wells. **Open:** All year
01749 840469 **D:** £15.00–£17.00 **S:** £15.00–£17.00 **Beds:** 1F 2D 1T **Baths:** 1 Sh 🛏 🄿⌨🛏 📺, ♨

Halse

ST1327

New Inn, *Halse, Taunton, Somerset, TA4 3AF.* Typical village inn, friendly atmosphere, relax and enjoy excellent home cooked fayre. **Open:** All year
01823 432352 Ms Hayes **D:** £18.00–£21.00 **S:** £20.00–£35.00 **Beds:** 2T 3D 5S **Baths:** 6 En 4 Sh 🄿⌨📺 ✕ 📺, ♨ cc

Hatch Beauchamp

ST2920

The Hatch Inn, *Hatch Beauchamp, Taunton, Somerset, TA3 6SG.* Situated in heart of village, we've been offering 'inn' hospitality for over 200 years. **Open:** All year
01823 480245 **Fax: 01823 481149** *isobel@ thehatchinn.co.uk* www.thehatchinn.co.uk **D:** £21.50–£30.00 **S:** £25.50–£32.50 **Beds:** 2F 6D **Baths:** 2 En 2 Sh 🛏 (14) 🄿 (26) ⌨ 📺 ✕ 📺 🛏, ✼ ♨ cc

Hawkridge

SS8530

East Hollowcombe Farm, *Hawkridge, Dulverton, Somerset, TA22 9QL.* Ideal Two Moors Way, views open moorland. Home cooked meals, fresh veg from garden. **Open:** All year (not Xmas/New Year)
01398 341622 H Floyd **D:** £14.00 **S:** £17.50 **Beds:** 1F 1T 1D 1S **Baths:** 1 Sh 🛏 🄿 (8) 📺 🛏 ✕ 📺 🛏, ♨

Henstridge

ST7219

Quiet Corner Farm, *Henstridge, Templecombe, Somerset, BA8 0RA.* Country house atmosphere with lovely garden; imaginative breakfasts. Recommended by 'Which?'. **Open:** All year **Grades:** ETC 4 Diamond
01963 363045 (also fax) Mrs Thompson *quietcorner.thompson@virgin.net* **D:** £21.00–£23.00 **S:** £27.00–£30.00 **Beds:** 1F 2D **Baths:** 1 En 1 Sh 🛏 🄿 (8) ⌨ 📺 🛏 📺 🛏, ♨

Henton

ST4945 🍺 *The Pheasant, Panborough Inn, Burcott Inn*

Rose Farm, *Henton, Wells, Somerset, BA5 1PD.* Lovely Georgian farmhouse, overlooking the Mendip Hills. Just outside beautiful Wells. **Open:** All year (not Xmas/ New Year)
01749 672908 Mrs Doherty *rosefarm5@ yahoo.co.uk* **D:** £23.00–£25.50 **Beds:** 1D **Baths:** 1 En 🄿 (2) ⌨ 📺 🛏, ♨

Hinton St George

ST4212

Rookwood, *West Street, Hinton St George, Somerset, TA17 8SA.* Comfortable accommodation in tranquil setting Listed NGS Garden. **Open:** All year (not Xmas/ New Year)
01460 73450 Mrs Hudspith *betty.hudspith@ virgin.net* **D:** £18.00–£19.00 **S:** £18.00–£19.00 **Beds:** 2T **Baths:** 1 En 1 Sh 🛏 (10) 🄿 (2) ⌨ 📺 🛏, ♨

Ludneymead, *Hinton St George, Somerset, TA17 8TD.* Family run farm close to many attractions. Secluded, peaceful, open views. **Open:** Easter to Oct
01460 57145 Mrs Chapman **D:** £19.00–£21.00 **Beds:** 1D **Baths:** 1 Pr 📺 ✕ 📺 ♨

All details shown are as supplied by B&B owners in Autumn 2001

Howley

ST2609

Howley Tavern, *Howley, Chard, Somerset, TA20 3DX.* C16th free house. Idyllic setting overlooking the beautiful Yarty Valley. **Open:** All year
01460 62157 K Leaf **D:** £25.00 **S:** £29.50
Beds: 1F 1T 1D 1S **Baths:** 3 En ⌂ 🖬 🖳 🗙
🖂 🎔 ⚓ cc

Hutton

ST3458

Moorlands Country Guest House,
Hutton, Weston-super-Mare, Somerset, BS24 9QH. Fine Georgian house, extensive landscaped gardens, village pub serves meals. **Open:** All year **Grades:** ETC 3 Diamond
01934 812283 (also fax) Mr & Mrs Holt
margaret_holt@email.com www.guestaccom.co.uk **D:** £20.00–£25.00 **S:** £20.00–£30.00
Beds: 3F 2D 1T 1S **Baths:** 5 En 1 Sh ⌂ 🖬 (7)
🖂 🎔 🖂 🖳 ♿3 ⚓ cc

Ilminster

ST3614   ⚑ *Crown Inn, Dolphin Inn*

Hermitage, *29 Station Road, Ilminster, Somerset, TA19 9BE.* Friendly, listed C17th house. Beams, inglenooks, fourposters. 2 acres delightful garden. **Open:** All year (not Xmas) **Grades:** ETC 3 Diamond
01460 53028 G Phillips www.smoothhound.co.uk/hotels/hermitagebb.html **D:** £19.00–£22.00 **S:** £22.00–£36.00 **Beds:** 1T 1D
Baths: 1 En 🖬 (2) 🖂 🖂 ⚓

Hylands, *22 New Road, Ilminster, Somerset, TA19 9AF.* Attractive Edwardian end-of-terrace. Small country town. Family home **Open:** All year (not Xmas/New Year)
01460 52560 Mrs Hayter *hayterbandb@talk21.com* **D:** £12.50–£15.00 **S:** £15.00
Beds: 1F 1D **Baths:** 2 Sh ⌂ 🖬 (2) 🗡 🖂 🖂 🖳

Keinton Mandeville

ST5430

Stangray House, *Church Street, Keinton Mandeville, Somerton, Somerset, TA11 6ER.* Family run country house in pleasant rural surroundings. Garden. Parking. **Open:** All year **Grades:** ETC 4 Diamond
01458 223984 Mr Moran **Fax:** 01458 224295
david.moran@btinternet.com stangrayguesthouse.co.uk **D:** £20.00–£22.50
S: £20.00–£25.00 **Beds:** 1F 1T 1D **Baths:** 1 En 1 Sh ⌂ 🖬 (6) 🗡 🖂 🗙 🖳 ⚓

Planning a longer stay? Always ask for any special rates

Kilve

ST1443

The Old Rectory, *Kilve, Bridgwater, Somerset, TA5 1DZ.* Foot of Quantocks; scenic walking/touring, local beach, pub, comfortable. **Open:** All year (not Xmas)
01278 741520 Chris & Jan Alder
oldrectorykilve@yahoo.co.uk **D:** £22.00–£25.00
S: £20.00–£25.00 **Beds:** 1F 1D 1T **Baths:** 3
En 🖬 (4) 🖂 🖳 ⚓

Kingston St Mary

ST2229

Lower Marsh Farm, *Kingston St Mary, Taunton, Somerset, TA2 8AB.*
Only 10 mins M5 J25. Warm welcome assured at tastefully refurbished farmhouse. **Open:** All year **Grades:** AA 3 Diamond
01823 451331 (also fax) Mr & Mrs Gothard
mail@lowermarshfarm.co.uk
www.lowermarshfarm.co.uk **D:** £22.50–£25.00 **S:** £25.00–£28.00 **Beds:** 1F 1T 1D
Baths: 2 En 1 Pr ⌂ 🖬 🗡 🖂 🗙 🖳 ⚓

Langport

ST4126

Amberley, *Long Load, Langport, Somerset, TA10 9LD.* Quality accommodation with far-reaching views on edge of Somerset Levels.
Open: All year (not Xmas) **Grades:** ETC 4 Diamond
01458 241542 Ms Jarvis *jeanatamberley@talk21.com* **D:** £17.00–£18.00 **S:** £17.00–£18.00 **Beds:** 1F 1T 1D **Baths:** 1 En 1 Sh ⌂ 🖬 (4) 🗡 🖂 🎔 🗙 🖳 ⚓

Long Load

ST4623

Fairlight, *Martock Road, Long Load, Langport, Somerset, TA10 9LG.* Detached bungalow, magnificent views. 2.5 acre garden, orchard & plantation. **Open:** All year (not Xmas/New Year)
01458 241323 Mrs Hook **D:** £17.50–£18.50
S: £18.50–£19.00 **Beds:** 1D 1T **Baths:** 1 En 1 Pr ⌂ (10) 🖬 (6) 🖂 🎔 🖳 ⚓

Lopen

ST4214   ⚑ *Royal Oak*

Rathmore, *Main St, Lopen, South Petherton, Somerset, TA13 5JU.* Attractive village, central for NT properties, Dorset coast, beautiful countryside. **Open:** All year
01460 240279 Mrs Webster **D:** £17.00–£18.00
S: £16.00 **Beds:** 2D 1S **Baths:** 1 Sh ⌂ (6)
🖬 (3) 🗡 🖂 🎔 🗙 🖳 ⚓

Martock

ST4619   ⚑ *Nag's Head*

Madey Mills, *Martock, Somerset, TA12 6NN.* Peaceful accommodation on working dairy farm, country views, riverside walk. **Open:** All year
01935 823268 Ms Clarke **D:** £18.00 **S:** £18.00
Beds: 1D 1S ⌂ 🖬 🖂 ⚓

The Nags Head, *East Street, Martock, Somerset, TA12 6NF.* The Nags Head is a charming village pub which dates back over 150 years. **Open:** All year
01935 823432 Fax: 01935 824265 **D:** £25.00
S: £30.00 **Beds:** 1F **Baths:** 1 En ⌂ 🖬 (24) 🖂
🖂 🎔 🗙 🖂 🖳 ⚓ cc

Mells

ST7249

The Talbot 15th Cenury Coaching Inn, *Mells, Frome, Somerset, BA11 3PN.*
Open: All year **Grades:** AA 4 Diamond
01373 812254 Fax: 01373 813599 *roger@talbotinn.com* www.talbotinn.com **D:** £35.00–£37.50 **S:** £39.50–£45.00 **Beds:** 1F 3T 4D
Baths: 7 En 1 Pr ⌂ 🖬 (10) 🖂 🎔 🗙 🖂 🖳 ⚓ cc
Beautiful coaching inn with ensuite and 4-poster bedrooms, tythe barn bar, award-winning oak-beamed restaurant and private cobbled courtyard. Located just south of Bath on the Mendip Hills, ideal for tourists, weddings, meetings and functions.

Wadbury House, *Mells, Frome, Somerset, BA11 3PA.* Historic house, quiet surroundings, close to many places of interest. **Open:** All year **Grades:** ETC 3 Diamond
01373 812359 Mrs Brinkmann *sbrinkman@btinternet.com* **D:** £28.00–£36.00 **S:** £28.00–£36.00 **Beds:** 1F 3T 1D **Baths:** 3 En 1 Pr ⌂
🖬 (10) 🖂 🎔 🗙 🖂 🖳 ⚓

Please respect a B&B's wishes regarding children, animals and smoking

BATHROOMS

En = Ensuite
Pr = Private
Sh = Shared

Midsomer Norton

ST6554

Ellsworth, Fosseway, Midsomer Norton, Bath, Somerset, BA3 4AU. Situated on the A367 on Somerset border 9 miles from city of Bath. **Open:** All year **01761 412305 (also fax)** Mrs Gentle *accommodation@ellsworth.fsbusiness.co.uk* www.ellsworth.fsbusiness.co.uk **D:** £25.00–£30.00 **S:** £25.00–£35.00 **Beds:** 2F 2T 3D **Baths:** 7 En ⅁ (2) ⊡ (4) ⥿ ⊡ ⲏ ⊻ ▥, ⸙

Minehead

SS9646 ⛴ Royal Oak, Old Ship, Queen's Head

The Parks Guest House, 26 The Parks, Minehead, Somerset, TA24 8BT. Comfortable, listed family-run establishment close gardens, Town centre, seafront, Exmoor. **Open:** All year (not Xmas/New Year) **01643 703547** Mr & Mrs Gibson **Fax: 01643 708088** *rng@theparks26.freeserve.co.uk* **D:** £17.00–£19.00 **S:** £19.00–£22.00 **Beds:** 4F 1T 1D **Baths:** 4 En 1 Sh ⅁ ⊡ (8) ⊡ ✕ ⊻ ▥, ⸙

Moorlands B&B, Moor Road, Minehead, Somerset, TA24 5RT. Elevated position, panoramic views. Warm welcome. Wonderful Exmoor touring base. **Open:** All year (not Xmas/New Year) **Grades:** ETC 3 Diamond **01643 703453** Mrs Beakes *moorlands@amserve.net* **D:** £17.50 **Beds:** 1T 2D **Baths:** 1 Sh ⅁ (12) ⊡ (3) ⥿ ⊡ ⊻ ▥, ⸙

Wyndcott Hotel, Martlet Road, Minehead, Somerset, TA24 5QE. A superb country house hotel adjacent to beach and Exmoor. **Open:** All year (not Xmas/New Year) **01643 704522 Fax: 01634 707577** *mineheadhotel@msn.com* **D:** £35.00–£55.00 **S:** £30.00–£40.00 **Beds:** 2F 4T 4D 1S **Baths:** 11 En ⅁ ⊡ (8) ⥿ ⊡ ⲏ ▥, ⸙ ⸙ cc

---

Old Ship Aground, The Quay, Minehead, Somerset, TA24 5UL. Located on the harbour, well-placed for Exmoor and coast. **Open:** All year **Grades:** ETC 3 Diamond **01643 702087 Fax: 01643 709066** *enquiries@oldshipaground.co.uk* oldshipaground.co.uk **D:** £20.00–£25.00 **S:** £25.00–£30.00 **Beds:** 3F 2T 1D 1S **Baths:** 7 En ⅁ ⊡ (3) ⊡ ⲏ ✕ ⊻ ▥, ⸙ cc

1 Glenmore Road, Minehead, Somerset, TA24 5BQ. Superior Victorian family-run guest house, excellent range of breakfasts including vegetarian. **Open:** All year **01643 706225** Mrs Sanders **D:** £17.00–£19.00 **S:** £17.00 **Beds:** 1F 1D 1T 1S **Baths:** 2 En 1 Sh ⅁ (6) ⊡ (2) ⥿ ⊡ ⊻ ▥, ⸙

St Audries Bay Holiday Park, West Quantockhead, Minehead, Somerset, TA4 4DY. Family holiday centre overlooking sea. Indoor pool. Entertainment. Licensed restaurant. **Open:** May to Oct **01984 632515 Fax: 01984 632785** *mrandle@staudriesbay.co.uk* www.staudriesbay.co.uk **D:** £22.00–£34.00 **Beds:** 20F 20T 20D 20S **Baths:** 80 En ⅁ ⊡ ⲏ ✕ ⊻ ▥, ⸙ ⸙ cc

Beaconwood Hotel, Church Road, North Hill, Minehead, Somerset, TA24 5SB. Edwardian country house hotel, set in 2 acres of terraced gardens with panoramic views. **Open:** All year **01643 702032 (also fax)** Mr Roberts *beaconwood@madasafish.com* www.beaconwoodhotel.co.uk **D:** £30.00–£35.00 **S:** £33.00–£40.00 **Beds:** 2F 6D 6T **Baths:** 14 En ⅁ ⊡ (25) ⊡ ⲏ ✕ ⊻ ▥, ⸙ cc

Monkton Combe

ST7762

The Manor House, Monkton Combe, Bath, BA2 7HD. Restful rambling medieval manor by millstream in Area of Outstanding Natural Beauty. **Open:** All year **01225 723128** Mrs Hartley **Fax: 01225 722972** *beth@manorhousebath.co.uk* www.manorhousebath.co.uk **D:** £22.50–£35.00 **S:** £30.00–£35.00 **Beds:** 2F 5D 1T **Baths:** 8 En ⅁ ⊡ (12) ⊡ ⲏ ✕ ⊻ ▥, ⸙2 ⸙

Montacute

ST4916

Mad Hatters Tea Rooms, 1 South Street, Montacute, Somerset, TA15 6XD. Listed Georgian property in picturesque village. Idyllic walks, Near NT properties. **Open:** All year **01935 823024** Mrs Hicken **D:** £17.50–£21.00 **S:** £23.00–£29.00 **Beds:** 1D 1T 1S **Baths:** 1 Pr 2 En ⥿ ⊡ ⊻ ⸙

National Grid References given are for villages, towns and cities – not for individual houses

---

RATES

D = Price range per person sharing in a double or twin room
S = Price range for a single room

Muchelney Ham

ST4323

Muchelney Ham Farm, Muchelney Ham, Langport, Somerset, TA10 0DJ. **Open:** All year **Grades:** ETC 5 Diamond, Gold **01458 250737** Mrs Woodborne www.muchelneyhamfarm.co.uk **D:** £25.00–£35.00 **S:** £25.00–£35.00 **Beds:** 1F 3D 2T 1S **Baths:** 6 En 1 Pr ⅁ (8) ⊡ (8) ⥿ ⊡ ▥, ⸙ ⸙ B&B with country house atmosphere. Beautiful traditional Somerset farmhouse mainly C17th, tastefully furnished with period furniture, beams and inglenook. Situated on the Somerset levels with peaceful and relaxing garden. Ideal centre for touring many NT properties, air museum, golf, fishing. Somerset/Dorset coasts 25 miles.

North Cadbury

ST6327

Ashlea House, High Street, North Cadbury, Yeovil, Somerset, BA22 7DP. 1 km A303, centre village, highly commended service, accommodation, home cooking. **Open:** All year (not Xmas/New Year) **01963 440891** Mr & Mrs Wade *ashlea@btinternet.com* www.ashlea.btinternet.co.uk **D:** £22.00–£25.00 **S:** £25.00–£27.00 **Beds:** 1T 1D **Baths:** 1 En 1 Pr ⊡ (2) ⥿ ⊡ ✕ ⊻ ▥, ⸙

North Perrott

ST4709

The Manor Arms, North Perrott, Crewkerne, TA18 7SG. Lovely C16th Listed inn overlooking village green, high standard of ensuite accommodation. **Open:** All year *manorarmshotel.co.uk* www.manorarmshotel.co.uk **D:** £19.00–£24.00 **S:** £35.00–£38.00 **Beds:** 1F 5D 3T **Baths:** 9 En ⅁ ⊡ (24) ⥿ ⊡ ✕ ⊻ ▥, ⸙ ⸙ cc

North Petherton

ST2832

Quantock View House, *Bridgwater Road, North Petherton, Bridgwater, Somerset, TA6 6PR.* Central for Cheddar, Wells, Glastonbury, the Quantocks and the sea. **Open:** All year
01278 663309 Mrs Howlett and Mrs Terry
irene@quantockview.freeserve.co.uk
www.quantockview.freeserve.co.uk
D: £19.00–£23.00 **S:** £23.00–£27.00 **Beds:** 2F 1D 1T **Baths:** 4 En ➤ 🄿 (8) 🗲 📺 🚻 ✕ 📺 🛲 🛊 cc

North Wootton

ST5641

Riverside Grange, *Tanyard Lane, North Wootton, Wells, Somerset, BA4 4AE.* A charming converted tannery, quietly situated on the River edge. **Open:** All year
01749 890761 Mrs English **D:** £19.50–£22.00 **S:** £25.00–£29.00 **Beds:** 1D 1T **Baths:** 2 Pr 🄿 (6) 📺 🚻 🛲 🛊

Norton-sub-Hamdon

ST4715

Courtfield, *Norton-sub-Hamdon, Stoke-sub-Hamdon, Somerset, TA14 6SG.* Comfortable, relaxed, peaceful. Breakfast in conservatory. Special accommodation, beautiful gardens. **Open:** All year (not Xmas)
01935 881246 Mrs Constable *courtfield@ hotmail.com* **D:** £25.00–£28.00 **S:** £38.00
Beds: 1D 1T **Baths:** 2 Pr ➤ (8) 🄿 (4) 📺 🚻 ✕ 📺 🛲 🛊

Brook House, *Norton-sub-Hamdon, Stoke-sub-Hamdon, Somerset, TA14 6SR.* Gracious Georgian family home in unspoilt quiet Hamstone village with pub providing good food. **Open:** Easter to Nov
01935 881789 (also fax) Mr & Mrs Fisher
D: £25.00 **S:** £35.00 **Beds:** 1D 1T **Baths:** 2 Pr ➤ (10) 🄿 (2) 🗲 📺 📺 🛲 🛊

Peasedown St John

ST7057   ◀ *Prince of Wales*

Eastfield Farm and Guest House, *Dunkerton Hill, Peasedown St John, Bath, Somerset, BA2 8PF.* Peaceful, sturdy house set in 3 acres. Beautiful views. **Open:** Easter to Oct **Grades:** ETC 3 Diamond
01761 432161 Mrs Newland **D:** £17.00–£20.00 **S:** £24.00–£30.00 **Beds:** 1F 1T 1D **Baths:** 3 Sh ➤ 🄿 (4) 🗲 📺 📺 🛲 🛊

BATHROOMS
En = Ensuite
Pr = Private
Sh = Shared

Peasmarsh

ST3412

Graden, *Peasmarsh, Donyatt, Ilminster, Somerset, TA19 0SG.* Comfortable house in rural situation, close to Somerset, Devon & Dorset border. **Open:** All year **Grades:** ETC 3 Diamond
01460 52371 G E Bond **D:** £16.00–£34.00 **S:** £17.00–£18.00 **Beds:** 1F 1T 2D **Baths:** 2 En ➤ 🗲 📺 🚻 ✕ 📺 🛲 🛊

Pilton

ST5940

The Long House, *Pylle Road, Pilton, Shepton Mallet, Somerset, BA4 4BP.* Picturesque, quiet village. Friendly, comfortable, unpretentious. **Open:** All year (not Xmas/New Year)
01749 890701 Mr & Mrs Case **D:** £40.00–£65.00 **S:** £27.00–£35.00 **Beds:** 1F 1D 1T **Baths:** 3 En ➤ (10) 🄿 (7) 📺 📺 🛲 🛊

Porlock

SS8846   ◀ *Castle Hotel*

West Porlock House, *Country House Hotel, West Porlock, Porlock, Minehead, Somerset, TA24 8NX.* Superbly set in beautiful woodland garden with magnificent sea views.
Open: Feb to Nov **Grades:** ETC 4 Diamond
01643 862880 Mrs Dyer **D:** £26.00–£28.00 **S:** £30.00 **Beds:** 1F 2D 2T **Baths:** 2 En 3 Pr ➤ (6) 🄿 (8) 🗲 📺 🛲 🛊 cc

Silcombe Farm, *Culbone, Porlock, Minehead, Somerset, TA24 8JN.* Comfortable secluded Exmoor farmhouse overlooking sea in beautiful walking country. **Open:** All year (not Xmas)
01643 862248 Mrs Richards **D:** £18.00–£20.00 **S:** £20.00 **Beds:** 1D 2T 1S **Baths:** 1 En 1 Sh ➤ (4) 🄿 (6) 📺 🚻 ✕ 📺 🛲 🛊

Hurlstone, *Sparkhayes Lane, Porlock, Minehead, Somerset, TA24 8NE.* Quiet house near village centre sea and moorland views. **Open:** All year (not Xmas)
01643 862650 Mrs Coombs **D:** £18.00 **S:** £18.00 **Beds:** 1D 1T **Baths:** 1 Sh ➤ 🄿 🚻 🛊

Leys, *The Ridge, Bossington Lane, Porlock, Minehead, Somerset, TA24 8HA.* Beautiful family home, delightful garden, with magnificent views. **Open:** All year (not Xmas)
01643 862477 (also fax) Mrs Stiles-Cox
D: £19.00 **S:** £19.00 **Beds:** 1D/T 2S **Baths:** 1 Sh ➤ 🄿 (4) 🗲 📺 🚻 📺 🛲 🛊

Overstream Hotel, Parsons Street,
Porlock, Minehead, Somerset, TA24 8QJ. Situated in the centre of Porlock, between Exmoor and the sea. **Open:** Easter to Nov
01643 862421 (also fax) **D:** £21.00–£30.00 **S:** £30.00 **Beds:** 1F 2T 4D 2S **Baths:** 9 En ➤ 🄿 🗲 📺 ✕ 📺 🛲 🛊

Puriton

ST3241

Rockfield House, *Puriton Hill, Puriton, Bridgwater, Somerset, TA7 8AG.* Just off M5 (J23). Good food and friendly atmosphere. **Open:** All year (not Xmas)
01278 683561 (also fax) Mrs Pipkin
rockfieldhouse@talk21.com **D:** £16.00–£20.00
S: £16.00 **Beds:** 1F 1D 1T 1S **Baths:** 2 En 1 Sh ➤ 🄿 (5) 🗲 📺 ✕ 📺 🛲 🛊

Saltford

ST6866

Long Reach House Hotel, *321 Bath Road, Saltford, Bristol, BS31 1TJ.* Gracious house standing in 2 acres midway between Bath and Bristol. **Open:** All year
01225 400500 Fax: 01225 400700 *lrhouse@ aol.com* bath.co.uk.visitbritain.co.uk
D: £22.50–£45.00 **S:** £45.00–£50.00 **Beds:** 2F 7T 7D 2S **Baths:** 18 En ➤ 🄿 🗲 📺 🚻 ✕ 📺 🛲 ♿ ✱ 🛊 cc

Sandyway

SS7933

Barkham, *Sandy, Exmoor, Devon, EX36 3LU.* Tucked away in hidden valley in the heart of Exmoor. **Open:** All year (not Xmas) **Grades:** ETC 4 Diamond
01643 831370 (also fax) Mrs Adie
adie.exmoor@btinternet.com holidays.exmoor.com **D:** £28.00–£32.00 **Beds:** 2D 1S **Baths:** 2 En 1 Pr ➤ (12) 🄿 (6) 🗲 📺 ✕ 📺 🛲 🛊

Selworthy

SS9146

Selworthy Farm, *Selworthy, Minehead, Somerset, TA24 8TL.* Comfortable farmhouse, peaceful, ideal for exploring Exmoor. Walkers paradise. **Open:** Jan to Nov
01643 862577 Mrs Leeves **D:** £20.00–£25.00 **S:** £25.00 **Beds:** 1T 1D 1S **Baths:** 2 En ➤ (11) 🄿 (3) 🗲 📺 📺 🛊

B&B owners may vary rates – be sure to check when booking

All details shown are as supplied by B&B owners in Autumn 2001

Shepton Mallet

ST6143 🍴 *Thatched Cottage, Kings Arms*

Burnt House Farm, *Waterlip, Cranmore, Shepton Mallet, Somerset, BA4 4RN.* **Open:** All year **Grades:** ETC 4 Diamond, Silver **01749 880280 Fax: 01749 880004 D:** £22.00–£25.00 **S:** £25.00–£30.00 **Beds:** 1F 1D 1T **Baths:** 1 En 2 Pr ⛄(4) 🅿(10) 🖺 📺 Ⅴ 🛏, 🎿 Amazing breakfasts in happy cottage-style period farmhouse. Tea/cake on arrival. Wine for multiple night stays. TVs in bedrooms. Full-sized snooker table. Hot hydro garden spa tub. Summerhouse. Organic farm. Organic home-made bread/ jam. Great mid-Somerset location. ETC 4 Diamond Silver Award.

Belfield House, *34 Charlton Road, Shepton Mallet, Somerset, BA4 5PA.* Impressive Georgian house. Ideally situated for Mendips, Cheddar, Longleat and Bath **Open:** All year (not Xmas/New Year) **Grades:** ETC 3 Diamond **01749 344353** Mr & Mrs Smith *reservations@ belfield-house.co.uk* www.belfield-house.co.uk **D:** £20.00–£24.00 **S:** £25.00–£30.00 **Beds:** 1F 2T 1D 2S **Baths:** 4 En 1 Sh ⛄🅿(6)🖺📺Ⅴ🛏, 🎿 cc

Park Farm House, *Forum Lane, Bowlish, Shepton Mallet, Somerset, BA4 5JL.* Comfortable C17th house with peaceful garden and private off-road parking. **Open:** All year **01749 343673 Fax: 01749 345279 D:** £17.50–£18.50 **S:** £17.50–£18.50 **Beds:** 2T 1D **Baths:** 1 En 2 Pr ⛄🅿(3)📺Ⅴ🛏, 🎿

Shipham

ST4457

Herongates, *Horseleaze Lane, Shipham, Winscombe, Somerset, BS25 1UQ.* Noted for quality, peaceful location. **Open:** All year (not Xmas/New Year) **01934 843280** Mrs Stickland **D:** £15.50–£18.50 **S:** £15.50–£18.50 **Beds:** 2D 1T **Baths:** 2 En 1 Pr ⛄🅿(3)🖺📺✗Ⅴ🛏, 🎿

Simonsbath

SS7739 🍴 *Poltimore Arms, Sportsman, Exmoor Forest Hotel*

Emmett's Grange Farm, *Simonsbath, Minehead, Somerset, TA24 7LD.* **Open:** All year (not Xmas/New Year) **01643 831138 & 01643 831093** T Barlow **Fax: 01643 831138** *emmetts.grange@virgin.net* **D:** £29.00–£38.00 **S:** £34.00–£43.00 **Beds:** 1T 2D ⛄🅿🖺📺🛏✗Ⅴ🛏, 🎿 cc Emmett's Grange provides oasis of friendly civilisation within its own 900 acres amidst the stunning wild and rugged Exmoor National Park. Luxurious B&B with moorland views. Guests own elegant drawing room. Gourmet food available and many local pubs. Fully licensed.

South Petherton

ST4316

Rathmore, *Main St, Lopen, South Petherton, Somerset, TA13 5JU.* Attractive village, central for NT properties, Dorset coast, beautiful countryside. **Open:** All year **01460 240279** Mrs Webster **D:** £17.00–£18.00 **S:** £17.00 **Beds:** 2D 1S **Baths:** 1 Sh ⛄(6) 🅿(3)🎿📺🛏✗Ⅴ🛏, 🎿

Kings Pleasure, *24 Silver Street, South Petherton, Somerset, TA13 5BZ.* Listed hamstone house, beautiful garden; in centre of conservation village. **Open:** All year **01460 241747** Mr & Mrs Veit *n.veit@ kingspleaure.fsnet.co.uk* **D:** £25.00 **S:** £35.00 **Beds:** 1D 1T **Baths:** 2 En 🅿(2)🎿🖺📺🛏, 🎿

Watergore House, *Watergore, South Petherton, Somerset, TA13 5JG.* Picturesque old hamstone house with large garden just off A303. **Open:** All year (not Xmas) **01460 240677 (also fax)** Mr & Mrs Gordon **D:** £20.00 **S:** £20.00 **Beds:** 2D 1T **Baths:** 2 Sh ⛄(6)🅿(4)🎿Ⅴ🛏, 🎿

RATES

D = Price range per person sharing in a double or twin room

S = Price range for a single room

Stanton Prior

ST6762

Poplar Farm, *Stanton Prior, Bath, BA2 9HX.* Spacious C17th farmhouse. Family-run farm. Idyllic village setting. **Open:** All year (not Xmas) **Grades:** ETC 3 Diamond **01761 470382 (also fax)** Mrs Hardwick *poplarfarm@talk21.com* **D:** £20.00–£27.00 **S:** £20.00–£30.00 **Beds:** 1F 1D 1T **Baths:** 2 En ⛄(4) 🅿(6)🎿📺🛏

Stanton Wick

ST6061 🍴 *Carpenters' Arms*

Greenacres Guest House, *Stanton Wick, Pensford, Bristol, BS39 4BX.* Comfortable family home in rural hamlet. Convenient towns and touring. **Open:** All year **Grades:** ETC 3 Diamond **01761 490397** Mrs Bond **D:** £20.00–£25.00 **S:** £20.00–£25.00 **Beds:** 1F 1T 1D 2S **Baths:** 1 En 2 Sh ⛄(1)🅿🎿📺🛏, 🎿

Staplegrove

ST2126

Yallands Farmhouse, *Staplegrove, Taunton, Somerset, TA2 6PZ.* Warm welcome assured at our beautiful C16th house. An oasis of 'old England'. **Open:** All year **Grades:** ETC 4 Diamond, Silver, AA 4 Diamond **01823 278979** Mr & Mrs Kirk *mail@ yallands.co.uk* www.yallands.co.uk **D:** £27.00–£28.00 **S:** £30.00–£34.00 **Beds:** 1F 2D 1T 2S **Baths:** 6 En ⛄🅿(6)📺Ⅴ🛏, 🎿 cc

Stathe

ST3728

Black Smock Inn, *Stathe, Bridgwater, Somerset, TA7 0JN.* Overlooking River Parrett. Panoramic views Somerset Levels. Home-made food speciality. **Open:** All year **Grades:** ETC 3 Diamond **01823 698352** Mr Horsham **Fax: 01823 690138** *blacksmock@aol.co.uk* www.blacksmock.co.uk **D:** £17.50–£22.00 **S:** £21.00–£26.00 **Beds:** 3D/T 1S **Baths:** 2 En 1 Sh ⛄🅿(30)📺✗Ⅴ🛏, 🎿 cc

Stogursey

ST2042

Acland Hood Arms, *11 High Street, Stogursey, Bridgewater, Somerset, TA5 1TB.* C17th pub in picturesque village between M5 and Exmoor. **Open:** All year (not Xmas) **01726 732489** Mrs Goulding **D:** £17.50–£20.00 **S:** £20.00–£25.00 **Beds:** 2T 2D **Baths:** 4 En ⛄(10) 🅿(20)🎿✗🛏, 🎿

Stoke St Gregory

ST3427

Parsonage Farm, Stoke St Gregory, Taunton, Somerset, TA3 6ET. Georgian farmhouse situated on the Somerset Levels. Working dairy farm. **Open:** All year (not Xmas/New Year)
01823 698205 Mrs House **D:** £17.00–£20.00 **S:** £19.00–£23.00 **Beds:** 1F **Baths:** 1 Sh ☜
🅿 (2) 📺 🍴 🛄 🕏

Stratton-on-the-Fosse

ST6550　◀ Ring O'Roses

Oval House, Stratton-on-the-Fosse, Bath, Somerset, BA3 4RB. Charming, friendly C17th home, ideal for visiting Bath, etc. **Open:** All year (not Xmas/New Year)
01761 232183 (also fax) Mrs Mellotte
mellotte@clara.co.uk www.mellotte.clara.co.uk
D: £19.00–£20.00 **S:** £20.00 **Beds:** 1T 1S
Baths: 2 Sh ☜ 🅿 (10) 💺 📺 🍴 🛄 🕏 cc

Taunton

ST2324　◀ King's Arms

The Old Mill, Bishops Hull, Taunton, Somerset, TA15AB. **Open:** All year (not Xmas)
01823 289732
(also fax) Mr & Mrs Slipper **D:** £22.00–£24.00 **S:** £30.00–£35.00 **Beds:** 2D **Baths:** 1 En 1 Pr 🅿 💺 📺 🛄 🕏
Grade II Listed former corn mill in lovely riverside setting, retaining many original workings. Two delightful bedrooms overlooking the river. Enjoy breakfast from our extensive menu amidst the wheels and cogs of a bygone era. Enjoyed by all who stay.

Yallands Farmhouse, Staplegrove, Taunton, Somerset, TA2 6PZ. **Open:** All year
Grades: ETC 4 Diamond, Silver, AA 4 Diamond
01823 278979 Mr & Mrs Kirk *mail@ yallands.co.uk* www.yallands.co.uk **D:** £27.00–£28.00 **S:** £30.00–£34.00 **Beds:** 1F 2D 1T 2S **Baths:** 6 En ☜ 🅿 (6) 📺 📺 🛄 🕏 cc
A warm welcome is assured at our beautiful C16th house. An oasis of 'old England' close to town centre yet unexpectedly peaceful and secluded. Comfortable, attractive ensuite rooms with ground floor room available. Out of season discounts. Phone for brochure.

Planning a longer stay? Always ask for any special rates

BEDROOMS
D = Double
T = Twin
S = Single
F = Family

Lower Marsh Farm, Kingston St Mary, Taunton, Somerset, TA2 8AB. **Open:** All year
Grades: AA 3 Diamond
01823 451331 (also fax) Mr & Mrs Gothard
mail@lowermarshfarm.co.uk
www.lowermarshfarm.co.uk **D:** £22.50–£25.00 **S:** £25.00–£28.00 **Beds:** 1F 1T 1D
Baths: 2 En 1 Pr ☜ 🅿 💺 📺 × 🛄 🕏
Only 10 mins M5 J25. A warm welcome is assured at our tastefully refurbished farmhouse on a working farm overlooking the vale of Taunton, nestling at the foot of the Quantock Hills. Attractive ensuite rooms, dining room and gardens, with traditional home cooking breakfast.

Blorenge Guest House, 57 Staplegrove Road, Taunton, Somerset, TA1 1DG. We are situated within 10 minutes of all Taunton's amenities. **Open:** All year **Grades:** AA 4 Diamond
01823 283005 (also fax) Mr Painter
enquiries@blorengehouse.co.uk
www.blorengehouse.co.uk **D:** £23.00–£40.00 **S:** £28.00–£42.00 **Beds:** 3F 5T 9D 7S
Baths: 17 En 2 Sh ☜ 🅿 (18) 💺 📺 🛄 🕏 cc

Hillview Guest House, Bishop's Hull, Taunton, Somerset, TA1 5EG. Spacious accommodation, warm and friendly atmosphere in attractive village near Taunton. **Open:** All year
01823 275510 (also fax) Mr Morgan
D: £17.50–£22.50 **S:** £17.50–£25.00 **Beds:** 2F 1D 1T 1S **Baths:** 2 En 3 Sh ☜ 🅿 (6) 💺 📺 🍴 📺 🛄 🕏 cc

Thorn Falcon

ST2723

Lower Farm, Thorn Falcon, Taunton, Somerset, TA3 5NR. Picturesque C15th thatched farmhouse, log fires, peaceful location, 3 miles Taunton. **Open:** All year (not Xmas)
01823 443549 (also fax) Mrs Titman
lowerfarm@talk21.com www.somersite.co.uk/lowerfarm.htm **D:** £23.00–£25.00 **S:** £30.00 **Beds:** 1F 1D 1T **Baths:** 1 En 1 Pr ☜ 🅿 (10) 💺 📺 × 🛄

Timberscombe

SS9542

Wellum, Brook Street, Timberscombe, Minehead, Somerset, TA24 7TG. Lovely, spacious old house situated in Avil Valley, spectacular views. **Open:** Mar to Nov
01643 841234 Mrs Kelsey **D:** £16.00–£20.00 **S:** £16.00–£20.00 **Beds:** 1D 1T **Baths:** 1 Pr 1 Sh ☜ 📺 🍴 × 🛄 🕏

Tivington

SS9345

Clements Cottage, Tivington, Minehead, Somerset, TA24 8SU. C16th cross-passage house with spectacular views of the Bristol Channel. **Open:** All year
01643 703970 *clementscottage@ exmoorbandb.co.uk* **D:** £18.50–£20.00 **S:** £18.50–£20.00 **Beds:** 1F 1T 1D **Baths:** 1 En 1 Sh ☜ 🅿 (3) 📺 🍴 × 📺 🛄 🕏

Watchet

ST0643　◀ The Anchor

Downfield House, 16 St Decuman's Road, Watchet, Somerset, TA23 0HR. **Open:** All year
01984 631267 Fax: 01984 634369 **D:** £24.00–£29.00 **S:** £36.00–£41.00 **Beds:** 5D 2T **Baths:** 7 En ☜ (12) 🅿 (15) 💺 📺 🍴 × 📺 🛄 🕏 cc
Spacious Victorian country house with converted and modernised coach house within a large garden in an elevated location. Views over the town and harbour from some rooms, comfortable lounge with open fire, chandeliered dining rooms, residents licence. Self-catering flat and available.

Esplanade House, Watchet, Somerset, TA23 0AJ. Comfortable Georgian farmhouse, with pretty garden, in historic harbour/marina setting. **Open:** All year (not Xmas/New Year) **Grades:** ETC 4 Diamond
01984 633444 Mrs Fawcus **D:** £18.50–£22.00 **S:** £23.50–£27.00 **Beds:** 1T 2D **Baths:** 2 En 1 Pr ☜ (8) 🅿 (3) 💺 📺 🍴 📺 🛄 🕏

Wayford

ST4006

Manor Farm, Wayford, Crewkerne, Somerset, TA18 8QL. Beautiful Victorian home in a peaceful location with undulating views. **Open:** All year **Grades:** AA 4 Diamond
01460 78865 & 07767 620031 (M) Mr Emery
www.manorfarm.com **D:** £22.00–£25.00 **S:** £22.00–£25.00 **Beds:** 3F 1T **Baths:** 4 En 🅿 (50) 💺 📺 📺 🛄 🕏

Wedmore

ST4347

The George Hotel, Church Street, Wedmore, Somerset, BS28 4AB. C16th coaching inn set in centre of village in heart of the Somerset Levels. **Open:** All year **01934 712124** Mr Hodge **Fax: 01934 712251** *reception@thegeorgewedmore.co.uk* www.thegeorgewedmore.co.uk **D:** £17.50–£25.00 **S:** £20.00–£25.00 **Beds:** 2F 3D 3T **Baths:** 3 En 1 Sh ♿ 🖬 (30) ⌿ 🖾 ♀ ✕ 🖾 🖩 ☕ cc

Wells

ST5445 🍺 Wookey Hole Inn, New Inn, Slab House, Fountain, City Arms

Burcott Mill Historic Watermill & Guest House, Wookey, Wells, Somerset, BA5 1NJ. **Open:** All year (not Xmas/New Year) **Grades:** ETC 3 Diamond **01749 673118** Mr & Mrs Burt **Fax: 01749 677376** *theburts@burcottmill.com* www.burcottmill.com **D:** £21.00–£32.00 **S:** £24.00–£37.00 **Beds:** 4F 1D 1S **Baths:** 5 En 1 Pr ♿ 🖪 (40) ⌿ 🖾 ♀ 🖾 ☕ ⌀
A rare working watermill dating from Domesday, still stonegrinding flour daily. Enjoy private tours with our miller. Families especially welcome: playground, ponies, small animals. Tea room, craft shops. Opposite country pub for dinner. Ideal for Wells, Cheddar, Glastonbury. You won't be disappointed.

Rose Farm, Henton, Wells, Somerset, BA5 1PD. **Open:** All year (not Xmas/New Year) **01749 672908** Mrs Doherty *rosefarm5@ yahoo.co.uk* **D:** £23.00–£25.50 **Beds:** 1D **Baths:** 1 En 🖪 (2) ⌿ 🖾 🖾 🖩 ☕
You will be well looked after at our lovely Georgian farmhouse, overlooking the Mendip Hills. Just outside the beautiful city of Wells. Cheddar, Glastonbury, Street and coast are all nearby. Delicious breakfasts served by Inglenook fireplace. Attractive, stylish accommodation.

17 Priory Road, Wells, Somerset, BA5 1SU. Large Victorian house. Home-made bread and preserves. Few mins walk shops, cathedral, bus station. **Open:** All year (not Xmas) **01749 677300** Mrs Winter www.smoothhound.co.uk/hotels/brian. html **D:** £17.50–£20.00 **S:** £20.00 **Beds:** 3F 3S **Baths:** 2 Sh ♿ 🖪 (5) ⌿ 🖾 🖾 🖩 ☕

The Crown at Wells, Market Place, Wells, Somerset, BA5 2RP. C15th inn situated in heart of Wells. Delicious meals, snacks, refreshments available all day. **Open:** All year **Grades:** ETC 2 Star, AA 2 Star **01749 673457** Sara Hodges **Fax: 01749 679792** *reception@crownatwells.co.uk* www.crownatwells.co.uk **D:** £30.00–£40.00 **S:** £45.00 **Beds:** 4F 5D 4T 2S **Baths:** 15 En ♿ 🖪 (15) 🖾 ♀ ✕ 🖾 🖩 ☕ cc

Double Gate Farm, Godney, Wells, Somerset, BA5 1RX. Comfortable, friendly, award-winning accommodation. Wonderful breakfasts - lots to see and do. **Open:** All year (not Xmas/New Year) **Grades:** ETC 4 Diamond, Gold, AA 4 Diamond, RAC 4 Diamond, Sparkling **01458 832217** Mrs Millard **Fax: 01458 835612** *hilary@doublegate.demon.co.uk* www.doublegatefarm.com **D:** £22.50 **S:** £30.00 **Beds:** 1F 3D 2T **Baths:** 6 En ♿ 🖪 (8) ⌿ 🖾 🖾 🖩 ☕

30 Mary Road, Wells, Somerset, BA5 2NF. Small, friendly family home, 10 mins' walk city centre, bright modern rooms, breakfast choice. **Open:** Feb to Nov **Grades:** ETC 3 Diamond **01749 674031 (also fax)** Mrs Bailey *triciabailey30@hotmail.com* www.travelengland. org.uk **D:** £18.00 **S:** £18.00 **Beds:** 2D 2S **Baths:** 1 Sh ♿ (3) 🖪 (5) 🖾 🖩 ☕

Cadgwith House, Hawkers Lane, Wells, Somerset, BA5 3JH. Delightfully furnished spacious family house, backing onto field. Beautiful bathrooms. **Open:** All year **Grades:** ETC 4 Diamond **01749 677799** Mr & Mrs Pletts *rplettscadgwith@aol.com* **D:** £18.00–£20.00 **S:** £18.00–£25.00 **Beds:** 1F 1D 1T 1S **Baths:** 3 En 1 Pr ♿ 🖪 (3) 🖾 ♀ 🖾 🖩 ☕

The Limes, 29 Chamberlain Street, Wells, Somerset, BA5 2PQ. Beautifully restored Victorian town house in the centre of historic Wells. **Open:** All year (not Xmas) **01749 675716 Fax: 01749 674874** *accommodation@thelimes.uk.com* www.thelimes. uk.com **D:** £20.00–£22.50 **S:** £30.00 **Beds:** 1D 1T ♿ 🖪 (2) ⌿ 🖾 🖾 🖩 ☕ cc

Broadleys, 21 Wells Road, Wookey Hole, Wells, Somerset, BA5 1DN. Large detached house situated between Wells and Wookey Hole with panoramic countryside views. **Open:** All year (not Xmas) **01749 674746 (also fax)** Mrs Milton *broadleys@bobmilton.totalserve.co.uk* **D:** £20.00–£22.50 **S:** £25.00–£35.00 **Beds:** 3D **Baths:** 2 En 1 Pr ♿ (10) 🖪 (4) ⌿ 🖾 🖾 🖩 ☕

Bekynton House, 7 St Thomas Street, Wells, Somerset, BA5 2UU. Old established B&B, 5 minutes max to cathedral and restaurants. **Open:** All year (not Xmas/New Year) **01749 672222 (also fax)** D & R Gripper *reservations@bekynton.freeserve.co.uk* **D:** £23.00–£28.00 **S:** £32.00–£40.00 **Beds:** 1F 1T 2D **Baths:** 3 En 1 Pr ♿ (5) 🖪 (6) 🖾 🖩 ☕ cc

Number One Portway, 1 Portway, Wells, Somerset, BA5 2BA. Comfortable Victorian house in comfortable setting. **Open:** All year **Grades:** AA 3 Diamond **01749 678864 & 07970 969354 (M) D:** £18.00–£25.00 **S:** £20.00–£25.00 **Beds:** 1F 1D **Baths:** 1 En 1 Pr ♿ ⌿ 🖾 🖾 ☕

Wembdon

ST2837 🍺 Malt Shovel

Ash-Wembdon Farm, Hollow Lane, Wembledon, Bridgwater, Somerset, TA5 2BD. Enjoy a refreshing and memorable stay at our elegant yet homely farmhouse. **Open:** All year (not Xmas) **Grades:** ETC 4 Diamond, Silver **01278 453097** Mr Rowe **Fax: 01278 445856** *mary.rowe@btinternet.com* www.farmaccommodation.co.uk **D:** £22.00–£25.00 **S:** £25.00–£30.00 **Beds:** 2D 1T **Baths:** 2 En 1 Pr ♿ (10) 🖪 (4) ⌿ 🖾 🖾 🖩 ☕ cc

Model Farm, Perry Green, Wembdon, Bridgwater, Somerset, TA5 2BA. Between Quantocks and Levels. Comfortable Victorian farmhouse in peaceful rural setting. **Open:** All year (not Xmas/New Year) **01278 433999** Mr & Mrs Wright *rmodelfarm@ aol.com* **D:** £25.00–£30.00 **S:** £35.00 **Beds:** 1F 1D 1T **Baths:** 3 En ♿ 🖪 ⌿ 🖾 ♀ ✕ 🖾 🖩 ☕ cc

West Monkton

ST2628

Prockters Farm, West Monkton, Taunton, Somerset, TA2 8QN. Beautiful C17th beamed farmhouse, large garden, 2 pubs easy walking. **Open:** All year **01823 412269 (also fax)** Mrs Besley *info@ scoot.co.* www.scoot.co.uk **D:** £21.00–£23.00 **S:** £21.00–£30.00 **Beds:** 2D 2T 2S 6F **Baths:** 2 En 2 Pr 2 Sh ♿ 🖪 (6) 🖾 ♀ 🖾 🖾 ♿ ☕ cc

West Pennard

ST5438

The Lion at Pennard, Glastonbury Road, West Pennard, Glastonbury, Somerset, BA6 8NH. C15th coaching inn offering excellent ales, fine food and friendly atmosphere. **Open:** All year **01458 832 941** Mr Moore **Fax: 01458 830 660** *thelion@pennardsbusiness.co.uk* **D:** £25.00–£35.00 **S:** £45.00–£50.00 **Beds:** 1F 2T 4D **Baths:** 7 En ♿ 🖪 🖾 🖩 ❋ ☕ cc

West Wick

ST3661

Orchard House, Summer Lane, West Wick, Weston-super-Mare, Somerset, *BS24 7TF.* A luxury guest house close to M5 (J21). **Open:** All year
01934 520948 (also fax) D: £21.00–£27.00 **S:** £36.00–£49.00 **Beds:** 2D **Baths:** 2 En ⚑ (4)
⊁ ⊡ ✕ ▥ ♨

Westbury-sub-Mendip

ST5048

Lana Hollow Farm, The Hollow, Westbury-sub-Mendip, Wells, Somerset, *BA5 1HH.* **Open:** All year (not Xmas/New Year)
01749 870635 S M Stott **D:** £20.00–£22.00 **S:** £22.00–£25.00 **Beds:** 1T 2D **Baths:** 3 En ⊅ ⚑ (3) ⊁ ⊡ ▥ ♨
Modern farmhouse accommodation on working farm. Gently elevated site offering beautiful views over the moors and Mendips. Lovely comfortable family home. Breakfast room for sole guest use, breakfast served at separate tables. Full English breakfast and a varied menu. (Quiet location).

Westhay

ST4342

New House Farm, Burtle Road, Westhay, Glastonbury, Somerset, *BA69TT.* **Open:** All year
Grades: ETC 4 Diamond, Silver
01458 860238 Mrs Bell **Fax: 01458 860568**
newhousefarm@farmersweekly.net **D:** £23.00–£24.00 **S:** £26.00–£27.00 **Beds:** 1F 2D **Baths:** 3 En ⊅ ⚑ ⊁ ⊡ ♔ ✕ ▥ ♨ ⚬ cc
Large Victorian farmhouse on working dairy farm on Somerset Levels, ideally situated for touring Wells Cheddar, Bath etc. Enjoy our large farmhouse breakfasts, 4 course evening meals on request-own or local produce used. A warm welcome is assured.

Please respect a B&B's wishes regarding children, animals and smoking

Weston-super-Mare

ST3261   ⚐ Balmoral Hotel

The Weston Rose, 2 Osborne Road, Weston-super-Mare, BS23 3EL. **Open:** All year
01934 412690 Mrs Trueman westonrose@ beeb.net
D: £14.00–£19.00 **S:** £15.00–£23.00 **Beds:** 4F 3D 2T **Baths:** 4 En 2 Sh ⊅ ⚑ (5) ⊡ ✕ ▥ ♨
Hearty traditional breakfasts - a feast for the eye and stomach. Our own prize winning preserves, yoghurts and fresh fruits always available. All rooms have fridges and hair dryers - most have ceiling fans. Our motto is 'Comfort is our concern', let us prove it!

Braeside Hotel, 2 Victoria Park, Weston-super-Mare, Somerset, *BS23 2HZ.* **Open:** All year (not Xmas/New Year) **Grades:** ETC 4 Diamond, AA 4 Diamond
01934 626642 (also fax) Mr & Mrs Wallington www.braesidehotel.co.uk
D: £25.00 **S:** £25.00 **Beds:** 1F 5D 1T 2S **Baths:** 9 En ⊅ ⊡ ♔ ▥ ♨
Fabulous views over Weston Bay; two minutes' walk from sandy beach. Quiet location. Directions: with sea on left, take first right after Winter Gardens, then first left into Lower Church Road. Victoria Park is on the right after the left hand bend.

Moorlands Country Guest House, Hutton, Weston-super-Mare, Somerset, *BS24 9QH.* Fine Georgian house, extensive landscaped gardens, village pub serves meals. **Open:** All year **Grades:** ETC 3 Diamond
01934 812283 (also fax) Mr & Mrs Holt margaret_holt@email.com www.guestaccom.co.uk **D:** £20.00–£25.00 **S:** £20.00–£30.00 **Beds:** 3F 2D 1T 1S **Baths:** 5 En 1 Sh ⊅ ⚑ (7) ⊡ ♔ ▥ ♨ ⚬ 3 ⚬ cc

Beverley Guest House, 11 Whitecross Road, Weston-super-Mare, Somerset, *BS23 1EP.* Victorian-style, many original features. Close beach, town, railway station. **Open:** All year (not Xmas)
01934 622956 Mr & Mrs Morgan www.smoothhound.co.uk/hotels/bevergh.html **D:** £18.00–£23.00 **S:** £21.00–£23.00 **Beds:** 2F 1D 1T 1S **Baths:** 5 En ⊅ ⊁ ⊡ ♨ 3

Kenilworth B&B, 115 Locking Road, Weston-super-Mare, Somerset, *BS23 3ER.* Free tea/coffee making - TV - English breakfast - central heating - Car space. **Open:** All year (not Xmas)
01934 629398 Mrs Searle **D:** £14.00–£16.00 **S:** £16.00–£20.00 **Beds:** 1F 3D 2T 1S **Baths:** 2 Sh ⊅ ⚑ ⊡ ▥ ♨

Planning a longer stay? Always ask for any special rates

Courtland Guest House, 41 Severn Road, Weston-super-Mare, Somerset, *BS23 1DP.* Friendly, family run guest house, close to seafront and town. **Open:** All year
01934 621117 M & G Woods **D:** £16.00–£20.00 **S:** £16.00–£20.00 **Beds:** 1F 1T 4D 1S **Baths:** 2 En 2 Sh ⊅ (6) ⊡ ♔ ▥ ♨

Arilas, 78 Clevedon Road, Weston-super-Mare, Somerset, *BS23 1DF.* Family guest house close to beach, parks and local shops. **Open:** All year
01934 628283 Mrs Watkins **D:** £15.00–£18.00 **S:** £15.00–£18.00 **Beds:** 1F 1D 1T 1S **Baths:** 1 En 2 Sh ⊅ ⊡ ♔ ✕ ▥ ♨ ⚬ ♨

Clifton Villa B&B, 11 Clifton Road, Weston-super-Mare, Somerset, *BS23 1BJ.* Bed and breakfast in family home, near town and beach. **Open:** All year (not Xmas)
01934 413243 Mr Weeks **D:** £13.00–£17.00 **S:** £15.00–£20.00 **Beds:** 1F 1D 1T **Baths:** 2 En 1 Sh ⊁ ⊡ ▥ ♨

Everley Villa, 35 Clevedon Road, Weston-Super-Mare, Somerset, *BS23 1DB.* Your comfort, our pleasure. Spacious accommodation, short walk beach, station. **Open:** All year
01934 643856 Mr & Mrs Howes **D:** £20.00–£25.00 **S:** £20.00–£35.00 **Beds:** 2F 3D **Baths:** 2 En 1 Pr ⊅ ⚑ ⊁ ✕ ♨ ⚬

Westonzoyland

ST3434   ⚐ Sedgemoor Inn

Staddlestones, 3 Standards Road, Westonzoyland, Bridgwater, Somerset, *TA7 0EL.* **Open:** All year (not Xmas/New Year) **Grades:** ETC 4 Diamond, Silver
01278 691179 Mrs Eldridge **Fax: 01278 691333** staddlestones@euphony.net www.staddlestonesguesthouse.co.uk
D: £26.00 **S:** £31.00 **Beds:** 1T 2D **Baths:** 2 En 1 Pr ⚑ ⊁ ⊡ ✕ ▥ ♨ ⚬ cc
Spacious, comfortable Georgian home in village close to M5 offering warm welcome, quality hospitality and a good base for exploring. With the Quantock and Mendip hills, Exmoor National Park, Somerset Levels and coast all to hand, the area offers a wide range of natural, historical and tourist attractions. Good walking, fishing and cycling and excellent golf courses.

Phoenicia, *31 Liney Road, Westonzoyland, Bridgwater, Somerset, TA7 0EU.* Private suite in modern detached house village location. comfortable beds. **Open:** All year
01278 691385 Mr & Mrs Pumfrey **D:** £21.00–£22.50 **S:** £21.00–£22.50 **Beds:** 2S 1D **Baths:** 1 Pr ⛱ (10) 🅿 ≒ 📺 ▥ ☂

Wheddon Cross

SS9238 ◄ *Rest & Be Thankful, Royal Oak*

Cutthorne Farm, *Luckwell Bridge, Wheddon Cross, Minehead, Somerset, TA24 7EW.* **Open:** All year (not Xmas/New Year) **Grades:** ETC 4 Star
01643 831255 (also fax) Mrs Durbin *durbin@ cutthorne.co.uk* www.cutthorne.co.uk
D: £25.00–£34.00 **S:** £35.00–£40.00 **Beds:** 1T 2D **Baths:** 3 En ⛱ (12) 🅿 (6) ≒ 📺 🐕 ✕ 📺 ▥ ☂
Tucked away in the heart of Exmoor, hidden in its own private valley, Cutthorne is a country house which is truly 'off the beaten track'. Log fires. Ensuite bathrooms. Four poster bedroom. Candlelit dinners. Licensed. No smoking. Fly-fishing. Dogs welcome.

Little Quarme Farm, *Wheddon Cross, Minehead, Exmoor, Somerset, TA24 7EA.* Old farmhouse, beautifully furnished and decorated. Outstanding, peaceful location, superb views. **Open:** Mar to Nov **Grades:** ETC 5 Diamond, Silver
01643 841249 (also fax) Mrs Cody-Boutcher *106425.743@compuserve.com*
www.littlequarme.co.uk **D:** £20.00–£25.00 **S:** £25.00–£30.00 **Beds:** 2D 1T **Baths:** 3 En 🅿 (6) ≒ 📺 ▥ ☂

BEDROOMS

D = Double
T = Twin
S = Single
F = Family

Planning a longer stay? Always ask for any special rates

Sundial Guest House, *Wheddon Cross, Minehead, Somerset, TA24 7DP.* All ensuite, residents' lounge, log fires, cosy and welcoming. **Open:** Mar to Nov **Grades:** ETC 4 Diamond, Silver
01643 841188 Fax: 01643 841870 *admin@ sundialguesthouse.co.uk* sundialguesthouse.co. uk **D:** £18.00–£23.00 **S:** £20.00–£26.00 **Beds:** 2T 1D 1S **Baths:** 4 En 🅿 (5) ≒ 📺 📺 ▥ ☂

Rest & Be Thankful Inn, *Wheddon Cross, Exmoor, Minehead, Somerset, TA24 7DR.* Old coaching inn, ideal Exmoor location for walking and touring. **Open:** All year (not Xmas)
01643 841222 (also fax) Mr Weaver *enquiries@restandbethankful.co.uk*
www.restandbethankful.co.uk **D:** £27.00–£30.00 **S:** £27.00–£30.00 **Beds:** 3D 1T 1S **Baths:** 5 En 1 Sh ⛱ (11) 🅿 (30) ≒ 📺 ✕ 📺 ▥ ☂ cc

Triscombe Farm, *Wheddon Cross, Minehead, Somerset, TA24 7HA.* Nestling in its own secluded valley with a stream cascading through the garden. **Open:** All year (not Xmas/New Year)
01643 851227 (also fax) Mrs Brinkley **D:** £20.00–£30.00 **S:** £25.00–£40.00 **Beds:** 1T 2D **Baths:** 1 En 2 Pr ⛱ ≒ 📺 ▥ ☂

Wick St Lawrence

ST3665

Icleton Farm, *Wick St Lawrence, Weston-super-Mare, BS22 7YJ.* C15th farmhouse 5 mins from M5 J21, ideal for touring West Country. **Open:** All year (not Xmas)
01934 515704 Mrs Parsons **D:** £17.00–£20.00 **S:** £17.00–£20.00 **Beds:** 1F 1D **Baths:** 1 Pr ⛱ (2) 🅿 (2) 📺 📺 ▥ ☂

Williton

ST0741

Foresters Arms Hotel, *55 Long Street, Williton, Taunton, Somerset, TA4 4QY.* C17th coaching inn on A39 between Quantock and Brendon Hills. **Open:** All year
01984 632508 Mr Goble **D:** £17.50–£21.00 **S:** £18.50–£22.00 **Beds:** 2F2T 4D 1S **Baths:** 6 En 1 Sh ⛱ 🅿 (20) 📺 ✕ 📺 ☂ cc

Winscombe

ST4056

Home Farm, *Barton, Winscombe, Somerset, BS25 1DX.* Delightful Listed building adjacent C15th farmhouse in 2 acres. Private lounge, working inglenook fireplace. **Open:** All year
01934 842078 Mr & Mrs Marlow *info@ homefarmcottages.co.uk*
www.homefarmcottages.co.uk **D:** £22.00–£24.00 **S:** £22.00–£24.00 **Beds:** 2D 🅿 (4) ≒ 📺 🐕 ▥ ☂

Withypool

SS8435

The Old Rectory, *Withypool, Minehead, Somerset, TA24 7QP.* Pleasant view, comfortable beds and a good, hearty English breakfast. **Open:** Easter to Oct
01643 831553 Mr Clatworthy **D:** £16.00 **S:** £16.00 **Beds:** 1D 1T 1S **Baths:** 1 Sh ⛱ 🅿 (4) ≒ 📺 🐕 📺 ▥ ☂

Wookey

ST5145 ◄ *Burcott Inn*

Burcott Mill Historic Watermill & Guest House, *Wookey, Wells, Somerset, BA5 1NJ.* A rare working watermill dating from Domesday, still stonegrinding flour daily. **Open:** All year (not Xmas/New Year) **Grades:** ETC 3 Diamond
01749 673118 Mr & Mrs Burt **Fax: 01749 677376** *theburts@burcottmill.com*
www.burcottmill.com **D:** £21.00–£32.00 **S:** £24.00–£37.00 **Beds:** 4F 1D 1S **Baths:** 5 En 1 Pr ⛱ 🅿 (40) ≒ 📺 🐕 📺 ☂ cc

Wookey Hole

ST5347

Broadleys, *21 Wells Road, Wookey Hole, Wells, Somerset, BA5 1DN.* Large detached house situated between Wells and Wookey Hole with panoramic countryside views. **Open:** All year (not Xmas)
01749 674746 (also fax) Mrs Milton *broadleys@bobmilton.totalserve.co.uk* **D:** £20.00–£22.50 **S:** £25.00–£35.00 **Beds:** 3D **Baths:** 2 En 1 Pr ⛱ (10) 🅿 (4) ≒ 📺 📺 ▥ ☂

Woolverton

ST7854

The Old School House, *Woolverton, Bath, Somerset, BA3 6RH.* Homely accommodation. Converted Victorian school, 10 minutes south of Bath. **Open:** All year (not Xmas/New Year)
01373 830200 (also fax) Peter & Mary Thornton **D:** £20.00–£25.00 **S:** £25.00–£30.00 **Beds:** 1F 1T 2D **Baths:** 1 Sh ⛱ 🅿 ≒ ▥ ☂

Staffordshire

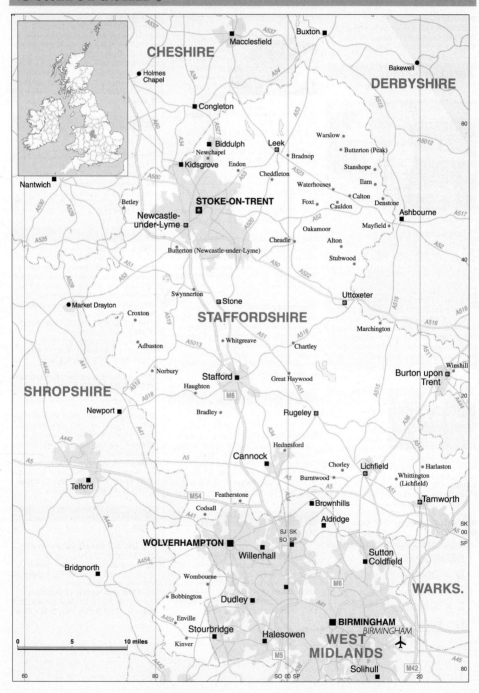

Adbaston
SJ7627

Offley Grove Farm, Adbaston, Eccleshall, Stafford, Staffordshire, ST20 0QB. You'll consider this a good find! Excellent breakfasts. Many guests return. **Open:** All year (not Xmas)
01785 280205 (also fax) Mrs Hiscoe James accom@offleygrovefarm.freeserve.co.uk www.offleygrovefarm.freeserve.co.uk
D: £18.00–£22.00 **S:** £18.00–£22.00 **Beds:** 2D 1T **Baths:** 2 En � 🄿 (4) 📺 �📺 ▥ ⚹

Alton
SK0742

Hillside Farm and Cottages, Alton Road, Denstone, Uttoxeter, Staffs, ST14 5HG.
Victorian farmhouse adjacent Alton Towers. Large gardens/orchard, views, cottages available. **Open:** All year
Grades: ETC 3 Diamond
01889 590760 (also fax) Mrs Johnson www.smoothhound.co.uk/hotels/hillside.html **D:** £15.00–£18.00 **S:** £18.00–£20.00 **Beds:** 2F 1D 1T **Baths:** 2 En 2 Sh ▷ 🄿 ▥ 📺 ▥ ⚹

The Dale, Alton, Stoke-on-Trent, Staffs, ST10 4BG. Ideal overnight base if visiting Alton Towers. Friendly family home. **Open:** All year (not Xmas)
01538 702394 Mrs Burrows thedalealton@ talk21.com **D:** £17.00 **S:** £22.00 **Beds:** 2T 1D **Baths:** 1 Sh ▷ 🄿 (6) 📺 ⚹ ▥ ⚹

Betley
SJ7548

The White Cottage, Main Road, Betley, Crewe, CW3 9BH. C16th cottage, tastefully decorated, peaceful gardens, excellent breakfasts. **Open:** All year (not Xmas)
01270 820218 Mrs Chisnall **D:** £17.50 **S:** £25.00 **Beds:** 1T/1D 1S **Baths:** 1 Sh ▷ (11) 🄿 (4) ⚹ ▥ ⚹

Bobbington
SO8090

Whittmere Farm, Bobbington, Stourbridge, West Midlands, DY7 5DX. Georgian farmhouse on working farm. **Open:** All year (not Xmas/New Year)
01384 221232 Mr & Mrs Snelson **D:** £15.00–£20.00 **S:** £15.00–£20.00 **Beds:** 1F 1T **Baths:** 1 Sh ▷ 🄿 ⚹ 📺 ⚹ ▥ ⚹

Planning a longer stay? Always ask for any special rates

Bradley
SJ8717

Littywood House, Bradley, Stafford, Staffordshire, ST18 9DW. Littywood is a beautiful double moated C14th manor house, set in its own grounds. **Open:** All year (not Xmas) **Grades:** ETC 4 Diamond
01785 780234 Mrs Busby **Fax:** 01785 780770 **D:** £21.00–£24.00 **S:** £25.00–£35.00 **Beds:** 1D 1T **Baths:** 1 En 1 Pr ▷ 🄿 (10) 📺 ▥ ⚹

Bradnop
SK0155

Middle Farm Guest House, Apesford, Bradnop, Leek, Staffordshire, ST13 7EX. Old farmhouse converted to B&B. Ensuite rooms. Half-price children in family rooms. **Open:** All year
01538 382839 (also fax) Ms Sheldon **D:** £20.00–£25.00 **S:** £25.00–£30.00 **Beds:** 4F 2D 1T ▷ 🄿 ⚹ 📺 ⚹ ✕ ▥ ⚹

Burntwood
SK0610

Davoll's Cottage, 156 Woodhouses Road, Burntwood, Staffs, WS7 9EL. Country cottage by woodland with easy access to Lichfield and the surrounding areas. **Open:** All year
01543 671250 Mrs Chrisfield **D:** £20.00–£22.00 **S:** £20.00–£25.00 **Beds:** 2T **Baths:** 1 En 1 Pr ▷ 🄿 (4) ⚹ ▥ ⚹ ✕ ▥ ⚹

Butterton (Newcastle-under-Lyme)
SJ8242 ⚓ Slater's Country Inn

New Hayes Farm, Trentham Road, Butterton, Newcastle-under-Lyme, Staffordshire, ST5 4DX. Perfectly situated for visiting the famous potteries and Alton Towers. **Open:** All year (not Xmas/New Year) **Grades:** ETC 4 Diamond
01782 680889 D: £20.00–£30.00 **S:** £25.00–£30.00 **Beds:** 1F 1T 1D **Baths:** 2 En 1 Pr ▷ (1) 🄿 (4) ⚹ 📺 ▥ ⚹

Butterton (Warslow)
SK0756

Coxon Green Farm, Butterton, Leek, Staffordshire, ST13 7TA. C17th farmhouse in Peak District village overlooking Manifold Valley. **Open:** All year (not Xmas/New Year)
01538 304221 Ms Tomkinson **D:** £20.00–£22.00 **S:** £22.00–£25.00 **Beds:** 3D **Baths:** 3 En 🄿 ⚹ 📺 ▥ ⚹

Calton
SK1050

Broadhurst Farm, Calton, Waterhouses, Stoke-on-Trent, Staffs, ST10 3LQ. Lovely farmhouse edge of Peak Park. Close to Alton Towers. **Open:** Easter to Nov
01538 308261 Mr & Mrs Mycock **D:** £18.00–£20.00 **S:** £19.00–£22.00 **Beds:** 1F 1D **Baths:** 2 En ▷ 🄿 (14) 📺 ⚹ ✕ ▥ ▥ ⚹

Cauldon
SK0749 ⚓ The Forge, Cross Inn, George Inn

The Cross Caravan Park, Cauldon Lowe, Cauldon, Waterhouses, Stoke on Trent, Staffordshire, ST10 3EX. Warm welcoming inn set in heart of the Staffordshire countryside. **Open:** All year
01538 308338 Mr Wilkinson **Fax:** 01538 308767 adrian_weaver@hotmail.com **D:** £20.00–£25.00 **S:** £20.00–£25.00 **Beds:** 2F 1T 4D 1S **Baths:** 8 En ▷ 🄿 ⚹ 📺 ✕ ▥ ▥ ⚹ ⚹ cc

Chartley
SK0028

Mill Cottage B&B, Chartley, Stafford, Staffordshire, ST18 0LH. Homely country cottage overlooking open countryside. A518 Stafford/Uttoxeter. **Open:** All year
01889 271109 & 07711 381669 (M) Ms Schuller **Fax:** 01889 271109 jennifer@ millcottagebandb.freeserve.co.uk www.millcottagebandb.co.uk **D:** £15.00–£17.50 **S:** £17.50–£20.00 **Beds:** 1F 1D **Baths:** 1 Sh ▷ 🄿 (2) 📺 ⚹ ▥ ▥ ⚹ ✱ ⚹

Cheadle
SK0143 ⚓ Waggon & Horses

Abbot's Haye, Cherry Lane, Cheadle, Stoke-on-Trent, Staffs, ST10 4QS. Country guest house with Tudor roots, quietly situated. Comfortable beds, breakfasts, light suppers, snacks. **Open:** All year (not Xmas/New Year)
01538 750645 Mr Piers-Leake **Fax:** 01538 754951 abbots.haye@btopenworld.com freespace.virgin.net/robert.james.leake **D:** £25.00 **S:** £37.50 **Beds:** 4F 1D **Baths:** 5 En ▷ 🄿 (5) ⚹ 📺 ✕ ▥ ▥ ⚹ cc

Leyfields Farm, Leek Road, Cheadle, Stoke on Trent, Staffs, ST10 2EF. Georgian farmhouse. High standard accommodation. Good food. Warm welcome. **Open:** All year (not Xmas/New Year) **Grades:** ETC 4 Diamond
01538 752875 (also fax) Mrs Clowes kathryn@leyfieldsfarm.freeserve.co.uk **D:** £20.00–£22.00 **S:** £22.00–£24.00 **Beds:** 2F 1T 2D **Baths:** 5 En ▷ 🄿 (5) ⚹ 📺 ▥ ⚹

Cheddleton

SJ9752

Choir Cottage, Ostlers Lane, Cheddleton, Leek, Staffs, ST13 7HS. C17th cottage in quiet location. Ideal honeymoon or special anniversary treat. **Open:** All year (not Xmas)
01538 360561 Mr & Mrs Sutcliffe
elaine.sutcliff@ic24 **D:** £27.50–£29.50
S: £35.00–£45.00 **Beds:** 1F 1D **Baths:** 2 En
ఆ (5) 🅿 (6) ⏦ 🖵 ▥ ♨

Chorley

SK0710

'Stone House' Farm, Farewell, Chorley, Lichfield, Staffs, WS13 8DS. C17th stone cottage surrounded by beautiful countryside. Peaceful hamlet. **Open:** All year
01543 682575 (also fax) Mrs Cowell
D: £17.00–£22.00 **S:** £17.00–£24.00 **Beds:** 3D 1S **Baths:** 1 En 2 Sh ఆ (5) 🅿 ⏦ 🖵 ⛄ 🖵 ▥ ♨

Codsall

SJ8703

Moors Farm & Country Restaurant, Chillington Lane, Codsall, Wolverhampton, Staffs, WV8 1QF. **Open:** All year **Grades:** AA 3 Diamond, RAC 3 Diamond
01902 842330 Mrs Moreton **Fax: 01902 847878** *enquiries@moorsfarm-hotel.co.uk*
www.moorsfarm-hotel.co.uk **D:** £25.00–£30.00 **S:** £30.00–£40.00 **Beds:** 1F 3D 2T 1S **Baths:** 4 En 2 Sh ఆ (4) 🅿 (20) ⏦ 🖵 × 🖵 ▥ ♨ ♣ cc
A cosy farmhouse in a picturesque valley. Codsall Village 1 mile, Wolverhampton 5 miles. Bedrooms have lovely views and very good facilities. Mrs Moreton is an excellent cook; dinner served in the oak-beamed dining room accompanied by some wine from the bar is a must.

Croxton

SJ7831

Glenwood, Croxton, Eccleshall, Staffordshire, ST21 6JA. C16th timber framed cottage in small country village. **Open:** All year
01630 620238 Mr & Mrs Martin **D:** £17.00–£19.00 **S:** £18.00–£20.00 **Beds:** 2T 1D **Baths:** 1 En 🅿 (6) ⏦ 🖵 ⛄ 🖵 ▥ ♨

Denstone

SK0940

Hillside Farm and Cottages, Alton Road, Denstone, Uttoxeter, Staffs, ST14 5HG. Victorian farmhouse adjacent Alton Towers. Large gardens/orchard, views, cottages available. **Open:** All year
Grades: ETC 3 Diamond
01889 590760 (also fax) Mrs Johnson
www.smoothhound.co.uk/hotels/hillside.
html **D:** £15.00–£18.00 **S:** £18.00–£20.00 **Beds:** 2F 1D 1T **Baths:** 2 En 2 Sh ఆ 🅿 🖵 🖵 ▥ ♨

Endon

SJ9253

The Hollies, Clay Lake, Endon, Stoke on Trent, Staffs, ST9 9DD. Beautiful Victorian house, set in lovely garden, with country view. **Open:** All year (not Xmas)
Grades: ETC 3 Diamond
01782 503252 Mrs Hodgson **D:** £20.00–£22.00 **S:** £22.00–£35.00 **Beds:** 1F 2D 2T **Baths:** 5 En ఆ (2) 🅿 (5) ⏦ 🖵 ⛄ 🖵 ▥ ♨

Reynolds Hey, Park Lane, Endon, Stoke-on-Trent, Staffordshire, ST9 9JB. Built 1640, modernised farmhouse. Superb views, close to Doultons, Alton Towers. **Open:** All year (not Xmas) **Grades:** ETC 4 Diamond
01782 502717 Mrs Weaver **D:** £18.00–£20.00 **S:** £25.00 **Beds:** 1F 1D 1T **Baths:** 3 En ఆ 🅿 (3) ⏦ 🖵 × 🖵 ▥ ♨

Hollinhurst Farm, Park Lane, Endon, Stoke on Trent, Staffs, ST9 9JB. Working farm, panoramic views, close to Alton Towers, the Potteries. **Open:** All year
01782 502633 Mr Clowes *hjball@ukf.net*
D: £18.00–£20.00 **S:** £18.00–£20.00 **Beds:** 1F 1D 1T **Baths:** 2 En 1 Pr ఆ 🅿 (5) ⏦ 🖵 ⛄ 🖵 ▥ ⛄ ♨

Enville

SO8287

Morfe Hall, Enville, Stourbridge, Staffs, DY7 5JU. Lovely old house surrounded by beautiful open country. **Open:** All year
01384 877004 Mrs Hobbs *morfehall@hotmail.com* **D:** £25.00–£30.00 **S:** £25.00 **Beds:** 1D **Baths:** 1 En ఆ 🅿 (20) ⏦ 🖵 ⛄ × 🖵 ▥ ♨

Featherstone

SJ9405

Featherstone Farm Hotel, New Road, Featherstone, Wolverhampton, W Mids, WV10 7NW. **Open:** All year
01902 725371 & 07836 315258 (M) Fax: 01902 731741 *Lewisprice@*
featherstoneFarm.co.uk www.featherstonefarm.co.uk **D:** £25.00–£35.00 **S:** £35.00–£45.00 **Beds:** 4D 2T 2S **Baths:** 4 En 2 Pr 2 Sh ఆ (2) 🅿 ⏦ 🖵 ⛄ × 🖵 ▥ ♨
Restaurant offering Indian cuisine. Rolls Royce available. 1/2 hour from NEC and NIA. C17th complex.

Foxt

SK0348

Shaw Gate Farm, Foxt, Stoke on Trent, Staffs, ST10 2HN. Overlooking Churnet Valley, residents bar, near Alton Towers. **Open:** All year (not Xmas/New Year)
01538 266590 (also fax) Mr Morris
D: £20.00–£25.00 **S:** £30.00–£50.00 **Beds:** 2F 3D **Baths:** 5 En ఆ 🅿 ⏦ 🖵 ▥ ♨ cc

Great Haywood

SK0023

Common Farm Motel, Pasturefields, Great Haywood, Stafford, ST18 0RB. Converted farm building giving the motel and 'old world' feeling. **Open:** All year (not Xmas/New Year)
01889 270209 Mrs Pickard *BOBPICKARD99@yahoo.com* **D:** £19.00–£25.00 **S:** £20.00–£29.00 **Beds:** 3F 3T 4D 4S **Baths:** 12 En 1 Sh ఆ (5) 🅿 (14) ⏦ 🖵 ▥ ⛄ ♨ cc

Harlaston

SK2111   ◀ White Lion

Harlaston Post Office, Main Road, Harlaston, Tamworth, Staffs, B79 9JU. **Open:** All year **Grades:** ETC 4 Diamond
01827 383324 Mrs Rowe **Fax: 01827 383746**
D: £22.50–£25.00 **S:** £25.00–£28.00 **Beds:** 1F 2T 1D 1S **Baths:** 5 En ఆ 🅿 (6) ⏦ 🖵 ▥ ♨
Harlaston won the Best Kept Small Village 2001 in Staffordshire. Within easy reach of Lichfield National Arboretum, NEC, Drayton Manor, Alton Towers, Tamworth's Castle and Snowdome. 4m M42 J11. A warm welcome assured.

Haughton

SJ8620

The Old School, Newport Road, Haughton, Stafford, Staffordshire, ST18 9JH. Listed building (1841) in centre of attractive village close to Stafford. **Open:** All year
Grades: AA 3 Diamond
01785 780358 (also fax) Mrs Jenks *info@theoldsc.co.uk* www.theoldsc.co.uk **D:** £20.00 **S:** £20.00–£25.00 **Beds:** 1D 1T 1S **Baths:** 2 Sh ఆ ⏦ 🖵 ▥ ⛄ ♨

Hednesford

SK0012

York House Guest House, *34 Anglesey Street, Hednesford, Cannock, Staffs, WS12 5AA.* Quiet, comfortable, spacious Edwardian house to accommodate worker or player. **Open:** All year
01543 422502 Ms Brown **D:** £18.00 **S:** £26.00 **Beds:** 1F 4T 1D **Baths:** 2 En 1 Sh ♥ ⊞ (8) ▥ ⊁ ▥ ⊞ ⬥

Ilam

SK1350 ⬦ *Watts Russell Arms, Crown Inn, Forge Inn, George Innm Izaak Walton*

Throwley Hall Farm, *Ilam, Ashbourne, Derbyshire, DE6 2BB.* Comfortable, large, rural Georgian farmhouse with delicious full breakfasts. **Open:** All year (not Xmas) **Grades:** ETC 4 Diamond **01538 308202** Mrs Richardson **Fax: 01538 308243** *throwleyhall@talk21.com* www.throwleyhallfarm.co.uk **D:** £22.00–£26.00 **S:** £22.00–£26.00 **Beds:** 2F 1T 1D **Baths:** 3 En 1 Pr ♥ ⊟ ⊁ ▥ ⊁ ▥ ⊞ ⬥

Kinver

SO8483

The Old Vicarage, *Vicarage Drive, Kinver, Stourbridge, W Mids, DY7 6HJ.* Very quiet position near village and NT Rock House. **Open:** All year (not Xmas)
01384 872784 Mr & Mrs Harris **D:** £20.00–£22.00 **S:** £20.00–£22.00 **Beds:** 2T 1S **Baths:** 1 En 1 Sh ⊟ (6) ▥ ⊁ ▥ ⊞ ⬥

Leek

SJ9856

Beechfields, *Park Road, Leek, Staffordshire, ST13 8JS.* Large Victorian house in spacious gardens. Delicious breakfast. Warm and relaxing. **Open:** All year (not Xmas)
01538 372825 Mrs Rider *judith@ beech-fields.fsnet.co.uk* **D:** £20.00 **S:** £25.00 **Beds:** 1F 2D **Baths:** 3 En ♥ ⊟ (4) ⊁ ▥ ▥ ⊞ ⬥

Lichfield

SK1109

Netherstowe House North, *Netherstowe Lane, Eastern Avenue, Lichfield, Staffs, WS13 6AY.* Grade II Listed Georgian building 3/4 mile from Lichfield city centre. **Open:** All year
01543 254631 Mrs Marshall **D:** £19.00–£21.00 **S:** £21.00–£22.00 **Beds:** 1F 1T **Baths:** 1 Pr 1 Sh ♥ (1) ⊟ (6) ⊁ ▥ ▥ ⊞ ⁕ ⬥

Marchington

SK1330

Forest Hills, *Moisty Lane, Marchington, Uttoxeter, Staffs, ST14 8JY.* **Open:** All year **01283 820447**
Mrs Brassington **D:** £21.00 **S:** £25.00 **Beds:** 3D 2T **Baths:** 5 En ♥ (5) ⊟ (6) ⊁ ▥ ▥ × ▥ ⊞, ⬥
Quiet Edwardian house enjoying views across River Dove Valley. Situated in a rural village with two pubs and a post office, good connection A50/M1. Easy access to Peak District and Alton Towers. Comfortable bedrooms, generous breakfasts and friendly atmosphere.

Mayfield

SK1546

Dove House, *Bridge Hill, Mayfield, Ashbourne, Derbyshire, DE6 2HN.* Large detached Victorian house close to Peak District and Alton Towers. **Open:** All year (not Xmas/New Year)
01335 343329 Mrs Green **D:** £20.00 **S:** £28.00 **Beds:** 1D **Baths:** 1 En ⊟ (1) ▥ × ▥ ▥ ⊞ ⬥

Newcastle-under-Lyme

SJ8546

Durlston Guest House, *Kimberley Road 'off A34, Newcastle under Lyme, Staffs, ST5 9EG.* Ten mins walk from town centre, convenient for Alton Towers and Potteries. **Open:** All year (not Xmas)
01782 611708 Mr & Mrs Stott **Fax: 01782 639770** *durlston@cwcom.net* **D:** £17.50–£18.00 **S:** £20.00–£21.00 **Beds:** 2F 1D 1T 3S **Baths:** 2 Sh ♥ ⊁ ▥ ⊁ ⊞ ⬥ cc

Newchapel

SJ8654

The Old Vicarage, *Birchenwood Road, Newchapel, Stoke-on-Trent, Staffordshire, ST7 4QT.* Built 1848 in tranquil gardens. 10 minute M6. Rural retreat. **Open:** All year
01782 785270 Mrs Kent-Baguley *oldvicarageb&b@birchenwood.freeserve.co.uk* **D:** £20.00–£25.00 **S:** £20.00–£25.00 **Beds:** 1F 1D 1S **Baths:** 2 En 1 Pr ♥ (8) ⊟ (6) ⊁ ▥ ⊁ ▥ ⊞, ⬥

Norbury

SJ7823 ⬦ *Plough Inn, Junction Inn, Swan Inn*

Oulton House Farm, *Norbury, Stafford, Staffordshire, ST20 0PG.* Visit our warm, comfortable Victorian farmhouse with marvellous countryside views. **Open:** All year (not Xmas) **Grades:** ETC 4 Diamond **01785 284264 (also fax)** Mrs Palmer *judy@ oultonhousefarm.co.uk* www.oultonhousefarm.co.uk **D:** £22.50 **S:** £30.00 **Beds:** 2D 1T **Baths:** 3 En ♥ ⊟ (3) ▥ ▥ ⊞, ⬥ cc

Oakamoor

SK0544

Ribden Farm, *Oakamoor, Stoke on Trent, Staffs, ST10 3BW.* Listed stone farmhouse (1748). Some rooms with four poster beds, all ensuite with TVs. **Open:** All year (not Xmas)
01538 702830 Mrs Shaw **D:** £20.00–£24.00 **S:** £30.00–£35.00 **Beds:** 5F 2D 1T **Baths:** 7 En 1 Pr ♥ ⊟ (10) ▥ ⊞, ⬥ cc

Stafford

SJ9223

Littywood House, *Bradley, Stafford, Staffordshire, ST18 9DW.* **Open:** All year (not Xmas)
Grades: ETC 4 Diamond **01785 780234** Mrs Busby **Fax: 01785 780770** **D:** £21.00–£24.00 **S:** £25.00–£35.00 **Beds:** 1D 1T **Baths:** 1 En 1 Pr ♥ ⊟ (10) ▥ ⊞, ⬥
Littywood is a beautiful double moated C14th manor house, set in its own grounds, secluded, yet easily accessible from the M6. Centrally heated, all rooms having antique furniture and tapestries. Ideally situated for Shugborough, Weston Park and the Potteries.

Bailey Hotel, *63 Lichfield Road, Stafford, Staffordshire, ST17 4LL.* Modern detached hotel, comfortably furnished, parking in own grounds. **Open:** All year (not Xmas)
01785 214133 Mr & Mrs Ayres **Fax: 01785 227920 D:** £18.00–£23.00 **S:** £21.50–£30.00 **Beds:** 1F 5D 3T 2S **Baths:** 4 En 2 Sh ♥ ⊟ (11) ▥ ⊁ ⊞, ⬥

Stanshope

SK1254

Stanshope Hall, *Stanshope, Ashbourne, Derbyshire, DE6 2AD.* Peace and quiet and lovely views over Peak District hills.
Open: All year (not Xmas)
01335 310278 Miss Chambers **Fax: 01335 310470** *naomi@stanshope.demon.co.uk*
D: £25.00–£40.00 **S:** £25.00–£40.00 **Beds:** 2D 1T **Baths:** 3 En ⛭ P (3) TV V ▥ ☕ cc

Stoke-on-Trent

SJ8747

The Hollies, *Clay Lake, Endon, Stoke on Trent, Staffs, ST9 9DD.* Beautiful Victorian house, set in lovely garden, with country view.
Open: All year (not Xmas) **Grades:** ETC 3 Diamond
01782 503252 Mrs Hodgson **D:** £20.00–£22.00 **S:** £22.00–£35.00 **Beds:** 1F 2D 2T **Baths:** 5 En ⛭ (2) P (5) ⚟ TV ♞ V ▥ ☕

Reynolds Hey, *Park Lane, Endon, Stoke-on-Trent, Staffordshire, ST9 9JB.* Built 1640, modernised farmhouse. Superb views, close to Doultons, Alton Towers. **Open:** All year (not Xmas) **Grades:** ETC 4 Diamond
01782 502717 Mrs Weaver **D:** £18.00–£20.00 **S:** £25.00 **Beds:** 1F 1D 1T **Baths:** 3 En ⛭ P (3) ⚟ TV ✕ V ▥ ☕

The Corrie Guest House, *13 Newton Street, Stoke-on-Trent, Staffs, ST4 6JN.* Victorian house, quiet central location.
Open: All year **Grades:** RAC 3 Diamond, Sparkling
01782 614838 (also fax) Burton *the.corrie@talk21.com* **D:** £19.00–£22.00 **S:** £22.00–£31.00 **Beds:** 3T 3D 2S **Baths:** 3 En 3 Sh ⛭ (5) P (9) ⚟ TV V ▥ ☕

Stone

SJ9034

Field House, *Stafford Road, Stone, Staffs, ST15 0HE.* **Open:** All year
01785 605712 Mrs Busfield
D: £16.00–£18.00 **S:** £25.00–£29.00 **Beds:** 1F 1D 1T **Baths:** 1 En 1 Sh ⛭ P (4) ⚟ TV ▥ ☕
Listed Georgian house offering charming spacious accommodation in warm, relaxed atmosphere, situated in beautiful grounds close to canal, town centre and excellent choice of restaurants. Ideal for Wedgwood Potteries, Shugborough, Alton Towers and the Peak District. Non-smoking bedrooms.

Stubwood

SK0939

Rowan Lodge, *Stubwood, Denstone, Ulloxeter, Staffordshire, ST14 5HU.* A short drive to Alton Towers/Peak District.
Open: All year (not Xmas/New Year)
01889 590913 Mrs Warren **D:** £17.00–£20.00 **S:** £18.00–£22.00 **Beds:** 1F 1D **Baths:** 2 En ⛭ P (2) ⚟ TV ✕ ▥ ☕

Swynnerton

SJ8535

Home Farm, *Swynnerton, Stone, Staffs, ST15 0RA.* Elizabethan farmhouse, easy access to Alton towers and potteries.
Open: All year
01782 796241 Mrs Cope *homefarm@cope32.fsnet.co.uk* **D:** £17.50–£20.00 **S:** £17.50 **Beds:** 1F 3D 3T 3S **Baths:** 2 En 2 Pr 2 Sh ⛭ P (10) TV ♞ ✕ V ▥ ☕

Tamworth

SK2203

Victoria Court Hotel, *42 Victoria Road, Tamworth, Staffs, B79 7HU.* Minutes from railway station and town centre. In-house Italian restaurant. **Open:** All year
01827 64698 Mrs Morlini **Fax: 01827 312368** *victoriacourthotel@btinternet.com* **D:** £19.00–£27.50 **S:** £22.00–£38.00 **Beds:** 2F 1T 2D 4S **Baths:** 5 Pr 1 Sh ⛭ P (20) TV ✕ V ▥ ☕ cc

Uttoxeter

SK0933

White Hart Hotel, *Carter Street, Uttoxeter, Staffs, ST14 8EU.* Friendly C16th coaching inn, close to Alton towers.
Open: All year
01889 562437 Mr Wood **Fax: 01889 565099** *white.hart.hotel.104111@punchgroupe.co.uk*
D: £31.50–£63.00 **S:** £56.00 **Beds:** 3F 5T 11D 2S **Baths:** 21 En ⛭ P (40) TV ♞ ✕ V ▥ ☕ cc

Warslow

SK0858

The Greyhound Inn, *Warslow, Buxton, Derbyshire, SK17 0JN.* Cosy village pub, open fires, good home cooking, exceptionally friendly. **Open:** All year
01298 84249 Mr Mullarkey **D:** £17.50 **Beds:** 2D 2S **Baths:** 1 Sh P (20) ✕ ▥ ☕ cc

Waterhouses

SK0850

Lee House Farm, *Waterhouses, Stoke On Trent, Staffordshire, ST10 3HW.* Lovely Georgian farmhouse, village setting, close to the Manifold Valley. **Open:** All year **Grades:** ETC 4 Diamond, Silver
01538 308439 Ms Little **D:** £20.00–£25.00 **S:** £25.00–£30.00 **Beds:** 2D 1T **Baths:** 3 En ⛭ P (4) ⚟ TV V ▥ ☕

Please respect a B&B's wishes regarding children, animals and smoking

Whitgreave

SJ8928 *Greyhound*

Whitgreave Manor, *Whitgreave, Stafford, ST18 9SP.* Beautiful Victorian manor house in own mature grounds. Peaceful setting. **Open:** All year
01785 251767 (also fax) Mrs Challinor *whitgreave.uk@virgin.net* **D:** £27.50–£35.00 **S:** £30.00–£40.00 **Beds:** 1F 3T 2D 5S **Baths:** 5 En ⚟ TV ✕ V ▥ ☕

Whittington (Lichfield)

SK1608

Hawthorns House, *44a Church Street, Whittington, Lichfield, Staffs, WS14 9JX.* Old Victorian house. 15 minutes Belfry and most motorways. **Open:** All year (not Xmas/New Year)
01543 432613 Mrs Christie **D:** £38.00–£40.00 **S:** £19.00–£20.00 **Beds:** 2T 1D **Baths:** 1 Sh ⚟ TV ✕ V ▥ ☕

Winshill

SK2623

Meadow View, *203 Newton Road, Winshill, Burton-upon-Trent, Staffs, DE15 0TU.* Double-fronted house overlooking River Trent in attractive wooded garden.
Open: All year (not Xmas)
01283 564046 Mrs Hancox **D:** £17.00 **S:** £17.00 **Beds:** 1T 1S **Baths:** 1 Pr ⛭ (10) P (3) ⚟ TV ♞ V ▥ ☕

Wombourne

SO8792

24 Dinkinson Road, *Wombourne, Wolverhampton, W Mids, WV5 0NH.* Central to many Midland attractions. **Open:** All year
01902 895614 Mrs Whitmore **D:** £13.50 **S:** £13.50 **Beds:** 1T P TV ♞ ▥

RATES
D = Price range per person sharing in a double or twin room
S = Price range for a single room

Suffolk

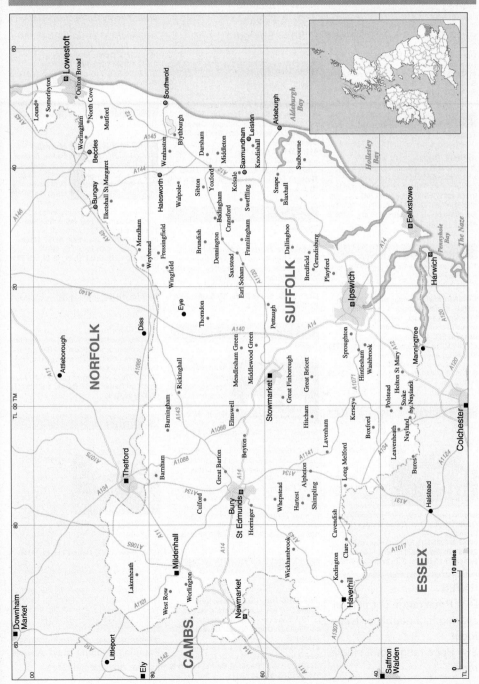

Aldeburgh

TM4656 🍺 *Mill Inn, Cross Keys, The Victoria, Railway Inn*

Faraway, *28 Linden Close, Aldeburgh, Suffolk, IP15 5JL.* Quiet, being off main road. Garden, car parking, dogs welcome. **Open:** Easter to Nov **Grades:** ETC 3 Diamond
01728 452571 Mrs Burrell **D:** £18.00–£20.00 **S:** £18.00–£20.00 **Beds:** 1F 1T 1S **Baths:** 2 Sh ⅊ ☐ ✠ ☐ ★ ☑ ▥

Alpheton

TL8850

Amicus, *Old Bury Road, Alpheton, Sudbury, Suffolk, CD10 9BT.* Just off A134 amid peaceful surroundings, ideal for garden lovers. **Open:** All year (not Xmas)
01284 828579 & 07779 076519 (M)
Mrs Burcham **D:** £17.50–£20.00 **S:** £20.00–£25.00 **Beds:** 1D 1T **Baths:** 2 Pr ☐ (2) ✠ ☑ ▥ ▥, ★

Badingham

TM3068 🍺 *Queens Head (Dennington), Queens Head (Bramfield)*

Colston Hall, *Badingham, Woodbridge, Suffolk, IP13 8LB.* Antique 4 poster bed. Excellent breakfasts. Surrounded by peaceful countryside. **Open:** All year **Grades:** ETC 4 Diamond, Silver
01728 638375 Mrs Bellefontaine **Fax: 01728 638084** *lizjohn@colstonhall.com*
www.colstonhall.com **D:** £25.00–£35.00 **S:** £30.00–£50.00 **Beds:** 2T 4D **Baths:** 6 En ☐ ✠ ▥, ★ cc

Barnham

TL8779

East Farm, *Barnham, Thetford, Norfolk, IP24 2PB.* Come and stay in large welcoming farmhouse and enjoy the farm countryside. **Open:** All year (not Xmas) **Grades:** ETC 4 Diamond
01842 890231 Mrs Heading **Fax: 01842 890457 D:** £22.00–£23.50 **S:** £24.00–£27.00 **Beds:** 1D 1T **Baths:** 2 En ⅊ ☐ (6) ✠ ☑ ▥, ★

BATHROOMS
En = Ensuite
Pr = Private
Sh = Shared

Barningham

TL9676 🍺 *Royal George*

College House Farm, *Bardwell Road, Barningham, Bury St Edmunds, Suffolk, IP31 1DF.* Self-catering cottages. **Open:** All year (not Xmas/New Year) **Grades:** ETC 4 Diamond
01359 221512 (also fax) Mrs Brightwell
www.abreakwithtradition.co.uk **D:** £25.00–£28.00 **S:** £25.00–£28.00 **Beds:** 1F 1T 1D 1S **Baths:** 1 En 1 Pr 1 Sh ⅊ (5) ☐ (8) ✠ ☑ ★ ✕ ☑ ▥, ⚄ ★

Beccles

TM4289

Catherine House, *2 Ringsfield Road, Beccles, Suffolk, NR34 9PQ.* Well furnished family home, excellent facilities, view over Waveney Valley. **Open:** All year
01502 716428 (also fax) Mrs Renilson **D:** £20.00 **S:** £20.00 **Beds:** 3D **Baths:** 2 En 1 Pr ⅊ ☐ (4) ☑ ☑ ▥, ★

Beyton

TL9363

Manorhouse, *The Green, Beyton, Bury St Edmunds, Suffolk, IP30 9AF.* **Open:** All year (not Xmas)
Grades: ETC 5 Diamond, Gold, AA 5 Diamond
01359 270960 Mrs Dewsbury *manorhouse@beyton.com* www.beyton.com **D:** £25.00–£27.00 **S:** £38.00–£45.00 **Beds:** 2D 2T **Baths:** 4 En ☐ (6) ✠ ☑ ☑ ▥, ★

This C15th timbered longhouse overlooks the Green in centre of pretty village and unwind. Large luxurious rooms, king-size beds. Excellent breakfasts at wonderful tables. 4 miles east of Bury St Edmunds.

Blaxhall

TM3656

The Ship Inn, *Blaxhall, Woodbridge, Suffolk, IP12 2DY.* Quiet rooms in stables of C17th village inn. Cask ales and home-cooked food. **Open:** All year **Grades:** ETC 2 Diamond
01728 688316 *shipinnblaxhall@aol.com*
www.shipinnblaxhall.co.uk **D:** £20.00–£22.50 **S:** £25.00–£32.00 **Beds:** 4T **Baths:** 4 En ⅊ ☐ ✠ ☑ ✕ ☑ ▥, ❋ ★ cc

---

Blythburgh

TM4475

Little Thorbyns, *The Street, Blythburgh, Halesworth, Suffolk, IP19 9LS.* Comfortable accommodation. Close to beaches, RSPB reserve, Southwold and East Anglia attractions. **Open:** All year
01502 478664 (also fax) Mrs Harris **D:** £20.00 **S:** £20.00–£40.00 **Beds:** 2T 2D 1S **Baths:** 3 En ⅊ ☐ (8) ✠ ☑ ✕ ☑ ▥, ★

Boxford

TL9640

Hurrels Farm, *Boxford Lane, Boxford, Sudbury, Suffolk, CO10 5JY.* An attractive Grade II Tudor farmhouse, ideal for visiting Suffolk/Essex border. **Open:** All year (not Xmas/New Year) **Grades:** ETC 4 Diamond, Silver
01787 210215 Dr Alok **Fax: 01787 211806** *hurrells@aol.com* **D:** £20.00 **S:** £25.00 **Beds:** 2D 1S **Baths:** 2 Sh ⅊ (10) ☐ (6) ✠ ☑ ▥, ★

Bredfield

TM2652

Moat Farmhouse, *Dallinghoo Road, Bredfield, Woodbridge, Suffolk, IP13 6BD.* Ideal family home accommodation. Reductions for children. Self contained on ground floor. **Open:** Mar to Oct
01473 737475 Mrs Downing **D:** £17.00 **S:** £17.00 **Beds:** 1D 1T **Baths:** 1 Sh ⅊ (1) ☐ (4) ✠ ☑ ▥, ★

Brundish

TM2669

Woodlands Farm, *Brundish, Woodbridge, Suffolk, IP13 8BP.* **Open:** All year (not Xmas/New Year) **Grades:** AA 4 Diamond
01379 384444 Mrs Graham *woodlandsfarm@hotmail.com* **D:** £20.00–£22.50 **S:** £25.00–£27.50 **Beds:** 2D 1T **Baths:** 3 En ⅊ (10) ☐ (6) ✠ ☑ ▥, ★

A warm friendly welcome awaits at our comfortable cottage-style farmhouse. Perfectly situated among orchards near Framlingham. Ideal for exploring coast/ countryside by foot, cycle or car. Excellent breakfasts using fresh local produce and our own free-range eggs.

Planning a longer stay? Always ask for any special rates

RATES
D = Price range per person sharing in a double or twin room
S = Price range for a single room

Bungay
TM3389

36, Fairfield Road, *Bungay, Suffolk, NR35 1RY.*
Open: All year
01986 893897
Mr & Mrs Tate
heather.tate@talk21.com **D:** £20.00–£22.00 **S:** £30.00–£35.00 **Beds:** 1D 1T **Baths:** 1 En 1 Pr ⑤ 🄿 (2) ⠵ 📺 ✕ Ⓥ ▥, 🛈
Comfortable family home overlooking open countryside. 10 minute walk to public indoor pool and to Bungay with its ancient castle, fine Georgian buildings, market place, butter cross and antiques. The River Waveney, Otter Trust, Aviation Museum, a short journey away.

Bures
TL9034

Queens House Guest House, *Church Square, Bures, Suffolk, CO8 5AB.* C17th coaching inn. Set in Stone Valley. Ideal for walks and cycling. **Open:** All year
Grades: ETC 4 Star
01787 227760 Mr Arnold **Fax:** 01787 227082
rogerarnold@cs.com **D:** £26.00 **S:** £33.00
Beds: 1F 2T 2D **Baths:** 4 En 1 Pr ⠵ 🄿 (6) ⠵ 📺 🐾 ✕ Ⓥ ▥, ✹ cc

Bury St Edmunds
TL8564

Hilltop, *22 Bronyon Close, Bury St Edmunds, Suffolk, IP33 3XB.* Home from Home. Quiet area. Ground floor bedroom, ensuite. **Open:** All year **Grades:** ETC 2 Diamond
01284 767066 & 07719 660142 (M)
Mrs Hanson *bandb@hilltop22br.freeserve.co.uk*
www.hilltop22br.freeserve.co.uk **D:** £16.00–£20.00 **S:** £16.00–£25.00 **Beds:** 1F 1T 1S
Baths: 1 Pr 1 Sh ⠵ 🄿 (2) ⠵ 📺 🐾 ✕ ▥, 🛈

Oak Cottage, *54 Guildhall Street, Bury St Edmunds, Suffolk, IP33 1QF.* Listed Tudor cottage, 2 mins from theatre, museums, shops, restaurants, cathedral, abbey gardens. **Open:** All year
01284 762745 & 07887 638553 (M)
Sheila Mann **Fax:** 01284 762745 **D:** £16.00–£26.50 **S:** £16.00–£20.00 **Beds:** 1F 1D 1T 1S
Baths: 1 En 1 Pr 1 Sh ⠵ 🄿 (1) ⠵ 📺 🐾 ✕ Ⓥ ▥, 🛈

Kiln Farm, *Kiln Lane, Elmswell, Bury St Edmunds, Suffolk, IP30 9QR.* Situated in the heart of Suffolk. Self-catering also Available. **Open:** All year
01359 240442 Mrs Knights *barry-sue@kilnfarm.fsnet.co.uk* **D:** £20.00–£25.00
S: £25.00–£35.00 **Beds:** 1F 1D 1T 1S
Baths: 4 En ⠵ 🄿 (10) 📺 🐾 ▥, 🛈

Cavendish
TL8046 ⌕ *The Bull*

The Red House, *Stour Street, Cavendish, Sudbury, Suffolk, CO10 8BH.* C16th house in delightful garden. Homely atmosphere. Delicious breakfasts.
Open: All year (not Xmas/New Year)
01787 280611 (also fax) M P Theaker
bg.theaker@btinternet.com **D:** £24.00–£26.50
Beds: 2T **Baths:** 1 En 1 Pr ⠵ 🄿 (2) ⠵ 📺 Ⓥ ▥, 🛈

The Grape Vine, *The Green, Cavendish, Sudbury, Suffolk, CO10 8BB.* Tudor house facing village green in Upper Stour Valley.
Open: All year
01787 280423 Morley *peterj_morley@hotmail.com* **D:** £14.25–£18.50 **S:** £24.00
Beds: 1T 1D **Baths:** 2 En ⠵ 📺 Ⓥ ▥, 🛈

Clare
TL7645

Ship Stores, *22 Callis Street, Clare, Sudbury, Suffolk, CO10 8PX.* Set in the beautiful small town of Clare, all rooms ensuite, breakfast to remember. **Open:** All year
01787 277834 Mrs Bowles *shipclare@aol.co.uk*
www.ship-stores.co.uk **D:** £20.50–£23.00
S: £25.00–£41.00 **Beds:** 1F 3D 1T **Baths:** 5 En ⠵ 🄿 (3) 📺 ✕ ▥, 🛈 cc

Cransford
TM3164

High House Farm, *Cransford, Framlingham, Woodbridge, Suffolk, IP13 9PD.* Beautiful oak-beamed C15th farmhouse on family farm. Spacious and comfortable accommodation. **Open:** All year
01728 663461 Mrs Kindred **Fax:** 01728 663409 *bb@highhousefarm.co.uk*
www.highhousefarm.co.uk **D:** £20.00
S: £25.00–£30.00 **Beds:** 1F 1D **Baths:** 1 En 1 Pr ⠵ 🄿 (4) 📺 🐾 Ⓥ ▥, 🛈

Culford
TL8369

47 Benyon Gardens, *Culford, Bury St Edmunds, Suffolk, IP28 6EA.* A modern bungalow overlooking fields and quietly situated. **Open:** All year (not Xmas/New Year)
01284 728763 Mrs Townsend **D:** £16.00–£32.00 **S:** £18.00 🄿 (4) ⠵ 📺 ▥,

Dallinghoo
TM2655

Old Rectory, *Dallinghoo, Woodbridge, Suffolk, IP13 0LA.* Rare, restful, rural retreat, relaxing, remedial, regularly revisited, room service. **Open:** All year (not Xmas)
01473 737700 Mrs Quinlan **D:** £16.00–£18.00
Beds: 1D 1T **Baths:** 1 Pr 1 Sh ⠵ 🄿 (6) ⠵ Ⓥ ▥,

Darsham
TM4169

Priory Farm, *Priory Lane, Darsham, Saxmundham, Suffolk, IP17 3QD.* B&B in comfortable C17th farmhouse, peaceful countryside. Ideal base for exploring Suffolk coast. **Open:** Mar to Oct
Grades: ETC 3 Diamond
01728 668459 Mrs Bloomfield **Fax:** 01728 668744 *www.prioryfarm.ision.co.uk*
D: £25.00–£30.00 **S:** £35.00–£40.00 **Beds:** 1D 1T **Baths:** 2 Pr ⠵ (12) 🄿 (2) ⠵ 📺 Ⓥ ▥, 🛈

White House Farm, *Main Road, Darsham, Saxmundham, Suffolk, IP17 3PP.* Period farmhouse. Extensive gardens. Close Minsmere/Dunwich/Southwold. All facilities. **Open:** All year **Grades:** ETC 3 Diamond, AA 3 Diamond, RAC 3 Diamond
01728 668632 & 07810 511804 (M)
Mrs Newman **D:** £20.00–£27.50 **S:** £25.00–£35.00 **Beds:** 1T 2D **Baths:** 1 En 1 Sh ⠵ (5) 🄿 (20) ⠵ 📺 Ⓥ ▥, 🛈

Dennington
TM2867

Fieldway, *Saxtead Road, Dennington, Woodbridge, Suffolk, IP13 8AP.* Stylish house in quiet location facing village green. All rooms overlook beautiful garden. **Open:** All year (not Xmas)
01728 638456 (also fax) Mrs Turan **D:** £20.00
S: £22.00 **Beds:** 1D 1T **Baths:** 1 Pr 1 Sh ⠵ (5) 🄿 (4) ⠵ 📺 ✕ ▥, 🛈

Earl Soham
TM2363

Bridge House, *Earl Soham, Woodbridge, Suffolk, IP13 7RT.* Beautiful C16th house. Warm welcome, good food, varied menu. **Open:** All year **Grades:** ETC 4 Diamond, Silver
01728 685473/685289 J A Baker
bridgehouse46@hotmail.com **D:** £25.00–£27.50
S: £28.00 **Beds:** 1T 2D **Baths:** 3 En 🄿 (5) ⠵ 📺 ✕ Ⓥ ▥, 🛈

Elmswell
TL9863 ⌕ *Gardeners Arms, Brewers Arms, Dog Inn, The Fox*

Elmswell Hall, *Elmswell, Bury St Edmunds, IP30 9EN.* Ideally situated for exploring East Anglia. Warm welcome, hearty breakfast.
Open: All year (not Xmas/New Year)
Grades: ETC 4 Diamond
01359 240215 (also fax) K Over *kate@elmswellhall.freeserve.co.uk www.elmswellhall.co.uk* **D:** £25.00 **S:** £30.00 **Beds:** 1T 1D
Baths: 1 En 1 Pr ⠵ (0) 🄿 (6) ⠵ 📺 🐾 Ⓥ ▥, 🛈

RATES

D = Price range per person sharing in a double or twin room

S = Price range for a single room

Kiln Farm, *Kiln Lane, Elmswell, Bury St Edmunds, Suffolk, IP30 9QR.* Situated in the heart of Suffolk. Self-catering also Available. **Open:** All year
01359 240442 Mrs Knights *barry-sue@ kilnfarm.fsnet.co.uk* **D:** £20.00–£25.00 **S:** £25.00–£35.00 **Beds:** 1F 1D 1T 1S **Baths:** 4 En ⊃ 🅿 (10) 📺 ⊁ 🖿 ⬩

Felixstowe

TM3034

Iddesleigh Private Guest House, *11 Constable Road, Felixstowe, IP11 7HL.* We offer a cordial welcome in a friendly atmosphere. **Open:** All year
01394 670546 & 01394 270167 Fax: 01394 273214 D: £16.50–£21.00 **S:** £17.50–£21.00 **Beds:** 2F 2T 2D 2S **Baths:** 1 En 1 Pr 2 Sh ⊃ 🅿 (3) ⊁ 📺 ⊁ ✕ 📺 🖿 ❋ ⬩

Framlingham

TM2863

Boundary Farm, *off Saxmundham Road, Framlingham, Woodbridge, Suffolk, IP13 9NU.*
C17th farmhouse, open countryside, ideal touring base. Brochure on request. **Open:** All year (not Xmas)
01728 723401 Mrs Cook **Fax: 01728 723877 D:** £18.00–£25.00 **S:** £20.00–£25.00 **Beds:** 2D 1T **Baths:** 1 En 1 Sh ⊃ 🅿 (4) 📺 ✕ 📺 🖿 ⬩

Shimmens Pightle, *Dennington Road, Framlingham, Woodbridge, Suffolk, IP13 9JT.* Comfortable home, beautiful garden. Home-made preserves, locally cured bacon. Ground-floor rooms. **Open:** Easter to Nov **Grades:** ETC 3 Diamond
01728 724036 Mrs Collett **D:** £22.00–£25.00 **S:** £25.00 **Beds:** 1D 2T **Baths:** 1 Sh ⊃ (8) 🅿 (5) ⊁ 📺 📺 🖿 ⬩

BEDROOMS

D = Double
T = Twin
S = Single
F = Family

Fressingfield

TM2677   ◁ *Swan Inn, Fox & Goose*

Elm Lodge Farm, *Chippenhall Green, Fressingfield, Eye, Suffolk, IP21 5SL.*
Open: Mar to Oct **Grades:** ETC 4 Diamond
01379 586249 Mrs Webster *sheila-webster@ elm-lodge.fsnet.co.uk www.elm-lodge.fsnet.co. uk* **D:** £18.00–£22.00 **S:** £21.00–£25.00 **Beds:** 1T 2D **Baths:** 1 En 1 Sh ⊃ (10) 🅿 (3) 📺 ✝ ⬩
Peace and quiet, a warm welcome and comfortable accommodation await you in our Victorian farmhouse. In a completely rural situation - overlooking a large common - yet within easy reach of the coast and many other beautiful and interesting areas of Suffolk.

Great Barton

TL8866

Cherry Trees, *Mount Road, Cattishall, Great Barton, Bury St Edmunds, Suffolk, IP31 2QU.* **Open:** All year (not Xmas) **Grades:** ETC 3 Diamond
01284 787501 Mrs Salmon **D:** £19.00–£20.00 **S:** £24.00–£26.00 ⊃ (4) 🅿 (5) ⊁ 📺 🖿 ⬩
Surrounded by lovely garden with fields beyond, yet only 2 miles from the centre of historic Bury St Edmunds. Comfortable beds and full English breakfast. Pub nearby for good meals.

Great Bricett

TM0350

Riverside Cottage, *The Street, Great Bricett, Ipswich, IP7 7DH.* Charming and extremely comfortable ensuite rooms overlooking half-acre garden. **Open:** All year (not Xmas) **Grades:** ETC 4 Diamond
01473 658266 & 07811 837728 (M) Mr Horne *chasmhorne@aol.com* **D:** £23.00–£27.50 **S:** £25.00–£30.00 **Beds:** 1D 1T **Baths:** 2 En ⊃ (1) 🅿 (3) 📺 ✕ 📺 🖿 ⬩

Great Finborough

TM0157

Dairy Farmhouse, *Valley Lane, Great Finborough, Stowmarket, Suffolk, IP14 3BE.* C16th thatched farmhouse in 5 acres with delightful views. Open fires, beams and antiques. **Open:** All year (not Xmas/New Year)
01449 615730 C Watson **D:** £25.00–£30.00 **S:** £30.00–£35.00 **Beds:** 2D **Baths:** 1 Sh ⊃ 🅿 (10) ⊁ 📺 ✝ ✕ 🖿 ⬩

Grundisburgh

TM2250   ◁ *The Dog, The Green*

Hawthorn Cottage, *Lower Road, Grundisburgh, Woodbridge, Suffolk, IP13 6UQ.* Super detached barn conversion in quiet village. **Open:** All year
01473 738199 Lady Hutchison **D:** £22.00–£25.00 **Beds:** 2T **Baths:** 1 Pr ⊃ 🅿 (6) 🖿 ⬩

Halesworth

TM3877   ◁ *The Plough*

Rumburgh Farm, *Halesworth, Suffolk, IP19 0RU.* Attractive C17th timber framed farmhouse on a mixed enterprise farm. **Open:** All year (not Xmas) **Grades:** ETC 4 Diamond
01986 781351 (also fax) Mr & Mrs Binder *binder@rumburghfarm.freeserve.co.uk www.rumburghfarm.freeserve.co.uk* **D:** £17.00–£22.50 **S:** £21.00–£27.00 **Beds:** 1F 1D **Baths:** 2 En ⊃ 🅿 ⊁ 📺 📺 🖿 ⬩

Hartest

TL8352

Giffords Hall, *Hartest, Bury St Edmunds, Suffolk, IP29 4EX.* Lovely Georgian house set among vineyards, flower meadows and animals. **Open:** All year (not Xmas)
01284 830464 Mr Kemp *inquiries@ giffords.co.uk www.giffordshall.co.uk* **D:** £22.00–£25.00 **S:** £22.00–£25.00 **Beds:** 2T **Baths:** 3 En ⊃ 🅿 (5) ⊁ 📺 ✝ 📺 🖿 ⬩ cc

Hintlesham

TM0843   ◁ *The George*

College Farm, *Hintlesham, Ipswich, Suffolk, IP8 3NT.* Peaceful C15th farmhouse near 'Constable Country'. Overlooks fields. Spacious rooms, large breakfasts. **Open:** Jan to Dec **Grades:** ETC 4 Diamond
01473 652253 (also fax) Mrs Bryce *bryce1@ agripro.co.uk* **D:** £20.00–£24.00 **S:** £19.00–£28.00 **Beds:** 1T 2D 1S **Baths:** 2 En 1 Sh ⊃ (12) 🅿 (5) ⊁ 📺 📺 🖿 ⬩

Birch Farm, *Hintlesham, Ipswich, Suffolk, IP8 3NJ.* Ideal for touring Suffolk or for businessmen working in Ipswich/ Hadleigh **Open:** All year
01473 652249 Mrs Bryce **Fax: 01473 652825** *birchfarm@lineone.net* **D:** £45.00–£50.00 **S:** £25.00–£30.00 **Beds:** 2D **Baths:** 2 En ⊃ 🅿 ⊁ 📺 📺 🖿 ♿ ⬩

B&B owners may vary rates – be sure to check when booking

Hitcham

TL9750

Pansy Cottage, *The Causeway, Hitcham, Ipswich, Suffolk, IP7 7NE.* Pansy Cottage is set in the heart of rolling countryside. **Open:** All year (not Xmas/New Year)
01449 740858 R Edden **D:** £18.00 **S:** £20.00 **Beds:** 1D 1S ⊁ ▣ ½ ▦ ▦ ⚓

Holton St Mary

TM0636

Stratford House, *Holton St Mary, Colchester, Essex, CO7 6NT.* **Open:** All year (not Xmas)

Grades: ETC 4 Diamond
01206 298246 (also fax) Mrs Selleck
D: £20.00–£25.00 **S:** £20.00–£25.00 **Beds:** 1D 1T 1S **Baths:** 1 Sh ⊁ (10) ▣ (10) ½ ▣ ✕ ▦ ⚓
A warm welcome in a very comfortable family home in Constable country. Easy access to A12, A14 and Harwich. Traditional breakfast. Good pubs and restaurants locally.

Horringer

TL8261

12 The Elms, *Horringer, Bury St Edmunds, Suffolk, IP29 5SE.* Friendly modern house close to Ickworth NT House and Gardens. **Open:** All year
01284 735400 Ms Pemberton **D:** £18.00–£20.00 **S:** £25.00–£40.00 **Beds:** 1D 1T 1S **Baths:** 1 Sh ▣ (3) ½ ▣ ▦ ⚓

Ilketshall St Margaret

TM3585

Shoo-Devil Farmhouse, *Ilketshall St Margaret, Bungay, Suffolk, NR35 1QU.* Enchanting thatched C16th farm house in secluded garden near St. Peters Brewery. **Open:** All year (not Xmas)
01986 781303 (also fax) Mrs Lewis **D:** £20.00 **S:** £25.00 **Beds:** 1D 1T **Baths:** 2 En ▣ (4) ½ ▣ ✕ ▣ ▦ ⚓

Ipswich

TM1644

Maple House, *114 Westerfield Road, Ipswich, Suffolk, IP4 2XW.* Attractive house one mile from town centre; close to park. **Open:** All year (not Xmas)
01473 253797 Mrs Seal **D:** £12.50–£15.00 **S:** £15.00–£18.00 **Beds:** 1D 3S **Baths:** 4 En ⊁ ▣ (3) ½ ▣ ✕ ▦ ▦ ⚓ ⚓

Cliffden Guest House, *21 London Road, Ipswich, Suffolk, IP1 2EZ.* Close to town centre. Full Sky TV. Family run. **Open:** All year
01473 252689 Mrs Staples **Fax:** 01473 252685 *cliffden.hotel@virgin.net* **D:** £21.00–£32.00 **S:** £25.00–£35.00 **Beds:** 3F 1D 3T 8S **Baths:** 7 Pr 3 Sh ⊁ ▣ (5) ▣ ✕ ▦ ⚓ ⚓ cc

Redholme, *52 Ivry Street, Ipswich, IP1 3QP.* Victorian house, ensuite bathrooms, quiet central area, friendly and helpful. **Open:** All year **Grades:** ETC 4 Diamond
01473 250018 Mr & Mrs McNeil **Fax:** 01473 233174 *johnmcneil@redholmeipswich.co.uk* www.redholmeipswich.co.uk **D:** £21.00–£25.00 **S:** £26.00–£32.00 **Beds:** 1F 2D 2T 1S **Baths:** 5 En 1 Pr ⊁ ▣ (5) ½ ▣ ✕ ▦ ▦ ⚓ ⚓

Craigerne, *Cauldwell Avenue, Ipswich, Suffolk, IP4 4DZ.* Large Victorian house, 3/4 acre pretty gardens. Friendly welcome. **Open:** All year (not Xmas)
01473 714061 Mrs Krotunas **D:** £18.00 **S:** £18.00–£26.00 **Beds:** 1D 1T 2S **Baths:** 2 En 2 Sh ▣ (6) ▣ ▣ ▦ ⚓

Kedington

TL7046 ◀ *The Plough, Red Lion, White Horse*

Orchard House, *Mill Road, Kedington, Suffolk, CB9 7NN.* Friendly, comfortable accommodation. Antique emporiums, Long Melford. Near Cambridge University. **Open:** All year (not Xmas/New Year)
01440 713113 (also fax) Mrs Osborne **D:** £20.00–£25.00 **S:** £18.00–£25.00 **Beds:** 2D 2S **Baths:** 1 En 1 Sh ⊁ (5) ▣ (6) ½ ▣ ▦ ⚓

Kelsale

TM3865

Mile Hill Barn, *Main Road, North Green, Kelsale, Saxmundham, Suffolk, IP17 2RG.* Luxury ensuite accommodation, converted barn, centrally located-Minsmere Heritage Coast. **Open:** All year **Grades:** ETC 5 Diamond, Gold
01728 668519 Mr Covington *b&b@ milehillbarn.freeserve.co.uk* www.abreakwithtradition.co.uk/prop_8.html **D:** £30.00–£38.00 **Beds:** 2D 1T **Baths:** 3 En ▣ (20) ½ ▣ ✕ ▦ ⚓

Touch Wood, *Main Road, Kelsale, Saxmundham, Suffolk, IP17 2NS.* Quiet positioned house, convenient for Aldeburgh, Heritage Coast and countryside. **Open:** All year (not Xmas/New Year)
01728 603214 & 07976 223378 (M) Mrs Craddock **D:** £18.50 **S:** £20.50 **Beds:** 2D **Baths:** 2 En ⊁ ▣ (2) ½ ▣ ▦ ⚓

Kersey

TM0044 ◀ *The Bell, White Hart*

Red House Farm, *Kersey, Ipswich, Suffolk, IP7 6EY.* Comfortable Listed farmhouse between Kersey and Boxford. Central for Constable country. **Open:** All year
01787 210245 Mrs Alleston **D:** £20.00–£22.00 **S:** £25.00–£28.00 **Beds:** 1T 1S **Baths:** 1 Pr 1 Sh ▣ (4) ▣ ♥ ✕ ▣ ▦ ⚓

Knodishall

TM4261

Sun Cottage, *Snape Road, Knodishall, Saxmundham, Suffolk, IP17 1UT.* Warm, friendly welcome in pink washed cottage adjoining village common. **Open:** Easter to Oct
01728 833892 (also fax) J Gadsby *suncottage@supanet.com* **D:** £20.00–£22.00 **S:** £24.00 **Beds:** 1T 1D **Baths:** 1 En ▣ (3) ½ ▣ ▦ ⚓

Lakenheath

TL7182

Bell Inn, *20 High Street, Lakenheath, Brandon, Suffolk, IP27 9DS.* Old coaching house. **Open:** All year
01842 860308 (also fax) C F Guy **D:** £20.00–£45.00 **S:** £20.00–£30.00 **Beds:** 2F 1T 2D 1S **Baths:** 6 En ⊁ ▣ (20) ▣ ♥ ✕ ▣ ▦ ⚓ cc

Lavenham

TL9149 ◀ *Angel, Greyhound, Cock, Swan Hotel, Great House*

The Red House, *29 Bolton Street, Lavenham, Suffolk, CO10 9RG.* **Open:** Feb to Dec **Grades:** ETC 4 Diamond
01787 248074 D Schofield www.lavenham.co.uk/redhouse **D:** £25.00–£27.50 **S:** £40.00–£50.00 **Beds:** 1T 2D **Baths:** 3 En ⊁ (5) ▣ (5) ½ ▣ ♥ ✕ ▣ ▦ ⚓
In the heart of medieval Lavenham, the Red House is a comfortable friendly home. Attractively decorated bedrooms, pretty sitting room, sunny country garden to relax in, candlelit dinner by arrangement. The town has a wealth of timber-framed houses and a magnificent church.

Planning a longer stay? Always ask for any special rates

Brett Farm, The Common, Lavenham, Sudbury, Suffolk, CO10 9PG. **Open:** All year (not Xmas/New Year)
01787 248533 M Hussey **D:** £22.50–£25.00 **S:** £30.00 **Beds:** 1T 2D **Baths:** 2 En 1 Pr ➢ ⊟ ⊬ ⊞ ⊠ ▥ ▴
Riverside bungalow in picturesque countryside yet only 5 minutes walk from the centre of the historic village of Lavenham. Comfortable, well-presented rooms. Full English breakfast. Tea/coffee served by the river.

Leiston
TM4462

White Horse Hotel, Station Road, Leiston, Suffolk, IP16 4HD. Ideally located to enjoy many delights of region including bird sanctuaries at Minsmere, Havergate. **Open:** All year
01728 830694 Fax: 01728 833105 *whihorse@ globalnet.co.uk* www.whitehorsehotel.co.uk **D:** £28.00 **S:** £35.00 **Beds:** 2F 5D 3T 3S **Baths:** 13 En ➢ ⊟ (14) ⊬ ⊠ ⊁ ✕ ⊠ Y ✱ ▴

Long Melford
TL8645

1 Westropps, Long Melford, Sudbury, Suffolk, CO10 9HW. **Open:** All year (not Xmas/New Year)
01787 373660 (also fax) Mrs Fisher *audgrabase@tesco.net* **D:** £22.50–£25.00 **S:** £25.00–£27.00 **Beds:** 1T 1D 1S **Baths:** 1 En 1 Sh ⊟ (3) ⊬ ⊠ ▥ ▴
This comfortable modern house situated in Long Melford is an ideal base for touring Suffolk with its many pretty villages, old churches, antique shops and pubs. Audrey Fisher, born in nearby Lavenham, is happy to share her local knowledge.

High Street Farm House, Long Melford, Sudbury, Suffolk, CO10 9BD. Warm welcome. C15th beamed farmhouse. Pretty garden. Good food. **Open:** All year (not Xmas)
01787 375765 (also fax) Mr Simmonds *anroy@lineone.net* **D:** £25.00–£27.00 **S:** £27.00–£35.00 **Beds:** 2D 1T 1S **Baths:** 2 En 2 Pr ⊟ (5) ⊬ ⊠ ⊁ ⊠ ▥ ▴

Lound
TM5099

Hall Farm, Jay Lane/Church Lane, Lound, Lowestoft, Norfolk, NR32 5LJ. Peaceful, traditional Suffolk farmhouse - spacious rooms, field views, huge breakfast.
Open: Easter to Oct
01502 730415 Ms Ashley *josephashley@ compuserve.com* **D:** £18.00–£22.00 **S:** £18.00–£25.00 **Beds:** 1F 1D 2S **Baths:** 2 En 2 Sh ➢ ⊟ (6) ⊬ ⊠ ⊁ ⊠ ▥ ▴

Lowestoft
TM5493

Royal Court Hotel, 146 London Road South, Lowestoft, Suffolk, NR33 0AZ. The hotel at bed and breakfast prices; central position. **Open:** All year
01502 568901 (also fax) D: £18.00–£20.00 **S:** £20.00–£25.00 **Beds:** 6F 1D 9T 2S **Baths:** 18 En ➢ ⊟ (12) ⊠ ⊁ ✕ ⊠ ▥ ♣2 ✱ ▴ cc

The Albany Hotel, 400 London Road, Lowestoft, Suffolk, NR33 0QB. Comfortable, homely accommodation guaranteed with our attention focused on your requirements. **Open:** All year **Grades:** AA 4 Diamond
01502 574394 Fax: 01502 581198 *geoffry.ward@btclick.com* www.albanyhotel-lowestoft.co.uk **D:** £22.00–£27.00 **S:** £20.00–£30.00 **Beds:** 1F 2T 2D 3S **Baths:** 6 En 1 Sh ➢ ⊬ ⊠ ⊁ ✕ ⊠ ▥ ▴ cc

The Jays Guest House, 14 Kirkley Cliff, Lowestoft, Suffolk, NR33 0BY. Licensed seafront guest house - for sensible rate, just phone for details. **Open:** All year
01502 561124 B Smith **D:** £15.00–£20.00 **S:** £15.00–£20.00 **Beds:** 1F 2D 1T 2S **Baths:** 2 En 2 Sh ➢ ⊟ (6) ⊠ ✕ ▥ ▴ cc

Kingfisher Guest House, 39 Marine Parade, Lowestoft, Suffolk, NR33 0QN. Centrally located seafront guest house, close to shops and amenities. **Open:** All year (not Xmas/New Year)
01502 582483 Mr & Mrs Davis **D:** £15.00–£16.50 **S:** £16.00–£17.50 **Beds:** 2F 3T **Baths:** 1 Sh ➢ ⊟ (3) ⊠ ⊁ ⊠ ▥ ▴

Mendham
TM2782

Weston House Farm, Mendham, Harleston, Norfolk, IP20 0PB. Attractive farmhouse, comfortably furnished, with large garden in peaceful rural setting. **Open:** Mar to Nov **Grades:** ETC 3 Diamond, AA 3 Diamond
01986 782206 Mrs Holden **Fax: 01986 782414** *holden@farmline.com* **D:** £20.00–£25.00 **S:** £25.00–£30.00 **Beds:** 2D 1T **Baths:** 3 En ➢ ⊟ (6) ⊬ ⊠ ⊁ ✕ ▥ ▴

Mendlesham Green
TM0963

Cherry Tree Farm, Mendlesham Green, Mendlesham Green, Suffolk, IP14 5RQ. Quality home cooking, garden fresh vegetables, wine from the Suffolk Vineyards. **Open:** All year (not Xmas/New Year)
01449 766376 Mr Ridsdale **D:** £25.00–£30.00 **S:** £35.00–£40.00 **Beds:** 3D **Baths:** 3 En ⊟ (3)

Middleton
TM4367

Rose Villa, The Street, Middleton, Saxmundham, Suffolk, IP17 3NJ. Private house, close to Minsmere. **Open:** All year
01728 648489 Mrs Crowden **D:** £15.00 **S:** £15.00 **Beds:** 1D 1T **Baths:** 1 Sh ⊟ (3) ⊠ ▥ ▴

Middlewood Green
TM0961

The Bears House, Mulberrytree Farm, Blacksmiths Lane, Middlewood Green, Stowmarket, Suffolk, IP14 5EU. B&B self-contained, converted barn sleeps 6. Indoor swimming pool. **Open:** All year
01449 711707 & 07711 112114 (M) Mr Beckett **Fax: 01449 711707 D:** £19.00–£21.00 **S:** £19.00–£21.00 ➢ ⊟ (5) ⊠ ⊁ ▥ ▴ ▵

Mutford
TM4888 ◁ Three Horseshoes, Swan Inn

Ash Farm, Dairy Lane, Mutford, Beccles, Suffolk, NR34 7QJ. C16th farmhouse, quiet countryside, close to seaside (5 miles), warm welcome. **Open:** All year
01502 476892 Mrs Warnes **D:** £18.00–£20.00 **S:** £20.00 **Beds:** 1F **Baths:** 1 En ➢ ⊟ (2) ⊬ ⊠ ⊠ ▥ ▴

Nayland
TL9734 ◁ The Angel

Hill House, Gravel Hill, Nayland, Colchester, Essex, CO6 4JB. **Open:** All year (not Xmas/New Year)
01206 262782 Mrs Heigham **D:** £24.00–£25.00 **S:** £25.00–£30.00 **Beds:** 1T 1D 1S **Baths:** 1 En 1 Pr ➢ (10) ⊟ (6) ⊬ ⊠ ⊠ ▥ ▴
C15th beamed house on edge of village overlooking valley.

Gladwins Farm, Harpers Hill, Nayland, Colchester, Essex, CO6 4NU. Traditional Suffolk farmhouse B&B, ensuite rooms, 22 acres beautiful rolling Constable country. **Open:** All year (not Xmas)
01206 262261 Mrs Dossor **Fax: 01206 263001** *gladwinsfarm@compuserve.com* www.gladwinsfarm.co.uk **D:** £28.00–£30.00 **S:** £25.00–£30.00 **Beds:** 2D 1S **Baths:** 2 En 1 Pr ➢ (8) ⊟ (14) ⊬ ⊠ ✕ ▥ ▴ cc

Newmarket
TL6463

29 Manderston Road, Newmarket, Suffolk, CB8 0NL. B&B in historic Newmarket. **Open:** All year
01638 603245 J Marshall **D:** £20.00 **Beds:** 1T **Baths:** 1 Sh ⊬ ⊠

17 Rous Road, *Newmarket, CB8 8DH.*
Open: All year (not Xmas)
01638 667483 Mr & Mrs Crichton *crighton@ rousnewmarket.freeserve.co.uk* **D:** £22.00–£25.00
S: £22.00–£25.00 **Beds:** 2T **Baths:** 1 Sh ⚡ ⚒
📺 ⬥
We are a family home offering good basic accommodation, comfortable rooms and full English breakfasts. Centrally situated in town, ideal for racing enthusiasts and tourists alike. Midway between Cambridge and Bury St Edmunds. Connections to Ely and London.

North Cove
TM4689

Fairfields Guest House, *Old Lowestoft Road, North Cove, Beccles, NR34 7PD.* Within easy reach of Norfolk Broads. Private car park, walking distance local pub. **Open:** All year
01502 476261 Mrs Charalambous **D:** £17.50–£19.00 **S:** £25.00 **Beds:** 2F 1T 2D **Baths:** 3 En 1 Sh ⚡ 🅿 (6) ⚒ 📺 🐾 📺 ⬥

Oulton Broad
TM5192

Toad Hall Bed And Breakfast, *129 Bridge Road, Oulton Broad, Lowestoft, Suffolk, NR33 9JU.*
Open: Jan to Dec
01502 518884 (also fax) Ms Dickinson
D: £18.00 **S:** £18.00 **Beds:** 1T 1D **Baths:** 1 Sh⚒ 📺 ⬛ ⬥
Homely accommodation, situated very close to Oulton Broad. Ideal for walking, fishing, touring Suffolk and Norfolk coastal towns including Southwold, Dunwich, Norwich 25 miles. River trips, beaches two miles, pubs and restaurants close to house, Lowestoft is only 2 miles.

Playford
TM2147 ⚑ *Admiral's Head, The Falcon, The Garland*

Glenham, *Hill Farm Road, Playford, Ipswich, Suffolk, IP6 9DU.* Situated in the Fynn valley. Warm welcome. Confirm e-mail by phone.
Open: All year (not Xmas) **Grades:** ETC 3 Diamond
01473 624939 Mr & Mrs Booker *glenham@ tesco.net* glenham.hypermart.net **D:** £16.00–£25.00 **S:** £16.00–£20.00 **Beds:** 1F 1T 1S
Baths: 1 Pr 1 Sh ⚡ 🅿 (3) ⚒ 📺 📺 ⬛

BEDROOMS
D = Double
T = Twin
S = Single
F = Family

Polstead
TL9938 ⚑ *Angel Inn, Cock Inn, Crown Inn, White Hart*

Polstead Lodge, *Mill Street, Polstead, Colchester, Essex, CO6 5AD.*
Village of outstanding beauty. Perfectly situated for exploring south Suffolk and Constable country. **Open:** All year (not Xmas/New Year) **Grades:** ETC 4 Diamond
01206 262196 (also fax) Mrs Howard *polsteadlodge@bushinternet.com* **D:** £25.00–£30.00 **S:** £25.00–£50.00 **Beds:** 1F 1T 1D
Baths: 1 En 1 Sh ⚡ 🅿 (9) ⚒ 📺 🐾 ⬛ ⬥

Rickinghall
TM0375

The Bell Inn, *The Street, Rickinghall, Diss, IP22 1BN.* Delightful C17th coaching inn, tastefully converted and individually furnished.
Open: All year (not Xmas/New Year)
Grades: ETC 4 Diamond
01379 898445 *bell-inn@ rickinghall.fsworld.co.uk* www.thebellrickinghall.com **D:** £25.00
S: £26.00–£30.00 **Beds:** 4T 3D 1S **Baths:** 8 En 🅿 (20) 📺 ✕ ⬛ ⬥ **cc**

Saxmundham
TM3863

Kiln Farm, *Kiln Lane, Benhall, Saxmundham, Suffolk, IP17 1HA.* Cosy country home with inviting garden terrace and bountiful breakfasts. **Open:** All year
01728 603166 Mr Potter *comfort@ kilnfarm33.freeserve.co.uk* **D:** £25.00 **S:** £35.00
Beds: 2T 1D **Baths:** 2 Sh ⚡ (5) 🅿 (4) 📺 🐾 ⬛

Saxtead
TM2525 ⚑ *Queen's Head*

Bantry, *Chapel Road, Saxtead, Woodbridge, Suffolk, IP13 9RB.* B&B in self-contained ensuite private apartments separate from house. **Open:** All year
01728 685578 Mrs Jones *cheryl.jones@ sleepysuffolk.co.uk* www.sleepysuffolk.co.uk
D: £20.00–£25.00 **S:** £30.00–£40.00 **Beds:** 1T 2D **Baths:** 3 En ⚡ (9) 🅿 (3) ⚒ 📺 ⬛ ⬥

Shimpling
TL8551

Gannocks House, *Old Rectory Lane, Shimpling, Bury St Edmunds, Suffolk, IP29 4HG.* Country house in quiet setting, rooms with luxury ensuite facilities/ fine furnishings. **Open:** All year
01284 830499 (also fax) *gannocks-house@ lineone.net* www.countrybreak.co.uk
D: £22.50–£25.00 **S:** £25.00–£45.00 **Beds:** 1F 1D 1T **Baths:** 3 En ⚡ (8) 🅿 (5) ⚒ 📺 📺 ⬛ ⬥ ⬥

Sibton
TM3669 ⚑ *Griffin, Queen's Head*

Park Farm, *Sibton, Saxmundham, Suffolk, IP17 2LZ.* Enjoy a friendly farmhouse welcome with your every comfort assured. **Open:** All year (not Xmas) **Grades:** ETC 4 Diamond
01728 668324 Mrs Gray **Fax: 01728 668564** *margaret.gray@btinternet.com* www.farmstayanglia.co.uk/parkfarm
D: £22.00–£25.00 **S:** £25.00–£30.00 **Beds:** 1D 2T **Baths:** 2 En 1 Pr 🅿 (6) ⚒ 📺 ✕ 📺 ⬛ ⬥

Snape
TM3959

Flemings Lodge, *Gromford Lane, Snape, Saxmundham, Suffolk, IP17 1RG.* Very quiet lane, friendly welcome, hearty breakfasts in quality accommodation. **Open:** All year (not Xmas)
01728 688502 (also fax) Mrs Edwards
D: £20.00–£22.00 **S:** £28.00–£35.00 **Beds:** 1D 1T **Baths:** 1 Sh 🅿 (4) ⚒ 📺 📺 ⬛ ⬥

Somerleyton
TM4897

Dove Wood Cottage, *5 Station Cottages, Somerleyton, Lowestoft, Norfolk, NR32 5QN.* Charming Edwardian cottage. Peaceful garden. Woodland walks, beautiful Broadland views. **Open:** All year (not Xmas/New Year)
01502 732627 Ms Spencer **D:** £20.00
S: £22.00 **Beds:** 1F 1D **Baths:** 1 Pr 1 Sh ⚡ 🅿 (4) ⚒ 📺 🐾 📺 ⬛ ⬥ ⬥

Southwold
TM5076 ⚑ *Nelson, Red Lion, Kings Head, Sole Bay*

Amber House, *North Parade, Southwold, Suffolk, IP18 6LT.* Victorian seafront house, with magnificent views, comfortable and homely atmosphere. **Open:** All year (not Xmas)
01502 723303 (also fax) Mrs Spring *spring@ amberhouse.fsnet.co.uk* www.southwold. blythweb.co.uk/amber_house/index.htm
D: £27.50–£30.00 **S:** £35.00–£50.00 **Beds:** 1F 3D 1T **Baths:** 5 En ⚡ (5) 📺 📺 ⬛ ⬥

Victoria House, 9
Dunwich Road, Southwold, Suffolk, IP18 6LJ.
Open: All year
Grades: ETC 4
Diamond
01502 722317 Mr & Mrs Henshaw *victoria@ southwold.ws* www.southwold.ws.co. uk/victoria_house/ **D:** £22.50–£32.50
S: £25.00–£30.00 **Beds:** 1D 1T 1S **Baths:** 2 En 1 Pr 🖻 📺 📶 🛁
Situated close to beach and town centre of charming unique Southwold. Double room has half tester bed and balcony, with sea views. We pride ourselves in providing high standard comfortable accommodation with a hearty English breakfast to start your day.

Prospect Guest House,
33 Station Road, Southwold, Suffolk, IP18 6AX.
Situated in the heart of Southwold, fine food and accommodation, car park. **Open:** All year (not Xmas/New Year) **Grades:** ETC 4 Diamond
01502 722757 Mr Whyman *sally@ prospect-place.demon.co.uk* **D:** £20.00–£25.00
S: £25.00–£30.00 **Beds:** 5D **Baths:** 5 En 🖻 (5) 🖻 📺 🛏 📺 📶 🛁

Acton Lodge, 18 South Green,
Southwold, Suffolk, IP18 6HB. Victorian merchant's mansion; superb location on Green 50 yards from beach **Open:** All year **01502 723217** Mrs Smith **D:** £25.00–£35.00
S: £30.00–£50.00 **Beds:** 1T 3D **Baths:** 2 En 1 Pr 📶 (6) 🖻 📺 📺 📶 🛁

Northcliffe Guest House, 20 North
Parade, Southwold, Suffolk, IP18 6LT.
Charming Victorian terrace. Panoramic sea view, relaxed atmosphere, individually designed rooms, licensed. **Open:** All year **01502 724074** Mrs Henshaw **Fax:** 01502 722218 www.s-h-systems.co. uk/hotels/northcli.html **D:** £20.00–£30.00
S: £25.00–£45.00 **Beds:** 5D 1T 1S **Baths:** 5 En 1 Sh 🖻 📺 🛏 🗙 📺 📶 🛁

No 21 North Parade, 21 North Parade,
Southwold, Suffolk, IP18 6LT. Peace, tranquillity and stunning sea views overlooking Blue Flag beach. **Open:** All year (not Xmas/New Year)
01502 722573 *richard.comrie@cw.com.net*
D: £50.00–£65.00 **S:** £35.00 **Beds:** 1T 2D 📶 📺 📺 📶 🛁

BEDROOMS

D = Double
T = Twin
S = Single
F = Family

Sproughton
TM1244

Finjaro Guest House, *Valley Farm
Drive, Hadleigh Road, Sproughton, Ipswich, Suffolk, IP8 3EL.* Deluxe accommodation 10 minutes from Ipswich, surrounded by open fields. **Open:** All year (not Xmas)
01473 652581 Mrs Finbow **Fax:** 01473 652139 www.s-h-systems.co. uk/hotels/finjaro.html **D:** £20.00–£23.00
S: £20.00 **Beds:** 1D 2S 1T **Baths:** 2 Sh 🖻 (3) 🖻 (5) 📶 📺 🗙 📺 📶 🛁

Stoke-by-Nayland
TL9836   🍴 The Angel, The Rose, White Hart

Nether Hall, *Thorington Street, Stoke-by-Nayland, Colchester, Essex, CO6 4ST.*
Open: All year
01206 337373 Mr & Mrs Jackson **Fax:** 01206 337496 *patrick.jackson@talk21.com* **D:** £30.00
S: £30.00 **Beds:** 1T 1D 1S **Baths:** 2 En 1 Pr 📶 (6) 📶 📺 🛏 📺 📶 🛁 🐾
Nether Hall is a C15th gem. The bedrooms are extremely comfortable and spacious. The River Box borders the 3-acre garden and old roses cascade over the house, barn and walls. A spectacle during the summer. Hard tennis court. Excellent local pubs.

Thorington Hall, *Stoke-by-Nayland,
Colchester, Essex, CO6 4SS.* Beautiful C17th house belonging to the National Trust.
Open: Easter to Sept
01206 337329 Mrs Wollaston **D:** £20.00–£24.00 **S:** £28.00–£32.00 **Beds:** 1F 1D 1TS **Baths:** 1 Sh 🖻 📶 (4) 🛏 📺

Sudbourne
TM4153

Long Meadow,
Gorse Lane, Sudbourne, Woodbridge, Suffolk, IP12 2BD.
Comfortable, friendly, home from home, lovely garden, quiet rural location. **Open:** All year (not Xmas)
Grades: ETC 3 Diamond
01394 450269 Mrs Wood **D:** £19.00–£21.00
S: £18.00–£20.00 **Beds:** 1D 1T 1S **Baths:** 1 Pr 1 Sh 🖻 (12) 📶 (6) 📶 📺 🛏 📺 📶 🛁

Sweffling
TM3463

Wayside, *Glemham Road, Sweffling,
Saxmundham, Suffolk, IP17 2QB.* Comfortable accommodation on edge of village near Heritage Coast attractions. **Open:** All year (not Xmas/New Year) **Grades:** ETC 4 Diamond
01728 663256 M Wilkinson **D:** £20.00–£22.00
S: £22.00–£25.00 **Beds:** 1T 1D **Baths:** 2 En 🖻 (5) 📶 (4) 📶 📺 📶 🛁

Thorndon
TM1369

Moat Farm, *Thorndon, Eye, Suffolk,
IP23 7LX.* Moat Farm is an old Suffolk house in peaceful village. **Open:** All year (not Xmas/New Year)
01379 678437 (also fax) J & G Edgecombe *gerolde@clara.co.uk* **D:** £20.00–£23.00
S: £24.00–£28.00 **Beds:** 1F 2T 2D **Baths:** 2 En 1 Pr 1 Sh 🖻 📶 📺 📺 📶 🛁

Walpole
TM3674

The Old Vicarage, *Walpole, Halesworth,
Suffolk, IP19 9AR.* Spacious bedrooms, lovely views from every room. **Open:** All year **01986 784295** Mr Calver **D:** £20.00–£25.00
S: £25.00–£30.00 **Beds:** 1T 1D **Baths:** 2 Pr 📶 (6) 📺 🛏 📶 🛁

Washbrook
TM1142   🍴 The Brook

Stebbings,
Back Lane, Washbrook, Ipswich, IP8 3JA.
Open: All year (not Xmas)
Grades: ETC 4
Diamond
01473 730216 & 07989 061088 (M) Mrs Fox *carolinefox@netscapeonline.co.uk* **D:** £19.00
S: £45.00 **Beds:** 2T 1S 📶 📶 (2) 📶 📺 📶 🛁
Detached Georgian cottage, quiet village location, secure parking, mature pretty gardens and outbuildings. Full English breakfast with local produce. 3 miles Ipswich town centre. Ideally situated, Suffolk countryside and Constable country. Easy access A12, A14. Pets and children welcome. No smoking.

High View,
Back Lane, Washbrook, Ipswich, Suffolk, IP8 3JA.
Comfortable Edwardian house set in secluded garden. Quiet village location. **Open:** All year (not Xmas/New Year) **Grades:** ETC 4 Diamond
01473 730494 Mrs Steward *rosanna.steward@ virgin.net* **D:** £20.00–£22.00 **S:** £20.00–£22.00
Beds: 1T 1D 1S **Baths:** 1 Sh 📶 (12) 📶 (5) 📶 📺 📺 📶 🛁

Wenhaston

TM4175

The Old Vicarage, Wenhaton, Halesworth, Suffolk, IP19 9EG. Period house in large grounds. Very peaceful, warm welcome assured. **Open:** All year **01502 478339** Mr & Mrs Heycock **Fax: 01502 478068** *theycock@aol.com* **D:** £25.00–£30.00 **S:** £28.00–£33.00 **Beds:** 1T 2D **Baths:** 1 Pr 1 Sh ⛺ (12) ⱷ (3) ⱷ ⱷ ⱷ

West Row

TL6775   🍺 Red Lion

Pear Tree House, Chapel Road, West Row, Mildenhall, Bury St Edmunds, Suffolk, IP28 8PA. C1750 former village inn, handy for touring East Anglia. **Open:** All year **01638 711112 (also fax)** Mr Knight *peartree@ 12stay.co.uk* www.peartree.12stay.co.uk **D:** £20.00–£25.00 **S:** £25.00–£35.00 **Beds:** 1T 2D **Baths:** 2 En 1 Pr ⱷ (2) ⱷ ✕ ⱷ ⱷ ⱷ cc

Weybread

TM2480

The Crown Inn, The Street, Weybread, Diss, Norfolk, IP21 5TL. Traditional English pub. Excellent fishing. Countryside walks. Coastline driving distance. **Open:** All year **01379 586710** L Rice **D:** £25.00–£30.00 **S:** £25.00–£30.00 **Beds:** 1T 1D **Baths:** 2 En ⱷ (15) ⱷ ⱷ ✕ ⱷ ⱷ ⱷ

Whepstead

TL8357

Folly House B&B, Folly Lane, Whepstead, Bury St Edmunds, IP29 4TJ. Bed & Breakfast in the country, indoor pool. Excellent breakfasts. **Open:** All year (not Xmas) **01284 735207** L Lower **D:** £20.00–£25.00 **S:** £25.00–£35.00 **Beds:** 1F 1D 1T **Baths:** 1 En 1 Sh ⛺ ⱷ (10) ⱷ ⱷ ✕ ⱷ ⱷ ⱷ

Wickhambrook

TL7554

The Old Bakery, Off Mill Lane, Farley Green, Wickhambrook, Newmarket, Suffolk, CB8 8PX. C17th house, quiet countryside, large rooms, comfortable beds, quality breakfasts. **Open:** All year (not Xmas) **01440 820852 (also fax)** L Lambert *info@ theoldbakery.freeserve.co.uk* www.theoldbakery. freeserve.co.uk **D:** £20.00–£22.50 **S:** £30.00– £35.00 **Beds:** 2D 1T **Baths:** 3 En ⱷ (4) ⱷ ⱷ ✕ ⱷ ⱷ ⱷ

Wingfield

TM2276

Gables Farm, Wingfield, Diss, Norfolk, IP21 5RH. Timbered C16th moated farmhouse, all rooms furnished to highest standards. Well-kept gardens for guests. **Open:** Jan to Dec **Grades:** ETC 4 Diamond **01379 586355** Sue Harvey **Fax: 01379 588058** *gables-farm@ntlworld.com* www.gablesfarm.co. uk **D:** £22.00–£26.00 **S:** £25.00–£30.00 **Beds:** 1T 2D **Baths:** 3 En ⛺ ⱷ (6) ⱷ ⱷ ⱷ ⱷ ⱷ ⱷ

Worlingham

TM4490

Colville Arms Motel, Lowestoft Road, Worligham , Beccles, Suffolk, NR34 7EF. Village location close to Lowestoft, Norwich, Yarmouth, Broads, golf and fishing. **Open:** All year **01502 712571 (also fax)** P & N Brooks *pat@ thecolvillearms.freeserve.co.uk* **D:** £22.50–£27.50 **S:** £32.50–£40.00 **Beds:** 4T 5D 2S **Baths:** 11 En ⱷ ⱷ ✕ ⱷ ⱷ ⱷ cc

Worlington

TL6973

The Old Forge, Newmarket Road, Worlington, Bury St Edmunds, Suffolk, IP28 8RZ. An attractive C18th cottage across road from pub near golf course. **Open:** All year (not Xmas/New Year) **01638 718014** Mrs Wilson **Fax: 01638 711616 D:** £28.00–£40.00 **S:** £28.00 **Beds:** 1T **Baths:** 1 Pr ⛺ ⱷ (2) ⱷ ⱷ ⱷ ⱷ

Yoxford

TM3968

The Old Mill House, Yoxford, Saxmundham, Suffolk, IP17 3HE. Comfortable secluded Regency house. Peaceful grounds. Good food. Warm welcome. **Open:** All year **01728 668536** R J Draper **D:** £17.50–£23.00 **S:** £23.00 **Beds:** 1F 1D **Baths:** 1 Pr ⛺ ⱷ (6) ⱷ ⱷ ⱷ ✕ ⱷ ⱷ ⱷ

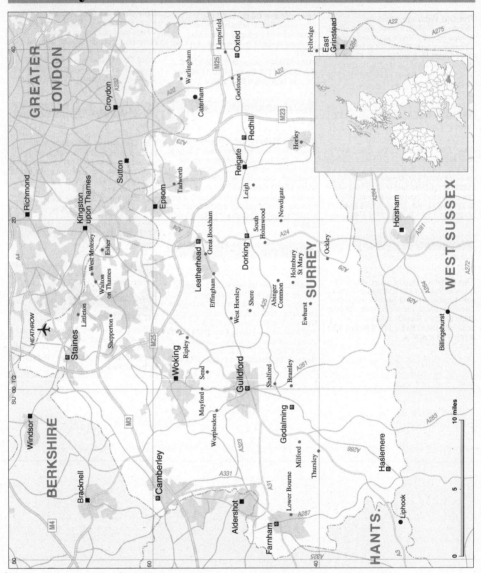

Abinger Common

TQ1145

Park House Farm, *Leith Hill Road, Abinger Common, Dorking, Surrey, RH5 6LW.* Spacious home with bright, tastefully decorated rooms, all with excellent views. **Open:** All year (not Xmas/New Year) **01306 730101** Mr & Mrs Wallis **Fax: 01306 730643** *peterwallis@msn.com* **D:** £20.00–£30.00 **S:** £30.00–£50.00 **Beds:** 1T 2D **Baths:** 3 En ☒ (12) 🅿 (10) 🗇 🗇 🔟 🕮 🕯

Bramley

TQ0044

Beevers Farm, *Chinthurst Lane, Bramley, Guildford, Surrey, GU5 0DR.* Peaceful surroundings, friendly atmosphere. Own preserves, honey, eggs. Nearby villages. **Open:** Feb to Dec **01483 898764 (also fax)** Mr Cook *beevers@ onetel.net.uk* **D:** £18.00–£25.00 **S:** £30.00 **Beds:** 1F 2T **Baths:** 1 Pr 1 Sh ☒ 🅿 (10) 🗇 🔟 🕮 🕯

Camberley

SU8860

Youlden Lodge, *12 Youlden Drive, Camberley, Surrey, GU15 1AL.* Spacious Tudor-style private house. Ample private parking. Convenient M3. **Open:** All year **01276 61793** Mrs Bennie **D:** £22.50 **S:** £25.00 **Beds:** 1D 1T 2S **Baths:** 2 Sh ☒ 🅿 (5) 🗇 🔟 🕮 🕯

Dorking

TQ1649

Shrub Hill, *3 Calvert Road, Dorking, Surrey, RH4 1LT.* Quiet comfortable family home with excellent views. **Open:** All year (not Xmas) **01306 885229** Mrs Scott Kerr *jackiesk@ ntlworld.com* **D:** £25.00–£26.00 **S:** £30.00–£35.00 **Beds:** 1T 1S 1D **Baths:** 1 Sh 1 En ☒ (8) 🅿 (2) 🗇 🔟 🔝 🔟 🕮 🕯

Steyning Cottage, *Horsham Road, South Holmwood, Dorking, Surrey, RH5 4NE.* Special rates for long term, including dinner. French spoken. **Open:** All year (not Xmas) **01306 888481** Mrs Treays **D:** £20.00–£22.00 **S:** £20.00–£22.00 **Beds:** 1T 1S **Baths:** 1 Sh ☒ 🅿 (4) 🔟 🔝 🗙 🕮

The Waltons, *5 Rose Hill, Dorking, Surrey, RH4 2EG.* Listed house in conservation area. Beautiful views and friendly atmosphere. **Open:** All year **01306 883127 & 07802 469953 (M)** Mrs Walton **Fax: 01306 883127** *thewaltons@ rosehill5.demon.co.uk* **D:** £17.50–£20.00 **S:** £20.00–£32.50 **Beds:** 1F 1D 1T 1S **Baths:** 3 Sh ☒ 🅿 (3) 🗇 🔟 🔝 🗙 🔟 🕮 ❄ 🕯

Effingham

TQ1153 🍴 *Sir Douglas Haig, Lord Howard, Black Swan, Plough*

Chalklands, *Beech Avenue, Effingham, Surrey, KT24 5PJ.* Large detached house overlooking golf course. Good pub food nearby. **Open:** All year (not Xmas) **Grades:** ETC 3 Diamond **01372 454936** Mrs Reilly **Fax: 01372 459569** *rreilly@onetel.net.uk* **D:** £23.00–£25.00 **S:** £30.00–£35.00 **Beds:** 1F 1D 1T **Baths:** 2 En 1 Pr ☒ 🅿 (8) 🗇 🔟 🔝 🗙 🔟 🕮 🕯

Crosslands Guest House, *Guildford Road, Effingham, Surrey, KT24 5PE.* Date of house 1280, 1775 & 1904 - pub for 400 years. **Open:** All year (not Xmas/New Year) **01372 453479** J Gifford **D:** £22.00–£25.00 **S:** £22.00–£25.00 **Beds:** 1T 1D 1S **Baths:** 1 En 1 Sh ☒ 🔟 🔝 🗙 🔟 🕮 🕯

Esher

TQ1464

Lilac Cottage, *14 Greenways, Hinchley Wood, Esher, Surrey, KT10 0QD.* Luxury friendly family home convenient London, Hampton Court, Wisley, Sandown. **Open:** All year **020 8398 7546 (also fax)** Mrs Evans *evans@ greenways.demon.co.uk* **D:** £30.00 **S:** £35.00 **Beds:** 1D 1T **Baths:** 2 En 🗇 🔟 🕮 🕯 cc

Ewhurst

TQ0940

Malricks, *The Street, Ewhurst, Cranleigh, Surrey, GU6 7RH.* Modern detached house, village location. Large attractive garden overlooking fields. **Open:** All year **01483 277575** Mrs Budgen **D:** £19.00 **S:** £19.00 **Beds:** 1F 1T **Baths:** 1 En 1 Sh ☒ 🅿 (3) 🗇 🔟 🔝 🔟

High Edser, *Shere Road, Ewhurst, Cranleigh, Surrey, GU6 7PQ.* C16th farmhouse in Area of Outstanding Natural Beauty, a beautiful setting. **Open:** All year (not Xmas) **Grades:** ETC 3 Diamond **01483 278214** Mrs Franklin-Adams **Fax: 01483 278200** *franklinadams@ highedser.demon.co.uk* **D:** £27.50 **S:** £25.00–£35.00 **Beds:** 2D 1T **Baths:** 1 Sh ☒ 🅿 (6) 🗇 🔟 🔝 🔟 🕮 🕯

Planning a longer stay? Always ask for any special rates

Farnham

SU8446 🍴 *Cherry Tree*

Orchard House, *13 Applelands Close, Farnham, Surrey, GU10 4TL.* Visitors warmly welcomed at our quietly located home overlooking countryside. **Open:** All year (not Xmas/New Year) **01252 793813** D C Warburton **D:** £20.00–£22.00 **S:** £20.00–£22.00 **Beds:** 1T 1S **Baths:** 1 Sh ☒ 🅿 (3) 🗇 🔟 🔟 🕮 🕯

Hawkridge, *20 Upper Old Park Lane, Farnham, Surrey, GU9 0AT.* Large family home in beautiful countryside. One mile from town. **Open:** All year (not Xmas/New Year) **01252 722068** Mr & Mrs Ackland *chris.ackland@tesco.net* **D:** £22.00–£27.00 **S:** £27.00–£35.00 **Beds:** 1T 1D 1S **Baths:** 1 Sh ☒ (10) 🅿 (4) 🗇 🔟 🕮 🕯

Felbridge

TQ3639

Toads Croak House, *30 Copthorne Road, Felbridge, East Grinstead, W Sussex, RH19 2NS.* Beautiful Sussex cottage-style house, gardens. Gatwick parking. 18th independent year. **Open:** All year **01342 328524 (also fax)** *toadscroakhouse@ aol.com* **D:** £19.00–£24.00 **S:** £25.00–£33.00 **Beds:** 1F 1D 2T **Baths:** 2 En 1 Sh ☒ 🅿 (7) 🗇 🔟 🕮 🕯

Gatwick (Surrey side)

TQ2843

Southbourne Guest House, *34 Massetts Road, Horley, Surrey, RH6 7DS.* **Open:** All year (not Xmas/New Year) **01293 771991** Breda & Tony Breen **Fax: 01293 820112** *reservations@ southbournegatwick.com* www.southbournegatwick.com **D:** £22.00–£25.00 **S:** £27.00–£36.00 **Beds:** 2F 3T 2D 2S **Baths:** 2 En 2 Sh ☒ 🅿 (20) 🗇 🔟 🕯 cc A warm welcome awaits you in our family-run guest house. Five minutes drive from Gatwick in our courtesy car from 9.30am to 9.30pm. Five minutes walk from local pubs, restaurants and shops. Thirty minutes by train from London.

Melville Lodge Guest House, 15
Brighton Road, Gatwick, Horley, Surrey, RH6 7HH. Friendly house, airport 5 minutes drive, train to London/Brighton. **Open:** All year **Grades:** ETC 2 Diamond, RAC 2 Diamond **01293 784951** Mr & Mrs Brooks **Fax: 01293 785669** *melvillelodge.guesthouse@tesco.net* **D:** £19.00–£22.50 **S:** £25.00–£35.00 **Beds:** 1F 3D 2T 1S **Baths:** 3 En 2 Sh 🛏 (0) 🅿 📺 ▥ ♨

Berrens Guest House, 62
Massetts Road, Horley, Surrey, RH6 7DS. Five minutes Gatwick Airport, walking distance town, trains 40 minutes London. **Open:** All year (not Xmas/New Year) **Grades:** ETC 2 Diamond **01293 786125 & 01293 430800** Mr Worham **Fax: 01293 786125 D:** £20.00–£25.00 **S:** £28.00–£36.00 **Beds:** 1F 2T 1D 2S 🛏 (5) 🅿 (6) ⌁ 📺 ▥ ♨ cc

Victoria Lodge Guest House, 161
Victoria Road, Horley, Surrey, RH6 7AS. 5 mins from Gatwick Airport and Horley town. Families welcome. **Open:** All year **01293 432040** Mr & Mrs Robson **Fax: 01293 432042** *prnrjr@globalnet.co.uk* *www.gatwicklodge.co.uk* **D:** £19.00–£25.00 **S:** £30.00–£48.00 **Beds:** 2F 2D 2S **Baths:** 2 En 2 Sh 🛏 🅿 (14) ⌁ 📺 ▥ ♨ cc

Gorse Cottage, 66
Balcombe Road, Horley, Surrey, RH6 9AY. Friendly, family run. 2 miles Gatwick Airport. Five mins station, serving London/South Coast. **Open:** All year (not Xmas/New Year) **01293 784402 (also fax) D:** £18.00–£20.00 **S:** £25.00–£28.00 **Beds:** 1T 2S **Baths:** 1 En 1 Sh 🛏 (2) 🅿 (3) ⌁ 📺 🏇 ✕ ▥ ♨

Godalming
SU9643

Sherwood, *Ashstead Lane, Godalming, Surrey, GU7 1SY.* We have 4 cats and one Cavalier King Charles Spaniel - we welcome animal lovers. **Open:** All year **01483 427545 (also fax)** Mr & Mrs Harrison *amandauk43@hotmail.com* **D:** £27.00 **S:** £27.00 **Beds:** 1T 2S **Baths:** 1 Sh 🛏 (5) 📺 ♨

Godstone
TQ3551

Godstone Hotel, *The Green, Godstone, Surrey, RH9 8DT.* C16th coaching house, original features, inglenook fireplaces. Our restaurant is renowned in the vicinity. **Open:** All year **01883 742461 (also fax)** Mr Howe **D:** £27.50 **S:** £39.00 **Beds:** 6D 2T **Baths:** 8 Pr 🛏 🅿 📺 🏇 ✕ ▥ ♨

Great Bookham
TQ1354

Selworthy, *310 Lower Road, Great Bookham, Leatherhead, Surrey, KT23 4DW.* Attractive location overlooking Green Belt. Convenient, M25, Gatwick and Heathrow airports. **Open:** All year (not Xmas) **Grades:** ETC 3 Diamond **01372 453952 (also fax)** Mrs Kent *bnb@selworthy.fslife.co.uk* **D:** £20.00–£23.00 **S:** £25.00–£28.00 **Beds:** 1D 1T **Baths:** 1 Sh 🛏 (10) 🅿 (4) ⌁ 📺 ▥ ♨

Guildford
SU9949 ⌖ *Astolat*

Quietways, 29
Liddington Hall Drive, Guildford, Surrey, GU3 3AE. **Open:** Jan to Nov **Grades:** ETC 3 Diamond **01483 232347 & 07799 626198 (M)** Mr White *bill.white@amserve.net* **D:** £20.00 **S:** £25.00 **Beds:** 1D 1T **Baths:** 1 En 1 Pr 🅿 (2) ⌁ 📺 ▥ ♿ ♨
Off A323, quiet cottage, end of cul-de-sac. Lounge, conservatory, pleasant garden.

Atkinsons Guest House, *129 Stoke Road, Guildford, Surrey, GU1 1ET.* Small, comfortable, family-run guest house close to town centre and all local amenities. **Open:** All year **01483 538260** Mrs Atkinson **D:** £21.00–£24.00 **S:** £30.00–£45.00 **Beds:** 1D 1T 2S **Baths:** 2 En 1 Sh 🛏 (6) 🅿 (2) 📺 ▥ ♨

Westbury Cottage, *Waterden Road, Guildford, Surrey, GU1 2AN.* Cottage-style house in large secluded garden, 5 mins town centre, 2 mins station. **Open:** All year (not Xmas) **01483 822602 (also fax)** Mrs Smythe *smythe.smythe@ntlworld.com* **D:** £25.00 **S:** £30.00 **Beds:** 1D 2T **Baths:** 1 Sh 🛏 (6) 🅿 (3) ⌁ 📺 ▥ ♨

2 Wodeland Avenue, *Guildford, GU2 4JX.* Centrally located rooms with panorama. Friendly and modernised family home. **Open:** All year (not Xmas) **01483 451142** Mrs Hay **Fax: 01483 572980** *rozanne.hay@talk21.com* **D:** £20.00–£22.00 **S:** £20.00–£25.00 **Beds:** 1D 1T **Baths:** 1 Pr 1 Sh 🛏 (3) 🅿 (3) ⌁ 📺 ▥ ♿ ♨

Beevers Farm, *Chinthurst Lane, Bramley, Guildford, Surrey, GU5 0DR.* Peaceful surroundings, friendly atmosphere. Own preserves, honey, eggs. Nearby villages. **Open:** Feb to Dec **01483 898764 (also fax)** Mr Cook *beevers@onetel.net.uk* **D:** £18.00–£25.00 **S:** £30.00 **Beds:** 1F 2T **Baths:** 1 Pr 1 Sh 🛏 🅿 (10) ⌁ 📺 ▥ ♨

The Old Malt House, *Worplesdon, Guildford, Surrey, GU3 3PT.* Old country house standing in extensive grounds with swimming pool. **Open:** All year **Grades:** ETC 3 Diamond **01483 232152** Mrs Millar **D:** £17.50–£19.00 **S:** £20.00–£25.00 **Beds:** 1S 2T **Baths:** 2 Sh 🅿 (6) 📺 ▥ ♨

Hampton B&b, *38 Poltimore Road, Guildford, GU2 5PN.* Panoramic views. Walking distance of station and town centre. Quality accommodation. **Open:** All year (not Xmas/New Year) **Grades:** ETC 4 Diamond **01483 572012** Mrs Morris *vgmorris@aol.com* **D:** £23.00–£27.00 **S:** £30.00–£45.00 **Beds:** 1T 2D **Baths:** 1 En 1 Sh 🅿 (1) ⌁ 📺 ▥ ♨

Haslemere
SU8932

Deerfell,
Fernden Lane, Haslemere, Surrey, GU27 3LA. **Open:** Feb to Dec **01428 653409** Mrs Carmichael *deerfell@tesco.net* **D:** £24.00 **S:** £29.00 **Beds:** 2T 1S **Baths:** 2 En 🛏 (6) 🅿 (3) ⌁ 📺 🏇 ✕ ▥ ♨
Wonderfully peaceful and scenic, Deerfell offers comfortable ensuite rooms, bath/shower, tea/coffee, TV, lounge with open fire. Breakfast served in handsome dining room. Many places of interest. London accessible from Haslemere train station: 4 miles.

Holmbury St Mary
TQ1144 ⌖ *The Bull, King's Arms, Royal Oak*

Woodhill Cottage,
Holmbury St Mary, Dorking, Surrey, RH5 6NL. Comfortable family home on outskirts of lovely rural village. **Open:** All year **01306 730498** Mrs McCann *woodhillcottage@amserve.net* **D:** £21.00–£25.00 **S:** £26.00–£32.00 **Beds:** 1T 2D **Baths:** 1 En 1 Sh 🛏 (5) 🅿 (3) ⌁ 🏇 📺 ▥ ♨

Bulmer Farm, Holmbury St Mary, Dorking, Surrey, *RH5 6LG.* Quiet, modernised C17th farmhouse/barn, large garden, picturesque village, self-catering. **Open:** All year **Grades:** ETC 4 Diamond **01306 730210** Mrs Hill **D:** £23.00–£25.00 **S:** £23.00–£37.00 **Beds:** 3D 5T **Baths:** 5 En 2 Sh ⊁ (12) ▣ (12) ⊬ 🖾 🐾 �V 🕮 ₼3 ⸙

Horley

TQ2843 ⚫ Six Bells, Thistle Hotel

Southbourne Guest House, 34 Massetts Road, Horley, Surrey, *RH6 7DS.* A warm welcome awaits you in our family-run guest house. 5 mins drive Gatwick. **Open:** All year (not Xmas/New Year) **01293 771991** Breda & Tony Breen **Fax:** **01293 820112** *reservations@ southbournegatwick.com* www.southbournegatwick.com **D:** £22.00–£25.00 **S:** £27.00–£36.00 **Beds:** 2F 3T 2D 2S **Baths:** 2 En 2 Sh ⊁ ▣ (20) 🖾 🕮 ⸙ cc

Berrens Guest House, 62 Massetts Road, Horley, Surrey, *RH6 7DS.* Five minutes Gatwick Airport, walking distance town, trains 40 minutes London. **Open:** All year (not Xmas/New Year) **Grades:** ETC 2 Diamond **01293 786125 & 01293 430800** Mr Worham **Fax: 01293 786125 D:** £20.00–£25.00 **S:** £28.00–£36.00 **Beds:** 1F 2T 1D 2S ⊁ (5) ▣ (6) ⊬ 🖾 🕮 ⸙ cc

Victoria Lodge Guest House, 161 Victoria Road, Horley, Surrey, *RH6 7AS.* 5 mins from Gatwick Airport and Horley town. Families welcome. **Open:** All year **01293 432040** Mr & Mrs Robson **Fax: 01293 432042** *prnrjr@globalnet.co.uk* www.gatwicklodge.co.uk **D:** £19.00–£25.00 **S:** £30.00–£48.00 **Beds:** 2F 2D 2S **Baths:** 2 En 2 Sh ⊁ ▣ (14) ⊬ 🖾 🕮 ⸙ cc

Gorse Cottage, 66 Balcombe Road, Horley, Surrey, *RH6 9AY.* Friendly, family run. 2 miles Gatwick Airport. Five mins station, serving London/South Coast. **Open:** All year (not Xmas/New Year) **01293 784402 (also fax)** **D:** £18.00–£20.00 **S:** £25.00–£28.00 **Beds:** 1T 2S **Baths:** 1 En 1 Sh ⊁ (2) ▣ (3) ⊬ 🖾 🐾 ✗ 🕮 ⸙

Prinsted Guest House, Oldfield Road, Horley, Surrey, *RH6 7EP.* Spacious Victorian house in quiet situation ideal for Gatwick Airport. **Open:** All year (not Xmas) **Grades:** ETC 3 Diamond, AA 3 Diamond **01293 785233** Mrs Kendall **Fax: 01293 820624** *kendall@prinstedguesthouse.co.uk* www.prinstedguesthouse.co.uk **D:** £18.50–£23.50 **S:** £32.00 **Beds:** 2D 3T 2S **Baths:** 6 En 1 Pr ⊁ ▣ (10) 🖾 cc

The Gables, 50 Bonehurst Road, Horley, Surrey, *RH6 8QG.* Family run guest house, near Gatwick Airport. Local pubs nearby. **Open:** All year (not Xmas/New Year) **01293 774553 & 01293 453345** Mr Hinojosa **Fax: 01243 430006** *enquiries@ thegablesguesthouse.co.uk* www.thegablesguesthouse.co.uk **D:** £18.00–£21.00 **S:** £30.00–£33.00 **Beds:** 2F 9T 4D 2S **Baths:** 3 En 3 Sh ⊁ ▣ 🖾 🕮 ⸙ cc

Yew Tree, 31 Massetts Road, Horley, Surrey, *RH6 7DQ.* Tudor-style house, 1/2 acre gardens, close Gatwick Airport, near town centre. **Open:** All year **01293 785855 (also fax)** Mr Stroud **D:** £15.00–£20.00 **S:** £20.00–£25.00 **Beds:** 1F 2D 1T 2S **Baths:** 1 En 1 Sh ⊁ (2) ▣ (10) 🖾 ⸙ cc

Leatherhead

TQ1656

Selworthy, 310 Lower Road, Great Bookham, Leatherhead, Surrey, *KT23 4DW.* Attractive location overlooking Green Belt. Convenient, M25, Gatwick and Heathrow airports. **Open:** All year (not Xmas) **Grades:** ETC 3 Diamond **01372 453952 (also fax)** Mrs Kent *bnb@ selworthy.fslife.co.uk* **D:** £20.00–£23.00 **S:** £25.00–£28.00 **Beds:** 1D 1T **Baths:** 1 Sh ⊁ (10) ▣ (4) ⊬ 🕮 ⸙

Leigh

TQ2246

Barn Cottage, Church Road, Leigh, Reigate, Surrey, *RH2 8RF.* Converted C17th barn, gardens with swimming pool, 100 yards from pub, 0.25 hr Gatwick. **Open:** All year **01306 611347** Mrs Comer **D:** £25.00–£30.00 **S:** £35.00–£40.00 **Beds:** 1D 1T **Baths:** 1 Sh ⊁ ▣ (3) ⊬ 🖾 🐾 ✗ V 🕮 ⸙

Limpsfield

TQ4052

Arawa, 58 Granville Road, Limpsfield, Oxted, Surrey, *RH8 0BZ.* Friendly, comfortable, welcoming. Lovely garden, excellent breakfast, good London trains. **Open:** All year **Grades:** ETC 3 Diamond **01883 714104 & 0800 2985732** D J Gibbs **Fax: 01883 714104** *david@arawa.co.uk* **D:** £25.00–£40.00 **S:** £25.00–£40.00 **Beds:** 1F 1T 1D **Baths:** 1 En 1 Pr 1 Sh ⊁ ▣ (3) ⊬ 🖾 V 🕮 ₼3 ⸙

Littleton

TQ0668

Old Manor House, Squires Bridge Road, Littleton, Shepperton, Middx, *TW17 0QG.* Listed building dating from reign of Henry VII, set in 5 acres of garden. **Open:** All year **01932 571293** Mrs Bouwens *victor@ oldmanorhouse.demon.co.uk* www.oldmanorhouse.demon.co.uk **D:** £25.00–£27.50 **S:** £30.00 **Beds:** 1D 1T 1S **Baths:** 1 En 1 Sh ⊁ (10) ▣ (6) 🖾 🐾 🕮 ⸙

Lower Bourne

SU8444

49 Burnt Hill Road, Lower Bourne, Farnham, Surrey, *GU10 3NA.* 300 year old cottage, overlooking paddocks. London 45 mins train. **Open:** All year **01252 715058** Mrs Sendall *diana@ sendall.screaming.net* **D:** £25.00 **S:** £28.00–£35.00 **Beds:** 1T 1D 2S **Baths:** 2 En 1 Sh ⊁ (10) ▣ (6) ⊬ 🖾 ⸙

Mayford

SU9956

East House, Beech Hill, Mayford, Woking, Surrey, *GU22 0SB.* Charming, quiet, Old English-style house, beautiful garden. **Open:** All year **01483 763218 (also fax)** A Moss *vladmoss@ aol.com* **D:** £20.00 **S:** £22.00 **Beds:** 1T 1D 1S **Baths:** 1 Sh ⊁ (5) ▣ (2) ⊬ 🕮 ⸙

Milford

SU9442

Coturnix House, Rake Lane, Milford, Godalming, Surrey, *GU8 5AB.* Modern house, family atmosphere, countryside position, easy access road/rail. **Open:** All year **01483 416897** Mr Bell *100523.1037@ compuserve.com* www.coturnix.freeserve.co.uk **D:** £20.00 **S:** £20.00 **Beds:** 1D 1T 1S **Baths:** 1 Pr 1 Sh ⊁ (1) ▣ (6) ⊬ 🖾 🐾 V 🕮 ⸙

Newdigate

TQ1942

Sturtwood Farm, Partridge Lane, Newdigate, Dorking, Surrey, *RH5 5EE.* Comfortable welcoming farmhouse in beautiful wooded countryside. Many historic properties nearby. **Open:** All year (not Xmas/New Year) **01306 631308** Mrs MacKinnon **Fax: 01306 631908 D:** £22.50–£25.00 **S:** £30.00–£35.00 **Beds:** 1T 1S 1D **Baths:** 1 En 1 Sh ⊁ ▣ (6) ⊬ 🖾 🐾 V 🕮 ⸙

Oxted

TQ3852

Arawa, 58 Granville Road, Limpsfield, Oxted, Surrey, *RH8 0BZ.* Friendly, comfortable, welcoming. Lovely garden, excellent breakfast, good London trains. **Open:** All year **Grades:** ETC 3 Diamond **01883 714104 & 0800 2985732** D J Gibbs **Fax: 01883 714104** *david@arawa.co.uk* **D:** £25.00–£40.00 **S:** £25.00–£40.00 **Beds:** 1F 1T 1D **Baths:** 1 En 1 Pr 1 Sh ⊁ ▣ (3) ⊬ 🖾 🐾 V 🕮 ₼3 ⸙

RATES

D = Price range per person sharing in a double or twin room

S = Price range for a single room

Pinehurst Grange Guest House,
East Hill (Part of A25), Oxted, Surrey, RH8 9AE. Comfortable Victorian ex-farmhouse with traditional service and relaxed friendly atmosphere. **Open:** All year (not Xmas/New Year)
01883 716413 & 07790 607658 (M)
Mr Rodgers **D:** £21.00 **S:** £26.00 **Beds:** 1D 1T 1S **Baths:** 1 Sh ⌾ (5) 🅿 (3) ⚹ �📺 🆅 🍽 🛗

Meads, *23 Granville Road, Oxted, Surrey, RH8 0BX.* Tudor-style house on Kent/Surrey border. Station to London. **Open:** All year
Grades: ETC 4 Diamond
01883 730115 Mrs Holgate *Holgate@ meads9.fsnet.co.uk* **D:** £25.00–£28.00 **S:** £30.00 **Beds:** 1T 1D **Baths:** 1 En 1 Pr ⌾🅿⚹⚹📺🆅🍽 🛗

Old Forge House, *Merle Common, Oxted, Surrey, RH8 0JB.* Welcoming family home in rural surroundings. Ten minutes from M25. **Open:** All year (not Xmas)
01883 715969 Mrs Mills **D:** £18.00–£20.00 **S:** £18.00–£20.00 **Beds:** 1D 1T 1S **Baths:** 1 Sh ⌾ 🅿 (4) 📺 🐾 🍽 **cc**

Redhill
TQ2750

Lynwood Guest House, *50 London Road, Redhill, Surrey, RH1 1LN.* Adjacent to a lovely park, within 6 minutes walk from railway station, town centre. **Open:** All year **Grades:** AA 3 Diamond
01737 766894 Mrs Trozado **Fax: 01737 778253** *lynwoodguesthouse@yahoo.co.uk* www.lynwoodguesthouse.co.uk **D:** £26.00–£28.00 **S:** £35.00 **Beds:** 4F 2D 1T 2S **Baths:** 3 En 6 Pr 1 Sh ⌾🅿 (8) 📺 🍽 🛗 **cc**

Ripley
TQ0456

The Half Moon, *High Street, Ripley, Woking, GU23 6AN.* Old world inn, all rooms colour TV, washbasins, tea/coffee. **Open:** All year
01483 224380 (also fax) Mr Beale **D:** £20.00–£22.50 **S:** £40.00–£45.00 **Beds:** 1D 6T **Baths:** 4 Pr 1 Sh ⌾ (7) 🅿 (20) 📺 ✕ 🍽 🛗

Send
TQ0255

Grantchester, *Boughton Hall Avenue, Send, Woking, Surrey, GU23 7DF.* **Open:** All year (not Xmas/New Year)
01483 225383 Mrs Winterbourne *gary@ hotpolmail.com* **D:** £24.00 **S:** £25.00 **Beds:** 3T 2S **Baths:** 3 Sh ⌾ 🅿 (9) ⚹ 📺 🍽 🛗
Attractive family house with large garden. 4 miles from Guildford, Woking, and close to M25 and A3. Wisley Gardens, Clandon Park and golf courses nearby. Own transport recommended. Parking available. Long term stays very welcome.

Shalford
TQ0046

The Laurels, *23 Dagden Road, Shalford, Guildford, Surrey, GU4 8DD.* Quiet detached house. Direct access to footpaths. Near Guildford centre. **Open:** All year
01483 565753 Mrs Deeks **D:** £20.00–£23.00 **S:** £22.00 **Beds:** 1T 1D ⌾ (6) 🅿 (5) ⚹ 📺 🐾 ✕ 🆅 🍽 🛗

Shepperton
TQ0767   🕯 *The Kingfisher, Thames Court Hotel*

The Bull Inn, *152 Laleham Road, Shepperton, TW17 0DB.* Perfect for visiting all main attractions in Surrey. Friendly Atmosphere. **Open:** All year
01932 221667 D: £21.00 **S:** £16.00 **Beds:** 3T 1S **Baths:** 3 En 1 Sh 🅿 (20) 📺 🍽 🛗 **cc**

Splash Cottage, *91 Watersplash Road, Shepperton, TW17 0EE.* Olde worlde cottage with pretty bedrooms and old fashioned hospitality. **Open:** All year **Grades:** ETC 3 Diamond
01932 229987 (also fax) Mr Shaw www.lazy-river.co.uk **D:** £20.00–£25.00 **S:** £27.00–£35.00 **Beds:** 2D 1T ⌾ ⚹ 📺 🍽 🛗

Shere
TQ0747   🕯 *White Horse*

Cherry Trees, *Gomshall Lane, Shere, Guildford, Surrey, GU5 9HE.* Quiet comfortable house, lovely garden, village foot of North Downs. **Open:** All year (not Xmas/New Year)
01483 202288 Mrs Warren **D:** £25.00 **S:** £25.00–£30.00 **Beds:** 2D 3F 1S **Baths:** 2 En 1 Sh ⌾ 🅿 (4) ⚹ 📺 🆅 🍽 🛗 ⚤ 🛗

Lockhurst Hatch Farm, *Lockhurst Hatch Lane, Shere, Guildford, Surrey, GU5 9JN.* Farmhouse dating from C15th. Area of Outstanding Natural Beauty. **Open:** All year
01483 202689 G Gellatly **D:** £25.00 **S:** £30.00 **Beds:** 1F **Baths:** 1 En ⌾ 🅿 (2) ⚹ 📺 🍽 🛗

South Holmwood
TQ1745

Steyning Cottage, *Horsham Road, South Holmwood, Dorking, Surrey, RH5 4NE.* Special rates for long term, including dinner. French spoken. **Open:** All year (not Xmas)
01306 888481 Mrs Treays **D:** £20.00–£22.00 **S:** £20.00–£22.00 **Beds:** 1T 1S **Baths:** 1 Sh ⌾ 🅿 (4) 📺 🐾 ✕ 🍽

Staines
TQ0471

The Penton, *39 Penton Road, Staines, TW18 2JL.* Homely character cottage close to River Thames, access to scenic walks and historic surroundings. **Open:** All year
01784 458787 D: £20.00–£25.00 **S:** £20.00–£26.00 **Beds:** 4F 1D 1T 1S **Baths:** 2 En 1 Sh ⌾ 🅿 (2) ⚹ 📺 🆅 🍽 ⚹ 🛗

Thursley
SU9039

Little Cowdray Farm, *Thursley, Godalming, Surrey, GU8 6QJ.* Farmhouse built early 50's with excellent views. 1.5 miles from A5. **Open:** All year (not Xmas/New Year)
01428 605016 Mrs Goble **D:** £36.00 **S:** £18.00 **Beds:** 1T **Baths:** 1 Sh 🅿 📺 🐾 ✕ 🆅 🍽 🛗

Hindhead Hill Farm, *Portsmouth Road, Thursley, Godalming, Surrey, GU8 6NN.* Small Christian family farm. Our own free-range eggs for breakfast. **Open:** All year (not Xmas)
01428 684727 Mrs Roe **Fax: 01428 685004** *cproe@supanet.uk* **D:** £20.00 **S:** £21.00 **Beds:** 1F 1T **Baths:** 1 En 1 Pr 🅿 (4) ⚹ 📺 ✕ 🆅 🍽 🛗

Walton-on-Thames
TQ1066   🕯 *Badgers Rest*

Beech Tree Lodge, *7 Rydens Avenue, Walton-on-Thames, Surrey, KT12 3JB.* In quiet avenue, close BR station, local shops. Foreign languages spoken. **Open:** All year **Grades:** ETC 3 Diamond
01932 242738 & 01932 886667 Mrs Spiteri *joanspiteri@aol.com* **D:** £20.00–£21.00 **S:** £22.00–£36.00 **Beds:** 1F 1T 1S **Baths:** 2 Sh ⌾ 🅿 (8) ⚹ 📺 🐾 🆅 🍽 🛗

Warlingham

TQ3558

Glenmore, *Southview Road, Warlingham, Surrey, CR6 9JE.* Victorian House in the large grounds close to the countryside and London. **Open:** All year
01883 624530 Fax: 01883 624199 D: £17.50 **S:** £22.00 **Beds:** 2F 1T 2D **Baths:** 1 En 2 Sh
🏠 🅿 (6) ⊬ 📺 🎹 ☕

West Horsley

TQ0752

Brinford, *Off Shere Road, West Horsley, Leatherhead, KT24 6EJ.* Comfortable modern house in peaceful rural location with panoramic views. **Open:** All year
Grades: ETC 3 Diamond
01483 283636 Mrs Wiltshire **D:** £21.00–£26.00 **S:** £26.00–£36.00 **Beds:** 1D 1T 1S
Baths: 1 En 1 Sh 🅿 (4) ⊬ 📺 📺 🎹 ☕

West Molesey

TQ1268

Pilgrim's Retreat, *43 Grange Road, West Molesey, Surrey, KT8 2PR.* Friendly, family home, one mile from Hampton Court. Continental breakfast. **Open:** All year (not Xmas/New Year)
020 8224 2460 Ms Vaughan-Spruce
vaughan_spruce@hotmail.com **D:** £16.50
S: £22.00 **Beds:** 1T 1S **Baths:** 1 Sh 🅿 (1) ⊬ 📺 🎹 ☕

Worplesdon

SU9753

The Old Malt House, *Worplesdon, Guildford, Surrey, GU3 3PT.* Old country house standing in extensive grounds with swimming pool. **Open:** All year
Grades: ETC 3 Diamond
01483 232152 Mrs Millar **D:** £17.50–£19.00 **S:** £20.00–£25.00 **Beds:** 1S 2T **Baths:** 2 Sh
🅿 (6) 📺 🎹 ☕

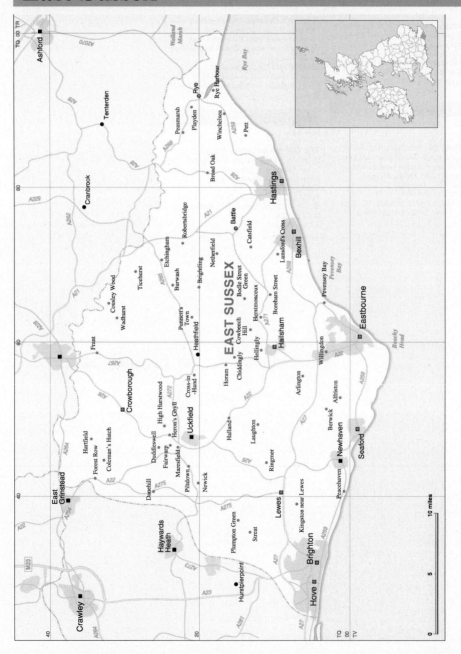

Alfriston

TQ5103 🍺 *The George, Wingrove Inn, Smugglers, Star Inn, Rose Cottage, Market Inn*

Dacres, *Alfriston, Polegate, East Sussex, BN26 5TP.* Studio apartment in pretty cottage. Beautiful gardens. Organic breakfasts. **Open:** All year **01323 870447** Mrs Embry **D:** £25.00 **S:** £40.00 **Beds:** 1T **Baths:** 1 Pr 🖻 (1) ⊁ 🗹 🎦 👶 👱

Meadow-bank, *Sloe Lane, Alfriston, East Sussex, BN26 5UR.* Lovely tranquil

accommodation. Close village centre. Superb breakfasts. **Open:** All year (not Xmas/New Year) **Grades:** ETC 4 Diamond **01323 870742** Mrs Petch **D:** £20.00–£25.00 **S:** £30.00–£35.00 **Beds:** 1T 2D **Baths:** 1 En 2 Sh 🖻 (4) ⊁ 🗹 🎦 🗹 🎦 👱

Arlington

TQ5407 🍺 *Old Oak, Rose Cottage, Yew Tree*

Bates Green, *Arlington, Polegate, E. Sussex, BN26 6SH.* Peaceful location. Tranquil garden. Close Sussex towns. **Open:** All year (not Xmas/New Year) **Grades:** ETC 5 Diamond **01323 482039 (also fax)** C McCutchan **D:** £30.00–£35.00 **Beds:** 2T 2D **Baths:** 3 En 🖻 (3) ⊁ 🗹 🎦

Battle

TQ7515 🍺 *White Hart, Netherfield Arms, Chequers*

Bell Cottage, *Vinehall Road, Robertsbridge, Battle, E Sussex, TN32 5JN.* C17th converted inn beamed throughout. Delightful gardens. Warm welcome assured. **Open:** All year (not Xmas) **Grades:** ETC 4 Diamond **01580 881164** Mrs Lowe **Fax: 01580 880519** *patricia.lowe@tesco.net* www.bellcottage.co.uk **D:** £20.00–£25.00 **S:** £25.00–£30.00 **Beds:** 1D 2T **Baths:** 1 En 1 Pr 1 Sh 🖻 (3) ⊁ 🗹 🎦 👱

Kelklands, *Off Chain Lane, Battle, East Sussex, TN33 0HG.* Peaceful situation, short walk into town. No smoking, easy parking. **Open:** All year **01424 773013** M Burgess **D:** £20.00 **S:** £20.00 **Beds:** 1F 1T 1S **Baths:** 2 En 1 Sh 🕿 (2) 🖻 (5) ⊁ 🗹 🗹 🎦 👱

Fox Hole Farm, *Kane Hythe Road, Battle, E Sussex, TN33 9QU.* A restored country cottage. Perfect place to relax and unwind. **Open:** All year **01424 772053** Mr Collins **Fax: 01424 773771** **D:** £24.50–£27.50 **S:** £29.00–£39.00 **Beds:** 3D **Baths:** 3 En 🖻 (6) ⊁ 🗹 🎦 ✕ 🗹 🎦 👱 **cc**

Berwick

TQ5104

Dawes House, *Berwick, Polegate, E Sussex, BN26 5QS.* Delightful period country home near Alfriston in scenic Cuckmere Valley. **Open:** Feb to Nov **01323 871276 (also fax)** Mrs Wardroper **D:** £22.50–£27.50 **S:** £25.00–£30.00 **Beds:** 1D 1T **Baths:** 1 En 1 Pr 🕿 🖻 (4) ⊁ 🗹 ✕ 🎦 👱

Bexhill-on-Sea

TQ7308 🍺 *The Mermaid*

Buenos Aires, *24 Albany Road, Bexhill-on-Sea, E Sussex, TN40 1BZ.* **Open:** All year **Grades:** ETC 3 Diamond **01424 212269 (also fax)** Mr & Mrs Robson **D:** £17.50–£22.50 **S:** £20.00–£30.00 **Beds:** 1F 1D 1T 1S **Baths:** 1 En 2 Sh 🕿 (5) ⊁ 🗹 🎦 👱 Well-established guest house offering a high standard of comfortable accommodation in a warm and friendly atmosphere. Situated close to sea front, town centre and De La Warr Pavilion, offering both ensuite and standard rooms.

Wakeford House, *Potmans Lane, Lunsford's Cross, Bexhill-on-Sea, E. Sussex, TN39 5JL.* Edwardian-style house in country setting with peaceful one acre garden. **Open:** All year **Grades:** ETC 3 Diamond, AA 4 Diamond **01424 892013** Mrs Skinner **Fax: 01424 893978** *keltie@globalnet.co.uk* **D:** £22.50–£25.00 **S:** £25.00–£30.00 **Beds:** 3F 1D 1S 1T **Baths:** 1 En 1 Sh 🕿 (5) 🗹 🎦 ✕ 🗹 🎦 👱

Manor Barn, *Lunsford's Cross, Bexhill on Sea, E. Sussex, TN39 5JJ.* Ensuite chalets, semi-rural setting on A269, 3 miles sea. **Open:** All year **Grades:** ETC 3 Diamond **01424 893018 (also fax)** Mrs Gillingham **D:** £16.50–£19.50 **S:** £23.50–£26.50 **Beds:** 1F 1D 1T 1S **Baths:** 4 En 🕿 🖻 (6) ⊁ 🗹 🗹 🎦 👶 👱

16 Magdalen Road, *Bexhill-on-Sea, E. Sussex, TN40 1SB.* Large, friendly, family house close to station, shops and sea front. **Open:** All year (not Xmas/New Year) **Grades:** ETC 3 Diamond **01424 218969** Barker **D:** £15.00–£20.00 **S:** £15.00–£30.00 **Beds:** 1F 1T 1D **Baths:** 2 Sh 🗹 🎦 🎦 👱

Bodle Street Green

TQ6514

The Stud Farm, *Bodle Street Green, Hailsham, E. Sussex, BN27 4RJ.* Comfortable farmhouse on working farm. Situated between Heathfield, Hailsham, Battle. **Open:** All year (not Xmas/New Year) **01323 833201 (also fax)** Mr & Mrs Gentry **D:** £20.00–£21.00 **S:** £22.00–£25.00 **Beds:** 1D 2T **Baths:** 1 Pr 1 Sh 🖻 (3) ⊁ 🗹 🎦 👱

Boreham Street

TQ6611

Baldocks, *Boreham Street, Hailsham, E Sussex, BN27 4SQ.* **Open:** All year (not Xmas) **01323 832107** **D:** £20.00 **S:** £20.00–£30.00 **Beds:** 1D 1T **Baths:** 1 Sh 🕿 🖻 (2) ⊁ 🗹 🎦 ✕ 🗹 🎦 👱 A warm welcome awaits you at this part C16th cottage in 1066 country with many local walks. Situated 2 miles from beautiful Herstmonceux Castle and grounds and 5 miles from Pevensey Castle - a good bird watching area especially around the marshes.

Brightling

TQ6821

Swallowfield Farm, *Brightling, Robertsbridge, East Sussex, TN32 5HB.* Elizabethan farmhouse and self-contained cottage in thirty acres of outstanding beauty. **Open:** All year **Grades:** ETC 4 Diamond **01424 838225** Mrs Page **Fax: 01424 838885** *jssp@swallowfieldfarm.freeserve.co.uk* www.swallowfieldfarm.co.uk **D:** £23.00–£25.00 **S:** £25.00–£30.00 **Beds:** 1F 2T **Baths:** 2 En 🕿 🖻 (20) 🗹 🎦 ✕ 🗹 🎦 👱

Brighton

TQ3106 🍺 *St James, Lion & Lobster*

Ambassador Hotel, *23 New Steine, Brighton, E. Sussex, BN2 1PD.* **Open:** All year (not Xmas) **Grades:** ETC 4 Diamond **01273 676869** Mr Koullas **Fax: 01273 689988** **D:** £28.00–£40.00 **Beds:** 5F 5D 4T 6S **Baths:** 20 En 🕿 🖻 🎦 👱 **cc** Situated in a seafront garden square, excellent location from where you can explore the sights, shops and entertainments that Brighton has to offer. Overlooking the sea and Palace Pier. You'll enjoy our freshly cooked English or vegetarian breakfast in our spacious dining room.

RATES

D = Price range per person sharing in a double or twin room

S = Price range for a single room

Claremont House Hotel, Second Avenue, Hove, E Sussex, BN3 2LL. **Open:** All year
01273 735161 (also fax) *claremonthove@aol.com* www.claremonthousehotel.co.uk **D:** £40.00–£70.00 **S:** £45.00–£90.00 **Beds:** 2D/F 6D/T 4S **Baths:** 12 En 🛏 ⅙ ⊠ ✕ 🖂 🕮 ⚓ **cc**
Claremont House is an elegantly presented Victorian villa, situated just a few hundred yards from the seafront and minutes from the centre of Brighton. The individually decorated rooms are very comfortably furnished, all benefiting from ensuite facilities. Bar available.

Brighton Marina House Hotel, 8 Charlotte Street, Brighton, E. Sussex, BN2 1AG. **Open:** All year
01273 605349 Mr Jung **Fax:** 01273 679484 *rooms@jungs.co.uk* www.s-h-systems.co.uk/hotels/brightma **D:** £25.00–£99.00 **S:** £25.00–£55.00 **Beds:** 3F 7D 4T 3S **Baths:** 7 Pr 1 Sh 🛏 ⊠ 🕮 ⚓
Ideal location, 2 mins' walk to the beach. Unique and innovative experience in today's B&B. Rooms only offer (without breakfast). Most rooms non-smoking. Free Internet and email facility. We cater for vegans, vegetarians, English and Continental.

Arlanda Hotel, 20 New Steine, Brighton, E. Sussex, BN2 1PD.
Open: All year
Grades: ETC 4 Diamond, Silver, AA 4 Diamond, RAC 4 Diamond
01273 699300 Mr Mathews **Fax:** 01273 600930 *arlanda@brighton.co.uk* www.arlandahotel.co.uk **D:** £30.00–£60.00 **S:** £30.00–£60.00 **Beds:** 3T 7D 5S **Baths:** 15 En 🛏 ⅙ ⊠ 🕮 ⚓ **cc**
A charming Grade II Regency townhouse, situated in a garden square adjacent to the seafront. The hotel provides a peaceful and relaxing base for exploring historic yet vibrant Brighton. You are assured a warm welcome and a clean and comfortable stay.

Avalon House, 7 Upper Rock Gardens, Brighton, East Sussex, BN2 1QE.
Open: All year (not Xmas)
01273 692344
D: £22.50–£30.00 **S:** £25.00–£30.00 **Beds:** 1F 2T 5D 1S **Baths:** 8 En 🛏 (12) ⅙ ⊠ ⊻ 🖂 🕮 ⚓ **cc**
A Grade II Listed building, being two minutes from seafront and ten minutes walk from town centre, Royal Pavilion and the famous 'Lanes'. All rooms tastefully decorated, most equipped with CD players and fridges. A friendly welcome awaits you.

Fyfield House, 26 New Steine, Brighton, E. Sussex, BN2 1PD.
Welcoming, clean home from home with superb views of sea. **Open:** All year (not Xmas)
01273 602770 (also fax) Mr & Mrs Culpeck *fyfield@aol.com* www.brighton.co.uk/hotels/fyfield **D:** £22.50–£45.00 **S:** £22.50–£45.00 **Beds:** 1F 5D 1T 4S **Baths:** 6 En 1 Sh 🛏 ⊠ 🛉 🖂 🕮 ⚓ **cc**

Dudley House, 10 Madeira Place, Brighton, E. Sussex, BN2 1TN. Grade 2 listed Victorian town house, centrally located, near seafront. **Open:** All year **Grades:** ETC 3 Diamond
01273 676794 Mr & Mrs Lacey *office@dudleyhousebrighton.com* www.dudleyhousebrighton.com **D:** £20.00–£35.00 **S:** £20.00–£50.00 **Beds:** 6D **Baths:** 3 En 3 Sh 🛏 (10) ⅙ ⊠ 🛉 🕮 ⚓ **cc**

Planning a longer stay? Always ask for any special rates

Trouville Hotel, 11 New Steine, Brighton, E. Sussex, BN2 1PB. Listed Regency townhouse restored to high standard and situated in a seafront square. **Open:** Feb to Dec
01273 697384 Mr Hansell **D:** £29.50–£32.50 **S:** £29.00–£45.00 **Beds:** 2F 3D 1T 2S **Baths:** 6 Pr 1 Sh 🛏 ⊠ ⊻ 🕮 ⚓ **cc**

Ainsley House Hotel, 28 New Steine, Brighton, E. Sussex, BN2 1PQ. Regency town house. Comfortable rooms. Excellent breakfasts, warm welcome, sea views.
Open: All year (not Xmas) **Grades:** ETC 4 Diamond, AA 4 Diamond
01273 605310 Mrs King **Fax:** 01273 688604 *ahhotel@fastnet.co.uk* www.ainsleyhotel.com **D:** £23.00–£45.00 **S:** £25.00–£35.00 **Beds:** 2F 4D 2T 3S **Baths:** 9 En 2 Sh ⅙ ⊠ ⊻ 🕮 ⚓ **cc**

Brighton Royal Hotel, 76 Grand Parade, Brighton, E. Sussex, BN2 2JA. Opposite Brighton's Royal Pavilion. Close to bars, clubs, shops, sea front **Open:** All year
01273 604182 (also fax) **D:** £20.00–£30.00 **S:** £20.00–£45.00 **Beds:** 1F 1T 7D 1S **Baths:** 1 En 1 Pr 1 Sh 🛏 (10) ⊠ 🕮 ✳ **cc**

Diana House, 25 St Georges Terrace, Brighton, E. Sussex, BN2 1JJ. Friendly run guest house. Close to seafront and town centre. **Open:** All year
01273 605797 Mrs Burgess **Fax:** 01273 600533 *diana@enterprise.net* www.dianahouse.co.uk **D:** £22.00–£25.00 **S:** £44.00–£50.00 **Beds:** 5F 5D 1S **Baths:** 9 En 2 Sh 🛏 ⊠ ⊻ 🕮 ⚓ **cc**

Market Inn, 1 Market Street, Brighton, East Sussex, BN1 1HH. Traditional inn, in the centre of Brighton's famous 'Lanes' area close to sea front. **Open:** All year
01273 329483 **Fax:** 01273 777227 *marketbrighton@aol.com* **D:** £30.00 **S:** £45.00 **Beds:** 2D **Baths:** 2 En ⊠ 🕮 ⚓ **cc**

14 Roedean Way, Brighton, East Sussex, BN2 5RJ. Situated above Brighton Marina. Stunning sea views. Quiet. Lovely garden.
Open: All year (not Xmas/New Year)
01273 605369 Mrs Shepherd *rube@rshepherd.freeserve.co.uk* **D:** £20.00–£25.00 **S:** £20.00–£25.00 **Beds:** 1T 1D **Baths:** 2 Pr 🅿 (2) ⅙ ⊠ 🕮 ⚓

Oriental Hotel, 9 Oriental Place, Brighton, E. Sussex, BN1 2LJ. Very friendly and relaxed hotel with contemporary decor, centrally located. **Open:** All year (not Xmas/New Year)
01273 205050 **Fax:** 01273 821096 *info@orientalhotel.co.uk* www.orientalhotel.co.uk **D:** £27.25–£45.00 **Beds:** 1F 7D 4S **Baths:** 8 En 2 Sh 🛏 ⊠ 🛉 ✕ ⊻ 🕮 ⚓ **cc**

New Steine Hotel, 12a New Steine, Brighton, E. Sussex, BN2 1PB. With 4 Diamonds, New Steine Hotel offers high standard of service with personal touch.
Open: All year
01273 681546 Mr Guyat **Fax:** 01273 679118 **D:** £20.00–£41.00 **S:** £25.00–£35.00 **Beds:** 2T 7D 2S **Baths:** 7 En 3 Sh 🛏 (12) ⊠ ✕ ⊻ 🕮 ⚓ **cc**

B&B owners may vary rates – be sure to check when booking

Paskins Hotel, *19 Charlotte Street, Brighton, E. Sussex, BN2 1AG.* Organic and natural food. Delicious traditional and vegetarian breakfasts. Stylish. **Open:** All year
01273 601203 Fax: 01273 621973 *Welcome@ paskins.co.uk* www.paskins.co.uk **D:** £22.50–£45.00 **S:** £22.50–£35.00 **Beds:** 2F 10D 2T 6S **Baths:** 17 En 3 Sh ♿ ☺ 🔭 ⊁ ☑ 🛏 ⁂ 🅿

Broad Oak (Rye)

TQ8220   🍺 *Rainbow Trout, Broad Oak*

Furnace Lane Oast, *Broad Oak (Rye), Rye, E. Sussex, TN31 6ET.* Double oasthouse in peaceful rural setting. Ideal for local touring. **Open:** All year **Grades:** ETC 4 Diamond
01424 882407 (also fax) Mr Sevastopulo *furnacelane@pavilion.co.uk* www.seetb.org. uk/furnace-lane-oast **D:** £25.50–£30.00 **S:** £25.00–£40.00 **Beds:** 1F 1T 1D **Baths:** 3 En ♿ 🅿 (5) ☑ 🔭 ⊁ ☑ 🛏 & 🅿

Burwash

TQ6724

Woodlands Farm, *Heathfield Road, Burwash, Etchingham, E. Sussex, TN19 7LA.* Comfortable, quiet, friendly C16th farmhouse, 0.25 mile off road. **Open:** All year
01435 882794 (also fax) Mrs Sirrell *liz.sir@ lineone.net* **D:** £20.00–£23.00 **S:** £20.00–£26.00 **Beds:** 2D 2T **Baths:** 1 En 2 Sh ♿ 🅿 (6) ⊁ ☑ ✗ 🛏 🅿

Catsfield

TQ7214

Farthings Farm, *Catsfield, Battle, East Sussex, TN33 9BA.* Edwardian house on a 70-acre farm set half mile off the road. **Open:** All year (not Xmas)
01424 773107 Mrs Rodgers www.farthingsfarm.co.uk **D:** £25.00 **S:** £30.00 **Beds:** 2D 1T **Baths:** 2 Pr 🅿 (3) ⊁ ☑ 🛏 🅿

Chiddingly

TQ5414

Hale Farm House, *Chiddingly, Lewes, E Sussex, BN8 6HQ.* C14th Listed beamed farmhouse, spacious rooms, situated on Wealdway overlooking South Downs. **Open:** All year
01825 872619 (also fax) Mrs Burrough *s.burrough@virgin.net* www.cuckmere-valley. co.uk/hale **D:** £18.00–£25.00 **S:** £18.00–£25.00 **Beds:** 1F 2T **Baths:** 1 En 1 Sh ♿ 🅿 (3) ⊁ ☑ 🔭 ✗ ☑ 🛏 🅿

Coleman's Hatch

TQ4533   🍺 *The Hatch*

Gospel Oak, *Sandy Lane, Coleman's Hatch, Hartfield, E. Sussex, TN7 4ER.* A charming county cottage in heart of Ashdown Forest. **Open:** All year
01342 823840 Mrs Hawker **D:** £22.50–£50.00 **S:** £25.00–£28.00 **Beds:** 1T 1D **Baths:** 2 En ♿ 🅿 (4) ⊁ ☑ 🔭 ✗ ☑ 🛏 🅿

Cousley Wood

TQ6533   🍺 *Old Vine*

Cheviots, *Cousley Wood, Wadhurst, E. Sussex, TN5 6HD.* Country house in beautiful Weald, good base for many NT properties. **Open:** Easter to Oct
01892 782952 Mr Field *cheviots.guesthouse@ dial.pipex.com* **D:** £22.50–£27.50 **S:** £22.00–£27.00 **Beds:** 1T 1D 2S **Baths:** 2 En 1 Sh 🅿 (4) ⊁ ☑ 🛏 🅿 cc

Cowbeech Hill

TQ6113

Batchelors, *Cowbeech Hill, Hailsham, E Sussex, BN27 4JB.* Situated perfectly for exploring East Sussex, warm welcome, farmhouse breakfast. **Open:** All year **Grades:** ETC 3 Diamond
01323 832215 Mrs Barrow **D:** £22.50–£25.00 **S:** £30.00 **Beds:** 1D 2T **Baths:** 1 En 1 Pr 2 Sh ♿ (10) 🅿 (3) ⊁ ☑ ☑ 🛏 🅿

Cross-in-Hand

TQ5521

Old Corner Cottage, *Little London Road, Cross-in-Hand, Heathfield, E. Sussex, TN21 0LT.* Pretty cottage situated conveniently between Eastbourne and Tunbridge Wells. **Open:** All year **Grades:** AA 5 Diamond
01435 863787 (also fax) Mrs Brown **D:** £20.00–£24.00 **S:** £25.00–£28.00 **Beds:** 2D 1T **Baths:** 3 En ♿ 🅿 (10) ⊁ ☑ 🔭 ☑ 🛏 🅿

Crowborough

TQ5230

Wareham Lodge, *Boarshead, Crowborough, E Sussex, TN6 3HE.* Comfortable country house with beautiful one-acre plantsman's garden. **Open:** All year (not Xmas)
01892 653444 Mrs Collins **D:** £21.00–£22.50 **S:** £25.00–£30.00 **Beds:** 2D **Baths:** 2 En 🅿 (3) ⊁ ☑ 🔭 ☑ 🛏 🅿

Danehill

TQ4027   🍺 *Coach & Horses, The Sloop, The Griffin*

New Glenmore, *Sliders Lane, Furners Green, Danehill, East Sussex, TN22 3RU.* Spacious bungalow set in 6 acres near Bluebell Railway and Sheffield Park. **Open:** All year (not Xmas/New Year) **Grades:** ETC 4 Diamond
01825 790783 (also fax) Mr Robinson *alan.robinson@bigfoot.com* **D:** £20.00 **S:** £35.00 **Beds:** 1F 1T 1D **Baths:** 1 En 1 Sh ♿ 🅿 ⊁ ☑ ☑ 🛏 🅿

Sliders Farmhouse, *Furners Green, Danehill, Uckfield, E. Sussex, TN22 3RT.* Picturesque C16th country house, peacefully situated down a country lane. **Open:** All year (not Xmas)
01825 790258 (also fax) Mr Salmon *jean&davidsalmon@freeserve.co.uk* **D:** £22.00–£30.00 **S:** £34.00–£40.00 **Beds:** 1F 1D 1T **Baths:** 3 En ♿ 🅿 (10) ☑ ☑ 🛏 🅿

Duddleswell

TQ4628

Toll Platt, *Duddleswell, Nutley, Uckfield, E. Sussex, TN22 3JB.* Self-contained wing of country cottage high in Ashdown Forest. Prior arrangement only. **Open:** All year (not Xmas/New Year)
01825 712683 D Bradbury **Fax: 01825 713120** *dianabradbury@hotmail.com* **D:** £22.00 **S:** £22.00 **Beds:** 1D **Baths:** 1 En 🅿 (2) ⊁ ☑ 🔭 🛏 🅿

Eastbourne

TQ5900   🍺 *The Marine*

Camberley Hotel, *27-29 Elms Avenue, Eastbourne, E. Sussex, BN21 3DN.* **Open:** Mar to Oct
01323 723789 **D:** £19.00–£22.00 **S:** £19.00–£22.00 **Beds:** 4F 3D 3T 2S **Baths:** 7 En 2 Sh ♿ 🅿 (3) ☑ ✗ ☑ 🛏 🅿
Situated in a pleasant avenue close to town centre, sea front and all amenities. Licensed, ensuite, tea-making, colour TV in bedrooms. English breakfast.

Edelweiss Hotel, *10-12 Elms Avenue, Eastbourne, E. Sussex, BN21 3DN.* Central family-run hotel just off sea front. Comfortable and welcoming. **Open:** All year
01323 732071 (also fax) Mr & Mrs Butler *peterbutler@fsbdial.co.uk* **D:** £16.00–£20.00 **S:** £16.00–£25.00 **Beds:** 1F 6D 5T 2S **Baths:** 3 En 4 Sh ♿ ☺ ✗ ☑ 🛏 ⁂ 🅿 cc

Planning a longer stay? Always ask for any special rates

Innisfree House, *130a Royal Parade, Eastbourne, East Sussex, BN22 7JY.* **Open:** All year (not Xmas)
01323 646777 & 01323 416674 Mrs Petrie **Fax: 01323 646777** *dave@medico-oil.fsnet.co.uk* www.eastbournehotels.com **D:** £22.50–£25.00 **S:** £25.00–£35.00 **Beds:** 1F 1D 1T **Baths:** 3 En
Small family-run B&B on seafront, close to amenities, (with international clientele), refurbished to high standards. Exclusive location with sea views, easy parking on road outside. Motorcycle storage. Stay a day or stay a week, your comfort and praise we aim to seek.

Ambleside Private Hotel, *24 Elms Avenue, Eastbourne, E. Sussex, BN21 3DN.* **Open:** All year **01323 724991** Mr Pattenden **D:** £18.00–£22.00 **S:** £18.00–£22.00 **Beds:** 4D 4T 2S **Baths:** 2 Sh 2 En
Situated on quiet avenue adjacent to seafront, pier, town centre, theatres, convenient for railway and coach stations. Short distance from South Downs Way, Wealdway. Colour TV in bedrooms. Compliant with environmental and fire regulations.

Cherry Tree Hotel, *15 Silverdale Road, Eastbourne, E. Sussex, BN20 7AJ.* Award-winning family-run hotel, close to sea front, downlands and theatres. **Open:** All year **Grades:** ETC 4 Diamond, Silver
01323 722406 Mr Henley **Fax: 01323 648838** *anncherrytree@aol.com* www.eastbourne.org/cherrytree-hotel **D:** £28.00–£36.00 **S:** £28.00–£36.00 **Beds:** 1F 4D 3T 2S **Baths:** 10 En (7) cc

The Manse, *7 Dittons Road, Eastbourne, East Sussex, BN21 1DW.* Character house located in quiet area yet within 5 mins' walk of town centre. **Open:** All year (not Xmas)
01323 737851 Mrs Walker **D:** £15.00–£20.00 **S:** £20.00–£25.00 **Beds:** 1F 2T **Baths:** 2 En 1 Pr (8) (1)

Sheldon Hotel, *9-11 Burlington Place, Eastbourne, East Sussex, BN21 4AS.* Situated within a few minutes walk of sea front, theatres. Licensed. **Open:** All year
01323 724120 Fax: 01323 430406 *gmeyer@sheldonhotel.fsbusiness.co.uk* www.smoothhound.co.uk/hotels/sheldon.html **D:** £25.00–£31.00 **S:** £25.00–£31.00 **Beds:** 4F 6T 8D 6S **Baths:** 24 En cc

Meridale Guest House, *91 Royal Parade, Eastbourne, East Sussex, BN22 7AE.* Quality B&B, sea front, quiet end of town, excellent value. **Open:** All year **01323 729686 Fax: 01323 419042** *crcmeridale@talk21.com* **D:** £18.50 **S:** £21.50 **Beds:** 2F 1T 3D **Baths:** 6 En cc

Southcroft Hotel, *15 South Cliff Avenue, Eastbourne, E. Sussex, BN20 7AH.* Friendly, family-run, non-smoking hotel. Close to Downs, sea and theatre. **Open:** All year **Grades:** ETC 4 Diamond
01323 729071 Mrs Skriczka *southcroft@eastbourne34.freeserve.co.uk* www.southcrofthotel.co.uk **D:** £25.00–£30.00 **S:** £25.00–£30.00 **Beds:** 2D 2T 1S **Baths:** 5 En

Heatherdene Hotel, *26-28 Elms Avenue, Eastbourne, E. Sussex, BN21 3DN.* Good food and comfortable rooms. Train and coach stations nearby. **Open:** All year
01323 723598 (also fax) Mrs Mockford **D:** £17.00–£45.00 **S:** £16.00–£25.00 **Beds:** 1F 4D 8T 3S **Baths:** 6 En 3 Sh 3

Etchingham

TQ7126 *The Bull, Rose & Crown*

King Johns Lodge, *Sheepstreet Lane, Etchingham, East Sussex, TN19 7AZ.* Historic Listed house in 7 acres of gardens. Exceptional furnishings and settings. **Open:** All year (not Xmas/New Year)
01580 819232 Fax: 01580 819562 D: £35.00–£40.00 **S:** £50.00–£55.00 **Beds:** 1F 1T 2D **Baths:** 2 En 2 Pr (7) (12)

All details shown are as supplied by B&B owners in Autumn 2001

RATES
D = Price range per person sharing in a double or twin room
S = Price range for a single room

Fairwarp

TQ4626

Broom Cottage, *Browns Brook, Fairwarp, Uckfield, E Sussex, TN22 3BY.* Victorian cottage in lovely garden on Ashdown Forest. Very peaceful. **Open:** All year **Grades:** ETC 4 Diamond
01825 712942 D: £24.00–£30.00 **S:** £30.00 **Beds:** 1D 1T **Baths:** 1 Sh

Forest Row

TQ4234

Woodcote, *Park Road, Forest Row, RH18 5BX.* Friendly family home in private road adjacent to Ashdown Forest. **Open:** All year (not Xmas/New Year)
01342 822170 S Hillen **Fax: 01342 823134** *shhillen@hotmail.com* **D:** £30.00–£60.00 **S:** £30.00–£60.00 **Beds:** 1T 1D **Baths:** 1 En (2)

Frant

TQ5935

Melling, *The Green, Frant, Tunbridge Wells, E Sussex, TN3 9ED.* Pretty house overlooks village green. Walkers welcome. **Open:** All year (not Xmas)
01892 750380 D: £20.00 **S:** £20.00 **Beds:** 1T **Baths:** 1 Sh

Hailsham

TQ5809 *King's Head*

Longleys Farm Cottage, *Harebeating Lane, Hailsham, E Sussex, BN27 1ER.* Quiet country location near prime tourist attractions. Informal and friendly. **Open:** All year **Grades:** ETC 3 Diamond
01323 841227 (also fax) J Hook **D:** £19.00 **S:** £22.00–£25.00 **Beds:** 1F 1D 1T **Baths:** 2 En 1 Pr (4)

National Grid References given are for villages, towns and cities – not for individual houses

Halland

TQ5016 *Blackboys Inn, Black Lion*

Shortgate Manor Farm, Halland, Lewes, E Sussex, BN8 6PJ. **Open:** All year **Grades:** ETC 4 Diamond, Silver **01825 840320 (also fax)** *ewalt@shortgate.co.uk* www.shortgate.co.uk **D:** £27.50–£30.00 **S:** £35.00–£40.00 **Beds:** 1T 2D **Baths:** 3 En ⬧ (10) 🅿 (6) ⚄ ⚄ ⚄ 🍴 ⚄
Enchanting C18th farmhouse set in 8 acres, with 2 acres of landscaped gardens which are open under the NGS every June. The 3 charming bedrooms all offer ensuite facilities with TVs, courtesy trays and bathrobes. Glyndebourne 4 miles.

Tamberry Hall, Eastbourne Road, Halland, Lewes, East Sussex, BN8 6PS. **Open:** All year (not Xmas/New Year) **Grades:** ETC 4 Diamond **01825 880090 (also fax)** Ms Baynham *bedandbreakfast@tamberryhall.fsbusiness.co.uk* www.fsbusiness.co.uk **D:** £22.50–£30.00 **S:** £35.00–£45.00 **Beds:** 1F 2D **Baths:** 3 En ⬧ 🅿 (4) 🍴 ⚄ ⚄ ⚄
Enjoy the warm and friendly surroundings of this delightful country house, savour your sumptuous breakfast overlooking secluded gardens. Relax in the comfort of your beautiful room with every amenity. Truly a stay to remember. Glyndebourne 10 minutes. Golf 2 minutes.

Hartfield

TQ4735

The Paddocks, Chuck Hatch, Hartfield, East Sussex, TN7 4EX. In the Ashdown Forest, 0.25 mile from Pooh Sticks Bridge. Walkers and children welcome. **Open:** All year (not Xmas) **01892 770623** Ms McAll **D:** £22.00 **S:** £22.00 **Beds:** 1D 1T 1S **Baths:** 1 Pr 1 Sh ⬧ 🅿 🍴 ⚄ ⚄ ⚄ ⚄

Hastings

TQ8110 *Hastings Arms*

Lavender and Lace, 106 All Saints Street, Old Town, Hastings, E. Sussex, TN34 3BE. **Open:** Mar to Dec (not New Year) **Grades:** ETC 4 Diamond **01424 716290 (also fax)** Ms Gould **D:** £20.00–£25.00 **Beds:** 1T 2D **Baths:** 1 En 1 Pr ⬧ (10) ⚄ ⚄ ⚄ 🍴 ⚄
Situated in heart of historic Old Town of Hastings, charming period house just 400 yards from the fishing harbour. The area contains a wealth of interest for the visitor who is able to browse amongst the many antique shops, wine bars, bistros and restaurants.

Emerydale, 6 King Edward Avenue, Hastings, E. Sussex, TN34 2NQ. Warm welcome. Perfectly situated for exploring 1066 country. Off A21. **Open:** All year (not Xmas) **Grades:** ETC 4 Diamond **01424 437915** Mrs Emery **Fax:** 01424 444124 **D:** £19.00–£21.00 **S:** £19.00–£23.00 **Beds:** 1D 1T 1S **Baths:** 1 En 1 Sh ⬧ (12) 🍴 ⚄ ⚄ ⚄

White Cottage, Battery Hill, Hastings, E. Sussex, TN35 4AP. Friendly family-run B&B on outskirts of peaceful Fairlight, beautiful gardens, far-reaching channel views. **Open:** Feb to Oct **Grades:** ETC 4 Diamond **01424 812528 Fax:** 01424 812285 **D:** £22.50–£25.00 **S:** £22.50–£30.00 **Beds:** 1T 3D **Baths:** 3 En 1 Pr ⬧ (7) 🅿 (4) 🍴 ⚄ ⚄ ⚄

Grand Hotel, Grand Parade, St Leonards On Sea, Hastings, E. Sussex, TN38 0DD. Seafront family hotel in heart of 1066 country. **Open:** All year **Grades:** ETC 3 Diamond **01424 428510 (also fax)** Mr & Mrs Mann **D:** £18.00–£35.00 **S:** £24.00–£45.00 **Beds:** 3F 6D 4T 4S **Baths:** 3 En 4 Pr 12 Sh ⬧ 🍴 ⚄ × ⚄ ⚄ ⚄ 🍴 ⚄

Westwood Farm, Stonestile Lane, Hastings, E. Sussex, TN35 4PG. Working sheep farm, peaceful, rural. Outstanding views over Brede Valley. **Open:** All year (not Xmas) **01424 751038 (also fax)** Mr York *york@westwood-farm.fsnet.co.uk* **D:** £19.00–£27.00 **S:** £23.00–£30.00 **Beds:** 1F 1D 1T **Baths:** 2 En 1 Pr ⬧ (5) 🅿 (8) 🍴 ⚄ ⚄ ⚄ ⚄ ⚄

All details shown are as supplied by B&B owners in Autumn 2001

Planning a longer stay? Always ask for any special rates

Millifont Guest House, 8/9 Cambridge Gardens, Hastings, E. Sussex, TN34 1EH. Centrally situated 15-bedroom guest house, lounge / games room. **Open:** All year (not Xmas) **01424 425645** Mr Main **D:** £16.00–£22.50 **S:** £16.00–£22.50 **Beds:** 3F 6D 4T 4S **Baths:** 2 En 1 Pr 4 Sh ⬧ 🅿 ⚄ ⚄ ⚄ ⚄ ⚄

Lansdowne Hotel, 1 Robertson Terrace, Hastings, E. Sussex, TN34 1JE. Family run for 25 years; great value for money and very high standards. **Open:** All year **01424 429605** Mr Rumble *lansdowne.hotel@btinternet.com* **D:** £23.50–£28.50 **S:** £24.50–£31.00 **Beds:** 6F 15D 3T 4S **Baths:** 28 En 2 Sh ⬧ ⚄ × ⚄ ⚄ 🍴 ⚄ cc

Cambridge Guest House, 18 Cambridge Gardens, Hastings, E. Sussex, TN34 1EH. Friendly, clean, family guest house. 3 minutes walk to town centre **Open:** All year **01424 712995** **D:** £16.00–£22.00 **S:** £14.00–£20.00 **Beds:** 1F 4T 1D 3S **Baths:** 3 En 2 Sh ⬧ 🍴 ⚄ ⚄ × ⚄ ⚄ ⚄ ⚄

Heathfield

TQ5821

Iwood, Mutton Hall Lane, Heathfield, E Sussex, TN21 8NR. **Open:** All year (not Xmas/New Year) **Grades:** ETC 4 Diamond, Silver **01435 863918 Fax:** 01435 868575 *iwoodbb@aol.com* www.iwoodbb.co.uk **D:** £21.00–£23.00 **S:** £20.00–£25.00 **Beds:** 1F 1D 1S **Baths:** 1 En 2 Pr ⬧ 🅿 (2) 🍴 ⚄ ⚄ ⚄ ⚄
Secluded chalet bungalow in lovely gardens with distant views South Downs and sea. Situated within coastal towns including 1066 attractions around Hastings and historic towns of Battle, Lewes and Royal Tunbridge Wells. Be prepared for an excellent breakfast!

Spicers Cottages, 21 Cade Street, Heathfield, E Sussex, TN21 9BS. Old beamed cottage on the High Weald of East Sussex. **Open:** All year **Grades:** ETC 4 Diamond **01435 866363** Mr Gumbrell **Fax:** 01435 868171 *sleep@spicersbb.co.uk* www.spicersbb.co.uk **D:** £21.00–£22.50 **S:** £22.00–£25.00 **Beds:** 1D 1T 1S **Baths:** 1 En 2 Pr ⬧ 🅿 🍴 ⚄ × ⚄ ⚄ ⚄ ⚄ cc

All details shown are as supplied by B&B owners in Autumn 2001

Old Corner Cottage, *Little London Road, Cross-in-Hand, Heathfield, E. Sussex, TN21 0LT.* Pretty cottage situated conveniently between Eastbourne and Tunbridge Wells. **Open:** All year **Grades:** AA 5 Diamond **01435 863787 (also fax)** Mrs Brown **D:** £20.00–£24.00 **S:** £25.00–£28.00 **Beds:** 2D 1T **Baths:** 3 En ♿ �🅿 (10) ⚲ 📺 ♒ Ⅴ ▥ 🔥

Hellingly
TQ5812

Grove Hill House, *Hellingly, Hailsham, E Sussex, BN27 4HG.* Period farmhouse in beautiful quiet setting in over 2 acres of grounds. **Open:** All year **01435 812440 (also fax)** Mrs Berthon **D:** £19.00–£22.00 **S:** £25.00–£30.00 **Beds:** 1D 1T **Baths:** 1 En 1 Pr ♿ �🅿 (4) ⚲ ✕ ▥

Heron's Ghyll
TQ4826

Tanglewood, *Oldlands Hall, Heron's Ghyll, Uckfield, E Sussex, TN22 3DA.* Peaceful setting on Ashdown Forest. Large pretty garden, warm welcome. **Open:** All year (not Xmas) **01825 712757** Mrs Clarke **D:** £24.00 **S:** £25.00–£30.00 **Beds:** 2D 1T **Baths:** 1 Pr 1 Sh �🅿 (6) ⚲ 📺 Ⅴ ▥ & 🔥

Herstmonceux
TQ6312

Sandhurst, *Church Road, Herstmonceux, Hailsham, E Sussex, BN27 1RG.* Large bungalow in countryside. Easy access to village and coast. **Open:** All year (not Xmas) **01323 833088** *junerussell@compuserve.com* **D:** £20.00–£25.00 **S:** £20.00–£30.00 **Beds:** 2F 2D **Baths:** 3 En 1 Pr ♿ �🅿 (4) ⚲ 📺 ▥

High Hurstwood
TQ4926 ◁ *Maypole Inn*

Huckleberry, *Perryman's Lane, High Hurstwood, Uckfield, W Sussex, TN22 1AG.* Pretty country house, prize winning garden. Near Ashdown Forest and many country houses. **Open:** All year (not Xmas/New Year) **Grades:** ETC 4 Diamond **01825 733170** Ms White **D:** £22.50–£27.50 **S:** £22.50–£30.00 **Beds:** 1F 1T 1D 1S **Baths:** 3 En 1 Pr 1 Sh ♿ �🅿 📺 ♒ ▥ 🔥

Horam
TQ5717

Oak Mead Nursery, *Cowden Hall Lane, Horam, Heathfield, E. Sussex, TN21 9ED.* Set in beautiful, quiet countryside, off road parking, good breakfasts. **Open:** Jan to Dec **Grades:** ETC 3 Diamond **01435 812962** Mrs Curtis **D:** £19.00 **S:** £19.00–£24.00 **Beds:** 1D 1T 1S **Baths:** 2 En 1 Pr ♿ �🅿 (4) ⚲ 📺 ♒ Ⅴ ▥ 🔥

Hove
TQ2805

Claremont House Hotel, *Second Avenue, Hove, E Sussex, BN3 2LL.* Elegantly presented Victorian villa, situated just a few hundred yards from the seafront. **Open:** All year **01273 735161 (also fax)** *claremonthove@ aol.com* www.claremonthousehotel.co.uk **D:** £40.00–£70.00 **S:** £45.00–£90.00 **Beds:** 2D/F 6D/T 4S **Baths:** 12 En ♿ ⚲ 📺 ✕ Ⅴ ▥ 🔥 cc

Lichfield House, *30 Waterloo Street, Hove, E. Sussex, BN3 1AN.* Town centre location, close to sea and night life. **Open:** All year **01273 777740** Mr Byrne *feelgood@ lichfieldhouse.freeserve.co.uk* www.lichfieldhouse.freeserve.co.uk **D:** £16.00–£35.00 **S:** £32.00–£80.00 **Beds:** 2F 5D 2T 1S **Baths:** 4 En 1 Pr 1 Sh ♿ (2) 📺 ♒ Ⅴ ▥ 🔥

Adastral Hotel, *8 Westbourne Villas, Hove, E. Sussex, BN3 4GQ.* The Adastral Hotel is a Victorian villa situated 200 metres from the sea front. **Open:** All year **01273 888800** Mr Salanson **Fax:** 01273 883839 *adastral@mistral.co.uk* www.adastralhotel.co.uk **D:** £41.00–£50.00 **S:** £44.00 **Beds:** 8S 2D 7T/F **Baths:** 11 En 3 Sh ♿ �🅿 (2) 📺 ♒ ✕ Ⅴ ▥ & ✿ 🔥 cc

Kingston near Lewes
TQ3908 ◁ *The Juggs*

Settlands, *Wellgreen Lane, Kingston near Lewes, Lewes, E Sussex, BN7 3NP.* Delightful, spacious accommodation, close to Lewes, Brighton, Glyndebourne and Downland walks. **Open:** All year (not Xmas) **Grades:** ETC 4 Diamond **01273 472295** Mrs Arlett *diana-a@ solutions-inc.co.uk* **D:** £22.50–£27.50 **S:** £25.00–£30.00 **Beds:** 1D 1T **Baths:** 2 Sh ♿ �🅿 (3) ⚲ 📺 Ⅴ ▥ 🔥

Planning a longer stay? Always ask for any special rates

Laughton
TQ5013

Holly Cottage, *Lewes Road, Laughton, Lewes, E. Sussex, BN8 6BL.* Charming C18th Listed country cottage. **Open:** All year **01323 811309** Mrs Clarke **Fax:** 01323 811106 **D:** £23.00–£25.00 **S:** £30.00–£35.00 **Beds:** 1F 1T 1D **Baths:** 3 En ♿ �🅿 (3) ⚲ 📺 ▥ 🔥

Lewes
TQ4110 ◁ *The Juggs*

Crown Inn, *191 High Street, Lewes, East Sussex, BN7 2NA.* Welcoming C17th inn, centrally located. Meeting room available. **Open:** All year **Grades:** ETC 2 Diamond **01273 480670** **Fax:** 01273 480679 *sales@ crowninn-lewes.co.uk* www.crowninn-lewes.co. uk **D:** £25.00–£35.00 **S:** £37.50–£48.00 **Beds:** 1F 3T 4D **Baths:** 6 En 1 Sh ♿ 📺 ♒ ✕ Ⅴ 🔥 cc

Coombe Barn, *Lewes, E Sussex, BN7 3PE.* Converted barn. Foot of South Downs Way. Stunning views. Farm eggs. **Open:** All year (not Xmas/New Year) **01273 477388** Mrs Greenwood *sara.greenwood@btinternet.com* **D:** £22.00–£25.00 **S:** £30.00 ♿ �🅿 (4) ⚲ 📺 Ⅴ ▥ 🔥

Sussex Country Accommodation, *Crink House, Barcombe Mills, Lewes, E. Sussex, BN8 5BJ.* Victorian farmhouse with panoramic views. Welcoming rural family home, ideal base for exploring Sussex. **Open:** All year (not Xmas) **01273 400625** Mrs Gaydon **D:** £25.00–£30.00 **S:** £30.00–£40.00 **Beds:** 2D 1T **Baths:** 3 En ♿ �🅿 (10) ⚲ 📺 Ⅴ ▥ 🔥

Castle Banks Cottage, *4 Castle Banks, Lewes, E. Sussex, BN7 1UZ.* Beamed cottage, pretty garden, quiet lane, close to castle, shops, restaurants. **Open:** All year (not Xmas) **01273 476291 (also fax)** Mrs Wigglesworth *awigglesworth@iname.com* **D:** £22.50 **S:** £22.50–£30.00 **Beds:** 1T 1S **Baths:** 1 Sh ⚲ 📺 Ⅴ ▥ 🔥

Phoenix House, *23 Gundreda Road, Lewes, E. Sussex, BN7 1PT.* Comfortable family home, quiet road, 5 minutes to town centre. **Open:** All year (not Xmas/New Year) **01273 473250** Mrs Greene *charg55@yahoo.com* **D:** £17.50–£22.50 **S:** £25.00 **Beds:** 1T 1D 1S **Baths:** 1 Pr 1 Sh ♿ �🅿 (2) ⚲ 📺 Ⅴ ▥ 🔥

Lunsford's Cross
TQ7210

Wakeford House, *Potmans Lane, Lunsford's Cross, Bexhill-on-Sea, E. Sussex, TN39 5JL.* Edwardian-style house in country setting with peaceful one acre garden. **Open:** All year **Grades:** ETC 3 Diamond, AA 4 Diamond **01424 892013** Mrs Skinner **Fax:** 01424 893978 *keltie@globalnet.co.uk* **D:** £22.50–£25.00 **S:** £25.00–£30.00 **Beds:** 3F 1D 1S 1T **Baths:** 1 En 1 Sh ♿ �🅿 (5) 📺 ♒ ✕ Ⅴ ▥ 🔥

BATHROOMS
En = Ensuite
Pr = Private
Sh = Shared

Manor Barn, *Lunsford's Cross, Bexhill on Sea, E. Sussex, TN39 5JJ.* Ensuite chalets, semi-rural setting on A269, 3 miles sea. **Open:** All year **Grades:** ETC 3 Diamond **01424 893018 (also fax)** Mrs Gillingham **D:** £16.50–£19.50 **S:** £23.50–£26.50 **Beds:** 1F 1D 1T 1S **Baths:** 4 En ☎ ▤ (6) ⌕ ▥ ▥ ▥ ♿ ♨

Maresfield
TQ4623   ◀ *The Chequers*

The Old Oast, *Underhill, Maresfield, Uckfield, E Sussex, TN22 3AY.* **Open:** Easter to Xmas
01825 768886 *stay@oldoast.demon.co.uk* **D:** £26.00–£28.00 **S:** £50.00–£52.00 **Beds:** 3D **Baths:** 2 En 1 Pr ☎ ▤ (10) ▥ ⌃ ⌕ ▥ ▥ ♦ ♨ ♨ Luxury Oast house in outstandingly beautiful rural location. 3 acres of landscaped gardens, woodland and carp pond. Relaxed atmosphere. Heated swimming pool. Ashdown Forest 2 mins. Coast 45 mins. Glyndebourne 15 mins. Most bedrooms ensuite. Children and pets welcome.

Netherfield
TQ7118

Roseneath, *Netherfield Road, Netherfield, Battle, E Sussex, TN33 9PY.* Situated in an area of outstanding natural beauty-1066 country. **Open:** All year **01424 772953** Mrs Vane *roseneath00@ mircosoft.com* **D:** £40.00–£60.00 **S:** £25.00–£30.00 **Beds:** 1T 2D **Baths:** 1 En 1 Sh ☎ ▤ ⌕ ⌃ ▥ ▥ ♨

Newick
TQ4121

Holly Lodge, *Oxbottom Lane, Newick, Lewes, E Sussex, BN8 4RA.* Georgian family house in pretty garden on outskirts of village. **Open:** All year **01825 722738 Fax:** 01825 723624 **D:** £22.50–£24.50 **S:** £25.00 **Beds:** 1F 2D 1T **Baths:** 1 En 1 Pr ☎ ▤ (6) ⌕ ▥ ▥ ♨

Pinecroft, *Allington Road, Newick, Lewes, E Sussex, BN8 4NA.* Easy reach of Lewes, Brighton, National Trust gardens and Gatwick. **Open:** All year **01825 723824 (also fax)** Mrs Thomas *diane.pinecroft@ic24.net* **D:** £36.00 **S:** £20.00 **Beds:** 1F 1T **Baths:** 1 Sh ☎ ▤ (2) ⌕ ▥ ▥ ♨

Peasmarsh
TQ8723

Kimbley Cottage, *Main Street, Peasmarsh, Rye, E. Sussex, TN31 6UL.* Friendly country house. 5 minutes' drive to historic Rye, beaches 15 minutes. **Open:** All year (not Xmas)
01797 230514 Mrs Richards **D:** £21.00–£22.00 **S:** £27.00 **Beds:** 3D **Baths:** 3 En ☎ ▤ (4) ⌕ ▥ ▥ ♨

Pett
TQ8714   ◀ *Two Sawyers, Royal Oak*

Pendragon Lodge, *Watermill Lane, Pett, Hastings, E Sussex, TN35 4HY.* Rye (near) luxury accommodation amidst Sussex countryside. Home-made bread, preserves. **Open:** All year **Grades:** ETC 5 Diamond, AA 5 Diamond
01424 814051 *pendragon_lodge@hotmail.com* www.pendragonlodge.co.uk **D:** £25.00–£30.00 **S:** £30.00–£35.00 **Beds:** 1F 1T 1D **Baths:** 3 En ☎ (5) ▤ (5) ⌕ ▥ ▥ ♨ cc

Pevensey Bay
TQ6504   ◀ *The Moorings*

Napier House, *The Promenade, Pevensey Bay, E. Sussex, BN24 6HD.* An enviable location. Glorious sea views. Rooms with balconies. **Open:** All year **01323 766242** Mrs Gregory **D:** £20.00–£25.00 **S:** £25.00–£30.00 **Beds:** 1F 2T 2D **Baths:** 2 En 2 Sh ☎ (5) ▤ (8) ▥ ⌃ ▥ ♨

Piltdown
TQ4422

Holly Farm, *Piltdown, Uckfield, E. Sussex, TN22 3XB.* Comfortable Victorian house, near Bluebell Railway, Sheffield Park, Fletching, Buxted. **Open:** All year **01825 722592 (also fax)** Ms Mayes **D:** £25.00 **S:** £25.00 **Beds:** 1F 2D **Baths:** 1 Pr 1 Sh ☎ ▤ ⌕ ▥ ♨

Playden
TQ9221

The Corner House, *Peasmarsh Road, Playden, Rye, E. Sussex, TN31 7UL.* A warm welcome awaits. Friendly country house. Excellent accommodation, hearty breakfast. **Open:** All year **Grades:** ETC 3 Diamond
01797 280439 *richardturner5@virgin.net* www.smoothhound.co.uk/hotels/corner2. html **D:** £18.00–£25.00 **S:** £20.00–£25.00 **Beds:** 1F 1D 1T **Baths:** 1 Sh ☎ ▤ (3) ⌕ ▥ ▥ ♨

Planning a longer stay? Always ask for any special rates

Plumpton Green
TQ3616

Farthings, *Station Road, Plumpton Green, Lewes, E. Sussex, BN7 3BY.* Relaxed friendly atmosphere in village setting under South Downs **Open:** All year (not Xmas) **01273 890415** M Baker **D:** £20.00–£25.00 **S:** £25.00–£30.00 **Beds:** 1T 2D **Baths:** 1 En 1 Sh ☎ ▤ ⌕ ▥ ⌃ ⌃ ▥ ▥

Punnett's Town
TQ6320

Ringwood, *Forest Lane, Punnetts Town, Heathfield, E Sussex, TN21 9JA.* Detached Victorian annexe situated in beautiful countryside. Ideal walking, cycling. **Open:** Apr to Oct **01435 830630** Mrs Batehup **D:** £22.50 **S:** £30.00 **Beds:** 1T **Baths:** 1 En ▤ (2) ▥ ▥ ♨

Ringmer
TQ4412

Gote Farm, *Gote Lane, Ringmer, Lewes, E. Sussex, BN8 5HX.* Traditional Sussex farmhouse near Glyndebourne, Newhaven, Brighton and South Downs Way. **Open:** All year (not Xmas) **01273 812303 (also fax)** Mrs Craig *janecraig@ukgateway.net* **D:** £22.50 **S:** £25.00–£30.00 **Beds:** 1D 1T 1S **Baths:** 2 Sh ☎ ▤ (4) ⌕ ▥ ▥ ♨

Robertsbridge
TQ7423   ◀ *Netherfield Arms*

Bell Cottage, *Vinehall Road, Robertsbridge, Battle, E Sussex, TN32 5JN.* C17th converted inn beamed throughout. Delightful gardens. Warm welcome assured. **Open:** All year (not Xmas) **Grades:** ETC 4 Diamond **01580 881164** Mrs Lowe **Fax:** 01580 880519 *patricia.lowe@tesco.net* www.bellcottage.co.uk **D:** £20.00–£25.00 **S:** £25.00–£30.00 **Beds:** 1D 2T **Baths:** 1 En 1 Pr 1 Sh ▤ (3) ⌕ ▥ ♨

Rye
TQ9120   ◀ *Globe Inn, Mermaid Inn, Peace & Plenty, Playden Oasts, Queen's Head, Standard Inn, Top of the Hill, Ypres Inn*

Little Saltcote, *22 Military Road, Rye, East Sussex, TN31 7NY.* Genuine welcome in Edwardian family home, generous English/vegetarian breakfasts. **Open:** All year (not Xmas) **Grades:** AA 3 Diamond **01797 223210** D Martin **Fax:** 01797 224474 *littlesaltcote.rye@virgin.net* **D:** £20.00–£24.00 **S:** £24.50–£29.00 **Beds:** 3F 2D **Baths:** 3 En 1 Sh ☎ ▤ (3) ▥ ⌃ ⌃ ⌃ ▥ ▥ ♨

Four Seasons, 96 Udimore Road, Rye, East Sussex, TN31 7DY. **Open:** All year **Grades:** ETC 4 Diamond, Silver
01797 224305 Fax: 01797 229450 coxsam@btinternet.com **D:** £18.00–£22.00 **S:** £23.00–£25.00 **Beds:** 1T 2D **Baths:** 2 En 1 Pr ☎ (10) 🄿 (3) 📺✕ 🎥 📶 ♿
Situated on Cadborough Cliffs, we have glorious views across Brede Valley to the sea. Ideal spot for touring, walking, cycling, 6 minutes walk from medieval heart of Rye. Breakfast on local organic, free-range produce. Convenient for Dover-Hastings cycle path.

The Old Vicarage, 66 Church Square, Rye, E. Sussex, TN31 7HF. Splendid Georgian house, peaceful and picturesque setting. Superb breakfast. Award hotel. **Open:** All year (not Xmas) **Grades:** AA 5 Diamond, Premier
01797 222119 Mr Masters **Fax: 01797 227466** oldvicaragerye@tesco.net www.oldvicaragerye.co.uk **D:** £30.00–£42.00 **S:** £45.00–£60.00 **Beds:** 1F 3D 1T **Baths:** 5 En ☎ (8) 🄿 (5) ⚡ 📺 📶 ♿

Magnolia House, 15 Udimore Road, Rye, E. Sussex, TN31 7DS. Situated within a few minutes walk to Rye. **Open:** All year **Grades:** RAC 3 Diamond, Sparkling
01797 222561 www.magnoliaguesthouse.co.uk **D:** £22.50–£25.00 **S:** £22.50–£25.00 **Beds:** 2F 1T 2D 1S **Baths:** 6 En ☎🄿⚡📺✕ 🎥 📶 ✱ ♿ cc

Vine Cottage, 25a Udimore Road, Rye, E Sussex, TN31 7DS. Situated in pretty gardens opposite 1066 Walk. 7 min walk town centre and station. **Open:** Apr to Oct **Grades:** ETC 3 Diamond
01797 222822 (also fax) Mrs Thomson **D:** £17.00–£18.00 **S:** £22.00–£25.00 **Beds:** 1T 1S ☎ (2) 🄿 (2) 📺 🎥 📶 ♿

Western House, 113 Winchelsea Road, Rye, E. Sussex, TN31 7EL. Charming C18th Listed house few minutes walk from town centre. **Open:** All year (not Xmas/New Year)
01797 223419 M Dellar **D:** £22.50–£25.00 **S:** £25.00–£30.00 **Beds:** 1F 1T 1T **Baths:** 3 En ☎ (10) 🄿 (3) 📺 📶 ♿

Strand House, Tanyards Lane, Winchelsea, Rye, E. Sussex, TN36 4JT. Charming C15th house, beams, inglenooks, pretty gardens, lounge, licensed, four-poster. **Open:** All year (not Xmas) **Grades:** RAC 4 Diamond, Sparkling
01797 226276 Mr & Mrs Woods **Fax: 01797 224806** strandhouse@winchelsea98.fsnet.co.uk **D:** £24.00–£36.00 **S:** £30.00–£38.00 **Beds:** 2F 7D 1T **Baths:** 9 En 1 Pr ☎ (4) 🄿 (10) ⚡ 📺 📶 ♿ cc

The Corner House, Peasmarsh Road, Playden, Rye, E. Sussex, TN31 7UL. A warm welcome awaits. Friendly country house. Excellent accommodation, hearty breakfast. **Open:** All year **Grades:** ETC 3 Diamond
01797 280439 richardturner5@virgin.net www.smoothhound.co.uk/hotels/corner2.html **D:** £18.00–£25.00 **S:** £20.00–£25.00 **Beds:** 1F 1D 1T **Baths:** 1 Sh ☎ 🄿 (3) ⚡ 📺 📶 ♿

Aviemore Guest House, 28/30 Fishmarket Road, Rye, E. Sussex, TN31 7LP. Imposing Tudor-style Victorian house, town centre 2 minute walk, situated on the A259. **Open:** All year
01797 223052 (also fax) Mr & Mrs Cogan aviemore@lineone.net www.smoothhound.co.uk/hotels/aviemore.html **D:** £20.00–£23.00 **S:** £25.00 **Beds:** 3D 4T 1S **Baths:** 4 En 2 Sh ☎ 📺 🎥 ♿ cc

Jeakes House, Mermaid Street, Rye, E. Sussex, TN31 7ET. Award-winning C16th B&B hotel in cobbled old town-centre. Traditional elegance with modern amenities. **Open:** All year
01797 222828 (also fax) Mrs Hadfield jeakeshouse@btinternet.com www.jeakeshouse.com **D:** £28.50–£48.50 **S:** £29.50–£63.00 **Beds:** 2F 8D 1T 1S **Baths:** 9 En 1 Pr 2 Sh ☎ (12) 🄿 (20) 📺 ⚡ 🎥 📶 ♿ cc

The Rise, 82 Udimore Road, Rye, E. Sussex, TN31 7DY. Pleasant comfortable house, terraced gardens, all bedrooms facing green fields to distant sea. **Open:** All year (not Xmas/New Year)
01797 222285 T E Francis therise@bb-rye.freeserve.co.uk **D:** £25.00–£30.00 **S:** £30.00–£35.00 **Beds:** 1T 3D ☎ (1) 🄿 (4) ⚡ 📺 🛏 📶 ♿

Culpeppers, 15 Love Lane, Rye, E. Sussex, TN31 7NE. 5 minutes walk Rye in quiet position adjacent countryside. Parking. **Open:** All year (not Xmas)
01797 224411 (also fax) P Ciccone peppersrye@aol.com www.rye-tourism.co.uk/culpeppers **D:** £24.00–£25.00 **S:** £23.00–£25.00 **Beds:** 1T 2S **Baths:** 1 En 1 Sh ☎⚡ 📺 🎥 📶 ♿

Rye Harbour

TQ9319

The Old Vicarage, Rye Harbour, Rye, E. Sussex, TN31 7TT. Victorian former vicarage, quietly situated, antique furniture, open fires, sumptuous breakfasts, near sea. **Open:** All year
01797 222088 Mr Bosher **D:** £19.50 **S:** £22.50 **Beds:** 1D 1T **Baths:** 1 Sh ☎🄿 (2) ⚡ 📺 🛏 🎥 📶 ♿

Seaford

TV4898 🍺 White Lion, Old Boot

Holmes Lodge, 72 Claremont Road, Seaford, East Sussex, BN25 2BJ. **Open:** All year **Grades:** ETC 3 Diamond
01323 898331 M D Parr **Fax: 01323 491346** holmes.lodge@freemail.co.uk www.seaford.co.uk/holmes/holmes.htm **D:** £20.00–£28.00 **S:** £25.00–£35.00 **Beds:** 3F 2D 1T **Baths:** 1 Pr 2 Sh ☎ 🄿 (10) ⚡ 📺 🎥 📶 ✱ ♿
Sherlock Holmes theme. Convenient for Downs, walks/cycling, Cuckmere Haven, 7 Sisters, Beachy Head, Newhaven Ferry. Beach/town/trains 300 metres, bus-stop outside, singles/groups welcome all year. Bar/restaurant adjacent. Tea/coffee in rooms. Conservatory, large garden, sea views.

Silverdale, 21 Sutton Park Road, Seaford, E. Sussex, BN25 1RH. Family run, town centre house hotel. Excellent value for money. **Open:** All year
01323 491849 Mr Cowdrey **Fax: 01323 891131** silverdale@mistral.co.uk www.mistral.co.uk/silverdale/silver.htm **D:** £13.00–£33.00 **S:** £25.00–£45.00 **Beds:** 2F 6D **Baths:** 6 En 2 Sh ☎🄿 (5) 📺 🛏 ✕ 🎥 📶 ♿ ♨ ♿ cc

Streat

TQ3515

North Acres, Streat, Hassocks, E. Sussex, BN6 8RX. Unique Victorian country house in tiny hamlet near South Downs. **Open:** All year (not Xmas)
01273 890278 (also fax) J & V Eastwood eastwood_streat@yahoo.com **D:** £20.00 **S:** £20.00–£25.00 **Beds:** 2F 2T 1S **Baths:** 3 Sh ☎🄿 (20) ⚡ 📶 ♿

Please respect a B&B's wishes regarding children, animals and smoking

Ticehurst

TQ6930

Pashley Farm, *Pashley Road, Ticehurst, Wadhurst, East Sussex, TN5 7HE.* Peaceful Victorian farmhouse with glorious views of the Sussex Weald. **Open:** All year (not Xmas/New Year)
01580 200362 Mrs Humphrey **Fax: 01580 200832** *colina@pashleyfarm.co.uk* www.pashleyfarm.co.uk **D:** £40.00 **S:** £30.00
Beds: 1T 1D **Baths:** 1 Sh ☺ 🅿 (4) ⚡ 📺 🐾 🛏.

Wadhurst

TQ6431

Spring Cottage, *Best Beech Hill, Wadhurst, E. Sussex, TN5 6JH.* Modern family house, split level. Close National Trust Properties - views! **Open:** All year (not Xmas) **Grades:** ETC 3 Diamond
01892 783896 Ms Bones **Fax: 01892 784866**
D: £18.00–£25.00 **S:** £25.00–£35.00 **Beds:** 1F 1D **Baths:** 1 En 1 Sh ☺ 🅿 (4) 📺 📺 🛏. ≛

Planning a longer stay? Always ask for any special rates

Kirkstone, *Mayfield Lane, Wadhurst, E. Sussex, TN5 6HX.* Large Victorian house with fine views in rural East Sussex. **Open:** All year (not Xmas)
01892 783204 Mr & Mrs Inman *colininman@onetelnet.uk* **D:** £20.00–£22.00 **S:** £22.00–£25.00 **Beds:** 1F 1T **Baths:** 2 Sh ☺ 🅿 (4) 📺 🛏. ≛

Willingdon

TQ5802

Butlers Gate, *24 Wish Hill, Willingdon, Eastbourne, BN20 9EX.* Attractive room, quiet family home, Victorian brass bed, sea views. **Open:** All year (not Xmas)
01323 509897 **D:** £20.00 **S:** £25.00 **Beds:** 1F **Baths:** 1 En ☺ (6) 🅿 (2) ⚡ 📺 📺 🛏. ≛

Winchelsea

TQ9017

Strand House, *Tanyards Lane, Winchelsea, Rye, E. Sussex, TN36 4JT.* Charming C15th house, beams, inglenooks, pretty gardens, lounge, licensed, four-poster. **Open:** All year (not Xmas) **Grades:** RAC 4 Diamond, Sparkling
01797 226276 Mr & Mrs Woods **Fax: 01797 224806** *strandhouse@winchelsea98.fsnet.co.uk* **D:** £24.00–£36.00 **S:** £30.00–£38.00 **Beds:** 2F 7D 1T **Baths:** 9 En 1 Pr ☺ (4) 🅿 (10) ⚡ 📺 🛏. ≛ cc

---

BEDROOMS
D = Double
T = Twin
S = Single
F = Family

West Sussex

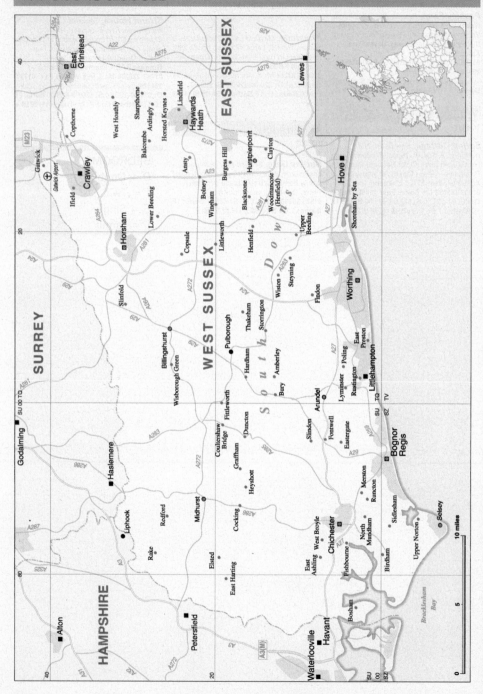

Amberley

TQ0313

Bacons, *Amberley, Arundel, W. Sussex,*
BN18 9NJ. Pretty, old cottage in the heart of the village. **Open:** All year (not Xmas)
01798 831234 Mrs Jollands **D:** £20.00
S: £20.00 **Beds:** 2T **Baths:** 1 Sh ⌂ ⌨ 🕭.

Ansty

TQ2823

Netherby,
Bolney Road,
Ansty, Haywards
Heath, W Sussex,
RH17 5AW.
Open: All year
Grades: ETC 4
Diamond
01444 455888
(also fax) Mr & Mrs Gilbert *susan@*
gilbert58.freeserve.co.uk **D:** £20.00 **S:** £25.00
Beds: 2D 1T **Baths:** 1 Sh ⌂ 🅿 (4) ⌨ ⌨ 🕭 🕭
🕭.
Cosy Victorian detached country cottage on A272. 1.25 miles from A23, convenient for Gatwick Airport, Hickstead, Ardingly Showground, Brighton, Glyndebourne Opera, Bluebell Railway and National Trust Gardens. Firm beds, full English breakfast, sinks in all rooms, warm welcome.

Ardingly

TQ3429

Stonelands
West Lodge,
Ardingly Road,
West Hoathly,
East Grinstead,
West Sussex,
RH19 4RA.
Victorian lodge
on B2028 between Turners Hill and Ardingly. Close Wakehurst Place. **Open:** All year **Grades:** ETC 3 Diamond
01342 715372 Mrs Hutchings **D:** £25.00–
£35.00 **S:** £20.00–£25.00 **Beds:** 1T 1D 1S
Baths: 1 En 1 Sh ⌂ 🅿 (2) ⌨ ⌨ 🕭 🕭 ⅊ 🕭

The Mount, *Little London, Ardingly,*
Haywards Heath, West Sussex, RH17 6TJ.
Wakehurst Place, Bluebell Railway, Ardingly Showground, South Downs, Sheffield Park. **Open:** All year (not Xmas/New Year)
01444 892252 Dr Dale **Fax: 01444 892974**
jwdale@ardingly.demon.co.uk **D:** £20.00
S: £20.00 **Beds:** 2D 2S ⌂ 🅿 ⅊ 🕭 ⌨ 🕭 🕭

BEDROOMS

D = Double
T = Twin
S = Single
F = Family

Please respect a B&B's wishes regarding children, animals and smoking

---

Arundel

TQ0106

Pindars, *Lyminster, Arundel, West Sussex,*
BN17 7QF. **Open:** All year (not Xmas/New Year) **Grades:** ETC 4 Diamond
01903 882628 (also fax) **D:** £19.00–£24.00
S: £30.00–£40.00 **Beds:** 1T 2D **Baths:** 1 En 1
Sh ⌂ (10) 🅿 (4) ⅊ ⌨ ⌨ 🕭 🕭 ⅊ cc
An excellent centre for exploring this historic area. Pindars is an attractive country house for the discerning traveller. Welcoming ambience, great home-cooking, beautiful gardens with heated swimming pool in summer. Picturesque villages, stately homes, old towns all abound nearby.

Portreeves Acre, *The Causeway,*
Arundel, W. Sussex, BN18 9JL. 3 minute from station, castle and town centre. **Open:** All year (not Xmas/New Year)
01903 883277 Mr Rogers **D:** £21.00–£23.00
S: £30.00–£35.00 **Beds:** 1F 1D 1T **Baths:** 2
En 1 Pr ⌂ (12) 🅿 (6) ⌨ 🕭 🕭 🕭

Balcombe

TQ3130 ◁ *Half Moon*

Rocks Lane Cottage, *Rowhill Lane,*
Balcombe, Haywards Heath, W. Sussex,
RH17 6JG. Stone cottage with spectacular views and private, comfortable accommodation. **Open:** All year
01444 811245 Mrs Parry **Fax: 01444 811986**
kpa@fsbdial.co.uk **D:** £25.00 **S:** £30.00–£35.00
Beds: 1D **Baths:** 1 En 🅿 (1) ⅊ ⌨ 🕭 🕭

Billingshurst

TQ0825

Groom Cottage, *Station Road,*
Billingshurst, W Sussex, RH14 9RF.
Comfortable rooms. Five minutes from station and village. English breakfast.
Open: All year (not Xmas/New Year)
01403 782285 Ms Gander **D:** £20.00–£22.50
S: £25.00–£30.00 **Beds:** 2T **Baths:** 2 En 🅿 (2)
⅊ ⌨ 🕭 🕭

Birdham

SU8200

Seldens, *Bell Lane, Birdham, Chichester,*
W. Sussex, PO20 7HY. Lovely, spacious, secluded bungalow, large attractive gardens. 2 miles beach. **Open:** All year (not Xmas)
01243 512358 Mrs Hepburn **D:** £22.50
S: £25.00 **Beds:** 2D **Baths:** 1 En 1P 🅿 (3) ⅊
⌨ ⌨ 🕭 🕭

The Red House, *Lock Lane, Birdham*
Pool, Birdham, Chichester, W Sussex,
PO20 7BB. Listed Georgian property with stunning views over Birdham Pool. Warm welcome, quiet location. **Open:** All year
01243 512488 Mrs Groom **Fax: 01243 514563**
susie.redhouse@ukonline.co.uk
www.redhousehideaway.co.uk **D:** £30.00–
£35.00 **S:** £35.00–£40.00 **Beds:** 1T 1D
Baths: 2 En 🅿 ⅊ ⌨ ✕ 🕭 🕭

Blackstone

TQ2416

Yeomans Hall, *Blackstone, Henfield, W*
Sussex, BN5 5TB. Medieval house with cottage garden. Conservation area in rural hamlet. **Open:** All year (not Xmas)
01273 494224 (also fax) Mr Kerridge *stay@*
yeomanshall.fsnet.co.uk **D:** £24.00–£27.50
S: £38.00–£40.00 **Beds:** 2D 1S **Baths:** 2 En
🅿 (2) ⅊ ⌨ ⌨ 🕭 🕭

Bognor Regis

SZ9398

Jubilee Guest
House,
Gloucester Road,
Bognor Regis, W
Sussex, PO21 1NU.
Family-run
business 75 yds
seafront, beach.
Easy reach
Brighton,
Arundel, Chichester, Portsmouth, South Downs. **Open:** All year (not Xmas/New Year) **Grades:** ETC 3 Diamond, AA 3 Diamond
01243 863016 **Fax: 01243 868017**
jubileeguesthouse@breathemail.net
www.jubileeguesthouse.com **D:** £20.00–
£35.00 **S:** £20.00–£35.00 **Beds:** 3F 1D 2S
Baths: 2 En 1 Sh ⌂ 🅿 (4) ⌨ 🕭 🕭 cc

Regis Lodge, *Gloucester Road, Bognor*
Regis, W. Sussex, PO21 1NU. Attractive seaside guest house, comfortable and clean throughout. Ideal base. **Open:** Apr to Nov **Grades:** ETC 3 Diamond, AA 3 Diamond
01243 827110 (also fax) Mr Rider *frank@*
regislodge.fsbusiness.co.uk regislodge.tripod.
com **D:** £20.00–£30.00 **S:** £20.00–£30.00
Beds: 4F 4D 4T **Baths:** 12 En ⌂ (5) 🅿 (9) ⌨ ⌨
🕭 🕭

Selwood Lodge, *93 Victoria Drive, Bognor Regis, W. Sussex, PO21 2DZ.* Friendly family hotel. Licensed bar. Games room. Garden. No restrictions. **Open:** All year **01243 865071 (also fax)** Mrs Bodle **D:** £17.00–£20.00 **S:** £20.00–£25.00 **Beds:** 2F 2D 1T **Baths:** 1 En 2 Sh ⵊⴲ▣(3) ▥⊁✕▣⚹⅋

Bolney
TQ2623

Butchers, *Ryecroft Road, Bolney, Haywards Heath, W Sussex, RH17 5PS.* Comfortable bedroom with ensuite bathroom. Breakfast room overlooking landscaped gardens. **Open:** All year (not Xmas) **01444 881503** Mrs Darby **D:** £25.00–£27.50 **S:** £30.00–£35.00 **Beds:** 1D ▣(1)⅋ ▥▦⅋

Bosham
SU8004

Good Hope, *Delling Lane, Old Bosham, Chichester, W. Sussex, PO18 8NR.* Friendly comfortable ground floor accommodation in beautiful historic harbour village. **Open:** All year (not Xmas) **Grades:** ETC 4 Diamond **01243 572487** Mrs Jones **Fax: 01243 530760 D:** £22.50–£28.00 **S:** £25.00–£45.00 **Beds:** 1T **Baths:** 1 En ▣(2)⅋▥ ▥▦⅋

Barford, *Bosham Lane, Bosham, Chichester, W Sussex, PO18 8HL.* Cottage-style bungalow near Saxon church and quay, cycle hire. **Open:** All year **Grades:** ETC 3 Diamond **01243 573393 (also fax)** Mr & Mrs Flanagan *Tony@aflanagan.freeserve.co.uk* **D:** £20.00–£22.00 **S:** £25.00–£30.00 **Beds:** 2D 1T **Baths:** 1 Sh ⵊⴲ▣(1)▥⊁✕▥▦⅋

Burgess Hill
TQ3119

The Homestead, *Homestead Lane, Valebridge Road, Burgess Hill, West Sussex, RH15 0RQ.* **Open:** All year **Grades:** ETC 4 Diamond, AA 4 Diamond **0800 0640015 & 01444 246899 Fax: 01444 241407** *homestead@burgess-hill.co.uk* www.burgess-hill.co.uk **D:** £25.00–£30.00 **S:** £25.00–£30.00 **Beds:** 1S 1D 1T 1F **Baths:** 4 En ⵊⴲ(12)▣⅋▥ ▥▦⅋⅋cc Peaceful home in 7.5 acres at end of private lane. Ground floor bedrooms with wheelchair access, Bluebell steam railway, Glyndebourne, South Downs Way, National Trust locations and gardens nearby. Railway station 1 km, Brighton, Gatwick, Lewes 15 mins. London 50 mins.

Bury
TQ0113

Pulborough Eedes Cottage, *Bignor Park Road, Bury Gate, Bury, Pulborough, W Sussex, RH20 1EZ.* Quiet country house surrounded by farmland, very warm personal welcome. **Open:** All year (not Xmas) **Grades:** ETC 4 Diamond **01798 831438 Fax: 01798 831942 D:** £22.50–£25.00 **S:** £25.00–£30.00 **Beds:** 1D 2T **Baths:** 1 En 1 Sh ⵊ▣(10) ▥⊁▦⅋⅋

Tanglewood, *Houghton Lane, Bury, Pulborough, W Sussex, RH20 1PD.* Warm welcome in our comfortable home, with beautiful views of South Downs. **Open:** All year **01798 831606 (also fax)** Mrs House **D:** £22.00–£25.00 **S:** £18.00–£20.00 **Beds:** 1D 1S **Baths:** 1 Sh ▣(3) ▥▦⚹⅋

Chichester
SU8604 ⵊ*Woody's*

Cedar House, *8 Westmead Road, Chichester, W Sussex, PO19 3JD.* Beautiful accommodation, close to city centre and many local attractions. **Open:** All year **Grades:** ETC 4 Diamond, AA 4 Diamond **01243 787771** Mr & Mrs Woodcock *mel.judi@talk21.com* **D:** £22.50–£25.00 **S:** £20.00–£25.00 **Beds:** 2D 1T 1S **Baths:** 2 En 1 Sh ▣(5)⅋▥ ▥▦⅋

112 St Pancras, *Chichester, W Sussex, PO19 4LH.* Listed Georgian town house, part converted brewery. Central Chichester. **Open:** All year **Grades:** ETC 3 Diamond **01243 789872** Mrs Jaeger **Fax: 01243 785474** *liz@jaegerl.freeserve.co.uk* freeserve.co.uk **D:** £23.00–£25.00 **S:** £25.00–£30.00 **Beds:** 2D 1S **Baths:** 1 En 1 Sh ⅋▥▥ ▦⅋

Englewood, *East Ashling, Chichester, W. Sussex, PO18 9AS.* Chichester 6 mins, easy access Bosham, theatres, Goodwood, Fishbourne, Singleton, Westdean. **Open:** All year (not Xmas) **Grades:** ETC 4 Diamond **01243 575407 (also fax)** Ms Jones *sjenglewood@tinyworld.co.uk* **D:** £23.50–£28.00 **S:** £34.00–£37.00 **Beds:** 2D **Baths:** 2 En ▣(4) ▥ ▥▦⅋

Abelands Barn, *Merston, Chichester, West Sussex, PO20 6DY.* Traditional Sussex stone barn and annexe converted into a family home by present owners. **Open:** All year (not Xmas) **Grades:** ETC 4 Diamond, Silver **01243 533826** Mr Richardson **Fax: 01243 555533 D:** £25.00–£30.00 **Beds:** 1F 1D 1T **Baths:** 3 En ⵊⴲ▣(5) ▥▦⅋cc

Riverside Lodge, *7 Market Avenue, Chichester, W. Sussex, PO19 1JU.* Traditional brick and flint house near city centre. **Open:** All year (not Xmas) **Grades:** ETC 3 Diamond **01243 783164** Mrs Tregear *tregeardavid@hotmail.com* www.riverside-lodge-chichester.co.uk **D:** £22.00–£25.00 **S:** £25.00 **Beds:** 2D **Baths:** 2 En ▣(2)⅋▦⅋

17 Grenville Gardens, *Donnington, Chichester, W. Sussex, PO19 2XB.* Petite modern accommodation quietly situated near historic Chichester. Goodwood nearby. **Open:** All year **01243 775825 (also fax)** D Johnson **D:** £20.00–£30.00 **S:** £20.00 **Beds:** 1D/T **Baths:** 1 Pr ▣(5)⅋▦⅋

Litten House, *148 St Pancras, Chichester, W. Sussex, PO19 1SH.* Unexpectedly quiet Georgian house with garden, king-sized bed; city centre. **Open:** All year **Grades:** ETC 4 Diamond **01243 774503** Mrs Steward **Fax: 01243 539187** *victoria@littenho.demon.co.uk* www.littenho.demon.co.uk **D:** £22.00–£30.00 **S:** £27.00–£35.00 **Beds:** 1F 1D 1T **Baths:** 3 Sh ⵊⵊ⅋ ▥▦⅋

Friary Close, Friary Lane, *Chichester, W Sussex, PO19 1UF.* Grade II Listed Georgian house built astride the ancient city wall in central Chichester. **Open:** All year **01243 527294** Mr & Mrs Taylor **Fax: 01243 533876** *friaryclose@argonet.co.uk* **D:** £25.00–£35.00 **S:** £35.00 **Beds:** 3T **Baths:** 3 En ▣(3) ⅋▥▦⅋cc

Please respect a B&B's wishes regarding children, animals and smoking

Clayton

TQ3014 ◀ *Jack & Jill, The Bull*

Dower Cottage, *Underhill Lane, Clayton, Hassocks, W. Sussex, BN6 9PL.* **Open:** All year (not Xmas)
01273 843363 Mrs Bailey **Fax: 01273 846503**
andy@dowerbailey.freeserve.co.uk
www.dowercottage.co.uk **D:** £27.50–£32.50
S: £35.00–£50.00 **Beds:** 2F 2D 1T 1S
Baths: 2 En 1 Sh ⌂ ▣ (8) ⊬ ▥ ▧ ▦.
Large country house in beautiful location overlooking the Sussex Weald. Ideal for walking, cycling, riding the South Downs Way yet only 15 mins from Brighton for nightlife. Library for guest use and colour TVs in all rooms. Peace and quiet away from city stress!

Cocking

SU8717

Moonlight Cottage Tea Rooms, *Chichester Road, Cocking, Midhurst, W. Sussex, GU29 0HN.* Warm welcome, pretty tea rooms/ garden, comfortable bed, excellent breakfast. **Open:** All year
01730 813336 Mrs Longland *bedtime@ moonlightcottage.net* *www.moonlightcottage. net* **D:** £20.00–£23.00 **S:** £20.00–£23.00
Beds: 2D 1T **Baths:** 1 Sh ⌂ ▣ (5) ▥ ▦.

Copsale

TQ1724

Copsale Farm, *Copsale, Horsham, W. Sussex, RH13 6QU.* C14th beamed farmhouse amid 37 acres. Rurally situated, easy access Horsham. **Open:** All year
01403 732237 Mrs Churcher **Fax: 01403 731114 D:** £20.00 **S:** £20.00 **Beds:** 1F 2D
Baths: 1 En 1 Sh ⌂ ▣ (7) ⊬ ▥ ♁ ▥ ▦.

Copthorne

TQ3139

Homesteads, *58 Church Lane, Copthorne, Crawley, W Sussex, RH10 3QF.* Semi-detached family home, warm welcome. M23 5 mins, Gatwick 8 mins. **Open:** All year
01342 713221 Mrs Nixon **D:** £20.00 **S:** £20.00
Beds: 2T **Baths:** 2 En ⌂ ▣ (2) ⊬ ▥ ▦.

BEDROOMS
D = Double
T = Twin
S = Single
F = Family

Planning a longer stay? Always ask for any special rates

Coultershaw Bridge

SU9618

The Old Railway Station, *Coultershaw Bridge, Petworth, W Sussex, GU28 0JF.* Without a doubt the most beautiful railway station in Britain. **Open:** All year
01798 342346 (also fax) Mrs Rapley *mlr@ old-station.co.uk* *www.old-station.co.uk*
D: £32.00–£47.00 **S:** £40.00–£65.00 **Beds:** 1T 5D **Baths:** 6 En ⌂ (12) ▣ (20) ⊬ ▥ ▥ ▦. & ♠ cc

Duncton

SU9517

Drifters, *Duncton, Petworth, W. Sussex, GU28 0JZ.* Quiet comfortable country house. TV, tea & coffee making facilities in rooms. **Open:** All year (not Xmas)
01798 342706 Mrs Folkes **D:** £20.00–£25.00 **S:** £25.00 **Beds:** 1D 2T 1S **Baths:** 1 En 1 Sh ▣ (3) ⊬ ▥ ✕ ▥ ▦. ♠

East Ashling

SU8207

Englewood, *East Ashling, Chichester, W. Sussex, PO18 9AS.* Chichester 6 mins, easy access Bosham, theatres, Goodwood, Fishbourne, Singleton, Westdean. **Open:** All year (not Xmas) **Grades:** ETC 4 Diamond
01243 575407 (also fax) Ms Jones *sjenglewood@tinyworld.co.uk* **D:** £23.50–£28.00
S: £34.00–£37.00 **Beds:** 2D **Baths:** 2 En ▣ (4) ▥ ▥ ▦. ♠

East Grinstead

TQ3938

Cranston House, *Cranston Road, East Grinstead, W. Sussex, RH19 3HW.* Attractive large detached house in residential area. Gatwick 15 minutes. **Open:** All year (not Xmas) **Grades:** ETC 3 Diamond
01342 323609 (also fax) Mr Linacre *accomodation@cranstonhouse.sereaming.net* *www.cranstonhouse.co.uk* **D:** £30.00–£35.00
S: £30.00–£35.00 **Beds:** 1F 2D 4T **Baths:** 7 En ⌂ (6) ▣ (6) ⊬ ▥ ♁ ▥ ▦. ♠

Grinstead Lodge Guest House, *London Road, East Grinstead, W Sussex, RH19 1QE.* Friendly family run with ample parking. Open all year round. **Open:** All year
01342 317222 (also fax) **D:** £22.00–£28.00
S: £20.00–£33.00 **Beds:** 1F 4T 2D 2S **Baths:** 7 En 1 Sh ⌂ ▣ (8) ▥ ▥ ▦. ♠ cc

---

East Harting

SU7919

Oakwood, *Eastfield Lane, East Harting, Petersfield, Hampshire, GU31 5NF.* Foot of South Downs, beautiful countryside, Chichester, Portsmouth easy reach. **Open:** All year
01730 825245 Mrs Brightwell **D:** £20.00–£22.50 **S:** £20.00–£25.00 **Beds:** 2T **Baths:** 2 Pr ▣ ⊬ ▥ ♁ ♠ ✕ ▥ ♠

East Preston

TQ0602 ◀ *Spotted Cow*

Roselea Cottage, *2 Elm Avenue, East Preston, Littlehampton, West Sussex, BN16 1HJ.* Near Goodwood, Arundel, Worthing and beach. Warm welcome, home-made bread. **Open:** All year
Grades: ETC 3 Diamond
01903 786787 Mrs Bartram **Fax: 01903 770220** *roselea.cottage@tesco.net* **D:** £20.00–£25.00 **S:** £25.00–£35.00 **Beds:** 1T 1D
Baths: 1 En 1 Pr ⌂ (12) ▣ (3) ⊬ ▥ ▦. ♠

Eastergate

SU9404

Downfields, *Level Mare Lane, Eastergate, Chichester, W Sussex, PO20 6SB.* Country house near Chichester, Arundel, Goodwood, Bognor Regis. 6m from coast, large garden. **Open:** All year (not Xmas)
01243 542012 & **01243 542306** Mrs Cane
D: £18.00–£25.00 **S:** £20.00–£27.00 **Beds:** 1T
Baths: 1 Pr ▣ (4) ⊬ ▥ ▥ ▦. ♠

Elsted

SU8119

Three, *Elsted, Midhurst, W Sussex, GU29 0JY.* Oldest house in village (1520). Pub, cricket ground, church nearby. Warm welcome. **Open:** Mar to Nov
01730 825065 Mrs Hill **Fax: 01730 825496** *rh@rhill.ftech.co.uk* **D:** £25.00 **S:** £22.50
Beds: 1D 1T 1S **Baths:** 1 Pr 1 Sh

Findon

TQ1208

The Coach House, *41 High Street, Findon, Worthing, West Sussex, BN14 0SU.* Village location in South Downs. Excellent walks/cycling. Close to coast. **Open:** All year
01903 873924 A Goble **D:** £19.50–£22.00
S: £25.00–£27.50 **Beds:** 1F 1T 1D **Baths:** 3 En ⌂ ▣ (3) ▥ ♁ ▥ ▦. ♠

Racehorse Cottage, *Nepcote, Findon, Worthing, W Sussex, BN14 0SN.* Cottage sheltering under Cissbory Rine. Breakfast provided. **Open:** All year (not Xmas)
01903 873783 Mr Lloyd **D:** £20.00 **S:** £25.00
Beds: 2T **Baths:** 1 Sh ⌂ (5) ▣ (2) ⊬ ▥ ♁ ▥ ▦. ♠ cc

Fishbourne

SU8304

Wilbury House, *Main Road, Fishbourne, Chichester, W Sussex, PO18 8AT.* Attractive home near Fishbourne Roman Palace, overlooking farmland and Bosham's picturesque harbour, 1.5 miles. **Open:** All year (not Xmas) **Grades:** AA 3 Diamond
01243 572953 (also fax) Mrs Penfold
jackie.penfold@talk21.com **D:** £22.50–£27.50
S: £25.00–£35.00 **Beds:** 1F 1D 1T 1S
Baths: 1 En 2 Sh 🏷 (5) 🅿 (4) 🕪 🕅 🐾 🕅 🖭 🛆

Fittleworth

TQ0019   🍺 *The Swan*

The Swan Inn, *Lower Street, Fittleworth, Pulborough, W Sussex, RH20 1EN.* Traditional C14th coaching inn. Home-made food and log fires. **Open:** All year
01798 865429 Fax: 01798 865721 *hotel@ swaninn.com* www.swaninn.com **D:** £30.00–£37.00 **S:** £35.00–£75.00 **Beds:** 4T 8D 3S
Baths: 15 En 🏷 🅿 (15) 🕅 ✕ 🕅 🖭 🛆 cc

Fontwell

SU9506

Woodacre, *Arundel Road, Fontwell, Arundel, W Sussex, BN18 0QP.* Set in beautiful garden surrounded by woodland. Everyone made welcome. **Open:** All year
01243 814301 Ms Richards **Fax:** 01243 814344 *wacrebb@aol.com* www.woodacre.co.uk
D: £20.00–£25.00 **S:** £20.00–£30.00 **Beds:** 1F 2T 1D **Baths:** 1 En 1 Pr 2 Sh 🏷 🅿 (20) 🕪 🕅 🐾 ✕ 🕅 🖭 🛆 🛆 cc

Gatwick

TQ2740

April Cottage, *10 Langley Lane, Ifield, Crawley, West Sussex, RH11 0NA.* Warm and friendly 200-year-old house in quiet lane, near pubs, churches, station, shops. **Open:** All year
01293 546222 Mrs Pedlow **Fax:** 01293 518712 *aprilcottage.guesthouse@tesco.net* www.aprilcottageguesthouse.co.uk
D: £22.50–£30.00 **S:** £38.00 **Beds:** 1F 1D 2T
Baths: 2 En 2 Sh 🅿 (8) 🕪 🕅 🕅 🖭 🛆

Planning a longer stay? Always ask for any special rates

Brooklyn Manor Hotel, *Bonnetts Lane, Gatwick, Crawley, W. Sussex, RH11 0NY.* Ideal location for Gatwick overnight stopover. Courtesy transport & holiday parking. **Open:** All year (not Xmas)
01293 546024 Mr Davis **Fax:** 01293 510366
D: £19.50–£26.00 **S:** £32.00–£43.50 **Beds:** 3F 4D 3T 1S **Baths:** 4 En 3 Sh 🏷 🅿 🕪 🕅 🖭 🛆 cc

Graffham

SU9217

Brook Barn, *Selham Road, Graffham, Petworth, W Sussex, GU28 0PU.* Large double bedroom with ensuite bathroom, leads directly to own conservatory. **Open:** All year (not Xmas)
01798 867356 Mr & Mrs Jollands **D:** £25.00
S: £30.00 **Beds:** 1D **Baths:** 1 En 🏷 🅿 (2) 🕅 🐾 🖭 🛆

Hardham

TQ0417

Moseley's Barn, *London Road, Hardham, Pulborough, West Sussex, RH20 1LB.* Converted C17th barn with galleried beamed hall with panoramic views of South Downs. **Open:** All year
01798 872912 (also fax) Mrs Newton
D: £22.50–£27.50 **S:** £30.00–£40.00 **Beds:** 1T 2D **Baths:** 2 En 1 Pr 🏷 (10) 🅿 🕪 🕅 🐾 🕅 🖭 🛆

Haywards Heath

TQ3324

12 Petlands Road, *Haywards Heath, W Sussex, RH16 4HH.* Homely cottage atmosphere. **Open:** All year
01444 454473 Mrs Hartley **D:** £22.00
S: £22.00 **Beds:** 1D 1T 1S **Baths:** 1 Sh 🏷 (1) 🕪 🕅 🐾 🖭 🛆

Pinehurst, *Tylers Green, Haywards Heath, W. Sussex, RH16 4BW.* Beautiful oak-beamed country house set in mature gardens backing onto nature reserve. **Open:** All year
01444 456578 Mrs O'Riordan **D:** £25.00–£35.00 **S:** £35.00–£40.00 **Beds:** 1D 2T
Baths: 4 En 🏷 (8) 🅿 (4) 🕪 🕅 🕅 🖭 🛆 🌸 🛆

Henfield

TQ2116   🍺 *George Inn, White Hart*

1 The Laurels, *Martyns Close, Henfield, West Sussex, BN5 9RQ.* Quiet village location. Easy access to Brighton, Gatwick and many places of interest. **Open:** All year
01273 493518 Mr Harrington **D:** £22.50–£30.00 **S:** £20.00–£30.00 **Beds:** 2D 1S
Baths: 2 En 1 Sh 🅿 (3) 🕅 🕅 🖭 🛆

Leeches, *West End Lane, Henfield, W Sussex, BN5 9RG.* Rural Tudor farmhouse. River and country walks. Heated swimming pool. **Open:** All year
01273 492495 Mrs Abbott **Fax:** 01273 493000
D: £22.50–£25.00 **S:** £25.00 **Beds:** 1D 2T 2S
Baths: 2 Pr 2 Sh 🏷 (5) 🅿 (6) 🕪 🕅 🐾 🖭 🛆

Heyshott

SU8917

Little Hoyle, *Hoyle Lane, Heyshott, Midhurst, W Sussex, GU29 0DX.* Comfortable, welcoming, peaceful, large garden, splendid views to South Downs, near Petworth, Goodwood, Chichester. **Open:** All year (not Xmas)
01798 867359 (also fax) Mr & Mrs Ralph
D: £23.00–£26.00 **S:** £35.00 **Beds:** 1D
Baths: 1 En 🏷 🅿 (2) 🕪 🕅 🕅 🖭 🛆

Horsham

TQ1731

The Larches, *28 Rusper Road, Horsham, West Sussex, RH12 4BD.* Friendly family house close to stations and attractive town centre. Separate visitors' entrance. **Open:** All year
01403 263392 Mrs Lane **Fax:** 01403 249980
D: £23.00–£25.00 **S:** £20.00–£25.00 **Beds:** 1F 2T 2S **Baths:** 2 En 🏷 🅿 (3) 🕅 ✕ 🖭 🌸 🛆

The Wirrals, *1 Downsview Road, Horsham, W Sussex, RH12 4PF.* Attractive detached home with a welcoming atmosphere and comfortable accommodation. **Open:** All year (not Xmas)
Grades: ETC 3 Diamond
01403 269400 (also fax) Mrs Archibald
p.archibald@lineone.net website.lineone. net/~p.archibald/webba.htm **D:** £22.00–£25.00 **S:** £22.00–£25.00 **Beds:** 1D 1S
Baths: 1 Sh 🅿 (2) 🕪 🕅 🖭 🛆

The Studio at The Hermitage, *Tower Hill, Horsham, West Sussex, RH13 7JS.* Private, self-contained, semi-rural location. 1 mile Horsham town. **Open:** All year
01403 270808 *hermitagejem@ netscapeonline.co.uk* **D:** £22.50–£27.50
S: £30.00–£35.00 **Beds:** 1T **Baths:** 1 En 🅿 (2) 🕪 🛆 🛆

Alton House, *29 Rusper Road, Horsham, W Sussex, RH12 4BA.* 15 mins Gatwick Airport, Leonardslee and Nymans Gardens, 35 minutes Worthing, Brighton. **Open:** All year
01403 211825 Mrs Ashton **D:** £22.50–£25.00
S: £35.00 **Beds:** 3D 1T **Baths:** 3 Pr 1 Sh 🏷 (1) 🅿 (4) 🕅 🐾 🖭 🛆

Please respect a B&B's wishes regarding children, animals and smoking

Horsted Keynes

TQ3827

The Croft, Lewes Road, Horsted Keynes, Haywards Heath, W Sussex, RH17 7DP. Warm welcome assured in comfortable family house situated in a quiet village location. **Open:** All year
01825 790546 Mrs Ollif **D:** £22.50–£25.00 **S:** £25.00–£30.00 **Beds:** 1T 1D **Baths:** 1 Sh
🛇 🄿 (4) ⌇ 🖾 🛏 ✕ 🖵 ⬛ ⚲

Hurstpierpoint

TQ2816   🍺 White Horse, New Inn

Bankyfield, 21 Hassocks Road, Hurstpierpoint, W. Sussex, BN6 9QH. Georgian house in Downland village. Brighton 5 miles. **Open:** All year (not Xmas/New Year)
01273 833217 Mrs Norris **D:** £23.00–£25.00 **S:** £25.00 **Beds:** 1T **Baths:** 1 Pr 🄿 (1) ⌇ ⬛

Ifield

TQ2537

April Cottage, 10 Langley Lane, Ifield, Crawley, West Sussex, RH11 0NA. Warm and friendly 200-year-old house in quiet lane, near pubs, churches, station, shops. **Open:** All year
01293 546222 Mrs Pedlow **Fax:** 01293 518712 aprilcottage.guesthouse@tesco.net www.aprilcottageguesthouse.co.uk **D:** £22.50–£30.00 **S:** £38.00 **Beds:** 1F 1D 2T **Baths:** 2 En 2 Sh 🄿 (8) ⌇ 🖾 🖵 ⬛ ⚲

Waterhall Country House, Prestwood Lane, Ifield Wood, Ifield, Crawley, W Sussex, RH11 0LA. Attractive country house set in 28 acres - ideal for Gatwick bed & breakfast. **Open:** All year (not Xmas)
01293 520002 Mrs Dawson **Fax:** 01293 539905 info@waterhall.co.uk **D:** £22.50 **S:** £35.00 **Beds:** 4D 3T 1S 2F **Baths:** 10 En 🛇 🄿 (25) ⌇ 🖾 ⬛ ⚲ cc

Lindfield

TQ3425

2 Hickmans Close, Lindfield, Haywards Heath, W Sussex, RH16 2PS. Detached house, quiet, 5 minutes walk picturesque village high street. **Open:** All year
01444 482006 Mr & Mrs Robinson **D:** £15.00–£17.50 **S:** £20.00 **Beds:** 1D 1T **Baths:** 2 Sh 🛇 (6) 🄿 (2) ⌇ 🖾 ⚲

Littlehampton

TQ0202

Victoria Hotel, 59 New Road, Littlehampton, W. Sussex, BN17 5AU. Comfortable accommodation. Warm welcome. Full English breakfast and seaside walks. **Open:** All year (not Xmas/New Year)
01903 717175 **D:** £18.00–£25.00 **S:** £20.00–£30.00 **Beds:** 2F 3D 1S **Baths:** 2 Sh 🛇 (5) 🄿 (5) 🖾 ⬛ ⚲

Littleworth

TQ1920

Pound Cottage, Mill Lane, Littleworth, Partridge Green, W. Sussex, RH13 8JU. Comfortable detached country house, warm welcome and good English breakfasts. **Open:** All year
01403 710218 Mrs Brown **Fax:** 01403 711337 poundcottagebb@amserve.net **D:** £20.00–£22.00 **S:** £20.00–£22.00 **Beds:** 1D 1T 1S **Baths:** 1 Sh 🛇 🄿 (8) ⌇ 🖾 ⬛ ⚲

Lower Beeding

TQ2128

The Old Posthouse, Plummers Plain, Lower Beeding, Horsham, W. Sussex, RH13 6NU.
Victorian house, beautiful garden, close to Leonardslee, Nymans, Bluebell Railway, Horsham, Brighton. **Open:** All year (not Xmas)
01403 891776 (also fax) Dr Crisp russell@oldposthouse.com www.oldposthouse.com **D:** £22.50 **S:** £28.00 **Beds:** 2D 2T 1S **Baths:** 6 En 🛇 🄿 (6) 🖾 🖵 ⬛ ⚲ cc

Village Pantry, Handcross Road, Plummers Plain, Lower Beeding, Horsham, W Sussex, RH13 6NU. Superb comfortable rooms, lovely garden, close Gatwick, Horsham, Brighton, Crawley. Warm welcome. **Open:** All year (not Xmas)
01403 891319 (also fax) Mrs Jays **D:** £20.00–£25.00 **S:** £26.00–£40.00 **Beds:** 1F 2D 1T 1S **Baths:** 3 En 1 Sh 🛇 🄿 (6) ⌇ 🖾 🛏 🖵 ⬛ ⚲

Lyminster

TQ0204

Pindars, Lyminster, Arundel, West Sussex, BN17 7QF. An excellent centre for exploring this historic area. Pindars is an attractive country house. **Open:** All year (not Xmas/New Year) **Grades:** ETC 4 Diamond
01903 882628 (also fax) **D:** £19.00–£24.00 **S:** £30.00–£40.00 **Beds:** 1T 2D **Baths:** 1 En 1 Sh 🛇 (10) 🄿 (4) ⌇ 🖾 ✕ 🖵 ⬛ ⚲ cc

Merston

SU8902

Abelands Barn, Merston, Chichester, West Sussex, PO20 6DY. Traditional Sussex stone barn and annexe converted into a family home by present owners. **Open:** All year (not Xmas) **Grades:** ETC 4 Diamond, Silver
01243 533826 Mr Richardson **Fax:** 01243 555533 **D:** £25.00–£30.00 **Beds:** 1F 1D 1T **Baths:** 3 En 🛇 🄿 (5) 🖾 ⬛ ⚲ cc

Midhurst

SU8821

Oakhurst Cottage, Carron Lane, Midhurst, W. Sussex, GU29 9LF. Beautiful cottage in lovely surroundings within easy reach of Midhurst amenities. **Open:** All year
01730 813523 Mrs Whitmore Jones **D:** £25.00–£30.00 **S:** £25.00–£30.00 **Beds:** 1D 1T 1S **Baths:** 1 En 1 Sh 🛇 (4) 🄿 (2) ⌇ 🖾 ⬛

North Mundham

SU8702

Enford Mead, Post Office Lane, North Mundham, Chichester, W Sussex, PO20 6JY. Welcoming family house, quiet country village, convenient Chichester, Goodwood, coast. **Open:** All year (not Xmas)
01243 783946 (also fax) Mrs Sampson **D:** £19.00–£23.00 **S:** £19.00–£25.00 **Beds:** 2D **Baths:** 2 En 🛇 🄿 (6) ⌇ 🖾 ⬛ ⚲

Poling

TQ0404

Medlar Cottage, Poling, Arundel, W. Sussex, BN18 9PT. Attractive country home in quiet village location. Restful and relaxing. **Open:** All year (not Xmas)
01903 883106 (also fax) Mr & Mrs Mercer **D:** £20.00–£22.50 **S:** £20.00–£25.00 **Beds:** 2D 1T 1S **Baths:** 1 En 2 Sh 🛇 (2) 🄿 (3) ⌇ 🖾 🛏 🖵 ⬛ ⚲

Rake

SU8027

Glendale, Hatch Lane, Rake, Liss, Hampshire, GU33 7NJ. Large family house in 4.5 acres, garden with tennis court set in country woodland. **Open:** All year (not Xmas)
01730 893451 Mrs Browse **Fax:** 01730 892626 carol@cbrowse.fsnet.co.uk **D:** £22.50–£25.00 **S:** £25.00–£30.00 **Beds:** 1D 1T 1S **Baths:** 1 En 1 Pr 🄿 ⌇ 🖾 ⬛ ⚲

Redford

SU8625

Redford Cottage, Redford, Midhurst, W Sussex, GU29 0QF. Warm welcome in old beamed cottage in quiet country location. **Open:** All year (not Xmas)
01428 741242 (also fax) C Angela **D:** £30.00–£35.00 **S:** £35.00–£40.00 **Beds:** 1T 2D **Baths:** 3 En 🄿 (10) ⌇ 🖾 ⬛ ⚲

Runcton

SU8801

Springdale Cottage, Runcton, Chichester, W Sussex, PO20 6PS. Beautiful C18th cottage in delightful gardens down country lane. **Open:** All year
01243 783912 Mr & Mrs Davey **D:** £20.00–£25.00 **S:** £20.00–£25.00 **Beds:** 1F 1T 1D 1S **Baths:** 1 En 1 Pr 1 Sh 🛇 🄿 (6) ⌇ ⬛ ⚲

Rustington

TQ0502

Kenmore Guest House, *Claigmar Road, Rustington, Littlehampton, W. Sussex, BN16 2NL.* Secluded Edwardian house in the heart of the village close to the sea. **Open:** All year
01903 784634 (also fax) Mrs Dobbs
kenmoreguesthouse@amserve.net **D:** £23.50–£26.00 **S:** £23.50–£26.00 **Beds:** 3F 3D 1T 1S **Baths:** 8 En ⮕ 🏠 (8) �🗲 🖸 ⚲ ▥, ⚲ cc

Selsey

SZ8593   🍴 *Rushmere, Lifeboat, Beaches*

St Andrews Lodge, *Chichester Road, Selsey, Chichester, W. Sussex, PO20 0LX.* Friendly family run small hotel 7 miles south of Chichester. **Open:** All year (not Xmas/New Year) **Grades:** ETC 4 Diamond **01243 606899** Mrs Kennedy **Fax: 01243 607826** *selseyrg@arunet.co.uk* **D:** £29.00–£42.00 **S:** £30.00–£50.00 **Beds:** 2F 3T 4D 1S **Baths:** 10 En ⮕ 🏠 (15) �🗲 🖸 ⚲ × 🖸 ▥, ⚲ cc

Sharpthorne

TQ3732

Saxons, *Horsted Lane, Sharpthorne, East Grinstead, W. Sussex, RH19 4HY.* Detached country house, beautiful countryside. Near National Trust properties. **Open:** All year **01342 810821** Mrs Smith *excol@aol.com*
D: £20.00–£25.00 **S:** £25.00–£30.00 **Beds:** 2D 1T **Baths:** 1 Sh 1 En ⮕ 🏠 (6) �🗲 🖸 🖸 ▥, ⚲

Shoreham-by-Sea

TQ2205

The Crabtree, *6 Buckingham Road, Shoreham-by-Sea, W. Sussex, BN43 5UA.* All rooms comfortably decorated. Close to sea front, station, local attractions. **Open:** All year
01273 463508 L B Dove **D:** £17.50–£20.00 **S:** £20.00–£25.00 **Beds:** 2F 1T 1D **Baths:** 1 Sh ⮕ 🏠 (10) �🗲 🖸 ⚲ × 🖸 ▥, ⚲

Sidlesham

SZ8597   🍴 *Black Horse, Selsey Tram*

Meadow-view, *Jury Lane, Sidlesham, Chichester, W. Sussex, PO20 7PX.* Large bungalow in acre of lovely gardens, four poster beds. **Open:** All year **Grades:** ETC 3 Diamond **01243 641316** Mrs Shepherd *shep.jen.dave@ bushinternet.com* **D:** £25.00 **S:** £28.00–£35.00 **Beds:** 3D **Baths:** 3 En 🏠 (3) 🖸 🖸 ▥, ⚲ ⚲

Planning a longer stay? Always ask for any special rates

Slindon

SU9608

Mill Lane House, *Mill Lane, Slindon, Arundel, W. Sussex, BN18 0RP.* In peaceful village on South Downs, views to coast. **Open:** All year
01243 814440 Mrs Fuente **Fax: 01243 814436**
D: £22.50 **S:** £28.50 **Beds:** 2D 1T **Baths:** 3 En ⮕ 🏠 (7) 🖸 ⚲ 🖸 ▥, ⚲

Slinfold

TQ1131

Wendys Cottage, *Five Oaks Road, Slinfold, Horsham, West Sussex, RH13 7RQ.* Farmhouse 3 miles from Horsham. Ample parking. English breakfast. **Open:** All year **01403 782326 (also fax)** **D:** £20.00–£22.50 **S:** £25.00–£30.00 **Beds:** 1F 1T **Baths:** 2 En ⮕ ▥ ⚲ 🖸 ⚲ ▥, ⚲

Steyning

TQ1711   🍴 *Star Inn, The Fountain*

Buncton Manor Farm, *Steyning Road, Wiston, Steyning, W. Sussex, BN44 3DD.* C15th partly moated farmhouse close to the South Downs Way. **Open:** All year **Grades:** ETC 4 Diamond
01903 812736 C Rowland **Fax: 01903 814838**
bunctonmanor@email.com
www.bunctonmanor.supanet.com **D:** £20.00–£22.00 **S:** £30.00 **Beds:** 1T 1D **Baths:** 1 Sh ⮕ 🏠 (5) �🗲 🖸 × 🖸 ▥, ⚲

Wappingthorn Farmhouse, *Horsham Road, Steyning, West Sussex, BN44 3AA.* Traditional farmhouse, recently refurbished, set in 2 acres of gardens. **Open:** All year **Grades:** ETC 4 Diamond **01903 813236** Mr Shapland *arianne@ wappingthorn.demon.co.uk* www.wappingthorn.demon.co.uk **D:** £22.50–£30.00 **S:** £27.50–£35.00 **Beds:** 1F 1T 1D 1S **Baths:** 4 En ⮕ 🏠 (8) �🗲 🖸 🖸 ▥,

Storrington

TQ0814

Chardonnay, *Hampers Lane, Storrington, Pulborough, W Sussex, RH20 3HZ.* Warm welcome in quiet South Downs location. Excellent home-cooked breakfast. **Open:** All year **Grades:** ETC 4 Diamond
01903 746688 Mrs Searancke *annsearancke@ bigfoot.com* **D:** £22.50–£24.50 **S:** £22.50–£24.50 **Beds:** 1T 2D **Baths:** 3 En ⮕ 🏠 (5) �🗲 🖸 ⚲ × 🖸 ▥, ⚲

Thakeham

TQ1017   🍴 *Half Moon on the Anchor*

Oak Field House, *Merrywood Lane, Thakeham, Pulborough, West Sussex, RH20 3HD.* Individual character home. Great location, rural views. Delicious breakfast. **Open:** All year (not Xmas/New Year) **01903 740843 (also fax)** Mrs Arter
D: £23.00–£28.00 **S:** £23.00–£30.00 **Beds:** 1T 1D 1S **Baths:** 2 Pr 🏠 (3) �🗲 🖸 🖸 ▥, ⚲

Upper Beeding

TQ1910

The Rising Sun, *Upper Beeding, Steyning, W. Sussex, BN44 3TQ.* **Open:** All year (not Xmas)
01903 814424 Mr & Mrs Taylor-Mason **D:** £17.00 **S:** £20.00 **Beds:** 2D 1T 2S **Baths:** 1 Sh 🏠 (20) 🖸 ⚲ × 🖸 ▥, ⚲ cc
A delightful Georgian country inn, set amidst the South Downs. Tony and Sue offer a warm welcome, fine selection of real ales and traditional home-cooked food lunchtime and evenings. Comfortable rooms, all with wash basin. Renowned full English breakfast.

West Broyle

SU8406

Primrose Cottage, *Old Broyle Road, West Broyle, Chichester, W. Sussex, PO19 3PR.* Victorian house 1.75 miles Chichester, close to theatre, Goodwood, countryside. **Open:** All year
01243 788873 Mrs Brooks **D:** £22.00–£28.00 **S:** £25.00–£44.00 **Beds:** 1T 1D 1S **Baths:** 2 Sh 🏠 (4) �🗲 🖸 🖸 ▥, ⚲

West Hoathly

TQ3632

Stonelands West Lodge, *Ardingly Road, West Hoathly, East Grinstead, West Sussex, RH19 4RA.* Victorian lodge on B2028 between Turners Hill and Ardingly. Close Wakehurst Place. **Open:** All year **Grades:** ETC 3 Diamond
01342 715372 Mrs Hutchings **D:** £25.00–£35.00 **S:** £20.00–£25.00 **Beds:** 1T 1D 1S **Baths:** 1 En 1 Sh ⮕ 🏠 (2) �🗲 🖸 ⚲ ▥, ⚲ ⚲

Wineham

TQ2320   🍴 *The Plough*

Frylands Farm, *Wineham, Henfield, W. Sussex, BN5 9BP.* Tudor farmhouse, large garden, swimming pool. Fishing available. **Open:** All year
01403 710214 Mr & Mrs Fowler www.frylands. co.uk **D:** £20.00–£23.00 **S:** £25.00 **Beds:** 1F 1T 1D **Baths:** 1 Pr 1 Sh ⮕ 🏠 (6) �🗲 🖸 🖸 ▥, ⚲

Wisborough Green

TQ0425 🍺 *Cricketers Arms, Three Crowns*

Lower Sparr Farm, *Skiff Lane, Wisborough Green, W Sussex, RH14 0AA.* Farmhouse set in quiet surroundings overlooking large garden and pastureland. **Open:** All year (not Xmas) **Grades:** ETC 4 Diamond
01403 820465 Mrs Sclater **Fax: 01403 820678**
sclater@lowersparrbb.f9.co.uk
www.lowersparrbb.f9.co.uk **D:** £23.00
S: £25.00 **Beds:** 1D 1T 1S **Baths:** 2 Pr 🐾
🅿 (4) ⌿ 📺 ✕ 🍽 🖢

Wiston

TQ1414

Buncton Manor Farm, *Steyning Road, Wiston, Steyning, W. Sussex, BN44 3DD.* C15th partly moated farmhouse close to the South Downs Way. **Open:** All year **Grades:** ETC 4 Diamond
01903 812736 C Rowland **Fax: 01903 814838**
bunctonmanor@email.com
www.bunctonmanor.supanet.com **D:** £20.00–£22.00 **S:** £30.00 **Beds:** 1T 1D **Baths:** 1 Sh 🐾
🅿 (5) ⌿ 📺 ✕ 📺 🍽 🖢

Woodmancote (Henfield)

TQ2314

The Tithe Barn, *Brighton Road, Woodmancote, Henfield, West Sussex, BN5 9ST.* Woodmancote - West Sussex. Converted flint barn with views of South Downs. **Open:** All year
01273 492986 (also fax) Mrs Warren
chriswarren@breathenet.com **D:** £18.00–£25.00
S: £18.00–£25.00 **Beds:** 2T 1S **Baths:** 1 Sh
🐾 🅿 (3) ⌿ 📺 ✈ 📺 🍽 🖢

BATHROOMS
En = Ensuite
Pr = Private
Sh = Shared

Worthing

TQ1303 🍺 *Charles Dickens*

Rosedale House, *12 Bath Road, Worthing, W. Sussex, BN11 3NU.* Delightful Victorian house run by friendly Nightingale. **Open:** All year
01903 233181 Mrs Nightingale *rosedale@amserve.net* **D:** £24.00–£26.50 **S:** £25.00–£33.00 **Beds:** 1T 1D 1S **Baths:** 1 En 2 Pr 1 Sh
🐾 ⌿ 📺 🍽 🖢

Marina, *191 Brighton Road, Worthing, W Sussex, BN11 2EX.* Charming Victorian house offering comfortable accommodation set in seafront location. **Open:** All year (not Xmas/New Year)
01903 207844 *marinaworthing@aol.com*
D: £22.50–£26.00 **S:** £22.50–£40.00 **Beds:** 1F 1T 1D 2S **Baths:** 1 En 4 Sh 🐾 ⌿ 📺 📺 🍽 🖢 cc

Tudor Lodge, *25 Oxford Road, Worthing, W. Sussex, BN11 1XQ.* Victorian house near amenities for warm welcome and excellent breakfast. **Open:** All year (not Xmas)
01903 234401 Mrs Colbourn **D:** £18.00–£20.00 **S:** £18.00–£20.00 **Beds:** 1D 1T 1S
Baths: 1 Sh 🐾 🅿 (2) ⌿ 📺 📺 🍽 🖢

Merton Guest House, *96 Broadwater Road, Worthing, W Sussex, BN14 8AW.* Friendly and attentive service with high standard accommodation. **Open:** All year **Grades:** ETC 3 Diamond
01903 238222 (also fax) Mr Smith *stay@mertonhouse.freeserve.co.uk* **D:** £26.00–£28.00 **S:** £27.50–£35.00 **Beds:** 3D 1T 1S **Baths:** 5 En 🐾 (8) 🅿 (5) ⌿ 📺 ✕ 📺 🍽 🖢 cc

Manor Guest House, *100 Broadwater Road, Worthing, West Sussex, BN14 8AN.* Detached cottage-style house. Ideally situated for business and pleasure.
Open: All year
01903 236028 Mr Emms **Fax: 01903 230404**
stay@manorworthing.com
www.manorworthing.com **D:** £20.00–£30.00
S: £20.00–£35.00 **Beds:** 2F 3D 1S **Baths:** 3 En 1 Sh 🐾 🅿 (8) ⌿ 📺 ✈ 📺 🍽 🖢 cc

Teesside

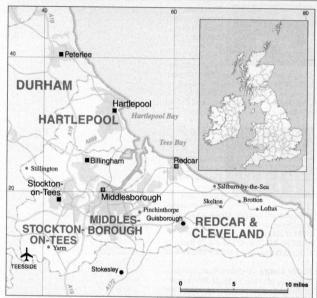

Redcar

NZ6124

Central Private Hotel, 44 Queen Street, Redcar, TS10 1BD. Centre of town, near race course, station golf club, pubs, beach. **Open:** All year
01642 482309 D: £16.00–£24.00 **S:** £18.00–£27.00 **Beds:** 5F 10T 5D 5S **Baths:** 9 En 5 Pr 5 Sh ⊗ 🖾 🖵 🖳 🕸

Saltburn-by-the-Sea

NZ6722 ⬥ The Spa , The Ship

Westerlands Guest House, 27 East Parade, Skelton, Saltburn-by-the-Sea, N. Yorks, TS12 2BJ. Large modern detached house, beautiful views sea/countryside, alongside Cleveland way long-distance path. **Open:** Mar to Oct
01287 650690 Mr Bull **D:** £15.00 **S:** £15.00
Beds: 6F 3D 3S **Baths:** 3 Pr ⊗ 🖸 (5) ⊭ 🖾 🕈 ✕ 🖾 🖳 🕸

Merhba, 11 Dundas Street, Saltburn-by-the-Sea, Teesside, TS12 1BL. Warm welcome. Full English breakfast. Ideal centre for touring area. **Open:** Feb to Dec
01287 622566 pcookmerhba@ntlworld.co.uk
D: £14.00–£16.00 **S:** £15.00–£17.00 **Beds:** 1F 1T 1D 1S **Baths:** 4 Sh ⊗ 🖸 🖾 🕈 🖾 🖳 🕸

Runswick Bay Hotel, Runswick Bay, Saltburn-by-the-Sea, Cleveland, TS13 5HR. In well-known village of Runswick Bay and within North York Moors National Park. **Open:** All year (not Xmas/New Year)
01947 840997 D: £22.50–£25.00 **S:** £25.00–£28.00 **Beds:** 1F 1T 4D **Baths:** 6 En ⊗ 🖸 🖾 🕈 ✕ 🖾 🖳 🕸 cc

Skelton (Saltburn)

NZ6518 ⬥ The Spa, The Ship

Westerlands Guest House, 27 East Parade, Skelton, Saltburn-by-the-Sea, N. Yorks, TS12 2BJ. Large modern detached house, beautiful views sea/countryside, alongside Cleveland way long-distance path. **Open:** Mar to Oct
01287 650690 Mr Bull **D:** £15.00 **S:** £15.00
Beds: 6F 3D 3S **Baths:** 3 Pr ⊗ 🖸 (5) ⊭ 🖾 🕈 ✕ 🖾 🖳 🕸

Brotton

NZ6820

Hunley Hall Lodge, Hunley Hall Golf Club and Hotel, Brotton, Saltburn-by-the-Sea, TS12 2QQ. **Open:** All year
Grades: AA 2 Star Hotel
01287 676216 E Lillie **Fax: 01287 678250**
enquiries@hunleyhall.co.uk www.hunleyhall.co.uk **D:** £30.00–£33.00 **S:** £30.00–£40.00
Beds: 1F 5T 2D **Baths:** 8 En ⊗ 🖸 (80) 🖾 🖾 🖳 ⅙ cc
Occupying a peaceful country location with unrivalled panoramic views of the golf course and dramatic coastline. Family owned and run hotel with professional, yet informal friendly service, well-equipped bedrooms and a wide selection of quality meals and beverages.

The Arches Hotel, Birkbeck Low Farm, Brotton, Saltburn-by-the- Sea, TS12 2QX. Beautiful coastal and golf course views. Special terms for long stays. **Open:** All year
01287 677512 Fax: 01287 677150 birkralysc@aol.com www.gorally.co.uk **D:** £20.00–£30.00
S: £30.00–£35.00 **Beds:** 11F 5T 6D **Baths:** 22 Pr 🖸 (20) ⊭ 🖾 🖾 🖳 🕸 cc

Loftus

NZ7118

White Horse Inn, 73 High Street, Loftus, Saltburn-by-the-Sea, TS13 4HG. Friendly village pub near to Yorkshire moors and seaside. **Open:** All year (not Xmas)
01287 640758 C Rowe **D:** £15.00–£18.00
S: £15.00–£18.00 **Beds:** 2F 1T **Baths:** 1 En 1 Sh ⊗ 🖸 (5) 🖾 🕈 ✕ 🖾 🖳 🕸

Middlesbrough

NZ5118

White House Hotel, 311 Marton Road, Middlesbrough, TS4 2HG. Family run, close to centre, good English breakfast, car parking. **Open:** All year
01642 244531 D: £15.00–£17.50 **S:** £18.50–£22.00 **Beds:** 2F 2D 6T 5S **Baths:** 4 En 3 Sh ⊗ 🖾 🕈 🖳 🕸

Pinchinthorpe (Middlesbrough)

NZ5418

Pinchinthorpe Hotel, Pinchinthorpe, Guisborough, TS14 8HG. In N Yorks National Park close to Heartbeat & Herriot country **Open:** All year
01287 630200 (also fax) G Tinsley **D:** £45.00–£65.00 **S:** £65.00–£85.00 **Beds:** 6D **Baths:** 6 En 🖸 🖾 ✕ 🖳 ⅙ 🕸

Wharton Arms Hotel, High Street, Skelton (Saltburn), Saltburn-by-the-Sea, N. Yorks, TS12 2DY. Friendly pub 3 miles from North York moors. 2 miles from Saltburn.
Open: All year (not Xmas/New Year)
Grades: ETC 2 Diamond
01287 650618 Ms Cummings **D:** £20.00
S: £20.00 **Beds:** 1F 2T 1D 1S **Baths:** 5 En ✋
🅿 (15) 📺 ✖ 📖 ✠

Stillington

NZ3724

Post Office House, Redmarshall Street, Stillington, Stockton-on-Tees, Cleveland, TS21 1JS. Spacious modern rooms. Private entrance with own keys. **Open:** All year
01740 630301 (also fax) *harewood@tesco.net*
D: £20.00 **S:** £25.00 **Beds:** 2D **Baths:** 2 En 📺
📖, ✠

Yarm

NZ4112

2 Valley Close, Yarm, Cleveland, TS15 9SE. Friendly, comfortable, modern, detached house in peaceful wooded surroundings.
Open: All year (not Xmas)
01642 780633 Mrs Bond **D:** £23.00–£30.00
S: £23.00–£30.00 **Beds:** 1T 2S 1D **Baths:** 1 En 1 Sh ✋ (5) 🅿 (2) ✗ 📺 Ⓥ 📖, ✠

Tyne & Wear

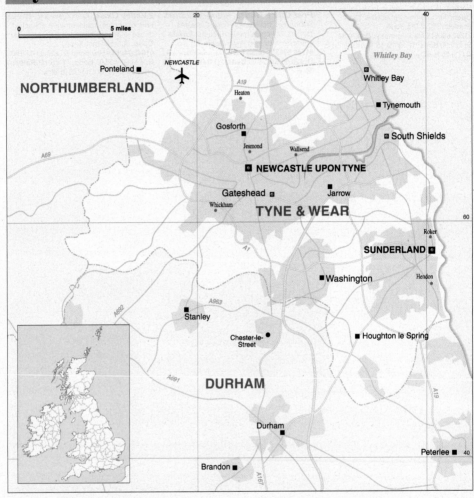

NORTHUMBERLAND

Ponteland ■

NEWCASTLE ✈

A19

Heaton

Gosforth ■

Jesmond

Wallsend

◙ **NEWCASTLE UPON TYNE**

Gateshead ◙

Whickham

Jarrow ■

TYNE & WEAR

Whitley Bay

■ Whitley Bay

■ Tynemouth

◙ South Shields

A69

Roker

SUNDERLAND ◙

■ Washington

Hendon

A1

A692

A963

Stanley ■

Chester-le-
Street ●

DURHAM

■ Houghton le Spring

A691

A19

Durham ■

Peterlee ■

Brandon ■

A167

Planning a longer stay? Always
ask for any special rates

Gateshead

NZ2561

Bellevue Guest House, *31-33 Belle Vue
Bank, Low Fell, Gateshead, NE9 6BQ.*
Victorian terrace, centrally located for
Metro Centre, Newcastle stadium, Beamish
Museum. **Open:** All year
0191 487 8805 Mr Wallace **D:** £18.00–£20.00
S: £18.00–£28.00 **Beds:** 1F 1D 2T 2S
Baths: 2 En 1 Sh ⮂ ❒ ☑ ✕ Ⓥ ▥ ⭗ ☙

Cox Close House, *Ravensworth,
Gateshead, NE11 0HQ.* Unique C16th
building. Secluded yet near city and tourist
attractions. **Open:** All year
0191 488 7827 *johnpat@
grayravensworth.freeserve.co.uk* **D:** £18.00–
£22.00 **S:** £18.00–£22.00 **Beds:** 1F 1D 1T
Baths: 1 En 1 Sh ⮂ ❒ ⇙ ☑ ⛐ ☼ ✕ Ⓥ ▥ ☙

Hendon

NZ3956

Acorn Guest House, *10 Mowbray Road,
Hendon, Sunderland, SR2 8EN.* Situated near
town centre, Mowbray Park and all local
amenities. **Open:** All year
0191 514 2170 A Morrison
theacornguesthouse@hotmail.com **D:** £15.00
S: £16.00 **Beds:** 3F 5T 1D ⮂ ❒ (9) ☑ ⛐ ✕ Ⓥ
▥ ☙

Jesmond

NZ2566

Grosvenor Hotel, *24-28 Grosvenor Road, Jesmond, Newcastle-upon-Tyne, NE2 2RR.* Ideally situated to explore Newcastle-upon-Tyne and experience its legendary nightlife. **Open:** All year
0191 281 0543 Fax: 0191 281 9217 D: £35.00–£45.00 **S:** £35.00–£45.00 **Beds:** 3F 25T 11D 14S **Baths:** 53 En ⇨ (7) ⊠ 🎟 ⚓ cc

Roker

NZ4059 🍺 *Queen Vic*

8 St Georges Terrace, *Roker, Sunderland, SR6 9LX.* Friendly, family run guest house near seafront and city centre. **Open:** All year **Grades:** ETC 3 Diamond **0191 567 2438** R L Dawson
belmontguesthouse@hotmail.com
www.belmontguesthouse.com **D:** £17.00–£19.00 **S:** £20.00–£28.00 **Beds:** 2F 2T 2D 1S **Baths:** 3 En 2 Sh ⇨ ⊠ 🎟 ⚓ cc

South Shields

NZ3666

Saraville Guest House, *103 Ocean Road, South Shields, NE33 2JL.* Family-run & centrally located. Close to Metro. **Open:** All year
0191 454 1169 (also fax) Mrs Taylor *emma@saraville.freeserve.co.uk* **D:** £20.00 **S:** £25.00–£28.00 **Beds:** 1F 1D 1T 2S **Baths:** 3 En ⇨ (6) 🅿 ⮠ ⊠ 🎟 ⚓

Sunderland

NZ3957

Braeside Guest House, *26 Western Hill, Beside University, Sunderland, SR2 7PH.* Experience our unique theme rooms, hearty northern breakfasts, Northumbria's beautiful countryside. **Open:** Jan to Nov **0191 565 4801 Fax: 0191 552 4198** *george@the20thhole.co.uk* www.the20thhole.co.uk **D:** £15.00–£17.50 **S:** £18.00–£23.00 **Beds:** 2T 1D **Baths:** 1 En 1 Sh ⇨ (12) 🅿 ⊠ 🎟 ⚓

BATHROOMS
En = Ensuite
Pr = Private
Sh = Shared

Wallsend

NZ3066 🍺 *Anson Pub, Hadrian Lodge Hotel*

Imperial Guest House, *194 Station Road, Wallsend, Newcastle-upon-Tyne, NE28 8RD.* Behind the unassuming terraced frontage lies a guest house with a difference. **Open:** All year **Grades:** ETC 4 Diamond, AA 4 Diamond **0191 236 9808 (also fax)** Mr Brownlee
enquiries@imperialguesthouse.co.uk
www.imperialguesthouse.co.uk **D:** £20.00–£25.00 **S:** £20.00–£35.00 **Beds:** 1T 1D **Baths:** 1 En 1 Sh ⇨ (12) ⊠ ✕ 🎟 ⚓

Whickham

NZ2161

East Byermoor Guest House, *Fellside Road, Whickham, Newcastle upon Tyne, NE16 5BD.* Formal farmhouse. Rural location. Convenient for cities and coast. **Open:** All year **Grades:** ETC 4 Diamond
01207 262687 *eastbyermoor-gh.arbon@virgin.net* **D:** £22.00–£25.00 **S:** £22.00–£25.00 **Beds:** 2T 4D **Baths:** 5 En 1 Pr ⇨ 🅿 (13) ⮠ ⊠ 🎟 ⚓ 🎟 cc

Whitley Bay

NZ3572 🍺 *Fitzgeralds*

Park Lodge Hotel, *160-164 Park Avenue, Whitley Bay, NE26 1AU.* **Open:** All year (not Xmas/New Year)
0191 253 0288 *parklodgehotel@hotmail.com*
www.the-parklodgehotel.co.uk **D:** £25.00–£30.00 **S:** £50.00–£55.00 **Beds:** 3F 4T 5D 4S **Baths:** 16 En ⇨ 🅿 (8) ⮠ ⊠ ✕ 🎟 ⚓ cc
You are assured a warm welcome in friendly, relaxed accommodation. An excellent location for business and pleasure. Close to Newcastle and surrounding business districts. Discover the delights of Northumbria's plentiful castles, beaches and Roman ruins. Sea views from some rooms.

BEDROOMS
D = Double
T = Twin
S = Single
F = Family

Cherrytree House, *35 Brook Street, Whitley Bay, NE26 1AF.* Edwardian town house near sea front in a quiet street. **Open:** All year **Grades:** AA 3 Diamond **0191 251 4306 (also fax)** Mr Coleman
cherrytreehouse@cherrytreehouse.free-online.co.uk
D: £16.00–£25.00 **S:** £20.00–£35.00 **Beds:** 1F 2T 2D 2S **Baths:** 1 En 3 Pr ⊠ 🎟 ⚓ 🎟 ✳ ⚓

The Lindsay Guest House, *50 Victoria Avenue, Whitley Bay, NE26 2BA.* Small family-run guest house, overlooking tennis courts and bowling green. **Open:** All year **0191 252 7341** A Ward **Fax: 0191 252 7505** *info@lindsayguesthouse.co.uk*
www.lindsayguesthouse.co.uk **D:** £20.00–£25.00 **S:** £25.00–£30.00 **Beds:** 4F 2D **Baths:** 4 En 2 Sh ⇨ 🅿 (3) ⊠ 🎟 ⚓

Marlborough Hotel, *20-21 East Parade, Whitley Bay, NE26 1AP.* Traditional family hotel on sea front overlooking the beach, 5 mins' walk town centre. **Open:** All year (not Xmas)
0191 251 3628 J A Thompson **Fax: 0191 252 5033** *reception@marlborough-hotel.com*
www.marlborough-hotel.com **D:** £28.00–£32.00 **S:** £22.00–£38.00 **Beds:** 4F 5D 3T 5S **Baths:** 14 En 1 Pr 2 Sh ⇨ (3) 🅿 (5) ⮠ ⊠ ✕ 🎟 🎟 & 3 ⚓ cc

Metro Guest House, *26 Percy Road, Whitley Bay, NE26 2AX.* A comfortable and friendly guest house in the centre of Whitley Bay. **Open:** All year
0191 253 0123 E Douglas **D:** £14.00–£15.00 **S:** £14.00–£15.00 **Beds:** 2F 1T 2S **Baths:** 2 Sh ⇨ 🅿 (3) ⊠ 🎟 ✕ 🎟 ⚓

RATES
D = Price range per person sharing in a double or twin room
S = Price range for a single room

Warwickshire

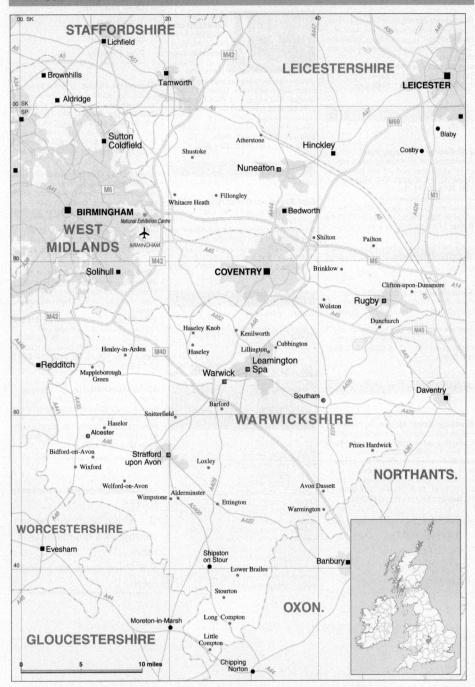

STILWELL'S BRITAIN: BED & BREAKFAST

Alcester

SP0857

Roebuck Inn, Birmingham Road, Alcester, Warks, B49 5QA. Traditional country inn, non-smoking, restaurants, excellent food, beer, beds. **Open:** All year
01789 762410 Fax: 01789 765794 D: £22.50–£30.00 **S:** £35.00–£45.00 **Beds:** 1F 6D 4T **Baths:** 11 En ⓢ ⓟ ⓚ ⓣⓥ ⓧ ⓥ Ⓜ ⓐ ⁂ ⓔ

Orchard Lawns, Wixford, Alcester, Warks, B49 6DA. Delightful house and grounds in small village, ideal touring centre. **Open:** All year (not Xmas) **Grades:** ETC 4 Diamond, Silver
01789 772668 Mrs Kember
margaret.orchardlawns@farmersweekly.net
D: £22.00–£25.00 **S:** £22.00–£25.00 **Beds:** 1D 1T 1S **Baths:** 1 En 1 Sh ⓟ (6) ⓚ ⓥ ⓣ Ⓜ

Alderminster

SP2248 ⬥ The Bell

Stour View, Alderminster, Stratford-upon-Avon, Warwickshire, CV37 8NY. Country bungalow, quiet, private accommodation. Central for Warwick, Cotswolds and Stratford-upon-Avon. **Open:** All year (not Xmas/New Year)
01789 450593 (also fax) Mrs Moody
moody.stourview@btinternet.com **D:** £17.50–£19.50 **S:** £25.00–£30.00 **Beds:** 1T **Baths:** 1 En ⓟ (3) ⓚ ⓥ ⓥ Ⓜ ⓐ ⓔ

Atherstone

SP3197

Manor Farm, Ratcliffe Culey, Atherstone, Warks, CV9 3NY. Victorian house located in small quiet friendly village in beautiful countryside. **Open:** All year
01827 712269 Mrs Trivett *jane@ousbey.com*
D: £17.00–£18.00 **S:** £20.00 **Beds:** 3D **Baths:** 2 Sh ⓢ ⓟ (3) ⓚ ⓣ ⓧ Ⓜ ⓔ cc

Abbey Farm, Merevale Lane, Atherstone, Warks, CV9 2LA. Period farmhouse in attractive surroundings, by a lake, set in beautiful countryside. **Open:** All year (not Xmas)
01827 713119 Mrs Noble *merevale_abbey@msn.com* **D:** £20.00–£22.50 **S:** £22.50–£25.00 **Beds:** 2T **Baths:** 1 Sh ⓢ (8) ⓟ (3) ⓚ ⓥ Ⓜ ⓔ

Planning a longer stay? Always ask for any special rates

All details shown are as supplied by B&B owners in Autumn 2001

Avon Dassett

SP4150

Crandon House, Avon Dassett, Leamington Spa, Warks, CV33 0AA. Luxury farmhouse accommodation, quiet location, superb views, extensive breakfast menu. **Open:** All year (not Xmas) **Grades:** ETC 5 Diamond, Silver
01295 770652 Miss Lea **Fax: 01295 770632**
crandonhouse@talk21.com www.crandonhouse.co.uk **D:** £20.00–£26.00 **S:** £30.00–£35.00 **Beds:** 3D 2T **Baths:** 4 En 1 Pr ⓢ (8) ⓟ (8) ⓥ ⓥ Ⓜ ⓔ cc

Barford

SP2760

Avonside Cottage, 1 High Street, Barford, Warwick, CV35 8BU. C17th riverside cottage. Luxurious and spacious guest rooms. Delightful garden. **Open:** All year (not Xmas)
01926 624779 D: £23.00–£27.00 **Beds:** 1D 1T **Baths:** 2 En ⓟ (4) ⓚ ⓥ ⓥ Ⓜ ⓔ

Bidford-on-Avon

SP0952 ⬥ Frog & Bullrush, Cottage of Content

Forsbrook House, 4 High Street, Bidford-on-Avon, Alcester, Warks, B50 4BU. Welcoming period house in riverside village. Ideal touring centre. **Open:** All year (not Xmas) **Grades:** ETC 4 Diamond
01789 772327 Mr & Mrs Newbury
www.smoothhound.co.uk/hotels/fosbroke.html **D:** £22.00–£25.00 **S:** £25.00–£30.00 **Beds:** 1F 2D 1T 1S **Baths:** 5 En ⓢ ⓟ (8) ⓥ ⓥ Ⓜ ⓔ

Brinklow

SP4379

The White Lion, Broad Street, Brinklow, Rugby, Warks, CV23 0LN. A warm welcome awaits you at our traditional country inn. **Open:** All year
01788 832579 Mr Yeend *brinklowlion@aol.com*
www.thewhitelion-inn.co.uk **D:** £20.00
S: £25.00 **Beds:** 1D 3T **Baths:** 4 En ⓢ ⓟ ⓥ ⓧ Ⓜ ⓐ ⓔ

Clifton-upon-Dunsmore

SP5376

Dunsmore Home Farm, Watling Street, Clifton-upon-Dunsmore, Rugby, Warks, CV23 0AQ. Victorian farmhouse in Warwickshire countryside. Rugby and motorways 3 miles. **Open:** All year (not Xmas/New Year)
01788 860168 (also fax) Ms Yates **D:** £20.00–£22.00 **S:** £24.00–£25.00 **Beds:** 1F 1T 1D **Baths:** 3 En 1 Sh ⓢ ⓟ ⓥ Ⓜ ⓔ

Cubbington

SP3468

Bakers Cottage, 52/54 Queen Street, Cubbington, Leamington Spa, CV32 7NA. C17th cottage. Ideal sightseeing base for Leamington Spa, Warwick, Stratford. **Open:** All year
01926 772146 E Soden **D:** £20.00–£23.00 **S:** £20.00–£25.00 **Beds:** 3T **Baths:** 2 En 1 Pr ⓢ ⓟ (4) ⓚ ⓥ ⓣ ⓥ Ⓜ ⓔ

Dunchurch

SP4871

Toft Hill, Dunchurch, Rugby, Warks, CV22 6NR. Country house situated on outskirts of picturesque village of Dunchurch. **Open:** All year **Grades:** ETC 4 Diamond
01788 810342 Mary Wells **D:** £22.50 **S:** £22.50 **Beds:** 1F 1D 1S **Baths:** 1 Pr 1 Sh ⓢ ⓟ ⓥ ⓣ Ⓜ ⓔ

Ettington

SP2648

Thornton Manor, Ettington, Stratford upon Avon, Warks, CV37 7PN. Friendly welcome to working farm in quiet relaxing C16th home. **Open:** Easter to Dec
01789 740210 Mrs Hutsby **D:** £21.00–£25.00 **S:** £25.00–£30.00 **Beds:** 2D 1T **Baths:** 2 En 1 Pr ⓢ (5) ⓟ (4) ⓚ ⓥ Ⓜ ⓔ

The Leys, 64 Banbury Road, Ettington, Stratford-upon-Avon, Warks, CV37 7SU. Comfortable stylish family village home tastefully decorated. Excellent full English breakfast. **Open:** All year (not Xmas/New Year)
01789 740365 & 07836 366615 (M)
Mrs Brewer **Fax: 01789 740365** *bobbrewer@beeb.net* **D:** £18.00–£20.00 **S:** £20.00–£25.00 **Beds:** 1D 1T **Baths:** 2 Pr ⓢ (10) ⓟ (2) ⓚ ⓥ Ⓜ ⓔ

Fillongley

SP2887

Bourne Brooke Lodge, Mill Lane, Fillongley, Coventry, W Mids, CV7 8EE. Peace and tranquillity, high standards of comfort and cleanliness, no smoking **Open:** All year
01676 541898 (also fax) Mrs Chamberlain
D: £20.00–£25.00 **S:** £20.00–£30.00 **Beds:** 1D 2T 1S **Baths:** 3 En ⓟ (6) ⓚ ⓥ Ⓜ ⁂ ⓔ

Haseley

SP2268

Shrewley Pools Farm, *Haseley, Warwick, CV35 7HB.* Glorious early C17th Listed farmhouse, beautiful 1 acre gardens. Working farm. **Open:** All year (not Xmas) **01926 484315** Mrs Dodd **D:** £22.50–£30.00 **S:** £30.00–£35.00 **Beds:** 1F 1T **Baths:** 2 En 🛏 🅿 (6) ⌁ 🆅 ✕ 🆅 🔥

Haseley Knob

SP2371

Croft Guest House, *The Croft, Haseley Knob, Warwick, CV35 7NL.* Friendly family country guest house. Near Warwick, Coventry, Stratford, NEC/NAC. **Open:** All year (not Xmas) **Grades:** ETC 4 Diamond **01926 484447 (also fax)** Mr & Mrs Clapp *david@croftguesthouse.co.uk* www.croftguesthouse.co.uk **D:** £23.00–£25.00 **S:** £34.00–£35.00 **Beds:** 2F 3D 3T 1S **Baths:** 7 En 2 Pr 🛏 🅿 (8) ⌁ 🆅 🔥 🍴 ▥ 🔥 cc

Haselor

SP1257 🍺 *King's Head*

Walcote Farm, *Walcote, Haselor, Alcester, Warks, B49 6LY.* C16th oak-beamed farmhouse in tranquil picturesque hamlet. **Open:** All year **Grades:** ETC 4 Diamond **01789 488264 (also fax)** Mr & Mrs Finnemore *john_finnemore@compuserve.com* **D:** £21.00–£24.00 **S:** £28.00–£34.00 **Beds:** 1T 2D **Baths:** 3 En 🅿 (6) ⌁ 🆅 🔥 🔥

Henley-in-Arden

SP1566

Holland Park Farm, *Buckley Green, Henley-in-Arden, Solihull, W Mids, B95 5QF.* **Open:** All year **01564 792625 (also fax)** Mrs Connolly **D:** £25.00 **S:** £30.00 **Beds:** 2F **Baths:** 2 En 🛏 🅿 (4) 🆅 🔥 🍴 ▥ 🔥 A Georgian-style house set in centre of peaceful farmland including the historic grounds of the mount and other interesting walks. Ideally situated in Shakespeare country. Convenient to airport NEC NAC and Cotswolds. Closed on Christmas day. H of E 3 stars.

Kenilworth

SP2872 🍺 *Clarendon Arms, Virgin & Castle, Queen & Castle*

Banner Hill Farm, *Rouncil Lane, Kenilworth, Warks, CV8 1NN.* Homely Georgian farmhouse. Middle of nowhere. No distance from anywhere. **Open:** All year (not Xmas) **01926 852850** Mr Snelson **D:** £16.00–£20.00 **S:** £16.00–£25.00 **Beds:** 1F 1D 2T 2S **Baths:** 3 En 1 Pr 2 Sh 🛏 🅿 (8) ⌁ 🆅 🔥 ✕ 🆅 ▥ 🔥

The Cottage Inn, *36 Stoneleigh Road, Kenilworth, Warks, CV8 2GD.* Friendly family-run free house - great traditional ales and fine wines. Real home-cooked specials. **Open:** All year **Grades:** ETC 3 Diamond **01926 853900** Mr Jones **Fax: 01926 856032** **D:** £18.00–£25.00 **S:** £30.00 **Beds:** 4D 2T **Baths:** 6 En 🛏 🅿 (20) 🆅 ✕ 🆅 ▥ 🔥 cc

Howden House, *170 Warwick Road, Kenilworth, CV8 1HS.* Comfortable home conveniently located for Warwick University, NAC, NEC, Airports. **Open:** All year (not Xmas) **Grades:** ETC 2 Diamond **01926 850310** Mrs Allen **D:** £18.00–£20.00 **S:** £20.00–£24.00 **Beds:** 1D 1T 2S 🛏 ⌁ 🆅 🆅 ▥ 🔥 🔥

Hollyhurst Guest House, *47 Priory Road, Kenilworth, Warks, CV8 1LL.* Friendly, relaxed atmosphere in comfortable Victorian town house near centre. **Open:** All year (not Xmas) **Grades:** AA 3 Diamond **01926 853882** Mr & Mrs Wheat **Fax: 01926 855211** *admin@hollyhurstguesthouse.co.uk* www.hollyhurstguesthouse.co.uk **D:** £20.00–£22.50 **S:** £25.00–£30.00 **Beds:** 1F 2D 4T 1S **Baths:** 3 Pr 2 Sh 🛏 🅿 (7) ⌁ 🆅 ▥ 🔥

Victoria Lodge Hotel, *180 Warwick Road, Kenilworth, CV8 1HU.* Built in 1850, completely refurbished luxury accommodation, beautiful Victorian walled garden. **Open:** All year (not Xmas) **01926 512020** Mr Woolcock **Fax: 01926 858703** *info@victorialodgehotel.co.uk* www.victorialodgehotel.co.uk **D:** £29.50 **S:** £40.00–£48.00 **Beds:** 6D 2T 1S **Baths:** 9 En 🛏 (14) 🅿 (10) ⌁ 🆅 ▥ 🔥 cc

Enderley Guest House, *20 Queens Road, Kenilworth, Warwickshire, CV8 1JQ.* Friendly, homely, family run guest house close to town centre. **Open:** All year **Grades:** ETC 4 Diamond **01926 855388** **Fax: 01926 850450** **D:** £22.00–£30.00 **S:** £27.00–£30.00 **Beds:** 1F 1T 2D 1S **Baths:** 5 En 🅿 (2) ⌁ 🆅 🆅 ▥ 🔥

Abbey Guest House, *41 Station Road, Kenilworth, Warks, CV8 1JD.* Comfortable Victorian house, well-equipped bedrooms, close to town centre. **Open:** All year (not Xmas) **01926 512707** Mrs Jefferies *the-abbey@virgin.net* **D:** £22.50 **S:** £26.00 **Beds:** 3D 2T 2S **Baths:** 6 En 1 Pr 🛏 🅿 (2) ⌁ 🆅 🆅 ▥ 🔥

All details shown are as supplied by B&B owners in Autumn 2001

Castle Laurels Hotel, *22 Castle Road, Kenilworth, CV8 1NG.* Beautiful Victorian house opposite the castle in Kenilworth old town. **Open:** All year (not Xmas) **01926 856179** N C Moore **Fax: 01926 854954** *moores22@aol.com* www.castlelaurelshotel.co.uk **D:** £28.50 **S:** £36.00–£45.00 **Beds:** 5D 3T 3S **Baths:** 11 En 🛏 🅿 (12) ⌁ 🆅 ▥ 🔥 cc

Leamington Spa

SP3165 🍺 *Benjamin Satchwell's*

Victoria Park Hotel, *12 Adelaide Road, Royal Leamington Spa, Warwickshire, CV31 3PW.* A cosy, comfortable establishment in a quiet, yet convenient location. **Open:** All year (not Xmas/New Year) **01926 424195** **Fax: 01926 421521** *info@victoriaparkhotelleamingtonspa.co.uk* www.victoriaparkhotelleamingtonspa.co.uk **D:** £30.00–£37.50 **S:** £39.50 **Beds:** 7F 1T 6D 6S **Baths:** 20 En 🛏 🅿 (15) 🆅 ✕ ▥ 🔥 cc

Charnwood Guest House, *47 Avenue Road, Leamington Spa, Warks, CV31 3PF.* Comfortable, informal atmosphere, close to town centre, also Warwick Castle. **Open:** All year (not Xmas) **01926 831074 (also fax)** Mr Booth **D:** £18.00–£20.00 **S:** £18.00–£30.00 **Beds:** 1F 2D 2T 1S **Baths:** 2 En 2 Sh 🛏 🅿 (6) 🆅 🔥 🍴 ✕ 🆅 ▥ 🔥 cc

11 St Andrews Road, *Leamington Spa, Warks, CV32 7EU.* Relax and enjoy our peaceful home. Special welcome. Delicious food. **Open:** All year (not Xmas) **01926 428864** Mrs Poultney **D:** £15.00–£18.00 **Beds:** 1D 1T **Baths:** 1 En 1 Sh 🅿 (1) ⌁ 🆅 ✕ 🆅 ▥ 🔥

Hedley Villa Guest House, *31 Russell Terrace, Leamington Spa, Warks, CV31 1EZ.* Friendly house within walking distance of railway station and town. **Open:** All year **01926 424504** Mr Tocker & Mrs P Ashfield **Fax: 01926 745801** **D:** £19.00–£25.00 **S:** £25.00–£30.00 **Beds:** 2F 1T 1D 3S **Baths:** 1 En 4 Sh 🛏 🆅 🔥 ✕ 🆅 ▥ 🔥 🔥

Lillington

SP3267 🍺 *The Rugby*

Almond House, *8 Parklands Avenue, Lillington, Leamington Spa, Warwickshire, CV32 7BA.* Quietly located, convenient for NEC, M40, NAC five minutes away. **Open:** All year **Grades:** ETC 4 Diamond **01926 424052** Mrs Mewett **D:** £20.00–£22.50 **S:** £25.00 **Beds:** 1T 1D **Baths:** 2 Pr 🛏 (14) 🅿 (4) ⌁ 🆅 ▥ 🔥

Little Compton

SP2630

Rigside, Little Compton, Moreton-in-Marsh, Glos, GL56 0RR. Lovely landscaped gardens backing onto farmland. **Open:** All year **01608 674128 (also fax)** Ms Cox *rigside@lineone.net* **D:** £22.00–£23.00 **S:** £20.00–£22.00 **Beds:** 2D 1S 1T **Baths:** 2 En 1 Sh ❦ (9) 🅿 (6) 📺 Ⓥ 🔲 ⚓

Long Compton

SP2832

Tallet Barn, Yerdley Farm, Long Compton, Shipston-on-Stour, Warks, CV36 5LH. Comfortable annexed rooms, a warm welcome and a quiet village location. **Open:** All year **01608 684248** Mrs Richardson **Fax: 01068 684248 D:** £20.00–£21.00 **S:** £25.00 **Beds:** 1D 1T **Baths:** 2 En ❦ (6) 🅿 (2) ⅌ 📺 🔲 ✿ ⚓

Lower Brailes

SP3139

The George Hotel, High Street, Lower Brailes, Banbury, Oxon, OX15 5NU. **Open:** All year **01608 685223 Fax: 01608 685916 D:** £25.00–£60.00 **S:** £25.00–£60.00 **Beds:** 1F 8T 1D 1S **Baths:** 1 En 9 Pr 1 Sh ❦ (1) 🅿 (80) ⅌ 📺 ➹ ✗ 📺 🔲 ✿ cc
A C12th inn, good, friendly public bar, large gardens with undercover outside eating area. In Cotswolds near Stratford-upon-Avon (14 miles). Well-kept local, off-road foot ways. Good centre to visit entire Cotswold area.

New House Farm, Lower Brailes, Banbury, Oxon, OX15 5BD. New House Farm is set between two villages in outstanding area of beauty. **Open:** All year (not Xmas) **01608 686239** Ms Taylor **Fax: 01608 686455** *helen@brailes88.fsnet.co.uk* **D:** £20.00–£22.50 **S:** £25.00–£28.00 **Beds:** 2D 1T **Baths:** 2 En 1 Pr ❦ 🅿 (10) 📺 ➹ Ⓥ 🔲 ⚓

Loxley

SP2552

Elm Cottage, Stratford Road, Loxley, Warks, CV35 9JW. Private house in open countryside. Stratford-upon-Avon 3 miles. **Open:** All year (not Xmas) **Grades:** ETC 4 Diamond **01789 840609** Mrs Brocklehurst **D:** £22.00 **S:** £25.00 **Beds:** 1D 1T 1S **Baths:** 1 Sh 🅿 (6) ⅌ 🔲 ⚓

Mappleborough Green

SP0765

The Woodlands, Birmingham Road, Mappleborough Green, Studley, Warwickshire, B80 7DE. Comfortable family home, M42 4 miles. Convenient NEC and Shakespeare Country. **Open:** All year (not Xmas/New Year) **01527 852693** Mrs Johnson **Fax: 01527 852001** *djohn2693@aol.com* **D:** £25.00 **S:** £25.00–£30.00 **Beds:** 1T 1D **Baths:** 1 En 1 Pr ❦ (12) 🅿 (8) ⅌ 📺 Ⓥ 🔲 ⚓

Nuneaton

SP3691

La Tavola Calda, 68 & 70 Midland Road, Nuneaton, Warks, CV11 5DY. A family-run Italian restaurant and hotel. Handy for M69 - M6. **Open:** All year (not Xmas/New Year) **07747 010702 (M)** Mr Emanuele **D:** £32.00–£35.00 **S:** £20.00–£25.00 **Beds:** 2F 5T 1S **Baths:** 8 En ❦ (5) 📺 🔲 ⚓ cc

Pailton

SP4781

White Lion Inn, Coventry Road, Pailton, Rugby, Warks, CV23 0QD. C17th coaching inn recently modernised retaining all the olde worlde atmosphere. **Open:** All year **01788 832359 (also fax)** Mr Brindley **D:** £19.50–£24.50 **S:** £21.00–£31.00 **Beds:** 9D **Baths:** 5 En 2 Sh ❦ 🅿 (60) ⅌ 📺 ➹ ✗ 📺 Ⓥ 🔲 ♿ ⚓ cc

Priors Hardwick

SP4756 🍺 *Butcher's Arms, Hollybush, The Plough*

Hill Farm, Priors Hardwick, Southam, Warwickshire, CV23 8SP. Outstanding westerly views over peaceful countryside. A real rural retreat! **Open:** All year (not Xmas/New Year) **Grades:** ETC 3 Diamond **01327 260338** Ms Darbishire *hillfarmbandb@farming.co.uk* www.warwicksfarmhols.co.uk **D:** £20.00 **S:** £25.00 **Beds:** 1T 1D **Baths:** 1 Sh ❦ 🅿 (100) ⅌ 📺 Ⓥ 🔲 ⚓

B&B owners may vary rates – be sure to check when booking

Rugby

SP5075 🍺 *Sheaf & Sickle, Old Smithy*

Dunsmore Home Farm, Watling Street, Clifton-upon-Dunsmore, Rugby, Warks, CV23 0AQ. Victorian farmhouse in Warwickshire countryside. Rugby and motorway 3 miles. **Open:** All year (not Xmas/New Year) **01788 860168 (also fax)** Ms Yates **D:** £20.00–£22.00 **S:** £24.00–£25.00 **Beds:** 1F 1T 1D **Baths:** 3 En 1 Sh ❦ 🅿 📺 🔲 ⚓

Lawford Hill Farm, Lawford Heath Lane, Rugby, Warks, CV23 9HG. Enjoy a stay at our farmhouse set in beautiful gardens. **Open:** All year (not Xmas/New Year) **Grades:** ETC 4 Diamond **01788 542001** Mr & Mrs Moses **Fax: 01788 537880** *lawford.hill@talk.com* www.lawfordhill.co.uk **D:** £22.00–£24.00 **S:** £26.00–£30.00 **Beds:** 3T 3D **Baths:** 6 En ❦ 🅿 ⅌ 📺 ➹ ⚓

Shilton

SP4085

Barnacle Hall, Shilton Lane, Shilton, Coventry, CV7 9LH. C16th farmhouse; excellent spacious accommodation. Attractive gardens. Warm welcome. **Open:** All year (not Xmas/New Year) **Grades:** ETC 5 Diamond, Silver **024 7661 2629 (also fax)** Mrs Grindal **D:** £23.50–£26.00 **S:** £30.00–£33.00 **Beds:** 1T 2D **Baths:** 2 En 1 Pr ❦ 🅿 ⅌ 📺 Ⓥ 🔲 ⚓

Shipston on Stour

SP2540

Shipston Guest House, 42 Church Street, Shipston on Stour, Warks, CV36 4AS. Charming C17th cottage in delightful country town of Shipston-on-Stour. **Open:** All year (not Xmas) **01608 661002** Mrs Roberts **Fax: 01608 664008** *petelain@aol.com* **D:** £19.00 **S:** £35.00 **Beds:** 1F 1D 1T **Baths:** 2 En 1 Pr ❦ ⅌ 📺 ➹ Ⓥ 🔲 ♿ ⚓

BATHROOMS
En = Ensuite
Pr = Private
Sh = Shared

Shustoke
SP2290   🍺 *The Plough, Bull's Head*

The Old Vicarage, *Shustoke, Coleshill, Birmingham, Warks, B46 2LA.*
Open: All year
(not Xmas)
01675 481331 (also fax) R A Hawkins
jbhawk@doctors.org.uk **D:** £20.00 **S:** £22.00–£25.00 **Beds:** 3D **Baths:** 1 En 2 Sh ♥ 🅿 (6) ⅙ ▦ ✕ ▥. ♨
This friendly old house set in a large leafy garden is by the village church and near 'The Griffin', famous for its beers. Comfort and country hospitality in the peace of rural Warwickshire, within easy reach of NEC, Belfry Golf, Birmingham Airport and Midlands motorways.

Snitterfield
SP2159

The Hill Cottage, *Kings Lane, Snitterfield, Stratford upon Avon, Warks, CV37 0QA.* Country house in 1.5 acres and bluebell wood. Glorious views to Stratford (3 miles). **Open:** All year (not Xmas)
01789 731830 Mrs Waldron **Fax: 01789 730288** *hilcott_bb@hotmail.com* **D:** £24.00–£25.00 **S:** £28.00 **Beds:** 1D 1T 1S **Baths:** 1 En 1 Sh ♥ 🅿 (4) ⅙ ▥. ♨

Southam
SP4162

Briarwood, *34 Warwick Road, Southam, Leamington Spa, Warwickshire, CV47 0HN.* Edwardian house on the outskirts of a small market town. **Open:** All year (not Xmas)
01926 814756 Mrs Bishop **D:** £20.00–£25.00 **S:** £20.00–£30.00 **Beds:** 1D 1S **Baths:** 2 En 🅿 (1) ⅙ ▥ ▦. ♨

Stourton
SP2937

Brook House, *Stourton, Shipston-on-Stour, Warwickshire, CV36 5HQ.* Lovely old house, edge pretty Cotswold village. Ideal touring Stratford, Oxford, Cotswolds.
Open: All year (not Xmas/New Year)
01608 686281 Mrs McDonald *graemedonald@msn.com* **D:** £22.00–£23.00 **S:** £27.00–£30.00
Beds: 1F 1D **Baths:** 1 En 1 Pr ♥ (7) 🅿 (4) ▥ ▥ ▦. ♨

Stratford-upon-Avon
SP1955   🍺 *Garrick Inn, The Bell*

Stretton House, *38 Grove Road, Stratford-upon-Avon, Warks, CV37 6PB.*
Open: All year (not Xmas) **Grades:** ETC 3 Diamond
01789 268647 (also fax) Mr Machin *skyblues@strettonhouse.co.uk* **D:** £15.00–£28.00
S: £20.00–£40.00 **Beds:** 1F 2D 3T 1S
Baths: 4 En ♥ (8) 🅿 (6) ⅙ ▥ ⧖ ▥ ▦. ♨
We've got a home from home where a warm and friendly welcome awaits you from Michael and Yvonne. Comfortable accommodation at reasonable prices. Ensuite and standard rooms. Best B&B Recommended, Stratford in Bloom Guest House 1997/98. Just 3 minutes' walk to town centre.

Minola Guest House, *25 Evesham Place, Stratford-upon-Avon, Warks, CV37 6HT.*
Open: All year (not Xmas)
01789 293573 Mr & Mrs Castelli **Fax: 01789 551625 D:** £22.00–£25.00 **S:** £22.00–£35.00
Beds: 2D 1T 2S **Baths:** 4 Pr 1 Sh ♥ 🅿 (2) ⅙ ▥ ▥ ▦. ♨
Minola's is situated in the old town of Stratford. The theatres, being major attractions, are within easy walking distance as is the town centre and the railway station. Minola's is a stopping point for the open air bus tour.

Penshurst, *34 Evesham Place, Stratford-upon-Avon, Warks, CV37 6HT.* **Open:** All year **Grades:** ETC 3 Diamond
01789 205259 Mrs Cauvin **Fax: 01789 295322** *karen@penshurst.net* www.penshurst.net
D: £16.00–£24.00 **S:** £18.00–£24.00 **Beds:** 2F 3D 1T 1S **Baths:** 4 En 1 Pr 2 Sh ♥ ⅙ ▥ ▥ ▦. ♨2 ♨
A prettily refurbished Victorian town house 5 minutes' walk from centre. Totally non-smoking. Delicious breakfasts, either English or Continental, served from 7.00 am right up until 10.30 am. Excellent value for money. Brochure available.

Planning a longer stay? Always ask for any special rates

BEDROOMS
D = Double
T = Twin
S = Single
F = Family

Travellers Rest Guest House, *146 Alcester Road, Stratford-upon-Avon, Warwickshire, CV37 9DR.* **Open:** All year (not Xmas/New Year) **Grades:** AA 3 Diamond
01789 266589 (also fax) *travellersrest146@hotmail.com* **D:** £20.00–£28.00 **S:** £25.00–£35.00 **Beds:** 1F 1T 1D **Baths:** 3 En ♥ (2) 🅿 (3) ⅙ ▥ ▥ ▦. ♨
Traditional luxury ensuite accommodation with home comforts. Hearty English breakfast, vegetarian or continental. Payphone and private parking. Easy walk to railway station, town centre, Ann Hathaway's cottage, theatre, riverside walks and restaurants. Good location for Warwick Castle and Cotswold villages.

Parkfield Guest House, *3 Broad Walk, Stratford-upon-Avon, Warks, CV37 6HS.* Lovely Victorian house in quiet side street, 5 mins' walk from town centre.
Open: All year **Grades:** ETC 3 Diamond, AA 3 Diamond
01789 293313 R Pettitt *parkfield@btinternet.com* www.parkfieldbandb.co.uk
D: £23.00–£24.00 **S:** £25.00–£35.00 **Beds:** 3F 1T 2D 1S **Baths:** 6 En 1 Pr 🅿 (7) ⅙ ▥ ▥ ▦. ♨ cc

Faviere, *127 Shipston Road, Stratford-upon-Avon, Warks, CV37 7LW.* A ten minute walk will bring you to the theatres and town centre. **Open:** All year **Grades:** ETC 4 Diamond
01789 293764 Mr & Mrs Martinez **Fax: 01789 269365** *guestsfaviere@cwcom.net* www.faviere.com **D:** £17.00–£24.00 **S:** £20.00–£25.00 **Beds:** 1F 1D/T 1T 1S **Baths:** 3 En 1 Pr ♥ (0) 🅿 (5) ⅙ ▥ ▥ ▦. ♨

Curtain Call, *142 Alcester Road, Stratford-upon-Avon, Warwickshire, CV37 9DR.* Romantic four-poster beds for that special night away. **Open:** All year **Grades:** ETC 3 Diamond, AA 3 Diamond
01789 267734 (also fax) J Purlan
curtaincall@btinternet.com
www.curtaincallguesthouse.co.uk **D:** £20.00–£30.00 **S:** £20.00–£30.00 **Beds:** 1F 2D 1T 2S **Baths:** 4 En 1 Sh � ⏚ (6) ⊬ ⏶ ⏶ × ⏶ ⏶, ₰ cc

Whitchurch Farm, *Wimpstone, Stratford-upon-Avon, Warks, CV37 8NS.* Lovely Georgian farmhouse set in park-like surroundings, 4.5 miles south of Stratford-upon-Avon. **Open:** All year (not Xmas) **Grades:** ETC 3 Diamond
01789 450275 (also fax) Mrs James
D: £19.00–£20.50 **S:** £20.00–£22.00 **Beds:** 2D 1T **Baths:** 1 En ⏚ (0) ⏚ (3) ⊬ ⏶ ⏶ ⏶, ₰

Newlands, *7 Broad Walk, Stratford-upon-Avon, Warks, CV37 6HS.* Elegant Victorian townhouse, quiet cul-de-sac, close to centre and theatres. **Open:** All year
01789 298449 Mrs Walter **Fax: 01789 267806**
newlandslynwalter@hotmail.com **D:** £23.00–£25.00 **S:** £25.00 **Beds:** 2F 1D/T 1S **Baths:** 4 En 1 Pr ⏚ (5) ⏚ (2) ⊬ ⏶ × ⏶ ₰ cc

Cymbeline House, *24 Evesham Place, Stratford-upon-Avon, Warks, CV37 6HT.* Clean, comfortable, convenient Victorian house. 5 mins theatre, town, river. **Open:** All year (not Xmas/New Year) **Grades:** ETC 3 Diamond, RAC 3 Diamond
01789 292958 (also fax) *cymbelinebb-s-on-a@amserve.net* **D:** £18.00–£30.00 **S:** £36.00–£60.00 **Beds:** 1F 1T 3D 2S **Baths:** 7 En ⏚ ⏚ (4) ⊬ ⏶ ⏶ ⏶, ₰

Moonlight Guest House, *144 Alcester Road, Stratford-upon-Avon, Warks, CV37 9DR.* Most bedrooms have coffee-making facilities, hairdryers most bedrooms. **Open:** All year
01789 298213 E Dionisi **D:** £16.00–£19.00 **S:** £16.00–£19.00 **Beds:** 5F 2T 2D 2S **Baths:** 3 En 3 Pr 1 Sh ⏚ (1) ⏚ ⊬ ⏶ ⏶ ⏶,

Linhill Guest House, *35 Evesham Place, Stratford-upon-Avon, Warks, CV37 6HT.* Family-run Victorian guest house, 5 mins town centre. Choice of breakfasts, home-cooked evening meals. **Open:** All year
01789 292879 Ms Tallis **Fax: 01789 299691**
linhill@bigwig.net **D:** £15.00–£25.00 **S:** £15.00–£25.00 **Beds:** 2F 4D 4T 1S **Baths:** 3 En ⏚ ⏚ ⏶ × ⏶ ⏶, ⋇ ₰

Arrandale Guest House, *208 Evesham Road, Stratford-upon-Avon, Warks, CV37 9AS.* Comfortable, double-glazed, family run. 15 min walk Shakespearean properties. **Open:** All year (not Xmas)
01789 267112 Mrs Mellor **D:** £16.00–£18.50 **S:** £26.00–£28.50 **Beds:** 2D 1T **Baths:** 2 En 1 Sh ⏚ (3) ⏶ ⏶ × ⏶, ₰ cc

Broadlands Guest House, *23 Evesham Place, Stratford-upon-Avon, Warks, CV37 6HT.* Relaxed and friendly atmosphere five minutes to town centre. **Open:** All year (not Xmas) **Grades:** ETC 3 Diamond
01789 299181 Mr P Gray & Mr J L Worboys
Fax: 01789 551382 *broadlands.com@virgin.net*
www.stratford-upon-avon.co.uk/broadlands.htm **D:** £20.00–£30.00 **S:** £25.00–£35.00 **Beds:** 3D 1T 2S **Baths:** 5 En ⏚ (12) ⏶ ⏶, ₰

Clomendy, *10 Broad Walk, Stratford-upon-Avon, Warwickshire, CV37 6HS.* Small Victorian house, central, rail/coach guests met, non smoking. **Open:** All year (not Xmas/New Year) **Grades:** AA 3 Diamond
01789 266957 Mr Jones **D:** £20.00–£23.00 **S:** £30.00 **Beds:** 1T 1D 1S **Baths:** 2 En 1 Pr ⏚ (5) ⏚ (1) ⊬ ⏶ ⏶ ⏶, ₰

Nandos, *18-19 Evesham Place, Stratford-upon-Avon, Warks, CV37 6HT.* Close to Stratford town centre, attractions and theatre and Cotswolds. **Open:** All year
01789 204907 Mrs Morris **D:** £18.00–£25.00 **S:** £18.00–£45.00 **Beds:** 3F 13D 4T 3S **Baths:** 17 En 17 Pr 3 Sh

Acer House, *44 Albany Road, Stratford-upon-Avon, Warks, CV37 6PQ.* Quality accommodation, quiet, near town centre. Rooms overlook pleasant garden. **Open:** All year (not Xmas/New Year)
01789 204962 Mrs Hall **D:** £18.00–£19.00 **S:** £18.00–£20.00 **Beds:** 1T 1S **Baths:** 1 Sh ⊬ ⏶ ⏶ ⏶,

Stour View, *Alderminster, Stratford-upon-Avon, Warwickshire, CV37 8NY.* Country bungalow, quiet, private accommodation. Central for Warwick, Cotswolds and Stratford-upon-Avon. **Open:** All year (not Xmas/New Year)
01789 450593 (also fax) Mrs Moody
moody.stourview@btinternet.com **D:** £17.50–£19.50 **S:** £25.00–£30.00 **Beds:** 1T **Baths:** 1 En ⏚ (3) ⊬ ⏶ ⏶ ⏶, ₰

The Dylan Guest House, *10 Evesham Place, Stratford-upon-Avon, Warks, CV37 6HT.* Charming Victorian house, 5 minutes town centre, theatre and river. **Open:** All year (not Xmas)
01789 204819 Mr Elmy *elmy@lineone.net*
D: £23.00–£25.00 **S:** £24.00–£26.00 **Beds:** 1F 3D 1T 1S **Baths:** 5 En ⏚ (5) ⏚ (5) ⊬ ⏶ ⏶ ⏶, ₰

Hunters Moon Guest House, *150 Alcester Road, Stratford-upon-Avon, Warks, CV37 9DR.* Modern, detached, run by Stratfordians. **Open:** All year (not Xmas)
01789 292888 (also fax) Mrs Austin
thehuntersmoon@compuserve.com **D:** £18.00 **S:** £20.00 **Beds:** 2F 2D 1T 2S **Baths:** 7 Pr ⏚ (2) ⏚ (6) ⊬ ⏶ ⏶,

Hampton Lodge, *38 Shipston Road, Stratford-upon-Avon, Warwickshire, CV37 7LP.* Just minutes from RSC theatre - your ideal base in Stratford. **Open:** All year (not Xmas/New Year)
01789 299374 (also fax) Mr Brewerton
hamptonlodge@aol.com **D:** £23.00–£30.00 **S:** £35.00–£45.00 **Beds:** 2F 5D **Baths:** 7 En ⏚ ⏚ (9) ⊬ ⏶ × ⏶ ⏶, ₰ cc

Warmington

SP4147 ⏽ The Plough

Pond Cottage, *The Green, Warmington, Banbury, Oxon, OX17 1BU.* 6m from M40 (J11/12). Double room. Shower and basin ensuite. Nearby pub. **Open:** Feb to Nov
01295 690682 V G Viljoen **D:** £24.00 **S:** £24.00–£33.00 **Beds:** 1D 1S **Baths:** 1 Sh ⏚ (2) ⊬ ⏶ ⏶, ₰

The Old Rectory, *Warmington, Banbury, Oxfordshire, OX17 1BU.* Beautiful C18th house with lovely garden on the green in idyllic peaceful village. **Open:** All year (not Xmas)
01295 690531 Mrs Cockcroft **Fax: 01295 690526** *sirwhcockcroft@clara.co.uk* **D:** £25.00–£30.00 **S:** £35.00 **Beds:** 2T 1D **Baths:** 3 En ⏚ (3) ⊬ ⏶ ⏶, ₰

Warwick

SP2865 ⏽ Tilted Wig, Richochet

The Seven Stars, *Friars Street, Warwick, CV34 6HD.* Quality Bed/Breakfast. Large beamed rooms. Town centre. Car park. **Open:** All year **Grades:** ETC 4 Diamond
01926 492658 A Flynn **Fax: 01926 411747**
7stars-warwick@gofornet.co.uk **D:** £25.00–£30.00 **S:** £38.00–£45.00 **Beds:** 1D **Baths:** 1 En ⏚ (11) ⊬ ⏶ ⏶ ⏶, ₰ cc

Chesterfields, *84 Emscote Road, Warwick, CV34 5QJ.* The ideal location for Warwick Castle, Stratford and the Cotswolds. **Open:** All year (not Xmas)
01926 774864 Mr & Mrs Chapman **D:** £17.50–£19.00 **S:** £18.00–£22.00 **Beds:** 2F 2D 1T 2S **Baths:** 1 Sh ⏚ ⏚ (8) ⏶ ⏶ ⏶, ₰

Please respect a B&B's wishes regarding children, animals and smoking

Ashburton Guest House, *74 Emscote Road, Warwick, CV34 5QG.* Extremely high standard of accommodation and close to town centre. **Open:** All year (not Xmas) **Grades:** ETC 3 Diamond **01926 401082** Mrs Whitelaw **Fax: 01926 774642** *ashburtongh@cs.com* **D:** £20.00 **S:** £20.00–£25.00 **Beds:** 2F 1T 4S **Baths:** 4 En 1 Pr 2 Sh ⌚ (1) 🅿 (3) 📺 🛏 🖾 ♨ **cc**

Austin Guest House, *96 Emscote Road, Warwick, CV34 5QJ.* Black and white Victorian house, one mile from town centre and castle. **Open:** All year (not Xmas) **Grades:** ETC 3 Diamond, AA 3 Diamond **01926 493583** Mr & Mrs Winter **Fax: 01926 493679** *mike@austinhouse96.freeserve.co.uk* www.austinhousewarwick.co.uk **D:** £19.00–£23.00 **S:** £19.00–£46.00 **Beds:** 2F 2D 2T 1S **Baths:** 5 En 1 Sh ⌚ 🅿 (6) 📺 📵 ♨ **cc**

Croft Guest House, *The Croft, Haseley Knob, Warwick, CV35 7NL.* Friendly family country guest house. Near Warwick, Coventry, Stratford, NEC/NAC. **Open:** All year (not Xmas) **Grades:** ETC 4 Diamond **01926 484447 (also fax)** Mr & Mrs Clapp *david@croftguesthouse.co.uk* www.croftguesthouse.co.uk **D:** £23.00–£25.00 **S:** £34.00–£35.00 **Beds:** 2F 3D 3T 1S **Baths:** 7 En 2 Pr ⌚ 🅿 (8) ✂ 📺 🛏 🖾 ♨ **cc**

Agincourt Lodge Hotel, *36 Coten End, Warwick, CV34 4NP.* Walking distance to castle & all amenities. Four-poster beds. Non-smoking bedrooms. **Open:** All year (not Xmas/New Year) **01926 499399 (also fax)** A & M Black-Band **D:** £26.50–£35.00 **S:** £37.50–£47.00 **Beds:** 1F 1T 4D **Baths:** 5 En ⌚ 🅿 ✂ 📺 🖾 ♨ **cc**

National Grid References given are for villages, towns and cities – not for individual houses

Welford-on-Avon

SP1451

One Acre Guest House, *Barton Road, Welford-on-Avon, Stratford upon Avon, Warks, CV37 8EZ.* Pretty Shakespearean village 4 miles Stratford-upon-Avon, 6 miles Cotswolds. **Open:** Mar to Nov **01789 750477** Ms Clifton **D:** £20.00 **S:** £30.00 **Beds:** 3D ⌚ (12) 🅿 (3) ✂ 📺 ✗ 📵 ♨

Springfields Farm, *Welford Road, Welford-on-Avon, Stratford upon Avon, Warks, CV37 8RA.* Farmhouse - walk in Shakespeare's paths. **Open:** All year **01789 720361 & 01789 720361** Mrs Reid **Fax: 01789 720885** *enquiries@reidgroup.co.uk* www.reidgroup.co.uk **D:** £16.00–£20.00 **S:** £16.00 **Beds:** 1F 1D 2T 1S **Baths:** 1 En 1 Sh 🅿 (12) ✂ 📵

Whitacre Heath

SP2192

Heathland Farm, *Birmingham Road, Whitacre Heath, Coleshill, W Mids, B46 2ER.* Comfortable, quiet secluded farmhouse, outskirts of village, courtyard parking. **Open:** All year **01675 462129 & 07970 754521 (M)** Mr Barnes **D:** £21.00–£22.00 **S:** £25.00–£28.00 **Beds:** 3T 2S **Baths:** 5 En 1 Pr 🅿 (10) 📺 🖾 ♨

Wimpstone

SP2148

Whitchurch Farm, *Wimpstone, Stratford-upon-Avon, Warks, CV37 8NS.* Lovely Georgian farmhouse set in park-like surroundings, 4.5 miles south of Stratford-upon-Avon. **Open:** All year (not Xmas) **Grades:** ETC 3 Diamond **01789 450275 (also fax)** Mrs James **D:** £19.00–£20.50 **S:** £20.00–£22.00 **Beds:** 2D 1T **Baths:** 1 En ⌚ (0) 🅿 (3) ✂ 📺 📵 🖾 ♨

RATES

D = Price range per person sharing in a double or twin room

S = Price range for a single room

Wixford

SP0854

Orchard Lawns, *Wixford, Alcester, Warks, B49 6DA.* Delightful house and grounds in small village, ideal touring centre. **Open:** All year (not Xmas) **Grades:** ETC 4 Diamond, Silver **01789 772668** Mrs Kember *margaret.orchardlawns@farmersweekly.net* **D:** £22.00–£25.00 **S:** £22.00–£25.00 **Beds:** 1D 1T 1S **Baths:** 1 En 1 Sh 🅿 (6) ✂ 📺 🛏 📵 🖾

Wolston

SP4175

The Byre, *Lords Hill Farm, Wolston, Coventry, Warks, CV8 3GB.* Homely hospitality, Food Hygiene Award 1998. 2 miles from Ryton Gardens. **Open:** All year (not Xmas) **Grades:** ETC 4 Diamond, Silver **024 7654 2098** Mrs Gibbs **D:** £22.00–£38.00 **S:** £22.00–£38.00 **Beds:** 2D 1T **Baths:** 1 En 1 Sh ⌚ (5) 🅿 (4) ✂ 📺 🖾 ♨

Lords Hill Farm, *Coalpit Lane, Wolston, Coventry, Warks, CV8 3GB.* Lovely views, very peaceful and private. Convenient for motorway network. **Open:** All year (not Xmas/New Year) **024 7654 4430** Mrs Gibbs **D:** £27.00 **S:** £27.00 **Beds:** 1D **Baths:** 1 Pr 🅿 (2) ✂ 📺 🖾 ♨

West Midlands

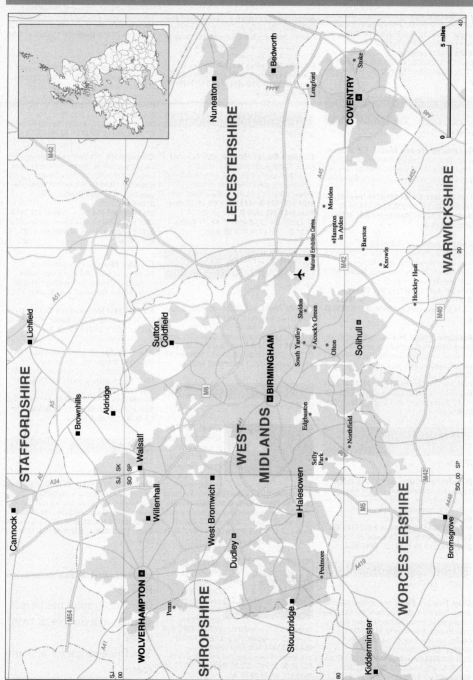

Barston

SP2078

The Gatehouse, *Barston Lane, Barston, Solihull, W Mids, B92 0JN.* Large Victorian house - close to Junction 5 M42. **Open:** All year (not Xmas/New Year)
01675 443274 (also fax) Mr Emmett
D: £20.00–£30.00 **S:** £20.00–£30.00 **Beds:** 1D 2T 3S **Baths:** 2 En 1 Sh ⑮ ☐ (20) ⊬ ⑰ ★ ⑰ ⑩. ⚘

BIRMINGHAM
Acock's Green

SP1183

Greenway House Hotel, *978 Warwick Road, Acock's Green, Birmingham, B27 6QG.* Small, privately run hotel, friendly service, very close to motorway network. **Open:** All year (not Xmas)
0121 706 1361 & 0121 624 8356 Fax: 0121 706 1361 **D:** £15.00–£18.00 **S:** £18.00–£25.00 **Beds:** 3F 3D 2T 6S **Baths:** 8 En 6 Sh ⑮ ☐ (18) ⑰ ★ ✕ ⑰ ⑩. ⚘

Atholl Lodge, *16 Elmdon Road, Acock's Green, Birmingham, B27 6LH.* Friendly guest house, convenient for NEC, airport, Birmingham, Solihull centres. **Open:** All year (not Xmas)
0121 707 4417 (also fax) Mrs Davey
D: £18.00–£23.00 **S:** £23.00–£27.00 **Beds:** 1F 1D 1T 5S **Baths:** 2 En 4 Sh ⑮ ☐ (10) ⑰ ★ ⑩. ⚘

Ashdale House Hotel, *39 Broad Road, Acock's Green, Birmingham, B27 7UX.* Victorian house overlooking park, near to airport, station, NEC and city centre. **Open:** All year
0121 706 3598 Mrs Read **Fax:** 0121 707 2324 **D:** £20.00–£23.00 **S:** £22.00–£28.00 **Beds:** 2F 1D 6S **Baths:** 4 En 1 Pr 4 Sh ⑮ (1) ☐ (4) ⑰ ★ ⑰ ⑩. ⚘ cc

BIRMINGHAM
Edgbaston

SP0584

Woodville House, *39 Portland Road, Edgbaston, Birmingham, B16 9HN.* First class accommodation, 1m city centre. All rooms colour TV, tea/coffee making facilities. **Open:** All year (not Xmas)
0121 454 0274 Mr Desousa **Fax:** 0121 454 5965 **D:** £17.00 **S:** £17.00 **Beds:** 2F 3D 5T 6S **Baths:** 4 En 3 Pr ⑮ ☐ (12) ⑰ ★ ⑩. ⚘

BIRMINGHAM Northfield

SP0279   🚩 *Black Horse*

Clay Towers B&B, *51 Frankley Beeches Road, Northfield, Birmingham, B31 5AB.* Very comfortable, warm welcome, easy access, near Birmingham centre, M5/M42. **Open:** All year (not Xmas/New Year)
Grades: ETC 3 Diamond
0121 628 0053 (also fax) Mr Clay **D:** £22.50–£25.00 **S:** £25.00–£30.00 **Beds:** 1T 2D **Baths:** 2 En 1 Pr ⑮ ☐ (4) ⊬ ⑰ ⑩. ⚘

BIRMINGHAM Selly Park

SP0582

Awentsbury Hotel, *21 Serpentine Road, Selly Park, Birmingham, B29 7HU.* Victorian country house set in own gardens, close to Birmingham University. **Open:** All year
Grades: AA 2 Diamond
0121 472 1258 (also fax) Mr Kerr
www.awentsbury.co.uk **D:** £26.00 **S:** £36.00 **Beds:** 1F 2D 8T 5S **Baths:** 6 Pr 2 Sh ⑮ ☐ (12) ⑰ ★ ✕ ⑰ ⑩. ⚘ ⚘

BIRMINGHAM Sheldon

SP1584

Elmdon Guest House, *2369 Coventry Road, Sheldon, Birmingham, B26 3PN.* Situated close to NEC, NIA, airport, railway, restaurants, pubs and town centre.
Open: All year (not Xmas/New Year)
0121 742 1626 & 0121 688 1720 Mr Gardner **Fax:** 0121 742 1626 **D:** £22.50–£27.50 **S:** £32.00–£42.00 **Beds:** 1F 4T 2D **Baths:** 7 Pr ⑮ ☐ (7) ⊬ ⑰ ★ ✕ ⑰ ⑩. ⚘ cc

BIRMINGHAM
South Yardley

SP1284

Gables Nest, *1639 Coventry Road, South Yardley, Birmingham, B26 1DD.* Friendly family-run guest house situated near to the National Exhibition Centre. **Open:** All year
0121 708 2712 M A Page **Fax:** 0121 707 3396 **D:** £20.00–£25.00 **S:** £20.00–£30.00 **Beds:** 1F 3T 1S **Baths:** 4 En1 Pr ⑮ ☐ ⑰ ⑰ ★ ⑩. ⚘

Coventry

SP3378   🚩 *Binley Park Inn*

Croft On The Green, *23 Stoke Green, Coventry, CV3 1FP.* Friendly, family-run guest house in a quiet conservation area. **Open:** All year **Grades:** AA 3 Diamond
024 7645 7846 (also fax) Mr & Mrs Barnby
croftonthegreen@aol.com www.croftonthegreen.
co.uk **D:** £22.50–£25.00 **S:** £22.50–£30.00 **Beds:** 2F 3T 4D 6S **Baths:** 6 En 1 Pr 2 Sh ⑮ ☐ (10) ⊬ ⑰ ⑰ ⑩. ⚘ cc

Abigail Guest House, *39 St Patricks Road, Coventry, W Mids, CV1 2LP.* Small, comfortable, convenient, city-centre, near NEC, NAC and universities. **Open:** All year (not Xmas)
024 7622 1378 Mrs Ford ag002a@
netgates.co.uk www.abigailuk.com **D:** £19.00–£22.00 **S:** £19.00–£22.00 **Beds:** 1F 1D 1T 3S **Baths:** 2 Sh ⑮ ⑰ ⑩. ⚘

Gilcrist Guest House, *106 St James Lane, Coventry, W Mids, CV3 3GS.* Accommodation near local motorways, Marconi, Jaguar, NEC and Peugeot.
Open: All year (not Xmas)
024 7630 2001 Mrs Howes **D:** £20.00–£22.00 **S:** £20.00–£22.00 **Beds:** 1T 1S **Baths:** 1 Sh ☐ (3) ⑰ ⑰ ⑩. ⚘

Albany Guest House, *121 Holyhead Road, Coventry, W Mids, CV1 3AD.* Located near city centre, NEC, NAC. Skating, cinema close by. **Open:** All year
Grades: ETC 3 Diamond
024 7622 3601 (also fax) Mr Jones
D: £17.00–£18.00 **S:** £18.00–£20.00 **Beds:** 1F 3T 1S **Baths:** 2 Sh ⑮ (5) ⑰ ★ ✕ ⑰ ⑩. ⚘

Brookfields, *134 Butt Lane, Allesley, Coventry, W Mids, CV5 9FE.* Well appointed, friendly. 6 mile NEC, 3 miles Coventry. Local amenities, semi-rural location. **Open:** All year (not New Year) **Grades:** ETC 4 Diamond
024 7640 4866 Mrs Marson **Fax:** 024 7640 2022 brookfieldscoventry@easicom.com **D:** £25.00 **S:** £28.00 **Beds:** 1D 1T 2S **Baths:** 4 En ⑮ (16) ☐ (4) ⑩. ⚘

Chester House, *3 Chester Street, Coventry, W Mids, CV1 4DH.* Large white building in Chester-le-Street, ten minute walk to town. **Open:** All year **Grades:** ETC 3 Diamond
024 7622 3857 Mrs Saunders **D:** £17.00–£22.50 **S:** £17.00–£22.50 **Beds:** 1F 2D 1T 1S **Baths:** 1 En 1 Sh ⑮ ⑰ ⑩. ⚘ ⚘

Almar Lodge, *37 Mount Nod Way, Coventry, W Mids, CV5 7GY.* Homely accommodation, quiet location, near NEC/NAC, A45, transport available. **Open:** All year (not Xmas)
024 7646 8841 Mrs Bastock **D:** £16.00–£20.00 **S:** £16.00–£20.00 **Beds:** 1T 1S **Baths:** 1 En 1 Sh ⑮ ☐ (2) ⊬ ⑰ ✕ ⑩. ⚘

Dudley

SO9390

Merdeka, *16 Dawlish Road, Woodsetton, Dudley, W Mids, DY1 4LU.* Detached residence 1 mile from Dudley town centre; no smoking. **Open:** All year (not Xmas)
01902 884775 Mrs Green **D:** £20.00 **S:** £20.00 **Beds:** 1T 1S **Baths:** 1 Sh ⑮ ☐ (3) ⊬ ⑰ ★ ✕ ⑰ ⑩. ⚘

RATES

D = Price range per person sharing in a double or twin room

S = Price range for a single room

Hampton in Arden

SP2081

The Cottage, *Kenilworth Road, Hampton in Arden, Solihull, W Mids, B92 0LW.* Excellent accommodation in a charming cosy cottage close to the NEC. **Open:** All year (not Xmas) **Grades:** ETC 3 Diamond, AA 3 Diamond **01675 442323** Mr Howles **Fax:** 01675 443323 **D:** £20.00–£24.00 **S:** £28.00–£30.00 **Beds:** 2F 2D 1T 4S **Baths:** 8 En 1 Pr ॐ🖪(10)🖵🏠▥🕭

Hockley Heath

SP1573

Illshaw Heath Farm, *Kineton Lane, Hockley Heath, Solihull, B94 6RX.* Working farm close to NEC, Birmingham airport and Shakespeare country. **Open:** All year (not Xmas) **Grades:** ETC 4 Diamond **01564 782214** Ms Garner **D:** £20.00–£22.50 **S:** £25.00–£30.00 **Beds:** 1D 4T **Baths:** 4 En 1 Pr ॐ🖪(8)🖵▥▥🕭

Knowle

SP1876   🍺 *Wilsons Arms*

Achill House, *35 Hampton Road, Knowle, Solihull, W. Mids, B93 0NR.* High standard affordable family run guest house. 100 yards Knowle High Street. **Open:** All year **01564 774090 (also fax)** Mrs Liszewski *achill5@aol.com* **D:** £35.00–£45.00 **S:** £20.00–£35.00 **Beds:** 2F 2T 1D **Baths:** 4 En 2 Sh ॐ 🖪(6)🖵🏠▥▥🕭 cc

Longford

SP3584

Chogan Bed & Breakfast, *33 Longford Road, Longford, Coventry, Warwickshire, CV6 6DY.* Old cottage-style building, very modern accommodation, sky digital lounge. **Open:** All year **024 7666 1861 Fax:** 024 7668 9733 **D:** £18.00–£25.00 **S:** £18.00–£25.00 **Beds:** 1F 3T 3S **Baths:** 2 En 2 Sh ॐ🖪▥✕▥▥ ✳ 🕭 cc

Meriden

SP2482   🍺 *Bull's Head*

Grange Farm, *Fillongley Road, Meriden, Coventry, W Mids, CV7 7HU.* NEC, Airport, 8 mins. Countryside setting. Annexe accommodation. Farmhouse breakfast. **Open:** All year (not Xmas/New Year) **01676 22312** Ms Byrne **D:** £20.00 **S:** £25.00 **Beds:** 1T 1D **Baths:** 2 En 🖪(10)🖵▥▥🕭

Olton

SP1382

Abberose, *18 Victoria Road, Olton, Birmingham, B27 7YA.* Comfortable, private, detached home guest house. Convenient to Airport, NEC, ICC, NIA. **Open:** All year (not Xmas/New Year) **0121 708 0867 D:** £40.00–£46.00 **S:** £21.00–£28.00 **Beds:** 1F 2T 1D 2S **Baths:** 2 En 1 Pr 1 Sh ॐ🖪(4)▥▥✕▥▥🕭

Pedmore

SO9182

The Limes Hotel, *260 Hagley Road, Pedmore, Stourbridge, W Mids, DY9 0RW.* Quiet comfortable Victorian property serving excellent food. **Open:** All year **01562 882689** E Rix **D:** £28.00–£32.50 **S:** £40.00–£49.00 **Beds:** 3T 4D 1S **Baths:** 8 En ॐ🖪(12)🖵🏠✕▥▥🕭 cc

Penn

SO8996   🍺 *Mount Tavern*

Pencroft Guest House, *100 Coalway Road, Penn, Wolverhampton, W Mids, WV3 7NB.* Warm welcome friendly guest house. Homely with private parking. **Open:** All year (not Xmas/New Year) **01902 340906 & 07961 810420 (M)** Ms Hall **D:** £34.00 **S:** £19.00 **Beds:** 2T 2D 2S **Baths:** 1 Sh ॐ(1)🖪(3)▥▥▥🕭

Solihull

SP1579

Ammonds, *11 Clifton Crescent, Solihull, W Mids, B91 3LG.* Friendly, quiet, 5 mins Solihull, M42. Near NEC, Stratford, Warwick. Weekday let. **Open:** All year (not Xmas/New Year) **0121 704 9399** Mrs Hammond **S:** £19.00 **Beds:** 3S **Baths:** 1 Sh ॐ(8)🖪(3)▥▥▥▥🕭

Ravenhurst Guest House, *56 Lode Lane, Solihull, W Mids, B91 2AW.* Solihull centre, leisure centre, pubs, restaurants, railway station on doorstep. **Open:** All year **Grades:** ETC 3 Diamond **0121 705 5754** Mr Keppy **Fax:** 0121 704 0717 **D:** £19.00–£24.00 **S:** £25.00–£40.00 **Beds:** 1F 2D 2T **Baths:** 2 En 3 Sh ॐ🖪(6)🖵🏠▥▥🕭 cc

Acorn Guest House, *29 Links Drive, Solihull, W Mids, B91 2DJ.* Homely service in a quiet family house overlooking golf course. **Open:** All year (not Xmas) **Grades:** ETC 4 Diamond **0121 705 5241** Mrs Wood *acorn.wood@btinternet.com* **D:** £20.00–£25.00 **S:** £20.00–£25.00 **Beds:** 1D 2T 2S **Baths:** 1 En 1 Pr 1 Sh 🖪(5)▥▥▥🕭

Bibury House, *Kenilworth Road, Solihull, West Midlands, B92 0LR.* Imposing refurbished country house 5 mins NEC and airport. **Open:** All year **01675 443518 (also fax)** A Hardwick *biburyhouse@aol.com* **D:** £22.00–£24.00 **S:** £28.00 **Beds:** 2F 3T 2D **Baths:** 7 En ॐ 🖪(9)▥🏠▥▥▥🕭

Michaelmas House, *1159 Warwick Road, Solihull, West Midlands, B91 3HQ.* An elegant Georgian-style house with mature gardens. 1m Solihull town centre. **Open:** All year (not Xmas/New Year) **0121 705 1414 (also fax)** Mrs Horton **D:** £25.00 **S:** £25.00–£30.00 **Beds:** 3F 1T 1D 1S **Baths:** 2 En 1 Pr 1 Sh ॐ🖪(6)▥▥✕▥▥🕭

Stoke

SP3679

Avon Gables, *33 Avon Street, Stoke , Coventry, West Midlands, CV2 3GJ.* Elegant Edwardian house, comfortable airy rooms. **Open:** All year (not Xmas/New Year) **024 7644 9521** Mrs Lewis *avongables_marion@yahoo.co.uk* **D:** £20.00–£25.00 **Beds:** 2T 1D **Baths:** 1 En 2 Sh ॐ(2)🖪(3)▥▥✕▥▥🕭

Wolverhampton

SO9198

Haven Hotel and Restaurant, *15 Claremont Street, Wolverhampton, W Mids, WV14 6BA.* Public bar and restaurants, home-cooked food. Family run hotel. **Open:** All year **01902 491661 (also fax)** Mr Foster **D:** £17.00 **S:** £18.00–£30.00 **Beds:** 3F 7T 6S **Baths:** 9 En 3 Sh ॐ🖪▥✕▥▥🕭 cc

Wiltshire

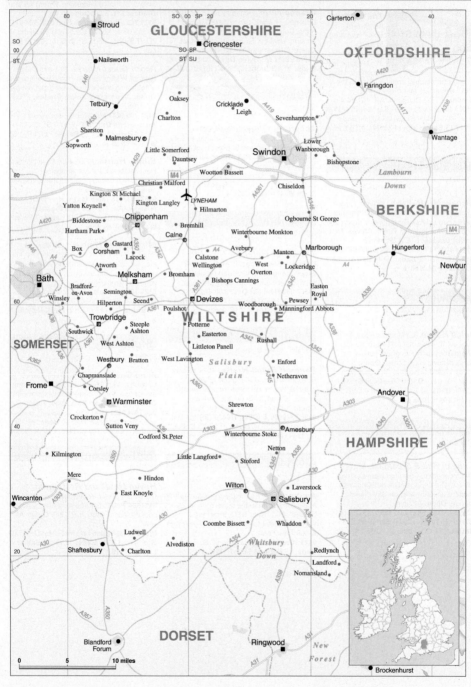

Alvediston

ST9723

The Crown Inn, *Alvediston, Salisbury, SP5 5JY.* Thatched pub, delicious food, central for great walks, cycle rides. **Open:** All year
01722 780335 Fax: 01722 780836 D: £23.75 **S:** £25.00 **Beds:** 1T 2D **Baths:** 3 En ⌂ 🖪 (30) ⤝ 📺 🛏 ✕ 🖂 ♨ cc

Amesbury

SU1541 ◀ *Stonehenge Inn*

Westavon, *76 Countess Road, Amesbury, Salisbury, SP4 7AT.* **Open:** All year
Grades: ETC 3 Diamond
01980 623698 (also fax) Mrs Walker
D: £20.00 **S:** £30.00 **Beds:** 1T 2D **Baths:** 2 En 1 Pr ⌂ 🖪 (4) ⤝ 📺 🖂 ♨ ⚓
Well-appointed detached house set in attractive landscaped gardens, with ample safe parking. Just 2 miles from Stonehenge, with the lovely south Wiltshire countryside all around us. Winter breaks 3 nights - 4th night free. A warm and friendly reception assured.

Catkin Lodge, *93 Countess Road, Amesbury, Salisbury, SP4 7AT.* The nearest B&B to Stonehenge. Friendly, comfortable and good value. **Open:** All year **Grades:** AA 3 Diamond
01980 624810 Mr Grace **Fax: 01980622139**
catkin@amesbury.in2home.co.uk
www.catkinlodge.fsnet.co.uk **D:** £22.00–
£27.00 **S:** £25.00–£38.00 **Beds:** 2F 1D 1T **Baths:** 1 En 1 Sh ⌂ (5) 🖪 (5) ⤝ 📺 🖂 ♨ ⚓

Atworth

ST8665 ◀ *Golden Fleece*

Church Farm, *Atworth, Melksham, Wilts, SN12 8JA.* Working dairy farm. Large garden/patio area. Walking distance to pubs. **Open:** Easter to Nov **Grades:** ETC 3 Diamond
01225 702215 Mrs Hole *churchfarm@ tinyonline.co.uk* www.churchfarm-atworth. freeserve.co.uk **D:** £20.00–£25.00 **S:** £25.00–£35.00 **Beds:** 1F 1T 1D **Baths:** 1 En 1 Sh ⌂ 🖪 ⤝ 📺 🛏 🖂 ♨ ⚓

Kings Stile Cottage, *153 Bath Road, Atworth, Melksham, Wiltshire, SN12 8JR.* Cottage in village location. Convenient for Bath, Bradford-on-Avon, NT properties. Delicious breakfasts. **Open:** All year
01225 706202 (also fax) Mr & Mrs Hughes
sean@kingstile.freeserve.co.uk **D:** £18.00–£20.00 **S:** £20.00–£25.00 **Beds:** 1T 1D ⌂ 🖪 (2) ⤝ 📺 🖂 ♨ ⚓

Avebury

SU1069

6 Beckhampton Road, *Avebury, Marlborough, Wilts, SN8 1QT.* Nearby Avebury Stone Circle, Ridgeway Walk, Silbury Hill, bus route. **Open:** All year (not Xmas)
01672 539588 Mrs Dixon **D:** £16.00–£20.00 **S:** £25.00–£30.00 **Beds:** 1D 1T **Baths:** 1 Sh ⌂ 🖪 (6) 📺 ♨ ⚓

Biddestone

ST8673 ◀ *White Horse*

Home Farm, *Biddestone, Chippenham, Wilts, SN14 7DQ.* C17th Cotswold stone farmhouse in village centre. Visit Bath and Stonehenge. **Open:** All year (not Xmas/New Year)
01249 714475 I Smith **Fax: 01249 701488**
audrey.smith@homefarmandb.co.uk
www.homefarmband b.co.uk **D:** £22.50–
£25.00 **S:** £27.00–£32.00 **Beds:** 2F 1D 1S **Baths:** 3 En 1 Pr ⌂ 🖪 (4) ⤝ 📺 🖂 ♨ ⚓ cc

Home Place, *Biddestone, Chippenham, Wiltshire, SN14 7DG.* End of farmhouse, on village green. Opposite duck pond. **Open:** All year
01249 712928 Ms Hall **D:** £15.00–£17.50 **S:** £15.00–£17.50 **Beds:** 1F 1T 1S **Baths:** 1 Sh ⌂ 🖪 (2) ⤝ 📺 ♨

Bishopstone (Swindon)

SU2483 ◀ *Royal Oak, True Heart*

Prebendal Farm, *Bishopstone, Swindon, Wilts, SN6 8PT.* Farmhouse serving local organic produce, short walk to excellent pubs. **Open:** All year (not Xmas/New Year)
01793 790485 Mrs Selbourne **D:** £25.00 **S:** £25.00 **Beds:** 3D 1T 1S **Baths:** 2 Sh ⌂ 🖪 (12) 📺 🛏 📺 ♨

Box

ST8268 ◀ *Fox & Hounds, Six Bells, Northey Arms, Quarrymans' Arms*

Owl House, *Lower Kingsdown Road, Kingsdown, Box, Corsham, Wilts, SN13 8BB.* **Open:** All year **Grades:** AA 5 Diamond
01225 743883 A Venus **Fax: 01225 744450**
venus@zetnet.co.uk www.owlhouse.co.uk
D: £27.50–£32.50 **S:** £35.00–£38.00 **Beds:** 1F 1D 1T 1S **Baths:** 3 En 1 Pr ⌂ (8) 🖪 (4) ⤝ 📺 ♨
Situated 4m from Bath, offering spectacular views over the Avon Valley.

Saltbox Farm, *Drewetts Mill Lane, Box, Corsham, Wilts, SN13 8PT.* C18th farmhouse set in conservation area of the Box Valley. **Open:** Feb to Nov **Grades:** ETC 3 Diamond
01225 742608 (also fax) M M Gregory
D: £21.00–£23.00 **Beds:** 1F 1D **Baths:** 1 En 1 Pr ⌂ 🖪 (3) ⤝ 📺 🖂 ♨ ⚓

Bradford-on-Avon

ST8261 ◀ *Seven Stars, Hop Pole*

Chard's Barn, *Leigh Grove, Bradford-on-Avon, Wilts, BA15 2RF.* **Open:** All year (not Xmas)
01225 863461 Mr & Mrs Stickney *stickney@ chardsbarn.freeserve.co.uk* **D:** £23.00–£25.00 **S:** £25.00–£35.00 **Beds:** 1D 1T 1S **Baths:** 2 En 1 Pr ⌂ 🖪 (4) ⤝ 📺 🛏 📺 ♨ ⚓ ⚓
Quiet C17th barn in unspoilt countryside with lovely gardens, view and walks. All ground floor, individually styled bedrooms, choice of breakfasts. Historic town and golf course, one mile. Close - Bath, Castle Combe, Longleat. Easy for Salisbury Plain and Stonehenge.

The Locks, *265 Trowbridge Road, Bradford-on-Avon, Wilts, BA15 1UA.* Adjoining canal tow path. Ideal walking/cycling 1m town centre. **Open:** All year
01225 863358 Mrs Benjamin **D:** £17.50–£20.00 **S:** £20.00–£30.00 **Beds:** 1F 2T **Baths:** 1 En 1 Pr 1 Sh ⌂ (3) 🖪 (6) ⤝ 📺 ♨ ⚓

Great Ashley Farm, *Ashley Lane, Bradford-on-Avon, Wilts, BA15 2PP.* Delightful rooms. Great hospitality. Delicious breakfast. Colour brochure. Sliver Award. **Open:** All year (not Xmas)
01225 864563 (also fax) Mrs Rawlings
greatashleyfarm@farmersweekly.net **D:** £20.00–£24.00 **S:** £25.00–£45.00 **Beds:** 1F 2D **Baths:** 3 En ⌂ 🖪 ⤝ 📺 📺 ♨ ⚓

Springfields, *182a Great Ashley, Bradford on Avon, Wilts, BA15 2PP.* Unique ground-level ensuite double room with adjoining dining room/lounge. Peaceful countryside setting. **Open:** All year
01225 866125 Ms Rawlings **D:** £20.00–£22.50 **S:** £30.00–£35.00 **Beds:** 1D **Baths:** 1En ⤝ 📺 ✕ ♨

Bratton

ST9152

The Duke Inn, *Melbourne Street, Bratton, Westbury, Wilts, BA13 4RW.* Traditional oak-beamed village inn serving good fresh food, real ale. **Open:** All year
01380 830242 Mr Overend **Fax: 01380 831239 D:** £25.00 **S:** £30.00 **Beds:** 2D 1T **Baths:** 2 Sh ⌂ (14) 🖪 (30) ⤝ 📺 ✕ 📺 ♨ ⚓ ❋ ⚓ cc

Bremhill

ST9773

Lowbridge Farm, *Bremhill, Calne, Wilts, SN11 9HE.* Old thatched farmhouse. Varied stock. Scenic views. Places to visit. **Open:** All year **01249 815889** Miss Sinden **D:** £25.00 **S:** £25.00 **Beds:** 1F 1D 1T **Baths:** 1 Sh ⑤ 🄿 (8) ⚥ 📺 🍴 ✕ 📹 🛏 ✿ ▦

Bromham

ST9665

Wayside, *Chittoe Heath, Bromham, Chippenham, Wilts, SN152EH.* **Open:** All year **01380 850458 (also fax)** Mr Collins *andrew.imi@virgin.net* **D:** £22.50–£25.00 **S:** £30.00 **Beds:** 1F 1D 1T **Baths:** 2 En 1 Pr ⑤ 🄿 (6) ⚥ 📺 🍴 ▦ ♿ ▦
Situated in the heart of the Wiltshire countryside yet within easy distance of Bath.

Calne

ST9971

Lower Sands Farm, *Low Lane, Calne, Wilts, SN11 8TR.* Old farmhouse, v. quiet, homely and friendly. Good breakfast, large garden. **Open:** All year (not Xmas) **01249 812402** Mrs Henly **D:** £20.00 **S:** £20.00 **Beds:** 1D 1T 1S **Baths:** 1 Sh 🄿 (10) 📺 ▦ ▦

Calstone Wellington

SU0268

Manor Farmhouse, *Calstone Wellington, Calne, Wiltshire, SN11 8PY.* Unique, secluded downland location. Interesting house with genuine history and Victorian 4 poster. **Open:** All year **01249 816804** Mrs Maundell **Fax:** 01249 817966 *calstonebandb@farmersweekly.net* www.calstone.co.uk **D:** £27.50–£32.50 **S:** £30.00–£40.00 **Beds:** 2D **Baths:** 2 En ⑤ (12) 🄿 (2) ⚥ 📺 ✕ 📹 ▦ ▦

Chapmanslade

ST8348

Spinney Farm, *Thoulstone, Chapmanslade, Westbury, Wilts, BA13 4AQ.* In heart of Wiltshire countryside. Easy reach of Bath, Longleat. **Open:** All year **01373 832412** Mrs Hoskins **D:** £19.00 **S:** £20.00 **Beds:** 1F 1D 1T **Baths:** 2 Sh ⑤ 🄿 (8) 📺 🍴 ✕ 📹 ▦ ▦

Charlton (Malmesbury)

ST9588   🍺 *Horse & Groom*

Stonehill Farm, *Charlton (Malmesbury), Malmesbury, Wilts, SN16 9DY.* C15th farmhouse on dairy farm, warm welcome, delicious breakfasts. **Open:** All year **01666 823310 (also fax)** Mr & Mrs Edwards *johnedna@stonehillfarm.fsnet.co.uk* **D:** £22.00–£25.00 **S:** £22.00–£27.00 **Beds:** 2D 1T **Baths:** 1 En 1 Sh ⑤ 🄿 (3) 📺 🍴 ▦ ▦

Charlton (Shaftesbury)

ST9022

Charnwood Cottage, *Charlton, Shaftesbury, Dorset, SP7 9LZ.* C17th thatched cottage with lovely garden. Good base for touring. **Open:** All year (not Xmas/New Year) **01747 828310 (also fax)** Mr & Mrs Morgan **D:** £19.00 **Beds:** 1T 1D **Baths:** 1 Sh 🄿 (2) 📺 ▦

Chippenham

ST9173

Beanhill Farm, *Main Road, Christian Malford, Chippenham, Wiltshire, SN15 4BS.* **Open:** All year **Grades:** ETC 3 Diamond **01249 720672 & 07775 660000 (M)** Mrs Kimber **Fax:** 01249 720672 *bb@ beanhillfarm.fsbusiness.co.uk* **D:** £20.00–£25.00 **S:** £20.00–£25.00 **Beds:** 1F 1D 1S **Baths:** 1 Sh ⑤ 🄿 (9) ⚥ 📺 📹 ▦ ♿ ▦
Beautiful Cotswold stone farmhouse on working livestock farm, offering a warm welcome for the business person and tourist alike. Generous quality breakfasts. Convenient for M4 (J17 3m). Excellent base for exploring the Cotswolds, Bath, Chippenham and Avebury. Also for visiting the racing at Castle Combe Circuit.

Bramleys, *73 Marshfield Road, Chippenham, Wilts, SN15 1JR.* Large Victorian house, Grade II Listed. **Open:** All year **Grades:** ETC 1 Diamond **01249 653770** Mrs Swatton **D:** £18.00–£20.00 **S:** £17.00–£19.00 **Beds:** 1F 3T 1S **Baths:** 1 Pr 1 Sh ⑤ 🄿 (4) ⚥ 📺 📹 ▦ ▦

Chiseldon

SU1879

Courtleigh House, *40 Draycott Road, Chiseldon, Swindon, Wilts, SN4 0LS.* Large well-appointed country home; large garden with downland views. **Open:** All year (not Xmas) **Grades:** ETC 4 Diamond **01793 740246** Ms Hibberd *rhib494369@ aol.com* **D:** £20.00–£22.50 **S:** £22.00–£27.00 **Beds:** 2T 1S **Baths:** 1 En 1 Sh ⑤ 🄿 (3) ⚥ 📺 ▦

Christian Malford

ST9678   🍺 *Mermaid, Rising Sun*

Beanhill Farm, *Main Road, Christian Malford, Chippenham, Wiltshire, SN15 4BS.* Beautiful Cotswold stone farmhouse on working livestock farm, offering a warm welcome. **Open:** All year **Grades:** ETC 3 Diamond **01249 720672 & 07775 660000 (M)** Mrs Kimber **Fax:** 01249 720672 *bb@ beanhillfarm.fsbusiness.co.uk* **D:** £20.00–£25.00 **S:** £20.00–£25.00 **Beds:** 1F 1D 1S **Baths:** 1 Sh ⑤ 🄿 (9) ⚥ 📺 ▦ ♿ ▦

Codford St Mary

ST9739

Glebe Cottage, *Church Lane, Codford St. Mary, Warminster, Wiltshire, BA12 0PJ.* 250-year-old former home of the Sexton, situated in attractive Wylye Valley. **Open:** All year (not Xmas/New Year) **01985 850565 & 01985 850666** Mrs Richardson-Aitken **Fax:** 01985 850666 *bobr-a@care4free.net* **D:** £25.00–£27.00 **S:** £25.00–£27.00 **Beds:** 1F 1T **Baths:** 2 Pr ⑤ (3) 🄿 (3) ⚥ 📺 ▦ ▦

Codford St Peter

ST9640

The George Hotel, *Codford St Peter, Warminster, Wilts, BA12 0NG.* Friendly village, family pub. **Open:** All year **01985 850270 (also fax)** *georgepub@tesco.net* **D:** £21.25 **S:** £28.50 **Beds:** 3F 1T **Baths:** 2 En 1 Sh ⑤ ⚥ 📺 ✕ 📹 ▦ ▦ cc

Coombe Bissett

SU1026   🍺 *Radnor Arms, Fox & Goose, Yew Tree*

Swaynes Firs Farm, *Grimsdyke, Coombe Bissett, Salisbury, SP5 5RF.* Spacious farmhouse on working farm with horses, cattle, poultry, geese and duck ponds. **Open:** All year (not Xmas) **Grades:** ETC 3 Diamond **01725 519240** Mr Shering *swaynes.firs@ virgin.net* www.swaynesfirs.co.uk **D:** £20.00–£22.00 **S:** £25.00–£30.00 **Beds:** 1F 2T **Baths:** 3 En ⑤ 🄿 (6) 📺 ▦ ▦

Cross Farm, *Coombe Bissett, Salisbury, Wilts, SP5 4LY.* Farmhouse in peaceful setting. Attractive village. Good walking. Many places to visit. **Open:** All year **01722 718293** Mrs Kittermaster **Fax:** 01722 718665 *s.j.kittermaster@talk21.com* **D:** £20.00 **S:** £20.00 **Beds:** 1F 1T 1S **Baths:** 2 Sh ⑤ 🄿 (4) ⚥ 📺 🍴 📹 ▦ ✿ ▦

Please respect a B&B's wishes regarding children, animals and smoking

BEDROOMS

D = Double
T = Twin
S = Single
F = Family

Corsham

ST8670 🍺 The George

Park Farm Barn, Westrop, Corsham, Wiltshire, SN13 9QF. **Open:** All year **01249 715911** Mrs Waldron **Fax: 01249 701107** thewaldrons@lineone.net www.parkfarm.co.uk **D:** £22.50–£25.00 **S:** £30.00 **Beds:** 1T 2D **Baths:** 3 En ⚡ 🅿 (4) ⅍ 📺 📺 🖾 ♨
Situated in the delightful hamlet of Westrop, one mile from Corsham. Our converted C18th tithe barn offers superb B&B in recently rebuilt farm buildings adjacent to our barn. Corsham Court, Bath, Lacock, Castle Combe and Bradford-on-Avon are within easy reach.

Church Farm, Hartham Park, Corsham, Wiltshire, SN13 0PU. Cotswold farmhouse in rural location, stunning views, quiet and peaceful. **Open:** All year (not Xmas/New Year) **Grades:** ETC 4 Diamond **01249 715180** Mrs Jones **Fax: 01249 715572** kmjbandb@aol.com www.churchfarm.cjb.net **D:** £22.50–£25.00 **S:** £25.00–£32.00 **Beds:** 1F 1D 1S **Baths:** 2 En 1 Pr ⚡ (1) 🅿 (6) ⅍ 📺 📺 🖾 ♨

Corsley

ST8246

Sturford Mead Farm, Corsley, Warminster, Wilts, BA12 7QU. Farmhouse in Area of Outstanding Natural Beauty close to Longleat. **Open:** All year **01373 832213 (also fax)** Mrs Corp lynn_sturford.bed@virgin.net **D:** £22.00 **S:** £30.00 **Beds:** 1D 2T **Baths:** 2 En 1 Pr ⚡ 🅿 (6) ⅍ 📺 📺 🖾 ♨

Crockerton

ST8642 🍺 Bath Arms

Tanhouse Cottage, Crockerton, Warminster, Wilts, BA12 8AU. C16th farmhouse, log fires, beams. **Open:** All year (not Xmas/New Year) **01985 214816** S J Dickinson **D:** £20.00 **S:** £20.00 **Beds:** 1T 1D 2S **Baths:** 2 Sh ⚡ 🅿 (6) 📺 ♨ 🖾 ♨

Stoneyside, PottersHill, Crockerton, Warminster, Wiltshire, BA12 8AS. Lovely peaceful bungalow, easy access, garden to relax in with lovely views of valley. **Open:** All year (not Xmas) **Grades:** ETC 3 Diamond **01985 218149** Mrs Elkins **D:** £21.00–£23.00 **S:** £27.00–£32.00 **Beds:** 1D 1T **Baths:** 1 En 1 Pr ⚡ 🅿 (2) ⅍ 📺 🖾 ♨ ♨

Dauntsey

ST9982

Olivemead Farm, Olivemead Lane, Dauntsey, Chippenham, Wilts, SN15 4JQ. Delightful C18th farmhouse, convenient M4, Bath, Cotswolds, Stonehenge. **Open:** All year (not Xmas) **01666 510205 (also fax)** Mrs Candy olivemead@farming.co.uk **D:** £20.00 **S:** £20.00–£22.00 **Beds:** 1F 1D 1T **Baths:** 1 Sh ⚡ 🅿 (6) ⅍ 📺 🐾 ♨

Devizes

SU0061 🍺 Moonrakers, Bell By The Green

Littleton Lodge, Littleton Panell, Devizes, Wilts, SN10 4ES. Comfortable Victorian house. In conservation village, garden, good pubs nearby. **Open:** All year **Grades:** ETC 4 Diamond, AA 4 Diamond **01380 813131** Mr & Mrs Linton **Fax: 01380 816969** stay@littletonlodge.co.uk www.littletonlodge.co.uk **D:** £25.00–£30.00 **S:** £30.00–£40.00 **Beds:** 2D 1T **Baths:** 3 En ⚡ 🅿 (5) ⅍ 📺 📺 🖾 ♨ ♨ cc

Eastleigh House, 3 Eastleigh Road, Devizes, Wilts, SN10 3EE. Relaxed atmosphere in comfortable accommodation, centrally located for Bath, Salisbury and Avebury. **Open:** All year (not Xmas/New Year) **Grades:** ETC 4 Diamond **01380 726918 (also fax)** Mrs Davis **D:** £22.50–£23.50 **S:** £25.00–£30.00 **Beds:** 1T 1S **Baths:** 2 En ⚡ 🅿 (3) 📺 📺 🖾 ♨

Lower Foxhangers Farm, Rowde, Devizes, Wilts, SN10 1SS. Relax with pleasant dreams in our rural retreat amid the Wiltshire countryside. **Open:** May to Oct **Grades:** ETC 3 Diamond **01380 828254 (also fax)** Mr & Mrs Fletcher sales@foxhangers.co.uk www.foxhangers.co.uk **D:** £20.00–£22.00 **S:** £22.00–£25.00 **Beds:** 2D 1T **Baths:** 1 Pr 2 En ⚡ 🅿 (4) ⅍ 📺 🐾 📺 ♨

▬▬▬▬▬▬▬▬▬
Planning a longer stay? Always ask for any special rates

Craven House, Station Road, Devizes, Wilts, SN10 1BZ. Victorian house 50 yds from centre for restaurants and pubs. **Open:** All year **01380 723514** Mrs Shaw **D:** £20.00 **S:** £20.00 **Beds:** 1F 1D 2T **Baths:** 2 En 1 Pr 1 Sh ⚡ 📺 ✕ 🖾 ♨

Gate House, Wick Lane, Devizes, Wilts, SN10 5DW. Spacious, comfortable, peaceful, in quiet road. A few minutes from Devizes. **Open:** All year (not Xmas/New Year) **Grades:** ETC 3 Diamond **01380 725283** Mrs Stratton **Fax: 01380 722382** laura@gatehouse-b-and-b.freeserve.co.uk freeserve.co.uk **D:** £20.00–£22.50 **S:** £25.00 **Beds:** 1T 1D 1S **Baths:** 1 En 1 Sh 🅿 (8) ⅍ 📺 📺 🖾 ♨

Eastcott Manor, Easterton, Devizes, Wilts, SN10 4PL. Elizabethan manor house in own grounds. Tranquil location. **Open:** All year (not Xmas) **01380 813313** Mrs Firth **D:** £24.00–£27.00 **S:** £24.00–£27.00 **Beds:** 1D 1T 2S **Baths:** 2 En 2 Pr ⚡ 🅿 (10) 📺 🐾 ✕ ♨

Glenholme Guest House, 77 Nursteed Road, Devizes, Wilts, SN10 3AJ. Friendly, comfortable house. Warm welcome. Lovely historic town. **Open:** All year **Grades:** ETC 2 Diamond **01380 723187** Mrs Bishop **D:** £36.00 **S:** £20.00 **Beds:** 1F 1T **Baths:** 1 Sh ⚡ 🅿 📺 🐾 📺 🖾 ♨

East Knoyle

ST8830 🍺 Fox & Hounds

Moors Farmhouse, East Knoyle, Salisbury, Wilts, SP3 6BU. A perfect countryside retreat. Beautiful and interesting area. **Open:** All year (not Xmas/New Year) **01747 830385** Mrs Reading **Fax: 01747 830877** romreading@moorsfarm.demon.co.uk **D:** £27.00 **S:** £35.00 **Beds:** 1F 1T ⚡ 🅿 (6) 📺 📺 ♨

Easterton

SU0255

Eastcott Manor, Easterton, Devizes, Wilts, SN10 4PL. Elizabethan manor house in own grounds. Tranquil location. **Open:** All year (not Xmas) **01380 813313** Mrs Firth **D:** £24.00–£27.00 **S:** £24.00–£27.00 **Beds:** 1D 1T 2S **Baths:** 2 En 2 Pr ⚡ 🅿 (10) 📺 🐾 ✕ ♨

Easton Royal

SU2060

Follets, Easton Royal, Pewsey, Wilts, SN9 5LZ. Convenient for Kennet & Avon canal. Stonehenge and Avebury. **Open:** All year (not Xmas/New Year) **01672 810619 (also fax)** Mrs Landless margaretlandless@talk21.com **D:** £22.50–£25.00 **S:** £30.00–£35.00 **Beds:** 2D 1T **Baths:** 3 En 🅿 (6) ⅍ 📺 ✕ 📺 🖾 ♨

Enford

SU1351

Enford House, Enford, Pewsey, Wilts, *SN9 6DJ.* Salisbury Plain. River village, old rectory, beautiful garden, thatched wall. **Open:** All year (not Xmas) **01980 670414** Mr Campbell **D:** £18.00 **S:** £20.00 **Beds:** 1D 2T **Baths:** 2 Sh ⌂ ▣ (5) ⏚ ▥ ↑ ✕ Ⓥ ▦ ⚲

Gastard

ST8868

Heatherly Cottage, Ladbrook Lane, Gastard, Corsham, Wilts, *SN13 9PE.* C17th cottage set in quiet location with large garden. Guests have separate wing. **Open:** All year (not Xmas/New Year) **01249 701402** Mrs Daniel **Fax: 01249 701412** *ladbrook1@aol.com* **D:** £23.00–£25.00 **S:** £27.00–£30.00 **Beds:** 1T 2D **Baths:** 3 En ⌂ (10) ▣ (8) ⏚ Ⓥ Ⓥ ▦ ⚲

Hartham Park

ST8672

Church Farm, Hartham Park, Corsham, Wiltshire, *SN13 0PU.* Cotswold farmhouse in rural location, stunning views, quiet and peaceful. **Open:** All year (not Xmas/New Year) **Grades:** ETC 4 Diamond **01249 715180** Mrs Jones **Fax: 01249 715572** *kmjbandb@aol.com* www.churchfarm.cjb.net **D:** £22.50–£25.00 **S:** £25.00–£32.00 **Beds:** 1F 1D 1S **Baths:** 2 En 1 Pr ⌂ (1) ▣ (6) ⏚ Ⓥ Ⓥ ▦ ⚲

Hilmarton

SU0275   ⌖ White Horse

Burfoots, 1 The Close, Hilmarton, Calne, Wilts, *SN11 8TQ.* Situated between Bath/ Swindon, Lacock Castle Combe, Avebury. M4 nearby. **Open:** All year (not Xmas/New Year) **Grades:** ETC 4 Diamond **01249 760492** Mr & Mrs Cooke **Fax: 01249 760609** *cookeburfoots@aol.com* www.burfoots. co.uk **D:** £20.00–£25.00 **S:** £27.00 **Beds:** 1T 1D 1S **Baths:** 3 En ⌂ (10) ▣ (5) ⏚ Ⓥ ▦ ⚲

Hilperton

ST8759

62b Paxcroft Cottages, Devizes Road, Hilperton, Trowbridge, Wiltshire, *BA14 6JB.* Small friendly house on the outskirts of Trowbridge. Far-reaching views overlooking the Wiltshire Downs. **Open:** All year (not Xmas) **Grades:** ETC 4 Diamond **01225 765838** S J Styles *paxcroftcottages@ hotmail.com* **D:** £22.00 **S:** £22.00–£25.00 **Beds:** 1F 1T 1D **Baths:** 2 En 1 Pr ⌂ ▣ (6) ⏚ Ⓥ ✕ Ⓥ ▦ ⚲

Hindon

ST9132

Chicklade Lodge, Chicklade, Hindon, Salisbury, Wilts, *SP3 5SU.* Charming Victorian cottage. Under 2 hours' drive from Heathrow. **Open:** All year **01747 820389** Mrs Jerram *aud.jerram@ virgin.net* **D:** £20.00 **S:** £25.00 **Beds:** 2T 1D **Baths:** 1 Sh ⌂ (5) ▣ (4) ⏚ ↑ ✕ Ⓥ ▦ ⚲

Kilmington

ST7736

The Red Lion Inn, On B3092 (Mere to Frome road), Kilmington, Warminster, Wilts, *BA12 6RP.* Unspoilt C15th traditional inn. Stourhead 1 mile. Comfortable beds, good breakfasts. **Open:** All year (not Xmas/New Year) **01985 844263** Mr Gibbs **D:** £17.50 **S:** £25.00 **Beds:** 1D 1T **Baths:** 1 Sh ⌂ (4) ▣ (25) ⏚ ↑ ▦ ⚲

Kington Langley

ST9277   ⌖ Wellesley Arms

Finnygook, Days Lane, Kington Langley, Chippenham, Wilts, *SN15 5PA.* Secluded house and garden overlooking countryside, ideal touring base, Cotswolds, Mendips, Wiltshire Downs M4 J17 1 mile. **Open:** All year (not Xmas/New Year) **01249 750411 (also fax)** Mrs Weston *accommodation@finnygook.fsnet.co.uk* **D:** £18.50–£25.00 **S:** £18.50–£30.00 **Beds:** 2T 2D 1S **Baths:** 1 Pr 1 Sh ▣ (4) ⏚ Ⓥ Ⓥ ▦ ⚲

Kington St Michael

ST8977

The Jolly Huntsman Inn, Kington St Michael, Chippenham, Wilts, *SN14 6JB.* Very friendly country pub, lots of local amenities. Easily accessible. **Open:** All year **01249 750305** Mr Lawrence **Fax: 01249 750182 D:** £30.00 **S:** £45.00 **Beds:** 3F 3D **Baths:** 6 En ⌂ ▣ (15) ⏚ Ⓥ ↑ ✕ Ⓥ ▦ ⚲ cc

---

RATES

D = Price range per person sharing in a double or twin room

S = Price range for a single room

National Grid References given are for villages, towns and cities – not for individual houses

Lacock

ST9168

The Old Rectory, Lacock, Chippenham, Wilts, *SN15 2JZ.* **Open:** All year **Grades:** ETC 4 Diamond **01249 730335** Mrs Sexton **Fax: 01249 730166** *elaine@oldrectorylacock.co.uk* **D:** £22.50–£27.50 **S:** £25.00–£45.00 **Beds:** 2F 3D 1T **Baths:** 4 En ⌂ ▣ (6) ⏚ Ⓥ ↑ ▦ ⚲ Superb Gothic Victorian architecture, in 8 acres of grounds and gardens, many original features, 4-poster beds. Excellent pubs a stroll away in medieval Lacock. Good location for tourists and business people, M4 J17 close by. Bath 12m, London 2 hrs. Recomm in 'Independent on Sunday'.

Lacock Pottery, The Tanyard, Lacock, Chippenham, Wilts, *SN15 2LB.* Stay at Lacock's working pottery. Rooms overlooking beautiful medieval church. **Open:** All year (not Xmas/New Year) **Grades:** ETC 4 Diamond **01249 730266** Mrs McDowell **Fax: 01249 730948** *simone@lacockbedandbreakfast.com* www.lacockbedandbreakfast.com **D:** £29.50– £39.50 **S:** £37.00–£59.00 **Beds:** 1T 2D **Baths:** 2 En 1 Pr ⌂ ▣ (6) ⏚ Ⓥ ↑ Ⓥ ▦ ⚲ cc

Landford

SU2619

Springfields, Lyndhurst Road, Landford, Salisbury, Wilts, *SP5 2AS.* Friendly hospitality close to New Forest, Salisbury, Southampton. Lovely rooms. **Open:** All year **01794 390093 (also fax)** Mrs Westlake *springfields_bb@libertysurf.co.uk* web.libertysurf.co.uk/springfieldsbandb **D:** £17.00–£20.00 **S:** £25.00 **Beds:** 2D 1S **Baths:** 2 Sh ⌂ ▣ (6) ⏚ Ⓥ ↑ ▦ ⚲

Laverstock

SU1530

The Twitterings, 73 Church Road, Laverstock, Salisbury, Wiltshire, *SP11QZ.* Quiet location. Comfortable self contained rooms. English breakfast a speciality. **Open:** All year (not Xmas/New Year) **01722 321760** Mrs Henly **D:** £20.00 **S:** £25.00– £30.00 **Beds:** 1T 1D **Baths:** 2 En ⌂ ▣ (4) ⏚ Ⓥ Ⓥ ▦ ⚲ ⚲

Planning a longer stay? Always ask for any special rates

Leigh

SU0692 ◀ *Forresters Arms*

Waterhay Farm, *Leigh, Cricklade, Swindon, Wilts, SN6 6QY.* Working farm. Cotswold stone beamed farmhouse set in peaceful surroundings. **Open:** All year (not Xmas/New Year) **01285 861253** Mrs Rumming **D:** £20.00–£25.00 **S:** £21.00–£30.00 **Beds:** 1T 1D **Baths:** 2 En ▣ (2) ⌫ ⊡ ▥ ♨

Little Langford

SU0436

Little Langford Farmhouse, *Little Langford, Salisbury, Wilts, SP3 4NR.* Elegant Victorian farmhouse. Beautiful countryside. Excellent sightseeing area. **Open:** Feb to Nov **Grades:** ETC 5 Diamond **01722 790205** Mrs Helyer **Fax: 01722 790086** *bandb@littlelangford.co.uk* www.dmac.co.uk/llf **D:** £26.00–£28.00 **S:** £40.00–£45.00 **Beds:** 1F 1T 1D **Baths:** 1 En 2 Pr ▣ (5) ⌫ ⊡ ⊡ ▥ ♨

Little Somerford

ST9684

Lovett Farm, *Little Somerford, Chippenham, Wilts, SN15 5BP.* Delightful farmhouse on working farm with beautiful views from the attractive ensuite bedrooms. **Open:** All year **01666 823268 (also fax)** Mrs Barnes *lovetts_farm@hotmail.com* **D:** £23.00–£25.00 **S:** £25.00–£30.00 **Beds:** 1D 1T **Baths:** 2 En ⌂ (3) ▣ (5) ⌫ ⊡ ▥ ♨

Littleton Panell

ST9954

Littleton Lodge, *Littleton Panell, Devizes, Wilts, SN10 4ES.* Comfortable Victorian house. In conservation village, garden, good pubs nearby. **Open:** All year **Grades:** ETC 4 Diamond, AA 4 Diamond **01380 813131** Mr & Mrs Linton **Fax: 01380 816969** *stay@littletonlodge.co.uk* www.littletonlodge.co.uk **D:** £25.00–£30.00 **S:** £30.00–£40.00 **Beds:** 2D 1T **Baths:** 3 En ⌂ ▣ (5) ⌫ ⊡ ▥ ♨ ⅄ ⚑ cc

Lockeridge

SU1467

The Taffrail, *Back Lane, Lockeridge, Marlborough, Wilts, SN8 4ED.* Great welcome, comfort, tranquillity. Delightful modern home and lovely garden. **Open:** Jan to Nov **01672 861266 (also fax)** Mrs Spencer *spencer.taffrail@ukgateway.net* **D:** £17.50 **S:** £20.00 **Beds:** 1D 1T 1S **Baths:** 1 Sh ⌂ (8) ▣ (3) ⌫ ⊡ ▥

Lower Wanborough

SU2083

Iris Cottage, *Bury Croft, Lower Wanborough, Swindon, Wilts, SN4 0AP.* Very comfortable village cottage. Swindon 4 miles. Near Ridgeway Path. **Open:** All year (not Xmas) **01793 790591** Mrs Rosier **D:** £19.00 **S:** £20.00 **Beds:** 2S **Baths:** 1 Sh ▣ (2) ⌫ ⊡ ▥

Ludwell

ST9122

Ye Olde Wheelwrights, *Birdbush, Ludwell, Shaftesbury, Dorset, SP7 9NH.* Accommodation in separate annexe. Children and families welcome. Hearty breakfast. **Open:** Apr to Oct **01747 828955** C Dieppe *charles@cdieppe.freeserve.co.uk* **D:** £17.50–£20.00 **S:** £20.00–£22.00 **Beds:** 1T 1D **Baths:** 1 Sh ⌂ ▣ ⌫ ⊡ ♨

Malmesbury

ST9387

Bremilham House, *Bremilham Road, Malmesbury, Wilts, SN16 0DQ.* **Open:** All year (not Xmas) **Grades:** ETC 3 Diamond **01666 822680** Mrs Ball **D:** £18.00 **S:** £20.00 **Beds:** 2D 1T **Baths:** 2 Sh ⌂ ▣ (3) ⌫ ⊡ ⚑ ▥ ♨

Delightful Edwardian cottage set in a mature walled garden in a quiet location on the edge of historic Malmesbury, England's oldest borough. The town, dominated by a stunning Norman Abbey, is central for Bath, Cheltenham, Salisbury and the glorious Cotswolds.

Stonehill Farm, *Charlton, Malmesbury, Wilts, SN16 9DY.* C15th farmhouse on dairy farm, warm welcome, delicious breakfasts. **Open:** All year **01666 823310 (also fax)** Mr & Mrs Edwards *johnedna@stonehillfarm.fsnet.co.uk* **D:** £22.00–£25.00 **S:** £22.00–£27.00 **Beds:** 2D 1T **Baths:** 1 En 1 Sh ⌂ ▣ (3) ⊡ ⚑ ▥ ♨

Kings Arms Hotel, *High Street, Malmesbury, Wilts, SN16 9AA.* Warm welcome. Meals served using fresh produce. Excellent restaurant. **Open:** All year **Grades:** ETC 4 Diamond **01666 823383** Mr Timms www.malmesburywilts.freeserve.co.uk **D:** £27.00–£33.00 **S:** £35.00–£45.00 **Beds:** 1F 1T 5D 1S **Baths:** 8 En ⌂ ▣ (20) ⌫ ⊡ ▥ ♨ cc

All details shown are as supplied by B&B owners in Autumn 2001

BEDROOMS
D = Double
T = Twin
S = Single
F = Family

Manningford Abbots

SU1459 ◀ *French Horn, Seven Stars*

Huntlys, *Manningford Abbotts, Pewsey, Wilts, SN9 6HZ.* Thatched farmhouse in Vale of Pewsey. Comfortable, peaceful, wonderful breakfasts. **Open:** All year **Grades:** ETC 3 Diamond **01672 563663** Mrs Andrews **Fax: 01672 851249 D:** £20.00–£23.00 **S:** £22.00–£25.00 ⌂ (6) ▣ (2) ⌫ ⊡ ⚑ ✕ ⊡ ▥ ♨

Manton

SU1768

Sunrise Farm, *Manton, Marlborough, Wilts, SN8 4HL.* Peacefully located approximately 1 mile from Marlborough. Friendly, comfortable, relaxing atmosphere. **Open:** Mar to Oct **01672 512878 (also fax)** Mrs Couzens **D:** £19.00–£20.00 **S:** £19.00–£25.00 **Beds:** 1D 2T **Baths:** 2 Pr ⌂ (14) ▣ (3) ⌫ ⊡ ▥ ♨

Marlborough

SU1869 ◀ *The Sun*

Browns Farm, *Marlborough, Wilts, SN8 4ND.* Peaceful farmhouse on edge of Savernake Forest. Overlooking open farmland. **Open:** All year **01672 515129** Mrs Crockford *crockford@farming.co.uk* **D:** £16.00–£20.00 **S:** £20.00–£25.00 **Beds:** 1F 1T 2D **Baths:** 1 En 1 Sh ⌂ ▣ (6) ⌫ ⊡ ⚑ ▥ ♨

13 Hyde Lane, *Marlborough, Wiltshire, SN8 1JL.* Comfortable home in town centre and near lovely walking country. **Open:** Easter to Oct **Grades:** ETC 3 Diamond **01672 514415** Mrs Luxton **D:** £19.00 **S:** £20.00–£25.00 **Beds:** 2T **Baths:** 1 Pr ⌂ (5) ⌫ ▥ ♨

West View, *Barnfield, Marlborough, Wiltshire, SN8 2AX.* Delightful peaceful, rural home, close to town. Ideal walkers, cyclists. **Open:** All year **01672 515583** Maggie Trevelyan-Hall **Fax: 01672 519014** *maggiestewart@euphony.net* www.westviewb-b.co.uk **D:** £20.00–£25.00 **S:** £35.00–£45.00 **Beds:** 1F 3D **Baths:** 2 Pr 1 Sh ⌂ ▣ (3) ⌫ ⚑ ✕ ⊡ ▥ ♨ ♨

Melksham

ST9063   ◀ The Barge, Three Magpies, King's Arms

Springfield B&B, *403 The Spa, Melksham, Wiltshire, SN12 6QL.* Charming 'historic' family home. Lovely gardens. Quiet location. Returning clients. **Open:** All year **Grades:** ETC 4 Diamond **01225 703694 (also fax)** J & P Jory **D:** £23.00–£26.00 **S:** £25.00–£36.00 **Beds:** 1F 1T 1D **Baths:** 1 En 1 Pr ॐ ▣ (3) 📺 🅥 💷 🖎

The Old Manor, *48 Spa Road, Melksham, Wiltshire, SN12 7NY.* Old manor house in 0.75 acre. Splendid breakfast. **Open:** All year **Grades:** ETC 3 Diamond **01225 793803** *theoldmanor@yahoo.co.uk* **D:** £20.00–£23.00 **S:** £25.00–£35.00 **Beds:** 1F 2T 1D **Baths:** 1 En 2 Sh ॐ ▣ (8) ⌇ 📺 🅥 💷 🖎

Mere

ST8132

Downleaze, *North Street, Mere, Warminster, Wilts, BA12 6HH.* Comfortable red brick house, quiet, close to town centre. Warm welcome. Stourhead - 2 miles. **Open:** All year (not Xmas/New Year) **01747 860876** Mrs La D: £16.00–£18.00 **S:** £17.50–£20.00 **Beds:** 1D 1T **Baths:** 1 Sh ॐ (5) ▣ (6) ⌇ 📺 🅥 💷 🖎

Netheravon

SU1549

Paddock House, *High Street, Netheravon, Salisbury, Wiltshire, SP4 9QP.* Comfortable village house in Netheravon. Close to Stonehenge and Avebury. **Open:** All year (not Xmas/New Year) **01980 670401 (also fax)** MrDavis **D:** £18.00–£20.00 **S:** £18.00–£20.00 **Beds:** 1T 1D **Baths:** 1 En 1 Sh ॐ (3) ▣ (2) ⌇ 📺 💷 🖎

Netton

SU1336

The Old Bakery, *Netton, Salisbury, Wilts, SP4 6AW.* The Old Bakery is a pleasantly modernised former village bakery in the Woodford Valley. **Open:** All year (not Xmas) **Grades:** ETC 3 Diamond **01722 782351** Mrs Dunlop *valahen@aol.com* www.members.aol.com/valahen **D:** £18.00–£22.00 **S:** £25.00–£30.00 **Beds:** 1D 1T 1S **Baths:** 3 En ॐ (5) ▣ (3) 📺 💷 🖎

Thorntons, *Netton, Salisbury, Wilts, SP4 6AW.* Tranquil village convenient for Salisbury and Stonehenge. Home cooking a speciality. **Open:** All year (not Xmas) **01722 782535 (also fax)** Mrs Bridger **D:** £19.00–£25.50 **S:** £20.00–£27.00 **Beds:** 1F 1D 1S **Baths:** 2 Sh ॐ (5) ▣ ⌇ 📺 ✕ 🅥 💷 🖎 & 🖎

Avonbank, *Netton, Salisbury, Wilts, SP4 6AW.* Comfortable modern house with very pretty garden overlooking water meadow and River Avon. **Open:** All year (not Xmas) **01722 782331** Mrs Vincent *vincent@netton.freeserve.co.uk* **D:** £16.00–£20.00 **S:** £20.00–£25.00 **Beds:** 3F 2T 1D **Baths:** 1 En 1 Sh ॐ ▣ (3) 📺 🅥 💷 & 🖎

Nomansland

SU2517

Clovenway House, *Forest Road, Nomansland, Sailsbury, Wiltshire, SP5 2BN.* Country house, garden overlook New Forest, close village pub, restaurant. **Open:** All year **01794 390620 (also fax)** Mrs Fryer **D:** £18.00–£22.00 **S:** £20.00–£30.00 **Beds:** 1F 1T 1D **Baths:** 1 En 2 Pr ॐ (5) ▣ (4) ⌇ 📺 🐾 🅥 💷 🖎

Oaksey

ST9993   ◀ Wheatsheaf , Bakers' Arms

Manby's Farm, *Oaksey, Malmesbury, Wiltshire, SN16 9SA.* **Open:** All year **Grades:** ETC 4 Diamond **01666 577399** Mr Shewry-Fitzgerald **Fax: 01666 577241** *manbys@oaksey.junglelink.co.uk* www.cotswoldbandb.co **D:** £23.00–£25.00 **S:** £30.00–£35.00 **Beds:** 1F 1T 1D **Baths:** 3 En ॐ (3) ▣ ⌇ 📺 🅥 💷 & 🖎 ⊹ **cc** A warm welcome awaits guests at our farmhouse, situation on the Wilts/Glos border. Bright, cheerful rooms, ground and first floor, adaptable accommodation. Relax over breakfast in our elegant dining room. Ideal location for visiting Bath, Cotswolds, Oxford. Wheelchair friendly.

Ogbourne St George

SU1974

The Inn With The Well, *Marlborough Road, Ogbourne St George, Marlborough, Wilts, SN8 1SQ.* Explore the Marlborough Downs. Friendly, good food and excellent rooms. **Open:** All year (not Xmas/New Year) **01672 841445** Mr & Mrs Shaw **Fax: 01672 841056** *theinnwiththewell@compuserve.com* www.theinnwiththewell.com **D:** £25.00–£30.00 **S:** £40.00–£45.00 **Beds:** 3T 2D 1F **Baths:** 6 Pr ॐ ▣ (15) ⌇ 📺 🐾 ✕ 🅥 💷 🖎 ⊹ **cc**

Foxlynch, *Bytham Road, Ogbourne St George, Marlborough, Wilts, SN8 1TD.* Bunkroom, 2 bunks make up double bed, TV, central heating, ensuite, camping - 4 tents. **Open:** All year **01672 841307** Mr Edwins **D:** £15.00 **S:** £15.00 **Beds:** 1F **Baths:** 1 En ॐ ▣ (4) 📺 🐾 💷 🖎

Pewsey

SU1660

Old Dairy House, *Sharcott, Pewsey, Wilts, SN9 5PA.* Thatched dairy house in four acres. Pewsey 1 mile. **Open:** All year **01672 562287** Mr & Mrs Stone *old.dairy@virgin.net* business.virgin.net/neville.burrell/sharcott **D:** £30.00 **S:** £35.00

Potterne

ST9958

Blounts Court Farm, *Coxhill Lane, Potterne, Devizes, Wiltshire, SN10 5NQ.* Traditional farmhouse set in 150 acres; beautiful rooms, homely atmosphere. **Open:** All year **01380 727180** Mr & Mrs Cary **D:** £25.00 **S:** £32.00–£37.00 **Beds:** 1D 1T **Baths:** 2 En ॐ (8) ▣ ⌇ 📺 🐾 🅥 💷 🖎

Poulshot

ST9659

Poulshot Lodge Farm, *Poulshot, Devizes, Wilts, SN10 1RQ.* Picturesque farmhouse in Poulshot; centrally situated for exploring historic Wiltshire. **Open:** All year (not Xmas) **01380 828255** Mr & Mrs Hues **D:** £19.00–£20.00 **S:** £20.00–£22.00 **Beds:** 2T **Baths:** 1 Sh ॐ (5) ▣ (2) ⌇ 📺 🅥 💷 🖎

Redlynch

SU2021

Yew Tree Cottage, *Grove Lane, Redlynch, Salisbury, Wilts, SP5 2NR.* Spacious country house in large garden overlooking paddock. In pretty New Forest village. **Open:** All year **01725 511730** Mr & Mrs Churchill **D:** £18.00–£20.00 **S:** £18.00–£20.00 **Beds:** 1D 1T 1S **Baths:** 1 Sh ॐ (5) ▣ (6) ⌇ 📺 🅥 💷 🖎

Rushall

SU1256

Little Thatch, *Rushall, Pewsey, Wilts, SN9 6EN.* A picturesque thatched house with a beautiful garden in heart of Wiltshire countryside. **Open:** All year **Grades:** ETC 3 Diamond **01980 635282 (also fax)** Mrs Newton **D:** £21.50 **S:** £25.00 **Beds:** 1T **Baths:** 1 En ▣ (2) ⌇ 💷 🖎

Salisbury

SU1430 🚂 *Coach & Horses, George & Dragon, Avon Brewerie, Old Castle*

Griffin Cottage, 10 St Edmunds Church
Street, Salisbury, Wilts, SP1 1EF. **Open:** All year (not Xmas/New Year) **Grades:** ETC 4 Diamond
01722 328259 Mrs Brandon **Fax: 01722 416928** *mark@brandonasoc.demon.co.uk* www.smoothhound.co.uk/hotels/griffinc.html **D:** £20.00–£22.00 **S:** £40.00–£44.00 **Beds:** 2D **Baths:** 1 Sh ⚡ 📺 📖 🅿
400-year old cottage 3 mins' walk from Salisbury's Market Square. Ideal for visiting Cathedral and Stonehenge. Inglenook logfire, lavender-scented beds and homebaked bread. Organic ingredients where possible and breakfasts healthily grilled not fried. Vegetarian and coeliac diets a speciality.

Hayburn Wyke Guest House, 72
Castle Road, Salisbury, Wilts, SP13RL. **Open:** All year **Grades:** AA 3 Diamond, RAC 3 Diamond
01722 412627 Mrs Curnow **Fax: 01722 412 627** *hayburn.wyke@tinyonline.co.uk* www.hayburnwykeguesthouse.co.uk **D:** £22.00–£27.00 **S:** £30.00–£50.00 **Beds:** 2F 3D 2T **Baths:** 4 En 3 Sh ⏳🅿(7) 📺📺📖 ⚡ cc
A family-run friendly guest house, Hayburn Wyke is a fine Victorian house, situated by Victoria Park, half a mile riverside walk from Salisbury Cathedral and city centre. Many places to visit locally, including Stonehenge, Wilton House and Old Sarum.

Malvern Guest House, 31 Hulse Road,
Salisbury, Wilts, SP1 3LU. Friendly guest house, but non-smoking. **Open:** All year **Grades:** ETC 4 Diamond
01722 327995 (also fax) Mrs Elkins *malvern_gh@madasafish.com* **D:** £45.00–£50.00 **S:** £30.00–£45.00 **Beds:** 2T 1D **Baths:** 2 En 1 Sh ⚡ 📺 📖 ⚡

Holly Tree House, 53 Wyndham Road,
Salisbury, Wilts, SP1 3AH. Detached family home close to city centre - parking, No Smoking. **Open:** All year **Grades:** ETC 2 Diamond
01722 322955 Mrs Middleton **D:** £18.00–£20.00 **Beds:** 1T 1D **Baths:** 1 Sh ⏳🅿(2) ⚡ 📖 ⚡

The Old Rectory B&B,
Belle Vue Road, Salisbury, Wiltshire, SP1 3YE. **Open:** All year **Grades:** ETC 4 Diamond
01722 502702
Ms Smith **Fax: 01722 501135** *stay@ theoldrectory.co.uk* **D:** £20.00–£30.00 **S:** £30.00–£45.00 **Beds:** 2T 1D **Baths:** 2 En 1 Pr ⏳(10) 🅿(1) ⚡ 📺 📺 📖 ⚡
Welcoming Victorian home, nestled in rich green English garden on a quiet street. Offering warm hospitality, bright airy bedrooms, quiet breakfast/sitting room with picture window and open fire. Short walk to city centre. Perfect for a quiet comfortable stay.

Swaynes Firs Farm,
Grimsdyke, Coombe Bissett, Salisbury, Wilts, SP55RF. **Open:** All year (not Xmas) **Grades:** ETC 3 Diamond
01725 519240 Mr Shering *swaynes.firs@ virgin.net* www.swaynesfirs.co.uk **D:** £20.00–£22.00 **S:** £25.00–£30.00 **Beds:** 1F 2T **Baths:** 3 En ⏳🅿(6) 📺 ⚡ 📖 ⚡
Spacious farmhouse on working farm with horses, cattle, poultry, geese and duck ponds. All rooms ensuite with colour TV and nice views. Ideal for visiting historic sites in area, with a Bronze Age Celtic ditch on the farm.

Highbank, 299A Castle Road, Salisbury,
Wiltshire, SP1 3SB. **Open:** All year (not Xmas/New Year)
01722 337819 Mr & Mrs Wilcox **D:** £21.00–£23.50 **S:** £30.00–£35.00 **Beds:** 1F 2T **Baths:** 1 En 1 Sh ⏳🅿(5) ⚡ 📺 📖 ⚡
Purpose built, quiet accommodation, situated 1.5 miles north of city centre in elevated position overlooking Old Sarum and Avon Valley. 8 miles from Stonehenge and New Forest. Excellent base for sightseeing. Warm welcome assured. Comfortable rooms. Full English breakfast.

Byways House, 31 Fowlers Road,
Salisbury, Wilts, SP1 2QP. Attractive Victorian house, quiet, parking. Fowlers Road opposite youth hostel. **Open:** All year (not Xmas/New Year) **Grades:** ETC 3 Diamond
01722 328364 Mr & Mrs Arthey **Fax: 01722 322146** *byways@bed-breakfast-salisbury.co.uk* www.stonehenge-uk.com **D:** £22.50–£39.00 **S:** £35.00–£60.00 **Beds:** 3F 7T 7D 4S **Baths:** 19 En 1 Sh ⏳🅿(15) 📺 📺 📖 ⚡ ⚡ cc

Farthings, 9 Swaynes Close, Wyndham
Road, Salisbury, Wilts, SP1 3AE. Comfortable old house in quiet street near city centre. **Open:** All year **Grades:** ETC 3 Diamond
01722 330749 (also fax) Mrs Rodwell *farthings@shammer.freeserve.co.uk* www.shammer.freeserve.co.uk **D:** £20.00–£25.00 **S:** £20.00–£25.00 **Beds:** 1D 1T 2S **Baths:** 2 En 1 Sh 🅿(1) ⚡ 📺 ⚡

Weaver's Cottage, 37 Bedwin Street,
Salisbury, Wilts, SP1 3UT. C15th city centre cottage, cosy, oak-beamed, 2 mins market square and bus station. **Open:** All year (not Xmas)
01722 341812 Mrs Bunce **D:** £15.00–£20.00 **S:** £23.00–£25.00 **Beds:** 1F 1D **Baths:** 1 Sh 📺 📖 ⚡

Cross Farm, Coombe Bissett, Salisbury,
Wilts, SP5 4LY. Farmhouse in peaceful setting. Attractive village. Good walking. Many places to visit. **Open:** All year
01722 718293 Mrs Kittermaster **Fax: 01722 718665** *s.j.kittermaster@talk21.com* **D:** £20.00 **S:** £20.00 **Beds:** 1F 1T 1S **Baths:** 2 Sh ⏳ 🅿(4) ⚡ 📺 ⚡ 📺 📖 ⚡ ⚡

Wyndham Park Lodge, 51 Wyndham
Road, Salisbury, Wilts, SP1 3AB. Large Victorian house, close to city centre. Friendly family-run establishment. **Open:** All year
01722 416517 P Legg & S Coppen **Fax: 01722 328851** *wyndham@wyndham51.freeserve.co.uk* **D:** £19.00–£21.00 **S:** £26.00–£32.00 **Beds:** 1F 1T 1D 1S **Baths:** 4 En ⏳🅿(3) ⚡ 📺 📖 ⚡ ⚡ cc

Cricket Field House Hotel, Wilton
Road, Salisbury, Wilts, SP2 7NS. All rooms ensuite. Ample car parking. Beautiful garden. **Open:** All year (not Xmas)
01722 322595 (also fax) Mrs James www.cricketfieldhousehotel.com **D:** £30.00–£35.00 **S:** £40.00–£45.00 **Beds:** 1F 7D 3T 3S **Baths:** 14 En ⏳🅿(14) ⚡ 📺 ✕ 📺 📖 ⚡ ⚡ ⚡

Websters, 11 Hartington Road, Salisbury,
Wilts, SP2 7LG. Set on the end of a delightfully colourful terrace with sumptuous choices for breakfast. **Open:** All year
01722 339779 (also fax) Mrs Webb *websters.salis@eclipse.co.uk* **D:** £19.00–£21.00 **S:** £30.00–£34.00 **Beds:** 1D 2T 2S **Baths:** 5 En ⏳(12) 🅿(5) 📺 ✕ 📺 📖 ⚡ ⚡ cc

The White Horse Hotel, 38 Castle
Street, Salisbury, SP1 1BN. Traditional pub/ inn offering a beautiful Cathedral view and only 10 mins' walk. **Open:** All year
01722 327844 Fax: 01722 336226 D: £35.00–£50.00 **S:** £27.00–£35.00 **Beds:** 2F 3T 4D **Baths:** 1 En 2 Sh ⏳🅿(9) 📺 ✕ 📖 ⚡ cc

Seend Cleeve

ST9261

Rew Farm, Seend Cleeve, Melksham,
Wiltshire, SN12 6PS. Working dairy farm. Few mins' walk to Kennet and Avon Canal. **Open:** All year (not Xmas/New Year)
01380 828289 & 07967 894328 (M) A Newman **D:** £20.00 **S:** £25.00 **Beds:** 1T ⏳ 🅿(2) ⚡ 📺 📖 ⚡

BATHROOMS
En = Ensuite
Pr = Private
Sh = Shared

Semington

ST8960

New House Farm, *Littleton, Semington, Trowbridge, Wilts, BA14 6LF.* Victorian former farmhouse, open countryside, lovely gardens, good touring centre. **Open:** All year **Grades:** ETC 4 Diamond
01380 870344 Mrs Ball **D:** £23.00 **S:** £27.00 **Beds:** 2D 1T **Baths:** 3 En ⌂ ⚑ (10) ⊬ ⊡ × ⊡ ⊞, ⚲ ⚸

Sevenhampton

SU2090

Roves Farm, *Sevenhampton, Swindon, Wilts, SN6 7QG.* Spacious comfortable quiet accommodation surrounded by beautiful countryside on a working farm. **Open:** All year
01793 763939 (also fax) *joanna@ rovesfarm.co.uk* www.rovesfarm.co.uk
D: £20.00–£22.00 **S:** £26.00–£27.00 **Beds:** 1F 1T **Baths:** 2 En ⌂ ⚑ (4) ⊬ ⊡ ⊡ ⊞, ⚲

Sherston

ST8586

Widleys Farm, *Sherston, Malmesbury, Wilts, SN16 0PY.* 200-year-old farmhouse. Peaceful and quiet. Log fires in season. Working farm. **Open:** All year (not Xmas) **Grades:** ETC 3 Diamond
01666 840213 Mrs Hibbard **Fax: 01666 840156 D:** £20.00–£25.00 **S:** £22.00–£27.00 **Beds:** 1F 1D 1T **Baths:** 1 En 1 Sh ⌂ ⚑ (6) ⊡ ⊞, ⚲

Shrewton

SU0644   ⚐ *George Inn*

Maddington House, *Shrewton, Salisbury, Wilts, SP3 4JD.* Listed house, 3 miles from Stonehenge in pretty village. **Open:** All year (not Xmas/ New Year) **Grades:** ETC 4 Diamond
01980 620406 (also fax) J Robothan *rsrobathan@freenet.co.uk* **D:** £22.50–£25.00 **S:** £30.00 **Beds:** 1F 1T 1D **Baths:** 2 En 1 Pr ⌂ (7) ⚑ (4) ⊬ ⊡ ⊡ ⊞, ⚲

All details shown are as supplied by B&B owners in Autumn 2001

Planning a longer stay? Always ask for any special rates

Sopworth

ST8286   ⚐ *The Rattlebone*

Manor Farm, *Sopworth, Chippenham, Wilts, SN14 6PR.* Quiet, working farm in beautiful countryside. Spacious rooms. Warm welcome. **Open:** Easter to Oct
01454 238676 (also fax) Mrs Barker
manor.farm@virgin.net **D:** £19.00–£22.00 **S:** £25.00–£30.00 **Beds:** 2F **Baths:** 1 En 1 Sh ⌂ ⚑ (4) ⊡ ⌖ ⊡ ⚲

Stapleford

SU0737

Elm Tree Cottage, *Stapleford, Salisbury, Wilts, SP3 4LH.* Light airy rooms with conservatory or large garden for relaxation. **Open:** Easter to Oct
01722 790507 Mrs Sykes *jan.sykes@virgin.net*
D: £22.50–£25.00 **S:** £22.00 **Beds:** 1F 2D **Baths:** 3 Pr ⌂ ⚑ (3) ⊡ ⌖ ⊡ ⊞, ⚲

Steeple Ashton

ST9056   ⚐ *Long's Arms, Somerset Arms*

Ashton Mill Farm, *Steeple Ashton, Trowbridge, Wilts, BA14 6HQ.* **Open:** All year
01380 870083
Mrs Langley *ashtonmillfarm@tiscali.co.uk*
D: £15.00–£20.00 **S:** £20.00–£25.00 **Beds:** 1F 1D **Baths:** 2 Sh ⌂ (0) ⚑ (4) ⊬ ⊡ ⌖ × ⊡ ⊞, ⚲
Get away from bustle and stress to a warm welcome at a unique, extremely peaceful farmhouse retreat in West Wiltshire. Conveniently located for Bath, Salisbury, and many National Trust properties including Stourhead, Lacock and Avebury. Ideal for walking, cycling, gliding.

Spiers Piece Farm, *Steeple Ashton, Trowbridge, Wilts, BA14 6HG.* Fantastic views, spacious garden and farmhouse, peace in countryside location. **Open:** Feb to Nov
01380 870266 (also fax) Ms Awdry
D: £16.50–£18.00 **S:** £17.00–£19.00 **Beds:** 2D 1T **Baths:** 2 Sh ⌂ (1) ⚑ (10) ⊡ ⌖ ⊡ ⊞, ⚲

Stoford

SU0835

The Swan Inn, *A36 Warminster Road, Stoford, Salisbury, Wilts, SP2 0PR.* Family-run coaching inn set in the picturesque Wylye Valley. **Open:** All year
01722 790236 Mr Ringwood **Fax:** 01722 790115 *info@theswanatstoford.co.uk* www.the swanatstoford.co.uk **D:** £22.50–£30.00 **S:** £35.00–£65.00 **Beds:** 2F 4T 3D **Baths:** 9 En ⌂ ⚑ (90) ⊬ ⊡ × ⊡ ⊞, ⚲ cc

---

Sutton Veny

ST9041

The Beeches Farm, *Deverill Road, Sutton Veny, Warminster, BA12 7BY.* Many animals, lovely views, adaptable relaxed atmosphere, Longleat 10 mins. **Open:** All year
01985 840796 (also fax) Mrs Ridout
D: £17.50–£20.00 **S:** £20.00–£25.00 **Beds:** 1F **Baths:** 1 En ⌂ ⚑ (5) ⊬ ⊡ ⌖ × ⊡ ⚲

Swindon

SU1685

Bradford Guest House, *40 Devizes Road, Old Town, Swindon, Wilts, SN1 4BG.* Small friendly guest house. **Open:** All year (not Xmas/New Year)
01793 642427 Ms McCalla **Fax:** 01793 430381 *sam@smccalla.freeserve.co.uk*
www.zednet.co.uk/bradfordshire **D:** £21.00–£24.00 **S:** £27.00–£33.00 **Beds:** 2T 4D 2S **Baths:** 8 En ⊬ ⊡ ⊞, ⚲ cc

Trowbridge

ST8557

62b Paxcroft Cottages, *Devizes Road, Hilperton, Trowbridge, Wiltshire, BA14 6JB.* **Open:** All year (not Xmas) **Grades:** ETC 4 Diamond
01225 765838 S J Styles *paxcroftcottages@ hotmail.com* **D:** £22.00 **S:** £22.00–£25.00 **Beds:** 1F 1T 1D **Baths:** 2 En 1 Pr ⌂ ⚑ (6) ⊬ ⊡ × ⊡ ⊞, ⚲
Small friendly house on the outskirts of Trowbridge. Far-reaching views overlooking the Wiltshire Downs. Lovely gardens. Tastefully furnished throughout. Centrally situated for Bath, Salisbury, Bristol. Many attractions in easy reach. Visitors' lounge with digital television and free email facilities.

44 Wingfield Road, *Trowbridge, Wilts, BA14 9ED.* Fine Victorian house. 'Home from home'. **Open:** All year
01225 761455 Mr & Mrs Dobbin **D:** £20.00 **Beds:** 1F 1D 1T 1S ⌂ ⊡ ⌖ ⊡ ⊞, ⚲

Warminster

ST8745

Belmont, *9 Boreham Road, Warminster, BA12 9JP.* Well-situated for town, spacious rooms, friendly welcome, good facilities. **Open:** All year
01985 212799 (also fax) Mrs Monkcom *monkcom@freeuk.com* **D:** £17.00–£20.00 **S:** £16.00–£25.00 **Beds:** 2D **Baths:** 1 Sh ⌂ (5) ⚑ (6) ⊬ ⊡ ⊞, ⚲

West Ashton

ST8755

Water Gardens, *131 Yarnbrook Road, West Ashton, Trowbridge, Wiltshire, BA14 6AF.* Detached bungalow, large gardens ideally situated for Bath and area. **Open:** All year (not Xmas)
01225 752045 Mrs Heard *lucy@ heard28.freeserve.co.uk* www.s-h-systems.co. uk/hotels/water2html **D:** £18.00 **Beds:** 1F 1D 1T **Baths:** 3 En ⚑ (3) ⚡ �📺 ✿ ✕ ☑ ⊞ ♨

West Lavington

SU0052

Parsonage House, *West Lavington, Devizes, Wilts, SN10 4LT.* Welcoming relaxed family home in peaceful surroundings overlooking the church. **Open:** All year (not Xmas/New Year)
01380 813345 Mrs West **D:** £20.00–£25.00 **S:** £25.00–£30.00 **Beds:** 1D 1T **Baths:** 1 Sh ⚡ ⚑ (3) ⚡ ⊞ ♨

West Overton

SU1268

Cairncot, *West Overton, Marlborough, Wilts, SN8 4ER.* Situated between Avebury and Marlborough, Cairncot offers comfortable accommodation with superb country views. **Open:** All year
01672 861617 Mrs Leigh *aaw@ comms-audit.co.uk* **D:** £20.00–£25.00 **S:** £20.00 **Beds:** 1D 1S **Baths:** 1 Sh ⚡ ⚑ (6) ⚡ 📺 ✿ ☑ ⊞ ♨

Westbury

ST8650

Brokerswood House, *Brokerswood, Westbury, Wilts, BA13 4EH.* Situated in front of 80 acres of woodland, open to the public. **Open:** All year (not Xmas)
01373 823428 Mrs Phillips **D:** £15.00–£18.00 **S:** £15.00–£18.00 **Beds:** 3F 1D 1T 1S **Baths:** 1 En 1 Pr 1 Sh ⚡ (1) ⚑ (6) ✿ ✿ ✿ ☑ ♨

Please respect a B&B's wishes regarding children, animals and smoking

---

BEDROOMS
D = Double
T = Twin
S = Single
F = Family

Whaddon

SU1926

Three Crows Inn, *Old Southampton Road, Whaddon, Salisbury, Wiltshire, SP5 3HB.* Quiet country inn, oak beams, home cooked food, country walks. **Open:** All year (not Xmas/New Year)
01722 710211 (also fax) Ms Sutton *lsu4210600@aol.com* www.threecrowns.co.uk **D:** £36.00–£48.50 **S:** £18.00–£25.00 **Beds:** 2T 2D **Baths:** 2 En 2 Sh ⚡ ⚑ ✿ 📺 ✿ ✕ ☑ ⊞ ♨ cc

Winsley

ST7961

Conifers, *4 King Alfred Way, Winsley, Bradford-on-Avon, Wilts, BA15 2NG.* Quiet area, pleasant outlook, friendly atmosphere, convenient Bath, lovely walks. **Open:** All year
01225 722482 Mrs Kettley **D:** £17.00–£18.00 **S:** £18.00–£20.00 **Beds:** 1T 1D **Baths:** 1 Sh ⚡ ⚑ ✿ ☑ ✿ ⊞ ♨

3 Corners, *Cottles Lane, Winsley, Bradford-on-Avon, Wilts, BA15 2HJ.* House in quiet village edge location, attractive rooms and gardens. **Open:** All year (not Xmas)
01225 865380 Mrs Cole *sandra@ turleigh.freeserve.co.uk* **D:** £22.50–£25.00 **S:** £26.00–£30.00 **Beds:** 1F 1D **Baths:** 1 En 1 Pr ⚡ ⚑ (4) ✿ ☑ ✕ ☑ ⊞ ♨

Winterbourne Monkton

SU1072

The New Inn, *Winterbourne Monkton, Swindon, Wilts, SN4 9NW.* Friendly 200-year-old Inn within 1 mile of Avebury Stone Circle. **Open:** All year **Grades:** ETC 3 Diamond
01672 539240 Fax: 01672 539150 *mick@ folliard.fsnet.co.uk* **D:** £25.00–£30.00 **S:** £45.00–£50.00 **Beds:** 1F 2T 2D **Baths:** 5 En ⚡ ⚑ (20) ✿ ☑ ✕ ☑ ♨ cc

---

Winterbourne Stoke

SU0741

Scotland Lodge, *Winterbourne Stoke, Salisbury, SP3 4TF.* Spacious comfortable rooms, easy access. Good touring centre. Personal service. **Open:** All year **Grades:** ETC 2 Star, AA 4 Diamond
01980 620943 Mrs Singleton **Fax: 01980 621403** *scotland.lodge@virgin.net.co.uk* www.scotland-lodge.co.uk **D:** £17.50–£27.50 **S:** £25.00–£30.00 **Beds:** 1F 2T 1D **Baths:** 4 En ⚡ ⚑ ✿ ☑ ☑ ⊞ ♨

Woodborough

SU1159

St Cross, *Woodborough, Pewsey, Wilts, SN9 5PL.* Pewsey Vale - heart of crop circles, beautiful countryside, Kennet & Avon Canal 8 mins' walk. **Open:** All year
01672 851346 (also fax) Mrs Gore **D:** £25.00–£35.00 **Beds:** 1D 1T **Baths:** 1 Sh ⚡ ⚑ (6) ⚑ (1) ✿ ☑ ✿ ☑

Wootton Bassett

SU0683 ⚑ *The Churchill*

The Hollies, *Greenhill Hook, Wootton Bassett, Swindon, SN4 8EH.* Ideal for business or touring. Beautiful views, peaceful attractive gardens. **Open:** All year (not Xmas/New Year) **Grades:** ETC 3 Diamond
01793 770795 (also fax) **D:** £19.00–£22.50 **S:** £22.00–£38.00 **Beds:** 2D 2S **Baths:** 1 En 2 Sh ⚡ (5) ⚑ (5) ✿ ☑ ⊞ ♨

Yatton Keynell

ST8676

Oakfield Farm, *Easton Piercy Lane, Yatton Keynell, Chippenham, Wilts, SN14 6JU.* Cotswold stone farmhouse in open countryside. Ideal for Cotswolds, Bath, Stonehenge. **Open:** Mar to Oct
01249 782355 Mrs Read **Fax: 01249 783458** **D:** £20.00–£22.50 **S:** £25.00–£30.00 **Beds:** 2D 1T **Baths:** 1 En 1 Sh ⚡ ⚑ (8) ✿ ☑ ☑ ⊞ ♨

Worcestershire

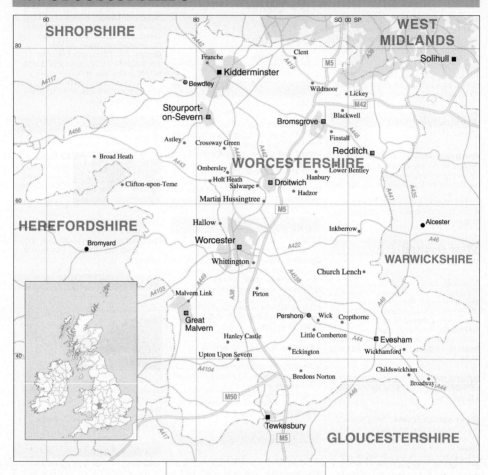

Astley

SO7868

Wood-hampton House, *Weather Lane, Astley, Stourport-on-Severn, Worcestershire, DY13 0SF.* Set in rural Worcestershire, delightful coach house. Always warm welcome. **Open:** All year (not Xmas/New Year) **Grades:** ETC 3 Diamond **01299 826510** Mrs Knight **Fax: 01299 827059** *pete-a@sally-a.freeserve.co.uk* **D:** £22.50–£25.00 **S:** £25.00–£30.00 **Beds:** 1F 1T 1D 1S **Baths:** 2 En ⌂ ☐ (3) ⊬ ⊡ ⟲ ⟲ ⒤ ᵭ

Bewdley

SO7875 ◢ *Cape of Good Hope, Ye Olde New Inn, Eagle & Serpent*

Bank House, *14 Lower Park, Bewdley, Worcs, DY12 2DP.* Warm family atmosphere, superb breakfasts, close to town centre/countryside/river. **Open:** All year (not Xmas) **Grades:** ETC 3 Diamond **01299 402652 (also fax)** Mrs Nightingale *fleur.nightingale@virgin.net* **D:** £20.00 **S:** £20.00 **Beds:** 1F 1T 1S **Baths:** 2 Sh ⌂ ☐ (2) ⊬ ⟲ ⟲ ⒤ ᵭ

Tarn B&B, *Long Bank, Bewdley, Worcs, DY12 2QT.* Unusual House in Acres of Gardens, fields with spectacular views. **Open:** Feb to Nov **01299 402243** T Beves **D:** £19.00–£21.00 **S:** £23.00–£25.00 **Beds:** 2T 2S **Baths:** 3 Sh ⌂ ☐ (6) ⊬ ⟲ ⒤

Lightmarsh Farm, *Crundalls Lane, Bewdley, Worcs, DY12 1NE.* Elevated position, outstanding views, peaceful location. Comfortable accommodation, quality breakfasts. **Open:** All year (not Xmas/New Year) **01299 404027** Mrs Grainger **D:** £22.50 **S:** £30.00 **Beds:** 1D 1T **Baths:** 1 En 1 Pr ⌂ (10) ☐ (6) ⟲ ⟲ ⒤ ᵭ

Blackwell

SO9972

Rosa Lodge, *38 Station Road, Blackwell, Bromsgrove, B60 1PZ.* Country village house in Blackwell, near Bromsgrove. Superb food in Edwardian-style dining robm. **Open:** All year
0121 445 5440 (also fax) *sandra@ rosalodge.co.uk* www.rosalodge.co.uk **D:** £25.00 **S:** £30.00 **Beds:** 2D 1T 1S **Baths:** 3 En 1 Pr ⑮ 🄿 (6) ⚡ 📺 ⋔ ✗ Ⅴ Ⅲ ❋ ♨ cc

Bredons Norton

SO9339

Round Bank House, *Lampitt Lane, Bredons Norton, Tewkesbury, Glos, GL20 7HB.* Beautiful views and countryside very peaceful homely and comfortable. **Open:** All year (not Xmas/New Year) **01684 772983 & 01684 772142** Mr & Mrs Thornton **Fax:** 01684 773035 **D:** £37.00–£40.00 **S:** £23.00–£25.00 **Beds:** 1T 1D **Baths:** 1 En ⑮ 🄿 Ⅴ Ⅲ ♨

Broad Heath

SO6665 🍺 *Tally Ho Inn, Fox Inn, Lion Inn*

Court Farm, *Hanley Childe, Broad Heath, Tenbury Wells, Worcs, WR15 8QY.* Court farm is a C15th oak-beamed and very spacious farmhouse. **Open:** All year (not Xmas/New Year) **Grades:** ETC 4 Diamond **01885 410265** Mrs Yarnold **D:** £22.50 **S:** £25.00–£30.00 **Beds:** 1T 1D **Baths:** 1 En 1 Pr ⑮ 🄿 (10) ⚡ 📺 Ⅴ ♨

Broadway

SP0937 🍺 *Horse & Hound, Dormy House, Lygon Arms*

Olive Branch Guest House, *78 High Street, Broadway, Worcs, WR12 7AJ.* **Open:** All year **Grades:** ETC 4 Diamond, AA 4 Diamond
01386 853440 D Talboys **Fax:** 01386 859070 *broadway@theolive-branch.co.uk* theolivebranch-broadway.com **D:** £27.50–£35.00 **S:** £35.00–£60.00 **Beds:** 2F 2T 3D 1S **Baths:** 7 En 1 Pr ⑮ 🄿 (7) ⚡ 📺 ⋔ ✗ Ⅴ Ⅲ ♿ ♨ cc
Perfect base to tour Cotswolds, C16th Grade II Listed building, on Broadway's famous High Street. We have a reputation of being a warm and friendly family-run house, and the owners go out of their way to take care of all guests.

Southwold House, *Station Road, Broadway, Worcs, WR12 7DE.* Spacious tastefully decorated Edwardian house in picturesque Cotswold village. 4 mins' walk pubs, restaurants. **Open:** All year **01386 853681** Mrs Smiles **Fax:** 01386 854610 **D:** £24.00–£25.00 **S:** £25.00–£27.00 **Beds:** 1F 4D 2T 1S **Baths:** 7 En ⑮ 🄿 (8) ⚡ 📺 ⋔ Ⅲ ♨ cc

Brook House, *Station Road, Broadway, Worcs, WR12 7DE.* **Open:** All year (not Xmas) **01386 852313** Mr & Mrs Thomas **D:** £21.00–£26.00 **S:** £21.00–£40.00 **Beds:** 2F 2D 1T 1S **Baths:** 3 En 1 Pr 1 Sh ⑮ 🄿 (6) 📺 ⋔ Ⅲ ♨ Traditional Victorian house with large rooms, overlooking fields, hills and gardens. 5 mins' walk from the village centre. Brookhouse is an ideal centre for exploring Cotswold villages gardens, wildlife centres. With golf courses, fishing river trips and horseriding nearby. Reductions for 3 or more nights.

Bowers Hill Farm, *Bowers Hill, Willersey, Evesham, Worcs, WR11 7HG.* Peaceful Cotswold location, offering high quality facilities and spectacular views. **Open:** All year **Grades:** ETC 4 Diamond, AA 4 Diamond **01386 834585** Ms Bent **Fax:** 01386 830234 *sarah@bowershillfarm.com* www.bowershillfarm.com **D:** £25.50 **S:** £30.00–£35.00 **Beds:** 1F 1T 1D **Baths:** 3 En ⑮ 🄿 ⚡ 📺 Ⅴ Ⅲ ♨ cc

Whiteacres Guest House, *Station Road, Broadway, Worcs, WR12 7DE.* Tastefully decorated Victorian house, two rooms having 4-poster beds. **Open:** All year (not Xmas) **01386 852320** Mr Allen *whiteacres@ btinternet.com* **D:** £25.00–£27.50 **Beds:** 4D 1T **Baths:** 5 En 🄿 (8) ⚡ 📺 Ⅲ ♨

Crown & Trumpet Inn, *Church Street, Broadway, Worcs, WR12 7AE.* C17th Cotswold inn in picturesque village (also on the Cotswold Way). **Open:** All year **01386 853202 & 0870 0750500** Mr Scott **Fax:** 01386 834650 *ascott@cotswoldholidays.co.uk* www.cotswoldholidays.co.uk **D:** £24.00 **Beds:** 3D 1T **Baths:** 4 En ⑮ 🄿 (6) ⋔ ✗ Ⅴ Ⅲ ❋ ♨

BATHROOMS
En = Ensuite
Pr = Private
Sh = Shared

Windrush House, *Station Road, Broadway, Worcs, WR12 7DE.* Elegant Edwardian detached house located near Broadway village green. **Open:** All year **01386 853577** Susan & Richard Pinder **Fax:** 01386 853790 *richard@ broadway-windrush.co.uk* www.broadway-windrush.co.uk **D:** £25.00–£30.00 **S:** £25.00–£40.00 **Beds:** 3D 2T **Baths:** 5 En ⑮ 🄿 (6) ⚡ 📺 ⋔ ✗ Ⅴ Ⅲ ❋ ♨

Quantocks, *Evesham Road, Broadway, Worcs, WR12 7PA.* Large detached house in 3 acres with superb views of Cleeve/Bredon/ Malvern Hills. **Open:** Mar to Nov **01386 853378** Mr & Mrs Stephens *quantocks_broadway@yahoo.co.uk* **D:** £22.50–£25.00 **S:** £30.00–£35.00 **Beds:** 1F 1T **Baths:** 2 En ⑮ 🄿 ⚡ 📺 Ⅴ Ⅲ ♿ ♨

Bromsgrove

SO9570 🍺 *Ewe & Lamb*

Woodcote Farm, *Kidderminster Road, Bromsgrove, Worcs, B61 9EA.* Attractive C18th farmhouse with moated garden on organic working farm. **Open:** All year **01562 777795 & 07767 617968 (M)** Mrs Prichard **Fax:** 01562 777024 **D:** £20.00–£25.00 **S:** £25.00–£27.50 **Beds:** 1F 1D 1T **Baths:** 2 En 1 Sh ⑮ 🄿 (10) ⚡ 📺 ⋔ Ⅴ Ⅲ ♿ ♨

Avoncroft Guest House, *77 Redditch Road, Bromsgrove, Worcs, B60 4JP.* Located on A38. M5, M42 five mins away. **Open:** All year **Grades:** ETC 4 Diamond **01527 832819** Mrs Gilmore **D:** £22.00 **S:** £30.00 **Beds:** 2T 1D 1S **Baths:** 4 En ⑮ 🄿 (9) ⚡ 📺 ✗ Ⅴ Ⅲ ♨

Lower Bentley Farm, *Lower Bentley Lane, Lower Bentley, Bromsgrove, Worcs, B60 4JB.* Victorian farmhouse in rural location close to M5/M42. **Open:** All year **01527 821286** C Gibbs **Fax:** 01527 821193 *aj.gibbs@farmline.com* www.lowerbentleyfarm. co.uk **D:** £22.00 **S:** £27.00–£30.00 **Beds:** 2T 1D **Baths:** 2 En 1 Pr ⑮ 🄿 (3) 📺 ⋔ Ⅴ Ⅲ ♨

Home Farm, *Mill Lane, Wildmoor, Bromsgrove, Worcs, B61 0BX.* Modern comfortable extension of farmhouse. **Open:** All year **01527 874964** Mr Lees **D:** £20.00 **S:** £20.00–£25.00 **Beds:** 3T 2S **Baths:** 3 Sh 🄿 (5) 📺 Ⅲ ♨

Bea's Lodge, *245 Pennine Road, Bromsgrove, Worcs, B61 0TG.* Modern house in quiet area, convenient for M5, M6, M40, M42. **Open:** All year **01527 877613** Mrs Lodge **D:** £20.00 **S:** £20.00 **Beds:** 1T 1S **Baths:** 1 Sh ⑮ (3) 🄿 (2) ⚡ 📺 ✗ Ⅲ ♨

Childswickham

SP0738

Mount Pleasant Farm, *Childswickham, Broadway, Worcs, WR12 7HZ.*
Working farm 3 miles from Broadway. Very quiet accommodation, excellent views.
Open: All year
01386 853424 Mrs Perry *helen@ mount_pleasant.fslife.co.uk* **D:** £25.00 **S:** £30.00
Beds: 2D 1T 1S **Baths:** 4 Pr ⊁ (5) ⊟ (10) ⊬ ⊡ ⊠ ≗

Church Lench

SP0251

Hill Barn Orchard, *Evesham Road, Church Lench, Evesham, Worcs, WR11 4UB.*
Stylish house and garden, trout lakes all in 50 acres. **Open:** Easter to Oct
01386 871035 (also fax) Mr & Mrs Badger
D: £25.00 **S:** £40.00 **Beds:** 2T **Baths:** 2 En
⊁ (6) ⊟ (6) ⊬ ⊠ ⊡ ⊠ ⊡ ⊡

Clent

SO9279

St Elisabeths Cottage, *Woodman Lane, Clent, Stourbridge, W Mids, DY9 9PX.*
Large country cottage close to motorway links. Excellent pubs nearby. **Open:** All year **Grades:** ETC 4 Diamond
01562 883883 Mrs Blankstone **Fax:** 01562 885034 *st_elizabeth_cot@btconnect.com*
D: £26.00–£30.00 **S:** £28.00–£30.00 **Beds:** 2D 1T **Baths:** 3 En ⊟ (6) ⊬ ⊡ ⊡ ⊡ ≗

Clifton upon Teme

SO7161   ⊈ *Lion Inn, Talbot*

Pitlands Farm, *Clifton upon Teme, Worcester, WR6 6DX.* C15th beamed farmhouse. Ideally situated for exploring Heart of England/Welsh Marshes.
Open: Feb to Nov
01886 812220 (also fax) Mrs Mann
D: £20.00–£23.00 **S:** £23.00–£25.00 **Beds:** 1F 2T **Baths:** 2 En 1 Pr ⊁ (3) ⊟ (10) ⊬ ⊡ ⊡ ≗

Cropthorne

SO9944

Cedars Guest House, *Evesham Road, Cropthorne, Pershore, Worcs, WR10 3JU.* Ideal for touring Cotswolds, Malverns, Stratford-upon-Avon & Cheltenham. **Open:** All year
01386 860219 Mrs Ward *cedarsguesthouse@ ukonline.co.uk* **D:** £18.00–£22.00 **S:** £18.00–£25.00 **Beds:** 1F 2D 2T **Baths:** 3 En 2 Sh ⊁ ⊟ (6) ⊬ ⊡ ⊡ ⊡ ≗

Crossway Green

SO8468

Garden Cottages, *Crossway Green, Hartlebury, Stourport-on-Severn, Worcs, DY13 9SJ.* Oak-beamed cottage in rural position close to main roads.
Open: All year (not Xmas/New Year)
Grades: ETC 4 Diamond, Silver
01299 250626 (also fax) Mr & Mrs Terry *accomodation@mamod.co.uk*
www.gardencottages.co.uk **D:** £25.00–£30.00 **S:** £25.00–£30.00 **Beds:** 1F 1T 1D 1S **Baths:** 3 En 1 Pr ⊁ ⊟ ⊬ ⊡ ⊡ ⊠ ⊠ ⊡ ⊠ ≗

Yew Tree House, *Norchard, Crossway Green, Stourport on Severn, DY13 9SN.*
Open: All year
01299 250921 & 07971 112621 (M)
Mrs Knight **Fax:** 01299 253472 *paul@ knightp.swinternet.co.uk*
www.yewtreeworcester.co.uk **D:** £25.00
S: £30.00 **Beds:** 1F 2T 2D **Baths:** 5 En ⊁ ⊟ ⊡ ⊡ ⊠ ⊡ ≗
Built in 1754, stepping over the threshold is a fascinating mix of elegance and atmosphere. Peacefully tucked away but convenient to all motorways systems and sightseeing. Splendid breakfasts provided, weather permitting served in beautiful gardens. Tennis court on site by arrangement.

Droitwich

SO8963

Temple Broughton Farm, *Broughton Green, Droitwich, WR9 7EF.* Listed manor house, elegantly furnished, spectacular views with tennis court. **Open:** All year (not Xmas/New Year)
01905 391456 Mrs Lawson **Fax:** 01905 391515 **D:** £25.00–£27.50 **S:** £30.00–£35.00 **Beds:** 1T 3D **Baths:** 3 En 1 Sh ⊟ (6) ⊬ ⊡ ⊡ ⊡ ≗

BATHROOMS
En = Ensuite
Pr = Private
Sh = Shared

Eckington

SO9241

The Anchor Inn and Restaurant, *Catheridge Lane, Eckington, Pershore, Worcs, WR10 3BA.* **Open:** All year
01386 750356 (also fax) Mr Kelly *anchoreck@ aol.com* www.anchoreckington.co.uk
D: £22.50–£30.00 **S:** £25.00–£40.00 **Beds:** 3T 2D **Baths:** 5 Pr ⊟ (25) ⊡ ⊠ ⊡ ⊡ ≗ ⊡ **cc**
Traditional village inn off the main road, comfortable lounge, separate restaurant. Chef-prepared cuisine. Central for Worcester, Evesham, Cheltenham and Tewkesbury. Situated between the Cotswolds and the Malvern Hills.

Evesham

SP0343   ⊈ *The Bell*

6 Fountain Gardens, *Waterside, Evesham, Worcs, WR11 1JY.*
Evesham town house, non-smoking, friendly, comfortable beds, good food.
Open: All year
01386 47384 (also fax) Mrs Roberts *sheila.roberts@care4free.net* **D:** £15.00
S: £15.00–£17.00 **Beds:** 1D 1S **Baths:** 1 Sh ⊟ (4) ⊬ ⊡ ⊠ ⊡ ⊡ ❀

Bowers Hill Farm, *Bowers Hill, Willersey, Evesham, Worcs, WR11 7HG.* Peaceful Cotswold location, offering high quality facilities and spectacular views.
Open: All year **Grades:** ETC 4 Diamond, AA 4 Diamond
01386 834585 Ms Bent **Fax:** 01386 830234 *sarah@bowershillfarm.com* www.bowershillfarm.com **D:** £25.50
S: £30.00–£35.00 **Beds:** 1F 1T 1D **Baths:** 3 En ⊁ ⊟ ⊬ ⊡ ⊠ ⊡ ⊡ ≗ **cc**

Anglers View, *90 Albert Road, Evesham, Worcs, WR11 4LA.* 5 minutes form town/bus stations and River Avon. **Open:** All year
01386 442141 S Tomkotwicz *sarahbandb2000@yahoo.co.uk* **D:** £17.50–£30.00 **S:** £20.00–£35.00 **Beds:** 1F 3T **Baths:** 1 Pr 2 Sh ⊁ ⊟ (2) ⊬ ⊡ ⊠ ⊡ ⊡ ≗

Finstall
SO9770

Stoke Cross Farm, *Dusthouse Lane, Finstall, Bromsgrove, Worcs, B60 3AE.* Quiet rural setting on outskirts of town, convenient for motorways. **Open:** All year (not Xmas/New Year)
01527 876676 J Orford **Fax: 01527 874729**
D: £16.00–£17.00 **S:** £20.00–£22.00 **Beds:** 1F 1T 1D **Baths:** 2 Sh ⌂ (2) ⊞ (6) ⌿ ⊡ ⊀ ⊞ ⚲

Franche
SO8178

Hollies Farm Cottage, *Franche, Kidderminster, Worcestershire, DY11 5RW.* Country cottage. Just off the beaten track. Wonderful views. Farmhouse breakfast. **Open:** All year (not Xmas/New Year)
01562 745677 Mrs Glover **Fax: 01562 824580**
pete@top-floor.fsbusiness.co.uk **D:** £22.00–£24.00 **S:** £24.00 **Beds:** 1T 1D **Baths:** 2 En ⌂ ⊞ ⌿ ⊡ ⊀ ⊞ ⚲

Hadzor
SO9162

Hadzor Court, *Hadzor, Droitwich, Worcs, WR9 7DR.* **Open:** All year (not Xmas)
01905 794401 Mrs Brooks **Fax:**
01905 794636 *hadzorcourt_droitwichspa@hotmail.com* **D:** £20.00 **S:** £25.00–£30.00 **Beds:** 1D 1T **Baths:** 2 En ⊞ ⌿ ⊡ × ⊡ ⊞ ⚲
Listed farmhouse in historic hamlet. Wonderful character, antiques, countryside, sun-terrace, business and meeting facilities, cellar bar, country weddings. 40 mins Stratford-upon-Avon, 25 mins Worcester, 40 mins Birmingham Airport, NEC.

Hallow
SO8258

Ivy Cottage, *Sinton Green, Hallow, Worcester, WR2 6NP.* Charming cottage in quiet village, 4m from Worcester centre. **Open:** Mar to Oct
01905 641123 Mrs Rendle **D:** £21.00 **S:** £25.00–£30.00 **Beds:** 1D 1T 1S **Baths:** 1 En 1 Pr ⌂ ⊞ (4) ⌿ ⊡ ⊡ ⊞ ⚲

Hanbury
SO9663   ⊲ *Eagle & Sun, Red Lion*

Upper Hollowfields Farm, *Hollowfields Road, Hanbury, Redditch, Worcs, B96 6RJ.* Country house. Beautifully appointed rooms. Convenient for motorways and towns. **Open:** All year
01527 821461 (also fax) Mrs Terry
D: £18.00–£21.00 **S:** £23.00–£30.00 **Beds:** 1T 1D 1S **Baths:** 3 En ⌂ ⊞ ⊡ ⊞ ⚲

Hanley Castle
SO8341

Four Hedges, *The Rhydd, Hanley Castle, Malvern, Worcester, WR8 0AD.* Friendly family house, spacious garden. Three Counties Showground 4 miles. **Open:** All year (not Xmas)
01684 310405 (also fax) Mrs Cooper
fredgies@aol.com **D:** £15.00–£17.00 **S:** £15.00–£17.00 **Beds:** 1D 1T 2S **Baths:** 1 En 1 Sh ⌂ ⊞ (5) ⌿ ⊡ ⊀ ⚲

The Chestnuts, *Gilberts End, Hanley Castle, Worcester, Worcs, WR8 0AS.* Delightful family home with a relaxed welcoming atmosphere in a tranquil setting. **Open:** All year
01684 311219 Ms Parker **D:** £20.00–£25.00 **S:** £20.00–£30.00 **Beds:** 1F 1T 1D **Baths:** 3 En ⌂ ⊞ ⌿ ⊡ ⊡ ⊞ ⚲

Holt Heath
SO8163   ⊲ *Red Lion*

Heathwood, *Holt Heath, Worcester, Worcs, WR6 6NA.* Large Victorian family house. Perfectly placed for touring and business. **Open:** All year
01905 621771 (also fax) Ms Beare-Wolfenden **D:** £25.00–£35.00 **Beds:** 1D **Baths:** 1 En ⌂ ⊞ (2) ⌿ ⊡ ⊞ ⚲

Inkberrow
SP0057

Perrymill Farm, *Little Inkberrow, Inkberrow, Worcester, WR7 4JQ.* Attractive Georgian farmhouse set in rural Worcestershire - family run. **Open:** All year
01386 792177 Mrs Alexander **Fax: 01386 793449** *alexander@estatesgazette.net* **D:** £25.00 **S:** £25.00 **Beds:** 1T 1D 1S **Baths:** 1 Sh ⌂ ⊞ (8) ⊡ ⊀ × ⊡ ⊞ ⚲

Lickey
SO9975

Honeypot, *305 Old Birmingham Road, Lickey, Bromsgrove, Worcs, B60 1HQ.* Attractive detached house, large garden and comfortable guests lounge. **Open:** All year **Grades:** ETC 4 Diamond
0121 445 2580 E Stanworth **D:** £21.00–£22.00 **S:** £21.00–£22.00 **Beds:** 1D 1T **Baths:** 1 Sh ⌂ ⊞ ⌿ ⊡ ⊡ ⊞ ⚲

Merrivale, *309 Old Birmingham Road, Lickey, Bromsgrove, Worcs., B60 1HQ.* Attractive bungalow in 5 acres of woodland and pastures. **Open:** All year (not Xmas/New Year) **Grades:** ETC 4 Diamond
0121 445 1694 (also fax) Mr Smith
alincolnsmith@bushinternet.com **D:** £20.00 **Beds:** 1T 1D **Baths:** 2 En ⌂ ⊞ (5) ⊡ ⊡ ⊞ ⚲

Little Comberton
SO9643

Byeways, *Pershore Road, Little Comberton, Pershore, Worcs, WR103EW.* Countryside location centrally situated for visiting Stratford, Broadway, Cheltenham, Oxford. **Open:** Jan to Nov
01386 710203 (also fax) G Wright **D:** £16.00–£20.00 **S:** £18.00–£20.00 **Beds:** 1F

Lower Bentley
SO9865   ⊲ *Red Lion*

Lower Bentley Farm, *Lower Bentley Lane, Lower Bentley, Bromsgrove, Worcs, B60 4JB.* Victorian farmhouse in rural location close to M5/M42. **Open:** All year
01527 821286 C Gibbs **Fax: 01527 821193** *aj.gibbs@farmline.com* www.lowerbentleyfarm.co.uk **D:** £22.00 **S:** £27.00–£30.00 **Beds:** 2T 1D **Baths:** 2 En 1 Pr ⌂ ⊞ (3) ⊡ ⊀ ⊞ ⚲

Malvern
SO7846   ⊲ *The Lamb*

Nether Green Farm, *Ridge Way Cross, Malvern, Worcs, WR13 5JS.* 5 Miles to spa town of Malvern and Malvern Hills for great walking. **Open:** All year (not Xmas)
01886 880387 Mrs Orford **D:** £17.50–£20.00 **S:** £16.00 **Beds:** 1D 1T 1S **Baths:** 1 Sh ⌂ ⊞ (3) ⊀ ⊞ ⚲

Cowleigh Park Farm, *Cowleigh Road, Malvern, Worcs, WR13 5HJ.* Peacefully situated C17th timbered farmhouse at foot of Malvern Hills. **Open:** All year (not Xmas/New Year) **Grades:** ETC 4 Diamond
01684 566750 (also fax) Mrs Stringer
cowleighparkfarm@talk21.com **D:** £27.00–£28.00 **S:** £38.00–£40.00 **Beds:** 2T 1D **Baths:** 3 En ⌂ (7) ⊞ (8) ⌿ ⊡ ⊀ × ⊡ ⊞ ⚲

Mellor Heights, *46a West Malvern Road, Malvern, Worcestershire, WR14 4NA.* Modern, comfortable family home high in the Malvern Hills. **Open:** All year (not Xmas/New Year) **Grades:** ETC 3 Diamond
01684 565105 Ms Mellor *mellorheights@onetei.net.uk* **D:** £20.00 **S:** £20.00 **Beds:** 1T 1D **Baths:** 1 Sh ⌂ (10) ⊡ ⊀ ⊡ ⊞ ⚲

Malvern Link
SO7847

Edgeworth, *4 Carlton Road, Malvern Link, Worcs, WR14 1HH.* Edwardian family home near station and access to hill walks. **Open:** All year
01684 572565 Mrs Garland *susan.garland@talk21.com* **D:** £18.00–£20.00 **S:** £19.00–£22.00 **Beds:** 1D 2S **Baths:** 1 Sh ⌂ ⊞ (2) ⌿ ⊡ ⊀ ⊡ ⊞ ⚲

Rathlin, *1 Carlton Road, Malvern Link, Worcs, WR14 1HH.* A private family home offering friendly B&B accommodation. **Open:** All year
01684 572491 Mrs Guiver **D:** £18.00–£22.00 **S:** £18.00–£22.00 **Beds:** 1T 2D **Baths:** 1 En 2 Sh ⊞ (1) ⌿ ⊡ ⊀ ⊡ ⊞ ⚲

Martin Hussingtree
SO8860

Knoll Farm, *Ladywood Road, Martin Hussingtree, Worcester, Worcs., WR3 7SY.* **Open:** All year
01905 455565 Mrs Griggs *aligriggs@ hotmail.com* **D:** £25.00 **S:** £25.00–£30.00
Beds: 1T 2D **Baths:** 2 En 1 Sh ✆🖥(10)🖥🛏 ♿
The house is set in a rural location with wonderful views towards Abberley and Malvern Hills. Comfortable rooms, full English breakfast and a warm welcome. Between the historic towns of Worcester and Droitwich. Close to M5, off-road parking.

Ombersley
SO8463

The Old Farmhouse, *Hadley Heath, Ombersley, Droitwich, Worcs, WR9 0AR.* Beautiful country house, peaceful location. Tennis. 5 mins M5 J6. Warm welcome. **Open:** All year **Grades:** ETC 5 Diamond, Silver
01905 620837 J M Lambe **Fax: 01905 621722** *judylambe@ombersley.demon.co.uk* www.the-old-farmhouse.com **D:** £27.50–£30.00 **S:** £30.00 **Beds:** 2T 2D 1S **Baths:** 3 En 1 Sh ✆🖥🖥✍🖥🖥♿

Greenlands, *Uphampton, Ombersley, Droitwich, Worcs, WR9 0JP.* C16th picturesque house. Peaceful conservation hamlet. Character bedrooms. Every comfort. **Open:** All year
01905 620873 Mrs Crossland *xlandgreenlands@onetel.net.uk* **D:** £18.00–£25.00 **S:** £20.00–£40.00 **Beds:** 2D 1T 1S **Baths:** 1 En 2 Sh 🖥(6)✍🖥🖥♿

Pershore
SO9445

Besford Bridge House, *Besford Bridge, Pershore, Worcs, WR10 2AD.* Georgian farmhouse in rural location just 2 miles from Pershore. **Open:** All year (not Xmas/New Year)
01386 553117 Mrs Dodwell *sallydodwell@ classicfm.net* **D:** £18.00–£24.00 **S:** £20.00–£24.00 **Beds:** 2D **Baths:** 1 Sh 🖥(2)✍🖥✕🖥♿

BEDROOMS
D = Double
T = Twin
S = Single
F = Family

Planning a longer stay? Always ask for any special rates

Pirton
SO8747

The Old Smithy, *Pirton, Worcester, WR8 9EJ.* C17th black and white country house, quiet location near M5. **Open:** All year (not Xmas) **Grades:** ETC 4 Diamond
01905 820482 Mrs Wynn *welcome@ TheOldSmithy.co.uk* www.smoothhound.co.uk/hotels/oldsmith.htmlhotels/oldsmith.html **D:** £20.00–£25.00 **S:** £25.00–£27.00 **Beds:** 1D 1T **Baths:** 1 Pr 1 Sh 🖥(6)✍🖥✕🖥♿ **cc**

Redditch
SP0368

Walcote, *Dagnell End Road, Bordesley, Redditch, Worcs, B98 9BH.* Comfortable country home, 3m to M42, opposite golf course. **Open:** All year (not Xmas/New Year)
01527 68784 Mrs Smith **D:** £17.50 **S:** £17.50 **Beds:** 2T 1S **Baths:** 1 Sh ✆(1)🖥(7)🖥♿

Oakland, *64 Ledbury Close, Matchborough East, Redditch, Worcs, B98 0BS.* Detached family home with easy access to Warwick, Stratford, motorway network. **Open:** All year
01527 524764 Mr & Mrs Lewis **D:** £20.00–£25.00 **Beds:** 1D **Baths:** 1 En 🖥(3)🖥🖥♿

Salwarpe
SO8762

Middleton Grange, *Ladywood Road, Salwarpe, Droitwich Spa, Worcestershire, WR9 5PA.* C18th farmhouse set in picturesque gardens in rural location. **Open:** All year **Grades:** ETC 4 Diamond
01905 451678 S Harrison **Fax: 01905 453978** *salli@middletongrange.com* www.middletongrange.com **D:** £25.00–£30.00 **S:** £25.00–£30.00 **Beds:** 2T 3D **Baths:** 4 En 1 Pr 🖥(8)🖥🛏🖥♿

Stoulton
SO9050

Caldewell, *Stoulton, Worcester, WR7 4RL.* Georgian mansion in parkland setting with animals and miniature railway. **Open:** All year (not Xmas) **Grades:** ETC 3 Diamond
01905 840894 (also fax) Mrs Booth *sheila@ caldewell.demon.co.uk* www.caldewell.demon.co.uk **D:** £20.00–£22.50 **S:** £23.00–£27.00 **Beds:** 3D 1T **Baths:** 2 En 2 Sh ✆🖥(6)✍🖥 🛏🖥♿

Stourport-on-Severn
SO8171

Baldwin House, *8 Lichfield Street, Stourport-on-Severn, Worcs, DY13 9EU.* Grade II Listed Georgian town house, close to historic canal basins. **Open:** All year
01299 877221 & 07966 365541 (M)
Mrs Barclay **Fax: 01299 877221** *balwinhousebb@aol.com* **D:** £20.00–£25.00 **S:** £22.50–£30.00 **Beds:** 2F 4D 2T 2S **Baths:** 7 En 1 Sh ✆🖥✍🖥🛏✕🖥♿ ♿

Upton-upon-Severn
SO8540 🍴 *Anchor Inn*

Bridge House, *Welland Stone, Upton-upon-Severn, Worcester, WR8 0RW.*
Open: All year (not Xmas/New Year)
Grades: ETC 4 Diamond, Silver
01684 593046 Ms Worrell *merrymichael@ clara.net* **D:** £25.00–£30.00 **S:** £30.00–£38.00 **Beds:** 1T 2D **Baths:** 2 En 1 Pr ✆(10)🖥(6)✍🖥🖥♿
Located in the peaceful hamlet of Welland Stone with glorious views of the Malvern Hills. Bridge House is perfectly situated for visiting the Three Counties Showground and local towns. A wonderful breakfast, attention to detail and many little extras ensures a pampered stay.

Lockeridge Farm, *Upton-upon-Severn, Worcester, WR8 0RP.* **Open:** All year (not Xmas)
01684 592193 Mrs Albert *frank@ albert85.freeserve.co.uk* **D:** £16.00–£18.00 **S:** £21.00–£23.00 **Beds:** 2F 1T **Baths:** 1 Sh ✆🖥(4)🖥🛏✕🖥♿
C16th farmhouse in quiet location, central to Worcester, Hereford, Gloucester, Cheltenham, Stratford on Avon. Off-road parking for larger vehicles. Ideally situated for 3 counties. Showground site of various events, comfortable accommodation all rooms showers ensuite. Friendly service, visitor satisfaction.

Jasmin, *21 School Lane, Upton-upon-Severn, Worcester, WR8 0LD.* Comfortable modern bungalow in quiet road and near town centre. **Open:** All year
01684 593569 D Leighton **D:** £20.00–£25.00 **S:** £25.00–£27.50 **Beds:** 1T 1D **Baths:** 1 Sh 🖥✍🖥🛏🖥♿

Please respect a B&B's wishes regarding children, animals and smoking

---

Four Hedges, *The Rhydd, Hanley Castle, Malvern, Worcester, WR8 0AD.* Friendly family house, spacious garden. Three Counties Showground 4 miles. **Open:** All year (not Xmas)
01684 310405 (also fax) Mrs Cooper
fredgies@aol.com **D:** £15.00–£17.00 **S:** £15.00–£17.00 **Beds:** 1D 1T 2S **Baths:** 1 En 1 Sh ⛻ 🅿 (5) ⽝ 📺 🐾 ⚐

Whittington

SO8753

Woodview, *High Park, Whittington, Worcester, WR5 2RS.* Comfortable friendly accommodation set in 10 acres garden, donkey paddocks. **Open:** All year (not Xmas)
01905 351893 Mrs Wheeler *betty.wheeler@ talk21.com* **D:** £19.00–£22.00 **S:** £20.00–£25.00 **Beds:** 2D 2T **Baths:** 1 En 2 Sh ⛻ 🅿 (4) ⽝ 📺 �:V: 🛏 ⚐

Wick

SO9545

6 Hopney Cottage, *Wick, Pershore, Worcs, WR10 3JT.* Spacious cottage providing a friendly atmosphere, comfortable bedrooms with views. **Open:** All year (not Xmas)
01386 556341 (also fax) Mrs Shakespeare
hopneycottage@hotmail.com **D:** £18.00–£25.00 **S:** £18.00 **Beds:** 2D 2T 1S **Baths:** 1 En 1 Sh 🅿 (10) ⽝ 📺 🛏 ⚐

Wickhamford

SP0642

Avonwood, *30 Pitchers Hill, Wickhamford, Evesham, Worcestershire, WR11 6RT.* High standard of furnishings and decor. 3 miles from Broadway. **Open:** All year (not Xmas/New Year)
01386 834271 (also fax) Ms Morgan
D: £19.50 **S:** £19.50–£26.00 **Beds:** 1T 2D **Baths:** 3 En ⛻ (12) 🅿 (8) ⽝ 📺 🛏 🛏 ⚐

Wildmoor

SO9575 🍺 *Wildmoor Oak*

Home Farm, *Mill Lane, Wildmoor, Bromsgrove, Worcs, B61 0BX.* Modern comfortable extension of farmhouse. **Open:** All year
01527 874964 Mr Lees **D:** £20.00 **S:** £20.00–£25.00 **Beds:** 3T 2S **Baths:** 3 Sh 🅿 (5) 📺 🛏 ⚐

Worcester

SO8555

Oaklands B&B, *Grange Lane, Claines, Worcester, WR3 7RR.* Peaceful, rural outlook, yet easy access Worcester city, Stratford, Cotswolds. **Open:** All year (not Xmas)
Grades: ETC 4 Diamond
01905 458871 Mrs Gadd **Fax: 01905 759362**
barbaragadd@hotmail.com **D:** £25.00–£30.00 **S:** £30.00 **Beds:** 1F 1D 1T 1S **Baths:** 4 En ⛻ 🅿 (6) 📺 🛏 ⚐

The Old Smithy, *Pirton, Worcester, WR8 9EJ.* C17th black and white country house, quiet location near M5. **Open:** All year (not Xmas)
Grades: ETC 4 Diamond
01905 820482 Mrs Wynn *welcome@ TheOldSmithy.co.uk* www.smoothhound.co. uk/hotels/oldsmith.htmlhotels/oldsmith. html **D:** £20.00–£25.00 **S:** £25.00–£27.00 **Beds:** 1D 1T **Baths:** 1 Pr 1 Sh 🅿 (6) ⽝ 📺 ✕ :V: 🛏 ⚐ cc

Burgage House, *4 College Precincts, Worcester, WR1 2LG.* Georgian house in perfect location next to Worcester Cathedral. **Open:** All year (not Xmas/New Year) **Grades:** AA 3 Diamond
01905 25396 (also fax) Mrs Ratcliffe
www.burgagehouse.co.uk **D:** £25.00–£27.50 **S:** £30.00 **Beds:** 1F 1T 2D **Baths:** 4 En ⛻ ⽝ 📺 👶 ⚐

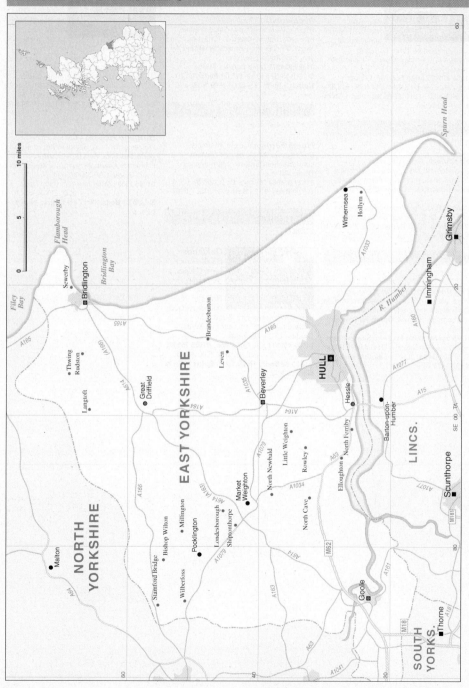

Beverley

TA0440 ◀ *Holescroft Inn, Hayride*

Number One, *1 Woodlands, Beverley, E. Yorks, HU17 8BT.* Victorian house, home cooking, open fires, library, lovely gardens. **Open:** All year
01482 862752 Mrs King *neilandsarah@ mansle.karoo.co.uk* **D:** £18.00–£22.00 **S:** £19.50–£29.00 **Beds:** 1D 1T 1S **Baths:** 1 En 1 Sh ⌣ ❚ (1) ⚓ 📺 ✗ Ⅴ 🍽 ♨

Bishop Wilton

SE7955

High Belthorpe, *Bishop Wilton, York, YO42 1SB.* Large comfortable farmhouse in peaceful setting with wonderful views, private fishing. **Open:** All year (not Xmas)
01759 368238 M Hamdan *keebyah@ netscapeonline.co.uk* **D:** £17.63 **S:** £20.00 **Beds:** 1F 1D ⌣ ❚ 📺 ♘ ✗ Ⅴ 🍽

Brandesburton

TA1247

Burton Lodge Hotel, *Brandesburton, Driffield, E. Yorks, YO25 8RU.* Charming country hotel, set in 2 acres of grounds adjoining golf course. **Open:** All year (not New Year)
01964 542847 Fax: 01964 544771 www.burtonlodge.fsnet.co.uk **D:** £24.00–£26.00 **S:** £34.00–£36.00 **Beds:** 2F 4T 2D 1S **Baths:** 9 En ⌣ ❚ (15) 📺 ♘ ✗ Ⅴ 🍽 ♨ cc

Bridlington

TA1867 ◀ *St Quintin Arms*

Grantlea Guest House, *2 South Street, Bridlington, E Yorks, YO15 3BY.* **Open:** All year (not Xmas) **Grades:** ETC 3 Diamond
01262 400190 M J Odey www.bridlington. net/accommodation/hotels/grantlea/ **D:** £16.00 **S:** £16.00 **Beds:** 2D 2T 2S **Baths:** 3 En 1 Sh 📺 Ⅴ 🍽 ♨
Situated on south side of Bridlington, 1 min from beach & Spa Theatre. 2 mins from harbour and town centre. Ideal for walking, fishing and golf as well as beach holidays. All rooms have colour TVs and tea/coffee making facilities.

Longleigh B&B, *12 Swanland Avenue, Bridlington, E. Yorks, YO15 2HH.* Quiet location, 4 minutes from town and sea front. **Open:** All year
01262 676234 D: £16.00–£18.00 **S:** £16.00–£17.00 **Beds:** 2D 1S 📺 🍽 ♨

The Bay Court Hotel, *35A Sands Lane, Bridlington, E Yorks, YO15 2JG.* **Open:** Mar to Nov **Grades:** ETC 4 Diamond
01262 676288 *bay.court@virgin.net* www.baycourt.co.uk **D:** £25.00–£28.00 **S:** £25.00 **Beds:** 2T 3D 2S **Baths:** 5 En 2 Pr ❚ (4) ⚓ 📺 ♘ ✗ Ⅴ 🍽 ♿ ♨ cc
Perfectly situated opposite Bridlington's quiet North Bay promenade, also giving easy access to the harbour and nearby cliffs. You will receive a warm friendly welcome, be assured of both tasteful and comfortable accommodation as well as delicious food. Licensed bar with wide selection of wines.

Stonmar Guest House, *15 Flamborough Road, Bridlington, E. Yorks, YO15 2HU.* An excellent family run guest house with traditional home-cooked meals. **Open:** All year
01262 674580 (also fax) D: £18.50–£24.00 **S:** £18.50–£24.00 **Beds:** 3F 5D 1S **Baths:** 2 En 2 Sh ⌣ ❚ (4) 📺 ✗ Ⅴ 🍽 ✾ ♨

Central Guest House, *1 Springfield Avenue, Bridlington, E. Yorks, YO15 3AA.* Perfectly situated for exploring the coast and countryside of Yorkshire. **Open:** All year (not Xmas/New Year)
01262 409283 Ms Evans **D:** £15.00–£20.00 **S:** £25.00–£35.00 **Beds:** 1F 1T 1D **Baths:** 1 En 1 Pr 1 Sh

Victoria Hotel, *25 Victoria Road, Bridlington, E. Yorks, YO15 2AT.* Family run. Ideal for beach, town centre and harbour. **Open:** All year **Grades:** ETC 3 Diamond
01262 673871 Fax: 01262 609431 *victoria.hotel@virgin.net* www.victoriahotelbridlington.co.uk **D:** £22.00 **S:** £27.00 **Beds:** 6F 2T 2D 2S **Baths:** 12 En ⌣ ❚ (6) 📺 ✗ Ⅴ 🍽 ✾ ♨ cc

Gables Private Hotel, *16 Landsowne Road, Bridlington, YO15 2QS.* Prime location, 50 yds from promenade, close to all amenities. **Open:** Easter to Oct
01262 672516 D: £15.00–£16.00 **S:** £15.00–£16.00 **Beds:** 1F 1T 1D 1S **Baths:** 2 Sh ⌣ ❚ (3) 📺 ✗ Ⅴ 🍽 ♨

Richmond Guest House, *9 The Crescent, Bridlington, E Yorks, YO15 2NX.* Welcoming B&B looking out over the sea **Open:** All year (not Xmas)
01262 674366 J Brewer **D:** £19.00–£24.00 **S:** £20.00–£22.00 **Beds:** 5F 2T 3D 1S **Baths:** 2 En 2 Sh ⌣ ❚ (4) ⚓ 📺 ♨

Planning a longer stay? Always ask for any special rates

Seawind's Guest House, *48 Horsforth Avenue, Bridlington, E Yorks, YO15 3DF.* Quiet location, close to beach, town centre and Spa Theatre. **Open:** All year
01262 676330 M J Chambers *seawinds@ btinternet.com* **D:** £16.00–£18.00 **S:** £20.00–£25.00 **Beds:** 1T 4D 1S **Baths:** 1 En 2 Sh ❚ (4) 📺 🍽 ♨

Elloughton

SE9428 ◀ *Red Hawk, Buccaneer, Half Moon*

Chat Moss, *16 Larchmont Close, Elloughton, Brough, E. Yorks, HU15 1AW.* Modern, quiet, 0.75m from Brough station, buses and shops. **Open:** All year (not Xmas/New Year)
01482 666514 Mrs Dixon **D:** £18.00–£18.50 **S:** £18.00 **Beds:** 1T 1D **Baths:** 1 Sh ⌣ (10) ❚ (3) ✗ 📺 Ⅴ 🍽

Goole

SE7423

Briarcroft Hotel, *49-51 Clifton Gardens, Goole, East Yorkshire, DN14 6AR.* Comfortable, friendly, licensed, ideally situated for touring Yorkshire. **Open:** All year
01405 763024 Mr Ramsdale **Fax: 01405 767317** *ianmr58@hotmail.com* www.briarcroft. co.uk **D:** £20.00–£24.00 **S:** £26.00–£39.00 **Beds:** 2F 6D 4T 5S **Baths:** 10 Pr 6 Sh ⌣ ❚ (6) ✗ 📺 Ⅴ 🍽 ♨

Great Driffield

TA0257

The Wold Cottage, *Wold Newton, Driffield, E Yorks, YO25 0HL.* Award-winning spacious C18th farmhouse away from roads. Ideal for Bampton cliffs and historic house. **Open:** All year
01262 470696 (also fax) Mrs Gray *woldcott@ wold-newton.freeserve.co.uk* **D:** £24.00–£30.00 **S:** £25.00–£30.00 **Beds:** 2D 1T **Baths:** 3 En ⌣ ❚ (10) ⚓ 📺 ✗ Ⅴ 🍽 ♨ cc

Hessle

TA0326

Redcliffe House, *Redcliffe Road, Hessle, E Yorks, HU13 0HA.* Elegant spacious rooms. Friendly service. Idyllic secluded gardens. Close Hull. **Open:** All year **Grades:** ETC 4 Diamond
01482 648655 S Skiba **D:** £25.00–£30.00 **S:** £30.00–£40.00 **Beds:** 2D 2T 2F 1S **Baths:** 4 En 1 Sh ⌣ ❚ (6) 📺 ♘ Ⅴ 🍽 ♨

Hollym

TA3425

Plough Inn, *Northside Road, Hollym, Withernsea, E Yorks, HU19 2RS.* Relaxed friendly atmosphere, open coal fires, large beer garden. **Open:** All year
01964 612049 Mr Robinson **D:** £16.00–£20.00 **S:** £20.00 **Beds:** 1F 4T **Baths:** 3 En ⌣ ❚ (20) 📺 ✗ Ⅴ 🍽 ♨

Planning a longer stay? Always ask for any special rates

Hull

TA0929

Beck House, *628 Beverley High Road, Hull, HU6 7LL.* Traditional town house, B&B, fine accommodation, close to university etc. **Open:** All year **01482 445468** Mrs Aylwin **D:** £19.00–£22.00 **S:** £19.00–£22.00 **Beds:** 3D 2S **Baths:** 5 En ⌨ 🅿 (4) 📺 🍽 🛜 cc

Marlborough Hotel, *232 Spring Bank, Hull, HU3 1LU.* Family run. Near to city centre. Victorian building. **Open:** All year **01482 224479 (also fax)** Mr Norman **D:** £18.00 **S:** £18.00 **Beds:** 3F 7T 3D 14S **Baths:** 5 Sh ⌨ 🅿 📺 🍽 🗙 📺 📺

Roseberry Guest House, *86 Marlborough Avenue, Hull, HU5 3JT.* Warm, clean Victorian B&B on tree-lined avenue. **Open:** All year **Grades:** ETC 4 Diamond **01482 445256 D:** £17.00–£21.00 **S:** £19.00–£30.00 **Beds:** 1F 1T 2D 2S **Baths:** 1 En 3 Pr 1 Sh ⌨ 📺 📺 🍽 * 🛜 cc

The Earlsmere Hotel, *76-78 Sunnybank, Hull, HU3 1LQ.* Comfortable, quiet home. One mile from city centre. **Open:** All year **Grades:** ETC 3 Diamond **01482 41977 D:** £17.00–£20.00 **S:** £19.00–£28.00 **Beds:** 4F 4T 7D 2S **Baths:** 7 En 2 Sh ⌨ 📺 🍽 📺 🛜 cc

Allandra Hotel, *5 Park Avenue, Hull, HU5 3EN.* Charming Victorian town house hotel, family run, close all amenities, convenient universities/town centre. **Open:** All year **01482 493349 Fax: 01482 492680 D:** £19.50 **S:** £26.00 **Beds:** 2F 1T 7D **Baths:** 10 En ⌨ 🅿 (5) 📺 🍽 🗙 📺 🛜 cc

Langtoft

TA0166

The Ship Inn, *Scarborough Road, Langtoft, Driffield, East Yorks, YO25 3TH.* C17th coaching inn, guest rooms overlooking rolling Wolds countryside. **Open:** All year **Grades:** ETC 3 Diamond **01377 267243 D:** £19.95–£21.95 **S:** £29.50–£31.50 **Beds:** 2T 2D 2S ⌨ 🅿 🍽 📺 🍽 🗙 📺 🛜 * 🛜 cc

Leven

TA1144

New Inn, *44 South Street, Leven, Beverley, HU17 5NZ.* Old Georgian coaching house adjacent to rural canal - fishing allowed. **Open:** All year **01964 542223** P T Oliver **D:** £17.50 **S:** £23.00 **Beds:** 1F 3D 1T 1S **Baths:** 6 En ⌨ 🅿 (50) 📺 🍽 🗙 📺 🛜 cc

Little Weighton

SE9933

Rosedale B&B, *9 Skidby Road, Little Weighton, Cottingham, E Yorks, HU20 3UY.* Bungalow accommodation set in large beautiful garden at the foot of the Yorkshire Wolds. **Open:** All year **01482 846074** I Wilkinson **D:** £15.00 **S:** £20.00 **Beds:** 1F 2T **Baths:** 1 En 1 Sh ⌨ 🅿 (6) 📺 🍽 📺 🍽 📺

Londesborough

SE8645

Towthorpe Grange, *Towthorpe, Market Weighton, York, YO43 3LB.* On Wolds Way Link Route and near Cycle Route 66. **Open:** All year (not Xmas/New Year) **Grades:** ETC 2 Diamond **01430 873814** Mrs Rowlands **D:** £16.50 **S:** £16.50 **Beds:** 1T 1D 1S **Baths:** 2 Sh ⌨ (6) 🅿 (2) 🍽 🗙 📺 📺

Millington

SE8351   🍴 *Gate Inn*

Laburnum Cottage, *Millington, York, YO42 1TX.* Comfortable home. Warm welcome. Good food and facilities. **Open:** Feb to Oct **01759 303055** Mrs Dykes **D:** £20.00–£22.00 **S:** £22.00 **Beds:** 1F 1D ⌨ 🅿 (2) 🍽 📺 🗙 📺 📺 📺

North Cave

SE8932

Albion House, *18 Westgate, North Cave, Brough, E Yorks, HU15 2NJ.* Warm welcome in pleasant family home decorated in Victorian style. **Open:** All year **01430 422958 D:** £15.00–£20.00 **S:** £15.00–£20.00 **Beds:** 1F 1D 1S **Baths:** 1 En 1 Sh ⌨ 🅿 (6) 🍽 📺 🍽 🗙 📺 🛜 📺

North Ferriby

SE9826

B&B at 103, *103 Ferriby High Road, North Ferriby, East Yorks, HU14 3LA.* Comfortable house, large garden, overlooking river near Humber Bridge and Hull. **Open:** All year **Grades:** ETC 3 Diamond **01482 633637 & 07808 387651 (M)** Mrs Simpson *info@bnb103.co.uk* www.bnb103.co.uk **D:** £15.00 **S:** £15.00 **Beds:** 1D 1T 1S **Baths:** 1 Sh ⌨ (7) 🅿 (2) 🍽 🗙 📺 📺

North Newbald

SE9136

The Gnu Inn, *The Green, North Newbald, York, YO43 4SA.* Traditional country inn in picturesque surroundings; good for walkers and cyclists. **Open:** All year **01430 827799 D:** £20.00–£30.00 **S:** £20.00–£30.00 **Beds:** 1F 1D 1T **Baths:** 3 En ⌨ 🅿 (25) 🍽 📺 🗙 📺 🍽 🛜 cc

Rowley

SE9832

Rowley Manor Hotel, *Rowley, Little Weighton, Cottingham, E. Yorks, HU20 3XR.* Situated in 35 acres of gardens & lawns, farmland. **Open:** All year **01482 848248   Fax: 01482 849900** *info@ rowleymanir.com* **D:** £55.00–£95.00 **S:** £55.00–£70.00 **Beds:** 3T 10D 3S **Baths:** 16 En ⌨ 🅿 (50) 🍽 📺 🍽 🗙 📺 🍽 * 🛜 cc

Rudston

TA0966

Bosville Arms, *High Street, Rudston, Driffield, East Yorkshire, YO25 4UB.* Quality country retreat in historic Yorkshire village near east coast. **Open:** All year **01262 420259 (also fax)** *hogan@ bosville.freeserve.co.uk* www.bosville.freeserve. co.uk **D:** £24.95–£28.75 **S:** £29.95–£34.95 **Beds:** 3T 3D ⌨ 🅿 (40) 📺 🗙 📺 🍽 * 🛜 cc

Sewerby

TA2068   🍴 *Martonian Inn*

The Poplars Motel, *45 Jewison Lane, Sewerby, Bridlington, East Yorkshire, YO15 1DX.* Purpose built, close to coastal paths, golf courses, RSPB reserve. **Open:** All year (not Xmas/New Year) **Grades:** ETC 3 Diamond **01262 677251 (also fax)** Mr Lewis **D:** £16.50–£19.00 **S:** £23.50–£26.00 **Beds:** 1T 5D **Baths:** 6 En ⌨ 🅿 (6) 📺 📺 🍽 📺

Shiptonthorpe

SE8543

Robeanne House Farm & Stables, *Driffield Lane, Shiptonthorpe, York, YO43 3PW.* Comfortable family house, large spacious rooms countryside views. **Open:** All year **01430 873312 (also fax)** Mrs Wilson *robert@ robeannefreeserve.co.uk* **D:** £20.00–£40.00 **S:** £20.00–£25.00 **Beds:** 3F 2D 1T **Baths:** 6 En ⌨ 🅿 (10) 📺 🍽 🗙 📺 🍽 * 🛜 cc

All details shown are as supplied by B&B owners in Autumn 2001

Stamford Bridge

SE7155

High Catton Grange, Stamford Bridge, York, YO41 1EP. A warm welcome awaits you at this C18th farmhouse in peaceful rural location. **Open:** All year (not Xmas/New Year)
01759 371374 (also fax) Ms Foster
D: £19.00–£23.00 **S:** £28.00–£35.00 **Beds:** 1F 1D **Baths:** 1 En 1 Pr ➳ 🅿 (6) 🖾 🛧 🖂 🎹 ₤

BEDROOMS

D = Double

T = Twin

S = Single

F = Family

Thwing

TA0569 ◀*Rampant Horse, Boswell Arms, Burton Arms*

Garth House, Main Street, Thwing, Driffield, E Yorks, YO25 3DY. **Open:** All year (not Xmas)
01262 470843 (also fax) Mr Dell *plasdell@ thwing.freeserve.co.uk.* **D:** £20.00 **S:** £20.00
Beds: 2D **Baths:** 1 En 1 Pr ➳ 🅿 (1) 🖾 🛧 🎹 ₤

Thwing is a quiet Yorkshire Wolds village off the beaten track. We offer a warm welcome, privacy and the choice to relax or explore the coast, Yorkshire Wolds, North York Moors and places of historic interest at your own pace.

Planning a longer stay? Always ask for any special rates

Wilberfoss

SE7351

Cuckoo Nest Farm, Wilberfoss, York, YO41 5NL. Red brick traditional house, park and ride nearby for York. **Open:** All year (not Xmas)
01759 380365 J M Liversidge **D:** £20.00–£25.00 **S:** £23.00 **Beds:** 1T 1D **Baths:** 1 Pr ➳ 🅿 ⅛ 🖾 🎹 ₤

Withernsea

TA3427

Vista Mar Guest House, 48 Promenade, Withernsea, E. Yorks, HU19 2DW. Seafront location, residents lounge, central for all amenities. **Open:** All year
01964 612858 Mr & Mrs Hirst **D:** £13.00–£16.00 **S:** £15.00–£20.00 **Beds:** 1F 1D 2T 3S
Baths: 2 En 2 Sh ➳ 🖾 🎹 ₤

North Yorkshire

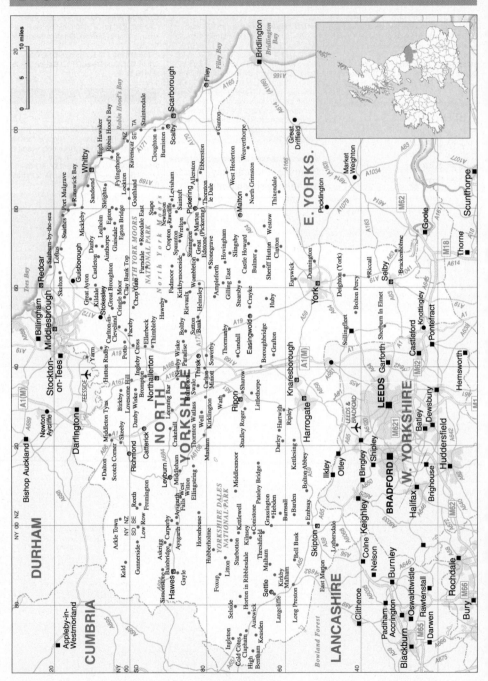

Ainthorpe

NZ7008

Rowantree Farm, Ainthorpe, Danby, Whitby, N. Yorks, *YO21 2LE.* Situated in the heart of the North York Moors, with panoramic moorland views. **Open:** All year (not Xmas/New Year) **Grades:** ETC 3 Diamond **01287 660396** Mrs Tindall *krbsatindall@ aol.com* **D:** £17.00–£18.00 **S:** £17.00–£18.00 **Beds:** 1F 1T **Baths:** 2 Pr ⌂ ▣ (4) ▥ ⚊ ✕ ☒ ▥.

Ampleforth

SE5878 ◀ *White Horse, White Swan*

Carr House Farm, Shallowdale, Ampleforth, York, *YO62 4ED.* Idyllic C16th farmhouse, romantic 4-poster bedrooms, internationally recommended, Heartbeat countryside. **Open:** All year (not Xmas) **Grades:** ETC 3 Diamond **01347 868526 & 07977 113197 (M)** Mrs Lupton *ampleforth@hotmail.com* www.guestaccom.co.uk/912.htm **D:** £20.00 **S:** £20.00 **Beds:** 3D **Baths:** 3 En ⌂ (7) ▣ (5) ⚊ ▥ ✕ ☒ ▥.

Arkle Town

NZ0002 ◀ *Charles Bathurst*

The Ghyll, Arkle Town, Arkengarthdale, Richmond, *DL11 6EU.* Perfectly situated for exploring Yorkshire Dales. Warm welcome, farmhouse breakfast. **Open:** All year (not Xmas) **Grades:** ETC 3 Diamond **01748 884353** Mr & Mrs Good **Fax: 01748 884015** *bookings@theghyll.co.uk* www.theghyll. co.uk **D:** £20.00 **S:** £20.00–£30.00 **Beds:** 1T 2D **Baths:** 3 En ⌂ ▣ (6) ⚊ ▥ ⚊ ▥ ▥. ⚊ cc

Askrigg

SD9491 ◀ *King's Arms, The Crown*

Milton House, Askrigg, Leyburn, N. Yorks, *DL8 3HJ.* Lovely old Dales family home situated in Askrigg village in beautiful countryside. **Open:** All year (not Xmas) **Grades:** ETC 4 Diamond **01969 650217** Mrs Percival **D:** £20.00–£22.00 **S:** £25.00–£30.00 **Beds:** 3D **Baths:** 3 En ⌂ (10) ▣ (3) ⚊ ▥ ⚊ ☒ ▥.

Austwick

SD7668

Dalesbridge, Austwick, Settle, N Yorks, *LA2 8AZ.* Friendly relaxing ensuite B&B. Outstanding views and a great atmosphere. **Open:** All year **Grades:** ETC 3 Diamond **015242 51021** Mr Beavan *info@ dalesbridge.co.uk* www.dalesbridge.co.uk **D:** £24.00 **S:** £29.00 **Beds:** 1F 2T 2D 1S **Baths:** 4 En 1 Sh ⌂ ▣ (60) ⚊ ▥ ⚊ ✕ ☒ ▥. ⚊ cc

Aysgarth

SE0088 ◀ *George & Dragon, Fox and Hound*

Cornlee, Aysgarth, Leyburn, North Yorks, *DL8 3AE.* Yorkshire Dales B&B overlooking village green. **Open:** All year **01969 663779 (also fax)** *cornlee@tesco.net* www.cornlee.co.uk **D:** £18.00–£22.00 **S:** £25.00 **Beds:** 1T 2D **Baths:** 2 En 1 Pr ⌂ (10) ⚊ ▥ ⚊ ☒ ▥. ⚊

Aysgarth Falls

SE0188

Wensleydale Farmhouse, Aysgarth Falls, Leyburn, N. Yorks, *DL8 3SR.* Situated 300 yards from the famous Aysgarth Falls. Superb views. **Open:** All year **01969 663534 (also fax)** Mr & Mrs Wykes *wykesarego@aol.com* www.wensleydalefarmhouse.fsnet.co.uk **D:** £22.00 **S:** £25.00 **Beds:** 2D 1T **Baths:** 3 En ⌂ (6) ▣ (4) ⚊ ▥.

Barden (Skipton)

SE0557

Howgill Lodge, Barden, Skipton, N. Yorks, *BD23 6DJ.* Uninterrupted views over beautiful Wharfedale. Once experienced, you will return. **Open:** All year (not Xmas) **01756 720655** Mrs Foster www.yorkshirenet. co.uk/stayat/howgill **D:** £27.00–£30.00 **S:** £32.00–£35.00 **Beds:** 1F 2D 1T **Baths:** 4 En ⌂ ▣ (10) ▥ ✕ ☒ ▥. ⚊ cc

Little Gate Farm, Drebley, Barden, Skipton, N Yorks, *BD23 6AU.* Beautiful Grade I Listed C15th Dales farmhouse; all rooms look down to River Wharfe. **Open:** Easter to Nov **01756 720200** **D:** £19.00 **S:** £19.00 **Beds:** 1F 1D 1T **Baths:** 1 Pr 1 Sh ⌂ ▣ ⚊ ▥ ☒ ▥.

Bedale

SE2688

Waggon And Horses, 20 Market Place, Bedale, N. Yorks, *DL8 1EQ.* Traditional cosy pub c1680 in attractive market town, selection of real ales, large bedrooms. **Open:** All year **01677 422747** Mr Young **D:** £22.50–£25.00 **S:** £25.00–£30.00 **Beds:** 3F **Baths:** 3 En ⌂ ▣ (10) ▥ ⚊ ▥.

Bell Busk

SD9056

Tudor House, Bell Busk, Skipton, N Yorks, *BD23 4DT.* Formerly a Victorian railway station retaining its character and charm yet with modern amenities. **Open:** Feb to Dec **01729 830301 (also fax)** Mr Hitchen *bellbusk.hitch@virgin.net* www.tudorbellbusk. co.uk **D:** £25.00 **S:** £21.00–£35.00 **Beds:** 1T 3D 1S **Baths:** 4 En 1 Sh ⌂ ▣ (10) ⚊ ▥ ✕ ▥. ⚊ cc

Birkby

NZ3202 ◀ *Cavalry Arms, Black Bull*

Woods End, 46 Inglewood Avenue, Birkby, Huddersfield, West Yorkshire, *HD2 2DS.* Easy access to the Dales and West Yorkshire's commercial centres. **Open:** All year **Grades:** ETC 4 Diamond **01484 513580 & 07710 691151 (M)** Ms Smith-Moorhouse *smithmoorehouse@ntlworld.com* **D:** £25.00 **S:** £25.00 **Beds:** 1D 1S **Baths:** 1 Pr 1 Sh ▣ ⚊ ▥ ▥.

Boltby

SE4986

Town Pasture Farm, Boltby, Thirsk, N. Yorks, *YO7 2DY.* Comfortable farmhouse in beautiful village, central for Yorkshire Dales. **Open:** All year (not Xmas) **Grades:** ETC 3 Diamond **01845 537298** Mrs Fountain **D:** £17.50–£19.50 **S:** £18.50–£20.00 **Beds:** 1F 1T **Baths:** 2 En ⌂ ▣ (3) ⚊ ▥ ⚊ ✕ ☒ ▥.

Willow Tree Cottage, Boltby, Thirsk, North Yorkshire, *YO7 2DY.* Large luxurious room with kitchenette. Quiet hillside village, spectacular views. **Open:** All year (not Xmas) **Grades:** ETC 4 Diamond **01845 537406** S C E Townsend **Fax: 01845 537073** *townsend.sce@virgin.net* **D:** £22.00–£30.00 **S:** £30.00–£38.00 **Beds:** 1F **Baths:** 1 En ⌂ (5) ▣ (2) ⚊ ▥ ⚊ ✕ ☒ ▥.

Low Paradise Farm, Boltby, Thirsk, N. Yorks, *YO7 2HS.* Warm welcome. Hill walking, cycling and Herriot Museum nearby. **Open:** Mar to Nov **01845 537253** Mrs Todd **D:** £17.00–£18.00 **S:** £20.00 **Beds:** 1D 2T **Baths:** 1 Sh ⌂ (6) ▣ (7) ⚊ ▥ ⚊ ✕ ☒ ▥.

Planning a longer stay? Always ask for any special rates

Bolton Abbey

SE0753

Hesketh Farm Cottage, *Bolton Abbey, Skipton, N. Yorks, BD23 6HA.* Beautiful views, situated 0.75m from village, Priory and river. **Open:** All year
01756 710332 Mrs Heseltine **D:** £18.00–£20.00 **S:** £18.00–£20.00 **Beds:** 2D 1S **Baths:** 1 En 1 Pr ⏚ 🅿 (4) ⸝ 🖙 🐾 🖾 ⚲

Bolton Percy

SE5341

Beckside House, *Main Street, Bolton Percy, York, YO23 7AQ.* Self contained ground floor accommodation in very peaceful village near York. **Open:** All year (not Xmas)
01904 744246 Mrs Rhodes *peter.rhodes@ tesco.net* **D:** £17.50 **S:** £20.00 **Beds:** 1D **Baths:** 1 En 🅿 (1) ⸝ 🖙 🐾 🖾 ⚲

Boroughbridge

SE3966   ◀ *Punch Bowl*

Primrose Cottage, *Marton-cum-Grafton, York, YO51 9QJ.* Warm hospitality in country cottage in picturesque village 1 mile east of A1(M). **Open:** All year **Grades:** ETC 4 Diamond
01423 322835 & 01423 322711 P M Styan **Fax: 01423 322835 & 01423 323985**
primrosecottage@btinternet.com **D:** £20.00 **S:** £20.00–£25.00 **Beds:** 2T 1D **Baths:** 1 Pr 1 Sh ⏚ 🅿 (8) 🖙 🐾 🖾 ⚲

Heaton House, *York Road, Boroughbridge, York, YO51 9HE.* Elegant Georgian farmhouse - landscaped gardens. **Open:** All year (not Xmas/New Year)
01423 323777 Mr & Mrs Rhodes
www.heatonhouse.co.uk **D:** £45.00 **S:** £30.00 **Beds:** 1F 1T 2D **Baths:** 1 En 2 Pr 1 Sh ⏚ (12) 🅿 (20) ⸝ 🖙 🖾 ⚲

Brackenholme

SE7030

Hagthorpe House, *Selby Road, Brackenholme, Selby, N. Yorks, YO8 6EL.* Beautiful country house, large garden, tennis, golf, fishing nearby. **Open:** All year (not Xmas)
01757 638867 Mrs Jackson *hagthorpe@ supanet.com* **D:** £16.00–£18.00 **S:** £18.00–£20.00 **Beds:** 1D 1T **Baths:** 1 Sh ⏚ 🅿 (3) ⸝ 🖙 🖾 ⚲

Brawby

SE7378   ◀ *Golden Lion*

Brawby Grange, *Brawby, Malton, N. Yorks, YO17 6PZ.* Comfortable farmhouse quiet location, central heating, wash basins all rooms, TV in lounge. **Open:** All year (not Xmas/New Year)
01653 668245 N Fairweather **D:** £17.00–£18.00 **Beds:** 1T 2D **Baths:** 1 Pr ⏚ 🅿 🖙 🖾 ⚲

Brompton

SE3796   ◀ *Green Tree, Village Inn*

Hallikeld House, *Brompton, Northallerton, N. Yorks, DL6 2UE.* Comfortable country setting. **Open:** Easter to Nov
01609 773613 Mrs Saxby **Fax: 01607 770262** **D:** £16.00–£18.00 **S:** £16.00–£18.00 ⏚ 🅿 (2) 🖙 🖾 ⚲

Bulmer

SE6967   ◀ *White Horse*

Lower Barn, *Bulmer, Castle Howard, York, YO60 7ES.* 200-year-old converted barn. Recommended by Which? magazine and B&B Guide. **Open:** All year (not Xmas/New Year)
01653 618575 Mr Hall **Fax: 01653 618183** www.lowerbarn.fsnet.co.uk **D:** £18.00–£20.00 **Beds:** 1T 1D **Baths:** 2 Sh ⏚ (5) 🅿 ⸝ 🖙 🖾 ⚲

Burniston

TA0192

Harmony Country Lodge, *Limestone Road, Burniston, Scarborough, N Yorks, YO13 0DG.* Octagonal peaceful retreat with superb sea views and 360 deg panorama. Aromatherapy massage available. **Open:** All year **Grades:** ETC 4 Diamond
0800 2985841 Mr & Mrs Hewitt
harmonylodge@cwcom.net www.spiderweb.co. uk/Harmony **D:** £23.50–£29.50 **S:** £23.50–£32.00 **Beds:** 1F 5D 1T 1S **Baths:** 5 En 3 Sh ⏚ (7) 🅿 (12) ⸝ 🖙 🐾 ✕ 🖾 ❋ ⚲

Burnsall

SE0361   ◀ *Fountain Inn*

Burnsall Manor House Hotel, *Burnsall, Skipton, N. Yorks, BD23 6BW.* Comfortable, friendly, relaxed. Good food. Ideal walking and cycling base. **Open:** All year
01756 720231 (also fax) Mr Lodge
manorhouse@burnsall.fsnet.co.uk manorhouseuk.co.uk **D:** £24.50–£28.50 **S:** £24.50–£28.50 **Beds:** 5D 3T **Baths:** 5 En 1 Pr 2 Sh ⏚ 🅿 (9) ⸝ 🖙 🐾 ✕ 🖾 ❋ ⚲

Holly Tree Farm

Holly Tree Farm, *Thorpe, Burnsall, Skipton, N. Yorks, BD23 6BJ.* Relax in a quiet, homely Dales sheep farm. **Open:** All year (not Xmas)
01756 720604 A Hall *hollytreefarm@amserve.net* **D:** £18.00–£20.00 **S:** £18.00–£20.00 **Beds:** 1D 1S **Baths:** 1 Sh ⏚ (5) 🅿 (2) ⸝ 🖙 🖾 ⚲

Carlton Miniott

SE3981

Carlton House Farm, *Carlton Miniott, Thirsk, N. Yorks, YO7 4NJ.* Warm Yorkshire welcome awaits in comfortable home. Lovely gardens and lanes to walk. **Open:** All year
01845 524139 Mrs Lee **D:** £15.00–£20.00 **S:** £15.00 **Beds:** 2D **Baths:** 1 Sh ⏚ (10) 🅿 (4) ⸝ 🖙 🖾

Grove Dene, *Carlton Miniott, Thirsk, N., YO7 4NJ.* Very homely bungalow 2 miles west of Thirsk, friendly B&B. **Open:** All year
01845 524257 Mrs Corner **D:** £16.00 **S:** £20.00 **Beds:** 1D **Baths:** 1 Sh ⏚ 🅿 (3) ⸝ 🖙 🐾 🖾 🖾 ♿ ⚲

Carlton-in-Coverdale

SE0684

Abbots Thorn, *Carlton-in-Coverdale, Leyburn, N. Yorks, DL8 4AY.* Traditional Yorkshire Dales home. Oak-beamed guest lounge, open fire, fabulous dinners. Superb scenery. **Open:** Jan to Dec
01969 640620 Mrs Lashmar *abbots.thorn@ virgin.net* www.abbotsthorn.co.uk **D:** £18.00–£25.00 **S:** £28.00 **Beds:** 2D 1T **Baths:** 2 En 1 Pr ⏚ (12) ⸝ 🖙 🐾 ✕ 🖾 ⚲

Carperby

SE0089

Crossouse, *Carperby, Leyburn, N Yorks, DL8 4DQ.* Old farmhouse, near Aysgarth Falls, excellent walking centre. Quiet. **Open:** All year (not Xmas/New Year)
01969 663457 Mrs Mason **D:** £16.00–£20.00 **S:** £16.00–£20.00 **Beds:** 1T 1D **Beds:** 1 En 1 Pr ⏚ 🅿 ⸝ 🖙 🖾 ⚲

Castle Howard

SE7170

High Gaterley Farm, *Castle Howard, York, YO60 7HT.* **Open:** All year
01653 694636 (also fax) Mrs Turner *relax@ highgaterley.com* www.highgaterley.com **D:** £19.00–£25.00 **S:** £25.00 **Beds:** 2D 1T 1S **Baths:** 1 En 1 Sh ⏚ 🅿 (10) ⸝ 🖙 🐾 ✕ 🖾 ⚲ Within the parkland of the estate with magnificent views over the Howardian Hills.

Lower Barn, Bulmer, Castle Howard, York, YO60 7ES. 200-year-old converted barn. Recommended by Which? magazine and B&B Guide. **Open:** All year (not Xmas/New Year)
01653 618575 Mr Hall **Fax:** 01653 618183
www.lowerbarn.fsnet.co.uk **D:** £18.00–£20.00
Beds: 1T 1D **Baths:** 2 Sh ☎ (5) ▣ ⅛ ▦ ▥.

Castleton
NZ6808

Greystones Bed & Breakfast, 30 High Street, Castleton, Whitby, N. Yorks, YO21 2DA. Between sea and moor's Greystone's makes the perfect resting place. **Open:** All year **Grades:** ETC 3 Diamond
01287 660744 D Wedgwood thewedgwood@aol.com **D:** £16.00 **S:** £16.00 **Beds:** 3D
Baths: 1 Pr 1 Sh ☎ ⅛ ▥ ▦.

Catterick
SE2497

Rose Cottage Guest House, 26 High Street, Catterick, Richmond, N. Yorks, DL10 7LJ. Small cosy stone-built guest house, midway London-Edinburgh. **Open:** All year (not Xmas) **Grades:** ETC 3 Diamond, AA 3 Diamond
01748 811164 Mrs Archer **D:** £18.50–£21.00
S: £22.00–£27.00 **Beds:** 1D 2T 1S **Baths:** 2 En 1 Sh ☎ ▣ (4) ▥ ♀ × ▦.

Chop Gate
SE5599

Hill End Farm, Chop Gate, Middlesbrough, TS9 7JR. Beautiful views down the valley of Bilsdale, midway between Helmsley and Stokesley. **Open:** Easter to Nov
01439 798278 Mrs Johnson **D:** £21.00
S: £25.00 **Beds:** 1F 1T **Baths:** 2 En ☎ (5) ▣ (3) ⅛ ▥ ♀ ▦.

Clapham
SD7469

Arbutus Guest House, Riverside, Clapham, Lancaster, LA2 8DS. Situated in heart of village, overlooking river. Excellent food and parking. **Open:** All year
015242 51240 Mrs Cass **Fax:** 015242 51197
info@arbutus.co.uk www.arbutus.co.uk
D: £20.00–£26.00 **S:** £20.00–£36.00 **Beds:** 2F 1D 2T 1S **Baths:** 5 En 1 Pr ☎ ▣ (6) ⅛ ▥ × ▥ ▦. ✿.

Claxton
SE6960

Claxton Hall Cottage, Malton Road, Claxton, York, YO60 7RE. Peaceful cottage, beams and log fires. Home baked cake on arrival. **Open:** All year
01904 468697 (also fax) Mrs Brough
claxcott@aol.com members.aol.com/claxcott
D: £20.00–£27.50 **S:** £20.00–£27.50 **Beds:** 1T 2D **Baths:** 1 En 2 Sh ☎ ▣ (10) ⅛ ▥ × ▥ ▦.
cc

Clay Bank Top
NZ5701

Maltkiln House, Clay Bank Top, Bilsdale, Middlesbrough, TS9 7HZ. Warm welcome. Home cooking. Wonderful views. Licensed. Convenient footpaths/bridleways. **Open:** All year (not Xmas/New Year)
01642 778216 (also fax) G D Broad stay@maltkiln.co.uk www.maltkiln.co.uk **D:** £18.00–£19.50 **S:** £18.00–£19.50 **Beds:** 1T 1D 1S **Baths:** 1 En 1 Sh ☎ (10) ▣ (2) ⅛ ▥ × ▥ ✿ cc

Cloughton
TA0094

Gowland Farm, Gowland Lane, Cloughton, Scarborough, N. Yorks, YO13 0DU. Warm, friendly, peaceful, beautiful views, quiet, convenient Whitby/Scarborough/coast. **Open:** Easter to Sept
01723 870924 Mr Martin www.gowlandfarm.co.uk **D:** £16.50–£18.00 **S:** £16.50–£18.00
Beds: 1D 1T 1S **Baths:** 1 Sh ☎ (3) ▣ (6) ▥ × ▥ ▦.

Cold Cotes
SD7171   🚂 Goat Gap

Moor View, Cold Cotes, Clapham, N Yorks, LA2 8JA. **Open:** All year (not Xmas)
015242 42085 Mrs Woodhead Garynjenny@hotmail.com **D:** £25.00 **S:** £30.00 **Beds:** 1T 1D **Baths:** 1 En 1 Pr ☎ (2) ⅛ ▥ ▦.
Beautiful detached home peacefully situated just off the A65 at the foot of Ingleborough in the Dales National Park. Stunning views (and sunsets if you're lucky!) Ideally situated for walking, cycling, touring, or just simply relaxing. A warm welcome awaits.

Conistone
SD9867   🚂 Tennants Arms

Ebony House, Conistone, Skipton, N Yorks, BD23 5HS. Peaceful, picturesque hamlet. Excellent walking. Spectacular views. **Open:** Mar to Oct **Grades:** ETC 4 Diamond
01756 753139 Mrs Robinson **D:** £22.00–£25.00 **S:** £30.00 **Beds:** 2D **Baths:** 2 En ▣ (4) ⅛ ▥ ▥ ▦.

Crakehall
SE2489

Waterside, Glenaire, Great Crakehall, Bedale, N. Yorks, DL8 1HS. Country house in 1-acre garden, trout stream. Bedrooms overlook garden to water's edge. **Open:** All year (not Xmas)
01677 422908 Mrs Smith **Fax:** 01677 422280
D: £19.00–£22.00 **S:** £25.00 **Beds:** 1D 2T
Baths: 2 En 1 Pr ☎ (5) ▣ (4) ⅛ ▥ ♀ ▥ ▦.

Crayke
SE5670

The Hermitage, Crayke, York, YO61 4TB. Stone-built house set in large garden, located on edge of small pretty village. **Open:** All year
01347 821635 Mr Moverley **D:** £26.00–£27.00
S: £26.00–£27.00 **Beds:** 1D 2T **Baths:** 1 En 1 Sh ☎ ▣ (4) ▥ ▥ ▦.

Cringle Moor
NZ5503

Beakhills Farm, Cold Moor, Cringle Moor, Chop Gate, Stokesley, Middlesbrough, TS9 7JJ. Cosy farmhouse on working farm. **Open:** All year
01642 778371 Mrs Cook **D:** £16.00 **S:** £16.00
Beds: 1F 1T 1D ☎ ▣ ▥ ♀ × ▥

Cropton
SE7589

High Farm, Cropton, Pickering, N. Yorks, YO18 8HL. Lovely Victorian house, beautiful garden overlooking National Parkland, home baking. **Open:** All year
01751 417461 Mrs Feaster **Fax:** 01751 473250 **D:** £20.00 **Beds:** 3D **Baths:** 3 En ☎ (10) ▣ (10) ▥ ▦. ✿. cc

Burr Bank Cottage, Cropton, Pickering, N. Yorks, YO18 8HL. Walks, rides, drives to coast, Moors, Dales, Wolds, York less than 45 mins away. **Open:** All year
01751 417777 Ms Richardson **Fax:** 01751 417789 bandb@burrbank.com www.burrbank.com **D:** £27.00 **S:** £27.00 **Beds:** 1D 1T **Baths:** 2 En ☎ (12) ▣ (10) ⅛ ▥ × ▥ ▦.

Cundall
SE4272   🚂 Farmers Inn, Angel Inn

Lodge Farm, Cundall, York, YO61 2RN. Warm welcome. Peaceful, quiet, panoramic views, explore North Yorkshire. **Open:** Mar to Dec **Grades:** ETC 4 Diamond
01423 360203 (also fax) Mrs Barker
D: £20.00–£25.00 **S:** £30.00–£35.00 **Beds:** 1F 1T 1D 1S **Baths:** 1 En 1 Pr ▣ (6) ⅛ ▥ ▥ ▦.

Dalton (Richmond)

NZ1108   ◀ *Travellers' Rest*

Broaches Farm, *Dalton, Richmond, North Yorkshire, DL11 7HW.* Idyllic situation between historic towns of Richmond and Barnard Castle. **Open:** All year (not Xmas/New Year) **01833 621369 (also fax)** Mrs Hutchinson *ahutchinson@promar-international.com* **D:** £18.00–£25.00 **S:** £20.00–£25.00 **Beds:** 1F 1D **Baths:** 1 Sh ⓣ 🅿 (4) ⌇ 📺 ♒ 🎔 Ⓥ 🏠 🏃

Stonesthrow, *Dalton, Richmond, North Yorkshire, DL11 7HS.* Quiet village between Richmond and Barnard Castle. Close to Yorkshire Dales. **Open:** All year **01833 621493 & 07970 655726 (M)** Mrs Lawson **D:** £18.00 **S:** £20.00 **Beds:** 2D 1S **Baths:** 1 Sh ⓣ (8) 🅿 (3) ⌇ 📺 Ⓥ 🏠 🏃

Danby

NZ7008

Sycamore House, *Danby, Whitby, N. Yorks, YO21 2NW.* C17th farmhouse with stunning views. Ideal area for walking/touring. **Open:** All year (not Xmas) **01287 660125** Mr Lowson **Fax: 01287 669122** *sycamore.danby@btinternet.com* **D:** £20.00 **S:** £20.00 **Beds:** 1F 1D 1T 1S **Baths:** 1 En 1 Sh ⓣ 🅿 (6) ⌇ 📺 🎔 ✗ Ⓥ 🏠 🏃

Holly Lodge Farm, *Danby Head, Danby, Whitby, N Yorks, YO21 2NW.* Beautiful views over Danby Dale near to Heartbeat and Herriot country, Whitby, York. **Open:** Easter to Oct **01287 660469** Mrs Shirley **D:** £18.00–£19.00 **S:** £18.00–£20.00 **Beds:** 1D 1T 1S **Baths:** 1 Pr ⓣ 🅿 (4) ⌇ 📺 ✗ Ⓥ 🏠 🏃

Danby Wiske

SE3398   ◀ *White Swan*

The Manor House, *Danby Wiske, Northallerton, N. Yorks, DL7 0LZ.* C16th house built of hand-made brick. **Open:** All year (not Xmas/New Year) **01609 774662** Mrs Sanders **D:** £17.00 **S:** £17.00 **Beds:** 1T 1D 2S **Baths:** 2 Sh ⓣ 🅿 (4) ⌇ 📺 🎔 Ⓥ 🏠 🏃

Darley

SE2059

Brimham Guest House, *Silverdale Close, Darley, Harrogate, N. Yorks, HG3 2PQ.* Family-run guest house, set in beautiful gardens. Winner of 1999 'Yorkshire In Bloom' competition. **Open:** All year (not Xmas) **01423 780948** Mrs Barker **D:** £15.00 **S:** £20.00 **Beds:** 2D 1T **Baths:** 3 En ⓣ (1) 🅿 (4) ⌇ 📺 Ⓥ 🏠 🏃

Deighton (York)

SE6244   ◀ *White Swan, Black Bull*

Rush Farm, *York Road, Deighton, York, YO19 6HQ.* **Open:** Mar to Oct **01904 728459** Mr Newsholme *david@ rushfarm.fsnet.co.uk* www.rushfarm.fsnet.co. uk **D:** £18.50–£20.00 **S:** £22.00–£25.00 **Beds:** 2F 3D 2S **Baths:** 5 En 1 Sh 🅿 (8) ⌇ 📺 🏠 🏃 cc
Family farmhouse standing in open countryside with pleasant views, ideally situated for visiting the city of York, the moors, the Dales and coast. Quality accommodation offering family care. Situated approximately 4 miles south of York.

Grimston House, *Deighton, York, YO19 6HB.* **Open:** All year **01904 728328   Fax: 01904720093** *grimstonhouse@talk21.com* www.grimstonhouse.com **D:** £48.00–£50.00 **S:** £30.00–£32.00 **Beds:** 1F 1T 5D **Baths:** 5 En ⓣ 🅿 📺 🎔 🏠 🏃
Built in the 1930s, Grimston House is an attractive place standing within a walled garden. Easy reach of York and on good bus route. Good local pub with bar meals.

Dunnington

SE6652

Brookland House, *Hull Road, Dunnington, York, YO19 5LW.* Private detached house, country area. Wholesome breakfast, home-made preserves. **Open:** Mar to Dec **01904 489548** Mrs Foster **D:** £16.00–£18.00 **S:** £17.00–£19.00 **Beds:** 1D 1T 1S **Baths:** 1 Sh 🅿 (3) ⌇ 📺 🏠 🏃

Earswick

SE6257

The Lodge, *302 Strensall Rd, Earswick, York, YO32 9SW.* Comfortable Christian house in countryside, 3.5 miles north of York. **Open:** All year **01904 761387 (also fax)** Mrs Edmondson *the.lodge@talk21.com* thelodgebandb.co.uk **D:** £20.00 **S:** £25.00 **Beds:** 1F 1D 1T **Baths:** 2 En 1 Sh ⓣ 🅿 (3) ⌇ 📺 Ⓥ 🏠 🏃

Fairthorne, *356 Strenshall Road, Earswick, York, YO32 9SW.* Peaceful country setting, dormer bungalow. 3 miles from York, easy reach North York Moors. **Open:** Dec to Dec **01904 768609 (also fax)** J W Harrison **D:** £16.00–£20.00 **S:** £20.00 **Beds:** 1F 1D **Baths:** 1 En ⓣ 🅿 (2) 📺 Ⓥ 🏃

Easingwold

SE5369

Garbutts Ghyll, *Thornton Hill, Easingwold, York, YO61 3PZ.* Traditional farm within own wooded valley. Period furnishings, organic cooking. **Open:** Easter to Nov **01347 868644** Mrs Glaister **Fax: 01347 868133 D:** £16.00–£18.00 **S:** £18.00–£22.00 **Beds:** 1T 1D **Baths:** 1 En ⓣ (0) 🅿 ⌇ 📺 🎔 Ⓥ 🏠 🏃

Yeoman's Course House, *Thornton Hill, Easingwold, York, YO61 3PY.* Set in an elevated position overlooking the beautiful Vale of York. **Open:** Easter to Oct **01347 868126** Mr & Mrs Addy **Fax: 01347 868129** *chris@yeomanscourse.fsnet.co.uk* **D:** £18.50–£19.50 **S:** £18.50–£19.50 **Beds:** 1T 2D ⓣ (12) 🅿 (8) ⌇ 📺 🏠 🏃

East Marton

SD9050

Sawley House, *East Marton, Skipton, N. Yorks, BD23 3LP.* C12th farmhouse - farm and stables by canal on Pennine Way. **Open:** All year (not Xmas) **01282 843207** Mrs Pilling *sawleyhouse@ pilling23.freeserve.co.uk* www.pilling23. freeserve.co.uk **D:** £22.00 **S:** £25.00 **Beds:** 1T 1D **Baths:** 2 Sh 🅿 (12) 📺 🎔 Ⓥ 🏃

Drumlins, *Heber Drive, East Marton, Skipton, North Yorkshire, BD23 3LS.* In quiet cul-de-sac off A59. Open views, easy access Dales, Pennine Way, Skipton. **Open:** All year **01282 843521** Ms Moran www.yorkshirenet. co.uk/stayat/drumlins/index.htm **D:** £22.00 **S:** £26.00 **Beds:** 1F 1D 1T 1D **Baths:** 3 En ⓣ 🅿 ⌇ 📺 ✗ Ⓥ 🏠 👥 🏃

Ebberston

SE8982 🛏 Foxholme Hotel, Grapes Inn, Caley Arms

Givendale Head Farm, *Ebberston, Scarborough, N. Yorks, YO13 9PU.* Beautiful views in a quiet location. Warm welcome. Farmhouse breakfast. **Open:** All year (not Xmas/New Year) **Grades:** ETC 3 Diamond **01723 859383** Mrs Gwilliam *sue.gwillam@ talk21.com* **D:** £20.00–£23.00 **S:** £23.00–£25.00 **Beds:** 1T 2D **Baths:** 3 En ⭐ 🅿 (3) ✔ 📺 ✕ 🏧 🐾

Foxholm Hotel, *Ebberston, Scarborough, N. Yorks, YO13 9NJ.* Peaceful, licensed ground floor rooms country inn in quiet picturesque village. **Open:** All year (not Xmas) **01723 859550 (also fax)** Mrs Clyde *kay@ foxholm.freeserve.co.uk* www.foxholm.freeserve. co.uk **D:** £25.50–£28.50 **S:** £30.50–£33.50 **Beds:** 2D 2T **Baths:** 4 En ⭐ 🅿 (20) ✔ 📺 🐾 ✕ 🏧 🐾 cc

Egton

NZ8006

Flushing Meadow, *Egton, Whitby, N Yorks, YO21 1UA.* Superb moorland views. Ideal base for Esk Valley and steam railway. **Open:** All year **01947 895395** Mrs Johnson *flushing_meadow_egton@yahoo.co.uk* **D:** £15.00–£19.50 **S:** £15.00–£17.00 **Beds:** 1D 1T 1S **Baths:** 1 En 1 Sh 🅿 (3) ✔ 📺 🏧 🐾

Egton Bridge

NZ8005 🛏 Horseshoe Hotel

Broom House, *Broom House Lane, Egton Bridge, Whitby, N Yorks, YO21 1XD.* Perfect location, accommodation, food, welcome etc. Visit website for details. **Open:** All Year (not Xmas) **Grades:** ETC 4 Diamond **01947 895279** Mr & Mrs White **Fax: 01947 895657** *welcome@ broomhouseegtonbridge.freeserve.co.uk* www.egton-bridge.co.uk **D:** £21.50–£23.50 **S:** £26.00 **Beds:** 1F 1T 4D **Baths:** 6 En ⭐ 🅿 (7) ✔ 📺 ✕ 🏧 🐾 🅗 🐾

Ellerbeck

SE4397

Old Mill House, *Ellerbeck, Osmotherley, Northallerton, N. Yorks, DL6 2RY.* Delightful C17th mill set central for walking touring North Yorkshire. **Open:** Easter to Nov **01609 883466** Mrs Shepherd **D:** £20.00–£25.00 **S:** £20.00–£25.00 **Beds:** 1T 2D **Baths:** 1 En 1 Sh 🅿 (4) ✔ 📺 🐾

Ellingstring

SE1684

Holybreen, *Ellingstring, Masham, Ripon, HG4 4PW.* Good home cooking at this spacious C18th cottage. **Open:** All year **01677 460216** Mrs Wright **Fax: 01677 460106** *anne.wright@virgin.net* **D:** £14.00–£15.00 **S:** £15.00–£16.00 **Beds:** 1F 1D **Baths:** 1 Sh ⭐ 🅿 (2) 📺 🐾 ✕ 📺 🏧 🐾

Embsay

SE0053

Bondcroft Farm, *Embsay, Skipton, N Yorks, BD23 6SF.* Sheep and beef farm, well known for training and breeding sheep dogs. **Open:** All year **01756 793371** Ms Clarkson *bondcroftfarm@ bondcroftfarm.yorks.net* **D:** £20.00–£22.50 **Beds:** 1T 2D **Baths:** 3 En ⭐ 🅿 (6) ✔ 📺 📺 🏧 cc

Faceby

NZ4903

Four Wynds, *Whorl Hill, Faceby, Middlesbrough, TS9 7BZ.* Small holding in beautiful countryside. Located off A172 between Swainby/Faceby. **Open:** All year **01642 701315** Mr Barnfather **D:** £18.00–£20.00 **S:** £18.00–£20.00 **Beds:** 1F 1D 1T **Baths:** 1 En 1 Sh ⭐ 🅿 (8) 📺 🐾 ✕ 📺 🏧 🐾 🐾

Fadmoor

SE6789

Mount Pleasant, *Rudland, Fadmoor, York, YO62 7JJ.* Friendly welcome. Ideal for walking, touring from moors. Brochure available. **Open:** All year (not Xmas) **Grades:** ETC 3 Diamond **01751 431579** Mary Clarke *info@ mountpleasantbedandbreakfast.co.uk* www.mountpleasantbedandbreakfast.co.uk **D:** £15.00–£17.00 **S:** £15.00–£17.00 **Beds:** 1F 1T **Baths:** 1 Sh ⭐ (4) 🅿 (6) 📺 ✕ 📺 🏧 🐾

Farndale

SE6697

Olive House Farm, *Farndale, Kirkbymoorside, York, YO60 7JY.* Homely farmhouse B&B on a working farm. Beautiful views. **Open:** Easter to Oct **01751 433207** Mrs Blacklock **D:** £14.00 **Beds:** 2F **Baths:** 1 Sh ⭐ 🅿 (4) 📺 🐾

Planning a longer stay? Always ask for any special rates

Filey

TA1180 🛏 Ship Inn, White Lodge

The Gables, *2a Rutland Street, Filey, N Yorks, YO14 9JB.* Characteristic Edwardian guest house. Friendly accommodation, comfortable ensuite rooms, colour TV. Central all amenities. **Open:** All year **Grades:** ETC 4 Diamond, AA 4 Diamond **01723 514750** R & K Broome *kate_gables@ talk21.com* **D:** £18.00–£20.00 **S:** £24.00–£25.00 **Beds:** 1F 2T 2D **Baths:** 5 En ⭐ 📺 🐾 ✕ 📺 🏧 🐾 🐾

Abbots Leigh Guest House, *7 Rutland Street, Filey, N. Yorks, YO14 9JA.* Close to the beach, gardens and town centre amenities. **Open:** All year **01723 513334** B E Illinworth and Miss C. Cullen **D:** £19.00–£20.00 **S:** £24.00–£25.00 **Beds:** 1F 2T 3D **Baths:** 6 En ⭐ (3) 🅿 (4) ✔ 📺 ✕ 📺 🏧 🐾 cc

Foxup

SD8676

Bridge Farm, *Foxup, Arncliffe, Skipton, N. Yorks, BD23 5QP.* Working Dales farm situated in Littondale (the forgotten valley). **Open:** Easter to Oct **01756 770249** Mrs Lund **D:** £15.00 **S:** £18.00 **Beds:** 1T 2D **Baths:** 1 Sh ⭐ 🅿 (4) 📺 🐾

Fremington

SE0499

Broadlands, *Fremington, Richmond, DL11 6AW.* Peaceful village setting 5 mins from Reeth, spectacular views, comfortable accommodation. **Open:** All year **01748 884297 (also fax)** Mrs Rudez **D:** £19.00 **S:** £27.00 **Beds:** 1D 1T 1S **Baths:** 1 Sh ⭐ (12) 🅿 (4) ✔ 📺 🐾 🏧 🅗 🐾

Fylingthorpe

NZ9404

South View, *Sledgates, Fylingthorpe, Robin Hood's Bay, Whitby, N. Yorks, YO22 4TZ.* Comfortable detached house. Sea and country views. Touring area. Bed time drink. **Open:** Easter to Oct **01947 880025** Mrs Reynolds **D:** £16.00–£18.00 **Beds:** 2D **Baths:** 1 Sh ⭐ (5) 🅿 (2) 📺 🐾

Red House, *Thorpe Lane, Fylingthorpe, Whitby, North Yorkshire, YO22 4TH.* Large Victorian house and garden. Panelled staircase and gallery. Beautiful views. **Open:** Easter to Oct **01947 880079** Mrs Collinson **D:** £18.00–£22.50 **S:** £20.00–£25.00 **Beds:** 1T 2D **Baths:** 1 En 1 Sh 🅿 (3) 📺 🐾 📺 🏧 🐾

Planning a longer stay? Always ask for any special rates

Low Farm, Fylingthorpe, Whitby, N Yorks, YO22 4QF. Imposing Georgian farmhouse built from local stone, set in beautiful countryside on working farm. **Open:** May to Nov
01947 880366 (also fax) Mrs Hodgson
D: £18.00–£21.00 **Beds:** 1F **Baths:** 1 En 🅿 (1)
⚡ 📺 Ⅴ 🛏 ⚓

Ganton
SE9977

The Ganton Greyhound, Main Street, Ganton, Scarborough, N Yorks, YO12 4NX. Family and country inn/hotel, 9 miles from coast. **Open:** All year (not Xmas)
01944 710116 T Bennet **Fax: 01944 710738**
gantongreyhound@supanet.com **D:** £25.00
S: £40.00 **Beds:** 6F 4D 6T 2S **Baths:** 16 En ⅌
🅿 (20) ⚡ 📺 ✕ Ⅴ 🛏 ⚓ cc

Gayle
SD8789

East House, Gayle, Hawes, N. Yorks, DL8 3RZ. Delightful house. Superb views, ideal centre for touring the Dales.
Open: Feb to Nov
01969 667405 Mrs Ward *loraward@lineone.net*
www.dalesaccommodation.com/easthouse
D: £18.00–£21.00 **S:** £18.00 **Beds:** 1T 1D 1S
Baths: 1 En 1 Sh ⅌ 🅿 ⚡ 📺 Ⅴ 🛏 ⚓

Gilling East
SE6177

Hall Farm, Gilling East, York, YO62 4JW. Warm family welcome, fantastic views, close to Moors, Helmsley, York. **Open:** All year (not Xmas)
01439 788314 Virginia Collinson *virginia@collinson2.fsnet.co.uk* **D:** £18.00–£20.00
S: £15.00–£20.00 **Beds:** 1D **Baths:** 1 En ⅌ 🅿
⚡ 📺 Ⅴ 🛏 ⚓3 ⚓

Glaisdale
NZ7603   ⚐ Moon & Sixpence, Horseshoe Inn

Arncliffe Arms Hotel, Glaisdale, Whitby, N. Yorks, YO21 2QL. Very friendly & comfortable accommodation. Romantic area along River Esk, close Beggars' Bridge. **Open:** All year
01947 897209 (also fax) Mr Westwood
D: £15.00 **S:** £15.00 **Beds:** 2D 2T 1S **Baths:** 1 Sh ⅌ 🅿 📺 ⚡ ✕ Ⅴ 🛏 ⚓

Hollins Farm, Glaisdale, Whitby, N. Yorks, YO21 2PZ. Comfortable C16th farmhouse near moors, 8 miles coast, wonderful scenery. **Open:** All year (not Xmas)
01947 897516 Mrs Mortimer **D:** £15.00
Beds: 3F 1D 2T **Baths:** 2 Sh ⅌ 🅿 (6) 📺 🛏 Ⅴ
🛏 ⚓

Red House Farm, Glaisdale, Whitby, N. Yorks, YO21 2PZ. **Open:** All year
01947 897242 (also fax) T J Spashett
spashettredhouse@talk21.com
www.redhousefarm.net **D:** £25.00 **S:** £25.00–£35.00 **Beds:** 1F 1T 2D 1S **Baths:** 3 En 1 Pr
⅌ 🅿 (4) ⚡ 📺 🛏 Ⅴ 🛏 ⚓
Listed Georgian farmhouse featured in 'Houses of the North York Moors'. Completely refurbished to highest standards but retaining original features. Excellent walks, bridleways from doorstep. 400 yds Coast to Coast walk. Friendly animals, stabling and billiards room, sitting in middle of NP just 8m coast & Whitby.

Postgate Farm, Glaisdale, Whitby, N Yorks, YO21 2PZ. C17th Listed farmhouse in beautiful Esk Valley, a walkers' paradise. Whitby 10 miles. **Open:** All year (not Xmas)
01947 897353 (also fax) Mrs Thompson
j-m.thompson.bandb@talk21.com **D:** £16.00–£21.00 **S:** £20.00–£30.00 **Beds:** 2D 1T
Baths: 3 En 🅿 (4) ⅌ 📺 Ⅴ 🛏 ⚓

Goathland
NZ8301   ⚐ Goathland Hotel, Inn on the Moor

Fairhaven Country Hotel, The Common, Goathland, Whitby, N. Yorks, YO22 5AN.
Edwardian country house, superb moorland views in centre of village.
Open: All year
01947 896361 Mr Ellis **Fax: 01947 896099**
royellis@thefairhavenhotel.co.uk
www.thefairhavenhotel.co.uk **D:** £27.00–£35.00 **S:** £22.00–£35.00 **Beds:** 3F 2T 2D 2S
Baths: 5 En 2 Sh ⅌ 🅿 (9) ⅌ 📺 🛏 ✕ Ⅴ 🛏 ⚓⚓
cc

The Beacon Country House, Goathland, Whitby, N Yorks, YO22 5AN. Late Victorian country house in 1 acre grounds. **Open:** All year
01947 896409 Mrs Katz **Fax: 01947 896431**
stewartkatz@compuserve.com
www.beacongoathland.co.uk **D:** £22.50–£25.00 **S:** £22.50 **Beds:** 1F 2T 2D **Baths:** 4 En
1 Pr ⅌ 🅿 ⅌ 📺 🛏 ✕ Ⅴ 🛏 ⚓ cc

Grafton
SE4163

Primrose Cottage, Marton-cum-Grafton, York, YO51 9QJ. Warm hospitality in country cottage in picturesque village 1 mile east of A1(M). **Open:** All year
Grades: ETC 4 Diamond
01423 322835 & 01423 322711 P M Styan
Fax: 01423 322835 & 01423 323985
primrosecottage@btinternet.com **D:** £20.00
S: £20.00–£25.00 **Beds:** 2T 1D **Baths:** 1 Pr 1
Sh ⅌ 🅿 (8) 📺 🛏 🛏 ⚓

Grassington
SE0064   ⚐ Angel Inn, Old Hall, Black Horse, Grassington House, King's Head, Devonshire Hotel

Raines Close, 13 Station Road, Grassington, Skipton, N. Yorks, BD23 5LS.
Close to village amenities.
Lovely views. Ideal touring or walking base.
Open: All year (not Xmas/New Year)
Grades: ETC 4 Diamond
01756 752678 Mr Benson *rainesclose@yorks.net*
www.rainesclose.co.uk **D:** £24.00–£30.00
S: £30.00 **Beds:** 1T 3D **Baths:** 3 En 1 Pr
⅌ (10) 🅿 (4) ⅌ 📺 Ⅴ 🛏 ⚓ cc

Mayfield Bed & Breakfast, Low Mill Lane, Grassington, Skipton, N. Yorks, BD23 5BX.
Beautiful Dales longhouse. Guest rooms overlook fells and river. **Open:** All year
01756 753052 Mr & Mrs Trewartha
suzanneatmayfield@talk21.com
www.yorkshirenet.co.uk/stayat/mayfield
D: £22.00–£25.00 **S:** £25.00 **Beds:** 1F 1D 1T
Baths: 1 En 1 Sh ⅌ 🅿 (5) ⅌ 🛏 Ⅴ 🛏 ⚓ ⚓

Craiglands, 1 Brooklyn, Threshfield, Grassington, Skipton, BD23 5ER.
Elegant Edwardian house offering quality accommodation and superb breakfasts. **Open:** All year (not Xmas)
Grades: ETC 4 Diamond
01756 752093 Mrs Wallace *craiglands@talk21.com* www.craiglands.com **D:** £23.00–£30.00 **S:** £21.00–£28.00 **Beds:** 2D 1T 1S
Baths: 3 En 1 Pr 🅿 (3) ⅌ 📺 🛏 ⚓ cc

Please respect a B&B's wishes regarding children, animals and smoking

BATHROOMS
En = Ensuite
Pr = Private
Sh = Shared

Ashfield House Hotel, Grassington, Skipton, N. Yorks, *BD23 5AE*. Quality food and accommodation in spectacular Yorkshire Dales National Park. **Open:** All year (not Xmas)
01756 752584 (also fax) Harrison *info@ ashfieldhouse.co.uk* www.ashfieldhouse.co.uk
D: £30.00–£34.00 **S:** £30.00–£54.00 **Beds:** 3T 4D **Baths:** 6 En 1 Pr ⌣ (5) ▣ (8) ⌇ ▥ ✕ ▣ 🖰 cc

Town Head Guest House, 1 Low Lane, Grassington, Skipton, N. Yorks, *BD23 5AU*. Friendly guest house at the head of the village between cobbled streets and moors. **Open:** All year (not Xmas)
01756 752811 Mrs Lister **D:** £25.00 **S:** £30.00 **Beds:** 3D 1T **Baths:** 4 En ▣ (3) ⌇ ▥ ▣ 🖰

Lythe End, Wood Lane, Grassington, Skipton, N. Yorks, *BD23 5DF*. Modern stone detached house, stunning views, quiet village location. **Open:** All year (not Xmas)
01756 753196 Mrs Colley *colley@ grassington.fsnet.co.uk* **D:** £22.00–£25.00 **S:** £30.00 **Beds:** 1F 1D **Baths:** 1 En 1 Pr ⌣ (12) ▣ (2) ⌇ ▥ 🖰

Great Ayton
NZ5611 ⬙ *Dudley Arms*

Eskdale Cottage, 31 Newton Road, Great Ayton, Middlesbrough, *TS9 6DT*. Victorian cottage in Picturesque village with River Lever running through it. Warm welcome. **Open:** All year (not Xmas)
01642 724306 Mrs Houghton *info@ mhoughton.co.uk* **D:** £18.00–£20.00 **S:** £20.00–£22.00 **Beds:** 2T **Baths:** 1 Pr ⌣ (0) ▣ (2) ⌇ ▥ ✕ ▥ 🖰

The Wheelhouse, Langbaurgh Grange, Great Ayton, Middlesbrough, Cleveland, *TS9 6QQ*. Converted barn/mill in half acre gardens with open views to Cleveland Hills. **Open:** All year
01642 724523 D: £17.00 **S:** £19.00 **Beds:** 1F 1D **Baths:** 2 Pr ⌣ ▣ (3) ▥ ↑ ▥ 🖰

Great Broughton
NZ5406

Ingle Hill, Ingleby Road, Great Broughton, North Yorks, *TS9 7ER*. Spectacular views North York Moors, warm welcome, transport to walks. **Open:** All year (not Xmas)
01642 712449 Mrs Sutcliffe www.spotlight osmotherley.co.uk **D:** £17.50 **S:** £18.50 **Beds:** 1F 1D 2T **Baths:** 2 En 2 Sh ⌣ ▣ (4) ⌇ ▥ ↑ ▥ 🖰 cc

Great Edstone
SE7084

Cowldyke Farm, Great Edstone, Kirkbymoorside, York, *YO62 6PE*. Family-run working farm set in idyllic peaceful Yorkshire countryside. **Open:** All year (not Xmas)
01751 431242 Mrs Benton www.cowldyke-farm.co.uk **D:** £20.00 **S:** £20.00 **Beds:** 1F 1D **Baths:** 2 En ⌣ (3) ▣ (10) ▥ 🖰 🖰

Gunnerside
SD9598 ⬙ *Kings Head*

Dalegarth House, Gunnerside, Richmond, *DL11 6LD*. Traditional breakfast. Home-made bread and preserves. Warm welcome. **Open:** Feb to Nov **Grades:** ETC 3 Diamond
01748 886275 Mrs Calvert **D:** £18.00–£20.00 **S:** £20.00 **Beds:** 1T **Baths:** 1 En ⌣ (4) ⌇ ▥ 🖰 🖰

Harrogate
SE3055 ⬙ *Joiners Arms, Hales Bar*

The Coppice, 9 Studley Road, Harrogate, N. Yorks, *HG1 5JU*. **Open:** All year
01423 569626 Mr & Mrs Richardson **Fax: 01423 569005** *coppice@harrogate.com* www.harrogate.com/coppice **D:** £23.00–£28.00 **S:** £28.00–£40.00 **Beds:** 1F 1T 2D 1S **Baths:** 5 En ⌣ (5) ⌇ ▥ ✕ ▥ 🖰 🖰 cc
A high standard of comfortable, clean accommodation, excellent food and warm friendly welcome awaits you. Our beautiful Victorian guest house is quietly situated yet close to the elegant town centre. Ideal for exploring the Dales. Halfway stop London to Edinburgh.

Staveleigh, 20 Ripon Road, Harrogate, *HG1 2JJ*. Luxury award-winning accommodation. Large rooms, excellent breakfasts. Walking distance town and conference centre. **Open:** All year **Grades:** ETC 4 Diamond, SIlver
01423 524175 Ms Sutton **Fax: 01423 524178** *enquiries@staveleigh.co.uk* www.staveleigh.co. uk **D:** £25.00–£30.00 **S:** £35.00–£55.00 **Beds:** 1F 1D 1T **Baths:** 2 En 1 Pr ⌣ ▣ (3) ⌇ ▥ ↑ ✕ ▥ 🖰 🖰 cc

Parnas Hotel, 98 Franklin Road, Harrogate, N. Yorks, *HG1 5EN*. **Open:** All year **Grades:** ETC 4 Diamond
01423 564493 Mr & Mrs Naylor **Fax: 01423 563554** *info@parnashotel.co.uk* www.parnashotel.co.uk **D:** £27.50 **S:** £40.00 **Beds:** 2F 3D 1T 3S **Baths:** 9 En ⌣ ▣ (8) ▥ ▥ 🖰 🖰 cc
Warm welcome to family-run licensed hotel in pleasant garden. Easy walk to town centre, Conference Centre, Valley Gardens. Great touring base. York half hour. Close to Emmerdale, Heartbeat country and Dales. Stop over on your way to Scotland.

The Belmont Hotel, 86 Kings Road, Harrogate, N. Yorks, *HG1 5JX*. **Open:** All year (not Xmas/New Year)
01423 528086 Mrs Buchanan *marilyn@ thebelmont86.fsnet.co.uk* www.smoothhound. co.uk/hotels/belmonthotel.html **D:** £25.00–£27.50 **S:** £30.00–£48.00 **Beds:** 2T 3D 2S **Baths:** 7 En ▣ (6) ⌇ ▥ ▥ 🖰 cc
We are about 200 yards from the Conference Centre/Exhibition Halls and five minutes walk into town - wonderful restaurants, cosmopolitan cafe-bars and very special shops. Returning to this mellow, comfortable house is a delight. Superb breakfasts. A warm welcome assured.

Ashley House Hotel, 36-40 Franklin Road, Harrogate, N. Yorks, *HG1 5EE*. **Open:** All year **Grades:** ETC 4 Diamond, AA 4 Diamond, RAC 4 Diamond
01423 507474 Mr & Mrs Thomas **Fax: 01423 560858** *ashleyhousehotel@btinternet.com* www.ashleyhousehotel.com **D:** £29.75–£42.50 **S:** £39.50–£75.00 **Beds:** 2F 5D 6T 5S **Baths:** 18 En ⌣ ▣ (4) ▥ 🖰 🖰 cc
High standard of accommodation at reasonable prices. Friendly hotel aiming to give you a memorable stay and value for money. Delightful bar with extensive collection of whiskies. Excellent restaurants within walking distance. Tour Dales and Moors from convenient location in this lovely spa town.

Alamah, 88 Kings Road, Harrogate, N. Yorks, *HG1 5JX*. Delightful Victorian guest house, 100 yds Exhibition Centre, 5 mins' walk town centre. **Open:** All year **Grades:** ETC 4 Diamond
01423 502187 Mr Wilkinson **Fax: 01423 566175 D:** £26.00–£28.00 **S:** £27.00–£33.00 **Beds:** 1F 2T 2D 2S **Baths:** 6 En 1 Pr ⌣ ▣ (10) ▥ ▥ 🖰 🖰

Planning a longer stay? Always ask for any special rates

Oakbrae Guest House, *3 Springfield Avenue, Harrogate, N. Yorks, HG1 2HR.* Centrally situated for all amenities, warm and friendly. **Open:** All year **01423 567682 (also fax) D:** £25.00 **S:** £30.00 **Beds:** 2T 3D 3S **Baths:** 7 En 1 Pr ⛣ (12) 🅿 (6) 📺 ⻗ 🆅 ▥ ⚓

Spring Lodge, *22 Spring Mount, Harrogate, N. Yorks, HG1 2HX.* Centrally situated Edwardian town house in a quiet cul-de-sac. Non-smoking. **Open:** All year (not Xmas) **Grades:** ETC 3 Diamond **01423 506036** Mr Vinter **Fax: 01423 506066** www.yorkshirenet.co.uk **D:** £19.00–£22.00 **S:** £20.00–£40.00 **Beds:** 1F 3D 1S **Baths:** 2 En 1 Sh ⛣ 🅿 (1) ⫫ 📺 🆅 ▥ ⚓

Geminian House, *13 Franklin Road, Harrogate, N. Yorks, HG1 5ED.* Family-run guest house close to town centre. **Open:** All year **Grades:** ETC 3 Diamond **01423 523347 & 01423 561768 Fax: 01423 523347** *geminian@talk21.com* www.geminian. org.uk **D:** £20.00–£25.00 **S:** £25.00–£30.00 **Beds:** 1F 2T 3D 2S **Baths:** 8 En ⛣ 🅿 ⻗ 🆅 ▥ ⁕ ⚓

Sunflower House, *61 Grantley Drive, Harrogate, North Yorkshire, HG3 2XU.* Friendly, quiet family home. Non-smoking. Near golf, swimming, leisure centres. **Open:** All year (not Xmas/New Year) **Grades:** ETC 3 Diamond **01423 503261 D:** £19.00–£25.00 **S:** £25.00–£30.00 **Beds:** 1T 1S **Baths:** 1 Sh 🅿 (1) ⫫ 📺 ✕ 🆅 ⚓

Knabbs Ash, *Skipton Road, Kettlesing, Felliscliffe, Harrogate, N. Yorks, HG3 2LT.* Peaceful country home six miles west of Harrogate. **Open:** All year (not Xmas/New Year) **Grades:** ETC 4 Diamond, Gold **01423 771040** S Smith **Fax: 01423 771515** *colin+sheila@knabbsash.freeserve.co.uk* www.yorkshirebandb.co.uk **D:** £22.50–£25.00 **S:** £35.00 ⛣ (10) ⫫ 📺 🆅 ▥ ⚓

The Alexander, *88 Franklin Road, Harrogate, N. Yorks, HG1 5EN.* Elegant friendly fully restored Victorian residence close to the town centre. **Open:** All year **01423 503348** Mrs Toole **Fax: 01423 540230 D:** £24.00–£25.00 **S:** £24.00–£25.00 **Beds:** 3F 2D 2S **Baths:** 5 En 1 Sh ⛣ 📺 🆅 ▥ ⚓

Hollins House, *17 Hollins Road, Harrogate, N. Yorks, HG1 2JF.* Clean, quiet spacious accommodation in a warm and friendly family-run Victorian house. **Open:** All year **01423 503646 (also fax)** Mr Hamblin **D:** £21.00–£24.00 **S:** £28.00–£30.00 **Beds:** 3T 2D 1S **Baths:** 3 En 3 Sh ⛣ (5) ⫫ 📺 🆅 ▥ ⚓ cc

Sherwood, *7 Studley Road, Harrogate, N. Yorks, HG1 5JU.* Centrally located near Harrogate town centre, in a quiet tree-lined street. **Open:** All year **01423 503033** C Grant **Fax: 01423 564659** *sherwood@hotels.harrogate.com* www.sherwood-hotel.com **D:** £20.00–£25.00 **S:** £30.00–£50.00 **Beds:** 1T 4D 1S **Baths:** 4 En 1 Sh 📺 ✕ 🆅 ▥ cc

Eton House, *3 Eton Terrace, Knareborough Road, Harrogate, N. Yorks, HG2 7SU.* Our home was built in 1876 and stands on the edge of the Stray. **Open:** All year (not Xmas) **01423 886850 (also fax)** Mrs Wyatt *janbounds@aol.com* **D:** £20.00–£25.00 **S:** £20.00–£30.00 **Beds:** 2F 2D 2T 1S **Baths:** 4 En 2 Sh ⛣ 🅿 (10) 📺 ⻗ 🆅 ▥ ⚓

Hartwith

SE2161   ◁ *Bay Horse, Boar's Head*

Holly Cottage, *Mill Lane, Hartwith, Harrogate, N. Yorks, HG3 3EU.* 200-year-old Yorkshire stone cottage with extensive views. **Open:** All year **01423 770746** Mrs Drake **D:** £20.00–£25.00 **S:** £25.00–£30.00 **Beds:** 1T 2D **Baths:** 3 En ⛣ 🅿 📺 ⻗ 🆅 ▥ ⚓

Hawes

SD8789   ◁ *Fountain, White Hart, Crown, Simonstone Hall Hotel, Stonehouse Hotel*

Ebor House, *Burtersett Road, Hawes, N. Yorks, DL8 3NT.* Family-run friendly and central. Off road parking and cycle store. **Open:** All year (not Xmas) **Grades:** ETC 3 Diamond **01969 667337 (also fax)** Mrs Clark *gwen@ eborhouse.freeserve.co.uk* **D:** £18.00–£22.00 **S:** £19.00–£25.00 **Beds:** 2D 1T **Baths:** 2 En 1 Sh ⛣ 🅿 (5) ⫫ 📺 ⻗ 🆅 ▥ ⚓

Overdales View, *Simonstone, Hawes, N Yorks, DL8 3LY.* Friendly welcome. Lovely views, rural surroundings, comfortable beds good food. **Open:** Easter to Oct **01969 667186** Mrs Sunter **D:** £17.00–£18.00 **S:** £18.00–£20.00 **Beds:** 1F/T 1D 1S **Baths:** 1 Sh ⛣ 🅿 (5) ⫫ 📺 🆅 ▥ ⚓

The Bungalow, *Springbank, Hawes, N. Yorks, DL8 3NW.* Large bungalow, excellent views, quiet, off-road parking. **Open:** Easter to Oct **01969 667209** Mrs Garnett **D:** £18.00–£20.00 **Beds:** 2D 1T **Baths:** 2 En 1 Sh ⛣ (4) 🅿 📺 ⻗ 🆅 ▥ ⚓

Hawnby

SE5489

Laskill Farm, *Hawnby, Helmsley, York, YO62 5NB.* Laskill Farm is built on a medieval site once belonging to Rievaulx Abbey. **Open:** All year **01439 798268** Mrs Smith **Fax: 01439 798498** *suesmith@laskillfarm.fsnet.co.uk* www.laskillfarm.co.uk **D:** £27.50–£30.00 **S:** £27.50–£30.00 **Beds:** 3D 2T 1S **Baths:** 5 En 1 Pr ⛣ 🅿 (20) 📺 ⻗ ✕ 🆅 ▥ ⚓ cc

B&B owners may vary rates – be sure to check when booking

Hebden

SE0263

Court Croft, *Church Lane, Hebden, Skipton, BD23 5DX.* Family farmhouse in quiet village close to the Dales Way. **Open:** All year **01756 753406** Mrs Kitching **D:** £17.50 **S:** £17.50–£20.00 **Beds:** 2T **Baths:** 1 Sh ⛣ 🅿 (4) 📺 ⻗ 🆅 ▥ ⚓

Helmsley

SE6184   ◁ *Crown, Feathers, Black Swan, Royal Oak, Feversham Arms*

Laskill Farm, *Hawnby, Helmsley, York, YO62 5NB.* **Open:** All year **01439 798268** Mrs Smith **Fax: 01439 798498** *suesmith@laskillfarm.fsnet.co.uk* www.laskillfarm.co.uk **D:** £27.50–£30.00 **S:** £27.50–£30.00 **Beds:** 3D 2T 1S **Baths:** 5 En 1 Pr ⛣ 🅿 (20) 📺 ⻗ ✕ 🆅 ▥ ⚓ cc Laskill Farm is built on a medieval site once belonging to Rievaulx Abbey. Recommended on BBC 'Holiday Programme' and Sunday Times. High standard of accommodation at reasonable rates.

The Carlton Lodge, *53 Bondgate, Helmsley, York, YO62 5EY.* **Open:** All year **Grades:** ETC 4 Diamond **01439 770557 Fax: 01439 770623** *stwls@ carlton-lodge.com* www.carlton-lodge.com **D:** £25.00–£30.00 **S:** £27.00–£30.00 **Beds:** 1F 3T 7D **Baths:** 10 En 1 Pr ⛣ 🅿 (35) 📺 ⻗ ✕ 🆅 ▥ ⚓ ⁕ ⚓ cc Congratulations on discovering the 'picture postcard' hamlet of C12th Helmsley in North York Moors NP. Ideal exploring, local heritage sites, attractions, East Coast, Dales, Moors, York. Yorkshire hospitality, cosy bedrooms, dry cured bacon, scrumptious award-winning sausages and farm fresh eggs guarantee a memorable stay!

4 Ashdale Road, *Helmsley, York, YO62 5DD.* Quiet private house 5 mins from Market Square and shops. **Open:** All year (not Xmas) **01439 770375** Mrs Barton **D:** £15.00–£16.00 **S:** £16.00 **Beds:** 1D 1T **Baths:** 1 Sh 🅿 (2) ⫫ 📺 ⻗ 🆅 ⚓

14 Elmslac Road, Helmsley, York, YO62 5AP. Quiet house 4 mins' walk from market square. Pleasant situation. **Open:** All year
01439 770287 Mrs Holding **D:** £13.50–£14.50 **S:** £14.00 **Beds:** 1D **Baths:** 1 Pr ⮪ (12) ⚮ �

Ashberry, 41 Ashdale Road, Helmsley, York, YO62 5DE. Warm welcome in comfortable home, start of Cleveland Way. **Open:** All year
01439 770488 Mrs oneil@ashberry.co.uk **D:** £17.50 **S:** £17.50–£21.00 **Beds:** 1T 1D 1S **Baths:** 1 Sh ⮪ (4) 🅿 (2) ⚮ � 📺 Ⅴ ▦ ⚱

Stilworth House, 1 Church Street, Helmsley, York, YO62 5AD. Elegant rooms, beautiful location overlooking castle, hearty breakfast, warm welcome. **Open:** All year (not Xmas)
01439 771072 Mrs Swift **D:** £17.50–£27.50 **S:** £30.00–£40.00 **Beds:** 1F 2D 1T **Baths:** 3 Pr 1 Sh 🅿 (4) ⚮ ⚯ ⅤⅤ ▦ ⚱

High Bentham
SD6669

Fowgill Park Farm, High Bentham, Lancaster, LA2 7AH. Beamed farmhouse enjoying panoramic views, close to caves and waterfalls. **Open:** Easter to Oct
015242 61630 Mrs Metcalfe **D:** £19.00–£22.00 **Beds:** 1D 1T **Baths:** 2 En ⮪ 🅿 (4) ⚮ ⅤⅥ ⚯ ⚱

High Hawsker
NZ9207

Old Blacksmiths Arms, High Hawsker, Whitby, N. Yorks, YO22 4LH. Originally first pub in village. Large garden with pond. **Open:** Easter to Oct
01947 880800 Mrs Stubbs **D:** £18.00–£19.00 **S:** £21.00–£24.00 **Beds:** 1T 2D **Baths:** 2 Sh ⮪ (12) 🅿 (3) ⅤⅤ ▦ ⚱

Holme-on-Swale
SE3582

Glen Free, Holme-on-Swale, Thirsk, N Yorks, YO7 4JE. Secluded cottage, one mile from A1. Ideal for Herriot country and Dales. **Open:** All year (not Xmas)
01845 567331 Mrs Bailes **D:** £16.00–£18.00 **S:** £16.00–£18.00 **Beds:** 1F 1D **Baths:** 1 Sh ⮪ 🅿 (4) ⚮ ⚯ ⚯ ▦ ⚱

Horsehouse
SE0481

The Thwaite Arms, Horsehouse, Leyburn, N. Yorks, DL8 4TS. Warm and cosy traditional Dales inn set in beautiful tranquil Coverdale. **Open:** All year (not Xmas/New Year)
01969 640206 Mrs Powell **D:** £23.00 **S:** £40.00 **Beds:** 1T 1D **Baths:** 1 Pr 🅿 (10) ✗ ⅤⅥ ⚱

Horton-in-Ribblesdale
SD8072 🍴 Golden Lion, Crown Hotel

The Golden Lion Hotel, Horton-in-Ribblesdale, Settle, N. Yorks, BD24 0HB. Friendly, comfortable village hotel. **Open:** All year
01729 860206 Mrs Johnson **D:** £18.00–£21.00 **Beds:** 2T 2D 1S **Baths:** 1 En 1 Sh 🅿 ⅤⅥ ▦ ⚱ cc

Studfold House, Horton-in-Ribblesdale, Settle, N. Yorks, BD24 0ER. Georgian house in beautiful grounds with panoramic views. **Open:** All year (not Xmas/New Year)
01729 860200 Mr & Mrs Horsfall **D:** £16.00–£20.00 **S:** £20.00 **Beds:** 1F 1T 1D 1S **Baths:** 2 En 1 Pr 1 Sh ⮪ 🅿 (8) ⅤⅥ ⚯ ✗ ⅤⅥ ⚱

The Willows, Horton-in-Ribblesdale, Settle, N. Yorks, BD24 0HT. Large detached house, luxurious bedrooms in lovely Yorkshire Dales. **Open:** Easter to Sept
01729 860373 (also fax) Mrs Barker **D:** £20.00–£24.00 **S:** £20.00–£25.00 **Beds:** 1F 1D 1T **Baths:** 1 En 1 Pr 1 Sh ⮪ 🅿 (5) ⅤⅥ ⚯ ✗ ⅤⅥ ▦ ⚱

Hovingham
SE6675 🍴 Malt Shovel, Worsley Arms

Sedgwick Country Guest House, Park Street, Hovingham, York, YO62 4JZ. North from York A64. Left Castle Howard. Left (2 miles) Hovington. **Open:** All year
01653 628740 (also fax) F J Smurthwaite sedgwick.ges-ho@amserve.net www.sedgwickcountryguest.co.uk **D:** £21.00–£25.00 **S:** £21.00–£30.00 **Beds:** 2F 2T 2D 1S **Baths:** 8 En ⮪ 🅿 ⚮ ⅤⅥ ▦ ✳ ⚱ cc

Hubberholme
SD9278

Church Farm, Hubberholme, Skipton, N. Yorks, BD23 5JE. Traditional C16th Dales farmhouse on working hill farm. Ideal for walking/touring. **Open:** All year
01756 760240 Mrs Huck **D:** £20.00 **S:** £20.00 **Beds:** 2D 2T **Baths:** 1 En 1 Pr 🅿 ⚮ ⅤⅥ ▦ ⚱

Huby (Easingwold)
SE5665

New Inn Motel, Main Street, Huby, York, YO61 1HQ. Huby, 'twixt York and Easingwold, for coast, Moors, Dales, Herriot/Heartbeat country. **Open:** All year **Grades:** AA 3 Diamond
01347 810219 Mrs Birkinshaw **D:** £24.00–£25.00 **S:** £28.00–£35.00 **Beds:** 3F 2D 2T 1S **Baths:** 8 En ⮪ 🅿 (8) ⅤⅥ ⚯ ✗ ⅤⅥ ▦ ⚱

National Grid References given are for villages, towns and cities – not for individual houses

Hutton Rudby
NZ4606

Greenview, 13 Eastside, Hutton Rudby, Yarm, N Yorks, TS15 0DB. **Open:** All year
01642 701739 Mrs Ashton **D:** £18.00 **S:** £18.00 **Beds:** 1D 1T **Baths:** 2 En ⮪ (3) ⚮ ⅤⅥ ▦ ⚱

Overlooking the village green at Hutton Rudby, Greenview offers you a delightful stay bordering the National Park in North Yorkshire. Rooms have showers, comfortable beds, with a hearty breakfast. Ideal for Coast to Coast, Cleveland Way and new cycle route.

Ingleby Cross
NZ4500

North York Moors Adventure Ctr, Park House, Ingleby Cross, Northallerton, N. Yorks, DL6 3PE. Park House, traditional sandstone farmhouse set in the National Park. **Open:** Easter to Oct
01609 882571 (also fax) Mr Bennett www.coast-to-coast.org.uk **D:** £15.00 **S:** £15.00 **Beds:** 3F 1D 3T **Baths:** 2 Sh ⮪ (1) 🅿 (20) ⅤⅥ ⅤⅥ ▦ ⚱

Ingleton
SD6973 🍴 Wheatsheaf, Whoop Hall, Hill Inn, Three Horseshoes, Bridge Inn

Springfield Country House Hotel, 26 Main Street, Ingleton, Carnforth, Lancs, LA6 3HJ. **Open:** All year (not Xmas)
Grades: ETC 3 Diamond, RAC 3 Diamond
015242 41280 (also fax) Mr Thornton **D:** £23.00–£25.00 **S:** £23.00–£25.00 **Beds:** 1F 3D 1T **Baths:** 5 En 1 Pr ⮪ 🅿 (12) ⚮ ⚯ ✗ ⅤⅥ ▦ ⚱ cc
Detached Victorian villa; large garden at rear running down to River Greta. Patio, small pond and waterfall. Home-grown vegetables in season. Front garden with patio, conservatory and fountain.

Seed Hill Guest House, Ingleton, Carnforth, LA6 3AB. A wonderful old Listed guest house in the centre of Ingleton. **Open:** All year
015242 41799 Mr & Mrs Brown adrianseedhill@hotmail.com www.come2ingleton.com **D:** £19.00–£22.00 **S:** £25.00–£30.00 **Beds:** 1F 1T 2D 1S **Baths:** 5 En ⮪ 🅿 (5) ⚮ ⅤⅥ ▦ ⚱

Planning a longer stay? Always ask for any special rates

Planning a longer stay? Always ask for any special rates

Inglenook Guest House, 20 Main Street, Ingleton, Carnforth, North Yorkshire, *LA6 3HJ.* Picturesque riverside location offering superb views. Family-run. Excellent service. **Open:** All year (not Xmas) **Grades:** ETC 3 Diamond, AA 3 Diamond **015242 41270** C & P Smith *phillsmith@ inglenookguesthouse.fsbusiness.co.uk* www.nebsweb.co.uk/inglenook **D:** £21.00 **S:** £21.00–£42.00 **Beds:** 1F 2T 2D **Baths:** 4 En 1 Pr ⌂ (5) ⌖ 🖂 ✕ 📺 📖 🎂 **cc**

Ingleborough View Guest House, Main Street, Ingleton, Carnforth, Lancashire, *LA6 3HH.* Picturesque riverside location. Ideal for local walks/touring Dales. **Open:** All year **Grades:** ETC 4 Diamond **015242 41523** Mrs Brown *ame@ ingleborough.view.co.uk* www.ingleborough. view.co.uk **D:** £19.00–£21.00 **S:** £25.00– £28.00 **Beds:** 1F 2T 2D **Baths:** 2 En 3 Pr ⌂ 📖 (5) 📺 📖 🎂

Gatehouse Farm, Far West House, Ingleton, Carnforth, Lancs, *LA6 3NR.* Working farm, home cooking, in Yorkshire Dales National Park. **Open:** All year (not Xmas/ New Year) **015242 41458 & 015242 41307** Mrs Lund **D:** £21.00–£22.00 **S:** £21.00–£22.00 **Beds:** 1T 2D **Baths:** 2 En 1 Pr ⌂ 📖 (3) ⌖ 🖂 🐾 📺 📖 🎂

Nutstile Farm, Ingleton, Carnforth, Lancs, *LA6 3DT.* Secluded working Dales farm with outstanding views. **Open:** All year **015242 41752** Mrs Brennand **D:** £20.00 **Beds:** 1F 1T 2D **Baths:** 2 En 1 Pr ⌂ 📖 (3) ⌖ 📺 📖 🎂

The Dales Guest House, Main Street, Ingleton, Carnforth, North Yorkshire, *LA6 3HH.* Cosy rooms with views, substantial home-cooked meals, ideal base for exploring Dales, Bowland, Lakes. **Open:** All year **015242 41401** P D Weaire *dalesgh@ hotmail.com* www.ingleton.yorks.net **D:** £19.00–£22.00 **S:** £19.00–£22.00 **Beds:** 1T 3D 1S **Baths:** 5 En ⌂ ⌖ 🖂 🐾 ✕ 📖 **cc**

Bridge End Guest House, Mill Lane, Ingleton, Carnforth, Lancs, *LA6 3EP.* Georgian Listed building, riverside location adjacent to Waterfalls Walk entrance. **Open:** All year **015242 41413** Mrs Garner *garner01@ tinyworld.co.uk* **D:** £19.00–£22.00 **S:** £25.00 **Beds:** 3D **Baths:** 3 En ⌂ (8) 📖 (8) 📺 ✕ 📖 🎂 **cc**

Keasden
SD7266

Lythe Birks, Keasden, Lancaster, *LA2 8EZ.* Converted barn in its own grounds overlooking three peaks. **Open:** All year **015242 51688** Mrs Phinn **D:** £19.50 **S:** £25.00 **Beds:** 2D 1T ⌂ 📖 ⌖ 🖂 📺 🐾 ✕ 📺 📖 🎂

Keld
NY8901

Greenlands, Keld, Richmond, *DL11 6DY.* Refurbished farmhouse amidst the peace and beauty of upper Swaledale. **Open:** All year **01748 886576** Mrs Thompson **D:** £19.50 **Beds:** 2D **Baths:** 2 En 📖 (2) ⌖ 📺 📖 🎂

Kettlesing
SE2256   🍴 *Queen's Head, Black Bull*

Knabbs Ash, Skipton Road, Kettlesing, Felliscliffe, Harrogate, N. Yorks, *HG3 2LT.* Peaceful country home six miles west of Harrogate. **Open:** All year (not Xmas/New Year) **Grades:** ETC 4 Diamond, Gold **01423 771040** S Smith **Fax: 01423 771515** *colin+sheila@knabbsash.freeserve.co.uk* www.yorkshirebandb.co.uk **D:** £22.50–£25.00 **S:** £35.00 ⌂ (10) 📖 ⌖ 📺 📖 🎂

Kettlewell
SD9772

Lynburn, Kettlewell, Skipton, N. Yorks, *BD23 5RF.* Well-preserved property with well tended grounds. Peaceful surroundings. **Open:** Mar to Oct **01756 760803** Mrs Thornborrow **D:** £19.00–£20.00 **S:** £25.00 **Beds:** 1D 1T **Baths:** 1 Sh ⌂ (12) 📖 (2) 📺 📖 🎂

Kildale
NZ6009

Bankside Cottage, Kildale, Whitby, North Yorkshire, *YO21 2RT.* Homely country cottage, beautiful views. Taxi service available. **Open:** All year (not Xmas/New Year) **01642 723259** Mrs Addison **D:** £19.00 **S:** £19.00 **Beds:** 1F 1T 1D **Baths:** 1 Sh ⌂ 📖 (4) ⌖ 📺 ✕ 📖 🎂

Kilnsey
SD9767

Skirfare Bridge Dales Barn, Kilnsey, Skipton, N. Yorks, *BD23 5PT.* Converted stone barn in beautiful limestone countryside of upper Wharfedale. **Open:** All year **01756 752465 (also fax)** Mrs Foster www.yorkshirenet.co. uk/ydales/bunkbarns/kilnsey **D:** £8.00 **S:** £8.00 **Beds:** 5F 1T **Baths:** 3 Sh ⌂ 📖 (8) ✕ 📖

RATES
D = Price range per person sharing in a double or twin room
S = Price range for a single room

Kirkby Malham
SD8961   🍴 *Buck Inn*

Yeoman's Barn, Kirkby Malham, Skipton, North Yorks, *BD23 4BL.* **Open:** All year (not Xmas/New Year) **Grades:** ETC 4 Diamond **01729 830639** Mrs Turner **D:** £20.00–£25.00 **S:** £25.00–£35.00 **Beds:** 2D **Baths:** 2 En ⌂ (5) ⌖ 📺 📖 🎂 Converted C17th barn, large oak beams, newly decorated bedrooms. Warm welcome, tea tray on arrival, open fire. Market towns of Skipton, Settle and Hawes all nearby. Malham Cove, Janets Foss and Gordale Scar - all suitable for the weekend walker.

Kirkbymoorside
SE6987   🍴 *George & Dragon, King's Head*

Sinnington Common Farm, Kirkbymoorside, York, *YO62 6NX.* Spacious ground floor. Panoramic views, family farm. **Open:** All year **Grades:** ETC 4 Diamond **01751 431719 (also fax)** Mrs Wiles *felicity@ scfarm.demon.co.uk* **D:** £18.00–£22.00 **S:** £23.00–£27.00 ⌂ 📖 📺 🐾 ✕ 📺 📖 🎂 ♿

Red Lion House, Crown Square, Kirkbymoorside, York, *YO62 6AY.* Lovely Georgian house, situated in quiet square in centre of small market town. **Open:** All year (not Xmas) **01751 431815** S & A Thompson *angela.thomson@red-lion-house.freeserve.co.uk* **D:** £20.00–£22.50 **S:** £25.00 **Beds:** 2D 1T **Baths:** 1 En 1 Sh ⌂ ⌖ 📺 📖 🎂

Kirklington
SE3181   🍴 *The Bull*

Morar House, Kirklington, Bedale, N Yorks, *DL8 2NE.* **Open:** All year (not Xmas/New Year) **01845 567293** Mrs Webb **D:** £19.00–£25.00 **S:** £19.00– £25.00 **Beds:** 1T 1D **Baths:** 2 En 📖 (4) ⌖ 📺 ✕ 📺 📖 🎂 Charming C17th cottage in picturesque village in heart of North Yorkshire. Traditional breakfast in farmhouse kitchen, stone-flagged floors, acre of garden. Two miles from A1, perfectly situated for York, Harrogate, Dales, Moors, East Coast and local places of interest.

Upsland Farm, *Lime Lane, Well, Bedale, N. Yorks, DL8 2PA.* **Open:** All year (not Xmas) **Grades:** ETC 4 Diamond, AA 5 Diamond **01845 567709 (also fax)** Mrs Hodgson *upsland@Btinternet.com* **D:** £27.50 **S:** £35.00 **Beds:** 1T 2D **Baths:** 3 En 🛏 🏠(4)⊬ 🗺 ★ ✕ 🆅 🍴🖂. Beautiful house rebuilt to an award winning design in delightful open countryside, situated on ancient moated site on land once owned by Katherine Parr. Close to moors, dales, castles, abbeys, stately homes, golf, fishing, riding. Ideal London-Scotland stopover.

Knaresborough
SE3557

Holly Corner, *3 Coverdale Drive, Knaresborough, N Yorks, HG5 9BW.* **Open:** All year **Grades:** ETC 4 Diamond **01423 864204 (also fax)** Mrs MacLellan *www.tuckedup.com/hollycorner.html* **D:** £24.00–£26.00 **S:** £28.00–£35.00 **Beds:** 1T 1D 1S **Baths:** 2 Pr 1 Sh 🏠(2)⊬ 🗺 🆅 ❀ ✱. Large, private, Tudor-style home in quiet private drive. Guaranteed friendly and personal service. Easy access Dales, York, Harrogate, Ripon, A1(M). Town centre and riverside walking distance 8 minutes. Plants and preserves for sale. No smoking. Proprietor: Mrs Jan MacLellan.

Newton House Hotel, *5/7 York Place, Knaresborough, N Yorks, HG5 0AD.* Situated in picturesque Knaresborough, a C17th former coaching inn. **Open:** All year (not Xmas) **01423 863539** Mr & Mrs Elliott **Fax:** 01423 869748 *newtonhouse@btinternet.com* *www.newtonhousehotel.com* **D:** £27.50–£32.50 **S:** £35.00–£45.00 **Beds:** 2F 7D 2T 1S **Baths:** 11 En 1 Pr 🛏 🏠(12)🗺 ★ ✕ 🆅 🍴. ✱ cc

Watergate Haven, *Ripley Road, Knaresborough, N Yorks, HG5 9BU.* B&B/Self-catering accommodation. Close to main attractions. **Open:** All year **Grades:** ETC 3 Star **01423 864627 Fax:** 01423 861087 *watergate.haven@virgin.net* **D:** £25.00–£27.00 **S:** £30.00–£35.00 **Beds:** 1F 1T 1D 1S **Baths:** 4 En 🛏 🏠(12)🗺 ★ 🆅 🍴. ✱ cc

Kirkgate House, *17 Kirkgate, Knaresborough, N Yorks, HG5 8AD.* Friendly non-smoking accommodation near the market place, bus and train station. **Open:** All year **01423 862704 (also fax)** S F Giesen **D:** £22.00 **S:** £26.00–£32.00 **Beds:** 2D 1T **Baths:** 3 En 🏠(2)⊬ 🗺 ✕ 🆅 🍴. ✱

Langcliffe
SD8264

Bowerley Hotel & Conference Centre, *Langcliffe, Settle, BD24 9LY.* Country house hotel in 3 acres, bar, restaurant, warm welcome. **Open:** All year **01729 823811** G Ralph **Fax:** 01729 822317 *bowerleyhotel@aol.com* **D:** £25.00–£29.00 **S:** £32.00–£39.00 **Beds:** 2F 8T 6D 2S **Baths:** 18 En 🛏 🏠(50)⊬ 🗺 ★ ✕ 🆅 🍴. ✆ ✱ cc

Lealholm
NZ7607 🍺 *Ye Old Horse Shoe*

High Park Farm, *Lealholm, Whitby, YO21 2AQ.* Peaceful location. 15 minutes from the coast many attractions close by. **Open:** Easter to Oct **Grades:** ETC 3 Diamond **01947 897416** Mrs Welford **D:** £18.50 **S:** £23.50 **Beds:** 1D **Baths:** 1 En 🛏 (5) 🏠(1) ⊬ 🗺 🆅 🍴. ✱

Leeming Bar
SE2890

Little Holtby, *Leeming Bar, Northallerton, N. Yorks, DL7 9LH.* **Open:** All year (not Xmas) **01609 748762** Mrs Hodgson *littleholtby@yahoo.co.uk* *www.littleholtby.co.uk* **D:** £22.50–£25.00 **S:** £25.00 **Beds:** 3D 1T **Baths:** 2 En 1 Pr 1 Sh 🛏 (10) 🏠(10) ⊬ ✕ 🆅 🍴. ✱ Today the discerning traveller is looking for somewhere special, where the warmth of welcome will remain a treasured feature. All guest rooms have wonderful views - treat yourself to a really memorable stay.

Levisham
SE8390

Rectory Farmhouse, *Levisham, Pickering, N. Yorks, YO18 7NL.* Picturesque village surrounded by beautiful scenery; excellent walking, horseriding or just relaxing. **Open:** All year **01751 460304** Mrs Holt *rectoryfarmhouse@barclays.net* *www.levisham.com* **D:** £20.00–£25.00 **S:** £24.00 **Beds:** 2D 1T **Baths:** 3 En 🛏 🏠(8)⊬ 🗺 ★ ✕ 🆅 🍴. ✱

Leyburn
SE1190 🍺 *Sandpiper Inn, Boulton Arms, Golden Lion*

Secret Garden House, *Grove Square, Leyburn, N. Yorks, DL8 5AE.* Georgian house, acre-walled garden. Central Leyburn. Off-street parking. **Open:** All year (not Xmas/New Year) **01969 623589** Mr Digges *njdigges@yahoo.co.uk* **D:** £22.00–£28.00 **S:** £22.00–£28.00 **Beds:** 1T 2D 1S **Baths:** 3 En 🛏 (12) 🏠(10) 🗺 ★ 🆅 🍴. ✱

Littlethorpe
SE3269

Moor End Farm, *Knaresborough Road, Littlethorpe, Ripon, N. Yorks, HG4 3LU.* Friendly, non-smoking first-class accommodation. Pleasantly situated. Ideal for touring. **Open:** All year (not Xmas) **Grades:** ETC 4 Diamond **01765 677419** Mrs Spensley *pspensley@ukonline.co.uk* yorkshirebandb.co.uk **D:** £22.00–£25.00 **S:** £30.00–£40.00 **Beds:** 2D 1T **Baths:** 2 En 1 Pr 🏠(5)⊬ 🗺 🍴. ✱

Litton
SD9074

Park Bottom, *Litton, Skipton, BD23 5QJ.* Peaceful setting, wonderful views, ideal for walking, Which? recommended. **Open:** All year (not Xmas) **01756 770235** Mr & Mrs Morgan **D:** £25.00 **S:** £30.00 **Beds:** 1F 2D 1T **Baths:** 4 En 🛏 🏠(5) ★ 🗺 🆅 🍴. ✱

Lockton
SE8489 🍺 *Fox & Rabbit Inn*

Farfields Farmhouse, *Lockton, Pickering, North Yorkshire, YO18 7NQ.* Peacefully situated working farm overlooking beautiful Newton Dale. Comfortable rooms. **Open:** All year (not Xmas/New Year) **Grades:** ETC 4 Diamond **01751 460239** Mrs Stead *farfieldsfarm@btinternet.com* **D:** £22.00–£25.00 **S:** £25.00–£27.50 **Beds:** 1T 2D **Baths:** 3 En 🛏 (8) 🏠(4) ⊬ 🗺 ✕ 🆅 🍴. ✱

National Grid References given are for villages, towns and cities – not for individual houses

Long Preston

SD8358

Inglenook, 22 Main Street, Long Preston, Skipton, *BD23 4PH.* Traditional mullion-windowed cottage, village setting, ideal for Dales exploration. **Open:** All year
01729 840511 Mrs Parton **D:** £18.00–£20.00 **S:** £25.00–£30.00 **Beds:** 1F **Baths:** 1 Pr 🅿 (4)
📺 🛏 📹 💷 ⚓

Lothersdale

SD9645   🍺 Hare & Hound

Burlington House, Lothersdale, Keighley, W. Yorks, BD20 8EL. Between Howarth and Dales, friendly old house on Pennine Way. **Open:** All year
01535 634635 Mrs Wood **D:** £17.00 **S:** £17.00 **Beds:** 1T 1D **Baths:** 1 Sh 🛏 🅿 (3) 📺 🛏 📹 💷 ⚓

Lynmouth, Dale End, Lothersdale, Skipton, N Yorks, BD20 8EH. On path, pretty bungalow set in lovely grounds. **Open:** All year (not Xmas)
01535 632744 (also fax) Mrs Foster *g.foster488@aol.com* **D:** £17.50 **S:** £17.50 **Beds:** 1F 1D 1T **Baths:** 3 En 🛏 🅿 (4) ⚡ 📺 📹 💷 ⚓ ♿ ⚓

Lovesome Hill

SE3599

Lovesome Hill Farm, (off A167), Lovesome Hill, Northallerton, N. Yorks, DL6 2PB. Ideal situation for exploring Herriot's Dales and Moors. Traditional working farm and welcome. **Open:** All year (not Xmas/New Year) **Grades:** ETC 4 Diamond
01609 772311 M Pearson **Fax:** 01609 774715 **D:** £42.00–£60.00 **S:** £26.00–£35.00 **Beds:** 1F 1T 3D 1S **Baths:** 6 En 🛏 🅿 ⚡ 📺 ✕ 📹 💷 ♿ ⚓

Low Row

SD9897   🍺 Farmers Arms, Punch Bowl

Summer Lodge, Low Row, Richmond, North Yorks, DL11 6NP. Set in a valley of its own in beautiful Swaledale. **Open:** Mar to Oct **Grades:** ETC 3 Diamond
01748 886504 Mr Porter **D:** £23.00–£26.00 **S:** £23.00–£26.00 **Beds:** 1F **Baths:** 1 En 🛏 🅿 ⚡ 📺 📹 ⚓

Malham

SD9062

Beck Hall, Malham, Skipton, N. Yorks, BD23 4DJ. Set in large streamside. Family run. Garden. **Open:** All year (not Xmas/New Year) **Grades:** ETC 3 Diamond
01729 830332 Mr & Mrs Boatwright **D:** £19.00–£28.00 **S:** £22.00–£35.00 **Beds:** 2F 3T 7D 2S **Baths:** 11 En 2 Sh 🛏 🅿 (30) 📺 🛏 ✕ 📹 💷 ⚓ cc

Eastwood Guest House, Malham, Skipton, North Yorkshire, BD23 4DA. High quality B&B in central village location. **Open:** All year
01729 830409 Mrs McIntyre *eastwood_house@hotmail.com* **D:** £20.00–£25.00 **S:** £18.00–£30.00 **Beds:** 1F 1T 1D **Baths:** 3 En 🛏 ⚡ 📺 💷 ⚓

Malton

SE7871

Suddabys Crown Hotel, Wheelgate, Malton, N. Yorks, YO17 0HP. **Open:** All year (not Xmas)
01653 692038 Mr & Mrs Suddaby **Fax:** 01653 691812 *suddaby@crownhotel.plus.net* *suddabyscrown.co.uk* **D:** £17.00–£30.00 **S:** £18.00–£40.00 **Beds:** 2F 2D 4T **Baths:** 2 En 2 Sh 🛏 🅿 (10) 📺 🛏 📹 💷 ⚓ Former Georgian coaching inn, located in historic market town close by all the attractions of Ryedale and the North Yorkshire Moors. Seven Real Ales always available in the Public Bar. Malton Brewery to the rear of the hotel - visits arranged.

The Brow, York Road, Malton, N. Yorks, YO17 0AX. Georgian House, garden, fantastic riverside views, private parking. **Open:** All year (not Xmas)
01653 693402 Mrs Hopkinson **D:** £18.00–£30.00 **S:** £18.00–£30.00 **Beds:** 1F 2D 1T 1S **Baths:** 3 En 1 Sh 🛏 🅿 (6) 📺 🛏 💷 ⚓

Marton (Pickering)

SE7383   🍺 Apple Tree

Wildsmith House, Marton, Sinnington, York, YO62 6RD. Former farmhouse in pretty village. Ideally situated for exploring N Yorks. **Open:** Mar to Nov **Grades:** ETC 4 Diamond
01751 432702 Mr & Mrs Steele *wildsmithhouse@talk21.com* **D:** £22.00–£26.00 **S:** £27.00–£31.00 **Beds:** 2T **Baths:** 2 En 🛏 🅿 ⚡ 📺 📹 💷 ⚓

B&B owners may vary rates – be sure to check when booking

Masham

SE2280   🍺 Blue Lion, Black Sheep

Bank Villa, Masham, Ripon, North Yorks, HG4 4DB. **Open:** All year (not Xmas) **Grades:** AA 4 Diamond
01765 689605 (also fax) Lucy & Bobby Thomson **D:** £20.00–£27.50 **S:** £30.00–£40.00 **Beds:** 1F 3D 2T **Baths:** 3 En 1 Pr 🛏 (5) ⚡ 📺 ✕ 📹 💷 ⚓ Welcoming Grade II Listed home in half-acre terraced gardens, 2 mins' walk from Masham's unique market place, refurbished to a high standard with individually decorated ensuite bedrooms, 2 delightful lounges, ideal base for exploring the Dales and Herriot country.

Haregill Lodge, Ellingstring, Masham, Ripon, North Yorkshire, HG4 4PW. C18th farmhouse. Excellent views, superb cooking. Ideal base for Dales/Moors. **Open:** All year (not Xmas) **Grades:** ETC 4 Diamond
01677 460272 (also fax) Ms Greensit *haregilllodge@freenet.co.uk* **D:** £20.00–£23.00 **S:** £21.00–£23.00 **Beds:** 2T 1D **Baths:** 2 En 1 Pr 🛏 🅿 (4) 📺 🛏 ✕ 📹 💷 ⚓

Mickleby

NZ8012

Northfield Farm, Mickleby, Saltburn-by-the-Sea, N Yorks, TS13 5NE. Quiet, friendly, comfortable farmhouse. Open views, ideal situation for walking. **Open:** Easter to Oct
01947 840343 Mrs Prudom **D:** £15.00–£20.00 **S:** £18.00 **Beds:** 1F 1D 1T **Baths:** 1 En 1 Sh 🛏 🅿 ⚡ 📺 📹 💷 ⚓

Middleham

SE1287

Yore View, Leyburn Road, Middleham, Leyburn, DL8 4PL. Former 1921 picture house situated 200 yards from Middleham centre. **Open:** All year
01969 622987 Mrs Roper **D:** £20.00–£25.00 **S:** £25.00–£30.00 **Beds:** 1F 2D **Baths:** 2 En 1 Pr 🛏 🅿 (5) 📺 🛏 ✕ 📹 ❊ ⚓ cc

Middlesmoor

SE0874

Dovenor House, *Middlesmoor, Harrogate, HG3 5ST.* Beautiful stone house on edge of village with unsurpassed views. **Open:** All year
01423 755697 (also fax) Mrs Thurland
www.nidderdale.co.uk **D:** £18.00 **S:** £18.00–£20.00 **Beds:** 2F 1T **Baths:** 1 Sh ⑁ ▤ (3) ⠵ �📺 🐾 ▥ 🍴 ❄ ⚓

Middleton Tyas

NZ2206

Greencroft, *Middleton Tyas, Richmond, DL10 6PE.* Friendly family home ideal for Dales, York and east coast. **Open:** All year
01325 377392 Mrs Alsop **Fax:** 01833 621423
greencroft@madasafish.com **D:** £18.00–£20.00
S: £25.00 **Beds:** 1F 1T **Baths:** 2 En ⑁ ▤ (4) ⠵ 📺 🍴 ⚓

Newby Wiske

SE3688

Well House, *Newby Wiske, Northallerton, N. Yorks, DL7 9EX.* Beautiful landscaped gardens of one acre. Ideal for touring Yorkshire. **Open:** All year
01609 772253 (also fax) Mrs Smith
D: £18.00–£25.00 **S:** £20.00–£25.00 **Beds:** 2D **Baths:** 2 En ⑁ ▤ (6) ⠵ 📺 🐾 ✗ 🍴 ⚓

Newton-on-Rawcliffe

SE8190 ⓐ *New Inn, White Swan, Apple Tree, Horseshoe*

Rawcliffe House Farm, *Newton-on-Rawcliffe, Pickering, N Yorks, YO18 8JA.* Charming, ensuite ground floor rooms with every convenience and comfort. **Open:** Easter to Oct **Grades:** ETC 4 Diamond
01751 473292 Mrs Ducat **Fax:** 01751 473766
sheilarh@yahoo.com
www.yorkshireaccommodation.com
D: £25.50 **S:** £30.50 **Beds:** 2D 1T **Baths:** 3 En ⑁ (8) ▤ (10) 📺 ✗ 🍴 ▥ & ⚓ cc

Swan Cottage, *Newton-on-Rawcliffe, Pickering, N. Yorks, YO18 8QA.* Picturesque tranquil village, Quiet pub next door, wide breakfast choice. **Open:** All year
01751 472502 Mrs Heaton **D:** £15.50–£16.50
S: £15.50–£16.50 **Beds:** 1D 1T 1S **Baths:** 1 Sh ⑁ ▤ (2) 📺 🐾 ✗ 🍴 ▥ ❄ ⚓

North Grimston

SE8467

Middleton Arms, *North Grimston, Malton, N. Yorks, YO17 8AX.* Friendly country pub with excellent reputation for quality food and homely accommodation.
Open: All year (not Xmas)
01944 768255 Mrs Grayston **Fax:** 01944
768389 **D:** £20.00 **S:** £27.50 **Beds:** 2D 1T
Baths: 1 Pr 1 Sh ⑁ ▤ 📺 ✗ ▥ 🍴 ⚓

Northallerton

SE3794

Porch House, *68 High Street, Northallerton, N. Yorks, DL7 8EG.* Built 1584 original fireplaces and beams between Yorkshire Dales and Moors. **Open:** All year (not Xmas)
01609 779831 J A Barrow **Fax:** 01609 778603
D: £24.50–£26.00 **S:** £33.00–£35.00 **Beds:** 4D 2T **Baths:** 6 En ⑁ (12) ▤ (6) ⠵ 📺 ▥ 🍴 ⚓

Honeypots, *4 Pennine View, Northallerton, DL7 8HP.* Well-recommended guest house (visitors love it!) decorated to extremely high standard. **Open:** All year (not Xmas/New Year)
01609 777264 *val@lougnu.demon.co.uk*
D: £18.00–£20.00 **S:** £18.00–£20.00 **Beds:** 1T
Baths: 1 Pr ⑁ (12) ▤ (1) ⠵ 📺 ✗ 🍴 ⚓

Paradise

SE4687

High Paradise Farm, *Boltby, Thirsk, N Yorks, YO7 2HT.* Set between the forest and the moors in Herriot country. **Open:** All year
01845 537235 Mr & Mrs Skilbeck **Fax:** 01845
537033 *info@highparadise.co.uk*
www.highparadise.co.uk **D:** £20.00 **S:** £23.00
Beds: 1F 1T 1D **Baths:** 3 En ⑁ ▤ 🐾 ✗ 🍴 ▥ & ⚓ cc

Pateley Bridge

SE1565 ⓐ *Birch Tree, Crown, Harefield, Grassfields, Miner's Arms, Sportsman's Arms, Talbot*

Dale View, *Old Church Lane, Pateley Bridge, Harrogate, N. Yorks, HG3 5LY.* Comfortable ensuite rooms, Beautiful views over Yorkshire Dales. Private parking. **Open:** All year
01423 711506 Mrs Simpson **Fax:** 01423
711892 *bandb@daleview.com* **D:** £19.00–£25.00
S: £25.00–£30.00 **Beds:** 1F 2D **Baths:** 3 En ⑁ ▤ (5) 📺 🐾 ✗ 🍴 ▥ ⚓

Greengarth, *Greenwood Road, Pateley Bridge, Harrogate, N. Yorks, HG3 5LR.* Central detached bungalow in lovely Dales town. Ground floor rooms. **Open:** All year (not Xmas/New Year) **Grades:** ETC 3 Diamond
01423 711688 Mrs Ravilious **D:** £18.00–£20.00 **S:** £18.00–£30.00 **Beds:** 1T 2D 1S
Baths: 2 En 1 Sh ⑁ (5) ▤ (4) ⠵ 📺 🍴 ▥ & ⚓

Pickering

SE7984 ⓐ *Apple Tree Inn, White Swan*

Barker Stakes Farm, *Lendales Lane, Pickering, N Yorks, YO18 8EE.* Superb location, excellent food, comfortable rooms Yorkshire welcome = fantastic holiday.
Open: All year (not Xmas/New Year)
01751 476759 Mrs Hardy **D:** £18.00–£20.00
S: £18.00–£20.00 **Beds:** 1T 2D **Baths:** 1 Pr 1 Sh ⑁ (5) ▤ (6) 📺 ✗ 🍴 ▥ ⚓

Rawcliffe House Farm, *Newton-on-Rawcliffe, Pickering, N Yorks, YO18 8JA.*
Open: Easter to Oct **Grades:** ETC 4 Diamond
01751 473292 Mrs Ducat **Fax:** 01751 473766
sheilarh@yahoo.com
www.yorkshireaccommodation.com
D: £25.50 **S:** £30.50 **Beds:** 2D 1T **Baths:** 3 En ⑁ (8) ▤ (10) 📺 ✗ 🍴 ▥ & ⚓ cc
Charming, ensuite ground floor rooms with every convenience and comfort. Idyllic and spectacular setting in the North Yorkshire Moors. Home cooked food using fresh local produce. A warm welcome awaits you. Easy access Coast and York. Highly recommended. ETC 4 Diamond.

Heathcote Guest House, *100 Eastgate, Pickering, N. Yorks, YO18 7DW.*
Open: All year (not Xmas/New Year)
Grades: ETC 4 Diamond
01751 476991 (also fax) Mrs Lovejoy
joanlovejoy@lineone.net **D:** £21.00–£24.00
S: £21.00 **Beds:** 3D 2T **Baths:** 5 En ▤ (5) ⠵ 📺 ✗ 🍴 ⚓ cc
Our beautiful Victorian house is ideally situated for exploring the North Yorkshire Moors, visiting historic Whitby and the fascinating city of York. We provide superb breakfasts and delicious evening meals in a lovely setting; an ideal place to relax.

The Huntsman Restaurant and Guest House, *Main Street, Wrelton, Pickering, N. Yorks, YO18 8PG.* **Open:** All year **Grades:** ETC 3 Diamond
01751 472530 Mr Lower *howard@ thehuntsman.freeserve.co.uk* www.europage.co. uk/huntsman **D:** £16.00–£24.00 **S:** £18.00–£26.00 **Beds:** 1T 2D **Baths:** 3 En ⑁ ▤ (10) 📺 🐾 ✗ 🍴 ▥ ❄ ⚓ cc
Quiet village location, 2 miles Pickering, leading to Rosedale and Moors. Converted stone-built farmhouse, rustic character beamed ceilings, garden, patio, private parking. Comfortable ensuite beds, licensed bar, Carol's home cooking. Special offer 3 for 2. Short breaks - brochure.

Kirkham Garth, *Whitby Road, Pickering, N. Yorks, YO18 7AT.* Quiet, private, homely residence, Ideal for York, forests, moors and coast. **Open:** All year (not Xmas)
01751 474931 Mrs Rayner **D:** £20.00–£22.00
Beds: 1F 1D 1T **Baths:** 1 Sh ▤ (3) ⠵ 📺 🍴 ⚓

Clent House,
15 Burgate, Pickering, North Yorkshire, YO18 7AU. Late C18th house, comfortable ensuite bedrooms, close to town centre, castle, moors railway. **Open:** All year (not Xmas) **Grades:** ETC 3 Diamond **01751 477928** K & I Loveday *swiftlink-bb-1315@pb-design.com* www.pb-design.com/swiftlink/bb/1315.htm **D:** £20.00 **S:** £20.00–£25.00 **Beds:** 1F 1T 1D **Baths:** 3 En ⛥ 🅿 (3) ⅙ 📺 Ⅵ 🏠 🐾

Potto
NZ4703

Dog & Gun Country Inn, Potto,
Northallerton, DL6 3HQ. Traditional country inn situated beside North York Moors NP. Warm friendly welcome. **Open:** All year **01642 700232 D:** £20.00–£25.00 **S:** £25.00–£30.00 **Beds:** 2F 2T 2D **Baths:** 5 En ⛥ 🅿 (30) 📺 ✕ Ⅵ 🏠 🐾 cc

Ravenscar
NZ9801

Bide A While Guest House,
3 Loring Road, Ravenscar, Scarborough, N. Yorks, YO13 0LY. Small family guest house, home comforts, home cooking a speciality. Edge North York Moors. **Open:** All year **Grades:** ETC 3 Diamond **01723 870643** Mr & Mrs Leach **Fax:** 01723 871577 **D:** £16.50–£21.50 **S:** £20.00 **Beds:** 1F 2D 1T **Baths:** 3 En 1 Pr ⛥ 🅿 📺 ✕ Ⅵ 🏠 🐾

Dunelm, Raven Hall Road, Ravenscar,
Scarborough, N. Yorks, YO13 0NA. Friendly, flexible B&B. Heather moors, dramatic cliffs, splendid bay view. **Open:** All year (not Xmas) **01723 870430** Jenny Bartlet **D:** £16.00–£18.00 **S:** £16.00–£18.00 **Beds:** 1D 1T 1S **Baths:** 2 Sh ⛥ 🅿 ⅙ 🐕 🐾 ✕ Ⅵ 🏠 🐾

Smugglers Rock Country Guest House, Ravenscar, Scarborough, N. Yorks,
YO13 0ER. Former smuggling inn twixt Whitby and Scarborough, refurbished and restored. **Open:** All year (not Xmas) **01723 870044** Mr & Mrs Gregson **D:** £23.00–£25.00 **S:** £26.00–£28.00 **Beds:** 1F 4D 2T 1S **Baths:** 8 En ⛥ 🅿 (12) ⅙ 📺 🐕 ✕ 🏠 🐾

B&B owners may vary rates – be sure to check when booking

Reeth
SE0399   🍺 *King's Arms, Buck Inn, Black Bull, Bridge Hotel*

Arkle House,
Mill Lane, Reeth, Richmond, North Yorks, DL11 6SJ. **Open:** All year **Grades:** ETC 4 Diamond **01748 884815** **(also fax)** *info@arklehouse.com* www.arklehouse.com **D:** £22.00–£27.00 **S:** £30.00–£40.00 **Beds:** 1F 1D **Baths:** 2 En ⛥ 🅿 (2) ⅙ 📺 Ⅵ 🏠 🐾 Quietly located alongside the Arkle Beck, Reeth, Swaledale. A beautiful old Georgian house full of character. Picturesque village full of beautiful rolling countryside. Excellent base for walking and touring the Dales. Family room available as double or twin. Friendly welcome.

Elder Peak, Arkengarthdale Road, Reeth,
Richmond, N Yorks, DL11 6QX. Friendly welcome. Good food. Peaceful, beautiful views. Ideal walking, touring. **Open:** Easter to Oct **01748 884770** Mrs Peacock **D:** £17.00 **S:** £17.00–£20.00 **Beds:** 1D 1T **Baths:** 1 Sh ⛥ (5) 🅿 (2) 📺 Ⅵ 🏠 🐾

2 Bridge Terrace, Reeth, Richmond, N.
Yorks, DL11 6TP. Dry - cured Gloucester old spot bacon, local bread, fresh fruit, yoghurt. **Open:** Easter to Nov **01748 884572** Mrs Davies *davidsizer@freenetname.co.uk* **D:** £16.50–£17.50 **S:** £22.00 **Beds:** 1D 1T **Baths:** 1 Sh ⛥ ⅙ Ⅵ 🏠

Riccall
SE6237

South Newlands Farm, Selby
Road, Riccall, York, YO19 6QR. Home from Home. Comfortable beds, fresh cooked food, well located. **Open:** All year **01757 248203** Mrs Swann **Fax:** 01757 249450 *pswann3059@aol.com* **D:** £18.00–£22.00 **S:** £20.00–£25.00 **Beds:** 1F 1D 1T **Baths:** 2 En ⛥ (3) 🅿 ⅙ 🐕 🐕 ✕ 🏠 🐾 ♿ cc

Richmond
NZ1701   🍺 *King's Head, Penny Farthing, Farmer's Arms, Black Lion, Golden Lion, Angel, Bay Horse, French Gate, New Inn, Turf Hotel*

Channel House, 8 Frenchgate,
Richmond, N. Yorks, DL10 4JG. Georgian town house near castle, shops, restaurants. Warm friendly welcome. **Open:** All year **01748 823844 (also fax)** Mrs Gould **D:** £19.00–£21.00 **S:** £20.00–£25.00 **Beds:** 1F 1D **Baths:** 1 En 1 Sh ⛥ ⅙ Ⅵ 🏠 🐾

Nuns Cottage, 5
Hurgill Road, Richmond, N Yorks, DL10 4AR. **Open:** All year **Grades:** ETC 4 Diamond **01748 822809** Mrs Parks *alan.parks@btinternet.com* www.richmond.org.uk/business/nunscottge **D:** £22.00–£25.00 **S:** £30.00–£39.00 **Beds:** 1T 2D **Baths:** 3 Pr ⛥ (10) 🅿 (270) ⅙ 📺 🐕 ✕ Ⅵ 🏠 🐾 Close to Richmond's centre, Grade II Listed, surrounded by stone walls and gardens. Decorated in period style and furnished with antiques. Beams, open fire and guests sitting-room. Bedrooms with all facilities / private bathrooms. Excellent meals. Welcoming and comfortable.

The Buck Inn, 27 Newbiggin, Richmond,
N. Yorks, DL10 4DX. **Open:** All year **01748 822259** E Fluen **D:** £22.00–£25.00 **S:** £25.00 **Beds:** 3F 1T 1D 1S **Baths:** 6 En ⛥ 📺 🏠 🐾 Elevated beer garden with magnificent views overlooking River Swale Valley, Castle and views of Colloden Tower all from a pub with character and old world charm, excellent accommodation of the highest standard, and breakfasts to satisfy the keenest appetite.

The Restaurant On The Green, 5-7
Bridge Street, Richmond, N. Yorks, DL10 4RW. Gateway to Dales. Good food, fine wines in historic house. **Open:** All year **01748 826229 (also fax)** Bennett *accom.bennett@talk21.com* www.coast2coast.co.uk/restaurantonthegreen **D:** £20.00 **S:** £25.00 **Beds:** 1T 1D **Baths:** 2 En ⛥ (10) ⅙ 📺 ✕ 🏠 🐾

Pottergate Guest House, 4 Pottergate,
Richmond, N Yorks, DL10 4AB. Comfortable guest house, friendly service, excellent value for money. **Open:** All year **01748 823826** Mrs Firby **D:** £19.00 **S:** £20.00 **Beds:** 1F 3D 1T 2S **Baths:** 3 Sh ⛥ 🅿 (3) ⅙ 📺 ✕ Ⅵ 🏠 🐾

Caldwell Lodge, Gilling West,
Richmond, N. Yorks, DL10 5JB. Friendly welcome. Pretty village. 1 mile Scotch Corner. **Open:** Easter to Oct **01748 825468** Mrs Bolton **D:** £18.00–£20.00 **S:** £20.00–£22.00 **Beds:** 1F 1D **Baths:** 1 Sh 🅿 (4) 📺 Ⅵ 🏠 🐾

66 Frenchgate, Richmond, DL10 7AG.
Comfortable rooms in beautiful old house. Stunning views of Richmond. **Open:** All year (not Xmas) **01748 823421** Mrs Woodward *paul@66french.freeserve.co.uk* **D:** £20.00–£21.00 **S:** £25.00–£26.00 **Beds:** 2D 1T **Baths:** 2 En 1 Pr ⛥ 📺 🐕 Ⅵ 🏠 🐾

Planning a longer stay? Always ask for any special rates

Rievaulx

SE5785

Barn Close Farm, *Rievaulx, Helmsley, York, YO62 5LH.* Barn close. Hill farm in valley of Rievaulx. Recommended in Telegraph. **Open:** All year
01439 798321 Mrs Milburn **D:** £20.00–£25.00 **Beds:** 1F 1D **Baths:** 1 En 1 Pr ⏰♿🅿(6) 📺🏠×
📺🖼.♿

Ripley

SE2860

Newton Hall, *Ripley, Harrogate, N. Yorks, HG3 3DZ.* Close to Harrogate, Fountains Abbey, the Dales, Skipton, Bolton Abbey, York. **Open:** All year
01423 770166 Mrs Iveson **D:** £20.00–£25.00 **S:** £30.00 **Beds:** 2D 1T **Baths:** 1 Sh ⏰🅿⤶📺
📺🖼.♿

Slate Rigg Farm, *Birthwaite Lane, Ripley, Harrogate, N. Yorks, HG3 3JQ.* Secluded working family farm with beautiful views of Lower Nidderdale. **Open:** All year (not Xmas/New Year) **Grades:** ETC 3 Diamond
01423 770135 Mrs Bowes **D:** £20.00–£22.50 **S:** £25.00–£30.00 **Beds:** 1F 1T **Baths:** 2 Sh
⏰🅿(4) 📺📺🖼.♿

Ripon

SE3171 ⚓ *Stanley Arms*

Bishopton Grove House, *Ripon, N. Yorks, HG4 2QL.* Large comfortable Georgian house near Fountains Abbey and River Laver. **Open:** All year **Grades:** ETC 3 Diamond
01765 600888 Mrs Wimpress *wimpress@ bronco.co.uk* **D:** £18.00–£20.00 **S:** £20.00–£25.00 **Beds:** 1F 1D 1T **Baths:** 2 En ⏰🅿(3)
📺🏠📺🖼.♿

Moor End Farm, *Knaresborough Road, Littlethorpe, Ripon, N. Yorks, HG4 3LU.* Friendly, non-smoking first-class accommodation. Pleasantly situated. Ideal for touring. **Open:** All year (not Xmas) **Grades:** ETC 4 Diamond
01765 677419 Mrs Spensley *pspensley@ ukonline.co.uk* yorkshirebandb.co.uk
D: £22.00–£25.00 **S:** £30.00–£40.00 **Beds:** 2D 1T **Baths:** 2 En 1 Pr 🅿(5) ⤶📺🖼.♿

Middle Ridge, *42 Mallorie Park Drive, Ripon, HG4 2QF.* Traditional,family owned, tastefully furnished, quiet, garden, conservatory, city outskirts. **Open:** Easter to Sept
01765 690558 Mrs Parker *john@ midrig.demon.co.uk* **D:** £18.00–£20.00 **S:** £25.00–£30.00 **Beds:** 1D 1T **Baths:** 1 Sh
⏰🅿(3) 📺📺🖼.♿

Robin Hood's Bay

NZ9504 ⚓ *The Dolphin, The Falcon, Bay Hotel, Victoria Hotel, Fylingdales Inn, Laurel Inn, Flask Inn*

Glen-lyn, *Station Road, Robin Hood's Bay, Whitby, N Yorks, YO22 4RA.* **Open:** All year
01947 880391 Mrs Price *jmpglenlyn@aol.com* **D:** £21.00–£22.00 **Beds:** 1T 1D **Baths:** 2 En 🅿
⤶📺📺🖼.♿&
Come and sample the delights of Robin Hood's Bay and stay in a tastefully decorated, well appointed detached bungalow. You can relax in the large, well-maintained mature gardens with seating area around a pond with water feature.

Clarence Dene, *Station Road, Robin Hood's Bay, Whitby, North Yorks, YO22 4RH.* **Open:** All year
01947 880272 Mrs Howard *dhcdene@aol.com* www.robinhoodsbay.net **D:** £20.00 **Beds:** 1F 1T 3D **Baths:** 5 En ⏰🅿⤶📺📺🖼.♿
Situated above this historic village. Clarence Dene retains many original Art Nouveau features. The spacious bedrooms have been sympathetically decorated and furnished, all are clean, comfortable and well appointed with ensuite facilities.

The White Owl, *Station Road, Robin Hood's Bay, Whitby, N. Yorks, YO22 4RL.* Interesting house and garden. Centre of village near cliff edge. **Open:** All year
01947 880879 Mr & Mrs Higgins **D:** £21.00 **S:** £21.00 **Beds:** 1F 1D 1T 1S **Baths:** 4 En ⏰
🅿(3) 📺🏠🖼.♿*.♿

Rosegarth, *Thorpe Lane, Robin Hood's Bay, Whitby, N. Yorks, YO22 4RN.* Friendly, comfortable accommodation. **Open:** Easter to Nov
01947 880578 Mr Stubbs **D:** £19.00 **Beds:** 1T 1D ⏰🅿(9) 📺🏠×📺🖼.♿ cc

Muir Lea Stores, *Robin Hood's Bay, Whitby, N. Yorks, YO22 4SF.* C18th smugglers' retreat. **Open:** All year
01947 880316 Mrs Leaf **D:** £17.00 **S:** £20.00 **Beds:** 3D 1S 📺🖼.♿ cc

Devon House, *Station Road, Robin Hood's Bay, Whitby, N. Yorks, YO22 4RL.* Devon House is a family-run B&B offering guests clean and comfortable accommodation. **Open:** All year (not Xmas/New Year)
01947 880197 D H Duncalfe *duncalfe@ devonhouserhb.freeserve.co.uk* devonhouserhb.freeserve.co.uk **D:** £21.00–£22.00 **S:** £42.00–£44.00 **Beds:** 1F 1T 2D **Baths:** 4 En ⏰(10) 🅿(4) ⤶📺📺🖼.♿

Meadowfield, *Mount Pleasant North, Robin Hood's Bay, Whitby, N. Yorks, YO22 4RE.* Refurbished Victorian house. Friendly, comfortable, plenty of food. Non-smoking. **Open:** All year (not Xmas)
01947 880564 Mrs Luker **D:** £17.00–£19.50 **S:** £20.00–£24.00 **Beds:** 2D 1T 2S **Baths:** 1 En 1 Sh ⤶📺📺🖼.♿

Rosedale East

SE7197

The Orange Tree, *Dale Head, Rosedale East, Pickering, N. Yorks, YO18 8RH.* In the heart of National Park. Spectacular views. Ideal touring, walking, cycling. **Open:** All year (not Xmas)
01751 417219 Mr Davies **D:** £21.00–£23.00 **S:** £26.00–£28.00 **Beds:** 1F 2T 2D ⏰🅿(6) 📺
🏠×📺🖼.♿

Runswick Bay

NZ8016

Cockpit House, *The Old Village, Runswick Bay, Saltburn-by-the-Sea, N Yorks, TS13 5HU.* Seafront position, near pub, beach, cafe, all sea views. **Open:** All year **Grades:** ETC 2 Diamond
01947 840504 & 01947 603047 Mrs Smith **D:** £17.00 **S:** £17.00–£21.00 **Beds:** 1D 2T **Baths:** 1 Sh ⏰(5) 📺🏠📺🖼.♿

Saintoft

SE7989

Beech Cottage, *Saintoft, Pickering, North Yorkshire, YO18 8QQ.* Large garden property nestled amongst trees, a particularly beautiful area. **Open:** All year
01751 417625 P & E Bramley **D:** £16.00–£18.00 **S:** £20.00–£24.00 **Beds:** 1F 1T **Baths:** 2 En ⏰🅿(2) ⤶📺🏠📺🖼.♿

BATHROOMS
En = Ensuite
Pr = Private
Sh = Shared

Sandsend

NZ8612

Estbek House, Sandsend, Whitby, N. Yorks, YO21 3SU. Fully equipped designer bedrooms. Fresh food, licensed restaurant. **Open:** All year
01947 893424 (also fax) Mr Cooper
R.C.Hill@Onyxnet.co.uk www.fastfix.co.uk/estbek **D:** £29.50 **S:** £27.50–£39.50 **Beds:** 1F 2D 2T **Baths:** 4 En 1 Pr ⌂ ⅄ ✕ ☒ ☑ ▥ ⚹ ⚐ cc

Scarborough

TA0388   🍴 *Rosette Inn*

Ryndle Court Hotel, 47 Northstead Manor Drive, Scarborough, N. Yorks, YO12 6AF. Delightfully situated overlooking Peasholm Park and near the sea. **Open:** Feb to Nov **Grades:** ETC 2 Star, RAC 2 Star
01723 375188 (also fax) Mr & Mrs Davies
enquiries@ryndlecourt.co.uk www.ryndlecourt.co.uk **D:** £28.00–£30.00 **S:** £28.00–£38.00 **Beds:** 1F 6D 5T 2S **Baths:** 14 En ⌂ ☒ (10) ☑ ✕ ☑ ▥ ⚹ ⚐ cc

Villa Marina Hotel, 59 Northstead Manor Drive, Scarborough, N. Yorks, YO12 6AF. Detached, quiet location overlooking Peasholm Park, close to north side attractions. **Open:** Easter to Oct **Grades:** ETC 4 Diamond
01723 361088 Mr & Mrs Pearson **D:** £22.00–£25.00 **Beds:** 2F 6D 2T **Baths:** 10 En ⌂ ☒ (9) ⅄ ✕ ☑ ▥ ⚐ cc

Russell Hotel, 22 Ryndleside, Scarborough, N Yorks, YO12 6AD. Detached 10-bedroom hotel, licensed, overlooking Peasholm Glen. Convenient all North Bay attractions. **Open:** All year **Grades:** ETC 3 Diamond
01723 365453 Lyn Stanley & Glen Martin *russellhotel.scarb@tinyworld.co.uk* **D:** £20.00–£30.00 **S:** £22.00–£33.00 **Beds:** 7F 2D 1T **Baths:** 7 En ⌂ ☒ (6) ☑ ⚐ ✕ ☑ ▥ ♺2 ⚹ ⚐

Clog and Garland, 26 Eastborough, Scarborough, N. Yorks, YO11 1NW. 100 yards from beach and town centre, close to all attractions. **Open:** All year
01723 362865 M Walker
www.clogandgarland.freeserve.com
D: £18.00–£22.00 **S:** £18.00–£25.00 **Beds:** 2F 1T 2D **Baths:** 5 En ⌂ ☑ ✕ ▥ ⚐

Howdale Hotel, 121 Queens Parade, Scarborough, N. Yorks, YO12 7HU. Comfortable hotel, panoramic sea views, memorable breakfasts, 10 mins town. **Open:** Easter to Oct **Grades:** ETC 3 Diamond
01723 372696 (also fax) Mr & Mrs Abbott
maria_keith-howdalehotel@yahoo.co.uk www.howdalehotel.moonfruit.com
D: £18.00–£23.00 **S:** £25.00–£28.00 **Beds:** 1F 11D 2T 1S **Baths:** 13 En 2 Sh ⌂ ☒ (9) ☑ ⚐ ☑ ▥ ⚐ cc

Richmond Private Hotel, 135 Columbus Ravine, Scarborough, N. Yorks, YO12 7QZ. Small, comfortable, family-run hotel. Friendly atmosphere, good home cooking. **Open:** All year
01723 362934 Mr & Mrs Shaw **D:** £15.00–£18.00 **S:** £15.00–£18.00 **Beds:** 2F 4D 1T 1S **Baths:** 3 En 1 Sh ⌂ ☑ ⚐ ✕ ☑ ▥ ⚐

Red Lea Hotel, Prince Of Wales Terrace, Scarborough, N. Yorks, YO11 2AJ. Traditional hotel with good facilities and expansive sea views. **Open:** All year **Grades:** ETC 2 Star, AA 2 Star, RAC 2 Star
01723 362431 Mr & Mrs Lee **Fax:** 01723 371230 *redlea@globalnet.com* www.redleahotel.co.uk **D:** £27.00–£38.00 **S:** £27.00–£38.00 **Beds:** 7F 16D 23T 22S **Baths:** 68 En ⌂ ☑ ✕ ☑ ▥ ⚹ ⚐ cc

Leeway Hotel, 71 Queens Parade, Scarborough, YO12 7HT. A family-run licensed hotel overlooking the North Bay and Castle. **Open:** Easter to Nov
01723 374371 Mr Saville *leenay@supanet.com* **D:** £17.00–£20.00 **S:** £17.00–£18.00 **Beds:** 2F 5D 2S **Baths:** 6 En ⌂ ☒ (6) ⅄ ✕ ▥ ⚐

Princess Court, 11 Princess Royal Terrace, Scarborough, N. Yorks, YO11 2RP. Spotless rooms with warm friendly service and home cooking. **Open:** All year
01723 501922 Rose *andy@princesscourt.co.uk* www.princesscourt.co.uk **D:** £20.00–£21.00 **S:** £30.00–£31.00 **Beds:** 1F 2T 2D 2S **Baths:** 6 En 1 Pr ⌂ ☒ ☑ ✕ ☑ ▥ ⚐

Blands Cliff Lodge and Restaurant, Blands Cliff, Scarborough, N. Yorks, YO11 1NR. Town centre located. Licensed family hotel. 100m from beach. **Open:** Easter to Oct
01723 351423 Fax: 01723 353211 *flats@scarborough-flats.co.uk* www.scarborough-flats.co.uk **D:** £15.00–£20.00 **S:** £15.00–£20.00 **Beds:** 5F 2T 5D 4S **Baths:** 6 En 10 Sh ⌂ ⅄ ☑ ✕ ⚐ cc

Gordon Hotel, 24 Ryndleside, Scarborough, N. Yorks, YO12 6AD. Detached private hotel, warm welcome, good food, free off-road parking. **Open:** All year **Grades:** ETC 4 Diamond
01723 362177 Mr Strickland *sales@gordonhotels.co.uk* www.gordonhotel.co.uk. or www.scarborough-hotels.com **D:** £20.00–£25.00 **S:** £25.00–£30.00 **Beds:** 3F 1T 5D 1S **Baths:** 7 En 3 Pr ⌂ ☒ (8) ☑ ✕ ☑ ▥ ⚐ cc

Wheatcroft Lodge, 156 Filey Road, Scarborough, N. Yorks, YO11 3AA. High standards at reasonable rates. RAC Sparkling Diamond Award. **Open:** All year (not Xmas)
01723 374613 Mrs Batty **D:** £21.50 **S:** £21.50 **Beds:** 4D 2T 1S **Baths:** 7 En ☒ (10) ⅄ ☑ ☑ ▥ ⚐ cc

Fixton, Scarborough, N Yorks, YO11 3UD. Rural location near coast, Moors, Wolds, warm welcome, secure parking. **Open:** All year (not Xmas)
01723 890272 (also fax) Mrs Wheater **D:** £18.00–£20.00 **S:** £18.00 **Beds:** 2F 2D 1S **Baths:** 2 En 1 Sh

Scotch Corner

NZ2105

Vintage Hotel, Scotch Corner, Richmond, N. Yorks, DL10 6NP. Conveniently situated roadside inn on A66, only quarter mile from A1 at Scotch Corner. **Open:** All year (not Xmas/New Year)
01748 824424 Mr & Mrs Fothergill **D:** £19.00–£27.00 **S:** £27.50–£42.50 **Beds:** 3D 2T 3S **Baths:** 5 En 1 Sh ⌂ (7) ☒ (40) ☑ ✕ ☑ ▥ ⚐ cc

Selby

SE6132

Hazeldene Guest House, 32-34 Brook Street, Selby, N. Yorks, YO8 4AR. Attractive period house, featuring spacious ensuite rooms, market town location. **Open:** All year (not Xmas) **Grades:** ETC 2 Diamond
01757 704809 Mr Leake **Fax:** 01757 709300 *selbystay@breathe.com* www.hazeldene-selby.co.uk **D:** £20.00–£23.00 **S:** £22.00–£32.00 **Beds:** 3D 3T 2S **Baths:** 5 En 2 Sh ☒ (6) ⅄ ☑ ☑ ▥ ⚐ cc

Selside

SD7875

South House Farm, Selside, Settle, N. Yorks, BD24 0HU. Comfortable farmhouse accommodation set in the centre of the Peaks. **Open:** Easter to Oct
01729 860271 Ms Kenyon **D:** £20.00 **S:** £20.00 **Beds:** 1F 2D 1T **Baths:** 1 En ⌂ (1) ☒ (6) ⅄ ☑ ⚐ ✕ ▥ ⚐

Settle

SD8163   🍴 *Golden Lion, Royal Oak, Falcon Manor*

Liverpool House, Chapel Square, Settle, N. Yorks, BD24 9HR. Situated in quiet area yet within 3 mins' walk town square. **Open:** All year **Grades:** AA 3 Diamond
01729 822247 Mr & Mrs Duerden **D:** £19.00–£23.00 **S:** £19.00–£20.00 **Beds:** 4D 1T 2S **Baths:** 2 En 2 Sh ⌂ ☒ (8) ⅄ ☑ ☑ ▥ ⚐ cc

Sharow

SE3271

Half Moon Inn, *Sharow Lane, Sharow, Ripon, N. Yorks, HG4 5BP.* Quiet C18th country inn on outskirts of historic Ripon. **Open:** All year (not Xmas/New Year) **01765 600291 D:** £20.00 **S:** £24.50 **Beds:** 1T 2D **Baths:** 3 En 1 Sh ⏺ 🅿 (10) 📺 ✕ 🎗 ♿ cc

Sherburn in Elmet

SE4933

Church Hill Guest House, *3 Church Hill, Sherburn in Elmet, Leeds, LS25 6AX.* **Open:** All year **01977 681000** A Beattie **Fax:** 01977 681333 **D:** £17.50–£20.00 **S:** £18.50–£25.00 **Beds:** 1D 2T 1S **Baths:** 2 En 1 Sh ⏺ 🅿 (8) 📺 ♋ 🎗 🎗 ⛟ ♿ cc

The accommodation is a purpose-built annexe joined to owners' house, all recently refurbished to high standard. Our register has many glowing testimonials. Very easy to find and extremely convenient for York, Dales, Moors, Pennines. Relaxed, easygoing and friendly.

Wheelgate Guest House, *7 Kirkgate, Sherburn in Elmet, Leeds, West Yorkshire, LS25 6BH.* Olde worlde cottage-style house, convenient for Leeds, York, Selby. **Open:** All year (not Xmas) **Grades:** ETC 3 Diamond **01977 682231 (also fax)** Mrs Tomlinson **D:** £18.00–£23.00 **S:** £23.00–£28.00 **Beds:** 1D 3T **Baths:** 1 En 2 Sh ⏺ 🅿 (4) 📺 ♋ ✕ 🎗 ⛟ 🎗

Sheriff Hutton

SE6466   🍺 *Blacksmith's Arms*

Hall Farm, *High Stittenham, Sheriff Hutton, York, YO60 7TW.* Perfectly situated for visiting York, Castle Howard and the North York Moors. **Open:** All year **Grades:** ETC 4 Diamond **01347 878461** Mrs Hemingway *hallfarm@ btinternet.com* www.hallfarm.btinternet.co.uk **D:** £20.00–£23.00 **S:** £25.00–£30.00 **Beds:** 1F 1T 1D **Baths:** 3 En ⏺ (0) 🅿 (20) 🎗 📺 🎗 ⛟ 🎗

Simonstone

SD8791

Overdales View, *Simonstone, Hawes, N Yorks, DL8 3LY.* Friendly welcome. Lovely views, rural surroundings, comfortable beds good food. **Open:** Easter to Oct **01969 667186** Mrs Sunter **D:** £17.00–£18.00 **S:** £18.00–£20.00 **Beds:** 1F/T 1D 1S **Baths:** 1 Sh ⏺ 🅿 (5) 🎗 📺 🎗 ⛟ 🎗

Sinnington

SE7486

Green Lea, *Sinnington, York, YO62 6SH.* Large converted bungalow in lovely pretty village off A170. Lovely garden to relax in. **Open:** Mar to Oct **01751 432008** Mr & Mrs Turnbull **D:** £18.00– £22.50 **S:** £18.00–£22.50 **Beds:** 1F 1T 1D **Baths:** 2 En 1 Sh ⏺ (5) 🅿 (4) 🎗 📺 ✕ 🎗 ⛟ 🎗

Skeeby

NZ1903

The Old Chapel, *Richmond Road, Skeeby, Richmond, North Yorks, DL10 5DR.* Beautifully converted Victorian chapel situated in small village near Richmond. **Open:** All year (not Xmas/New Year) **01748 824170 & 07803 103871 (M)** H Allan *hazel@theoldchapel.fsnet.co.uk* **D:** £20.00 **S:** £25.00 **Beds:** 2D **Baths:** 2 En ⏺ 🅿 (2) 🎗 📺 🎗 ⛟ 🎗

Skipton

SD9851   🍺 *Bull, Elm Tree, Sailor, Craven Heifer, Devonshire Arms, Albion, White Swan, Bay Horse, Angel*

Spring Gardens Cottage, *20 Queens Street, Skipton, BD23 1HE.* **Open:** All year (not Xmas/New Year) **Grades:** ETC 3 Diamond **01756 790739 D:** £20.00 **Beds:** 1D **Baths:** 1 En 🅿 (2) 🎗 📺 🎗 ⛟ 🎗 Cottage-style building featuring luxury double room ensuite. Private Sky TV lounge. Within 10 mins' walk of Skipton town centre with its historic castle and markets, yet situated in a tranquil area, for a peaceful break. Gateway to the Dales.

Low Skibeden Farmhouse, *Harrogate Road, Skipton, N. Yorks, BD23 6AB.* C16th farmhouse with little luxuries and fireside treats at no extra charge. **Open:** All year **Grades:** AA 4 Diamond **01756 793849 & 07050 207787 (M)** Mrs Simpson **Fax:** 01756 793804 *skibhols.yorksdales@talk21.com* www.yorkshirenet.uk/accgde/lowskibeden **D:** £20.00–£24.00 **S:** £30.00–£40.00 **Beds:** 3F 1D 1T **Baths:** 4 En 1 Sh ⏺ (12) 🅿 (5) 🎗 📺 ⛟ 🎗 cc

Dalesgate Lodge, *69 Gargrave Road, Skipton, N. Yorks, BD23 1QN.* Comfortable rooms, friendly welcome. Special winter breaks available. **Open:** All year **01756 790672** Mr & Mrs Mason **D:** £17.50– £20.00 **S:** £20.00–£25.00 **Beds:** 2D/T 2S **Baths:** 4 En ⏺ 🅿 (2) 🎗 📺 ⛟ 🎗

Bourne House, *22 Upper Sackville Street, Skipton, N Yorks, BD23 2EB.* Edwardian townhouse, quiet location, close to town centre, easy parking. **Open:** All year (not Xmas/New Year) **01756 792633** Mr & Mrs Barton **Fax: 01756 701609** *bournehouse@totalise.co.uk* www.bournehouseguesthouse.co.uk **D:** £16.00–£18.00 **S:** £17.00–£25.00 **Beds:** 1T 2D 1S **Baths:** 1 En 2 Sh ⏺ (3) 🎗 📺 🎗 ⛟ 🎗 cc

Sleights

NZ8607   🍺 *White Horse, Huntsman*

Ryedale House, *154-8 Coach Road, Sleights, Whitby, N. Yorks, YO22 5EQ.* National Park country. Magnificent moor/dale/ coastal scenery. Relaxing house for non-smokers. **Open:** Apr to Oct **Grades:** ETC 4 Diamond **01947 810534 (also fax)** Mrs Beale **D:** £20.00–£22.00 **S:** £18.00–£24.00 **Beds:** 2D 2S **Baths:** 2 En 1 Pr 🅿 (3) 🎗 📺 🎗 ⛟ 🎗 cc

Slingsby

SE6975

Beech Tree House Farm, *South Holme, Slingsby, York, YO62 4BA.* Working farm. Beautiful area between York and Scarborough. Children welcome. **Open:** All year (not Xmas) **01653 628257 D:** £18.00 **S:** £18.00 **Beds:** 2F 1D 1T **Baths:** 3 Pr ⏺ 🅿 (6) 📺 ✕ 🎗 ⛟ 🎗

Sowerby

SE4281

The Old Manor House, *27 Front Street, Sowerby, Thirsk, N. Yorks, YO7 1JQ.* Charming C16th Manor house overlooking village Green Herriot Museum town. **Open:** Mar to Oct **Grades:** ETC 4 Diamond **01845 526642** Mr Jackson **Fax:** 01845 526568 **D:** £20.00–£30.00 **S:** £35.00–£40.00 **Beds:** 3D **Baths:** 3 En 🅿 (5) 🎗 📺 ⛟ 🎗 cc

Spaunton

SE7289

Holywell House, *Spaunton Bank Foot, Spaunton, Appleton Le Moors, York, YO62 6TR.* C18th beamed cottage with large garden. **Open:** All year (not Xmas/New Year) **01751 417624** Mrs Makepeace **D:** £36.00 **S:** £18.00 **Beds:** 1D 1T 1S ⏺ (5) 🅿 (4) 🎗 📺 ⛟ 🎗

Staintondale

SE9998

Island House, *Island Farm, Staintondale, Scarborough, N Yorks, YO13 0EB.* Space, tranquillity, relaxation, tennis, snooker, on organic farm. Beautiful countryside. **Open:** Easter to Nov **Grades:** ETC 4 Diamond
01723 870249 M Clarke *roryc@tinyworld.co.uk*
www.islandhousefarm.co.uk **D:** £20.00–£25.00 **S:** £25.00–£27.00 **Beds:** 1T 2D **Baths:** 3 En ➲ ▣ (6) ⅍ ▨ ★ ▨ ▥. ♨

Staithes

NZ7718   ◀ *Cod & Lobster, Black Lion*

Brooklyn, *Brown's Terrace, Staithes, Saltburn-by-the-Sea, TS13 5BG.* Sea captain's house, central, but quiet, in picturesque fishing village. **Open:** All year (not Xmas)
01947 841396 Ms Heald **D:** £18.50 **S:** £18.50 **Beds:** 1T 2D **Baths:** 2 Sh ➲ ▨ ★ ▨ ▥. ♨

Springfields, *42 Staithes Lane, Staithes, Saltburn-by-the-Sea, N Yorks, TS13 5AD.* Victorian house with countryside views. Lounge available. In National Park. **Open:** All year
01947 841011 Mrs Verrill **D:** £15.00 **S:** £15.00 **Beds:** 1D 1S **Baths:** 1 En 1 Sh ▣ (1) ⅍ ▨ ▥. ♨

Stape

SE7993

Seavy Slack Farm, *Stape, Pickering, N. Yorks, YO18 8HZ.* Comfortable farmhouse on a working farm serving good food. **Open:** All year (not Xmas)
01751 473131 Mrs Barrett **D:** £20.00–£25.00 **S:** £25.00 **Beds:** 1T 2D **Baths:** 3 En ➲ (5) ▣ (6) ▨ ★ ✕ ▨ ▥. ♨

Starbotton

SD9574

Fox & Hounds Inn, *Starbotton, Skipton, N. Yorks, BD23 5HY.* Traditional cosy Dales inn. **Open:** Mar to Dec
01756 760269 Mr & Mrs McFadyen **Fax:** **01756 760862** *hilarymcfadyen@supanet.com*
D: £27.50 **S:** £35.00 **Beds:** 1D 1T ▣ (12) ⅍ ▨ ★ ▥. ♨ cc

Stearsby

SE6172

The Granary, *Stearsby, Brandsby, York, YO61 4SA.* Converted C18th granary set in beautiful 1-acre garden located in quiet Yorkshire hamlet. **Open:** All year (not Xmas/New Year)
01347 888652 (also fax) Mr & Mrs Turl *roberturl@thegranary.org.uk* **D:** £22.00–£25.00 **S:** £25.00–£30.00 **Beds:** 3D **Baths:** 3 En ➲ ▣ (6) ⅍ ▨ ★ ▥. ♨

Stonegrave

SE6578

Manor Cottage, *Stonegrave , York, YO62 4LJ.* Quiet friendly home offering comfortable spacious accommodation on peaceful garden. **Open:** All year (not Xmas/New Year)
01653 628599 Trudy Visser *gideon.v@ virgin.net* business.virgin.net/gideon. v/index.html **D:** £17.50–£20.00 **S:** £20.00–£25.00 **Beds:** 2T **Baths:** 2 En ▣ (4) ⅍ ▨ ▥. ♨

Studley Roger

SE2870

The Wheelhouse, *2 Parklands, Studley Roger, Ripon, HG4 3AY.* Renovated mill next to Studley Royal Oak Park and Fountains Abbey. **Open:** All year (not Xmas)
01765 604508 J Burton *itis@itis.slv.co.uk* **D:** £23.00–£25.00 **Beds:** 1D **Baths:** 1 En ➲ (8) ▣ (4) ⅍ ▨ ▨ ▥. ♨

Sutton Bank

SE5182

Cote Faw, *Hambleton Cottages, Sutton Bank, Thirsk, N. Yorks, YO7 2EZ.* Comfortable cottage in National Park, central for visiting North Yorkshire. **Open:** All year (not Xmas)
01845 597363 Mrs Jeffray **D:** £16.00–£17.00 **S:** £16.00–£17.00 **Beds:** 1F 1D 1S **Baths:** 1 Sh ➲ ▣ (3) ▨ ▨ ▥. ♨

Thimbleby

SE4495

Stonehaven, *Thimbleby, Osmotherly, Northallerton, DL6 3PY.* Comfortable farmhouse, super view, lovely walks, good beds and good food. **Open:** Easter to Nov **Grades:** ETC 3 Diamond
01609 883689 Mrs Shepherd **D:** £20.00–£22.00 **S:** £20.00–£22.00 **Beds:** 1D 1T **Baths:** 1 Pr ➲ (1) ▣ (3) ⅍ ▨ ▨ ▥. ♨ cc

Thirsk

SE4282   ◀ *Crown & Anchor, Dog & Gun, Angel Inn, Sheppard Hotel, Golden Fleece, Oak Tree, The George*

Fourways Guest House, *Town End, Thirsk, N. Yorks, YO7 1PY.* Ideal holiday base for touring the North York Moors/Dales. **Open:** All year **Grades:** ETC 2 Star
01845 522601 Mrs Baukar *fourways@ nyorks.fsbusiness.co.uk* **D:** £19.00–£21.00 **S:** £21.00–£24.00 **Beds:** 1F 2T 2D 3S **Baths:** 7 En 1 Pr 1 Sh ➲ ▣ (6) ▨ ★ ✕ ▨ ▥. ♨ cc

Town Pasture Farm, *Boltby, Thirsk, N. Yorks, YO7 2DY.* Comfortable farmhouse in beautiful village, central for Yorkshire Dales. **Open:** All year (not Xmas) **Grades:** ETC 3 Diamond
01845 537298 Mrs Fountain **D:** £17.50–£19.50 **S:** £18.50–£20.00 **Beds:** 1F 1T **Baths:** 2 En ➲ ▣ (3) ⅍ ▨ ★ ✕ ▨ ▥. ♨

St James' House, *36 The Green, Thirsk, N Yorks, YO7 1AQ.* Two minutes' walk from market place. **Open:** All year **Grades:** ETC 3 Diamond
01845 526565 Mr Ogleby **D:** £20.00 **S:** £30.00 **Beds:** 3D **Baths:** 2 En ➲ (1) ▣ (3, ⅍ ▨ ★ ▨ ▥. ♨. ♨

The Old Manor House, *27 Front Street, Sowerby, Thirsk, N. Yorks, YO7 1JQ.* Charming C16th Manor house overlooking village Green Herriot Museum town. **Open:** Mar to Oct **Grades:** ETC 4 Diamond
01845 526642 Mr Jackson **Fax: 01845 526568** **D:** £20.00–£30.00 **S:** £35.00–£40.00 **Beds:** 3D **Baths:** 3 En ▣ (5) ⅍ ▨ ▥. ♨ cc

Thixendale

SE8461

Manor Farm, *Thixendale, Malton, N. Yorks, YO7 9TG.* Working farm. Private spacious accommodation, overlooking pretty garden. Substantial breakfasts. **Open:** All year (not Xmas/New Year)
01377 288315 (also fax) Mrs Brader **D:** £20.00 **S:** £20.00 **Beds:** 2F 1D 1T 1S **Baths:** 1 Pr ➲ ▣ ⅍ ▨ ▥. ♨

Thormanby

SE4974   ◀ *Black Bull*

The Old Rectory, *Thormanby, Easingwold, York, YO61 4NN.* Early C18th Listed rectory in the heart of Yorkshire. **Open:** All year (not Xmas)
01845 501417 Mrs Ritchie **D:** £16.00–£18.00 **S:** £18.00 **Beds:** 1F 1D 1T **Baths:** 2 En 1 Sh ➲ ▣ (6) ▨ ★ ▨ ▥. ♨

Thornton le Dale

SE8382   ◀ *Buck Inn, New Inn, Old Hall*

Tangalwood, *Roxby Road, Thornton le Dale, Pickering, N. Yorks, YO18 7SX.* Friendly comfortable accommodation, quietly situated. Ideal for York, Moors, Coast. **Open:** Easter to Oct **Grades:** ETC 3 Diamond
01751 474688 Mrs Wardell **D:** £17.00–£19.00 **S:** £20.00–£25.00 **Beds:** 1D 1T **Baths:** 1 En 1 Sh ➲ (7) ▣ (2) ▨ ★ ▨ ▥. ♨

Nabgate, *Wilton Road, Thornton le Dale, Pickering, N. Yorks, YO18 7QP.* **Open:** All year **Grades:** ETC 4 Diamond
01751 474279 & 07703 804859 (M)
Mrs Pickering **D:** £20.00–£22.00 **S:** £22.00–£25.00 **Beds:** 2D 1T **Baths:** 3 En ⏰ 🅿 (4) 📺 ⛏
📺 🛏 ♿ ⚘
Situated on the edge of beautiful Thornton le Dale, in TV's heartbeat country, this clean and friendly home offers excellent Yorkshire breakfasts. Central for Moors, Coast, Steam railway, York, Castle Howard and Dalby Forest. Garden for guest to relax in. Own keys.

Thornton Watlass

SE2385

Buck Inn, *Thornton Watlass, Ripon, N. Yorks, HG4 4AH.* **Open:** All year (not Xmas)
Grades: ETC 1 Star, AA 1 Star
01677 422461 Mr & Mrs Fox **Fax: 01677 422447** *buckwatlass@btinternet.com*
www.smoothhound.co.uk/hotels/buckinn.html **D:** £27.50–£32.00 **S:** £38.00–£42.00 **Beds:** 1F 3D 2T 1S **Baths:** 5 En 1 Sh ⏰ 🅿 (20)
📺 🛏 ✗ 📺 🛏 ♿ ⚘ cc
Delightful country inn overlooking the cricket green in a quiet village just 5 mins from the A1. Relax in our comfortable bedrooms, enjoy our superb home-cooked food and drink from our selection of five real ales. Large secluded garden with children's playground.

Threshfield

SD9863

Grisedale Farm, *Threshfield, Skipton, N Yorks, BD23 5NT.* Friendly traditional Dales farmhouse near Grassington with beautiful rural location. **Open:** All year (not Xmas/New Year)
01756 752516 Mrs Kitching *janette.kitching@tesco.net* **D:** £15.00–£18.00 **S:** £20.00 **Beds:** 1T 1D **Baths:** 1 Sh ⏰ 🅿 (2) 📺 ⛏ 📺 🛏 ⚘

Wath

SE3277

George Inn Hotel, *Wath, Ripon, N. Yorks, HG4 5EN.* Friendly country inn set in picturesque village. **Open:** All year
01765 640202 (also fax) **D:** £48.00–£55.00 **S:** £29.50–£32.50 **Beds:** 2F 1T 3D **Baths:** 6 En ⏰ 🛏 ⚡ ⏰ ⛏ ✗ 📺 🛏 ⚘ cc

Weaverthorpe

SE9670

The Star Inn, *Weaverthorpe, Malton, N. Yorks, YO17 8EY.* Country inn, quiet locality, fine food, traditional ales and open log fires. **Open:** All year
01944 738273 Mr Richardson *starinn@quista.net* www.starinn.net **D:** £20.00–£26.00 **S:** £20.00–£26.00 **Beds:** 1F 1D 1T **Baths:** 3 En ⏰ (5) 🅿 (30) 📺 ✗ 📺 🛏 ⚘ cc

Well

SE2682

Upsland Farm, *Lime Lane, Well, Bedale, N. Yorks, DL8 2PA.* Beautiful house rebuilt to an award winning design in delightful open countryside. **Open:** All year (not Xmas)
Grades: ETC 4 Diamond, AA 5 Diamond
01845 567709 (also fax) Mrs Hodgson *upsland@Btinternet.com* **D:** £27.50 **S:** £35.00 **Beds:** 1T 2D **Baths:** 3 En ⏰ 🅿 (4) ⚡ 📺 ⛏ ✗ 📺 🛏 ⚘

West Heslerton

SE9176

The Old Rectory, *West Heslerton, Malton, North Yorkshire, YO17 8RE.* B&B in fine Georgian house set in 2 acres of garden. **Open:** All year (not Xmas/New Year) **Grades:** ETC 4 Diamond
01944 728285 Mr & Mrs Hillas *bhillas@supanet.com* www.theoldrectoryny.co.uk **D:** £19.00–£21.00 **S:** £19.00–£21.00 **Beds:** 1F 1T 1D **Baths:** 3 En ⏰ 🅿 (10) ⚡ 📺 ⛏ 📺 🛏 ♿ ⚘ cc

West Witton

SE0688 🍺 *Fox & Hounds*

The Old Star, *West Witton, Leyburn, N. Yorks, DL8 4LU.* **Open:** All year (not Xmas) **Grades:** ETC 3 Diamond
01969 622949 Mr & Mrs Martin **D:** £17.00–£20.00 **S:** £17.00–£20.00 **Beds:** 1F 2T 4D **Baths:** 5 En ⏰ 🅿 (12) 📺 ⛏ 📺 🛏 ⚘
Former C17th coaching inn now a family-run guest house. Oak beams, log fire and informal relaxing atmosphere. Situated in the Yorkshire Dales National Park, the Old Star is an ideal base for touring, walking or cycling.

BATHROOMS

En = Ensuite
Pr = Private
Sh = Shared

Westow

SE7565

Woodhouse Farm, *Westow, York, YO60 7LL.* Beautiful peaceful traditional farmhouse with views. Home-made bread etc. **Open:** May to Nov
01653 618378 (also fax) Mrs Wardle *woodhousefarm@farmersweekly.net* **D:** £17.50–£20.00 **S:** £17.50–£20.00 **Beds:** 1F 1D **Baths:** 1 En 1 Sh ⏰ 🅿 (6) 📺 📺 🛏 ⚘

Whitby

NZ8910 🍺 *White Horse & Griffin, The Granby*

Wheeldale Hotel, *North Promenade, Whitby, YO21 3JX.* **Open:** Feb to Nov **Grades:** ETC 4 Diamond
01947 602365 Mr & Mrs Bouttell *wheeldale_hotel@lineone.net* www.wheeldale-hotel.co.uk **D:** £25.00–£30.00 **Beds:** 1T 8D **Baths:** 9 En 🅿 (9) ⚡ 📺 ✗ 📺 🛏 ⚘ cc
Set in a quiet peaceful location overlooking Whitby's West Cliff. The harbour and town are only minutes' walk away. Owned and run by Liz and Ian who guarantee a warm welcome and a comfortable and relaxing stay.

Arches Guest House, *8 Havelock Place, Hudson Street, Whitby, YO21 3ER.* **Open:** All year **Grades:** ETC 3 Diamond
01947 601880 Mr Brew *archeswhitby@freeola.com* www.whitbyguesthouses.co.uk **D:** £17.00–£22.00 **S:** £25.00–£32.00 **Beds:** 3F 2T 5D 1S **Baths:** 8 En 1 Pr 2 Sh ⏰ ⚡ 📺 ⛏ 📺 🛏 ♿ ❄ ⚘ cc
Friendly family-run guest house, where a warm welcome and a large breakfast is always assured. The ideal base for experiencing the old world charms of this historic seaside town, exploring the beautiful North Yorkshire Moors or simply relaxing.

Ryedale House, 154-8 Coach Road, Sleights, Whitby, N. Yorks, YO22 5EQ. **Open:** Apr to Oct **Grades:** ETC 4 Diamond **01947 810534 (also fax)** Mrs Beale **D:** £20.00–£22.00 **S:** £18.00–£24.00 **Beds:** 2D 2S **Baths:** 2 En 1 Pr 🅿 (3) 🗡 🏧 Ⅴ ▥ ♨ cc National Park country 3.5 miles Whitby. Magnificent moor/dale/coastal scenery. Relaxing house for non-smokers; high standard private facilities with many extras. Lovely gardens, valley views, extensive traditional wholefood/vegetarian breakfasts, regret no pets or children. Minimum 2 nights.

Kirklands Hotel, 17 Abbey Terrace, Whitby, North Yorkshire, YO21 3HQ. **Open:** Feb to Nov **01947 603868 (also fax)** Mr Halton **D:** £25.00 **S:** £35.00 **Beds:** 6F 3D 2T 1S **Baths:** 6 En 3 Pr 3 Sh 🏧 ▥ ★ ★ Ⅴ ♨ The Kirkland's is a privately run, close to all amenities, comfortable rooms (ensuite) some with private bathrooms, TVs, coffee and tea faculties, an excellent breakfast. Pets and schools welcome, easy access to the North York Moors and villages, and other major tourist attractions.

Rosslyn Guest House, 11 Abbey Terrace, Whitby, YO21 3HQ. Quality accommodation at affordable prices, close to harbourside and moorlands. **Open:** All year (not Xmas) **Grades:** ETC 3 Diamond **01947 604086 (also fax)** A Briers *rosslynhouse@bushinternet.com* www.guesthousewhitby.co.uk **D:** £18.00– £19.50 **S:** £20.00–£25.00 **Beds:** 2F 2D 1T 1S **Baths:** 5 En 1 Pr 🏧 🅿 (2) ▥ ✕ Ⅴ ♨

Falcon Guest House, 29 Falcon Terrace, Whitby, N. Yorks, YO21 1EH. Quiet private house near centre. Sunny breakfast room, organic produce. **Open:** All year **01947 603507** Mr Lyth **D:** £18.00 **S:** £20.00 **Beds:** 2F **Baths:** 1 Sh 🏧 🗡 🏧 Ⅴ ♨

The Yorkshire House, Moorlands, North Promenade, Whitby, N. Yorks, YO21 3JX. Fine sea views. Warm Christian welcome. Special interest breaks available. **Open:** All year **01947 603584** L Atkinson **Fax: 01947 821668 D:** £20.60–£32.60 **S:** £20.60–£32.60 **Beds:** 2F 10T 8D 10S **Baths:** 14 En 7 Sh 🏧 🅿 (20) 🗡 🏧 ✕ Ⅴ ▥ ♨ ♨ cc

White Horse and Griffin, Church Street, Whitby, YO22 4BH. Historic inn with echoes of Captain Cook, Scorsby, Stephenson and Dickens. **Open:** All year **01947 604857** Mr Perkins **D:** £24.00–£35.00 **S:** £24.00–£35.00 **Beds:** 3F 2T 6D 1S **Baths:** 12 En 🏧 🅿 🏧 ★ ✕ Ⅴ ▥ ♨ ♨ cc

Haven Guest House, 4 East Crescent, Whitby, N. Yorks, YO21 3HD. Comfortable friendly guest house with sea views. Comprehensive breakfast menu. **Open:** Easter to Oct **01947 603842** Mrs Smith **D:** £18.00–£24.00 **S:** £21.00–£23.00 **Beds:** 1F 5D 2S **Baths:** 5 En 1 Sh 🏧 (5) ▥ ♨ ♨

Havelock Guest House, 30 Hudson Street, Whitby, YO21 3ED. Conveniently situated for the spa, beach, harbour and shops. Sauna available. **Open:** All year (not Xmas) **01947 602295 (also fax)** M J Ryder **D:** £17.00–£19.50 **S:** £17.00 **Beds:** 2F 5D 1T 5S **Baths:** 7 En 2 Sh 🏧 ▥ ★ Ⅴ ▥ ♨

Seaview Guest House, 5 East Crescent, Whitby, N Yorks, YO21 3HD. Family-run guest house with high standard of cleanliness. Close to beach and town. **Open:** All year (not Xmas/New Year) **01947 604462** L Boettger *cview@supanet.com* **D:** £19.00–£22.00 **S:** £19.00–£21.00 **Beds:** 1F 5D 2S **Baths:** 6 En 1 Sh 🏧 🏧 ★ Ⅴ ▥ ♨

Wombleton

SE6684

Rockery Cottage, Main Street, Wombleton, York, YO62 7RX. Quiet village location, ideally placed for touring Moors/coast. **Open:** All year **Grades:** ETC 4 Diamond, Silver **01751 432257 & 07771 657222 (M)** Mrs Sleight **D:** £22.50–£25.00 **S:** £25.00 **Beds:** 1D 1S **Baths:** 2 En 🏧 (12) 🅿 (3) 🗡 🏧 Ⅴ ▥ ♨

Wrelton

SE7686   ◄ New Inn, Apple Tree

The Huntsman Restaurant and Guest House, Main Street, Wrelton, Pickering, N. Yorks, YO18 8PG. Converted stone-built farmhouse, rustic character beamed ceilings, garden, patio, private parking. **Open:** All year **Grades:** ETC 3 Diamond **01751 472530** Mr Lower *howard@ thehuntsman.freeserve.co.uk* www.europage.co. uk/huntsman **D:** £16.00–£24.00 **S:** £18.00– £26.00 **Beds:** 1T 2D **Baths:** 3 En 🏧 (10) ▥ ★ ✕ Ⅴ ▥ ✳ ♨ cc

York

SE5951   ◄ Nag's Head

Bank House, 9 Southlands Road, York, YO23 1NP. Privately-owned guest house in quiet position adjacent to the Racecourse. **Open:** All year **01904 627803 & 07713 639596 (M)** Mr Farrell **D:** £16.00–£25.00 **S:** £20.00–£25.00 **Beds:** 2F 1T 3D 1S **Baths:** 7 En 🏧 🅿 🗡 🏧 ★ ✕ Ⅴ ▥ ♨ ♨

Ascot House, 80 East Parade, York, YO31 7YH. **Open:** All year (not Xmas) **Grades:** ETC 4 Diamond, AA 4 Diamond, RAC 4 Diamond **01904 426826** Mrs Wood **Fax: 01904 431077** *J&K@ascot-house-york.demon.co.uk* www.smoothhound.co.uk/hotels/ascothou. html **D:** £22.00–£26.00 **S:** £22.00–£46.00 **Beds:** 3F 8D 3T 1S **Baths:** 12 En 1 Pr 1 Sh 🏧 🅿 (14) ▥ ★ Ⅴ ▥ ♨ ♨ cc A family-run Victorian villa, built in 1869, with rooms of character and many four-poster or canopy beds. Superb English breakfasts. Fifteen minutes' walk to Jorvik Viking Centre, Castle Museum or York Minster. Residential licence, sauna, private enclosed car park.

The Hazelwood, 24-25 Portland Street, Gillygate, York, YO31 7EH. **Open:** All year **Grades:** ETC 4 Diamond, Silver, AA 4 Diamond, RAC 4 Diamond, Sparkling **01904 626548   Fax: 01904 628032** www.thehazelwoodyork.com **D:** £35.00– £47.50 **S:** £35.00–£80.00 **Beds:** 2F 8D 3T 1S **Baths:** 14 En 🏧 (8) 🅿 (8) 🗡 🏧 Ⅴ ▥ ♨ ♨ cc High quality B&B in the very heart of York, only 400 yards from York Minster. Elegant Victorian townhouse in quiet residential area with own car park. Individually styled ensuite bedrooms. Wide choice of quality breakfasts including vegetarian. Non smoking.

St Raphael Guest House, 44 Queen Annes Road, Bootham, York, YO30 7AF. Family-run mock Tudor guest house, tastefully decorated. **Open:** All year **01904 645028** Mrs Foster **Fax: 01904 658788** *straphael2000@yahoo.com* **D:** £20.00–£25.00 **S:** £21.00–£28.00 **Beds:** 3F 2D 1T 2S **Baths:** 8 En 🏧 🅿 (2) 🏧 ★ ▥ ♨ ♨ cc

Holly Lodge, *206 Fulford Road, York, YO10 4DD.* **Open:** All year **Grades:** ETC 4 Diamond, AA 4 Diamond, RAC 4 Diamond **01904** 646005 Mr Gallagher www.thehollylodge.co.uk **D:** £29.00–£34.00 **S:** £48.00–£58.00 **Beds:** 1F 3D 1T **Baths:** 5 En 5 Pr ⌣ (7) ▣ ⌇ ▧ Ⓥ ▥, ▙ cc
Ideally located 10 mins' riverside walk from the centre, convenient for all York's amenities. This fine Georgian building, with comfortable rooms, walled garden and car park, offers a warm welcome. Booking recommended. Located on A19,1.5 miles towards the city from A19/A64 intersection.

Avenue Guest House, *6 The Avenue, Clifton, York, YO30 6AS.* **Open:** All year (not Xmas/New Year) **Grades:** ETC 3 Diamond **01904** 620575 *allen@avenuegh.fsnet.co.uk* www.avenuegh.fsnet.co.uk **D:** £17.00–£22.00 **S:** £20.00–£25.00 **Beds:** 4F 3D **Baths:** 4 En 3 Sh ⌣ (4) ⌇ ▧ Ⓥ ▥, ▙
This family-run charming Victorian guest house is quietly situated in a beautiful tree-lined avenue. The city centre is a ten minute riverside walk. Some rooms are ensuite. Families are welcome. Non-smoking throughout. Free, easy permit parking always available.

The Beckett, *58 Bootham Crescent, York, YO30 7AH.* City centre, Victorian, magnificent breakfast, warm welcome, elegant, comfortable, friendly. **Open:** All year (not Xmas/New Year) **01904** 644728 Mrs Brown **Fax: 01904 639915** *abrownyork@aol.com* www.mywebsite. net/thebeckett **D:** £25.00–£35.00 **S:** £25.00–£45.00 **Beds:** 2T 4D 1S **Baths:** 5 En 1 Sh ⌇ ▧ ▥, ▙ cc

Planning a longer stay? Always ask for any special rates

Blakeney Hotel, *180 Stockton Lane, York, YO31 1ES.* **Open:** All year (not Xmas) **Grades:** ETC 3 Diamond **01904** 422786 (also fax) Mr Whiteford *reception@blakeneyhotel-york.co.uk* www.blakeneyhotel-york.co.uk **D:** £24.00–£29.00 **S:** £30.00–£35.00 **Beds:** 11F 2T 2D 2S **Baths:** 9 En 1 Pr 2 Sh ⌣ ▣ (12) ▧ ✕ Ⓥ ▥, ▙ cc
Superb location for visiting York city centre and exploring the Yorkshire Dales, Moors and Coast. Friendly, family-run hotel offering a warm welcome, comfortable accommodation, excellent cuisine, fine wines and guaranteed personal service. Our aim is to persuade you to return!

Warrens Guest House, *30 Scarcroft Road, York, YO23 1NF.* **Open:** All year (not Xmas/New Year) **Grades:** ETC 3 Diamond **01904** 643139 Mr & Mrs Warren **Fax: 01904 658297** www.warrens.ndo.co.uk **D:** £25.00–£30.00 **S:** £35.00–£50.00 **Beds:** 2F 2T 2D **Baths:** 6 En ⌣ ▣ (6) ⌇ ▧ Ⓥ ▥, ▙
Family-run Victorian town house built 1880, 350 yds from medieval city walls. Close to race course and city centre. Four poster and ground floor rooms available. Private car park. No smoking house.

Cumbria House, *2 Vyner Street, Haxby Road, York, YO31 8HS.* Lovely family-run guest house. Private car park. Ideal for city centre. **Open:** All year **Grades:** ETC 3 Diamond, AA 3 Diamond **01904** 636817 Mrs Clark *reservation@ cumbriahouse.freeserve.co.uk* www.cumbriahouse.com **D:** £20.00–£25.00 **S:** £22.00–£30.00 **Beds:** 2F 2D 1T 1S **Baths:** 2 En 4 Sh ⌣ ▣ (5) ⌇ ▧ Ⓥ ▥, ▙ cc

Barrington House, *15 Nunthorpe Avenue, Scarcroft Road, York, YO23 1PF.* **Open:** All year (not Xmas/New Year) **01904** 634539 **D:** £18.00–£23.00 **S:** £18.00–£23.00 **Beds:** 2F 1T 3D 1S **Baths:** 7 En ⌣ ▧ ▥, ♿ ▙ cc
Beautiful Edwardian guest-house in quiet cul-de-sac. Ten minutes walk from city centre and all York's attractions. Near station, racecourse and theatres. All ensuite and hearty breakfasts. Spotlessly clean. Unrestricted parking. A perfect base for exploring Dales, Moors and coast.

Nunmill House, *85 Bishopthorpe Road, York, YO23 1NX.* **Open:** Feb to Nov **Grades:** ETC 4 Diamond, Silver, AA 4 Diamond **01904** 634047 Mr & Mrs Whitbourn-Hammond **Fax: 01904 655879** *b&b@ nunmill.co.uk* www.nunmill.co.uk **D:** £26.00–£32.00 **S:** £45.00 **Beds:** 1F 6D 1T **Baths:** 7 En 1 Pr ⌣ ▣ (6) ⌇ ▧ Ⓥ ▥, ▙
Splendid Victorian house, lovingly furnished and smoke-free, for those looking for comfortable yet affordable accommodation. Easy walk to all attractions. SAE for brochure. Please visit our website.

Friars Rest Guest House, *81 Fulford Road, York, YO10 4BD.* **Open:** All year **01904** 629823 (also fax) Mr Armitage *friarsrest@ btinternet.com* www.friarsrest. co.uk **D:** £19.00–£32.00 **S:** £18.00–£35.00 **Beds:** 2F 1T 4D **Baths:** 6 En 1 Pr ⌣ ▣ (4) ▧ ▙ cc
Friars Rest is a comfortable, clean and friendly guest house just 10 mins' walk from York centre. A pleasant riverside walk is nearby and you can leave your car in our free car park. Our ensuite rooms are equipped with col TVs and tea-making.

National Grid References given are for villages, towns and cities – not for individual houses

Foss Bank Guest House, *16 Huntington Road, York, YO31 8RB.* Overlooking the River Foss. 10-minute stroll to city centre. **Open:** All year (not Xmas/New Year) **Grades:** ETC 3 Diamond
01904 635548 D: £21.00–£26.00 **S:** £23.00–£25.00 **Beds:** 1T 3D 2S **Baths:** 2 En (7) (4)

Briar Lea Guest House, *8 Longfield Terrace, Bootham, York, YO30 7DJ.* Small friendly guest house 5 mins' walk from city centre. **Open:** All year **Grades:** ETC 3 Diamond
01904 635061 Fax: 01904 330356 *briargh81@aol.com* www.briarlea.co.uk **D:** £22.00–£25.00 **S:** £25.00–£40.00 **Beds:** 2F 2T 2D **Baths:** 6 En (2) **cc**

The Limes, *135 Fulford Road, York, YO10 4HE.* Perfectly situated for City, University and golf club. Warm welcome. **Open:** All year (not Xmas) **Grades:** ETC 4 Diamond
01904 624548 Fax: 01904 624944 *queries@limeshotel.co.uk* www.limeshotel.co.uk **D:** £25.00–£35.00 **S:** £35.00–£60.00 **Beds:** 5F 3D **Baths:** 8 En (8) **cc**

Northholme Guest House, *114 Shipton Road, York, YO30 5RN.* Warm welcome, comfortable accommodation, hearty breakfast. Handy for city centre. **Open:** All year (not Xmas) **Grades:** ETC 3 Diamond
01904 639132 J L Liddle *g.liddle@tesco.net* **D:** £15.50–£22.50 **S:** £19.00–£28.00 **Beds:** 1F 1D 2T 1S **Baths:** 3 En 1 Sh (4)

Ivy House Farm, *Kexby, York, YO41 5LQ.* C19th farmhouse, central for York, East Coast, Dales, Herriot country. **Open:** All year (not Xmas) **Grades:** AA 3 Diamond, RAC 3 Diamond
01904 489368 (also fax) Mrs Daniel *ivyhousefarm@faxvia.net* **D:** £16.00–£20.00 **S:** £20.00–£22.00 **Beds:** 1F 1D 1T 1S **Baths:** 2 En 1 Sh (10)

Ivy House Farm, *Kexby, York, YO41 5LQ.* C19th farmhouse, central for York, East Coast, Dales, Herriot country. **Open:** All year (not Xmas) **Grades:** AA 3 Diamond, RAC 3 Diamond
01904 489368 (also fax) Mrs Daniel *ivyhousefarm@faxvia.net* **D:** £16.00–£20.00 **S:** £20.00–£22.00 **Beds:** 1F 1D 1T 1S **Baths:** 2 En 1 Sh (10)

Cornmill Lodge, *120 Haxby Road, York, YO31 8JP.* Vegetarian/vegan guest house. 15 mins' walk to York Minster. **Open:** All year **Grades:** ETC 3 Diamond
01904 620566 (also fax) Mrs Williams *cornmillyork@aol.com* www.cornmillyork.co.uk **D:** £20.00–£28.00 **S:** £20.00–£28.00 **Beds:** 2D 1T/F 1S **Baths:** 3 En 1 Pr (4) **cc**

Bay Tree Guest House, *92 Bishopthorpe Road, York, YO23 1JS.* Tastefully decorated Victorian town house, 10 mins' walk from attractions. **Open:** All year (not Xmas) **Grades:** ETC 3 Diamond
01904 659462 (also fax) Mr Ridley *d.ridley.baytree@ondigital.co.uk* **D:** £25.00 **S:** £25.00 **Beds:** 1F 1D 1T 2S **Baths:** 2 En 1 Sh (1)

Sagar B&B The Bungalow, *Kexby, York, YO41 5LA.* A modern bungalow, four miles east of York on A1079. **Open:** All year (not Xmas)
01759 380247 Mrs Sagar *lynnesagar@btinternet.com* www.sagarsbed-breakfast.ukf.net **D:** £18.00 **S:** £20.00–£22.00 **Beds:** 1D 1T **Baths:** 2 En (2)

Fairthorne, *356 Strenshall Road, Earswick, York, YO32 9SW.* Peaceful country setting, dormer bungalow. 3 miles from York, easy reach North York Moors. **Open:** Dec to Dec
01904 768609 (also fax) J W Harrison **D:** £16.00–£20.00 **S:** £20.00 **Beds:** 1F 1D **Baths:** 1 En (2)

Crescent Guest House, *77 Bootham, York, YO30 7DQ.* Georgian building built in 1770. 5 mins' walk to Minster and town centre. **Open:** All year
01904 623216 (also fax) E H Whitelegg www.guesthousesyork.net **D:** £18.00–£25.00 **S:** £20.00–£30.00 **Beds:** 4F 3T 5D 1S **Baths:** 8 En 2 Pr **cc**

Avimore House Hotel, *78 Stockton Lane, York, YO31 1BS.* Small friendly family-run B&B. 15 mins' walk to city. **Open:** All year (not Xmas/New Year) **Grades:** ETC 3 Diamond
01904 425556 Mrs Lewis **Fax: 01904 426264** *aviemore.house@tinyonlinr.co.uk* **D:** £23.00–£25.00 **S:** £24.00–£26.00 **Beds:** 1F 1T 1D 2S **Baths:** 5 En (3)

Grange Lodge, *52 Bootham Crescent, Bootham, York, YO30 7AH.* Lovely family-run guest house. **Open:** All year
01904 621137 Mrs Robinson *grangeldg@aol.com* **D:** £16.00–£22.00 **S:** £18.00–£20.00 **Beds:** 2F 3D 1T 1S **Baths:** 1 En 5 Pr 2 Sh

Planning a longer stay? Always ask for any special rates

Bronte Guesthouse, *22 Grosvenor Terrace, Bootham, York, YO30 7AG.* Award-winning Victorian guest house. 5 mins' walk from city centre. **Open:** All year (not Xmas/New Year) **Grades:** ETC 4 Diamond, AA 4 Diamond
01904 621066 Fax: 01904 653434 *100754.300@compuserve.com* **D:** £26.00–£30.00 **S:** £30.00–£40.00 **Beds:** 1F 1T 2D 2S **Baths:** 6 En (1) **cc**

Acer Hotel, *52 Scarcroft Hill, York, YO24 1DE.* Accommodation and hospitality at its best. Licensed. Substantial breakfasts. Door porter. **Open:** All year (not Xmas/New Year) **Grades:** ETC 4 Diamond, Silver
01904 653839 Fax: 01904 677017 *info@acerhotel.co.uk* **D:** £26.00–£38.00 **S:** £35.00–£40.00 **Beds:** 1F 2D **Baths:** 3 En **cc**

Park View Guest House, *34 Grosvenor Terrace, Bootham, York, YO30 7AG.* Victorian town house close to centre. Front rooms have views of Minster. **Open:** All year (not Xmas)
01904 620437 (also fax) Mrs Ashton *park_view@talk21.com* **D:** £22.00–£25.00 **S:** £25.00–£30.00 **Beds:** 1F 3D 2T 1S **Baths:** 5 En 1 Pr

Wold View House Hotel, *171-175 Haxby Road, York, YO31 8JL.* Turn-of-the-20th-Century hotel, tea and coffee facilities, clock radio alarms, all ensuite. **Open:** All year (not Xmas/New Year)
01904 632061 (also fax) Mr & Mrs Wheeldon www.woldviewhousehotel.co.uk **D:** £19.00–£26.00 **S:** £19.00–£26.00 **Beds:** 2F 2T 10D 3S **Baths:** 17 En (1)

Newton Guest House, *Neville Street, Haxby Road, York, YO31 8NP.* Few mins' walk from city. Friendly, family run. Non-smoking. **Open:** All year (not Xmas)
01904 635627 Mrs Tindall **D:** £19.00–£22.00 **S:** £20.00–£25.00 **Beds:** 1F 2D 1T 1S **Baths:** 4 En 1 Pr (5)

Bowen House, *4 Gladstone Street, Huntington Road, York, YO31 8RF.* Small, family-run, Victorian guest house with period furnishings throughout. **Open:** All year (not Xmas)
01904 636881 Mrs Wood **Fax: 01904 338700** *info@bowenhouse.co.uk* www.bowenhouse.co.uk **D:** £18.50–£24.00 **S:** £23.00–£28.00 **Beds:** 1F 2D 1T 1S **Baths:** 2 En 1 Sh (4) **cc**

Bishopgarth Guest House, *3 Southlands Road, Bishopthorpe Road, York, YO23 1NP.* In a quiet Victorian terrace, just 10 mins' pleasant walk from York's historic heart. **Open:** All year (not Xmas/New Year)
01904 635220 Mrs Spreckley **D:** £15.00–£23.00 **S:** £20.00–£46.00 **Beds:** 2F 2D 1T **Baths:** 5 En 2 Sh **cc**

Ashbourne House, *139 Fulford Road, York, YO10 4HG.* Friendly family-run Victorian establishment. Providing the highest of standards. **Open:** All year (not Xmas/New Year)
01904 639912 Mr & Mrs Minns **Fax: 01904 631332** *ashbourneh@aol.com* **D:** £20.00–£30.00 **S:** £34.00–£40.00 **Beds:** 2F 2T 3D **Baths:** 6 En 1 Pr ☺ ▣ (6) ⚡ ▦ Ⅴ ▥, ▦ cc

---

Planning a longer stay? Always ask for any special rates

Heworth Court Hotel, *76 Heworth Green, York, YO31 7TQ.* Established recommended hotel. Ample parking, York Minster within 1 mile. **Open:** All year
01904 425156 Mr Smith *hotel@heworth.co.uk* **D:** £30.00–£52.50 **S:** £46.00–£65.00 **Beds:** 2F 5T 10D 8S **Baths:** 25 En ☺ ▣ (25) ⚡ ▦ ✕ Ⅴ ▥. ✳ ▦ cc

Chimney's Bed and Breakfast, *18 Bootham Cresent, York, YO30 7AH.* Beautiful olde-worlde house, 5 mins' walk from York Minster/city walls. **Open:** All year
01904 644334 **D:** £18.00–£25.00 **S:** £18.00–£25.00 **Beds:** 2T 2D 1S ☺ (10) ⚡ ▦ Ⅴ ▥, ♿

Kismet Guest House, *147 Haxby Road, York, YO31 8JW.* Close to city centre, friendly welcome, substantial breakfast. Cleanliness foremost. **Open:** All year
01904 621056 B Chamberlain & N Summers *kismetguesthouse@yahoo.com* **D:** £25.00–£30.00 **S:** £20.00–£25.00 **Beds:** 1F 1T 4D **Baths:** 1 Sh ☺ ▣ (6) ⚡ ▦ ✕ ▥, ▦

Please respect a B&B's wishes regarding children, animals and smoking

South Yorkshire

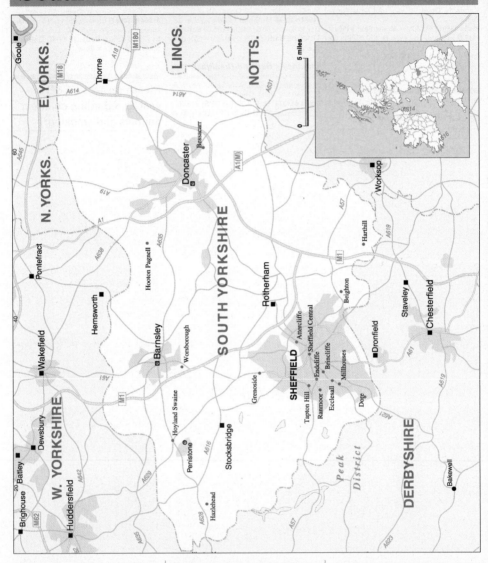

Beighton

SK4483

Beighton Bed and Breakfast, *50 High Street, Beighton, Sheffield, S20 1EA.* Within easy reach for arena, Don Valley, Meadowhall, Chatsworth and Rother Valley. **Open:** All year
0114 269 2004 Fax: 0114 2692004 **D:** £16.00–£18.00 **S:** £17.00–£28.00 **Beds:** 1F 1T 1D 3S
Baths: 6 En 🛇 🅿 ⊁ 🗹 🖢 🏢 📠

Bessacarr

SE6101

10 Saxton Avenue, *Bessacarr, Doncaster, South Yorkshire, DN4 7AX.* Friendly 1930 house, quiet, leafy residential area. Near Dome, Racecourse. **Open:** All year
01302 535578 A Gibbs **D:** £18.00–£22.00 **S:** £22.50–£27.50 **Beds:** 2T 1D 1S **Baths:** 1 En 1 Sh 🅿 (2) ⊁ 🗹 ✕ 🗹 🏢 📠

Doncaster

SE5702

Rockingham Arms Hotel, *Bennetthorpe, Doncaster, DN2 6AA.* Not far from Doncaster centre, racecourse, railway station and Doncaster Dome. **Open:** All year
01302 360980 D: £25.00 **S:** £30.00 **Beds:** 5F 9T 2D 2S **Baths:** 1 En 6 Pr 🛇 🅿 ⊁ 🗹 🏸 ✕ 🗹 🏢 🛇 ♨ cc

Dore
SK3181

Critchleys, *6 Causeway Head Road, Dore, Sheffield, S17 3DJ.* A modern guest house near city and country. Friendly, clean, excellent food. **Open:** All year **Grades:** ETC 3 Diamond
0114 236 4328 (also fax) M L Critchleys
D: £17.50–£22.50 **S:** £25.00–£35.00 **Beds:** 1F 3D 3T 2S **Baths:** 5 En 3 Sh ⌂ (9) ▣ (4) ▣ 🐾 ▣ ▦ ❋ ♨

Grenoside
SK3393   ◁ *Red Lion*

Middleton Green Farm, *Cinder Hill Lane, Grenoside, Sheffield, S35 8NH.* C17th farmhouse. Sauna and jacuzzi available.
Open: All year
0114 245 3279 (also fax) Ms Mennell
D: £25.00 **S:** £30.00 **Beds:** 1F 2T 1D **Baths:** 3 En ⌂ ▣ (10) ⅟ ▣ 🐾 ▣ ▦ ♨

Harthill
SK4980   ◁ *Bee Hive*

57 Firvale, *Harthill, Sheffield, S26 7XP.* Delightful cottage, warm conservatory.
Open: All year
01909 773605 D Stevens **D:** £20.00 **S:** £20.00 **Beds:** 1T 1D **Baths:** 2 En ⌂ ▣ ⅟ ▣ ✕ ▣ ▦ ❋ ♨

Hazlehead
SE1800

Delmont Grange, *Flouch, Hazlehead, Sheffield, S36 4HH.* Moorland views near 'Summer Wine' country. Penistone market town. **Open:** All year
01226 767279 Mrs Cuss *nancuss@lineone.net*
D: £22.50 **S:** £22.50 **Beds:** 1F 1T 1D **Baths:** 2 En ⌂ ▣ (8) ▣ ✕ ▣ ▦ ♿ ♨

Hooton Pagnell
SE4808

Rock Farm, *Hooton Pagnell, Doncaster, S. Yorks, DN5 7BT.* Traditional stone farmhouse in picturesque village 2m NW of A1. **Open:** All year
01977 642200 (also fax) Mrs Harrison
D: £20.00 **S:** £18.00–£20.00 **Beds:** 1F 1D 1S **Baths:** 1 En 1 Sh ⌂ ▣ (6) ▣ ▦ ♨

RATES
D = Price range per person sharing in a double or twin room
S = Price range for a single room

BATHROOMS
En = Ensuite
Pr = Private
Sh = Shared

Hoyland Swaine
SE2604

Fell House, *354 Barnsley Road, Hoylandswaine, Sheffield, S36 7HD.* 1830s cottage. Beautiful views, private suite to relax in comfort. **Open:** All year (not Xmas)
01226 790937 & 07808 355 329 (M) Ms Sykes
D: £18.00 **S:** £23.00 **Beds:** 1F **Baths:** 1 En ⌂ ▣ (2) ▣ 🐾 ▣ ▦ ♨

Penistone
SE2403

Millhouse Guest Centre, *Carr House Farm, Royd Lane, Penistone, Sheffield, S36 9NY.* Converted barn in summer wine country overlooking open countryside. **Open:** All year (not Xmas)
01226 762917 Mr Worboys *mgc@uworboys.freeserve.co.uk* **D:** £12.50 **S:** £15.00 **Beds:** 1F 1D 1T **Baths:** 2 Sh ⌂ ▣ (4) ⅟ ▣ ▦ ♨

Old Vicarage Guest House & Tea Rooms, *Shrewsbury Road, Penistone, Sheffield, S36 6DY.* Situated in centre of Penistone, close to Pennine Way trail.
Open: All year
01226 376607 Mr Storer **Fax: 01226 766521** *enquires@old vicarage.co.uk* **D:** £25.00–£55.00 **S:** £25.00–£35.00 **Beds:** 2F 4D 4S **Baths:** 5 En 5 Sh ⌂ ▣ (10) ▣ ▦ ♨ cc

SHEFFIELD   Attercliffe
SK3788

Swan Hotel, *756 Attercliffe Road, Sheffield, S9 3RQ.* Family-run hotel, close Sheffield city centre, next to Don Valley Stadium and Sheffield Arena. **Open:** All year
0114 244 7978 Fax: 0114 242 4928 *swansheffield@btinternet.com* www.swansheffield.co.uk **D:** £17.50–£24.00 **S:** £25.00–£35.00 **Beds:** 4F 4D 4T 1S **Baths:** 10 En 3 Sh ⌂ ▣ (15) ⅟ ▣ 🐾 ▣ ▦ ♨ cc

SHEFFIELD   Brincliffe
SK3385

Peace Guest House, *92 Brocco Bank, Hunters Bar, Sheffield, S11 8RS.* B&B close to centre, university, hospitals. Friendly, comfortable, family run. **Open:** All year
0114 268 5110 & 0114 267 0760 Mr Manavi **D:** £18.00–£40.00 **S:** £22.00–£27.00 **Beds:** 1F 2D 2T 3S **Baths:** 2 En 1 Pr 1 Sh ⌂ ▣ (6) ⅟ ▣ ❋ ♨ cc

SHEFFIELD   Central
SK3586

Beech House, *44 Broomgrove Road, Sheffield, S10 2NA.* Large homely Victorian house, close to universities, hospitals, Peak District. **Open:** All year (not Xmas)
0114 266 2537 Miss Boler **D:** £20.00 **S:** £22.00 **Beds:** 1F 3D 3T 1S **Baths:** 2 Sh ⌂ (12) ▣ (4) ▣ ▣ ▦ ♨

SHEFFIELD   Ecclesall
SK3284

Hillside, *28 Sunningdale Mount, Ecclesall, Sheffield, S11 9HA.* Your comfort is our interest. Quiet, modern, welcoming, close buses and town (2.5 miles). **Open:** All year **Grades:** ETC 3 Diamond
0114 262 0833 Mrs Whitehead **D:** £19.00 **S:** £19.00 **Beds:** 1T 1S **Baths:** 1 Sh ⌂ (1) ▣ (2) ⅟ ▣ ▦ ♨

SHEFFIELD   Endcliffe
SK3286

Nini's Guest House, *41 Endcliffe Rise Road, Sheffield, S11 8RU.* Family-run, offering a friendly and welcoming atmosphere. **Open:** All year
0114 266 9114 A Kocura **D:** £20.00 **S:** £22.00 **Beds:** 1D 2T 1S ⌂ (3) ⅟ ▣ 🐾 ▣ ▦ ♨

SHEFFIELD   Millhouses
SK3283

Tyndale, *164 Millhouses Lane, Sheffield, S7 2HE.* **Open:** All year **Grades:** ETC 3 Diamond
0114 236 1660
(also fax) Mr & Mrs Wilmshurst **D:** £19.00 **S:** £19.00 **Beds:** 1F 1D 1S **Baths:** 1 Sh ⌂ ▣ (3) ⅟ ▣ 🐾 ▣ ▦ ♨
A warm welcome awaits you at our clean, comfortable home in the pleasant southwest of Sheffield. Ecclesall Woods and Millhouses Park nearby. 3 miles from Peak Park. Universities, shops (including Meadowhall), theatres and nightclubs all within easy reach.

BEDROOMS
D = Double
T = Twin
S = Single
F = Family

SHEFFIELD   Ranmoor

SK3186   🍺 *Bull's Head, Rising Sun*

Martins Guest House, *397 Fulwood Road, Sheffield, S10 3GE.* Victorian mansion on bus route. **Open:** All year
0114 230 8588 Martins **D:** £22.00–£25.00 **S:** £25.00–£30.00 **Beds:** 3F 2T **Baths:** 2 En 2 Pr 1 Sh ॐ �🅿 (10) ⊬ 📺 ▥ ⚉

SHEFFIELD   Tapton Hill

SK3286

St Pellegrino Hotel, *2 Oak Park, Sheffield, S10 5SD.* Friendly family-run hotel. Situated near to the centre of Sheffield. **Open:** All year
0114 268 1953 A Lawera **Fax: 0114 266 0151 D:** £25.00–£35.00 **S:** £24.00–£35.00 **Beds:** 5F 2D 3T 4S **Baths:** 1 En 5 Pr 3 Sh ॐ �🅿 (20) ⊬ 📺 ✕ ▥ ▥.

Worsbrough

SE3503   🍺 *Burton Inn*

The Button Mill Inn, *Park Road, Worsbrough, Barnsley, South Yorkshire, S70 5LJ.* **Open:** All year (not Xmas)
01226 282639 (also fax) Mr Loftus **D:** £22.50 **S:** £25.00 **Beds:** 1F 1D 3T 2S **Baths:** 7 Pr ॐ (14) ⅊ (60) ⊬ ✕ ▥ ▥. & ⚉ cc
Olde worlde inn opposite Worsborough Country Park and Mill. Fishing reservoir and public walkways in walking distance. Comfortable rooms with televisions. Good food cooked fresh. Large menu to choose from. Vegetarian meals. Large wine list. Good selection of cask beers.

West Yorkshire

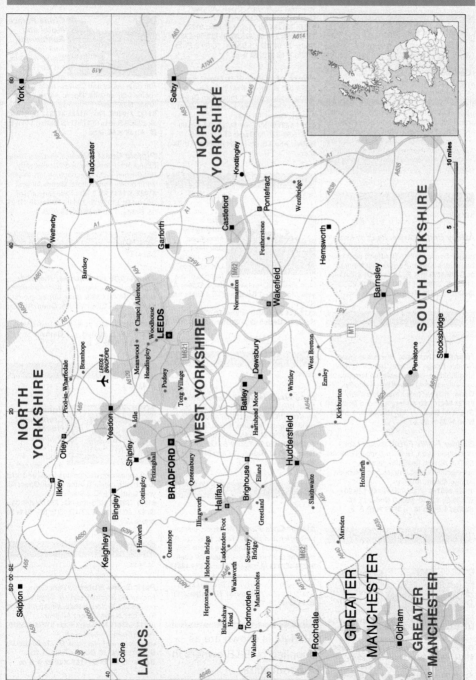

Bardsey

SE3643

Gables B&B,
*Mill Lane,
Bardsey, Leeds,
West Yorkshire,
LS17 9AN.*
Open: All year
(not Xmas)
01937 574163 Mr & Mrs Gregory **D:** £20.00–
£24.00 **S:** £22.00–£27.00 **Beds:** 3D 1T 2S
Baths: 2 En 2 Sh ⌷ 🄿 (6) ⠉ 🖂 🛏 ⺌ 🖵, ⚍
Distinctive detached family home, in half
acre gardens, offers friendly hospitality for
any visitors to North Leeds, immediately
adjacent extensive nature reserve, country
walks. 4 miles Harewood House. 4 miles
Wetherby. 4m several premier W Yorks golf
courses.

Bingley

SE1139

Ashley End, *22 Ashley Road, off Ashfield
Crescent, Bingley, W. Yorks, BD16 1DZ.* Quiet,
private house 5 miles Bradford; near main
bus routes. **Open:** All year (not Xmas)
01274 569679 Mrs Robertson **D:** £18.00–
£19.00 **S:** £18.00–£19.00 **Beds:** 1T 2S
Baths: 1 Sh ⌷ (4) ⠉ 🖂 🖵, ⚍

Blackshaw Head

SD9527

Higher Earnshaw, *Blackshaw Head,
Hebden Bridge, W. Yorks, HX7 7JB.* Family
smallholding, comfortable old farmhouse
in lovely countryside. Warm welcome.
Open: All year (not Xmas/New Year)
01422 844117 Mr & Mrs Redmond **D:** £20.00
S: £21.00 **Beds:** 1F 1D 1S **Baths:** 1 Sh ⌷
🄿 (4) ⠉ 🖂 🛏 🖵, ⚍

Badger Fields Farm, *Badger Lane,
Blackshaw Head, Hebden Bridge, W. Yorks,
HX7 7JX.* Amidst beautiful gardens,
spectacular views, 2 miles from Hebden
Bridge. **Open:** All year
01422 845161 Mrs Whitaker **D:** £19.00–
£20.00 **S:** £20.00–£22.00 **Beds:** 1F 1D
Baths: 1 Sh ⌷ 🄿 (3) ⠉ 🐾 🖵, ⚅ ⚍

Bradford

SE1632

Carnoustie, *8
Park Grove,
Bradford, W.
Yorks, BD9 4JY.*
Detached
Victorian house
near Lister Park
and University Management School.
Open: All year **Grades:** ETC 3 Diamond
01274 490561 (also fax) Mr Sugden
carnoustie1@activemail.co.uk **D:** £19.00–£21.00
S: £25.00–£27.00 **Beds:** 1D 1T 1S **Baths:** 3
En ⌷ 🄿 (1) ⠉ 🖂 🖵, ⚍

New Beehive Inn, *Westgate, Bradford,
W. Yorks, BD1 3AA.* Renowned gaslit inn.
Centrally situated. Characterful and
spacious bedrooms. **Open:** All year
Grades: ETC 3 Diamond
01274 721784 Mr Wagstaff **Fax: 01274
735092 D:** £19.00–£23.00 **S:** £24.00–£30.00
Beds: 2F 6T 4D 1S **Baths:** 10 En 2 Pr ⌷
🄿 (20) ⠉ 🖂 ✕ 🖵, ⚍ cc

Prince of Wales, *91 Harrogate Road,
Eccleshill, Bradford, West Yorkshire, BD2 3ES.*
Warm friendly pub 10 mins from Bradford,
15 mins Leeds, 10 mins Leeds-Bradford
Airport. **Open:** All year
01274 638729 Mr Peat **D:** £15.00–£25.00
S: £15.00–£25.00 **Beds:** 1F 3D 3T 1S
Baths: 4 En 4 Sh ⌷ (1) 🄿 (30) ⠉ 🛏 ✕ 🖂 🖵, ⚅
⚍ cc

Bramhope

SE2543

**The
Cottages,**
*Moor Road,
Bramhope,
Leeds, LS16 9HH.*
Old cottages,
furnished to a
high standard, fringe of village. **Open:** All
year (not Xmas) **Grades:** ETC 4 Diamond,
Silver
0113 284 2754 Mrs Adams **D:** £24.00
S: £35.00 **Beds:** 4D 1T **Baths:** 5 En 🄿 (5) ⠉ 🖂
🖵, ⚍

Brighouse

SE1423

Lane Head Hotel, *2 Brighouse Wood
Lane, Brighouse, Huddersfield, HD6 2AL.* A
renovated C17th coaching inn retaining
many original features. **Open:** All year
01484 714108 Mr & Mrs Mccue **Fax: 01484
380540 D:** £20.00–£23.50 **S:** £29.38–£35.25
Beds: 10D 4T **Baths:** 14 En ⌷ 🄿 ⠉ 🖂 ✕ 🖂
🖵, ⚍ cc

Cottingley

SE1137

March Cote Farm, *Woodside Avenue,
Cottingley, Bingley, W. Yorks, BD16 1UB.* A
friendly welcome awaits you in our fully
modernised farmhouse. **Open:** All year
01274 487433 Mrs Warin **Fax: 01274 488153**
jeanwarin@nevisuk.net www.yorkshire.co.
uk/accgde/marchcote **D:** £20.00–£25.00
S: £22.00–£25.00 **Beds:** 1F 2D **Baths:** 2 En 1
Pr ⌷ 🄿 (6) ⠉ 🖂 🖵, ⚍

All details shown are as
supplied by B&B owners in
Autumn 2001

Elland

SE1121

**China Palace
Hotel and
Restaurant,**
*Park Road,
Elland, W. Yorks,
Hx5 9HP.* High
quality English
run rural house and Chinese restaurant. All
rooms fully ensuite. **Open:** All year (not
Xmas/New Year)
01422 310408   Fax: 01422 377232 D: £19.95
S: £29.50 **Beds:** 1F 4T 5D 4S **Baths:** 14 En ⌷
🄿 (90) ⠉ ✕ 🖵, ⚍ cc

Pinfold Guest House, *Dewsbury Road,
Elland, West Yorkshire, HX5 9JU.* Recently
refurbished Victorian coaching inn. Warm
and homely atmosphere. **Open:** All year
01422 372645 Mr & Mrs Parr *parrpinfold@
aol.com* **D:** £19.00 **S:** £26.00 **Beds:** 1F 1D 2T
3S **Baths:** 7 En ⌷ 🄿 (10) ⠉ 🖂 🖵, ⚍

Emley

SE2413

Thorncliffe Farmhouse, *Thorncliffe
Lane, Emley, Huddersfield, West Yorkshire,
HD8 9RS.* Rural C18th stone farmhouse on
Kirklees Way. Close M1 J38. **Open:** All year
(not Xmas)
01924 848277 Mrs Judd **D:** £17.50–£20.00
S: £19.50–£25.00 **Beds:** 2T **Baths:** 2 En 1 Pr
🄿 (4) ⠉ ✕ 🖂 🖵, ⚅ ⚍

Featherstone

SE4219

**Rolands
Croft Guest
House,**
*Rolands Croft,
Featherstone,
Pontefract, W
Yorks, WF7 6ED.* A
barn conversion overlooking fields and next
to pub with meals at great prices. **Open:** All
year **Grades:** ETC 2 Star
01977 790802 Mr Sutton **D:** £39.00–£44.00
S: £27.00 **Beds:** 1F 2T 1D 1S ⌷ 🄿 🖂 🛏 🖵,
⚅ ✷ ⚍ cc

Frizinghall

SE1435

Park Grove Hotel, *28 Park Grove,
Frizinghall, Bradford, W. Yorks, BD9 4JY.* Quietly
positioned, Victorian style, situated 2 mins
from city centre. **Open:** All year
01274 543444 Mr Singh **Fax: 01274 495619**
enquiry@parkgrovehotel.co.uk
www.parkgrovehotel.co.uk **D:** £25.00–£30.00
S: £40.00–£47.00 **Beds:** 2F 9D 2T 2S
Baths: 15 En ⌷ 🄿 (9) ⠉ ✕ 🖂 🖵, ✷ ⚍ cc

Greetland

SE0821

Crawstone Knowl Farm, *Rochdale Road, Greetland, Halifax, W. Yorks, HX4 8PX.* Large comfortable Pennine farmhouse, convenient for Halifax Huddersfield and Dales. **Open:** All year **Grades:** ETC 3 Diamond
01422 370470 Mrs Shackleton **D:** £16.00–£20.00 **S:** £16.00–£20.00 **Beds:** 1F 1D 1T **Baths:** 3 En 🚸 P (7) 🚭 📺 🐕 ✕ V ▦ ☕

Halifax

SE0925 *The Quays*

Tower House Hotel, *Master Lane, Halifax, HX2 7EW.* **Open:** All year
01422 345000 Fax: 01422 320875
www.towerhousehotel.co.uk **D:** £27.50–£30.00 **S:** £39.50–£60.00 **Beds:** 3F 2T 10D 1S **Baths:** 16 En 🚸 P (65) 🚭 📺 ✕ V ▦ ♿ ❄ ☕ cc
This country-style hotel is situated at the foot of 'Wainhouse Tower' (the famous folly). The older part of the hotel lays claim to 'ghostly goings on'! The family restaurant 'La Terraza' opens every day from 4.00pm.

Heathleigh Guest House, *124 Skircoat Road, Halifax, West Yorkshire, HX1 2RE.* A beautiful Victorian house offering a warm welcome, comfortable beds and a delicious breakfast. **Open:** All year **Grades:** ETC 4 Diamond
01422 323957 Ms Eccles **D:** £20.00 **S:** £20.00–£25.00 **Beds:** 1F 1D 2S **Baths:** 2 En 1 Pr 1 Sh 🚸 P (2) 🚭 📺 V ▦ ☕

Mozart House, *34 Prescott Street, Halifax, West Yorkshire, HX1 2QW.* Large Victorian terrace house, 3-minute walk from town centre. **Open:** All year **Grades:** ETC 3 Diamond
01422 340319 D: £18.00 **S:** £20.00–£25.00 **Beds:** 5T 1D **Baths:** 5 En 1 Pr 🚸 P (4) 📺 V ▦ ☕ cc

Field House, *Staups Lane, Stump Cross, Halifax, West Yorkshire, HX3 6XW.* Charming Listed country farmhouse in the picturesque Shibden Valley. **Open:** All year **Grades:** ETC 4 Diamond
01422 355457 & 07720 626580 (M) Mr Taylor *stayatfieldhouse@yahoo.co.uk*
www.fieldhouse-bb.co.uk **D:** £20.00–£27.50 **S:** £25.00–£35.00 **Beds:** 2T 1D **Baths:** 2 En 1 Pr 🚸 (3) P (6) 🚭 📺 🐕 ✕ V ▦ ☕ cc

Hartshead Moor

SE1624

The Barn House, *Harefield Farm, Halifax Road, Hartshead Moor, Cleckheaton, West Yorkshire, BD19 6PH.* Renovated barn, perfectly situated for M62. Full farmhouse breakfast. **Open:** All year
01274 874134 Mr & Mrs Gibson **D:** £20.00–£25.00 **S:** £20.00–£25.00 **Beds:** 2T 1S **Baths:** 1 Sh 🚸 P (4) 📺 ▦ ☕

Haworth

SE0337 *Old Hall, Black Bull, Old White Lion, Silent Inn, King's Arms, Three Sisters, King's Head*

Cobwebs Guest House, *West Lane, Haworth, Keighley, West Yorkshire, BD22 8DU.* **Open:** All year **Grades:** ETC 4 Diamond
01535 642501 *Aitches@talk21.com*
www.aitches.co.uk **D:** £20.00–£25.00 **S:** £20.00–£30.00 **Beds:** 1T 3D 1S **Baths:** 4 En 1 Pr 🚸 P 🚭 📺 ✕ V ▦ ❄ ☕ cc
Large Victorian house, tastefully furnished, nestling on the cobbled street of Haworth, famous for the Bronte sisters, situated between the Pennines and the Yorkshire Dales. Ideal base for touring West. North Yorkshire, home of the Keighley and Worth Valley Railway.

BATHROOMS
En = Ensuite
Pr = Private
Sh = Shared

B&B owners may vary rates – be sure to check when booking

Hole Farm, *Dimples Lane, Haworth, Keighley, W. Yorks, BD22 8QS.* Perfectly situated for Bronte museum and Moors. Warm welcome. **Open:** All year (not Xmas/New Year) **Grades:** ETC 4 Diamond
01535 644755 (also fax) Mrs Milner *janet@bronteholidays.co.uk* www.bronteholidays.co.uk **D:** £20.00 **S:** £30.00 **Beds:** 1D **Baths:** 1 En 🚭 📺 V ▦ ☕

Kershaw House, *90 West Lane, Haworth, Keighley, West Yorkshire, BD22 8EN.* Situated on the edge of the Moors, in the heart of Bronte country. **Open:** All year (not Xmas)
01535 642074 & 0973 734758
kershawhouse.guesthouse@talk21.com **D:** £20.00 **S:** £25.00 **Beds:** 1T 2D 1S **Baths:** 3 En 1 Pr P (4) 📺 V ▦ ☕

Woodlands Drive Private Hotel, *Woodlands Grange, Haworth, Keighley, W. Yorks, BD22 8PB.* 4-bedroom detached house, quiet location, 1 mile town centre. Near woods/nature trails. **Open:** All year **Grades:** ETC 2 Diamond
01535 646814 Ms Harker **D:** £17.00 **S:** £17.00 **Beds:** 1D 1S **Baths:** 1 Sh 🚸 P (1) 🚭 📺 🐕 ✕ V ▦ ☕

Weavers Restaurant And Bar, *15 West Lane, Haworth, Keighley, W. Yorks, BD22 8DU.* Set on the cobbles in the heart of the village. **Open:** All year (not Xmas/New Year) **Grades:** ETC 4 Diamond
01535 643822 Mr & Mrs Rushworth *weavers@amserve.net* www.weaversmallhote.co.uk
D: £35.00 **S:** £50.00 **Beds:** 1T 2D 1S 🚸 P (10) 📺 ✕ V ▦ ☕ cc

The Old Registry, *4 Main Street, Haworth, Keighley, West Yorkshire, BD22 8DA.* Victorian guest house, where courtesy and charm extend, 4-poster beds, ensuite rooms. **Open:** All year
01535 646503 Mrs Herdman
www.oldregistry.co.uk **D:** £18.00–£25.00 **S:** £18.00–£30.00 **Beds:** 1F 3T 5D 1S **Baths:** 9 En 1 Pr P 🚭 📺 ✕ V ▦ ❄ ☕ cc

Hebden Bridge

SD9927

Prospect End, *8 Prospect Terrace, Hebden Bridge, West Yorkshire, HX7 6NA.* Town edge location. Very private guest rooms. Extensive breakfast menu. **Open:** All year **Grades:** ETC 3 Diamond
01422 843586 (also fax) Ann Anthon
D: £17.00–£19.00 **S:** £21.00–£25.00 **Beds:** 1T 1D **Baths:** 2 En 🚭 📺 V ▦ ♿ ☕

BEDROOMS

D = Double
T = Twin
S = Single
F = Family

Heptonstall

SD9728

Poppyfields House, *29 Slack Top, Heptonstall, Hebden Bridge, West Yorkshire, HX7 7HA.* Pennine House set amidst the dramatic hills of Calderdale. Wooded valleys, tumbling streams. **Open:** All year **Fax:** 01422 843636 Mrs Simpson **Fax:** 01422 845621 **D:** £19.00–£22.00 **S:** £22.00–£25.00 **Beds:** 1F 1D **Baths:** 2 En ♿ �📶 (4) ✓ 🖂 ☆ ✕ 🖂 🍴 ⚿

Holmfirth

SE1408

Holme Castle Country Hotel, *Holme Village, Holmfirth, Huddersfield, W. Yorks, HD7 1QG.* Unusual mill house in Peak Park. Splendid views. Oak panelling, antiques, open fires. **Open:** All year **Fax:** 01484 680680 Ms Hayfield **Fax:** 01484 686764 *jill.hayfield@virgin.net* www.holmecastle.com **D:** £27.50–£37.50 **S:** £35.00–£55.00 **Beds:** 1F 2T 4D 1S **Baths:** 5 Pr 1 Sh ♿ 🖂 (12) ✓ 🖂 ✕ 🖂 🍴 ⚿ cc

Idle

SE1737

Glengarry Guest House, *175 Albion Road, Idle, Bradford, W. Yorks, BD10 9QP.* Within easy reach of Bronte land/Moors/ industrial heritage/TVs 'Emmerdale'. **Open:** All year 01274 613781 Mr Swain **D:** £14.50–£15.00 **S:** £16.00–£16.50 **Beds:** 2T 1S **Baths:** 2 Sh ♿ (5) 🖂 🍴 ⚿

Ilkley

SE1147

63 Skipton Road, *Ilkley, W. Yorks, LS29 9BH.* Imposing stone detached house, gardens and ground-floor ensuite bedrooms. **Open:** All year **Grades:** ETC 3 Diamond 01943 817542 (also fax) Mrs Roberts *petraroberts1@activemail.co.uk* **D:** £18.00–£20.00 **S:** £25.00–£30.00 **Beds:** 2D 1T **Baths:** 2 En 1 Sh ♿ 🖂 (5) ✓ 🖂 ✕ 🖂 🍴 ⚿ cc

Archway Cottage, *24 Skipton Road, Ilkley, W. Yorks, LS29 9EP.* Beautiful Victorian cottage in central Ilkley with outstanding moorland views. **Open:** All year 01943 603399 Mrs Green **D:** £17.50–£20.00 **S:** £20.00–£25.00 **Beds:** 1F 2D 1T **Baths:** 1 En 2 Sh ♿ 🖂 (2) 🖂 🍴 🖂 🍴 ⚿

Illingworth

SE0728

The Elms, *Keighley Road, Illingworth, Halifax, W. Yorks, HX2 8HT.* Detached Victorian house set in three-quarter acre walled garden. **Open:** All year (not Xmas) **Grades:** ETC 3 Diamond 01422 244430 Mrs Davis-Crowther *sylvia@ theelms.force9.co.uk* **D:** £21.00–£22.00 **S:** £21.00–£23.00 **Beds:** 1F 1D 2S **Baths:** 3 En 1 Pr ♿ 🖂 (6) 🖂 🍴 ✕ 🖂 🍴 ⚿

Keighley

SE0541

Currer Laithe Farm, *Moss Carr Road, Long Lee, Keighley, W. Yorks, BD21 4SL.* **Open:** All year (not Xmas) 01535 604387 Miss Brown *www.edgey8843. free-online.co.uk/currer/index.htm* **D:** £15.00 **S:** £15.00 **Beds:** 2F 1D 3T **Baths:** 3 En 3 Pr 1 Sh ♿ 🖂 (10) 🖂 ✕ ☆ ⚿ C16th working Pennine hill farm in Bronte Country. Splendid views of Airedale, Ilkley Moor, Ingleborough. Traditional fare. Guests returning for twenty years. Groups welcome. Excellent base for Haworth, Dales, museums, abbeys, markets, mill shops. Inglenook fireplace, beams and mullions.

Kirkburton

SE1912

Manor Mill Cottage, *21 Linfit Lane, Kirkburton, Huddersfield, West Yorkshire, HD8 0TY.* Warm welcoming cottage twixt Huddersfield and Wakefield in rural peaceful countryside. **Open:** All year 01484 604109 Ms Askham *manormill@ paskham.freeserve.co.uk* **D:** £17.00–£19.00 **S:** £17.00–£19.00 **Beds:** 1D 1T **Baths:** 1 En 1 Sh 🖂 (3) ✓ 🖂 🍴 🖂 🍴 ⚿

LEEDS   Chapel Allerton

SE3037

Highbank Hotel & Restaurant, *83 Harehills Lane, Leeds, LS7 4HA.* Convenient, affordable, comfortable traditional hotel with modern facilities and secure car park. **Open:** All year 0870 7456744 & 0113 262 2164 Mr Thomas **Fax:** 0870 7456734 *info@highbank.co.uk* www.highbankhotel.co.uk **D:** £17.78–£25.00 **S:** £20.00–£39.50 **Beds:** 4F 4D 5T 8S **Baths:** 8 En 3 Sh ♿ 🖂 (30) 🖂 ✕ 🖂 🍴 ☆ ⚿ cc

LEEDS   Headingley

SE2836

Number 23, *23 St Chad's Rise, Far Headingley, Leeds, West Yorkshire, LS6 3QE.* Quiet cul-de-sac overlooking church grounds. Easy access to public transport. **Open:** All year (not Xmas/New Year) **Grades:** ETC 3 Diamond 0113 275 7825 Mr & Mrs Sheldrake **D:** £18.00 **S:** £17.00–£18.00 **Beds:** 1T 4S **Baths:** 1 Sh ♿ 🖂 (2) ✓ 🖂 ✕ 🖂 🍴 ⚿

49 St Chad's Drive, *Headingley, Leeds, West Yorkshire, LS6 3PZ.* Pleasant, comfortable semi-detached family home near park and universities. **Open:** All year **Grades:** ETC 2 Diamond 0113 275 0703 Mrs Ballantine **D:** £20.00–£22.00 **S:** £23.00–£25.00 ♿ 🖂 (1) ✓ 🖂 🖂 🍴 ⚿

LEEDS   Meanwood

SE2837

Aragon Hotel, *250 Stainbeck Lane, Leeds, LS7 2PS.* Large Victorian house set in large gardens, quiet and non-smoking. **Open:** All year (not Xmas) 0113 275 9306 R & D Woodward **Fax:** 0113 275 7166 www.aragonhotel.co.uk **D:** £24.90–£26.50 **S:** £39.90–£43.90 **Beds:** 2F 6D 2T 2S **Baths:** 12 En ♿ 🖂 (20) ✓ 🖂 ✕ 🖂 🍴 ⚿ cc

LEEDS   Woodhouse

SE2835

Moorlea Hotel, *146 Woodsley Road, Leeds, LS2 9LZ.* **Open:** All year 0113 243 2653 **Fax:** 0113 246 5393 **D:** £20.00–£25.00 **S:** £27.00–£35.00 **Beds:** 2F 2T 2D 5S **Baths:** 7 En 2 Sh ♿ 🖂 🍴 ✕ 🖂 🍴 ⚿ Small, friendly hotel situated 5 mins from Leeds University and fifteen minutes from the town centre. Headingley cricket ground is a 5-minute walk from our front door. We serve good, wholesome food and have a fully licensed residents' bar.

Luddenden Foot

SE0424

Rockcliffe West, *Burnley Road, Luddenden Foot, Halifax, W. Yorks, HX2 6HL.* Spacious, friendly Victorian home with delightful gardens and hillside views. **Open:** All year (not Xmas/New Year) **Grades:** ETC 4 Diamond 01422 882151 (also fax) Mrs Hodgeson *rockcliffe.b.b@virgin.net* **D:** £19.00 **S:** £24.00 **Beds:** 1T 1D **Baths:** 1 En 1 Pr ♿ 🖂 (2) 🖂 ✕ 🖂 🍴 ⚿

Mankinholes
SD9623

Cross Farm, *Mankinholes, Todmorden, West Yorkshire, OL14 7JQ.* 400-year-old stone Pennine farmhouse and barn with hillside views. **Open:** All year
01706 813481 Mrs Hancock **D:** £19.50
S: £19.50 **Beds:** 2T 2D **Baths:** 3 Pr ⌂ ▣ (4) ⅋
▣ ✕ ▥ ▦ ⚓

Marsden
SE0411

Forest Farm, *Mount Road, Marsden, Huddersfield, W Yorks, HD7 6NN.* Come as a guest, leave as a friend. **Open:** All year (not Xmas)
01484 842687 (also fax) Mr & Mrs Fussey
mayandted@aol.com **D:** £18.00 **S:** £20.00
Beds: 1F 1D 1T **Baths:** 2 Sh ⌂ ▣ (6) ▣ ↑ ✕
▥ ▦ ⚓ cc

Pear Tree Cottage, *18 Grange Avenue, Marsden, Huddersfield, West Yorkshire, HD7 6AQ.* Cosy former millworkers' cottage amid dramatic South Pennine scenery. Convenient transport, village amenities, canal. **Open:** All year (not Xmas)
01484 847518 & 07833 112981 (M) Mr & Mrs Goodall **Fax: 01484 847518** *john@ jgoodall.fsnet.co.uk* www.jgoodall.fsnet.co.uk
D: £15.00–£17.50 **S:** £15.00–£17.50 **Beds:** 1F 1S **Baths:** 2 Sh ⌂ ⅋ ▣ ↑ ✕ ▥ ▦ ⚓

Throstle Nest Cottage, *3 Old Mount Road, Marsden, Huddersfield, West Yorkshire, HD7 6DU.* Olde worlde C17th country cottage in beautiful Colne Valley. Close to all amenities. **Open:** All year (not Xmas)
01484 846371 (also fax) Ms Hayes
throstle-nest@faxvia.net **D:** £15.00–£20.00
S: £18.00–£20.00 **Beds:** 1F 1T **Baths:** 1 Sh
▣ (3) ▣ ↑ ▥ ▦ ⚓

Otley
SE2045

18 Harecroft Road, *Otley, W. Yorks, LS21 2BQ.* Quiet, friendly, private residence near River Wharfe and all amenities. **Open:** All year
01943 463643 Mrs Mandy **D:** £17.00 **S:** £17.00
Beds: 1T 2S **Baths:** 2 Sh ⌂ ▣ (2) ⅋ ▣ ↑ ▦ ⚓

All details shown are as supplied by B&B owners in Autumn 2001

Oxenhope
SE0335

Springfield Guest House, *Shaw Lane, Oxenhope, Keighley, W. Yorks, BD22 9QL.* Large Victorian residence set in large well-kept grounds. **Open:** All year
01535 643951 Mrs Hargreaves **Fax: 01535 644672** *best_bb_uk@msm.com* www.s-h-systems. co.uk/hotels/sprungfi.html **D:** £20.00
S: £22.50–£25.00 **Beds:** 1F 3D 1T 3S
Baths: 2 En 2 Sh ⌂ ▣ (6) ▣ ↑ ✕ ▥ ▦ ⚓

Pontefract
SE4521

Tudor Guest House, *18 Tudor Close, Pontefract, W. Yorks, WF8 4NJ.* Private house, residential area, near to town centre and racecourse. **Open:** All year (not Xmas)
01977 701007 Mrs Kilby **D:** £17.50–£18.00
S: £25.00–£27.00 **Beds:** 2D **Baths:** 2 En 2 Pr
⌂ ▣ (2) ▣ ▦ ⚓

Pool-in-Wharfedale
SE2445

Rawson Garth, *Pool Bank Farm, Pool-in-Wharfedale, Otley, W. Yorks, LS21 1EU.* Attractively converted coach house, open country views in heart of Emmerdale country. **Open:** All year (not Xmas)
0113 284 3221 Mrs Waterhouse **D:** £20.00
S: £30.00 **Beds:** 2D 1T **Baths:** 2 En 1 Pr
⌂ (12) ▣ (4) ⅋ ▣ ▦ ⚓ cc

Pudsey
SE2233

Heatherlea House, *105 Littlemoor Road, Pudsey, Leeds, West Yorkshire, LS28 8AP.* Tastefully furnished, friendly, award-winning gardens. Near motorways, airport, Dales. **Open:** All year **Grades:** ETC 3 Diamond
0113 257 4397 Mr & Mrs Barton **D:** £18.00
S: £20.00–£24.00 **Beds:** 1T 1S **Baths:** 1 Sh
⌂ ▣ (2) ⅋ ▣ ✕ ▥ ▦ ⚓

Queensbury
SE1030

Mountain Hall, *Brighouse & Denholme Road, Queensbury, Bradford, W. Yorks, BD13 1LH.* Former mill owners social institute. Situated 1200' overlooking Bradford-dale. Rural area. **Open:** All year (not Xmas)
01274 816258 Mrs Ledgard **Fax: 01274 884001 D:** £20.00–£25.00 **S:** £20.00–£25.00
Beds: 3T 5D 5S **Baths:** 9 En 1 Sh ⌂ (16)
▣ (10) ⅋ ▣ ↑ ✕ ▥ ▦ ⚓ cc

Sowerby Bridge
SE0523

The Dene, *Triangle, Sowerby Bridge, W Yorks, HX6 3EA.* Georgian stone house in walled garden with wooded valley views. **Open:** July to Open
01422 823562 Mr & Mrs Noble *noble@ thedene-triangle.freeserve.co.uk* **D:** £22.50
S: £25.00 **Beds:** 1F 1T 1D **Baths:** 3 En ▣ (4)
⅋ ▣ ▥ ▦ ⚓

Stanbury
SE0137

Wuthering Heights Inn, *26 Main Street, Stanbury, Keighley, W. Yorks, BD22 0HB.* Warm & friendly country pub, excellent food and traditional ales. **Open:** All year
01535 643332 Mrs Mitchell **D:** £17.00
S: £17.00 **Beds:** 1F 1D 1T 1S **Baths:** 2 Sh ⌂
▣ (20) ▣ ↑ ✕ ▥ ▦ ⚓

Todmorden
SD9424

The Berghof Hotel, *Cross Stone Road, Todmorden, W. Yorks, OL14 8RQ.* Authentic Austrian hotel and restaurant, function suite and conference facilities. **Open:** All year
01706 812966 (also fax) Mrs Brandstatter
berghof@tinyworld.co.uk www.berghof.co.uk
D: £27.50–£35.00 **S:** £42.50–£55.00 **Beds:** 5D 2T **Baths:** 7 En ⌂ ▣ (40) ▣ ↑ ✕ ▥ ▦ ⚓ cc

Cherry Tree Cottage, *Woodhouse Road, Todmorden, W. Yorks, OL14 5RJ.* C17th detached country cottage nestling amidst lovely Pennine countryside. **Open:** All year (not Xmas)
01706 817492 Mrs Butterworth **D:** £16.00–£24.50 **S:** £16.00 **Beds:** 1F 1D 1T 1S **Baths:** 3 En 1 Pr 1 Sh ⌂ ▣ ▣ ↑ ✕ ▥ ▦ ⚓

Wadsworth
SE0126

Hare & Hounds, *Wadsworth, Hebden Bridge, HX7 8TN.* A family-run country pub, ensuite bedrooms, Good Beer Guide. **Open:** All year
01422 842671 (also fax) S Greenwood
www.hare.and.hounds.connectfree.co.uk
D: £22.50–£25.00 **S:** £35.00–£40.00 **Beds:** 4D **Baths:** 4 En ▣ (25) ⅋ ▣ ✕ ▦ ⚓ cc

Wakefield
SE3220

Savile Guest House, *78 Savile Street, Wakefield, W. Yorks, WF1 3LN.* Savile Guest House is a small, friendly place to stay. **Open:** All year
01924 374761 Mrs Herbert **Fax:** 01924 382740 **D:** £18.00–£20.00 **S:** £20.00–£25.00 **Beds:** 2F 4T 2D 2S
Baths: 8 En 8 Pr 2 Sh ⌂ ▣ (10) ⅋ ▣ ↑ ▦ ⚓ cc

Walsden

SD9322

Highstones Guest House, *Lane Bottom, Walsden, Todmorden, W. Yorks, OL14 6TY.* Large house set in half an acre with lovely views over open countryside.
Open: All year
01706 816534 Mrs Pegg **D:** £17.00 **S:** £17.00 **Beds:** 2D 1S **Baths:** 2 Sh 🛏 🅿 (3) ⠧ 📺 🐾 ✕ 🛏

Wentbridge

SE4817

Bridge Guest House, *Wentbridge, Pontefract, W. Yorks, WF8 3JJ.* Picturesque village close A1 & M62 with a friendly welcome. **Open:** All year
01977 620314 **D:** £21.00–£25.00 **S:** £21.00–£25.00 **Beds:** 4T 2D 1S **Baths:** 2 En 2 Sh 🛏 🅿 (8) 📺 🐾 ✕ 📺 🛏 ⅙ ♨

Planning a longer stay? Always ask for any special rates

West Bretton

SE2813

Birch Laithes Farm, *Bretton Lane, West Bretton, Wakefield, W. Yorks, WF4 4LF.* C18th house in countryside, 4 miles from Wakefield. **Open:** All year (not Xmas/New Year)
01924 252129 Mrs Hoyland **D:** £18.00–£20.00 **S:** £18.00–£20.00 **Beds:** 1F 1T 1D **Baths:** 2 Sh 🛏 (3) 🅿 📺 🐾 📺 🛏 ♨

Wetherby

SE4048

The Red House, *12 The Spinney, Wetherby, West Yorkshire, LS22 6SH.* Comfortable house in quiet, private grounds. Wetherby 10 mins' walk.
Open: All year **Grades:** ETC 3 Diamond
01937 585497 Mr & Mrs Forsyth **D:** £23.00–£25.00 **S:** £26.00–£28.00 **Beds:** 1D **Baths:** 1 En 🅿 (6) ⠧ 📺 🛏 ♨

14 Woodhill View, *Wetherby, W. Yorks, LS22 4PP.* Quiet residential area near to town centre. **Open:** All year **Grades:** ETC 3 Diamond
01937 581200 & 07967 152091 (M) Mr Green **D:** £19.00 **S:** £29.00 **Beds:** 1D 1T **Baths:** 1 Sh 🛏 🅿 (3) ⠧ 📺 🐾 🛏 ♨ cc

Whitley

SE2217

The Woolpack Country Inn, *Whitley Road, Whitley, Dewsbury, West Yorkshire, WF12 0LZ.* Charming country inn equidistant from Huddersfield, Wakefield & Dewsbury.
Open: All year
01924 499999 (also fax) V Barraclough
enquiries@woolpackhotel.co.uk
www.woolpackhotel.co.uk **D:** £27.50 **S:** £44.50 **Beds:** 5T 6D **Baths:** 11 En 🛏 🅿 (80) ⠧ 📺 ✕ 📺 🛏 ⅙ ♨ cc

National Grid References given are for villages, towns and cities – not for individual houses

Isle of Man

Isle of Man

ISLE OF MAN

Point of Ayre

Bride
Andreas
Ramsey Bay
Sulby
Ballaugh
Ramsey
Maughold
Kirk Michael
Glen Mona
Peel
Laxey
Laxey Bay
St John's
Patrick
Greeba
Crosby
Foxdale
Onchan
Douglas
Ballasalla
Port Erin
Castletown
Port St Mary
Calf of Man

Douglas
SC3875 Marine Hotel

All Seasons Hotel, *Broadway, Douglas, Isle of Man, IM2 3HX.* Low cost travel arranged. Indoor heated pool. Ideal central location. **Open:** All year **Grades:** IOMTB 3 Crown, Comm, AA 3 Diamond
01624 676323 (also fax) Mr & Mrs Hanson
D: £18.50–£23.50 **S:** £18.50–£30.50 **Beds:** 3D 1T 2S **Baths:** 4 En 1 Sh ▯ ✕ ▯ ▥ ▮ cc

Ramblin, *32 Murrays Road, Douglas, Isle Of Man, IM2 3HP.* Friendly B&B near coastal footpath. Hikers and bikers welcome, also railway enthusiasts. **Open:** All year
01624 610484 & 07624 497391 (M)
Mrs Conning *e.conning@talk21.com*
D: £18.00–£25.00 **S:** £18.00–£25.00 **Beds:** 1D 1T **Baths:** 1 En 1 Pr ⊬ ▯ ▮ ✕ ▥ ▮

Planning a longer stay? Always ask for any special rates

Glen Mona
SC4588

Ballasholague Farm, *Main Road, Glen Mona, Maughold, Isle of Man, IM7 1HR.*
Open: All year (not Xmas/New Year)
01624 861750 D: £18.00–£20.00 **S:** £18.00–£20.00 **Beds:** 1T 2D **Baths:** 1 Sh ▭ ▯ (4) ⊬ ▯ ⊯ ✕ ▯ ▥ ▮
Perfect holidays are the aim at Ballasholague, so be spoiled in an elegant Edwardian farmhouse. Good food, good company, in elegant surroundings. Situated conveniently for walking, fishing, birdwatching or just being on the farm with the animals. A welcome awaits.

Greeba
SC3080

Kerrow Garrow Farm, *Greeba, St Johns, Isle of Man, IM4 3LG.* Kerrow Garrow is a dairy farm with a homely atmosphere.
Open: Easter to Oct
01624 801871 Mrs Jackson **Fax: 01624 801543 D:** £18.00–£22.00 **S:** £18.00–£22.00
Beds: 1F 1D **Baths:** 1 En 1 Pr ▭ ▯ (2) ⊬ ▯ ⊯ ▥ ▮

Kirk Michael
SC3190

Lyngarth, *Station Road, Kirk Michael, Isle of Man, IM6 1HB.* Large secluded garden with patio/barbecue. Unbelievable views of sunrise over Kirk Michael Mountains.
Open: Jan to Dec
01624 878607 E & M Collister **D:** £16.00–£22.00 **S:** £22.00–£25.00 **Beds:** 3T **Baths:** 1 En 1 Sh ▯ ⊬ ▯ ▥

Laxey

SC4383

The Greaves, *Ramsey Road, Laxey, Isle of Man, IM4 7PD.* Homely guest house, perfectly situated for exploring Laxey and east coast. **Open:** All year (not Xmas) **01624 861500** Mrs Quirk **D:** £18.00–£25.00 **S:** £18.00–£25.00 **Beds:** 2D 2S **Baths:** 1 En 1 Sh ▣ ▦ ✕

Onchan

SC3978

Mullen Beg, *Little Mill, Onchan, Douglas, Isle of Man, IM4 5BD.* **Open:** All year **01624 624495** (also fax) Mr Ward **D:** £22.00 **S:** £24.00 **Beds:** 1F 1D **Baths:** 2 En ⌕ (3) ▣ (6) ⊬ ▦ ✕ �authV ▦ ☕

A beautiful country house set in tranquil surroundings overlooking glen and stream. One acre garden, sun patio, private parking. Manx farmhouse kitchen with home-cooking, conservatory, TV, tea/coffee making facilities, evening meal on request. 5 mins from Douglas.

Banks Howe, *23 The Fairway, Onchan, Douglas, Isle of Man, IM3 2EG.* Fully refurbished dormer bungalow set in attractive garden with pool. **Open:** All year **01624 661660** Mr & Mrs Leventhorpe **D:** £24.00–£26.00 **S:** £29.00–£31.00 **Beds:** 1D 2T **Baths:** 2 En 1 Pr ⌕ (10) ▣ (3) ▦ ✕ ▦ ⅙ ☕

Planning a longer stay? Always ask for any special rates

Peel

SC2484   ⚓ *Creek Inn*

The Merchant's House, *18 Castle Street, Peel, IM5 1AN.* Georgian merchant's house. Conservation area. Near sea, harbour, castle, hills and town centre. **Open:** All year **01624 842541 (also fax)** *jslater@enterprise.net* **D:** £20.00–£25.00 **S:** £25.00–£30.00 **Beds:** 2D 1T **Baths:** 1 En 2 Sh ⌕ ⊬ ▦ �authV ▦ ☕

Seaforth House, *4 Crown Street, Peel, Isle of Man, IM5 1AJ.* Family-run Victorian house near river and beach. **Open:** All year (not Xmas/New Year) **01624 843404** Mr & Mrs Plumley *plumelyr@ hotmail.com* **D:** £17.00–£20.00 **S:** £18.00–£21.00 **Beds:** 1F 1T 2S **Baths:** 2 Sh ⌕ ▦ ⅞ ✕ ▦ ▦ ☕

Port Erin

SC1969   ⚓ *Cherry Orchard*

Port Erin Hotels, *The Promenade, Port Erin, Isle of Man, IM9 6LH.* Comfortable hotels overlooking beautiful Port Erin Bay with heavenly sunsets. **Open:** Feb to Nov **01624 833558** Mrs Gowing **Fax: 01624 835402** *enq@porterinhotels.com* www.porterinhotels.com **D:** £25.00–£37.00 **S:** £25.00–£45.00 **Beds:** 42F 32D 36T 19S **Baths:** 129 En ⌕ ▣ (99) ▦ ✕ ▦ ▦ ☕ cc

Regent House, *The Promenade, Port Erin, Isle of Man, IM9 6LE.* Family-run guest house in beautiful seaside location. **Open:** All year **01624 833454 (also fax)** Mrs McGiffin **D:** £22.50–£23.50 **S:** £25.00–£26.00 **Beds:** 2F 3D 2T 2S **Baths:** 7 En 2 Sh ⌕ ▣ ⊬ ▦ ⅞ ✕ ▦ ▦ ☕

Port St Mary

SC2067

Mallmore, *The Promenade, Port St Mary, Isle Of Man, IM9 5DE.* Spacious Victorian terrace house above sandy beach with outstanding views across bay and harbour. **Open:** All year (not Xmas) **01624 836048 (also fax)** J Galjaardt www.mallmore.org **D:** £13.50–£27.00 **S:** £20.25–£40.50 **Beds:** 6F 3T 2D 11S **Baths:** 2 En 8 Sh ⌕ ⅞ ▦ ⅞ ✕ ▦ ▦

Ramsey

SC4594

The Whitehouse, *12 Cooil Breyrk, Ramsey, Isle Of Man, IM8 3HJ.* Quiet, comfortable house. Back garden overlooks fields to the sea. **Open:** May to Oct **Grades:** IOMTB 3 Crown, Comm **01624 813654** Mrs White *clementsbrooch@ aol.com* **D:** £19.00 **S:** £19.00 **Beds:** 1D **Baths:** 1 Pr ▣ (2) ⊬ ▦ ✕ ▦ ☕

Stanleyville Guest House, *Stanley Mount West, Ramsey, Isle of Man, IM8 1LR.* Minutes from all amenities, only yards away from seaside. **Open:** All year (not Xmas) **01624 814420** Mr & Mrs Gillings **D:** £17.00 **S:** £17.00 **Beds:** 1F 2D 2T 3S **Baths:** 1 Sh ⌕ ▣ (6) ▦ ⅞ ✕ ▦ ☕

Sulby

SC3894

Ballacowell, *Cooilbane, Sulby, Isle of Man, IM7 2HR.* Manx cottage near village pub and shop. Bikes/hikers welcome. **Open:** All year **01624 897773 (also fax)** Ms Bedey *majbedey@ ballacowell.co.uk* **D:** £20.00–£25.00 **S:** £25.00–£27.00 **Beds:** 2D **Baths:** 2 En ⌕ (7) ▣ ⊬ ▦ ▦ ☕

Aberdeenshire & Moray

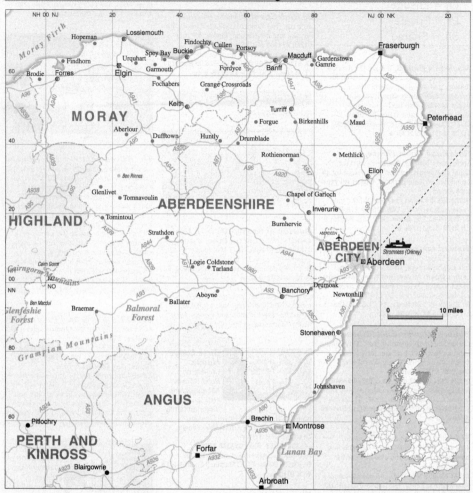

Moray Firth

Hopeman
Lossiemouth
Findochty   Cullen
Spey Bay   Buckie   Portsoy
Findhorn   Urquhart   Macduff   Gardenstown   Fraserburgh
Brodie   Forres   Garmouth   Fordyce   Banff   Gamrie
Elgin   Fochabers   Grange Crossroads
Keith
Turriff   Peterhead
Forgue   Birkenhills   Maud
Aberlour   Dufftown   Huntly   Drumblade
Rothienorman   Methlick
Ben Rinnes   Ellon
Glenlivet   Tomnavoulin   **ABERDEENSHIRE**   Chapel of Garioch
Tomintoul   Inverurie
HIGHLAND   Strathdon   Burnhervie
ABERDEEN   Stromness (Orkney)
Caim Gorm   Logie Coldstone   **CITY**   Aberdeen
Ben Macdui   Tarland
Braemar   Aboyne   Banchory   Drumoak
Balmoral   Ballater   Newtonhill
Forest
Glenfeshie   **Grampian Mountains**   Stonehaven
Forest

0   10 miles

Johnshaven

ANGUS

Pitlochry   Brechin
PERTH AND   Montrose
KINROSS   Forfar
Blairgowrie   Lunan Bay

Arbroath

BATHROOMS
En = Ensuite
Pr = Private
Sh = Shared

Maclean's BandB, *8 Boyd Orr Avenue, Aberdeen, AB12 5RG.* Perfectly situated for fishing, golf, bowling, walks, flower gardens, swimming. **Open:** All year **01224 248726 (also fax)** *j.maclean@ abdn.ac.uk* www.cableol.net/jonathan **D:** £16.00–£20.00 **S:** £18.00–£20.00 **Beds:** 2T 1D ↻ ▣ (3) ⅟ ⊠ ▥. ♨

Roselodge Guest House, *3 Springbank Terrace, Aberdeen, AB11 6LS.* Quiet city centre location, convenient for all amenities. Private parking. **Open:** All year (not Xmas) **01224 586794 (also fax)** Mrs Wink *marywink@onetel.net.uk* **D:** £16.00–£18.00 **S:** £20.00–£22.00 **Beds:** 3F 2T 1S **Baths:** 2 Sh ↻ ▣ (3) ▣ ▥. ♨

Stewart Lodge Guest House, *89 Bon Accord Street, Aberdeen, AB11 6ED.* Family-run establishment, situated in the city centre. **Open:** All year (not Xmas/New Year) **01224 573823** L Wann **Fax: 01224 592624** *stewartlodge@talk21.com* **D:** £16.00–£20.00 **S:** £20.00–£25.00 **Beds:** 1F 3T 3S **Baths:** 3 Sh ↻ ▣ (4) ▣ ⚹ ▣ ▥. ♨ cc

Butler's Islander Guest House, *122 Crown Street, Aberdeen, AB11 6HJ.* City centre location near rail, bus and ferry links. **Open:** All year (not Xmas/New Year) **Grades:** STB 3 Star GH **01224 212411** A Butler **Fax: 01224 586448** *bookings@butlerigh.demon.co.uk* www.butlerigh. demon.co.uk **D:** £13.50–£22.00 **S:** £22.00–£35.00 **Beds:** 3T 3D 1S **Baths:** 2 En 2 Sh ⚹ ▣ ▣ ▥. ♨ cc

St Elmo, *64 Hilton Drive, Aberdeen, AB24 4NP.* Traditional granite family home, near historic university and city centre. **Open:** All year **01224 483065** Mrs Watt *stelmobandb@aol.com* www.home.aol.com/stelmobandb **D:** £16.00–£17.00 **S:** £20.00–£24.00 **Beds:** 1D 2T **Baths:** 1 Sh ↻ (1) ▣ (2) ⚹ ▣ ▥. ♨

Crown Private Hotel, *10 Spring Bank Terrace, Aberdeen, AB1 2LS.* Small, central, family-run private hotel. **Open:** All year **01224 586842** Mr Buthlay **Fax: 01224 573787** *crown_hotel@yahoo.co.uk* crownprivatehotel.ourfamily.com **D:** £18.00–£22.00 **S:** £16.00–£28.00 **Beds:** 2F 2D 2T 3S **Baths:** 7 En 1 Sh ↻ ▣ ⚹ ▣ ▥. ♨

The Ferndale Private Hotel, *62 Bon-Accord Street, Aberdeen, AB11 6EL.* City centre, easy walk to station, shopping, clubs, etc. **Open:** All year (not Xmas/New Year) **01224 584835** A Noble **Fax: 01224 584724** **D:** £17.00–£20.00 **S:** £20.00–£25.00 **Beds:** 7F 2T 2S **Baths:** 6 Sh ↻ ▣ (4) ▣ ♨ cc

Aberlour
NJ2642

83 High Street, *Aberlour, Banffshire, AB38 9QB.* The heart of a village famous for whisky and shortbread. **Open:** All year **01340 871000** Miss Gammack *ruth@ resolute.fsnet.co.uk* www.resolute.fsnet.co.uk **D:** £15.00–£16.00 **S:** £15.00–£16.00 **Beds:** 1T 2D **Baths:** 2 Sh ↻ ⚹ ▣ ▣ ▥. ♨ cc

Aboyne
NO5298   ◁ *Boat Inn*

Newton of Drumgesk, *Dess, Aboyne, Aberdeenshire, AB34 5BL.* **Open:** Mar to Oct **013398 86203 (also fax)** Mrs Selwyn Bailey *crogerbailey@cs.com* **D:** £19.50–£25.00 **S:** £19.50–£25.00 **Beds:** 1T 1D **Baths:** 2 En ↻ ▣ (6) ⚹ ▣ ⚹ ▥. ♨ Comfortable, quiet, typical Scottish farmhouse in own acreage. Newly modernised. Cot/high chair available. Beautiful views of hills and woods. Nice walks. Horse riding by appointment only.

Birse Lodge House, *Charleston Road, Aboyne, Aberdeenshire, AB34 5EL.* Friendly Victorian family home in the heart of Royal Deeside. **Open:** All year (not Xmas/New Year) **Grades:** STB 3 Star **013398 86253 Fax: 013398 87796** *birselodgehouse@btinternet.com* **D:** £27.00 **S:** £32.00 **Beds:** 1T 2D **Baths:** 3 En ▣ (3) ⚹ ▣ ⚹ ✗ ▣ ▥. ♨

Struan Hall, *Ballater Road, Aboyne, Aberdeenshire, AB34 5HY.* We are quietly situated in 2 acres of woodland garden. **Open:** Mar to Oct **013398 87241 (also fax)** Mrs Ingham *struanhall@zetnet.co.uk* www.accomodata.co. uk/struanhall.htm **D:** £26.00–£28.50 **S:** £26.00–£34.00 **Beds:** 1D 2T 1S **Baths:** 3 En 1 Pr ↻ (7) ▣ (6) ⚹ ▣ ⚹ ▣ ▥. ♨ cc

BEDROOMS
D = Double
T = Twin
S = Single
F = Family

Ballater
NO3695   ◁ *Monaltrie Hotel, Green Inn, Loch Kinord Hotel, Glen Lui, Highlander, Prince of Wales, Auld Kirk, Alexandra, Darroch Learg Hotel*

The Belvedere, *Station Square, Ballater, Aberdeenshire, AB35 5QB.* **Open:** All year (not Xmas/New Year) **Grades:** STB 4 Star, AA 4 Diamond **013397 55996** Mrs Ingram **Fax: 013397 55110** *flora-ingram@freeuk.com* **D:** £20.00–£55.00 **S:** £25.00 **Beds:** 2F 1T 1D **Baths:** 4 En ↻ (5) ▣ (4) ⚹ ▣ ▣ ▥. ♨ Victorian town house in the centre of Ballater. Ideal base for visiting the many castles, touring, hill walking & golf. Wonderful views from bedroom windows. All rooms ensuite with many thoughtful extras. Good breakfast menu, individual tables.

Celicall, *3 Braemar Road, Ballater, Aberdeenshire, AB35 5RL.* **Open:** Easter to Oct **Grades:** STB 3 Star **01339 755699** Mrs Cowie *celicall@euphony.net* **D:** £18.00–£20.00 **S:** £25.00 **Beds:** 2T 2D **Baths:** 4 En ▣ (4) ▣ ▣ ▥. ♨ Small family-run guest house in centre of Royal Deeside village of Ballater with its Royal Warrant shops. Close to bars and restaurants. Short drive from Glen Muck and on the Castle and Whisky Trail. Secure overnight off-road parking.

Morvada Guest House, *Braemar Road, Ballater, Aberdeenshire, AB35 5RL.* **Open:** All year (not Xmas) **Grades:** STB 4 Star **013397 56334 (also fax)** Mr Campbell *morvada@aol.com* www.morvada.com **D:** £20.00–£22.00 **S:** £20.00–£25.00 **Beds:** 5D 1T **Baths:** 6 En ▣ (6) ⚹ ▣ ⚹ ▥. ♨ cc Allan and Thea Campbell welcome you to this lovely Victorian villa set in the beautiful village of Ballater. Excellent rooms, quality breakfasts, and a prime location for fine restaurants, Balmoral Castle, the Cairngorm Mountains, the Whisky and Castle Trails.

Planning a longer stay? Always ask for any special rates

Deeside Hotel, *Braemar Road, Ballater, Aberdeenshire, AB35 5RQ.* Quiet location. Informal dining. Good touring base. Two ground floor bedrooms. **Open:** Feb to Dec **Grades:** STB 3 Star
013397 55420 Mr Brooker **Fax: 013397 55357**
deesidehotel@btconnect.com www.deesidehotel.co.uk **D:** £23.00–£28.00 **S:** £28.00–£31.50 **Beds:** 1F 4D 4T **Baths:** 9 Pr ⚡ 🛏 ✕ 📺 🍴 🕭 🕭 cc

Darrochlee, *5a Monaltrie Road, Ballater, Aberdeenshire, AB35 5QE.* Centrally located in beautiful highland village. Balmoral Castle 7m away. **Open:** Apr to Oct
01339 755287 Mrs Wilkie **Fax: 013397 56006**
lynewilkie@fsbdial.co.uk **D:** £17.50 **S:** £20.00 **Beds:** 1T 2D **Baths:** 1 Sh ⚡ ⅊ 📺 🛏 🍴 🕭

Inverdeen House BandB, *11 Bridge Square, Ballater, Aberdeenshire, AB35 5QJ.* Beautifully restored Georgian townhouse with en-suite rooms and superb breakfasts. **Open:** All year **Grades:** STB 4 Star, AA 4 Diamond, RAC 4 Diamond
013397 55759 Ms Mote **Fax: 013397 55993**
info@inverdeen.com www.inverdeen.com
D: £22.50–£35.00 **S:** £22.50–£28.00 **Beds:** 1F 1T 2D 1S **Baths:** 4 En 1 Pr ⚡ (0) ⅊ (2) ⅊ 📺 🍴 ❋ 🕭 cc

Dee Valley, *26 Viewfield Road, Ballater, Aberdeenshire, AB35 5RD.* Large detached Victorian house. Quiet location. Stair lift. Beautiful countryside. **Open:** Apr to Nov
013397 55408 (also fax) Mrs Gray **D:** £17.00–£20.00 **S:** £22.00–£25.00 **Beds:** 2F 1D 1T **Baths:** 1 En 2 Sh ⚡ (1) ⅊ (3) ⅊ 📺 🍴 🕭

Banchory
NO7095

Dorena, *Strachan, Banchory, Kincardineshire, AB31 6NL.* Modern bungalow, panoramic views over River Feugh, hills and woodlands. **Open:** All year (not Xmas/New Year)
01330 822540 (also fax) D Mutch **D:** £20.00 **S:** £25.00–£30.00 **Beds:** 1T 2D **Baths:** 3 En ⅊ (4) ⅊ 📺 📺 🍴 🕭

Banff
NJ6864

Clayfolds Farm, *Banff, AB45 3UD.* Warm, comfortable accommodation on working farm. 3 miles from Banff. **Open:** Easter to Sept
01261 821288 Mrs Eddison *clayfolds@ farming.co.uk* **D:** £15.00 **S:** £15.00 **Beds:** 1F 1D 1S **Baths:** 1 Sh ⚡ (2) ⅊ (4) ⅊ ✕ 🍴 🕭

The Trinity and Alvah Manse, *21 Castle Street, Banff, AB45 1DH.* Trinity Manse is restored and tastefully decorated to highest standards. **Open:** All year (not Xmas)
01261 812244 (also fax) Ms Grant *oldmanse@ tesco.net* **D:** £18.00–£20.00 **S:** £18.00–£23.00 **Beds:** 2D 1T **Baths:** 1 En 2 Pr ⚡ ⅊ 📺 📺 🍴 🕭

Birkenhills
NJ7445 ⬧ *Fife Arms*

Lendrum Farm, *Birkenhills, Turriff, Aberdeenshire, AB53 8HA.* Comfortable historic farmhouse, traditional Scottish hospitality, home cooking, ensuite and peaceful. **Open:** All year (not Xmas/New Year) **Grades:** STB 3 Star
01888 544285 (also fax) Mrs Roebuck *christina@lendru.fs.business.co.uk* **D:** £20.00–£22.00 **S:** £22.00 **Beds:** 1F 1T **Baths:** 1 En ⚡ (3) ⅊ ⅊ 📺 📺 🍴 🕭

Braemar
NO1491 ⬧ *Braemar Lodge, Invercauld Hotel*

Balnellan House, *Braemar, Aberdeenshire, AB35 5YQ.* A charming renovated Victorian family home offering traditional Scottish hospitality. **Open:** All year (not Xmas)
013397 41474 Mrs Sharp *balnellan@ hotmail.com* **D:** £22.00 **S:** £25.00–£30.00 **Beds:** 2D 1T **Baths:** 3 En ⚡ (1) ⅊ (4) ⅊ 🛏 ✕ 📺 🍴

Brodie
NH9757

Invercairn House, *Brodie, Forres, Moray, IV36 2TD.* **Open:** All year (not Xmas)
01309 641261 (also fax) Mrs Malin **D:** £17.00 **Beds:** 1F 2T 1S **Baths:** 1 Sh ⚡ ⅊ 📺 🛏 ✕ 📺 🍴 🕭 Formerly Brodie Castle Station C1857. Perfectly situated for historic castles, whisky route, beaches, golfing, walking, delicious evening meals served. Accent on Scottish produce, enjoy a glass of wine or a malt, we have a table licence.

Buckie (Spey Bay)
NJ4165 ⬧ *Old Coach House Hotel, Marine Hotel, Highlander Hotel*

Rosemount, *62 East Church Street, Buckie, Banffshire, AB56 1ER.* Large Victorian house overlooking Moray Firth. **Open:** All year (not Xmas/New Year) **Grades:** STB 4 Star
01542 833434 (also fax) N Pirie *rosemount_bck@btinternet.com* **D:** £20.00–£22.50 **S:** £25.00–£27.50 **Beds:** 2T 1D **Baths:** 2 En 1 Sh 📺 📺 🍴 🕭

Cluny Hotel, *2 High Street, Buckie, Banffshire, AB56 1AL.* Family-run, centrally located hotel overlooking the Moray Firth **Open:** All year
01542 832922 D: £22.00–£28.00 **S:** £26.00–£28.00 **Beds:** 1F 2D 2T 1S **Baths:** 6 En ⚡ 📺 (40) 📺 🛏 ✕ 📺 🍴 🕭 cc

Burnhervie
NJ7219

Broadsea, *Burnhervie, Inverurie, Aberdeenshire, AB51 5LB.* Homely accommodation on a working family farm. Good home cooking, quiet rural location. **Open:** All year
01467 681386 Mrs Harper *elizharber@ broadsea99.freeserve.co.uk* **D:** £19.00–£21.00 **S:** £22.00–£26.00 **Beds:** 1F **Baths:** 1 En ⚡ 📺 ⅊ 📺 🛏 ✕ 📺 🍴 🕭 🕭

Chapel of Garioch
NJ7124

Kirkton Park Bed And Breakfast, *5 Kirkton Park, Chapel of Garioch, Inverurie, AB51 5HF.* Convenient for Whisky/Castle Trails - close to Bennachie. Good views. **Open:** All year (not Xmas/New Year)
01467 681281 *kirkton-park@msn.com* **D:** £16.00–£22.00 **S:** £16.00–£22.00 **Beds:** 2T **Baths:** 1 En 1 Pr ⚡ ⅊ (4) ⅊ ✕ 📺 🍴 🕭

Cullen
NJ5167 ⬧ *Seafield Arms, Three Kings Inn, Bayview Hotel, Waverley Hotel, Grant Arms, Royal Oak, Cullen Bay Hotel*

Torrach, *147 Seatown, Cullen, Buckie, Banffshire, AB56 4SL.* Traditional house, near beach and golf course. Warm friendly atmosphere. **Open:** Easter to Oct **Grades:** STB 3 Star
01542 840724 Mrs Mair **D:** £16.00 **S:** £18.00 **Beds:** 1F 1D **Baths:** 1 Sh ⚡ 📺 📺 🍴 🕭

The Elms Guest House, *2 Seafield Place, Cullen, Buckie, Banffshire, AB56 2UU.* Family-run guest house offering very comfortable accommodation. Close to Speyside Way. **Open:** All year
01542 841271 (also fax) Mr Welford **D:** £16.00–£20.00 **S:** £16.00–£20.00 **Beds:** 1F 2D 2T 1S **Baths:** 1 En 1 Pr 1 Sh ⚡ (4) ⅊ 📺 🛏 📺 🍴 🕭

Drumblade
NJ5840

Annandale House, *Drumblade, Huntly, AB54 6EN.* Beautifully furnished early Victorian manse, idyllic location. Ideal for touring. **Open:** Mar to Jan
01466 740233 (also fax) Ms Staunton *susan.staunton@virgin.net* **D:** £20.00–£27.50 **S:** £20.00–£25.00 **Beds:** 1T 2D 1S **Baths:** 4 En ⚡ (4) ⅊ 📺 🛏 ✕ 📺 🍴 🕭 cc

Drumoak

NO7898   ⚓ *Irvine Arms, Ploughman*

Mains Of Drum Farmhouse BandB,
*Drum Castle Road, Drumoak, Banchory,
Aberdeenshire, AB31 5AE.* Modernised
farmhouse. Convenient for Aberdeen,
castles, attractions on Royal Deeside.
Open: All year
01330 811295 **Fax:** 01330 811335 **D:** £15.00
S: £18.00 **Beds:** 2F 2T **Baths:** 3 En 1 Pr ➢
🅿(20) 📺 ✕ 📺 🛏, ✳ �ं&

Dalmaik Manse, *Drumoak, Banchory,
Aberdeenshire, AB31 5AT.* Beautiful, peaceful
riverside location. Warm and comfortable.
Close to Aberdeen and Royal Deeside.
Open: All year
01330 811746 (also fax) Mrs Fowler
dalmaikmanse@btinternet.com **D:** £20.00
S: £20.00 **Beds:** 1F 1D **Baths:** 1 En ➢ 🅿 📺
🛏, ☰

Dufftown

NJ3240

Fife Arms Hotel, *2 The Square,
Dufftown, Keith, Banffshire, AB55 4AD.* Small,
modern town centre hotel. Steaks - beef
and ostrich our speciality. **Open:** All year
01340 820220 Mr Widdowson **Fax:** 01340
821137 **D:** £20.00–£25.00 **S:** £22.00–£27.00
Beds: 2F 4T **Baths:** 6 En ➢ (1) 🅿 (6) 🛏 ✕
📺 🛏, ☰ & cc

Errolbank, *134 Fife Street, Dufftown,
Keith, Banffshire, AB55 4DP.* Friendly local
hosts. Scottish breakfasts our speciality.
On Whisky Trail. **Open:** All year
01340 820229 Mrs Smart **D:** £15.00
S: £15.50–£16.00 **Beds:** 3F 1D 1S **Baths:** 1
Sh ➢ 🅿 (5) 📺 🛏 ✕ 📺 🛏, ☰

Nashville, *8a Balvenie Street, Dufftown,
Keith, Banffshire, AB55 4AB.* Large C18th
rooms. Whisky Trail, castles, walks. Warm
welcome. **Open:** All year **Grades:** STB 2
Star
01340 820553 & 07703 984634 (M)
Mrs Morrison **Fax:** 01340 820553 *lynn-gil@
ntlworld.com* **D:** £15.00–£18.00 **S:** £20.00–
£23.00 **Beds:** 1F 1T 1D **Baths:** 1 Sh ➢ 🅿 (2)
📺 🛏 📺 🛏, ☰

Davaar, *Church Street, Dufftown, Keith,
Banffshire, AB55 4AR.* Nice Victorian house.
Some guest rooms overlooking garden at
rear. **Open:** All year (not Xmas/New Year)
01340 820464 Mrs Macmillan **D:** £16.00–
£18.00 **S:** £25.00–£30.00 **Beds:** 1T 2D
Baths: 2 En 1 Sh ➢ 📺 ✕ 📺 🛏, ☰

BATHROOMS
En = Ensuite
Pr = Private
Sh = Shared

**Planning a longer stay? Always
ask for any special rates**

Elgin

NJ2162   ⚓ *Laichmoray Hotel, Flanagan's*

Ardgowan, *37 Duff Avenue, Elgin, Moray,
IV30 1QS.* Whisky castle, coastal trails and
golf courses, all close by. **Open:** All year
(not Xmas/New Year)
01343 541993 (also fax) Mrs McGowan
ardgowan@mac.com www.scotland-info.co.
uk/ardgowan **D:** £18.00–£20.00 **S:** £25.00–
£30.00 **Beds:** 1T 1D **Baths:** 1 En 1 Pr 🅿 (3) ⊬
📺 🛏, & ☰

Woodlea, *38 Academy Street, Elgin,
Moray, IV30 1LR.* Detached villa with garden
near city centre and railway station.
Open: All year
01343 547114 Mrs Mckenzie *muriel@
woodlea18.freeserve.co.uk* **D:** £15.00–£18.00
S: £15.00–£18.00 **Beds:** 1F 2T **Baths:** 1 En 1
Sh ➢ 🅿 (4) ⊬ 📺 🛏 🛏, ☰

Foresters House, *Newton, Elgin, Moray,
IV30 8XW.* Situated on B9013, 3 miles west of
Elgin, near sandy beaches and Whisky Trail.
Open: All year
01343 552862 Mrs Goodwin *goodwin@
forestershouse.fsnet.co.uk* **D:** £15.00 **S:** £17.00
Beds: 2F **Baths:** 1 Sh ➢ 🅿 (2) 📺 🛏 📺 🛏, ☰

5 Forrestry Cottages, *Newton , Elgin,
IV30 8XP.* Family home - providing warm,
clean rooms. Lounge for relaxing with a TV.
Open: All year
01343 546702 Ms Whyte **D:** £14.00 **S:** £14.00
Beds: 1T 1D **Baths:** 1 Sh ➢ 🅿 (2) 📺 🛏 ✕ 📺
🛏, ☰

Ellon

NJ9530

**58 Station
Road,** *Ellon,
Aberdeenshire,
AB4 9AL.* Victorian
house in town
centre near
Whisky/Castle
Trails, cycle routes. **Open:** All year (not
Xmas)
01358 720263 Mrs Thomson **D:** £16.00–
£18.00 **S:** £18.00–£23.00 **Beds:** 2T **Baths:** 1
Sh 🅿 (4) ⊬ 📺 📺 🛏, ☰

Findhorn

NJ0464   ⚓ *Kimberley Inn*

Crown and Anchor Inn, *Findhorn,
Forres, Moray, IV36 0YF.* C18th coaching inn.
Fresh fish, real ales, bayside. **Open:** All year
01309 690243 Mr Burrell *crownanchorinn@
aol.com* **D:** £25.00–£30.00 **S:** £25.00–£30.00
Beds: 2F 2T 4D **Baths:** 8 En ➢ 🅿 (30) ⊬ 📺 🛏
✕ 📺 🛏, ☰

Findochty

NJ4668   ⚓ *Harbour Bar, The Admiral*

15 Station Road, *Findochty, Buckie,
Banffshire, AB56 2PJ.* Between Inverness and
Aberdeen. Home cooking, good breakfast.
Ideal dolphin watching. **Open:** Easter to
Nov
01542 834992 Mrs Loades **D:** £16.00
S: £16.00 **Beds:** 1F 1T 1D **Baths:** 1 Sh ➢ 📺
✕ 📺 🛏, ☰

Fochabers

NJ3458   ⚓ *Garmouth Hotel*

Castlehill Farm, *Blackdam, Fochabers,
Moray, IV32 7LJ.* Ideally situated for exploring
the area. Panoramic views of Ben Aigen.
Open: All year (not Xmas/New Year)
Grades: STB 3 Star
01343 820351 A Shand **Fax:** 01343 821856
D: £16.00–£20.00 **S:** £17.00–£22.00 **Beds:** 2D
Baths: 1 En 1 Sh 🅿 (5) ⊬ 📺 📺 🛏, ☰

Fordyce

NJ5563

Academy House, *School Road, Fordyce,
Portsoy, Banffshire, AB45 2SJ.* Tastefully
decorated and furnished country house.
Paintings and pottery throughout.
Open: All year
01261 842743 Mrs Leith *academy_house@
hotmail.com* www.fordyceaccommodation.
com **D:** £20.00–£24.00 **S:** £25.00–£27.00
Beds: 1D 1T **Baths:** 1 En 1 Sh ➢ 🅿 (5) 📺 🛏
✕ 📺 🛏, ☰

Forgue

NJ6145   ⚓ *Bognie Arms Hotel, Rothie Inn*

Yonder Bognie, *Forgue, Huntly,
Aberdeenshire, AB54 6BR.* **Open:** All year
Grades: STB 3 Star
01466 730375 Mrs Ross **D:** £16.00–£18.00
S: £20.00 **Beds:** 2D **Baths:** 2 En ➢ 🅿 (6) ⊬ 📺
🛏, ☰
Comfortable accommodation near Huntly,
on Castle and Whisky Trails. Central
heating throughout, residents lounge with
colour TV. En-suite bedrooms have electric
blankets, colour TV, tea/coffee making
facilities and hairdryers. Food hygiene
certificate held. French and Italian spoken.
Warm welcome assured.

RATES
D = Price range per person
sharing in a double or twin
room
S = Price range for a single
room

National Grid References given are for villages, towns and cities – not for individual houses

Forres

NJ0358   🍺 *Mosset Tavern*

Morven, Caroline Street, Forres, Moray, IV36 0AN. Beautiful house, town centre location. Warm, friendly atmosphere. Private parking. Brochure available. **Open:** All year **Grades:** STB 3 Star **01309 673788 (also fax)** Mrs MacDonald *morven2@globalnet.co.uk* www.golfgreenfees. com/morven **D:** £17.00–£19.00 **S:** £18.00–£25.00 **Beds:** 3T **Baths:** 2 En 1 Pr 🛇 🖪 (5) 🗹 🍴 Ⓥ 🛋 🕏

Mayfield Guest House, Victoria Road, Forres, Moray, IV36 3BN. Mayfield is centrally located with spacious rooms and a quiet, relaxed ambience. **Open:** All year (not Xmas) **Grades:** STB 4 Star **01309 676931** W Hercus *bill-hercus@ mayfieldghouse.freeserve.co.uk* www.mayfieldghouse.freeserve.co.uk **D:** £18.00–£20.00 **S:** £25.00–£30.00 **Beds:** 1D 2T **Baths:** 2 En 1 Pr 🖪 (4) 🗹 🛋 🕏 **cc**

Heather Lodge, Tytler Street, Forres, Moray, IV36 0EL. Situated in quiet area near town. **Open:** All year **Grades:** STB 2 Star **01309 672377** Mr Ross **D:** £18.00–£20.00 **S:** £18.00–£20.00 **Beds:** 2T 3S **Baths:** 7 En 🖪 (12) 🗹 🍴 Ⓥ 🛋 🕏

Gamrie

NJ7965

The Palace Farm, Gamrie, Banff, AB45 3HS. Late C18th farmhouse. Hearty Scottish breakfasts. Scenic clifftop villages close by. **Open:** All year (not Xmas/New Year) **01261 851261** P Duncan **Fax: 01261 851 401** *robbie@palace-farm.freeserve.co.uk* **D:** £19.00–£20.00 **S:** £20.00–£25.00 **Beds:** 1F 1T 1D **Baths:** 3 En 🛇 🖪 (6) 🗹 ✕ 🛋 🕏

Roughwards, Gamrie, Gardenstown, Banff, AB45 3HA. Warm comfortable former farmhouse, walking, bird watching, near scenic Gardenstown, Crovie. **Open:** All year (not Xmas) **01261 851758** Mrs Hawick *hawick@ btinternet.com* roughwards.20m.com **D:** £15.00–£17.00 **S:** £15.00–£18.00 **Beds:** 1D 1T **Baths:** 1 Sh 🛇 (2) 🖪 (3) 🗹 🍴 ✕ Ⓥ 🛋 🕅 🕏

Gardenstown

NJ8064

Bankhead Croft, Gamrie, Banff, Aberdeenshire & Moray, AB45 3HN. Modern country cottage, offering high standards of comfort in tranquil surroundings. **Open:** All year **01261 851584 (also fax)** Mrs Smith *lucinda@ bankheadcroft.freeserve.co.uk* www.destination. scotland.com/bankhead **D:** £15.00–£18.00 **S:** £18.00–£20.00 **Beds:** 1F 1D 1T **Baths:** 1 Pr 🛇 🖪 (6) ✗ 🗹 🍴 ✕ Ⓥ 🛋 🕏 ❀ 🕏

Garmouth

NJ3364

Rowan Cottage, Station Road, Garmouth, Fochabers, Moray, IV32 7LZ. C18th cottage with garden in rural village at Spey estuary. **Open:** Jan to Nov **01343 870267** Mrs Bingham **Fax: 01343 870621** *patricia@pbingham.fsnet.co.uk* **D:** £17.00 **S:** £17.00 **Beds:** 1D 1T 1S **Baths:** 1 Sh 🛇 🖪 (4) 🗹 🛋 🕏

Glenlivet

NJ1929

Craighed, Glenlivet, Ballindalloch, Banffshire, AB37 9DR. Traditional country house, overlooking beautiful heather hills, pine trees and stream. **Open:** All year (not Xmas) **01807 590436** R Wilson **D:** £16.00–£18.00 **S:** £16.00–£18.00 **Beds:** 1T 1D 🖪 (4) ✗ 🗹 ✕ Ⓥ 🛋 **cc**

Grange Crossroads

NJ4754

Chapelhill Croft, Grange Crossroads, Keith, Banffshire, AB55 3LQ. Warm welcome, rural location. Ideal for Whisky and Castle Trails. **Open:** All year (not Xmas/New Year) **01542 870302** Mrs Fleming *chapelhill@ btinternet.com* www.scottishholidays. net/chapelhill **D:** £14.00–£17.00 **S:** £17.00–£20.00 **Beds:** 1T 1D **Baths:** 1 En 1 Sh 🛇 🖪 🗹 ✕ Ⓥ 🛋 🕏

All details shown are as supplied by B&B owners in Autumn 2001

Hopeman

NJ1469   🍺 *Station Hotel, Duffus Inn*

Ardent House, 43 Forsyth Street, Hopeman, Elgin, Moray, IV30 2SY. Traditional stone built house with conservatory overlooking secluded rose garden. **Open:** All year (not Xmas/New Year) **Grades:** STB 4 Star, AA 4 Diamond **01343 830694 (also fax)** N McPherson *normaardent@aol.com* www.ardenthouse.fsnet. co.uk **D:** £16.00–£22.00 **S:** £18.00–£30.00 **Beds:** 1T 2D **Baths:** 1 En 1 Sh 🛇 (6) 🖪 (4) ✗ 🗹 🛋 🕏

Huntly

NJ5240   🍺 *Fjord Inn*

Greenmount, 43 Gordon Street, Huntly, Aberdeenshire, AB54 8EQ. Family-run Georgian house. Excellent base for touring NE Scotland. **Open:** All year (not Xmas) **Grades:** STB 3 Star **01466 792482** Mr Manson **D:** £17.00–£20.00 **S:** £17.00–£25.00 **Beds:** 2F 4T 2S **Baths:** 4 En 1 Pr 1 Sh 🛇 🖪 (6) ✗ 🗹 ✕ 🛋 🕏

Dunedin Guest House, 17 Bogie Street, Huntly, Aberdeenshire, AB54 5DX. Dunedin Guest House. A few minutes walk from town centre. All rooms ensuite. **Open:** All year **01466 794162** Mrs Keith *dunedin.guesthouse@ btinternet.uk* **D:** £18.50–£23.00 **S:** £18.50–£23.00 **Beds:** 6F 1D 4T **Baths:** 6 En 🛇 🖪 (8) ✗ 🗹 🛋 🕏

Inverurie

NJ7721

Kingsgait, 3 St. Andrews Gardens, Inverurie, Aberdeenshire, AB51 3XT. Friendly family run establishment close to town centre. **Open:** All year **01467 620431 (also fax)** Mrs Christie *muriel@mchrstie25.freeserve.co.uk* **D:** £18.00–£23.00 **S:** £18.00–£23.00 **Beds:** 2T 1S **Baths:** 1 En 1 Sh 🛇 (2) 🖪 (3) ✗ 🗹 🍴 Ⓥ 🛋 🕏

Johnshaven

NO7966

Ellington, Station Place, Johnshaven, Montrose, DD10 0JD. Comfortable modern family home in old fishing village. Ground-floor twin room. **Open:** All year (not Xmas) **01561 362756** Mrs Gibson *ellington13@ supanet.com* **D:** £18.00–£20.00 **S:** £20.00 **Beds:** 1T 1D **Baths:** 2 En 🖪 (2) 🗹 🍴 🛋 🕏

Keith
NJ4250

The Haughs, Keith, Banffshire, *AB55 6QN.*
Large comfortable farmhouse. Lovely view
from dining room over rolling countryside.
Open: Easter to Oct **Grades:** STB 3 Star, AA
4 Diamond
01542 882238 (also fax) Mrs Jackson
jiwjackson@aol.com **D:** £19.00–£21.00
S: £22.00–£25.00 **Beds:** 1F 2D 1T **Baths:** 3
En 1 Pr ☎ (2) 🅿 (6) 🖂 ✕ 🎞 ♨

Logie Coldstone
NJ4304

**Migvie
House,** Logie
Coldstone,
Aboyne,
Aberdeenshire,
AB34 4XL. Off the
beaten track in
Royal Deeside. Luxury, peace and personal
attention. **Open:** Mar to Oct **Grades:** STB 4
Star
01339 881313 C Luffman **Fax:** 01339 81635
bluffman.cu@aberdeenshire.gov.uk
www.b-and-b-scotland.co.uk/migrie.htm
D: £25.00 **S:** £35.00 **Beds:** 2T 1 D **Baths:** 3
En

Lossiemouth
NJ2370

Skerryhill, 63 Dunbar Street,
Lossiemouth, Moray, *IV31 6AN.* Near beaches
and golf course. Convenient for Castle and
Whisky Trails. **Open:** All year
01343 813035 Mrs Stewart **D:** £16.00–£18.00
S: £17.00 **Beds:** 1F 2D 1T **Baths:** 1 Sh ☎ 🅿
🖂 ♈ 🎞 ♨

Laburnum, 54 Queen Street,
Lossiemouth, Moray, *IV31 6PR.* Family run
home close to all amenities, including
beaches. **Open:** All year
01343 813482 (also fax) Mrs Stephen *bstep@*
talk21.com **D:** £16.00–£20.00 **S:** £17.00–
£20.00 **Beds:** 1F 1S 1D **Baths:** 1 En 1 Pr 1 Sh
☎ 🅿 (2) 🖂 ♈ 🎞 ♨

Maud
NJ9248

Pond View, Brucklay, Maud, Peterhead,
AB42 4QN. Quiet house with panoramic view
close to the National Cycle Route. **Open:** All
year
01771 613675 & 07929 594168 (M) J & M
Hepburn *mhepburn@lineone.net* **D:** £20.00
S: £22.00–£25.00 **Beds:** 1T 1D 🅿 (4) ⚲ 🖂 🎞

All details shown are as
supplied by B&B owners in
Autumn 2001

National Grid References given
are for villages, towns and
cities – not for individual houses

Methlick
NJ8537   ⚓ Gight House Hotel

Sunnybrae Farm, Gight, Methlick, Ellon,
Aberdeenshire, *AB41 7JA.* Traditional
farmhouse; comfort in a peaceful location
with lovely views. **Open:** All year
01651 806456 (also fax) Mrs Staff
sunnybrae-farm@faxvia.net **D:** £18.00–£20.00
S: £18.00–£20.00 **Beds:** 1T 1D 1S **Baths:** 2
En ☎ 🅿 🖂 ♈ 🎞 ♨

Newtonhill
NO9193

3 Greystone Place, Newtonhill,
Stonehaven, Kincardineshire, *AB39 3UL.*
Beautiful coastal village within easy reach
Aberdeen and Royal Deeside. **Open:** All
year (not Xmas)
01569 730391 & 07808 439683 (M) Mrs Allen
Fax: 01569 730391 *patsbb@supanet.com*
D: £15.00–£17.00 **S:** £15.00–£18.00 **Beds:** 1F
1T **Baths:** 2 Sh ☎ 🅿 (2) 🖂 ♈ ✕ 🎞 ♨

Portsoy
NJ5866

The Boyne Hotel, 2 North High Street,
Portsoy, Banff, Aberdeenshire & Moray,
AB45 2PA. Family run hotel situated 100 yards
from C17th harbour. **Open:** All year
01261 842242 Mr Christie *enquiries@*
boynehotel.co.uk www.boynehotel.co.uk
D: £20.00–£25.00 **S:** £20.00–£25.00 **Beds:** 4D
4T 4S **Baths:** 12 En 🅿 🖂 ♈ ✕ 🎞 ❋ ♨ cc

Rothienorman
NJ7235

Rothie Inn, Main Street, Rothienorman,
Inverurie, Aberdeenshire, *AB51 8UD.* Family-
run village inn in the heart of castle country.
Open: All year (not Xmas) **Grades:** STB 3
Star
01651 821206 (also fax) Miss Thomson
rothieinn@accom90.freeserve.co.uk **D:** £20.00–
£25.00 **S:** £25.00–£30.00 **Beds:** 1F 1D 1T
Baths: 3 En ☎ 🅿 (20) ⚲ 🖂 ♈ ✕ 🎞 ♨ cc

Spey Bay
NJ3565

31 The Muir, Bogmoor, Spey Bay,
Fochabers, *IV32 7PN.* 1 Mile from Spey
estuary, sighting of dolphins, seals, osprey.
Open: All year
01343 820196 J Philpott **D:** £15.00–£16.00
S: £15.00–£16.00 **Beds:** 2D ☎ 🅿 ⚲ 🖂 ✕ 🖂
♨

Stonehaven
NO8786   ⚓ Marine Hotel

Glencairn, 9
Dunnottar
Avenue,
Stonehaven,
AB39 2JD. Coastal
location close to
open-air
swimming pool and picturesque fishing
harbour. **Open:** All year
01569 762612 M Sangster *msangster@*
amserve.net www.glen-cairn.fsbusiness.co.uk
D: £18.00–£20.00 **S:** £20.00–£22.00 **Beds:** 1T
1D 1S **Baths:** 2 En 1 Pr ☎ 🅿 (5) 🖂 🎞 ♨

Arduthie House, Ann Street,
Stonehaven, Kincardineshire, *AB3 2DA.*
Elegant detached Victorian guest house
with attractive garden, central Stonehaven.
Open: All year (not Xmas) **Grades:** STB 4
Star, AA 4 Star
01569 762381 Mrs Marr **Fax:** 01569 766366
arduthie@talk21.com **D:** £24.00–£26.00
S: £18.00 **Beds:** 1F 2D 2T 1S **Baths:** 5 En 1
Pr ☎ 🖂 ✕ 🎞 ♨

The Grahams, 71 Cameron Street,
Stonehaven, Kincardineshire, *AB39 2HE.*
Traditional Scottish home. Town centre/
harbour within ten minutes' walk.
Open: Apr to Dec **Grades:** STB 2 Star
01569 763517 *arthur@grahams71.fsnet.co.uk*
D: £17.50 **S:** £20.00 **Beds:** 1F 1T 1S **Baths:** 2
Sh 🎞 cc

Alexander Guest House, 36 Arduthie
Road, Stonehaven, Kincardineshire,
AB39 2DP. Friendly, comfortable. Convenient
for town centre, harbour, train. Superb
breakfast. **Open:** All year **Grades:** STB 3
Star
01569 762265 (also fax) Mrs Peterkin
marion@alexanderguesthouse.com
www.alexanderguesthouse.com **D:** £22.00–
£30.00 **S:** £20.00–£30.00 **Beds:** 3F 1T 1D 2S
Baths: 5 En 2 Sh ☎ ⚲ 🖂 ♈ 🖂 ♨

44 Evan Street, Stonehaven,
Aberdeenshire, *AB39 2ET.* Victorian town
house. Near sea. Handy for Dunnottar
Castle. **Open:** All year (not Xmas/New Year)
Grades: STB 3 Star
01569 763494 Mrs Horne *lorrainehorne@*
tinyworld.co.uk **D:** £18.00 **S:** £25.00 **Beds:** 2D
Baths: 2 Sh 🖂 ♈ 🖂 🎞 ♨

Strathdon
NJ3512   ⚓ Glenkindie Arms

Buchaam Farm, Strathdon,
Aberdeenshire, *AB36 8TN.* Enjoy Scottish
hospitality on 600-acre family-run farm in an
area of unspoilt beauty. **Open:** Apr to Oct
Grades: STB 3 Star
019756 51238 (also fax) Mrs Ogg *e.ogg@*
talk21.com **D:** £17.00 **S:** £17.00 **Beds:** 1F 1D
1T **Baths:** 2 Sh ☎ 🅿 (3) 🖂 ♨

Tarland

NJ4704 🏨 *Aberdeen Arms, Loch Kinnord, Boat Inn*

Kirklands of Cromar, *Bridge Street, Tarland, Aboyne, Aberdeenshire, AB34 4YN.* By same architect as Balmoral Castle. Visit castles and Whisky Trail. **Open:** All year **013398 81082** Ms Stewart *morna@ kirkland.u-net.com* kirklandsofcromar.co.uk **D:** £17.00–£18.00 **S:** £17.00–£30.00 **Beds:** 2F 1T 1D **Baths:** 1 En 🛇 🖬 📺 🍴 ✕ 📺 🛋

Tomintoul

NJ1618

Findron Farm, *Braemar Road, Tomintoul, Ballindalloch, Banffshire, AB37 9ER.* Situated in the Castle, Distillery area. Warm welcome. Farmhouse breakfast. **Open:** All year (not Xmas/New Year) **Grades:** STB 3 Star **01807 580382 (also fax)** Mrs Turner *elmaturner@talk21.com* www.cometo/findronfarmhouse **D:** £15.00–£17.00 **S:** £15.00–£17.00 **Beds:** 1F 1D 1T **Baths:** 2 En 1 Pr 🛇 🖬 📺 🍴 ✕ 📺 🛋

Bracam House, *32 Main Street, Tomintoul, Ballindalloch, AB37 9EX.* Enjoy a warm welcome to the Highlands from the Camerons. **Open:** All year **01807 580278 (also fax)** Mr & Mrs Cameron *camerontomintoul@compuserve.com* **D:** £15.00–£16.00 **S:** £15.00–£16.00 **Beds:** 1D 1T 1S **Baths:** 1 En 1 Sh 🛇 🖬 (2) ⅙ 📺 🍴 📺 🛋

Croughly Farm, *Tomintoul, Ballindalloch, Banffshire, AB37 9EN.* Farmhouse with breathtaking views of Cairngorm mountains. Overlooking River Conglas. **Open:** May to Oct **01807 580476 (also fax)** Mrs Shearer *johnannecroughly@tinyworld.co.uk* **D:** £16.00–£18.00 **S:** £18.00–£20.00 **Beds:** 1F 1D **Baths:** 1 Pr 1 En 🛇 🖬 (3) 📺 🍴 🛋 👤

Tomnavoulin

NJ2126

Roadside Cottage, *Tomnavoulin, Glenlivet, Ballindalloch, Banffshire, AB37 9JL.* Warm welcome, cool prices. Total customer care in glorious countryside. **Open:** All year (not Xmas) **01807 590486 (also fax)** Mrs Marks **D:** £16.00–£18.00 **S:** £16.00–£18.00 **Beds:** 1F 1D 1S **Baths:** 2 Sh 🛇 🖬 (4) 📺 🍴 ✕ 📺 🛋 👤

Turriff

NJ7250

Lower Plaidy, *Turriff, Aberdeenshire, AB53 5RJ.* Traditional farmhouse. On castle trail, golf, fishing, sporting activities locally. **Open:** All year (not Xmas/New Year) **Grades:** STB 2 Star **01888 551679** Mr & Mrs Daley *lowplaidy@ aol.com* www.lowerplaidy.co.uk **D:** £18.00–£22.00 **S:** £18.00–£22.00 **Beds:** 1T 1D 1S **Baths:** 1 Sh 🖬 (5) ⅙ 📺 🍴 ✕ 📺 🛋 👤

Lendrum Farm, *Birkenhills, Turriff, Aberdeenshire, AB53 8HA.* Comfortable historic farmhouse, traditional Scottish hospitality, home cooking, ensuite and peaceful. **Open:** All year (not Xmas/New Year) **Grades:** STB 3 Star **01888 544285 (also fax)** Mrs Roebuck *christina@lendru.fs.business.co.uk* **D:** £20.00–£22.00 **S:** £22.00 **Beds:** 1F 1T **Baths:** 1 En 🛇 (3) 🖸 ⅙ 📺 📺 🛋 👤

Urquhart

NJ2862

The Old Church of Urquhart, *Parrandier, Meft Road, Urquhart, Elgin, IV30 8NH.* Distinctly different place to explore malt whisky country, sea and Highlands. **Open:** All year **Grades:** STB 4 Star **01343 843063 (also fax)** A Peter *parrandier@ freeuk.com* www.oldkirk.co.uk **D:** £18.00–£27.50 **S:** £23.00–£28.00 **Beds:** 1F 2T 1D **Baths:** 2 En 1 Pr 🛇 🖬 (5) 📺 🍴 ✕ 🛋 👤 cc

All details shown are as supplied by B&B owners in Autumn 2001

Angus

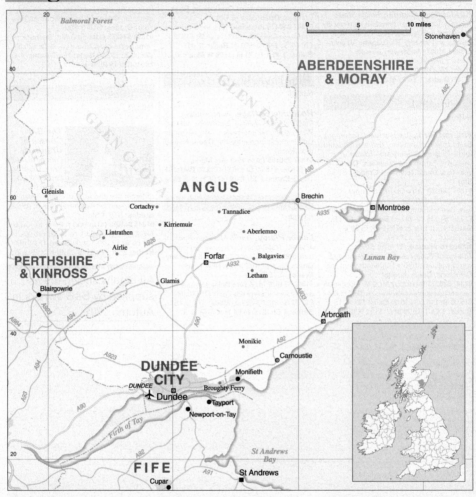

Balmoral Forest

ABERDEENSHIRE
& MORAY

Stonehaven

0   5   10 miles

ANGUS

Glenisla

Cortachy

Tannadice

Brechin

Montrose

Kirriemuir

Lintrathen

Aberlemno

Airlie

PERTHSHIRE
& KINROSS

Forfar

Balgavies

Lunan Bay

Glamis

Letham

Blairgowrie

Arbroath

Monikie

Carnoustie

DUNDEE
CITY

DUNDEE

Monifieth

Dundee

Broughty Ferry

Tayport

Newport-on-Tay

Firth of Tay

St Andrews
Bay

FIFE

Cupar

St Andrews

Aberlemno

NO5255

Blibberhill Farmhouse, *Aberlemno,
Brechin, Angus, DD9 6TH.* Glamis nearby.
Perth (1 hr), St. Andrews (40 mins),
Aberdeen (50 mins). **Open:** All year
Grades: STB 3 Star
01307 830323 Mrs Stewart
www.farmhouse-holidays.co.uk **D:** £17.00–
£20.00 **S:** £18.00 **Beds:** 1F 1T 1D **Baths:** 3 En
2 Sh ♿ 🅿 (5) ⅋ 📺 🛏 ✗ 🎥 ▦ ₺ cc

Planning a longer stay? Always
ask for any special rates

Airlie

NO3150

The Brae Of Airlie Farmhouse, *The
Kirkton of Airlie, Airlie, Kirriemuir, Angus,
DD8 5NJ.* Fabulous, relaxing views. Large
garden, many facilities. Telephone for
brochures. **Open:** All year
01575 530293 (also fax) M Gardyne
mamie.gardyne@tesco.net www.angusglens.co.
uk **D:** £20.00 **S:** £20.00 **Beds:** 2T **Baths:** 1 En
1 Sh 🅿 (4) ✗ 🎥 ▦ ₺ ₺

National Grid References given
are for villages, towns and
cities – not for individual houses

Arbroath

NO6441 🍴 *Old Brewhouse, Letham Grange Hotel,
Colliston Inn*

***Fairway View
B and B,*** *2
Fairway View,
Letham Grange,
Arbroath,
DD11 4XE.* Rural
setting. Warm
welcome. Hearty
breakfast. Golf courses of Angus. **Open:** All
year **Grades:** STB 3 Star
01241 890762 Mrs Mackie **Fax: 01241
890213** *chris_mackie1952@hotmail.com*
D: £25.00 **S:** £25.00 **Beds:** 1T 1D 1S **Baths:** 1
En 1 Sh ♿ 🅿 (3) 🎥 🛏 ▦ ₺

RATES

D = Price range per person sharing in a double or twin room

S = Price range for a single room

Balgavies

NO5350

Redroofs, *Balgavies, Guthrie, Forfar, Angus, DD8 2TN.* **Open:** All year **Grades:** STB 3 Star
01307 830268 (also fax) Mr & Mrs Milne
redroofs.forfar@virgin.net **D:** £20.00 **S:** £22.50
Beds: 1F 1T 1D **Baths:** 3 En ♿ ▣ (10) 📺 ♉ ✕
📺 ▥ ♿3 ⚄
Warm welcome in house set in large wooded area. All rooms on ground floor. TVs and refrigerators in all rooms. Ideal base for touring and activities, golf, fishing, walks, glens and seaside. Private secluded parking off B9113 Forfar-Montrose road. Discount on five or more days stay.

Broughty Ferry

NO4630   ⬛ *Tay Cregan Hotel*

Homebank, *9 Ellislea Road, Broughty Ferry, Dundee, DD5 1JH.* Splendid Victorian mansion house. Charming ambience, elegant gardens and decor. **Open:** All year **Grades:** STB 4 Diamond
01382 477481 (also fax) Mrs Moore
pat.moore.homebank@bushinternet.com
D: £25.00–£30.00 **S:** £25.00–£40.00 **Beds:** 1F 1T 1D 1S **Baths:** 2 En 1 Pr 1 Sh ♿ ▣ (7) ⤶ 📺
📺 ▥ ⚄

BEDROOMS

D = Double

T = Twin

S = Single

F = Family

Carnoustie

NO5634

Park House, *Park Avenue, Carnoustie, Angus, DD7 7JA.* Victorian house, three minutes from championship golf course, sea views. **Open:** All year (not Xmas)
Grades: STB 4 Star, AA 4 Diamond
01241 852101 (also fax) R Reyner
parkhouse@bbcarnoustie.co.uk
www.bbcarnoustie.fsnet.co.uk **D:** £25.00
S: £25.00 **Beds:** 1D 1T 2S ▣ (3) ⤶ 📺 📺 ▥ ⚄
cc

16 Links Parade, *Carnoustie, Angus, DD7 7JE.* Stone built villa overlooking 18th fairway of championship golf course.
Open: All year
01241 852381 (also fax) Bill & Mary Brand
billbrand@dechmont16.freeserve.co.uk
www.dechmont16.freeserve.co.uk **D:** £18.00
S: £18.00 **Beds:** 1D 1T 1S **Baths:** 1 Sh ▣ 📺
▥ ⚄

Cortachy

NO3959

Muirhouses Farm, *Cortachy, Kirriemuir, Angus, DD8 4QG.* Beautiful farmhouse in extensive mature garden on busy farm.
Open: All year (not Xmas/New Year)
01575 573128 (also fax) Mrs McLaren
muirhousesfarm@farming.co.uk
www.angusglens.co.uk **D:** £20.00 **S:** £20.00
Beds: 1F 1D 1S **Baths:** 1 Pr 1 Sh ♿ ▣ (4) ⤶
📺 ▥ ⚄

Dundee

NO3632

Aberlaw Guest House, *230 Broughty Ferry Road, Dundee, Angus, DD4 7JP.* Victorian house overlooking River Tay. Warm welcome from Brian and Aileen. **Open:** All year **Grades:** STB 3 Star
01382 456929 (also fax) Mr McCormick
D: £25.00–£30.00 **S:** £20.00–£25.00 **Beds:** 1T 2D 2S **Baths:** 1 En 1 Sh ♿ (12) ▣ (6) ⤶ 📺 ▥ ⚄

Ardmoy, *359 Arbroath Road, Dundee, Angus, DD4 7SQ.* Ardmoy is a family-run lovely house, overlooking the River Tay. **Open:** All year **Grades:** STB 3 Star
01382 453249 Mrs Taylor *taylord@sol.co.uk*
D: £18.00–£25.00 **S:** £18.00–£25.00 **Beds:** 1F 1D 1T 1S **Baths:** 2 En 1 Sh ♿ (5) ▣ (4) ⤶ 📺 ♉
✕ ▥ ⚄

Elm Lodge, *49 Seafield Road, Dundee, Angus, DD1 4NW.* Large Victorian Listed family home. Rooms with river view.
Open: Jan to Dec
01382 228402 Mrs McDowall **D:** £18.00–
£25.00 **S:** £18.00–£25.00 **Beds:** 1D 1T 1S
Baths: 1 Sh ▣ (4) 📺 ♉ 📺 ▥ ⚄

Ash Villa, *216 Arbroath Road, Dundee, Angus, DD4 7RZ.* Friendly family guest house. Nearby sea, river, mountains. ideal walking, exploring, castles, wildlife. **Open:** All year
Grades: STB 3 Star
01382 450831 (also fax) J M Hill
ash-villa-guesthouse@talk21.com **D:** £18.00–
£22.00 **S:** £18.00–£25.00 **Beds:** 1F 1T 1S
Baths: 1 En 2 Sh ♿ ▣ (4) ⤶ ♉ ⚄ ⚄

Homebank, *9 Ellislea Road, Broughty Ferry, Dundee, DD5 1JH.* Splendid Victorian mansion house. Charming ambience, elegant gardens and decor. **Open:** All year
Grades: STB 4 Diamond
01382 477481 (also fax) Mrs Moore
pat.moore.homebank@bushinternet.com
D: £25.00–£30.00 **S:** £25.00–£40.00 **Beds:** 1F 1T 1D 1S **Baths:** 2 En 1 Pr 1 Sh ♿ ▣ (7) ⤶ 📺 ▥ ⚄

Forfar

NO4550

Wemyss Farm, *Montrose Road, Forfar, Angus, DD8 2TB.* 190 acre mixed farm situated 2.5 miles along B9113. **Open:** All year
Grades: STB 3 Star
01307 462887 (also fax) Mrs Lindsay
wemyssfarm@hotmail.com **D:** £17.00–£18.00
S: £20.00–£21.00 **Beds:** 1F 1D **Baths:** 2 Sh
♿ ▣ (6) 📺 ♉ ✕ ▥ ⚄ ⚄ cc

Glamis

NO3846

Arndean, *Linross, Glamis, Forfar, Angus, DD8 1QN.* Close to Glamis Castle and in ideal walking country. **Open:** All year (not Xmas)
01307 840535 Mrs Ruffhead *arndean@ btinternet.com www.arnbog.btinternet.co.uk*
D: £16.00 **S:** £16.00–£20.00 **Beds:** 2T
Baths: 1 Sh ▣ (3) 📺 ♉ ▥ ⚄ ⚄

Glenisla

NO2160

The Kirkside House Hotel, *11 Conigre Close, Glenisla, Blairgowrie, Perthshire, PH11 8PH.* Overlooking upper River Isla; peace, tranquility, good food, friendly service. Ideal for touring. **Open:** All year
01575 582313 Janice Appleby & Tony Willis
D: £22.50 **S:** £22.50 **Beds:** 1F 3D 1S **Baths:** 3 En 1 Sh ♿ ▣ (50) ⤶ 📺 ♉ ✕ ▥ ⚄ ✳ ⚄ cc

Planning a longer stay? Always ask for any special rates

Kirriemuir

NO3853 🍴 *Clova Hotel, Royal Jubilee Arms, Woodville Inn, Thrums Hotel, Airlie Arms*

Crepto, *Kinnordy Place, Kirriemuir, Forfar, Angus, DD8 4JW.* 10 minutes walk from town centre. Friendly, warm welcome. Comfortable. **Open:** All year
01575 572746 Mrs Lindsay *daveandjessma@ bun.com* **D:** £22.00–£25.00 **S:** £22.00–£25.00 **Beds:** 1D 1T 1S **Baths:** 2 Sh ♿ 🅿 (3) ✄ 📺 🛈 ♨

Muirhouses Farm, *Cortachy, Kirriemuir, Angus, DD8 4QG.* Beautiful farmhouse in extensive mature garden on busy farm. **Open:** All year (not Xmas/New Year) **01575 573128 (also fax)** Mrs McLaren *muirhousesfarm@farming.co.uk* www.angusglens.co.uk **D:** £20.00 **S:** £20.00 **Beds:** 1F 1D 1S **Baths:** 1 Pr 1 Sh ♿ 🅿 (4) ✄

Letham

NO5248

Whinney-Knowe, *8 Dundee Street, Letham, Forfar, DD8 2PQ.* Large semi-detached villa in friendly rural surroundings. Guests lounge.
Open: All year **Grades:** STB 3 Star **01307 818288** E Mann *whinneyknowe@ btinternet.com* **D:** £18.00–£20.00 **S:** £20.00–£25.00 **Beds:** 1T 2D **Baths:** 1 En 1 Sh ♿ 🅿 (4) 📺 🍴 🛈 ♨

Lintrathen

NO2853

Lochside Lodge, *Bridgend of Lintrathen, Lintrathen, Kirriemuir, Angus, DD8 5JJ.* In Angus Glens, a picturesque converted farm steading alongside Linstrathen Loch.
Open: All year **01575 560340 Fax: 01575 560202** *enquiries@ lochsidelodge.com* www.lochsidelodge.com **D:** £30.00–£35.00 **S:** £35.00–£40.00 **Beds:** 1F 2T 1D **Baths:** 4 Pr ♿ 🅿 (20) ✄ 📺 🍴 ✕ 🛈 ♨ cc

Monikie

NO4938

Lindford House, *8 West Hillhead Road, Monikie, Angus, DD5 3QS.* Deluxe accommodation overlooking country park and close to local amenities. **Open:** All year (not Xmas) **01382 370314 (also fax)** M Milton **D:** £18.00–£25.00 **S:** £20.00–£25.00 **Beds:** 2F 1D **Baths:** 2 Pr ♿ 🅿 (6) 📺 🛈 ♨

Montrose

NO7157

Byeways, *11 Rossie Terrace, Ferryden, Montrose, Angus, DD10 9RX.* Very comfortable, home from home. Turn sharp right past pub. **Open:** All year (not Xmas/New Year) **01674 678510** Mrs Docherty **D:** £15.00 **S:** £20.00 **Beds:** 2D 1T **Baths:** 1 En 2 Pr ✄ 📺 🛈 ♨

Tannadice

NO4758 🍴 *Finavon Hotel, Drovers Arms*

Glencoul House, *Tannadice, Forfar, Angus, DD8 3SF.* Near Glamis Castle, Angus Glens, beaches. Golf courses, St. Andrews, fishing. **Open:** All year (not Xmas/New Year) **Grades:** STB 3 Star **01307 860248 (also fax)** Mrs Kirby *glencoul@ waitrose.com* **D:** £19.00–£20.00 **S:** £20.00 **Beds:** 1F 1T **Baths:** 2 Sh ♿ 🅿 (3) ✄ 📺 🍴 ✕ 🛈 ♨

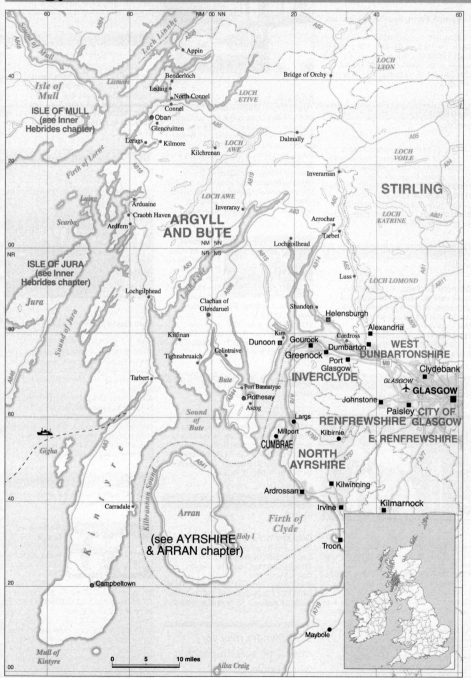

Appin

NM9346   *Creggan Inn, Pier House*

Lurignish Farm, *Appin, Argyll, PA38 4BN.* Traditional lochside hill farm, good home-cooking, golf, boating, riding nearby. **Open:** May to Sept **Grades:** STB 2 Star **01631 730365** Mrs Macleod *lurignish@ amserve.net* **D:** £18.00–£21.00 **S:** £20.00–£23.00 **Beds:** 1F 1D **Baths:** 1 Sh ⌂ ▯ (4) ▢ ⌂ ▢ ▥ ⌂

Ardfern

NM8004

Lunga, *Ardfern, Lochgilphead, Argyll, PA31 8QR.* C17th estate mansion overlooks islands & Firth of Lorne. 3,000 acre private coastal estate. **Open:** All year **01852 500237** Mr Lindsay-MacDougall **Fax: 01852 500639** *colin@lunga.demon.co.uk* www.lunga.demon.co.uk **D:** £19.00–£22.00 **S:** £18.00 **Beds:** 1F 2D 1T 1S **Baths:** 4 Pr 1 Sh ⌂ ▯ ▢ ⌂ × ▢ ⌂

Arduaine

NM8010

Asknish Cottage, *Arduaine, Oban, Argyll, PA34 4XQ.* Halfway between Oban & Lochgilphead. Warm welcome in hillside cottage overlooking islands Jura to Luing. **Open:** All year **01852 200247** Miss Campbell **D:** £16.50–£17.50 **S:** £17.00–£22.00 **Beds:** 2D 1T **Baths:** 1 Sh ⌂ ▯ (3) ⅍ ▢ ⌂ ▢ ▥ ⌂

Arrochar

NN2904   *Callums Bar, Village Inn*

Ferry Cottage, *Ardmay, Arrochar, Dunbartonshire, G83 7AH.* **Open:** All year (not Xmas) **01301 702428** Mrs Bennetton **Fax: 01301 702729** *caroleferrycott@aol.com* **D:** £18.50–£25.00 **S:** £22.00–£35.00 **Beds:** 1F 2D 1T **Baths:** 3 En 1 Sh ⌂ (2) ▯ (6) ⅍ ▢ × ▥ ⌂ cc Quietly situated 1 mile south of Arrochar (A814) 5 minutes drive from Loch Lomond. All ensuite rooms have breathtaking views overlooking Loch Long towards the 'Cobbler'. Major credit cards, private parking. Excellent base for touring the surrounding area. Non Smoking establishment.

Seabank, *Main Road, Arrochar, G83 7AG.* **Open:** All year **Grades:** STB 2 Star **01301 702555 (also fax)** S Smillie *sam@ seabankarrochar.fsnet.co.uk* **D:** £16.00–£20.00 **S:** £20.00–£28.00 **Beds:** 1F 1D 1T **Baths:** 1 Sh ⌂ (8) ▯ (6) ⅍ ▢ ⌂ ▢ ▥ ⌂ Lovely old house, beautiful views Loch and Arrochar Alps. Great base hill-walking, touring, fishing. Loch Lomond 2 miles, Glasgow 40 miles, historic Stirling 50 miles. 200 metres walking distance village pub. Great food, reasonably priced, warm welcome from Sam and Kathleen.

Fascadail, *Shore Road, Arrochar, G83 7AB.* Magnificent loch and mountain views. Ideal base touring and walking. **Open:** All year **Grades:** STB 3 Star **01301 702344** *fascadail@easynet.co.uk* www.fascadail.com **D:** £20.00–£27.50 **S:** £30.00–£45.00 **Beds:** 2T 5D **Baths:** 6 En 1 Pr ▯ (8) ⅍ ▢ ⌂ ▢ ▥ ⌂ cc

Benderloch

NM9038

Hawthorn, *Benderloch, Oban, Argyll, PA37 1QS.* Delightful bungalow situated in 20 acres of farming land. All rooms ensuite, peaceful accommodation. **Open:** All year **01631 720452** Mrs Currile **D:** £18.00–£22.00 **S:** £25.00–£30.00 **Beds:** 1F 1D 1T **Baths:** 2 En 1 Pr ▯ (5) ▢ × ▥ ⌂ cc

Bridge of Orchy

NN2939

Glen Orchy Farm, *Glen Orchy, Bridge of Orchy, Argyll, PA33 1BD.* Remote sheep farm. Enjoy wildlife, birdwatching, walking, climbing amongst beautiful scenery. **Open:** Mar to Nov **01838 200221** Mrs MacLennan **Fax: 01838 200231** **D:** £16.00–£18.00 **S:** £16.00–£18.00 **Beds:** 2F **Baths:** 1 Sh ⌂ ▯ ▢ × ▥ ⌂

B&B owners may vary rates – be sure to check when booking

Planning a longer stay? Always ask for any special rates

BUTE   Ascog

NS1062   *Black Bull*

Ascog Farm, *Ascog, Rothesay, Isle of Bute, PA20 9LL.* Features on BBC TV's 'Holidays Out' - come and be spoilt. **Open:** All year (not Xmas/New Year) **01700 503372** I Watson **D:** £17.00 **S:** £17.00 **Beds:** 1D 3S **Baths:** 2 Sh ⌂ (8) ▯ (4) ⅍ ▢ ▥ ⌂

BUTE   Port Bannatyne

NS0867

Port Royal Hotel, *37 Marine Road, Port Bannatyne, Isle of Bute, PA20 0LW.* **Open:** All year **01700 505073** *portroyal@uk-entertainment.com* www.uk-entertainment.com/portroyalhotel **D:** £22.00–£26.00 **S:** £22.00–£35.00 **Beds:** 1F 4T **Baths:** 2 En 1 Pr 1 Sh ⌂ ▯ (5) ▢ ⌂ × ▥ ⌂ ⌂ ✳ ⌂ A traditional village inn, The Port Royal Hotel looks across Kames Bay to the stunning Argyll mountains. Sparking cottage rooms, real ale, fine wine and fresh local produce, blessed by a dedicated Russian chef, await nature lovers, yachtsmen and travellers.

BUTE   Rothesay

NS0864   *Black Bull Inn, Ardmory House Hotel, Port Royal Hotel, Kingarth Hotel*

Battery Lodge, *25 Battery Place, Rothesay, Isle of Bute, PA20 9DU.* **Open:** All year **01700 502169** M Leyden **D:** £20.00–£22.00 **S:** £18.00–£20.00 **Beds:** 2F 1T 4D 1S **Baths:** 4 En 2 Pr 1 Sh ⌂ ▯ (7) ▢ × ▥ ⌂ ⌂ Built in 1865, Battery Lodge is a splendid mid-Victorian enjoying spectacular views across Rothesay Bay to the Argyllshire Hills. Your hosts Martin and Lorraine offer attractive bedrooms, most with ensuite facilities, plus warm Scottish hospitality with home cooking.

BUTE

Alamein House Hotel, *28 Battery Place, Rothesay, Isle of Bute, PA20 9DU.* Magnificent views from seafront bedrooms. Yachting, fishing, riding, cycling closeby. **Open:** All year **01700 502395** J F Hutchings **D:** £19.00–£21.00 **S:** £20.00–£22.00 **Beds:** 1F 3T 3D **Baths:** 3 En 1 Pr 2 Sh ⅏ ⚐ (5) ⊠ ⌇ ⛨ ⬛ ⬥ ⚘

Campbeltown

NR7220 ⚓ Ardsheil Hotel

Homestone Farm, *Campbeltown, Argyll, PA28 6RL.* Wonderfully, peaceful location on working farm/riding centre. Excellent food. **Open:** Easter to Oct **01586 552437** L McArthur *lorna@ relaxscotland.com* **D:** £18.00 **S:** £18.00 **Beds:** 3D 2S **Baths:** 3 En 1 Sh ⚐ (10) ⊠ ✕ ⚘

Glen Mhairi, *Craigown Road, Campbeltown, Argyll, PA28 6HQ.* Superb location overlooking town and loch. Modern bungalow, warm welcome. **Open:** Easter to Oct **Grades:** STB 3 Star **01586 552952** Mrs Craig **D:** £18.50–£20.00 **S:** £20.00–£22.50 **Beds:** 1T 1D **Baths:** 1 Pr 1 Sh ⅏ ⚐ (2) ⊠ ⌇ ⬛ ⚘

Cardross

NS3477

Kirkton House, *Darleith Road, Cardross, Dumbarton, G82 5EZ.* Old farmstead hotel. Tranquil setting. Clyde views. Wine and dine. **Open:** Feb to Nov **Grades:** STB 4 Star, AA 5 Diamond, RAC 5 Diamond **01389 841951 Fax: 01389 841868** *stil@ kirktonhouse.co.uk* www.kirktonhouse.co.uk **D:** £30.50–£35.00 **S:** £40.50–£45.00 **Beds:** 4F 2T **Baths:** 6 En ⅏ ⚐ (12) ⊠ ⌇ ✕ ⬛ ⬥ ⚘ cc

Glengate Cottage, *Main Road, Cardross, Dumbarton, G82 5NZ.* Picturesque village. Minutes from Helensburgh seaside town. NTS properties and golf nearby. **Open:** All year **01389 841737** Miss Mackie **D:** £19.00–£21.00 **S:** £17.00 **Beds:** 2D 1S **Baths:** 1 Pr 1 Sh ⚐ (2) ⅄ ⊠ ⬛ ⚘

Carradale

NR8138 ⚓ Ashbank Hotel, Carradale Hotel

Kiloran Guest House, *Carradale, Campbeltown, Argyll, PA28 6QG.* Lovely Victorian house. Warm welcome. Good home cooking. Sandy beaches. **Open:** All year **01583 431795** J A Nicholson **D:** £18.50–£25.00 **S:** £22.00–£28.00 **Beds:** 1F 3T 1D **Baths:** 2 En 1 Pr 1 Sh ⅏ ⚐ (6) ⊠ ⌇ ✕ ⬛ ⚘

Clachan of Glendaruel

NS0083

Glendaruel Hotel, *Clachan of Glendaruel, Colintraive, Argyll, PA22 3AA.* Charming family run hotel. Ideal for fishing, touring, walking etc. **Open:** All year (not Xmas) **01369 820274 Fax: 01369 820317** *info@ glendaruel-hotel.com* www.glendaruel-hotel. com **D:** £30.00–£35.00 **S:** £35.00–£40.00 **Beds:** 3T 2D 1S **Baths:** 6 En ⚐ (10) ⊠ ⌇ ✕ ⊠ ⬛ ⚘ cc

Colintraive

NS0374

Colintraive Hotel, *Colintraive, Argyll, PA22 3AS.* Former Victorian hunting lodge. Comfortable and informal family run hotel. **Open:** All year **01700 841207** Mr Williamson *kyleshotel@ aol.com* **D:** £22.00–£28.00 **S:** £26.00–£30.00 **Beds:** 1F 1D 1T **Baths:** 4 Pr ⅏ ⚐ ⊠ ⌇ ✕ ⊠ ⬛ ⚘

Connel

NM9133 ⚓ Lcoknell Arms, Dunstaffanage Arms, Falls of Lora

Rosebank, *Connel, Oban, Argyll, PA37 1PA.* **Open:** May to Sept **01631 710316** R L MacKechnie **D:** £14.00–£16.00 **S:** £15.00–£17.00 **Beds:** 1D 1T 1S **Baths:** 1 Sh ⅏ ⊠ ⌇ ⚘ Family house in quiet situation in Connel village overlooking Loch Etive, 5 miles from Oban. Excellent touring centre, large garden at rear. Home made preserves a speciality. Hand-knitted articles for sale. A warm welcome to home and overseas visitors.

Craobh Haven

NM7907

Buidhe Lodge, *Craobh Haven, Lochgilphead, Argyll, PA31 8UA.* Swiss-style lodge located on shores of Loch Shuna. Near NTS Arduaine Gardens. **Open:** All year (not Xmas) **01852 500291** Mr & Mrs Twinn www.buidhelodge.com **D:** £23.00–£26.00 **S:** £33.00 **Beds:** 2D 4T **Baths:** 6 Pr ⅏ ⚐ (8) ⊠ ⌇ ✕ ⊠ ⬛ ⬥ ⚘

Dalmally

NN1626

Orchy Bank Guest House, *Dalmally, Argyll, PA33 1AS.* Victorian house on the bank of the River Orchy. **Open:** All year **Grades:** STB 2 Star **01838 200370** Mr Burke *a.j.burke@talk21.com* **D:** £17.00–£20.00 **S:** £20.00–£25.00 **Beds:** 2D 2T **Baths:** 4 Sh ⅏ ⚐ (8) ⊠ ⌇ ⬛ ⚘

Dunoon

NS1776

Craigieburn Hotel, *Alexandra Parade, East Bay, Dunoon, Argyll, PA23 8AN.* Friendly family-run private hotel with superb sea views. **Open:** All year (not Xmas) **Grades:** STB 2 Star **01369 702048** Mrs Hutchinson *emma.hutchinson@btinternet.com* www.btinternet.com/~emma.hutchinson **D:** £16.00–£20.00 **S:** £16.00–£20.00 **Beds:** 3F 2D 2T 2S **Baths:** 3 Sh ⅏ ⚐ (5) ⊠ ⌇ ✕ ⬛ ⚘

Lyall Cliff Hotel, *Alexandra Parade, East Bay, Dunoon, Argyll, PA23 8AW.* Beautifully situated family-run seafront hotel. 3 ground floor rooms. **Open:** Jan to Oct **Grades:** STB 3 Star **01369 702041 (also fax)** Mr & Mrs Norris *lyallcliff@talk21.com* www.in-uk.com/lyallcliff **D:** £20.00–£25.00 **S:** £23.00–£30.00 **Beds:** 2F 4D 4T **Baths:** 10 En ⅏ (4) ⚐ (10) ⅄ ⊠ ✕ ⊠ ⬛ ⚘ cc

Moncrieff, *133 Alexandra Parade, Dunoon, Argyll, PA23 8AW.* Family Tudor style home, panoramic sea views, private gardens, wheelchair users catered for. **Open:** All year **01369 707945 (also fax)** Mrs Peel *willypeel@ aol.com* **D:** £16.00–£20.00 **S:** £19.00–£25.00 **Beds:** 1T 2D **Baths:** 1 En 2 Sh ⅏ ⊠ ⌇ ⊠ ⬛ ⬥ ⚘

Glencruitten

NM8729

Barranrioch Farm, *Glencruitten, Oban, Argyll, PA34 4QD.* Peaceful working farm close to Oban. Enclosed play area. **Open:** All year **Grades:** STB 2 Star **01631 770223** Mrs Nicholson *barranrioch@ crosswinds.net* **D:** £15.00–£20.00 **S:** £15.00–£20.00 **Beds:** 1F 1D **Baths:** 1 En 1 Pr ⅏ ⚐ (10) ⊠ ⌇ ✕ ⊠ ⬛ ⚘

Helensburgh

NS2982

Eastbank, *10 Hanover Street, Helensburgh, Argyll, G84 7AW.* Upper flat of Victorian house 30 minutes from Glasgow airport. **Open:** All year (not Xmas) **Grades:** STB 3 Star **01436 673665 (also fax)** Mrs Ross *enquries@ eastbankscotland.com* **D:** £18.00–£23.00 **S:** £18.00–£20.00 **Beds:** 1F 1T 1S **Baths:** 1 En 1 Sh ⅏ (3) ⚐ (4) ⊠ ⊠ ⬛ ⚘ cc

County Lodge Hotel, *Old Luss Road, Helensburgh, Dunbartonshire, G84 7BH.* Travel Lodge style accommodation. Twin/Double rooms ensuite at £39.95. **Open:** All year
01436 672034 Fax: 01436 672033 D: £22.95 **S:** £22.95 **Beds:** 7T/D **Baths:** 7 En ⮢ 🅿 📺 ⼐ ✕ 📺 🕮 ☕ **cc**

Maybank, *185 East Clyde Street, Helensburgh, Dunbartonshire, G84 7AG.* Attractive early Victorian home in a level location. **Open:** All year **Grades:** STB 3 Star
01436 672865 Mrs Barella **D:** £18.00 **S:** £22.00 **Beds:** 2D/T 1S **Baths:** 2 Sh ⮢ 🅿 📺 ⼐ 📺 🕮 ♿ ☕

Yetholm, *103 East Princes Street, Helensburgh, Dunbartonshire, G84 7DN.* Near Hill House - Rennie Mackintosh. 10 mins Loch Lomond. Good base golf, sailing, Trossachs. **Open:** All year (not Xmas) **Grades:** STB 3 Star
01436 673271 Mrs Mackenzie **D:** £18.00–£22.00 **S:** £20.00–£22.00 **Beds:** 1D 1T **Baths:** 1 Pr 1 En ⮢ (5) 🅿 (3) ⼐ 📺 📺 🕮 ☕

Ravenswood, *32 Suffolk Street, Helensburgh, Dunbartonshire, G84 9PA.* Member walkers and cyclists scheme - Sliver Green Tourism award. **Open:** All year **01436 672112 (also fax)** Mrs Richards *ravenswood@breathemail.net* **D:** £25.00–£40.00 **S:** £25.00–£50.00 **Beds:** 2D 1T 1S **Baths:** 2 En 1 Pr 1 Sh ⮢ 🅿 (4) ⼐ 📺 ✕ 📺 🕮 ☕

Arran View, *32 Barclay Drive, Helensburgh, Dunbartonshire, G84 9RA.* Panoramic sea views, Convenient NT. Hill House, Loch Lomond, golf. **Open:** All year **01436 673713** Mr & Mrs Sanders **Fax: 01436 672595** *arranview@btinternet.com* www.btinternet.com/arranview **D:** £19.00–£22.00 **S:** £20.00–£25.00 **Beds:** 1D 1T 2S **Baths:** 2 En 1 Pr 1 Sh 🅿 (5) ⼐ 📺 📺 🕮 ☕

28 Macleod Drive, *Helensburgh, Dunbartonshire, G84 9QS.* Stunning views near Loch Lomond, golf, walking and the Highlands. **Open:** June to Sept **01436 675206** Mr & Mrs Calder *g.calder@talk21.com* **D:** £17.00–£19.00 **S:** £18.00–£20.00 **Beds:** 1F 1T 1S **Baths:** 2 Sh ⮢ 🅿 (3) ⼐ 📺 📺 🕮 ☕

4 Redclyffe Gardens, *Helensburgh, Dunbartonshire, G84 9JJ.* Modern family home; sea views, quiet cul-de-sac, adjacent Mackintosh Hill House. **Open:** All year (not Xmas)
01436 677688 (also fax) Mrs Weston *dweston440@aol.com* www.stayatlochlomond.com/bweston **D:** £21.00–£24.00 **S:** £25.00–£30.00 **Beds:** 1D 1T **Baths:** 1 Pr 1 En ⮢ 🅿 (3) ⼐ 📺 📺 🕮 ☕

\rumfork Farm, *Helensburgh, G84 7JY.* \rking farm with friendly family, 20 utes from Loch Lomond. **Open:** All year Xmas/New Year)
\72329 (also fax)** Mrs Howie *fm@aol.com* **D:** £20.00–£25.00 –£40.00 **Beds:** 2T 1D **Baths:** 3 En 📺 ✕ 📺 🕮 ♿ ☕ **cc**

Inveraray

NN0908   🏚 George Hotel

Minard Castle, *Minard, Inveraray, Argyll, PA32 8YB.* Warm welcome in our nineteenth-century castle beside Loch Fyne. **Open:** Apr to Oct **Grades:** STB 4 Star
01546 886272 (also fax) Mr Gayre *reinoldgayre@minardcastle.com* www.minardcastle.com **D:** £35.00–£40.00 **S:** £35.00–£40.00 **Beds:** 2F 1T **Baths:** 3 En ⮢ 🅿 (6) ⼐ 📺 ⼐ 📺 🕮 ☕ **cc**

The Old Rectory, *Inveraray, Argyll, PA32 8UH.* Family-run Georgian house overlooking Loch Fyne. **Open:** All year (not Xmas)
01499 302280 Mrs Maclaren **D:** £15.00–£20.00 **S:** £15.00–£20.00 **Beds:** 4F 3D 1T 1S **Baths:** 3 Sh ⮢ (3) 🅿 (9) ⼐ 📺 📺 🕮

Claonairigh House, *Bridge of Douglas, Inveraray, Argyll, PA32 8XT.* Historic country house ideally situated for Argyll countryside and coast. Excellent breakfasts, beautiful rooms. **Open:** All year (not Xmas) **Grades:** STB 3 Star
01499 302160 Fax: 01499 302774 *fiona@argyll-scotland.demon.co.uk* **D:** £16.00–£25.00 **S:** £16.00–£25.00 **Beds:** 1D 2T **Baths:** 3 En ⮢ 🅿 (8) ⼐ 📺 ⼐ 📺 🕮 ☕

Creag Dhubh, *Inveraray, Argyll, PA32 8XF.* Family run B&B. Unrestricted views across Loch Fyne. **Open:** All year (not Xmas/New Year)
01499 302430 J MacLugash *creagdhubh@freeuk.com* **D:** £20.00–£25.00 **S:** £25.00–£30.00 **Beds:** 2F 3D **Baths:** 5 En ⮢ (2) 🅿 (6) ⼐ 📺 📺 🕮 ☕ **cc**

Inverarnan

NN3118   🏚 Drovers Inn

Rose Cottage, *Inverarnan, Glen Falloch, Arrochar, Dunbartonshire, G83 7DX.* Renovated C18th cottage on West Highland Way, Loch Lomond. **Open:** All year (not Xmas/New Year) **Grades:** STB 2 Star
01301 704255 Mr & Mrs Fletcher *fletcher.j3@talk21.com* **D:** £19.00–£25.00 **Beds:** 2D **Baths:** 2 En ⮢ 🅿 (4) ⼐ ✕ 📺 🕮 ☕

Kilchrenan

NN0322   🏚 Lcoknell Arms, Dunstaffnage Arms, Falls of Lora, Kilchrenan Inn

Innisfree, *Kilchrenan, Taynuilt, Argyll, PA35 1HG.* Wonderful scenery, modern croft house, quiet. Oban 19 miles, popular destination. **Open:** Easter to Sept
01866 833352 Mrs Wright **D:** £18.00 **S:** £18.00 **Beds:** 1D 1T **Baths:** 2 Sh ⮢ 🅿 (4) 📺 🕮

Kilfinan

NR9378

Auchnaskeoch Farm House, *Kilfinan, Tighnabruaich, Argyll, PA21 2ER.* Enjoy unspoiled countryside and magnificent scenery; a warm Scottish welcome awaits you. **Open:** All year (not Xmas)
01700 811397 Mrs Mackay **Fax: 01700 811799 D:** £17.50–£20.00 **S:** £18.00–£21.00 **Beds:** 1D **Baths:** 1 En 🅿 (1) 📺 ✕ 📺 🕮 ☕

Kilmore

NM8825

Invercairn, *Musdale Road, Kilmore, Oban, Argyll, PA34 4XX.* Beautiful spot, 10-minute drive Oban town centre. Wonderful base for splendours of Argyll. **Open:** Easter to Oct
01631 770301 (also fax) Mrs MacPherson *invercairn.kilmore@virgin.net* www.bandboban.com **D:** £20.00–£25.00 **S:** £25.00–£30.00 **Beds:** 2D 1T **Baths:** 3 En 🅿 (4) ⼐ 📺 📺 🕮 ☕

Kirn

NS1877

Rosscairn Hotel, *51 Hunter Street, Kirn, Dunoon, Argyll, PA23 8JR.* Quiet, friendly atmosphere, excellent food. Ideal base to explore Argyll. **Open:** All year (not Xmas/New Year) **Grades:** STB 3 Star
01369 704344 (also fax) Mr & Mrs Jones *rosscairn@kirn.fsnet.co.uk* rosscairn.freeserve.co.uk **D:** £22.00–£26.00 **S:** £25.00–£30.00 **Beds:** 3F 2T 2D 1S **Baths:** 7 En 1 Pr ⮢ 🅿 (10) ⼐ 📺 ✕ 📺 🕮 ☕ **cc**

Ledaig

NM9037

An Struan, *Ledaig, Oban, Argyll, PA37 1QS.* Large modern bungalow in the picturesque village of Benderloch, 7 miles north of Oban. **Open:** All year (not Xmas)
01631 720301 Mrs Knowles **Fax: 01631 720734** *frankwop@btinternet.com* www.oban.org.uk/accommodation/anstruan.index.html **D:** £18.00–£22.00 **S:** £20.00–£25.00 **Beds:** 2D 1T **Baths:** 1 En 1 Sh ⮢ 🅿 ⼐ 📺 ⼐ 📺 🕮 ♿

Lerags

NM8424

Lerags House, *Lerags, Oban, Argyll, PA34 4SE.* Enchanting country house in mature gardens on Loch Feochan shore. **Open:** Easter to Oct
01631 563381 (also fax) N A Hill *leragshouse@supanet.com* www.leragshouse.com **D:** £22.50–£30.00 **S:** £22.50–£30.00 **Beds:** 4D 2T 1S **Baths:** 7 En ⮢ (12) 🅿 (7) ⼐ 📺 ✕ 📺 🕮 ☕

Lochgilphead

NR8687

Kilmory House, Paterson Street, Lochgilphead, Argyll, PA31 8JP. Lovely house and gardens situated lochside. Most rooms with loch views. **Open:** All year
01546 603658 Mr Moore **D:** £16.50–£20.00 **S:** £20.00–£25.00 **Beds:** 2D 3T **Baths:** 3 En 2 Pr ⌖ (10) ▣ (16) ⊬ ▣ ✕ ▣ ▦. ♣ **cc**

Empire Travel Lodge, Union Street, Lochgilphead, Argyll, PA31 8JS. Former cinema converted to create quality travel lodge. **Open:** All year (not Xmas)
01546 602381 Mr Haysom **Fax:** 01546 606606 **D:** £23.00 **S:** £23.00 **Beds:** 2F 5D 2T **Baths:** 9 En ⌖ ▣ (9) ▣ ▣ ▦. ♣1 ♣ **cc**

Corbiere, Achnabreac, Lochgilphead, Argyll, PA31 8SG. Bedrooms are spacious, comfortable, thoughtfully equipped. Peaceful, rural location. **Open:** All year (not Xmas/New Year)
01546 602764 Mrs Sinclair **D:** £16.50–£17.50 **S:** £20.00 **Beds:** 1T 1D **Baths:** 2 Sh ⌖ ▣ ▣ ⋔ ▣ ▦. ♣

Luss

NS3592

Shantron Farm, Shantron Cottage, Luss, Alexandria, Dunbartonshire, G83 8RH. 5000-acre farm with spectacular views of loch and surrounding area. **Open:** Mar to Nov **Grades:** STB 3 Star
01389 850231 (also fax) Mrs Lennox rjlennox@shantron.u-net.com www.staylochlomond.com **D:** £22.00–£25.00 **S:** £25.00–£30.00 **Beds:** 1F 1D 1T **Baths:** 3 En ⌖ ▣ (3) ▣ ▣ ♣ **cc**

Doune of Glen Douglas Farm, Luss, Loch Lomond, Alexandria, Argyll & Bute, G83 8PD. Remote working hill sheep farm set in 6000 acres hills above Loch Lomond. **Open:** Easter to Oct
01301 702312 Mrs Robertson **Fax:** 01301 702916 pjrobertson@glendouglas.u-net.com **D:** £22.00–£30.00 **S:** £25.00–£35.00 **Beds:** 2D 1T **Baths:** 1 En 2 Sh ⌖ ▣ ▣ ⋔ ▣ ▦. ♣ **cc**

North Connel

NM9134 ⬗ Lochnell Arms, Dunstaff Nage Arms, Falls of Lora Hotel

Santana Lodge, Bonawe Road, North Connel, Oban, PA37 1RA. Beautiful bungalow. Quiet area. Perfect for touring West Highlands Islands. **Open:** Easter to Sept
01631 710380 Mrs Scott **D:** £16.00–£20.00 **S:** £20.00–£25.00 **Beds:** 1FN 2T 1D 1S **Baths:** 2 Sh ⌖ (5) ▣ (6) ⊬ ⋔ ▣ ▦.

Oban

NM8630 ⬗ Cuilfail Hotel, Kings Knoll Hotel, Lorne Hotel

Glenara Guest House, Rockfield Road, Oban, Argyll, PA34 5DQ. **Open:** All year **Grades:** STB 4 Star
01631 563172 Mrs Bingham **Fax:** 01631 571125 glenara_oban@hotmail.com www.smoothhound.co.uk/hotels/glenara.html **D:** £21.00–£27.00 **S:** £25.00–£35.00 **Beds:** 1F/T 3D **Baths:** 4 En ⌖ (12) ▣ (5) ⊬ ▣ ▣ ▦. ♣
We offer to our guests a quality of room, breakfast and welcome which will ensure your return. Centrally situated, sea views, off-street parking. Individually furnished rooms with king-sized beds reflecting Dorothy's commitment to quality. Glenara is a no-smoking guest house.

Corriemar House, Esplanade, Oban, Argyll, PA34 5AQ. **Open:** All year **Grades:** STB 3 Star, AA 3 Diamond
01631 562476 A Russell **Fax:** 01631 564339 corriemar@tinyworld.co.uk **D:** £24.00–£40.00 **S:** £24.00–£45.00 **Beds:** 2F 6D 4T 2S **Baths:** 12 En 2 Pr ⌖ ▣ (10) ⊬ ▣ ✕ ▣ ▦. ♣ ♣ **cc**
Large Victorian house in prime location on Oban's seafront. Ideal for use as a base for touring local islands and loch or just relax and watch the sun setting over Oban Bay.

Dana Villa, Dunollie Road, Oban, Argyll, PA34 5PJ. Scottish hospitality, family run. Close to all amenities and waterfront. **Open:** All year
01631 564063 Mrs Payne edna.payne@btopenworld.com www.danavilla.com **D:** £15.00 **Beds:** 2F 2D 3T 1S **Baths:** 3 En 1 Pr 2 Sh ⌖ ▣ ⋔ ✕ ▣ ▦. ♣

Greencourt, Benvoulin Lane, Oban, Argyll, PA34 5EF. Great hospitality. Immaculate rooms, delicious breakfast, peaceful location. **Open:** All year (not Xmas/New Year) **Grades:** STB 4 Diamond
01631 563987 Mr & Mrs Cook relax@greencourt-oban.fsnet.co.uk **D:** £22.00–£28.00 **S:** £35.00–£45.00 **Beds:** 2T 5D 1S ▣ (8) ⊬ ▣ ▦. ♣ **cc**

Please respect a B&B's wishes regarding children, animals and smoking

---

Roseneath Guest House, Dalriach Road, Oban, Argyll, PA34 5EQ. Quiet yet conveniently located for all terminals, towns and amenities. **Open:** Feb to Nov **Grades:** STB 4 Star, AA 4 Diamond
01631 562929 **Fax:** 01631 567218 quirkers@aol.com www.oban.org.uk/accommodation.roseneath **D:** £20.00–£27.00 **S:** £26.00 **Beds:** 2T 6D **Baths:** 8 En ⌖ (6) ▣ (8) ⊬ ▣ ⋔ ▣ ▦. ♣ **cc**

Barranrioch Farm, Glencruitten, Oban, Argyll, PA34 4QD. Peaceful working farm close to Oban. Enclosed play area. **Open:** All year **Grades:** STB 2 Star
01631 770223 Mrs Nicholson barranrioch@crosswinds.net **D:** £15.00–£20.00 **S:** £15.00–£20.00 **Beds:** 1F 1D **Baths:** 1 En 1 Pr ⌖ ▣ (10) ▣ ⋔ ✕ ▣ ▦. ♣

Santana Lodge, Bonawe Road, North Connel, Oban, PA37 1RA. Beautiful bungalow. Quiet area. Perfect for touring West Highlands Islands. **Open:** Easter to Sept
01631 710380 Mrs Scott **D:** £16.00–£20.00 **S:** £20.00–£25.00 **Beds:** 1FN 2T 1D 1S **Baths:** 2 Sh ⌖ (5) ▣ (6) ⊬ ⋔ ▣ ▦.

The Torrans, Drummore Road, Oban, Argyll, PA34 4JL. Detached bungalow overlooking Oban in pleasant peaceful residential area. Private parking. **Open:** All year
01631 565342 Mrs Calderwood **D:** £16.00 **S:** £20.00 **Beds:** 1T 2D **Baths:** 2 En 1 Pr ⌖ ▣ (3) ▣ ⋔ ▦. ♣

Harbour View Guest House, Shore Street, Oban, Argyll, PA34 4LQ. Centrally situated town house. **Open:** All year (not Xmas)
01631 563462 Mrs McDougall **D:** £15.00–£17.00 **Beds:** 2F 1D 1T **Baths:** 2 Sh ⌖ ▣ ⋔ ▦. ♣

Feorlin, Longsdale Road, Oban, Argyll, PA34 5DZ. Charming bungalow less than 8 mins' walk from town and leisure sports complex. **Open:** Mar to Nov
01631 562930 Mrs Campbell **Fax:** 01631 564199 campbellsmith@btinternet.com **D:** £17.50–£20.00 **S:** £27.50 **Beds:** 1F **Baths:** 1 En ⌖ ▣ (2) ⊬ ▣ ▣ ▦. ♣

Alltavona, Corran Esplanade, Oban, Argyll, PA34 5AQ. Victorian villa lying on Oban's esplanade. Outstanding views of Oban Bay and surrounding islands. **Open:** Feb to Nov
01631 565067 (also fax) Ms Harris carol@alltavona.co.uk **D:** £20.00–£33.00 **S:** £20.00–£55.00 **Beds:** 1F 5D 2T ⌖ (5) ▣ ⊬ ▣ ▣ ▦. ♣

Thelwillows, Glenslellgh Road, Oban, Argyll, PA34 4PP. Large garden, private road, idyllic wooded country hillside, overlooking pleasant mile walk to town. **Open:** All year (not Xmas/New Year)
01631 566240 & 07833 504094 (M) D F Coates **Fax:** 01631 566783 enquiries@obanaccommodation.com **D:** £20.00–£25.00 **S:** £20.00–£25.00 **Beds:** 1T 1D **Baths:** 2 En ▣ (4) ⊬ ▣ ▣ ▦. ♣

Shandon
NS2586

Garemount Lodge, *Shandon, Helensburgh, G84 8NP.* Delightful lochside home, large garden, convenient Loch Lomond, Glasgow, Highlands. **Open:** All year (not Xmas)
01436 820780 (also fax) Mrs Cowie
nickcowie@compuserve.com
www.stayatlochlomond.com/garemount
D: £20.00–£23.00 **S:** £28.00–£36.00 **Beds:** 1F 1D **Baths:** 1 En 1 Pr ⊃ � ⊡ (4) ⚥ ⊡ ⼑ ⓥ ▥ ♨

Tarbert (Kintyre)
NR8668   ⚓ Anchor Hotel, Columba Hotel, Victoria Hotel, Tarbert, Islay Frigate, Stonefield Hotel

Kintarbert Lodge, *Kilberry Road, Tarbert, Argyll, PA29 6XX.* **Open:** Apr to Oct **Grades:** STB 4 Star
01880 820237 Mrs Chainey **Fax: 01880 821149** *bdchainey@aol.com* **D:** £20.00–£22.00 **S:** £20.00–£22.00 **Beds:** 1F 2T **Baths:** 2 En 1 Pr ⊃ ⊡ ⊡ ⼑ ⓥ ▥ ♿ ♨ cc
Former farm house, 200 ft above West Loch Tarbert with panoramic views. Outside play area for children. 3 miles from Tarbert and 7,10 miles from Islay, Arran ferries. A quiet place to relax from the stresses of daily life.

Tarbert Hotel, *Harbour Street, Tarbert, Argyll, PA29 6UB.* **Open:** All year **Grades:** STB 2 Star, AA 2 Star
01880 820264   Fax: 01880 820847
iain.robertson@tarberthotel.com **D:** £25.00–£27.50 **S:** £27.50–£30.00 **Beds:** 1F 5D 10T 4S **Baths:** 18 En 1 Sh ⊃ ⊡ ⼑ ✕ ⓥ ▥ ♨ cc
The hub of the local community - a lively meeting place, giving a true reflection of Scottish hospitality. Our food is famous and its value unsurpassed. Ideal base for touring or relaxing overlooking the bustling fishing and sailing harbour of Tarbert.

Tarbet
NN3104   ⚓ Callum's Bar

Corner Stone, *7 Ballyhennan Cresent, Tarbet, Arrochar, G83 7DB.* Beautiful stone built house, overlooking Loch Lomond's breathtaking mountains. **Open:** All year (not Xmas/New Year)
01301 702592 Mr & Mrs McKinley
s_mckinley@talk21.com **D:** £16.00–£18.00 **S:** £20.00–£25.00 **Beds:** 1T 1F **Baths:** 1 Sh ⊃ ⊡ ⚥ ⓥ ▥

Planning a longer stay? Always ask for any special rates

BATHROOMS
En = Ensuite
Pr = Private
Sh = Shared

Lochview, *Tarbet, Arrochar, Dunbartonshire, G83 7DD.* Clean, comfortable, friendly welcome in 200-year-old Georgian house. **Open:** All year (not Xmas)
01301 702200 Mrs Fairfield *e.fairfield@lineone.net* **D:** £16.00–£18.00 **S:** £20.00 **Beds:** 1F 1T 1D **Baths:** 1 Sh ⊃ ⊡ ⓥ ⼑ ▥ ♨

Aye Servus, *Tyneloan Road, Tarbet Loch Lomond, Arrochar, Argyll and Bute, G83 7DD.* Elevated position with magnificent views over Ben and Loch Lomond. **Open:** All year **Grades:** STB 3 Star
01301 702491 Mrs McDonald *ayeservus@talk21.com* www.accomodata.co.uk/ayeservus.htm **D:** £17.00–£19.00 **S:** £22.00–£25.00 **Beds:** 1T 1D **Baths:** 1 Sh ⊃ (6) ⊡ (2) ⓥ ✕ ⓥ ▥ ✱ ♨

Tighnabruaich
NR9773

The Kyles Hotel, *Shore Road, Tighnabruaich, Argyll, PA21 2BE.* **Open:** All year
01700 811674
Fax: 01700 811721 *thekyleshotel@netscape.net* **D:** £25.00–£30.00 **S:** £45.00–£50.00 **Beds:** 2T 3D **Baths:** 5 En ⊃ ⊡ (30) ⓥ ⼑ ✕ ⓥ ▥ ♿ ♨ cc
Cosy family-run hotel, with renowned hospitality, offering regular entertainment and an extensive home-made bar menu. Ideally situated in the beautiful 'Kyles of Bute' where walking, fishing, golfing and sailing are all minutes away. Function suite

Ayrshire & Arran

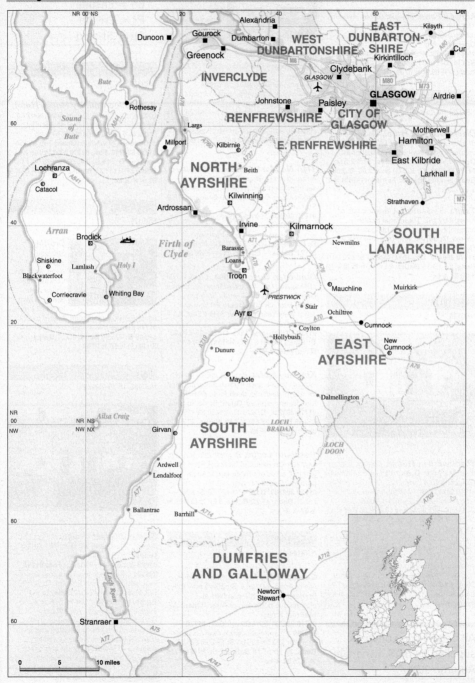

Ardwell

NX1693

Ardwell Farm, *Ardwell, Girvan, Ayrshire, KA26 0HP.* Picturesque farmhouse with rooms overlooking the Firth of Clyde. **Open:** All year
01465 713389 Mrs Melville **D:** £14.00–£15.00 **S:** £14.00–£16.00 **Beds:** 2T 1D **Baths:** 1 Sh
⌂ 🅿 (3) ⊬ 🖵 🐂 ✕ 🆅 ▥. ♨

ARRAN   Blackwaterfoot

NR8928   ⚓ *Blackwater Hotel, Kinloch Hotel*

Blackwaterfoot Hotel, *Blackwaterfoot, Brodick, Isle of Arran, KA27 8EU.* Creature comforts on the windswept west coast. **Open:** Easter to Oct **Grades:** STB 2 Star
01770 860202 D: £25.00 **S:** £25.00–£50.00 **Beds:** 2F 4T 2D **Baths:** 7 En 🅿 (6)⊬ 🖵 🐂 ✕ 🆅 ♨ cc

Tsalta, *Blackwaterfoot, Brodick, Isle of Arran, KA27 8HB.* Traditional Scottish hospitality in newly built bungalow - locally owned. **Open:** All year (not Xmas/New Year)
01770 860405 D: £20.00–£22.00 **S:** £22.00 **Beds:** 1T 1D 1S **Baths:** 2 En 1 Sh ⌂ 🅿 ⊬ 🖵 🐂 🆅 ▥. ♨ cc

ARRAN   Brodick

NS0136

Strathwhillan House, *Brodick, Isle of Arran, KA27 8BQ.* **Open:** All year (not Xmas) **Grades:** STB 3 Star
01770 302331 Mrs Williams *strathwhillan@talk21.com* www.strathwhillan.co.uk
D: £16.00–£25.00 **S:** £16.00–£20.00 **Beds:** 1F 2T 2D 3S **Baths:** 2 En 3 Sh ⌂ 🅿 ⊬ 🖵 🐂 🆅 ▥. ♿1 ♨ cc
Beautifully situated, award winning guest house with sea and mountain views, convenient for ferry (150m) and local amenities, with a fine reputation for hospitality, value, and superb breakfasts, Strathwhillan is an ideal holiday base. Ground floor accommodation. Totally non-smoking.

All details shown are as supplied by B&B owners in Autumn 2001

Sunnyside, *Kings Cross, Brodick, Isle of Arran, KA27 8RG.* **Open:** All year (not Xmas) **Grades:** STB 3 Star
01770 700422 D: £17.50–£19.50 **S:** £17.50–£19.50 **Beds:** 1T 1S **Baths:** 1 En 1 Sh ⌂ ⊬ 🖵 🐂 ▥. ♨
Welcome to Sunnyside - a warm, comfortably furnished modern bungalow with superb views across The Clyde, and secluded suntrap garden. A full wholesome breakfast is assured. Private parking, and separate entrance for guests. Kings Cross: a picturesque hamlet 8 miles SE of Brodick.

Tigh Na Mara, *Seafront, Brodick, Isle of Arran, KA27 8AJ.* Beautifully situated on seafront overlooking the mountains and Brodick Bay. **Open:** All year **Grades:** STB 2 Star
01770 302538 Terry & Leslie Dunleavy **Fax: 01770 302546** *arran.tighnamara@btinternet.com* www.arran.net/brodick/tighnamara
D: £20.00–£24.00 **S:** £20.00–£24.00 **Beds:** 2F 5D 2T **Baths:** 2 En 3 Sh ⌂ (4) 🖵 🆅 ▥. ♨ cc

Dunvegan Guest House, *Brodick, Isle of Arran, KA27 8AJ.* Award-winning Dunvegan House is situated 500 yards from pier, facing Brodick Bay. **Open:** All year (not Xmas/New Year) **Grades:** STB 4 Star, AA 4 Diamond
01770 302811 (also fax) D: £29.00–£35.00 **S:** £35.00 **Beds:** 3T 7D **Baths:** 9 En 1 Pr 🅿 (10) ⊬ 🖵 ✕ ▥. ♨

Kingsley Hotel, *Brodick, Isle of Arran, KA27 8AJ.* Well-known Arran hotel, reputation for warm welcome, good food, relaxing friendly atmosphere. **Open:** Easter to Sept
01770 302226 D: £29.00–£29.50 **S:** £29.00–£29.50 **Beds:** 2F 6D 11T 8S **Baths:** 27 En ⌂ 🅿 (30) 🖵 🐂 ✕ 🆅 ▥. ♨ cc

Rosaburn Lodge, *Brodick, Isle of Arran, KA27 8DP.* On beautiful banks of River Rosa within 2 acres of private landscaped gardens. **Open:** All year
01770 302383 D: £24.00–£27.50 **S:** £24.00–£27.50 **Beds:** 1T 2D **Baths:** 3 En ⌂ 🅿 ⊬ 🖵 🐂 🆅 ▥. ♿ ♨ ♨

ARRAN   Catacol

NR9149

Catacol Bay Hotel, *Catacol, Brodick, Isle of Arran, KA27 8HN.* Small friendly fully licensed hotel nestling in hills at picturesque north end of Arran. **Open:** All year (not Xmas)
01770 830231 Mr Ashcroft **Fax: 01770 830350** *davecatbay@lineone.net* www.catacol.co.uk **D:** £20.00–£25.00 **S:** £20.00–£25.00 **Beds:** 3F 1D 1T 1S **Baths:** 2 Sh ⌂ 🅿 (30) 🐂 ✕ 🆅 ▥. ♨ cc

---

BATHROOMS

En = Ensuite
Pr = Private
Sh = Shared

ARRAN   Lochranza

NR9349

Butt Lodge Country House Hotel, *Lochranza, Brodick, Isle of Arran, KA27 8JF.* Beautiful family-run hotel, residential licence. 2 acres of gardens with an abundance of wildlife. **Open:** Feb to Jan
01770 830240 Fax: 01770 830211 *butt.lodge@virgin.net* **D:** £25.00–£40.00 **S:** £25.00–£48.00 **Beds:** 5F 1D 1T 3S **Baths:** 1 Pr ⌂ 🅿 ⊬ 🖵 ✕ 🆅 ▥. ♿ ♨ ♨ cc

ARRAN   Shiskine

NR9129

Croftlea, *Shiskine, Brodick, Isle of Arran, KA27 8EN.* Comfortable house with garden. Quiet location 2 miles beach/golf course. **Open:** Easter to Oct
01770 860259 Mrs Henderson **D:** £18.00–£20.00 **S:** £25.00 **Beds:** 2D 3T **Baths:** 3 En 1 Sh 🅿 (5) ⊬ 🖵 🐂 🆅 ▥.

Ayr

NS3422   ⚓ *The Pickwick*

Belmont Guest House, *15 Park Circus, Ayr, KA7 2DJ.* **Open:** All year (not Xmas) **Grades:** STB 3 Diamond
01292 265588 Mr Hillhouse **Fax: 01292 290303** *belmontguesthouse@btinternet.com* www.belmontguesthouse.co.uk **D:** £20.00–£22.00 **S:** £22.00–£24.00 **Beds:** 2F 2D 1T **Baths:** 5 En ⌂ 🅿 (5) 🖵 🐂 🆅 ▥. ♿ ♨
Try a breath of fresh 'Ayr'. Warm, comfortable hospitality assured in this Victorian town house, situated in a quiet residential area within easy walking distance of the town centre and beach. Ground floor bedrooms available. Glasgow (Prestwick) Airport 6 miles. Green Tourism Silver Award.

Inverlea Guest House, *42 Carrick Road, Ayr, KA7 2RB.* **Open:** All year **01292 266756 (also fax)** Mr & Mrs Bryson **D:** £15.00–£20.00 **S:** £20.00–£25.00 **Beds:** 3F 2D 2T 1S **Baths:** 3 En 2 Pr 3 Sh ⅔ ▣ (5) ▢ ⌇
▢ ▥. ▪
Family-run Victorian guest house which has ensured personal attention for 16 years. Few minutes walk from beach and town centre. Burns Cottage and 7 golf courses nearby. Large enclosed car park at rear of house.

Sunnyside, *26 Dunure Road, Doonfoot, Ayr, KA7 4HR.* Close to Burns Cottage, Brig O'Doon, spacious rooms, family welcome. **Open:** All year (not Xmas) **Grades:** STB 3 Star **01292 441234 (also fax)** Mrs Malcolm **D:** £20.00–£22.00 **S:** £26.00–£28.00 **Beds:** 2F **Baths:** 2 En ⅔ ▣ (4) ⌇ ▢ ▥. ▪

Kilkerran, *15 Prestwick Road, Ayr, KA8 8LD.* Friendly family-run guest house on main A79 Ayr-Prestwick route. **Open:** All year **Grades:** STB 2 Star **01292 266477** Ms Ferguson *margaret@ kilkerran-gh.demon.co.uk* **D:** £16.00–£20.00 **S:** £16.00–£20.00 **Beds:** 3F 2D 2T 2S **Baths:** 2 En 1 Pr 3 Sh ⅔ ▣ (10) ▢ ⌇ ▢ ▥. ▴ ✳
▪

The Dunn Thing Guest House, *13 Park Circus, Ayr, KA7 2DJ.* Warm welcome at this Victorian house, close to town centre. **Open:** All year **Grades:** STB 2 Star **01292 284531** Mrs Dunn **Fax:** **01292 262944** *thedunnthing@compuserve.com* www.smoothhound.co. uk/hotels/dunnthing.html **D:** £18.00–£22.00 **S:** £18.00–£24.00 **Beds:** 1F 1T 1D **Baths:** 3 En ⅔ ▢ ▢ ▥. ▪

Deanbank, *44 Ashgrove Street, Ayr, KA7 3BG.* Convenient for town centre, station, golf and Burns Country. **Open:** All year (not Xmas) **Grades:** STB 4 Star **01292 263745** Ms Wilson **D:** £18.00–£20.00 **S:** £20.00–£25.00 **Beds:** 1F 1T **Baths:** 1 Sh ⅔ (1) ⌇ ▢ ⌇ ▢ ▥. ▪

23 Dalblair Road, *Ayr, KA7 1UF.* Central town, five minutes from beach. Golf courses nearby. Friendly. **Open:** All year (not Xmas/New Year) **Grades:** STB 3 Star **01292 264798** Mr & Mrs Gambles *jacmar23@ aol.com* **D:** £22.00–£30.00 **S:** £25.00–£30.00 **Beds:** 4F 1T 1D 2S **Baths:** 3 En 1 Pr ▣ (4) ▢ ✕ ▥. ▪

Lochinver, *32 Park Circus, Ayr, KA7 2DL.* Town centre B&B establishment with reasonable rates. **Open:** All year **01292 265086 (also fax)** Mr Young *young.lochinver@talk21.com* www.smoothhound.co.uk/hotels **D:** £18.00–£25.00 **S:** £18.00–£25.00 **Beds:** 1F 1T 1D 1S **Baths:** 3 En 1 Pr ⅔ ▢ ▥. ▪

Finlayson Arms Hotel, *Coylton, Ayr, KA6 6JT.* Superbly located for golfing holidays - over 30 courses nearby including Turnberry and Royal Troon. **Open:** All year (not Xmas/New Year) **01292 570298 (also fax)** **D:** £22.50–£27.50 **S:** £25.00–£35.00 **Beds:** 1F 7T **Baths:** 8 En ⅔ ▣ (12) ⌇ ▢ ✕ ▢ ▥. ▴ ▪ cc

Ballantrae

NX0982 ⌇ *King's Arms*

Orchard Lea, *14 Main Street, Ballantrae, Girvan, Ayrshire, KA26 0NB.* Comfortable house offers superb breakfast. Quiet coastal village, ferries nearby. **Open:** All year (not Xmas) **01465 831509** Mr & Mrs Ward **D:** £17.00 **S:** £17.00 **Beds:** 2D 1T **Baths:** 1 Sh ⅔ ▣ (12) ⌇ ▢ ⌇ ▥. ✳ ▪

Ardstinchar Cottage, *81 Main Street, Ballantrae, Girvan, Ayrshire, KA26 0NA.* Beautiful cottage in magnificent countryside. **Open:** All year (not Xmas/New Year) **01465 831343** Mrs Drummond **D:** £16.00–£20.00 **S:** £20.00–£25.00 **Beds:** 2D 1T **Baths:** 1 Sh ⅔ ▣ (3) ▢ ▥. ✳ ▪

Barassie

NS3232

Fordell, *43 Beach Road, Barassie, Troon, KA10 6SU.* Ideal spot for many reasons. Quiet, comfortable accommodation overlooking sea. **Open:** All year (not Xmas/New Year) **Grades:** STB 3 Star **01292 313224** Mrs Mathieson **Fax:** **01292 312141** *morag@fordell-troon.co.uk* www.fordell-troon.co.uk **D:** £20.00–£25.00 **S:** £25.00–£30.00 **Beds:** 2T **Baths:** 2 Sh ⌇ ▢ ▢ ▥. ▪

Barrhill

NX2382

14 Main Street, *Barrhill, Girvan, Ayrshire, KA26 0PQ.* Comfortable, homely, in small village. Central for local beauty spots. **Open:** All year **01465 821344** Mrs Hegarty **D:** £15.00–£18.00 **S:** £18.00 **Beds:** 1F **Baths:** 1 Pr 1 Sh ⅔ ⌇ ▢ ⌇ ✕ ▥. ▪

Blair Farm, *Barrhill, Girvan, Ayrshire, KA26 0RD.* Beautiful farmhouse, lovely views. Enjoy peace, comfort & friendly hospitality. **Open:** Easter to Nov **01465 821247** Mrs Hughes www.dalbeattie. com/farmholidays/qblfb.htm **D:** £20.00–£22.00 **S:** £25.00 **Beds:** 1D 1T **Baths:** 1 En 1 Pr ⅔ ▣ ▢ ⌇ ▥. ▪

Beith

NS3553 ⌇ *Burnhouse Manor*

Shotts Farm, *Barmill, Beith, Ayrshire, KA15 1LB.* Ideal for exploring south-west Scotland, located between A736/737. **Open:** All year **Grades:** AA 3 Star **01505 502273** Mrs Gillan **D:** £15.00 **S:** £17.00 **Beds:** 1F 2D **Baths:** 1 En 1 Sh ⅔ ▣ (4) ⌇ ▢ ⌇ ✕ ▢ ▥. ▪

Townend of Shuterflat Farm, *Beith, Ayrshire, KA15 2LW.* Comfortable farmhouse, warm welcome, 15 minutes Glasgow Airport and city centre. **Open:** All year **01505 502342** Mrs Lamont **D:** £17.50 **S:** £17.50 **Beds:** 1T 2D **Baths:** 1 Sh ⅔ ▣ (4) ▢ ⌇ ▥. ▪

Coylton

NS4219

The Kyle Hotel, *Main Street, Coylton, Ayr, KA6 6JW.* Close to many Ayrshire top golf courses and Ayr Racecourse. **Open:** All year **01292 570312** Mr Finlayson **Fax:** **01292 571493** **D:** £22.50–£25.00 **S:** £22.50–£25.00 **Beds:** 3F 1T **Baths:** 2 En 1 Sh ⅔ ▢ ⌇ ✕ ▢ ▥. ▪ cc

Dalmellington

NS4805

Bellsbank House, *Bellsbank Road, Dalmellington, Ayr, KA6 7PR.* **Open:** All year **01292 550248 (also fax)** *enquiries@ bellsbankhouse.fsnet.co.uk* **D:** £20.00–£40.00 **S:** £25.00–£40.00 **Beds:** 1F 2D 1S **Baths:** 2 En 1 Pr ⅔ ▣ (30) ▢ ⌇ ✕ ▢ ▥. ✳ ▪ cc
Deep in Burns country. Dating from 1700's, a warm and friendly experience is assured. Sited high on a hill with panoramic views of Doon valley, fishing, shooting and championship golf courses. Forest parks, trails and walks all on your doorstep.

Please respect a B&B's wishes regarding children, animals and smoking

Dunure

NS2515 ⚓ *Anchorage, Heads of Ayr*

Cruachan, *38 Station Road, Dunure, Ayr, KA7 4LL.* Magnificent views to Arran. Close to harbour and castle park. **Open:** Apr to Oct **01292 500494** Mr Evans **Fax: 01292 500266** *dnevans@lineone.net* **D:** £20.00–£25.00 **S:** £20.00–£30.00 **Beds:** 1D 1T **Baths:** 1 En 1 Pr 🅿 (4) 🛏 📺 💻 ♨

Fisherton Farm, *Dunure, Ayr, KA7 4LF.* Delightful traditional Scottish farmhouse. Coastal location on working farm. **Open:** All year (not Xmas/New Year) **Grades:** STB 3 Star **01292 500223 (also fax)** Mrs Wilcox *lesleywilcox@hotmail.com* **D:** £20.00–£25.00 **S:** £20.00–£25.00 **Beds:** 1D 1S **Baths:** 2 Pr �🖰 🅿 (6) 📺 🛏 📺 💻 ♨

Girvan

NX1897

Hotel Westcliffe, *15-16 Louisa Drive, Girvan, Ayrshire, KA26 9AH.* Family run hotel on sea front, all rooms ensuite. Spa/steam room. **Open:** All year **Grades:** STB 2 Star **01465 712128 (also fax)** Mrs Jardine **D:** £23.00–£26.00 **S:** £24.00–£28.00 **Beds:** 6F 5D 8T 5S **Baths:** 24 En 🖰 🅿 (6) 📺 ✕ 💻 ♨ ✾ ♨ cc

Hollybush

NS3914

Malcolmston Farm, *Hollybush, Ayr, KA6 6EZ.* Farmhouse on A713 near Ayr, (near Turnberry and Troon). **Open:** Easter to Nov **01292 560238** Mrs Drummond **D:** £16.00–£18.00 **S:** £16.00–£18.00 **Beds:** 1F 2D **Baths:** 1 En 2 Sh 🖰 🅿 (4) 📺 🛏 💻 ♨ ♨

Kilbirnie

NS3154 🏨 *Mossend Hotel*

Alpenrose, *113 Herriot Avenue, Kilbirnie, Ayrshire, KA25 7JB.* Ideal for tour cycle coast. Wonderful home cooked breakfast. **Open:** All year **01505 683122** E Cameron **D:** £11.00–£15.00 **S:** £11.00–£15.00 **Beds:** 1F 1T 1D 1S **Baths:** 1 Sh 🖰 (1) 🅿 (2) 📺 🛏 ✕ 📺 💻 ♨

BATHROOMS

En = Ensuite
Pr = Private
Sh = Shared

Kilmarnock

NS4238 ⚓ *Wheatsheaf Inn, Cochrane Inn*

Hillhouse Farm, *Grassyards Road, Kilmarnock, Ayrshire, KA3 6HG.* **Open:** All year **Grades:** STB 4 Star **01563 523370** Mrs Howie www.smoothhound.co.uk/hotels/hillhouse.html **D:** £18.00–£21.00 **S:** £18.00–£21.00 **Beds:** 3F 1T **Baths:** 3 En 1 Pr 🖰 🅿 (8) 📺 🛏 📺 💻 ♨.
The Howie family extend a warm welcome to their working dairy farm. Large bedrooms with superb views over garden and Ayrshire countryside. Central location for coast, golf, fishing, Glasgow and Prestwick Airports. Real farmhouse breakfast, home baking for supper in lounge.

Tamarind, *24 Arran Avenue, Kilmarnock, Ayrshire, KA3 1TP.* Large ranch-style bungalow on one level. Located at end of quiet tree-lined avenue. **Open:** All year **Grades:** STB 3 Star **01563 571788** Mrs Turner **Fax: 01563 533515** *james@tamarind25.freeserve.co.uk* **D:** £17.50–£20.00 **S:** £25.00–£30.00 **Beds:** 1F 2T 1S **Baths:** 4 En 🖰 🅿 (4) 📺 💻 ♿ ♨ cc

Kilwinning

NS3043

Claremont Guest House, *27 Howgate, Kilwinning, Ayrshire, KA13 6EW.* Friendly family B&B close to town centre and public transport. **Open:** All year (not Xmas) **01294 553905** Mrs Filby **D:** £18.00–£20.00 **S:** £18.00–£20.00 **Beds:** 1F 1S **Baths:** 2 Sh 🖰 🅿 (10) 📺 💻.

Largs

NS2059

Belmont House, *2 Broomfield Place, Largs, Ayrshire, KA30 8DR.* Interesting old waterfront house. Spacious rooms. Views of islands and highlands. **Open:** All year **Grades:** STB 3 Star **01475 676264** Mr & Mrs Clarke *belmont.house@i12.com* www.belmont.i12.com **D:** £20.00–£25.00 **S:** £20.00–£25.00 **Beds:** 2D 1T **Baths:** 1 En 2 Pr 🖰 (4) 🅿 (2) 🛏 📺 💻 ♨

South Whittleburn Farm, *Brisbane Glen, Largs, Ayrshire, KA30 8SN.* Superb farmhouse accommodation. Enormous, delicious breakfasts. Warm, friendly hospitality, highly recommended. **Open:** All year (not Xmas) **Grades:** STB 4 Star, AA 4 Diamond **01475 675881** Mrs Watson **Fax: 01475 675080** www.smoothhound.co.uk/hotels/whittlie.html **D:** £20.00–£25.00 **S:** £20.00–£25.00 **Beds:** 1F 1D 1T **Baths:** 3 En 🖰 🅿 (10) 📺 💻 ♨

Rutland Guest House, *22 Charles Street, Largs, Ayrshire, KA30 8HJ.* Ideal base for diving, golfing, walking and visiting islands. **Open:** All year **01475 675642** Mrs Russell **Fax: 01475 672422** *rutlandhouse@btinternet.com* **D:** £17.00–£18.00 **S:** £18.00–£20.00 **Beds:** 3F 1D 1T **Baths:** 1 En 1 Pr 2 Sh 🖰 📺 🛏 💻 ♨

Stonehaven Guest House, *8 Netherpark Crescent, Largs, KA30 8QB.* Overlooking Largs Bay and Isles of Cumbrae, Arran and Bute. **Open:** All year (not Xmas) **Grades:** STB 4 Star **01475 673319** Mr Martin *stonehaven.martin@virgin.net* **D:** £20.00–£25.00 **S:** £18.00–£23.00 **Beds:** 1D 1T 1S **Baths:** 1 En 1 Sh 📺 💻 ♨

Lendalfoot

NX1389

The Smiddy, *Lendalfoot, Girvan, KA26 0JF.* Make yourself at home in comfortable home with panoramic views. **Open:** May to Sept **01465 891204** Mrs Bell **D:** £14.00 **S:** £14.00 **Beds:** 1D 1T **Baths:** 1 Sh 🖰 🅿 📺 ✕ 📺 💻 ♨

Loans

NS3431 ⚓ *Old Loans Inn*

Craikslamd Cottage, *Loans, Troon, Ayrshire, KA10 7HN.* Attractive rural situation. Easy reach of golf courses and beach. **Open:** All year (not Xmas/New Year) **01292 314924** Mrs Webster *tomwebster@supanet.com* **D:** £20.00–£22.00 **S:** £22.00–£25.00 **Beds:** 1F **Baths:** 1 En 🖰 🅿 📺 📺 💻.

Mauchline

NS4927

Treborane, *Dykefield Farm, Mauchline, Ayrshire, KA5 6EY.* This is a new cottage on farm with friendly atmosphere. **Open:** All year **01290 550328** Ms Smith **D:** £12.00–£15.00 **Beds:** 2F **Baths:** 1 En 1 Sh 🖰 🅿 📺 🛏 ✕ 📺

Dykefield Farm, *Mauchline, KA5 6EY.*
Farmhouse B&B with friendly, family
atmosphere. Private lounge for guests.
Open: All year
01290 553170 Mrs Smith **D:** £12.00 **S:** £12.00
Beds: 2F **Baths:** 1 Sh ⌂ ❒ (3) ▣ ▥.

Ardwell, *103 Loudoun Street, Mauchline,
KA5 5BH.* Beautiful rooms, near centre of
historic village. Great golf locally. **Open:** All
year
01290 552987 Mrs Houston **D:** £15.00–£17.00
S: £17.00–£19.00 **Beds:** 2F **Baths:** 2 En ⌂
❒ (2) ⊬ ▣ ▥ ⚓

Maybole
NS2909

Homelea, *62 Culzean Road, Maybole,
Ayrshire, KA19 8AH.* Attractive Victorian
family home near Culzean Castle, Burns
country and Turnberry Golf. **Open:** Easter to
Oct
01655 882736 Mrs McKellar **Fax: 01655
883557** *gilmour_mck@msn.com* **D:** £18.50
S: £22.00 **Beds:** 1F 1T 1S **Baths:** 2 Sh ⌂
❒ (3) ⊬ ▣ ▥ ⚓

Muirkirk
NS6927   ⌨ *Dumfries Arms*

La Orilla, *29 Garronhill, Muirkirk,
Cumnock, Ayrshire, KA18 3RY.* Central for
Ayrshire/Lanarkshire. Warm welcome.
Relaxed atmosphere. Good breakfast.
Open: All year (not Xmas/New Year)
01290 661335 (also fax) Mrs Kirk **D:** £15.00
S: £15.00 **Beds:** 2T **Baths:** 1 Sh ⌂ ❒ (2) ▣
▥ ⚓

New Cumnock
NS6113

Low Polquheys Farm, *New Cumnock,
Cumnock, Ayrshire, KA18 4NX.* Warm
welcome in modern farmhouse. Situated
near Dumfriesshire/Ayrshire border.
Open: Feb to Dec
01290 338307 Mrs Caldwell *marjorie@
low-polquheys.freeserve.co.uk* **D:** £15.00–£18.00
S: £15.00–£18.00 **Beds:** 1F 1T 1S **Baths:** 1
Sh ⌂ (2) ▣ ▥ ⚓

Newmilns
NS5237

Whatriggs Farm, *Newmilns, Ayrshire,
KA16 9LJ.* Family-run 700-acre farm, with golf
and family attractions nearby. **Open:** All
year (not Xmas)
01560 700279 Mrs Mitchell *whatriggs@
farming.co.uk* www.whatriggs.co.uk **D:** £15.00–
£17.50 **S:** £15.00–£17.50 **Beds:** 2F **Baths:** 1
Sh ⌂ ❒ (6) ▣ ⊢ ✕ ▣ ⚓

Ochiltree
NS5121

**Laigh Tarbeg
Farm,**
*Ochiltree,
Cymnock,
KA18 2RL.* Modern
working dairy
farm traditional
farmhouse of great character with a warm
family welcome. **Open:** Easter to Oct
Grades: STB 3 Star
01290 700242 (also fax) Mrs Watson
D: £18.00–£20.00 **S:** £18.00–£22.00 **Beds:** 2F
Baths: 1 Pr 1 Sh ⌂ (1) ❒ ▣ ⊢ ▥ ⚓

Stair
NS4423

Stair Inn, *Stair, Mauchline, KA5 5HW.*
Conservation area. Guest rooms of a very
high standard. **Open:** All year
01292 591562 Mr Boyd **Fax: 01292 591650**
D: £22.50–£25.00 **S:** £35.00–£39.00 **Beds:** 2F
3T 1D **Baths:** 6 En ⊬ ▣ ✕ ▣ ▥ ⚓ cc

Troon
NS3230

The Cherries,
*50 Ottoline Drive,
Troon, Ayrshire,
KA10 7AW.*
Beautiful quiet
home on golf
course near
beaches and restaurants. **Open:** All year
Grades: STB 3 Star
01292 313312 Mrs Tweedie **Fax: 01292
319007** *thecherries50@hotmail.com*
www.smoothhound.co.uk/hotels/cherries
D: £20.00–£25.00 **S:** £20.00–£25.00 **Beds:** 1F
1T 1S **Baths:** 1 En 1 Pr 1 Sh ⌂ ❒ (5) ⊬ ▣ ⊢ ▣
▥ ⚓

Fordell, *43 Beach Road, Barassie, Troon,
KA10 6SU.* Ideal spot for many reasons. Quiet,
comfortable accommodation overlooking
sea. **Open:** All year (not Xmas/New Year)
Grades: STB 3 Star
01292 313224 Mrs Mathieson **Fax: 01292
312141** *morag@fordell-troon.co.uk*
www.fordell-troon.co.uk **D:** £20.00–£25.00
S: £25.00–£30.00 **Beds:** 2T **Baths:** 2 Sh ⊬ ▣
⊢ ▣ ▥ ⚓

Borders

EDINBURGH

CITY OF EDINBURGH

Livingston

Haddington

Musselburgh

Dalkeith

E. LOTHIAN

St Abb's Head

St Abbs

Coldingham

Coldingham

Eyemouth

Bonnyrigg

Penicuik

MIDLOTHIAN

West Linton

Longformacus

Duns

Allanton

Berwick-upon-Tweed

Lauder

Greenlaw

Uplands

Langshaw

Peebles

Biggar

Galashiels

Birgham

Innerleithen

Gattonside

Melrose

St Boswells

Kelso

NORTHUMBERLAND

Bowden

Selkirk

Heiton

Town Yetholm

Yarrow Feus

BORDERS

Eckford

Kirk Yetholm

Ashkirk

Jedburgh

Southern

Ettrick

Hawick

Langlee

The Cheviot Hills

Moffat

Teviothead

NORTHUMBERLAND NATIONAL PARK

NS NT
NX NY

DUMFRIES AND GALLOWAY

The Borders

KIELDER RESERVOIR

Newcastleton

Lochmaben

Lockerbie

Langholm

0   5   10 miles

Allanton

NT8654

Allanton Inn, *Allanton, Chirnside, Duns, Berwickshire, TD11 3JZ.* Historic coaching inn, set in a Scottish Borders Conservation village. **Open:** All year (not Xmas/New Year)
01890 818260 Mrs Ward **Fax: 01890 817186**
allantoninn@supanet.com **D:** £40.00 **S:** £46.00
Beds: 1F 1D 2T 🛏 🖵 🅟 ⊁ ✕ Ⓥ ▥ ♨ cc

Ashkirk

NT4722   🍺 *Cross Keys, Coach House*

Ashkirktown Farm, *Ashkirk, Selkirk, TD7 4PB.* Farmhouse in beautiful countryside. Tastefully furnished. Warm welcome assured.
Open: All year (not Xmas/New Year)
01750 32315 (also fax) Mrs Lamont
D: £20.00 **S:** £20.00–£24.00 **Beds:** 1F 2D
Baths: 2 Sh 🛏 🅟 (6) ⊁ Ⓥ ▥ ♨

Birgham

NT7939

Tweedview, *Birgham, Coldstream, Berwickshire, TD12 4NF.* Friendly family house in beautiful Scottish Borders. Good touring base. **Open:** All year
018908 30312 Mrs Jarvis **D:** £14.00 **S:** £14.00
Beds: 1D 1T 🛏 🅟 (4) Ⓥ 🍴 ✕ Ⓥ ▥ ♨

Planning a longer stay? Always ask for any special rates

National Grid References given are for villages, towns and cities – not for individual houses

Bowden
NT5530

Glenwhilt, Bowden, Melrose, Roxburghshire, TD6 0SX. Small country house in Scottish Borders, lovely gardens. Warm welcome. **Open:** All year **Grades:** STB 3 Star
01835 822408 Mrs Pryde **D:** £15.00–£23.00 **S:** £20.00–£30.00 **Beds:** 1T 2D **Baths:** 1 En 1 Sh ⌂ 🅿 ⽊ �📺 ⽊ ✕ 🍴 ⛿

Coldingham
NT9066 🍺 Anchor Inn

Rhovanion, Burnhall, Coldingham, Berwickshire, TD14 5NR. Pretty village setting. Peaceful stay assured with our adult only policy. **Open:** All year (not Xmas/New Year) **Grades:** STB 3 Star
018907 71760 Mr & Mrs Jones *info@ 'rhovanion.org* www.rhovanion.org **D:** £20.00 **S:** £25.00 **Beds:** 1T 2D **Baths:** 3 En ⌂ (14) 🅿 ✄ 📺 📺 🍴 ⛿

St Abbs Haven Hotel, Coldingham Sands, Coldingham, Eyemouth, Berwickshire, TD14 5PA. Spectacular sea views overlooking bay. Exceptional wildlife and sealife, excellent walks. **Open:** All year **018907 71779** Mrs Ross **Fax:** 01907 71847 **D:** £30.00–£35.00 **S:** £30.00–£35.00 **Beds:** 2F 6D 4T 3S **Baths:** 12 En ⌂ 🅿 📺 ⽊ ✕ 📺 🍴 ⛿

Duns
NT7854

St Albans, Clouds, Duns, Berwickshire, TD11 3BB. Georgian manse, with period furnishings, overlooking small town. **Open:** All year (not Xmas/New Year) **01361 883285 Fax: 01361 884534** *st_albans@ email.msn.com* **D:** £19.50–£25.00 **S:** £22.00–£30.00 **Beds:** 2D/T 2S **Baths:** 2 Sh ⌂ (12) ✄ 📺 ⽊ 📺 🍴 ⛿ cc

Eckford
NT7126

The Old Joiners Cottage, Eckford, Kelso, Roxburghshire, TD5 8LG. Charming Borders style cottage with picturesque views over rolling countryside. **Open:** All year **01835 850323 (also fax)** Mr Butterfield *joiners.cottage@virgin.net* www.destination-scotland.com **D:** £18.00–£21.00 **S:** £21.00–£30.00 **Beds:** 1F 1D **Baths:** 2 En ⌂ 🅿 (3) ✄ 📺 ⽊ ✕ 📺 🍴 ⛿ cc

Ettrick
NT2714

West Deloraine Farm, Ettrick, Selkirk, TD7 5HR. 1000 acre farm situated in James Hogg and Sir Walter Scott country. **Open:** Easter to Oct
01750 62207 Mrs Bernard **D:** £16.00 **S:** £16.00 **Beds:** 1T 2D **Baths:** 2 Sh ⌂ 🅿 🍴

Galashiels
NT4936 🍺 Abbotsford Arms, King's Hotel

Kirklands, Gala Terrace, Galashiels, Selkirkshire, TD1 3JT. Large house (1900), town centre area, easy parking, quality location on Southern Upland Way. **Open:** All year **Grades:** STB 2 Star
01896 753762 (also fax) Mrs McLauchlan *kirklandsguesthouse@BTinternet.com* www.kirklandsguesthouse.co.uk **D:** £16.50 **S:** £16.50 **Beds:** 1F 1D 1S **Baths:** 1 Sh ⌂ 🅿 (1) 📺 ⽊ 🍴 ⛿

Ettrickvale, 33 Abbotsford Road, Galashiels, Selkirkshire, TD1 3HW. Warm, comfortable bungalow, ideally situated for touring Borders and Edinburgh. **Open:** All year (not Xmas) **Grades:** STB 2 Star
01896 755224 Mrs Field **D:** £16.00 **S:** £20.00 **Beds:** 1D 2T **Baths:** 2 Sh ⌂ 🅿 (3) 📺 ⽊ ✕ 📺 🍴 ⛿ 🛁 ⛿

Watson Lodge, 15 Bridge Street, Galashiels, Selkirkshire, TD1 1SW. **Open:** All year
01896 750551 Mrs Reid *watsonlodge@mac.com* **D:** £17.50–£20.00 **S:** £18.00–£25.00 **Beds:** 2F 2D 1T **Baths:** 3 En 1 Sh ⌂ ✄ 📺 📺 🍴 ⛿ Charming central yet peaceful Victorian town house. Newly refurbished throughout. Bright, comfortable rooms. Pleasant garden area open to guests. Perfect touring base for Borders/Edinburgh. Excellent choice of eating places closeby. Transport arranged to/from anywhere in the UK. Friendly and relaxing.

Planning a longer stay? Always ask for any special rates

Island House, 65 Island Street, Galashiels, Selkirkshire, TD1 1PA. Comfortable family home. Town centre. Ideally situated for touring the Borders. **Open:** All year **Grades:** AA 3 Diamond
01896 752649 Mr Brown **D:** £16.00–£20.00 **S:** £15.00–£20.00 **Beds:** 1D 2T **Baths:** 2 En 1 Sh ⌂ 🅿 (2) ✄ 📺 ⽊ 🍴 ⛿

Sunnybrae, 160 Magdala Terrace, Galashiels, Selkirkshire, TD1 2HZ. Comfortable, friendly family-run home. Convenient for touring Borders and Edinburgh. **Open:** All year (not Xmas/New Year) **Grades:** STB 3 Star
01896 758042 Mrs Anderson *bandb@ sunnybrae.co.uk* www.sunnybrae.co.uk **D:** £18.00–£20.00 **S:** £18.00–£20.00 **Beds:** 1T 2D **Baths:** 2 En 1 Pr ⌂ 🅿 (3) ✄ 📺 ⽊ 📺 🍴 ⛿

Wakefield Bank, 9 Abbotsford Road, Galashiels, Selkirkshire, TD1 3DP. Award-winning B&B. Ideal base for touring Scottish Borders/Edinburgh. **Open:** Easter to Oct
01896 752641 (also fax) A M Platt *wakefieldbank@netscapeonline.co.uk* www.smoothhound.co. uk/hotels/wakefieldbank.html **D:** £18.50–£21.00 **S:** £24.00 **Beds:** 1T 2D **Baths:** 2 Sh ⌂ (12) 🅿 (2) ✄ 📺 ✕ 📺 🍴 ⛿

Gattonside
NT5435

Fauhope House, Fauhope, Gattonside, Melrose, Roxburghshire, TD6 9LU. An Edwardian house looking over the River Tweed to Melrose Abbey. **Open:** All year **01896 823184 & 01896 822245** Mrs Robson **Fax: 01896 823184 D:** £25.00 **S:** £32.00 **Beds:** 2T 1D **Baths:** 3 En 🅿 ✄ ⽊ 🍴 ⛿ cc

Greenlaw
NT7146

Bridgend House, West High Street, Greenlaw, Duns, Berwickshire, TD10 6XA. Built 1816 with trout fishing in pretty riverside garden.
Open: All year **Grades:** STB 2 Star
01361 810270 (also fax) Mrs Carruthers *aproposdes@fsbdial.co.uk* **D:** £18.00–£20.00 **S:** £24.00–£26.00 **Beds:** 1F 1D 2T **Baths:** 3 En 1 Pr ⌂ 🅿 (4) ✄ 📺 ⽊ ✕ 📺 🍴 ⛿

Hawick
NT5015

Kirkton Farmhouse, Hawick, Roxburghshire, TD9 8QJ. Welcome to our spacious farmhouse - we look forward to looking after you. **Open:** All year **01450 372421 (also fax)** Mrs Bell *bell.kirton@ virgin.net* **D:** £16.00 **S:** £22.00 **Beds:** 1T 2D **Baths:** 1 Sh ⌂ 🅿 ✄ 📺 ⽊ ✕ 📺 🍴 ⛿

Wiltonburn Farm, *Hawick, Roxburghshire, TD9 7LL.*
Delightful setting on hill farm with designer cashmere knitwear shop. **Open:** All year (not Xmas)
01450 372414 & 07719 154173 (M) Mrs Shell
Fax: 01450 378098 *shell@ wiltonburnfarm.u-net.com* www.smoothhound. co.uk/hotels/wiltonbu **D:** £20.00–£22.50 **S:** £20.00–£25.00 **Beds:** 1F 1D 1T **Baths:** 1 En 1 Pr 1 Sh ⏰ 🖨 (6) �🗙 📺 ★ ✕ 📺 ⛰ ♨ cc

Ellistrin, *6 Fenwick Park, Hawick, Roxburghshire, TD9 9PA.* Welcoming family home in quiet area, close to all amenities.
Open: Easter to Oct **Grades:** STB 3 Star
01450 374216 Mrs Smith **Fax: 01450 373619** *ellistrin@compuserve.com* www.ellistrin.co.uk
D: £18.00 **S:** £18.00 **Beds:** 2D 1T **Baths:** 3 En ⏰ 🖨 (3) 📺 ★ 📺 ⛰ ♨

Heiton

NT7130

Goldilands, *Roxburgh Road, Heiton, Kelso, TD5 8TP.* New bungalow, 2 miles from Kelso, adjacent to golf course. **Open:** All year
01573 450671 (also fax) Mrs Brotherston *jimbroth@aol.com* **D:** £20.00 **S:** £25.00 **Beds:** 2T 1D **Baths:** 3 En ⏰ (2) 🖨 (3) ✕ 📺 ★ 📺 🖐 ♨ ⛰

Innerleithen

NT3336

Caddon View Hotel, *14 Pirn Road, Innerleithen, Peebles-shire, EH44 6HH.*
Open: All year (not Xmas)
01896 830208 Mr & Mrs Djellil *caddonview@ aol.com* www.caddonview.co.uk **D:** £28.00–£35.00 **S:** £38.00–£55.00 **Beds:** 1F 3D 2T **Baths:** 6 En ⏰ 🖨 (6) ⛱ 📺 ★ ✕ 🖐 ❉ ⛰ cc Charming Victorian family house by the River Tweed, ideally situated for walking, fishing, touring or just relaxing. All rooms individually designed and equipped to make you feel at home. Fine dining experience at reasonable price in the French restaurant. 30 miles from Edinburgh.

Planning a longer stay? Always ask for any special rates

Jedburgh

NT6520 🛏 *Forester's Arms, Carters' Arms, The Pheasant*

Meadhon House, *48 Castlegate, Jedburgh, Roxburghshire, TD8 6BB.* **Open:** All year (not Xmas/New Year) **Grades:** STB 3 Diamond
01835 862504 (also fax) Mrs Poloczek *meadhon@aol.com* **D:** £20.00–£22.00 **S:** £30.00 **Beds:** 3F 2D **Baths:** 5 En ⏰ (12) 🖨 (3) ✕ 📺 📺 ⛰ ♨ cc
C17th stone-built house with views overlooking Jedburgh Abbey and Castle. Perfectly situated for exploring Scottish Borders, ancient monuments and historic buildings. You are assured a warm welcome and extremely comfortable accommodation just over 1 hour's drive from Edinburgh and Newcastle on A68.'

Edgerston Rink Smithy, *Jedburgh, Roxburghshire, TD8 6PP.*
Open: All year **Grades:** STB 3 Star
01835 840328 Mr & Mrs Smart *royglen.rink@ btinternet.com* **D:** £18.00–£20.00 **S:** £23.00–£25.00 **Beds:** 2D **Baths:** 2 Pr ⏰ (12) 🖨 (4) 📺 ★ ✕ 📺 ♨
Converted smithy overlooking the Cheviot Hills backing on to natural woodland, with walks from garden. Very private facilities of a superior standard. Warm welcome assured. Private visitors lounge with TV, music centre etc. Rural location, 7 miles south of Jedburgh.

Windyridge, *39 Dounehill, Jedburgh, Roxburghshire, TD8 6LJ.* Quiet location, stunning views, great food, warm hospitality, modern comfortable house. **Open:** All year **Grades:** STB 4 Star
01835 864404 Mrs Lowe *jlowelowc6r@ supanet.com* **D:** £18.00–£20.00 **S:** £18.00–£25.00 **Beds:** 1F 1T 1D 1S **Baths:** 1 En 1 Sh ⏰ 🖨 (3) ✕ 📺 ★ ✕ 📺 ♨

Froylehurst, *The Friars, Jedburgh, Roxburghshire, TD8 6BN.* Detached Victorian house in large garden. Spacious guest rooms, 2 mins town centre. **Open:** Mar to Nov **Grades:** STB 4 Star
01835 862477 (also fax) Mrs Irvine **D:** £18.00–£20.00 **S:** £20.00–£25.00 **Beds:** 2F 1D 1T **Baths:** 2 Sh ⏰ (5) 🖨 (5) 📺 📺 ♨

Ferniehirst Mill Lodge, *Jedburgh, Roxburghshire, TD8 6PQ.* Modern guest house in peaceful setting, country lovers' paradise. **Open:** All year **Grades:** STB 1 Star, AA 3 Diamond, RAC 3 Diamond
01835 863279 (also fax) Mr Swanston *ferniehirstmill@aol.com* **D:** £23.00 **S:** £23.00 **Beds:** 1F 3D 4T 1S **Baths:** 9 En 1 Sh ⏰ 🖨 (10) 📺 ★ ✕ 📺 ⛰ ♨ cc

Riverview, *Newmill Farm, Jedburgh, Roxburghshire, TD8 6TH.* Spacious modern villa overlooking River Jed with country views. **Open:** Apr to Oct
01835 862145 & 01835 864607 Mrs Kinghorn **D:** £18.00–£20.00 **S:** £25.00 **Beds:** 1T 2D **Baths:** 3 En 🖨 (4) 📺 📺 ♨

Willow Court, *The Friars, Jedburgh, Roxburghshire, TD8 6BN.* Willow Court is in a quiet location yet only two minutes from Market Square. **Open:** All year **Grades:** STB 3 Star GH
01835 863702 Mr McGovern **Fax: 01835 864601** *mike@willowcourtsedburgh.co.uk* www.willowcourtsedburgh.co.uk **D:** £18.00–£22.00 **S:** £22.00–£30.00 **Beds:** 1F 1T 2D **Baths:** 3 En 1 Pr ⏰ 🖨 (4) ✕ 📺 ★ 📺 ♨

Hundalee House, *Jedburgh, Roxburghshire, TD8 6PA.* Large Victorian private house. **Open:** Mar to Nov
01835 863011 (also fax) Mrs Whittaker *sheila.whittaker@btinternet.com* **D:** £20.00–£23.00 **S:** £25.00–£35.00 **Beds:** 1F 3D 1T **Baths:** 4 En 1 Pr ⏰ (5) 🖨 (10) ✕ 📺 📺 ♨ ⛰

Kelso

NT7234 🛏 *Cross Keys Hotel, Cobbles Inn, White Swan, Waggon Inn, Ednam House Hotel*

Lochside, *Town Yetholm, Kelso, Roxburghshire, TD5 8PD.* Victorian country house. Peaceful, spacious, ensuite bedrooms. Beautiful countryside. **Open:** Apr to Oct **Grades:** STB 3 Star B&B
01573 420349 Mrs Hurst **D:** £22.50 **S:** £22.50 **Beds:** 1D 1T **Baths:** 2 En ⏰ (2) 🖨 (2) ✕ 📺 🖐 ♨ ⛰

Craignethan House, *Jedburgh Road, Kelso, Roxburghshire, TD5 8AZ.* Comfortable welcoming family home, relaxed informal atmosphere. Breakfast to suit all tastes & times. **Open:** All year **01573 224818** Mrs McDonald **D:** £19.00 **S:** £19.00 **Beds:** 2D 1T **Baths:** 1 Pr 1 Sh ❧ 🄿 (6) ⊠ ⊁ ♥ 🎟 ♨ ♨3 ★

Duncan House, *Chalkheugh Terrace, Kelso, Roxburghshire, TD5 7DX.* Georgian riverside house, spectacular views river & castle. 2 mins to centre town. **Open:** All year (not Xmas) **01573 225682** Mrs Robertson **D:** £15.00–£17.00 **S:** £20.00–£30.00 **Beds:** 3F 1D **Baths:** 3 En 3 Pr 1 Sh ❧ 🄿 (6) ⊠ ⊁ ♥ 🎟 ♨ ♨ ★

Kirk Yetholm
NT8228

Valleydene, *High Street, Kirk Yetholm, Kelso, Roxburghshire, TD5 8PH.* Traditional Scottish welcome. Log fire. Comfortable rooms with excellent views. **Open:** All year **01573 420286** Mrs Campbell **D:** £22.00 **S:** £25.00–£30.00 **Beds:** 2T 1D **Baths:** 2 En 1 Pr ❧ (12) 🄿 (4) ⊠ ⊁ ♥ × 🎟 ★

Langlee
NT6417

The Spinney, *Langlee, Jedburgh, Roxburghshire, TD8 6PB.* Spacious house in main house and in nearby pine cabins. **Open:** Mar to Nov **01835 863525** Mrs Fry **Fax: 01835 864883** *thespinney@btinternet.com* **D:** £21.00–£23.00 **Beds:** 2D 1T 3F **Baths:** 5 En 1 Pr ❧ 🄿 (6) ⊁ ⊠ ♥ 🎟 ★ **cc**

Langshaw
NT5139

Over Langshaw Farm, *Langshaw, Galashiels, Selkirkshire, TD1 2PE.* Welcoming family farm superb location in unspoilt border countryside. **Open:** All year **Grades:** STB 3 Star **01896 860244 (also fax)** Mrs Bergius *bergius@overlangshaw.fsnet.co.uk* **D:** £20.00–£22.00 **S:** £25.00 **Beds:** 1F 1D **Baths:** 1 En 1 Pr 1 Sh ❧ 🄿 ⊁ ⊠ ♥ × ⊠ ♨ ♨ ★

Lauder
NT5247

The Grange, *6 Edinburgh Road, Lauder, Berwickshire, TD2 6TW.* A peaceful haven from which to explore the tranquil Scottish Borders. **Open:** All year (not Xmas) **01578 722649 (also fax)** Tricia and Peter Gilardi *trishnpete.lauder@amserve.net* **D:** £17.00–£20.00 **S:** £18.00–£20.00 **Beds:** 1D 2T **Baths:** 1 Sh ❧ 🄿 (3) ⊁ ⊠ ⊠ 🎟 ★

Longformacus
NT6957

Eildon Cottage, *Longformacus, Duns, Berwickshire, TD11 3NX.* Leave crowds behind set in beautiful rolling Lammermuir Hill village. **Open:** All year (not Xmas/New Year) **01361 890230** Mrs Amos **D:** £20.00–£25.00 **S:** £20.00–£25.00 **Beds:** 1F 1T 1D **Baths:** 2 En 1 Pr 🄿 (3) ⊠ ♥ × ⊠ 🎟 ★

Kintra Ha, *Gifford Road, Longformacus, Duns, Berwickshire, TD11 3NZ.* Recently converted, detached property. Edinburgh 50 mins. Access to rural pursuits. **Open:** All year **01361 890660 (also fax)** Mrs Lamb *lamb@kintrastell.co.uk* **D:** £20.00 **S:** £25.00 **Beds:** 1D 1T **Baths:** 2 En ⊁ ⊠ ♥ × ⊠ 🎟 ♨ ★

Melrose
NT5433

Old Abbey School House, *Waverley Road, Melrose, Roxburghshire, TD6 9SH.* Charming old school house with character. Large bedrooms, restful atmosphere. **Open:** Mar to Nov **Grades:** STB 3 Star **01896 823432** Mrs O'Neill *oneill@abbeyschool.fsnet.co.uk* **D:** £18.00–£22.00 **S:** £25.00 **Beds:** 1T 2D **Baths:** 1 Pr 1 Sh ❧ 🄿 (5) ⊁ ⊠ ⊠ 🎟 ★

Glenwhilt, *Bowden, Melrose, Roxburghshire, TD6 0SX.* Small country house in Scottish Borders, lovely gardens. Warm welcome. **Open:** All year **Grades:** STB 3 Star **01835 822408** Mrs Pryde **D:** £15.00–£23.00 **S:** £20.00–£30.00 **Beds:** 1T 2D **Baths:** 1 En 1 Sh ❧ 🄿 ⊁ ⊠ ♥ × 🎟 ★

Newcastleton
NY4887

Bailey Mill, *Bailey, Newcastleton, Roxburghshire, TD9 0TR.* Courtyard apartments in converted C18th grain mill. Ideal retreat. Jacuzzi, pony trekking, bar meals. **Open:** All year **016977 48617 & 016977 48027** Mrs Copeland **Fax: 016977 48074** *pam@baileymill.fsnet.co.uk* www.holidaycottagescumbria.co.uk **D:** £20.00–£22.00 **S:** £22.00–£28.00 **Beds:** 4F 6T 3D 4S **Baths:** 6 En 4 Pr 6 Sh ❧ 🄿 ⊠ ♥ ⊠ 🎟 ♨ ✳ ★ **cc**

Peebles
NT2540 🍷 *Crown Inn, Horseshoe Inn*

Lyne Farmhouse, *Lyne Farm, Peebles, EH45 8NR.* **Open:** All year (not Xmas) **01721 740255 (also fax)** Mrs Waddell *awaddell@farming.co.uk* www.lynefarm.co.uk **D:** £18.00–£20.00 **S:** £20.00–£22.00 **Beds:** 2D 1T **Baths:** 2 Sh ❧ 🄿 ⊠ ♥ 🎟 ★ Beautiful Georgian farmhouse, with tastefully decorated rooms overlooking scenic Stobo Valley. Walled garden plus hill-walking, picnic areas and major Roman fort all on farm. Ideally placed for Edinburgh and picturesque town of Peebles, plus Border towns and historic houses.

Selkirk
NT4728 🍷 *Queen' Head*

Ettrickshaws Hotel, *Ettrickbridge, Selkirk, TD7 5HW.* **Open:** All year **Grades:** STB 4 Star, RAC 5 Diamond **01750 52229 (also fax)** J Oldhead *jenny@ettrickshaws.co.uk* www.ettrickshaws.co.uk **D:** £45.00–£60.00 **S:** £55.00–£70.00 **Beds:** 1T 4D **Baths:** 5 En ❧ (12) 🄿 (10) ⊠ ♥ × ⊠ 🎟 **cc** This splendid Victorian country house nestling in 12 acres of woodland, boasts private salmon and trout fishing. 12 golf courses within half an hour and the opportunity to enjoy riding and walking in the Scottish Borders. Excellent home cooking and service.

Hillholm, *36 Hillside Terrace, Selkirk, TD7 4ND.* Victorian house, warm welcome, 5 mins walk to centre or golf. **Open:** Mar to Oct **Grades:** STB 3 Star **01750 21293** Mrs Hannah **D:** £20.00–£25.00 **S:** £25.00–£27.00 **Beds:** 1T 2D **Baths:** 2 En 1 Pr ❧ (10) ⊁ ⊠ ⊠ 🎟 ★

Ivy Bank, *Hillside Terrace, Selkirk, TD7 2LT.* Set back from A7 with fine views over hills beyond. **Open:** Easter to Dec **01750 21270** Mrs MacKenzie *nettamackenzie@ivybankselkirk.freeserve.co.uk* **D:** £17.50–£18.00 **S:** £18.00 **Beds:** 1D 1T 1S **Baths:** 2 En 1 Pr 1 Sh ❧ 🄿 (4) ⊠ ♥ ⊠ 🎟 ★ **cc**

Please respect a B&B's wishes regarding children, animals and smoking

St Abbs

NT9167

Castle Rock Guest House,
*Murrayfield, St Abbs, Eyemouth,
Berwickshire, TD14 5PP.* Victorian house with
superb views over sea and rocks. **Open:** Feb
to Nov
018907 71715 Mrs Wood **Fax: 018907 71520**
boowood@compuserve.com **D:** £23.00–£25.00
S: £23.00–£25.00 **Beds:** 1F 1D 1T 1S
Baths: 4 En ♿ ⴾ (4) ⴽ ⺌ ⴑ ✕ Ⅴ ⴏ ♨ cc

St Boswells

NT5930

Whitehouse Farmhouse, *St Boswells,
Melrose, Roxburghshire, TD6 0ED.* Large
welcoming country house, log fires, home-
cooked dinners. Spectacular views.
Open: All year **Grades:** STB 4 Star
01573 460343 Mrs Tyrer **Fax: 01573 460361**
tyrer.whitehouse@lineone.net **D:** £28.00–£35.00
S: £32.00–£45.00 **Beds:** 2T 1D **Baths:** 3 En
♿ ⴾ (10) ⺌ ⴑ ✕ Ⅴ ⴏ ♨ cc

Planning a longer stay? Always
ask for any special rates

Teviothead

NT4004

The Quiet Garden, *Hislop , Teviothead,
Hawick, Roxburghshire, TD9 0PS.* Small
privately run eco-friendly B&B with ground
floor accommodation. Need own transport.
Open: Easter to Oct
01450 850310 (also fax) Mrs Armitage
D: £16.00–£18.00 **S:** £16.00–£18.00 **Beds:** 1T
1D **Baths:** 1 Sh 1 Pr ♿ ⴾ (2) ⴽ Ⅴ ✕ ⴏ ♨ ⴜ ♨

Town Yetholm

NT8127

Lochside, *Town Yetholm, Kelso,
Roxburghshire, TD5 8PD.* Victorian country
house. Peaceful, spacious, ensuite
bedrooms. Beautiful countryside.
Open: Apr to Oct **Grades:** STB 3 Star B&B
01573 420349 Mrs Hurst **D:** £22.50 **S:** £22.50
Beds: 1D 1T **Baths:** 2 En ♿ (2) ⴾ (2) ⴽ Ⅴ ⴑ
ⴏ ♨

Blunty's Mill, *Kirk Yetholm, Kelso,
Roxburghshire, TD5 6PG.* Fabulous rural
location set in 6 acres. Friendly welcome
guaranteed. **Open:** All year
01573 420288 Mrs Brooker *gail_rowan@
hotmail.com* **D:** £22.00–£30.00 **Beds:** 2T
Baths: 1 Sh ♿ ⴾ (10) Ⅴ ⴑ ✕ Ⅴ ⴜ ✾ ♨

B&B owners may vary
rates – be sure to check
when booking

West Linton

NT1551

The Gordon Arms Hotel, *Dolphinton
Road, West Linton, Peebles-shire, EH46 7DR.*
Small, friendly country inn, award winning
food, traditional bar. **Open:** All year
01968 660208 **D:** £24.00 **S:** £28.00 **Beds:** 1F
1T 2D 1S **Baths:** 1 Sh ♿ ⴾ Ⅴ ⺌ ⴑ ✕ Ⅴ ⴏ ♨ cc

Yarrow Feus

NT3426

Ladhope Farm, *Yarrow Feus, Yarrow
Valley, Selkirk, TD7 5NE.* Beautiful farmhouse,
log fires, very peaceful. Ideal for hunting,
touring. **Open:** Easter to Oct
01750 82216 Mrs Turnbull *anne@
scottish.borders.com* **D:** £18.00–£20.00
S: £20.00–£22.00 **Beds:** 1F 1D **Baths:** 1 Sh
♿ ⴾ (4) Ⅴ ⴑ ♨

Dumfries & Galloway

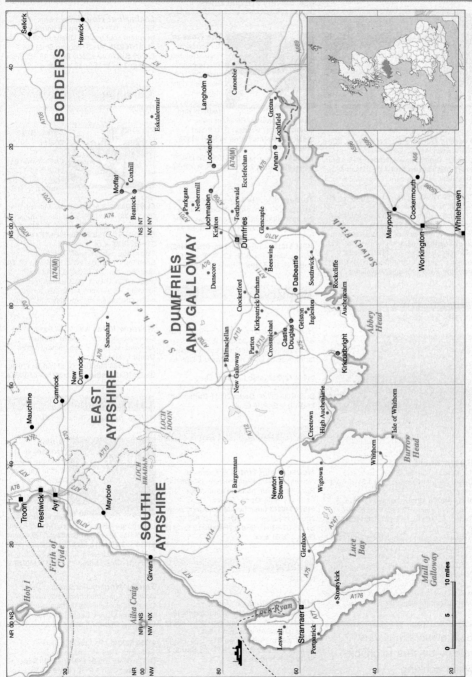

Annan
NY1966

The Old Rectory Guest House, *12 St Johns Road, Annan, Dumfriesshire, DG12 6AW.* **Open:** All year **Grades:** STB 4 Star **01461 202029 (also fax)** J Buchanan & J Alexander *old-rectory-guest1@supanet.com* www.theoldrectoryscotland.co.uk **D:** £24.00–£28.00 **S:** £35.00 **Beds:** 4D 1T **Baths:** 5 En 🄿 (6) 📺 🏃 ✕ 📖 ♣ ♨
Charming C19th manse in the centre of Annan, 7 miles from famous wedding town Gretna. Warm welcome, ensuite bedrooms, great Scottish breakfasts, home cooking, licensed. Main Euro and Irish routes. Walkers, cyclists, small wedding parties welcome. Smoking lounge available.

Auchencairn
NX7951   *Old Smugglers'*

Balcary Mews, *Balcary Bay, Auchencairn, Castle Douglas, DG7 1QZ.* **Open:** All year **Grades:** STB 4 Star, AA 4 Diamond **01556 640276** Mrs Davies www.geocities.com/BalcaryMews **D:** £26.00 **S:** £34.00 **Beds:** 1T 2D **Baths:** 3 En 🄾 (3) 📺 📖 ♨
Discover our tranquil hideaway superbly situated on the shores of Balcary Bay on the beautiful Solway Coast. Ideal for spectacular coastal walks, birdwatching, fishing, etc and exploring unspoilt Galloway. We offer excellent food, friendly service and stunning seaviews from every room. Brochure available.

B&B owners may vary rates – be sure to check when booking

Planning a longer stay? Always ask for any special rates

The Rossan, *Auchencairn, Castle Douglas, Kirkcudbrightshire, DG7 1QR.* Georgian style house 1869. Large secluded garden - bird watchers paradise. Resident owls. **Open:** All year **Grades:** STB 2 Star **01556 640269** Mrs Bardsley **Fax: 01556 640278** *bardsley@rossan.freeserve.co.uk* www.the-rossan.co.uk **D:** £15.00 **S:** £20.00 **Beds:** 3D **Baths:** 2 Sh 🄿 (4) 📺 🏃 ✕ 📖 ♨ ♣

Torbay, *Blue Hill, Auchencairn, Castle Douglas, DG7 1QW.* Enjoy the tranquillity of the unspoilt countryside and relax in the tastefully furnished rooms. **Open:** Easter to Oct **01556 640180** J T Cannon **Fax: 01556 640228** *cannontorbay@aol.com* **D:** £25.00 **S:** £30.00 **Beds:** 1T 1D **Baths:** 2 En 🄿 📺 📖 ♨

Balmaclellan
NX6579

High Park, *Balmaclellan, Castle Douglas, Kirkcudbrightshire, DG7 3PT.* A warm welcome awaits you at our comfortable farmhouse by Loch Ken. **Open:** Easter to Oct **01644 420298 (also fax)** Mrs Shaw *high.park@farming.co.uk* **D:** £16.00–£17.00 **S:** £16.00–£17.00 **Beds:** 2D 1T **Baths:** 1 Sh 🄾 🄿 (4) 📺 🏃 📺 📖 ♨

Bargrennan
NX3576

House O'Hill Hotel, *Bargrennan, Newton Stewart, Wigtownshire, DG8 6RN.* Rural family run hotel on edge of the Galloway Hills. **Open:** All year **01671 840243 (also fax)** Mrs Allwood *john@allwood33.freeserve.co.uk* **D:** £20.00–£25.00 **S:** £25.00–£30.00 **Beds:** 2F **Baths:** 2 En 🄾 📺 🏃 ✕ 📖 ♨ cc

Beattock
NT0802

Middlegill, *Beattock, Moffat, Dumfriesshire, DG10 9SW.* Manor farmhouse, 4 miles from Moffat. Deer, peacocks, lovely walks. **Open:** All year (not Xmas) **01683 300612** Mr Ramsden **D:** £15.00–£19.00 **S:** £15.00–£19.00 **Beds:** 2F 2D 3S **Baths:** 2 Sh 🄾 📺 🏃 ✕ 📖 ♨

Beeswing
NX8969

Locharthur House, *Beeswing, Dumfries, DG2 8JG.* Georgian house in beautiful countryside. **Open:** All year **01387 760235** Mrs Schooling **D:** £18.00–£20.00 **S:** £20.00–£22.00 **Beds:** 1F 1D **Baths:** 2 En 🄾 🄿 (6) 📺 ✕ 📺 📖 ♨

Canonbie
NY3876

Cross Keys Hotel, *Canonbie, Dumfriesshire, DG14 0SY.* **Open:** All year **Grades:** STB 3 Star **01387 371382 & 01387 371205** Mrs Kitching **Fax: 01387 371878** www.gretnaweddings.com/crosskeys.html **D:** £26.00 **S:** £30.00 **Beds:** 1F 4T 3D 2S **Baths:** 9 En 1 Pr 🄾 🄿 (30) 📺 🏃 ✕ 📖 ♨ cc
One of the oldest Coaching Inns in Scotland. The Cross Keys Hotel is a C17th building standing in the heart of the picturesque village of Canonbie. Bar-lunches and evening meals are served daily, carvery meals Saturday and Sunday.

Meadow View, *Watch Hill Road, Canonbie, DG14 0TF.* A warm Scottish welcome assured in this friendly home. **Open:** Easter to Oct **013873 71786** Mrs Bell **D:** £17.50 **S:** £20.00 **Beds:** 1F 1D **Baths:** 2 En 🄾 🄿 (3) ✕ 📺 📺 📖 ♨

Castle Douglas
NX7662   *Crown Hotel, Station Hotel*

Albion House, *49 Ernespie Road, Castle Douglas, Kircudbrightshire, DG7 1LD.* Substantial Victorian house, set in attractive, large garden. Every comfort. **Open:** All year (not Xmas/New Year) **Grades:** STB 4 Star **01556 502360 (also fax)** Mrs Kirk *pikoe007@aol.com* **D:** £20.00–£25.00 **S:** £25.00–£35.00 **Beds:** 1F 1T 1D **Baths:** 2 En 🄿 📺 🏃 ✕ 📺 📖 ♨

Smithy House, *The Buchan, Castle Douglas, Kirkcudbrightshire, DG7 1TH.* Comfortable Galloway cottage overlooking Carlingwark Loch. Central for exploring Galloway. **Open:** All year (not Xmas/New Year) **01556 503841** Mrs Carcas *enquiries@smithyhouse.co.uk* www.smithyhouse.co.uk **D:** £20.00–£27.50 **S:** £30.00–£35.00 **Beds:** 1T 2D **Baths:** 2 En 1 Pr 🄿 (4) ✕ 📺 📖 ♨ cc

Coxhill
NT0904

Coxhill Farm, *Old Carlisle Road, Coxhill, Moffat, Dumfriesshire, DG10 9QN.* Stylish farmhouse set in 70 acres, outstanding views, private parking. **Open:** All year (not Xmas/New Year)
01683 220471 Mrs Long **Fax: 01683 220871**
D: £22.50 **S:** £30.00 **Beds:** 1D 1T **Baths:** 2 En
⚊ 📺 ▦ 🌢

Creetown
NX4758 🍺 *Ellangowan Hotel, Barholm Arms*

Wal-d-mar,
Mill Street, Creetown, Newton Stewart, Wigtownshire, DG8 7JN.
Open: All year (not Xmas)
01671 820369 M Lockett **Fax: 01671 820266**
howie@thebogue.freeserve.co.uk **D:** £16.50
S: £16.50 **Beds:** 1D 1S **Baths:** 1 Sh ⅁ 🅿 (3)
📺 🍴 📺 ▦ 👶 🌢
Modern bungalow in quiet village location, ideal base for touring, walking, golf, etc. Comfortable beds, good breakfasts, private off-road parking, warm Scottish welcome assured. Situated between Dumfries and Stranraer on the Cree estuary.

Crocketford
NX8372

Henderland Farm, *Crocketford Road, Crocketford or Ninemile Bar, Dumfries, DG2 8QD.* Substantial farmhouse, comfortably furnished with views of lovely open countryside. **Open:** All year (not Xmas) **Grades:** STB 3 Star
01387 730270 Mrs Smyth **D:** £18.00–£20.00
S: £20.00 **Beds:** 1F 1D 1T **Baths:** 3 En ⅁
🅿 (4) 📺 🍴 ✕ 📺 ▦ 🌢

Crossmichael
NX7366

Culgruff House Hotel, *Crossmichael, Castle Douglas, Kirkcudbrightshire, DG7 3BB.* Victorian baronial mansion, own grounds, overlooking loch, village, Galloway Hills.
Open: All year
01556 670230 Mr Grayson **D:** £18.50–£28.50
S: £21.00–£28.50 **Beds:** 4F 4D 7T 2S
Baths: 4 En 4 Sh ⅁ 📺 (40) 📺 🍴 ✕ 📺 ▦ 🌢 cc

Airds Farm, *Crossmichael, Castle Douglas, Kirkcudbrightshire, DG7 3BG.* Scenic views over Loch Ken and the Galloway Hills. **Open:** All year
01556 670418 (also fax) Mrs Keith *tricia@ airds.com* www.airds.com **D:** £18.00–£23.00
S: £23.00–£27.00 **Beds:** 1F 1T 2D 1S
Baths: 2 En 1 Sh ⅁ 🅿 (6) ⚊ 📺 🍴 ▦ 🌢

Dalbeattie
NX8361 🍺 *Pheasant, Anchor, Smugglers, Laurie Arms, Clonyard House*

13 Maxwell Park, *Dalbeattie, Kirkcudbrightshire, DG5 4LR.* Perfectly situated for walks, beaches, golf. Warm welcome. Farmhouse breakfast. **Open:** All year
01556 610830 & 07808 146505 (M)
Mrs Tattersfield **D:** £18.00–£22.00 **S:** £26.00
Beds: 1T 2D **Baths:** 1 En 1 Sh ⅁ 🅿 (2) ⚊ 📺 🌢

Dumfries
NX9776

Fernwood, *4 Casslands, Dumfries, DG2 7NS.* Victorian sandstone villa, close to golf course and town centre. **Open:** All year (not Xmas)
01387 253701 (also fax) Mrs Vaughan
pamelavaughan@yahoo.com **D:** £18.00–£19.00
S: £18.00–£25.00 **Beds:** 1F 1D 2S **Baths:** 2
Sh ⅁ 🅿 (6) ⚊ 📺 ▦ 🌢

Lindean, *50 Rae Street, Dumfries, DG1 1JE.* Town centre house in quiet residential area, near railway station.
Open: All year **Grades:** STB 3 Star
01387 251888 Mrs Stein **D:** £18.00–£20.00
S: £25.00 **Beds:** 2T 1D **Baths:** 2 En 1 Pr ⅁ 🅿
⚊ 📺 📺 ▦ 🌢

Waverley Guest House, *21 St Mary's Street, Dumfries, DG1 1HB.* 5 minutes from town centre, across from railway station. On main road. **Open:** All year
01387 254080 F Meikle-Latta **Fax: 01387 254848** *southwest.lumber@virgin.net* **D:** £16.00–£20.00 **S:** £16.00–£24.00 **Beds:** 5F 3T 1D 5S
Baths: 6 En ⅁ 📺 🍴 ▦ 🌢 cc

Henderland Farm, *Crocketford Road, Crocketford or Ninemile Bar, Dumfries, DG2 8QD.* Substantial farmhouse, comfortably furnished with views of lovely open countryside. **Open:** All year (not Xmas) **Grades:** STB 3 Star
01387 730270 Mrs Smyth **D:** £18.00–£20.00
S: £20.00 **Beds:** 1F 1D 1T **Baths:** 3 En ⅁
🅿 (4) 📺 🍴 ✕ 📺 ▦ 🌢

17 Rotchell Road, *Dumfries, DG2 7SE.* Small, friendly, family establishment, near town centre. **Open:** All year
01387 255615 Mrs Kempsell *joank@ tinyworld.co.uk* **D:** £20.00 **S:** £20.00 **Beds:** 1F 1T 1D **Baths:** 3 En ⅁ 🅿 (4) 📺 🍴 ▦ 🌢

30 Hardthorn Avenue, *Dumfries, DG2 9JA.* Non-smoking private house with car parking in quiet residential area.
Open: Easter to Oct
01387 253502 (also fax) Ms Sloan
anniesbandb@aol.com **D:** £16.00–£18.00
S: £23.00–£25.00 **Beds:** 1D 1T **Baths:** 1 Sh
🅿 (2) ⚊ 📺 ▦ 🌢

Brackenbridge, *67 New Abbey Road, Dumfries, DG2 7JY.* Brackenridge Bed & Breakfast, walking distance into the town centre and all local attractions. **Open:** All year
01387 263962 Mr & Mrs Thomson **D:** £18.50–£25.00 **S:** £20.00 **Beds:** 3F 3T 1D 1S **Baths:** 2 En 1 Pr ⅁ 🅿 📺 🍴 ✕ 📺 ▦ 👶 🌢

Dunscore
NX8684

Low Kirkbride Farmhouse, *Dunscore, Dumfries, DG2 0SP.* Warm comfortable farmhouse with beautiful views, superb breakfasts, tasty home baking. **Open:** All year **Grades:** STB 3 Star
01387 820258 (also fax) Mrs Kirk
lowkirkbride@btinternet.com www.lowkirkbride. com **D:** £16.00–£18.00 **S:** £16.00–£18.00
Beds: 1F 1T 1D **Baths:** 3 En ⅁ 🅿 (4) 📺 ✕ 📺 ▦ 🌢

Ecclefechan
NY1974

Carlyle House, *Ecclefechan, Lockerbie, Dumfriesshire, DG11 3DG.* C18th house in small village. Central to Dumfries & Galloway and Borders. **Open:** All year (not Xmas/New Year) **Grades:** STB 1 Star
01576 300322 (also fax) Mrs Martin
D: £14.50 **S:** £14.50 **Beds:** 1F 1T 1S **Baths:** 2
Sh ⅁ 🅿 (6) 📺 🍴 ▦ 🌢

Eskdalemuir
NY2597

Hart Manor, *Eskdalemuir, Langholm, Dumfriesshire, DG13 0QQ.*
Open: All year
013873 73217
visit@hartmanor.co.uk www.hartmoor.co.uk
D: £36.50–£39.50 **S:** £46.50–£49.50 **Beds:** 1T 3D **Baths:** 4 En ⅁ (10) 🅿 ⚊ 📺 🍴 ✕ 📺 ▦ 🌢 cc
Something a little special. Superb food and a restful break. You can be sure of warm and relaxed personal service. All the food is home-made, the style British-country but with an individuality and flair that lifts it above the rest.

Gelston

NX7658 *Smuggler's Inn, Crows Nest, Douglas Arms*

Oakleaf Cottage, *Nether Linkins, Gelston, Castle Douglas, DG7 1SU.*
Open: All year
01556 680247 Mr Driver and Mrs D Cook
D: £21.00–£23.00 **S:** £23.00–£25.00 **Beds:** 1T
Baths: 1 En ⊞ (2) ⚟ 🖵 🛏 ✕ 🏛 ≗
Newly renovated cottage with woodland garden. Stunning views, hill and forest backdrop. Mild climate. The area beckons you to walk, paint, cycle and much more. We have bantams, ducks, dogs and abundant wildlife. Conservatory, guest kitchen for your added convenience.

Rose Cottage Guest House, *Gelston, Castle Douglas, Kirkcudbrightshire, DG7 1SH.*
Quiet country guest house in small village, 2.5 miles from Castle Douglas. **Open:** All year (not Xmas)
01556 502513 (also fax) Mr Steele
D: £18.00–£20.50 **S:** £18.00 **Beds:** 2D 3T 1S
Baths: 1 En 2 Sh ⏁ ⊞ (10) 🖵 🛏 ✕ 🗡 🏛 ≗

Glencaple

NX9968 *Nith Hotel*

Riverside, *Shore Park, Glencaple, Dumfries, DG1 4RF.* Detached house in small village, superb views over River Nith.
Open: All year (not Xmas/New Year)
01387 770423 Mrs Anderson **D:** £17.50
S: £20.00 **Beds:** 1F **Baths:** 1 Pr ⏁ ⊞ (1) ⚟ 🖵
🏛 & ≗

Glenluce

NX1957

Bankfield Farm, *Glenluce, Newton Stewart, Wigtownshire, DG8 0JF.* Large spacious farmhouse on the outskirts of quiet country village. **Open:** All year
01581 300281 (also fax) Mrs Stewart
D: £18.00 **S:** £20.00 **Beds:** 1F 1D 1T **Baths:** 2
En 1 Pr ⊞ 🖵 🏛 ≗

Gretna

NY3167

The Braids, *Annan Road, Gretna, Dumfriesshire, DG16 5DQ.* **Open:** All year
01461 337409 (also fax) Mrs Copeland
D: £16.00–£18.00 **S:** £25.00–£28.00 **Beds:** 2T
Baths: 1 Sh ⏁ ⊞ (2) 🖵 🗡 🏛 ≗
Small, friendly, family B&B in bungalow inside the entrance to our (BGHP Grade 4) caravan park. Open all year. Gretna marriage centre, golf, Sunday market. Good area for birdwatching in winter months. Advice on fishing in the area.

High Auchenlarie

NX5353

High Auchenlarie Farmhouse, *High Auchenlarie, Gatehouse of Fleet, Castle Douglas, Kirkcudbrightshire, DG7 2HB.* Traditional farmhouse overlooking Fleet, Wigtown Bay, Isle of Man. Superb location.
Open: Feb to Dec
01557 840231 (also fax) Mrs Johnstone
D: £22.00–£26.00 **S:** £30.00–£36.00 **Beds:** 1F
1T 1D **Baths:** 3 En ⏁ ⊞ (4) ⚟ 🖵 ✕ 🏛 ≗

Ingleston

NX7757 *Kings Arms*

Ingleston Farm, *Ingleston, Castle Douglas, Kirkcudbrightshire, DG7 1SW.*
Open: May to Oct
01556 502936 Mrs Smith **Fax: 01556 502757**
D: £19.00 **S:** £19.00 **Beds:** 1T 1D **Baths:** 1 En
1 Pr ⏁ ⊞ 🖵 🏛 ≗
Our charming old farmhouse, offering comfortable, spacious accommodation is centrally situated amidst beautiful rolling Galloway countryside. We rear beef cattle and sheep. Ideal base for touring. Double bedroom en suite. Twin bedroom private facilities. Home baking. Nearby lovely Solway Beaches.

Isle of Whithorn

NX4737 *Steam Packet*

Dubar House, *Tonderghie Road, Isle of Whithorn, Newton Stewart, Wigtownshire, DG8 8LQ.* Views of picturesque harbour. Modern comforts, retaining original character. **Open:** All year (not Xmas/New Year)
01988 500336 Mr & Mrs Lewis **D:** £15.00
S: £18.00 **Beds:** 3T **Baths:** 2 Sh ⏁ 🖵 ✕ 🗡 🏛

Kirkcudbright

NX6850 *Selkirk, Commercial Hotel, Arden House*

Number 3 B&B, *3 High Street, Kirkcudbright, DG64JZ.* **Open:** All year
Grades: STB 4 Star
01557 330881 Miriam Baker *ham_wwk@hotmail.com* www.number3-bandb.co.uk
D: £25.00 **S:** £30.00 **Beds:** 2T 1D **Baths:** 2 En
1 Pr ⏁ ⚟ 🖵 🛏 🏛 ≗
A 'B' listed Georgian townhouse with a C17th dining area and elegant guest drawing room. No 3 is at the end of Kirkcudbright's historic Old High Street behind MacLellans Castle. Featured in Scotland's Best B&Bs. Weekly and short breaks.

Parkview, *22 Millburn Street, Kirkcudbright, Kirkcudbrightshire, DG6 4EA.* Quiet situation, warm welcome guaranteed. **Open:** Easter to Oct
Grades: STB 3 Star
01557 330056 Mrs McIlwraith **D:** £17.00–£19.00 **S:** £17.00–£20.00 **Beds:** 1T 1D
Baths: 1 Sh ⊞ (2) ⚟ 🖵 🏛 ≗

Kirkpatrick Durham

NX7870

Glenhill, *Kirkpatrick Durham, Castle Douglas, Kirkcudbrightshire, DG7 3HE.* Traditional Scottish home, offering warm welcome and excellent home cooking.
Open: Easter to Oct
01556 650274 M Mathie **D:** £17.00–£20.00
S: £17.00–£20.00 **Beds:** 1T 1D **Baths:** 1 Pr 1
Sh ⊞ ⚟ 🖵 ✕ 🗡 🏛 ≗

Kirkton

NX9782

Wallamhill House, *Kirkton, Dumfries, DG1 1SL.* Country house, beautiful views, spacious rooms, leisure suite, safe parking.
Open: All year (not Xmas)
01387 248249 (also fax) Mrs Hood
wallamhill@aol.com **D:** £19.00–£22.00
S: £22.00–£28.00 **Beds:** 1F 2D 1T **Baths:** 4
En ⏁ ⊞ (8) ⚟ 🖵 🗡 🏛 ≗ cc

Langholm

NY3684 *Reiver's Rest, Riverside Inn, Eskdale Arms, Cross Keys*

Burnfoot House, *Westerkirk, Langholm, Dumfriesshire, DG13 0NG.* **Open:** Mar to Jan
01387 370611 Mr & Mrs Laverack **Fax: 01387 370616** *sg.laverack@burnft.co.uk* www.burnft.co.uk **D:** £20.00–£29.00 **S:** £23.00–£32.00
Beds: 1T 3D **Baths:** 3 En 1 Pr ⏁ ⚟ 🖵 🗡 🏛 ≗ cc
A C19th country home set in the beautiful Eskdale Valley. The rooms are ensuite and very spacious, all having panoramic views of the surrounding countryside. The library-sitting room is available to guests throughout the day. Ample private parking.

BATHROOMS
En = Ensuite
Pr = Private
Sh = Shared

Leswalt

NX0163

Windyridge, *Auchnotteroch, Leswalt, Stranraer, Wigtownshire, DG9 0XL.* Set in rolling countryside between Stranraer and Portpatrick 10 mins all ferries. **Open:** All year (not Xmas)
01776 870280 (also fax) Mrs Rushworth
rushworth@windyridge96.fsnet.co.uk **D:** £15.00
S: £15.00 **Beds:** 1D 1T **Baths:** 1 Sh ⛤ 🖩 (3)
�📺 🛉 📖 ♨

Lochfield

NY2066

20 Hardthorn Road, *Lochfield, Dumfries, DG2 9JQ.* Comfortable accommodation in family home. Full Scottish breakfast. Warm welcome.
Open: Mar to Oct
01387 264415 Mrs Cherrington *pcherrington@ hotmail.com* **D:** £15.00 **S:** £20.00 **Beds:** 1D
Baths: 1 Pr ⛤ 🖩 (1) ⚡ 📺 📖 ♨

Lochmaben

NY0882

Ardbeg Cottage, *19 Castle Street, Lochmaben, Lockerbie, Dumfriesshire, DG11 1NY.* **Open:** Feb to Dec **Grades:** STB 3 Star
01387 811855 (also fax) Mr & Mrs Neilson
bill@neilson.net **D:** £19.00 **S:** £19.00 **Beds:** 1D 1T **Baths:** 2 En ⚡ 📺 ✕ 📖 ♿ ♨
Warm comfortable peaceful ground floor B&B near centre of friendly ancient Royal Burgh, built round three Lochs. Four miles from motorway, a good staging point and base for exploring beautiful South West Scotland. Walkers and Cyclists welcome, drying room available.

Smallrigg, *Lochmaben, Lockerbie, DG11 1JH.* Only 10 mins' drive from motorway network, small working dairy farm, extensive views. **Open:** All year (not Xmas/ New Year)
01387 810462 Janet Newbould *jnewbould@ ukgateway.net* **D:** £15.00 **S:** £18.00 **Beds:** 1T 1D **Baths:** 1 En 1 Pr ⛤ 🖩 (4) ⚡ 📺 ✕ 📖 ♨

Lockerbie

NY1381 ⚑ *Murray Arms*

Rosehill Guest House, *9 Carlisle Road, Lockerbie, Dumfriesshire, DG11 2DR.* Victorian sandstone house (1871). Half-acre garden. Easy access M74. **Open:** All year (not Xmas)
Grades: STB 3 Star, AA 4 Diamond
01576 202378 Mr & Mrs Callander **D:** £20.00–£25.00 **S:** £20.00–£25.00 **Beds:** 1F 1D 2T 1S **Baths:** 3 En 2 Pr ⛤ 🖩 (5) 📺 🛉 📖 ♨

Ravenshill House Hotel, *Dumfries Road, Lockerbie, Dumfriesshire, DG11 2EF.* Large Victorian house, good food, quiet location, gardens, private car park.
Open: All year
01576 202882 (also fax) Ms Tindal *reception@ ravenshillhotellockerbie.co.uk*
www.ravenshillhotellockerbie.co.uk
D: £25.00–£27.00 **S:** £37.00 **Beds:** 2F 3D 3T
Baths: 7 En 1 Pr ⛤ 🖩 (30) 📺 🛉 ✕ 📖 ♨ cc

Kings Arms Hotel, *29 High Street, Lockerbie, DG11 2JL.* C16th former coaching inn with cosy barn log fires. **Open:** All year
01576 202410 (also fax) Mr Spence
www.kingsarmshotel.co.uk **D:** £30.00
S: £35.00–£40.00 **Beds:** 3F 4D 2T 5S ⛤ 🖩 (10) ⚡ 📺 🛉 ✕ 📖 ♨ cc

The Elms, *Dumfries Road, Lockerbie, Dumfriesshire, DG11 2EF.* Comfortable detached house. Friendly personal welcome. Private parking **Open:** Mar to Nov
01576 203898 (also fax) Mrs Rae *theelms@ gofornet.co.uk* *www.lockerbie-lodging.com*
D: £19.00–£22.00 **S:** £22.00–£25.00 **Beds:** 1D 1T **Baths:** 2 En ⛤ (12) 🖩 (2) ⚡ 📺 📖 ♨

Moffat

NT0805 ⚑ *Black Bull, Chequers Inn, Old Sun, Star, Moffat House*

Annandale Arms Hotel, *High Street, Moffat, Dumfriesshire, DG10 9HF.* **Open:** All year (not Xmas)
01683 220013 *still@annandalearmshotel.co.uk*
www.annandalearmshotel.co.uk **D:** £35.00
S: £45.00 **Beds:** 1F 4T 4D 1S **Baths:** 10 En ⛤ 🖩 (40) 📺 🛉 ✕ ♿ ♨ cc
Gold Key Award Winner 2001. Attractive 240 year old Georgian Hotel standing in the centre of the tree-lined square of the beautiful town of Moffat. Private carpark. Only one mile off J15/A74 (M6)

Ericstane, *Moffat, Dumfriesshire, DG10 9LT.* Working hill farm in a peaceful valley. Moffat 4 miles.
Open: All year
Grades: STB 3 Star
01683 220127 Mr Jackson **D:** £22.00
S: £27.00 **Beds:** 1D 1S **Baths:** 2 En ⛤ (8) 🖩 📺 📖 ♨

Craigie Lodge, *Ballplay Road, Moffat, Dumfriesshire, DG10 9JU.* **Open:** All year
Grades: STB 4 Star
01683 221769 (also fax) Mrs Corlett
craigielodge@aol.com *www.craigielodge.co.uk*
D: £22.00 **S:** £30.00 **Beds:** 1F 1T 1D **Baths:** 3 En ⛤ 🖩 (6) ⚡ 📺 ✕ 📖 ♨ cc
Homely Victorian townhouse situated in extensive gardens in a quiet residential area, yet only 5 minutes walk from town centre. Only 1 mile from M74, 45m to Glasgow, 50m to Edinburgh, 20m to Dumfries. Renowned for scrumptious home cooking.

Woodhead Farm, *Moffat, Dumfriesshire, DG10 9LU.*
Open: All year
01683 220225 (also fax)
Mrs Jackson **D:** £25.00–£27.50 **S:** £35.00
Beds: 1D 2T **Baths:** 3 En ⛤ 🖩 (3) ⚡ 📺 ✕ 📖 ♨
Luxuriously appointed farmhouse. Breakfast served in large conservatory, overlooking mature garden and surrounding hills. Working sheep farm. Ample safe parking. 2 miles from spa town of Moffat. All bedrooms have panoramic views.

Seven Oaks B&B, *School Lane, Moffat, Dumfriesshire, DG10 9AX.*
Open: All year
01683 220584
Mrs Elliott **Fax:**
01683 221984 *mfelliott@aol.com*
www.seven-oaks-moffat.co.uk **D:** £22.00
S: £30.00 **Beds:** 1D **Baths:** 1 En ⛤ (3) ⚡ 📺 📖 ♨
A delightful secluded bungalow affording, an oasis of peace and tranquility, yet only 3 minutes' walk from town centre. Wonderful views of the surrounding hills. Many extras not always found in B&Bs. A friendly welcome is assured.

Kirkland House, *Well Road, Moffat, Dumfriesshire, DG10 9AR.* Listed former manse with many interesting features, set in peaceful gardens. **Open:** All year
01683 221133 (also fax) Mr Watkins
kirklandmoffat@aol.com **D:** £19.00–£22.00
S: £19.00–£24.00 **Beds:** 1F 1T 2D **Baths:** 2 En 2 Pr 🖩 (6) ⚡ 📺 📖 ♨

National Grid References given are for villages, towns and cities – not for individual houses

Nethermill
NY0487

Lochrigghead Farmhouse, *Nethermill, Parkgate, Dumfries, DG1 3NG.* Farmhouse, picturesque surroundings. Good food, hospitality. Ideal for touring Scotland. **Open:** All year
01387 860381 Mrs Burgoyne
lochrigghead.burgo@talk21.co **D:** £17.00
S: £17.00 **Beds:** 3F 1D 1T 1S **Baths:** 2 En 1 Pr 1 Sh ⇔ 🄿 (10) 📺 ⛾ ✕ Ⅴ ▥ ❋ ♿

New Galloway
NX6377   ♨ Cross Keys

Cross Keys Hotel, *High Street, New Galloway, Castle Douglas, Kirkcudbrightshire, DG7 3RN.* C18th olde worlde hotel. **Open:** All year (not Xmas/ New Year)
01644 420494 (also fax) Mr Berriman
www.crosskeys.com **D:** £19.50–£23.50
S: £25.00–£27.50 **Beds:** 2F 4T 3D 2S **Baths:** 3 En 2 Sh ⇔ 🄿 ▤ 📺 ⛾ ✕ Ⅴ ▥ ♿ cc

Newton Stewart
NX4065

Ivy Bank Cottage, *Minnigaff, Newton Stewart, Dumfries & Galloway, DG8 6PQ.* 300 year old secluded riverside cottage, where breakfasts are legendary. **Open:** All year (not Xmas/New Year) **Grades:** STB 3 Star
01671 403139 Mr Izod *chris@ ivybank.fslife.co.uk* **D:** £18.00–£21.00
S: £18.00–£21.00 **Beds:** 1T 1D **Baths:** 1 Sh ⇔ 🄿 (2) ⅙ 📺 ⛾ Ⅴ ▥ ♿

Parkgate
NY0288

Lochrigghead Farmhouse, *Nethermill, Parkgate, Dumfries, DG1 3NG.* Farmhouse, picturesque surroundings. Good food, hospitality. Ideal for touring Scotland. **Open:** All year
01387 860381 Mrs Burgoyne
lochrigghead.burgo@talk21.co **D:** £17.00
S: £17.00 **Beds:** 3F 1D 1T 1S **Baths:** 2 En 1 Pr 1 Sh ⇔ 🄿 (10) 📺 ⛾ ✕ Ⅴ ▥ ❋ ♿

Parton
NX6970

Drumrash Farm, *Parton, Castle Douglas, Kirkcudbrightshire, DG7 3NF.* Traditional farmhouse, 300 yards from working farm. Superb views over Loch Ken. **Open:** All year
01644 470274 & 07714 748509 (M)
Mrs Cruikshank **D:** £14.00–£16.00 **S:** £15.00– £18.00 **Beds:** 2F 1D **Baths:** 1 En 2 Sh ⇔ 🄿 (6) ⅙ 📺 ⛾ ✕ Ⅴ ▥ ♿

Portpatrick
NW9954

Crest House, *Heugh Road, Portpatrick, Stranraer, Wigtownshire, DG9 8TD.* Magnificent sea and harbour views. Peacefully situated close to golf course. **Open:** All year **Grades:** STB 3 Star
01776 810316 (also fax) Mr & Mrs Batts **D:** £19.00–£23.00 **S:** £20.00–£25.00 **Beds:** 1T 4D **Baths:** 5 En ⇔ 🄿 (6) 📺 ⛾ ✕ Ⅴ ▥ ♿

Melvin Lodge Guest House, *South Crescent, Portpatrick, Stranraer, Wigtownshire, DG9 8LE.* Very comfortable, friendly house starting Southern Upland Way. **Open:** All year
01776 810238 Mr & Mrs Pinder **D:** £20.00– £23.00 **S:** £20.00–£23.00 **Beds:** 4F 3D 1T 2S **Baths:** 5 En 1 Sh ⇔ 🄿 (8) ⅙ 📺 ⛾ Ⅴ ▥ ♿ cc

Rockcliffe
NX8453

The Cottage, *1 Barcloy Mill, Rockcliffe, Dalbeattie, Kirkcudbrightshire, DG5 4QL.* Quiet cottage in central village guest rooms overlooking garden and coast. **Open:** All year (not Xmas/New Year)
01556 630460 Mrs Bailey *elizabeth-bailey@ rockcliffe-bandb.freeserve.co.uk* **D:** £17.50– £18.50 **S:** £23.00–£25.00 **Beds:** 1T 1D **Baths:** 1 En 1 Sh ⇔ 🄿 ⅙ 📺 ✕ Ⅴ ▥ ♿

Sanquhar
NS7809

4 Barons Court, *Sanquhar, Dumfriesshire, DG4 6EB.* Comfortable self-contained flat. Ideal for fishing, walking, golf and touring. **Open:** All year (not Xmas)
01659 50361 Mrs Clark **D:** £17.00 **S:** £17.00
Beds: 1F 1D **Baths:** 2 En ✕ Ⅴ ▥

Southwick
NX9357

Boreland of Southwick, *Southwick, Dumfries, DG2 8AN.* Warm and friendly welcome awaits you on the beautiful Solway Coast. **Open:** All year
01387 780225 Mrs Dodd *boreland.southwic@ virgin.net www.dalbeattie. com/farmholidaysqbasb.htm* **D:** £20.00– £25.00 **S:** £20.00–£25.00 **Beds:** 1T 2D **Baths:** 3 En ⇔ 🄿 ⅙ 📺 ✕ Ⅴ ▥ ❋ ♿ cc

Please respect a B&B's wishes regarding children, animals and smoking

---

Hartfell House, *Hartfell Crescent, Moffat, Dumfriesshire, DG10 9AL.* Splendid Victorian manor house in peaceful location. **Open:** All year (not Xmas/New Year) **Grades:** STB 4 Star, AA 4 Diamond
01683 220153 Mrs White *robert.white@ virgin.net* freespace.virgin.net/robert.white **D:** £24.00 **S:** £28.00 **Beds:** 2F 4D 1T 1S **Baths:** 7 En 1 Sh ⇔ 🄿 (8) 📺 ⛾ ✕ Ⅴ ▥ ♿

Morag, *19 Old Carlisle Road, Moffat, Dumfriesshire, DG10 9QJ.* Beautiful quiet location in charming town near Southern Upland Way. **Open:** All year **Grades:** STB 3 Star
01683 220690 Mr & Mrs Taylor **D:** £17.00– £18.00 **S:** £18.00–£19.00 **Beds:** 1D 1T 1S **Baths:** 1 Sh ⇔ (10) 🄿 (5) ⅙ 📺 ⛾ ✕ Ⅴ ▥ ♿

Allanton Hotel, *21-22 High Street, Moffat, Dumfriesshire, DG10 9HL.* Small inn in the scenic town of Moffat. Home cooking. **Open:** All year
01683 220343 & 01461 338330 Mr Kennedy **Fax: 01683 220914 D:** £22.00–£30.00
S: £24.00–£32.00 **Beds:** 1F 2T 3D 1 S **Baths:** 2 En 6 Pr 1 Sh ⇔ ⅙ 📺 ⛾ ✕ Ⅴ ▥ ♿ cc

Black Bull Hotel, *Churchgate, Moffat, Dumfriesshire, DG10 9EG.* Family run hotel, open all year. Accommodation and meals available. **Open:** All year
01683 220206 Miss Hughes **Fax: 01623 220403** *hotels@blackbullmoffat.co.uk* www.blackbullmoffat.co.uk **D:** £26.50
S: £35.00 **Beds:** 2F 4T 5D 1S **Baths:** 12 En ⇔ 📺 ✕ ▥ ♿ ♿ cc

The Arden House Guest House, *High Street, Moffat, Dumfriesshire, DG10 9HG.* Former bank building off of town square with private car park. **Open:** Easter to Oct **Grades:** STB 2 Star
01683 220220 I Standingford **D:** £18.00– £20.00 **S:** £18.00–£20.00 **Beds:** 2F 2T 2D 1S **Baths:** 4 En 1 Pr 2 Sh 🄿 (7) ⅙ 📺 ✕ Ⅴ ▥ ♿

Morlich House, *Ballplay Road, Moffat, Dumfriesshire, DG10 9JU.* A superb Victorian country house set in quiet elevated grounds overlooking town. **Open:** Feb to Nov
01683 220589 Mrs Wells **Fax: 01683 221032** *morlich.house@ndirect.co.uk* www.morlich-house.ndirect.co.uk **D:** £20.00– £23.00 **S:** £20.00–£33.00 **Beds:** 2F 1D 1T 1S **Baths:** 4 En 1 Pr ⇔ 🄿 (6) ⅙ 📺 ⛾ ✕ Ⅴ ▥ ♿ cc

Waterside, *Moffat, Dumfriesshire, DG10 9LF.* Large country house in 12 acres woodland garden with private stretch of river. **Open:** Easter to Oct
01683 220092 Mrs Edwards **D:** £19.00– £21.00 **S:** £21.00 **Beds:** 2D 2T **Baths:** 1 Pr 1 Sh ⇔ 🄿 (4) ⅙ 📺 ▥ ♿

Stoneykirk

NX0853

Torrs Warren Hotel, *Stoneykirk, Portpatrick, Stranraer, Wigtownshire, DG9 9DH.* Delightful former manse set in peaceful countryside location. Warm welcome. **Open:** All year
01776 830298 Mrs Camlin **Fax: 01776 830204**
torrswarren@btinternet.com **D:** £24.00 **S:** £28.00
Beds: 2F 2T 2D 2S **Baths:** 8 En ☎ 🅿 (30) 🅲 ✕ 🅅 ⬛ ✳ 🌢 **cc**

Stranraer

NX0560 ⬤ *Bay Horse*

Ivy House, *London Road, Stranraer, DG9 8ER.* Lovely old town house, situated at the foot of Loch Ryan. **Open:** All year
01776 704176 Mr & Mrs Mcmillan
gregormcmillan@hotmail.com www.fortunecity.
co.uk/business/financial/40/index.html
D: £16.00–£19.00 **S:** £18.00–£25.00 **Beds:** 1F
1D 1T **Baths:** 2 En 1 Pr ☎ 🅿 (10) 🅲 ⴕ 🅅 ⬛ 🌢

Lorenza, *2 Birnam Place, Station Street, Stranraer, Wigtownshire, DG9 7HN.* Central location, walking distance from town, train, bus and ferries. **Open:** All year (not Xmas/New Year) **Grades:** STB 2 Star
01776 703935 Mrs Jameson **D:** £18.00
S: £20.00 **Beds:** 1T 2D **Baths:** 2 En 1 Pr 🅿 (3)
🅅 ⬛ 🌢

Neptune's Rest, *25 Agnew Crescent, Stranraer, Wigtownshire, DG9 7JZ.* Neptune's Rest overlooks Agnew Park with its boating lake and miniature railway. **Open:** All year
01776 704729 Mr McClymont **D:** £15.00–£20.00 **S:** £16.00–£22.00 **Beds:** 2F 2D 1T 1S
Baths: 3 En 2 Sh ☎ 🅲 ✕ 🅅 ✳ 🌢 **cc**

Windyridge Villa, *5 Royal Crescent, Stranraer, DG9 8HB.* Overlooking Loch Ryan. Convenient for ferry terminal and railway station. **Open:** All year (not Xmas/New Year)
01776 889900 (also fax) Mrs Kelly
windyridge_villa@hotmail.com **D:** £20.00–£22.00 **S:** £25.00–£28.00 **Beds:** 1T 1D
Baths: 2 En ☎ 🅿 (3) ↙ 🅲 ⴕ 🅅 ⬛ 🌢

Torthorwald

NY0378

Branetrigg Farm, *Torthorwald, Dumfries, DG1 3QB.* Farmhouse with panoramic views; ideal for touring, cycling, fishing and golfing. **Open:** Easter to Nov
01387 750650 Mrs Huston **D:** £16.00–£18.00
S: £18.00 **Beds:** 1F 1D **Baths:** 1 Sh 🅲 ⬛

Whithorn

NX4440

Belmont, *St John Street, Whithorn, Newton Stewart, Wigtownshire, DG8 8PG.* Comfortable home in beautiful area. Warm welcome. **Open:** All year **Grades:** STB 3 Star
01988 500890 (also fax) B J Fleming
D: £18.00–£20.00 **S:** £18.00–£20.00 **Beds:** 2D
Baths: 1 Pr 1 Sh ☎ (8) 🅿 (10) ↙ 🅲 ⴕ ✕ 🅅 🌢

The Steampacket Hotel, *Whithorn, Newton Stewart, Wigtownshire, DG8 8LA.* Family run harbourside inn. **Open:** All year (not Xmas/New Year) **Grades:** STB 1 Star
01988 500334 *steampacketinn@btconnect.com*
D: £25.00–£35.00 **S:** £25.00–£35.00 **Beds:** 1F
1T 5D **Baths:** 7 En ☎ ↙ 🅲 ⴕ ✕ 🅅 ⬛ 🌢 **cc**

Slan A Stigh, *34 George Street, Whithorn, Dumfries & Galloway, DG8 8NZ.* 1700 Georgian townhouse in historic Whithorn, site of earliest Christian community in Scotland. **Open:** All year
01988 500699 Mr Burford *alexburford@supanet.com* www.alexburford.supanet.com
D: £20.00 **S:** £20.00 **Beds:** 1F 2D **Baths:** 1
Sh ☎ 🅿 (2) ↙ 🅲 ✕ 🅅 ⬛ 🌢

Wigtown

NX4355 ⬤ *Corsemalzie Hotel, Bladnock Inn*

Craigmount Guest House, *High Street, Wigtown, Wigtownshire, DG8 9EQ.* **Open:** All year
01988 402291 / 0800 980 4510 P Taylor
taylorpat1@talk21.com **D:** £18.00–£20.00
S: £18.00–£25.00 **Beds:** 2F 2T 1S **Baths:** 2
En 1 Sh ☎ 🅿 (10) 🅲 ⴕ ✕ 🅅 ⬛ 🌢
Welcoming, licensed family-run home with space to relax. Close to Stranraer for ferries to Ireland, walk the Galloway hills and forests, play golf, shoot, visit the beaches, stone circle and historic monuments, browse the shops in Scotland's book town.

Glaisnock House, *20 South Main Street, Wigtown, Wigtownshire, DG8 9EH.* Set in the heart of Scotland's book town with licensed restaurant. **Open:** All year (not Xmas)
01988 402249 (also fax) Mr & Mrs Cairns
cairns@glaisnock1.freeserve.co.uk
www.glaisnock-house.co.uk **D:** £17.50–£18.50
S: £18.50–£19.50 **Beds:** 2F 1T 1S **Baths:** 2
En 1 Pr 1 Sh ☎ 🅲 ⴕ ✕ 🅅 ⬛ 🌢 **cc**

Fife

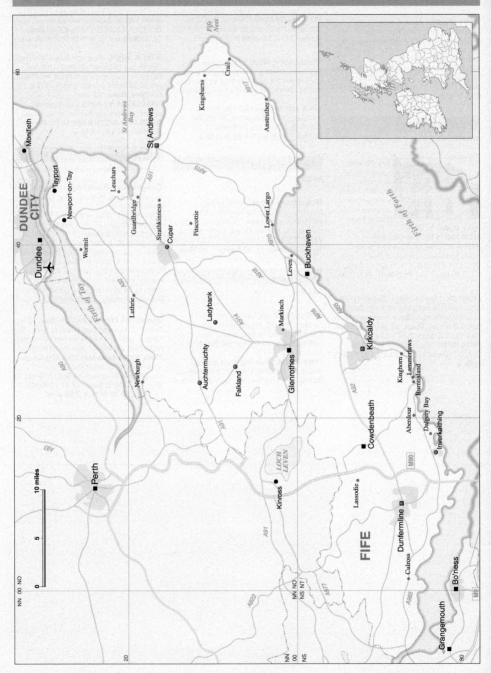

Planning a longer stay? Always
ask for any special rates

Aberdour

NT1985

**Aberdour
Hotel,** 38 High
Street, Aberdour,
Burntisland, Fife,
KY3 0SW. Friendly
village inn,
traditional
cooking, real ales, Edinburgh half hour car/
rail. **Open:** All year **Grades:** STB 3 Star, AA
2 Diamond
01383 860325 Mr Thomson **Fax: 01383
860808** *reception@aberdourhotel.co.uk*
www.aberdourhotel.co.uk **D:** £25.00–£30.00
S: £35.00–£45.00 **Beds:** 4F 7D 5T **Baths:** 16
En ⹁ 🅿 (8) 🅳 ⑂ ✕ 🆅 🔟 ☕ ⚿**1** ⚒ **cc**

Anstruther

NO5603

Royal Hotel,
20 Rodger Street,
Anstruther, Fife,
KY10 3HU. Family-
run hotel, 100
yards seashore.
Small harbour,
sea trips to May Island Bird Sanctuary.
Open: All year
01333 310581 Mr Cook **D:** £18.00–£22.00
S: £18.00–£25.00 **Beds:** 1F 4T 4D 2S
Baths: 1 En ⹁ 🅳 ⑂ ✕ 🆅 🔟 ⚒

The Sheiling, 32 Glenogil Gardens,
Anstruther, Fife, *KY10 3ET.* Pretty white
bungalow, ground floor bedrooms overlook
garden. Harbour 200m. **Open:** Easter to
Sept
01333 310697 Mrs Ritchie **D:** £16.00–£22.00
S: £22.00 **Beds:** 2D **Baths:** 1 Sh 1 Pr 🅿 (2) ⑂
🔟 ✕ 🆅 🔟 ⚿ ⚒

Harefield Cottage, Carvenom,
Anstruther, Fife, *KY10 3JU.* Large stone-built
single-storey cottage, large garden. All
rooms extensive views to Firth of Forth.
Open: Easter to Oct
01333 310346 Mrs Robinson **D:** £20.00–
£21.50 **S:** £24.00 **Beds:** 1T 1D **Baths:** 1 Pr 1
Sh 🅿 (4) 🔟 ⑂ 🆅 🔟

Burntisland

NT2386 ⚲ Inchuen Hotel, Kingswood Hotel

Gruinard, 148 Kinghorn Road,
Burntisland, Fife, *KY3 9JU.* Member of
Scotland's best B&B. Coastal location.
Spectacular views. **Open:** Mar to Nov
Grades: STB 4 Star
01592 873377 & 07798 738578 (M)
Mrs Bowman *gruinard@dircon.co.uk*
www.gruinardguesthouse.co.uk **D:** £21.00–
£26.00 **S:** £30.00–£45.00 **Beds:** 1T 1D
Baths: 2 En ⚿ 🅳 ⑂ 🆅 🔟 ⚒ **cc**

148a Kinghorn Road, Burntisland, Fife,
KY3 9JU. Panoramic views over River Forth,
golf courses and water sports nearby.
Open: All year
01592 872266 (also fax) Mrs Redford
c148m@aol.com **D:** £20.00–£25.00 **S:** £25.00–
£30.00 **Beds:** 1F 1D **Baths:** 2 En ⚲ 🅿 (2) 🔟 ⑂
🆅 🔟 ⚒

Crail

NO6107 ⚲ Golf Hotel, Cambo Arms, Balcomie
Hotel, East Neuk Hotel

Denburn House, 1 Marketgate North,
Crail, Anstruther, Fife, *KY10 3TQ.* **Open:** All
year **Grades:** STB 3 Star
01333 450253 *denburn@fsbdial.co.uk*
D: £18.00–£27.50 **S:** £25.00–£35.00 **Beds:** 3T
2D 1S **Baths:** 5 En 1 Pr ⚲ 🅿 ⚿ 🔟 ⑂ 🆅 🔟 ⚒ **cc**
Enjoy the special atmosphere of this
beautiful C18th house, the peaceful walled
garden, comfy guest lounge and splendid
sea views. Wander the quaint lanes to the
beaches and harbour, or challenge the
many links golf courses. St Andrews 9
miles.

Culross

NS9886 ⚲ Red Lion

**St Mungo's
Cottage,** Low
Causeway,
Culross,
Dunfermline,
Fife, *KY12 8HJ.*
Historic village.
Ideal for touring central Scotland.
Edinburgh 40 min. Gardens. **Open:** All year
(not Xmas/New Year)
01383 882102 Mrs Jackson *martinpjackson@*
hotmail.com www.milford.co.
uk/scotland/accom/h-a-1763.html
D: £16.00–£22.00 **S:** £20.00–£22.00 **Beds:** 1F
1T 1D **Baths:** 1 En 1 Sh 🅿 (6) ⑂ 🆅 🔟 **cc**

Dundonald Arms Hotel, Mid
Causeway, Culross, Dunfermline, Fife,
KY12 8HS. C16th time warp riverside village;
white cottages, cobbled causeways.
Open: All year
01383 882443 Mrs Finlayson **Fax: 01383
881137 D:** £20.00–£30.00 **S:** £30.00–£40.00
Beds: 7F 3D 2T **Baths:** 7 En 7 Pr ⚲ 🅿 (30) 🔟
✕ 🆅 🔟 ⚒ **cc**

Cupar

NO3714 ⚲ Springfield Tavern, Pitscottie Inn,
Meldrums Hotel, Ceres Inn

Scotstarvit Farm, Cupar, Fife, *KY15 5PA.*
Enviably located just off A916. Few minutes
Cupar, 10 minutes St Andrews. **Open:** All
year
01334 653591 (also fax) Mrs Chrisp
D: £16.00–£18.00 **S:** £18.00–£24.00 **Beds:** 1T
1D **Baths:** 1 Pr 1 Sh ⚲ (12) 🅿 ⚿ 🔟 🆅 🔟

Dalgety Bay

NT1583 ⚲ The Granary

Wickers B&B, 5 Main Street West, Dalgety
Bay, Dunfermline, *KY11 9HJ.* Edinburgh 20
mins, rail halt 3 min walk. **Open:** All year
Grades: STB 3 Star
01383 415326 Ms Harper **D:** £18.00–£25.00
S: £5.00–£10.00 **Beds:** 1T 1D 1S **Baths:** 1 En
2 Sh ⚲ 🅿 (2) 🔟 🔟 ⚒

Dunfermline

NT1087

Broomfield Guest House, 1
Bloomfield Drive, Dunfermline, Fife, *KY12 7DZ.*
Large Victorian house, near golf course,
swimming pool and town centre. **Open:** All
year (not Xmas/New Year)
01383 732498 Mrs Taylor **D:** £19.00–£25.00
S: £16.00–£20.00 **Beds:** 1F 2D 1T 2S
Baths: 5 En 1 Pr ⚲ 🅿 (7) 🔟 🆅 ⚿ ⚒

Bowleys Farm, Roscobie, Dunfermline,
Fife, *KY12 0SG.* Sample Scottish hospitality at
its best! (30 minutes from Edinburgh).
Open: Feb to Dec
01383 721056 Mrs Fotheringham
bowleysfarm@hotmail.com **D:** £18.00–£22.00
S: £25.00 **Beds:** 2F **Baths:** 1 En 1 Sh ⚲ 🅿 (6)
⚿ 🔟 ⑂ ✕ 🆅 🔟 ⚒

Falkland

NO2507

Templelands Farm, Falkland, Cupar,
Fife, *KY15 7DE.* Panoramic views, National
Trust properties nearby - abundance of golf
courses. **Open:** Easter to Oct
01337 857383 Ms McGregor **D:** £15.00
S: £15.00–£18.00 **Beds:** 1F 1D 1S **Baths:** 2
Sh ⚲ 🅿 (3) ⚿ 🔟 ⚒

Guardbridge

NO4519

The Larches, 7 River Terrace,
Guardbridge, St Andrews, Fife, *KY16 0XA.*
Perfectly situated for golf, wonderful
countryside, beaches and fantastic food.
Open: All year **Grades:** STB 4 Star, AA 4
Diamond
01334 838008 (also fax) V Mayner
thelarches@aol.com **D:** £18.00–£28.00
S: £25.00–£38.00 **Beds:** 2T 2D **Baths:** 2 En 2
Pr ⚲ (5) 🅿 ⚿ 🔟 🆅 🔟 ⚒

Inverkeithing

NT1382   The Granary

Elindil B and B, *10 Muckle Hill Park, Inverkeithing, KY11 1BX.* Relaxed, friendly, ideally situated for East and Central Scotland. 10 mins Edinburgh Airport. **Open:** All year **Grades:** STB 3 Star **01383 411367 (also fax)** Ms Scott *elendilscott@aol.com* **D:** £22.00–£25.00 **S:** £22.00–£25.00 **Beds:** 2T 1D **Baths:** 2 Pr ≥ ⊡ ⊬ ⊡ ⊁ × ⊻ ⊞ ⋅ ≜

The Roods, *16 Bannerman Avenue, Inverkeithing, Fife, KY11 1NG.* Award winning B&B set in quiet gardens close to coastal path. **Open:** All year **01383 415049 (also fax)** Mrs Marley *bookings@theroods.com* www.theroods.com **D:** £20.00–£25.00 **S:** £20.00–£25.00 **Beds:** 1D 1T 1F **Baths:** 3 En ≥ ⊡ ⊬ ⊡ × ⊞ ⋅ ≜ cc

Kinghorn

NT2687   Kingswood Hotel

Craigo-Er, *45 Pettycur Road, Kinghorn, Fife, KY3 9RN.* Victorian house, panoramic sea views, direct regular Edinburgh rail links. **Open:** All year **01592 890527** Mrs Thomson **D:** £19.00 **S:** £19.00 **Beds:** 1D 2T **Baths:** 2 Sh ≥ ⊡ (1) ⊡ ⊁ ⊞ ⋅ ≜

Kingsbarns

NO5912

Kingsbarns Bed & Breakfast, *3 Main Street, Kingsbarns, St Andrews, Fife, KY16 8SL.* Warm, friendly, comfortable B&B in picturesque coastal village. Golf courses nearby. **Open:** Apr to Oct **Grades:** STB 4 Star **01334 880234** Mrs Hay *farida@ kingsbarns-bb.co.uk* www.kingsbarns-bb.co.uk **D:** £22.00–£25.00 **S:** £22.00–£28.00 **Beds:** 2D 1T **Baths:** 3 En ≥ ⊡ (2) ⊡ ⊡ ⊞ ⋅ ≜

Kirkcaldy

NT2791   Parkway Hotel, Victoria Hotel

Crawford Hall, *2 Kinghorn Road, Kirkcaldy, Fife, KY1 1SU.* **Open:** All year (not Xmas) **01592 262658** Mrs Crawford **D:** £17.00–£19.00 **S:** £17.00–£19.00 **Beds:** 1F 1T **Baths:** 1 Sh ≥ ⊡ (4) ⊡ ⊁ × ⊞ ⋅ ≜ ⋅ Large, rambling old C19th house, once local manse, set in lovely gardens. 2 minutes from beach, 10 minute walk to town centre, bus/railway stations. Comfortable rooms, hearty breakfast, handy for golfers, near St Andrews.

Cameron House, *44 Glebe Park, Kirkcaldy, Fife, KY1 1BL.* Friendly, welcome, good home cooking, central location, main line station. **Open:** All year (not Xmas) **01592 264531** Mrs Nicol **D:** £16.00–£17.50 **S:** £17.00–£20.00 **Beds:** 1F 1D **Baths:** 1 Sh ≥ (1) ⊬ ⊡ ⊁ × ⊻ ⊞ ⋅ ≜

Castleview, *17 Dysart Road, Kirkcaldy, Fife, KY1 2AY.* Situated on Fife coast near M90, within reach Edinburgh, Perth, Dundee. **Open:** All year (not Xmas) **01592 269275** Mrs Dick **D:** £16.00–£17.00 **S:** £16.00–£17.00 **Beds:** 1F 2T **Baths:** 1 Sh ≥ ⊡ ⊡ ⊁ × ⊻ ⊞ ⋅ ≜

North Hall Guest House, *143 Victoria Road, Kirkcaldy, Fife, KY1 1DQ.* Victorian manse with modern comforts. Two minutes from railway station. **Open:** All year (not Xmas/New Year) **Grades:** STB 4 Star **01592 268864** Cairns *cairns@ northall.freeserve.co.uk* www.smoothhound.co. uk/hotels/northall.html **D:** £22.50–£26.00 **Beds:** 1T 2D **Baths:** 2 En 1 Pr ⊡ (3) ⊬ ⊡ ⊻ ⊞ ≜

Arboretum, *20 Southerton Road, Kirkcaldy, Fife, KY2 5NB.* Extended Bungalow overlooking large park close to all amenities. **Open:** All year **Grades:** STB 3 Star **01592 643673** E Duncan **D:** £19.00–£20.00 **S:** £20.00–£22.00 **Beds:** 1T 1D **Baths:** 2 En ⊡ (4) ⊡ ⊡ ⊁ ⊞ ⋅ ✻ ≜

Ladybank

NO3009

Redlands Country Lodge, *Pitlessie Road, Ladybank, Cupar, Fife, KY15 7SH.* Country cottage surrounded by trees and fields. **Open:** Feb to Nov **Grades:** STB 4 Star **01337 831091 (also fax)** Mr McGregor **D:** £25.00 **S:** £35.00 **Beds:** 2T 2D **Baths:** 4 En ≥ ⊡ (6) ⊬ ⊡ ⊡ ⊁ × ⊻ ⊞ ⋅ ≜ cc

Lammerlaws

NT2386   Inchview Hotel, Kingwoods Hotel

Inchcape Guest House, *1 South View, Lammerlaws, Burntisland, Fife, KY3 9BS.* 1 minute from beach. Centre view of river. **Open:** Apr to Oct **Grades:** STB 2 Star **01592 873270** Mrs Sharp **D:** £18.00 **S:** £18.00 ≥ ⊡ ⊬ ⊡ ⊞ ⋅ ≜

BATHROOMS

En = Ensuite

Pr = Private

Sh = Shared

Lassodie

NT1292

Loch Fitty Cottage, *Lassodie, Dunfermline, Fife, KY12 0SP.* Enjoy the comfort of a family home, in rural setting. **Open:** All year **01383 831081** Mr Woolley *n.woolley@ btinternet.com* www.lochfittybandb.btinternet. co.uk **D:** £18.00–£20.00 **S:** £18.00–£20.00 **Beds:** 1F 1D **Baths:** 1 En 1 Pr ≥ ⊡ (4) ⊡ ⊡ ⊻ ⊞ ⋅ ≜

Leuchars

NO4521

Pitlethie Farm, *Leuchars, St Andrews, Fife, KY16 0DP.* Comfortable farmhouse base for golf and the St Andrews area. **Open:** All year **01334 838649** Mrs Black **Fax: 01334 839281** www.aboutscotland.com/fife/pitlethie.html **D:** £25.00–£30.00 **S:** £30.00–£35.00 **Beds:** 2D **Baths:** 1 Sh ≥ (10) ⊬ ⊡ ⊞ ⋅ cc

Pinewood Country House, *Tayport Road, St Michaels, Leuchars, St Andrews, Fife, KY16 0DU.* A quiet wooded area, ideal setting for short breaks or golfing holidays. **Open:** All year (not Xmas/New Year) **01334 839860** Mr Bedwell **Fax: 01334 839868** *accommodation@pinewoodhouse.com* www.pinewoodhouse.com **D:** £22.00–£25.00 **S:** £32.00–£44.00 **Beds:** 2T 3D **Baths:** 4 En 1 Pr ⊡ ⊡ ⊁ × ⊻ ⊞ ⋅ ≜ cc

Leven

NO3800

Duniface Farm, *Windygates, Leven, Fife, KY8 5RH.* Charming C19th farmhouse - comfortable & welcoming, hearty breakfasts, ideal touring base. **Open:** All year **01333 350272 (also fax)** Mrs Hamilton *audreymhamilton@tinyworld.co.uk* **D:** £15.00–£17.00 **S:** £15.00–£20.00 **Beds:** 1D 1F **Baths:** 1 Sh ≥ ⊡ ⊡ ⊞ ⋅ ≜

Lower Largo

NO4102

Crusoe Hotel, *2 Main Street, Lower Largo, Leven, Fife, KY8 6BT.* Friendly family-run hotel. Harbour location, A la carte restaurant, bar meals. **Open:** All year **Grades:** STB 3 Star **01333 320759** D & P Ferries **Fax: 01333 320865** *info@crusoe-hotel.co.uk* www.crusoe-hotel.co.uk **D:** £25.00–£45.00 **S:** £45.00–£65.00 **Beds:** 2F 10T 2S **Baths:** 17 En ≥ ⊡ ⊡ ⊡ ⊡ ⊁ × ⊻ ⊞ ✻ ⋅ cc

Map page 436   *Fife*

Luthrie

NO3319

Easter Kinsleith, *Luthrie, Cupar, Fife, KY15 4NR.* Gaplair is ideally situated for touring east and central Scotland. **Open:** Feb to Nov
01337 870363 Mr Rieu-Clarke *gapplair@ compuserve.com* gapplairguesthouse.co.uk
D: £18.00–£20.00 **S:** £18.00–£20.00 **Beds:** 1F 1D **Baths:** 2 En ➳ (6) ▣ (2) ⽅ ▨ ⼘ ▥ ▥ cc

Markinch

NO2901

Wester Markinch Cottage, *Balbirnie Estate, Markinch, Glenrothes, Fife, KY7 6JN.* Extended Victorian cottage, convenient for Edinburgh, Glasgow and St. Andrews. **Open:** All year (not Xmas/New Year)
01592 756719 & 07774 622 497 (M) Ms Tjeransen **Fax:** 01592 756719 **D:** £18.00–£25.00 **S:** £16.00 **Beds:** 1D 2S 1T **Baths:** 1 En 1 Sh ➳ ▣ (4) ▨ ⼘ ▥ ▥

Shythrum Farm, *Markinch, Glenrothes, Fife, KY7 6HB.* Peaceful farmhouse. Markinch 1 mile golfers haven, excellent touring base. **Open:** Mar to Oct
01592 758372 Mrs Craig **D:** £19.00 **S:** £19.00 **Beds:** 1F 1T **Baths:** 1 En 1 Pr ➳ ▣ (3) ▨ ▥ ▥

Newburgh

NO2318   ◀ *Abbey Inn, Baigwe Inn, Cree's Inn*

Ninewells Farm, *Woodriffe Road, Newburgh, Cupar, Fife, KY14 6EY.* Quiet and comfortable with magnificent views. Well-furnished. Warm welcome, excellent breakfast. **Open:** Apr to Oct **Grades:** STB 4 Star
01337 840307 (also fax) B Baird *barbara@ ninewellsfarm.co.uk* www.ninewells.co.uk
D: £19.00–£24.00 **S:** £25.00–£34.00 **Beds:** 1F 1T 1D **Baths:** 1 En 2 Pr ➳ (14) ▣ (4) ⽅ ▨ ▥ ▥

Pitscottie

NO4113

Rockmount Cottage, *Dura Den Road, Pitscottie, Cupar, Fife, KY15 5TG.* Lovely C19th cottage tastefully modernised to a high standard just 7m from St. Andrews. **Open:** All year (not Xmas/New Year)
01334 828164 Mrs Reid *annmreid@ rockmount1.freeserve.co.uk* **D:** £18.00–£25.00
S: £18.00–£25.00 **Beds:** 1F 1D 1S **Baths:** 1 Pr 2 Sh ➳ ▣ (3) ⽅ ▨ ▥ ▥ ♿3 ▥

St Andrews

NO5116   ◀ *New Inn*

23 Kilrymont Road, *St Andrews, Fife, KY16 8DE.* Detached home, harbour area, East Sands, 10 mins famous golf course. **Open:** Apr to Dec
01334 477946 Mrs Kier *mkier@talk21.com*
D: £17.00–£19.00 **S:** £17.00–£20.00 **Beds:** 1D 1S ➳ (7) ▣ (1) ⽅ ▨ ▥ ♿ ▥

The Paddock, *Sunnyside, Strathkinness, St Andrews, KY16 9XP.* **Open:** All year (not Xmas/New Year)
01334 850888 Mrs Taylor **Fax:** 01334 850870 *thepaddock@btinternet.com* www.thepadd.co.uk
D: £20.00–£26.00 **S:** £25.00–£40.00 **Beds:** 1T 2D ▣ (8) ▨ ▥ ▥ ❋ ▥ cc
Quality ensuite accommodation in a modern residence with outstanding country views. Positioned in a secluded spot. Ample private parking. Guests may use the conservatory overlooking the gardens. St. Andrews 2 miles.

Glenderran Guest House, *9 Murray Park, St Andrews, Fife, KY16 9AW.* **Open:** All year **Grades:** STB 4 Star, AA 4 Diamond
01334 477951 Mr Wood **Fax:** 01334 477908 *glenderran@telinco.com* www.glenderran.com **D:** £30.00 **S:** £30.00 **Beds:** 1T 2D 2S **Baths:** 3 En 2 Pr ➳ (12) ⽅ ▨ ▥ ▥ ▥
250 yards from the first tee of the Old Course and St Andrews Bay. Glenderran is a smartly presented Guest House with thoughtful amenities throughout. A warm welcome awaits you from your host Patrick Wood.

Whitecroft Guest Lodges, *33 Strathkinness High Road, St Andrews, Fife, KY16 9UA.*
Open: All year **Grades:** STB 4 Star
01334 474448 Mr & Mrs Horn *whitecroft@ tesco.net* www.whitecroft-lodges.co.uk
D: £22.00–£28.00 **S:** £30.00–£50.00 **Beds:** 3F 1T 1D **Baths:** 5 En ▣ (5) ⽅ ▨ ⼘ ▥ ▥ cc
Whitecroft is a converted 1890's farm croft set in 1/3rd acre on Western edge of town. All rooms are ensuite with car parking and private entrances. Lovely views of Sidlaws and Eden Estuary, only 3 minutes by car to St Andrews.

All details shown are as supplied by B&B owners in Autumn 2001

B&B owners may vary rates – be sure to check when booking

Copper-cantie, *8 Lawhead Road West, St Andrews, Fife, KY16 9NE.* High standard of decor and breakfast, only minutes drive from centre. **Open:** All year (not Xmas) **Grades:** STB 4 Star
01334 476544 Mrs Dobson *f.dobson@ btinternet.com* www.coppercantie.co.uk
D: £20.00–£26.00 **S:** £34.00–£40.00 **Beds:** 1F 1D 1T **Baths:** 1 En 2 Sh ⽅ ▨ ▥ ▥ cc

The Larches, *7 River Terrace, Guardbridge, St Andrews, Fife, KY16 0XA.* Perfectly situated for golf, wonderful countryside, beaches and fantastic food. **Open:** All year **Grades:** STB 4 Star, AA 4 Diamond
01334 838008 (also fax) V Mayner *thelarches@aol.com* **D:** £18.00–£28.00
S: £25.00–£38.00 **Beds:** 2T 2D **Baths:** 2 En 2 Pr ➳ (5) ▣ ⽅ ▨ ▥ ▥ ▥

Cairnsden B&B, *2 King Street, St Andrews, Fife, KY16 8JQ.* Comfortable family house, 7 mins town centre, early breakfasts for golfers. **Open:** All year (not Xmas) **Grades:** STB 4 Star
01334 476326 Mrs Allan **Fax:** 01334 840355 **D:** £16.00–£20.00 **S:** £22.00–£25.00 **Beds:** 2D **Baths:** 1 Sh ▣ (1) ⽅ ▨ ⼘ ▥ ▥ ▥

Arden House, *2 Kilrymont Place, St Andrews, Fife, KY16 8DH.* Family run B&B. Convenient for golf, town centre, East Neuk. **Open:** All year (not Xmas/New Year) **Grades:** STB 3 Star
01334 475478 Mrs Finlay **D:** £20.00–£22.00 **S:** £25.00–£27.00 ⽅ ▨ ▥ ▥

Acorn B&B, *16 Priestden Road, St Andrews, Fife, KY16 8DJ.* Excellent accommodation, ideally placed for golfing, touring, walking or relaxing. **Open:** All year **Grades:** STB 4 Star
01334 476009 (also fax) Mrs Cameron *acorn@homeofgolf.fsnet.co.uk* www.acorn. standrews.btinternet.co.uk **D:** £20.00–£24.00 **Beds:** 1T 2D **Baths:** 3 En ▣ (4) ⽅ ▨ ▥ ▥ ▥

Edenside House, *Edenside, St Andrews, Fife, KY16 9SQ.* Pre 1775 farmhouse, 2.5 miles from St Andrews. Parking guaranteed. **Open:** All year (not Xmas)
01334 838108 Douglas & Yvonne Reid **Fax:** 01334 838493 *yreid19154@aol.com* www.topweb.free-online/e/index/htm.
D: £20.00–£27.00 **S:** £32.00–£38.00 **Beds:** 1F 2D 5T **Baths:** 8 En ➳ ▣ (10) ⽅ ▨ ⼘ ▥ ▥ ♿ ▥ cc

Strathkinness

NO4616

Brig-A-Doon, *6 High Road,*
Strathkinness, St Andrews, Fife, KY16 9XY.
Brig-A-Doon was one time a Toll House.
Panoramic views St Andrews Bay/Tay
Estuary. **Open:** Easter to Oct
01334 850268 Mrs Watson **D:** £20.00–£25.00
S: £25.00 **Beds:** 1T 1D **Baths:** 1 En 1 Pr ⌂ (5)
🅿 (2) ⌂ 📺 ▥

Wormit

NO3925

Newton Farm, *Wormit, Newport-on-Tay,*
Fife, DD6 8RL. Traditional farmhouse
overlooking our own trout loch, fly fishing,
quad biking. **Open:** Easter to Oct
01382 540125 K Crawford **Fax: 01382 542513**
ghcrawford@ukonline.co.uk **D:** £17.00 **Beds:** 1F
2T **Baths:** 1 Sh ⌂ 🅿 (8) ⌂ 📺 ⊁ 🌣

Glasgow & District

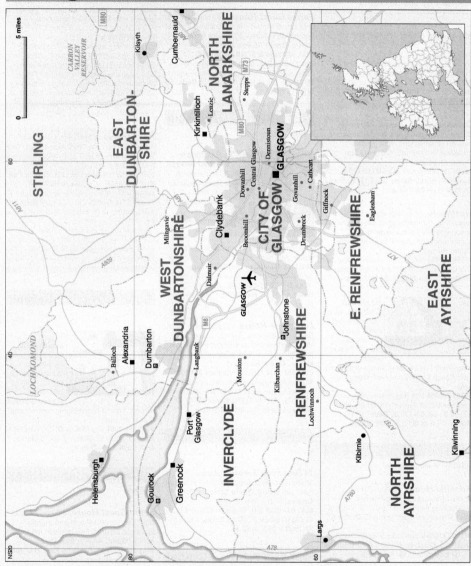

Balloch

NS3982　◀ *The Stables*

7 Carrochan Crescent, *Balloch,*
Alexandria, Dunbartonshire, G83 8PX. A warm
welcome awaits you, ideally situated for
touring etc. **Open:** Easter to Oct
Grades: STB 3 Star
01389 750078 Mrs Campbell **D:** £16.00
S: £18.00 **Beds:** 2D **Baths:** 1 Sh ⛨🅿(2) 📺 Ⅴ
📺, ⚘

Glyndale, *6 McKenzie Drive, Lomond*
Road Estate, Balloch, Alexandria,
Dunbartonshire, G83 8HL. Easy access to
Loch Lomond, Glasgow Airport, public
transport. **Open:** All year (not Xmas)
01389 758238 Mrs Ross *glyndale_b_and_b@*
tinyworld.co.uk **D:** £16.50–£17.50 **S:** £20.00
Beds: 1D 1T **Baths:** 1 Sh ⛨🅿(2) ⅙ 📺 🛏 Ⅴ
📺, ⚘

Gowanlea Guest House, *Drymen*
Road, Balloch, Alexandria, Dunbartonshire,
G83 8HS. Award-winning family-run guest
house B&B. Superior accommodation,
excellent hospitality. Ideal touring base.
Open: All year (not Xmas/New Year)
01389 752456 Mrs Campbell **Fax: 01389**
710543 *gowanlea@aol.com* members.aol.
com/gowanlea/gowanlea.htm **D:** £19.00–
£23.00 **S:** £22.00–£30.00 **Beds:** 1T 3D
Baths: 4 En ⛨🅿(4) ⅙ 📺 Ⅴ 📺, ⚘ cc

Planning a longer stay? Always ask for any special rates

Anchorage Guest House, *Balloch Road, Balloch, Alexandria, Dunbartonshire, G83 8SS.* Situated on the banks of Loch Lomond. Ideal base for touring, fishing, sailing & walking. **Open:** All year **01389 753336** Mr Bowman **D:** £18.00–£25.00 **Beds:** 1F 2D 4T **Baths:** 5 En 2 Sh ☎(1)🅿(6) 📺🏠📺🛍♨♿

Dumbain Farm, *Balloch, Alexandria, Dunbartonshire, G83 8DS.* Newly converted byre on working farm. Aga cooked breakfast. Homemade raspberry jam. **Open:** All year **01389 752263** Mrs Watson **D:** £20.00–£22.00 **S:** £18.00–£25.00 **Beds:** 1F 1T 1D **Baths:** 3 En ☎🅿(5)✒📺📺🛍♨

Heathpete, *24 Balloch Road, Balloch, Alexandria, Dunbartonshire, G83 8LE.* Superb hospitality offered in luxurious accommodation central to all amenities. **Open:** All year **01389 752195** Mrs Hamill *sheathpete@aol.com* **D:** £12.00–£25.00 **S:** £18.00–£25.00 **Beds:** 2F 2D **Baths:** 4 En ☎🅿(5)📺🏠📺🛍♨♿

Braeburn Cottage, *West Auchencarroch Farm, Balloch, Alexandria, G83 9LU.* Peaceful location, magnificent views, set in beautiful gardens. Farmhouse breakfast served. **Open:** All year **01389 710998** Mrs Kay *braeburn@bigfoot.com* www.braeburn.telinco.co.uk **D:** £16.00–£22.00 **S:** £20.00–£30.00 **Beds:** 1F 1D **Baths:** 2 En ☎🅿(3)✒📺🏠📺🛍♨

Dumbarton

NS4075　🍴 *Abbotsford Hotel*

Kilmalid House, *17 Glen Path, Dumbarton, G82 2QL.* Large manse overlooking castle and Clyde, 15 minutes from airport and Loch Lomond. **Open:** All year **01389 732030** Muirhead *kilmalid@ecossetel.com* **D:** £18.00–£25.00 **S:** £25.00–£40.00 **Beds:** 1F 1T 1D **Baths:** 1 Sh 🅿(8) 📺🛍♨

Eaglesham

NS5752　🍴 *Crosskeys, Swan Inn*

Annecy, *60 Montgomery Street, Eaglesham, Glasgow, G76 0AU.* Attractive cottage in conservation village. Lovely garden. **Open:** All year **01355 302413 (also fax)** Mrs Margetts **D:** £22.00 **S:** £22.00–£25.00 **Beds:** 1F 1T 1D 1S **Baths:** 2 Pr 🅿(2)✒📺📺🛍♨

Giffnock

NS5658

Forres Guest House, *10 Forres Avenue, Giffnock, Glasgow, G46 6LJ.* Located in quiet south side suburbs. 5 minutes from city centre. **Open:** All year (not Xmas) **0141 638 5554 & 07710 864151 (M)** Mrs Davies **Fax: 0141 571 9301** *june@10forres.freeserve.co.uk* www.junesdavies.com **D:** £18.00–£20.00 **S:** £18.00–£20.00 **Beds:** 2D 🅿(4)📺🛍♨

GLASGOW　Broomhill

NS5467　🍴 *Three Craws*

Barrisdale Guest House, *115 Randolph Road, Glasgow, G11 7DS.* Delightful Victorian townhouse, perfectly situated for exploring Glasgow's many highlights. **Open:** All year **0141 339 7589 (also fax)** Mr Phillips *barrisdale@btinternet.com* www.barrisdale-bnb.co.uk **D:** £22.50–£30.00 **S:** £30.00–£40.00 **Beds:** 1F 2T 1D **Baths:** 3 En 1 Pr ☎✒📺🏠🛍♨

Lochgilvie House, *117 Randolph Road, Broomhill, Glasgow, G11 7DS.* Luxurious Victorian town house situated in Glasgow's prestigious West End, adjacent to rail station. **Open:** All year **0141 357 1593** Mrs Ogilvie **Fax: 0141 334 5828** *reservations@lochgilvie.demon.co.uk* www.lochgilvie.demon.co.uk **D:** £25.00–£30.00 **S:** £25.00–£35.00 **Beds:** 1F 2D 3T **Baths:** 4 En ☎(10)🅿📺📺🛍♨

GLASGOW　Cathcart

NS5860

24 Greenock Avenue, *Glasgow, G44 5TS.* Modern architect designed villa, 12 minutes from city centre. **Open:** Easter to Oct **Grades:** STB 4 Star **0141 637 0608** Mrs Bruce **D:** £20.00–£22.50 **S:** £25.00 **Beds:** 2T 1D 1S **Baths:** 2 En 1 Pr 1 Sh ☎🅿✒📺✖📺🛍♨

GLASGOW　Central

NS5865

Adelaide's, *209 Bath Street, Glasgow, G2 4HZ.* Central location, close to all major attractions of revitalised city. **Open:** All year (not Xmas/New Year) **Grades:** STB 2 Star **0141 248 4970** A R Meiklejohn **Fax: 0141 226 4247** *info@adelaides.freeserve.co.uk* www.adelaides.co.uk **D:** £25.00–£28.00 **S:** £30.00–£45.00 **Beds:** 2F 2T 2D 2S **Baths:** 6 En 2 Sh ☎✒📺🛍♨ cc

Kirkland House, *42 St Vincent Crescent, Glasgow, G3 8NG.* **Open:** All year **0141 248 3458** Mrs Divers **Fax: 0141 221 5174** *admin@kirkland.gispnet.com* www.kirkland.gispnet.com **D:** £27.00–£30.00 **S:** £27.00–£30.00 **Beds:** 3D 2T 2S **Baths:** 6 En 2 Sh ☎(1)✒📺🛍♨ City centre guest house with excellent rooms on beautiful Victorian Crescent in Finnieston (Glasgow's 'little Chelsea'). Short walk to Scottish Exhibition Centre, Museum/Art Gallery, Kelvingrove Park and all West End facilities. Glasgow airport 10 minutes, member of the Harry James society.

Kelvingrove Hotel, *944 Sauchiehall Street, Glasgow, G3 7TH.* **Open:** All year (not Xmas) **Grades:** STB 3 Star, AA 3 Diamond, RAC 3 Star **0141 339 5011 & 0141 569 1121** Mr Wills **Fax: 0141 339 6566** *kelvingrove.hotel@business.ntl.com* www.kelvingrove-hotel.co.uk **D:** £24.00–£29.00 **S:** £33.00–£38.00 **Beds:** 8D 4T 4F **Baths:** 10 En ☎🅿(20)✒📺🏠✖📺🛍♨ cc Centrally located family-run hotel, set in Glasgow's fashionable West End. Close to pubs, clubs, art galleries, museums, University, shops, rail and bus links - all within walking distance.

GLASGOW　Dalmuir

NS4970

13 Southview, *Dalmuir, Clydebank, Dunbartonshire, G81 3LA.* Semi-villa. Near Station/Glasgow Airport. Tourist board highly commended. **Open:** All year **0141 952 7007** Mrs McCay **D:** £15.00–£18.00 **S:** £18.00–£20.00 **Beds:** 1T 1D 1S **Baths:** 1 En 1 Sh 🅿(1)✒📺🛍♨

GLASGOW　Dennistoun

NS6065

Seton Guest House, *6 Seton Terrace, Glasgow, G31 2HU.* Warm and friendly welcome assured. Five minutes from city centre. **Open:** All year (not Xmas) **0141 556 7654** Mr Passway **Fax: 0141 402 3655** *passway@seton.prestel.co.uk* www.vacations-scotland.co.uk/seton.html **D:** £17.00–£18.00 **S:** £24.00 **Beds:** 4F 2D 2T 1S **Baths:** 3 Sh ☎📺📺🛍♨

Rosewood Guest House, *4 Seton Terrace, Glasgow, G31 2HU.* Victorian House near city centre, close to many city attractions. **Open:** All year **0141 550 1500** Ms Turner **Fax: 01555 393876** *rosewoodguesthouse@hotmail.com* **D:** £17.00–£20.00 **S:** £19.00–£22.00 **Beds:** 3F 2T 1D 2S **Baths:** 3 Sh ☎🅿📺🏠📺🛍♨ cc

GLASGOW   Dowanhill
NS5667

Belgrave Guest House, *2 Belgrave Terrace, Glasgow, G12 8JD.* **Open:** All year **Grades:** AA 2 Diamond
0141 337 1850 Fax: 0141 337 1741
belgraveguesthse@hotmail.com **D:** £18.00–£25.00
S: £20.00–£25.00 **Beds:** 2F 2T 3D 4S
Baths: 2 En 9 Sh ⓢ 🅿 (8) 📺 🛏 ♣ cc
Perfectly situated in the popular bustling West End of Glasgow. Within walking distance of many local attractions, pubs and restaurants. Underground station and city centre minutes away. Full Scottish breakfast.

The Terrace House Hotel, *14 Belhaven Terrace, Glasgow, G12 0TG.* 'B' Listed terraced townhouse, built circa 1860, boasting fine period features. **Open:** All year
0141 337 3377 (also fax) Mrs Black *admin@ the-terrace.fsnet.co.uk* www.the-terrace.fsnet.co. uk **D:** £29.00–£39.00 **S:** £49.00–£65.00
Beds: 4F 3D 5T 1S **Baths:** 12 En 1 Pr ⓢ ⅍ 📺 🛏 ✕ 📺 🛏 ♣ cc

GLASGOW   Drumbreck
NS5663

Glasgow Guest House, *56 Dumbreck Road, Glasgow, G41 5NP.* Turn-of-the-20th-Century red sandstone house, antique decoration, friendly welcome. **Open:** All year
0141 427 0129 Mr Bristow *brian.muir@ ukonline.co.uk* **S:** £25.00 **Beds:** 3D 3T 1S 1F **Baths:** 8 En ⓢ 🅿 (2) 📺 🛏 🛏 ♿ ♣ cc

GLASGOW   Govanhill
NS5862

Dunkeld Hotel, *10-12 Queens Drive, Glasgow, G42 8BS.* Set in one of Glasgow's premier conservation streets overlooking Queen's Park. **Open:** All year
0141 424 0160 P Martin **Fax: 0141 423 4437**
dunkeldhot@aol.com www.dunkeld-hotel.co.uk
D: £22.00–£29.95 **S:** £30.00–£44.95 **Beds:** 4F 8T 11D 4S **Baths:** 21 En 6 Sh ⓢ 🅿 (10) ⅍ 📺 🛏 ✕ 📺 🛏 ♣ cc

Johnstone
NS4362   🍴 *Lynnhurst Hotel*

Northview Guest House, *11 North Road, Johnstone, PA5 8NE.* Situated near to Glasgow airport. **Open:** All year
Grades: STB 4 Star
01505 336690 *mail@northview.fsbusiness.co.uk*
www.northview.fsbusiness.co.uk **D:** £20.00–£25.00 **S:** £20.00–£30.00 **Beds:** 1F 1T 1D 2S
Baths: 5 En ⓢ 🅿 (5) 📺 cc

Kilbarchan
NS4063

Gladstone Farmhouse, *Burntshields Road, Kilbarchan, Johnstone, Renfrewshire, PA10 2PB.* Quiet countryside, 10 minutes Glasgow airport on direct route. **Open:** All year
01505 702579 (also fax) Mrs Douglas
D: £18.00 **S:** £20.00 **Beds:** 1F 1D 1T **Baths:** 1 Sh ⓢ 🅿 (6) 📺 🛏 ✕ 📺 🛏 ♿ ♣

Langbank
NS3872   🍴 *The Lodge*

The Croft By The Clyde, *Houston Road, Langbank, Port Glasgow, PA14 6XT.* Overlooking River Clyde, unique plantsperson's garden. 10 minutes Glasgow Airport. **Open:** All year
Grades: STB 3 Star
01475 540079 *info@croft-by-the-clyde.co.uk*
www.croft-by-the-clyde.co.uk **D:** £25.00–£30.00 **S:** £30.00–£35.00 **Beds:** 1F 1T 1D
Baths: 3 En 🅿 (3) ⅍ 📺 🛏 ♣

Lenzie
NS6572

16 Laurel Avenue, *Lenzie, Glasgow, G66 4RU.* Detached bungalow. Ideally situated for exploring central Scotland, Glasgow and Edinburgh. **Open:** All year
0141 776 1634 D Martyn **Fax: 0141 578 6418**
david.martyn@net.ntl.com **D:** £18.00 **S:** £24.00
Beds: 1T 1D **Baths:** 1 En 1 Pr ⓢ 🅿 (2) 📺 🛏 ✕ 🛏 ♣

Lochwinnoch
NS3559

Garnock Lodge, *Lochwinnoch, Renfrewshire, PA12 4JT.* **Open:** All year **Grades:** STB 4 Star
01505 503680 (also fax) Mr & Mrs McMeechan *garnocklodge@cwcom.net*
www.garnocklodge.cwc.net **D:** £18.00–£21.00
S: £25.00–£30.00 **Beds:** 1D 2T 1S **Baths:** 2 En 1 Sh ⓢ 🅿 (4) ⅍ 📺 🛏 ♣ cc
A warm welcome awaits you at detached house in rural situation. Easy access to Glasgow Airport via main route also Loch Lomond and Ayrshire coast, walking, fishing, golf, cycling and bird watching, home baking, log fires, ensuite, off road parking.

Milngavie
NS5574

13 Craigdhu Avenue, *Milngavie, Glasgow, G62 6DX.* Very comfortable family house where a warm welcome is assured.
Open: Mar to Oct
0141 956 3439 Mrs Ogilvie **D:** £18.00
S: £20.00–£25.00 **Beds:** 1F 1T ⓢ 🅿 (4) ⅍ 📺 🛏 📺 🛏 ♣

Stepps
NS6668

Avenue End B&B, *21 West Avenue, Stepps, Glasgow, G33 6ES.* Self-built family home situated down quiet tree-lined lane, on main route to Stirling. **Open:** All year
0141 779 1990 (also fax) Mrs Wells
avenueend@aol.com **D:** £20.00–£25.00
S: £25.00–£27.50 **Beds:** 1F 1D 1S **Baths:** 2 En 1 Pr ⓢ 🅿 (2) ⅍ 📺 🛏 ♣

Please respect a B&B's wishes regarding children, animals and smoking

Achintee

NG9441

The Shieling, Achintee, Strathcarron, Ross-shire, IV54 8YX. Comfortable, homely croft cottage, tastefully extended and modernised, only minutes from Strathcarron railway station. **Open:** All year **01520 722364** Mrs Levy *jlevyshieling@ talk21.com* **D:** £18.00–£20.00 **S:** £17.00 **Beds:** 2T 1S **Baths:** 1 En 1 Sh ⛺ 🖭 (3) 乂 🖭 🎹 🏧

Alcaig

NH5657

Dun Eistein, Alcaig, Conon Bridge, Dingwall, Ross-shire, IV7 8HS. Highland country cottage. **Open:** May to Oct **01349 862210** Mrs Morrison www.host.co.uk **D:** £18.50–£19.50 **S:** £24.00 **Beds:** 1F 1D **Baths:** 1 En 1 Pr ⛺ 🖭 (3) 乂 🖭 🎹 🏧

Alness

NH6569

An Laimhrig, 82 Obsdale Park, Alness, IV17 0TR. Modern detached house, ideal touring centre, cyclists' stopover for John O'Groats. **Open:** All year **Grades:** STB 3 Star **01349 882016 (also fax)** Ms MacDonald *m.mac4388@faxvia.net* **D:** £18.00–£25.00 **S:** £20.00–£30.00 **Beds:** 1F 2T 1D **Baths:** 2 En 1 Sh 乂 🖭 乂 🎹 🏧

Altnaharra

NC5635

1 Macleod Crescent, Altnaharra, Lairg, Sutherland, IV27 4UG. **Open:** All year **01549 411258** Mrs Barrie **D:** £18.00 **S:** £23.00 **Beds:** 1F 2T **Baths:** 3 En ⛺ 🖭 (3) 乂 🖭 🎹 🏧 Hamlet (pop. 31) nestling between 2 Munros, Ben Klebrig and Ben Hope, ideal base hillwalking. Cyclists welcome (CTC member) dry secure shelter for cycles, on direct inland route for End to End. Only B&B in Altnaharra so early booking is advisable.

Ardelve

NG8727 ⚫The Duich

Loch Duich Hotel, Ardelve, Kyle of Lochalsh, IV40 8DY. On the road to Skye and Kyle, facing Eilean Donan Castle. **Open:** All year (not Xmas/New Year) **Grades:** AA 2 Star, 1 Rosette **01599 555213 Fax: 01599 555214** *sales@ lochduich.fg.co.uk* www.lochduich.fg.co.uk **D:** £25.00–£35.00 **S:** £30.00–£35.00 **Beds:** 1F 4T 4D 2S **Baths:** 9 En 2 Pr ⛺ 🖭 (40) 🖭 🏃 乂 🖭 🏧 cc

Caberfeidh House

Caberfeidh House, Ardelve, Kyle of Lochalsh, IV40 8DY. Beautiful lochside house with superb views of Eilean Donan Castle. **Open:** All year (not Xmas/New Year) **01599 555293** Mr Newton **D:** £18.00–£22.00 **S:** £25.00–£30.00 **Beds:** 2T 3D 1S **Baths:** 2 En 1 Sh 🖭 (6) 乂 🖭 🎹 🏧 cc

Ardgour

NN0163

The Inn at Ardgour, Ardgour, Fort William, Inverness-shire, PH33 7AA. Top rated inn in the Highlands. **Open:** Mar to Nov **Grades:** STB 4 Star **01855 841225 Fax: 01855 841214** *ardgour@ ecosse.net* www.ardgour.com **D:** £27.50–£49.00 **Beds:** 2F 4T 4D **Baths:** 10 En ⛺ 🖭 (26) 乂 🖭 🏃 乂 🖭 🎹 🏧 🐾 cc

Arisaig

NM6586 ⚫Cnoc-na-Faire Hotel, Arisaig Hotel

Leven House, Borrodale, Arisaig, PH39 4NR. Ideal for walking, touring, sails to Skye, Rhum, Eigg, Muck. **Open:** All year (not Xmas/New Year) **Grades:** STB 3 Star **01687 450238** Mrs MacMillan *ejmacmillan@ aol.com* www.hexhome.fsnet.co.uk/thehouse. html **D:** £22.00 **S:** £30.00 **Beds:** 2F **Baths:** 2 En ⛺ 🖭 乂 🖭 🖭 🏧

Arnisdale

NG8410

Corran, Arnisdale, Kyle of Lochalsh, Ross-shire, IV40 8JJ. House is situated in small village surrounded by massive mountains overlooking Loch Horn. **Open:** All year **01599 522336** Mrs Nash **D:** £13.00–£16.00 **S:** £13.00–£16.00 **Beds:** 1F 1S **Baths:** 1 Sh 🖭 🏃 乂 🖭 🏧

Auldearn

NH9155

Covenanters Inn, Auldearn, Nairn, Inverness-shire, IV12 5TG. Friendly family run inn. Excellent location for exploring Highlands. **Open:** All year **Grades:** STB 3 Star **01667 452456** Mr Harrison *covenanters@ aol.com* www.covenantes-inn.co.uk **D:** £22.00–£35.00 **S:** £35.00–£48.00 **Beds:** 2F 6T 6D **Baths:** 14 En ⛺ 🖭 (30) 🖭 🏃 乂 🖭 🎹 🏧 cc

---

BATHROOMS

En = Ensuite

Pr = Private

Sh = Shared

Aultivullin

NC8167

Catalina Guest House, Aultivullin, Strathy Point, Thurso, Caithness, KW14 7RY. On the far North Coast, private suite for just two. **Open:** All year **01641 541279** J Salisbury **Fax: 0870 1247960** *petesalisbury@catalina72.freeserve.co.uk* **D:** £17.00–£20.00 **S:** £20.00–£30.00 **Beds:** 1T **Baths:** 1 En 🖭 (1) 乂 🖭 乂 🎹 🏧

Aviemore

NH8912 ⚫Winking Owl, Old Bridge Inn, Tyree House

Ravenscraig Guest House, Aviemore, Inverness-shire, PH22 1RP. **Open:** All year **Grades:** STB 2 Star, AA 3 Diamond, RAC 3 Diamond **01479 810278** Mr & Mrs Gatenby **Fax: 01479 812742** *ravenscrg@aol.com* www.aviemoreonline.com **D:** £18.00–£25.00 **S:** £18.00–£25.00 **Beds:** 2F 5D 4T 1S **Baths:** 12 En ⛺ 🖭 (16) 🖭 🏃 🎹 🏧 cc Family-run guest house, central village location. Rooms recently refurbished, some with views over the Cairngorm Mountains. Perfect base for exploring the Highlands or just discovering the delights of our local area. Our aim is to make your stay an enjoyable one.

Cairngorm Guest House, Grampian Road, Aviemore, Inverness-shire, PH22 1RP. Clean, comfortable, cosy, rooms. Home-made cake and hearty breakfast **Open:** All year **01479 810630 (also fax)** Mrs Conn *conns@ lineone.net* www.aviemore.co.uk **D:** £18.00–£25.00 **S:** £20.00–£30.00 **Beds:** 1F 5D 3T **Baths:** 9 En ⛺ (2) 🖭 (10) 乂 🖭 🎹 🏧 cc

Ardlogie Guest House, Dalfaber Road, Aviemore, Inverness-shire, PH22 1PU. Lovely, quiet, central location. Views over river to Cairngorm Mountains. **Open:** All year **01479 810747** Mrs Willies **D:** £20.00 **S:** £25.00 **Beds:** 4D 1T **Baths:** 5 En ⛺ 🖭 (3) 🖭 🏃 🎹 🏧 cc

Rowan Tree Country Hotel, Loch Alvie, Aviemore, Inverness-shire, PH22 1QB. C17th coaching inn. Characterful bedrooms. Comfortable lounges. A warm welcome. **Open:** All year **01479 810207 (also fax)** *enquires@ rowantreehotel.com* www.rowantreehotel.com **D:** £26.50–£31.50 **S:** £36.50–£41.50 **Beds:** 2F 3T 4D 1S **Baths:** 10 En 1 Sh ⛺ (12) 🖭 🖭 🏃 乂 🖭 🎹 🐾 cc

Badachro

NG7773

Lochside, *Aird Road, Badachro, Gairloch, Wester Ross, IV21 2AB.* All rooms face south across beautiful sheltered Badachro Bay with its many boats. **Open:** All year
01445 741295 Mrs Foster www.host.co.uk
D: £21.00–£22.00 **Beds:** 1F 1D **Baths:** 2 En
🛏 🅿 ⚲ 📺 🖾 ♨

Baddidarroch

NC0822

Veyatie, *66 Baddidarroch, Lochinver, Lairg, Sutherland, IV27 4LP.* Peaceful, relaxing location. Magnificent mountain views, walkers paradise. Fantastic breakfasts. **Open:** All year (not Xmas) **Grades:** STB 4 Star
01571 844424 (also fax) Mrs Chapman
veyatie@baddid.freeserve.co.uk www.host.co.uk
D: £20.00–£25.00 **S:** £25.00–£38.00 **Beds:** 2D 1T **Baths:** 2 En 1 Pr 🅿 (3) ⚲ 📺 🕇 🖾 ♨

Balblair (Cromarty Firth)

NH7066   🍴 *Crofters, The Plough*

Braelangwell House, *Balblair, Dingwall, Ross-shire, IV7 8LQ.* Beautiful Georgian mansion. Ideal for touring Scottish Highlands. Four-poster bed. **Open:** Apr to Oct **Grades:** STB 4 Star
01381 610353 Fax: 01381 610467
braelangwell@btinternet.com www.btinternet.com/~braelandwell **D:** £25.00–£35.00
S: £35.00–£50.00 **Beds:** 1T 1D **Baths:** 1 En 2 Pr 🛏 🅿 (40) ⚲ 📺 🕇 🖾 ♨

Ballachulish

NN0858   🍴 *Laroch Bar, Ballachulish Hotel, Glencoe Hotel, Clachaig Inn, Onich Hotel, Holly Tree Hotel*

Fern Villa Guest House, *Loanfern, Ballachulish, Argyll, PH49 4JE.* **Open:** All year **01855 811393**
Mr Chandler **Fax:** 01855 811727 *stil@ fernvilla.com* www.fernvilla.com **D:** £20.00–£23.00 **S:** £25.00–£28.00 **Beds:** 3D 2T **Baths:** 5 En 🛏 🅿 (5) ⚲ 📺 ✕ 🖾 ♨
A warm welcome awaits you in this beautifully upgraded Victorian house. The village is surrounded by the spectacular lochs and mountains of Glencoe. Natural cooking of Scotland forms the basis of our home made dinner menus. Non-smoking.

B&B owners may vary rates – be sure to check when booking

Planning a longer stay? Always ask for any special rates

Ardno House, *Lettermore, Ballachulish, Argyll, PA49 4JD.* **Open:** Mar to Oct
Grades: STB 4 Star
01855 811830 Mrs Weir *pamweir@ globalnet.co.uk* www.users.globalnet.co.uk~pamweir/index.html **D:** £21.00–£26.00
Beds: 1F 2D **Baths:** 3 En 🅿 (6) ⚲ 📺 🖾 ♨
Beautifully appointed luxury villa nestling on the shores of Loch Linnhe. Magnificent loch and mountain views. Each superior, spacious bedroom has an excellent private ensuite. Perfect base for touring the scenic splendour of the Scottish Highlands. Near Glencoe and Ben Nevis. Wonderful walks. Private parking. Warm welcome.

Lyn Leven Guest House, *West Laroch, Ballachulish, Argyll, PA39 4JP.* Very warm Highland welcome in modern comfortable family-run award-winning guest house. **Open:** All year **Grades:** STB 4 Star, AA 4 Diamond, RAC 4 Diamond
01855 811392 Mrs Macleod **Fax:** 01855 811600 www.lynleven.co.uk **D:** £20.00–£25.00 **S:** £25.00–£30.00 **Beds:** 4F 4D 4T **Baths:** 12 En 🛏 🅿 (10) 📺 🕇 ✕ 🖾 ♨ cc

Inverlaroch, *Albert Road, Ballachulish, Argyll, PH49 4JR.* Modern, comfortable, spacious, homely bungalow. Excellent for walking and climbing. **Open:** All year (not Xmas)
01855 811726 Mrs Castles *inverlaroch@ talk21.com* **D:** £17.00–£21.00 **S:** £34.00–£42.00 **Beds:** 1F 1D 1T **Baths:** 3 En 🛏 (3) 🅿 (5) ⚲ 📺 🖾 ♨

Riverside House, *Ballachulish, Argyll, PH49 4JE.* Spacious rooms in modern house overlooking river mountains and loch. **Open:** Easter to Oct
01855 811473 Mrs Watt **D:** £16.00–£20.00 **S:** £18.00–£22.00 **Beds:** 2D 1T **Baths:** 1 En 1 Sh 🛏 (2) 🅿 (4) ⚲ 📺 ♨

All details shown are as supplied by B&B owners in Autumn 2001

Balnain

NH4430   🍴 *Steading*

Glenurquhart House Hotel, *Balnain, Drumnadrochit, Inverness, IV63 6TJ.* **Open:** Mar to Dec
01456 476234 C Hughes *carol@ glenurquartlodges.co.uk* **D:** £20.00–£35.00
S: £20.00–£40.00 **Beds:** 2F 2D 2T 2S
Baths: 6 En 1 Sh 🛏 🅿 (8) 📺 ✕ 🖾 ♨ cc
Set in 6 acres of wooded grounds with fantastic views of Loch Heiklie. This small family-run hotel offers the perfect place to relax and unwind. Ideally situated for exploring the scenic highlands of Scotland and nearby Loch Ness.

Banavie

NN1177   🍴 *Moorings Hotel*

Rushfield House, *Tomonie, Banavie, Fort William, Inverness-shire, PH33 7LX.* Modern house with excellent views of Ben Nevis, 3m Fort William. **Open:** Mar to Oct **Grades:** STB 3 Star
01397 772063 Ms Corbett *rushbb0063@ aol.com* www.members.aol.com/rushbb0063/index.html **D:** £18.00–£25.00 **Beds:** 2F 1D **Baths:** 3 En 🛏 🅿 (3) ⚲ 📺 🖾 ♨

Fordon, *Badabrie, Banavie, Fort William, Inverness-shire, PH33 7LX.* Modern house with beautiful views **Open:** All year (not Xmas/New Year) **Grades:** STB 3 Star
01397 772737 P Wilkinson *fordon@ supanet.com* **D:** £17.00–£21.00 **S:** £17.00–£25.00 **Beds:** 3F 1D **Baths:** 1 En 1 Sh 🛏 🅿 ⚲ 📺 🖾 ♨

Beauly

NH5246   🍴 *Glass Rest, Lovat Arms, Cnoc Hotel*

Caledonian Hotel, *The Square, Beauly, Inverness-shire, IV4 7BY.* For families, fishing and food, come to the 'Caley'. 300 years of Highland hospitality. **Open:** All year
01463 782278 (also fax) Mr Campbell
caleyhotel123@hotmail.com **D:** £20.00–£25.00
S: £24.00–£28.00 **Beds:** 4F 2T 2D 1S
Baths: 9 En 🛏 🅿 (2) 📺 🕇 ✕ 🖾 ✳ ♨ cc

Please respect a B&B's wishes regarding children, animals and smoking

Bettyhill

NC7061 🏨 *Betty Hill Hotel*

Dunveaden House, *Bettyhill, Thurso, Caithness, KW14 7SP.* On A836 Thurso/ Tongue Road. Picturesque scenery, golden beaches, highland. **Open:** All year **01641 521273** Mr & Mrs MacKenzie **D:** £16.00–£17.00 **S:** £16.00–£17.00 **Beds:** 3T 2D 1S **Baths:** 2 Sh ⇆ 🅿 (8) 📺 🐾 🖾 🕭

Bhlaraidh

NH3816

Burnside Guest House, *Bhlaraidh, Glenmoriston, Inverness, IV63 7YH.* Comfortable family home situated in a forested mountain area of Glenmoriston. **Open:** Mar to Nov **01320 351269 (also fax)** Mr & Mrs Lowe **D:** £16.00–£17.50 **S:** £16.00–£17.50 **Beds:** 2D 1T 1S **Baths:** 2 Sh ⇆ 🅿 (5) 🗲 📺 🐾 🖾 🕭

Boat of Garten

NH9418 🏨 *Boat Hotel, Craigard Hotel, Old Bridge Inn, Heatherbrae, Skye of Curr Hotel, Strathspey Hotel*

The Old Ferrymans House, *Boat of Garten, Inverness-shire, PH24 3BY.* **Open:** All year
01479 831370 (also fax) Ms Matthews **D:** £20.00–£21.00 **S:** £20.00–£21.00 **Beds:** 1T 1D 2S **Baths:** 2 Sh ⇆ 🅿 (4) 🗲 🐾 🕻 📺 🖾 🕭 Which? Recommended former ferryman's house, just across River Spey from village, welcoming, homely, comfortable. Sitting room with wood stove, many books, no TV. No set breakfast times, home-cooked meals with Highland specialities. Numerous walks, beautiful Strathspey countryside and Cairngorm mountains, castles, distilleries.

Chapelton Steading, *Boat Of Garten, Inverness-shire, PH24 3BU.* Spacious rural retreat. Charming garden with views of Cairngorm Mountains. **Open:** Mar to Nov **01479 831327** Mrs Smyth *chapelton@ btinternet.com* boatofgarten.com/chapelton **D:** £22.00–£23.00 **S:** £25.00–£26.00 **Beds:** 1T 2D **Baths:** 3 En ⇆ (10) 🅿 (4) 🗲 📺 🕭

BEDROOMS
D = Double
T = Twin
S = Single
F = Family

Heathbank - The Victorian House, *Drumuillie Road, Boat of Garten, Inverness- shire, PH24 3BD.* Victorian house. Excellent cuisine. Some 4-poster beds! **Open:** All year **01479 831234 (also fax)** Mr Lawton *heathbankhotel@aol.com* **D:** £28.00–£40.00 **S:** £38.00 **Beds:** 1F 2T 4D **Baths:** 7 En ⇆ 🅿 (8) 🗲 📺 ✕ 📺 🖾 ❀ 🕭 cc

Avingormack Guest House, *Boat of Garten, Inverness-shire, PH24 3BT.* Breathtaking views of the mountains, award-winning food - just perfect. **Open:** All year **01479 831614** Mrs Ferguson *avin.gormack@ ukgateway.net* **D:** £19.00–£22.00 **S:** £19.50 **Beds:** 1F 2D 1T **Baths:** 2 En 1 Sh ⇆ 🅿 (6) 🗲 📺 ✕ 📺 🕭 cc

Bonar Bridge

NH6191

Kyle House, *Dornoch Road, Bonar Bridge, Argday, Sutherland, IV24 3EB.* Superb old Scottish house offering excellent accommodation. Ideal touring base. **Open:** Feb to Nov **Grades:** AA 3 Diamond, RAC 3 Diamond **01863 766360 (also fax)** Mrs Thomson *kyle.hse.@talk21.com* **D:** £19.00–£22.00 **S:** £24.00 **Beds:** 2F 1D 2T 1S **Baths:** 3 En 1 Sh ⇆ (4) 🅿 (6) 🗲 📺 🖾 🕭

Brora

NC9004 🏨 *Royal Marine Hotel, Links Hotel*

Clynelish Farm, *Brora, Sutherland, KW9 6LR.* Spacious, peaceful farmhouse with caring, friendly hosts. **Open:** Easter to Oct **Grades:** STB 2 Star **01408 621265 (also fax)** J Ballantyne *jane@ clynelish.fsnet.co.uk* **D:** £20.00 **S:** £20.00 **Beds:** 1F 1T 1D **Baths:** 2 En 1 Pr ⇆ 🐾 📺 🕭 cc

Non Smokers Haven, *Tigh Fada, 18 Golf Road, Brora, Sutherland, KW9 6QS.* Top quality welcoming home. Also self- catering, prime seaside location. **Open:** All year (not Xmas/New Year) **01408 621332 (also fax)** Mr & Mrs Clarkson **D:** £18.00 **S:** £20.00 **Beds:** 1D 2T **Baths:** 1 En 2 Pr ⇆ (5) 🅿 (6) 🗲 📺 🖾 🕭

Glenaveron, *Golf Road, Brora, Sutherland, KW9 6QS.* A luxurious Edwardian house in mature gardens close to Brora golf club and beaches. **Open:** All year **01408 621601 (also fax)** Mr Fortune *glenaveron@hotmail.com* **D:** £24.00–£28.00 **S:** £28.00–£34.00 **Beds:** 1F 1D 1T **Baths:** 3 En ⇆ 🅿 (3) 🗲 📺 🖾 ♿ 🕭

RATES
D = Price range per person sharing in a double or twin room
S = Price range for a single room

Canisbay

ND3472

Bencorragh House, *Upper Gills, Canisbay, John o' Groats, Wick, Caithness, KW1 4YB.* Working croft. Panoramic views across Pentland Firth near Orkney ferries. **Open:** All year **Grades:** STB 3 Star, AA 3 Star **01955 611449 (also fax)** Mrs Barton *bartonsandy@hotmail.com* www.bencorraghhouse.com **D:** £21.00– £22.00 **S:** £25.00–£30.00 **Beds:** 1F 2D 1T **Baths:** 4 En ⇆ (5) 🅿 (6) 🗲 📺 🕻 ✕ 📺 🖾 🕭 cc

Cannich

NH3331

Kerrow House, *Cannich, Beauly, Inverness-shire, IV4 7NA.* **Open:** All year **Grades:** STB 3 Star **01456 415243** Mr Basset **Fax: 01456 415425** *stephen@kerrow-house.demon.co.uk* www.kerrow-house.demon.co.uk **D:** £22.00– £34.00 **S:** £32.00–£42.00 **Beds:** 1F 1T 2D **Baths:** 2 En 2 Pr ⇆ 🅿 🗲 📺 🕻 📺 🖾 ♿ 🕭 cc A traditional Georgian hunting lodge, now a very comfortable home, set in 12 acres of woodland bordered by the River Glass, offering free trout fishing to guests. The Glen Affric area offers spectacular scenery, excellent walking, wildlife and tranquillity.

Caol

NN1076

Connamara, *27 Carnaghael Road, Caol, Fort William, PH33 7HU.* The front of the house faces Ben Nevis, back looks onto Caledonian Canal. **Open:** All year **01397 702901** Mrs Mcginlay **Fax: 01397 700566** *e.mcginlay@amserve.net* **D:** £17.00– £18.00 **S:** £20.00–£25.00 **Beds:** 2F ⇆ 🅿 🗲 📺 🕭

Carrbridge

NH9022 ◀ Cairn Hotel, Dalrachney Lodge, Struan House

Craigellachie House, *Main Street, Carrbridge, Inverness-shire, PH23 3AS.* Perfectly situated for exploring the Cairngorms and Loch Ness. Close to historic bridge. **Open:** All year **Grades:** STB 3 Star **01479 841641 (also fax)** Mrs Pedersen *e.pedersen@talk21.com* www.host.co.uk **D:** £16.00–£20.00 **S:** £17.00–£26.00 **Beds:** 2F 2D 2T 1S **Baths:** 3 En 2 Sh ॐ 🖸 (8) ⅍ 🖾 ✕ 🖾 🛲. ♨ cc

Carrmoor Guest House, *Carr Road, Carrbridge, Inverness-shire, PH23 3AD.* Licensed, family-run, warm welcome. Popular restaurant, chef proprietor. **Open:** All year **Grades:** STB 3 Star, AA 4 Diamond **01479 841244 (also fax)** Mrs Stitt *christine@ carrmoorguesthouse.co.uk* www.carrmoorguesthouse.co.uk **D:** £20.00– £22.00 **S:** £22.50–£27.00 **Beds:** 1F 3D 2T **Baths:** 6 En ॐ 🖸 (6) 🖾 ✕ 🖾 🛲. ♣ cc

Pine Ridge, *Carrbridge, Inverness-shire, PH23 3AA.* Pine Ridge is a beautiful 100-year-old home. **Open:** All year **01479 841646** Mrs Weston *jane.weston@ tesco.net* **D:** £16.00–£20.00 **S:** £20.00–£25.00 **Beds:** 1F 1D 1T **Baths:** 1 En 1 Sh ॐ 🖸 (6) ⅍ 🖾 ⊁ 🛲. ♨

Cruachan, *Carrbridge, Inverness-shire, PH23 3AA.* Modern bungalow **Open:** Easter to Nov **01479 841609** Mrs Campbell **Fax: 01479 841776** *iancc@tesco.net* **D:** £15.00–£18.00 **S:** £16.00–£18.00 **Beds:** 1T 1D 1S **Baths:** 1 En 1 Pr 1 Sh 🖸 (4) ⅍ 🖾 ⊁ 🛲. ♿ ♨

Cairn Hotel, *Main Road, Carrbridge, Inverness-shire, PH23 3AS.* Log fire, malt whiskies, real ales and affordable food in family-owned village centre hotel. **Open:** All year (not Xmas) **01479 841212** Mr Kirk **Fax: 01479 841362** *cairn.carrbridge@talk21.com* www.host.co.uk **D:** £19.00–£22.00 **S:** £19.00–£26.00 **Beds:** 2F 2D 1T 2S **Baths:** 4 En 1 Sh ॐ 🖸 (15) 🖾 ♨ cc

RATES

D = Price range per person sharing in a double or twin room

S = Price range for a single room

Cawdor

NH8449

Colonsay, *Piperhill Cawdor, Cawdor, Nairn, IV12 5SD.* **Open:** All year (not Xmas/New Year) **01667 404305** Mrs Murray *murray@micro-central.co.uk* **D:** £15.00 **S:** £18.00 **Beds:** 1F 1D **Baths:** 2 Sh ॐ 🖸 (3) ⅍ 🖾 🛲. ♨ Beautiful new traditionally built detached house set in rural area close to Inverness, Nairn, Cawdor castle and Culloden battlefield, Golf and Fishing close by. Comfortable beds, tastefully decorated rooms and good Scottish breakfasts and evening tea, private off road parking.

Charlestown (Gairloch)

NG8175 ◀ Creag Mor Hotel

Heatherdale, *Charlestown, Gairloch, Ross-shire, IV21 2AH.* Situated on hillside. Overlooking harbour. Seaviews, golf course and beach nearby. **Open:** Mar to Nov **Grades:** STB 4 Star **01445 712388** Mrs MacIver *BrochoD1@aol.com* **D:** £21.00–£23.00 **S:** £25.00–£30.00 **Beds:** 1T 2D **Baths:** 3 En 1 Sh ॐ (1) 🖸 (3) ⅍ ⊁ 🛲. ♨

Contin

NH4555 ◀ Baloan House

Hideaway BandB, *Craigdarroch Drive, Contin, Strathpeffer, Ross-shire, IV14 9EL.* Modern bungalow at gateway to Northwest Highlands. Consistent high standards **Open:** All year (not Xmas/New Year) **Grades:** STB 3 Star **01997 421127 (also fax)** *hideaway@ bushinternet.com* www.visithideaway.co.uk **D:** £15.00–£16.00 **S:** £16.00–£18.00 **Beds:** 1T 2D ॐ 🖸 (4) ⅍ 🖾 🖾 ♿ ♨

Millbrae, *Contin, Strathpeffer, Ross-shire, IV14 9EB.* Traditional Highland house, 100 years old, relax in peace, watch wildlife, feel welcome. **Open:** All year **01997 421368** Mrs Redfern **D:** £13.50–£15.00 **S:** £20.00 **Beds:** 1F 1D **Baths:** 1 Sh ॐ 🖸 (4) 🖾 ⊁ 🖾 🛲. ♨

Corpach

NN0976

Heston, *Corpach, Fort William, Inverness-shire, PH33 7LT.* Comfortable house with excellent views on road to the Isles. **Open:** Mar to Nov **01397 772425** Mrs Wynne **D:** £18.00–£20.00 **S:** £22.00 **Beds:** 1F 1D 1T **Baths:** 2 En ॐ (3) 🖸 (3) ⅍ 🖾 ⊁ 🛲. ♨

The Neuk, *Corpach, Fort William, Inverness-shire, PH33 7LR.* Modern, privately run, home cooking. Views over Ben Nevis. Private garden. **Open:** All year (not Xmas) **01397 772244** Mrs McCallum **D:** £18.00– £24.00 **S:** £27.00–£36.00 **Beds:** 2F 1D 1T **Baths:** 4 En ॐ 🖸 (6) ⅍ 🖾 ⊁ ✕ 🖾 🛲. ♨

Ben Nevis View, *Corpach, Fort William, Inverness-shire, PH33 7JH.* Modern, comfortable house, 5 minutes by car from Fort William. **Open:** Mar to Oct **01397 772131** Mrs Mooney **D:** £18.00–£20.00 **S:** £20.00–£25.00 **Beds:** 1F 1D **Baths:** 2 En 🖸 (4) ⅍ 🖾 🛲. ♨

Cromarty

NH7867 ◀ Royal Hotel

Braelangwell House, *Balblair, Dingwall, Ross-shire, IV7 8LQ.* Beautiful Georgian mansion. Ideal for touring Scottish Highlands. Four-poster bed. **Open:** Apr to Oct **Grades:** STB 4 Star **01381 610353 Fax: 01381 610467** *braelangwell@btinternet. com/~braelandwell* www.btinternet. com/~braelandwell **D:** £25.00–£35.00 **S:** £35.00–£50.00 **Beds:** 1T 1D **Baths:** 1 En 2 Pr ॐ 🖸 (40) ⅍ 🖾 🛲. ♨

7 Church Street, *Cromarty, Ross-shire, IV11 8XA.* 300-year-old house with warm welcome. **Open:** All year **01381 600488** Mrs Robertson **D:** £16.00 **S:** £16.00 ॐ 🖸 🖾 🛲. ♿

Culloden

NH7246

Easter Muckovie Farm House, *Westhill, Inverness, IV2 5BN.* Original farmhouse modernised set in a rural location overlooking Inverness town, Moray Firth. **Open:** All year **01463 791556** J H MacLellan *dot.westhill@ virgin.co.uk* **D:** £18.00–£20.00 **S:** £25.00 **Beds:** 2F **Baths:** 1 En 1 Pr ॐ 🖸 (5) ⅍ 🖾 ⊁ 🖾 ♨

Culloden Moor

NH7345

Westhill House, *Westhill, Inverness, IV1 5BP.* Spacious, comfortable family home in lovely garden. Close to Culloden and Inverness. **Open:** Easter to Oct **01463 793225** Mrs Honnor **Fax: 01463 792503** *janethon@piccolopress.demon.co.uk* www.scotland-info.co.uk/westhill.htm **D:** £18.00–£20.00 **S:** £18.00–£20.00 **Beds:** 1F 1T 1S **Baths:** 2 En 1 Sh ॐ 🖸 (4) ⅍ 🖾 ⊁ 🛲. ♨

Culdoich Farm, *Culloden Muir, Inverness, IV2 5EL.* Old farmhouse in peaceful surroundings. Good farmhouse breakfast. **Open:** May to Oct **Grades:** STB 3 Star
01463 790268 Mrs Alexander **D:** £17.00 **S:** £34.00 **Beds:** 1F 1T/D **Baths:** 1 Sh

Bayview, *Westhill, Culloden Moor, Inverness, IV2 5BP.* Modern 2-storey house situated in half acre landscaped garden. Beautiful views. **Open:** Easter to Oct
01463 790386 (also fax) Mrs Campbell *bayviewguesthouse@btinternet.com* **D:** £18.00–£22.00 **S:** £20.00–£25.00 **Beds:** 1T 2D **Baths:** 2 En 1 Pr (3)

Delny

NH7372

Under Beechwood, *Delny, Kilmvir Easter, Ross-shire, IV18 ONW.* Overlooking Cromarty Firth offering traditional and friendly accommodation with good cooking and baking. **Open:** Feb to Nov
01862 842685 (also fax) Mrs Horn **D:** £16.00–£17.00 **S:** £16.00–£17.00 **Beds:** 1F 1T 1D 1S **Baths:** 1 Sh (6)

Diabaig

NG7960

Ben Bhraggie, *Diabaig, Torridon, Achnasheen, Ross-shire, IV22 2HE.* Comfortable homely cottage - fishing and hill walkers' paradise. **Open:** Easter to Nov
01445 790268 Mrs Ross www.host.co.uk **D:** £14.00 **S:** £14.00 **Beds:** 1D 1T (3) (4)

Dornoch

NH8089 *Eagle Hotel, Dornoch Bridge Inn, Trentham Hotel, Burgh Field Hotel, Sutherland House, Castle Hotel, Mallin House Hotel*

Rosslyn Villa, *Castle Street, Dornoch, Sutherland, IV25 3SR.* Comfortable ensuite rooms (non-smoking). Beautiful scenery, beach, golf and wildlife. **Open:** All year
01862 810237 Mr Miles **D:** £16.00–£20.00 **S:** £16.00–£19.00 **Beds:** 1D 1T 1S **Baths:** 2 En 1 Pr (1)

Corven, *Station Road, Embo, Dornoch, Sutherland, IV25 3PR.* Detached bungalow with panoramic views. Ideal base for touring North Scotland. **Open:** Feb to Nov **Grades:** STB 2 Star
01862 810128 Mrs Fraser **D:** £17.00–£19.00 **S:** £20.00–£24.00 **Beds:** 2D 1T **Baths:** 1 En 1 Sh (10) (4)

Tordarroch, *Castle Street, Dornoch, Sutherland, IV25 3SN.* Traditional stone-built house set within walled gardens, ensuring peace & quiet. **Open:** Easter to Oct
01862 810855 Mrs Matherson **D:** £19.00–£21.00 **S:** £19.00–£21.00 **Beds:** 1D 1T 1S **Baths:** 1 En 1 Pr 1 Sh (3)

Achandean Bungalow, *The Meadows, Dornoch, Sutherland, IV25 3SF.* **Open:** Easter to Oct **Grades:** AA 3 Diamond
01862 810413 (also fax) Mrs Hellier **D:** £18.00–£22.00 **Beds:** 2D 1T **Baths:** 2 En 1 Pr (3)
Audrey Hellier extends a warm highland welcome to Achandean. Quiet, central position opposite fire station, comfortable ensuite bedrooms. Two minutes Cathedral, shops, OAPs,disabled welcomed. reductions- short breaks. Weekly rates. EM available. Lovely seaside town. Golf, birdwatching, walks, beach, relaxation.

Amalfi, *River Street, Dornoch, Sutherland, IV25 3LY.* Modern comfortable house alongside golf course. Award winning beach 300m. Friendly Highland hospitality. **Open:** All year (not Xmas/New Year)
01862 810015 Mrs MacKay *mackay.amalfi@talk21.com* **D:** £18.00–£21.00 **S:** £20.00–£33.00 **Beds:** 1F 1T **Baths:** 2 En (2) (2)

Drumnadrochit

NH5030 *Fiddlers Bar*

Glen Rowan House, *West Lewiston, Drumnadrochit, Inverness, IV63 6UW.* Very comfortable riverside village house near Urquhart Castle, Monster Exhibition. **Open:** All year (not Xmas) **Grades:** STB 3 Diamond
01456 450235 Mrs Harrod **Fax: 01456 450817** *glenrowan@loch-ness.demon.co.uk* www.loch-ness.demon.co.uk **D:** £16.00–£25.00 **S:** £25.00–£42.00 **Beds:** 1D 2T **Baths:** 3 Pr

Ferness Cottage, *Lewiston, Drumnadrochit, Inverness, IV3 6UW.* 200-year-old cottage within walking distance of Loch Ness. **Open:** Easter to Oct **Grades:** STB 3 Star
01456 450564 Mrs Campbell *morag@glenferness.com* www.host.co.uk **D:** £18.00–£23.00 **S:** £20.00–£30.00 **Beds:** 1F 1T 2D **Baths:** 4 En

Planning a longer stay? Always ask for any special rates

Westwood, *Lower Balmacaan, Drumnadrochit, Inverness, IV63 6WU.* Comfortable bungalow near Loch Ness. Ideal walking and touring base. **Open:** All year
01456 450826 (also fax) S Silke *sandra@westwoodbb.freeserve.co.uk* www.westwoodbb.freeserve.co.uk **D:** £17.00–£21.00 **S:** £20.00 **Beds:** 1D 1T 1S **Baths:** 2 En 1 Sh (8) (4) **cc**

Bridgend House, *The Green, Drumnadrochit, Inverness, IV63 6TX.* Highland home overlooking village green. Comfortable rooms. Imaginative evening meals. **Open:** Feb to Dec **Grades:** STB 3 Star
01456 450865 (also fax) Mrs Luffman www.host.co.uk **D:** £18.00–£25.00 **S:** £18.00–£28.00 **Beds:** 1F/T 1D 1S **Baths:** 1 En 1 Sh (10) (5)

Twin Birches, *Milton, Drumnadrochit, IV63 6UA.* Friendly, good breakfast, comfortable room. Loch Ness, Urquhart Castle nearby. **Open:** All year (not Xmas/New Year)
01456 450359 Mrs Seeburg **D:** £17.00 **S:** £17.00 **Beds:** 1D **Baths:** 1 Pr (3)

Drumsmittal

NH6449

Culbin Drumsmittal Croft, *Drumsmittal, North Kessock, Inverness, IV1 3XF.* Situated on a Highland working croft. Set in beautiful countryside, ideal touring base. **Open:** All year (not Xmas)
01463 731455 (also fax) Mrs Ross *ian-eliz@rossculbin.freeserve.co.uk* **D:** £15.00–£18.00 **Beds:** 1F 1T 1D **Baths:** 1 Pr 1 Sh (4)

Dulnain Bridge

NH9924

Broomlands, *Dulnain Bridge, Grantown-on-Spey, Moray, PH26 3LT.* A traditional Scottish house in a quiet village. Ideal centre for touring the Highlands.
Open: Easter to Sept
01479 851255 Mrs Noble *ernest@noble56.fsnet.co.uk* **D:** £16.00–£17.00 **S:** £16.00–£20.00 **Beds:** 1F 1D 1S **Baths:** 1 Sh (4)

Durness

NC4067 *Smoo Cave Hotel*

Rowan House, *90 Laid, Loch Eriboll, Lairg, Sutherland, IV27 4UN.* Set in a spectacular setting with uninterrupted views across Loch Eriboll to Ben Hope. **Open:** All year
01971 511347 (also fax) Mr MacLellan *h.maclellan@btinternet.com* drive.to/laid **D:** £15.00–£25.00 **S:** £15.00–£25.00 **Beds:** 1F/T 2D **Baths:** 3 En (6)

Port Na Con House, *Loch Eriboll, Lairg, Sutherland,* *IV27 4UN.* **Open:** All year **Grades:** AA 4 Diamond
01971 511367 (also fax) Mrs Black
portnacon70@hotmail.com www.smoothhound.
co.uk /hotels/portnaco.html **D:** £19.00–
£20.00 **S:** £27.00–£28.00 **Beds:** 1F 2D 1T
Baths: 1 En 1 Pr 1 Sh ⓢ ₽ (4) ⊬ ♀ ✕ ▦ ₤
cc
Former customs house, sited on the shore
of Loch Eriboll. All rooms overlook the sea
and our raised conservatory offers
magnificent views to Ben Hope (the
northernmost Munro) and Ben Loyal. We
have a restricted licence.

Glengolly House, *Durine, Durness, Lairg, Sutherland,* *IV27 4PN.* **Open:** All year
01971 511255
(also fax) Mr Mackay *mackaymm@talk21.com*
www.glengolly.co.uk **D:** £16.00–£18.00
S: £18.00–£20.00 **Beds:** 1F 1T 1D **Baths:** 1
En 1 Pr 1 Sh ⓢ ₽ (4) ⊬ ♀ ▦ ₤
Prepare to be enchanted by spectacular
sunsets and breathtaking scenery. Come
and stay at a traditional croft where you can
watch Border Collies at work or listen to the
corncrake. Enjoy outdoor pursuits in an
area steeped in history.

Caberfeidh Guest House, *Durness, Lairg, Sutherland,* *IV27 4QA.* Central village,
caves beaches and suited for exploring
North Coast. **Open:** Easter to Sept
01971 511215 J Marsham **Fax:** 01971 511339
D: £15.00–£20.00 **Beds:** 2F 1T 1D 1S
Baths: 1 Sh ⓢ ₽ (10) ⊬ ♀ ▦ ₤

Embo

NH8193

Corven, *Station Road, Embo, Dornoch, Sutherland,* *IV25 3PR.* Detached bungalow
with panoramic views. Ideal base for
touring North Scotland. **Open:** Feb to Nov
Grades: STB 2 Star
01862 810128 Mrs Fraser **D:** £17.00–£19.00
S: £20.00–£24.00 **Beds:** 2D 1T **Baths:** 1 En 1
Sh ⓢ (10) ₽ (4) ⊬ ▦ ♀ ▦ ₤ & ₤

Erbusaig

NG7629

Old Schoolhouse Restaurant, *Tigh Fasgaidh, Erbusaig, Kyle of Lochalsh, Ross-shire,* *IV40 8BB.* A house of special charm
where the mood is mellow! **Open:** All year
(not Xmas/New Year) **Grades:** STB 4 Star
01599 534369 (also fax) Mr & Mrs Cumine
cuminecandj@lineone.net www.highland.plus.
com/schoolhouse **D:** £28.00 **S:** £40.00–
£45.00 **Beds:** 1T 2D **Baths:** 3 En ⓢ ₽ (15) ⊬
▦ ♀ ✕ ▦ ₤ cc

Feshiebridge

NH8504

Balcraggan House, *Feshiebridge, Kincraig, Kingussie, Inverness-shire,* *PH21 1NG.* Wonderful setting where wildlife,
walks and cycle routes abound. **Open:** All
year
01540 651488 Mrs Gillies **D:** £25.00
S: £30.00–£35.00 **Beds:** 1D 1T **Baths:** 2 En
ⓢ (10) ₽ (3) ⊬ ▦ ✕ ▦ ▦ ₤

Fort Augustus

NH3709   ⚓ *Lock Inn*

Lorien House, *Station Road, Fort Augustus, Inverness-shire,* *PH32 4AY.* **Open:** All year
Grades: STB 3 Star
01320 366736
E Dickie **Fax:**
01320 366263 *lorienhouse@aol.com* www.ipw.
com/lorienhouse **D:** £20.00–£25.00
S: £35.00–£40.00 **Beds:** 2D 1F **Baths:** 3 En
₽ (2) ⊬ ▦ ♀ ▦ ₤
Luxurious family home overlooking Loch
Ness and the Caledonian Canal. Excellent
breakfasts- traditional, continental, fresh
fruits, smoked fish. Very central for pubs,
shops and restaurants, 10% discount at The
Bothy. Less than an hour from Skye,
Inverness and Ben Nevis.

Caledonian Cottage, *Station Road, Fort Augustus, Inverness-shire, PH32 4AY.*
Open: All year
01320 366401 Ms Graham *cal@ipw.com*
www.ipw.com/cal **D:** £18.00–£25.00
S: £15.00–£25.00 **Beds:** 1F 1T 1D **Baths:** 2
En 1 Pr ⓢ ₽ (5) ⊬ ▦ ♀ ▦ ₤
Warm, friendly and comfortable, the
cottage has beautiful views and situated
just minutes from the village with the
Caledonian Canal Locks which flow down
into Loch Ness. Perfect for walking, fishing,
boating, cycling. No need to take the car.

Old Pier House, *Fort Augustus, Inverness-shire, PH32 4BX.* Loch
Ness farmhouse
with panoramic
views, boats, riding, highland cattle.
Open: Apr to Nov
01320 366418 Mrs MacKenzie **Fax:** 01320
366770 *old.pier@talk21.com* **D:** £20.00–£30.00
S: £25.00–£35.00 **Beds:** 1F 1T 1D **Baths:** 3
En ⓢ (7) ₽ (10) ⊬ ▦ ✕ ▦ ₤

Sonas, *Inverness Road, Fort Augustus, Inverness-shire, PH32 4DH.* Modern
bungalow in very attractive Highland
village. Ideal touring centre. **Open:** All year
01320 366291 L H Service **D:** £15.00 **S:** £22.00
Beds: 1F 1T 1D **Baths:** 3 En ₽ (3) ⊬ ▦ ₤ & ₤

Fort William

NN1073   ⚓ *Ben Nevis Bar, Grand Hotel, Nevis Bank Hotel, West End Hotel*

Innseagan House Hotel, *Achintore Road, Fort William, Inverness-shire,* *PH33 6RW.* **Open:** Easter to Oct
01397 702452 Mr Maclean **Fax:** 01397
702606 *frontdesk@innseagan-holidays.com*
www.innseagan-holidays.com **D:** £22.50–
£31.50 **S:** £30.00–£40.00 **Beds:** 14D 8T 2S
Baths: 23 En 1 Pr ₽ ▦ ✕ ▦ ₤ cc
Spectacularly located on the shores of Loch
Linnhe only 1.5 miles from Fort William
town centre. We are large enough to
provide the facilities, privacy and services
of an hotel, yet small enough to give each
guest personal attention.

Glenlochy Guest House, *Nevis Bridge, Fort William, Inverness-shire, PH33 6PF.*
Open: All year **Grades:** STB 3 Star
01397 702909 Mrs MacBeth
glenlochyguesthouse@hotmail.com **D:** £17.00–
£27.00 **Beds:** 2F 5D 3T **Baths:** 8 En 2 Sh ⓢ
₽ (14) ▦ ▦ ₤
Situated in our extensive grounds
overlooking River Nevis, 1/2 mile North of
town and within easy walking distance of
Ben Nevis. The famous 'West Highland
Way Walk' officially ends in the grounds.
Large private carpark. Colour brochure
available.

RATES

D = Price range per person
sharing in a double or twin
room
S = Price range for a single
room

Glen Shiel Guest House,
Achintore Road, Fort William, Inverness-shire, PH33 6RW. Lochside location, panoramic views. Large car park. Tea makers, colour TV in all rooms. **Open:** Easter to Oct
01397 702271 D: £17.00–£21.00 **Beds:** 3D 1T **Baths:** 3 En 1 Pr 1 Sh ☎ (8) ▣ (7) ⊬ ⊡ Ⓥ ▥ ﹗

Ben View Guest House, Belford Road, Fort William, Inverness-shire, PH33 6ER. **Open:** Mar to Oct **Grades:** STB 3 Star, AA 3 Diamond
01397 702966 Mrs Smith *Benview@ gowanbrae.co.uk* www.benviewguesthouse.co. uk **D:** £18.00–£25.00 **S:** £18.00–£27.00 **Beds:** 1F 2T 6D 2S **Baths:** 10 En 1 Pr ☎ ▣ (20) ⊬ ⊡ Ⓥ ▥ ﹗
Perfectly situated close to Ben Nevis, Britain's highest mountain. 5 mins walk from town centre, sports, entertainments, bus and train links. Excellent touring base where visitors can enjoy walking, skiing, fishing, sailing, etc.

Rushfield House, Tomonie, Banavie, Fort William, Inverness-shire, PH33 7LX. **Open:** Mar to Oct **Grades:** STB 3 Star
01397 772063 Ms Corbett *rushbb0063@ aol.com* www.members.aol. com/rushbb0063/index.html **D:** £18.00–£25.00 **Beds:** 2F 1D **Baths:** 3 En ☎ ▣ (3) ⊬ ⊡ Ⓥ ▥ ﹗
Modern house with excellent views of Ben Nevis, situated within 3 miles of Fort William. All rooms ensuite, TVs, hospitality trays and ample parking. Restaurants/bars within easy walking distance.

Hillview Guest House,
Achintore Road, Fort William, Inverness-shire, PH33 6RW. Lochside location, magnificent views, home cooked food. Warm welcome assured. **Open:** All year
01397 704349 Mrs McLindon
hillview.fortwilliam@care4free.net www.hillview. fortwilliam.care4free.net **D:** £16.00–£23.00 **S:** £16.00–£22.50 **Beds:** 2F 3T 3D 1S **Baths:** 4 En 1 Pr 1 Sh ☎ (0) ▣ (9) ⊬ ⊡ ✕ Ⓥ ▥ ♿ ❋ ﹗ cc

Ferndale, Tomacharrich, Torlundy, Fort William, PH33 6SP. **Open:** All year **Grades:** STB 3 Star
01397 703593 Mrs Riley *ferndalebandb@ aol.com* **D:** £15.00–£20.00 **Beds:** 1F 2D **Baths:** 2 En 1 Pr ☎ ▣ (6) ⊬ ⊡ ✕ Ⓥ ▥ ﹗
Large bungalow in beautiful country setting, with wonderful views of Ben Nevis and Nevis Range Ski Slope. Ideal base for walking, cycling, skiing and touring. Pony trekking, trout fishing and golfing all nearby. Breakfast served in conservatory. Nearest B&B to skiing.

Alltonside,
Achintore Road, Fort William, Inverness-shire, PH33 6RW. **Open:** All year **Grades:** STB 3 Star
01397 703542 (also fax) Mrs Allton
altonside@aol.com **D:** £16.00 **S:** £20.00 **Beds:** 1F 3D 2T **Baths:** 6 Pr ☎ ▣ (8) ⊡ ⊀ Ⓥ ▥ ❋ ﹗
Alltonside guest house commands magnificent views over Loch Linnhe to the hills beyond. Being close to the town of Fort William and Ben Nevis makes it an ideal base for sightseeing and visiting the many beautiful places in the Highlands.

Rhu Mhor Guest House, Alma Road, Fort William, Inverness-shire, PH33 6BP. Old fashioned in acre of wild and enchanting garden. **Open:** Easter to Oct
01397 702213 Mr MacPherson *ian@ rhumhor.co.uk* www.rhumhor.co.uk **D:** £16.00–£24.00 **S:** £17.00–£44.00 **Beds:** 4F 1D 1T 1S **Baths:** 2 Sh 4 En ☎ (1) ▣ (7) ⊡ ⊀ Ⓥ ▥ ﹗ cc

Distillery House, Nevis Bridge, North Road, Fort William, Inverness-shire, PH33 6LR. Well-run guest house, ideally situated at end of Glen Nevis and West Highland Way. **Open:** All year
01397 700103 Mr Macpherson **Fax: 01397 702980** *disthouse@aol.com* **D:** £20.00–£36.00 **S:** £22.00–£38.00 **Beds:** 1F 3D 2T 1S **Baths:** 7 En ☎ ▣ (12) ⊬ ⊡ ▥ ﹗ cc

Stronchreggan View Guest House, Achintore Road, Fort William, Inverness-shire, PH33 6RW. Our house overlooks Loch Linnhe with views to Ardgour Hills. **Open:** Mar to Nov
01397 704644 & 01397 704707 Fax: 01397 704644 *patricia@apmac.freeserve.co.uk* www.stronchreggan.co.uk **D:** £19.00–£24.00 **Beds:** 5D/F 2T **Baths:** 5 En 2 Pr ☎ (8) ▣ (7) ⊬ ⊡ ✕ Ⓥ ▥ ﹗

Ossian's Hotel, High Street, Fort William, Inverness-shire, PH33 6DH. **Open:** All year
01397 700857 J Wallace **Fax: 01397 701030** *ossiansfw@aol.com* **D:** £16.00–£25.00 **S:** £18.00–£32.00 **Beds:** 10F 10D 10T 5S **Baths:** 32 En 3 Sh ☎ ▣ ⊡ ⊀ ✕ Ⓥ ▥ ﹗
Accommodation, food and drink for the budget traveller. Ideal town centre location. Couple of minutes walk from railway or bus. Warm, friendly and relaxed atmosphere.

Abrach, 4 Caithness Place, Fort William, Inverness-shire, PH33 6JP. Modern house in elevated position overlooking Loch Linnhe. **Open:** All year (not Xmas)
01397 702535 Mr & Mrs Moore **Fax: 01397 705629** *cmoore3050@aol.com* www.net-trak. com/~ecs/guest/abrach/ **D:** £17.50–£23.00 **S:** £20.00–£30.00 **Beds:** 1F 1D 1T 1S **Baths:** 2 En 1 Pr 1 Sh ☎ ▣ (6) ⊬ ⊡ ⊀ Ⓥ ▥ ﹗ cc

11 Castle Drive,
Lochyside, Fort William, PH33 7NR. **Open:** All year **Grades:** STB 3 Star
01397 702659 Mrs Grant *grantmoy@aol.com* **D:** £16.00–£18.00 **S:** £20.00–£24.00 **Beds:** 1T 1D **Baths:** 1 Sh ☎ ▣ (2) ⊬ ⊡ ⊀ ✕ Ⓥ ▥ ❋ ﹗
Quiet residential area near castle. Views to Ben Nevis. Ideal base for walking, climbing, skiing. Intimate family home with cosy log fire in lounge where you can be assured of a warm and friendly welcome. Breakfast is the best in the West.

Stobahn,
Fassifern Road, Fort William, Inverness-shire, PH33 6BD. Guest rooms overlooking Loch Linnhe. Just off High Street. **Open:** All year
01397 702790 (also fax) *boggi@supanet.com* **D:** £15.00–£20.00 **S:** £18.00–£23.00 **Beds:** 1F 1T 2D **Baths:** 2 En 2 Sh ☎ ▣ ⊡ ⊀ ✕ Ⓥ ▥ ﹗ cc

Planning a longer stay? Always ask for any special rates

RATES

D = Price range per person sharing in a double or twin room

S = Price range for a single room

Voringfoss, 5 Stirling Place, Fort William, Inverness-shire, PH33 6UW. Experience the best of the Highland hospitality in a quiet situation. **Open:** All year
01397 704062 Mr & Mrs Fraser **D:** £20.00–£26.00 **S:** £20.00–£26.00 **Beds:** 2D 1T **Baths:** 3 En 🅿 (4) 🔟 Ⅴ 🖳 🛋 cc

Melantee, Achintore Road, Fort William, Inverness-shire, PH33 6RW. Comfortable bungalow overlooking Loch Linnhe and the Ardgour hills. **Open:** All year (not Xmas)
01397 705329 Mrs Cook **Fax:** 01397 700453 **D:** £15.50–£16.00 **S:** £15.50–£16.00 **Beds:** 1F 1D 1T 1S **Baths:** 2 Sh ⅏ (5) 🅿 (6) 🔟 Ⅴ 🖳 🛋

Foyers
NH4920

Intake House, Foyers, Inverness, IV2 6YA. Overlooking the River Foyers near the famous Falls of Foyers. **Open:** Easter to Nov **Grades:** STB 4 Star
01456 486258 (also fax) Mrs Grant **D:** £15.00–£18.00 **S:** £20.00–£25.00 **Beds:** 1T 2D **Baths:** 1 En 1 Sh ⅏ (14) 🅿 (5) ⚲ 🔟 🖳 🛋

Gairloch
NG8076 🔹 Olde Inn, Sheildaig Lodge Hotel, Myrtle Bank Hotel, Millcroft Hotel, Badachro Inn

The Mountain Restaurant and Lodge, Strath Square, Gairloch, Ross-shire, IV21 2BX. **Open:** All year
01445 712316 (also fax) Mr Rudge **D:** £19.95–£27.95 **S:** £27.00 **Beds:** 1T 2D **Baths:** 3 En ⅏ 🅿 🔟 ⑂ 🗙 Ⅴ 🖳 🛋 cc
Mountain hospitality and informal atmosphere, lochside in Gairloch's Village Square. Themed ensuite bedrooms, most with ocean/mountain views. Four-poster bedroom also available. On-site, the unique 'Mountain Coffee Company' featuring cappuccino and mountain latte drinks with real mountain home-baking! Plus adventure travel bookstore and nature shop.

Whindley Guest House, Auchtercairn Brae, Gairloch, Ross-shire, IV21 2BN. Modern detached bungalow. Fantastic views. Warm welcome. Home cooking. **Open:** All year (not Xmas/New Year) **Grades:** STB 3 Star GH
01445 712340 (also fax) Mrs Nichols pam@whindley.co.uk www.whindley.co.uk **D:** £19.00–£21.00 **S:** £19.00–£31.00 **Beds:** 1F 1T 1D **Baths:** 3 En ⅏ 🅿 ⚲ 🔟 ⑂ 🗙 Ⅴ 🖳 🛋

Garve
NH3961

The Old Manse, Garve, Ross-shire, IV23 2PX. Former manse, c.1860, set in quiet location amidst beautiful scenery. **Open:** All year (not Xmas)
01997 414201 (also fax) Mr & Mrs Hollingdale petehollingdale@supanet.com **D:** £16.00–£17.00 **S:** £16.00–£17.00 **Beds:** 2D 1T **Baths:** 1 En 1 Sh ⅏ (10) 🅿 (6) ⚲ 🖳 🛋

Glencoe
NN1058 🔹 Glencoe Hotel, Lodge on the Loch, Clachaig Hotel, Laroch Bar, Glencoe Hotel

Glencoe Hotel, Glencoe, Ballachulish, Argyll, PA49 4HW. **Open:** All year (not Xmas)
01855 811245 Mr MacConnacher **Fax:** 01855 811687 glencoehotel@hotmail.com www.glencoehotel-scotland.com **D:** £20.00–£36.00 **S:** £32.00–£48.00 **Beds:** 3F 5T 6D 1S **Baths:** 15 En ⅏ 🅿 (40) 🔟 ⑂ 🗙 Ⅴ 🖳 🛋 cc
A family-run Highland hotel in Glencoe village where a warm welcome, comfortable rooms and very good food are standard. All rooms have private facilities. Local and long distance buses stop at our door. Ask for Bargain Break details.

Dunire Guest House, Glencoe, Ballachulish, Argyll, PA39 4HS. Family-run guest house. Great base for touring and walking. **Open:** All year (not Xmas/New Year)
01855 811305 Mrs Cameron **D:** £17.00–£23.00 **S:** £17.00–£23.00 **Beds:** 2T 4D **Baths:** 5 En 1 Pr 🅿 (8) 🔟 ⑂ 🔟 🛋

Craigavon House, West Laroch (beside Lochside Cottages), Ballachulish, Glencoe, Argyll, PH49 4JY. Stunning lochside location with panoramic views set amidst the heart of historic Glencoe. **Open:** All year **Grades:** STB 4 Star
01855 811608 & 07980 931556 (M) Mr MacCallum-Chisholm selfcatering_glencoe@btinternet.com www.assc.co.uk/glencoe **D:** £17.00–£23.00 **S:** £30.00 **Beds:** 1T 2D **Baths:** 3 En ⅏ 🅿 (5) ⚲ 🔟 Ⅴ 🖳 🛋 cc

Craigavon House, West Laroch (beside Lochside Cottages), Ballachulish, Glencoe, Argyll, PH49 4JY. **Open:** All year **Grades:** STB 4 Star
01855 811608 & 07980 931556 (M) Mr MacCallum-Chisholm selfcatering_glencoe@btinternet.com www.assc.co.uk/glencoe **D:** £17.00–£23.00 **S:** £30.00 **Beds:** 1T 2D **Baths:** 3 En ⅏ 🅿 (5) ⚲ 🔟 Ⅴ 🖳 🛋 cc
Craigavon House, stunning lochside location with panoramic views set amidst the heart of historic Glencoe. An ideal base for climbing, hillwalking, skiing or just exploring the West Highlands. All rooms ensuite and wonderfully comfortable, all you need after a hard day's adventuring.

Glenelg
NG8118 🔹 Glenelg Inn

Marabhaig, 7 Coullindune, Glenelg, Kyle of Lochalsh, Ross-shire, IV40 8JU. Marabhaig - Situated on the shore of Glenelg Bay. Fantastic views. **Open:** All year
01599 522327 Mrs Cameron **D:** £19.00–£21.00 **S:** £21.00–£23.00 **Beds:** 2T 3D **Baths:** 3 En 2 Sh 🅿 (6) ⚲ 🔟 🗙 🖳 ♨ 🛋

Glenfinnan
NM8980

Craigag Lodge Guest House, Glenfinnan, Inverness-shire, PH37 4LT. Victorian shooting lodge among superb mountain scenery. Ideal walking/wildlife. **Open:** Easter to Oct
01397 722240 Mr & Mrs Scott **D:** £15.00–£20.00 **S:** £18.00 **Beds:** 1F 1D 1T **Baths:** 1 Sh ⅏ (9) 🅿 (4) ⚲ 🔟 🗙 🛋

Glengolly
ND1066

Shinval, Glengolly, Thurso, Caithness, KW14 7XN. Modern house with large garden. Four miles from Orkney ferry. **Open:** Jan to Dec
01847 894306 Mrs Sinclair **Fax:** 01847 890711 mary@shinval.swinternet.co.uk **D:** £15.00 **S:** £15.00 **Beds:** 1F 1D 1T **Baths:** 1 En 2 Sh ⅏ 🅿 (4) 🔟 🖳 ♨ 🛋

Planning a longer stay? Always ask for any special rates

Grantown-on-Spey

NJ0327 🚃 *Strathspey Hotel, Tiree House Hotel, Ben Mhor Hotel*

Brooklynn, *Grant Road, Grantown-on-Spey, Moray, PH26 3LA.* **Open:** All year **Grades:** STB 3 Star
01479 873113 *brooklynn@woodier.com* www.woodier.com **D:** £19.00–£25.00
S: £24.00–£30.00 **Beds:** 2T 3D 2S **Baths:** 3 En 1 Sh
In our beautiful Victorian home enjoy a delicious home-cooked dinner with herbs and vegetables from the garden, relax in the lounge before retiring to your spacious, comfortable room. Tomorrow's for fishing, golf, birdwatching, the Malt Whisky Trail, walking, castles and so much more!

Rossmor Guest House, *Woodlands Terrace, Grantown-on-Spey, Moray, PH26 3JU.*
Open: Feb to Nov **Grades:** AA 4 Diamond
01479 872201 & 01479 872247 Mrs Steward **Fax: 01479 872201** *johnsteward.rossmore@lineone.net* www.rossmor.co.uk **D:** £23.00–£25.00 **S:** £25.00–£28.00 **Beds:** 2F 2T 2D
Baths: 6 En 🅿 (6) ⧖ 🖵 📖 ♨ cc
Built in 1887 Rossmor is a beautiful Victorian house with original staircase etched glass and brass fittings, ideally located to explore the Highlands, to fish in the river Spey, or play golf at the many surrounding courses. Full Scottish breakfast.

Strathallan House, *Grant Road, Grantown-on-Spey, Moray, PH26 3LD.*
Charming Victorian home, original features, first class accommodation. ensuite rooms.
Open: Easter to Oct **Grades:** STB 3 Star B&B
01479 872165 (also fax) Mr Pearson
strathallanhouse.co.uk **D:** £19.00–£25.00
S: £20.00–£25.00 **Beds:** 3D 2T 1F **Baths:** 5 En 1 Pr ⧖ (7) 🅿 (6) ⧖ × 📖 ♨ cc

Firhall Guest House, *Grant Road, Grantown-on-Spey, Moray, PH26 3LD.*
Beautiful Victorian house set in the heart of Scottish Highlands.
Open: All year (not Xmas) **Grades:** STB 3 Star GH
01479 873097 (also fax) Mr Salmon *firhall@cs.com* www.smoothhound.co.uk/hotels/firhall.html **D:** £17.00–£24.00
S: £17.00–£30.00 **Beds:** 3F 1D 1T 1S
Baths: 3 En 1 Pr 1 Sh ⧖ 🅿 (8) ⧖ × 📖 ♨

Ravenscourt House Hotel, *Seafield Avenue, Grantown-on-Spey, Moray, PH26 3JG.*
Victorian manse set in beautiful gardens within walking distance of River Spey. **Open:** All year **Grades:** RAC 5 Diamond
01479 872286 Mr & Mrs Lockey **Fax: 01479 873260 D:** £27.50–£35.00 **S:** £30.00–£35.00
Beds: 2F 3D 2T 1S **Baths:** 8 En ⧖ 🅿 (8) ⧖ 🖵 ⅋ × 🖤 📖 ♨ 🍴

Kinross Guest House, *Woodside Avenue, Grantown-on-Spey, Moray, PH26 3JR.* Relaxing in a stunning part of Scotland. Sauna, gyms and cycles **Open:** All year **Grades:** STB 4 Star
01479 872042 Mr Milne **Fax: 01479 873504** *milne@kinrosshouse.freeserve.co.uk* **D:** £20.00–£28.00 **S:** £20.00–£31.00 **Beds:** 2F 2T 1D 2S
Baths: 5 En 2 Pr ⧖ (13) 🅿 (6) ⧖ × 🖤 📖 ♨ ✿ cc

Gaich Farm, *Grantown-on-Spey, Moray, PH26 3NT.* Beautiful working farmhouse overlooking Cairngorms, comfortable beds, good breakfast. **Open:** May to Sept
01479 851381 Mrs Laing **Fax: 01479 851 381** *gaich@tinyworld.co.uk* **D:** £16.00–£17.00
S: £16.00–£17.00 **Beds:** 1T 1D **Baths:** 1 Sh ⧖ 🅿 🖵 🍴 × 📖 ♨

Helmsdale

ND0215

Bayview B&B, *Portgower, Helmsdale, Sutherland, KW8 6HL.*
Open: All year (not Xmas/New Year) **Grades:** STB 2 Star B&B
01431 821679 (also fax) Mr Leitch
www.bayview-helmsdale.org.uk **D:** £15.00
S: £15.00 **Beds:** 2D ⧖ 🅿 (2) 🖤 🍴 × 🖤 📖 ♨
A C19th cottage perfectly situated on the shore of the Moray Firth. Step through our garden gate and explore the beach and coastline which offer you peace, tranquillity and sea breezes. A warm welcome is offered by Alastair and Pat Leitch.

The Old Manse, *Stittenham Road, Helmsdale, Sutherland, KW8 6JG.* Beautiful village settings, garden, access to salmon river, fishing arranged. **Open:** All year
01431 821597 Mrs Goodridge **D:** £18.00–£20.00 **S:** £18.00–£20.00 **Beds:** 1F 2T
Baths: 1 En 1 Pr 1 Sh ⧖ 🅿 (4) ⧖ × 🖤 📖 ♨

Inverdruie

NH9011

Riverside Lodge, *Inverdruie, Aviemore, Inverness-shire, PH22 1QH.* Architect-designed house in own silver birch woodland with riverside location. **Open:** All year (not New Year)
01479 810153 Mrs Macintyre *riversidelodge@sol.co.uk* www.host.co.uk **D:** £20.00–£25.00
S: £25.00–£30.00 **Beds:** 1F 1T 1D **Baths:** 3 En ⧖ 🅿 (5) ⧖ 🖤 🍴 📖 ♨

Invergarry

NH3001 🚃 *Invergarry Hotel, Glengarry Castle, Lock Inn*

Forest Lodge, *South Laggan, Invergarry, Inverness-shire, PH34 4EA.* **Open:** All year (not Xmas/New Year) **Grades:** STB 3 Star
01809 501219 Mr & Mrs Shearer **Fax: 01809 501476** *info@flgh.co.uk* www.flgh.co.uk
D: £17.00–£22.00 **S:** £24.00–£29.00 **Beds:** 2F 2T 3D **Baths:** 6 En 1 Pr ⧖ 🅿 (10) ⧖ 🖤 × 🖤 📖 ♨ cc
Ian and Janet Shearer offer friendly hospitality, pleasant ensuite accommodation, and home cooking in their rurally set home close to the Great Glen Way. Walking or touring, Forest Lodge is the perfect stopover.

Ardfriseal, *Mandally Road, Invergarry, Inverness-shire, PH35 4HR.*
Modern comfortable bungalow, easy access for touring beautiful West Highlands. **Open:** May to Oct
01809 501281 Mrs Fraser *fraser@ardfriseal.freeserve.co.uk* **D:** £15.00–£16.00
S: £18.00–£20.00 **Beds:** 1T 2D **Baths:** 1 Sh ⧖ 🅿 (6) 🖤 📖 ♨

Lilac Cottage, *South Laggan, Invergarry, Inverness-shire, PH34 4EA.*
Comfortable accommo-dation, warm welcome in the heart of the Great Glen.
Open: All year
01809 501410 Mrs Jamieson *lilac.cottage@virgin.net* **D:** £14.00–£17.00 **S:** £13.00–£20.00
Beds: 2D 1T **Baths:** 1 Sh ⧖ 🅿 (4) 🖤 × 📖 ♨

Ardgarry Farm, *Faichem, Invergarry, Inverness-shire, PH35 4HG.* Comfortable accommodation, warm welcome, ideal for touring, beautiful forest walks. **Open:** Easter to Oct **01809 501226** Mr Wilson **Fax: 01809 501307** *ardgarry.farm@lineone.net* www.scottish-highlandholidays.glo.cc **D:** £14.00–£15.00 **Beds:** 1F 2T 1D **Baths:** 2 Sh ⊃ (5) 🅿 (5) 🖵 🖮 ✕ 🖵 🞔 ♨

Invergarry Hotel, *Invergarry, Inverness-shire, PH35 4HJ.* A wonderful base for touring the Highlands of Scotland. **Open:** All year (not Xmas/New Year) **01809 501206** R E MacCallum **Fax: 01809 501400** *hotel@invergarry.net* www.invergarry.net **D:** £25.00–£35.00 **S:** £30.00–£40.00 **Beds:** 1F 3T 5D **Baths:** 10 En ⊃ 🅿 (20) 🖵 🖮 ✕ 🖵 🞔 ♨ cc

Lundie View Guest House, *Invergarry, Inverness-shire, PH35 4HN.* Set in heart of Great Glen near Loch Ness, Ben Nevis, much more. **Open:** All year **01809 501291 (also fax)** Mr & Mrs Girdwood *lundieview@talk21.com* **D:** £18.00–£24.00 **S:** £20.00–£28.00 **Beds:** 2F 2D 1T **Baths:** 4 En 1 Pr ⊃ 🅿 (10) ✔ 🖵 🖮 ✕ 🖵 🞔 ♨ ✳ ♨ cc

Invergordon

NH7168

Craigaron, *17 Saltburn, Invergordon, Ross-shire, IV18 0JX.* Ground floor bedrooms (some seafront), good breakfast, friendly, value for money. **Open:** All year (not Xmas/New Year) **01349 853640** Mrs Brown **Fax: 01349 853619** *jobrown@craigaron.freeserve.co.uk* www.host.co.uk **D:** £18.00–£22.00 **S:** £20.00–£22.00 **Beds:** 4T 1S **Baths:** 2 En 1 Sh 🅿 (6) 🖵 🖮 🞔 ♨

Inverinate

NG9221 🔌 *Dornie Hotel, Old School House*

Foresters Bungalow, *Inverinate, Kyle of Lochalsh, Ross-shire, IV40 8HE.* Shores of Loch Duich on main A87, with superb views of the Kintail Mountains. **Open:** Easter to Oct **01599 511329** Mrs MacIntosh **Fax: 01599 511407** *Jean-MacIntosh@tesco.net* **D:** £17.50–£20.00 **Beds:** 1D 1T **Baths:** 1 En 1 Pr ⊃ 🅿 (2) 🖵 🞔 ♨ cc

Cruechan, *5 Glebe Road, Inverinate, Glenshiel, Kyle of Lochalsh, Ross-shire, IV40 8HD.* Seafront location, looking towards Mam Ratagan and Five Sisters of Kintail. **Open:** All year **01599 511328 (also fax)** Mrs Fraser **D:** £16.00–£18.00 **S:** £18.00–£20.00 **Beds:** 2F **Baths:** 1 Sh 🅿 🖵 🖮 🞔 ♨

Inverlochy

NN1174

19 Lundy Road, *Inverlochy, Fort William, Inverness-shire, PH33 6NY.* Family-run B&B. Views of Ben Nevis, passing steam trains. **Open:** All year **01397 704918** Mrs Campbell *acampbell@talk21.com* **D:** £13.00–£17.00 **S:** £15.00–£20.00 **Beds:** 2F **Baths:** 1 Sh 🅿 (2) 🖵 🖮 ✕ 🖵 🞔 ♨

Inverness

NH6645 🔌 *Johnny Fox's, Finlays, Barbazza*

Edenview, *26 Ness Bank, Inverness, IV2 4SF.* **Open:** Mar to Oct **01463 234397** Mrs Fraser **Fax: 01463 222742** **D:** £22.00–£25.00 **S:** £22.00–£28.00 **Beds:** 1F 1D 1T **Baths:** 2 En 1 Pr 🅿 (4) 🖵 🖵 🞔 ♨ Edenview Guest House occupies a beautiful situation overlooking the River Ness. Excellent touring centre for viewing the beautiful Scottish highlands, including (Glen Affric, Loch Ness and the Black Isle). Castles, exhibitions, shopping, golf, dolphin watching, monster hunting.

Strathmhor Guest House, *99 Kenneth Street, Inverness, IV35QQ.* **Open:** All year **Grades:** STB 3 Star **01463 235397** Mr & Mrs Reid www.smoothhound.co.uk/hotels/strathmh.html **D:** £18.00–£22.00 **S:** £20.00–£25.00 **Beds:** 2F 2T 2D 1S **Baths:** 6 En 1 Pr 🅿 (5) 🖵 🖮 ♨ Warm welcome awaits at refurbished Victorian home. Comfortable bedrooms and good food. 10 minutes walk into town centre, theatres, restaurants, leisure centre; golf course and fishing nearby. Easy access for all traffic off A9/A82

Rotherwood Guest House, *7 Midmills Road, Inverness, IV2 3NZ.* **Open:** All year **Grades:** STB 3 Star **01463 225732** *junejim.taylor@lineone.net* www.rotherwoodguesthouse.co.uk **D:** £20.00–£25.00 **S:** £25.00–£45.00 **Beds:** 1T 2D **Baths:** 3 En 🅿 (11) 🅿 (1) ✕ 🖵 🖵 🞔 ♨ cc Beautiful Victorian red sandstone villa, situated in a quiet side road, but only 3 mins walk from city centre. Central for restaurants, and ideal for touring all corners of the Highlands and Islands, including Isle of Skye and Loch Ness.

Ardaroul, *3 Fairfield Road, Inverness, IV3 4QA.* **Open:** All year (not Xmas/New Year) **01463 237741** Mr & Mrs Murray **D:** £16.00–£20.00 **S:** £16.00–£20.00 **Beds:** 1T 1D 2S **Baths:** 2 Sh 🅿 (2) ✔ 🖮 🞔 ♨ Ideally situated near city centre and for exploring the beautiful scenery of the Scottish Highlands. You are assured a warm welcome and excellent accommodation. Choice of menu including full Scottish breakfast. Footbridge to city centre 5 mins away.

30 Culduthel Road, *Inverness, IV2 4AP.* **Open:** All year **01463 717181** Mrs Dunnett **Fax: 01463 717188** *kathleensbnb@cs.com* www.puffinexpress.co.uk/bandb.htm **D:** £12.50–£15.00 **S:** £18.00–£22.00 **Beds:** 1D 1T **Baths:** 2 En 🅿 (2) 🖵 🖮 🞔 ♨ 1930s bungalow set in large garden, pleasant to relax in on summer evenings. Central heating. Lounge with open fire which you may have to share with a cat. Your hosts are both qualified local guides.

Eskdale Guest House, *41 Greig Street, Inverness, IV3 5PX.* **Open:** All year (not Xmas) **Grades:** STB 3 Star **01463 240933 (also fax)** Mrs Mazurek *eskdale.guesthouse@lineone.net* www.smoothhound.co.uk/hotels/eskdale.html **D:** £16.00–£25.00 **S:** £22.00–£25.00 **Beds:** 2F 2D 1T 1S **Baths:** 3 En 1 Sh 🅿 (5) ✔ 🖵 🖵 ♨ Situated in the heart of Inverness only 5 minutes from bus/rail stations, this impeccably run guest house offers all the comforts of home and a warm Highland welcome. Private parking, discounts for stays over 3 days. Please phone Vera and Alex.

Pitfaranne, *57 Crown Street, Inverness, IV2 3AY.* **Open:** All year **Grades:** STB 3 Star **01463 239338** Gwen & Jim Morrison **Fax: 01463 240356** *pitfaranne@talk21.com* www.pitfaranne.co.uk **D:** £16.00–£20.00 **S:** £18.00–£26.00 **Beds:** 1F 2D 4T **Baths:** 1 En 1 Pr 2 Sh 🅿 (5) 🖵 🖮 🖵 🞔 ♨ 5 minutes from town centre/rail/bus stations. Find true Highland hospitality in friendly relaxed atmosphere of 100-year-old town house in quiet location. Private showers in all cosy guest rooms. Daily room service. Extensive varied menu. Full Highland breakfast our speciality.

Abb Cottage, *11 Douglas Row, Inverness, IV1 1RE.* Central, quiet, riverside Listed terraced cottage. **Open:** Feb to Dec **01463 233486** Miss Storrar **D:** £16.00–£18.00 **S:** £18.00–£25.00 **Beds:** 3T **Baths:** 1 Sh 🅿 (12) 🅿 (2) ✔ 🖵 ✕ 🖵 🞔 ♨

Merlewood House, Merlewood Road, Inverness, IV2 4NL. UK winner of 'Mansion & Manor of the Year' 1999 and 2000 **Open:** All year **Grades:** STB 4 Star **01463 236060** Mrs Cordiner **Fax: 01463 711999** *merlewood@norcor.ltd.uk* www.merlewood.norcor.ltd.uk **D:** £25.00–£55.00 **S:** £50.00–£68.00 **Beds:** 1T 3D **Baths:** 4 En ⌂ (15) ▣ (10) ⌇ ▣ ▣ ▥ **cc**

Charden Villa, 11 Fairfield Road, Inverness, IV3 5QA. Warm comfortable family-run house situated 10 mins' walk town centre. **Open:** All year **01463 718058** Mrs Munro **D:** £18.00–£20.00 **S:** £20.00–£25.00 **Beds:** 3F 1D **Baths:** 2 En 1 Sh ⌂ ▣ ⍢ ▣ ▥ ⁂ ⚓

The Tilt, 26 Old Perth Road, Inverness, IV2 3UT. Family home convenient for A9. Ideal touring base. **Open:** All year (not Xmas) **01463 225352 (also fax)** Mrs Fiddes *thetilt26@ukonline.co.uk* **D:** £15.00–£17.00 **S:** £17.00–£19.00 **Beds:** 1F 1D 1T 1S **Baths:** 1 Sh ⌂ ▣ (4) ⌇ ▣ ▣ ▥

MacGregor's, 36 Ardconnel Street, Inverness, IV2 3EX. We are situated minutes from River Ness, shops and castle. **Open:** All year (not Xmas/New Year) **01463 238357** Mrs MacGregor *james@seafieldorms.orknet.co.uk* www.seafieldorms.orknet.co.uk **D:** £14.00–£18.00 **S:** £15.00–£20.00 **Beds:** 1F 3D 1T 3S **Baths:** 2 En 3 Sh ▣ ⍢ ▥ ⚓

Hazeldean House, 125 Lochalsh Road, Inverness, IV3 5QS. Friendly Highland welcome. Only 10 mins' walk to town centre. **Open:** All year **01463 241338** Mr Stuart **Fax: 01463 236387** *mail@hazeldeanhouse.co.uk* www.hazeldeanhouse.co.uk **D:** £14.00–£18.00 **S:** £16.00–£20.00 **Beds:** 2F 4D 3T 2S **Baths:** 3 En 2 Sh ⌂ ▣ (6) ⌇ ▣ ⍢ ▥ ⚓

East Dene, 6 Ballifeary Road, Inverness, IV3 5PJ. Near Eden Court Theatre. **Open:** All year (not Xmas/New Year) **Grades:** STB 3 Star **01463 232976 (also fax)** J Greig *dgreig@nildram.co.uk* www.eastdene-inverness.co.uk **D:** £23.00–£30.00 **S:** £30.00 **Beds:** 1T 2D **Baths:** 1 En 3 Pr ⌇ ▣ ▥ ⚓ **cc**

Cambeth Lodge, 49 Fairfield Road, Inverness, IV3 5QP. Victorian detached stone built house in quiet residential area. **Open:** All year (not Xmas/New Year) **Grades:** STB 3 Star **01463 231764** Mrs Carson-Duff *duffcambeth@tinyworld.co.uk* **D:** £16.00–£19.50 **Beds:** 1T 2D **Baths:** 1 En 1 Pr 1 Sh ▣ (6) ⌇ ▣ ⍢ ⚓

Macrae Guest House, 24 Ness Bank, Inverness, IV2 4SF. Non-smoking house overlooking river. 5 mins from town. **Open:** All year **Grades:** STB 3 Star **01463 243658** *joycemacrae@hotmail.com* **D:** £20.00–£24.00 **S:** £30.00–£35.00 **Beds:** 1T 2D **Baths:** 2 En 1 Pr ▣ (5) ⌇ ▣ ▣ ▥ ⚓ ⁂ ⚓

Alban House, Bruce Gardens, Inverness, IV3 5EN. Walking distance from town centre. Large garden, fish pond. Warm, relaxing ambience. **Open:** All year (not Xmas/New Year) **Grades:** STB 3 Star **01463 714301** *enquiries@alban-house.freeserve.co.uk* **D:** £25.00–£29.00 **S:** £30.00–£38.00 **Beds:** 1F 3T 3D 2S **Baths:** 9 En ⌂ ▣ ⌇ ▣ ⍢ × ▣ ▥ ⚓ **cc**

Torridon Guest House, 59 Kenneth Street, Inverness, IV3 5PZ. Comfortable, family-run house, 5 minutes from town centre, good food, good beds. **Open:** All year **01463 236449 (also fax)** Mrs Stenhouse *louise@torridon59.freeserve.co.uk* **D:** £17.00 **Beds:** 3F **Baths:** 2 En 1 Pr ⌂ (5) ▣ (4) ▣ ▥ ⚓

Loanfern Guest House, 4 Glenurquhart Road, Inverness, IV3 5NU. Victorian house with character. 15 minutes walk from town centre. **Open:** All year (not Xmas/New Year) **01463 221660 (also fax)** Mrs Campbell **D:** £16.00–£22.00 **S:** £18.00–£23.00 **Beds:** 1F 2T 2D **Baths:** 1 En 2 Sh ▣ (4) ⌇ ▣ ⚓

Winmar House Hotel, Kenneth Street, Inverness, IV3 5QG. Full Scottish breakfast and friendly welcome. Ample parking. **Open:** All year (not Xmas) **01463 239328 (also fax)** Mrs Maclellan *winmarguesthouse@invernessll.freeserve.co.uk* **D:** £16.00–£22.00 **S:** £16.00–£22.00 **Beds:** 1D 6T 3S **Baths:** 1 En 4 Pr 2 Sh ⌂ ▣ (10) ⌇ ▣ ⍢ ▥ ⚓ **cc**

Roseneath Guest House, 39 Greig Street, Inverness, IV3 5PX. 100-year-old building in centre location 200 yards from River Ness. **Open:** All year **01463 220201 (also fax)** Mr Morrison *roseneath@lineone.net* www.Scottish-holiday.com **D:** £15.00–£25.00 **Beds:** 3F 1T 2D **Baths:** 5 En 1 Pr ⌂ (7) ▣ (3) ▣ ▥ ⚓ **cc**

Melness Guest House, 8 Old Edinburgh Road, Inverness, IV2 3HF. Charming, award-winning guest house close to town centre. **Open:** All year **01463 220963 Fax: 01463 717037** *melness@joyce86.freeserve.co.uk* www.melnessie.co.uk **D:** £20.00–£26.00 **S:** £25.00–£40.00 **Beds:** 1F 1T 1D **Baths:** 1 En 1 Sh ▣ (3) ⌇ ▣ ▣ ▥ ⚓ **cc**

101 Kenneth Street, Inverness, IV3 5QQ. Ideal base for day trips to North Highland and Islands. **Open:** All year **01463 237224** Mrs Reid **Fax: 01463 712249** *dalmoreguesthouse@amserve.net* **D:** £16.00–£25.00 **S:** £20.00–£25.00 **Beds:** 2F 2D 1T 1S **Baths:** 1 En 1 Pr 2 Sh ⌂ ▣ (6) ⌇ ▣ ▣ ▥ ⚓ **cc**

John O' Groats

ND3773

Bencorragh House, Upper Gills, Canisbay, John o' Groats, Wick, Caithness, KW1 4YB. Working croft. Panoramic views across Pentland Firth near Orkney ferries. **Open:** All year **Grades:** STB 3 Star, AA 3 Star **01955 611449 (also fax)** Mrs Barton *bartonsandy@hotmail.com* www.bencorraghhouse.com **D:** £21.00–£22.00 **S:** £25.00–£30.00 **Beds:** 1F 2D 1T **Baths:** 4 En ⌂ (5) ▣ (6) ⌇ ▣ ⍢ × ▣ ▥ ⚓ **cc**

Seaview Hotel, John o' Groats, Wick, Caithness, KW1 4YR. Scenic seaside location. Family owned, five minutes from Orkney ferry. **Open:** All year **01955 611220 (also fax)** Mr Mowat **D:** £14.50–£25.00 **S:** £20.00–£35.00 **Beds:** 3F 3D 2T 1S **Baths:** 5 En 2 Sh ⌂ ▣ (20) ▣ ⍢ × ▣ ▥ ⚓

Links View, Keiss, Wick, Caithness, KW1 4XG. Attractive location overlooking Sinclair Bay. 10 minutes from Orkney Ferry. **Open:** All year **01955 631376** Mrs Brooks **D:** £16.00–£17.00 **S:** £17.00 **Beds:** 1T 2D **Baths:** 1 Pr 1 Sh ⌂ ▣ ⌇ ▣ ×

Keiss

ND3461 ⚓ Sinclair Bay

Charnwood B&B, Main Street, Keiss, Wick, Caithness, KW1 4UY. **Open:** Easter to Oct **Grades:** STB 2 Star **01955 631258** Mr & Mrs Hickman **D:** £18.00–£20.00 **S:** £20.00–£22.00 **Beds:** 1F 1D **Baths:** 1 Sh ⌂ ▣ (3) ⌇ ▣ ▣ ▥ ⚓ Charnwood is located in the peaceful village of Keiss which overlooks Sinclair Bay with its miles of sandy beach and harbour. Both within walking distance. Keiss is just 15 minutes' drive to John O'Groats and the Orkney passenger ferry.

Links View, Keiss, Wick, Caithness, KW1 4XG. Attractive location overlooking Sinclair Bay. 10 minutes from Orkney Ferry. **Open:** All year **01955 631376** Mrs Brooks **D:** £16.00–£17.00 **S:** £17.00 **Beds:** 1T 2D **Baths:** 1 Pr 1 Sh ⌂ ▣ ⌇ ▣ ×

National Grid References given are for villages, towns and cities – not for individual houses

Kentallen

NN0157

Ardsheal House, Kentallen, Appin, Argyll, *PA38 4BX*. Spectacularly situated on shores of Loch Linnhe, in 800 acres of woodlands, fields, gardens. **Open:** All year **01631 740227** N V C Sutherland **Fax: 01631 740342** *info@ardsheal.co.uk* www.ardsheal.co. uk **D:** £45.00 **S:** £45.00 **Beds:** 1F 2T 4D 1S **Baths:** 8 En ☎ 🖭 🛪 ✕ Ⅵ ⬛ 🎇 cc

Kiltarlity

NH5041 🏚 *Brockes Lodge, Priory Hotel*

Cherry Trees, Kiltarlity, Beauly, Inverness-shire, *IV4 7JD*. **Open:** Feb to Nov **Grades:** STB 3 Star **01463 741368 (also fax)** Mrs Matheson *cherrytrees@mathesonJ.freeserve.co.uk* **D:** £17.00–£21.00 **S:** £19.00–£23.00 **Beds:** 2D **Baths:** 1Pr ☎ (3) 🖭 (4) ⅙ Ⅵ 🛪 ⬛ 🎇 Come and visit this beautiful part of the Highlands of Scotland with excellent fishing, hill walking, golf. Visit the wonderful Glens of Affric and Strathfarrer, also Loch Ness. A warm welcome awaits you in this spacious, cosy, comfortable country house.

Kinbrace

NC8632

Tigh achen Echan, Kinbrace, Sutherland, *KW11 6UB*. Natural stone-built house. View of river and distant hills. **Open:** All year **01431 831207** Mrs MacKenzie **D:** £15.00 **S:** £15.00 **Beds:** 2F **Baths:** 1 Sh ☎ 🖭 Ⅵ ✕ Ⅵ ⬛ 🎇

Kincraig

NH8305 🏚 *Ossian Hotel, Kith & Kin, Loch Inch Boat House, Suie Hotel*

Ossian Hotel, Kincraig, Kingussie, Inverness-shire, *PH21 1QD*. Built in 1880s lochside village. Magnificent mountain views. **Open:** Feb to Dec **Grades:** STB 2 Star **01540 651242** Mrs Rainbow **Fax: 01540 651633** *ossian@kincraig.com* www.kincraig. com/ossian.htm **D:** £20.00–£31.00 **S:** £20.00–£31.00 **Beds:** 2F 3D 2T 2S **Baths:** 8 En 1 Pr ☎ 🖭 (20) ⅙ Ⅵ 🛪 ✕ ⬛ 🎇 cc

Insh House, Kincraig, Kingussie, Inverness-shire, *PH21 1NU*. Friendly family guest house in splendid rural location near loch and mountains. **Open:** All year **Grades:** STB 3 Star **01540 651377** Nick & Patsy Thompson *inshhouse@btinternet.com* www.kincraig. com/inshhouse.htm **D:** £18.00–£21.00 **S:** £18.00–£25.00 **Beds:** 1F 1T 1D 2S **Baths:** 2 En 1 Sh ☎ 🖭 ⅙ Ⅵ 🛪 ✕ Ⅵ ⬛ 🎇

Balcraggan House, Feshiebridge, Kincraig, Kingussie, Inverness-shire, *PH21 1NG*. Wonderful setting where wildlife, walks and cycle routes abound. **Open:** All year **01540 651488** Mrs Gillies **D:** £25.00 **S:** £30.00–£35.00 **Beds:** 1D 1T **Baths:** 2 En ☎ (10) 🖭 (3) ⅙ Ⅵ ✕ Ⅵ ⬛ 🎇

Kingussie

NH7500

The Osprey Hotel, Kingussie, Inverness-shire, *PH21 1EN*. **Open:** All year **Grades:** STB 3 Star Hotel, AA 2 Star **01540 661510 (also fax)** Mr & Mrs Burrow *aileen@ospreyhotel.co.uk* www.ospreyhotel.co. uk **D:** £24.00–£30.00 **S:** £24.00–£30.00 **Beds:** 3D 3T 2S **Baths:** 8 En ☎ 🖭 Ⅵ 🛪 ✕ Ⅵ ⬛ ♿ 🎇 cc Small hotel in area of outstanding beauty, offering a warm welcome, ensuite accommodation and award-winning food. Aileen and Robert hold AA Food Rosettes and are members of the 'Taste of Scotland'. Ideal base for touring, walking, golf, fishing, etc.

Dunmhor House, 67 High Street, Kingussie, Inverness-shire, *PH21 1HX*. Centrally situated for numerous attractions in beautiful scenic Highland village. **Open:** All year **01540 661809 (also fax)** **D:** £16.00–£18.00 **S:** £16.00–£20.00 **Beds:** 2F 2D 1S **Baths:** 2 Sh ☎ 🖭 (5) Ⅵ 🛪 ✕ Ⅵ ⬛ 🎇

All details shown are as supplied by B&B owners in Autumn 2001

Arden House, Newtonmore Road, Kingussie, Inverness-shire, *PH21 1HE*. Excellent food and accommodation, delightful centrally situated Victorian villa. **Open:** All year **Grades:** STB 3 Star GH **01540 661369 (also fax)** Mrs Spry *ardenhouse@compuserve.com* www.ardenhouse. org **D:** £18.00–£22.00 **S:** £18.00–£22.00 **Beds:** 1F 3D 1T **Baths:** 3 En 2 Sh ☎ (1) 🖭 (7) ⅙ Ⅵ 🛪 ✕ Ⅵ ⬛ ♿2 🎇 cc

The Hermitage, Spey Street, Kingussie, Inverness-shire, *PH21 1HN*. Warm Highland welcome in heart of Badenoch and Strathspey. Excellent touring base. **Open:** All year (not Xmas) **Grades:** STB 4 Star **01540 662137** Mr Taylor **Fax: 01540 662177** *thehermitage@clara.net* www.thehermitage-scotland.com **D:** £21.00–£23.00 **S:** £26.00–£28.00 **Beds:** 1F 1T 3D **Baths:** 5 En ☎ 🖭 Ⅵ ✕ Ⅵ ⬛ 🎇 cc

Kinlochbervie

NC2156

Beachview B&B, 165 Drumnaguie, Rhiconich, Lairg, Sutherland, *IV27 4RT*. **Open:** Easter to Oct **01971 521780 (also fax)** Mrs Macdonald **D:** £15.00–£18.00 **S:** £18.00 **Beds:** 1F/T 2D **Baths:** 2 Sh ☎ 🖭 (6) Ⅵ 🛪 ⬛ 🎇 Perfectly situated for exploring the delightful NW Highlands. Clean and comfortable accommodation overlooking sandy beach. Scottish breakfast. Near small fishing village. Ideal for walking, fishing, bird watching, golf, climbing and one mile from the famous Sandwood Bay Road End.

Kinlochleven

NN1861

Edencoille, Garbhien Road, Kinlochleven, Argyll, *PA40 4SE*. Friendly, comfortable B&B. Home cooking our speciality. Family run. **Open:** All year **Grades:** STB 3 Star **01855 831358 (also fax)** Mrs Robertson **D:** £18.00–£22.00 **S:** £26.00–£34.00 **Beds:** 2F 1D 2T **Baths:** 2 Sh 2 En ☎ 🖭 (5) Ⅵ ✕ Ⅵ ❋ 🎇

Hermon, Kinlochleven, Argyll, *PH50 4RA*. Spacious bungalow in village surrounded by hills on West Highland Way. **Open:** Easter to Sept **01855 831383** Miss MacAngus **D:** £16.00–£18.00 **S:** £18.00–£25.00 **Beds:** 1D 2T **Baths:** 1 En 1 Sh ☎ 🖭 (6) Ⅵ 🛪 ⬛ 🎇

Macdonald Hotel and Camp Site,
Fort William Road, Kinlochleven, Argyll,
PH50 4QL. Modern hotel in Highland style on
shore of Loch Leven. Superb views.
Open: Mar to Dec
01855 831539 Mr & Mrs Reece **Fax: 01855
831416** *martin@macdonaldhotel.demon.co.uk*
www.macdonaldhotel.demon.co.uk
D: £24.00–£32.00 **S:** £24.00–£44.00 **Beds:** 1F
4D 5T **Baths:** 10 En ♨ 🅿 (20) 📺 ⼦ 🛏 ✕ 📺 🗐 ⚿ ⚑
cc

Kyle of Lochalsh
NG7627

Kyle Hotel,
*Main Street, Kyle
of Lochalsh,
Ross-shire,
IV40 8AB.*
Open: All year
Grades: STB 3
Star
01599 534204 Fax: 01599 534932
thekylehotel@btinternet.com www.btinternet.
com/~thekylehotel **D:** £25.00–£47.00
S: £25.00–£47.00 **Beds:** 14T 8D 9S **Baths:** 31
En ♨ 🅿 ✕ 📺 ⼦ 🛏 ✕ 📺 🗐 ⚑ **cc**
Nestling in the village of Kyle of Lochalsh
and ideally situated for exploring the Isle of
Skye via the nearby bridge. Kyle Hotel
offers extremely comfortable rooms and a
fine restaurant specialising in fresh local
foods including seafood and game.

A'chomraich,
*Main Street, Kyle
of Lochalsh,
Ross-shire,
IV40 8DA.* Warm
welcome near
amenities.
Quiet, great touring centre. Olde-worlde
charm. **Open:** Easter to Oct **Grades:** STB 2
Star
01599 534210 Mrs Murchison **D:** £15.00–
£17.00 **S:** £20.00 **Beds:** 2D 1T **Baths:** 2 Sh
♨ (3) 🅿 (3) 📺 🛏 📺 ⚑

Ashgrove, *Balmacara Square, Kyle of
Lochalsh, Ross-shire, IV40 8DJ.* Very central
West Highland location for touring and
walking, including hill climbing. **Open:** All
year
01599 566259 Mrs Gordon **D:** £16.50–£20.00
Beds: 2D 1T **Baths:** 2 En 1 Pr ♨ 🅿 (3) 📺 🛏 📺
🗐 ⚑

Tigh-a-Cladach, *Badicaul, Kyle of
Lochalsh, Ross-shire, IV40 8BB.* Between Kyle
of Lochalsh and Plockton with superb views
of Isle of Skye. **Open:** Mar to Nov
01599 534891 (also fax) Mrs Matheson
D: £16.00–£17.50 **S:** £16.00–£17.50 **Beds:** 1T
2D 1S **Baths:** 2 Sh ♨ 🅿 (5) 📺 🛏 🗐 ⚿ ⚑

B&B owners may vary
rates – be sure to check
when booking

Kylesku
NC2233

Newton Lodge, *Kylesku, Lairg,
Sutherland, IV27 4HW.* Highly recommended
hotel overlooking small seal colony.
Open: Easter to Sept **Grades:** STB 4 Star
01971 502070 (also fax) Mr & Mrs Brauer
newtonlge@aol.com **D:** £28.00–£30.00 **Beds:** 3T
4D **Baths:** 7 En 🅿 (10) ⼦ 📺 🛏 ✕ 📺 🗐 ⚑ **cc**

Laggan (Newtonmore)
NN6194

Gaskmore House Hotel, *Laggan,
Newtonmore, Inverness-shire, PH20 1BS.* Set
in heart of the Highlands a wonderful place
just to be. **Open:** Easter to Oct
01528 544250 (also fax) *gaskmorehouse@
aol.com* **D:** £25.00–£45.00 **S:** £30.00–£50.00
Beds: 12T 12D 1S **Baths:** 25 En ♨ 🅿 ⼦ 📺 ✕
📺 🗐 ⚿ ⚑ **cc**

Laid
NC4159

Rowan House, *90 Laid, Loch Eriboll,
Lairg, Sutherland, IV27 4UN.* Set in a
spectacular setting with uninterrupted
views across Loch Eriboll to Ben Hope.
Open: All year
01971 511347 (also fax) Mr MacLellan
h.maclellan@btinternet.com drive.to/laid
D: £15.00–£25.00 **S:** £15.00–£25.00 **Beds:** 1F/
T 2D **Baths:** 3 En ♨ 🅿 (6) 📺 🛏 ✕ 📺 🗐 ⚿ ⚑ ⚑

Laide
NG8992 ⚑ *Sand Hotel*

**Cul Na Mara
Guest House,**
*Catalina
Slipway, Sand
passage, Laide,
Achnasheen,
Ross-shire,
IV22 2ND.* **Open:** All year (not Xmas/New
Year) **Grades:** STB 3 Star
01445 731295 Bill Hart **Fax: 01445 731570**
billhart@dircon.co.uk
www.culnamara-guesthouse.co.uk **D:** £22.00
S: £33.00 **Beds:** 1F 1D **Baths:** 2 En ♨ (5)
🅿 (4) 📺 🛏 ✕ 📺 🗐
A stay at Cul Na Mara (Gaelic - Song of the
Sea) is an enjoyable experience with
superior bed and breakfast
accommodation. Guest rooms fully ensuite
complete with colour television - private
dining room.

Lairg
NC5806 ⚑ *Nip Inn*

Muirness, *97 Lower Toroboll, Lairg,
Sutherland, IV27 4DH.* Comfortable croft
house, superb open views. Central for day
trips, close to railway. **Open:** All year
01549 402489 Mrs Grey **D:** £16.00–£18.00
S: £18.00 **Beds:** 2D 1T **Baths:** 1 Pr 1 Sh ♨ (2)
🅿 ⼦ 📺 ✕ 📺 ⚑

Latheron
ND1933

Tacher, *Latheron, Caithness, KW5 6DX.* On
A895 (Thurso). Modern, comfortable
farmhouse. **Open:** May to Oct
01593 741313 Mrs Falconer www.host.co.uk
D: £16.00–£18.00 **S:** £16.00–£20.00 **Beds:** 1F
1D 1T **Baths:** 1 En 1 Sh 1 Pr ♨ 🅿 (8) ⼦ 📺 🗐
⚑

Lochcarron
NG8939 ⚑ *Rockvilla Hotel, Strath Carron Hotel,
Loch Carron Hotel*

Aultsigh, *Croft
Road,
Lochcarron,
Strathcarron,
Ross-shire,
IV54 8YA.*
Spectacular
views over Loch Carron. Ideal base for
climbing or touring. **Open:** All year
01520 722558 Ms Innes *moyra.innes@
talk21.com* **D:** £16.00–£18.00 **S:** £18.00
Beds: 1F 1D 1T **Baths:** 2 Sh ♨ 🅿 (6) ⼦ 📺 🛏
🗐 ⚿ ⚑

Lochinver
NC0922

Veyatie, *66
Baddidarroch,
Lochinver, Lairg,
Sutherland,
IV27 4LP.*
Peaceful,
relaxing
location. Magnificent mountain views,
walkers paradise. Fantastic breakfasts.
Open: All year (not Xmas) **Grades:** STB 4
Star
01571 844424 (also fax) Mrs Chapman
veyatie@baddid.freeserve.co.uk www.host.co.uk
D: £20.00–£25.00 **S:** £25.00–£38.00 **Beds:** 2D
1T **Baths:** 2 En 1 Pr ♨ (3) ⼦ 📺 🛏 🗐 ⚑

Suilven, *Badnaban, Lochinver, Lairg,
Sutherland, IV27 4LR.* 3 miles from Lochinver,
off Achiltibuie Road. Sea angling available.
Open: All year (not Xmas/New Year)
01571 844358 Mrs Brown **D:** £17.00 **S:** £22.00
Beds: 1T 1D **Baths:** 1 Sh 🅿 (2) 📺 🛏 ✕ 🗐 ⚑

Lochluichart
NH3263

4 Mossford Cottages, *Lochluichart,
Garve, IV232QA.* Spectacular view across
loch. Friendly informal atmosphere. Central
touring position. **Open:** All year (not Xmas/
New Year)
01997 414334 Mr & Mrs Doyle **D:** £15.00–
£18.00 **S:** £15.00–£20.00 **Beds:** 1F 1T 1D 1S
Baths: 2 En 1 Pr 1 Sh ♨ ⼦ 🛏 ✕ 🗐 ⚑ ⚑

Lybster (Wick)

ND2435

Reisgill House, *Lybster, Caithness,*
KW3 6BT. **Open:** All year (not Xmas/New
Year) **Grades:** STB 3 Star
01593 721212 (also fax) Ms Harper *helen@*
reisgill-house.com www.reisgill-house.com
D: £18.00 **S:** £18.00 **Beds:** 1F 2T 2D 1S
Baths: 5 En 1 Pr ⟍ ▣ 🅿 (6) ⌿ ▥ ✕ 🐾 ▣ ▥ ▦ ♨
Our C18th 7-bedroomed house stands in its
own grounds one mile from Lybster. All the
ensuite rooms have a sea view and we pride
ourselves on home-baking and traditional
food, salmon and venison being the two
favourites.

Hamnavoe, *Norland Road, Lybster,*
Caithness, KW3 6AT. **Open:** Easter to Oct
01593 721411 Mrs Barnie *janebarnie@*
hotmail.com **D:** £16.00–£20.00 **S:** £16.00–
£20.00 **Beds:** 1F 1T 1D **Baths:** 1 En 1 Sh ⟍
🅿 (3) ⌿ ▥ ▣ ▦ ♨
Quiet, residential area of small fishing
village. Unwind in our comfortable
bungalow. Lovely scenery overlooking
fields and mountains. Enjoy our lovely
Scottish breakfasts before touring
beautiful, quiet countryside. Golf course,
bowling green and amenities nearby.
Orkney day trip and secluded beaches to
explore.

Mallaig

NM6796   ⚓ *Marine Hotel, West Highland Hotel*

Spring Bank Guest House, *East Bay,*
Mallaig, Inverness-shire, PH41 4QF.
Traditional Highland house, overlooking
harbour and ferry terminals to Skye, Small
Isles, Knoydart. **Open:** All year (not Xmas/
New Year)
01687 462459 (also fax) Mr Smith
j.t.smith0@talk21.com **D:** £16.00–£17.00
S: £16.00–£17.00 **Beds:** 1F 2D 3T 2S
Baths: 3 Sh ⟍ ▣ ▥ 🐾 ✕ ▥ ▦ ♨ cc

Marine Hotel, *Mallaig, Inverness-shire,*
PH41 4PY. **Open:** All year (not Xmas/New
Year) **Grades:** STB 3 Star, AA 2 Star
01687 462217 E Ironside **Fax: 01687 462821**
marinehotel@btinternet.com **D:** £28.00–£32.00
S: £30.00–£36.00 **Beds:** 2F 9T 5D 3S
Baths: 18 En 1 Pr ⟍ ▣ 🅿 (4) ▥ 🐾 ✕ ▥ ▦ ♨ cc
Comfortable family run hotel in the fishing
village of Mallaig, nearest to rail and ferry
terminals. Experience Highland hospitality,
our Scottish cuisine and fresh local
seafood. Ideal base for day trips to Skye and
Inner Hebrides.

Seaview, *Mallaig, Inverness-shire,*
PH41 4QS. Family run. Overlooking harbour,
perfectly situated for ferry, train and bus.
Open: All year (not Xmas/New Year)
Grades: STB 2 Star
01687 462059 C King **Fax: 01687 462768**
seaviewmallaig@talk21.com **D:** £16.00–£18.00
S: £18.00–£20.00 **Beds:** 1F 3T 3D **Baths:** 2
Sh 🅿 ▣ 🐾 ▥ ▦ ♨

Rockcliffe, *East Bay, Mallaig, Inverness-*
shire, PH41 4QF. Quality accommodation
overlooking bay. Trains, ferries and
restaurants very close. **Open:** Easter to Oct
01687 462484 Mrs Henderson **D:** £16.00–
£17.00 **S:** £18.00 **Beds:** 2D 1S **Baths:** 2 Sh
🅿 (2) ⌿ ▥ ▥ ▦ ♨

Mellon Charles

NG8491

Tranquillity, *21 Mellon Charles, Aultbea,*
Achnasheen, Ross-shire, IV22 2JN.
Comfortable house in quiet lochside
location with wonderful mountain views.
Open: All year (not Xmas)
01445 731241 (also fax) Mr & Mrs Bond
D: £20.00 **S:** £20.00–£30.00 **Beds:** 1F 1D 1S
Baths: 2 En 1 Pr ⟍ ▣ 🅿 ⌿ ▥ ✕ ▥ ♨

Melvich

NC8865

Tigh na Clash, *Melvich, Thurso,*
Caithness, KW14 7YJ. Modern building.
Country views. Ideally situated for touring
North Coast. **Open:** Easter to Oct
Grades: STB 3 Star
01641 531262 (also fax) Mrs Ritchie *joan@*
tighnaclash.co.uk www.tighnaclash.co.uk
D: £22.00–£23.00 **S:** £22.00–£23.00 **Beds:** 1F
2T 3D 2S **Baths:** 7 En 1 Pr 🅿 (8) ▥ ▦ ♨ cc

Melvich Hotel, *Melvich, Thurso,*
Caithness, KW14 7YJ. Stunning views. Brew
pubs. 100 malts. Comfortable rooms.
Open: All year (not Xmas/New Year)
Grades: STB 2 Star
01641 531206 Fax: 01641 531347 *melvichtl@*
aol.com www.smoothhound.co.
uk/hotels/melvichh.html **D:** £20.00–£25.00
S: £30.00–£35.00 **Beds:** 4T 6D 4S **Baths:** 14
En ⟍ 🅿 (8) ▥ ✕ ▥ ▦ ♨ cc

Planning a longer stay? Always
ask for any special rates

Morar

NM6793   ⚓ *Arisaig Hotel, Garramore House*

Sunset, *Morar, Mallaig, Inverness-shire,*
PH40 4PA. Family-run guest house, sea views,
Thai food our speciality. **Open:** All year (not
Xmas) **Grades:** STB 2 Star
01687 462259 Mrs Clulow **Fax: 01687 460085**
sunsetgh@aol.com www.sunsetguesthouse.co.
uk **D:** £14.00–£19.00 **S:** £14.00–£19.00
Beds: 1F 1D 1T **Baths:** 1 En 1 Sh ⟍ (2) 🅿 (6)
⌿ ▥ ✕ ▥ ▦ ♨

Glengorm, *Morar, Mallaig, Inverness-*
shire, PH40 4PA. In Morar Village. Silversand
beaches nearby. Ferry to Skye 2 miles.
Open: All year
01687 462165 Mrs Stewart *glengormmorar@*
talk21.com **D:** £15.00–£16.00 **Beds:** 1D 1T
Baths: 1 Sh 🅿 (4) ▥ 🐾 ▥ ▦ ♨

Muir of Ord

NH5250   ⚓ *Priory Hotel*

Blairdhu
Farmhouse,
Muir of Ord,
Ross-shire,
IV6 7RT. Relax in
renovated
farmhouse
surrounded by
superb open
views. **Open:** Easter to Oct
01463 870536 (also fax) Mrs Morrison
donaldmorrison@amserve.net **D:** £15.00–£20.00
S: £20.00 **Beds:** 1F 1D 1S **Baths:** 1 Pr 1 Sh
🅿 (6) ▥ 🐾 ✕ ♿ ♨

Birchgrove, *Arcan, Muir of Ord, Ross-*
shire, IV6 7UL. Comfortable country house in
quiet area. Guest rooms overlooking
garden. **Open:** All year (not Xmas)
01997 433245 Mrs Bell **Fax: 01997 433304**
D: £15.00–£16.50 **S:** £16.00–£17.00 **Beds:** 1F
1D 1T **Baths:** 1 En 1 Sh ⟍ 🅿 (3) ▥ 🐾 ▦ ♨

Hillview Park, *Muir of Ord, Ross-shire,*
IV6 7XS. Rural situation, adjacent to golf
course. Ground floor bungalow.
Open: Easter to Oct
01463 870787 Mrs Peterkin **D:** £17.00–£19.00
S: £18.00–£20.00 **Beds:** 1F 1D 1T **Baths:** 3
En 🅿 (3) ⌿ ▥ ▦ ♨

Muirshearlich

NN1380

Strone Farm, *Muirshearlich, Banavie,*
Fort William, Inverness-shire, PH33 7PB. Rural
setting, panoramic views Ben Nevis,
Caledonian Canal. Traditional food.
Open: Feb to Nov
01397 712773 (also fax) Mrs Cameron
D: £18.00–£20.00 **S:** £23.00–£25.00 **Beds:** 2D
1T 🅿 (3) ▥ ✕ ▥ ▦ ♨

Planning a longer stay? Always ask for any special rates

Munlochy

NH6453

Craigiehowe, *3 Forestry House, Munlochy, Ross-shire, IV8 8NH.* Quiet cul-de-sac near to all services. **Open:** All year (not Xmas)
01463 811402 Mrs Munro **D:** £15.00
S: £16.00–£18.00 **Beds:** 2D ⛄ 🅿 ⅙ 📺 🛆

Nairn

NH8856

Durham House, *4 Academy Street, Nairn, IV12 4RJ.* Elegant Victorian villa near beaches, golf, castles and historic sites. **Open:** All year (not Xmas) **Grades:** STB 3 Star
01667 452345 (also fax) P J Hudson
durhamhouse@nairn34.freeserve.co.uk
www.durhamhouse-nairn.co.uk **D:** £18.00–£22.00 **S:** £16.00–£18.00 **Beds:** 1F 1D 1T 1S
Baths: 2 En 1 Pr 1 Sh ⛄ 🅿 (4) ⅙ 📺 🏠 ✕ 📺 🛆
🛆 cc

Aurora Hotel, *2 Academy Street, Nairn, Inverness-shire, IV12 4RJ.* Close to championship golf courses, beach, harbour and shopping. **Open:** All year
01667 453551 Fax: 01667 456577
aurorahotelnairn@aol.com **D:** £25.00–£35.00
S: £34.50–£39.50 **Beds:** 1F 3T 3D 3S
Baths: 6 En 1 Pr 2 Sh

Redburn, *Queen Street, Nairn, IV12 4AA.* Extremely attractive Victorian villa, quiet location, close to all amenities.
Open: Easter to Oct
01667 452238 & 07747 090167 (M) Mr & Mrs Clucas *clucas@redburnvilla.fsnet.co.uk*
www.host.co.uk **D:** £17.00–£20.00 **S:** £17.00–£20.00 **Beds:** 1D 1T 1S **Baths:** 2 Sh ⛄ 🅿 (4)
⅙ 📺 📺 🛆

Fonthill, *King Street, Nairn, IV12 4NP.* Beautiful detached villa, central location, views on website. **Open:** All year
01667 455996 Mrs O'Grady *fonthill@classicfm.net* www.fonthill-nairn.co.uk
D: £18.00–£22.00 **S:** £18.00–£22.00 **Beds:** 1T 2D **Baths:** 1 En 1 Pr 1 Sh ⛄ 🅿 (6) ⅙ 📺 🏠 ✕ 📺
🛆 ✱ 🛆

Nethy Bridge

NJ0020 *◄ Heatherbraes Hotel*

Aspen Lodge, *Nethy Bridge, Inverness-shire, PH25 3DA.* Warm welcome and memorable breakfast in heart of picturesque village. **Open:** All year (not Xmas) **Grades:** STB 3 Star B&B
01479 821042 Mrs Renton *linda@aspenlodge.fsnet.co.uk* www.nethybridge.com/aspenlodge.htm **D:** £19.50 **S:** £25.00
Beds: 1D 1T **Baths:** 1 En 1 Pr ⅙ 📺 📺 🛆

Newtonmore

NN7199 *◄ Balaval Hotel, Glen Hotel, Braeriach Hotel*

The Pines,
Station Road, Newtonmore, Inverness-shire, PH20 1AR.
Open: All year (not Xmas)
01540 673271 Mr Walker **Fax: 01540 673882**
www.smoothhound.co.uk/hotels/thepines
D: £19.00–£24.00 **S:** £19.00–£24.00 **Beds:** 2D
1T 2S **Baths:** 5 En ⛄ (12) 🅿 (6) ⅙ 📺 🏠 ✕ 📺 🛆
🛆 cc
Enjoy river valley and mountain views from our comfortable Edwardian home in peaceful wooded gardens rich in bird and wildlife. Convenient for Cairngorm and Monadhliath mountains, RSPB reserves, walking, cycling, golf, or touring Badenoch ('Monarch of the Glen Country').

Alder Lodge Guest House, *Glen Road, Newtonmore, Inverness-shire, PH20 1EA.* Beautiful house, quiet situation, 0.25 mile from the shops and hotels. **Open:** All year
01540 673376 Mr Stewart **D:** £15.00 **S:** £15.00
Beds: 2 T 2D **Baths:** 1 Sh ⛄ 🅿 (6) 🏠 ✕ 📺 🛆
🛆

Nigg

NH8071

Nigg Ferry Hotel, *Nigg, Tain, Ross Shire, IV19 1QU.* **Open:** All year (not Xmas/New Year)
01862 851440 (also fax) N F Kimber
D: £25.00 **Beds:** 8F 7T 1D **Baths:** 8 En ⛄ (12)
🅿 (20) 📺 🏠 ✕ 📺 🛆 🛆 cc
Excellent views over water from lounge. Cruise ships are regular visitors in the Firth. Watch the dolphins at play from the lounge. Play golf at discount prices. Bird watching, shooting and fishing all available locally.

Carse of Bayfield, *Nigg, Tain, Ross-shire, IV19 1QW.* Overlooking Cromarty Firth on Pictish Trail. Walking, sandy beaches, golf courses & birdwatching nearby.
Open: All year (not Xmas)
01862 863230 (also fax) Mrs Campbell
D: £16.00–£18.00 **S:** £16.00–£18.00 **Beds:** 1D
1T **Baths:** 1 Sh ⛄ 🅿 (6) ⅙ 📺 🏠 ✕ 📺 🛆

North Kessock

NH6548

The Rowans, *Bogallan, North Kessock, Inverness, Highland, IV1 3XE.* Family-run bungalow, outskirts of Inverness in Black Isle, area of scenic beauty. **Open:** All year (not Xmas/New Year)
01463 731428 Mrs Davidson *ruth.davidson@ntlworld.com* **D:** £15.00–£17.50 **S:** £18.00–£20.00 **Beds:** 3D **Baths:** 2 En 1 Pr ⅙ 📺 🛆

Onich

NN0261

Camus House, *Lochside Lodge, Onich, Fort William, Inverness-shire, PH33 6RY.* Beautiful Victorian country house in outstanding location between Fort William - Glencoe. **Open:** Feb to Nov
01855 821200 Fax: 01855 821 200 *young@camushouse.freeserve.co.uk* **D:** £23.50–£30.00
S: £27.50–£35.00 **Beds:** 2F 2T 3D **Baths:** 6
En 1 Sh ⛄ 🅿 ⅙ 📺 ✕ 📺 🛆 🛆 cc

Plockton

NG8033 *◄ Plockton Hotel, Plockton Inn*

2 Frithard Road, *Plockton, Ross-shire, IV52 8TQ.* Modern, comfortable, 'home from home' accommodation **Open:** All year
01599 544226 (also fax) Mrs Cameron
ewen@frithard.freeserve.co.uk **D:** £15.00–£19.00
S: £15.00–£20.00 **Beds:** 1T 2D ⛄ 📺 🏠 📺 🛆 🛆
🛆

Poolewe

NG8580 *◄ Poolewe Hotel, Pool House Hotel*

Creagan, *Poolewe, Ross-shire, IV22 2LD.* Quiet country house in highland village. Private off-road parking, good breakfasts with home-baking. **Open:** Mar to Oct
01445 781424 (also fax) Mrs MacKenzie
D: £18.00–£20.00 **S:** £25.00 **Beds:** 2D 1T
Baths: 2 En 1 Pr ⛄ 🅿 (4) ⅙ 📺 🏠 🛆 🛆

Corriness Guest House, *Poolewe, Achnasheen, Ross-shire, IV22 2JU.* Cherished Edwardian villa by Inverewe Gardens and Loch Ewe. **Open:** Easter to Oct
01445 781262 Mrs Rowley **Fax: 01445**
781263 D: £23.00–£25.00 **Beds:** 3T 2D
Baths: 5 En 🅿 (10) ⅙ 📺 ✕ 📺 🛆 🛆 🛆 cc

Portgower

ND0013

Bayview BandB, *Portgower, Helmsdale, Sutherland, KW8 6HL.* A C19th cottage perfectly situated on the shore of the Moray Firth. **Open:** All year (not Xmas/New Year)
Grades: STB 2 Star B&B
01431 821679 (also fax) Mr Leitch
www.bayview-helmsdale.org.uk **D:** £15.00
S: £15.00 **Beds:** 2D ⛄ 🅿 (2) 📺 🏠 ✕ 📺 🛆 🛆

Portmahomack

NH9184

Wentworth House, *Tarbatness Road, Portmahomack, Tain, Ross-shire, IV20 1YB.* Historic former manse beside golf course, overlooking Dornoch Firth, home of the bottle-nosed dolphins. **Open:** All year
01862 871897 Mrs Elliott *monicaelliott@wentworth39.demon.co.uk* **D:** £20.00–£22.50
S: £25.00 **Beds:** 3T **Baths:** 1 En 2 Sh 🅿 (6) ⅙
📺 ✕ 🛆

Rhiconich

NC2552 ⚓ *Fisherman's Mission*

Beachview B&B, *165 Drumnaguie, Rhiconich, Lairg, Sutherland, IV27 4RT.* Perfectly situated for exploring the delightful NW Highlands. Clean and comfortable accommodation. **Open:** Easter to Oct
01971 521780 (also fax) Mrs Macdonald **D:** £15.00–£18.00 **S:** £18.00 **Beds:** 1F/T 2D **Baths:** 2 Sh ⛷ 🄟 (6) 🄫 🛏 🕮 ☕

Rogart

NC7303

Benview, *Lower Morness, Rogart, Sutherland, IV28 3XG.* Traditional country farmhouse offering peace and quiet, comfort, good food. **Open:** Easter to Oct
01408 641222 Mrs Corbett **D:** £15.00–£15.50 **S:** £16.00 **Beds:** 1T 1S 2D **Baths:** 2 Sh 🄟 ⤨ 🄫 ✕ 🕮

Rothiemurchus

NH9308

Loiste View, *2 Dell Mhor, Rothiemurchus, Aviemore, Inverness-shire, PH22 1QW.* Aviemore semi-detached bungalow near tennis, canoeing. Ideal for walking **Open:** All year (not Xmas/New Year)
01479 810230 Mrs Bruce **D:** £16.00 **S:** £18.00 **Beds:** 1T 1D **Baths:** 1 Sh 🄟 (2)⤨🄫🛏🄫🕮⚲

Scaniport

NH6239

Ballindar-roch, *Aldourie, Inverness, IV2 6EL.* A warm, friendly country house, set in extensive woodland gardens. **Open:** All year
01463 751348 Mrs Parsons **Fax: 01463 751372** *BandB@ballindarroch.fsnet.co.uk* www.milford.co.uk/go/ballindarroch.html **D:** £20.00–£30.00 **S:** £20.00–£30.00 **Beds:** 1F 1D 1T 1S **Baths:** 1 Pr 2 Sh ⛷🄟(8)🄫🛏🄫🕮 ⚲

Scourie

NC1544

Badcall Stoerview, *Scourie, Lairg, Sutherland, IV27 4TH.* This house overlooks Eddrachilles Bay, the Mountains of Assynt. Badcall Islands. **Open:** May to Oct
01971 502411 (also fax) Mrs MacKay *badcall@supanet.com* **D:** £16.00–£17.00 **S:** £25.00–£30.00 **Beds:** 1F 1D **Baths:** 1 Sh 🄟 (5) 🄟 ✕ 🕮 ☕ ⚲

Minch View, *Scouriemore, Scourie, Lairg, Sutherland, IV27 4TG.* Modern comfortable croft house. Home cooking. Outstanding views and hospitality. **Open:** Easter to Oct
01971 502010 Mrs MacDonald **D:** £18.50 **S:** £18.50 **Beds:** 2D 1T **Baths:** 2 Sh ⛷🄟⤨🄟 🛏✕🄫🕮

Shieldaig (Loch Shieldaig)

NG8153 ⚓ *Applecross Inn, Shieldaig Hotel, Torridon Hotel, Tigh an Eilean Hotel*

Tigh Fada, *117 Doireaonar, Shieldaig, Strathcarron, Ross-shire, IV54 8XH.* Family home on working croft, magnificent scenery. **Open:** Feb to Nov
01520 755248 (also fax) Mrs Calcott **D:** £14.50–£15.50 **S:** £16.00–£18.00 **Beds:** 1F 1D 1T **Baths:** 2 Sh ⛷🄟 (3) 🄟 ✕ 🕮 cc

Smithton

NH7145

3a Resaurie, *Smithton, Inverness, IV2 7NH.* Quiet residential area 3 miles east of Inverness. Public transport nearby. **Open:** All year
01463 791714 Mrs Mansfield *mbmansfield@uk2.net* www.host.co.uk **D:** £17.00–£21.00 **S:** £17.00–£21.00 **Beds:** 2D 1T **Baths:** 1 En 1 Sh ⛷🄟 (3) ⤨🄟 🛏✕🄫🕮 ☕ cc

South Laggan

NN2996

Forest Lodge, *South Laggan, Invergarry, Inverness-shire, PH34 4EA.* Friendly hospitality, pleasant ensuite accommodation, and home cooking in rurally set home. **Open:** All year (not Xmas/New Year) **Grades:** STB 3 Star
01809 501219 Mr & Mrs Shearer **Fax: 01809 501476** *info@flgh.co.uk* www.flgh.co.uk **D:** £17.00–£22.00 **S:** £24.00–£29.00 **Beds:** 2F 2T 3D **Baths:** 6 En 1 Pr ⛷🄟(10)⤨🄟🄫🕮 ☕ cc

Spean Bridge

NN2281

Coinachan Guest House, *Gairlochy Road, Spean Bridge, Inverness-shire, PH34 4EG.* **Open:** All year (not Xmas) **Grades:** STB 4 Star
01397 712417 H C Hoare **Fax: 01397 712528** *coinachan@supanet.com* **D:** £20.00–£25.00 **S:** £20.00–£35.00 **Beds:** 2D 1T **Baths:** 3 En 🄟 🄟✕🄫🕮 ☕ Enjoy a relaxing informal stay in a tastefully modernised C17th Highland home offering a high standard of comfort and attention to detail. Privately situated overlooking mountains and moorland, carefully prepared 4 course dinner. Perfect touring base, special 7 day rates.

Mahaar, *Corrie Choillie Road, Spean Bridge, Inverness-Shire, PH34 4EP.* Ideal base for walking, cycling or touring, good highland hospitality. **Open:** All year **Grades:** STB 3 Star
01397 712365 (also fax) *alan@mahaar.co.uk* www.mahaar.co.uk **D:** £16.50–£18.00 **S:** £17.00–£18.50 **Beds:** 1F 1T 1D 2S **Baths:** 2 Sh ⛷🄟⤨🄟🛏✕🄫🕮 ☕ cc

Dreamweavers, *Earendil, Mucomir, Spean Bridge, PH34 4EQ.* Traditional Scottish hospitality and cuisine amidst stunning Highland scenery. **Open:** All year
01397 712548 H Maclean *helen@dreamweavers.co.uk* www.dreamweavers.co.uk **D:** £15.00–£20.00 **S:** £15.00–£20.00 **Beds:** 1F 1T 1D **Baths:** 1 En 2 Pr ⛷🄟(5)⤨🄟🛏✕🄫🕮 ♨3 ⚲

Distant Hills Guest House, *Spean Bridge, Inverness-shire, PH34 4EU.* Perfectly situated for exploring Highlands. Panoramic views. **Open:** All year
01397 712452 *enquiry@distanthills.com* www.distanthills.com **D:** £20.00–£24.00 **S:** £30.00–£37.00 ⛷🄟(12)⤨🄟🛏✕🄫⚙ ☕ cc

Coire Glas Guest House, *Spean Bridge, Inverness-shire, PH34 4EU.* Spectacular views of Grey Corries. Ideal base for climbing / touring. **Open:** All year (not Xmas)
01397 712272 (also fax) Mr & Mrs Shaw *enquiry@coireglas.co.uk* www.coireglas.co.uk **D:** £14.50–£19.50 **S:** £14.50–£25.00 **Beds:** 2F 4D 4T 1S **Baths:** 8 En 3 Sh ⛷🄟(11)🄟✕🄫 ☕ cc

Stoer

NC0328

Cruachan Guest House, *Stoer, Lochinver, Lairg, Sutherland, IV27 4JE.* Friendly licensed accommodation. Beautiful beaches and mountains nearby. **Open:** Apr to Oct
01571 855303 Miss Gould **D:** £17.50–£20.00 **S:** £17.50–£20.00 **Beds:** 1D 2T 1S **Baths:** 1 Pr 1 Sh ⛷🄟 (4) 🄟🛏✕🄫🕮 ☕ ⚲

Stoer Villa, *Stoer, Lairg, Sutherland, IV27 4JE.* Victorian villa near Atlantic, sandy beaches, hill walkers and anglers paradise. **Open:** All year (not Xmas/New Year)
01571 855305 Mrs Spykers **D:** £15.00–£17.00 **S:** £15.00–£17.00 **Beds:** 1D 1T **Baths:** 1 Sh ⛷🄟 (5) 🄟 🕮

Strathan (Lochinver)

NC0821

Glenview, *Strathan, Lochinver, Lairg, Sutherland, IV27 4LR.* Peaceful location, 100 yards off minor road, easy parking. Home from home. **Open:** Mar to Oct
01571 844324 Mrs Palmer *jand1@nascr.net* **D:** £17.00–£18.00 **S:** £16.00–£20.00 **Beds:** 1T 2D 2S **Baths:** 2 Sh ⛷(14)🄟(6)⤨🄟✕🄫🕮 ⚲

BATHROOMS
En = Ensuite
Pr = Private
Sh = Shared

Strathkanaird
NC1402

Loch Dubh House, *Strathkanaird, Ullapool, Wester Ross, IV26 2TW.* Out of town. Quiet and comfortable. Excellent breakfast. Ideal base **Open:** All year **Grades:** STB 3 Star **01854 666224 Fax:** 0870 0569379 *stay@ lochdubhhouse.co.uk* www.lochdubhhouse.co. uk **D:** £18.00–£28.00 **S:** £20.00–£45.00 **Beds:** 1T 2D **Baths:** 1 En 1 Sh ⊞(4)⊁⊡✕⊡ ✻ ♨

Strathpeffer
NH4858 🍴 *Achilty Hotel, Coul House Hotel.*

Scoraig, *8 Kinnettas Square, Strathpeffer, Ross-shire, IV14 9BD.* Quiet location in Victorian village, ideal base for touring Highlands. **Open:** All year (not Xmas) **Grades:** STB 3 Star **01997 421847** Mrs MacDonald *macdonald@ kinnettas.freeserve.co.uk* **D:** £15.00–£17.00 **S:** £15.00–£20.00 **Beds:** 1F 1D 1T 1S **Baths:** 1 En 1 Sh ⊞⊡(6)⊡⼽⊡⊞♨

Burnhill, *Strathpeffer, Ross-shire, IV14 9DH.* Victorian house situated at entrance on former spa village. Excellent centre for touring. **Open:** Easter to Oct **01997 421292** Mrs Watt *jockwatt@ icscotland.net* **D:** £15.00–£18.00 **S:** £18.00 **Beds:** 1F 1T 1D **Baths:** 1 En 1 Pr ⊞⊡⊁⊡⊡ ♨

Strathy Point
NC8167

Catalina Guest House, *Aultivullin, Strathy Point, Thurso, Caithness, KW14 7RY.* On the far North Coast, private suite for just two. **Open:** All year **01641 541279** J Salisbury **Fax:** 0870 1247960 *petesalisbury@catalina72.freeserve.co.uk* **D:** £17.00–£20.00 **S:** £20.00–£30.00 **Beds:** 1T **Baths:** 1 En ⊡(1)⊁⊡✕⊞♨

Stromeferry
NG8634

Maple Lodge, *Stromeferry, Ross-shire, IV53 8UP.* Detached house in secluded Glen. Mountain views all rooms. **Open:** All year **01599 577276** Mrs McDermott *jim@ maple-lodge.co.uk* www.maple-lodge.co.uk **D:** £16.00–£20.00 **S:** £16.00–£20.00 **Beds:** 1F 1T **Baths:** 1 En 1 Pr ⊞⊡(2)⊡⼽✕⊡⊞♨

Strontian
NM8161

Carm Cottage, *Monument Park, Strontian, Acharacle, Argyll, PH36 4HZ.* Ideal stop for visiting Mull and smaller Isles, plus touring around Ardnamurchan. **Open:** Apr to Oct **01967 402268 & 01967 402112** Mrs Macnaughton **Fax: 01967 402095** **D:** £16.00–£19.00 **Beds:** 3F 1T 2D **Baths:** 1 En 1 Sh ⊞⊡(3)⊡⼽✕⊞♨

Tain (Dornoch Firth)
NH7881 🍴 *Morangie House*

Aldie House, *Tain, Ross-shire, IV19 1LZ.* **Open:** All year **Grades:** STB 4 Star, AA 4 Diamond **01862 893787 (also fax)** *info@ aldiehouse.co.uk* www.aldiehouse.co.uk **D:** £24.00–£26.00 **S:** £32.00 **Beds:** 1F 1T 1D **Baths:** 3 En ⊞⊡⊁⊡⊞♨ ♨ cc Chris and Charles are pleased to invite you to Aldie House. Situated in 6 acres of woods and gardens, providing an ideal setting for relaxation. This oasis of peace and tranquillity is the ideal base for touring the Northern Scottish Highlands.

Golf View Guest House, *13 Knockbreck Road, Tain, Ross-shire, IV19 1BN.* Secluded Victorian house, overlooking Tain golf course and Dornoch Firth. **Open:** Feb to Nov **01862 892856** Mrs Ross **Fax: 01862 892172** *booking@golf-view.co.uk* www.golf-view.co.uk **D:** £20.00–£25.00 **S:** £25.00–£40.00 **Beds:** 1F 1D 3T **Baths:** 3 En 1 Sh ⊞(5)⊡(7)⊁⊡⊡⊞ ♨ cc

National Grid References given are for villages, towns and cities – not for individual houses

Carringtons, *Morangie Road, Tain, Ross-shire, IV19 1PY.* Large Victorian house facing sea. Suitable stopover for Orkney Isles. **Open:** All year (not Xmas) **Grades:** STB 3 Star **01862 892635 (also fax)** Mrs Roberts *mollie1@btinternet.com* www.stelogic. com/carringtons **D:** £16.00–£18.00 **S:** £20.00–£25.00 **Beds:** 2F 1D **Baths:** 2 En ⊞⊡(6)⼽⊡⊞♨

Thurso
ND1168 🍴 *Pentland Hotel, Park Hotel*

3 Ravenshill Road, *Thurso, Caithness, KW14 7PX.* Easy access to rail and ferry, spectacular Highland scenery. Warm welcome assured. **Open:** May to Sept **01847 894801** Mrs Milne **D:** £16.00 **S:** £17.00 **Beds:** 1D 1T **Baths:** 1 Sh ⊞⊁⊡⼽⊡⊞♨

The St Clair Hotel, *Thurso, Caithness, KW14 7AJ.* Town centre, high standard, family run hotel. **Open:** All year **Grades:** STB 2 Star **01847 896481 (also fax)** Mrs Munro *stclairhotel@aol.com* www.stclairhotel.co.uk **D:** £25.00–£30.00 **S:** £25.00–£32.00 **Beds:** 2F 12T 12D 6S **Baths:** 32 En ⊞⊡⼽✕⊡⊞♨ cc

Tomatin
NH8029

Millcroft, *Old Mill Road, Tomatin, Inverness, IV13 7YN.* 1850 modernised crofthouse in quiet village. Ideal base for touring. **Open:** All year **01808 511405** Mrs Leitch *margaret_tomatin@ hotmail.com* **D:** £18.00 **S:** £20.00–£25.00 **Beds:** 1D 1F **Baths:** 1 En 1 Pr ⊞⊡(3)⊡⼽⊡ ⊞

Tongue
NC5956

Strathtongue Old Manse, *Tongue, Lairg, Sutherland, IV27 4XR.* Attractive Victorian Highland manse. Woodland setting. lovely gardens, spectacular views, beautiful beach nearby. **Open:** All year (not Xmas/ New Year) **01847 611252** Mrs MacKay *oldmanse@ strathtongue.freeserve.co.uk* **D:** £19.00–£21.00 **S:** £20.00–£25.00 **Beds:** 2D 1T **Baths:** 1 En 2 Pr ⊞⊡⼽⊡⼽⊞♨

77 Dalcharn, *Tongue, Lairg, Sutherland, IV27 4XU.* Croft cottage set in quiet valley. Families welcome. Phone for brochure. **Open:** All year **Grades:** STB 2 Star **01847 611251** Mrs MacIntosh **D:** £13.00–£15.00 **S:** £15.00 **Beds:** 1F 1D 1T 1S **Baths:** 1 En 1 Sh ⊞⊡(3)⊁⊡✕⊡⊞⚬✻♨

Planning a longer stay? Always ask for any special rates

Tore
NH6052

Fiveways Bed & Breakfast, *Tore, Muir of Ord, Ross-shire, IV6 7RY.* Ideal for touring highlands, dolphin, bird-watching, golf, ample parking. **Open:** All year (not Xmas/New Year) **01463 811408** Mrs MacKenzie **D:** £15.00–£17.00 **S:** £17.00 **Beds:** 1F 1D 1T **Baths:** 1 En 2 Sh ⛄ 🅿 🖵 ⛵ 🔭 📺 🛏 🕳

Ullapool
NH1294

Broombank Bungalow, *Castle Terrace, Ullapool, IV26 2XD.* A warm welcome awaits. Panoramic views over Loch Broom and Summer Isles. **Open:** All year **01854 612247** Mrs Couper *shirley.couper@ tesco.net* **D:** £17.50–£20.00 **Beds:** 1T 2D **Baths:** 3 En 🅿 (3) ⅍ 📺 🔭 🛏 🕳

Westhill
NH7144   🍺 *Tomatin Inn, Cawdor Tavern*

Easter Muckovie Farm House, *Westhill, Inverness, IV2 5BN.* Original farmhouse modernised set in a rural location overlooking Inverness town, Moray Firth. **Open:** All year **01463 791556** J H MacLellan *dot.westhill@ virgin.co.uk* **D:** £18.00–£20.00 **S:** £25.00 **Beds:** 2F **Baths:** 1 En 1 Pr ⛄ 🅿 (5) ⅍ 📺 🔭 ✕ 📺 🕳 🕳

Wick
ND3650

Quayside, *25 Harbour Quay, Wick, Caithness, KW1 5EP.* **Open:** All year **Grades:** STB 2 Star **01955 603229 (also fax)** Mr Turner *quaysidewick@compuserve.com* ourworld.compuserve. com/homepages/quaysidewick **D:** £15.50–£19.50 **S:** £18.00–£28.00 **Beds:** 2F 2D 1T 2S **Baths:** 2 En 2 Sh 🅿 (4) ⅍ 📺 📺 🕳 🕳 We provide comfortable accommodation within a relaxed atmosphere, overlooking a traditional harbour front. For motoring and motorcycle enthusiasts, we provide a warm welcome, secure parking and simple but adequate repair facilities. Advice on daily sightseeing runs is available for all guests.

Wellington Guest House, *41-43 High Street, Wick, Caithness, KW1 4BS.* Perfectly situated in the town centre close to railway station. **Open:** All year **01955 603287 D:** £22.50–£25.00 **S:** £20.00–£25.00 **Beds:** 6T **Baths:** 6 En ⛄ 🅿 (10) 📺 🔭 🕳, **cc**

The Clachan, *South Rd, Wick, Caithness, KW1 5NJ.* Family-run perfect for exploring the North and Orkney Islands. **Open:** All year (not Xmas) **01955 605384** Mrs Bremner *enquiry@ theclachan.co.uk* www.theclachan.co.uk **D:** £20.00–£25.00 **S:** £25.00–£30.00 **Beds:** 2D 1T **Baths:** 3 En ⛄ (12) 🅿 (4) ⅍ 📺 🕳 🕳

Inner Hebrides

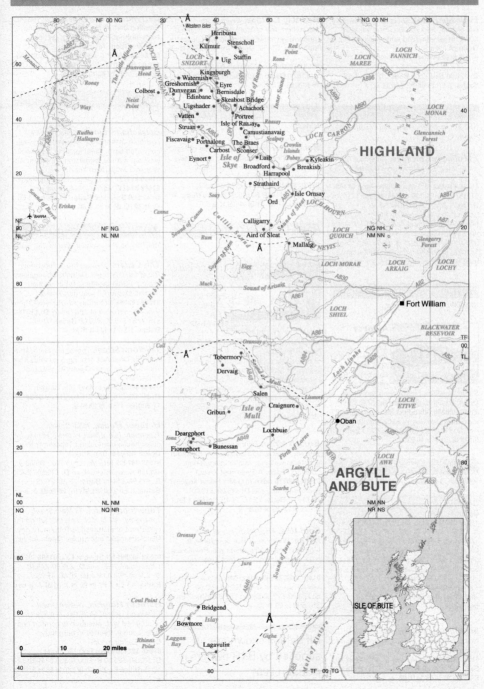

ISLAY Bowmore

NR3159

Lochside Hotel, *Shore Street, Bowmore, Isle of Islay, PA43 7LB.* Excellent value accommodation, food and whisky!
Open: All year
01496 810244 Mrs Birse *birse@lochsidehotel.co.uk* www.lochsidehotel.co.uk
D: £20.00 **S:** £20.00 **Beds:** 1F 1D 1T 5S
Baths: 8 En

ISLAY Bridgend

NR3361 *Bridgend Hotel, Port Charlotte Hotel, Harbour Inn*

2 Mulindry Cottages, *Bridgend, Isle Of Islay, PA44 7PZ.* **Open:** All year **Grades:** STB 3 Star
01496 810397 Mrs Macfarlane **Fax: 01469 810397 D:** £19.00 **S:** £22.00 **Beds:** 1T
Baths: 1 Sh 3
Comfortable accommodation in family home. All on ground floor. Good breakfast provided, quiet scenic area with views to surrounding hills and iron age fort. Ideal location for walking, bird watching and fishing.

MULL Bunessan

NM3821 *Argyll Arms Hotel*

Ardness House, *Tiraghoil, Bunessan, Isle of Mull, PA67 6DU.* Family-run B&B near Iona, Staffa, beaches, outstanding sea views.
Open: Easter to Oct **Grades:** STB 3 Star
01681 700260 (also fax) Messrs MacNeill *ardness@supanet.com* www.isleofmullholidays.com **D:** £18.00–£22.00 **Beds:** 2D 1T **Baths:** 3 En (3)

MULL Craignure

NM7136 *Craignure Inn, Ceildh Place*

Goldings, *Craignure, Isle of Mull, PA65 6AY.*
Open: All year
01680 812427 (also fax) Mr & Mrs Roberts
D: £20.00–£25.00 **S:** £20.00–£25.00 **Beds:** 1T 1D **Baths:** 1 Sh (3)
Comfortable, newly built bungalow in quiet position, overlooking Loch Linnhe and Sound of Mull. 200 yards from buses and main ferry to Oban. You are assured, a warm welcome and relaxing stay. Ideal walking centre. Food, drink and shop nearby.

Inverlussa, *Craignure, Isle of Mull, PA65 6BD.* Warm, spacious, elegant, relaxed home **Open:** Easter to Oct
01680 812436 Mrs Wilson **D:** £18.00–£20.00
S: £18.00–£20.00 **Beds:** 1F 2T 2D **Baths:** 1 En 1 Sh

MULL Deargphort

NM3025

Red Bay Cottage, *Deargphort, Fionnphort, Isle of Mull, PA66 6BP.* Isolated, modernised home with restaurant. Ideal for Mull, Iona, Staffa. **Open:** All year (not New Year)
01681 700396 Mr Wagstaff **D:** £16.50
S: £16.50 **Beds:** 1D 2T **Baths:** 3 Sh (10)

MULL Dervaig

NM4352

Kengharair Farm, *Dervaig, Isle of Mull, PA75 6QR.* Victorian farmhouse on hillside, overlooking glen and river beautiful scenery. **Open:** All year
01688 400251 (also fax) Mrs Caskie
D: £16.00–£17.00 **S:** £16.00–£18.00 **Beds:** 1F 2T **Baths:** 1 Sh (4)

MULL Fionnphort

NM3023

Staffa House, *Fionnphort, Isle of Mull, PA66 6BL.* **Open:** Mar to Oct **Grades:** STB 3 Star
01681 700677 (also fax) D: £20.00–£25.00 **S:** £25.00–£44.00 **Beds:** 2T 1D **Baths:** 3 En (5) cc
Full of antiques and individual touches which set Staffa House apart from similar establishments. 2 minutes walk Iona/Staffa (Fingals Cave) ferries. Conservatory dining room full of floral extravaganza. Ideal for dinner watching Hebridean sunset and views of Iona and Abbey.

Bruach Mhor, *Fionnphort, Isle of Mull, PA66 6BL.* Near Iona/Staffa ferries. Beautiful coastline, walking, wildlife. Vegetarian cooking. **Open:** All year (not Xmas)
01681 700276 (also fax) Mrs Heald *heather@bruachmhor.ndo.co.uk* **D:** £16.00–£18.00
S: £16.00 **Beds:** 1F 1D 1T 1S **Baths:** 1 En 1 Sh (4)

Caol-Ithe, *Fionnphort, Isle of Mull, PA66 6BL.* Warm, spacious bungalow. A highland hospitality awaits you. Private car parking. **Open:** All year (not Xmas/New Year)
01681 700375 (also fax) Mrs Dickson *mary@caol-ithe.demon.co.uk* **D:** £20.00–£22.00
S: £20.00–£22.00 **Beds:** 1T 2D **Baths:** 2 En 1 Sh

All details shown are as supplied by B&B owners in Autumn 2001

MULL Gribun

NM4534

Derryguaig, *Gribun, Isle of Mull, PA68 6EJ.* Situated bottom Ben More overlooking Loch na Keal. Ideal walking, cycling, wildlife. **Open:** All year
01680 300363 R & A MacKenzie **D:** £18.00–£20.00 **S:** £18.00–£20.00 **Beds:** 1T 2D
Baths: 2 Sh (4)

MULL Lochbuie

NM6124

Barrachandroman, *Kinlochspelve, Lochbuie, Isle of Mull, PA62 6AA.* Luxurious converted barn. Rural location, excellent walking, wildlife, birdwatching. **Open:** All year (not Xmas/New Year)
01680 814220 Mrs Railton Edwards **Fax: 01680 814247** *edwards@lochbuie.org.uk*
D: £25.00 **S:** £25.00 **Beds:** 2D **Baths:** 1 En 1 Pr (6)

MULL Tobermory

NM5055 *The Anchorage, Western Isles Hotel*

The Cedars, *Dervaig Road, Tobermory, Isle of Mull, PA75 6PY.* Detached bungalow, separate B&B facilities, set in wooded garden. **Open:** All year (not Xmas)
01688 302096 Mr Bettley *thecedars@talk21.com* www.tobermory.co.uk/thecedars **D:** £15.00–£16.00 **S:** £16.00–£20.00 **Beds:** 1D 1T
Baths: 1 Sh (4)

2 Victoria Street, *Tobermory, Isle of Mull, PA75 6PH.* On-street parking, 5 minutes from shops and harbour. **Open:** All year (not Xmas/New Year)
01688 302263 (also fax) Mrs Harper
D: £14.00–£16.00 **S:** £15.00–£18.00 **Beds:** 1D 1T **Baths:** 1 Sh

Harbour House, *Main Street, Tobermory, Isle of Mull, PA75 6NU.* Family-run guest house overlooking Tobermory Bay.
Open: All year (not Xmas)
01688 302209 Mrs MacLean **Fax: 01688 302750** *harbourhou@aol.com* **D:** £19.50–£22.00
S: £19.50–£44.00 **Beds:** 2F 3D 2T 2S
Baths: 5 En 2 Sh (10) cc

Tobermory Hotel, *53 Main Street, Tobermory, Isle of Mull, PA75 6NT.* Set on the waterfront of picturesque Tobermory Bay. Delicious meals and drinks. **Open:** All year (not Xmas)
01688 302091 Mr Stevens **Fax: 01688 302254** *tobhotel@tinyworld.co.uk* **D:** £35.00–£45.00
S: £39.00–£90.00 **Beds:** 2F 8D 4T 2S
Baths: 15 En 1 Pr cc

Harbour Heights, *Western Road, Tobermory, Isle of Mull, PA75 6PR.* Recently refurbished with attention to comfort and style. Lounge themed in burgundy.
Open: Easter to Oct
01688 302430 (also fax) Mr Stojak
D: £22.50–£25.00 **S:** £25.00–£30.00 **Beds:** 2T 4D **Baths:** 6 En (12) (20)

RAASAY   Isle of Raasay
NG5537

6 Osgaig Park, *Isle of Raasay, Kyle of Lochalsh, Ross-shire, IV40 8PB.* Modern croft house, working croft, overlooking sea to Cuillins of Skye. **Open:** All year
01478 660207 Mrs MacKay *osgaig@lineone.net*
D: £15.50 **S:** £20.00 **Beds:** 1T 1D **Baths:** 1
Sh 🅿 (4) ⚡ 📺 ✕ 🔽 🔟.

SKYE   Achachork
NG4745   🍴 *Royal Hotel, Isles Inn*

Myrtlebank, *Achachork, Portree, Isle of Skye, IV51 9HT.* Modern croft house overlooking Portree. Panoramic view towards Cuillin Mountains. **Open:** May to Aug
01478 612597 (also fax) Mrs Gilmour
skye.gilmour@lineone.net **D:** £16.00 **S:** £16.00
Beds: 2F 1D 1S **Baths:** 2 En 1 Sh 🅿 (5) 📺
🐾 🔽.

Jacamar, *5 Achachork Road, Achacork, Portree, Isle of Skye, IV51 9HT.* Country bungalow overlooks Portree and Cuillins. Excellent cooking Scottish breakfast.
Open: All year
01478 612274 Mrs Thorpe **Fax: 01478 61191**
normal.pat@jacamar.idps.co.uk **D:** £15.00–£19.00 **S:** £15.00–£19.00 **Beds:** 2F 1D 1S
Baths: 2 En 1 Sh 🏠 🅿 ⚡ 📺 ✕ 🔽.

Creag An Fhithich, *10 Achachork, Achachork, Portree, Isle of Skye, IV51 9HT.* Modern farmhouse with panoramic views, situated 2 miles north of Portree.
Open: Easter to Nov
01478 612213 (also fax) Mrs MacDonald
D: £16.50 **S:** £16.50 **Beds:** 1F 1D 1T 1S
Baths: 1 En 2 Sh 🏠 🅿 (6) 📺 🔽 🔟.

SKYE   Aird of Sleat
NG5900

The Old School House, *Aird of Sleat, Ardvasar, Isle of Skye, IV45 8RN.* Old school house idyllically situated, 30 yards shore. Panoramic views of mountains across sea.
Open: Mar to Oct
01471 844218 Mrs Newman
ourworld.compuserve.com/homepages/ChrisBrady/newman.htm
D: £19.50–£24.00 **S:** £19.50–£24.00 **Beds:** 1D 1T 1S **Baths:** 1 Sh 🏠 (12) 🅿 (6) ⚡ 🔟.

BEDROOMS
D = Double
T = Twin
S = Single
F = Family

SKYE   Bernisdale
NG4050

Rubislaw, *34 Bernisdale, Bernisdale, Skeabost Bridge, Portree, Isle of Skye, IV51 9NS.* Warm welcome to Highland hospitality, good food and comfortable accommodation. **Open:** Easter to Sept
01470 532212 (also fax) E M Macdonald
etta@rubislaw.u-net.com **D:** £16.00–£22.00
Beds: 1T 2D **Baths:** 2 En 🅿 (4) ⚡ 🐾 ✕ 🔽 🔟.

SKYE   Breakish
NG6623

Nethallan, *12 Lower Breakish, Breakish, Isle of Skye, IV42 8QA.* **Open:** All year (not Xmas/New Year) **Grades:** STB 4 Star
01471 822771 (also fax) Mrs Hyndman
nethallanskye@aol.com **D:** £20.00–£23.00
S: £25.00–£30.00 **Beds:** 1F 1D **Baths:** 2 En
🏠 🅿 ⚡ 🐾 🔽 🔟. 🔼
Warm, friendly welcome in spacious traditional Skye house. Set in a quiet water's edge location with stunning views and sunsets. Secluded sandy beach nearby. Local wildlife including otters, seals and many birds. Ideal touring/walking base. Every room faces the sea.

Ashfield, *Breakish, Isle of Skye, IV42 9PY.* Comfortable accommodation, overlooking sea and mountains. Short walk to beach.
Open: Easter to Oct **Grades:** STB 3 Star
01471 822301 Mrs Clarke **D:** £16.00–£20.00
S: £18.00–£20.00 **Beds:** 2D **Baths:** 1 En 1 Sh ⚡ 📺 🔽 🔟.

Hazelwood, *5 Lower Breakish, Breakish, Isle of Skye, IV42 8QA.* Peaceful location near sandy beach. Beautiful spot with beautiful views. **Open:** Easter to Oct
01471 822431 Mrs Munro **D:** £14.00–£17.00
S: £20.00 **Beds:** 1F 1T 1D **Baths:** 1 Sh 🏠 🅿 ⚡ 📺 🐾 🔽.

SKYE   Broadford
NG6423

Millbrae House, *Broadford, Isle of Skye, IV49 9AE.* **Open:** Feb to Nov
01471 822310 (also fax) P & V Tordoff
D: £16.00–£22.00 **S:** £16.00–£23.00 **Beds:** 2D 1T 1S **Baths:** 3 Pr 1 Sh ⚡ 📺 🔽 🔟. 🔼
A refurbished croft house looking to the sea and hills. Bedrooms have private facilities with tea/coffee trays. Non-smoking. Antiques. Many foreign languages spoken. Packed lunches. Help with walking/driving tours gladly given. Very friendly.

Tigh Na Mara, *Lower Harrapool, Broadford, Isle of Skye, IV49 9AQ.* **Open:** May to Oct **Grades:** STB 2 Star
01471 822475 Mrs Scott *jackieconder@talk21.com* www.host.co.uk **D:** £16.00–£18.00
Beds: 1F **Baths:** 1 Pr 🏠 (1) 🅿 ⚡ 🔟. 🔼
150-year-old traditional croft house in quiet position a few yards from the sea. Varied wildlife. Family room comprising double and single bed plus good sized bunks. Private sitting and bathrooms. French and Italian spoken. TV and toys. Restaurants nearby.

Ashgrove, *11 Black Park, Broadford, Isle of Skye, IV49 9DE.* **Open:** All year **Grades:** STB 3 Star
01471 822327 (also fax) Mrs Fletcher *ian.fletcher4@btinternet.com* www.isleofskye.net/ashgrove
D: £18.00–£20.00 **Beds:** 2D 1T **Baths:** 2 En 1 Pr 🅿 (4) 📺 🐾 🔟. 🔼
Comfortable accommodation in bungalow situated within walking distance of hotels and restaurant and other amenities. A warm welcome and a full Scottish breakfast.

National Grid References given are for villages, towns and cities – not for individual houses

The Sheiling, *2 Lower Harrapool, Broadford, Isle of Skye, IV49 9AQ.* **Open:** All year (not Xmas)
01471 822533 Mr & Mrs Shearer **D:** £14.00–£20.00 **S:** £14.00–£25.00 **Beds:** 1F 1T 1D 1S **Baths:** 1 En 1 Sh ⭐ 🖺 🏧 🕅 📺 �🖩 ⚲
A lovely old traditional Skye house where a friendly Scottish welcome and a good breakfast is always assured. An ideal base for touring Skye, close to Broadford village. The area has beautiful views over Broadford bay to the mountains beyond.

Caberfeidh, *1 Lower Harrapool, Broadford, Isle of Skye, IV49 9AQ.* Modern bungalow with spectacular views. Sea shore location. Warm welcome assured. **Open:** All year (not Xmas/New Year) **Grades:** STB 3 Star
01471 822664 Mrs MacKenzie **D:** £20.00–£23.00 **Beds:** 3D **Baths:** 3 En 🖺 (4) 🗲 🕅 🕇 📺 �🖩 ⚲

SKYE   Camustianavaig
NG5139

An Airigh Shamradh, *1/2 of 8 Camustianavaig, Camustianavaig, Portree, Isle of Skye, IV51 9LQ.* Outstanding sea views over Camustianavaig Bay to the Cuillin Hills. **Open:** All year
01478 650224 (also fax) Mrs Smith **D:** £20.00 **Beds:** 1T 1D **Baths:** 2 En 🖺 (4) 📺 �🖩 ⚲

SKYE   Dunvegan
NG2547   🍴 Stein Inn, Dunvegan Hotel Bar,

An Cala, *1 Colbost, Dunvegan, Isle of Skye, IV55 8ZT.* Modern bungalow overlooking Loch Dunvegan. Lavish breakfast is our speciality. **Open:** All year (not Xmas)
01470 511393 Mrs Bohndorf *B&B@ ancala.co.uk* www.ancala.co.uk **D:** £18.00–£19.00 **S:** £21.50 **Beds:** 1T **Baths:** 1 Pr ⭐ 🖺 📺 🕇 🕅 �🖩

6 Altavaid, *Harlosh, Dunvegan, Isle of Skye, IV55 8WA.* Modern house, small garden, open countryside. Loch Bracadale, MacLeods Tables, Dunvegan Castle. **Open:** Easter to Oct
01470 521704 Mrs Ewbank **D:** £18.00–£20.00 **S:** £18.00–£20.00 **Beds:** 1F 1T **Baths:** 2 En 🖺 (2) 📺 🕅 ⍰ ⚲

RATES
D = Price range per person sharing in a double or twin room
S = Price range for a single room

BATHROOMS
En = Ensuite
Pr = Private
Sh = Shared

SKYE   Edinbane
NG3451   🍴 Edinbane Hotel, Stein Inn, Skeaboat Lodge

Shorefield House, *Edinbane, Portree, Isle of Skye, IV51 9PW.* Peaceful lochside village. Ideal for touring, quality accommodation and food. **Open:** All year **Grades:** STB 4 Star, AA 4 Diamond, RAC 4 Diamond, Sparkling
01470 582444 Mrs Prall **Fax: 01470 582414** *shorefieldhouse@aol.com* www.shorefield.com **D:** £24.00–£30.00 **S:** £26.00–£32.00 **Beds:** 2F 1T 1D 1S **Baths:** 5 En ⭐ 🖺 (5) 🗲 🕅 📺 ⍰ ⚲ 1 ⚲ cc

SKYE   Eynort
NG3826

The Blue Lobster, *Glen Eynort, Isle of Skye, IV47 8SG.* Walkers haven: Secluded, relaxed, in forest, by sea-loch and eagles! **Open:** All year
01478 640320 Mr Van der Vliet *bluelobster_grula@yahoo.com* **D:** £18.00 **S:** £23.00 **Beds:** 1D 2T ⭐ 🖺 (4) 🕅 🕇 ✗ 📺 ⍰

SKYE   Eyre
NG4153

Cruinn Bheinn, *4 Eyre, Snizort, Portree, Isle of Skye, IV51 9XB.* Large modern crofthouse situated ten minutes' drive from Portree. We offer true Highland hospitality. **Open:** Easter to Oct
01470 532459 Mrs Gordon **D:** £17.00–£22.00 **Beds:** 2D 1T **Baths:** 3 En ⭐ 🖺 (3) 🗲 📺 ⍰ ⚲

All details shown are as supplied by B&B owners in Autumn 2001

BEDROOMS
D = Double
T = Twin
S = Single
F = Family

SKYE   Fiscavaig
NG3334

Ivanhoe, *19 Fiscavaig, Fiscavaig, Carbost, Isle of Skye, IV47 8SN.* **Open:** All year (not Xmas/New Year) **Grades:** STB 2 Star
01478 640360 P Wood **D:** £16.00–£18.00 **S:** £16.00–£18.00 **Beds:** 1T 1D **Baths:** 1 En 1 Sh ⭐ 🖺 (4) 📺 🕇 ⍰ ⚲
Modern bungalow in peaceful surroundings, situated above Fiscavaig Bay. Spectacular view over Loch Bracadale to 'Macleods Tables' in background. Ideal for exploring Skye, four miles from world famous 'Talisker Distillery'. Suitable for walkers and climbers, warm welcome awaits you.

SKYE   Greshornish
NG3454

Greshornish House Hotel, *Greshornish, Portree, Isle of Skye, IV51 9PN.* At the Isle of Skye B&B, pipers lead you into dinner **Open:** All year **Grades:** STB 3 Star
01470 582266 C & J Dickson **Fax: 01470 582345** *jane@greshornishhotel.co.uk* www.greshornishhotel.co.uk **D:** £25.00–£60.00 **S:** £55.00–£75.00 **Beds:** 2F 2T 4D **Baths:** 8 En ⭐ 🖺 (20) 📺 🕇 ✗ 📺 ⍰ ⚲ cc

SKYE   Heribusta
NG4070

1 Heribusta, *Kilmuir, Portree, Isle of Skye, IV51 9YX.* Panoramic sea views towards Outer Hebrides. Peaceful rural community, unrestricted views over unspoilt countryside. **Open:** Easter to Sept
01470 552341 Mrs Beaton *alanbeaton@ yahoo.com* **D:** £13.00–£15.00 **S:** £14.00–£15.00 **Beds:** 2D 2S **Baths:** 2 Sh ⭐ 🖺 📺 🕇 ⍰ ⚲

SKYE   Isle Ornsay
NG6912   🍴 Isle Ornsay Hotel

6 Duisdale Beag, *Isle Ornsay, Isle of Skye, IV43 8QU.* Beautiful, peaceful location just 10 minutes walk to pubs and restaurants. **Open:** All year (not Xmas/New Year) **Grades:** STB 3 Star
01471 833230 MacDonald *macdonald@ coillechalltainn.idps.co.uk* **D:** £19.00 **S:** £19.00–£24.00 **Beds:** 1T 2D **Baths:** 3 En 🖺 (4) 🗲 📺 🕅 ⍰ ⚲

SKYE   Kilmuir (Uig)
NG3870

Whitewave - Skye's Outdoor Centre, *19 Lincro, Kilmuir, Portree, Isle of Skye, IV51 9YN.* Imagine a cross between an outdoor centre, an inn, and a ceilidh place. **Open:** All year
01470 542414 (also fax) J White *info@ white-wave.co.uk* www.white-wave.co.uk
D: £16.00 **S:** £16.00 **Beds:** 4F **Baths:** 1 En 2 Sh ⏰ 🅿 (8) ⅏ 🛏 ✕ ▦ 🐾 cc

SKYE   Kingsburgh
NG3955

Iulan Dubh, *12 Kingsburgh, Kingsburgh, Snizort, Portree, Isle of Skye, IV51 9UT.* Panoramic views of Loch Snizort and Cuillins. **Open:** Apr to Sept
01470 532293 Mrs MacLean *r.campbell@ iodhlann.fsnet.co.uk* **D:** £17.00 **S:** £17.00
Beds: 1D **Baths:** 1 En ⏰ 🅿 (3) ▦ 🛏 🐾

SKYE   Kyleakin
NG7526   🍽 *Crofters' Kitchen*

White Heather Hotel, *Kyleakin, Isle of Skye, IV41 8PL.* **Open:** Mar to Oct
Grades: STB 3 Star
01599 534577 Fax: 01599 534427 *ian@ whiteheatherhotel.co.uk*
www.whiteheatherhotel.co.uk **D:** £20.00–£28.00 **Beds:** 1F 3T 4D **Baths:** 8 En ⏰ 🅿 ▦ ▦ 🐾 cc
Beautifully situated overlooking the sea and mountains, the hotel is an ideal base for visiting Skye, Lochalsh and Plockton. Visitors Centre next door. Otter spotting, seal cruises, castle walk. Large Scottish breakfast. Central for all road, rail and bus routes.

Blairdhu House, *Kyle Farm Rd, Kyleakin, Isle of Skye, IV41 8PR.* Beautifully situated house with panoramic views. Excellent spot for bird watching. **Open:** All year
01599 534760 Mrs Scott **Fax: 01599 534623** *blairdhuskye@compuserve.com* ourworld.compuserve. com/homepages/blairdhuskye **D:** £20.00
Beds: 1F 1D 1T **Baths:** 3 En ⏰ 🅿 (6) ⅏ ▦ ▦ 🐾 🐾 cc

West Haven, *Kyleakin, Isle of Skye, IV41 8PH.* Friendly family guest house. Nearby sea, river, mountains. Ideal walking, castles, wildlife. **Open:** Easter to Oct
01599 534476 Mrs MacAskill **D:** £18.00
S: £18.00–£18.20 **Beds:** 1D 1T 1S **Baths:** 3 En 🅿 (6) ▦ 🛏 ▦ ▦ 🐾

SKYE   Luib
NG5627

Luib House, *Luib, Broadford, Isle of Skye, IV49 9AN.* Our home is your home - and make full use of the guest lounge. **Open:** All year
01471 822724 Mrs Dobson **D:** £18.00–£19.00
S: £25.00 **Beds:** 2D 1T **Baths:** 2 En 1 Pr ⏰ 🅿 ▦ 🛏 ▦ 🐾

SKYE   Portree
NG4843   🍽 *Portree House, Isles Inn*

Half of Two, *Lower Ollach, Braes, Portree, Isle of Skye, IV51 9LJ.* **Open:** Easter to Sept
01478 650301 Mrs Scott *jan.scott@amserve.net*
D: £20.00–£22.00 **S:** £22.00–£24.00 **Beds:** 1D
Baths: 1 En 🅿 (1) ⅏ ▦ 🛏 ▦ 🐾
Welcome to our pretty little Skye crofter's cottage. Beautifully renovated in a timeless country style, to provide a high standard of warmth and comfort for our two guests, who can enjoy their own sitting room overlooking our beautiful quiet and peaceful garden with wonderful sea views.

Cnoc Iain, *3 Sluggans, Portree, Isle of Skye, IV51 9EQ.* Modern home with friendly atmosphere; good Scottish breakfast, panoramic views.
Open: Mar to Oct
01478 612143 Mrs MacSween *cnociain@ tinyworld.co.uk* www.cnociain.com **D:** £20.00–£25.00 **S:** £30.00–£42.00 **Beds:** 2D 1T
Baths: 3 En ⏰ 🅿 (3) ▦ 🛏 ▦ 🐾

Easdale Bridge Road, *Portree, Isle of Skye, IV51 9ER.* Centrally situated bungalow with view of Cuillins and warm welcome.
Open: All year
01478 613244 & 07769 922261 (M)
Mrs Macdonald **D:** £20.00–£25.00 **S:** £25.00–£30.00 **Beds:** 2D **Baths:** 2 En ⏰ 🅿 (2) ▦ ▦ 🐾

Brenitote, *9 Martin Crescent, Portree,.Isle of Skye, IV51 9DW.* Centrally situated for viewing the beautiful scenery of Skye, Dunvegan Castle and museums. **Open:** All year **Grades:** STB 3 Star
01478 612808 Mrs Matheson **D:** £16.00–£18.00 **Beds:** 1T 1D **Baths:** 2 En 🅿 ▦ ▦ ▦ 🐾

An Traigh, *3 Heatherfield, Portree, Isle of Skye, IV51 9NE.* Seaside location, splendid views. 3 miles from town. Full breakfast. **Open:** Easter to Oct **Grades:** STB 3 Star
01478 613236 Mrs McLeod *an_traigh@ yahoo.co.uk* **D:** £18.00–£20.00 **S:** £18.00–£22.00 **Beds:** 1T 1D 1S **Baths:** 2 En 1 Pr 🅿 (4) ⅏ ▦ 🛏 ▦ 🐾

Myrtlebank, *Achachork, Portree, Isle of Skye, IV51 9HT.* Modern croft house overlooking Portree. Panoramic view towards Cuillin Mountains. **Open:** May to Aug
01478 612597 (also fax) Mrs Gilmour *skye.gilmour@lineone.net* **D:** £16.00 **S:** £16.00 **Beds:** 2F 1D 1S **Baths:** 2 En 1 Sh ⏰ 🅿 (5) ▦ 🛏 ▦ 🐾

25 Urquart Place, *Portree, Isle of Skye, IV51 9HJ.* Warm welcome, excellent accommodation and breakfasts. Special off-season deals available. **Open:** All year **Grades:** STB 3 Star
01478 612374 Mrs Macdonald *elizabethmacdonald@talk21.com* **D:** £15.00–£20.00 **S:** £15.00–£20.00 **Beds:** 1F 1D 1S **Baths:** 1 En 1 Sh ⏰ 🅿 (2) ⅏ ▦ 🛏 ▦ 🐾

Jacamar, *5 Achachork Road, Achacork, Portree, Isle of Skye, IV51 9HT.* Country bungalow overlooks Portree and Cuillins. Excellent cooking Scottish breakfast.
Open: All year
01478 612274 Mrs Thorpe **Fax: 01478 61191** *normal.pat@jacamar.idps.co.uk* **D:** £15.00–£19.00 **S:** £15.00–£19.00 **Beds:** 2F 1D 1S **Baths:** 2 En 1 Sh ⏰ 🅿 ⅏ ▦ ✕ ▦ ▦ 🐾

12 Fraser Crescent, *Portree, Isle of Skye, IV51 9PH.* Family-run bed & breakfast, offering clean, comfortable accommodation, 5 mins from bus.
Open: Apr to Oct
01478 612529 Mr Speed **D:** £19.00–£20.00
S: £19.00–£20.00 **Beds:** 1T 1D **Baths:** 1 Pr 🅿 (2) ▦ 🛏 ▦ ▦ 🐾

National Grid References given are for villages, towns and cities – not for individual houses

12 Stormyhill Road, *Portree, Isle of Skye, IV51 9DY.* Centrally located in Portree village, within five minutes walking distance to shop, restaurants. **Open:** All year
01478 613165 Mrs Nicolson *audrey-nicolson3@ yahoo.co.uk* **D:** £17.50–£20.00 **S:** £20.00– £25.00 **Beds:** 1F 1T 2D **Baths:** 1 Pr 1 Sh ⅌ ⓟ (3) ⅌ ⓣⱴ ▥ ⚓

SKYE   Sconser
NG5131   ⬛ *Sligachan Hotel*

Old Schoolhouse, *Sconser, Isle of Skye, IV48 8TD.* **Open:** All year (not Xmas/New Year)
01478 650313 Mr & Mrs MacLeod *mcld@ aol.com* **D:** £13.00–£16.00 **Beds:** 1F 1T 1D **Baths:** 2 Sh ⅌ ⓣⱴ ▥ ⚓
A warm friendly welcome waits you from a Gaelic-speaking family. On a working croft nestling at the foot of the Red Cuillin with magnificent frontal views overlooking Loch Sligachan, this is an ideal base for walking, touring Skye.

SKYE   Skeabost Bridge
NG4148

Ardenlea, *Skeabost Bridge, Portree, Isle of Skye, IV51 9PB.* Ideal for touring Skye and Western Isles, warm welcome assured. **Open:** All year
01470 532270 Mrs Macinnes **D:** £15.00 **S:** £20.00 **Beds:** 1T 2D **Baths:** 2 Sh ⅌ (10) ⓟ (8) ⓣⱴ ▥ ⚓

SKYE   Staffin
NG4867

Gracelands, *5 Glasphein, Staffin, Portree, Isle of Skye, IV51 9LZ.* Fantastic sea and hill views. Boat/ fishing trips. Hill walking. **Open:** Apr to Nov
01470 562313 Mrs Nicolson **D:** £16.00– £18.00 **S:** £18.00 **Beds:** 1F 2D 1T 1S **Baths:** 2 Sh ⅌ (4) ⓟ (3) ⓣⱴ ▥ ⚓

SKYE   Stenscholl
NG4868

Quiraing Lodge, *Stenscholl, Staffin, Portree, Isle of Skye, IV51 9JS.* **Open:** All year
01470 562330
Mr Gardener *sam@quiraing-lodge.co.uk* www.quiraing-lodge.co.uk **D:** £22.00 **S:** £22.00 **Beds:** 2F 3T 1D 1S **Baths:** 3 Sh ⅌ ⓟ (10) ⅌ ✕ ⓥ ▥ ⚓
Spacious home, full of art, beautifully situated on Staffin Bay. Large walled garden leading to the sea. Our own home-made bread; and organic, locally grown produce whenever possible. Arts and Crafts workshops (programme available); cameras and bicycles for hire.

SKYE   Strathaird
NG5317   ⬛ *The Hayloft*

Strathaird House, *Strathaird, Broadford, Isle of Skye, IV49 9AX.* **Open:** Easter to Sept
01471 866269 & 01444 452990 (o/s)
Mr Kubale **Fax:** 01471 866320
straithairdhouse.@skye.co.uk
www.straithairdhouse.skye.co.uk **D:** £25.00– £30.00 **S:** £25.00–£30.00 **Beds:** 4F 1D 2S **Baths:** 1 En 1 Pr 3 Sh ⅌ ⓟ (6) ⅌ ▥ ⚓ cc
Family-run guest house above Kilmarie Bay on the Elgol Road. Ideal for walks to Camasunary Bay, Blaven, the Cuillins, seashore exploring and boat trips to Loch Coruisk. Rambling house with glorious views. Guests sitting room, library by the fireside

SKYE   Struan
NG3438   ⬛ *Ullinish Hotel, Harlosh Hotel, Old Inn, Taigh Ailean Hotel, Atholl House*

Ard-Bhealaidh, *Balgown, Struan, Isle of Skye, IV56 8FA.* Scenic lochside view, and a warm Highland welcome, await all who stay. **Open:** Easter to Oct **Grades:** STB 3 Star
01470 572334 (also fax) Mr MacKay *ard-bhealaidh@uk-bedandbreakfasts.com* **D:** £16.00–£18.00 **S:** £16.00–£18.00 **Beds:** 1F 1D 1S **Baths:** 1 En 1 Sh ⅌ ⓟ (5) ⓣⱴ ✕ ⚓

The Anchorage, *9 Eabost West, Struan, Isle of Skye, IV56 8FE.* Modern comfortable bungalow with panoramic sea and mountain views. **Open:** All year
01470 572206 Mrs Campbell *eabost@aol.com* www.host.co.uk **D:** £18.00–£20.00 **S:** £20.00 **Beds:** 2D 1T **Baths:** 2 En 1 Pr ⓟ (3) ⓣⱴ ✕ ⓥ ▥ ⚓ cc

Glenside, *4 Totarder , Struan, Isle of Skye, IV56 8FW.* Situated on working croft in lovely valley. Warm welcome assured. **Open:** Easter to Oct
01470 572253 Mrs MacCusbic **D:** £17.00– £20.00 **S:** £20.00–£22.00 **Beds:** 1D 1T **Baths:** 1 En 1 Pr ⅌ (12) ⓟ (3) ⅌ ⓥ

SKYE   The Braes
NG5234

Tianavaig, *Camustianavaig, The Braes, Portree, Isle of Skye, IV51 9LQ.* A pretty rural seashore location magnificent sea and mountain views. **Open:** All year (not Xmas)
01478 650325 Mrs Corry www.host.co.uk **D:** £17.50–£20.00 **S:** £17.50–£20.00 **Beds:** 2D **Baths:** 1 En 1 Pr ⅌ ⓟ (2) ⅌ ⓣⱴ ✕ ▥ ⚓

SKYE   Uig (Uig Bay)
NG3963

Ferry Inn Hotel, *Uig, Portree, Isle of Skye, IV51 9XP.* Family run hotel, close ferry terminal. Good food. Pets welcome. **Open:** All year
01470 542246 **Fax:** 01470 542377 **D:** £25.00– £30.00 **S:** £28.00–£35.00 **Beds:** 1F 2T 2D 1S **Baths:** 6 En ⅌ ⓟ (25) ⓣⱴ ✕ ⓥ ▥ ⚓ cc

SKYE   Uigshader
NG4346

Torwood, *1 Peiness, Uigshader, Portree, Isle of Skye, IV51 9LW.* Modern home offering warm, comfortable accommodation, in countryside yet only 10 mins from Portree. **Open:** Easter to Oct
01470 532479 Mrs Gillies *anne@selma.co.uk* **D:** £16.00–£20.00 **Beds:** 1F 1D 1T **Baths:** 2 En 1 Pr ⅌ (1) ⓟ (4) ⅌ ⓣⱴ ▥ ⚓

SKYE   Vatten
NG2843

Sea View, *3 Herebost, Vatten, Dunvegan, Isle of Skye, IV55 8GZ.* Modern bungalow with sea views, near the famous Dunvegan castle. **Open:** Easter to Oct
01470 521705 Mrs Campbell **D:** £16.00– £17.50 **Beds:** 1D 1T **Baths:** 1 En 1 Pr ⓟ (2) ⅌ ⓣⱴ ▥ ⚓

SKYE   Waternish
NG2658

Lusta Cottage, *11-12 Lochbay, Waternish, Isle of Skye, IV55 8GD.* Modern cottage set in 18 acre croft with waterfalls to shore of Loch Bay. **Open:** May to Oct
01470 592263 Mrs Smith *lustacottage@ supanet.com* www.isleofskyelustabandb.co.uk **D:** £20.00 **S:** £20.00 **Beds:** 1D 1T **Baths:** 1 En 1 Pr ⓟ (8) ⅌ ⓣⱴ ▥ ⚓

Lanarkshire

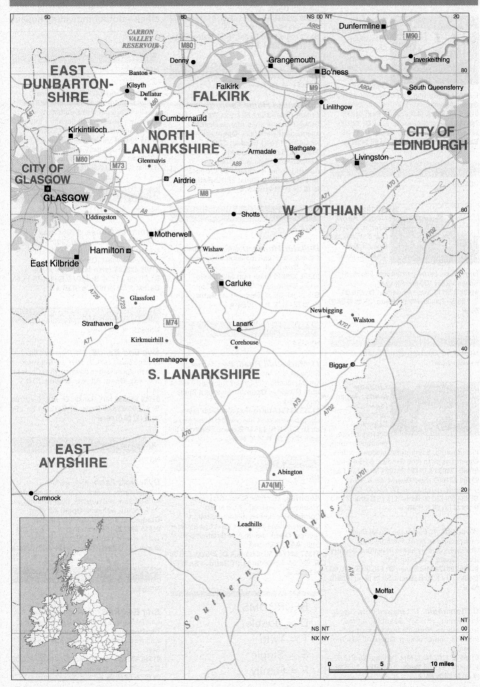

Airdrie

NS7665   🍺 *The Exchange*

Rosslee Guest House, *107 Forrest Street, Airdrie, Lanarkshire, ML6 7AR.* Central situation for Glasgow, Edinburgh, Stirling and Lanarkshire areas. **Open:** All year
01236 765865 A McFadzean **Fax: 01236 748535** *alanrgh@blueyonder.co.uk* **D:** £20.00–£25.00 **S:** £20.00–£30.00 **Beds:** 1F 3T 2S **Baths:** 4 En 2 Pr ⏤ (1) 🅿 (8) 📺 🍴 🛏 🖼 ♨

Banton

NS7579

Auchenrivoch Farm, *Banton, Kilsyth, Glasgow, G65 0OZ.* Beautifully situated, south facing farmhouse. Large garden and views of Kelvin Valley. **Open:** All year
01236 822113 Mrs Henderson **D:** £18.00–£21.00 **S:** £20.00–£22.00 **Beds:** 2T ⏤ 🅿 📺 📺 🖼 ♨

Biggar

NT0437   🍺 *Tinto Hotel, Elphinstone Hotel, Wyndales Hotel*

Lindsaylands, *Biggar, Lanarkshire, ML12 6EQ.* Beautiful country house, peaceful setting, local touring, Edinburgh/Glasgow borders. **Open:** Easter to Nov **Grades:** STB 4 Star
01899 220033 & 01899 221221 Mrs Stott **Fax: 01899 221009** *elspeth@lindsaylands.co.uk* www.lindsaylands.co.uk **D:** £24.00–£28.00 **S:** £28.00–£30.00 **Beds:** 2D 1T **Baths:** 2 En 1 Pr ⏤ 🅿 (8) 📺 🛏 × 📺 🖼 ♨

Woodgill, *12 Edinburgh Road, Biggar, Lanarkshire, ML12 6AX.* Friendly and welcoming family home in historic country town. **Open:** Easter to Oct
01899 220324 Mrs Brown **D:** £18.00 **S:** £20.00 **Beds:** 1D 1T 1S **Baths:** 1 Sh ⏤ 🅿 (4) ⠇ 📺 📺 🖼 ♨

Cultershogle, *12 Langvout Gate, Biggar, Lanarkshire, ML12 6UF.* Beautiful outlook from very comfortable bungalow; quiet location, home cooking. **Open:** All year (not Xmas)
01899 221702 Mr & Mrs Tennant **D:** £18.00–£19.00 **S:** £20.00 **Beds:** 2T **Baths:** 2 En ⏤ 🅿 (3) ⠇ 📺 🍴 🖼 ♨

Cormiston Cottage, *Cormiston Road, Biggar, ML12 6NS.* Delightful country cottage with beautiful views over the fields and hills beyond. **Open:** All year
01899 220 200 Mrs Wales **Fax: 0131 440 0272** *jwales4453@aol.com* **D:** £20.00–£25.00 **S:** £25.00–£30.00 **Beds:** 1F 1T **Baths:** 1 En ⏤ (3) 🅿 (2) 📺 × 📺 🖼 ♨ ♨

Corehouse

NS8841   🍺 *The Tavern*

Corehouse Home Farm, *Corehouse, Lanark, Lanarkshire, ML11 9TQ.* Working farm. Ground floor ensuite rooms. Near to spectacular waterfalls. **Open:** All year (not Xmas/New Year) **Grades:** STB 3 Star
01550 661377 (also fax) Mrs Hamilton *corehouse@thegallop.com* thegallop.com/corehouse **D:** £20.00–£22.00 **S:** £24.00–£26.00 **Beds:** 2F 1D **Baths:** 3 En ⏤ 🅿 (6) ⠇ 📺 🍴 📺 🖼 ♨

Dullatur

NS7476

Dullatur House, *Dullatur, Glasgow, G68 0AW.* Georgian mansion house circa 1740. **Open:** All year
01236 738855 (also fax) Mrs Moore *mooread@global.com* **D:** £19.50–£23.50 **S:** £21.50–£25.00 **Beds:** 1F 2T **Baths:** 2 En 1 Pr ⏤ 🅿 (4) 📺 🍴 × 📺 🖼 ♨

East Kilbride

NS6354

11 Markethill Road, *East Kilbride, Glasgow, G74 4AA.* 1920 sandstone villa, central location for Lanarkshire and 8 miles from Glasgow. **Open:** All year (not Xmas/New Year)
01355 231547 (also fax) Mrs Gibb *bb@ekgibb.freeserve.co.uk* www.ekgibb.freeserve.co.uk **D:** £18.50 **S:** £23.50 **Beds:** 5T **Baths:** 1 En 2 Sh 🅿 (5) 📺 🍴 × 📺 🖼 ♨

Glassford

NS7247

Avonlea, *46 Millar Street, Glassford, Strathaven, Lanarkshire, ML10 6TD.* Comfortable homely accommodation. Country village near M74 (junction 8). Rear garden. **Open:** Jan to Nov **Grades:** STB 3 Star, AA 2 Diamond
01357 521748 Miss Rankin **D:** £18.00–£20.00 **S:** £22.00–£25.00 **Beds:** 2T **Baths:** 1 Sh ⏤ (7) ⠇ 📺 🖼 ♨

BEDROOMS

D = Double
T = Twin
S = Single
F = Family

National Grid References given are for villages, towns and cities – not for individual houses

Glenmavis

NS7567

Rowan Lodge, *23 Condorrat Road, Glenmavis, Airdrie, Lanarkshire, ML6 0NS.* Excellent bungalow accommodation opposite village church. Ideal for touring. **Open:** All year **Grades:** STB 3 Star
01236 753934 *june@rowanlodge.demon.co.uk* www.rowanlodge.demon.co.uk **D:** £20.00–£30.00 **S:** £20.00–£30.00 **Beds:** 1T 1D 1S **Baths:** 3 En 🅿 (4) ⠇ 📺 🖼 ♨ cc

Hamilton

NS7255   🍺 *Gilts Bar*

Glenmhor House, *6 Bent Road, Hamilton, Lanarkshire, ML3 6QB.* Minutes coach/rail station. Country park nearby. Hearty breakfast. **Open:** All year
01698 423293 (also fax) Ms McCabe **D:** £17.00–£18.00 **S:** £20.00 **Beds:** 1F 1T 1S **Baths:** 2 Sh ⏤ 🅿 📺 🍴 📺 🖼 ♨

Kirkfieldbank

NS8643   🍺 *The Tavern*

Brig End BandB, *231 Riverside Road, Kirkfieldbank, Lanark, ML11 9JJ.* Between Two Bridges Garden down to River Clyde on walkway. **Open:** All year **Grades:** STB 2 Star
01555 663855 Mrs Rankin **D:** £19.00–£20.00 **S:** £22.00–£25.00 **Beds:** 2T **Baths:** 1 En 1 Pr ⏤ 🅿 (3) 📺 📺 🖼 ♨

Kirkmuirhill

NS7943

Dykecroft Farm, *Kirkmuirhill, Lesmahagow, Lanark, ML11 0JQ.* Convenient for Glasgow and airports, near Strathclyde Park. Warm welcome **Open:** All year **Grades:** STB 2 Star, AA 3 Diamond
01555 892226 I H McInally *dykecroftbandb@talk21.com* **D:** £19.50–£20.00 **S:** £22.00 **Beds:** 1T 2D **Baths:** 2 Sh ⏤ 🅿 ⠇ 📺 🍴 📺 🖼 ♨

Lanark

NS8843

Brig End B&B, *231 Riverside Road, Kirkfieldbank, Lanark, ML11 9JJ.* Between Two Bridges Garden down to River Clyde on walkway. **Open:** All year **Grades:** STB 2 Star
01555 663855 Mrs Rankin **D:** £19.00–£20.00 **S:** £22.00–£25.00 **Beds:** 2T **Baths:** 1 En 1 Pr ⏤ 🅿 (3) 📺 📺 🖼 ♨

5 Hardacres, *Lanark, ML11 7QP.* Peaceful, cheerful, well-appointed bungalow between Edinburgh-Glasgow. 'Lonely Planet' recommended. **Open:** All year (not Xmas) **01555 661002** Mrs Buchanan **D:** £16.00–£18.00 **S:** £17.00–£18.00 **Beds:** 1D 1T **Baths:** 1 En 1 Sh 🅿 (1) ⚡ 📺 🛋 🚲

Roselea, *9 Cleghorn Road, Lanark, ML11 7QT.* Edwardian House, original features. Close to New Lanark. Golf, fishing, riding and genealogy. **Open:** All year **01555 662540** Mrs Allen *margaretallen2@ tesco.net* **D:** £18.00–£20.00 **S:** £17.00–£26.00 **Beds:** 1F 1D 1S **Baths:** 1 En 1 Sh 🎀 🅿 (2) 📺 🍴 📺 🛋 ✳ 🚲

Leadhills

NS8815

Meadowfoot Cottage, *Gowanbank, Leadhills, Biggar, Lanarkshire, ML12 6YB.* Blending history and modern amenities with the warmest welcome and delicious home cooking. **Open:** All year (not Xmas) **01659 74369** Mrs Ledger *enquiries@ meadowfootcottage.co.uk* **www.meadowfootcottage.co.uk D:** £18.50–£20.00 **S:** £20.00–£25.00 **Beds:** 1F 1T **Baths:** 1 En 1 Sh 🎀 🅿 (4) ⚡ 📺 ✕ 📺 🛋 🚲

Lesmahagow

NS8139 ⬛ *Star Inn*

Auldtoun Farm, *Lesmahagow, Lanark, ML11 0JT.* **Open:** All year (not Xmas/New Year) **01555 892910 (also fax)** Mrs Muirhead **D:** £17.50–£20.00 **S:** £20.00–£25.00 **Beds:** 1F 1T 1D **Baths:** 1 En 1 Sh 🅿 (6) 📺 🛋 🚲 Perfectly situated 1 mile off M74 exit 10, 22 miles south of Glasgow, 40 miles west of Edinburgh, good stopover on your way to the Highlands. You are assured of a warm welcome, comfortable accommodation and full Scottish breakfast.

BATHROOMS
En = Ensuite
Pr = Private
Sh = Shared

Dykecroft Farm, *Kirkmuirhill, Lesmahagow, Lanark, ML11 0JQ.* Convenient for Glasgow and airports, near Strathclyde Park. Warm welcome **Open:** All year **Grades:** STB 2 Star, AA 3 Diamond **01555 892226** I H McInally *dykecroftbandb@ talk21.com* **D:** £19.50–£20.00 **S:** £22.00 **Beds:** 1T 2D **Baths:** 2 Sh 🎀 🅿 ⚡ 📺 🍴 📺 🛋 🚲

Newbigging

NT0145

Nestlers Hotel, *Newbigging, Lanark, ML11 8NA.* Small intimate family run hotel in rural South Lanarkshire. **Open:** All year **01555 840680** Mr Anderson *nestlers@ hotel98.freeserve.co.uk* **D:** £23.50–£27.50 **S:** £28.50–£35.00 **Beds:** 1F 2T 1D **Baths:** 4 En 🎀 🅿 (9) ⚡ 📺 🍴 ✕ 📺 🛋 🚲 ⚫ cc

Strathaven

NS7044

Avonlea, *46 Millar Street, Glassford, Strathaven, Lanarkshire, ML10 6TD.* Comfortable homely accommodation. Country village near M74 (junction 8). Rear garden. **Open:** Jan to Nov **Grades:** STB 3 Star, AA 2 Diamond **01357 521748** Miss Rankin **D:** £18.00–£20.00 **S:** £22.00–£25.00 **Beds:** 2T **Baths:** 1 Sh 🎀 (7) ⚡ 📺 🛋 🚲

Haroldslea, *3 Kirkhill Road, Strathaven, Lanarkshire, ML10 6HN.* Modern detached villa with garden in quiet residential area near village centre. **Open:** All year (not Xmas/New Year) **01357 520617** Mrs Goodwillie **D:** £20.00 **S:** £20.00 **Beds:** 1F 1D **Baths:** 2 Sh 🎀 🅿 (2) ⚡ 📺 🍴 🛋 🚲

Kypemhor, *West Kype Farm, Strathaven, Lanarkshire, ML10 6PR.* Bungalow with scenic rural views, 3 miles from busy market town. **Open:** All year **01357 529831** Mrs Anderson **D:** £17.00–£20.00 **S:** £18.00–£22.00 **Beds:** 1D 1T **Baths:** 1 Sh 🎀 🅿 (12) 📺 🍴 📺 🛋 🚲

Uddingston

NS6960

Phoenix Lodge Guest House, *4 Girdons Way, Uddingston, Glasgow, G71 7ED.* Modern building, near motorways, station, tourist attractions locally, walks, pubs, restaurants. **Open:** All year **01698 815296 & 01698 811529** Mr Boyce **Fax:** **01698 267567 D:** £19.00–£22.00 **S:** £23.00–£25.00 **Beds:** 6F 1T 1D **Baths:** 3 En 2 Sh 🎀 🅿 (8) 📺 🍴 ✕ 📺 🛋 ♿ ✳ 🚲 cc

Northcote Guest House, *2 Holmbrae Avenue, Uddingston, Glasgow, G71 6AL.* Large Victorian private house, quiet locality. Easily accessible. **Open:** All year (not Xmas) **01698 813319 (also fax)** Mrs Meggs *meggs@ accanet.com* **D:** £16.00–£17.00 **S:** £16.00–£17.00 **Beds:** 1F 1D 1S **Baths:** 1 Sh 🎀 🅿 (3) 📺 📺 🛋

Walston

NT0545

Walston Mansion Farmhouse, *Walston, Carnwath, Lanark, ML11 8NF.* A farmhouse that's 'home from home' **Open:** All year **Grades:** STB 3 Star **01899 810338 (also fax)** Mrs Kirby *kirby-walstonmansion@talk21.com* **D:** £16.00–£18.00 **S:** £18.00–£20.00 **Beds:** 1F 1T 1D 1S **Baths:** 2 En 1 Sh 🎀 🅿 (6) 📺 🍴 ✕ 📺 🛋 ✳ 🚲

Wishaw

NS7954

The Mill House, *Garrion Bridge, Wishaw, Lanarkshire, ML2 0RR.* Mill House, built 1907 with delightful garden, comfortable warm home. **Open:** All year **01698 881166** Mrs Pinkerton **Fax: 01698 886874** *alanphotog@aol.com* **D:** £15.00–£18.00 **S:** £22.50–£27.50 **Beds:** 1F 1D 1T **Baths:** 1 En 1 Sh 🅿 (6) ⚡ 📺 🛋 🚲

BEDROOMS
D = Double
T = Twin
S = Single
F = Family

Lothian & Falkirk

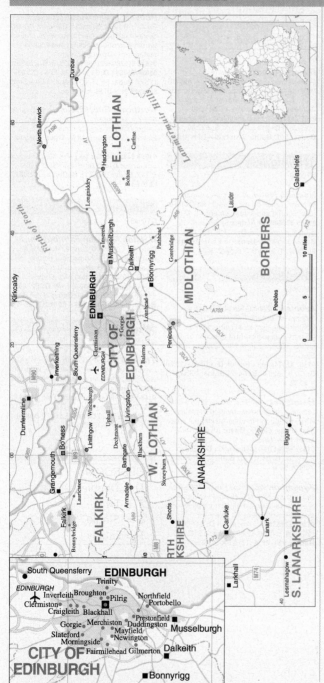

Armadale
NS9368

Tarrareoch Farm, *Armadale, Bathgate, W Lothian, EH48 3BJ.* C17th farmhouse all on one level. Midway Edinburgh/Glasgow. Beautiful countryside. **Open:** All year **Grades:** STB 3 Star **01501 730404 (also fax)** Mrs Gibb **D:** £16.00–£20.00 **S:** £20.00–£26.00 **Beds:** 1F 2T **Baths:** 1 En 1 Sh �🐾 🄿 (10) 📺 ⛄ Ⓥ 📖 ⚓

Balerno
NT1666

Newmills Cottage, *472 Lanark Road West, Balerno, EH14 5AE.* Delightful house set in own grounds with ample private off-road parking. **Open:** All year **0131 449 4300 (also fax)** Mrs Linn *newmillscottage@blueyonder.co.uk* www.planet-scotland.com/newmills **D:** £20.00–£27.50 **S:** £25.00–£35.00 **Beds:** 2T **Baths:** 1 En 1 Pr 🄿 ⛄ 📺 Ⓥ 📖 ⚓

Bathgate
NS9769

Hillview, *35 The Green, Bathgate, W Lothian, EH48 4DA.* Quality and friendly accommodation with spectacular views of West Lothian. **Open:** All year (not Xmas) **Grades:** STB 2 Star **01506 654830 (also fax)** Mrs Connell **D:** £15.00–£16.00 **S:** £20.00–£22.00 **Beds:** 1F 1T **Baths:** 1 Sh ⛄ ⛄ 📺 ⛄ Ⓥ 📖 ⚓

Blackburn
NS9865

Cruachan Guest House, *78 East Main Street, Blackburn, Bathgate, West Lothian, EH47 7QS.* Relaxed, friendly, high-quality. Airport nearby, rail service to Edinburgh. **Open:** All year (not Xmas) **01506 655221** Mr Harkins **Fax: 01506 652395** *cruachan.bb@virgin.net* www.cruachan.co.uk **D:** £20.00–£23.00 **S:** £25.00–£30.00 **Beds:** 1F 3D **Baths:** 3 En 1 Pr ⛄ 🄿 (5) ⛄ 📺 Ⓥ 📖 ⚓

BEDROOMS
D = Double
T = Twin
S = Single
F = Family

Bo'ness
NS9981

Haypark, *28 Grange Terrace, Bo'ness, EH51 9DS.* Attractive stone built house overlooking the Forth, convenient for Edinburgh and Stirling. **Open:** May to Sept **Grades:** STB 2 Star **01506 823193 (also fax)** Mrs Croxford *peter_croxford@tesco.net* **D:** £20.00–£25.00 **S:** £25.00 **Beds:** 1T 1D **Baths:** 1 Sh ⊬ ▥ ▦ ₤

Bolton
NT5070   ⬛ *The Goblin, Tweeddale Arms*

Fieldfare, *Upper Bolton Farm, Bolton, Haddington, E Lothian, EH41 4HL.* Quiet location on farm. Edinburgh, 1/2 mile. Near hills and sea. **Open:** All year (not New Year) **01620 810346** Mrs Clark **D:** £18.00–£22.00 **S:** £20.00–£24.00 **Beds:** 1F 1T 1D **Baths:** 2 Pr ⌖ ▥ ▣ ▦ & ₤

Bonnybridge
NS8380

Bandominie Farm, *Walton Road, Bonnybridge, Stirlingshire, FK4 2HP.* Farmhouse friendly atmosphere. 2 miles from A80, Castle Cary, B816. **Open:** All year (not Xmas/New Year) **01324 840284** Mrs Forrester **D:** £17.00–£18.00 **S:** £17.00–£18.00 **Beds:** 1D 1T 1S **Baths:** 1 Sh ⌖ ▣ (3) ⊬ ▥ ▦ ₤

Carfrae
NT5769

Carfrae Farm, *Carfrae, Haddington, E Lothian, EH41 4LP.* Peaceful farmhouse overlooking lovely gardens. Edinburgh, The Borders, Golf nearby. **Open:** Apr to Oct **01620 830242** Mrs Gibson **Fax: 01620 830320** *dgcarfrae@aol.com* **D:** £25.00–£27.00 **S:** £35.00–£40.00 **Beds:** 2D 1T **Baths:** 2 En 1 Pr ⌖ (10) ▣ (6) ⊬ ▥ ▦ ₤

Dalkeith
NT3467   ⬛ *Justinlees Inn, Dalhousie Castle*

Rathan House, *45 Eskbank Road, Eskbank, Dalkeith, Midlothian, EH22 3BH.* Conservation area by Midlothian Cycleway, croquet lawn. Low fat breakfasts. **Open:** All year **0131 663 3291 (also fax)** Mr & Mrs MacRae *bandb@edinvac.btinternet.co.uk* www.edinvac. btinternet.co.uk **D:** £24.00–£32.00 **S:** £28.00–£40.00 **Beds:** 1F 2T 1D **Baths:** 2 En 2 Pr ⌖ ▣ (8) ▥ ⊬ ▥ ▦ ₤ cc

Dechmont
NT0370

Bankhead Farm, *Dechmont, Broxburn, EH52 6NB.* Panoramic views of beautiful countryside yet easy access Edinburgh airport. **Open:** All year (not Xmas) **Grades:** STB 3 Star **01506 811209** H Warnock **Fax: 01506 811815** *bankheadbb@aol.com* bankheadfarm.com **D:** £22.00–£25.00 **S:** £28.00–£35.00 **Beds:** 2F 2D 3S **Baths:** 7 En ⌖ ▣ ⊬ ▥ ▥ ▦ ₤ cc

Dunbar
NT6779

Goldenstones Hotel, *Queens Road, Dunbar, E Lothian, EH42 1LG.* The Goldenstones is a friendly, family-run hotel. **Open:** All year **01368 862356** Mr Currie **Fax: 01368 862344** **D:** £30.00–£32.00 **S:** £40.00–£45.00 **Beds:** 4F 15T **Baths:** 19 En ⌖ ▣ ⊬ ▥ ✕ ▥ ▦ & ❋ ₤ cc

Overcliffe Guest House, *11 Bayswell Park, Dunbar, E Lothian, EH42 1AE.* Family-run, perfect for touring East Lothian's golf courses beaches. **Open:** All year **01368 864004** Mrs Bower **Fax: 01368 865995** *overcliffe@aol.com* **D:** £20.00–£35.00 **S:** £25.00–£35.00 **Beds:** 3F 2T **Baths:** 3 En 2 Sh ⌖ (1) ▣ (2) ⊬ ▥ ⊁ ▦ ₤

EDINBURGH   Blackhall
NT2174

Sandilands House, *25 Queensferry Road, Edinburgh, EH4 3HB.* 1930's bungalow with many art deco features. Near Murrayfield Stadium. **Open:** All year **0131 332 2057** Mrs Sandilands **Fax: 0131 315 4476** **D:** £20.00–£34.00 **S:** £25.00–£45.00 **Beds:** 1F 1D 1T **Baths:** 3 En ⌖ ▣ ⊬ ▥ ▦ ₤ cc

EDINBURGH   Broughton
NT2575

Ben Cruachan, *17 Mcdonald Road, Edinburgh, EH7 4LX.* Be assured of a very warm welcome at our family-run centrally situated guest house. **Open:** Apr to Oct **0131 556 3709** N Stark **D:** £25.00–£35.00 **Beds:** 1F 1T 1D **Baths:** 3 En ⌖ (10) ▣ ⊬ ▥ ▥ ▦ ₤

BEDROOMS

D = Double

T = Twin

S = Single

F = Family

EDINBURGH   Central
NT2573

6 Dean Park Crescent, *Edinburgh, EH4 1PN.* Warm friendly home. Large rooms. 10 mins walk to centre. **Open:** Easter to Oct **Grades:** RAC 4 Diamond **0131 332 5017** Mrs Kirkland *kirkland.b&b@ cableinet.co.uk* www.kirkland.pwp.blueyonder. co.uk **D:** £22.00–£29.00 **S:** £40.00–£55.00 **Beds:** 1F 1D 1T **Baths:** 1 En 1 Pr 1 Sh ⌖ ⊬ ▥ ▥ ▦ & ₤

17 Hope Park Terrace, *Edinburgh, EH8 9LZ.* Fifteen minutes' walk city centre. H&C in bedrooms. **Open:** All year **0131 667 7963** Mrs Frackelton **D:** £25.00 **S:** £25.00 **Beds:** 2D **Baths:** 1 Sh ⌖ (10) ⊬ ▥ ▦ ₤

37 Howe Street, *Edinburgh, EH3 6TF.* Quiet Georgian garden flat in historic New Town; few minutes walk to Princes Street **Open:** All year **Grades:** STB 2 Star **0131 557 3487 (also fax)** Mrs Collie **D:** £20.00 **Beds:** 1D **Baths:** 1 Sh ▥ ▥ ▦ & ₤

Glenora Hotel, *14 Rosebery Crescent, Edinburgh, EH12 5JY.* Small, city central hotel. Airport, bus stops nearby. **Open:** All year **Grades:** STB 3 Star **0131 337 1186** www.glenorahotel.co.uk **D:** £18.00–£45.00 **S:** £25.00–£65.00 **Beds:** 1F 1T 5D 4S **Baths:** 11 En ⊬ ▥ ✕ ▦ ₤ cc

Averon Guest House, *44 Gilmore Place, Edinburgh, EH3 9NQ.* Fully restored Georgian town house, built in 1770. Central Edinburgh with car park. **Open:** All year **0131 229 9932** Mr Cran **D:** £18.00–£38.00 **S:** £25.00–£38.00 **Beds:** 3F 2D 3T 1S **Baths:** 6 Pr ⌖ ▣ (10) ▥ ▦ & ₤ cc

Rothesay Hotel, *8 Rothesay Place, Edinburgh, EH3 7SL.* Heart of Edinburgh's Georgian new town in the city centre, short walk Princes Street. **Open:** All year **0131 225 4125** Mr Borland *info@ rothesay-hotel.demon.co.uk* **D:** £25.00–£45.00 **S:** £38.00–£65.00 **Beds:** 2F 4D 18T 12S **Baths:** 36 Pr ⌖ ▥ ✕ ✕ ▥ &

Amaryllis Guest House, *21 Upper Gilmore Place, Edinburgh, EH3 9NL.* Warm, comfortable, friendly, central all attractions. Walkable but quietly situated. **Open:** All year (not Xmas) **0131 229 3293 (also fax)** L Melrose *ghamaryllis@aol.com* **D:** £18.00–£30.00 **S:** £25.00–£40.00 **Beds:** 3F 1D 1T **Baths:** 4 En 1 Pr ⌖ (10) ▣ (2) ▥ ▦ ₤ cc

28 London Street, *Edinburgh, EH3 6NA.* Central Georgian 1st floor flat 5 minutes' walk from station. **Open:** Easter to Oct **0131 556 4641** Mr & Mrs Campbell **D:** £18.00–£25.00 **S:** £20.00–£27.00 **Beds:** 1F 1T 1D 1S **Baths:** 3 Sh ⌖ (5) ▣ (1) ▥ ▦

EDINBURGH   Clermiston

NT1974   ◄ *The Old Inn*

Crannoch But and Ben, *467 Queensferry Road, Edinburgh, EH4 7ND.* Highly recommended. Airport and city centre situated three miles. **Open:** All year **Grades:** STB 4 Star **0131 336 5688** *moiraconway@ crannoch467.freeserve.co.uk* **D:** £25.00–£28.00 **Beds:** 1F 1T 1D **Baths:** 2 En 1 Pr ⌿ (5) ⌿ ▣ ▥ ▦ ♨

EDINBURGH   Craigleith

NT2374

Six Marys Place Guesthouse, *Raeburn Place, Stockbridge, Edinburgh, EH4 1JN.* **Open:** All year **Grades:** STB 3 Star, AA 4 Diamond **0131 332 8965** The Manager **Fax: 0131 624 7060** *info@sixmarysplace.co.uk* www.sixmarysplace.co.uk **D:** £28.00–£35.00 **S:** £28.00–£40.00 **Beds:** 1F 2T 3D 2S **Baths:** 7 En 1 Pr ⌿ ▣ ⌿ ▣ ▥ ▦ ♨ cc Perfectly located, 10 minutes from the city centre and 5 minutes from the celebrated Royal Botanic Gardens. This beautifully restored Georgian townhouse, with its light, fresh decor, offers a warm, relaxed smoke-free atmosphere.

St Bernards Guest House, *22 St Bernards Crescent, Edinburgh, EH4 1NS.* Victorian townhouse, 10-15 minute walk from city centre. **Open:** All year **Grades:** STB 2 Star **0131 332 2339** Mr & Mrs Alsop **Fax: 0131 332 8842** *alexstbernards@aol.com* **D:** £24.00–£30.00 **S:** £25.00–£40.00 **Beds:** 4T 3D 1S **Baths:** 4 En 2 Sh ⌿ ▣ ▥ ▦ ♨ cc

Galloway Guest House, *22 Dean Park Crescent, Edinburgh, EH6 6PH.* City centre location 10 minutes walk, Princes Street, free street parking. **Open:** All year **Grades:** STB 3 Star, AA 3 Diamond, RAC 3 Diamond **0131 332 3672 (also fax)** Mr Clark **D:** £25.00–£30.00 **S:** £30.00–£45.00 **Beds:** 3F 3T 3D 1S **Baths:** 6 En 1 Pr 2 Sh ⌿ ▣ ▥ ▦ ♨ cc

BATHROOMS

En = Ensuite
Pr = Private
Sh = Shared

National Grid References given are for villages, towns and cities – not for individual houses

---

EDINBURGH   Duddingston

NT2973

Sure & Steadfast, *76 Milton Road West, Duddingston, Edinburgh, EH15 1QV.*

Open: Easter to Sept **0131 657 1189** Mr & Mrs Taylor *a_t_taylor@ ednet.co.uk* www.ednet.co.uk/~a_t_taylor **D:** £16.50–£22.00 **S:** £20.00–£44.00 **Beds:** 2D 1T **Baths:** 3 Sh ⌿ ▣ (3) ⌿ ▣ ▥ ▦ ♨ cc Small, family-run 3 star B&B situated about 2 miles from the city centre. The property is located on the main bus route and can be easily reached by taxi or bus from the railway station or airport.

EDINBURGH   Fairmilehead

NT2468

Valhalla, *35 Comiston View, Edinburgh, EH10 6LP.* Modern detached property; quiet; golf, full breakfast. Warm welcome guaranteed. **Open:** All year **0131 445 5354** Mrs Stevenson-Renwick **D:** £20.00–£32.00 **S:** £25.00–£35.00 **Beds:** 1D 1T 1S **Baths:** 2 En 1 Pr ⌿ ▣ (2) ⌿ ▣ ▥ ▦ ♨

EDINBURGH   Gilmerton

NT2968

Emerald Guest House, *3 Drum Street, Gilmerton, Edinburgh, EH17 8QQ.* Victorian villa situated on bus route to city centre. **Open:** All year (not Xmas/New Year) **0131 664 5918** Mrs O'Connor **D:** £20.00–£31.00 **S:** £35.00 **Beds:** 1F 2T 2D **Baths:** 3 En 1 Sh ⌿ (4) ▣ (5) ▥ ✕ ▥ ▦ ♨

EDINBURGH   Gorgie

NT2272   ◄ *Orwell Lodge Hotel, Royal Ettrick Hotel*

Invermark, *60 Polwarth Terrace, Edinburgh, EH11 1NJ.* On bus route into city, easy access from city bypass. **Open:** All year **0131 337 1066** Mrs Donaldson **D:** £20.00 **S:** £20.00 **Beds:** 1F 2T 1S **Baths:** 1 En 1 Pr ⌿ ▣ (2) ⌿ ▣ ♨ ▦

EDINBURGH   Inverleith

NT2475

The Inverleith Hotel, *5 Inverleith Terrace, Edinburgh, EH3 5NS.* Licensed Victorian Hotel, city centre, adjacent botanic gardens, groups accepted. **Open:** All year (not Xmas) **0131 556 2745** Mr & Mrs Case **Fax: 0131 557 0433** *hotel@inverleith.freeserve.co.uk* www.inverleith.freeserve.co.uk **D:** £25.00–£50.00 **S:** £30.00–£50.00 **Beds:** 2F 2D 2T 2S **Baths:** 8 En ⌿ ⌿ ▣ ♨ ▣ ✕ ▥ ▦ ♨ cc

EDINBURGH   Mayfield (Edinburgh)

NT2672

Ivy Guest House, *7 Mayfield Gardens, Edinburgh, EH9 2AX.* **Open:** All year **Grades:** STB 3 Star, AA 3 Diamond, RAC 4 Diamond, Sparkling **0131 667 3411** Mr Green **Fax: 0131 620 1422** *don@ivyguesthouse.com* www.ivyguesthouse.com **D:** £17.00–£35.00 **S:** £17.00–£65.00 **Beds:** 2F 3D 2T 1S **Baths:** 6 En 2 Pr ⌿ ▣ (7) ▥ ♨ ▦ ♨ Quiet, family-run Victorian villa guest house, many local restaurants, close to all Edinburgh's major cultural attractions, golf courses, Commonwealth swimming pool and university. A hearty Scottish breakfast and a warm welcome is assured.

Lauderville Guest House, *52 Mayfield Road, Edinburgh, EH9 2NH.* **Open:** All year **Grades:** STB 4 Star **0131 667 7788** Mrs Marriott **Fax: 0131 667 2636** *res@laudervilleguesthouse.co.uk* www.LaudervilleGuestHouse.co.uk **D:** £25.00–£40.00 **S:** £28.00–£48.00 **Beds:** 1F 6D 2T 1S **Baths:** 10 En ⌿ ▣ (6) ⌿ ▣ ▥ ▦ ♨ cc Restored Victorian town house minutes from the city sights, Royal Mile, Castle, Princes Street. Elegant non-smoking bedrooms and excellent breakfast awaits, with varied menu including vegetarian. Secluded garden and secure car park. Traditional Pubs and quality Restaurants nearby.

Glenalmond Guest House, 25
Mayfield Gardens, Edinburgh, EH9 2BX.
Open: All year (not Xmas)
0131 668 2392 (also fax) Mr & Mrs Fraser
glen@almond25.freeserve.co.uk
almond25.freeserve.co.uk **D:** £20.00–£35.00
S: £25.00–£40.00 **Beds:** 3F 4D 2T 1S
Baths: 10 En ☺ (5) 📺 Ⓥ 🛇 & 🌣
Deb and Dave warmly welcome you to their superb accommodation. Ground, four poster, ensuite rooms available. Close to Waverley Station. Varied breakfast served daily with home-made scones.

Rowan Guest House, 13 Glenorchy
Terrace, Edinburgh, EH9 2DQ. **Open:** All year
(not Xmas) **Grades:** STB 3 Star, AA 3
Diamond
0131 667 2463 (also fax) Mr & Mrs Vidler
angela@rowan-house.co.uk **D:** £23.00–£34.00
S: £24.00–£30.00 **Beds:** 1F 3D 2T 3S
Baths: 3 En 3 Sh ☺ (2) 🅿 (2) 📺 🛇 🌣 cc
Comfortable Victorian home in quiet, leafy, conservation area, a mile and a half from city centre, castle and Royal Mile. Delicious breakfast, including porridge and freshly baked scones. A warm welcome and personal service from Alan and Angela. Free parking.

Sylvern Guest House, 22 West
Mayfield, Edinburgh, EH9 1TQ. **Open:** All year
Grades: STB 2 Star
0131 667 1241 (also fax) Mr & Mrs Livornese
sylvernguesthouse@amserve.net **D:** £17.00–
£24.00 **S:** £24.00–£32.00 **Beds:** 2F 2T 2D
Baths: 4 En 2 Sh ☺ 🅿 (8) ≠ 📺 🛇 ♿
Detached Victorian villa one mile from Edinburgh City Centre, near Commonwealth Pool Festival Theatre, Edinburgh Castle, Royal Mile and University, good bus route, free private parking. TV in all rooms, full cooked breakfast.

RATES

D = Price range per person sharing in a double or twin room

S = Price range for a single room

Hopetoun, 15
*Mayfield Road,
Edinburgh,
EH9 2NG.*
Completely non-smoking. Small family-run B&B, close Edinburgh
University. Personal attention, relaxed, informal atmosphere. **Open:** All year (not Xmas) **Grades:** STB 3 Star
0131 667 7691 Mrs Mitchell **Fax:** 0131 466
1691 *hopetoun@aol.com* members.aol.
com/hopetoun **D:** £20.00–£30.00 **S:** £25.00–
£40.00 **Beds:** 1F 1D 1T **Baths:** 1 En 1 Pr 1 Sh
☺ (6) 🅿 (2) ≠ 📺 Ⓥ 🛇 cc

Sonas, 3 East Mayfield, Edinburgh, EH9 1SD.
Recommended by 'Which Guide'. Warm, friendly, comfortable, delicious breakfasts - Perfect! **Open:** All year (not Xmas)
Grades: STB 3 Star
0131 667 2781 Mrs Robins **Fax:** 0131 667
0454 *sonas.guesthouse@virgin.net* **D:** £19.00–
£35.00 **S:** £25.00–£35.00 **Beds:** 1F 2T 4D 1S
Baths: 8 En ☺ 🅿 ≠ 📺 🛇 🌣

The International, 37 Mayfield Gardens,
Edinburgh, EH9 2BX. Attractive stone-built Victorian house, 1.5m south of Princes Street. Magnificent views. **Open:** All year
Grades: STB 4 Star, AA 4 Diamond
0131 667 2511 Mrs Niven **Fax:** 0131 667 1112
intergh@easynet.co.uk **D:** £20.00–£40.00
S: £25.00–£45.00 **Beds:** 2F 2D 2T 3S
Baths: 9 Pr ☺ 📺 Ⓥ 🛇 & 🌣 🌣

Tania Guest House, 19 Minto Street,
Edinburgh, EH9 1RQ. Comfortable Georgian guest house, very good bus route, private parking available. Italian spoken. **Open:** All
year (not Xmas) **Grades:** STB 1 Star
0131 667 4144 Mrs Roscilli **D:** £18.00–£25.00
S: £20.00–£27.50 **Beds:** 3F 1D 1T 1S
Baths: 2 En ☺ 🅿 📺 Ⓥ 🛇 🌣

Ben Doran Guest House, 11 Mayfield
Gardens, Edinburgh, EH9 2AX. Beautiful refurbished Georgian house. Elegant, cosy, comfortable, central. Family run hotel.
Open: All year
0131 667 8488 Dr Labaki **Fax:** 0131 667 0076
info@bendoran.com www.bendoran.com
D: £25.00–£60.00 **S:** £25.00–£60.00 **Beds:** 4F
3D 2T 1S **Baths:** 6 En 4 Sh ☺ 🅿 (17) ≠ 📺 Ⓥ
🛇 🌣 cc

Lorne Villa Guest House, 9 East
Mayfield, Edinburgh, EH9 1SD. Festival city residence, serving fine Scottish cuisine with Scottish hospitality. **Open:** All year
0131 667 7159 (also fax) Mr McCulloch
lornevilla@cableinet.co.uk **D:** £18.00–£32.00
S: £18.00–£32.00 **Beds:** 1F 2D 3T 1S
Baths: 3 En 1 Pr 3 Sh ☺ 🅿 (6) 🛇 🍴 × 🛇 🌣

Crion Guest House, 33 Minto Street,
Edinburgh, EH9 2BT. Family run guest house near city centre. Most tourist attractions.
Open: All year
0131 667 2708 **Fax:** 0131 662 1946 *w.cheape@
gilmourhouse.freeserve.co.uk*
www.edinburghbedbreakfast.com **D:** £20.00–
£27.00 **S:** £20.00–£27.00 **Beds:** 1D 2T 1S
Baths: 1 Sh ☺ 🅿 📺 🛇 🌣 cc

Parklands Guest House, 20 Mayfield
Gardens, Edinburgh, EH9 2BZ. Comfortable well maintained Victorian guest house near city centre. **Open:** All year
0131 667 7184 Mr Drummond **Fax:** 0131 667
2011 *parklands_guesthouse@yahoo.com*
D: £22.00–£30.00 **S:** £25.00–£40.00 **Beds:** 1F
2D 2T 1S **Baths:** 5 En 1 Pr ☺ 🅿 (1) 📺 Ⓥ 🛇 🌣

EDINBURGH Merchiston
NT2472

**Villa Nina
Guest House,**
*39 Leamington
Terrace,
Edinburgh,
EH10 4JS.*
Open: All year
(not Xmas/New
Year) **Grades:** STB 1 Star
0131 229 2644 (also fax) Mr Cecco
villanina@amserve.net **D:** £18.00–£24.00
Beds: 1F 2D 2T **Baths:** 2 Sh 🅿 📺 Ⓥ 🛇 🌣
Good value Bed and Breakfast accommodation is offered in this comfortable Victorian town house in the centre of Edinburgh. Close to the Castle Kings theatre, International Conference centre and major attractions, 10 min walk to Princes Street.

Granville Guesthouse, 13 Granville
Terrace, Edinburgh, EH10 4PQ. Family-run guest house situated centrally in Edinburgh, all local amenities nearby.
Open: All year **Grades:** STB 2 Star, RAC 2
Star
0131 229 1676 & 0131 229 4633 Mr Oussallem
Fax: 0131 229 4633 *granvilleguesthouse@
tinyworld.co.uk* **D:** £18.00–£30.00 **S:** £18.00–
£30.00 **Beds:** 3F 2T 3D 1S **Baths:** 6 En 1 Sh
☺ 🅿 (2) 📺 × Ⓥ 🛇 & 🌣 cc

Nova Hotel, 5 Bruntsfield Crescent,
Edinburgh, EH10 4EZ. Victorian, city centre, quiet area, free parking, fully licensed, all rooms ensuite. Lovely views. **Open:** All year
0131 447 6437 & 0131 447 7349 Mr McBride
Fax: 0131 452 8126 (preferred for
bookings) *jamie@scotland-hotels.demon.co.uk*
www.novahotel.com **D:** £25.00–£55.00
S: £35.00–£70.00 **Beds:** 6F 2D 2T 2S
Baths: 13 En ☺ 🅿 ≠ 📺 🍴 × Ⓥ 🛇 &1 🌣 cc

EDINBURGH
Morningside

NT2471 🍺 *Montpelier Bar, King's Bar*

Sandeman House, 33 Colinton Road,
Edinburgh, EH10 5DR. Victorian family house centrally situated. Wonderful breakfasts. Street parking. **Open:** All year
0131 447 8080 (also fax) Ms Sandeman
joycesandeman@freezone.co.uk www.freeserve.
co.uk/sandemanhouse **D:** £30.00–£36.00
S: £38.00–£45.00 **Beds:** 1T 1D 1S **Baths:** 3
En ≠ 📺 Ⓥ 🛇 🌣

Dunedin, 21-23 Colinton Road, Edinburgh, EH10 5DR. 'B' Listed mid-Victorian terraced villas, furnished in period style. **Open:** All year
0131 447 0679 H Fortune **Fax: 0131 446 9358**
enquiries@dunedinprivatehouse.com
dunedinprivatehouse.com **D:** £24.00–£35.00 **S:** £24.00–£35.00 **Beds:** 3F 2T 2D 1S **Baths:** 5 En 2 Sh ⌂ ⚲ ⊞ ▥ ✻ ♣ cc

EDINBURGH   Newington

NT2671   🔲 Braidburn Inn

Ben Craig House, 3 Craigmillar Park, Edinburgh, EH16 5PG. Attractive Victorian villa. Conservatory breakfast room overlooking beautiful garden. Personally managed by owners. **Open:** All year (not Xmas/New Year)
0131 667 2593   Fax: 0131 667 1109
bencraighouse@dial.piper.com
www.bencraighouse.co.uk **D:** £25.00–£40.00 **S:** £30.00–£60.00 **Beds:** 1F 1T 3D **Baths:** 5 En ⌂ 🅿 ⚲ ⊞ ▥ ▥ ♿ ♣ cc

17 Crawfurd Road, Edinburgh, EH16 5PQ. Victorian family home, friendly welcome - easy access to city centre. **Open:** May to Sept **Grades:** STB 3 Star
0131 667 1191 Ms Simpson *ec_liz_simpson@talk21.com* **D:** £18.50–£25.00 **S:** £18.50–£25.00 **Beds:** 1D 1T 1S **Baths:** 2 Sh ⌂ 🅿 (1) ⚲ ▥ ▥ ♣

Gifford House, 103 Dalkeith Road, Edinburgh, EH16 5AJ. Elegant Victorian house. Superior rooms with Edinburgh's attractions within easy reach. **Open:** All year
0131 667 4688 (also fax) Mrs Dow
giffordhotel@btinternet.com **D:** £20.00–£38.00 **S:** £23.00–£50.00 **Beds:** 2F 2D 2T 1S **Baths:** 7 En ⌂ ⚲ ⊞ ▥ ▥ ✻ ♣ cc

Kingsley Guest House, 30 Craigmillar Park, Edinburgh, EH16 5PS. Friendly family run house on excellent bus route for sightseeing. **Open:** All year
0131 667 8439 (also fax) *accom.kingsley@virgin.net* **D:** £20.00–£35.00 **S:** £25.00–£40.00 **Beds:** 1F 2T 3D **Baths:** 3 En 2 Pr ⌂ (3) 🅿 (5) ⚲ ▥ ▥ ♣

EDINBURGH   Northfield

NT2973

Brae Guest House, 119 Willowbrae Road, Edinburgh, EH8 7HN. Friendly guest house. Meadowbank - Holyrood Palace, on main bus route. **Open:** All year
0131 661 0170 Mrs Walker *braeguesthouse@tinyworld.co.uk* **D:** £18.00–£40.00 **S:** £18.00–£40.00 **Beds:** 1F 1T 1D 1S **Baths:** 3 En 1 Pr ⌂ ⊞ ♟ ▥ ▥ ♣

EDINBURGH   Pilrig

NT2675

Glenburn Guest House, 22 Pilrig Street, Edinburgh, EH6 5AJ. Clean, welcoming, budget accommodation. 15 minutes from the city centre. **Open:** All year (not Xmas)
0131 554 9818 (also fax) Mrs McVeigh
glenburn@lineone.net www.candytape.com/glenburn **D:** £18.00–£30.00 **S:** £20.00–£36.00 **Beds:** 4F 4D 4T 2S **Baths:** 2 En 6 Sh ▥ ▥ ♣

Sunnyside Guest House, 13 Pilrig Street, Edinburgh, EH6 5AN. Beautiful Georgian family-run guest house. An easy atmosphere and ample breakfast. **Open:** All year (not Xmas)
0131 553 2084 Mr Wheelaghan
sunnyside.guesthouse@talk21.com **D:** £17.00–£30.00 **S:** £17.00–£30.00 **Beds:** 2F 4D 2T 1S **Baths:** 4 En 1 Pr 1 Sh ⌂ 🅿 ⚲ ⊞ ▥ ▥ ♣

Claymore Guest House, 68 Pilrig Street, Edinburgh, EH6 5AS. Warm, welcoming, personally run, centrally situated, close to all attractions. **Open:** All year (not Xmas)
0131 554 2500 (also fax) Mrs Dorrian **D:** £18.00–£30.00 **S:** £22.00 **Beds:** 2F 2D 2T **Baths:** 3 En 1 Pr 2 Sh ⌂ ⚲ ♟ ▥ ▥ ♣

EDINBURGH   Portobello

NT3074

Hopebank, 33 Hope Lane North, Portobello, Edinburgh, EH15 2PZ. **Open:** All year
0131 657 1149 Ms Williamson **D:** £20.00–£22.00 **S:** £20.00–£22.00 **Beds:** 2D 1T **Baths:** 2 Pr 1 Sh ⌂ 🅿 ⚲ ⊞ ▥ ▥ ♣ Victorian terraced villa, two minutes sea - beautiful promenade, 20 minutes city centre. Good food, Scottish hospitality, inexpensive bus service to centre. Non smoking, showers ensuite, TV in all rooms. Many golf courses nearby, good touring centre.

Cruachan, 6 Pittville Street, Edinburgh, EH15 2BY. Elegant Georgian villa adjacent to beach, promenade, city centre 2.5 miles. Good parking. **Open:** Easter to Oct
0131 669 2195 Mrs Thom **D:** £20.00–£22.00 **S:** £19.00–£21.00 **Beds:** 2D 1T 1S **Baths:** 2 Sh ⌂ (12) 🅿 (3) ⚲ ▥ ♟ ▥ ♣

EDINBURGH   Prestonfield

NT2771

Cameron Toll Guest House, 299 Dalkeith Road, Edinburgh, EH16 5JX. Eco-friendly family guest house on A7, 10 minutes from city centre. **Open:** All year
0131 667 2950 M Deans **Fax: 0131 662 1987**
stil@edinburghguesthouse.co.uk
www.edinburghguesthouse.co.uk **D:** £20.00–£35.00 **S:** £25.00–£37.00 **Beds:** 3F 2T 3D 3S **Baths:** 10 En 1 Pr ⌂ 🅿 (4) ⚲ ▥ ✕ ▥ ♿ ♣ cc

EDINBURGH   Slateford

NT2271

13 Moat Street, Edinburgh, EH14 1PE. Comfortable accommodation 2 miles city centre. Unrestricted street parking **Open:** Mar to Oct
0131 443 8266 Mrs Hume **D:** £17.00–£21.00 **S:** £18.00–£23.00 **Beds:** 1D 1T ⌂ 🅿 ▥ ▥ ♣

EDINBURGH   Trinity

NT2476   🔲 Old Chain Pier, Starbank Inn

Park View Villa Guest House, 254 Ferry Road, Edinburgh, EH5 3AN. Charming Edwardian house, well located for city breaks. Superb views. **Open:** All year **Grades:** STB 3 Star
0131 552 3456 *enquiries@parkviewvilla.com*
www.parkviewvilla.com **D:** £23.00–£40.00 **S:** £25.00–£70.00 **Beds:** 4F 2T 2D **Baths:** 8 En ⌂ 🅿 ⚲ ▥ ▥ ♣ cc

Fala

NT4361   🔲 Juniper Lea Hotel

Fala Hall Farm, Fala, Pathhead, Midlothian, EH37 5SZ. Secluded C16th farmhouse. 16m South East of Edinburgh. 0.5m from Fala (A 68). **Open:** All year (not Xmas/New Year)
01875 833249 (also fax) Lothian *H.Lothian@farming.co.uk* www.members.farmline.com/falahall_farm_BandB **D:** £17.00–£22.00 **S:** £22.00–£25.00 **Beds:** 1F 1T 1D **Baths:** 1 Sh ⌂ 🅿 ⊞ ♟ ▥ ♣

Falkirk

NS8680   🔲 Lawrie's Bar

Ashbank, Main Street, Falkirk, FK2 9UQ. Victorian cottage. Panoramic views. Near Grangemouth, M9 Motorway and trains. **Open:** All year **Grades:** STB 3 Star
01770 860 202 Mr & Mrs Ward **Fax: 01770 860 570** *ashbank@guest-house.freeserve.co.uk* **D:** £22.00–£25.00 **S:** £25.00–£35.00 **Beds:** 2T 1D 1S **Baths:** 4 En

Benaiah, *11 Culmore Place, Falkirk,*
FK1 2RP. Perfectly situated for exploring central Scotland. Warm welcome. Fantastic breakfast. **Open:** All year **Grades:** STB 2 Star
01324 621223 & 07931 616854 (M)
D Richardson *benaiah@onetel.net.uk*
D: £15.00–£18.00 **S:** £20.00–£24.00 **Beds:** 1F 1T 1D **Baths:** 1 Sh ⊁ ⬇ ⊠ ▦ ☙

Denecroft, *8 Lochgreen Road, Falkirk,*
FK1 5NJ. 1.5 miles from town centre, near railway station and hospital. **Open:** All year
01324 629258 (also fax) Mrs Stewart
D: £22.00–£26.00 **S:** £25.00–£30.00 **Beds:** 2T 1D 1S **Baths:** 3 En 1 Sh ⬇ (6) ⊁ ⊠ ▦ ☙ cc

Gorebridge

NT3460

Ivory House, *14 Vogrie Road, Gorebridge,*
EH23 4HH. Secluded Victorian house, 10 miles Edinburgh. Ideal base Borders/Coast.
Open: All year
01875 820755 Mrs Maton *ivory.house@*
talk21.com **D:** £25.00–£35.00 **S:** £27.50–
£40.00 **Beds:** 1F 1D 1T **Baths:** 3 En ⬇ ⬇ (6) ⊁ ⊠ ⓥ ▦ ☙ cc

Haddington

NT5173

28 Market Street,
Haddington, E Lothian, EH41 3JE.
Open: All year
Grades: STB 3 Star
01620 822465 Mrs Hamilton **Fax: 01620
825613 D:** £20.00–£26.00 **S:** £18.00–£22.00
Beds: 1F 1D 2T 1S **Baths:** 2 En 1 Pr 2 Sh ⬇ ⊁ ⊠ ⓥ ▦ ☙
Victorian building in centre of picturesque Haddington on Edinburgh (17 miles) bus route. Ample street parking and within walking distance of numerous excellent restaurants and pubs. Ideal base for golf. You are assured of a warm welcome and extremely comfortable accommodation.

Eaglescairnie Mains, *Haddington, E Lothian, EH41 4HN.* Superb farmhouse with wonderful views over conservation award-winning farm. **Open:** All year (not Xmas)
01620 810491 (also fax) Mrs Williams
williams.eagles@btinternet.com www.btinternet.
com/~williams.eagles **D:** £20.00–£27.00
S: £25.00–£35.00 **Beds:** 1D 1T 2S **Baths:** 2 En 1 Sh ⬇ ⬇ (6) ⊁ ⊠ ⓥ ▦ ☙ cc

Inveresk

NT3572

Delta House, *16 Carberry Road, Inveresk, Musselburgh, E Lothian, EH21 7TN.* A beautiful Victorian house, 7 miles east of central Edinburgh overlooking fields.
Open: All year (not Xmas)
0131 665 2107 (also fax) D: £20.00–£27.50
S: £30.00–£50.00 **Beds:** 1F 3D **Baths:** 2 En 1 Pr ⬇ (5) ⬇ (2) ⊁ ⊠ ⓥ ▦ ☙

Lasswade

NT3266 ⬅ *The Howgate, The Steading*

Gorton House, *Lasswade, Midlothian,*
EH18 1EH. Historic house overlooking Roslin Glen including tennis court. Edinburgh centre only 8 miles away. **Open:** All year
Grades: STB 2 Star
0131 440 4332 Mr & Mrs Young **Fax: 0131 440
1779** *jquintinyoung@hotmail.com* www.gorton.
plus.com **D:** £20.00–£25.00 **S:** £20.00–£25.00
Beds: 1F 2T **Baths:** 3 En ⬇ ⬇ (6) ⊠ ⋔ ⓥ ▦ ☙

Laurieston

NS9079

Oaklands, *32 Polmont Road, Laurieston, Falkirk, FK2 9QT.* **Open:** All year (not Xmas)
Grades: STB 4 Star
01324 610671 & 07050 675231 (M)
Mrs Fattori **Fax: 01324 610671** *b-and-b@*
oaklands.ndirect.co.uk **D:** £25.00–£35.00
S: £35.00 **Beds:** 1D 2T **Baths:** 3 En ⬇ ⬇ (4) ⊁ ⊠ ▦ ☙ cc
Edwardian house, 1.5 miles Falkirk, situated 5 mins M9 (J5), taking you to Edinburgh (east), Glasgow, Stirling (west). 20 mins by road to Edinburgh Airport. Near 2 mainline rail stations, frequent service to Edinburgh/Glasgow (approx 20 mins each way).

Linlithgow

NS9977 ⬅ *Four Marys*

Thornton,
Edinburgh Road, Linlithgow, EH49 6AA.
Open: All year (not Xmas/New Year)
Grades: STB 4 Star, AA 4 Diamond
01506 844 693 Mrs Inglis **Fax: 01506 844 876**
inglisthornton@hotmail.com
www.thornton-scotland.co.uk **D:** £22.00–
£25.00 **S:** £25.00–£30.00 **Beds:** 1T 1D
Baths: 2 En ⬇ (12) ⬇ (4) ⊁ ⊠ ⓥ ▦ ☙ cc
Victorian house near Union Canal, five minutes from station, town centre and Linlithgow Palace (Birthplace of Mary Queen of Scots). Easy road/rail access to Edinburgh, Stirling, Glasgow. Large garden. Winner AA 'Best Breakfast of the Year' award 2001 Scotland.

Belsyde Farm, *Lanark Road, Linlithgow, W Lothian, EH49 6QE.*
Looking for somewhere special? Go no further. Check out www.belsydehouse.co.uk **Open:** Jan to Dec **Grades:** STB 3 Star, AA 3 Diamond
01506 842098 (also fax) Mrs Hay
belsyde.guesthouse@vigin.net
www.belsydehouse.co.uk **D:** £19.00–£25.00
S: £20.00–£25.00 **Beds:** 1F 1D 2S **Baths:** 1 En 2 Sh ⬇ ⬇ (10) ⊁ ⊠ ⋔ ⓥ ▦ ☙ cc

Woodcockdale Farm, *Lanark Road, Linlithgow, W Lothian, EH49 6QE.* Look no further. Easy access to airport, Edinburgh, Stirling. Phone now. **Open:** All year
01506 842088 (also fax) Mrs Erskine
arnhouse@hotmail.com www.arnhouse.co.uk
D: £18.00–£25.00 **S:** £18.00–£25.00 **Beds:** 3F 2D 1T 1S **Baths:** 4 En 1 Pr 2 Sh ⬇ ⬇ ⊁ ⊠ ⋔ ⓥ ▦ ☙ cc

Loanhead

NT2765

Inveravon House Hotel, *9 Inveravon Road, Loanhead, Midlothian, EH20 9EF.* Large Victorian house. **Open:** All year
0131 440 0124 Mr Potter **D:** £20.00–£25.00
S: £25.00 **Beds:** 5F 5D 1T 3S **Baths:** 13 En ⬇ ⊠ ⋔ ▦ ☙ cc

Aaron Glen, *7 Nivensknowe Road, Loanhead, Edinburgh, EH20 9AU.* Hotel quality accommodation at B&B prices.
Open: All year
0131 440 1293 Mrs Davidson **Fax: 0131 440
2155** *aaronglen1@aol.com* www.members.
edinburgh.org/aaron **D:** £20.00–£30.00
S: £25.00–£60.00 **Beds:** 1F 3D 1T **Baths:** 5 En ⬇ ⬇ (8) ⊁ ⊠ ⋔ ⓥ ▦ ☙3 ☙ cc

Longniddry

NT4476

13 Glassel Park Road, *Longniddry,*
EH32 0NY. 20 minutes by train to Edinburgh. Easy access to golf courses. **Open:** Easter to Sept **Grades:** STB 3 Star
01875 852333 Mrs Morrison **D:** £18.00–
£20.00 **S:** £25.00 **Beds:** 1D 1T **Baths:** 2 Pr ⬇ (8) ⬇ (2) ⊠ ▦ ☙

Musselburgh

NT3573

Craigesk, *10 Albert Terrace, Musselburgh, Midlothian, EH21 7LR.* Terraced villa overlooking golf and racecourse. Bus/railway close by. **Open:** All year
Grades: STB 3 Star
0131 665 3344 & 0131 665 3170 Miss Mitchell
Fax: 0131 665 3344 *craigesk-b-b@faxvia.net*
D: £17.00–£19.00 **S:** £18.00–£20.00 **Beds:** 2F 1D 1T 1S **Baths:** 2 Sh ⬇ ⬇ (4) ⊠ ⋔ ⓥ ▦ ☙

18 Woodside Gardens, *Musselburgh, Midlothian, EH21 7LJ.* Quiet bungalow, easy access Edinburgh, seaside, countryside and golf parking. **Open:** All year
0131 665 3170 & 0131 665 3344 Mrs Aitken
D: £17.00–£19.00 **S:** £17.00–£19.00 **Beds:** 1F 1D 1T **Baths:** 2 Sh ♿ 🅿 (4) 📺 ⊁ Ⅴ 🅙 & ♨

North Berwick

NT5585   ⚐ *Tantallion Lodge, County Hotel*

Golf Hotel, *34 Dirleton Avenue, North Berwick, E Lothian, EH39 4BH.* Family run hotel in seaside town close to golf courses.
Open: All year **Grades:** STB 1 Star
01620 892202 Mr Searle **Fax:** 01620 892290
D: £28.00–£66.00 **S:** £28.00–£50.00 **Beds:** 5F 1D 3T 2S **Baths:** 10 Pr 1 Sh ♿ 🅿 (20) ⊁ 📺 ✕ Ⅴ 🅙 ♨

Troon, *Dirleton Road, North Berwick, E Lothian, EH39 5DF.* Comfortable, spacious, pleasant bungalow outskirts seaside town, 35 minutes Edinburgh. **Open:** Apr to Oct
Grades: STB 3 Star
01620 893555 Mrs Dixon **D:** £18.00–£25.00 **Beds:** 1D **Baths:** 1 En 🅿 (1) ⊁ 📺 🅙 ♨

The Belhaven Hotel, *28 Westgate, North Berwick, E Lothian, EH39 4AH.* Overlooking golf course and sea; convenient for town centre and railway station. **Open:** Dec to Oct
01620 893009 M Free **D:** £19.00–£26.00 **S:** £20.00–£35.00 **Beds:** 2F 5T 2S **Baths:** 5 En 4 Sh ♿ (9) 📺 ✕ Ⅴ 🅙 ♨

Pathhead

NT3964

The Old Farm House, *47 Main Street, Pathhead, Midlothian, EH37 5PZ.* Comfortable B&B, 12 miles south of Edinburgh on the A68. **Open:** All year
01875 320100 Mr Reid **Fax:** 01875 320501
oldfarmhouse@tinyworld.co.uk
scotland2000.com/oldfarmhouse **D:** £16.00–£18.00 **S:** £20.00–£25.00 **Beds:** 1F 1T 1D **Baths:** 2 En 1 Pr ♿ 🅿 (3) 📺 ⊁ 🅙 ♨ cc

Penicuik

NT2360

Loanstone House, *Loanstone, Penicuik, EH26 8PH.* A Victorian family house in peaceful country surroundings.
Open: Easter to Oct
01968 672449 Mrs Patch *the.patches@btinternet.com* **D:** £17.50 **S:** £20.00 **Beds:** 1D **Baths:** 1 Sh ♿ 🅿 (2) ⊁ 📺 ⊁ 🅙 ♨

South Queensferry

NT1277

Priory Lodge, *8 The Loan, South Queensferry, EH30 9NS.* Beautiful guest house in a tranquil village, twenty minutes from Edinburgh. **Open:** All year (not Xmas)
Grades: STB 4 Diamond
0131 331 4345 (also fax) C C Lamb *calmyn@aol.com* www.queensferry.com **D:** £27.00–£30.00 **S:** £40.00–£56.00 **Beds:** 3F 1D 1T **Baths:** 5 En ♿ 🅿 ⊁ 📺 Ⅴ 🅙 ♨ cc

Stoneyburn

NS9762

Eisenach, *1 Cannop Crescent, Stoneyburn, Bathgate, W Lothian, EH47 8EF.* Large detached countryside villa. **Open:** All year
01501 762659 Mrs Gray *cagray@eisenach.demon.co.uk* **D:** £15.00 **S:** £20.00 **Beds:** 1F 1D 1T 1S **Baths:** 1 Pr ♿ 🅿 (3) ⊁ 📺 ✕ Ⅴ 🅙

Uphall

NT0572

20 Houston Mains Holdings, *Uphall, Broxburn, EH52 6PA.* Charming guest house eleven miles from Edinburgh. Railway link nearby. **Open:** All year
01506 854044 Mr Fisher **Fax:** 01506 855118
michaelfisher@cmgh.freeserve.co.uk
www.coille-mhor.co.uk **D:** £23.00–£25.00 **S:** £35.00–£37.00 **Beds:** 1F 1T 4D **Baths:** 6 En ♿ ⊁ 📺 🅙 & ♨ cc

Winchburgh

NT0875

Turnlea, *123 Main Street, Winchburgh, Broxburn, EH52 6QP.* Central location. Edinburgh 12 miles and Linlithgow 6 miles. **Open:** All year (not Xmas/New Year) **Grades:** STB 3 Star
01506 890124 R W Redwood **Fax:** 01506 891573 *royturnlea@hotmail.com* **D:** £22.00–£25.00 **S:** £25.00–£30.00 **Beds:** 1D 2T **Baths:** 3 En ♿ 🅿 (3) ⊁ 📺 🅙 ♨ cc

Orkney

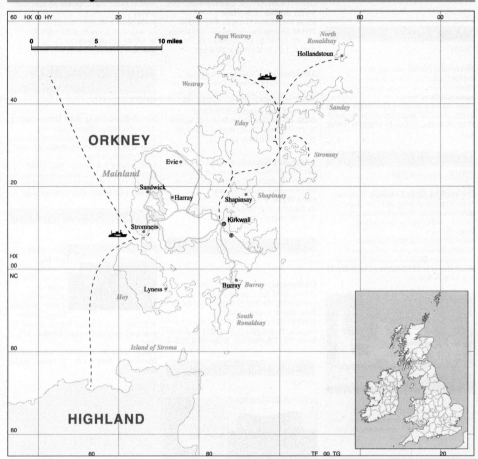

0   5   10 miles

Papa Westray

North Ronaldsay

Hollandstoun

Westray

ORKNEY

Sanday

Eday

Mainland

Stronsay

Evie

Sandwick

Harray

Shapinsay

Shapinsay

Stromness

Kirkwall

HX 00
NC

Lyness

Burray   Burray

Hoy

South Ronaldsay

Island of Stroma

HIGHLAND

BURRAY   Burray

ND4795   ⫘ *Galley Inn*

Ankersted, *Burray, Orkney,* KW17 2SS.
Purpose-built guest house, overlooking bay
into Scapa Flow and Churchill Barrier.
Open: All year
01856 731217 (also fax) Mrs Watt
ankerstead@tinyworld.co.uk **D:** £18.00–£20.00
S: £18.00–£20.00 **Beds:** 2D 2S **Baths:** 4 En
⯑ ⯑ 𝖯 (6) ⊡ ⯑ ⯑ ▥, ⯑

BEDROOMS
D = Double
T = Twin
S = Single
F = Family

All details shown are as
supplied by B&B owners in
Autumn 2001

HOY   Lyness

ND3094

Stoneyquoy, *Lyness, Hoy, Orkney,*
KW16 3NY. Orcadian/Dutch couple - 200 acre
farm - leaflet available, guided tours.
Open: All year (not Xmas/New Year)
Grades: STB 3 Star
01856 791234 (also fax) Mrs Budge
arthurlouise@talk21.com www.visithoy.com
D: £17.00–£19.00 **S:** £17.00–£19.00 **Beds:** 1T
1D 1S **Baths:** 2 En 1 Sh ⯑ 𝖯 (6) ⯑ ⊡ ✕ ⊡ ▥,
⯑

MAINLAND   Evie

HY3525

Woodwick House, *Evie, Orkney,*
KW17 2PQ. Historic country house, bluebell
Woodland, Burn secluded Bay, Open Fires.
Open: All year **Grades:** STB 3 Star
01856 751330 A Herdman **Fax: 01856 751383**
woodwickhouse@appleonline.net www.orknet.co.
uk/woodwick **D:** £27.00–£38.00 **S:** £30.00–
£46.00 **Beds:** 3T 5D **Baths:** 4 En ⯑ ⯑ ⊡ ✕
⊡ ▥, ⯑

BATHROOMS
En = Ensuite
Pr = Private
Sh = Shared

Planning a longer stay? Always ask for any special rates

MAINLAND   Harray
HY3218

Merkister Hotel, *Harray, Orkney, KW17 2LF.* Situated on the shores of Loch Harray. Panoramic views. **Open:** All year (not Xmas/New Year)
01856 771336 L Munson **Fax: 01856 771515**
D: £25.00–£47.00 **S:** £25.00–£55.00 **Beds:** 2F 3T 2D 2S **Baths:** 13 En 1 Pr ♿ 🄿 📺 📖 ★ × 📺 📖. ☕ cc

MAINLAND   Kirkwall
HY4510   ⬡ *Lynnfield Hotel*

Lav'rockha Guest House, *Inganess Road, Kirkwall, Orkney, KW15 1SP.* Superior accommodation at an affordable price, Finalist - 1999 Orkney Food awards. **Open:** All year
01856 876103 (also fax) J Webster
lavrockha@orkney.com www.norsecom.co.uk/lavrockha **D:** £20.00–£24.00 **S:** £24.00–£30.00 **Beds:** 1F 2T 2D **Baths:** 5 En ♿ 🄿 ⬇ 📺 ★ × 📺 📖. & ✳ ★ cc

Royal Oak Guest House, *Holm Road, Kirkwall, Orkney, KW15 1PY.* **Open:** All year (not Xmas/New Year)
01856 877177 (also fax) *royal.oak@btinternet.com* www.royal.oak.btinternet.co.uk
D: £18.00–£23.00 **S:** £20.00–£26.00 **Beds:** 2F 3T 2D 1S **Baths:** 8 En ♿ (0) 🄿 (10) ⬇ 📺 📺 📖. ☕ cc
Royal Oak Guest House is a modern, purpose built guest house with views of Scapa Flow, close to Highland Park Distillery and walking distance from St Magnus Cathedral. Ideally situated for touring the many historical and archaeological sites on Orkney.

Elderwood, *4 Park Loan, Kirkwall, Orkney, KW15 1PU.* Modern bungalow in quiet cul-de-sac.
Open: All year
01856 872657 Mrs Omand **D:** £15.00
S: £15.00 **Beds:** 1D 1T **Baths:** 2 Sh 🄿 (2) ⬇ 📺 📖. ★

Polrudden Guest House, *Peerie Sea Loan, Kirkwall, Orkney, KW15 1UH.* Peaceful location, ten minutes walk from town centre. Stunning view. **Open:** All year (not Xmas) **Grades:** STB 3 Star
01856 874761 Mrs Thornton **Fax: 01856 870950** *linda@polrudden.com* www.polrudden.com **D:** £24.00 **S:** £30.00 **Beds:** 2F 5T **Baths:** 7 En ♿ 🄿 (7) 📺 × 📖. ★ cc

Shearwood, *Muddiesdale Road, off Pickaquoy Road, Kirkwall, Orkney, KW15 1RR.* Quiet country location, 10 mins walk town centre. Wonderful archaeology nearby. **Open:** All year **Grades:** STB 2 Star
01856 873494 Mrs Braun **D:** £16.00–£20.00 **S:** £17.00 **Beds:** 2T 1D **Baths:** 2 Sh 1 En ♿ (12) 🄿 ⬇ 📺 📺 📖. & ★

7 Matches Square, *Kirkwall, Orkney, KW15 1AU.* Personally run neighbouring houses. Centrally situated, shops, buses, ferries nearby. **Open:** All year
01856 872440 Mrs Parkins **D:** £15.00–£17.00 **S:** £16.00–£18.00 **Beds:** 2T 1D 2S **Baths:** 1 En 2 Sh ♿ 🄿 (2) 📺 ★ 📺 📖. ★

MAINLAND   Sandwick
HY2519

Netherstove, *Sandwick, Stromness, Orkney, KW16 3LS.* Farmhouse B&B, overlooking the Bay of Skaill. Near Skara Brae. **Open:** Easter to Nov
01856 841625 (also fax) Mrs Poke *ann.poke@virgin.net* **D:** £16.00–£18.50 **S:** £16.00–£18.50 **Beds:** 1D 1T **Baths:** 2 Sh ♿ 🄿 ⬇ 📺 × 📺 📖. ★

MAINLAND   Stromness
HY2509

Lindisfarne, *Stromness, Orkney, KW16 3LL.* **Open:** Jan to Dec
01856 850828 MrsWorthington
Fax: 01856 850805 *epnworthington@hotmail.com* www.geocities.com/twworthington **D:** £20.00–£22.00
Beds: 1F 4T **Baths:** 5 En 🄿 📺 📖. ★
Modern detached house, set in a elevated rural location, overlooking the town of Stromness views of Scapa Flow, the island of Gramsay, Hoy Hills and the island of Hoy, also Stromness harbour.

RATES
D = Price range per person sharing in a double or twin room
S = Price range for a single room

Orca Hotel, *76 Victoria Street, Stromness, Orkney, KW16 3BS.* Harbourside guest house in romantic fishing village. All amenities nearby, cellar bistro. **Open:** All year (not Xmas)
01856 850447 Ms Fischler *info@orcahotel.com* www.orcahotel.com **D:** £18.00–£25.00 **S:** £20.00–£25.00 **Beds:** 2F 1S 1D 2T **Baths:** 6 En ♿ 🄿 (1) 📺 ★ × 📺 📖. ★

NORTH RONALDSAY   Hollandstoun
HY7553

North Ronaldsay Bird Observatory, *North Ronaldsay, Orkney, KW17 2BE.* Comfortable island guest accommodation. Solar and wind powered. **Open:** All year (not Xmas/New Year)
01857 633200 A E Duncan **Fax: 01857 633207** *alison@nrbo.prestel.co.uk* www.nrbo.f2s.com **D:** £18.00 **S:** £23.00 **Beds:** 2D 2T **Baths:** 4 En ♿ 🄿 ⬇ 📺 × 📺 📖. &2 ★ cc

SHAPINSAY   Shapinsay
HY5017

Harroldsgarth, *Shapinsay, Orkney, KW17 2EA.* Superior accommodation, peaceful island location, short ferry trip Orkney's capital **Open:** All year (not Xmas/New Year) **Grades:** STB 3 Star
01856 711262 Mrs Evans **D:** £20.00 **S:** £20.00 **Beds:** 1T 2D **Baths:** 1 Pr 1 Sh ♿ 🄿 (5) ⬇ 📺 × 📺 📖. ★

Perthshire & Kinross

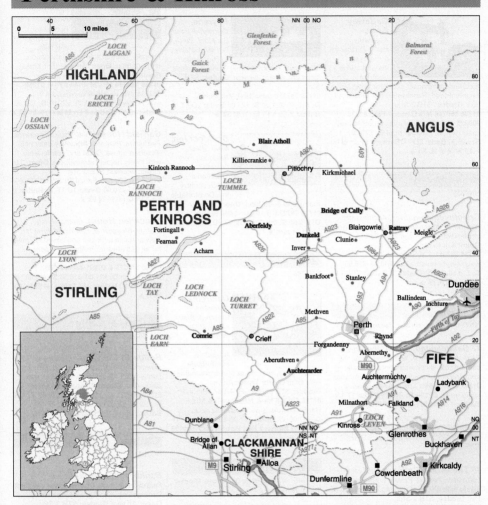

HIGHLAND

Glenfeshie
Forest

Gaick
Forest

Balmoral
Forest

80

LOCH
LAGGAN

A86

LOCH
ERICHT

LOCH
OSSIAN

Grampian

A9

ANGUS

60

Blair Atholl

Kinloch Rannoch

Killiecrankie

Pitlochry

Kirkmichael

LOCH
RANNOCH

LOCH
TUMMEL

A924

PERTH AND
KINROSS

Fortingall

Fearnan

Aberfeldy

Bridge of Cally

A923   Blairgowrie   Rattray

Dunkeld   Clunie

Meigle

A926

LOCH
LYON

Acharn

A827

A826

Inver

Bankfoot

Stanley

A94

A923

STIRLING

LOCH
TAY

LOCH
LEDNOCK

LOCH
TURRET

Ballindean   Inchture

Dundee

A85

A822

Methven

A85

Perth   Rhynd

Firth of Tay

A92

20

Comrie

Crieff

Forgandenny

Abernethy

FIFE

LOCH
EARN

Aberuthven

Auchterarder

Auchtermuchty

Ladybank

A84

A9

A823

Milnathort   Falkland

A914   A916

A81

Dunblane

A91   LOCH
LEVEN

NO   00

NT

Bridge of
Allan   CLACKMANNAN-
SHIRE

Kinross

Glenrothes

Buckhaven

M9   Stirling   Alloa

Dunfermline

A92   Kirkcaldy

Cowdenbeath

M90

Aberfeldy

NN8549   *Black Watch Inn*

Ardtornish, *Kenmore Street, Aberfeldy, PH15 2BL.* In beautiful friendly High-land Perthshire with walking, golf, cycling, water sports and more. **Open:** All year (not Xmas/New Year) **Grades:** STB 3 Star **01887 820629** Mrs Ross *ardtornish@ talk21.com* **D:** £16.00–£20.00 **S:** £16.00–£20.00 **Beds:** 1D 1T 1D/F **Baths:** 1 En 1 Sh 🅿 (3) ⅍ 📺 ⅴ 🏾 🛋

Tomvale, *Tom of Cluny Farm, Aberfeldy, Perthshire, PH15 2JT.* Modern farmhouse with outstanding views of Upper Tay Valley. **Open:** All year (not Xmas/New Year) **01887 820171 & 07808 515666 (M)** Mrs Kennedy **Fax: 01887 820171** *tomvale@ aol.com* tomvale.co.uk **D:** £18.00 **S:** £20.00 **Beds:** 1F 1D **Baths:** 1 Sh ⛲ 🛏 🅿 📺 ⅻ ✕ ⅴ 🏾 🛋

Handa, *Taybridge Road, Aberfeldy, PH15 2BH.* Pleasant views overlooking golf course and river. Quiet location. **Open:** All year (not Xmas/New Year) **01887 820334** Mrs Bassett-Smith **D:** £18.00 **Beds:** 1T 1D **Baths:** 2 En ⛲ 🅿 📺 ⅴ 🏾 🛋

Abernethy

NO1816

Gattaway Farm, *Abernethy, Perth, Perthshire & Kinross, PH2 9LQ.* Large Georgian/ Victorian farmhouse; excellent views, excellent food. Recommended. **Open:** All year **Grades:** STB 3 Star
01738 850746 Mrs Dawson **Fax: 01738 850925** *tarduff@aol.com* www.smoothhound. co.uk/hotels/gattaway.html **D:** £20.00
S: £25.00 **Beds:** 2D 1T **Baths:** 3 En ⌷ ₽ (4)

Aberuthven

NN9815

Craiginver, *Aberuthven, Auchterarder, PH3 1HE.* Victorian former manse in large garden with views over Earn Valley.
Open: Apr to Oct
01764 662411 J M Smith *jms@ craiginver.freeserve.co.uk* **D:** £18.50–£19.50
S: £19.50–£20.50 **Beds:** 2T **Baths:** 1 En 1 Pr
₽ (8)

Acharn

NN7543   ⌷ *Croft Na Caber, Kenmore Hotel*

12 Ballinlaggan, *Acharn, Aberfeldy, Perthshire, PH15 2HT.* Warm welcome, comfortable accommodation, hill walking, pony trekking, fishing, golf. **Open:** All year **01887 830409** Mrs Spiers *bandb.acharn@ virgin.net* **D:** £15.00 **S:** £15.00 **Beds:** 1T 1S
Baths: 1 Sh ⌷ ₽ (1)

Auchterarder

NN9412

10 The Grove, Collearn, *Auchterarder, Perthshire, PH3 1PT.* Private house in quiet estate with off-street parking. **Open:** Jan to Dec **Grades:** STB 2 Star
01764 662036 Mrs McFarlane **D:** £17.50– £18.50 **S:** £18.00–£20.00 **Beds:** 1T **Baths:** 1 Sh ₽ (1)

Ballindean

NO2529

The Orchard, *Easter Ballindean, Inchture, Perth, PH14 9QS.* Characterful cottage in lovely rural setting. Magnificent views. Sunny conservatory. **Open:** Apr to Oct
01828 686318 J.D Burrowes *theorchard@ exl.co.uk* www.theorchard.exl.co.uk **D:** £22.00
S: £25.00–£27.00 **Beds:** 1T 2D **Baths:** 2 En 1 Pr ⌷ ₽ (4)

Bankfoot

NO0635

Kayrene, *Cairneyhill Road, Bankfoot, Perth, PH1 4AD.* Gateway to Highlands. Ideal touring spot, golfing, fishing, castles, lochs etc. **Open:** All year **Grades:** STB 3 Star
01738 787338 (also fax) Mrs McKay
D: £19.50–£21.00 **S:** £25.00 **Beds:** 2D 1T
Baths: 2 En 1 Pr ₽ (3)

Bankfoot Inn, *Main Street, Bankfoot, Perth, PH1 4AB.* Traditional C19th country inn. Comfortable rooms and good food. **Open:** All year **01738 787243** *bankfootinn@barbox.net*
D: £19.00 **S:** £19.00 **Beds:** 2T 2D 2S **Baths:** 2 Sh ⌷ ⛄ × ⫿

Blair Atholl

NN8764

Dalgreine, *off St Andrews Crescent, Blair Atholl, Pitlochry, Perthshire, PH18 5SX.* Attractive comfortable guest house, set in beautiful surroundings near Blair Castle. **Open:** All year **Grades:** STB 3 Star GH, AA 4 Diamond
01796 481276 Mr & Mrs Pywell & Mrs F Hardie *mail@dalgreine-guest-house.co.uk*
D: £17.00–£20.00 **S:** £17.00–£20.00 **Beds:** 1F 2D 2T 1S **Baths:** 2 En 1 Pr 1 Sh ⌷ ₽ (6) ⫿ × ⫿ ⬛ ⌷

Blairgowrie

NO1745   ⌷ *Angus Hotel, Drumnacree, Moorfield, Kinloch House*

The Laurels Guest House, *Golf Course Road, Rosemount, Blairgowrie, Perthshire, PH10 6LH.* **Open:** Jan to Dec **Grades:** STB 3 Star
01250 874920 (also fax) Mr & Mrs McPherson **D:** £19.50–£20.00 **S:** £22.00– £30.00 **Beds:** 2D 3T 1S **Baths:** 4 En ⌷ ₽ (8) ⫿ ⫿ × ⬛ ⌷ cc
Converted C18th farmhouse. First class cooking, licensed. Our bedrooms are very well-equipped with power showers in ensuite rooms and bathroom.

Ridgeway,

Ridgeway, *Wester Essendy, Blairgowrie, Perthshire, PH10 6RA.* Bungalow overlooking loch and hills.
Friendly, comfortable accommodation, large garden. **Open:** All year (not Xmas)
Grades: STB 3 Star
01250 884734 Mrs Mathews **Fax: 01250 884735** *pam.mathews@btinternet.com*
www.ridgewayb-b.co.uk **D:** £22.00 **S:** £22.00
Beds: 1D 1T **Baths:** 2 En ⌷ ₽ (8) ⫿ ⫿ ⬛ ⌷

Garfield House, *Perth Road, Blairgowrie, Perthshire, PH10 6ED.* Attractive detached Victorian house. Quiet and comfortable with lovely homely atmosphere. **Open:** Jan to Dec **Grades:** STB 3 Star
01250 872999 Mrs Safsaf **D:** £17.00–£20.00
S: £17.00–£20.00 **Beds:** 1D 1T 1S **Baths:** 2 En 1 Pr ₽ (4) ⫿ ⫿ ⬛ ⌷

Shocarjen House, *Balmoral Road, Rattray, Blairgowrie, Perthshire, PH10 7AF.* New purpose built bed and breakfast. Ideal for all activities in Perthshire. **Open:** All year **Grades:** STB 3 Star
01250 870525 & 07801 436662 (M)
Mrs Beattie **D:** £17.00–£18.50 **S:** £19.00
Beds: 1T 1D **Baths:** 2 En ⌷ ₽ (6) ⫿ ⫿ ⫿ × ⫿ ⬛ ⌷

Bridge of Cally

NO1351

Bridge Of Cally Hotel, *Bridge of Cally, Blairgowrie, Perthshire, PH10 7JJ.* Small family hotel. Cooking award. Walk over 2000 acres. **Open:** All year (not Xmas)
01250 886231 Mr McCosh **D:** £20.00–£27.50
S: £20.00–£27.50 **Beds:** 1F 3D 4T 1S
Baths: 7 En 2 Pr ⌷ ₽ ⫿ ⫿ × ⫿ ⬛ ⌷

Clunie

NO1043

Bankhead, *Clunie, Blairgowrie, Perthshire, PH10 6SG.* Quiet house on small farm, golfing, fishing, walking nearby.
Open: All year **Grades:** STB 3 Star
01250 884281 (also fax) Mrs Wightman
ian@ihwightman.freeserve.co.uk **D:** £18.00
S: £20.00–£21.00 **Beds:** 1F 1T **Baths:** 2 En ⌷ ₽ (3) ⫿ ⫿ ⫿ × ⫿ ⬛ ⌷

Comrie

NN7722   ⌷ *Achray Hotel, St Fillands, Comrie Hotel*

St Margarets, *Braco Road, Comrie, Crieff, Perthshire, PH6 2HP.* Attractive Victorian family house, good fishing, golfing, walking, horse riding. **Open:** Mar to Nov **Grades:** STB 3 Star
01764 670413 Mr & Mrs Paterson **D:** £18.00– £20.00 **S:** £18.00–£20.00 **Beds:** 1D 2T
Baths: 1 En 1 Sh ⌷ (3) ₽ (4) ⫿ ⫿ ⫿ ⬛ ⌷

Planning a longer stay? Always ask for any special rates

Millersfield, *Dalginross, Comrie, Crieff, Perthshire, PH6 2HE.* Modern centrally heated bungalow. Peaceful location, attractive garden and warm welcome. **Open:** All year (not Xmas/New Year) **01764 670073** Mrs Rae **D:** £19.00–£20.00 **S:** £19.00–£20.00 **Beds:** 1D 1T ❄ (12) ▣ (3) ⅍ ▦ Ⅴ ▦ ⅋ ⅃

Crieff

NN8621 ◀ *Meadow Inn*

Merlindale, *Perth Road, Crieff, PH7 3EQ.* **Open:** Feb to Dec **Grades:** STB 4 Star, AA 4 Diamond **01764 655205 (also fax)** Mr & Mrs Clifford *merlin.dale@virgin.net* www.merlindale.co.uk **D:** £22.50–£27.00 **S:** £25.00–£35.00 **Beds:** 1F 1T **Baths:** 2 En ❄ ▣ ⅍ ▦ Ⅹ ▦ ⅃ Luxury Georgian house, all bedrooms ensuite with tea/coffee making facilities. We have a jacuzzi bath, garden, ample off-road parking, satellite television, and extensive library. Cordon Bleu cooking is our speciality. A warm welcome awaits you in this non-smoking house.

Crieff Holiday Village, *Turret Bank, Crieff, Perthshire, PH7 4JN.* Within easy walking distance from town centre. Quietly situated modern family home. **Open:** All year **01764 653513** Mrs Sloan **Fax: 01764 655028** *katie@turretbank7.freeserve.co.uk* **D:** £15.00–£19.00 **S:** £19.00–£23.00 **Beds:** 1F 1T 1D **Baths:** 3 En ❄ ▣ (6) ⅍ ⅄ Ⅴ ▦ ⅃

Dunkeld

NO0243

Taybank Hotel, *Tay Terrace, Dunkeld, Perthshire, PH8 0AQ.* Friendly music bar, spontaneous sessions, beautiful location, tasteful rooms. **Open:** All year **01350 727340** Mr Close **Fax: 01350 728606** *admin@dunkeld.co.uk* **D:** £17.50 **S:** £17.50–£22.50 **Beds:** 2F 1T 1D 1S **Baths:** 2 Sh ❄ ▣ Ⅹ cc

Fearnan

NN7244

Tigh An Loan Hotel, *Fearnan, Aberfeldy, Perthshire, PH15 2PF.* Old C19th inn; beautifully situated overlooking Loch Tay. **Open:** Easter to Oct **Grades:** STB 1 Star **01887 830249** Mr Kelloe **D:** £29.00–£31.00 **S:** £29.00–£31.00 **Beds:** 1F 3S **Baths:** 3 En 2 Sh ❄ ▣ (25) Ⅴ ⅄ Ⅹ Ⅴ ⅃ cc

Forgandenny

NO0818

Battledown, *Forgandenny, Perth, PH2 9EL.* Explore Scotland from this perfectly situated comfortable C18th cottage. **Open:** All year **Grades:** STB 4 Star **01738 812471** Mr & Mrs Dunsire **Fax: 01738 812 471** *ian@battledown34.freeserve.co.uk* **D:** £20.00–£23.00 **S:** £25.00 **Beds:** 1T 2D **Baths:** 3 En ▣ (3) ⅍ Ⅴ ⅄ Ⅴ ▦ ⅋ ⅃ cc

Fortingall

NN7347 ◀ *Fortingall Hotel, Kenmore Hotel, Coshieville Hotel, Farley House*

Fortingall Hotel, *Fortingall, Aberfeldy, Perthshire, PH15 2NQ.* Fine food, log fires, comfortable bedrooms and excellent Highland hospitality. **Open:** Mar to Dec **01887 830367 (also fax)** *hotel@fortingall.com* www.fortingall.com **D:** £27.50 **S:** £27.50 **Beds:** 2F 4T 4D **Baths:** 10 En ❄ ▣ (12) Ⅴ ⅄ Ⅹ Ⅴ ⅃ cc

Kinnighallen Farm, *Duneaves Road, Fortingall, Aberfeldy, Perthshire, PH15 2LR.* Come and have a relaxing stay in this sleepy, rural backwater where wildlife abounds. **Open:** Apr to Nov **Grades:** STB 1 Star **01887 830619 (also fax)** Mrs Kininmonth *a.kininmonth@talk21.com* www.heartlander. scotland.net/home/kinnighallen.htm **D:** £15.00 **S:** £15.00 **Beds:** 1D 1T 1S **Baths:** 1 Sh ❄ (2) ▣ (5) Ⅴ ⅄ ▦

Inver

NO0142 ◀ *Atholl Arms Hotel*

Neil Gow Cottage, *Inver, Dunkeld, Perthshire, PH8 0JR.* Neil Gow, C18th fiddler, lived here - lovely walks, central for touring. **Open:** Easter to Oct **01350 727278 (also fax)** Mrs Lyon **D:** £14.00–£15.00 **S:** £14.00–£15.00 **Beds:** 1T 1D **Baths:** 1 Sh ▣ (8) Ⅴ ▦ ⅃

National Grid References given are for villages, towns and cities – not for individual houses

Killiecrankie

NN9162 ◀ *Atholl Arms, Tilt Hotel, Claymore Hotel, Killiecrankie Hotel*

Tighdornie, *Killiecrankie, Pitlochry, Perthshire, PH16 5LR.* Modern house in historic Killiecrankie. 2.5 miles from Blair Castle. **Open:** All year **01796 473276 (also fax)** Mrs Sanderson *tigh_dornie@btinternet.com* **D:** £22.00–£25.00 **S:** £27.00–£30.00 **Beds:** 1T 2D **Baths:** 3 En ❄ (12) ▣ (4) ⅍ Ⅴ Ⅴ ▦ ⅃

Kinloch Rannoch

NN6658

Dunalastair Hotel, *Kinloch Rannoch, Pitlochry, Perthshire, PH16 5PW.* C18th former shooting lodge, now a wonderful hotel with luxurious rooms. **Open:** All year **01882 632323** Paul Edwards **Fax: 01882 632371** *reservations@dunalastair.co.uk* www.dunalastair.co.uk **D:** £27.50 **S:** £27.50 **Beds:** 2F 10D 10T 1S **Baths:** 25 En ❄ ▣ ⅄ Ⅹ Ⅴ ▦ ⅃ ✳ ⅃ cc

Bunrannoch House, *Kinloch Rannoch, Pitlochry, Perthshire, PH16 5QB.* Lovely country house, beautiful views, open fires. Warm welcome and excellent food. **Open:** All year (not Xmas/New Year) **01882 632407 (also fax)** Mrs Skeaping *bun.house@tesco.net* www.bunrannoch.co.uk **D:** £22.00–£24.00 **S:** £22.00–£24.00 **Beds:** 2F 3D 2T **Baths:** 5 Pr 2 Sh ❄ ▣ (10) ⅍ ⅄ Ⅹ Ⅴ ▦ ⅃ cc

Kinross

NO1102

Lochleven Inn, *6 Swansacre, Kinross, Fife, KY13 7TE.* Local friendly inn (public bar). **Open:** All year **01577 864185** Mr McGregor **D:** £18.00 **S:** £18.00 **Beds:** 1F 1T 1D **Baths:** 2 Pr ❄ ▣ (2) Ⅴ ⅄ Ⅹ Ⅴ ▦ ⅃

Kirkmichael

NO0860

Curran House, *Kirkmichael, Blairgowrie, Perthshire, PH10 7NA.* Traditional Scottish house. Log fire. Home baking on arrival. **Open:** Jan to Sept **01250 881229** Mr & Mrs Van der Veldt **Fax: 01250 881448** *a.m.vanderveldt@tesco.net* **D:** £18.00–£36.00 **Beds:** 2D 1T **Baths:** 1 Pr 1 Sh ❄ ▣ ⅍ Ⅴ Ⅴ ▦ ⅃

Meigle

NO2844

Loanhead House, *Dundee Road, Meigle, Blairgowrie, PH12 8SF.* Superb accommodation and food in edge of castle estate location. **Open:** All year (not Xmas/New Year) **01828 640358** Mr Taylor **Fax: 0870 132 9749** *gill@loanheadhouse.co.uk* **D:** £20.00–£24.00 **S:** £20.00–£28.00 **Beds:** 1D 1T **Baths:** 1 En 1 Pr ❄ ▣ (4) ⅍ Ⅴ Ⅴ ▦ ⅃

Methven

NO0226   *Methven Arms, Almondbank Inn*

Lismore, *1 Rorrie Terrace, Methven, Perth,
PH1 3PL.* True home from home in village 5
miles from Perth. **Open:** All year
Grades: STB 3 Star
01738 840441 (also fax) Mr Comrie
D: £13.50–£16.00 **S:** £17.50–£25.00 **Beds:** 1F
1D ⛔ (8) ⊞ (2) ⊁ ⊡ ⊻ ▥

Milnathort

NO1204

Hattonburn Farmhouse, *Milnathort,
Kinross, Fife, KY13 0SA.* Close to M90.
Edinburgh and airport 10 minutes, Perth 20
minutes. **Open:** All year (not Xmas/New
Year)
01577 862362 Mrs Todrick **D:** £20.00–£24.00
S: £20.00–£24.00 **Beds:** 1T **Baths:** 1 Pr ⛔
⊞ (6) ⊡ ⊁ ✕ ▥ ▲

Perth

NO1123   *Almondbank Inn, Letham Farmhouse
Hotel, Lovat Hotel*

**Hunting-
tower House,**
*Crieff Road,
Perth, PH1 3JJ.*
Open: Feb to
Dec
01738 624681
Mrs Lindsay **Fax: 01738 639770**
huntingtowerhouse@btinternet.com **D:** £22.00–
£25.00 **S:** £22.00–£25.00 **Beds:** 1D 2T
Baths: 1 Pr 1 Sh ⛔ (11) ⊞ (3) ⊁ ⊡ ⊻ ▥
Situated on the western outskirts of Perth,
this charming country house with large,
secluded garden nestles beside historic
Huntingtower Castle. There is easy access
to Perth and all main routes throughout
Scotland. A friendly welcome and delicious
breakfast are assured.

Comely Bank Cottage, *19 Pitcullen
Cres, Perth, Perthshire, PH2 7HT.* **Open:** All
year (not Xmas) **Grades:** STB 3 Star
01738 631118 Mrs Marshall **Fax: 01738
571245** *comelybankcott@hotmail.com* **D:** £18.00–
£22.00 **S:** £22.00–£30.00 **Beds:** 1F 1D 1T
Baths: 3 En ⛔ (3) ⊞ ⊁ ⊡ ⊻ ▥ ▲ cc
Perfectly situated for exploring Perthshire,
Fife and Central Scotland. Ten mins walk
town centre. Perth is known as the
flowering city with it's beautiful floral
displays. Enjoy true Scottish hospitality and
substantial breakfast at Comely Bank
Cottage.

The Darroch Guest House, *9 Pitcullen
Crescent, Perth, PH2 7HT.* Victorian semi,
friendly relaxed atmosphere, ideal base for
touring. **Open:** All year
01738 636893 (also fax) Mr & Mrs Hirst
D: £16.00–£21.00 **S:** £16.00–£25.00 **Beds:** 1F
1D 2T 2S **Baths:** 3 En 1 Sh ⛔ (8) ⊡ ⊁ ✕ ⊻
▥ ▲

**Achnacarry
Guest House,**
*3 Pitcullen
Crescent, Perth,
Perthshire and
Kinross, PH2 7HT.*
Perfectly
situated for
exploring
Central Scotland and Highlands. Warm
welcome. **Open:** All year **Grades:** STB 4
Star
01738 621421 David & Allison Golder **Fax:
01738 444110** *info@achnacarry.co.uk*
www.achnacarry.co.uk **D:** £20.00–£25.00
S: £25.00–£30.00 **Beds:** 1F 1T 2D **Baths:** 4
En ⛔ ⊞ (6) ⊁ ⊡ ▥ ▲ cc

**Dunallan
Guest House,**
*10 Pitcullen
Crescent, Perth,
PH2 7HT.* Well-
appointed
Victorian villa
within walking
distance Perth
City Centre. **Open:** All year **Grades:** STB 4
Star
01738 622551 (also fax) Mrs Brown
D: £20.00–£22.00 **S:** £21.50–£23.00 **Beds:** 1F
1D 2T 3S **Baths:** 7 En ⛔ ⊞ (7) ⊁ ⊡ ✕ ⊻ ▥ ▲
▲ cc

Beeches, *2 Comely Bank, Perth, PH2 7HU.*
Home from home Victorian house. Friendly,
relaxing, check web details! **Open:** All year
01738 624486 Mrs Smith **Fax: 01738 643382**
enquiries@beeches-guest-house.co.uk
www.beeches-guest-house.co.uk **D:** £18.00–
£22.00 **S:** £18.00–£22.00 **Beds:** 1D 1T 2S
Baths: 4 En ⛔ ⊞ (4) ⊁ ⊡ ⊻ ▥ ▲ cc

Parkview Guest House, *22 Marshall
Place, Perth, PH2 8AG.* Listed Georgian town
house. Very central, overlooking park.
Open: All year
01738 620297 (also fax) Mr Farquharson
fiona.farquharson@btinternet.com **D:** £16.00–
£19.00 **S:** £18.00–£20.00 **Beds:** 4F 1T
Baths: 3 En 1 Sh ⛔ ⊞ (4) ⊡ ⊁ ⊻ ▥ ▲

Arisaig Guest House, *4 Pitcullen
Crescent, Perth, Perthshire & Kinross,
PH2 7HT.* Late-Victorian family run guest
house situated on the A94. **Open:** All year
Grades: STB 4 Star
01738 628240 Stewart & Wilma Bousie **Fax:
01738 638521** *enquiries@arisaigguesthouse.co.uk*
www.arisaigguesthouse.co.uk **D:** £20.00–
£22.50 **S:** £25.00–£30.00 **Beds:** 1F 2D 1T 1S
Baths: 5 En ⛔ ⊞ (5) ⊁ ⊡ ▥ ▲ cc

Abercrombie, *85 Glasglow Road, Perth,
PH2 0PQ.* Abercrombie is ideally situated
near rail/bus stations, leisure pool, ice and
bowling rinks. **Open:** All year **Grades:** STB
4 Star
01738 444728 Mrs Dewar **Fax: 07138 444728**
D: £25.00–£30.00 **S:** £25.00–£30.00 **Beds:** 1T
1D 2S **Baths:** 2 En 2 Pr ⊞ (6) ⊁ ⊡ ▥ ▲ cc

Aberdeen Guest House, *Pitcullen
Crescent, Perth, PH2 7HT.* Beautiful Victorian
house where comfort and care is
paramount. **Open:** All year
01738 633183 (also fax) Mrs Buchan
buchan@aberdeenguesthouse.fsnet.co.uk
D: £18.00–£22.00 **S:** £18.00–£25.00 **Beds:** 2D
1T **Baths:** 1 En 2 Sh ⛔ ⊞ (4) ⊡ ⊻ ▥ ▲

Pitlochry

NN9458   *Moulin Inn, Killiecrankie Hotel,
Riverside Inn*

Auchlatt Steading, *Kinnaird, Pitlochry,
Perthshire, PH16 5JL.* **Open:** Easter to Nov
01796 472661 (also fax) Miss Elkins
D: £17.00 **S:** £17.00 **Beds:** 1T 1D **Baths:** 2 En
⊞ (2) ⊁ ⊡ ⊻ ▥
Newly converted Scottish barn comfortable
beds and a good honest breakfast
overlooking Pitlochry and surrounding
beautiful countryside close Edradour -
Scotland smallest distillery, good hill
walking and fishing, also the theatre and
much historic interest.

**Balrobin
Hotel,** *Higher
Oakfield,
Pitlochry,
Perthshire,
PH16 5HT.* Quality
accommodation
with panoramic
views at
affordable prices. **Open:** Apr to Oct
Grades: STB 3 Star, AA 2 Star, RAC 2 Star
01796 472901 Mr Hohman **Fax: 01796
474200** *info@balrobin.co.uk* www.balrobin.co.
uk **D:** £25.00–£33.00 **S:** £25.00–£39.00
Beds: 1F 10D 3T 1S **Baths:** 15 En ⛔ (5)
⊞ (15) ⊁ ⊡ ⊻ ✕ ⊡ ▥ ▲ cc

**Easter Dunfallandy Country House
B&B,** *Pitlochry, Perthshire, PH16 5NA.*
Beautifully presented country house with
fine views and gourmet breakfast. **Open:** All
year (not Xmas/New Year)
01796 474128 Mr Mathieson **Fax: 01796
473994** *sue@dunfallandy.co.uk*
www.dunfallandy.co.uk **D:** £28.00 **S:** £38.00
Beds: 1D 2T **Baths:** 3 En ⛔ (12) ⊞ (6) ⊁ ⊡ ⊻
▥

Planning a longer stay? Always
ask for any special rates

Lynedoch, *9 Lettoch Terrace, Pitlochry, Perthshire, PH16 5BA.* Stone-built semi-detached villa in beautiful Highland Perthshire, ideally situated for walking, golf, fishing etc. **Open:** Easter to Oct **01796 472119** Mrs Williamson *iwilliamson@talk21.com* **D:** £16.00–£18.00 **S:** £16.00–£18.00 **Beds:** 2D 1T **Baths:** 2 Sh 🅿 (3) ⏣ 📺 ⌇ 🛍 🖢

Wellwood House, *West Moulin Road, Pitlochry, Perthshire, PH16 5EA.* The Wellwood is a Victorian mansion house set in 2 acres of splendid gardens. **Open:** Mar to Nov **01796 474288** Ms Herd **Fax: 01796 474299** *wellwood@ukonline.co.uk* www.smouthhound.co.uk/hotels/wellwood.html **D:** £19.50–£25.00 **S:** £25.00–£35.00 **Beds:** 1F 5D 4T **Baths:** 8 En 2 Sh 🐾 🅿 (25) 📺 ⌇ 🛍 🖢

Atholl Villa, *29 Atholl Road, Pitlochry, Perthshire, PH16 5BX.* 10-bedroom Victorian detached house, typical Highland construction, edge of town. **Open:** All year **01796 473820** Mrs Bruce *athollvilla@aol.com* www.s-h-systems.co.uk/hotels/athollvilla. html **D:** £17.50–£25.00 **S:** £17.50–£25.00 **Beds:** 3F 2T 2D **Baths:** 7 En 🐾 🅿 (10) ⏣ 📺 ⌇ ✕ 📺 🛍 ♿ ⚹ 🖢 **cc**

Rattray

NO1845 ⚓ *Angus Hotel, Victoria Hotel*

Shocarjen House, *Balmoral Road, Rattray, Blairgowrie, Perthshire, PH10 7AF.* New purpose built bed and breakfast. Ideal for all activities in Perthshire. **Open:** All year **Grades:** STB 3 Star **01250 870525 & 07801 436662 (M)** Mrs Beattie **D:** £17.00–£18.50 **S:** £19.00 **Beds:** 1T 1D **Baths:** 2 En 🐾 🅿 (6) ⏣ 📺 ⌇ ✕ 📺 🛍 ♿ 🖢

Rhynd

NO1520

Fingask Farm, *Rhynd, Perth, Perthshire & Kinross, PH2 8QF.* Spacious accommodation in well-appointed farmhouse in a peaceful part of central Perthshire. **Open:** Easter to Oct **01738 812220** Mrs Stirrat **Fax: 01738 813325** *libby@agstirrat.sol.co.uk* **D:** £19.00–£21.00 **S:** £19.00–£21.00 **Beds:** 1D 1T 1S **Baths:** 2 Pr 🐾 (10) 🅿 (3) ⏣ 📺 ✕ 🛍 🖢 **cc**

Stanley

NO1133

Beechlea, *Stanley, Perth, Perthshire, PH1 4PS.* Luxury comfortable B&B, beautiful quiet countryside, excellent location off A9. **Open:** All year (not Xmas) **01738 828715** Mrs Lindsay *chaslizlin@aol.com* members.aol.com/chaslizlin/index.html **D:** £20.00–£27.00 **S:** £25.00–£27.00 **Beds:** 1F 1D 1T **Baths:** 3 En 🐾 (10) 🅿 (6) ⏣ 📺 🛍 🖢 **cc**

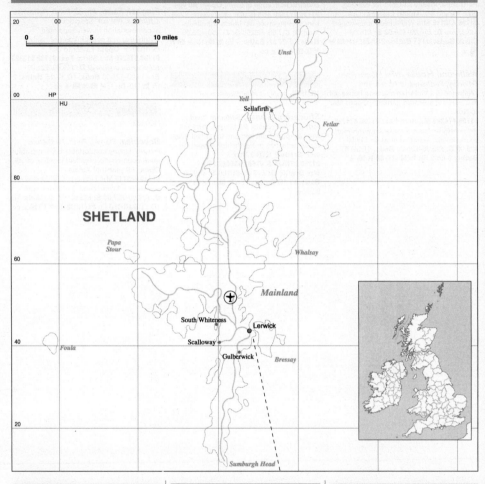

0   5   10 miles

Unst

HP

HU

Yell

Sellafirth

Fetlar

SHETLAND

Papa Stour

Whalsay

⊕   *Mainland*

South Whiteness   Lerwick

Foula

Scalloway

Gulberwick

Bressay

Sumburgh Head

FAIR ISLE   Fair Isle
HZ2271

Upper Leogh, *Fair Isle, Shetland, ZE2 9JU.* Working croft, hand spinning demonstration/ tuition available. Local crafts nearby. **Open:** All year **01595 760248** Mrs Coull *kathleen.coull@ lineone.net* **D:** £20.00–£22.00 **S:** £20.00– £22.00 **Beds:** 1T 1D 1S ♿ �ⓟ (3) ⊬ ⊠ ✕ ⓥ ☀

BATHROOMS
En = Ensuite
Pr = Private
Sh = Shared

B&B owners may vary rates – be sure to check when booking

MAINLAND   Gulberwick
HU4438

Virdafjell, *Shurton Brae, Gulberwick, Shetland, ZE2 9TX.* Peaceful Nordic home overlooking bay. Walks, ponies, bird watching, good touring base. **Open:** All year **01595 694336** Mrs Stove **Fax: 01595 696252** *d.stove@talk21.com* **D:** £25.00 **S:** £30.00 **Beds:** 1T 2D **Baths:** 3 En ♿ ⓟ (6) ⊬ ⊠ ⓥ ▥ ⅋

MAINLAND   Lerwick
HU4741

Whinrig, *12 Burgh Road, Lerwick, Shetland, ZE1 0LB.* Private bungalow. Centrally heated. Central to all amenities, warm welcome. **Open:** All year (not Xmas) **Grades:** STB 4 Star **01595 693554** Mrs Gifford *c.gifford@ btinternet.com* www.btinternet.com/~C. Gifford/ **D:** £20.00–£22.00 **S:** £22.00 **Beds:** 2T **Baths:** 1 En 1 Pr ⓟ (2) ⊬ ⊠ ⓥ ▥ ☀

Woosung, *43 St Olaf Street, Lerwick, Shetland, ZE1 0EN.* Very central - close to all amenities **Open:** All year (not Xmas/New Year) **01595 693687** S Conroy **D:** £17.00 **S:** £20.00 **Beds:** 2T **Baths:** 1 Sh ♿ ⊠ ⅋ ✕ ⓥ ▥ ☀

MAINLAND   Scalloway
HU4039

Broch Guest House, *Scalloway,*
Lerwick, Shetland, ZE1 0UP. Comfortable
guest house. **Open:** All year (not Xmas)
01595 880767 Mrs Young **D:** £17.00 **S:** £19.00
Beds: 3D **Baths:** 3 En ⍩ 🅿 (3) 📺 Ⓥ ▥ ♨

All details shown are as
supplied by B&B owners in
Autumn 2001

MAINLAND
South Whiteness
HU3844

The Inn on the Hill, *The Westings,*
Whiteness, Shetland, ZE2 9LJ. Country inn
with stunning views from all rooms.
Open: All year **Grades:** STB 3 Star
01595 840242 Fax: 01595 840500
westingsinn@aol.com www.westings.shetland.
co.uk **D:** £37.50–£40.00 **S:** £37.50–£45.00
Beds: 2T 1D 3S **Baths:** 6 En ⍩ (10) 🅿 (25) 📺
🍴 ✕ ▥ ♨ cc

YELL   Sellafirth
HU5297   🏨 *Glenmoriston Hotel*

North Isle Motel, *Sellafirth, Shetland,*
ZE2 9DG. Beautiful views, overlooking Basta
Voe. Wild life, birds. **Open:** All year
01957 744294 D: £19.00–£21.00 **S:** £22.00–
£25.00 **Beds:** 10T **Baths:** 2 Sh ⍩ (5) 🅿 (20) 📺
🍴 ✕ Ⓥ ♨

National Grid References given
are for villages, towns and
cities – not for individual houses

Stirling & the Trossachs

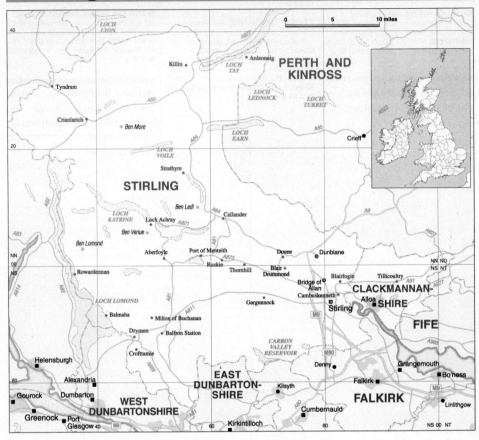

Aberfoyle

NN5200 🍴 *Black Bull, Rob Roy*

Creag Ard House B&B, *Aberfoyle, Stirling, FK8 3TQ.* A beautiful Victorian house with extensive and colourful gardens, set in magnificent scenery. **Open:** All year **Grades:** STB 4 Star **01877 382297** Mrs Wilson *cara@ creag-ardhouse.co.uk www.creag-ardhouse.co. uk* **D:** £29.00–£40.00 **S:** £35.00–£70.00 **Beds:** 4D 2T **Baths:** 6 En ⚭ 🖳 (7) ⮀ 🐾 ✕ 🆅 ▥ ▥ 🅲 🅲

Ardeonaig

NN6735

Abernethy Trust, *Ardeonaig, Killin, Perthshire, FK21 8SY.* Outdoor activity centre in 20 acre estate overlooking Loch Tay **Open:** Jan to Nov **01567 820523** *at@ardeonaig.org www.ardeonaig.org* **D:** £23.00 **S:** £28.00 **Beds:** 11F 3D **Baths:** 4 Sh ⚭ 🖳 (20) ⮀ ✕ 🆅 ▥

Planning a longer stay? Always ask for any special rates

Balfron Station

NS5289

Loaninghead Farm, *Balfron Station, Glasgow, G63 0SE.* Make this your base. Explore Scotland's first National Park. **Open:** All year **01360 440432 (also fax)** Mrs Paterson *paterson.loaninghead@virgin.net www.visit-lochlomod.com/loaninghead* **D:** £18.00–£25.00 **S:** £20.00–£25.00 **Beds:** 1F 1T 1D **Baths:** 1 En 1 Pr 1 Sh ⚭ 🖳 ⮀ ▥ 🆅 ▥ ⬛

Easter Balfunning Farm, Drymen, Glasgow, G63 0NF. A warm welcome awaits you in our attractive farmhouse, idyllically situated. **Open:** All year **01360 440755** Ms Black **D:** £18.00–£21.00 **S:** £21.00–£27.00 **Beds:** 1D 1F **Baths:** 1 Pr 1 En ⭑ 🅿 (4) ⚊ 📺 ♉ 🛏 Ⅲ 🔥 🎿

Balmaha

NS4290

Critreoch, Rowardennan Road, Balmaha, Glasgow, G63 0AW. Family home quiet location beautiful view over garden to Loch. **Open:** May to Sept **01360 870300** Mrs MacLuskie **D:** £20.00–£22.00 **S:** £25.00–£30.00 **Beds:** 1D 1T **Baths:** 1 En 1 Pr 🅿 (6) ⚊ 📺 🛏 Ⅲ 🔥

Mar Achlais, Milton of Buchanan, Balmaha, Glasgow, G63 0JE. Rural setting near Loch Lomond. Excellent touring centre for Scotland. **Open:** All year (not Xmas) **Grades:** STB 3 Star **01360 870300** Mr Nichols **Fax: 01360 870444** *marachlais@dial.pipex.com* **D:** £18.50 **S:** £23.50–£28.50 **Beds:** 1F 1D **Baths:** 2 En ⭑ 🅿 (2) 📺 🛏 ✕ 📺 Ⅲ 🔥 cc

Conic View Cottage, Balmaha, Glasgow, G63 0JQ. Beautifully situated near Loch Lomond and the West Highland Way, surrounded by forest walks. **Open:** Mar to Nov **01360 870297** Mrs Cronin *jenny@balmaha32.freeserve.co.uk* www.geocities.com/jenny_cronin **D:** £15.00–£20.00 **S:** £18.00–£20.00 **Beds:** 1D 1S **Baths:** 1 Sh 🅿 (2) ⚊ 📺 📺 Ⅲ 🔥

Blair Drummond

NS7299 🏨 Lion & Unicorn

The Linns, Kirk Lane, Blair Drummond, Stirling, FK9 4AN. Perfectly situated for exploring central Scotland. Warm welcome. Wholesome breakfast. **Open:** All year (not Xmas/New Year) **Grades:** STB 3 Star **01786 841679** Mr Darby **Fax: 01786 842473** *swell@hillview-cottage.com* www.hillview-cottage.com **D:** £21.00–£24.00 **S:** £30.00–£35.00 **Beds:** 2F 1T 2D **Baths:** 5 En ⭑ 🅿 (7) 📺 🛏 ✕ 📺 Ⅲ 🔥 🎿 cc

Blairlogie

NS8296

Blairmains Farm, Manor Loan, Blairlogie, Stirling, FK9 5QA. Traditional stone farmhouse. Working farm, beautiful country location. Coffee shop and farm shop. **Open:** All year (not Xmas/New Year) **Grades:** STB 2 Star **01259 761338** Mrs Logan **D:** £18.00–£20.00 **S:** £20.00–£23.00 **Beds:** 2T 1D **Baths:** 1 Sh 🅿 📺 ⚊ 📺 📺 Ⅲ 🔥

Bridge of Allan

NS7997

Lorraine, 10 Chalton Road, Bridge of Allan, Stirling, FK9 4DX. Listed building, off main road, lovely views, good walking country. **Open:** All year (not Xmas) **01786 832042** B Holliday **Fax: 01786 831066** *101567.2041@compuserve.com* **D:** £18.00 **S:** £18.00–£25.00 **Beds:** 1D 1T 1S **Baths:** 2 Sh ⭑ 🅿 (4) ⚊ 📺 📺 Ⅲ 🔥

Callander

NN6307 🏨 Claymore, Bridgend House

Arden House, Bracklinn Road, Callander, Perthshire, FK17 8EQ. **Open:** Apr to Oct **Grades:** STB 4 Star, AA 4 Diamond **01877 330235 (also fax)** Mr Mitchell & Mr W Jackson *ardenhouse@onetel.net.uk* www.smoothhound.co.uk/hotels/arden.html **D:** £27.50–£30.00 **S:** £30.00 **Beds:** 3D 2T 1S **Baths:** 6 En ⭑ (14) 🅿 (6) ⚊ 📺 Ⅲ 🔥 cc Tranquillity in the Trossachs. Peaceful Victorian country house with stunning views. Home of BBC TVs 'Dr Finlay's Casebook'. Comfortable, Elegant ensuite rooms with TV, tea/coffee and many thoughtful touches. Few minutes walk to village. Generous breakfasts and genuine hospitality.

Lamorna, Ancaster Road, Callander, Perthshire, FK17 8JJ. **Open:** Mar to Oct **01877 330868 D:** £19.00–£20.00 **S:** £22.00–£23.00 **Beds:** 1T 1D **Baths:** 1 Sh ⭑ (10) 🅿 (3) ⚊ 📺 📺 Ⅲ 🔥 Detached bungalow with panoramic views of Callander and surrounding countryside. Quiet location on main cycle route. Close to all local amenities.

Brook Linn Country House, Callander, Perthshire, FK17 8AU. Lovely comfortable Victorian house with magnificent views and personal attention. **Open:** Easter to Oct **Grades:** STB 4 Star, AA 4 Diamond **01877 330103 (also fax)** Mrs House *derek@blinn.freeserve.co.uk* www.brooklinn-scotland.co.uk **D:** £24.00–£30.00 **S:** £23.00–£27.00 **Beds:** 2S 2D 2T **Baths:** 6 En ⭑ 🅿 (8) ⚊ 📺 🛏 📺 Ⅲ 🔥 cc

Riverview House, Leny Road, Callander, Perthshire, FK17 8AL. Guesthouse and self-catering in scenic Trossachs National Park. **Open:** All year (not Xmas) **Grades:** STB 3 Star **01877 330635** Mr Little **Fax: 01877 339386** *auldtoll@netscapeonline.co.uk* www.nationalparkscotland.co.uk **D:** £21.00–£22.00 **S:** £22.00–£24.00 **Beds:** 3D 2T 1S **Baths:** 5 En 🅿 (6) ⚊ ✕ 📺 Ⅲ 🔥

Annfield House, North Church Street, Callander, Perthshire, FK17 8EG. Ideal as an overnight stop for exploring the Highlands. **Open:** All year **01877 330204** Mrs Greenfield **Fax: 01877 330674 D:** £21.00 **S:** £25.00 **Beds:** 1F 2T 4D 1S **Baths:** 4 En 1 Pr 1 Sh ⭑ (3) 🅿 (7) ⚊ 📺 🛏 📺 Ⅲ 🔥

East Mains House, Bridgend, Callander, Perthshire, FK17 8AG. Comfortable Georgian house with large garden and relaxed atmosphere. **Open:** All year **Grades:** STB 3 Star **01877 330535 (also fax)** Ms Alexander *east.mains@tesco.net* www.smoothhound.co.uk/hotels/eastm/html **D:** £22.00–£24.00 **S:** £27.00–£29.00 **Beds:** 2F 4D **Baths:** 4 En ⭑ 🅿 (6) ⚊ 📺 🛏 📺 Ⅲ ❄ cc

White Cottage, Bracklinn Road, Callander, FK17 8EQ. Situated in one acre garden. Magnificent views of Ben Ledi. **Open:** Apr to Nov **01877 330896** Mrs Hughes **D:** £17.50–£19.00 **S:** £20.00–£22.00 **Beds:** 2D **Baths:** 1 Sh 🅿 (3) ⚊ 📺 📺 Ⅲ 🔥

Glengarry Hotel, Stirling Road, Callander, Perthshire, FK17 8DA. Family-run hotel in own grounds. Hearty breakfast, traditional home-cooked evening meals. Easy access. **Open:** All year **01877 330216** *info@glengarryhotel.com* www.glengarryhotel.demon.co.uk **D:** £22.00–£25.00 **Beds:** 3F 1D **Baths:** 4 En ⭑ 🅿 (15) 📺 🛏 ✕ 📺 Ⅲ 🔥

National Grid References given are for villages, towns and cities – not for individual houses

Campfield Cottage, *138 Main Street, Callander, Perthshire, FK17 8BG.* Charming C18th cottage in heart of Callander, down a quiet lane. **Open:** All year (not Xmas/New Year)
01877 330597 Mrs Hunter **D:** £18.00
S: £18.00 **Beds:** 2D 1T 1S **Baths:** 1 Sh ⌷ ▣ ⌷ ⌷ ▣ ⌷ ⌷ ⌷

Linley Guest House, *139 Main Street, Callander, Perthshire, FK17 8BH.* Comfortable Victorian terraced house close to Callander busy centre. Stirling 25 minutes drive.
Open: All year
01877 330087 M McQuilton
linley_guesthouse@tinyworld.co.uk **D:** £16.00–£18.50 **S:** £20.00–£25.00 **Beds:** 1F 1T 3D **Baths:** 2 En 2 Sh ⌷ ▣ (4) ⌷ ▣ ⌷ ⌷

Cambuskenneth

NS8094

Carseview, *16 Ladysneuk Road, Cambuskenneth, Stirling, FK9 5NF.* Quiet conservation village, 15 mins' walk Stirling town centre, panoramic views. **Open:** All year **Grades:** STB 3 Star
01786 462235 (also fax) Mr & Mrs Seaton
D: £18.00 **S:** £18.00–£20.00 **Beds:** 2T 1S **Baths:** 1 Sh ⌷ ▣ (0) ⌷ ⌷ ⌷ × ▣ ⌷ ⌷ cc

Crianlarich

NN3825   ⌷ *Benmore Lodge*

Riverside Guest House, *Tigh-na Struith, Crianlarich, Perthshire, FK20 8RU.*
Open: All year
01838 300235 Mr & Mrs Chisholm **Fax:**
01838 300268 *jansan@btinternet.com*
www.riversideguesthouse.co.uk **D:** £18.00–£20.00 **S:** £20.00–£30.00 **Beds:** 2F 1D 1S **Baths:** 3 En 1 Sh ⌷ ▣ (6) ⌷ ⌷ ⌷ ▣ ⌷ ⌷ Lovely established guest house in super position on village outskirts. 200 yards off main road with unrestricted views of hills and river. Ideal for fishing, walking and touring by car. Discounts on stays for 3 nights and 5 nights.

Inverherive Cottage, *Crianlarich, Perthshire, FK20 8RU.* Beautifully situated. Private sitting area and entrance. Come and enjoy.
Open: All year (not Xmas/New Year)
01838 300336 Mr & Mrs Scott *inver@ herive.freeserve.co.uk* **D:** £15.00 **S:** £25.00 **Beds:** 1D **Baths:** 1 Pr ▣ (6) ⌷ ⌷ × ⌷ ▣ ⌷

Planning a longer stay? Always ask for any special rates

The Lodge House, *Crianlarich, Perthshire, FK20 8RU.* Superbly located guest house, magnificent views of Crianlarich hills. **Open:** All year
01838 300276 Mr Gaughan *admin@ lodgehouse.co.uk* www.lodgehouse.co.uk
D: £25.00–£30.00 **S:** £35.00–£45.00 **Beds:** 1F 3D 2T **Baths:** 6 En ⌷ ▣ (10) ⌷ ⌷ ⌷ × ⌷ ▣ ⌷ ⌷ cc

Ben More Lodge Hotel, *Crianlarich, Perthshire, FK20 8QS.* Family-run lodge hotel with spectacular setting beneath Ben More.
Open: All year **Grades:** STB 2 Star, AA 3 Diamond
01838 300210 Mr Goodale **Fax: 01838 300218** *john@ben-more.demon.co.uk* www.ben-more.co.uk **D:** £25.00 **S:** £28.00 **Beds:** 2F 8D 1T **Baths:** 11 En ⌷ ▣ ⌷ ⌷ × ⌷ ▣ ⌷ ⌷

Craigbank Guest House, *Crianlarich, Perthshire, FK20 8QS.* Situated one hour's drive from Glen Coe, Loch Lomond, the Trossachs. **Open:** All year (not Xmas)
01838 300279 Mr Flockhart **D:** £17.00–£19.00 **S:** £25.00 **Beds:** 2F 1D 3T **Baths:** 2 En 2 Sh ⌷ ▣ (6) ⌷ ⌷ ⌷ ▣ ⌷

Croftamie

NS4786

Croftburn, *Croftamie, Drymen, Glasgow, G63 0HA.* Former gamekeeper's cottage in one acre of beautiful gardens overlooking Strathendrick Valley & Campsie Fells.
Open: All year
01360 660796 Mrs Reid **Fax: 01360 661005** *johnreid@croftbarn.fsnet.co.uk* **D:** £18.00–£22.00 **S:** £20.00–£25.00 **Beds:** 2D 1T
Baths: 2 En 1 Pr ⌷ (12) ▣ (20) ⌷ ⌷ ⌷ × ⌷ ▣ ⌷ cc

Doune

NN7301   ⌷ *Creity Hall, Red Lion, Woodside Hotel*

Inverardoch Mains Farm, *Doune, Perthshire, FK15 9NZ.* Traditional farmhouse on working farm. View of Doune Castle close to Dunblane and Trossachs. **Open:** All year (not Xmas/New Year) **Grades:** STB 2 Star
01786 841268 (also fax) J Anderson
D: £20.00–£23.00 **S:** £22.00–£28.00 **Beds:** 1F 1T 1D **Baths:** 2 Pr 1 Sh ⌷ (3) ▣ (4) ⌷ ⌷ ⌷ ⌷ ▣ ⌷

Drymen

NS4788   ⌷ *Winnock Hotel, The Clachan, Buchanan Arms*

Easter Drumquhassle Farm, *Gartness Road, Drymen, Glasgow, G63 0DN.* Traditional farmhouse, beautiful views, home cooking, excellent base on the West Highland Way. **Open:** All year
01360 660893 Mrs Cross **Fax: 01360 660282** *juliamacx@aol.com* members.aol. com/juliamacx **D:** £18.00–£25.00 **S:** £25.00–£30.00 **Beds:** 1F 1D 1T **Baths:** 3 En ⌷ ▣ (10) ⌷ ⌷ ⌷ × ⌷ ▣ ⌷

Green Shadows, *Buchanan Castle Estate, Drymen, Glasgow, G63 0HX.* **Open:** All year (not Xmas) **Grades:** STB 3 Star
01360 660289 & 07775 690855 (M) Mrs Goodwin **D:** £21.00 **S:** £24.00 **Beds:** 1F 1D 1S **Baths:** 2 Sh ⌷ ▣ (8) ⌷ ⌷ ⌷ ▣ ⌷ Warm, friendly welcome in a beautiful country house with spectacular views over golf course and the Lomond Hills. Buchanan Castle to the rear. 1 mile from Drymen Centre, 2 miles from Loch Lomond. Glasgow Airport 40 mins away.

Ceardach, *Gartness Road, Drymen, Glasgow, G63 0BH.* 250-year-old coach house near shores of Loch Lomond. Large garden, good home cooking. **Open:** All year (not Xmas)
D: £18.00–£20.00 **S:** £18.00–£20.00 **Beds:** 1D 1T **Baths:** 1 Sh ⌷ (1) ▣ (3) ⌷ ⌷ ⌷ ▣ ⌷ ⌷

The Hawthorns, *The Square, Drymen, Glasgow, G63 0BH.* Built 1873 - The Doctors 'Auld Hoose'. Totally refurbished, all ensuite. **Open:** All year
01360 660916 Mrs Gallacher **Fax: 01360 661070** *pat@thehawthorns-drymen.com* www.thehawthorns-drymen.com **D:** £25.00–£30.00 **Beds:** 1F 1T 1D **Baths:** 3 En ▣ ⌷ ⌷ ⌷ ▣ ⌷

Dunblane

NN7801

Mossgiel, *Doune Road, Dunblane, Perthshire, FK15 9ND.* **Open:** Mar to Oct
01786 824325 Mrs Bennett *judy@mossgiel.com* **D:** £20.00–£22.00 **S:** £25.00–£30.00 **Beds:** 2T 1D **Baths:** 2 En 1 Pr ▣ (5) ⌷ ⌷ ▣ ⌷ ⌷ ⌷ Countryside house situated between Dunblane and Doune Castle. Nearby attractions include Stirling Castle, Wallace Monument and The Trossachs. Good road and rail services into Glasgow and Edinburgh. A full Scottish breakfast and well-equipped bedrooms ensure guests a memorable holiday.

BATHROOMS
En = Ensuite
Pr = Private
Sh = Shared

RATES

D = Price range per person sharing in a double or twin room

S = Price range for a single room

Gargunnock

NS7094

East Lodge, *Leckie, Gargunnock, Stirling, FK8 3BN.* C19th lodge house tastefully extended. In attractive woodland setting. 'Comfortable, peaceful and elegant'. **Open:** All year (not Xmas) **01786 860605** Mrs Currie *janc123456@aol.com* **D:** £20.00–£22.00 **S:** £25.00–£28.00 **Beds:** 1D 1T **Baths:** 1 Pr 1 Sh ᗧ 🅿 (3) ⊬ 🔟 ❅ 🎢 ᗺ1 ᐧ

Killin

NN5732 🚶 *Killin Hotel*

Falls of Dochart Cottage, *Killin, Perthshire, FK21 8SW.* C17th cottage, overlooking Falls, river. Central for magnificent mountain area. Home cooking. **Open:** All year (not Xmas) **01567 820363** Mr & Mrs Mudd **D:** £16.00–£17.00 **S:** £17.00 **Beds:** 1D 1T 1S **Baths:** 2 Sh ᗧ (1) 🅿 (4) ⊬ 🔟 🎢 ✕ 🔟 🌄

Main Street, *Killin, Perthshire, FK21 8TP.* Magnificent setting, overlooking River Lochay. Bistro - home-cooked dishes; lounge bar - stock of malt whiskies. **Open:** All year **01567 820296** Mr & Mrs Garnier **Fax: 01567 820647** *killinhotel@btinternet.com* www.killinhotel.com **D:** £19.00–£35.00 **S:** £19.00–£35.00 **Beds:** 3F 6T 17D 6S **Baths:** 32 En ᗧ 🅿 (20) ⊬ 🔟 🎢 ✕ 🔟 🌄 ᗺ ❆ cc

Allt Fulieach, *Maragowan, Killin, Perthshire, FK21 8TN.* Comfortable, modern house at the head of Loch Tay. **Open:** All year **01567 820962** Mr Judd **D:** £19.00 **S:** £19.00 **Beds:** 2T 1D **Baths:** 3 En ᗧ 🅿 (4) ⊬ 🔟 🌄 ᐧ

BEDROOMS

D = Double

T = Twin

S = Single

F = Family

Loch Achray

NN5106

Glenbruach Country House, *Loch Achray, Trossachs, Callander, Perthshire, FK17 8HX.* **Open:** All year **01877 376216 (also fax)** Mrs Lindsay *james.lindsay5@btinternet.com* www.nationalparkaccommodation.co.uk **D:** £22.00–£25.00 **S:** £22.00–£25.00 **Beds:** 2D 1T **Baths:** 2 En 1 Pr ᗧ (12) 🅿 (3) ⊬ 🎢 🔟 🌄 ᐧ

Unique country mansion in the heart of Rob Roy country. All rooms with Loch views. Interesting interior design and collections in this Scots-owned home. Situated in the centre of Scotland's First National Park, 1 mile from Loch Katrine.

Milton of Buchanan

NS4490

Mar Achlais, *Milton of Buchanan, Balmaha, Glasgow, G63 0JE.* Rural setting near Loch Lomond. Excellent touring centre for Scotland. **Open:** All year (not Xmas) **Grades:** STB 3 Star **01360 870300** Mr Nichols **Fax: 01360 870444** *marachlais@dial.pipex.com* **D:** £18.50 **S:** £23.50–£28.50 **Beds:** 1F 1D **Baths:** 2 En ᗧ 🅿 (2) 🔟 🎢 ✕ 🔟 🌄 ᐧ cc

Ochtertyre

NS7497

Broadford House, *Ochtertyre, Stirling, FK9 4UN.* Lovely country house in 2.5 acres of garden adorned with 300-year-old oak trees. **Open:** Easter to Oct **01786 464674** Mrs Littlejohn **Fax: 01786 463256** *simonlittlejohn@compuserve.com* **D:** £20.00–£23.00 **Beds:** 1T 1D **Baths:** 1 En 1 Pr ⊬ 🔟 🌄 ᐧ

Port of Menteith

NN5801 🚶 *Crown Hotel, Lion & Unicorn*

Inchie Farm, *Port of Menteith, Stirling, FK8 3JZ.* Family farm on shores of Lake Menteith. **Open:** Easter to Oct **Grades:** STB 3 Star **01877 385233 (also fax)** Mrs Erskine *inchiefarm@ecosse.net* **D:** £18.00 **S:** £22.00 **Beds:** 1F 1T ᗧ ⊬ 🔟 🌄

Rowardennan

NS3598

Anchorage Cottage, *Rowardennan, Drymen, Glasgow, G63 0AW.* Family home on eastern shore of Loch Lomond. Highest standards. **Open:** Easter to Oct **01360 870394 (also fax)** **D:** £26.00–£30.00 **S:** £36.00–£40.00 **Beds:** 2T 1D **Baths:** 2 En 1 Pr 🅿 (6) ⊬ 🔟 🌄 ᐧ

Ruskie

NN6200 🚶 *Crown Hotel, Lion & Unicorn*

Lower Tarr Farm, *Waterfoot, Ruskie, Stirling, Perthshire, FK8 3LG.* Peaceful situation and panoramic views **Open:** Easter to Nov **01786 850202 (also fax)** Mrs Bain *lowertarr@ ecosse.net* **D:** £20.00–£22.00 **S:** £20.00–£25.00 **Beds:** 1F 1D **Baths:** 1 En 1 Pr ᗧ 🅿 🔟 🎢 ✕ ᐧ

Stirling

NS7993

Woodside Guest House, *4 Back Walk, Stirling, FK8 2QA.* **Open:** All year **01786 475470** Mr Drummond **D:** £16.00–£18.00 **S:** £18.00–£20.00 **Beds:** 1F 3D 2T 1S **Baths:** 2 En 2 Pr 2 Sh ᗧ 🅿 ⊬ 🔟 🌄 ᐧ Beautifully situated on the old historic Wall of Stirling. Modern, comfortable, friendly, central to all amenities. Five minutes' walk from rail and bus stations. All rooms have private showers.

Anderson House, *8 Melville Terrace, Stirling, FK8 2NE.* **Open:** All year (not Xmas) **Grades:** STB 3 Star **01786 465185** Mrs Piggott *m.j.piggott@talk21.com* **D:** £22.00–£24.00 **S:** £25.00–£40.00 **Beds:** 1F 1T 1D 1S **Baths:** 3 En 1 Sh ᗧ 🅿 (5) 🔟 🎢 🌄 ᐧ Welcome to our 200 year old Georgian home within 2 minutes walk of historic Stirling. Large, bright rooms, antique furnishings, refurbished ensuites, a friendly atmosphere and and a great Scottish breakfast will make your stay a memorable one.

Neidpath Guest House, *24 Linden Avenue, Stirling, FK7 7PQ.* Refurbished friendly Edwardian home, 5 minutes walk from town centre. **Open:** All year **Grades:** STB 3 Star **01786 469017** *kayneidpathbanb@hotmail.com.* www.smoothhound.co.uk/hotels/neidpath **D:** £20.00–£22.00 **S:** £25.00–£35.00 **Beds:** 1F 1T 1D **Baths:** 3 En ⏰ ▣ ⚡ ▣ ✕ ▣ ▥ ⚹ ♨ ☕ ▪

12 Princes Street, *Stirling, FK8 1HQ.* Central for Stirling, buses, trains. Near to Castle and Wallace monument. **Open:** All year **01786 479228 (also fax)** Mrs Cairns **D:** £18.00–£20.00 **S:** £18.00–£20.00 **Beds:** 1D 1T 2S **Baths:** 2 En 2 Sh ⏰ (3) ▣ ⚡ ▣ ▣ ✕ ▣ ▥ ▪

16 Riverside Drive, *Stirling, FK8 1XF.* Our small family home in quiet area near to town. **01786 461105** Mrs Miller **D:** £13.50–£15.00 **S:** £13.50–£15.00 **Beds:** 2S **Baths:** 1 Sh ⚡ ▣ ▥ ▪

Hopeton, *28 Linden Avenue, Stirling, FK7 7PQ.* Ground floor flat of large detached stone building surrounded by attractive gardens. **Open:** All year **01786 473418** Mrs McDonald **D:** £18.00 **S:** £20.00 **Beds:** 1F 1D 1T **Baths:** 1 Pr 1 Sh ⏰ ▣ ▣ ▥ ♨ ☕ ▪

Wellgreen Guest House, *8 Pit Terrace, Stirling, FK8 2EZ.* Family-run guest house close to town centre and all its amenities. **Open:** All year **01786 472675** Mrs Mcphail **D:** £18.00 **S:** £18.00 **Beds:** 2F 1T 1S **Baths:** 2 Sh ⏰ ⚡ ▣ ▥ ▣ ▥ ▪

Linden Guest House, *22 Linden Avenue, Stirling, FK7 7PQ.* Situated in a tree-lined avenue only few minutes' walk to town centre. **Open:** All year **Grades:** STB 2 Star **01786 448850 (also fax)** Miss McGuinness *fay@lindenguesthouse.co.uk* www.lindenguesthouse.co.uk **D:** £20.00–£22.00 **S:** £25.00–£35.00 **Beds:** 2F 1D 1T **Baths:** 1 Sh ⏰ ▣ (2) ▣ ▥ ✕ ▣ ▥ ▪

Whinwell Cottage, *171 Glasgow Road, Whins of Milton, Stirling, FK7 0LH.* Immaculate, comfortable, accommodation, close to many tourist attractions and amenities. **Open:** All year **01786 818166 D:** £18.00–£22.00 **S:** £20.00–£30.00 **Beds:** 1F 1T 1D **Baths:** 1 Sh ⏰ ▣ ⚡ ▣ ▥ ▣ ▪

The Linns, *Kirk Lane, Blair Drummond, Stirling, FK9 4AN.* Perfectly situated for exploring central Scotland. Warm welcome. Wholesome breakfast. **Open:** All year (not Xmas/New Year) **Grades:** STB 3 Star **01786 841679** Mr Darby **Fax:** 01786 842473 *swell@hillview-cottage.com* www.hillview-cottage.com **D:** £21.00–£24.00 **S:** £30.00–£35.00 **Beds:** 2F 1T 2D **Baths:** 5 En ⏰ ▣ (7) ▣ ▥ ✕ ▣ ▥ ☕ ♨ ☕ cc

27 King Street, *Stirling, FK8 1DN.* Comfortable Edwardian town house, convenient bus/rail stations, town centre. **Open:** All year **01786 471082 (also fax)** Mr & Mrs Macgregor *jennifer@sruighlea.demon.co.uk* www.accommodation-stirling.co.uk **D:** £16.00–£20.00 **S:** £20.00–£25.00 **Beds:** 1F 1D 1T **Baths:** 2 Pr ⏰ (2) ⚡ ▣ ▣ ▥ ▪

Ravenscroft, *21 Clarendon Place, Stirling, FK8 2QW.* Beautiful Victorian house in conservation area, views over to castle. **Open:** All year (not Xmas) **01786 473815** Mr & Mrs Dunbar **Fax:** 01786 450990 *dunbar@ravenscroft3.freeserve.co.uk* **D:** £23.50 **S:** £35.00 **Beds:** 1D 1T **Baths:** 1 En 1 Pr ▣ (2) ⚡ ▣ ▥ ▪

Strathyre

NN5617

Rosebank House, *Strathyre, Callander, Perthshire, FK18 8NA.* Enjoy the taste of Scotland, 5 Star food and comforts **Open:** All year **01877 384208** Mr & Mrs Moor **Fax:** 01877 384201 *rosebank@tinyworld.co.uk* www.rosebankhouse.co.uk **D:** £21.00–£25.00 **S:** £21.00–£25.00 **Beds:** 1F 1T 2D **Baths:** 2 En 1 Sh ⏰ ▣ (3) ⚡ ▣ ▥ ✕ ▣ ☕ cc

Dochfour, *Strathyre, Callander, FK18 8NA.* Award-winning B&B in scenic glen, specialising in being the best! **Open:** All year **01877 384256 (also fax)** Mr & Mrs Ffinch *tony.ffinch@tesco.net* **D:** £17.00–£20.00 **S:** £23.00–£26.00 **Beds:** 2D 1T **Baths:** 2 En 1 Pr ⏰ ▣ (6) ✕ ▣ ▥ ⚹ ♨ cc

Thornhill

NS6699

The Granary, *West Moss Side, Thornhill, Stirling, FK8 3QJ.* Recently converted granary. Rooms overlooking gardens with spectacular views. **Open:** All year (not Xmas) **01786 850310** Mrs Cumming **D:** £20.00–£22.00 **S:** £25.00 **Beds:** 2D 1S **Baths:** 2 En 1 Sh ⏰ ▣ (6) ⚡ ▣ ▥ ▥ ☕ ⚹ ♨ ▪

Tillicoultry

NS9197

Wyvis, *70 Stirling Street, Tillicoultry, Clackmannanshire, FK13 6EA.* Converted mill worker's cottage with views to the Ochil Hills. **Open:** All year (not Xmas/New Year) **01259 751513** Mrs Goddard *terrygoddard@netscapeonline.co.uk* **D:** £21.00–£28.00 **S:** £25.00–£28.00 **Beds:** 1T 1D **Baths:** 1 Pr 1 En ⏰ ⚡ ▣ ▥ ✕ ▣ ▥ ▪

Tyndrum

NN3330   ⚐ *Invervey Hotel*

Glengarry Guest House, *Tyndrum, Crianlarich, Perthshire, FK20 8RY.* Ideal base for touring and outdoor activities. Scottish welcome awaits. **Open:** All year **01838 400224** Mr & Mrs Mailer *glengarry@altavista.net* ✕ www.glengarryhouse.co.uk **D:** £18.00–£22.00 **S:** £25.00 **Beds:** 1F 1T 1D **Baths:** 2 En 1 Pr ⏰ (2) ▣ (4) ⚡ ✕ ▣ ▥ ▪

Tigh na Froach, *Lower Station Road, Tyndrum, Crianlarich, Perthshire, FK20 8RY.* Home cooking a speciality. Ideal for walking, touring and golfing. **Open:** All year (not Xmas/New Year) **01838 400354 & 07776 428508 (M)** Ms Clement *tigh-na-froach@supanet.com* **D:** £17.50 **S:** £22.00 **Beds:** 1T 2D **Baths:** 2 Sh ⏰ ▣ ⚡ ▣ ▥ ▪

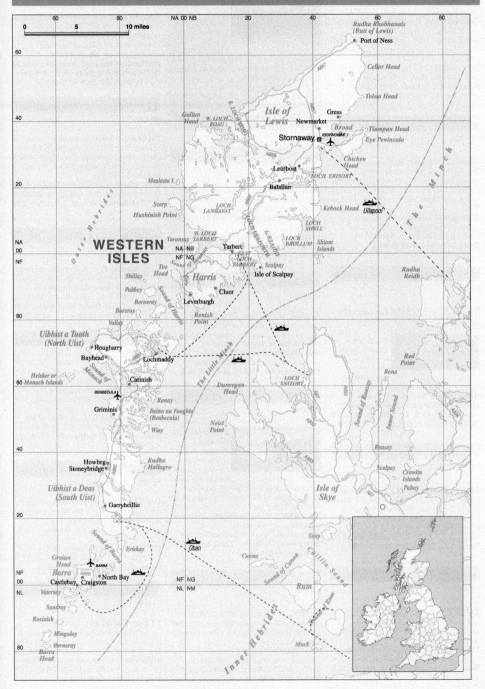

BARRA   Craigston
NF6601

Gearadhmor, *123 Craigston, Castlebay, Isle of Barra, HS9 5XS.* Beautiful surroundings. Home cooking a speciality. Traditional Highland hospitality. **Open:** All year
01871 810688 (also fax) Mrs Maclean
archie.b.maclean@tesco.net **D:** £15.00–£18.00 **S:** £15.00–£20.00 **Beds:** 2F 2T **Baths:** 1 En 3 Sh ⌨ 🖥 (6) 🖺 🗡 ✕ ☑ 🛏 🔅

BARRA   North Bay
NF7203

Northbay House, *Balnabodach, North Bay, Castlebay, Isle of Barra, HS9 5UT.* Attractive former school with comfortable and spacious accommodation. Warm hospitality. **Open:** All year (not Xmas/New Year)
01871 890255 (also fax) Mrs Savory
northbayhouse@isleofbarra.com **D:** £22.00–£26.00 **S:** £22.00–£26.00 **Beds:** 1T 1D **Baths:** 2 En 🖺 (4) 🗡 ☑ 🛏 🔅1

BENBECULA   Griminis
NF7851

Creag Liath, *15 Griminis, Griminish, Isle of Benbecula, HS7 5QA.* Rural working croft, ideal for birdwatching, fishing, cycling and beachcombing. **Open:** All year **Grades:** STB 3 Star
01870 602992 Mrs MacDonald *creagliath@ aol.com* **D:** £25.00 **S:** £25.00 **Beds:** 2F 1T 1D **Baths:** 2 En 2 Pr ⌨ 🖺 (5) ☑ 🗡 ✕ ☑ 🛏 🔅

HARRIS   Cluer
NG1490

Mount Cameron, *2 Cluer, Cluer, Isle of Harris, HS3 3EP.* Mount Cameron is a seven apartment house. Situated within scenic Bays of Harris. **Open:** All year
01859 530356 Mr Mackinnon *calmac2c@ aol.com* **D:** £15.00–£20.00 **S:** £20.00 **Beds:** 2D **Baths:** 1 En 1 Pr 1 Sh ⌨ 🖺 🗡 ☑ ✕

HARRIS   Isle of Scalpay
NG2395

Seafield, *Isle of Scalpay, Isle of Harris, HS4 3XZ.* Fantastic sea views, homely atmosphere. Free boat trip for two night stay. **Open:** Easter to Nov
01859 540250 Mrs Cunningham *roddy@ mjg.sol.uk* **D:** £16.00–£18.00 **S:** £20.00–£22.00 **Beds:** 1F 2D **Baths:** 2 Sh ⌨ 🖺 (4) 🗡 ✕ 🛏

New Haven, *15 Scalpay, Isle of Scalpay, Isle of Harris, HS4 3XZ.* **Open:** All year **Grades:** STB 3 Star
01859 540325
Mrs MacLennan **Fax: 07833527630**
D: £20.00–£25.00 **Beds:** 2D **Baths:** 2 En ⌨ (1) 🖺 (3) 🗡 ☑ ☑ 🛏 🔅
Spacious, comfortable accommodation with sea view. Ideal for hillwalking, fishing. Short drive to beautiful sandy beaches overlooking Atlantic. Residents lounge with open fire. 5 miles from ferry terminal.

HARRIS   Leverburgh
NG0186

St Kilda House, *Leverburgh, Isle of Harris, HS5 3UB.* Beautiful location, warm welcome, home cooking. Levenburgh ferry 2 minutes. **Open:** All year (not Xmas/New Year)
01859 520419 (also fax) Mrs Macleod **D:** £15.00–£20.00 **S:** £15.00–£20.00 **Beds:** 2D **Baths:** 1 En 1 Pr ⌨ 🖺 (2) ✕ ☑ 🛏

HARRIS   Tarbert
NB1500

Avalon, *12 West Side, Tarbert, Isle of Harris, HS3 3BG.* Magnificent views, 3/4 mile ferry terminal. Excellent base for touring Lewis & Harris. **Open:** All year
01859 502334 Mrs Morrison *info@ avalonguesthouse.co.uk* **D:** £20.00 **Beds:** 2T 1D **Baths:** 2 En 1 Pr ⌨ 🖺 (4) ☑ 🗡 ✕ ☑ 🛏 🔅

LEWIS   Balallan
NB2920

Clearview, *44 Balallan, Balallan, Isle of Lewis, HS2 9PT.* Central location for touring Lewis and Harris. Elevated position, panoramic views. **Open:** All year (not Xmas/New Year) **Grades:** STB 3 Star
01851 830472 Mr & Mrs Mackay *clearview@ tinyworld.co.uk www.witb.co. uk/links/clearview.htm* **D:** £20.00–£22.00 **S:** £22.00–£25.00 **Beds:** 1T 2D **Baths:** 2 En 1 Pr ⌨ 🖺 (6) 🗡 ☑ ✕ 🛏

LEWIS   Gress
NB4941

Caladh, *44 Gress, Isle of Lewis, Western Isles, HS2 0NB.* All rooms look overlook river and the sea. Even a talking parrot here. **Open:** All year
01851 820743 Mrs Evans *Eve@ caladh.fsbusiness.co.uk* **D:** £17.00–£19.00 **S:** £18.00–£20.00 **Beds:** 2T **Baths:** 2 En ⌨ (0) 🖺 (4) 🗡 ✕ ☑ 🛏 🔅

LEWIS   Leurbost
NB3725

Glen House, *77 Liurbost, Leurbost, Lochs, Isle of Lewis, HS2 9NL.* Quiet country residence overlooking scenic sea loch, offering high standard of food and accommodation. **Open:** All year
01851 860241 Mrs Reid *glenhouse@talk21.com* **D:** £19.00 **S:** £20.00 **Beds:** 2F 1D 1T **Baths:** 2 En 1 Pr ⌨ 🖺 (5) 🖺 🗡 ☑ 🛏 ✕ ☑ 🛏 🔅

LEWIS   Newmarket
NB4235

Lathamor, *Bakers Road, Newmarket, Isle of Lewis, HS2 0EA.* Spacious family home overlooking Stornoway. Cycle hire, large gardens. Home cooking. **Open:** All year **Grades:** STB 3 Star
01851 706093 (also fax) Mrs Ferguson **D:** £14.00–£20.00 **S:** £14.00–£20.00 **Beds:** 1F 1T 1D 1S **Baths:** 1 Pr ⌨ 🖺 (5) 🗡 ☑ 🛏 ✕ ☑ 🛏 🔅

LEWIS   Port of Ness
NB5363

Cliff House, *Port of Ness, Isle of Lewis, HS2 0XA.* Cliff house situated above sandy beach and harbour. **Open:** Easter to Oct
01851 810278 M Morrison **D:** £18.00–£20.00 **S:** £18.00–£20.00 **Beds:** 1D 2T **Baths:** 1 Sh ⌨ (5) 🖺 (4) ☑ 🗡 ✕ ☑ 🛏

LEWIS   Stornoway
NB4232

Dunroamin, *18 Plantation Road, Stornoway, Isle of Lewis, HS1 2JS.* Centrally located Victorian town house, warm welcome assured, hearty breakfasts. **Open:** All year
01851 704578 Mrs MacLeod **Fax: 01851 170578 D:** £17.00–£20.00 **S:** £18.00–£25.00 **Beds:** 3F 1D 1T 1S **Baths:** 1 En 1 Sh ⌨ 🛏 ✕ ☑ 🛏

NORTH UIST   Bayhead
NF7468   🏨 *Temple View Hotel*

Old Shop House, *Bayhead, Lochmaddy, Isle of North Uist, HS6 5DS.* Bungalow with nice view. Ideal for walking and bird watching. **Open:** All year **Grades:** STB 3 Star
01876 510395 Mrs Nicholson **D:** £19.00–£20.00 **S:** £20.00–£25.00 **Beds:** 1F 1T 1D **Baths:** 2 En ⌨ 🖺 (4) ☑ 🗡 ✕ ☑ 🛏

NORTH UIST   Carinish
NF8259

8 Cnoc Cuidehein, *Carinish, Lochmaddy, Isle of North Uist, HS6 5HW.* A warm welcome and good food awaits you in our comfortable home. **Open:** Easter to Nov
01876 580635 Mrs MacDonald **D:** £15.00–£16.00 **S:** £19.00 **Beds:** 1F 1D 1T **Baths:** 1 Pr 1 Sh ⌨ (5) 🖺 (5) 🗡 🛏 ☑ 🛏

NORTH UIST Hougharry

NF7071

Sgeir Ruadh, *Hougharry, Lochmaddy, Isle of North Uist, HS6 5DL.* On top of a deserted sandy beach, with panoramic views across the bay. **Open:** All year **01876 510312** Mrs Simpson *sgeirruadh@aol.com* **D:** £18.50–£22.00 **S:** £20.00–£22.00 **Beds:** 1T 2D **Baths:** 3 En ⿴ ▣ ⼁ 🖵 �animal ✕ Ⓥ 🔳 ⚲

SOUTH UIST
Garryheillie

NF7522

Clan Ranald, *247 Gearraidh Sheile, Garryheillie, Lochboisdale, Isle of South Uist, HS8 5SX.* Working croft, 3 miles from ferry, will collect from terminal. **Open:** Apr to Dec **01878 700263** Mr & Mrs MacDonald **D:** £23.00 **S:** £23.00 **Beds:** 1T 1D 1S **Baths:** 3 En ⿴ ▣ 🖵 �animal ✕ Ⓥ 🔳 ⚲

SOUTH UIST Howbeg

NF7535 🍺 *Palachar Inn, Orasay Inn*

6 Tobha Beag, *Howbeg, Lochboisdale, Isle of South Uist, HS8 5SQ.* Situated beside a loch, sandy beaches nearby. Haven for birdwatchers. **Open:** All year (not Xmas/New Year) **01870 620273** Mrs MacEachen **D:** £20.00 **S:** £20.00 **Beds:** 1F 1T **Baths:** 1 Pr ⿴ ▣ ⼁ 🖵 �animal ✕ Ⓥ 🔳 ⚲ ⚜ ⚲

SOUTH UIST
Stoneybridge

NF7433

Cross Roads, *Staionebrig, Stoneybridge, Lochboisdale, Isle of South Uist, HS8 5SD.* Ideal for hillwalking, fishing, birdwatching, 2 miles from sandy beaches. **Open:** All year (not Xmas/New Year) **Grades:** STB 2 Star **01870 620321** Mrs MacRury **D:** £18.00–£20.00 **S:** £18.00–£20.00 **Beds:** 2D ⿴ ▣ (6) 🖵 �animal ✕ Ⓥ 🔳 ⚲ ⚲

Anglesey

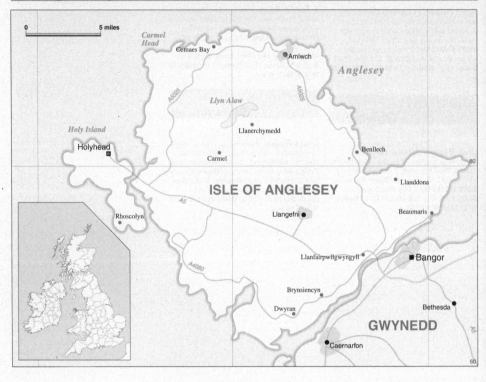

Beaumaris
SH6076

Mor Awel, *Beaumaris, Anglesey, LL58 8NP.*
Victorian house, village rural location, nice
walks, evening meal. Licensed. **Open:** All
year (not Xmas)
01248 490930 Mr Thomas **Fax: 01248 490826**
mor-awel@zetnet.co.uk **D:** £20.00 **S:** £30.00
Beds: 2D 1T 1S **Baths:** 1 En 2 Sh ⌘ 🅿 (4) ⊁
📺 🐾 ⅲ.

Please respect a B&B's
wishes regarding children,
animals and smoking

B&B owners may vary
rates – be sure to check
when booking

Benllech
SH5182

Belvoir, *8 Lon Fferam, Benllech, Tyn-y-
Gongl, Anglesey, LL74 8RL.* Detached house,
pleasant residential locality, quiet, and with
stunning seaviews. **Open:** Easter to Oct
Grades: WTB 4 Star
01248 852907 Mrs Evans
www.belvoirbenllech **D:** £21.50 **S:** £43.00
Beds: 2D **Baths:** 2 Pr 🅿 (2) ⊁ 🛏 📺 📺 ⅲ. ♨

Bay Court Hotel, *Beach Road, Benllech,
Tyn-y-Gongl, Anglesey, LL74 8SW.* 200 yds
from sandy beach. Nearby riding, golf,
fishing. Handy Snowdonia, ferries.
Open: All year
01248 852573 Mr Threfall **Fax: 01248 852606**
D: £23.00–£28.00 **S:** £23.00–£28.00 **Beds:** 4F
10D 3T 5S **Baths:** 10 En 3 Sh ⌘ 🅿 (50) 📺 🐾 ✗
📺 ⅲ. ♨ cc

BEDROOMS
D = Double
T = Twin
S = Single
F = Family

Brynsiencyn

SH4867

Fron Guest House, Brynsiencyn, Llanfairpwllgwyngyll, Anglesey, LL61 6TX. Traditional high class accommodation with magnificent views of Snowdonia. **Open:** Easter to Sept **01248 430310 (also fax)** Mr Geldard **D:** £16.00–£17.50 **S:** £16.50–£18.00 **Beds:** 3D **Baths:** 1 En 1 Sh ⅙ 🃏 🆅 🛏️ ⚓

Carmel

SH3882 ⚓ Old Wharf Boat House

Cefn Gribyn, Carmel,

LLannerchymedd, Anglesey, LL71 7BU. Central Anglesey. Easy reach Irish Ferries, Snowdonia. Peaceful. Vegetarian meals. **Open:** All year **01248 470606** Mrs Hayward lesh@ corfe-castle.demon.co.uk www.corfe-castle. demon.co.uk **D:** £14.30–£20.00 **Beds:** 1T 2D **Baths:** 2 Sh ⮭ (12) 🅿 (6) ⅙ 🃏 🆅 🛏️ ◬ ⚓

Cemaes Bay

SH3694

Woburn Hill Hotel, High Street, Cemaes Bay, Anglesey, LL67 0HU. Popular hotel in old fishing village. Serving local seafood dishes. **Open:** All year **Grades:** WTB 2 Star **01407 711388** Mrs Potter **Fax: 01407 711190** brian@woburnhill.freeserve.co.uk www.woburnhillhotel.co.uk **D:** £22.50–£25.00 **S:** £32.50–£45.00 **Beds:** 5D 2T 1S **Baths:** 5 En 1 Sh 🅿 (10) 🆅 🛏️ ✳ ⚓

Dwyran

SH4466

Tal-y-Foel, Dwyran, Llanfairpwllgwyngyll, LL61 6LQ. Spectacular waterfront location overlooking Snowdonia. Whirlpool baths. Birdwatching, walking, fishing. **Open:** All year (not Xmas/New Year) **01248 430377 Fax: 01248 430977** hutchings@ talyfoel.u-net.com www.tal-y-foel.co.uk **D:** £25.00 **S:** £25.00–£30.00 **Beds:** 2F 2T **Baths:** 4 En ⮭ 🅿 🆅 🛏 🆅 🛏️ ◬ ⚓ cc

Holyhead

SH2482 ⚓ Church Bay Inn, Bull Inn

Wavecrest, 93 Newry Road, Holyhead, Anglesey, LL65 1HU. Ideal ferry stopover for Ireland; close to the South Stack. **Open:** All year (not Xmas) **Grades:** AA 3 Diamond **01407 763637** Mr Hiltunen **Fax: 01407 764862** cwavecrest@aol.com www.holyheadhotels.com **D:** £16.00–£20.00 **S:** £18.00–£20.00 **Beds:** 3F 1D 1S **Baths:** 2 En 1 Pr 1 Sh ⮭ 🅿 (4) ⅙ 🆅 🛏 ✗ 🆅 🛏️ ⚓

Roselea, 26 Holborn Road, Holyhead, Anglesey, LL65 2AT. Good value B & B establishment 28 years, closest to ferry & station. **Open:** All year **Grades:** WTB 2 Star B&B **01407 764391 (also fax)** S Foxley sheila@ roselea73.freeserve.co.uk www.roselea73. freeserve.co.uk **D:** £16.00–£17.00 **S:** £18.00 **Beds:** 1F 1T 1D **Baths:** 1 Sh ⮭ ⅙ 🆅 ✗ 🆅 🛏️ ⚓

Monravon Guest House, Port-y-felin Road, Holyhead, LL65 1PL. Family-run business, 3 minutes to ferry/train terminals. Adjacent to park & beach. **Open:** All year (not Xmas) **Grades:** WTB 3 Star GH **01407 762944 (also fax)** len@monravon.co.uk www.monravon.co.uk **D:** £15.00–£20.00 **S:** £25.00 **Beds:** 8D **Baths:** 8 En ⅙ cc

Llanddona

SH5779 ⚓ Owain Glyndrw

Tyn Pistyll, Beach Road, Llanddona, Beaumaris, Anglesey, LL58 8UN. **Open:** All year (not Xmas/New Year) **Grades:** WTB 3 Star **01248 811224 (also fax)** Mrs Peacock carolynchilton@aol.com **D:** £25.00–£30.00 **S:** £24.00–£35.00 **Beds:** 1F 2D **Baths:** 2 En 1 Pr ⮭ 🅿 (10) ⅙ 🆅 🛏 🆅 🛏️ ⚓ A small piece of paradise set in two acres of lawned gardens surrounded by woodland giving private and panoramic views over Red Wharf Bay and beyond. Blue Flagged beach and miles of walks in this Area of Outstanding Natural Beauty.

RATES

D = Price range per person sharing in a double or twin room

S = Price range for a single room

Llanerchymedd

SH4184 ⚓ Ship Inn, Pilot Boat

Llwydiarth Fawr, Llanerchymedd, Anglesey, LL71 8DF. Secluded Georgian mansion set in 850 acres of woodland & farmland. **Open:** All year (not Xmas/New Year) **Grades:** WTB 4 Star **01248 470321 & 01248 470540** Mrs Hughes **Fax: 01248 470540** llwydiarth@hotmail.com llwydiarthfawr.com **D:** £25.00 **S:** £30.00 **Beds:** 1F 1T 1D 1S **Baths:** 4 En ⮭ 🅿 (8) ⅙ 🆅 ✗ 🆅 🛏️ ◬ ⚓ cc

Maenaddwyn

SH4584

Tre-Wyn, Maenaddwyn, Llangefni, LL71 8AE. A warm welcome. Comfortable accommodation and central to Anglesey's attractions. **Open:** All year (not Xmas/New Year) **01248 470874** Ms Brown **Fax: 01248 470875** nia@trewyn.fsnet.co.uk **D:** £20.00–£22.50 **S:** £25.00–£27.00 **Beds:** 1F 2T **Baths:** 3 En ⮭ ⅙ 🆅 🛏️ ⚓

Rhoscolyn

SH2675 ⚓ White Eagle, Anchorage Hotel

Gwynfryn House, Rhoscolyn, Holyhead, LL65 2EQ. Rural location. Distant views. Delightful coastal walks within five minutes. **Open:** All year (not Xmas/New Year) **Grades:** WTB 2 Star **01407 861107** Mr & Mrs Chadwick ann_dennis@tesco.net homepages.tesco. net/~Ann_Dennis **D:** £19.00 **S:** £17.50 **Beds:** 2D 2S **Baths:** 1 Sh ⮭ 🅿 (10) ⅙ 🆅 🛏 🛏️ ⚓

Valley

SH2979

Valley Hotel, London Road, Valley, Holyhead, LL65 3DU. Superior ensuite accommodation and pub situated 4 miles from ferry. Take exit marked 'valley (y fali)' on A55. **Open:** All year **Grades:** RAC 3 Diamond **01407 740203** K Snape **Fax: 01407 740686** valleyhotel@tinyworld.co.uk www.valley-hotel-anglesey.co.uk **D:** £25.00–£49.50 **S:** £37.50 **Beds:** 2F 9T 4D 5S **Baths:** 18 En 1 Sh ⮭ 🅿 (40) 🆅 🛏 ✗ 🆅 🛏️ ⚓ cc

Carmarthenshire

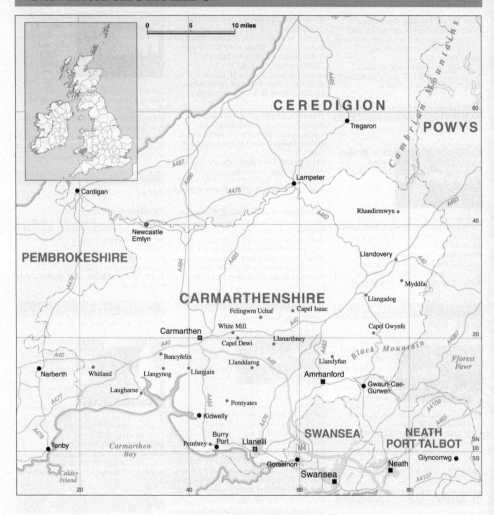

Bancyfelin

SN3217

Sarnau Mansion, *Llysonnen Road, Bancyfelin, Carmarthen, SA33 5DZ.* Beautiful Georgian mansion, large landscaped grounds, tennis court, easy access A40. **Open:** All year **Grades:** WTB 3 Star **01267 211404 (also fax)** Mrs Fernihough **D:** £20.00–£27.50 **S:** £25.00–£35.00 **Beds:** 1F 2D 1T **Baths:** 3 En 1 Pr ♿ 🅿 (10) ⌿ 📺 Ⓥ 🛏

Capel Dewi

SN4720

Farm Retreats, *Dewi Uchaf Country House, Capel Dewi, Carmarthen, SA32 8AY.* Large, traditional, comfortable secluded farmhouse. **Open:** All year **Grades:** WTB 4 Star **01267 290799** F M Burns **Fax: 01267 290003** *uchaffarm@aol.com* walescottageholidays.uk. com **D:** £28.00 **S:** £40.00 **Beds:** 1T 2D **Baths:** 3 En ♿ 🅿 ⌿ 📺 ✕ 🛏 Ⓥ 🛏 ⚓ cc

---

Capel Gwynfe

SN7222

Pencrug Farm, *Capel Gwynfe, Llangadog, Carmarthenshire, SA19 9RP.* C17th working farm house. National Park. Quiet. Glorious views. Good food. **Open:** All year (not Xmas/New Year) **Grades:** WTB 3 Star **01550 740686 (also fax)** Mrs Fleming **D:** £13.50 **S:** £14.00 **Beds:** 1D 2T **Baths:** 1 Sh ♿ 🅿 (4) ⌿ 📺 ✕ Ⓥ 🛏 ⚓

Capel Isaac

SN5827

The Manse, *Capel Isaac, Llandeilo, SA19 7TN.* Peaceful organic farm, beautiful area, many attractions, castles, Aberglasney's historic gardens. **Open:** All year
01558 668873 (also fax) Mr & Mrs Smith **D:** £16.00 **S:** £16.00 **Beds:** 1D 1T 1S **Baths:** 2 Pr 1 Sh 🅿 (6) ⌇ 📺 ✕ 🅅 🛏 ⚓

Carmarthen

SN4120

Trebersed Farmhouse, *Travellers Rest, St Peters, Carmarthen, SA31 3RR.* Relax in peaceful countryside staying on friendly working dairy farm.
Open: All year (not Xmas) **Grades:** WTB 3 Star
01267 238182 Mrs Jones **Fax: 01267 223633** *trebersed.farm@farmline.com* www.trebersed.co. uk **D:** £20.00 **S:** £25.00 **Beds:** 1F 1D 1T **Baths:** 3 En 🕭 🅿 (6) ⌇ 📺 🛏 ⚓ cc

Plas Farm, *Llangynog, Carmarthen, SA33 5DB.* Ideal touring base for South and West Wales. Easy to find. **Open:** All year **Grades:** WTB 3 Star
01267 211492 (also fax) Mrs Thomas **D:** £18.00–£20.00 **S:** £20.00–£25.00 **Beds:** 1F 1D 1T **Baths:** 2 En 1 Pr 🕭 🅿 (4) ⌇ 📺 ⚓

Y Dderwen Fach, *98 Priory Street, Carmarthen, SA31 1NB.* C17th town house of character. Convenient for shops, beaches, countryside. **Open:** All year (not Xmas) **Grades:** WTB 2 Star
01267 234193 Mr & Mrs Bowyer **Fax: 01267 235766 D:** £16.00–£18.50 **S:** £16.50–£22.50 **Beds:** 1D 1T 2S **Baths:** 2 En 1 Sh 🕭 (5) 📺 ✕ 🅅 ⚓

Sarnau Mansion, *Llysonnen Road, Bancyfelin, Carmarthen, SA33 5DZ.* Beautiful Georgian mansion, large landscaped grounds, tennis court, easy access A40.
Open: All year **Grades:** WTB 3 Star
01267 211404 (also fax) Mrs Fernihough **D:** £20.00–£27.50 **S:** £25.00–£35.00 **Beds:** 1F 2D 1T **Baths:** 3 En 1 Pr 🕭 🅿 (10) ⌇ 📺 🅅

53 Parcmaen Street, *Carmarthen, SA31 3DR.* Terraced house, walking distance town centre, bus/train stations, parking.
Open: All year
01267 238260 & 07779 468675 (M) Mrs Jones **D:** £14.00–£15.00 **S:** £15.00 **Beds:** 1D 1T 🕭 ⌇ 📺 🅅 ⚓

Meiros Hall Guest House, *2 Waterloo Terrace, Carmarthen, SA31 1DG.* Homely guest house minutes' walk from centre of quaint market county town of Carmarthen.
Open: All year (not Xmas/New Year)
01267 222708 J D C Lewis **D:** £17.00 **S:** £17.00 **Beds:** 1F 1T 1D 1S **Baths:** 1 Sh 🕭 ⌇ 📺 🛏 🅅 ⚓

Felingwm

SN5124

Dolau Guest House, *Felingwm Isaf, Nantgaredig, Carmarthen, SA32 7PB.* Attractive rural riverside location. Luxury accommodation, near botanic Aberglasney gardens **Open:** All year
01267 290464 Mr Bright *brightdolau@aol.com* www.visit-carmarthenshire.co.uk/dolau **D:** £18.00–£25.00 **S:** £21.00–£25.00 **Beds:** 1F 1D 1T **Baths:** 2 En 1 Pr 🕭 🅿 (6) ⌇ 📺 ✕ 🅅 ⚓

Laugharne

SN3010

Swan Cottage, *20 Gosport St, Laugharne, Carmarthen, SA33 4SZ.* Lovely stone cottage, one room only on ground floor, excellent breakfasts. **Open:** All year
01994 427409 Mrs Brown *rob.erts@talk21.com* **D:** £18.00–£20.00 **S:** £18.00–£25.00 **Beds:** 1D **Baths:** 1 En 🕭 🅿 (1) ⌇ 📺 🅅 ⚓ ⚓

Castle House, *Market Lane, Laugharne, Carmarthen, SA33 4SA.* Beautiful Georgian house with gardens, overlooking the estuary and castle. **Open:** All year
01994 427616 Mrs Mitchell *charles@ laugharne.co.uk* www.laugharne.co. uk/casthous.htm **D:** £25.00–£35.00 **S:** £30.00–£35.00 **Beds:** 1F 2D **Baths:** 2 En 1 Pr 🕭 🅿 (3) 🛏 🅅 ⚓

Llanarthney

SN5320 🍺 *Old Emlyn Arms*

Central House, *Llanarthney, Carmarthen, SA32 8JE.* Near Botanical Gardens, castles, Towy Valley, market towns. Homely atmosphere. **Open:** All year
01558 668595 Mr & Mrs Jonah *pjonah6442@ aol.com* **D:** £18.00 **S:** £18.00 **Beds:** 1F 1T 1D **Baths:** 1 Sh 🕭 🅿 (2) 📺 🛏 ✕ 🅅 ⚓

Llanboidy

SN2123

Castell Pigyn Farm, *Llanboidy, Whitland, Carmarthenshire, SA34 0LJ.* Situated on a peaceful hilltop with fabulous views in all directions. **Open:** Easter to Oct
01994 448391 Mrs Davies **Fax: 01994 448755 D:** £22.00 **S:** £27.00 **Beds:** 1F 1D 1T **Baths:** 2 En 1 Pr 🕭 🅿 📺 ✕ 🅅 ⚓ ⚓

Llanddarog

SN5016 🍺 *White Hart, Butcher's Arms*

Coedhirion Farm, *Llanddarog, Carmarthen, SA32 8BH.* Conveniently situated just off A48 dual carriageway, 5 mins National Botanical Garden of Wales. **Open:** All year
Grades: WTB 2 Star
01267 275666 Mr & Mrs Evans *welshfarmhouse@hotmail.com* www.smoothhound.co. uk/hotels/coedhirion.com **D:** £20.00–£22.50 **S:** £27.50–£30.00 **Beds:** 1F 1T 1D 1S **Baths:** 4 En 🕭 🅿 (5) ⌇ 📺 ⚓ ✳ ⚓

Llanddowror

SN2514

West Wood House, *Llanddowror, Carmarthen, SA33 4HL.* Village, not isolated, near Carmarthen, enroute Irish Ferries & Tenby. **Open:** All year
01994 230512 (also fax) Mrs Davies **D:** £18.00–£20.00 **S:** £20.00–£25.00 **Beds:** 2D 1S **Baths:** 1 En 1 Sh 🕭 🅿 (4) ⌇ 📺 🅅 ⚓

Llandovery

SN7634 🍺 *Castle, King's Head*

Pencerrig, *New Road, Llandovery, SA20 0EA.* Victorian house at edge of town. Local shops, pubs, restaurants 5 mins' walk. **Open:** All year
01550 721259 D: £19.00 **S:** £19.00 **Beds:** 1D 1T 1S **Baths:** 2 En 1 Pr 🅿 (1) ⌇ 📺 🅅 ⚓

Cwm Rhuddan Mansion, *Llandovery, Carmarthenshire, SA20 0DX.* Unique French chateau-style mansion with original features, antique furnishings. Landscaped gardens with panoramic view. **Open:** All year
01550 721414 (also fax) Mrs Wheadon www.visit-carmarthen-shire.co. uk/cwmrhuddan **D:** £25.00–£30.00 **S:** £25.00 **Beds:** 2F 1D **Baths:** 3 En 🕭 🅿 (10) 📺 🛏 🅅 ⚓ ⚓

Llandyfan

SN6417 🍺 *Square Compass*

Pen-y-banc Farm, *Llandyfan, Ammanford, SA18 2UD.* In Brecon National Park. Ideal base for touring, SW Wales. **Open:** All year (not Xmas/New Year)
01269 850530 *franhay@freeuk.com* www.penybancbandb.co.uk **D:** £19.00 **S:** £23.00 **Beds:** 3D **Baths:** 2 En 1 Pr 🅿 (6) 📺 ⚓ ⚓

Bryncoch Farm,
Llandyfan, Ammanford, SA18 2TY.
Open: All year
01269 850480
Mr Richardson **Fax: 01269 850888** *bryncoch@ tesco.net* **D:** £17.50 **S:** £20.00 **Beds:** 1F 1T 1D
Baths: 3 En ॐ ₱ 🎴 🔟 ⚡ 🍴 📺 🎍
Bryncoch, high above the Amman Valley in the Brecons National Park, overlooking Glynher Golf Course. 20 mins from the Botanic Gardens and Aberglasney. Comfortable ensuite bedrooms. English or vegetarian breakfast cooked by your host Graham in a homely atmosphere.

Llanelli
SN5000 🚂 *Farriers*

Southmead Guest House, *72 Queen Victoria Road, Llanelli, SA15 2TH.* Southmead Guest House, ensuite rooms, car park, town centre. **Open:** All year (not Xmas)
01554 758588 R Fouracre **D:** £15.00–£20.00 **S:** £15.00–£20.00 **Beds:** 1F 2D 2T 2S
Baths: 4 En 2 Sh

Llangadog
SN7028

Cynyll Farm, *Llangadog, Carmarthenshire, SA19 9BB.* Comfortable C17th farmhouse. Excellent home cooking. Overlooks Black Mountains. **Open:** All year (not Xmas/New Year)
01550 777316 (also fax) Mrs Dare
www.visit_camarthenshire.co.uk/cynyll/
D: £17.00 **S:** £17.00 **Beds:** 1F 1D **Baths:** 1 En 1 Pr ॐ ₱ 🔟 ✗ 🔟 ⚡

Llangain
SN3815

Brynderwen, *School Lane, Llangain, Carmarthen, SA33 5AE.* Family-run B&B, quiet village setting. Comfortable rooms, convenient coast, countryside & Irish ferries. **Open:** All year (not Xmas)
01267 241403 M Davies **D:** £20.00–£24.00 **S:** £18.00–£24.00 **Beds:** 1D 1T 1S **Baths:** 2 En 1 Sh ॐ ₱ (4) ⚡ 🔟 🔟 📺 ⚡

Llangynog
SN3316

Plas Farm, *Llangynog, Carmarthenshire, SA33 5DB.* Ideal touring base for South and West Wales. Easy to find. **Open:** All year
Grades: WTB 3 Star
01267 211492 (also fax) Mrs Thomas
D: £18.00–£20.00 **S:** £20.00–£25.00 **Beds:** 1F 1D 1T **Baths:** 2 En 1 Pr ॐ ₱ (4) ⚡ 🔟 📺 ⚡

Myddfai
SN7730

Erwlas, *Myddfai, Llandovery, Carmarthenshire, SA20 0JB.* Modern, comfortable bungalow, quiet location, magnificent countryside. Ideal walking area. **Open:** All year (not Xmas)
01550 720797 Mrs Holloway **D:** £13.50
S: £13.50 **Beds:** 1D 1T **Baths:** 1 Sh ॐ ₱ (3) ⚡ 🔟 🍴 ✗ 🔟 📺

Newcastle Emlyn
SN3040

Maes Y Derw Guest House, *Newcastle Emlyn, Carmarthenshire, SA38 9RD.* Large Edwardian family house full of original charm and character. **Open:** All year
01239 710860 (also fax) D Davies **D:** £19.00–£20.00 **S:** £25.00–£32.00 **Beds:** 1F 1T 1D
Baths: 1 En 2 Pr ॐ ₱ (8) ⚡ 🔟 🍴 ✗ 🔟 📺 ⚡ cc

Pembrey
SN4201

Four Seasons Guest House, *62 Gwscwm Road, Pembrey, Burry Port, SA16 0YU.* A friendly guest house with ground floor accommodation available. **Open:** All year
01554 833367 (also fax) **D:** £18.00–£20.00 **S:** £22.00–£27.00 **Beds:** 1F 3T 1D **Baths:** 2 En 1 Sh ॐ ₱ (10) ⚡ 🔟 📺 ⚡

Pontyates
SN4708

Glynfach Farm, *Pontyates, Llanelli, SA15 5TG.* Warm welcome to our organic small holding. Creative breakfasts, coast & country. **Open:** All year (not Xmas)
01269 861290 (also fax) J Pearce **D:** £18.00
S: £18.00 **Beds:** 1D 2T **Baths:** 1 Pr ॐ ₱ ⚡ 🔟 🍴 🔟 📺

Rhandirmwyn
SN7843

Nantybai Mill, *Rhandirmwyn, Llandovery, Carmarthenshire, SA20 0PB.* Historic farmhouse dating back to C15th. Spectacular scenery. Relaxing ambience.
Open: All year
01550 760211 A Jones *nantybai.mill@ ukonline.co.uk* **D:** £17.50–£18.50 **S:** £17.50–£18.50 **Beds:** 1T 1D 1S **Baths:** 1 Sh ॐ ₱ (10) ⚡ 🔟 🍴 ✗ 🔟 📺 ⚡

White Mill
SN4621

Penrhiw Farm Guest House, *White Mill, Carmarthen, SA32 7ET.* Situated 0.25 mile off A40 at Whitemill. Peaceful surroundings overlooking Towy Valley.
Open: All year
01267 290260 Mrs Jones **D:** £20.00 **S:** £25.00 **Beds:** 2D **Baths:** 1 En 1 Pr ॐ ₱ (10) 🔟 📺 ⚡

Whitland
SN2016

Fforest Farm, *Whitland, Carmarthenshire, SA34 0LS.* Farm set in Taf Valley near coast. Beautiful walks, fishing available **Open:** All year (not Xmas/New Year)
01994 240066 Mrs Windsor **D:** £18.00 **S:** £18.00 **Beds:** 2F **Baths:** 2 En ₱ ⚡ 🔟 📺

Ceredigion

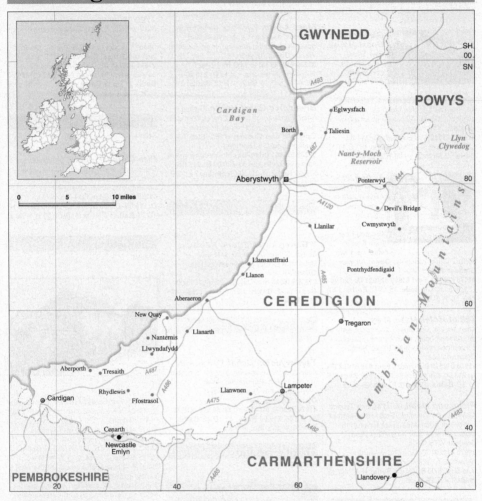

SH 00
SN

GWYNEDD

POWYS

Cardigan Bay

Eglwysfach

Borth • Taliesin

Nant-y-Moch Reservoir

Llyn Clywedog

Aberystwyth ▪   Ponterwyd   80

Devil's Bridge

Llanilar   Cwmystwyth

Llansantffraid

Llanon   Pontrhydfendigaid

Aberaeron

C E R E D I G I O N   60

New Quay   Tregaron

Nanternis   Llanarth
Llwyndafydd

Aberporth • Tresaith

Rhydlewis •   Llanwnen   Lampeter
Cardigan   Ffostrasol

Cenarth
Newcastle
Emlyn

Cambrian Mountains

CARMARTHENSHIRE

PEMBROKESHIRE   Llandovery

0   5   10 miles

Aberaeron

SN4562   Prince of Wales, Habour Master Hotel

Arosfa, Harbourside, Aberaeron, Ceredigion, *SA46 0BU.* Harbourside. Superb Welsh breakfast with highest AA Grade for 2002.
Open: All year **Grades:** WTB 3 Star, AA 4 Diamond
01545 570120 Mr Griffiths *arosfabandb@ aol.com* www.arosfaguesthouse.co.uk
D: £20.00–£25.00 **S:** £22.00–£35.00 **Beds:** 1F 2D 1T **Baths:** 4 En 1 Pr ➣ (6) ▣ (4) ⚡ 🗹 Ⅴ 🏠 ♿ ⚓

Aberporth

SN2651

Highcliffe Hotel, School Road, Aberporth, Cardigan, *SA43 2DA.* Unspoilt sandy coves, bar, restaurant, waterfalls, dolphins. Kids/pets welcome. **Open:** All year
01239 810534 (also fax) Mr Conway
www.highcliffehotel.co.uk **D:** £22.50–£29.75
S: £33.95–£39.60 **Beds:** 4F 6D 4T 1S
Baths: 14 En 1 Sh ➣ ▣ (18) 🗹 🛏 ✕ Ⅴ 🏠 ✿ ⚓ cc

Aberystwyth

SN5881   Tollgate Inn, Gogerddan Arms, Wetherspoons, Cambrian Hotel

Marine Hotel, Marine Terrace, Aberystwyth, Cardiganshire, *SY23 2BX.* Idyllic countryside setting new luxury guest house. Set in peaceful surroundings.
Open: Jan to Dec
0800 0190020 & 01970 612444 Mrs Evans
Fax: 01970 617435 D: £20.00–£35.00
S: £25.00–£35.00 **Beds:** 7F 14D 13T 5S
Baths: 38 En 1 Pr ➣ (1) ▣ (12) 🗹 🛏 ✕ Ⅴ 🏠 ♿ ✿ ⚓ cc

Planning a longer stay? Always ask for any special rates

Garreg Lwyd Guest House, Bow Street, Aberystwyth, Ceredigion, SY24 5BE. On A487. Private parking. Excellent breakfast. Television lounge. Tea & coffee facilities, snacks available. **Open:** All year (not Xmas) **Grades:** WTB 2 Star **01970 828830** Mrs Edwards **D:** £17.00–£21.50 **S:** £19.00–£23.00 **Beds:** 1F 2D 1T 1S **Baths:** 2 Sh ➤ 🖻 (6) 🎦 ⊁ 🔟 💷 ⚉

Aisling, 21 Alexandra Road, Aberystwyth, Ceredigion, SY23 1LN. Perfectly situated near train & bus stations, town centre. Warm welcome. **Open:** All year **Grades:** WTB 3 Star **01970 626980 Fax: 01970 624921 D:** £20.00–£23.00 **S:** £25.00 **Beds:** 1F 1T 1S **Baths:** 1 Sh ➤ ⊁ 🔟 🎦 🔟 💷 ⚉

Talbot Hotel, Market Street, Aberystwyth, Ceredigion, SY23 1DL. Newly refurbished hotel, town centre location, conference room. Close to sea front. **Open:** All year **01970 612575** E T Davies **Fax: 01970 412575 D:** £18.00–£30.00 **S:** £25.00–£30.00 **Beds:** 5F 8T 5D **Baths:** 18 En ➤ 🔟 🎦 ✕ 💷 ✿ cc

Richmond Hotel, 44-45 Marine Terrace, Aberystwyth, Ceredigion, SY23 2BX. Seafront family run hotel. Ideal base for touring. **Open:** All year (not Xmas/New Year) **Grades:** WTB 3 Star **01970 612201** Mr Griffiths *richard@richmondhotel.uk.com* www.richmondhotel.uk.com **D:** £38.00 **S:** £55.00 **Beds:** 4F 4T 4D 3S ➤ 🖻 🔟 ✕ 🔟 💷 ⚉ cc

Borth
SN6089

Glanmor Hotel, High Street, Borth, Ceredigion, SY24 5JP. Small friendly seaside hotel close to golf course. **Open:** All year **Grades:** WTB 1 Star **01970 871689** Mr Elliot **D:** £21.00 **S:** £21.00 **Beds:** 3F 2D 1T 1S **Baths:** 2 En 2 Sh ➤ 🖻 (6) 🔟 🎦 ✕ 🔟 💷 ⚉

Maesteg Guest House, High Street, Borth, Ceredigion, SY24 5JP. Comfortable, friendly sea front B&B - 2 minutes to village. **Open:** Easter to Oct **01970 871928** Mrs Fiorentino **D:** £16.00–£18.00 **S:** £16.00 **Beds:** 1F 1D 1T 1S **Baths:** 1 Sh ➤ ⊁ 🔟 🎦 🔟 💷 ⚉

Cardigan
SN1746 🍺 *Three Horse Shoes, White Hart, The Ship, Goggerdan Arms, Pendre Inn*

Maes-A-Mor, Park Place, Gwbert Road,- Cardigan, SA43 1AE. Centrally situated opposite the park. Ideal for coast & central Wales. **Open:** All year **01239 614929 (also fax)** Mr Jones *maesamor@jejones.demon.co.uk* **D:** £16.00–£20.00 **S:** £18.00 **Beds:** 1D 2T **Baths:** 3 En ➤ (8) 🖻 (3) ⊁ 🔟 💷 ⚉

Brynhyfryd Guest House, Gwbert Road, Cardigan, SA43 1AE. 2 miles Cardigan Bay; 6 minutes walk to town centre. **Open:** All year **Grades:** WTB 3 Star, AA 3 Diamond, RAC 3 Diamond **01239 612861 (also fax)** Mrs Arcus *g.arcus@btinternet.com* **D:** £18.00–£20.00 **S:** £18.00–£25.00 **Beds:** 1F 3D 1T 2S **Baths:** 3 En 2 Pr ➤ (5) ⊁ 🔟 ✕ 🔟 💷 ⚉

Cenarth
SN2641 🍺 *Nag's Head*

Y Garreg Lwyd, Cenarth, Newcastle Emlyn, Carmarthenshire, SA38 9RB. Delightful former farmhouse cottage. **Open:** All year **01239 710230** Mrs Daly **D:** £16.00–£25.00 **Beds:** 1T 1D **Baths:** 1 En 1 Pr ➤ (12) 🖻 (3) ⊁ 🔟 💷 ⚉

Cwmystwyth
SN7874

Tainewyddion Uchaf, Cwmystwyth, Aberystwyth, Ceredigion, SY23 4AF. Situated at over 1000 ft. Panoramic views overlooking the Ystwyth Valley. **Open:** Easter to Oct **01974 282672** Mrs Liford **D:** £15.00–£18.00 **S:** £15.00–£18.00 **Beds:** 1T 1D 1S **Baths:** 1 En 1 Sh ⊁ ✕ 🔟 💷

Devil's Bridge
SN7376

Mount Pleasant, Devil's Bridge, Aberystwyth, Ceredigion, SY23 4QY. **Open:** All year (not Xmas/New Year) **Grades:** WTB 3 Star **01970 890219** M B Connell **Fax: 01970 890239** *relax@mpleasant.co.uk* www.mpleasant.co.uk **D:** £20.00–£25.00 **S:** £20.00–£33.00 **Beds:** 1T 2D **Baths:** 2 En 1 Pr 🖻 (4) ⊁ 🔟 ✕ 🔟 💷 ⚉
Relax and enjoy excellent hospitality in our comfortable, well-furnished home, amidst peaceful, stunning scenery. Fully non-smoking, delicious breakfasts and candlelit dinners with menu choice, wine list. Delightful gardens. Ideal for birdwatching, walking, cycling or discovering our many surrounding attractions.

Eglwys Fach
SN6896

Tyglyneiddwen, Eglwysfach, Machynlleth, Powys, SY20 8SX. Warm welcome. Excellent breakfast amid beautiful scenery in Dovey Valley. **Open:** All year (not Xmas) **Grades:** WTB 2 Star **01654 781348** Mrs Greenwood *edna@aber.ac.uk* **D:** £18.00–£21.00 **S:** £18.00–£25.00 **Beds:** 2F 2D 1S **Baths:** 1 En 1 Sh ➤ 🖻 (6) ⊁ 🔟 🎦 ✕ 🔟 ⚉

Ffostrasol
SN3747

Plas Cerdin, Ffostrasol, Llandysul, Ceredigion, SA44 4TA. Large modern split-level house. Secluded position with breathtaking views. **Open:** All year **01239 851329 (also fax)** Mrs Hicks **D:** £19.00–£20.00 **S:** £20.00–£24.00 **Beds:** 1F 1D 1T **Baths:** 3 En ➤ (3) 🖻 (4) 🔟 🎦 💷 ⚉

Lampeter
SN5848

Pantycelyn Guest House, Llanwnnen, Lampeter, Ceredigion, SA48 7LW. **Open:** Feb to Oct **Grades:** WTB 3 Star **01570 434455 (also fax)** Mrs Jenkins *HuwAnnJ@aol.com* www.pantycelyn.co.uk **D:** £20.00–£24.00 **S:** £20.00–£24.00 **Beds:** 1D 1T 1S **Baths:** 3 En 🖻 (4) ⊁ 🔟 🎦 💷 ⚉
Relax in this peaceful branch of the Teify Valley. Pantycelyn, in 11 acres of meadows, 5 miles west of Lampeter, is ideal for enjoying Cardigan Bay and Ceredigion's many attractions. We promise a warm welcome, memorable breakfasts, plus friendly Welsh Cobs.

Penlanmedd, Llanfair Road, Lampeter, Ceredigion, SA48 8JZ. Cosy, secluded C18th farmhouse, between coast and mountains. Warm welcome. **Open:** All year (not Xmas) **Grades:** WTB 3 Star **01570 493438 (also fax)** Mrs Coombes *penlanmedd@coombes-e.freeserve.co.uk* **D:** £19.00–£20.00 **S:** £25.00 **Beds:** 1F 1D 1T **Baths:** 3 En ➤ 🖻 (20) 🔟 🔟 💷 ⚉

Haulfan, *6 Station Terrace, Lampeter, Ceredigion, SA48 7HH.* Central town position, near university, nature reserve and sea. **Open:** Jan to Dec **Grades:** WTB 3 Star, AA 3 Diamond
01570 422718 Mrs Williams **D:** £17.00–£19.00 **S:** £17.00–£20.00 **Beds:** 1F 1D 1S **Baths:** 1 En 1 Sh ♥ 🖻 ☑ ↑ Ⅵ ⅢⅡ. ☀

Llanarth
SN4257

Beechwood, *Llanarth, Ceredigion, SA47 0RE.* Friendly family-run bed and breakfast in a quiet village. **Open:** Easter to Sept
01545 580280 Mrs Evans **D:** £14.00 **S:** £16.00 **Beds:** 2F 1T **Baths:** 3 En ♥ 🖻 ⅉ ☑ ↑ Ⅵ ⅢⅡ. ☀

Llanilar
SN6275

Glynwern Guest House, *Llanilar, Aberystwyth, Ceredigion, SY23 4NY.* Picturesque riverside house - free fishing, beautiful views, golf, wildlife **Open:** All year (not Xmas/New Year)
01603 782193 Miss Evans **D:** £22.00 **S:** £22.00 **Beds:** 1T 2D **Baths:** 1 En 🖻 (2) ⅉ ☑ ✕ Ⅵ ⅢⅡ.

Llanon
SN5166

The Barn House, *Llanon, Aberystwyth, Ceredigion, SY23 5LZ.* Converted barn in landscaped gardens, sea views. Aromatherapy, reflexology available. **Open:** All year **Grades:** WTB 2 Star
01974 202581 Mrs Rees **D:** £18.00–£25.00 **S:** £18.00–£25.00 **Beds:** 1F 1T 2S **Baths:** 1 En 1 Pr 1 Sh ♥ 🖻 (6) ⅉ ☑ ↑ Ⅵ ⅢⅡ. ☀ ☀

Llansantffraid
SN5167

The Haven, *Winllan Road, Llansantffraid, Powys, SY22 6TR.* Detached bungalow, Shropshire-Powys border, with panoramic views. **Open:** All year
01691 828101 Mrs Wilde **D:** £17.00–£19.00 **S:** £20.00–£21.00 **Beds:** 1F 1T **Baths:** 1 En 1 Pr 🖻 (4) ⅉ ☑ ✕ Ⅵ ⅢⅡ. ♿1 ☀ ☀

Llanwnnen
SN5347

Pantycelyn Guest House, *Llanwnnen, Lampeter, Ceredigion, SA48 7LW.* Peaceful branch of the Teify Valley. Pantycelyn, in 11 acres of meadows. **Open:** Feb to Oct **Grades:** WTB 3 Star
01570 434455 (also fax) Mrs Jenkins *HuwAnnJ@aol.com* www.pantycelyn.co.uk **D:** £20.00–£24.00 **S:** £20.00–£24.00 **Beds:** 1D 1T 1S **Baths:** 3 En 🖻 (4) ⅉ ☑ ↑ Ⅵ ⅢⅡ. ☀

Planning a longer stay? Always ask for any special rates

Llwyndafydd
SN3755

Ty Hen Farm Hotel Cottages &, *Leisure Centre, Llwyndafydd, Llandysul, Ceredigion, SA44 6BZ.* Working sheep farm with private indoor pool and fitness room. **Open:** Feb to Nov
01545 560346 (also fax) Mr Kelly *tyhen@ouvip.com* **D:** £25.50–£29.00 **S:** £25.50–£29.00 **Beds:** 1D 1T **Baths:** 2 Pr 🖻 (20) ⅉ ☑ ↑ ✕ ⅢⅡ. ☀ cc

Nanternis
SN3756 🍺 *Crown Inn*

Llainfran House, *Nanternis, New Quay, Ceredigion, SA45 9RR.* **Open:** Mar to Oct
01545 561243 **D:** £20.00–£25.00 **Beds:** 1T 1D **Baths:** 2 En ♥ (8) 🖻 (4) ✕ ☑ ✕ ⅢⅡ. ☀
Sea views, scenic, secluded 16 acre setting. Warm welcome, lovely accommodation. Victorian country house, modern facilities. Heritage and Gulf Stream Coastline near Cwmtydu Cove. Dolphins, seals, red kites, buzzards, Cornwall without the crowds. Own dining TV lounge. Week holidays a speciality.

New Quay
SN3859 🍺 *Castle Bar, Hungry Trout*

Brynarfor Hotel, *New Road, New Quay, Ceredigion, SA45 9SB.* Watch dolphins play in the bay, sandy beaches, cliff walks. **Open:** Mar to Oct
01545 560358 Mr Jewess **Fax: 01545 561204** *enquiries@brynarfor.co.uk* www.brynarfor.co.uk **D:** £28.00–£32.00 **S:** £25.00–£35.00 **Beds:** 3F 2D 1T 1S **Baths:** 7 En ♥ 🖻 (10) ☑ ✕ Ⅵ ⅢⅡ. ♿ cc

Ponterwyd
SN7480

The George Borrow Hotel, *Ponterwyd, Aberystwyth, Ceredigion, SY23 3AD.* Famous old hotel set in beautiful countryside, overlooking Eagle Falls & Rheidol Gorge. **Open:** All year (not Xmas)
01970 890230 Mr & Mrs Wall **Fax: 01970 890587** *georgeborrow@clara.net* www.george-borrow.co.uk **D:** £25.00 **S:** £25.00 **Beds:** 2F 3D 2T 2S **Baths:** 9 En ♥ 🖻 (40) ☑ ↑ ✕ Ⅵ ⅢⅡ. ☀ cc

Pontrhydfendigaid
SN7366

Red Lion Hotel, *Pontrhydfendigaid, Ystrad Meurig, Ceredigion, SY25 6BH.* Friendly riverside country pub/inn with caravan/camping facilities. **Open:** All year
01974 831232 Mr Earey *red@redlionbont.com* www.redlionbont.com **D:** £18.50 **S:** £18.50 **Beds:** 1F 1T 2D **Baths:** 4 En ♥ 🖻 (50) ⅉ ☑ ✕ Ⅵ ⅢⅡ. ☀ ☀

Rhydlewis
SN3447

Llwyn-yr-eos, *Rhydlewis, Llandysul, Ceredigion, SA44 5QU.* Organic farm, peaceful, wide-sweeping views, stream, wildlife, beach: 3 miles. **Open:** All year (not Xmas/New Year)
01239 851268 Mrs Lalljee **Fax: 01239 851850** *lalljee@which.net* **D:** £19.00–£20.00 **S:** £19.00–£20.00 **Beds:** 1F 1D **Baths:** 2 En ♥ 🖻 ⅉ ↑ ✕ Ⅵ ⅢⅡ. ☀

Rhydlewis House, *Rhydlewis, Llandysul, Ceredigion, SA44 5PE.* Exceptional guest house, once a venue for drovers. Comfort, style, good locally-produced food. **Open:** All year (not Xmas)
01239 851748 (also fax) Ms Russill www.terradat.co.uk/rhydlewis **D:** £20.00–£22.00 **S:** £20.00–£22.00 **Beds:** 1T 1D 1S **Baths:** 2 En 1 Pr ♥ 🖻 (3) ⅉ ☑ ✕ Ⅵ ⅢⅡ. ☀

Taliesin
SN6591

Free Trade Hall, *Taliesin, Machynlleth, Powys, SY20 8JH.* Comfortable and welcoming, large garden, coastal views, interesting old shop. **Open:** All year (not Xmas)
01970 832368 (also fax) Ms Regan *info@freetradehall.co.uk* www.freetradehall.co.uk **D:** £18.00–£20.00 **S:** £20.00–£23.00 **Beds:** 1F 2D **Baths:** 1 En 1 Sh ♥ 🖻 (3) ⅉ Ⅵ Ⅵ ⅢⅡ. ☀

Tregaron
SN6759 🍺 *Talbot Hotel, Foelallt Arms*

Wern Newyd, *Llanio Road, Tregaron, Ceredigion, SY25 6UN.* **Open:** All year
01974 298356 **D:** £18.00 **S:** £18.00 **Beds:** 1F 1T 1D 1S **Baths:** 1 En 1 Sh ♥ 🖻 ⅉ ☑ ⅢⅡ. ☀
Fantastic value. Good breakfast. Friendly working family farm. Spectacular mountain runs renowned for Red Kites. Free fishing on Teifi River. Ample parking space. 18 miles from seaside. Perfectly situated to explore rural mid Wales. Opportunity not to be missed.

Lluest Guest House, *Lampeter Road, Tregaron, Ceredigion, SY25 6HG.* Large Victorian house, rambling gardens at the foot of the Cambrian Mountains. **Open:** All year (not Xmas)
01974 298936 (also fax) Mrs Bull *lluest@supanet.com* **D:** £16.00–£19.50 **S:** £16.00–£19.50 **Beds:** 2D 1T 1S **Baths:** 1 En 1 Sh ♥ 🖻 (5) ⅉ ☑ ↑ ✕ Ⅵ ⅢⅡ. ☀

Talbot Hotel, *The Square, Tregaron, Ceredigion, SY25 6JL.* Olde worlde comfortable family atmosphere, good food and real ales. **Open:** All year (not Xmas) **01974 298208** Mr Williams **Fax: 01974 299059** *talbothotel@btinternet.com* **D:** £21.00–£27.50 **S:** £25.00–£35.00 **Beds:** 1F 3D 8T 1S **Baths:** 10 En 5 Pr ⮟ 🅿 (10) 📺 ⊁ ✕ Ⓥ ▥ 🛏 cc

Tresaith

SN2751

Bryn Berwyn Guest House, *Tresaith, Ceredigon, SA43 2JG.* **Open:** All year **01239 811126** Mr & Mrs Oxborrow **Fax: 01239 811832** *enq@brynberwyn.com* www.brynberwyn.com **D:** £25.00–£30.00 **Beds:** 1F 4D 1T **Baths:** 6 En ⮟ 🅿 (12) 📺 ⊁ ✕ Ⓥ ▥ 🛏 cc
A stunning Edwardian property exuding an atmosphere of warmth. Spectacular sea views and sunsets help you unwind. Meals available every day except Sundays. On Fridays and Saturdays our Restaurant's A La Carte Menu is available - Gabby's desserts will amaze you! See our website now!

The Glamorgans

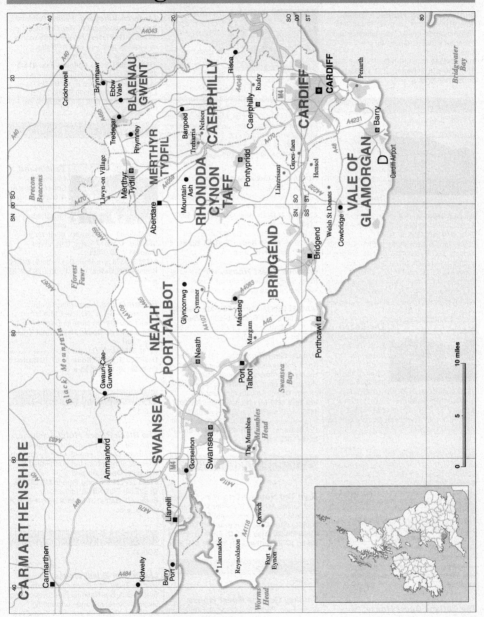

Barry

ST1067

Anglesea Guest House, *9 Romilly Road, Barry, S Glam, CF62 6AZ.* Small, late-Victorian guest house, near beaches and transport services. **Open:** All year (not Xmas)
01446 749660 Mr Griffith **D:** £15.00–£16.00 **S:** £15.00–£16.00 **Beds:** 1F 1T 1S **Baths:** 1 Sh ⌂ (5) ⊬ ▦ ⚊

Caerphilly

ST1586   🍺 *Brewsters*

Dugann, *Springfield Bungalow, Rudry Road, Caerphilly, Mid Glam, CF83 3DT.* **Open:** All year

Grades: WTB 2 Star
029 2086 6607 Mrs Powell **D:** £20.00–£30.00 **S:** £25.00–£30.00 **Beds:** 1F 1T **Baths:** 1 En 1 Pr ⌂ ⊬ ✦ ▦ ▣ ⚊ ♿ ⚊
Quiet, rural place. Private garden. Off-road parking. Warm welcome. Guests' private lounge with fridge, tea/coffee/fac. 4/C breakfast. Private bathroom. 2 pubs/restaurants 2/5 mins walk away. Caerphilly Castle nearby. On/line/bus/service. Private suite also available.

The Coach House, *2 Twyn Sych, Rudry, Caerphilly, CF83 3EF.* **Open:** All year
029 2088 4772 (also fax) Mr Davis **D:** £17.00–£20.00 **S:** £17.00–£25.00 **Beds:** 2F 1D 3T 4S **Baths:** 1 En 2 Pr 3 Sh ⌂ ▣ ✦ ▦ ⚊
Located in the heart of the country. 6 miles Cardiff or Newport.

Lugano Guest House, *Hillside Mountain Road, Caerphilly, Mid Glamorgan, CF83 1HN.* **Open:** All year (not Xmas)
Grades: WTB 3 Star
029 2085 2672 & 07970 906488 (M) **D:** £20.00 **S:** £25.00 **Beds:** 1D 2T **Baths:** 3 En ⌂ (1) ▣ (2) ⊬ ▦ ⚊
Charming character house, residents' own private garden and entrance. Upstairs bedrooms overlook Caerphilly Castle, all rodms ensuite. Minutes' walk to town centre, castle, train and bus stations for regular services to the capital, Cardiff. Warm friendly welcome assured. No smoking.

The Cottage Guest House, *Pwll y Pant, Caerphilly, Mid Glam, CF83 3HW.* 300 year old cottage. Castles, coastline, mountains nearby. Warm welcome. **Open:** All year
029 2086 9160 Mr Giles *thecottage@tesco.net* **D:** £17.00–£20.00 **S:** £26.00–£29.00 **Beds:** 3T **Baths:** 2 En 1 Pr ⌂ ▣ (5) ⊬ ▦ ⚊

Cardiff

ST1677

Rambler Court Hotel, *188 Cathedral Road, Pontcanna, Cardiff, S Glam, CF11 9JE.*
Open: All year
029 2022 1187 (also fax) Mrs Cronin **D:** £18.00–£20.00 **S:** £18.00–£25.00 **Beds:** 3F 3D 1T 3S **Baths:** 4 En 5 Sh ⌂ ▣ (4) ▦ ⚊
Friendly family-run hotel, ideally situated in a tree-lined conservation area, close to all of the city's main attractions, 10 minutes' walk to the city centre and Millennium Stadium. Good local restaurants and pubs.

Austins, *11 Coldstream Terrace, City Centre, Cardiff, CF11 6LJ.* In the centre of the city, 300 yards from Cardiff Castle. **Open:** All year **Grades:** WTB 2 Star
029 2037 7148 Mr Hopkins **Fax:** 029 2037 7158 *austins@hotelcardiff.com*
www.hotelcardiff.com **D:** £17.50–£19.50 **S:** £20.00–£27.50 **Beds:** 1F 5T 5S **Baths:** 4 En 2 Sh ⌂ ▦ ⚊ ⚊ cc

Maxines Guest House, *150 Cathedral Road, Cardiff, S Glam, CF1 9JB.* Large Victorian private guest house. **Open:** All year
029 2022 0288 Mr Barrett **Fax:** 029 2034 4884 **D:** £20.00–£30.00 **S:** £20.00–£30.00 **Beds:** 4F 2T 2D 2S **Baths:** 5 En 1 Pr 2 Sh ⌂ (13) ▦ ▦ ⚊ cc

Preste Gaarden Hotel, *181 Cathedral Road, Pontcanna, Cardiff, S Glam, CF11 9PN.* Highly recommended, modernised ex-Norwegian consulate offering olde-worlde charm. **Open:** All year (not Xmas)
029 2022 8607 Mrs Nicholls **Fax:** 029 2037 4805 *cardiff.hotel@btinternet.com* cardiff.hotel. btinternet.co.uk **D:** £18.00–£22.00 **S:** £22.00–£27.00 **Beds:** 1F 2D 3T 4S **Baths:** 7 En 3 Pr ⌂ ▣ (3) ▦ ▦ ⚊

Cymmer (Glyncorrwg)

SS8695

Bryn Teg House, *9 Craig-y-fan, Cymmer, Port Talbot, SA13 3LN.* Mountains, biking, cycleways, country walks and fishing in country park. **Open:** All year (not Xmas)
01639 851820 (also fax) **D:** £16.00 **S:** £16.00 **Beds:** 1D 2T **Baths:** 1 Sh ⌂ ▦ ✦ ✕ ▦ ⚊

Groes-faen

ST0680

Smokey Cottage Guest House, *Groes-Faen, Pontyclun, CF72 8NG.* Family-run guest house offering very best in accommodation. Rural location but close Cardiff M4. **Open:** All year
029 2089 1173 (also fax) *smokeycot@ talk21.com* **D:** £20.00–£25.00 **S:** £20.00–£25.00 **Beds:** 1F 2T **Baths:** 3 En ⌂ ▣ ⊬ ▦ ▦

Hensol

ST0478

Llanerch Vineyard, *Hensol, Pendoylan, Vale of Glamorgan, CF72 8JU.* One of Wales' 'Great Little Places'. Most ensuite rooms overlook largest vineyard in Wales.
Open: All year (not Xmas)
01443 225877 Peter Andrews **Fax:** 01443 225546 *llanerch@cariadwines.demon.co.uk* www.llanerch-vineyard.co.uk **D:** £24.00–£30.00 **S:** £38.00–£50.00 **Beds:** 2D 2T **Baths:** 4 En ⌂ (8) ▣ (20) ⊬ ▦ ▦ ⚊ cc

Llanmadoc

SS4493

Tallizmand, *Llanmadoc, Gower, Swansea, W Glam, SA3 1DE.* Tastefully furnished ensuites. Coastal and inland walks, quiet sandy beaches. **Open:** All year (not Xmas)
Grades: WTB 3 Star
01792 386373 Mrs Main **D:** £22.00 **S:** £25.00 **Beds:** 1D 2T **Baths:** 1 En 2 Pr ▣ (5) ▦ ✦ ▦ ▦ ⚊

Britannia Inn, *Llanmadoc, Gower, Swansea, W Glam, SA3 1DB.* C18th family-owned country inn close to Burry Inley & nature reserve. **Open:** All year (not Xmas/New Year)
01792 386624 Mr Downie *mikdow@freeuk.com* **D:** £25.00 **S:** £32.50 **Beds:** 1F 1T 3D **Baths:** 5 En ⌂ ▣ (50) ▦ ✕ ▦ ▦ ⚊ cc

Llantrisant

ST0483

The Black Prince Hotel, *Llantrisant Industrial Estate, Llantrisant, Pontyclun, Mid Glam, CF72 8LF.* Friendly, family-run pub. Informal atmosphere but guaranteed a welcome. **Open:** All year
01443 227723 Mr Long **Fax:** 01443 228655 **D:** £27.00–£30.00 **S:** £27.00–£30.00 **Beds:** 37F **Baths:** 37 En ⌂ ▣ (100) ⊬ ▦ ✦ ✕ ▦ ▦ ♿ ⚊ cc

Llwyn-on Village

SO0111

Llwyn Onn Guest House, *Cwmtaf, Merthyr Tydfil, Mid Glam, CF48 2HT.* In the Brecon Beacons National Park, overlooking Llwyn-on Reservoir and surrounding woodland. **Open:** All year (not Xmas/New Year) **Grades:** WTB 3 Star, AA 4 Diamond
01685 384384 Mr Evans **Fax:** 01685 359310 *reception@llwynonn.co.uk* www.llwynonn.co.uk **D:** £25.00 **S:** £20.00–£28.00 **Beds:** 1D 1T 1S **Baths:** 3 En ▣ (4) ⊬ ▦ ▦ ⚊ cc

Planning a longer stay? Always ask for any special rates

Manmoel
SO1703

Wyrloed Lodge, Manmoel, Blackwood, Gwent, NP12 0RW. Victorian-style home in mountain hamlet. Pub, views, peaceful, walking, touring, home-cooking. **Open:** All year (not Xmas/New Year)
01495 371198 (also fax) Mrs James **D:** £20.00 **S:** £20.00 **Beds:** 1F 2D 1T **Baths:** 4 En ♦ 🅿 (6) 📺 🏃 ✕ 📺 🛏 ⚑

Margam
SS7887

Ty'N-Y-Caeau, Margam, Port Talbot, W Glam, SA13 2NW. Original vicarage for Margam Abbey since C17th, in walled gardens. **Open:** Feb to Nov
01639 883897 Mrs Gaen **D:** £22.00–£25.00 **S:** £25.00–£27.00 **Beds:** 1F 2D 4T **Baths:** 6 En 1 Pr ♦ (2) 🅿 (8) ✗ 📺 🏃 ✕ 📺 🛏 ⚑

Merthyr Tydfil
SO0506

Llwyn Onn Guest House, Cwmtaf, Merthyr Tydfil, Mid Glam, CF48 2HT.
Open: All year (not Xmas/New Year) **Grades:** WTB 3 Star, AA 4 Diamond
01685 384384 Mr Evans **Fax: 01685 359310**
reception@llwynonn.co.uk www.llwynonn.co.uk
D: £25.00 **S:** £20.00–£28.00 **Beds:** 1D 1T 1S **Baths:** 3 En 🅿 (4) ✗ 📺 📺 🛏 ⚑ cc
In the Brecon Beacons National Park, overlooking Llwyn-on Reservoir and surrounding woodland. Close to Taff Trail, Pen-Y-Fan and Waterfalls. Walking, cycling, fishing, golf, all nearby. Warm Welsh welcome assured. Ideal location for business or leisure.

Brynawel Guest House, Queens Road, Merthyr Tydfil, Mid Glam, CF47 0HD. Large Victorian house, tastefully furnished, adjoining parks. Family home, friendly atmosphere. **Open:** All year **Grades:** WTB 3 Star
01685 722573 Mrs Johnson **D:** £23.00 **S:** £28.00 **Beds:** 1D 2T **Baths:** 3 En ♦ 🅿 (5) ✗ 📺 📺 🛏 ⚑

Maes Y Coed, Park Terrace, Pontmorlais West, Merthyr Tydfil, Mid Glam, CF47 8UT. Large comfortable house on edge of Brecon Beacons in 0.25 acre of gardens. **Open:** All year
01685 722246 (also fax) Mr Davies **D:** £16.00–£18.00 **S:** £18.00–£22.00 **Beds:** 4F 5T 1S **Baths:** 4 En ♦ 🅿 (4) 📺 🏃 ✕ 📺 🛏 ⚑

Neath
SS7497

Victoria Guest House, 10 Victoria Gardens, Neath, W Glam, SA11 3BE. Victorian house close to town centre and beautiful Victorian gardens. **Open:** All year (not Xmas/New Year)
01639 636233 Mr & Mrs Riando **D:** £15.00–£17.50 **S:** £16.00–£18.00 **Beds:** 1D 1T 2S **Baths:** 2 Sh ♦ ✗ 📺 📺 ⚑

Nelson
ST1195 🚂 Rowan Tree

Fairmead, 24 Gelligaer Road, Treharris, Nelson, Mid Glam, CF46 6DN. A small family-run quiet haven, offering a warm welcome. **Open:** All year
01443 411174 Mrs Kedward **Fax: 01443 411430** *fairmeadhouse@aol.com* **D:** £21.50–£35.00 **S:** £27.50–£35.00 **Beds:** 2D 1T **Baths:** 2 En 1 Pr ♦ 🅿 (5) ✗ 📺 🏃 ✕ 📺 🛏 ⚑

Wern Ganol Farm, Nelson, Treharris, Mid Glam, CF46 6PS. Working farm with pleasant views across valley. Main A472. **Open:** All year
01443 450413 Mrs Portlock **D:** £20.00 **S:** £21.00–£26.00 **Beds:** 2F 2T 2D ♦ 🅿 📺 🏃 📺 ⚑

Oxwich
SS4986

Little Haven Guest House, Oxwich, Swansea, W Glam, SA3 1LS.
Open: Jan to Nov
01792 390940
Mrs Lewis www.littlehaven.bt. internet.co.uk **D:** £17.00 **S:** £19.00 **Beds:** 2D 1T **Baths:** 1 En 1 Sh ♦ 🅿 (16) 📺 ⚑
Bed and Breakfast open all year in Oxwich, Gower. Close to beach. Ideal walking area. Outdoor heated swimming pool. Large family room ensuite, 2 Doubles and 1 Twin. www.littlehaven.oxwich.btinternet.co.uk

Surf Sound Guest House, Long Acre, Oxwich, Gower, Swansea, W Glam, SA3 1LS. Secluded, near to beach, ground floor bedrooms available. No-smoking establishment. **Open:** Easter to Oct **Grades:** WTB 3 Star
01792 390822 Fax: 01792 391230 D: £22.00–£26.00 **S:** £32.00–£40.00 **Beds:** 1F 1T 3D **Baths:** 5 En ♦ 🅿 (6) ✗ ✕ 📺 ⚑

BATHROOMS
En = Ensuite
Pr = Private
Sh = Shared

All details shown are as supplied by B&B owners in Autumn 2001

Penarth
ST1871

Glendale Hotel, 8-10 Plymouth Road, Penarth, CF64 3DH. **Open:** All year **Grades:** WTB 2 Star, RAC 2 Diamond
029 2070 6701 & 029 2070 8302 Fax: 029 2070 9269 www.infotel.co.uk **D:** £29.50–£36.50 **S:** £23.50–£33.50 **Beds:** 20F 9D 8S **Baths:** 18 En 15 Pr 3 Sh ♦ ✗ 📺 ✕ 📺 ⚑ cc
Listed building, warm and friendly welcome. Recognised for excellent food, standard, service, fresh fish, meats, traditional Italian dishes, lounge bar, private disco, full on licence, 3 miles from Cardiff train and bus station. Walking distance to Penarth promenade and marina, golf course, Cosmeston Lake.

Alandale Guest House, 17 Plymouth Road, Penarth, S Glam, CF64 3DA.
Open: All year
029 2070 9226
Mr Crothers www.alandaleguesthouse.co.uk
D: £25.00–£28.00 **S:** £20.00–£25.00 **Beds:** 12F 2T 2D 6S **Baths:** 3 En 4 Pr 3 Sh ♦ 🅿 📺 🏃 📺 ❄ ⚑ cc
The family-run Alandale Guest House is 5 minutes from the sea front. Cardiff Bay is 10 minutes by car and Cardiff is 10 minutes by train from Penarth station. Ideal guest house for holidays, work or short breaks.

Walton House Hotel, 37 Victoria Road, Penarth, CF64 3HY. Family-run, convenient for Cardiff Bay, Millennium Stadium, Welsh Coast. **Open:** All year (not Xmas/New Year) **Grades:** WTB 2 Star
029 2070 7782 Fax: 029 2071 1012 *reservations@waltonhouse.net* **D:** £17.50–£30.00 **S:** £20.00–£40.00 **Beds:** 1F 3T 5D 4S **Baths:** 11 En ♦ (5) 🅿 (13) 📺 🏃 ✕ 📺 ⚑ cc

Planning a longer stay? Always ask for any special rates

Penmark

ST0568

The Old Barn, The Croft, Penmark, Barry, S Glam, *CF62 3BP*. Converted C17th barn set in a beautiful rural village. **Open:** All year **Grades:** WTB 3 Star **01446 711352 (also fax)** *enquiries@ theoldbarnbedandbreakfast.com* www.theoldbarnbedandbreakfast.co.uk **D:** £20.00–£23.00 **S:** £25.00–£27.00 **Beds:** 1T 1D **Baths:** 2 En ♋ ▣ ⊬ ▥ ⚹

Pontypridd

ST0789

Market Tavern Hotel, Market Street, Pontypridd, Mid Glam, *CF37 2ST*. **Open:** All year (not Xmas) **01443 485331** Mr John **Fax:** **01443 491403** *bookings@ markettavernhotel.fsbusiness.co.uk* www.markettavernhotel.fsbusiness.co.uk **D:** £21.00–£24.00 **S:** £42.00–£46.00 **Beds:** 4D 3T 4S **Baths:** 11 En ♋ ▣ ▥ ⛬ ⚹ cc All bedrooms ensuite and delightfully furnished. Tavern bar offers good range of ales, wines and food. Chilli Pepper Cocktail Bar and Strads Nightclub are open late Friday and Saturday evenings. Centrally located. Ideal base for Cardiff and the Valleys.

Porthcawl

SS8277

Rockybank Guest House, 15 De Breos Drive, Porthcawl, Mid Glam, *CF36 3JP*. First guest house off M4/J37. Quiet area, private parking, golf. **Open:** All year (not Xmas) **Grades:** WTB 3 Star **01656 785823 (also fax)** Mrs Lewis *rockybank@totalise.co.uk* www.jeanlewis. members.beeb.net **D:** £21.00–£23.00 **S:** £25.00–£26.00 **Beds:** 1F 1D 1T **Baths:** 3 En ♋ ▣ (6) ⊬ ▥ ▥ ⚹

Rossett Guest House, 1 Esplanade Avenue, Porthcawl, *CF36 3YS*. Friendly seaside home situated on heritage coastline. Easy access surrounding areas. **Open:** All year (not Xmas) **01656 771664 D:** £17.00–£22.00 **Beds:** 1F **Baths:** 2 En 1 Sh ♋ ▣ (2) ▥ ⊬ ✕ ▥ ⚹

Reynoldston

SS4890

Greenways, Hills Farm, Reynoldston, Swansea, W Glam, *SA3 1AE*. Reynoldston is central to beautiful Tower Bays, Three Cliffs, Rhossili. **Open:** Easter to Nov **01792 390125** Mrs John **D:** £18.00–£20.00 **S:** £20.00–£25.00 **Beds:** 2D 1T ♋ (5) ▣ (3) ▥ ⊬ ▥ ⚹ cc

Rudry

ST1886

The Coach House, 2 Twyn Sych, Rudry, Caerphilly, *CF83 3EF*. Located in the heart of the country. 6 miles Cardiff or Newport. **Open:** All year **029 2088 4772 (also fax)** Mr Davis **D:** £17.00–£20.00 **S:** £17.00–£25.00 **Beds:** 2F 1D 3T 4S **Baths:** 1 En 2 Pr 3 Sh ♋ ▣ ▥ ⊬ ▥ ⚹

Swansea

SS6592   🍺 Abertawe Ale House, Wig & Pen

The Coast House, 708 Mumbles Road, The Mumbles, Swansea, W Glam, *SA3 4EH*. **Open:** Jan to Nov **Grades:** WTB 3 Star, RAC 3 Diamond **01792 368702** Mrs Clarke *thecoasthouse@ aol.com* **D:** £20.00–£24.00 **S:** £23.00–£28.00 **Beds:** 2F 3D 1S **Baths:** 6 En ♋ ▣ (3) ▥ ⊬ ▥ ⚹ Situated on the seafront, most rooms have spectacular views of Swansea Bay. High levels of cleanliness, with ensuite facilities, TV, tea-making, hairdryers and radiograms. Convenient for Swansea University, Cork Ferry and Gower Peninsular. Home from Home.

Mirador Guest House, 14 Mirador Crescent, Uplands, Swansea, W Glam, *SA2 0QX*. Proximity to university, beaches, Dylan Thomas trail, Gower, city centre & buses. **Open:** All year **01792 466976** Mr Anderson **D:** £20.00–£24.00 **S:** £20.00–£22.00 **Beds:** 1F 2D 1T 1S **Baths:** 3 En 2 Sh ♋ ⊬ ▥ ⊬ ✕ ▥ ⚹

BATHROOMS

En = Ensuite

Pr = Private

Sh = Shared

Rock Villa Guest House, 1 George Bank, The Mumbles, Swansea, W Glam, *SA3 4EQ*. Family-run, friendly guest house. Beautiful view of Swansea Bay. **Open:** All year (not Xmas/New Year) **Grades:** RAC 3 Diamond **01792 366794** Mrs Thomas *rockvilla@ tinyworld.co.uk* users.tinyworld.co. uk/rockvilla **D:** £22.00–£25.00 **S:** £22.00–£32.00 **Beds:** 1F 2T 2D 1S **Baths:** 3 En 2 Sh ♋ (3) ▣ ▥ ⊬ ▥ ⚹

The Lyndale, 324 Oystermouth Road, Swansea, W Glam, *SA1 3UJ*. Seafront. Central to city amenities. Ideal base for exploring Gower. **Open:** All year (not Xmas/New Year) **Grades:** WTB 2 Star **01792 653882** H M Williams **D:** £14.00–£18.00 **S:** £16.00–£25.00 **Beds:** 1F 3T 1D 1S **Baths:** 2 Sh ♋ (5) ▥ ▥ ⚹

Osprey Guest House, 244 Oystermouth Road, Swansea, W Glam, *SA1 3UH*. Sea front location. **Open:** All year (not Xmas/New Year) **01792 642369** Mrs Ellis **D:** £14.00–£16.00 **S:** £16.00–£18.00 **Beds:** 5F 2T 2D **Baths:** 3 Sh ♋ ▣ ▥ ✕ ▥ ⚹

The Mumbles

SS6187

The Coast House, 708 Mumbles Road, The Mumbles, Swansea, W Glam, *SA3 4EH*. Situated on the seafront, most rooms have spectacular views of Swansea Bay. **Open:** Jan to Nov **Grades:** WTB 3 Star, RAC 3 Diamond **01792 368702** Mrs Clarke *thecoasthouse@ aol.com* **D:** £20.00–£24.00 **S:** £23.00–£28.00 **Beds:** 2F 3D 1S **Baths:** 6 En ♋ ▣ (3) ▥ ⊬ ▥ ⚹

Rock Villa Guest House, 1 George Bank, The Mumbles, Swansea, W Glam, *SA3 4EQ*. Family-run, friendly guest house. Beautiful view of Swansea Bay. **Open:** All year (not Xmas/New Year) **Grades:** RAC 3 Diamond **01792 366794** Mrs Thomas *rockvilla@ tinyworld.co.uk* users.tinyworld.co. uk/rockvilla **D:** £22.00–£25.00 **S:** £22.00–£32.00 **Beds:** 1F 2T 2D 1S **Baths:** 3 En 2 Sh ♋ (3) ▣ ▥ ⊬ ▥ ⚹

Treharris

ST0997

Fairmead, 24 Gelligaer Road, Treharris, Nelson, Mid Glam, *CF46 6DN*. A small family-run quiet haven, offering a warm welcome. **Open:** All year **01443 411174** Mrs Kedward **Fax:** 01443 411430 *fairmeadhouse@aol.com* **D:** £21.50–£35.00 **S:** £27.50–£35.00 **Beds:** 2D 1T **Baths:** 2 En 1 Pr ♋ ▣ (5) ⊬ ▥ ⊬ ✕ ▥ ⚹

Welsh St Donats
ST0275

Bryn-y-Ddafad, *Welsh St Donats,*
Cowbridge, CF71 7ST. Panoramic views,
network of footpaths. Spacious, secluded
comfortable country guest house. **Open:** All
year (not Xmas)
01446 774451 & 07775 997397 (M)
Mrs Jenkins *junejenkins@bydd.co.uk*
www.bydd.co.uk **D:** £20.00–£22.50 **S:** £20.00–
£30.00 **Beds:** 2D 2S **Baths:** 1 En 1 Pr 1 Sh
➢ (10) ₽ (5) ⊁ ⊠ ✕ ⓥ ▥ ♨

Abergavenny

SO2914 ⚓ *Three Salmons, Hunters Moon, Walnut Tree, Crown Inn, Skirrid Mountain Inn*

Kings Head Hotel, Cross Street, Abergavenny, NP7 5EW. C16th coaching inn in centre of busy market town. **Open:** All year **Grades:** WTB 2 Star Inn
01873 853575 (also fax) *kingsheadhotel@hotmail.com* www.kingshead.2ofr.com
D: £25.00 **Beds:** 2T 2D 1S **Baths:** 5 En ⊠ ✕ �ておⅤ ▥ ♨

Planning a longer stay? Always ask for any special rates

Please respect a B&B's wishes regarding children, animals and smoking

Pentre House, Brecon Road, Abergavenny, Monmouthshire, NP7 7EW. Charming small Georgian award-winning country house in wonderful gardens.
Open: All year (not Xmas) **Grades:** WTB 3 Star
01873 853435 Mrs Reardon-Smith **Fax:**
01873 852321 *Treardonsm@aol.com* **D:** £17.00–£18.00 **S:** £20.00–£25.00 **Beds:** 1F 1D 1T
Baths: 2 Sh ⌕ 🅿 (6) ⊠ ✕ Ⅴ ▥ ♨

The Wenallt, Gilwern, Abergavenny, Monmouthshire, NP7 0HP. **Open:** All year
01873 830694 Mr Harris **D:** £19.50–£26.00
S: £24.00–£28.00 **Beds:** 1F 6D 2T 6S
Baths: 1 En 6 Pr ⌕ 🅿 (20) ⌕ ⊠ 🛏 ✕ Ⅴ ▥ ♨
A C16th Welsh longhouse set in 50 acres of farmland in the Brecon Beacons National Park, commanding magnificent views over the Usk Valley. Retaining its old charm with oak beams, inglenook fireplace, yet offering a high standard; ensuite bedrooms.

All details shown are as supplied by B&B owners in Autumn 2001

Black Lion, *Lion Street, Abergavenny,*
NP7 5PE. **Open:** All year
01873 853993 Fax: 01873 857885 D: £20.00–
£25.00 **S:** £20.00–£25.00 **Beds:** 1F 3T 5D 3S
Baths: 1 En 1 Sh ⓣ ⮐ 🅿 ⊡ ♈ ✕ Ⓥ 🔳 ⚓ cc
Family-run inn with a warm Welsh welcome
and friendly atmosphere. Hearty breakfast
awaits you. Located in market area of town.
Music nights, Karaoke Thurs, Fri, Sat. Ideal
situated for walkers, cyclists, boating,
narrowcast, pony-trekking, fishing, hand
gliding, and many more attractions all
situated closeby. Give us a try.

Tyn-y-bryn, *Deriside,*
Abergavenny,
Monmouthshire,
NP7 7HT.
Open: All year
Grades: WTB 3
Star
01873 856682 & 07855 038969 (M)
Ms Belcham **Fax: 01873 856682** *cbelcham@*
care4free.net www.tyn-y-bryn.co.uk **D:** £21.00
S: £25.00 **Beds:** 1F 1T 1D **Baths:** 1 En 1 Pr
🅿 (6) ⊡ ♈ ✕ Ⓥ 🔳 ⚓
Situated on the slopes of the Sugar Loaf
Mountain within Brecon Beacons National
Park, just 1.5 miles away from
Abergavenny, the cottage is comfortable
and well-equipped. Magnificent views, a
peaceful location, access to the hill directly
from the cottage.

Pentre Court, *Brecon Road,*
Abergavenny, NP7 9ND. Spacious,
welcoming Georgian house with open fires,
set in 3 acres of pretty gardens. **Open:** All
year
01873 853545 Mrs Candler *judith@*
pentrecourt.com www.pentrecourt.com
D: £18.00–£24.00 **S:** £18.00–£30.00 **Beds:** 3D
Baths: 3 En ⓣ ⮐ 🅿 ⊡ ♈ ✕ Ⓥ 🔳 ⚓

RATES

D = Price range per person
sharing in a double or twin
room

S = Price range for a single
room

BEDROOMS

D = Double

T = Twin

S = Single

F = Family

Abersychan
SO2603

Mill Farm, *Cwmavon, Abersychan,*
Pontypool, NP4 8XJ. **Open:** All year (not
Xmas/New Year) **Grades:** WTB 3 Star, AA 4
Diamond
01495 774588 (also fax) Mrs Jayne **D:** £25.00
S: £25.00–£30.00 **Beds:** 1T 2D 🅿 (6) ⊡ Ⓥ 🔳
⚓
Enjoy total relaxation in C15th farmhouse in
idyllic setting - antiques, log fires, oak
beams, spiral staircases, heated pool in
lounge. Breakfast until noon; boules,
croquet in garden. Woodland walks. Close
to attractions. Adults only for complete
tranquility. AA 4 Diamonds.

Bettws Newydd
SO3605

Thornbury
Farm, *Bettws*
Newydd, Usk,
Monmouthshire,
NP5 1JY. Family
farm. Warm
welcome,
beautiful views, attractions - castles, golf,
walks. **Open:** All year (not Xmas/New Year)
Grades: WTB 3 Star
01873 880598 Mrs Jones **D:** £20.00–£25.00
S: £22.00–£25.00 **Beds:** 1T 2D **Baths:** 1 Sh
ⓣ 🅿 ⧖ ⊡ Ⓥ 🔳 ⚓

BATHROOMS

En = Ensuite

Pr = Private

Sh = Shared

All details shown are as
supplied by B&B owners in
Autumn 2001

Caerleon
ST3390

Great House, *Isca Road, Old Village,*
Caerleon, NP18 1QG. **Open:** All year (not
Xmas) **Grades:** WTB 3 Star
01633 420216 Mrs Price **Fax: 01633 423492**
price.greathouse@tesco.net www.visitgreathouse.
co.uk **D:** £25.00–£30.00 **S:** £30.00–£32.50
Beds: 2T 1S **Baths:** 1 Sh ⓣ (10) 🅿 (2) ⧖ ⊡ Ⓥ
🔳
C16th, Grade II Listed, delightful village
home with clematis garden to river.
Comfortable, pretty rooms and very warm
welcome. 1.5 miles to M4. Good enroute
stop for Ireland and West Wales. 1.25 miles
Celtic Manor Golf and Resort Hotel.

Caldicot
ST4788

The Lychgate, *47 Church Road, Caldicot,*
Newport, Monmouthshire, NP6 4HW.
Convenient location within easy reach of
Wye Valley and Cardiff. **Open:** All year (not
Xmas/New Year) **Grades:** WTB 3 Star
01291 422378 Mrs Welch **D:** £18.00–£19.00
S: £25.00 **Beds:** 1T 2D 2S **Baths:** 5 En 🅿 (5)
⧖ ⊡ Ⓥ 🔳 ⚓

Chepstow
ST5393 🚉 *Pierce Field, Cross Keys, The George,*
Rising Sun

Afon Gwy
Restaurant,
28 Bridge Street,
Chepstow,
Monmouthshire,
NP6 6EZ. Victorian
house
overlooking the
river Wye, near
Chepstow
Castle. **Open:** All
year
01291 620158 (also fax) **D:** £25.00
S: £32.00–£37.00 **Beds:** 1F 3D **Baths:** 4 En
ⓣ (0) ⧖ ⊡ ✕ Ⓥ 🔳 ✳ ⚓ cc

Langcroft, 71 St Kingsmark Avenue, Chepstow, Monmouthshire, NP6 5LY. Modern family, friendly home. Town centre four minutes walk.
Open: All year (not Xmas/New Year)
Grades: WTB 2 Star
01291 625569 (also fax) Mrs Langdale
D: £20.00 **S:** £20.00 **Beds:** 1T 1D 1S **Baths:** 1 Sh ⌂ ▱ (2) ⠧ ▱ ⌖ ▥ ▦ ⚍

Lower Hardwick House, Mount Pleasant, Chepstow, Monmouthshire, NP16 5PT. Beautiful Georgian house, walled garden. Free car parking for duration.
Open: All year
01291 622162 Mrs Grassby **D:** £15.50–£18.00 **S:** £18.00–£25.00 **Beds:** 1F 1D 1T 1S
Baths: 2 Pr 1 Sh ⌂ ▱ (12) ▱ ⌖ ▥ ▦ ⚍

Clydach
SO2213

Rock & Fountain Hotel, Clydach, Abergavenny, NP7 0LL. Family-run hotel within the Brecon Beacons National Park.
Open: All year
01873 830393 Fax: 01873 730393 *archer@ rockandfountain.fsnet.co.uk* **D:** £23.00–£28.00 **S:** £29.50–£33.00 **Beds:** 3F 1T 2D **Baths:** 6 En ⌂ ▱ (20) ▱ ✕ ▥ ▦ ⚍ **cc**

Cwmbran
ST2894

Springfields, 371 Llantarnam Road, Llantarnam, Cwmbran, Monmouthshire, NP44 3BN. Large welcoming Victorian home, family-run for 27 years, Joan Graham.
Open: All year
01633 482509 Mrs Graham **D:** £15.75–£18.00 **S:** £18.00–£20.00 **Beds:** 2F 4D 3T **Baths:** 6 En 6 Pr 2 Sh ⌂ ▱ (16) ▱ ⌖ ▥ ▦ ⚍

Cwmyoy
SO2923   🖾 Skirrid Inn, Queens Head

Gaer Farm, Cwmyoy, Abergavenny, Monmouthshire, NP7 7NE. **Open:** Easter to Nov **Grades:** WTB 3 Star
01873 890345 S Judd *judd@farmersweekly.net abergavennyfarmholidaygroup.com*
D: £25.00 **S:** £25.00 **Beds:** 3D **Baths:** 3 En ▱ (4) ⠧ ▱ ⌖ ▦ ⚍
A perfect retreat for those wanting peace in the hills. Rooms have private sitting rooms, wonderful views. Our 'Wool Loft' suite has a Rayburn and fridge. Wide breakfast menu and idyllic surroundings in this period farmhouse.

B&B owners may vary rates – be sure to check when booking

Dingestow
SO4510

Lower Pen-y-Clawdd Farm, Dingestow, Monmouth, NP5 4BG. Very attractive house on working farm. Rooms overlook landscaped gardens. **Open:** Mar to Nov
01600 740223 & 01600 740677 Mrs Bayliss **D:** £18.00–£20.00 **S:** £20.00 **Beds:** 1F 1T
Baths: 1 Sh ⌂ (1) ⠧ ▱ ⌖ ▥ ▦ ⚍

Forest Coalpit
SO2821

New Inn Farm, Forest Coalpit, Abergavenny, Monmouthshire, NP7 7LT. Peaceful, welcoming mountain farmhouse. Superb views. Walking from the door. **Open:** All year (not Xmas) **Grades:** WTB 3 Star
01873 890466 (also fax) J Bull *newinn.farm@ virgin.net* **D:** £20.00 **S:** £20.00 **Beds:** 1F 1D 1T
Baths: 1 En 2 Pr ⌂ ▱ (10) ⠧ ▱ ⌖ ▥ ▦ ⚍ ⚇ ⚍

Gilwern
SO2414

The Wenallt, Gilwern, Abergavenny, Monmouthshire, NP7 0HP. C16th Welsh longhouse in 50 acres of farmland in Brecon Beacons NP. **Open:** All year
01873 830694 Mr Harris **D:** £19.50–£26.00 **S:** £24.00–£28.00 **Beds:** 1F 6D 2T 6S
Baths: 1 En 6 Pr ⌂ ▱ (20) ⠧ ▱ ⌖ ✕ ▥ ▦ ⚍

Grosmont
SO4024

Lawns Farm, Grosmont, Abergavenny, Monmouthshire, NP7 8ES. Beautiful C17th farmhouse set in unspoilt countryside. 'A real gem!'. **Open:** Feb to Nov
01981 240298 Mr & Mrs Ferneyhough **Fax:** **01981 241275** *edna@ ferneyhough8.freeserve.co.uk* www.downourlane.co.uk/7.html **D:** £20.00– £24.00 **S:** £25.00 **Beds:** 2D 1T **Baths:** 2 En 1 Sh ⌂ ▱ ⠧ ▱ ▥ ▦ ⚍

Llandenny
SO4004

The Peargoed, Llandenny, Usk, Monmouthshire, NP5 1DH. £15 pppn. Peargoed Farmhouse, Llandenny, Usk, Mon. 01291 690233. **Open:** Easter to Oct
01291 690233 K M James **D:** £15.00 **Beds:** 1D 1S **Baths:** 1 Pr ⌂ (8) ▱ (2) ⠧ ▱ ⚍

Llanellen
SO3010

Yew Tree Farm, Llanellen, Abergavenny, NP7 9LB. Exceptional self-contained accommodation on secluded farm with far-reaching views. **Open:** Apr to Oct
Grades: WTB 2 Star
01873 854307 (also fax) Mrs Rose **D:** £20.00 **S:** £25.00 **Beds:** 1F **Baths:** 1 En ⌂ ▱ (2) ⠧ ▱ ⌖ ▥ ⚍

Llanfihangel Crucorney
SO3221

Pen-y-dre Farm, Llanfihangel Crucorney, Abergavenny, Gwent, NP7 8DT. C17th farmhouse, situated in the picturesque village of Llanfihangel Crucorney. **Open:** All year
01873 890246 (also fax) Mrs Jones **D:** £20.00–£22.00 **S:** £20.00–£25.00 **Beds:** 2D 1D/F **Baths:** 2 En 1 Pr ⌂ ▱ (6) ▱ ⌖ ▥ ▦ ⚍ **cc**

Llanover
SO3107

Ty Byrgwm, Upper Llanover, Abergavenny, NP7 9EP. C18th cottage/barn, 26 acres in National Park meadows/ woodlands. **Open:** All year
01873 880725 Mrs Bloomfield **D:** £22.50 **S:** £22.00 **Beds:** 1D 2S **Baths:** 2 En 1 Pr ⌂ (2) ▱ (3) ⠧ ▱ ⌖ ✕ ▦ ⚍

Llantarnam
ST3093

Springfields, 371 Llantarnam Road, Llantarnam, Cwmbran, Monmouthshire, NP44 3BN. Large welcoming Victorian home, family-run for 27 years, Joan Graham.
Open: All year
01633 482509 Mrs Graham **D:** £15.75–£18.00 **S:** £18.00–£20.00 **Beds:** 2F 4D 3T **Baths:** 6 En 6 Pr 2 Sh ⌂ ▱ (16) ▱ ⌖ ▥ ▦ ⚍

Llanthony
SO2827

The Half Moon, Llanthony, Abergavenny, Monmouthshire, NP7 7NN. C17th, beautiful countryside. Serves good food and real ales. **Open:** All year (not Xmas)
01873 890611 Mrs Smith **D:** £20.00–£22.00 **S:** £22.00–£25.00 **Beds:** 2F 4D 2T 1S
Baths: 2 Sh ⌂ ▱ (8) ▱ ⌖ ✕ ▥ ▦ ⚍

Planning a longer stay? Always ask for any special rates

National Grid References given are for villages, towns and cities – not for individual houses

Planning a longer stay? Always ask for any special rates

Mamhilad

SO3003 🍲 *Horseshoe Inn*

Ty-Cooke Farm, *Mamhilad, Pontypool, Monmouthshire, NP4 8QZ.* Spacious C18th farmhouse in cobbled courtyard near Monmouthshire Brecon Canal. **Open:** All year
01873 880382 (also fax) M F Price
ty-cookefarm@hotmail.com www.downourlane.co.uk **D:** £25.00 **S:** £30.00 **Beds:** 1F 1T 1D
Baths: 3 En 🛏 ⅍ 🗹 🔟 🖩 ♨

Mitchel Troy

SO4910

Church Farm Guest House, *Mitchel Troy, Monmouth, NP25 4HZ.* C16th character (former) farmhouse set in large garden with stream. **Open:** All year (not Xmas)
Grades: WTB 2 Star, AA 3 Diamond
01600 712176 Mrs Ringer **D:** £20.00–£24.00
S: £20.00–£30.00 **Beds:** 2F 3D 2T 1S
Baths: 6 En 1 Sh 🛏 🖳 (12)⅍ 🔟 🔭 ✕ 🔟 🖩 ♨

Monmouth

SO5012 🍲 *Gatehouse, Three Horseshoes, Vine Tree*

Offa's Bed and Breakfast, *37 Brook Estate, Monmouth, NP5 3AN.* **Open:** Easter to Sept
01600 716934 Mr Ruston and Ms A West
rruston@surfaid.org www.offas-dyke.co.uk/offasb&b www.altourism.com/uk/offas.html **D:** £17.50 **S:** £17.50 **Beds:** 1F 1D
Baths: 1 Pr 1 Sh 🛏 🖳 ⅍ 🔟 ♨ 🔟 🖩 & ♨
Situated in the beautiful Wye Valley on Offa's Dyke Path, a friendly and comfortable family-run B&B. Also close to the Forest of Dean and not far from the Brecon Beacons National Park. Private off-road parking. Walkers especially welcome.

Riverside Hotel, *Cinderhill Street, Monmouth, NP25 5EY.* Located in the Wye Valley. Warm and friendly ambience. **Open:** All year
Grades: WTB 2 Star, AA 2 Star
01600 715577 Mr Dodd **Fax: 01600 712668**
riverside.hotel@amserve.net **D:** £25.00–£34.00
S: £40.00–£48.00 **Beds:** 2F 6D 9T **Baths:** 17 En 🛏 (1) 🖳 (25)⅍ 🔟 🔭 ✕ 🔟 🖩 & ✳ ♨ cc

Caseta Alta, *15 Toynbee Close, Osbaston, Monmouth, NP25 3NU.* Quiet, comfortable, artistic, upside-down house. Picturesque hillside views. Town - walking distance. **Open:** All year (not Xmas/New Year)
01600 713023 Mrs Allcock **D:** £16.00–£21.00
S: £23.00–£30.00 **Beds:** 2F 1T 2D 1S
Baths: 1 En 1 Sh 🛏 🖳 (2) 🔟 ✕ 🔟 🖩 & ♨

Llantrisant

ST3896

Royal Oak, *Llantrisant, Usk, Monmouthshire, NP15 1LG.* **Open:** All year
01291 673455 (also fax)
Mr Major *bb@oakroyal.co.uk* www.oakroyal.co.uk **D:** £20.00–£25.00 **S:** £25.00 **Beds:** 1F 1T 1D **Baths:** 2 En 1 Pr 🛏 🖳 (15)⅍ 🔟 🖩 ♨
Nestled in the green hills of the Caerleon/Usk Abergavenny 'Wye Valley Walk', this 500 year old property, one-time popular inn and medieval priory boasts beamed bedrooms, beautiful scenery for walking, cycling, fishing, sightseeing, local castles and Roman ruins. Welcome.

Llanvetherine

SO3617

Great Tre-Rhew Farm, *Llanvetherine, Abergavenny, Monmouthshire, NP7 8RA.* Warm welcome on a Welsh working farm. Peaceful, rural & friendly. **Open:** All year (not Xmas)
01873 821268 Ms Beavan **D:** £17.50–£20.00
S: £17.50–£20.00 **Beds:** 1F 2D 1T 1S
Baths: 2 Sh 🛏 🖳 🖳 🔭 ✕ 🔟 🖩 ♨

Llanvihangel Crucorney

SO3220

The Skirrid Mountain Inn,
Llanvihangel Crucorney, Abergavenny, Monmouthshire, NP7 8DH. An historic country inn of unique character. Wales' oldest inn. **Open:** All year
01873 890258 Miss Grant **D:** £34.50–£39.50
S: £34.50–£39.50 **Beds:** 2D 🛏 🖳 ⅍ ✕ 🖩 ♨

Penyclawdd Farm, *Llanvihangel Crucorney, Abergavenny, Monmouthshire, NP7 7LB.* Beef/sheep farm, very large garden. Easy reach Abergavenny, Hereford, Cardiff, Hay-on-Wye. **Open:** All year
01873 890591 (also fax) Mrs Davies
D: £20.00–£22.00 **S:** £20.00–£22.00 **Beds:** 2F
Baths: 1 Sh 🛏 🖳 ⅍ 🔟 ✕ 🖩 ♨

Lower Machen

ST2287

The Forge, *Lower Machen, Newport, NP1 8UU.* Warm welcome, ideal for walking in forests or on mountains. **Open:** All year (not Xmas/New Year)
01633 440226 Mrs Jones **D:** £16.50–£18.00
S: £18.00–£20.00 **Beds:** 1F 1D 1T **Baths:** 1 Sh 🛏 🖳 (3) 🔟 🔭 🔟 🖩 ♨

Wye Avon, *New Dixton Road, Monmouth, NP5 3PR.* Large, interesting stone-built Victorian house. A family home. **Open:** All year (not Xmas)
01600 713322 Mrs Cantrell **D:** £16.00
S: £16.00–£21.00 **Beds:** 1F 1D 1S **Baths:** 1 Sh 🛏 🖳 ⅍ 🖩

Newport

ST3188 🍲 *Toby Inn*

The West Usk Lighthouse, *Lighthouse Road, St Brides Wentlooge, Newport, Monmouthshire, NP10 8SF.* Super B&B in real lighthouse, with water & four poster beds. **Open:** All year
01633 810126 & 01633 815860 Mr & Mrs Sheahan *Lighthouse1@tesco.net* www.westusklighthouse.co.uk **D:** £40.00–£45.00 **S:** £50.00–£65.00 **Beds:** 1F 2D
Baths: 3 En 🛏 🖳 (10)⅍ 🔟 🔭 🖩 ♨

Pentre Tai Farm, *Rhiwderin, Newport, Monmouthshire, NP10 9RQ.* Peaceful Welsh sheep farm in Castle Country close to M4. **Open:** Feb to Nov
01633 893284 (also fax) Mrs Proctor *stay@pentretai.f9.co.uk* www.downourlane.co.uk
D: £20.00–£21.00 **S:** £25.00 **Beds:** 1F 1T
Baths: 2 En 🛏 🖳 (4) ⅍ 🔟 🖩 ♨

Chapel Guest House, *Church Road, St Brides Wentlooge, Newport, Monmouthshire, NP10 8SN.* Comfortable accommodation in converted chapel situated between Newport and Cardiff. **Open:** All year **Grades:** WTB 3 Star ✓
01633 681018 Mr Bushell **Fax: 01633 681431**
chapelguesthouse@hotmail.com www.smoothhound.co.uk/hotels/chapel1.html **D:** £20.00–£23.00 **S:** £23.00–£25.00
Beds: 1F 1D 1T 1S **Baths:** 4 En 🛏 🖳 (10)⅍ 🔟 🔭 🔟 🖩 ♨

Craignair, *44 Corporation Road, Newport, Monmouthshire, NP9 0AW.* Friendly guest house. Close to all amenities and shopping centres. **Open:** All year (not Xmas/New Year) **Grades:** WTB 2 Star
01633 259903 D: £15.00–£18.00 **S:** £16.00–£20.00 **Beds:** 1F 3T 2D 3S **Baths:** 3 Sh 🛏 🖳 (8) 🔟 🔟 🖩 ♨

Osbaston

SO5014

Caseta Alta, *15 Toynbee Close, Osbaston, Monmouth, NP25 3NU.* Quiet, comfortable, artistic, upside-down house. Picturesque hillside views. Town - walking distance. **Open:** All year (not Xmas/New Year)
01600 713023 Mrs Allcock **D:** £16.00–£21.00
S: £23.00–£30.00 **Beds:** 2F 1T 2D 1S
Baths: 1 En 1 Sh 🛏 🖳 (2) 🔟 ✕ 🔟 🖩 & ♨

Pandy

SO3322

Brynhonddu, *Pandy, Abergavenny, Monmouthshire, NP7 7PD.* Large C16th-C19th country house in great location. **Open:** All year (not Xmas) **Grades:** WTB 2 Star
01873 890535 Mrs White *kdwhite@clara.net* www.brynhonddu.co.uk **D:** £16.00–£20.00 **S:** £18.00–£25.00 **Beds:** 1F 1D 1T **Baths:** 1 Sh 1 En ⌘ (5) ₽ (6) ⊡ ⊞ ♨ ☆

Old Castle Court Farm, *Pandy, Abergavenny, Monmouthshire, NP7 7PH.* C13th farmhouse near Offa's Dyke path and River Monnow. **Open:** Feb to Nov **Grades:** WTB 1 Star
01873 890285 Mrs Probert **D:** £15.00 **S:** £16.00 **Beds:** 1F 1D 1T **Baths:** 3 En 3 Pr ⌘ ₽ (10) ⊡ ♨ ⊡ ☆

Lancaster Arms, *Pandy, Abergavenny, Monmouthshire, NP7 8DW.* Country pub on Offa's Dyke path, edge of Black Mountains. **Open:** All year **Grades:** WTB 2 Star
01873 890699 (also fax) Mr & Mrs Lyon **D:** £20.00 **S:** £21.00–£23.00 **Beds:** 2T **Baths:** 2 Pr ⌘ ₽ (10) ⊡ ♨ ✕ ⊡ ⊞ ☆

Penallt

SO5210

Cherry Orchard Farm, *Lone Lane, Penallt, Monmouth, NP5 4AJ.* Small C18th working farm situated in Lower Wye Valley. **Open:** All year (not Xmas)
01600 714416 Mrs Beale **Fax: 01600 714447** **D:** £18.00 **S:** £18.00 **Beds:** 2D **Baths:** 1 Sh ₽ (4) ✕ ♨ ✕ ⊞ ☆

Pontypool

SO2800

Ty Shon Jacob Farm, *Tranch, Pontypool, NP4 6BP.* Secluded hilltop farm. Panoramic views, home-grown vegetables and good cooking. **Open:** All year
01495 757536 A Harris *tyshonfarm@aol.com* www.s-h-systems.co.uk/hotels/tyshon.html **D:** £18.00–£20.00 **S:** £20.00–£22.00 **Beds:** 2T 1D **Baths:** 2 En 1 Pr ⌘ (1) ₽ (10) ⊡ ♨ ✕ ⊡ ⊞ ☆

Please respect a B&B's wishes regarding children, animals and smoking

Rhiwderin

ST2687

Pentre Tai Farm, *Rhiwderin, Newport, Monmouthshire, NP10 9RQ.* Peaceful Welsh sheep farm in Castle Country close to M4. **Open:** Feb to Nov
01633 893284 (also fax) Mrs Proctor *stay@pentretai.f9.co.uk* www.downourlane.co.uk **D:** £20.00–£21.00 **S:** £25.00 **Beds:** 1F 1T **Baths:** 2 En ⌘ ₽ (4) ✕ ⊡ ⊞ ☆

Rogiet

ST4687

Court Farm, *Rogiet, Newport, Gwent, NP26 3UR.* Comfortable farmhouse near Usk, Chepstow & Wye Valley. Cardiff 16, Bristol 17 miles. **Open:** All year
01633 880232 S Anstey **D:** £20.00–£25.00 **S:** £20.00–£25.00 **Beds:** 2F 2T **Baths:** 2 En 1 Pr ⌘ ₽ (10) ✕ ⊡ ♨ ⊡ ⊞ ☆

St Brides Wentlooge

ST2982

The West Usk Lighthouse, *Lighthouse Road, St Brides Wentlooge, Newport, Monmouthshire, NP10 8SF.* Super B&B in real lighthouse, with water & four poster beds. **Open:** All year
01633 810126 & 01633 815860 Mr & Mrs Sheahan *Lighthouse1@tesco.net* www.westusklighthouse.co.uk **D:** £40.00–£45.00 **S:** £50.00–£65.00 **Beds:** 1F 2D **Baths:** 3 En ⌘ ₽ (10) ✕ ⊡ ♨ ⊞ ☆

Chapel Guest House, *Church Road, St Brides Wentlooge, Newport, Monmouthshire, NP10 8SN.* Comfortable accommodation in converted chapel situated between Newport and Cardiff. **Open:** All year **Grades:** WTB 3 Star
01633 681018 Mr Bushell **Fax: 01633 681431** *chapelguesthouse@hotmail.com* www.smoothhound.co.uk/hotels/chapel1.html **D:** £20.00–£23.00 **S:** £23.00–£25.00 **Beds:** 1F 1D 1T 1S **Baths:** 4 En ⌘ ₽ (10) ✕ ⊡ ♨ ⊡ ⊞ ☆

Tintern

SO5300   ◆ *Moon & Sixpence, Rose & Crown, Wye Valley Hotel, Royal George*

Holmleigh, *Monmouth Road, Tintern, Chepstow, Monmouthshire, NP6 6SG.* Beautiful old house overlooking the river Wye. **Open:** All year
01291 689521 Mr & Mrs Mark **D:** £16.00 **S:** £16.00 **Beds:** 2D 1T 1S **Baths:** 1 Sh ⌘ ₽ (3) ⊡ ♨ ⊞ ☆

Highfield House, *Chapel Hill, Tintern, Chepstow, Monmouthshire, NP6 6TF.* Remarkable house - wondrous views of the Wye Valley. Close Offa's Dyke. **Open:** All year
01291 689838 Mr McCaffery **Fax: 01291 689890** **D:** £24.50–£29.50 **S:** £30.00–£37.50 **Beds:** 2F 1D **Baths:** 2 En 1 Pr ₽ (10) ⊡ ♨ ✕ ⊡ ⊞ ☆

Rose Cottage, *The Chase, Woolaston, Glos, GL15 6PT.* Self-contained converted barn, peaceful location. Evening meals a speciality, own organic produce. **Open:** All year
01291 689691 Mrs Dunbar *rosecottage@breathemail.net* **D:** £22.50 **S:** £45.00 **Beds:** 1T **Baths:** 1 En ✕ ⊡ ♨ ✕ ⊡ ⊞ ☆

Tranch

SO2600

Ty Shon Jacob Farm, *Tranch, Pontypool, NP4 6BP.* Secluded hilltop farm. Panoramic views, home-grown vegetables and good cooking. **Open:** All year
01495 757536 A Harris *tyshonfarm@aol.com* www.s-h-systems.co.uk/hotels/tyshon.html **D:** £18.00–£20.00 **S:** £20.00–£22.00 **Beds:** 2T 1D **Baths:** 2 En 1 Pr ⌘ (1) ₽ (10) ⊡ ♨ ✕ ⊡ ☆

Tregare

SO4110   ◆ *Cripple Creek Inn, Hostry Inn*

Court Robert, *Tregare, Raglan, Monmouthshire, NP5 2BZ.* Peaceful C16th home. Comfortable, spacious bedrooms, antique furnishings. **Open:** All year (not Xmas/New Year) **Grades:** WTB 2 Star
01291 690709 (also fax) Ms Paxton *courtrobert@virgin.net* **D:** £18.00 **Beds:** 2F **Baths:** 1 Sh ⌘ ₽ ⊡ ⊞ ☆

Trelleck

SO4901

Hollytree House, *Trelleck, Monmouth, NP25 4PA.* A Wye Valley rural village setting with pub and restaurant. **Open:** All year
01600 860181 Mr & Mrs Peckham *gerald.peckham@ic24.net* **D:** £19.50–£21.50 **S:** £20.50–£22.50 **Beds:** 1F 1T **Baths:** 1 Pr 1 Sh ⌘ (3) ₽ (3) ✕ ⊡ ♨ ✕ ⊡ ⊞ ☆

North East Wales

North East Wales

Scale: 0 — 5 — 10 miles

Bangor-on-Dee

SJ3742

Fraser Cottage, *High Street, Bangor-on-Dee, Wrexham, LL13 0AU.* Pure vegetarian B&B in Welsh Borderlands; rural village, informal atmosphere. **Open:** All year **01978 781068 (also fax)** Ms Knowles *101357.2201@compuserve.com* ourworld.compuserve. com/homepages/helenknowles **D:** £15.00–£19.00 **S:** £15.00–£19.00 **Beds:** 2D 1T **Baths:** 3 En ⏣ 🚳 🄿 (3) ⌿ 🆅 🄷 🆅 🆅 ▥ ❋ 🛁

Bodfari

SJ0970

Fron Haul, *Sodom, Bodfari, Denbigh, LL16 4DY.* An oasis of calm and taste overlooking the Vale of Clwyd. **Open:** Jan to Dec **01745 710301 (also fax)** Mrs Edwards *fronhaul@pantglasbodfari.freeserve.co.uk* www.fron-haul.com **D:** £20.00–£25.00 **S:** £25.00 **Beds:** 1F 1D 1T 1S **Baths:** 1 En 2 Sh ⏣ 🚳 🄿 (12) ⌿ 🆅 🄷 ✕ 🆅 ▥ 🛁

Bontuchel

SJ0857

Pantglas Ganol, *Bontuchel, Ruthin, LL15 2BS.* Stay in this beautiful and peaceful location, enjoy the wildlife. **Open:** All year (not Xmas/New Year) **01824 710639 (also fax)** Mrs Wilkinson **D:** £20.00–£21.00 **S:** £21.00–£22.00 **Beds:** 1F 1T 1D **Baths:** 1 En 1 Pr ⏣ 🄿 🆅 🆅 🄷 ✕ ▥ 🛁

RATES
D = Price range per person
sharing in a double or twin
room
S = Price range for a single
room

Caerwys
SJ1272

Plas Penucha, Caerwys, Mold, Flintshire,
CH7 5BH. Peaceful countryside, comfortable
farmhouse with large gardens overlooking
the Clwydian Hills. **Open:** All year
Grades: WTB 3 Star
01352 720210 Mrs Price **Fax: 01352 720881**
D: £22.00–£25.00 **S:** £22.00–£25.00 **Beds:** 2D
2T **Baths:** 2 En 1 Pr 1 Sh ♿ ☐ ⅛ ☑ ⊶ ✕ 🗏
⚘

Chirk
SJ2837

Sun Cottage, Pentre, Chirk, Wrexham,
LL14 5AW. Welcoming character cottage,
1723. Spectacular woodland views over
river valley. **Open:** All year (not Xmas)
01691 774542 Mrs Little *little@
suncottage-bb.freeserve.co.uk* **D:** £17.00 **S:** £17.00
Beds: 2F 1S **Baths:** 2 Sh ♿ (10) ☐ (3) ⅛ ⊶
☑ 🗏 ⚘

Clawdd-newydd
SJ0852

Bryn Coch,
Clawdd-newydd,
Ruthin, LL15 2NA.
Working farm
near Clocaenog
Forest
overlooking Vale
of Clwyd. Croeso. **Open:** Easter to Oct
01824 750603 (also fax) Mrs Jones
gaenorjones@hotmail.com **D:** £18.00–£20.00
S: £18.00–£22.00 **Beds:** 1T 1F **Baths:** 1 En 1
Sh ♿ ☐ ⅛ ☑ ✕ ☑ 🗏 ⚘

Corwen
SJ0743

Corwen Court Private Hotel, London
Road, Corwen, Denbighshire, LL21 0DP.
Converted old police station/courthouse;
six cells, now single bedrooms. **Open:** Mar
to Nov
01490 412854 Mr & Mrs Buckland **D:** £16.50
S: £16.00 **Beds:** 4D 6S **Baths:** 4 En 2 Sh
♿ (3) ☐ (6) ⊶ ✕ 🗏

Cynwyd
SJ0541   ⚑ Blue Lion

**Pen y Bont
Fawr,** Cynwyd,
Corwen, LL21 0ET.
Open: All year
Grades: WTB 3
Star
01490 412663
Mr Wivell **D:** £15.00–£17.00 **S:** £15.00
Beds: 1T 2D **Baths:** 2 En 1 Sh ♿ ☐ (5) ⅛ ☑ ✕
☑ 🗏 ⚘
Situated in the Edeyrnion Valley, close to
the Berwyn Mountains on the outskirts of
Cynwyd Village, near Corwen. Llangollen,
Bala, Betws-y-Coed & Snowdonia, are
nearby. Ideal for walking, cycling, fishing &
horse riding. Water sports in Bala. All
rooms have mountain views.

Denbigh
SJ0566

Cayo Guest House, 74 Vale Street,
Denbigh, LL16 3BW. Centrally-situated
townhouse. Ideal for viewing N. Wales.
Pickup from Bodfari (Offa's Dyke).
Open: All year (not Xmas/New Year)
01745 812686 Mrs MacCormack **D:** £18.00–
£19.00 **S:** £18.00–£19.00 **Beds:** 2D 3T 1S
Baths: 3 En 1 Pr 1 Sh ⅛ ☑ ⊶ ✕ ☑ 🗏 ⚘ cc

Flint
SJ2472

Oakenholt Farm, Chester Road, Flint,
Flintshire, CH6 5SU. Set in a beautiful
location, convenient for touring Chester,
North Wales & Liverpool. **Open:** All year
Grades: WTB 3 Star
01352 733264 Mrs Hulme *jenny@
oakenholt.freeserve.co.uk* www.smoothhound.
co.uk/oakenholt **D:** £20.00–£25.00
S: £25.00–£28.00 **Beds:** 1F 2D 1T **Baths:** 4
En ♿ ☐ ⅛ ☑ ⊶ ✕ ☑ 🗏 ⚘

Froncysyllte
SJ2740

Argoed Farm, Froncysyllte, Llangollen,
Clwyd, LL20 7RH. Old farmhouse, beamed
ceilings, inglenook fireplace in dining
room. **Open:** All year
01691 772367 Mrs Landon *llangollen@
argoedfm.freeserve.co.uk* **D:** £20.00–£22.00
S: £20.00–£22.00 **Beds:** 1F 1D 1T 1S
Baths: 4 En ♿ ☐ (6) ⅛ ☑ ⊶ ✕ ☑ 🗏 ⚘

BATHROOMS
En = Ensuite
Pr = Private
Sh = Shared

Glyn Ceiriog
SJ2038

Pant Farm, Glyn Ceiriog, Llangollen,
LL20 7BY. Spectacular views, walking, riding
on the doorstep, ideal touring base.
Open: All year (not Xmas)
01691 718534 (also fax) Mrs Tomlinson
chris@pantfarmholidays.com
www.pantfarmholidays.com **D:** £19.00
S: £19.00 **Beds:** 2D 1S **Baths:** 2 En ♿ ☐ (6)
⅛ ☑ ⊶ ✕ ☑ 🗏 ⚘

Hawarden
SJ3165

**The Coach
House,**
Hawarden,
Deeside,
CH5 3DH. A
converted
coaches 5 miles
from Chester.
Ideal for touring N. Wales. **Open:** All year
(not Xmas/New Year)
01244 532328 (also fax) Mrs Jacks **D:** £22.50
S: £25.00 **Beds:** 2D 2S **Baths:** 1 Sh ♿ (12)
☐ (4) ☑ 🗏 ⚘

St Deiniol's Library, Church Lane,
Hawarden, Deeside, CH5 3DF. William
Gladstone's library, Grade I Listed building
set in own grounds. **Open:** All year (not
Xmas) **Grades:** WTB 3 Star
01244 532350 G P Morris **Fax: 01244 520643**
deiniol.vistors@btinternet.com st-
deniols.chester.ac.uk **D:** £22.50–£24.40
S: £22.50–£24.40 **Beds:** 7D 10T 16S **Baths:** 9
Sh ☐ (20) ⅛ ☑ ✕ ☑ 🗏 ⚘ cc

Higher Kinnerton
SJ3261   ⚑ The Swan, Royal Oak

Green Cottage, Higher Kinnerton,
Chester, CH4 9BZ. 6 miles from historic
Chester, relaxing atmosphere, good food, in
a Welsh rural setting. **Open:** All year
01244 660137 Mrs Milner **D:** £19.00 **S:** £24.00
Beds: 1D 1T **Baths:** 1 Pr ♿ ☐ ⅛ ☑ ☑ 🗏 ⚘

Kinnerton Hall, 43 Main Street, Higher
Kinnerton, Chester, CH4 9AJ. C18th
farmhouse, providing luxury
accommodation overlooking the Cheshire
Plain. **Open:** All year
01244 660213 (also fax) Ms Cannon *gille@
kinnertonhall.co.uk* www.kinnertonhall.co.uk
D: £17.00–£19.50 **S:** £17.00–£24.50 **Beds:** 1F
1D 2S **Baths:** 1 En 1 Sh ♿ ☐ ⅛ ☑ ☑ 🗏 ⚘

Holywell
SJ1875

Greenhill Farm, Bryn Celyn, Holywell,
Denbigh & Flint, CH8 7QF. C16th timber
framed farmhouse with 'old world' charm.
Open: Feb to Nov
01352 713270 Mr & Mrs Jones *mary@
greenhillfarm.fsnet.co.uk* greenhillfarm.co.uk
D: £18.50–£20.50 **Beds:** 2F 1D 1T **Baths:** 2
En 2 Sh ♿ ☐ (6) ☑ ✕ 🗏 ⚘

Llandegla

SJ1952   *The Plough*

Saith Daran Farm, Llandegla, Wrexham, LL11 3BA. Ideally placed for touring North Wales, Chester and Offa's Dyke. **Open:** All year (not Xmas/New Year) **01978 790685** Mrs Thompson *ianjoy@ saithdaran.freeserve.co.uk* **D:** £18.00 **S:** £18.00 **Beds:** 1T 1S **Baths:** 2 En ☎ 🅿 ⽅ 📺 ✕ 🎦 🛒 🛉

Llandrillo

SJ0337

Y Llwyn Guest House, Llandrillo, Corwen, LL21 0ST. Enjoy beautiful views of Berwyn Mountains from your bedroom, restaurants in walking distance. **Open:** All year **01490 440455 & 07803 524526 (M)** Mrs Jones *aeron@yllwyn39.freeserve.co.uk* **D:** £20.00–£22.00 **S:** £26.00 **Beds:** 1D 1T **Baths:** 1 En 1 Pr ☎ 🅿 (3) 📺 ⽊ 🎦 🛒 🛉

Llanfair Dyffryn Clwyd

SJ1355

Eyarth Station, Llanfair Dyffryn Clwyd, Ruthin, Denbighshire, LL15 2EE. Converted old railway station. Perfect touring centre for N. Wales **Open:** Mar to Oct **01824 703643** Mrs Spencer **Fax: 01824 707464** *eyarthstation@amserve.net* www.smoothhound.co.uk/hotels/eyarth **D:** £23.00–£25.00 **S:** £30.00–£35.00 **Beds:** 2F 2T 2D 1S **Baths:** 6 En ☎ 🅿 (10) 📺 ⽊ ✕ 🎦 🛒 cc

Llanferres

SJ1860

The White House, Rectory Lane, Llanferres, Mold, Denbighshire, CH7 5SR. Victorian rectory with recently converted stables set in conservation area. **Open:** All year **01352 810259** *rarmst@hotmail.com* **D:** £19.00–£22.00 **S:** £23.00–£25.00 **Beds:** 2D 1T **Baths:** 3 Pr 🅿 (6) ⽅ 📺 🎦 🛒 🛉

Llangollen

SJ2141   *Bryn Derwen, Abbey Grange, Sarah Ponsonby, Wild Pheasant*

Dee Farm, Rhewl, Llangollen, LL20 7YT. Comfortable stone farmhouse. 4 miles upstream of Llangollen. Superb countryside. **Open:** Mar to Nov **01978 861598 (also fax)** M Harman *harman@ activelives.co.uk* **D:** £22.00–£23.00 **S:** £22.00–£25.00 **Beds:** 2T 1S **Baths:** 1 En 1 Pr ☎ 🅿 (6) ⽅ 📺 ⽊ ✕ 🎦 🛒 🛉

Bryn Meirion, Abbey Road, Llangollen, Clwyd, LL20 8EF. Edwardian house overlooking Dee, canal, steam railway and surrounding hills. **Open:** All year **Grades:** WTB 3 Star **01978 861911** Mrs Hurle *jhurle@ globalnet.co.uk* www.users.globalnet.co. uk/~jhurle/ **D:** £18.00–£20.00 **S:** £24.00–£35.00 **Beds:** 1F 2D **Baths:** 2 En 1 Pr ☎ 🅿 (4) ⽅ 📺 ⽊ ✕ 🎦 🛒 🛉

River Lodge, Mill Street, Llangollen, Clwyd, LL20 7UH. On the banks of the Dee, River Lodge is Llangollen's newest motel lodge. **Open:** Feb to Dec **01978 869019** Mr Byrne **Fax: 01978 861841** *chainbridge@hotmail.com* **D:** £15.00–£35.00 **S:** £15.00–£35.00 **Beds:** 4F 7D 7T **Baths:** 18 En ☎ 🅿 (30) ⽊ ✕ 🛒 🛉 🎦 cc

Lloc

SJ1376

Misty Waters Country Lodge Hotel, Lloc, Holywell, CH8 8RG. Country lodge set in peaceful area with a friendly atmosphere. **Open:** All year **01352 720497 (also fax)** Mr Edwards www.shepherdscottage.ntb.ore.uk **D:** £20.00 **S:** £30.00 **Beds:** 1F 4D **Baths:** 5 En ☎ 🅿 ⽅ 📺 ✕ 🎦 🛒 🛉

Maeshafn

SJ2061

Hafan Deg, Maeshafn, Mold, Flintshire, CH7 5LU. A comfortable country home surrounded by woods and hills. Relax on patio or gallery. **Open:** All year **01352 810465 (also fax)** Mrs Scruton *dave@ hafandeg.co.uk* www.hafandeg.co.uk **D:** £20.00 **S:** £20.00 **Beds:** 1F 1T 1D 1S **Baths:** 1 En 2 Pr 1 Sh ☎ 🅿 (4) ⽅ 📺 ⽊ 🎦 🛒 🛉

Minera

SJ2651   *Tyn y Capel*

Butterfields Guest House, Pen-y-Nant Cottage, Minera, Wrexham, LL13 3DA. Just outside Minera village, overlooking Minera Mountain. Utilises British sign language. **Open:** All year **01978 750547 (also fax)** **D:** £20.00 **S:** £20.00 **Beds:** 5S **Baths:** 1S ☎ 🅿 (3) ⽅ 📺 ⽊ 🎦 🛒 🛉

BATHROOMS

En = Ensuite
Pr = Private
Sh = Shared

Planning a longer stay? Always ask for any special rates

Mold

SJ2363

Heulwen, Maes Bodlonfa, Mold, Flintshire, CH7 1DR. Spacious well-furnished rooms. Quiet, convenient town centre. Friendly - nothing too much trouble. **Open:** All year (not Xmas) **Grades:** AA 3 Diamond **01352 758785** Mrs Hollywell **D:** £19.00 **S:** £19.00–£25.00 **Beds:** 1F 1S **Baths:** 2 Pr ☎ 🅿 (3) ⽅ 📺 🎦 🛒 🛉

Northop Hall

SJ2667   *Black Lion*

Brookside House, Northop Hall, Mold, Flintshire, CH7 6HR. Relax enjoy the hospitality or our beautifully refurbished cottage. **Open:** All year (not Xmas/New Year) **Grades:** WTB 3 Star **01244 821146** Mrs Whale *christine@ brooksidehouse.fsnet.co.uk* www.brooksidehouse.fsnet.co.uk **D:** £19.00–£22.00 **Beds:** 1F 1T 1D **Baths:** 1 En 1 Pr 1 Sh ☎ 🅿 ⽅ 📺 🛒 🛉

Penley

SJ4140

Bridge House, Penley, Wrexham, LL13 0LY. Comfortable house, idyllic setting, open views. Landscaped gardens with stream. **Open:** All year (not Xmas) **01978 710763** Mr & Mrs Clarke **D:** £16.00–£18.00 **S:** £18.00–£20.00 **Beds:** 1D 2T **Baths:** 2 Sh ☎ 🅿 ⽅ 📺 ⽊ 🎦 🛒 🛉

Pentre

SJ2940

Pentre Cottage, Pentre, Chirk, Wrexham, Flintshire, LL14 5AW. Beautiful Welsh cottage with friendly Lancashire welcome; dog-lovers paradise. **Open:** All year (not Xmas) **01691 774265** Mrs Vant *vant@ pentrecott.freeserve.co.uk* **D:** £16.00 **S:** £16.00–£18.00 **Beds:** 1D 1T **Baths:** 1 Pr 1 Sh 🅿 (3) 📺 ⽊ ✕ 🎦 🛒 🛉

Pentre Halkyn

SJ2072   *Glan-yr-Afon Inn, Calcot Arms*

The Hall, Lygan Y Wern, Pentre Halkyn, Holywell, CH8 8BD. Delightful cottage in large grounds adjoining Georgian mansion. **Open:** All year **01352 780215** Mrs Vernon **Fax: 01352 780187** *daviniavernon@aol.com* **D:** £20.00 **S:** £25.00 **Beds:** 1T 1D **Baths:** 1 En 1 Sh ☎ (5) 🅿 (4) ⽅ 📺 🎦 🛒 🛉 cc

Prestatyn

SJ0682

Roughsedge House, *26/28 Marine Road, Prestatyn, Denbighshire, LL19 7HG.* Victorian guest house, excellent breakfast. Walkers welcome, friendly atmosphere. **Open:** All year **Grades:** AA 1 Diamond **01745 887359** Mrs Kubler **Fax: 01745 852883** *roughsedge@ykubler.fsnet.co.uk* **D:** £17.00–£20.00 **S:** £17.00–£25.00 **Beds:** 2F 4D 2T 2S **Baths:** 3 Pr 3 Sh ⏰ ⅍ 📺 ✕ 📖 ♨ cc

Rhewl (Llangollen)

SJ1844   🍺 *Sun Inn*

Dee Farm, *Rhewl, Llangollen, LL20 7YT.* Comfortable stone farmhouse. 4 miles upstream of Llangollen. Superb countryside. **Open:** Mar to Nov **01978 861598 (also fax)** M Harman *harman@activelives.co.uk* **D:** £22.00–£23.00 **S:** £22.00–£25.00 **Beds:** 2T 1S **Baths:** 1 En 1 Pr ⏰ 📶 (6) ⅍ 📺 ⅏ ✕ 📖 ♨

Rhyl

SJ0181

Links Guest House, *20 Beechwood Road, Rhyl, LL18 3EU.* East Parade beach, ground floor available. 3 stars, ensuite **Open:** All year **01745 344381** Mrs Mariner *thelinksgh@cwcom.net* www.virtualrhyl.co.uk/links/index.htm **D:** £15.00–£20.00 **S:** £18.00–£25.00 **Beds:** 3F 4D 2S **Baths:** 6 En 1 Pr ⏰ (5) ⅍ 📺 📖 ♨

Normaz Guest House, *19 Aquarium Street, Rhyl, LL18 1PG.* Welcoming licensed guest house. Reasonable rates, clean, central and great food. **Open:** Easter to Sept **01745 334761** Mrs Harper *tom@normaz.fsnet.co.uk* **D:** £15.00 **S:** £15.00 **Beds:** 2F 1T 2D 1S **Baths:** 1 Sh ⏰ 📺 ✕ 📖 ♨

The Kensington Hotel, *17 East Parade, Rhyl, LL18 3AG.* Traditional Victorian bay property, now family-run hotel. Prominent position on the sea front. **Open:** All year (not Xmas/New Year) **01745 331868 (also fax)** Mr Dawson **D:** £20.00–£34.00 **S:** £25.00–£35.00 **Beds:** 10F 4T 10D 10S **Baths:** 10 En 10 Pr ⏰ 📶 📺 📖 ♨ cc

Rossett

SJ3657   🍺 *Golden Lion, Hand & Hart*

Corner House Farm, *Parkside, Rossett, Wrexham, LL12 0BW.* 9 luxury holiday houses & apartments suitable for meetings, family gatherings, lovely rural location. **Open:** All year **Grades:** WTB 5 Star **01829 270452** Mrs Coop **Fax: 01829 271260** **D:** £20.00–£28.00 **S:** £25.00 **Beds:** 1D 1T 1S **Baths:** 3 En ⏰ 📶 (14) 📺 ⅏ ✕ 📖 ♿1 ♨

Ruthin

SJ1258

Eyarth Station, *Llanfair Dyffryn Clwyd, Ruthin, Denbighshire, LL15 2EE.* Converted old railway station. Perfect touring centre for N. Wales **Open:** Mar to Oct **01824 703643** Mrs Spencer **Fax: 01824 707464** *eyarthstation@amserve.net* www.smoothhound.co.uk/hotels/eyarth **D:** £23.00–£25.00 **S:** £30.00–£35.00 **Beds:** 2F 2T 2D 1S **Baths:** 6 En ⏰ 📶 (10) 📺 ⅏ ✕ 📖 ♨ cc

St Asaph

SJ0374   🍺 *Bod Erw, Plas Elwy, The Plough*

Diddanfa, *The Roe, St Asaph, Denbighshire, L17 0LU.* Large Victorian B&B, 2 min off A55, set in the lovely Vale of Clwyd. **Open:** All year (not Xmas/New Year) **01745 582849 (also fax)** Mr & Mrs Thomas **D:** £15.00–£20.00 **S:** £20.00 **Beds:** 1F 1T 1S **Baths:** 1 Sh 📺 ✕ 📖 ♨

Pen-Y-Bryn Farm, *Boderw, St Asaph, Denbighshire, LL17 0LF.* Comfortable farmhouse in peaceful surroundings overlooking the city. Farmhouse breakfast. **Open:** All year **01745 583213** Mrs Williams **D:** £17.50–£20.00 **S:** £19.00–£20.00 **Beds:** 1F 2D 1S **Baths:** 1 En 1 Sh ⏰ 📶 📺 ⅏ 📺 📖 ♨

Worthenbury

SJ4146

The Manor, *Worthenbury, Wrexham, LL13 0AW.* **Open:** Mar to Nov **Grades:** WTB 3 Star **01948 770342** Mr Taylor **Fax: 01948 770711** **D:** £28.00–£35.00 **S:** £35.00–£45.00 **Beds:** 2D **Baths:** 1 En 1 Pr ⏰ (12) 📶 (4) ⅍ ✕ 📺 📖 ♨ Elizabeth and Ian warmly welcome you to a tranquil rural retreat. Relax in country house style and dine on local and home-grown produce. Then retire to a period bedroom and comfy four-poster bed. Explore Cheshire, North Wales and Shropshire.

Wrexham

SJ3350   🍺 *Fox & Hounds*

Plas Eyton, *Wrexham, LL13 0YD.* Large, easily accessible Victorian house. 3 acre small holding in own private grounds. **Open:** All year **01978 820642** Mrs Davies **D:** £17.00 **S:** £17.00 **Beds:** 1F 1T 1D 2S **Baths:** 1 En 2 Sh ⏰ 📶 (10) ⅍ 📺 📖 ♨

The Windings, *Cea Penty Road, Wrexham, LL12 9TH.* Delightful rural setting. Ideal base for Chester, North Wales, Wrexham. **Open:** All year **01978 720503** Mrs Rooks **Fax: 01978 757372** *windings@enterprise.net* **D:** £20.00 **S:** £20.00 **Beds:** 1T 2D **Baths:** 1 Sh 📶 (10) ⅍ 📺 ♨

North West Wales

Preswylfa, *Balkan Hill, Aberdovey, LL35 0LE.* Detached period house with garden, private parking and stunning views. **Open:** All year
01654 767239 Mrs Billingham **Fax: 01654 767983** *preswylfa@cwcom.net* **D:** £25.00–£30.00 **S:** £30.00–£60.00 **Beds:** 2D 1T **Baths:** 3 En ⅍ (10) ▣ (3) ⅄ ▦ ⅄ ╳ ▥ ▥. ⚹ ⚘

Bodfor Hotel, *Sea Front, Aberdovey, LL35 0EA.* Two Star family-run seafront hotel, on main promenade, overlooking sandy beach. **Open:** All year
01654 767475 Mr Evans **Fax: 01654 767679** *davidevans@bodforhotel.co.uk* **D:** £20.00–£29.50 **S:** £20.00–£29.50 **Beds:** 1F 6D 5T 4S
Baths: 10 En 2 Pr 4 Sh ⅍ ▣ ▥ ⅄ ╳ ▥ ▥.

Abergynolwyn

SH6706

Riverside House, *Abergynolwyn, Tywyn, LL36 9YR.* Victorian former quarry master's house, set in riverside gardens Magnificent views. **Open:** All year
01654 782235 (also fax) Ron Bott *ronbott@talyllyn.freeserve.co.uk www.snowdonia-wales.co.uk* **D:** £18.00–£20.00 **S:** £18.00–£20.00 **Beds:** 1F 3D 1S **Baths:** 1 En 1 Sh ⅍ ▣ (6) ⅄ ▥ ⅄ ╳ ▥ ▥. ⚹ ⚘

Eisteddfa, *Abergynolwyn, Tywyn, LL36 9UP.* Newly-built bungalow, suitable for disabled in wheelchair, overlooking Tal-y-llyn Railway. **Open:** Mar to Nov
01654 782385 Mrs Pugh **Fax: 01654 782228**
D: £20.00–£24.00 **S:** £20.00–£25.00 **Beds:** 2D 1T **Baths:** 2 En 1 Pr Ⓢ⒫🖳📺⌨✕Ⓥ▦♿♨

Abersoch

SH3128

Angorfa Guest House, *Lon Sarn Bach, Abersoch, Pwllheli, LL53 7EB.* Newly decorated bedrooms, superb breakfast, great beaches, scenery, walks & activities.
Open: All year (not Xmas)
01758 712967 (also fax) Mrs Stanworth
D: £19.00–£25.00 **S:** £22.00–£30.00 **Beds:** 1F 2D 1T **Baths:** 2 Pr 2 Sh � Ⓢ Ⓟ(4)⌁📺✕Ⓥ▦♨

Arthog

SH6414

Graig Wen Guest House, *Arthog, LL39 1BQ.* In 42 acres of woodland leading to Mawddach Estuary. Spectacular view from house. **Open:** All year
01341 250900 & 01341 250482 Mrs Ameson
Fax: 01341 250482 *graig-wen@supanet.com*
www.graig-wen.supernet.com **D:** £17.00–£19.00 **S:** £18.00–£24.00 **Beds:** 1F 4D 1T 1S **Baths:** 3 En 2 Sh Ⓢ(4)Ⓟ(20)⌁📺✕Ⓥ▦♿♨

Bala

SH9235

Traian, *95 Tegid Street, Bala, Gwynedd, LL23 7BW.* Welsh welcome, ideal for walking, sailing, canoeing, fishing. Local produce.
Open: All year (not Xmas) **Grades:** WTB 2 Star
01678 520059 Mrs Jones **D:** £14.00–£17.00 **S:** £16.00–£18.00 **Beds:** 1F 1D 1T **Baths:** 1 Sh Ⓢ⌁📺▦♨

Trem Aran House, *1 Glannau Tegid Tegid St, Bala, Gwynedd, LL23 7DZ.* A chalet-style detached house; car park maintained to a good standard. **Open:** Jan to Dec
01678 520848 Mrs Jones **D:** £16.50–£18.00 **S:** £16.50–£18.00 **Beds:** 1F 1T 1D **Baths:** 2 En Ⓢ Ⓟ(4)📺⌨✕Ⓥ▦♿♻♨

Bangor

SH5771   ⌂ *The Nelson*

The Guest House, *32 Glynne Road, Bangor, LL57 1AN.* Small, friendly accommodation close to centre. Large choice of breakfasts. **Open:** All year (not Xmas/New Year)
01248 352113 (also fax) Mrs Roberts
ragsroberts@aol.com **D:** £15.00 **S:** £15.00
Beds: 2D 2S **Baths:** 1 Sh Ⓟ(1)⌁📺▦♨

Barmouth

SH6115   ⌂ *Last Inn, George, Victoria Inn, Myn-Y-Mor Hotel*

Wavecrest Hotel, *8 Marine Parade, Barmouth, North West Wales, LL42 1NA.* Welcoming and relaxing 'Which?' recommended. Excellent food, wine and whisky. **Open:** Easter to Oct **Grades:** WTB 3 Star
01341 280330 (also fax) Mr & Mrs Jarman
thewavecrest@talk21.com www.lokalink.co.uk/wavecrest.htm **D:** £20.00–£28.00
S: £23.00–£40.00 **Beds:** 2F 3D 2T 2S **Baths:** 8 En 1 Pr Ⓢ Ⓟ(2)⌁📺⌨✕Ⓥ▦♨

Endeavour Guest House, *Marine Parade, Barmouth, LL42 1NA.* Sea front location. Beach 75 yards. Railway station 150 yards. **Open:** All year (not Xmas/New Year)
01341 280271 Mr & Mrs Every **D:** £18.00–£20.00 **S:** £20.00 **Beds:** 7F **Baths:** 4 En 1 Sh Ⓢ(2)Ⓟ(3)📺▦♨

Bryn Melyn Hotel, *Panorama Road, Barmouth, LL42 1DQ.* Stunning views of mountains, estuary and sea. **Open:** All year (not Xmas/New Year) **Grades:** WTB 2 Star
01341 280556 Mr Jukes MBII **Fax:** 01341 280342 **D:** £27.00–£80.00 **S:** £30.00–£47.00 **Beds:** 2F 2T 5D **Baths:** 8 En 1 Pr Ⓟ(9)📺⌨✕Ⓥ▦♨ **cc**

The Gables, *Fford Mynach, Barmouth, Gwynedd, LL42 1RL.* Victorian house of character lovely position near mountains - warm welcome. **Open:** Easter to Nov
01341 280553 Mr & Mrs Lewis **D:** £18.00–£20.00 **S:** £18.00–£20.00 **Beds:** 1F 2D 1S **Baths:** 2 En 1 Sh Ⓢ Ⓟ(4)⌁📺⌨✕Ⓥ▦♨

Beddgelert

SH5948   ⌂ *Prince Llewellyn, The Goat, Saracen's Head, Tanronnen Inn*

Plas Colwyn Guest House, *Beddgelert, Caernarfon, LL55 4UY.* Comfortable C17th house, centre of village, river and mountain views.
Open: All year (not Xmas)
01766 890458 Mrs Osmond *plascolwyn@hotmail.com* **D:** £18.00–£21.00 **S:** £18.00–£34.00 **Beds:** 2F 2D 1T 1S **Baths:** 3 En 3 Sh Ⓢ Ⓟ(6)⌁📺⌨✕Ⓥ▦♨ **cc**

Emrys House, *Beddgelert, Caernarfon, Gwynedd, LL55 4YB.* Friendly, comfortable accommodation at this spacious, centrally situated Victorian house. **Open:** All year
01766 890240 Mrs Gauler *gauler@lineone.net* www.emryshouse.co.uk **D:** £16.50–£18.00 **S:** £25.00 **Beds:** 1T 2D **Baths:** 1 Sh Ⓢ Ⓟ(2)⌁📺⌨▦♨

The Royal Goat Hotel, *Beddgelert, Caernarfon, LL55 4YE.* **Open:** All year
01766 890224 Fax: 01766 890422 *info@royalgoathotel.co.uk* www.royalgoathotel.co.uk
D: £39.50–£49.50 **S:** £39.50–£49.50 **Beds:** 2F 15T 15D 2S **Baths:** 34 En Ⓢ Ⓟ(80)📺⌨✕Ⓥ▦♿❀ **cc**
Our 200 year old listed building (Grade 2) offers 2 restaurants, 2 bars, and a residents' lounge set amidst glorious scenery. Beddgelert is a British and European winner for 'Prettiest Village' and 'Bloom in Britain' awards. Set at the foot of 'Snowdon', yet only 7 miles from the coast.

Ael-y-Bryn, *Caerarfon Road, Beddgelert, Caernarfon, LL55 4UY.* Centrally situated licensed guest house - award-winning village - wonderful views. **Open:** All year
01766 890310 Mrs Duffield *ay.b@virgin.net* www.plastangraig.co.uk **D:** £15.00–£22.50 **S:** £20.00–£40.00 **Beds:** 4F **Baths:** 1 Pr Ⓢ Ⓟ(2)⌁📺✕Ⓥ▦♨ **cc**

Betws-y-Coed

SH7956   ⌂ *Ty Gwyn, Royal Oak, Eagles, Glan Aber Hotel*

Fron Heulog Country House, *Betws-y-Coed, LL24 0BL.* **Open:** All year
Grades: RAC 4 Diamond, Sparkling
01690 710736 Jean & Peter Whittingham **Fax:** 01690 710920 *jean&peter@fronheulog.co.uk* www.fronheulog.co.uk
D: £22.00–£28.00 **Beds:** 2D 1T **Baths:** 3 En Ⓟ⌁📺▦♨
Elegant Victorian stone-built home in peaceful wooded riverside scenery. Excellent modern accommodation - comfort, warmth, style. Ideal Snowdonia location - tour, walk, relax. Enjoy hosts' personal hospitality & local knowledge. 'Which?' recommended. A5, B5106 Pont y Pair, left, 150 yds. Lower rates for longer stay.

Fairy Glen Hotel, *Betws-y-Coed, LL24 0SH.*
Open: Mar to Oct **Grades:** WTB 2 Star, AA 2 Star
01690 710269 (also fax) Mr & Mrs Youe *fairyglenhotel@amserve.net* www.fairyglenhotel.co.uk **D:** £22.00–£24.00 **S:** £22.00–£36.00 **Beds:** 2F 3D 2T 1S **Baths:** 6 En 2 Pr ⟩ ☐ (10) ☐ ☐ ⨯ ☐ ⊞, ☀ cc
Family-run 300-year-old small hotel, overlooking River Conwy in the Snowdonia National Park amongst mountains and forest. Private car park and licensed bar. Warm, friendly welcome with fresh home-cooked meals from local produce.

Cwmanog Isaf Farm, *Betws-y-Coed, LL24 0SL.*
Open: All year
01690 710225 & 07808 421634
(M) Mrs Hughes **Fax: 01690 710225**
h.m.hughes@amserve.net
www.cwmanogisaffarmholidays.co.uk
D: £19.00–£20.00 **S:** £24.00 **Beds:** 1F 2D **Baths:** 3 En ☐ (3) ⨯ ☐ ⨯ ☐ ⊞ ☀
Nestling in the spectacular scenery of the Snowdonia National Park, this traditional Welsh farmhouse enjoys a peaceful homely atmosphere, wonderful views, unforgettable cuisine - situated on a small working farm only 1 mile from the picturesque village of Betws-y-Coed, peace & tranquillity awaits.

Mairlys, *Betws-y-Coed, Gwynedd, LL24 0AN.*
Open: Mar to Nov

Grades: WTB 3 Star
01690 710190 *mairlys@betws-y-coed.co.uk*
www.betws-y-coed/accommodation/mairys
D: £21.00–£24.00 **S:** £21.00–£24.00 **Beds:** 1T 3D 1S **Baths:** 3 En 2 Sh ☐ (5) ⨯ ☐ ⊞, ☀
Situated in the beautiful village of Betws-y-Coed, Mairlys is an imposing Victorian house, set in attractive gardens. The village offers visitors a warm and welcoming atmosphere and is an ideal base from which to go walking, touring & golfing.

Royal Oak Farmhouse, *Betws-y-Coed, LL24 0AH.* **Open:** All year (not Xmas)
Grades: WTB 3 Star
01690 710427 Mrs Houghton **D:** £20.00–£22.00 **S:** £20.00–£25.00 **Beds:** 2D 1T **Baths:** 1 En 2 Sh ⟩ (10) ☐ ☐ ☐ ☐ ⊞, ☀
Part C13th water mill on beautiful meander of River Llugwy. Golf course adjacent, Fishing available from grounds, secluded, but only 3 minutes walk from village centre.

Dolweunydd Guest House, *Pentre Du, Betws-y-Coed, LL24 0BY.*
Open: All year
Grades: WTB 3 Star
01690 710693 (also fax) Mrs Shepherd *jenny.dolweunydd@virgin.net*
www.snowdonia-dolweunydd.co.uk
D: £20.00–£28.00 **S:** £25.00–£30.00 **Beds:** 2T 3D **Baths:** 5 En ⟩ (5) ☐ (7) ⨯ ☐ ⨯ ☐ ⊞, ☀ ☀
Runners-up of the North Wales Welcome Host of the Year Awards 2000. Jenny and Rob Shepherd offer guests a warm welcome. Quality ensuite accommodation with colour TV, hospitality tray and central heating. Excellent home cooked food using local produce.

Bryn Llewelyn Non-Smokers' Guest House, *Holyhead Road, Betws-y-Coed, LL24 0BN.*
Attractive Victorian guest house. Village centre, ample private car park. **Open:** All year **Grades:** WTB 2 Star, AA 3 Diamond
01690 710601 (also fax) Mr Parker *steveparker01690@yahoo.com*
www.betws-y-coed-snowdonia.co.uk
D: £17.50–£24.50 **S:** £19.50–£27.50 **Beds:** 2F 3D 1T 1S **Baths:** 4 En 3 Sh ⟩ (2) ☐ (9) ⨯ ☐ ☐ ⊞, ☀

Swallow Falls Hotel, *Betws-y-Coed, Wales, LL24 0DW.* Perfectly situated for exploring Snowdonia National Park. Opposite Swallow Falls.
Open: All year **Grades:** WTB 2 Star
01690 710796 Mr Jones **Fax: 01690 710191** *swallowfalls@virgin.net* **D:** £19.50–£29.50 **S:** £24.50–£34.50 **Beds:** 2F 2T 8D **Baths:** 12 En ⟩ ☐ ☐ ☐ ☐ ⨯ ⨯ ☐ ☀ cc

Park Hill Hotel, *Llanrwst Road, Betws-y-Coed, LL24 0HD.* Informal family-run hotel; our hotel is your castle; views; swimming-pool. **Open:** All year **Grades:** WTB 3 Star, AA 2 Star, RAC 2 Star
01690 710540 (also fax) *parkhill.hotel@virgin.net* www.betws-y-coed.co.uk/acc/parkhill **D:** £27.50–£38.00 **S:** £35.00–£47.00 **Beds:** 1F 5D 4T **Baths:** 9 En ☐ (10) ☐ ⨯ ☐ ⊞, ☀ cc

Royal Oak Farm Cottage, *Betws-y-Coed, LL24 0AH.* Picturesque C17th farmhouse in a quiet riverside setting.
Open: All year (not Xmas)
01690 710760 Mrs Houghton **D:** £18.00–£20.00 **S:** £20.00–£24.00 **Beds:** 2D 1T **Baths:** 3 Pr ☐ (4) ⨯ ☐ ☐ ⊞, ☀

Coed-y-Fron, *Vicarage Road, Betws-y-Coed, LL24 0AD.* Lovely Victorian house & garden in middle of village, superb outlook over Betws-y-Coed. **Open:** All year **Grades:** WTB 3 Star, AA 4 Diamond
01690 710365 Mr & Mrs Mills *mike&beth@coedyfron.enterprise-plc.com* www.coedyfron.co.uk **D:** £18.00–£24.00 **S:** £18.00–£21.00 **Beds:** 1F 3D 2T 1S **Baths:** 3 En 2 Sh ⟩ (2) ☐ (3) ☐ ⨯ ☐ ⊞, ☀ cc

Riverside, *Betws-y-Coed, LL24 0BN.* Centrally located in centre of village, comfortable accommodation and a superb restaurant. **Open:** All year
01690 710650 (also fax) *riverside4u@talk21.com* **D:** £17.00–£22.00 **S:** £18.00–£22.00 **Beds:** 2D 2T **Baths:** 1 En 1 Pr 1 Sh ⟩ (10) ⨯ ☐ ☐ ⊞, ☀

Bron Celyn Guest House, *Llanrwst Road, Betws-y-Coed, North West Wales, LL24 0HD.* Small Victorian-style guest house on outskirts of picturesque village.
Open: All year **Grades:** WTB 3 Star
01690 710333 Mr & Mrs Boughton **Fax: 01690 710111** *broncelyn@betws-y-coed.co.uk* www.betws-y-coed.co.uk/broncelyn **D:** £20.00–£26.00 **S:** £23.00–£50.00 **Beds:** 2F 1t 3D **Baths:** 3 En 2 Pr ⟩ ☐ (7) ☐ ⨯ ☐ ⊞, ☀ ☀ cc

Glan Llugwy, *Holyhead Road, Betws-Y-Coed, LL24 0BN.* Perfectly situated for exploring Snowdonia. A warm welcome. Superb breakfast. **Open:** All year
01690 710592 J Brayne *glanllugwy@beyws-y-coed.co.uk* **D:** £17.50–£19.00 **S:** £17.50–£19.00 **Beds:** 1F 1T 2D 1S **Baths:** 2 Sh ⟩ (6) ☐ (5) ⨯ ☐ ☐ ⊞, ☀

Aberconwy House, *Llanrwst Road, Betws-y-Coed, North West Wales, LL24 0HD.* Victorian guest house, elevated position overlooking the picturesque Snowdonia National Park. **Open:** All year
01690 710202 Mr Jones **Fax: 01690 710800** *aberconwy@betws-y-coed.co.uk* www.betws-y-coed.co.uk/aberconwy/ **D:** £22.00–£50.00 **S:** £22.00–£50.00 **Beds:** 1F 3T 4D **Baths:** 8 En ⟩ (8) ☐ (10) ⨯ ☐ ⊞, ☀ cc

Maes-y-Fedwen, *Llanrwst Road, Betws-y-Coed, LL24 0HD.* Panoramic views of Snowdonia are enjoyed from the dining room **Open:** All year
01690 710726 (also fax) Mr Roobottom *maes-y-fedwen@betws-y-coed.co.uk/acc/maes-y-fedwen/* **D:** £20.00–£25.00 **S:** £25.00–£30.00 **Beds:** 1F 1T 2D **Baths:** 3 En ⟩ (8) ☐ (4) ⨯ ☐ ⊞,

Betws-yn-Rhos
SH9073

Wheatsheaf Inn, *Betws-yn-Rhos, Abergele, LL22 8AW.* Olde worlde C17th inn in award-winning village. **Open:** All year
01492 680218 **D:** £22.00 **S:** £26.00 **Beds:** 1F 2D 1S **Baths:** 4 En ⟩ (1) ☐ (3) ⨯ ☐ ⨯ ⨯ ☐ ⊞, ☀ cc

Blaenau Ffestiniog

SH7045   ⚐ *Queen's Hotel, The Grapes*

Bryn Elltyd,
*Tanygrisiau,
Blaenau
Ffestiniog,
Gwynedd,
LL41 3TW.*
Mountain views:
in an acre of peaceful grounds. Guided
walking available. **Open:** All year
Grades: WTB 2 Star
01766 831356 (also fax) Mr & Mrs Cole
bob6annie9@aol.com
www.accommodation-snowdonia.com
D: £17.50–£19.50 **S:** £17.50–£19.50 **Beds:** 3T
1D **Baths:** 4 En ➤ ❒ (4) ⊡ ⊁ ⊻ ▥ ⅙ ✻ 🌣

Afallon Guest House, *Manod Road,
Blaenau Ffestiniog, LL41 4AE.* Situated in
Snowdonia National Park. Clean homely
accommodation with Welsh breakfast.
Open: All year (not Xmas)
01766 830468 Mrs Griffiths **D:** £15.00–£18.00
S: £15.00–£18.00 **Beds:** 1D 1T 1S **Baths:** 1
Sh ➤ ❒ (4) ⊡ ⊁ ⊻ ▥ 🌣

The Don Guest House, *High Street,
Blaenau Ffestiniog, LL41 3AX.* Victorian town
house with breathtaking mountain views.
Friendly welcome assured. **Open:** All year
(not Xmas/New Year)
01766 830403 (also fax) Mr Cotton
allan-cotton@supanet.com **D:** £14.00–£18.00
S: £15.00–£20.00 **Beds:** 3D 2T 1S **Baths:** 2
En 1 Sh ➤ ❒ (2) ⊡ ⊁ ⊻ ▥ 🌣

Brithdir

SH7618

Llwyn Talcen, *Brithdir, Dolgellau,
LL40 2RY.* Enjoy a holiday/short break at our
country house in rhododendron gardens.
Open: Easter to Oct
01341 450276 Mrs Griffiths **D:** £18.00–£20.00
S: £18.00–£20.00 **Beds:** 1D 1S **Baths:** 1 En 1
Sh ➤ (3) ❒ (3) ⊡ ⊁ ⊠ ▥ 🌣

Bryncrug

SH6003

Peniarth Arms, *Bryncrug, Tywyn,
Gwynedd, LL36 9PH.* Cosy village inn Cader
Idris. Tal-y-llyn railway nearby. Beautiful
scenery. **Open:** All year (not Xmas/New
Year)
01654 711505 Mrs Mountford **Fax:** 01654
712169 **D:** £17.00–£20.00 **S:** £18.00–£25.00
Beds: 4D **Baths:** 4 En ➤ (1) ❒ ⊠ × ⊻ 🌣 cc

Caerhun (Bangor)

SH5769

Penhower Bed & Breakfast, *Caerhun,
Bangor, Gwynedd, LL57 4DT.* Single-storey
stone-built house in peaceful setting,
panoramic views of Snowdonia, Anglesey.
Open: All year
01248 362427 Mr Farrar **D:** £18.00–£20.00
S: £20.00–£23.00 **Beds:** 1D 2T **Baths:** 3 En
➤ ❒ (10) ⊁ ⊡ ⊁ × ⊻ ▥ 🌣

Caernarfon

SH4862   ⚐ *Glyntwrog Inn, Vaynol Arms, Black Boy*

**The White
House,**
*Llanfaglan,
Caernarfon,
LL54 5RA.* Quiet,
isolated country
house.
Magnificent
views to mountains and sea. **Open:** Mar to
Nov **Grades:** WTB 3 Star
01286 673003 Mr Bayles *rwbayles@sjms.co.uk*
D: £20.00–£22.00 **S:** £26.00 **Beds:** 2D 2T
Baths: 3 En 1 Pr ➤ ❒ (8) ⊡ ⊁ ▥ 🌣

Swn-Y-Fenai, *8 Church Street,
Caernarfon, LL55 1SW.* Perfectly situated,
near castle and only 7 miles from Snowdon.
Open: All year
01286 671677 Mr Newell **Fax: 01745 334513**
philnewell73@hotmail.com **D:** £14.00–£20.00
S: £14.00–£20.00 **Beds:** 1F 4T 1S **Baths:** 2
Sh ➤ ⊁ ⊡ ⊁ × ⊻ 🌣

Pengwern Farm, *Saron, Llanwnda,
Caernarfon, LL54 5UH.* Charming, spacious
farmhouse of character, beautifully
situated between mountains & sea.
Open: Jan to Nov **Grades:** WTB 4 Star
01286 831500 & 07778 411780 (M) Mr & Mrs
Rowlands **Fax: 01286 831500** *jhjgr@
enterprise.net* **D:** £24.00–£28.00 **S:** £30.00–
£38.00 **Beds:** 1T 2D **Baths:** 3 En ➤ ❒ ⊁ ⊡ ×
⊻ 🌣 cc

Prince of Wales Hotel, *Bangor Street,
Caernarfon, LL55 1AR.* Town location, perfect
stopover enroute for Ireland's ferries or
exploring Snowdonia. **Open:** All year (not
Xmas)
01286 673367 Ms Parry **Fax: 01286 676610**
princeofwaleshotel@gofornet.co.uk **D:** £19.00–
£32.00 **S:** £19.00–£32.00 **Beds:** 2F 8D 7T 4S
Baths: 19 En 2 Sh ➤ ❒ (6) ⊡ ⊁ × ⊻ ▥ 🌣 cc

**Menai View Guest House &
Restaurant,** *North Road, Caernarfon,
North Wales, LL55 1BD.* Close to Caernarfon
Castle, overlooking Menai Straights .
Lounge/bar & restaurant. Spa-bath.
Open: All year (not Xmas/New Year)
01286 674602 (also fax) *menaiview@
walesuk4.freeserve.co.uk*
menaiviewguesthouse.co.uk **D:** £17.50–
£22.50 **S:** £22.50–£27.00 **Beds:** 3F 2T 4D
Baths: 9 En ➤ ⊡ ⊁ × ⊻ ▥ ⅙ 🌣 cc

Capel Curig

SH7258

Llugwy Guest House, *Capel Curig,
Betws-y-Coed, LL24 0ES.* Warm welcome,
hearty breakfast, forest and mountain
scenery. Easily located. **Open:** All year
01690 720218 Mrs Cousins **D:** £17.50–£18.50
S: £19.50–£21.50 **Beds:** 2D 1T 1S **Baths:** 2
Sh ❒ (4) ⊁ ⊡ ⊻ ▥ 🌣 cc

Can-yr-Afon, *Capel Curig, Betwys-y-
Coed, LL24 0DR.* Situated in the heart of
Snowdonia, near the famous Swallow Falls.
Open: All year (not Xmas/New Year)
01690 720375 Mrs Berry **D:** £18.00 **Beds:** 1F
1T 1D **Baths:** 2 Pr ➤ (10) ❒ (5) ⊁ ⊻ ▥ ⅙ 🌣

Capel Garmon

SH8155

**Llannerch Goch C17th Country
House,** *Capel Garmon, Betws-Y-Coed,
North Wales, LL26 0RL.* Peaceful. 2 miles from
picturesque Betws-y-Coed. Clear views of
Snowdonia. **Open:** All year (not Xmas)
01690 710261 Eirian Ifan *eirianifan@
talk21.com* www.croeso-betws.org.
uk/acc/bb/llangoch.htm **D:** £20.00–£25.00
S: £25.00–£28.00 **Beds:** 3D **Baths:** 3 En
➤ (8) ❒ (3) ⊁ ⊡ ⊻ ▥ 🌣

Colwyn Bay

SH8479   ⚐ *Wheatsheaf, White Lion, Queen's
Head, Mountain View, Weatherspoons*

St Margaret's Hotel, *Princes Drive,
Colwyn Bay, LL29 8RP.* **Open:** All year
01492 532718 *stmargarets@hotelcb.fsnet.co.uk*
www.st-margarets-hotel.co.uk **D:** £21.00–
£25.00 **S:** £21.00–£25.00 **Beds:** 1F 5D 3T 2S
Baths: 11 En ➤ ❒ (10) ⊡ ⊁ × ⊻ ▥ ⅙ 🌣 cc
Recommended by Which? Good Bed and
Breakfast Guide. We are dedicated to the
well-being of our guests. We provide
excellent food & comfortable bedrooms all
with ensuite facilities. Ground floor
accommodation available. Own car park. A
'particularly pleasant place to stay'.

**Cabin Hill
Hotel,** *College
Avenue, Colwyn
Bay, LL28 4NT.*
Quiet residential
area within easy
working
distance to promenade & shops. **Open:** All
year (not Xmas/New Year) **Grades:** WTB 2
Star, AA 3 Diamond
01492 544568 Mrs Ashton **D:** £18.00
S: £18.00 **Beds:** 2F 3T 3D 2S **Baths:** 7 En 2
Sh ➤ ❒ (2) ⊡ ⊁ × ⊻ ▥ 🌣

Planning a longer stay? Always
ask for any special rates

Llysfaen House, 58 Llysfaen Road, Colwyn Bay, LL29 9HB.

Magnificent sea views. Lovely house. Warm welcome. Good home cooking. Cleanliness assured. **Open:** All year **Grades:** WTB 2 Star **01492 517859** Mr & Mrs Hooker *views@compuserve.com* **D:** £18.00–£20.00 **S:** £18.00–£20.00 **Beds:** 1T 1D 1S **Baths:** 1 Sh ⏰ 🅿 (2) ⅟ 📺 🛏 ✕ 🆅 🛍 ♨

Holly Tree Guest House, 11 Marine Road, Colwyn Bay, LL29 8PH.

Friendly comfortable Victorian house. Modern facilities. Central to everywhere. Parking. **Open:** All year (not Xmas) **01492 533254** Mr Ross **Fax: 01492 532332** *ross@nationwideisp.net* www.avaweb.co.uk/hollytree **D:** £20.00 **S:** £25.00 **Beds:** 2F 4D 3T **Baths:** 9 En ⏰ 🅿 (12) 📺 🆅 🛍 ♨ cc

Marine Hotel, West Promenade, Colwyn Bay, LL28 4BP.

Superbly situated seafront hotel offering spacious comfortable ensuite accommodation. **Open:** Easter to Oct **01492 530295 & 0870 1689400** Mr & Mrs Owen *resrvations@marinehotel.co.uk* www.marinehotel.co.uk **D:** £23.00–£24.00 **S:** £24.00–£29.00 **Beds:** 1F 6D 4T 3S **Baths:** 12 En 2 Pr ⏰ 🅿 (10) ⅟ 📺 🛏 ✕ 🆅 🛍 ♨ cc

Edelweiss Hotel, Lawson Road, Colwyn Bay, LL29 8HD.

C19th house, wooded garden, a slice of countryside by the sea. **Open:** All year **01492 532314** Mr Baker **Fax: 01492 534707** www.hotelvenues.com/edelweiss **D:** £21.00 **S:** £21.00 **Beds:** 4F 10T 10D 3S **Baths:** 27 En ⏰ 🅿 (25) 📺 🛏 ✕ 🆅 🛍 ♿ ♨ cc

Conwy

SH7777

Henllys Farm, Llechwedd, Conwy, Gwynedd, LL32 8DJ.

Ideally placed for touring Snowdonia, North Wales coast, Bodnant Gardens. **Open:** Easter to Nov **Grades:** WTB 3 Star Farm **01492 593269** C Roberts **D:** £18.00–£20.00 **S:** £25.00 **Beds:** 1F 1D **Baths:** 2 En ⏰ 🅿 ⅟ 📺 ✕ 🛍 ♨

Glan Heulog Guest House, Llanrwst Road, Conwy, LL32 8LT.

Warm welcome, comfortable beds & a hearty breakfast in a fine Victorian house. **Open:** All year **01492 593845** Mr & Mrs Watson-Jones **D:** £15.00–£20.00 **S:** £18.00–£24.00 **Beds:** 2F 2D 2T **Baths:** 5 En 1 Pr ⏰ 🅿 (7) ⅟ 📺 🛏 ✕ 🆅 🛍 ♨ cc

Bryn Derwen, Woodlands, Conwy, LL32 8LT.

Warm welcome to a gracious Victorian home with panoramic views. **Open:** All year **01492 596134** Mr & Mrs Smith **D:** £18.00–£20.00 **S:** £18.00–£25.00 **Beds:** 1F 2D 3T **Baths:** 6 En ⏰ 🅿 (8) ⅟ 📺 🛏 🆅 🛍 ♨ ♨

Fishermore, Llanrwst Road, Conwy, LL32 8HP.

Rural setting close to historic town, NT gardens and mountains. **Open:** Easter to Oct **01492 592891** Mrs Dyer *dyers@tesco.net* www.northwalesbandb.co.uk **D:** £17.00–£19.00 **Beds:** 1T 2D **Baths:** 2 En 1 Pr 🅿 (5) ⅟ 📺 🛍 ♨

Craig-y-don

SH7981

Hotel Carmen, 4 Carmen Sylva Road, Craig-y-don, Llandudno, LL30 1LZ.

Situated in the quieter part with easy parking. Excellent cuisine. **Open:** Easter to Oct **01492 876361** Mr Newberry *peter1@plynch-greatxscape.net* **D:** £20.00–£23.00 **S:** £23.50–£25.00 **Beds:** 2F 9D 3T **Baths:** 16 En ⏰ (9) ⅟ 📺 ✕ 🆅 🛍 ♨ ♨

Criccieth

SH4938 ◀ The Goat, Gwyndy Hotel, The Feathers, Bryncir Arms

Mor Heli Guest House, Min Y Mor, Criccieth, LL52 0EL.

On sea front overlooking 100 miles of coastline. All bedrooms sea views. **Open:** All year (not Xmas) **01766 522802** **Fax: 01766 522878** **D:** £20.00 **S:** £20.00 **Beds:** 2F 2D 1T **Baths:** 5 Pr ⏰ 🅿 🆅 🛏 ✕ 🆅 ♨

Bron Rhiw Hotel, Caernarfon Road, Criccieth, LL52 0AP.

Cosy, comfortable non-smoking hotel; a truly warm welcome awaits you. **Open:** Mar to Nov **Grades:** WTB 3 Star Hotel **01766 522257** Ms Woodhouse & Ms S C Williams **D:** £22.50–£26.00 **S:** £22.50–£26.00 **Beds:** 7D 1T 1F **Baths:** 7 En 2 Pr ⏰ 🅿 (4) ⅟ 📺 🛏 ✕ 🆅 🛍 ♨ cc

Craig y Mor Guest House, West Parade, Criccieth, LL52 0EN.

Tastefully upgraded Victorian house overlooking sea into Tremadog Bay. **Open:** Mar to Oct **Grades:** WTB 3 Star GH **01766 522830** Mr Williamson *enquiries@craig-y-mor-bandb.freeserve.co.uk* **D:** £21.00–£25.00 **S:** £21.00 **Beds:** 4F 2D **Baths:** 6 En ⏰ 🅿 (6) 📺 🆅 🛍 ♨

Awel Mor Hotel, 29 Marine Terrace, Criccieth, LL52 0EL.

Spectacular sea views. An ideal base for touring Snowdonia/Llyn Peninsula. **Open:** Mar to Nov **Grades:** WTB 2 Star **01766 522086 (also fax)** Mr & Mrs Petch *sue.petch@virgin.net* www.cricciethaccommodation.com **D:** £19.00–£24.00 **S:** £19.00–£24.00 **Beds:** 3F 2T 2D 2S **Baths:** 8 En 1 Pr ⏰ ⅟ 🆅 ✕ 🆅 🛍 ♨ cc

Min y Gaer Hotel, Porthmadog Road, Criccieth, North West Wales, LL52 0HP.

Comfortable hotel with delightful coastal views. Ideal for touring Snowdonia. **Open:** Easter to Oct **Grades:** WTB 2 Star, AA 4 Diamond, RAC 4 Diamond **01766 522151** Mr Murray **Fax: 01766 523540** *info@minygaerhotel.co.uk* www.minygaerhotel.co.uk **D:** £22.00–£26.00 **S:** £22.00–£26.00 **Beds:** 3F 4D 2T 1S **Baths:** 10 En ⏰ 🅿 (12) ⅟ 📺 🆅 🛍 ♨ cc

Dinas Mawddwy

SH8514

The Red Lion Inn, Dinas-Mawddwy, Machynlleth, Powys, SY20 9JA.

Centuries-old traditional inn. In heart of village amid scenic beauty of southern Snowdonia. **Open:** All year (not Xmas) **01650 531247 (also fax)** Mr Jenkins *llewcoch@yahoo.co.uk* www.llewcoch.freeserve.co.uk **D:** £20.00–£25.00 **S:** £20.00–£25.00 **Beds:** 3F 1D 1T 1S **Baths:** 3 En ⏰ 🅿 (30) 📺 🛏 ✕ 🆅 🛍 ♨

Dolgellau

SH7217 ◀ George III, Royal Ship, The Unicorn, Torrent Hotel

Trem Idris, Llanelltyd, Dolgellau, LL40 2TB.

Open: All year **01341 423776** Ms Jones **D:** £20.00–£23.00 **S:** £25.00–£30.00 **Beds:** 1F 1D **Baths:** 2 En ⏰ (3) 🅿 (4) ⅟ 📺 🆅 🛍 ♨

Homely guest house situated in an elevated position overlooking the beautiful Mawddach estuary. One family ensuite and one double ensuite with own lounge. Both with colour TV, tea/coffee facilities. Ideally situated for exploring the coast and also Snowdonia. Non-smokers, please.

Fronallt, *Dolgellau, LL40 2YL.* Listed cottage, large conservatory, edge of town, several pets. Orchard/lawns. **Open:** All year (not Xmas/New Year) **01341 422296 & 07751 514261 (M)** Mrs Price **Fax: 01341 422286 D:** £20.00–£25.00 **S:** £20.00–£25.00 **Beds:** 1D 1F **Baths:** 1 En 1 Pr ☎ ⓟ (0) ⓥ ⓧ ⛤ ♨

Tanyfron, *Arran Road, Dolgellau, North West Wales, LL40 2AA.* Modernised, former stone farmhouse, beautiful views. 'Wales in Bloom' Winners 2000. **Open:** Feb to Nov **Grades:** WTB 4 Star **01341 422638** Mrs Rowlands **Fax: 01341 421251** *rowlands@tanyfron.freeserve.co.uk* www.tanyfron.co.uk **D:** £20.00–£22.00 **Beds:** 1D 2T **Baths:** 3 En ☎ (5) ⓟ (6) ⓨ ⓥ ⛤ ♨

Ivy House, *Finsbury Square, Dolgellau, North West Wales, LL40 1RF.* Attractive country town guest house, good home-made food. **Open:** All year **01341 422535** Mrs Bamford **Fax: 01341 422689** *marg.bamford@btconnect.com* www.ukworld.net/ivyhouse **D:** £19.00–£25.00 **S:** £25.00–£33.00 **Beds:** 1F 3D 2T **Baths:** 3 En 2 Sh ☎ ⓟ ⓧ ⓧ ⛤ ♨ cc

Dolgun Uchaf, *Dolgellau, Gwynedd, LL40 2AB.* Perfectly situated for exploring beautiful Snowdonia National Park. Warm welcome, farmhouse breakfast. **Open:** All year **Grades:** WTB 3 Star **01341 422269 Fax: 01341 422285** *dolgunuchaf@guesthousessnowdonia.com* www.guesthousessnowdonia.com **D:** £18.00–£22.00 **S:** £18.00–£25.00 **Beds:** 1F 1T 1D **Baths:** 3 En ☎ ⓟ ⓥ ⓧ ⛤ ♨ cc

Esgair Wen Newydd, *Garreg Feurig, Llanfachreth Road, Dolgellau, LL40 2YA.* Bungalow, mountain views. Relaxed atmosphere. High standards. Double Award Winners. **Open:** Feb to Nov **Grades:** WTB 3 Star **01341 423952** Mrs Westwood **D:** £19.50 **S:** £21.50 **Beds:** 2D 1T **Baths:** 1 Sh ☎ (3) ⓟ (3) ⓨ ⓧ ⓥ ⛤ ♨

Arosfyr Farm, *Penycefn Road, Dolgellau, North West Wales, LL40 2YP.* Homely friendly, farmhouse, flower, gardens, mountainous, views, self-catering available. **Open:** All year **Grades:** WTB 2 Star **01341 422355 (also fax)** Mrs Skeel Jones **D:** £16.00–£17.50 **S:** £19.00 **Beds:** 1F 1D 1T **Baths:** 2 Sh ☎ ⓟ (4) ⓥ ⓧ ⓥ ⛤ ♨

Gwelafon, *Caedeintur, Dolgellau, Gwynedd, LL40 2YS.* Beautiful, high-standard, spacious house. Panoramic views of town and mountains. **Open:** Mar to Oct **Grades:** WTB 3 Star **01341 422634** Mrs Roberts **D:** £20.00–£25.00 **S:** £20.00 **Beds:** 1D 2S **Baths:** 1 En 1 Sh ☎ (7) ⓟ (3) ⓨ ⓥ ⓥ ⛤ ♨

Penbryn Croft, *Cader Road, Dolgellau, LL40 1RN.* At the foot of Cader Idris, 200 yards Dolgellau centre, retaining original features. **Open:** All year (not Xmas) **01341 422815** Ms Dunne **D:** £20.00–£24.00 **Beds:** 4T 2D **Baths:** 2 Sh ☎ ⓥ ⓧ ⛤ ♨

Aber Cottage, *Smithfield Street, Dolgellau, Gwynedd, LL40 1DE.* Cosy market town stone cottage (1811) foot of Cader - comfortable welcoming hospitality. **Open:** All year **01341 422460 & 07885 547052 (M)** Mrs Mullin *gmullini@compuserve.com* **D:** £18.00–£20.00 **S:** £18.50–£25.00 **Beds:** 1F 2D 1T 2S **Baths:** 2 En 1 Pr 2 Sh ⓧ ⓥ ⛤ ♨

Dolwyddelan

SH7352   🖙 *Ty Gwyn, Gwydyr Hotel, Elan's Castle Hotel*

Rhiw y Goch, *Pont y Pant, Dolwyddelan, LL25 0PQ.* **Open:** All year (not Xmas/New Year) **01690 750231** Mrs King **D:** £22.00 **S:** £22.00 **Beds:** 3D **Baths:** 2 Sh ⓟ (4) ⓨ ⓧ ⓧ ⓥ ⛤. A warm welcome awaits you in our comfortable, lovely C17th longhouse. Set in 35 acres with wonderful gardens and marvellous views over Lledr Valley. Perfect for total relaxation and walking, exploring Snowdonia, coastline, castles, Bodnant Gardens, Portmeirion. Choice of traditional or continental breakfasts.

Bryn Tirion Farm, *Dolwyddelan, LL25 0JD.* C12th Dolwyddelan Castle, 100 yards on the farm, picturesque Lledr Valley. **Open:** All year (not Xmas/New Year) **Grades:** WTB 2 Star **01690 750366** Mrs Price **D:** £25.00 **S:** £25.00 **Beds:** 1F 1D 1T **Baths:** 2 En 1 Pr ☎ (12) ⓟ ⓨ ⓥ ⛤ ♨

Dwygyfylchi

SH7377

Caerlyr Hall Hotel, *Conwy Old Road, Dwygyfylchi, Penmaenmawr, LL34 6SW.* Country house set in natural amphitheatre with sea & mountain views. **Open:** All year **Grades:** WTB 3 Star **01492 623518** Mr & Mrs Warner **Fax: 01492 622070** www.caerlyrhallhotel.co.uk **D:** £25.00–£30.00 **S:** £25.00–£30.00 **Beds:** 5F 1D 3T **Baths:** 8 En 1 Pr ☎ ⓟ (12) ⓥ ⓧ ⓧ ⓥ ⛤ ♨ cc

Dyffryn Ardudwy

SH5822   🖙 *Ty Mawr*

Parc yr Onnen, *Dyffryn Ardudwy, Gwynedd, LL44 2DU.* Rural setting; superb sea and mountain views by peaceful lane. **Open:** All year **Grades:** WTB 3 Star **01341 247033** Mr & Mrs Bethell **D:** £18.00–£20.00 **S:** £20.00 **Beds:** 1D 1T **Baths:** 2 En ⓟ (3) ⓨ ⓧ ⓧ ⓥ ⛤ ♨

Friog

SH6112

Einion House, *Friog, Fairbourne, North West Wales, LL38 2NX.* Lovely old house in marvellous walking country. Good home cooking. **Open:** All year (not Xmas/New Year) **01341 250644** Mr Waterhouse *enquiries@einionhouse.freeserve.co.uk* **D:** £20.50 **S:** £22.00–£27.50 **Beds:** 4D 1T 1S **Baths:** 4 En 2 Pr ⓥ ⓧ ⓥ ⛤ ♨

Gellilydan

SH6839   🖙 *Bryn Arms*

Tyddyn Du Farm, *Gellilydan, Blaenau Ffestiniog, Gwynedd, LL41 4RB.* Superb central location. Spectacular scenery. Converted barn and stable suites. **Open:** All year **Grades:** WTB 5 Star **01766 590281** Ms Williams *stil@snowdonia.farm.com* www.snowdonia.farm.com **D:** £23.00–£35.00 **S:** £25.00 ☎ ⓟ (10) ⓨ ⓥ ⓧ ⓧ ⓥ ⛤ ♿ ♨

Gwynfryn, *Gellilydan, Blaenau Ffestiniog, LL41 4EA.* Detached house with character in a small village. Friendly welcome. **Open:** All year **01766 590225** Mrs Jones **D:** £17.00–£18.00 **Beds:** 1T 1D **Baths:** 1 Sh ☎ ⓟ ⓨ ⓥ ⓧ ⛤ ♨

Planning a longer stay? Always ask for any special rates

Glan-yr-afon (Druid)

SJ0242

Llawr-Betws Farm, *Glan-yr-afon, Corwen, LL21 0HD.* Modern, comfortable farmhouse. **Open:** All year
01490 460224 Mr Jones **D:** £15.00 **S:** £10.00 **Beds:** 3F 2D 1S **Baths:** 2 Pr (2)

Glan-yr-afon (Fron-goch)

SH9040

The Old Post Office, *Glan-yr-afon, Corwen, Gwynedd, LL21 0HB.* 7 miles Bala Lake. Incorporating North Wales's only dedicated teddy bear shop. **Open:** All year
01490 460231 (also fax) H J Jennings **D:** £18.00–£19.50 **S:** £16.00–£19.50 **Beds:** 1F 1D 1T 1S **Baths:** 2 En 1 Sh (2)

Harlech

SH5831

Tyddyn Y Gwynt, *Harlech, LL46 2TH.* Perfect setting for peaceful holidays; warm welcome, tourist attractions, mountain scenery, beaches. Car essential. **Open:** All year
01766 780298 Mrs Jones **D:** £16.00 **S:** £16.00–£18.00 **Beds:** 1F 1D 1T 1S **Baths:** 1 Sh (8)

Lion Hotel, *Harlech, LL46 2SG.* 2 bars & restaurant. Double rooms ensuite. **Open:** All year
01766 780731 Mr Morris **D:** £22.00 **S:** £34.00 **Beds:** 3D 1T 2S **Baths:** 5 En 1 Pr (3)

Gwrach Ynys Country Guest House, *Ynys, Talsarnau, North West Wales, LL47 6TS.* Edwardian country house, tranquil rural setting, close sea & mountains in Snowdonia NP. **Open:** Mar to Nov
01766 780742 Mrs Williams **Fax: 01766 781199** *gwynfor@btinternet.com* www.grwachynys.co.uk **D:** £23.00–£28.00 **S:** £30.00–£35.00 **Beds:** 2F 2D 2T 1S **Baths:** 6 En (8)

Llanbedr-y-cennin

SH7569

Waen Newydd, *Llanbedr-y-Cennin, Conwy, Gwynedd, LL32 8UR.* Secluded C19th farmhouse. Spacious grounds high above village in open countryside. **Open:** All year
01492 660527 Ms Jeffries **Fax: 01492 660155** *pauline@jeffries.fsnet.co.uk* www.waen-newydd.co.uk **D:** £20.00 **S:** £25.00 **Beds:** 1T **Baths:** 1 En

Llanberis

SH5760

Lake View Hotel, *Tan Y Pant, Llanberis, Caernarfon, LL55 4EL.* **Open:** All year **Grades:** WTB 2 Star, AA 2 Star, RAC 2 Star
01286 870422 Fax: 01286 872591 *reception@lakeviewhotel.co.uk* lakeviewhotel.co.uk **D:** £24.00–£29.00 **S:** £32.00 **Beds:** 3F 2T 5D **Baths:** 9 En 1 Pr (30) **cc**
Welsh country cottage hotel in unique position, overlooking Lake Padarn. Stunning mountains & lakes with many visitor amenities in nearby Llanberis (incl. mountain railway to Snowdon). Warm & cosy hotel, candlelit restaurant with choice of menus & full Welsh breakfast. Conference facilities now available.

Beech Bank Guest House, *High Street, Llanberis, Caernarfon, LL55 4EN.* Small friendly lake and mountain views, close to all amenities. **Open:** All year (not Xmas)
01286 870414 Mrs Watson **D:** £17.00 **S:** £17.50 **Beds:** 1F 2D 1T **Baths:** 1 Sh (6)

Mount Pleasant Hotel, *High Street, Llanberis, Caernarfon, LL55 4HA.* Friendly, family-run, foot of Snowdon. Cosy bar, real ale. **Open:** All year
01286 870395 (also fax) Mrs Waterton *mph@waterton.org.uk* www.waterton.org.uk **D:** £18.00–£22.00 **S:** £18.00–£25.00 **Beds:** 2F 3D 1T 2S **Baths:** 1 En 2 Sh (8)

Marteg, *High Street, Llanberis, Caernarfon, Gwynedd, LL55 4HA.* Within walking distance of Snowdon mountain railway and all amenities. **Open:** Jan to Dec **Grades:** WTB 3 Star
01286 870207 Mr & Mrs Torr *carol@marteg.freeserve.co.uk* **D:** £22.00–£25.00 **S:** £22.00–£25.00 **Beds:** 2D 1T **Baths:** 3 En (4)

Llandanwg

SH5628 *Victoria Inn*

Glan-Y-Gors, *Llandanwg, Harlech, LL46 2SD.* 3 star guest house near beach, with panoramic views. **Open:** All year **Grades:** WTB 3 Star
01341 241410 G Evans **D:** £17.00–£18.00 **S:** £19.00

BATHROOMS
En = Ensuite
Pr = Private
Sh = Shared

Llandudno

SH7881 *The Albert, Cross Keys, Kings Head*

Dolwen Guest House, *7 St Mary's Road, Llandudno, LL30 2UB.* **Open:** Mar to Nov **Grades:** WTB 3 Star
01492 877757 *david.kyffin@tesco.net* **D:** £18.00–£20.00 **Beds:** 1F 1T 1D **Baths:** 1 En 1 Pr 1 Sh
A warm welcome awaits you at Dolwen, which is a very comfortable Edwardian house. We are situated in the town centre within easy reach of beach, shops and theatre. Llandudno is ideally situated for exploring Snowdonia and North Wales.

Craiglands, *7 Carmen Sylva Road, Craig-y-don, Llandudno, LL30 1LZ.* Beautiful Victorian private hotel, seconds walk to Promenade. Delicious breakfasts. **Open:** Easter to Nov
01492 875090 (also fax) Mrs Jones www.craiglandsllandudno.co.uk **D:** £20.00–£25.00 **S:** £25.00 **Beds:** 2T 3D **Baths:** 6 En

Karden Hotel, *16 Charlton Street, Llandudno, LL30 2AA.* Pleasant clean and comfortable family-run hotel. Close to beach, shops, train and coach stations. Vegetarian diets available. **Open:** All year
01492 879347 Mr Roberts **D:** £15.00–£17.50 **S:** £15.00–£16.00 **Beds:** 4F 4D 2S **Baths:** 4 En 2 Sh

The Sunningdale, *59 Church Walks, Llandudno, Ll30 1HL.* Superior accommodation with lovely gardens and views. Walk to town and promenade. **Open:** All year (not Xmas/New Year)
01492 875915 (also fax) www.sunningdalebandb.co.uk **D:** £25.00–£32.50 **S:** £35.00–£40.00 **Beds:** 1T 5D **Baths:** 6 En (6)

Fernbank, *9 Chapel Street, Llandudno, LL30 2SY.* Friendly family-run guest house in a town centre location. **Open:** All year (not Xmas) **Grades:** WTB 1 Star GH
01492 877251 *jim42@lineone.net* website.lineone.net/~fernbank/ **D:** £12.00–£14.00 **S:** £12.00 **Beds:** 3F 2D 3T 1S **Baths:** 3 En 3 Sh 3

Stoneleigh Guest House, 10 St David Road, Llandudno, LL30 2UL. Family-run seaside guest house offering good home cooking. **Open:** All year **Grades:** WTB 3 Star
01492 875056 Mr & Mrs Roberts **D:** £20.00–£22.00 **S:** £25.00–£27.00 **Beds:** 1F 1T 2D **Baths:** 4 En ♿ 🅿 (6) ⌇ 📺 ⌂ ✕ 🎄 ▥ ⚓

Hafod y Mor Hotel, Hill Terrace, Llandudno, LL30 2LS. Superb views from all rooms. Quiet, comfortable, excellent food. **Open:** Easter to Sept
01492 876925 *enquiries@hafodymor.co.uk* www.hafodymor.co.uk **D:** £22.00–£29.00 **S:** £27.00–£29.00 **Beds:** 2F 2T 4D 2S **Baths:** 10 En ♿ 🅿 (4) 📺 ⌂ ▥ ⚓ cc

Ashdale Guest House, 3 St Davids Road, Llandudno, LL30 2UL. Halfway between North and West Shores, ideal for exploring Llandudno. **Open:** All year (not Xmas/New Year)
01492 877089 *bnbmccann@lineone.net* **D:** £19.00–£22.00 **S:** £19.00–£22.00 **Beds:** 2F 2T 4D 1S **Baths:** 7 En 2 Sh ♿ (4) 🅿 (3) ⌇ 📺 ⌂ ▥ ⚓

The Grafton Hotel, Promenade, Craig y Don, Llandudno, North West Wales, LL30 1BG. Only 5 mins' walk from North Wales Theatre and Conference Centre. **Open:** All year (not Xmas/New Year)
01492 876814 Derek Griffiths **Fax:** 01492 879073 *derek@thegraftonhotel.com* www.hotellink.co.uk/llandudno/grafton. html **D:** £20.00–£28.00 **S:** £22.00–£28.00 **Beds:** 2F 10D 5T 5S **Baths:** 22 Pr ♿ 🅿 (12) 📺 ⌂ ▥ ♿1

Ty Glandwr, 42 St Mary's Road, Llandudno, Gwynedd, LL30 2UE. Elegant Edwardian town house, convenient public transport, theatre, castles, Snowdonia. **Open:** All year (not Xmas/New Year)
01492 871802 Mrs Beesley *tyglandwr@talk21.com* **D:** £19.00–£25.00 **S:** £22.00–£25.00 **Beds:** 1T 2D 1S **Baths:** 3 En 1 Pr ⌇ 📺 ⌂ ▥ ⚓

Llanegryn
SH6005

Cefn Coch Country Guest House, Llanegryn, Tywyn, LL36 9SD. A former coaching inn, enjoying a beautiful garden with spectacular views. **Open:** Mar to Oct
01654 712193 (also fax) Mrs Sylvester *david@cefncoch.force9.co.uk* www.cefncoch. force9.co.uk/ **D:** £22.00–£24.00 **S:** £22.00–£29.00 **Beds:** 2D 3T **Baths:** 3 En 2 Sh ♿ (14) 🅿 (11) ⌇ ✕ 📺 ⌂ ⚓

Llanelltyd
SH7119   🍺 Halfway House

Trem Idris, Llanelltyd, Dolgellau, LL40 2TB. Homely guest house situated in an elevated position overlooking the beautiful Mawddach estuary. **Open:** All year
01341 423776 Ms Jones **D:** £20.00–£23.00 **S:** £25.00–£30.00 **Beds:** 1F 1D **Baths:** 2 En ♿ (3) 🅿 (4) ⌇ 📺 ⌂ ▥ ⚓

Llanfachreth
SH7522

Maesneuadd Farm, Llanfachreth, Dolgellau, LL40 2DH. 200-year-old farmhouse situated in a peaceful Area of Outstanding Natural Beauty. **Open:** All year
01341 450256 Mrs Smith **D:** £18.00–£22.00 **S:** £22.00 **Beds:** 1F 1T 1D **Baths:** 3 En ♿ (3) 🅿 (6) ⌇ 📺 ✕ ⌂ ▥ ⚓

Llanfaglan
SH4760

The White House, Llanfaglan, Caernarfon, LL54 5RA. Quiet, isolated country house. Magnificent views to mountains and sea. **Open:** Mar to Nov **Grades:** WTB 3 Star
01286 673003 Mr Bayles *rwbayles@sjms.co.uk* **D:** £20.00–£22.00 **S:** £26.00 **Beds:** 2D 2T **Baths:** 3 En 1 Pr ♿ 🅿 (8) 📺 ⌂ ⚓

Llanfairfechan
SH6874

Rhiwiau Riding Centre, Llanfairfechan, LL33 0EH. Magnificent views of mountains and sea; riding and walking. **Open:** All year (not Xmas)
01248 680094 Mrs Hill **Fax:** 01248 681143 *rhiwiau@aol.com* www.rhiwiau.co.uk **D:** £15.00–£16.50 **S:** £15.00–£16.50 **Beds:** 1F 1D 4T 1S **Baths:** 3 Sh ♿ 🅿 (12) ⌇ 📺 ✕ ⌂ ▥ ⚓

Llanfihangel Glyn Myfyr
SH9949   🍺 Saracen's Head

The Old Rectory, Llanfihangel Glyn Myfyr, Cerrigydrudion, Corwen, LL21 9UN. Luxury rural retreat in idyllic surroundings. Perfectly situated for exploring N. Wales. **Open:** All year (not Xmas/New Year)
01490 420568 & 07850 241795 (M) Mr & Mrs Hughes **Fax:** 01490 420773 **D:** £24.00–£30.00 **S:** £24.00–£30.00 **Beds:** 2F **Baths:** 1 En 1 Pr ♿ 🅿 (3) 📺 ⌂ ⌂ ▥ ⚓

Llanfor
SH9336

Melin Meloch (Water Mill) Guest House, Llanfor, Bala, Gwynedd, LL23 7DP. One of the most picturesque buildings and water gardens in this area. **Open:** All year
01678 520101 B M Gunn *theoldmill@mac.com* www.melin.co.uk **D:** £20.00–£25.00 **S:** £36.00–£42.00 **Beds:** 1F 3D 2T 2S **Baths:** 4 En 2 Pr 1 Sh ♿ (4) 🅿 (10) ⌇ 📺 ⌂ ▥ ⚓

Please respect a B&B's wishes regarding children, animals and smoking

Llangower
SH9032

Plas Gower, Llangower, Bala, LL23 7BY. A warm welcome in an old stone house, beautiful views over Bala Lake, mountains. **Open:** All year (not Xmas)
01678 520431 (also fax) Mrs Foreman *olwen@plasgower.com* **D:** £19.50–£21.00 **S:** £20.00–£22.00 **Beds:** 1D 1T **Baths:** 1 En 1 Pr ♿ 🅿 (4) ⌇ 📺 ⌂ ▥ ⚓

Llangwnnadl
SH2033

Carrog Farm, Llangwnnadl, Pwllheli, Gwynedd, LL53 7NL. Set in beautiful farmland with the sea visible across fields. **Open:** Easter to Oct
01758 770694 Mrs Thomas **D:** £18.00–£20.00 **S:** £18.00–£20.00 **Beds:** 3F 1T 1D 1S **Baths:** 2 Sh 📺 ✕ ▥ ⚓

Llanrwst
SH7961

Nant-Y-Glyn Isaf, Llanrwst, Gwynedd, LL26 0NN. Working farm. Spacious, well-appointed rooms. Magnificent views, quiet location. **Open:** All year
01492 640327 (also fax) Mrs Evans *maievans@farmwales.co.uk* **D:** £19.50–£25.00 **Beds:** 1F 1D 1T **Baths:** 3 En ♿ (8) 🅿 ⌇ 📺 ⌂ ▥ ⚓

Argoed Guest House, Crafnant Road, Trefriw, Conwy, LL27 OJX. Comfortable old-fashioned house. Beautiful views of Conwy Valley. Easy access to mountains & coast. **Open:** All year **Grades:** WTB 3 Star
01492 640091 Mr & Mrs Phillips *keithandanne@netscapeonline.co.uk* www.argoed.co.uk **D:** £18.50–£23.00 **S:** £28.50–£33.00 **Beds:** 3D 1T **Baths:** 1 En 3 Sh 🅿 (5) ⌇ 📺 ✕ ⌂ ⚓

Llansannan
SH9366   🍺 Saracens Head, Red Lion, Black Lion, Sportsman's Arms

Cleiriach, Llansannan, Denbigh, Conwy, LL16 5LW. Beautiful scenery, off the beaten track. Quiet and peaceful location. **Open:** All year (not Xmas/New Year)
01745 870695 Mrs Williams *katycleiriach@aol.com* **D:** £10.00–£15.00 **S:** £12.00–£17.00 **Beds:** 1T 1D **Baths:** 1 Sh ♿ 🅿 (2) ⌇ 📺 ⌂ ✕ ▥ ⚓

Planning a longer stay? Always ask for any special rates

Llanuwchllyn
SH8730

Eifionydd, Llanuwchllyn, Bala, LL23 7UB. Beautiful location; warm welcome. Enjoy your vacation in well-appointed rooms. **Open:** Easter to Oct **01678 540622 (also fax)** Mr & Mrs Murray *eifionydd@ntlworld.com* www.eifionydd.com **D:** £20.00–£22.00 **S:** £25.00–£27.00 **Beds:** 1F 1T 1D **Baths:** 3 En ⊁ 🅿 ⊬ 📺 Ⅴ 🏕 ♨

Llanycil
SH9134

Abercelyn Guest House, Llanycil, Bala, Gwynedd, LL23 7YF. Georgian residence set in landscaped gardens overlooking Bala Lake. **Open:** All year (not Xmas/New Year) **01678 521109** Mrs Hind **D:** £22.50–£26.50 **S:** £25.00–£28.00 **Beds:** 2F 1T 1D **Baths:** 2 En 1 Pr ⊁ 🅿 (4) ⊬ 📺 Ⅴ 🏕 ♨ cc

Llechwedd
SH7676

Henllys Farm, Llechwedd, Conwy, Gwynedd, LL32 8DJ. Ideally placed for touring Snowdonia, North Wales coast, Bodnant Gardens. **Open:** Easter to Nov **Grades:** WTB 3 Star Farm **01492 593269** C Roberts **D:** £18.00–£20.00 **S:** £25.00 **Beds:** 1F 1D **Baths:** 2 En ⊁ 🅿 ⊬ 📺 ✕ 🏕 ♨

Maentwrog
SH6640

The Old Rectory Hotel, Maentwrog, Blaenau Ffestiniog, LL41 4HN. Main house/budget annexe, 3 acre garden. Informal, peaceful. **Open:** All year (not Xmas) **01766 590305 (also fax)** Ms Herbert **D:** £22.50–£32.50 **S:** £30.00–£45.00 **Beds:** 2F 6D 2T **Baths:** 10 En ⊁ 🅿 📺 ★ ✕ Ⅴ 🏕 ♨

Manod
SH7244 ◀ Shilton Arms

Cae Du, Manod, Blaenau Ffestiniog, Gwynedd, LL41 4BB. **Open:** All year (not Xmas/New Year) **01766 830847 (also fax)** S Ashe *caedu@tinyworld.co.uk* **D:** £24.00 **S:** £24.00 **Beds:** 1T 2D **Baths:** 3 En 🅿 (4) ⊬ 📺 ✕ Ⅴ 🏕 ♨ Picturesque C16th former farmhouse in magnificent mountain setting. Ensuite rooms, stunning panoramic views, home-cooking and a warm, friendly atmosphere make Cae Du an ideal base for exploring the wonders of Snowdonia. It's our home - make it yours.

Morfa Nefyn
SH2840 ◀ Cliffs Inn

Llys Olwen Guest House, Morfa Nefyn, Pwllheli, LL53 6BT. Established 1972. Approximately 500 metres from beautiful cliff walks. **Open:** Mar to Nov **01758 720493 (also fax)** *llysolwen@beeb.net* www.llysolwen.co.uk **D:** £21.50 **S:** £21.50 **Beds:** 4F 2T 2D **Baths:** 4 Sh ⊬ 📺 ✕ Ⅴ 🏕 ♨

Mynytho
SH3030

Paradwys, Mynytho, Pwllheli, Gwynedd, LL53 7SA. Lovely sea and mountain views. Peaceful ideal walking, golfing, brochure **Open:** All year (not Xmas/New Year) **01758 740876 (also fax)** Mrs Roberts **D:** £20.00 **Beds:** 1D **Baths:** 1P 🅿 (1) ⊬ 📺 🏕 ♨

Nant Peris
SH6058

Tyn y Ffynnon, Nant Peris, Caernarfon, Gwynedd, LL55 4UH. Beautiful spacious cottage set in 2 acres below Llanberis pass. **Open:** All year (not Xmas/New Year) **01286 871723** Mrs Kelly **D:** £18.00–£20.00 **S:** £20.00–£22.00 **Beds:** 1F 1T 2D **Baths:** 1 Pr 1 Sh ⊱ 🅿 (6) 📺 ★ 🏕

Nantgwynant
SH6250

Pen-Y-Gwryd Hotel, Nantgwynant, Caernarfon, LL55 4NT. Famous mountain inn, heart of Snowdonia. Associated with Lord Hunt's Everest team (1953). **Open:** Mar to Nov **01286 870211** Mrs Pullee **D:** £23.00–£28.00 **S:** £33.00–£38.00 **Beds:** 16F 6T 9D 1S **Baths:** 5 En 5 Pr 5 Sh 🅿 (30) ★ ✕ 🏕 ♨ &

Pant-glas
SH4747

Hen Ysgol Old School Pant-glas, Bwlch Derwin, Pant-glas, Garndolbenmaen, LL51 9EQ. Beautiful mid-C19th Welsh country school. Perfectly situated for the attractions of Snowdonia. **Open:** All year **01286 660701** T J Gibbins *oldschoolpantglas@talk21.com* **D:** £17.00–£20.00 **S:** £20.00–£25.00 **Beds:** 2F 1D 1T **Baths:** 1 En 1 Sh ⊱ 🅿 (6) ⊬ 📺 ★ ✕ Ⅴ 🏕 ♨ & ♨

All details shown are as supplied by B&B owners in Autumn 2001

Penmaenmawr
SH7176

Bodlwyfan, Conwy Road, Penmaenmawr, LL34 6BL. Beautiful Victorian house, overlooking the sea and mountains in quiet location. **Open:** All year **01492 623506** Mr Anderton *Bodlwyfan@totalise.co.uk* www.bodlwyfan.co.uk **D:** £17.50–£20.00 **S:** £18.00–£21.00 **Beds:** 1F 3T 2D 1S **Baths:** 2 Sh ⊱ 🅿 (6) 📺 ★ ✕ Ⅴ 🏕 ♨

Pennal
SH6900

Marchlyn, Aberdovey Road, Pennal, Machynlleth, SY20 9YS. Quiet location near Aberdovey on a Welsh-speaking working farm. **Open:** All year **01654 702018** **D:** £17.00–£20.00 **S:** £17.00–£20.00 **Beds:** 1F 4D 1T 1S **Baths:** 2 En 1 Pr

Penrhyn Bay
SH8281

Awelfor Guest House, 74 Llandudno Road, Penrhyn Bay, Llandudno, LL30 3HA. Immaculately presented, close to all amenities. Completely non-smoking establishment. **Open:** All year **01492 549373** *i+s@awelfor.freeserve.co.uk* ukworld.net/awelfor **D:** £20.00–£23.00 **Beds:** 6D **Baths:** 6 Pr 🅿 ⊬ 📺 ✕ 🏕 ♨

Penrhyndeudraeth
SH6139

Wenallt, Penrhyndeudraeth, Gwynedd, LL48 6PW. Award-winning guest house near Portmeirion. Lovely views. Ideal touring base. **Open:** All year (not Xmas/New Year) **01766 770321 (also fax)** G Cooper *gh@wenallt.globalnet.co.uk* **D:** £22.00–£25.00 **S:** £27.00–£30.00 **Beds:** 1T 2D **Baths:** 3 En 🅿 (3) ⊬ 📺 ✕ Ⅴ 🏕 ♨ cc

Pentrefoelas
SH8751 ◀ Foelas Hotel, Saracens, White Horse

Maesgwyn Farm, Pentrefoelas, Betws-Y-Coed, LL24 0LR. On the edge of Snowdonia National Park in quiet countryside. **Open:** Apr to Nov **Grades:** WTB 3 Star **01690 770668** F Jones **D:** £34.00–£36.00 **S:** £18.00–£20.00 **Beds:** 1F 1D **Baths:** 1 Sh ⊱ 🅿 📺 ★ ♨

Penygroes
SH4753

Lleuar Fawr, Penygroes, Caernarfon, Gwynedd, LL54 6PB. Peaceful location, substantial farmhouse breakfast, comfortable bedrooms. Warm Welsh welcome. **Open:** All year (not Xmas) **01286 660268 (also fax)** Mrs Lloyd Jones *user@lleuarfawr.fsnet.co.uk* **D:** £18.00–£20.00 **S:** £25.00 **Beds:** 1D 1T **Baths:** 2 En ☲ ☐ ⌇ ☑ ★ ☑ ★

Porthmadog
SH5638

35 Madog Street, Porthmadog, LL49 9BU. Modern terraced house. **Open:** All year (not Xmas) **01766 512843** Mrs Skellern **D:** £14.00–£15.00 **S:** £14.00–£15.00 **Beds:** 1F 1D 1T 1S **Baths:** 2 Sh ☲ (3) ☑ ★ ☑ ▥ ★

Pwllheli
SH3735

Rhosydd, 26 Glan Cymerau, Pwllheli, Gwynedd, LL53 5PU. Detached bungalow, outskirts Pwllheli. Near beach, leisure centre, golf, marina. **Open:** All year **01758 612956** S Williams *helen@rhosydd.freeserve.co.uk* **D:** £15.00–£17.50 **S:** £15.00–£17.50 **Beds:** 1T 1D **Baths:** 1 En 1 Sh ☲ ☐ ⌇ ☑ ★ ☑ ▥ ☐ ✲ ▴

Rhos-on-Sea
SH8381 ⚓ The Ship, Toad Hall

Sunnyside, 146 Dinerth Road, Rhos-on-Sea, Colwyn Bay, LL28 4YF. Central for sea, country and mountains, golf and cricket, welcoming. **Open:** Easter to Oct **Grades:** WTB 2 Star **01492 544048** Mrs Pryce **D:** £16.00 **S:** £20.00 **Beds:** 1T 1D **Baths:** 1 Sh ☲ ⌇ ☑ ▥ ▴

Ashmount Hotel, College Avenue, Rhos-on-Sea, Colwyn Bay, LL28 4NT. Christian hotel, perfectly situated for beaches and Snowdonia. **Open:** All year **01492 545479 D:** £20.00–£28.50 **S:** £20.00–£28.50 **Beds:** 3F 3T 4D 2S **Baths:** 11 En 1 Pr ☲ (0) ☐ (8) ⌇ ☑ ▥ ☐ ✲ ▴

Sunnydowns Hotel, 66 Abbey Road, Rhos-on-Sea, Conwy, LL28 4NU. Perfectly situated for exploring Snowdonia and North Wales beaches. **Open:** All year **Grades:** WTB 3 Star **01492 544256** Mr Willington **Fax: 01492 543223** *sunnydowns-hotel@tinyworld.co.uk* www.hotelnorthwales.co.uk **D:** £22.00–£29.00 **S:** £25.00–£35.00 **Beds:** 3F 3T 7D 2S **Baths:** 15 En ☲ ☐ (12) ☑ ★ ☑ ▥ ✲ ▴

Rhyd
SH6341

Bodlondeb Farm, Rhyd, Penrhyndeudraeth, LL48 6ST. In small rural hamlet near Ffestiniog Railway, Portmeirion, mountains & beaches. **Open:** Easter to Oct **01766 770640** *bodlondeb.rhyd@virginnet.co.uk* **D:** £17.50–£19.50 **S:** £17.50–£19.50 **Beds:** 1T 2D ☲ ☐ (2) ⌇ ☑ ✕ ▥

Rhyd-Ddu
SH5652

Ffridd Isaf, Rhyd-Ddu, Caernarfon, LL54 6TN. **Open:** All year **01766 890452** Mrs Kent **D:** £15.00 **S:** £15.00 **Beds:** 1T 1D **Baths:** 1 Sh ☐ ⌇ ✕ ☑ ▥

Restored C16th Grade II farmhouse, beneath Snowdon. Magnificent views, log fires, good food, muddy boots no problem, secure parking. Last house before the summit on the Rhyd Ddu path. Come and get away from it all.

Rhydymain
SH7921

Rhaeadr Wnion, Rhydymain, Dolgellau, LL40 2AH. Victorian house in 3 acres of gardens in beautiful Snowdonia. **Open:** All year **01341 450249** Mrs Perkins **D:** £17.00–£19.00 **S:** £18.00–£20.00 **Beds:** 2D 2T **Baths:** 2 En 1 Sh ☲ ☐ (5) ☑ ★ ✕ ☑ ▥ ▴

Rowen
SH7571

Bulkeley Mill, Rowen, Conwy, Gwynedd, LL32 8TS. Converted water mill set in beautiful gardens and mountain scenery. **Open:** All year **Grades:** WTB 4 Star **01492 650481** Mrs Seville *SKenseville@cs.com* www.bulkeley-mill.co.uk **D:** £27.00–£29.00 **S:** £32.00 **Beds:** 1F 1D **Baths:** 2 En ☲ ☐ (4) ⌇ ☑ ★ ☑ ▥ ▴

Saron (Llanwnda)
SH4658

Pengwern Farm, Saron, Llanwnda, Caernarfon, LL54 5UH. Charming, spacious farmhouse of character, beautifully situated between mountains & sea. **Open:** Jan to Nov **Grades:** WTB 4 Star **01286 831500 & 07778 411780 (M)** Mr & Mrs Rowlands **Fax: 01286 831500** *jhjgr@enterprise.net* **D:** £24.00–£28.00 **S:** £30.00–£38.00 **Beds:** 1T 2D **Baths:** 3 En ☲ ☐ ⌇ ✕ ☑ ▥ ▴ cc

Tal-y-llyn
SH7109

Dolffanog Fach, Tal-y-llyn, Tywyn, North West Wales, LL36 9AJ. Stone-built farmhouse situated near Tal-y-llyn Lake and Cader Idris mountain. **Open:** Mar to Nov **Grades:** WTB 3 Star **01654 761235 (also fax)** Mrs Pugh *meirwen.pughe@talk21.com* www.walestouristsonline.co.uk **D:** £22.00–£24.00 **S:** £25.00–£30.00 **Beds:** 1T 2D **Baths:** 3 En ☲ ⌇ ☑ ★ ☑ ▥ ▴

Minffordd Hotel, Tal-y-Llyn, Tywyn, LL36 9AJ. 400 year old ex-drovers inn. **Open:** All year **01654 761665** G Holt **Fax: 01654 761517** *hotel@minffordd.com* www.minffordd.com **D:** £39.00–£61.00 **S:** £47.00–£69.00 **Beds:** 2T 4D 1S **Baths:** 7 En ☲ (13) ☐ (14) ⌇ ★ ✕ ☑ ▥ ☐ ✲ ▴ cc

Talsarnau
SH6135

Estuary Motel Y Traeth, Talsarnau, LL47 6TA. Snowdonia National Park, near Portmeirion. All modern ground floor rooms. **Open:** All year **01766 771155** Mr King **D:** £16.50–£24.50 **S:** £34.50 **Beds:** 1F 5D 4T **Baths:** 10 En ☲ (16) ☐ (30) ☑ ★ ✕ ☑ ▥ ☐ ✲ ▴ cc

Trawsfynydd
SH7035 ⚓ The Grapes, Rhiw Goch, Bryn Arms

Old Mill Farmhouse, Fron Oleu Farm, Trawsfynydd, Blaenau Ffestiniog, LL41 4UN. Olde Worlde charm, wonderful scenery, friendly animals, large good breakfasts. **Open:** All year **Grades:** WTB 3 Star **01766 540397 (also fax)** Miss Roberts & Mrs P Osborne *penmar@oldmillfarm.spacomputers.com* **D:** £21.00–£27.00 **S:** £21.00–£27.00 **Beds:** 2F 3D 2T **Baths:** 7 En ☲ ☐ (10) ⌇ ☑ ★ ✕ ☑ ▥ ☐ ✲ ▴

Trefriw
SH7863 ⚓ Fairy Falls, Old Ship

Craig y Felin, Trefriw, Betws-y-Coed, LL27 0RJ. Beautiful peaceful location. Panoramic views. Close to lakes & mountains. **Open:** All year **Grades:** WTB 3 Star **01492 640868** *gordon@couperg.freeserve.co.uk* www.snowdonia.org.uk/trefriw **D:** £20.00–£23.00 **S:** £30.00–£32.00 **Beds:** 1F 1T 1D **Baths:** 2 En 1 Pr ☲ ☐ (5) ⌇ ☑ ★ ☑ ▥ ▴

Argoed Guest House, *Crafnant Road, Trefriw, Conwy, LL27 OJX.* Comfortable old-fashioned house. Beautiful views of Conwy Valley. Easy access to mountains & coast. **Open:** All year **Grades:** WTB 3 Star **01492 640091** Mr & Mrs Phillips *keithandanne@netscapeonline.co.uk* www.argoed.co.uk **D:** £18.50–£23.00 **S:** £28.50–£33.00 **Beds:** 3D 1T **Baths:** 1 En 3 Sh ⊞ (5) ⊬ 📺 ✕ 🏠 ♨

Hafod Country Hotel, *Trefriw, Conwy, LL27 0RQ.* Converted farmhouse on edge of village nestling into heavily wooded Snowdonian foothills. **Open:** Feb to Jan **01492 640029 Fax: 01492 641351** *hafod@breathemail.net* www.hafodhouse.co.uk **D:** £27.50–£40.00 **S:** £32.00–£47.50 **Beds:** 4D 2T **Baths:** 6 En ⓢ ⊞ (12) ⊬ 📺 ✦ ✕ Ⅴ 🏠 ❀ ♨ cc

Tremadog
SH5640

Ty Newydd Guest House, *30 Dublin Street, Tremadog, Porthmadog, Gwynedd, LL49 9RH.* Close to the Ffestiniog Railway, Portmeirion and many other attractions. **Open:** All year (not Xmas/New Year) **01766 512553** *johnjulieo@aol.com* porthmadog.co.uk/tynewydd **D:** £18.50–£21.00 **S:** £28.50–£31.00 **Beds:** 1F 1T 2D **Baths:** 1 Sh ⓢ ⊞ (6) 📺 ✦ 🏠 ♨

Planning a longer stay? Always ask for any special rates

Tywyn (Aberdovey)
SH5800

Hendy Farm, *Tywyn, LL36 9RU.* Comfortable farmhouse near town and beach. Own halt on Tal-y-llyn railway. **Open:** Easter to Oct **Grades:** WTB 3 Star **01654 710457 (also fax)** Mrs Lloyd-Jones *jones@farmline.com* www.croesocaderidris.co.uk-hendy **D:** £20.00–£24.00 **S:** £24.00–£29.00 **Beds:** 2D 1T **Baths:** 2 En 1 Pr ⓢ ⊞ ⊬ 📺 ✦ Ⅴ 🏠 ♨

Pembrokeshire

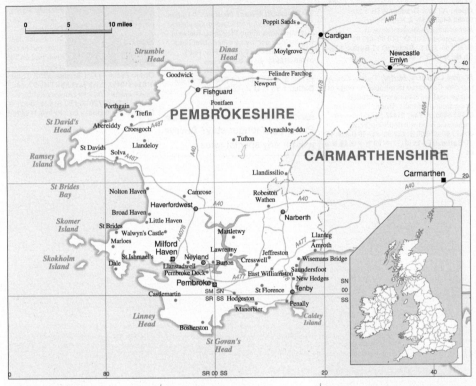

Abereiddy

SM7931 🍺 The Sloop

Murmur-y-Mor, *Abereiddy, Haverfordwest, Pembs, SA62 6DS.* Beautiful views. Ideal for Coastal Path walkers, near Abereiddy Beach. **Open:** Mar to Oct **01348 831670** L A Thomas **D:** £20.00 **S:** £25.00 **Beds:** 1T 1S **Baths:** 1 En 1 Sh
🛏(12) 🅿(4) ⅙ 📺 ✕ Ⓥ 🍽 🐾

Amroth

SN1607

Beach Haven Guest House, *Amroth, Narberth, SA67 8NG.* Quiet picturesque location, magnificent sea views, transfers available. **Open:** All year (not Xmas) **01834 813310** Mr Rickards **D:** £15.00–£17.00 **S:** £15.00–£17.00 **Beds:** 2D 1T 1S **Baths:** 2 En 2 Sh 🛏(5) 🅿 📺 🐾 ✕ Ⓥ 🐾

Planning a longer stay? Always ask for any special rates

Ashdale Guest House, Amroth,

Narberth, Pembs, SA67 8NA. Well situated for:- beaches, theme parks, Dylan Thomas, Irish ferries **Open:** Easter to Nov **01834 813853 (also fax)** Mrs Williamson **D:** £15.00–£16.00 **S:** £15.00–£16.00 **Beds:** 2F 1T 2D 1S **Baths:** 2 Sh 🛏 🅿(6) 📺 🐾 ✕ Ⓥ 🍽 ⅙ 🐾

Bosherston

SR9694

Trefalen Farm, *Bosherston, Pembroke, SA71 5DR.* 100 yards to Broadhaven beach. Short walk to village pub. **Open:** All year **Grades:** WTB 2 Star **01646 661643** Mr & Mrs Giardelli **Fax: 01646 661626** *trefalen@aol.com* **D:** £19.00 **S:** £22.50 **Beds:** 1S 1T 1D **Baths:** 2 Sh 🛏 🅿 ⅙ 📺 Ⓥ 🍽

Cornerstones, *Bosherston, Pembroke, SA71 5DN.* Immaculately contained accommodation. Half mile Broadhaven Beach & Coastal Path. **Open:** All year (not Xmas/New Year) **01646 661660** Mrs James **D:** £20.00–£21.00 **S:** £25.00 **Beds:** 1T 1F **Baths:** 1 En 1 Pr 🛏 🅿(4) ⅙ 📺 🐾 🍽 🐾

Broad Haven

SM8613 🍺 *Galleon Inn, Royal Hotel, Swan Inn, The Castle, St Brides Inn*

Lion Rock, *Broad Haven, Haverfordwest, Pembs, SA62 3JP.* **Open:** Feb to Oct **Grades:** WTB 3 Star **01437 781645** Mrs Main **Fax: 01437 781203** *lion.rock@btinternet.com* www.stayatlionrock. co.uk **D:** £24.00–£32.00 **S:** £24.00–£28.00 **Beds:** 1T 2D 2S **Baths:** 3 En 2 Pr 🛏(7) 🅿(8) ⅙ 📺 🐾 ✕ Ⓥ 🍽 🐾
Stunning quiet cliff top position in Pembrokeshire Coast National Park. Single storey house. Views over St. Brides Bay and Skomer Island. Owner Access to Coast Path. Warm welcome, help and information on local walks, beaches and watersports. Not to be missed.

BATHROOMS

En = Ensuite
Pr = Private
Sh = Shared

BEDROOMS

D = Double
T = Twin
S = Single
F = Family

Anchor Guest House, The Sea Front, *Broad Haven, Haverfordwest, Pembs, SA62 3JN.* Opposite sandy beach with magnificent sea views. Adjacent cafe, shop, restaurant. Coastal Path. **Open:** All year (not Xmas/New Year) **Grades:** WTB 2 Star **01437 781051** Mrs Morgan **Fax:** 01437 781050 *anch@bdhn.fsnet.co.uk* www.anchor-guesthouse.co.uk **D:** £18.00–£27.00 **S:** £20.00–£27.00 **Beds:** 8 **Baths:** 8 En ⌂ 🅿 📺 Ⅴ ⬛ ♨

Burton
SM9805

Beggars Reach Hotel, *Burton, Milford Haven, Pembs, SA73 1PD.* Quiet country house hotel. Ideal base for exploring Pembrokeshire. **Open:** All year **01646 600700** W Smallman **Fax:** 01646 600560 **D:** £26.25 **S:** £32.50 **Beds:** 3F 1T 6D 2S **Baths:** 12 En 🅿 (25) ⚸ 📺 ✕ ⬛ ✳ ♨ cc

Camrose
SM9219

The Fold, Cleddau Lodge, *Camrose, Haverfordwest, Pembrokeshire, SA62 6HY.* Converted C17th farmhouse, gardens, woodlands, river with otters, view of Preseli. **Open:** Easter to Oct **01437 710640** Mrs Brookman **Fax:** 01437 710663 *cleddau.lodge@btinternet.com* **D:** £15.00–£18.50 **S:** £18.50 **Beds:** 1D **Baths:** 1 Pr ⌂ 🅿 (10) 📺 Ⅴ ⬛ ♨

Castlemartin
SR9198

Chapel Farm, *Castlemartin, Pembroke, Pembrokeshire, SA71 5HW.* Large comfortable farmhouse overlooking sea, offers relaxing holidays to unwind. **Open:** All year **01646 661312 (also fax)** Mrs Smith *chapelfarm@aol.com* **D:** £20.00–£22.00 **S:** £25.00–£27.00 **Beds:** 1F 1T **Baths:** 1 En 1 Pr ⌂ 🅿 (10) 📺 ✕ Ⅴ ⬛ ♨

RATES

D = Price range per person sharing in a double or twin room

S = Price range for a single room

Planning a longer stay? Always ask for any special rates

Cresswell
SN0506

Cresswell House, *Cresswell Quay, Kilgetty, Pembs, SA68 0TE.* **Open:** All year **01646 651435** Mr Wright *phil@ cresswellhouse.co.uk* www.cresswellhouse.co.uk **D:** £25.00–£30.00 **S:** £30.00 **Beds:** 1T 2D **Baths:** 2 En 1 Pr 🅿 ✕ ⬛ ♨ Set on the banks of the Cleddau Estuary, centrally situated for South Pembrokeshire and coast. Wonderful food, breakfast choices include kedgeree, home-made fishcakes, smoked salmon, scrambled eggs. All rooms with a view, 100 yards from traditional ale house.

Croesgoch
SM8230

Bank House Farm, *Abereiddy Road, Croesgoch, Haverfordwest, Pembs, SA62 6XZ.* Picturesque sea views on country road between Croes-goch and Abereiddy. **Open:** All year (not Xmas) **01348 831305** Mrs Lloyd **D:** £15.00–£18.00 **S:** £18.00 **Beds:** 1D 1T **Baths:** 1 Sh ⌂ 🅿 📺 ♨ ✕ Ⅴ ⬛ ♨

Maes y Ffynnon, *Penygroes, Croesgoch, Haverfordwest, Pembs, SA62 5JN.* Modern large bungalow, private grounds; ideal base for walking or touring. **Open:** Mar to Oct **01348 831319** Mrs Evans **D:** £16.50 **S:** £18.50 **Beds:** 1F 1T **Baths:** 2 En ⌂ 🅿 (4) ⚸ 📺 ♨ Ⅴ ⬛ ♨

Dale
SM8005 ⊲ *The Griffin Inn*

Point Farm, *Dale, Haverfordwest, Pembs, SA62 3RD.* Large country house on sea front. Adjacent to Pembrokeshire coast. **Open:** All year (not Xmas/New Year) **Grades:** WTB 4 Star **01646 636254** Mrs Webber **D:** £25.00 **Beds:** 1T 2D 1S **Baths:** 2 En 🅿 (4) ⚸ 📺 ⬛ ♨

Please respect a B&B's wishes regarding children, animals and smoking

The Post House Hotel, *Dale, Haverfordwest, Pembs, SA62 3RE.* Licensed hotel, ensuite bedrooms, plus suite of rooms, TV lounge, conservatory. **Open:** Mar to Jan **01646 636201** Mr & Mrs Riley *posthousedale@ talk21.com* **D:** £24.00–£27.50 **S:** £26.00 **Beds:** 2T 2D 1S **Baths:** 5 En 🅿 (6) 📺 ✕ Ⅴ ♨

East Williamston
SN0904 ⊲ *The Lodge*

Whitehall Lodge, *Meadow Close Green, East Williamston, Tenby, SA70 8RU.* Perfect location for Pembrokeshire Coast. Warm welcome. Comfortable, quality accommodation. **Open:** All year **Grades:** WTB 3 Star **01834 812682** Mrs Keys **Fax:** 01834 810077 *ruth.keys@lineone.net* www.whitehall-lodge.co.uk **D:** £20.00–£25.00 **S:** £30.00 **Beds:** 1F 1T 1D **Baths:** 1 En 1 Sh ⌂ 🅿 ⚸ 📺 Ⅴ ⬛ ♨

Felindre Farchog
SN1039

The Salutation Inn, *Felindre Farchog, Crymych, Pembs, SA41 3UY.* **Open:** All year **Grades:** WTB 3 Star **01239 820564 Fax:** 01239 820355 *johndenley@ aol.com* www.salutationcountryhotel.co.uk **D:** £24.00–£30.00 **S:** £32.00–£38.00 **Beds:** 2F 2T 4D **Baths:** 8 En 🅿 ⚸ 📺 ♨ ✕ Ⅴ ⬛ ♨ C16th coaching inn in Pembrokeshire Coast National Park. Ground floor rooms. Ideally situated for walking, riding, golf, beaches etc. Riverside restaurant. Good food served using local produce. Bar meals, good selection of wines and real ales. Friendly staff.

BATHROOMS

En = Ensuite
Pr = Private
Sh = Shared

National Grid References given are for villages, towns and cities – not for individual houses

Fishguard

SM9537   🍴 *Cartref Hotel, Old Coach House*

Cartref Hotel, *13-19 High Street, Fishguard, Pembs, SA65 9AW.* Friendly, renovated hotel. Excellent family accommodation. Free garage. Open 24 hours. **Open:** All year **Grades:** WTB 2 Star, AA 2 Star
01348 872430 Mrs Bjorkquist **Fax: 01348 873664** *cartef@themail.co.uk* **D:** £24.00–£27.00 **S:** £32.00–£36.00 **Beds:** 2F 2D 2T 4S **Baths:** 10 En 🔄 🅿 (3) 📺 📻 🛏 ✕ 🔽 ▥, 🏃 cc

Stanley House, *Quay Road, Goodwick, Fishguard, Pembs, SA64 0BS.* Overlooking Fishguard, ferry terminal and bay and Preseli Hills beyond. **Open:** All year **Grades:** WTB 2 Diamond, AA 3 Diamond
01348 873024 Mr Hendrie **D:** £16.50–£19.50 **S:** £19.50 **Beds:** 2F 2D 2T 1S **Baths:** 1 En 1 Pr 2 Sh 🔄 🅿 (3) 📺 🔽 ▥, 🏃

The Beach House, *Fishguard Harbour, Fishguard, Pembs, SA64 0DH.* Seafront guest house on Fishguard Harbour (village location). **Open:** All year
01348 872085 & 01348 875491 Mrs Wagstaff **D:** £13.50–£18.00 **S:** £13.50–£18.00 **Beds:** 2F 2D 2T 2S **Baths:** 2 En 3 Pr 1 Sh 🔄 🅿 (5) 📺 🛏 🔽 ▥, 🏃 cc

Goodwick

SM9438   🍴 *Rose & Crown*

Ivybridge, *Drim Mill, Dyffryn, Goodwick, Fishguard, Pembs, SA64 0FT.* **Open:** All year (not Xmas)

Grades: AA 3 Diamond
01348 875366 Mrs Davies **Fax: 01348 872338** *ivybridge@cwcom.net* www.ivybridge.cwc.net **D:** £20.50–£24.50 **S:** £19.50–£24.50 **Beds:** 4F 4D 2T 1S **Baths:** 4 En 2 Pr 🔄 🅿 (12) 📺 🛏 ✕ 🔽 ▥, 🏃 cc
Friendly family-run guest house. Ensuite rooms with colour TV and hot drinks tray. Good home cooking, heated indoor pool, licensed, vegetarians welcome. Ample off-road parking. 2 minutes ferry port. Early/ late visitors welcome.

Stanley House, *Quay Road, Goodwick, Fishguard, Pembs, SA64 0BS.* Overlooking Fishguard, ferry terminal and bay and Preseli Hills beyond. **Open:** All year **Grades:** WTB 2 Diamond, AA 3 Diamond
01348 873024 Mr Hendrie **D:** £16.50–£19.50 **S:** £19.50 **Beds:** 2F 2D 2T 1S **Baths:** 1 En 1 Pr 2 Sh 🔄 🅿 (3) 📺 🔽 ▥, 🏃

Haverfordwest

SM9515   🍴 *Masons' Arms, Rising Sun*

East Hook Farm, *Portfield Gate, Haverfordwest, SA62 3LN.* **Open:** All year (not Xmas/New Year) **Grades:** WTB 3 Star
01437 762211 Fax: 01437 760310 *jen.easthook@virgin.net* www.easthookfarmhouse.co.uk **D:** £22.50–£24.00 **S:** £30.00 **Beds:** 1F 1T 1D **Baths:** 2 En 1 Pr 🅿 (3) 📺 🔽 🛏 ✕ 🔽 ▥, 🏃
Unwind in our Georgian farmhouse surrounded by peaceful unspoilt countryside. Large rooms furnished with antiques and all the home comforts you could wish for. Selection for breakfast, local produce used. Evening meals available by arrangement. Perfect place to relax.

Greenways, *Shoals Hook Lane, Haverfordwest, Pembs, SA61 2XN.* Quiet retreat. The best in the west - find peace in our heaven on earth **Open:** All year **Grades:** WTB 2 Star
01437 762345 Mr Tuson *keith2son@aol.co.uk* www.greenways-guesthouse.com **D:** £20.00–£25.00 **S:** £20.00–£25.00 **Beds:** 1F 3D 3T 4S **Baths:** 3 En 1 Sh 🔄 🅿 🔽 🛏 ✕ 🔽 ▥, 🏃 🏃

Cuckoo Mill, *Pelcomb Bridge, St Davids Road, Haverfordwest, Pembs, SA62 6EA.* Central Pembrokeshire. Quietly situated. Excellent food. Genuine welcome. Unrestricted access. **Open:** All year
01437 762139 Mrs Davies **D:** £20.00–£25.00 **S:** £20.00–£25.00 **Beds:** 1F 2D 1T **Baths:** 2 Sh 🔄 🅿 (4) 📺 🛏 ✕ 🔽 ▥, 🏃 🏃

College Guest House, *93 Hill Street, Haverfordwest, Pembs, SA61 1QX.* Friendly welcome, spacious rooms, good Welsh breakfast, smoking rooms available. **Open:** All year (not Xmas/New Year)
01437 763710 (also fax) Mr Gerson **D:** £20.00–£23.00 **S:** £22.00–£25.00 **Beds:** 1D 5T 2S 1F **Baths:** 9 En 🔄 ✕ 🔽 ▥, 🏃 cc

Hodgeston

SS0399

Rosedene, *Hodgeston, Freshwater East, Pembroke, SA71 5JU.* Peaceful village location, 1 mile Coastal Footpath. Affordable luxury! **Open:** Easter to Nov
01646 672586 E A Fallon **Fax:** 01646 672855 *eileen@rosedene85.freeserve.co.uk* www.rosedene85.freeserve.co.uk **D:** £22.00–£27.00 **S:** £32.00–£37.00 **Beds:** 1F 1D **Baths:** 7 En 🔄 🅿 (7) ✕ 📺 ✕ 🔽 ▥, 🏃1 🏃 cc

Please respect a B&B's wishes regarding children, animals and smoking

RATES
D = Price range per person sharing in a double or twin room
S = Price range for a single room

Jeffreston

SN0806

Jeffreyston Grange, *Jeffreyston, Kilgetty, Pembs, SA68 0RE.* Warm, friendly, cosy & comfortable, peacefully located opposite the ancient parish church. **Open:** All year (not Xmas)
01646 650159 Mr & Mrs Hesslegrave **Fax:** 01646 651124 **D:** £18.00–£20.00 **S:** £18.00–£20.00 **Beds:** 1D 2T **Baths:** 2 En 1 Pr 🔄 🅿 (4) ✕ 📺 ✕ ▥, 🏃

Lawrenny

SN0106

Knowles Farm, *Lawrenny, Kilgetty, Pembs, SA68 0PX.* Lovely farmhouse overlooking organic farm on estuary. Birding, walking, boating, relaxing! **Open:** Easter to Oct
01834 891221 V Lort-Phillips **Fax:** 01834 891344 *ginilp@lawrenny.org.uk* www.lawrenny.org.uk **D:** £23.00–£25.00 **S:** £33.00–£35.00 **Beds:** 1T 2D **Baths:** 2 En 1 Pr 🔄 🅿 (20) ✕ 📺 🛏 ✕ 🔽 ▥, 🏃

Little Haven

SM8512   🍴 *Royal Hotel*

The Bower Farm, *Little Haven, Haverfordwest, Pembs, SA62 3TY.* Friendly farmhouse, fantastic sea views. **Open:** All year
01437 781554 Mr Birt-Llewellin *bowerfarm@ lineone.net* www.a1tourism.com/uk/bower. html **D:** £22.00–£29.00 **S:** £25.00–£30.00 **Beds:** 2F 1D 1T 1S **Baths:** 5 En 🔄 🅿 (10) 📺 🛏 ✕ 🔽 ▥, 🏃

Whitegates, *Settlands Hill, Little Haven, Haverfordwest, Pembs, SA62 3LA.* Overlooking the sea & lovely fishing village, good eating places within easy walking distance. **Open:** All year (not Xmas)
01437 781386 (also fax) Mr & Mrs Llewellin **D:** £20.00–£27.00 **S:** £30.00–£35.00 **Beds:** 1F 4D 1T **Baths:** 4 En 2 Pr 🔄 🅿 📺 🛏 ✕ 🔽 ▥, 🏃 🏃 cc

Llandeloy

SM8526

Lochmeyler Farm, *Llandeloy, Pen Y Cwm, Solva, St Davids, Pembs, SA62 6LL.* **Open:** All year (not Xmas/New Year) **Grades:** WTB 4 Star, AA 5 Diamond, RAC 5 Diamond
01348 837724 Mrs Jones **Fax: 01348 837622** *stay@lochmeyler.co.uk* www.lochmeyler.co.uk **D:** £20.00–£25.00 **S:** £20.00–£35.00 **Beds:** 8F 4T 2D 2S **Baths:** 16 En (30) cc
Located on a working dairy farm. An ideal position for all enthusiasts of rural Wales. Just a short distance from the Coastal Path and the city of St Davids. Plenty of local attractions for all ages.

Llandissilio

SN1221

Plas-y-Brodyr, *Rhydwilym, Llandissilio, Clynderwen, Pembs, SA66 7QH.* Peaceful farmhouse in unspoilt valley. Ideal base for exploring Pembrokeshire & West Wales. **Open:** Mar to Nov
01437 563771 Mrs Pogson **Fax: 01437 563294** *janet@farmhols.freeserve.co.uk* www.pfh.co.uk/plasybrodyr **D:** £20.00–£22.00 **S:** £25.00–£27.00 **Beds:** 2D **Baths:** 1 En 1 Pr (4)

Llanstadwell

SM9405 *Ferry House*

Ferry House Inn, *Hazelbeach, Llanstadwell, Milford Haven, Pembs, SA73 1EG.* **Open:** All year (not Xmas/New Year)
01646 600270 Mr & Mrs Philips **Fax: 01646 600567** *ferryhouseinn@freenet.co.uk* **D:** £20.00–£25.00 **S:** £30.00–£45.00 **Beds:** 2F 2T 1D 1S **Baths:** 6 En (15) cc
Watch the yachts and the waves roll by and enjoy fresh fish, real ales, a hearty Welsh breakfast and a warm welcome at our family run riverside village inn, alongside Pembrokeshire's beautiful Coastal Path.

The Old Mill, *Hazelbeach, Llanstadwell, Milford Haven, Pembs, SA73 1EG.* Old farmhouse situated on Coastal Path between Milford and Hazelbeach. **Open:** Easter to Nov
01646 690190 Mr Johnson *sheila@hickey.ntlworld.com* **D:** £15.00–£20.00 **S:** £15.00–£20.00 **Beds:** 1F 2D **Baths:** 2 Sh (20)

Llanteg

SN1810

East Llanteg Farm, *Llanteg, Amroth, SA67 8QA.* **Open:** All year (not Xmas/New Year) **Grades:** WTB 3 Star
01834 831336 Mrs Lloyd *john@pembrokeshireholiday.co.uk* www.pembrokeshireholiday.co.uk **D:** £18.00–£22.00 **S:** £18.00–£22.00 **Beds:** 1F 1T 1D **Baths:** 2 En 1 Pr (6)
The comfortable farmhouse is ideally located for exploring Pembrokeshire's renowned coastline. Tenby is near at hand and Amroth only minutes away. Comfortable bedrooms with colour televisions and private guests' lounge. Good traditional home cooking. Guests assured of a warm welcome.

Manorbier

SS0697

Fernley Lodge, *Manorbier, Tenby, Pembs, SA70 7TH.* Victorian house in heart of beautiful coastal village. **Open:** All year (not Xmas)
01834 871226 Mrs Cowper *fernleylodge@yahoo.com* **D:** £20.00–£25.00 **S:** £20.00–£25.00 **Beds:** 1F 1D **Baths:** 2 Pr (2) (7)

Marloes

SM7908

Foxdale, *Glebe Lane, Marloes, Haverfordwest, Pembs, SA62 3AX.* Set in the heart of the Pembrokeshire Coast National Park. Close to cliff path. **Open:** All year
01646 636243 Mrs Roddam-King **Fax: 01646 636982** *foxdale.guest.house@totalise.co.uk* www.foxdale.guest.house.8m.com **D:** £18.00–£25.00 **S:** £23.00–£30.00 **Beds:** 2D 1T **Baths:** 2 En 1 Pr (6)

BEDROOMS
D = Double
T = Twin
S = Single
F = Family

BATHROOMS
En = Ensuite
Pr = Private
Sh = Shared

Martletwy

SN0310

The Peacock Tea Garden, *Hoarstone House, Martletwy, Narberth, Pembs, SA67 8AZ.* A country house situated in its own grounds amidst the tranquil countryside of mid-Pembrokeshire. **Open:** Easter to Sept
01834 891707 (also fax) Mrs Mooney *peacock@jpmarketing.co.uk* www.jpmarketing.co.uk/peacock **D:** £20.50–£27.50 **S:** £25.50–£32.50 **Beds:** 1D 1T **Baths:** 1 En 1 Pr (8)

Milford Haven

SM9005

Kings Arms, *Hakin Point, Milford Haven, Pembs, SA73 3DG.* Public house, home-cooking. Near marina, railway station. All rooms sea view. **Open:** All year (not Xmas)
01646 693478 Mrs Hutchings **D:** £25.00–£30.00 **S:** £17.50 **Beds:** 2F 4T **Baths:** 3 En

Moylgrove

SN1144 *Golden Lion, Ferry Inn*

Trewidwal, *Moylegrove, Cardigan, Pembrokeshire, SA43 3BY.* Beautiful ex-farmhouse. Extensive grounds. Outstanding coastal and hill views. Peace. **Open:** All year (not Xmas/New Year) **Grades:** WTB 2 Star
01239 881651 Mr & Mrs Bloss *alan.bloss@btinternet.com* www.trewidwal.co.uk **D:** £18.00–£22.00 **S:** £20.00–£24.00 **Beds:** 1F 1D **Baths:** 1 En 1 Pr (4)

The Old Vicarage, *Moylgrove, Cardigan, Pembrokeshire, SA43 3BN.* Edwardian country house, large lawned garden and glorious sea view. **Open:** Mar to Nov
01239 881231 Patricia & David Phillips **Fax: 01239 881341** *stay@old-vic.co.uk* www.old-vic.co.uk **D:** £24.00–£28.00 **S:** £26.00–£38.00 **Beds:** 1T 2D **Baths:** 3 En (5)

Mynachlog-ddu

SN1430

Dolau Isaf Farm, *Mynachlog-ddu, Clunderwen, Pembs, SA66 7SB.* Comfort and service in central tranquil settings. Quality farmhouse food. **Open:** All year (not Xmas/New Year) **Grades:** WTB 3 Star
01994 419327 (also fax) Mrs Lockton *dolau-isaf@pfh.co.uk* **D:** £22.00–£25.00 **S:** £22.00 **Beds:** 1T 2D **Baths:** 2 En 1 Pr

All details shown are as supplied by B&B owners in Autumn 2001

Narberth

SN1014

Woods Cross, Narberth, Pembrokeshire, SA67 8RQ. **Open:** Mar to Oct
01834 860694 Mrs Logan **D:** £16.50–£17.50
S: £20.00 **Beds:** 2D **Baths:** 1 Sh ⏰ (14) 🅿 (4)
⏼ 🛏.
Woods Cross is a cottage 8 miles from Tenby, 5 miles from Saundersfoot, 5 minutes from Oakwood. Views overlooking the Preseli Hills. Everyone given a warm, homely welcome. Folly Farm 3 miles. Car essential.

Canton House, Robeston Wathen, Narberth, Pembs, SA67 8EP. Large peach-coloured country house, panoramic views. Convenient touring, amenities. **Open:** All year (not Xmas/New Year) **Grades:** WTB 2 Star
01834 860104 Mrs Brown **D:** £20.00
S: £20.00–£35.00 **Beds:** 1F 1T 1D 1S
Baths: 1 Sh ⏰ (5) 🅿 🔲 ✕ 🔔

Great Canaston Farm, Robeston Wathen, Narberth, Pembrokeshire, SA67 8DE. River & woodland walks surround comfortable/spacious farmhouse. Breakfasts a speciality. **Open:** All year (not Xmas/New Year)
01437 541254 (also fax) Mrs Lewis *eleanor2@ tesco.net* **D:** £18.00–£23.00 **S:** £25.00 **Beds:** 2F
Baths: 1 Sh ⏰ 🅿 (5) ⏼ 🔲 ✕ 🔲 🛏 🔔

New Hedges

SN1302

Pen Mar Guest House, New Hedges, Tenby, Pembs, SA70 8TL. Friendly, comfortable, family-run hotel (Tenby 1 mile; Saundersfoot 1 1/2 miles). **Open:** All year (not Xmas/New Year) **Grades:** WTB 2 Star, AA 3 Diamond
01834 842435 Mr Hurton *penmarhotel@ jhurton.freeserve.co.uk* www.s-h-systems.co. uk/a15498.html **D:** £18.00–£25.00 **S:** £23.50–£30.00 **Beds:** 2F 2T 6D **Baths:** 6 En 4 Sh ⏰ 🅿 (12) 🔲 ✕ 🔲 🛏 🔔 **cc**

Newport

SN0539

Llysmeddyg Guest House, East Street, Newport, Pembrokeshire, SA42 0SY. Listed Georgian house and mews flat and mountain bike hire. **Open:** All year (not Xmas)
01239 820008 Ian & Penny Ross *penny@ ipross.freeserve.co.uk* **D:** £22.00–£24.00
S: £25.00–£35.00 **Beds:** 1F 1D 2T 1S
Baths: 2 En 1 Sh ⏰ 🅿 (5) ⏼ 🔲 ✕ 🔲 🛏 🔔

Neyland

SM9605 ⚓ Jolly Sailor

Y Ffynnon, 45 Honeyborough Road, Neyland, Milford Haven, Pembs, SA73 1RF. Comfortable, private house. Friendly welcome. Irish ferry by prior arrangement. **Open:** All year (not Xmas/New Year)
Grades: WTB 1 Star
01646 601369 (also fax) D Hawley **D:** £16.00
S: £16.00 **Beds:** 1T 1D 1S **Baths:** 1 Sh 🅿 (1)
🔲 🛏.

Nolton Haven

SM8618 ⚓ Mariners' Inn

Mariners Inn, Nolton Haven, Haverfordwest, Pembs, SA62 3NH. Adjacent to coastal path and beach. Owner managed. **Open:** All year
01437 710469 D: £21.00 **S:** £42.00 **Beds:** 1F 6T **Baths:** 7 En ⏰ ⏼ 🔲 🛏 ✕ 🔲 🛏. ❋ 🔔 **cc**

Nolton Haven Farm House, Nolton Haven, Haverfordwest, Pembs, SA62 4NH. Beachside farmhouse, working farm. 75 yards village inn, quiet, good walks. **Open:** All year (not Xmas)
01437 710263 (also fax) Mr Canton *stilbb@ noltonhaven.com* www.noltonhaven.com
D: £15.00 **S:** £15.00 **Beds:** 3F 2D 1T 1S
Baths: 2 Pr 4 Sh ⏰ 🅿 (20) 🔲 🛏 🔲 🛏.

Pembroke

SM9801 ⚓ Carew Inn, Milton Brewery

Merton Place House, 3 East Back, Pembroke, SA71 4HL. **Open:** All year
01646 684796 Mrs Pearce
D: £15.00–£17.50 **S:** £17.50–£20.00 **Beds:** 2D 2T 1S **Baths:** 1 Sh ⏰ 🔲 🛏. 🔔
Lovely old Victorian merchants' house, walled gardens at rear. Small, pretty bedrooms. Two twin rooms and double so only six guests taken at any one time. Centre of Pembroke, close castle, buses and trains. Full of books and pictures. Quiet house.

Rosedene, Hodgeston, Freshwater East, Pembroke, SA71 5JU. Peaceful village location, 1 mile Coastal Footpath. Affordable luxury! **Open:** Easter to Nov
01646 672586 E A Fallon **Fax:** 01646 672855 *eileen@rosedene85.freeserve.co.uk* www.rosedene85.freeserve.co.uk **D:** £22.00–£27.00 **S:** £32.00–£37.00 **Beds:** 1F 2T 4D
Baths: 7 En ⏰ 🅿 (7) ⏼ 🔲 ✕ 🔲 🛏. ♿1 🔔 **cc**

B&B owners may vary rates – be sure to check when booking

RATES

D = Price range per person sharing in a double or twin room
S = Price range for a single room

Pembroke Dock

SM9603

The Old Rectory, Cosheston, Pembroke Dock, Pembroke, SA72 4UJ. Large former rectory in 2 acre gardens. **Open:** All year (not Xmas)
01646 684960 Mrs Bailey **D:** £17.50–£20.00
S: £17.50–£20.00 **Beds:** 1F 1D 2T 1S
Baths: 2 Sh ⏰ 🅿 (4) 🔲 🛏 🛏. 🔔

Penally

SS1199

Giltar Grove Country House, Penally, Tenby, Pembs, SA70 7RY.
Open: All year
Grades: WTB 3 Star, AA 4 Diamond
01834 871568 Ms Diment *giltarbnb@aol.com* www.giltargrovecountryhouse.co.uk
D: £20.00–£25.00 **Beds:** 1F 3D 1T 1S
Baths: 4 En 1 Pr 1 Sh ⏰ 🅿 (10) ⏼ 🔲 🔲 🛏. 🔔
Late Victorian Welsh country house, totally refurbished with charm and character retained. Peaceful location, near unspoilt beaches and castles. Great walks, wildlife and scenery right outside the door - Coastal Path just 3 mins away. All bedrooms ensuite, 2 with four-posters. As mentioned in 'Which?', Sunday Times, Top 20 Finalist in AA Landlady of the Year.

Brambles Lodge, Penally, Tenby, Pembs, SA70 7QE. Detached guest house in picturesque coastal village only 1.5m Tenby. **Open:** Feb to Oct
Grades: WTB 3 Star
01834 842393 Mrs Nightingale *nightingales@ easicom.com* www.smoothhound.co. uk/hotels/brambles.html **D:** £16.00–£23.00
S: £18.00–£20.00 **Beds:** 1F 2T 4D 1S
Baths: 6 En 1 Sh ⏰ 🅿 (6) 🔲 🛏 ✕ 🔲 🛏.

BATHROOMS

En = Ensuite
Pr = Private
Sh = Shared

Pontfaen

SN0234

Gellifawr Country House, Pontfaen, Fishguard, Pembs, *SA65 9TX.* **Open:** All year **01239 820343 Fax: 01239 820128** *info@ gellifawr.co.uk* www.gellifawr.co.uk **D:** £23.00–£27.50 **S:** £28.00–£35.00 **Beds:** 1F 6D **Baths:** 7 En ♿ 🖪 (20) ⚡ 📺 ✕ 📺 🛏, ✻ 🚲 **cc** Welcoming country hotel, seven bedrooms, set in 12 acres in the Preseli National Coastal Park. Comfortable & relaxed, 4 miles to the beaches. Bar and restaurant, with excellent home-cooked food. Excellent walking country or a place to come & relax. 3 star.

Poppit Sands

SN1548

Glan-y-Mor, Poppit Sands, St Dogmaels, Cardigan, Pembs, *SA43 3LP.* Ex-farmhouse with sea view. **Open:** All year (not Xmas/New Year) **01239 612329** Mrs Sharp **D:** £15.00 **S:** £15.00 **Beds:** 1D **Baths:** 1 Sh 🖪 🛏 📺 🛏, 🚲

Porthgain

SM8132

Ynys Barry Country Hotel, Porthgain, Haverfordwest, Pembs, *SA62 5BH.* **Open:** All year **01348 831180 Fax: 01348 831800** *ynysbarry@ adl.com* www.ynysbarryhotel.co.uk **D:** £19.00–£26.00 **S:** £18.00–£25.00 **Beds:** 4F 4T 6D **Baths:** 14 En ♿ 🖪 (200) 📺 🛏 ✕ 📺 🛏, 🚲 **cc** Coastal hotel situated in the National Park. Close to Coastal Path and the beaches of Abereiddy and Traeth Llyfn, and the unspoilt harbourside village of Porthgain. Ideal walking and holiday centre. Self-catering cottages also available, fully licensed bar and restaurant.

Robeston Wathen

SN0815

Canton House, Robeston Wathen, Narberth, Pembs, *SA67 8EP.* Large peach-coloured country house, panoramic views. Convenient touring, amenities. **Open:** All year (not Xmas/New Year) **Grades:** WTB 2 Star **01834 860620** Mrs Brown **D:** £20.00 **S:** £20.00–£35.00 **Beds:** 1F 1T 1D 1S **Baths:** 1 Sh ♿ (5) 🖪 📺 ✕ 🚲

Planning a longer stay? Always ask for any special rates

Saundersfoot

SN1304

Pinewood, Cliff Road, Wisemans Bridge, Narberth, Pembs, *SA67 8NU.* Peaceful, comfortable accommodation. Beach: 350 yards. Lounge sea view, on Coastal Path. **Open:** All year **Grades:** WTB 3 Star **01834 811082** Mrs Grecian **D:** £19.50 **S:** £25.00 **Beds:** 1T 2D **Baths:** 3 En 🖪 (3) 📺 📺 🛏, 🚲

Solva

SM8024 🍴 Royal George, Harbour House, Ship Inn, Farmers Arms, Grove Hotel

Pendinas, St Brides View, Solva, Haverfordwest, Pembs, *SA62 6TB.* Glorious sea views from all rooms, good food, warm welcome. **Open:** Easter to Oct **Grades:** WTB 3 Star **01437 721283** Ms Davies *pendinas.solva@ talk21.com* www.pendinas.co.uk **D:** £20.00–£22.00 **S:** £20.00–£22.00 **Beds:** 2D 2S **Baths:** 1 Sh 🖪 (3) ⚡ 📺 📺 🛏, 🚲

St Brides

SM8010 🍴 Swan Inn, Castle Inn, The Griffin

Fopston Farm, St Brides, Haverfordwest, Pembs, *SA62 3AW.* C17th working farm of 282 acres with interesting features. Beautiful scenery, lovely safe beaches. **Open:** Easter to Oct **01646 636271 (also fax)** Mrs Price **D:** £22.00–£25.00 **S:** £28.00–£31.00 **Beds:** 1F 2T 1D **Baths:** 1 En 2 Sh 🖪 (6) ⚡ 📺 ✕ 📺 🛏, 🚲

St Davids

SM7525 🍴 Sloop Inn, Grove Hotel, Farmers' Arms, City Inn, St Non's Hotel, Old Cross

Ty Olaf, Mount Gardens, St Davids, Pembs, *SA62 6BS.* Quiet bungalow, within reach of cathedral, restaurants, coast path, beaches. **Open:** All year **Grades:** WTB 3 Star **01437 720885 (also fax)** Mrs Liggitt *rona.liggitt@which.net* www.stdavids.co. uk/bnb/tyolaf.htm **D:** £17.00–£19.00 **S:** £17.00–£19.00 **Beds:** 1F 1D 1T 1S **Baths:** 1 Sh 🖪 (3) ⚡ 📺 📺 🛏, 🚲 🚲

Pen Albro Guest House, 18 Goat Street, St Davids, Haverfordwest, Pembs, *SA62 6RF.* Cathedral 150 yards, coastal path 0.25 hr, pub next door. **Open:** All year **Grades:** WTB 1 Star **01437 721865 D:** £15.50 **S:** £15.50 **Beds:** 1D 1T 1S 📺 🛏 ✕ 🚲

Ramsey House, Lower Moor, St Davids, Haverfordwest, Pembs, *SA62 6RP.* **Open:** All year (not Xmas) **Grades:** WTB 4 Star, AA 4 Diamond, RAC 4 Diamond **01437 720321 & 01437 720332** Mr & Mrs Thompson **Fax: 01437 720025** *info@ ramseyhouse.co.uk* www.ramseyhouse.co.uk **D:** £31.00–£33.50 **S:** £31.00–£67.00 **Beds:** 4D 3T **Baths:** 6 En 1 Pr 🖪 (8) ⚡ 📺 🛏 ✕ 📺 🚲 **cc** Superior non-smoking 4 Star guest house exclusively for adults. Convenient location for Cathedral and Coast Path. Award-winning dinners/wines with Welsh emphasis. Licensed bar and friendly relaxed hospitality completes your enjoyment. Dinner B&B £46–£50 pppn, £276–£300 weekly.

St Florence

SN0801

La Ponterosa, Eastern Lane, St Florence, Tenby, *SA70 8LJ.* Enjoy warm friendly hospitality. Village location. Perfectly situated for exploring Pembrokeshire. **Open:** All year **Grades:** WTB 3 Star **01834 871674** Mrs Mayhew **D:** £18.00–£24.00 **S:** £20.00–£25.00 **Beds:** 1F 2T 3D **Baths:** 6 En 🖪 (10) 📺 ✕ 📺 🛏, 🚲

St Ishmael's

SM8307

Skerryback Farmhouse, Sandy Haven, St Ishmael's, Haverfordwest, Pembs, *SA62 3DN.* Welcoming C18th farmhouse, adjoining Coastal Path, relaxed atmosphere, tea/coffee on arrival. **Open:** Mar to Nov **01646 636598** Mrs Williams **Fax: 01646 636595** *williams@farmersweekly.net* www.pfh. co.uk **D:** £22.00–£25.00 **S:** £20.00–£25.00 **Beds:** 1D 1T 1S **Baths:** 1 Sh 2 En ♿ 🖪 ⚡ 📺 ✕ 📺 🛏, 🚲

BATHROOMS
En = Ensuite
Pr = Private
Sh = Shared

Tenby

SN1300   🍺 *Cross Inn, Paddock Inn*

Clarence House Hotel, *Esplanade, Tenby, Pembs, SA70 7DU.* **Open:** Feb to Dec
01834 844371 Mr Phillips **Fax: 01834 844372**
clarencehotel@freeuk.com
www.clarencehotel-tenby.co.uk **D:** £19.00–
£49.00 **S:** £19.00–£49.00 **Beds:** 8F 19S 16D
31T **Baths:** 74 Pr ⚡ 📺 ⊁ ✕ 📺 ⚿ 🅰️ Superbly situated in centre of esplanade overlooking South Beach. Steps to beach opposite hotel door. Panoramic views encompassing Castle Hill, Galdey Island and Giltar Point. Golf course short walk away. Town centre short level walk. Lift to all floors.

The Lynmaure, *26 Victoria Street, Tenby, Pembs, SA70 7DY.* Perfectly situated for Pembrokeshire Coastal Path or town centre. **Open:** All year (not Xmas)
01834 842844 (also fax) Mr Egginton
D: £16.00–£25.00 **S:** £22.00–£30.00 **Beds:** 3F
4T 8D 2S **Baths:** 17 Pr ⅋ 📺 ✕ 📺 🅰️ cc

Pen Mar Guest House, *New Hedges, Tenby, Pembs, SA70 8TL.* Friendly, comfortable, family-run hotel (Tenby 1 mile; Saundersfoot 1 1/2 miles). **Open:** All year (not Xmas/New Year) **Grades:** WTB 2 Star, AA 3 Diamond
01834 842435 Mr Hurton *penmarhotel@ jhurton.freeserve.co.uk* www.s-h-systems.co.uk/a15498.html **D:** £18.00–£25.00 **S:** £23.50–£30.00 **Beds:** 2F 2T 6D **Baths:** 6 En 4 Sh ⅂ 🅿 (12) 📺 ✕ 📺 ⬛ 🅰️ cc

Glenthorne Guesthouse, *9 Deer Park, Tenby, Pembs, SA70 7LE.* Situated 250 metres from Tenby's beautiful beaches and coast path. **Open:** All year (not Xmas)
01834 842300 Mr & Mrs Lapham **D:** £14.00–£20.00 **S:** £14.00–£20.00 **Beds:** 2F 5D 1T 1S
Baths: 5 En 1 Pr 3 Sh ⅂ 🅿 (5) 📺 ⊁ ✕ 📺 🅰️

St Oswalds Guest House, *Picton Terrace, Tenby, Pembs, SA70 7DR.* Fifty yards beach, Town two minutes, ensuite rooms, Private parking. **Open:** Apr to Oct
01834 842130 (also fax) Mr Nichols
D: £17.00–£25.00 **Beds:** 7D 4F **Baths:** 11 En
⅂ (2) 🅿 (10) 📺 ⬛ 🅰️

Ripley St Marys Hotel, *St Marys Street, Tenby, Pembs, SA70 7HN.* Central Floral Hotel, 75 yards from sea front, private garage parking. **Open:** Easter to Oct
01834 842837 (also fax) Mr Mace **D:** £25.00–£28.00 **S:** £25.00–£29.00 **Beds:** 3F 4D 3T 2S
Baths: 8 En 3 Sh ⅂ 🅿 (12) 📺 ⊁ ⬛ 🅰️

Trefin

SM8332

The Old Court House Vegetarian Guest House, *Trefin, Haverfordwest, SA62 5AX.* Cosy cottage close to spectacular coastal path; excellent vegetarian food.
Open: All year
01348 837095 L Brodie www.pembrokeshire.on-line.co.uk/courthouse **D:** £21.50–£23.50
S: £21.50–£23.50 **Beds:** 2D 1T **Baths:** 2 En
⅂ (5) 🅿 (2) ⅋ 📺 ✕ 📺 ⬛ 🅰️

Tufton

SN0428   🍺 *Bridge End Inn, Drovers' Arms*

Golwg-y-Fro, *Tufton, Haverfordwest, Pems, SA63 4UB.*
Open: Feb to Oct
01437 532379
Mrs Llewellyn **D:** £16.50–£18.00 **S:** £18.50–£19.50 **Beds:** 1F 2D **Baths:** 2 Sh ⅂ 🅿 📺 ⬛ Warm welcome awaits you, perfectly situated at the foot of Preseli Mountain. Panoramic view overlooking Llys-y-fran Reservoir. Ideal, fishing, walks, coastal paths, beaches, oak wood. Peaceful surroundings, comfortable beds for good night's rest. Full breakfast, ample parking. Recommended by guests. Off road.

Walwyns Castle

SM8711

Barley Villa Farm House, *Walwyns Castle, Haverfordwest, Pembs, SA62 3EB.* Spacious modern farmhouse in scenic countryside. Warm welcome awaits you.
Open: Easter to Nov
01437 781254 Mrs Davies *barley-villa@ pfh.co.uk* **D:** £18.00–£22.00 **S:** £21.00–£25.00
Beds: 2D 1T **Baths:** 2 En 1 Sh ⅂ (10) 🅿 (4) ⅋ 📺 ✕ 📺 ⬛ 🅰️

Wisemans Bridge

SN1406

Pinewood, *Cliff Road, Wisemans Bridge, Narberth, Pembs, SA67 8NU.* Peaceful, comfortable accommodation. Beach: 350 yards. Lounge sea view, on Coastal Path.
Open: All year **Grades:** WTB 3 Star
01834 811082 Mrs Grecian **D:** £19.50
S: £25.00 **Beds:** 1T 2D **Baths:** 3 En 🅿 (3) 📺 📺 ⬛ 🅰️

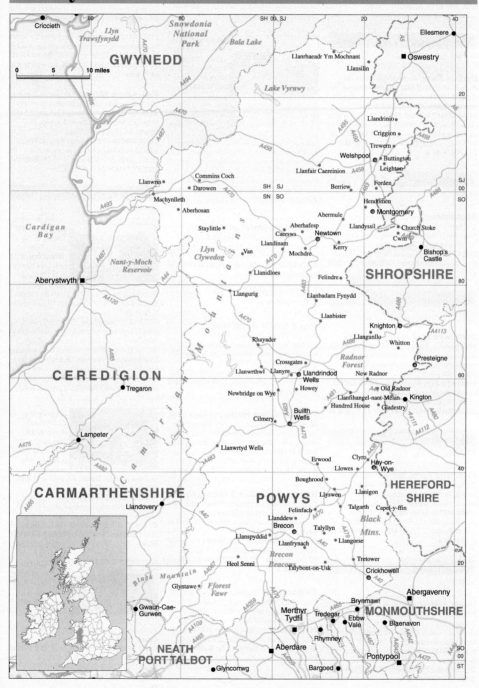

Planning a longer stay? Always ask for any special rates

Aberhafesp
SO0692

Dyffryn Farm, *Aberhafesp, Newtown, Powys, SY16 3JD.* 5 Star accommodation on organic hill farm - walks & nature reserve nearby. **Open:** All year (not Xmas) **01686 688817 & 07885 206412 (M)** Mr & Mrs Jones **Fax: 01686 688324** *dave&sue@clara.net* www.daveandsue.clara.net **D:** £24.00–£25.00 **S:** £24.00–£25.00 **Beds:** 1F 1D 1T **Baths:** 3 En ⅍ ⊠ Ⅴ ▥ ♨

Aberhosan
SN8097

Bacheiddon Farm, *Aberhosan, Machynlleth, Powys, SY20 8SG.* Working farm. Ideal walking, touring area. Close RSPB and MWT. **Open:** May to Oct **01654 702229** Mrs Lewis **D:** £18.00–£20.00 **S:** £20.00–£25.00 **Beds:** 3D **Baths:** 3 En ▣ ⊠ ♨

Abermule
SO1694

Dolforwyn Hall Hotel, *Abermule, Montgomery, Powys, SY15 6JG.* Picturesque country hotel with comfortable ensuite rooms overlooking the Severn Valley. **Open:** All year **01686 630221** K Galvin **Fax: 01686 630360** *enquiries@dolforwyn.co.uk* www.dolforwyn.co. uk **D:** £30.00 **S:** £39.50–£45.00 **Beds:** 1F 2T 3D 2S **Baths:** 8 En ⅍ ▣ (30) ⅍ ⊠ Ⅴ ▥ ♨ cc

Berriew
SJ1800

Plasdwpa Farm, *Berriew, Welshpool, Powys, SY21 8PS.* Magnificent Mountain setting in this very comfortable farmhouse, very tranquil. **Open:** Mar to Nov **01686 640298 (also fax)** Mrs Hughes *plas@ care4free.net* **D:** £15.00–£16.00 **S:** £18.00–£20.00 **Beds:** 1F 1D 1T **Baths:** 1 Sh ⅍ ▣ (4) ⅍ ⊠ ✕ ♨

Boughrood
SO1339

Upper Middle Road, *Boughrood, Brecon, Powys, LD3 0BX.* Quiet location overlooking mountains. Cycle route Hay-On-Wye 7 miles. **Open:** All year (not Xmas/ New Year) **Grades:** WTB 3 Star **01874 754407** K Kelleher *middleroad@ lineone.net* www.middleroad.free-online.net **D:** £19.00 **S:** £26.00 **Beds:** 1T 1D **Baths:** 1 En ⅍ ▣ (3) ⅍ ⊠ ✕ Ⅴ ▥ ♨

Brecon
SO0428   ♨ *Seland Newydd , White Swan, Old Ford, Traveller's Rest, Griffin Inn, Tai'r Bull, Castle Hotel, George Hotel, Camden Arms*

Old Ford Inn, *Brecon, LD3 7YB.* **Open:** All year **Grades:** WTB 3 Diamond **01874 665220** *enquiries@ theoldfordinn.co.uk* www.theoldfordinn.co.uk **D:** £24.00–£27.00 **S:** £26.00–£35.00 **Beds:** 2F 1T 4D 1S **Baths:** 8 En ⅍ ▣ (16) ⅍ ⊠ ♙ ✕ ▥ ♨ cc
Ancient coaching inn, traditional beamed bars & dining room, alongside the A40, 'twix Brecon & Abergavenny, enjoying a glorious setting with superb southerly views over the Beacons. Ideally situated for pony trekking, Llangorse Lake & hill walking, which are all available nearby.

Lansdowne Hotel, *39 The Watton, Brecon, Powys, LD3 7EG.* Warm & friendly family-run hotel & restaurant located in centre of Brecon. **Open:** All year **01874 623321** Mrs Mulley **Fax: 01874 610438** *reception@lansdownehotel.co.uk* www.lansdownehotel.co.uk **D:** £23.50–£25.00 **S:** £27.50–£30.00 **Beds:** 2F 5D 2T **Baths:** 9 Pr ⊠ ✕ Ⅴ ▥ ♨ cc

Flag & Castle Guest House, *11 Orchard Street, Llanfaes, Brecon, Powys, LD3 8AN.* Family-run guest house near to town centre and National Park. **Open:** All year **Grades:** WTB 3 Star **01874 625860** Mr & Mrs Richards **D:** £20.00–£25.00 **S:** £25.00 **Beds:** 2T 1D **Baths:** 3 En ⅍ ▣ ⅍ ⊠ Ⅴ ▥ ♨

Tir Bach Guest House, *13 Alexandra Road, Brecon, Powys, LD3 7PD.* Panoramic view of Brecon Beacons. Quiet road near town centre. **Open:** All year (not Xmas) **01874 624551** Mrs Thomas www.tirbach.co. uk **D:** £18.00–£19.00 **S:** £25.00–£30.00 **Beds:** 1F 1D 1T **Baths:** 1 Sh ⅍ ▣ ♙ ♨ ♨

Brecon Canal Guest House, *Canal Bank, The Watton, Brecon, Powys, LD3 7HG.* Situated adjacent to Brecon Canal, five minutes walk from town. **Open:** Feb to Nov **Grades:** WTB 2 Star **01874 623464 Fax: 01874 610930** *brecanal@ brecon112.freeserve.co.uk* **D:** £17.00–£20.00 **S:** £17.00 **Beds:** 1D 2T 1S **Baths:** 2 En ▣ (6) ⊠ ✕ Ⅴ ▥ ♨

Tir Bach, *Libanus, Brecon, Powys, LD3 8NE.* Beautiful C17th Welsh longhouse in Brecon Beacons National Park. **Open:** All year (not Xmas) **Grades:** WTB 3 Star **01874 625675** Mrs Norris **Fax: 01874 611198** *norris.tirbach@talk21.com* **D:** £20.00–£22.00 **S:** £23.00–£25.00 **Beds:** 1T 2D **Baths:** 2 En 1 Pr

Beacons Accommodation and Restaurant, *16 Bridge Street, Brecon, Powys, LD3 8AH.* Georgian town house. Variety of well-appointed standard ensuite & luxury period rooms. **Open:** All year (not Xmas) **01874 623339 (also fax)** Mr & Mrs Jackson *beacons@brecon.co.uk* www.beacons.brecon.co. uk **D:** £18.00–£29.50 **S:** £20.00 **Beds:** 6F 4D 3T 1S **Baths:** 11 En 1 Sh ⅍ ▣ (14) ⅍ ⊠ ♙ ✕ Ⅴ ▥ ⅍ ♨ cc

Pen-y-Bryn House, *Llangorse, Brecon, LD3 7UG.* Situated in the Brecon Beacons National Park, overlooking Llangorse Lake, large gardens, mountains beyond. **Open:** All year (not Xmas) **01874 658606** Mrs Thomas **Fax: 01874 658215** *jumt@pen-y-bryn79.freeserve.co.uk* **D:** £20.00 **S:** £25.00 **Beds:** 1F 1T 1D **Baths:** 2 En 1 Pr ⅍ ▣ ⅍ ⊠ ✕ Ⅴ ▥ ♨

Builth Wells
SO0350

Dollynwydd Farm, *Builth Wells, Powys, LD23RZ.* **Open:** All year (not Xmas) **01982 553660 (also fax)** Mrs Williams **D:** £18.00–£20.00 **S:** £18.00–£20.00 **Beds:** 1D 2T 2S **Baths:** 1 En 2 Sh ▣ (6) ⅍ ⊠ ✕ ▥.
C17th farmhouse lying beneath Eppynt Hills. Very comfortable house down quiet farm lane. Within easy distance of Elan Valley, Brecon Beacons, Black Mountains, Hay-on-Wye bookshops. Superb area for walking, touring, birdwatching. 1 mile from Builth Wells B4520 - 1st left down lane signed Tregare/Erwood.

Rhydfelin, *Builth Road, Builth Wells, Powys, LD2 3RT.* 1725 cosy stone guest house, restaurant, bar and tea garden. **Open:** All year (not Xmas) **Grades:** WTB 3 Star **01982 552493** E M Moyes *liz@ rhydfelinguesthouse.freeserve.co.uk* www.rhydfelinguesthouse.freeserve.co.uk **D:** £19.50–£22.50 **S:** £26.00–£44.00 **Beds:** 1F 2D 1T **Baths:** 1 En 2 Sh ⅍ ▣ (12) ⅍ ⊠ ♙ ✕ Ⅴ ▥.

The Cedar Guest House, *Hay Road, Builth Wells, Powys, LD2 3AR.* Built 1880, on A470 backing Wye Valley with good views, good food, parking. **Open:** All year **01982 553356** Mr Morris **Fax: 01982 553193** www.cedars.co.uk **D:** £20.00–£22.00 **S:** £27.50–£30.00 **Beds:** 1F 1D 3T 2S **Baths:** 5 En 2 Sh ⅍ ▣ (10) ⊠ ♙ ✕ Ⅴ ▥. ✽ ♨ cc

Planning a longer stay? Always ask for any special rates

Llewelyn Leisure Park, *Cilmery, Builth Wells, Powys, LD2 3NU.* Jacuzzi, snooker, views, hospitality, inn, cows, sheep; self-catering, camping. **Open:** All year **01982 552838** Mr Johnson **Fax: 01982 551090** *deejay1010@aol.com* **D:** £18.00–£22.00 **S:** £22.00–£26.00 **Beds:** 2F 1S **Baths:** 2 Sh ⚡ 🅿 📺 ⋔ ✕ 🆅 & ♨ cc

Woodlands, *Hay Road, Builth Wells, Powys, LD2 3BP.* Impressive Edwardian house, with ensuite facilities with secluded parking. **Open:** All year (not Xmas) **01982 552354 & 07967 387718 (M)** Mrs Nicholls **Fax: 01982 552354** *HeskethN@aol.com* **D:** £18.00–£20.00 **S:** £22.00–£25.00 **Beds:** 4T **Baths:** 4 En 🅿 (4) ✄ 📺 ▥ & ♨

Buttington
SJ2408

1 Plas Cefn, *Heldre Lane, Buttington, Welshpool, Powys, SY21 8SX.* Quiet private house. **Open:** All year (not Xmas/New Year) **01938 570225** Mr Broxton **D:** £15.00 **S:** £15.00 **Beds:** 1F 1D 1S **Baths:** 1 Sh ✄ ✕

Caersws
SO0391

The Talk House (Ty Siarad), *Pontdolgoch, Caersws, Powys, SY17 5JE.* Delightful C19th Inn, completely refurnished in recent years. **Open:** All year (not Xmas/New Year) **01686 688919** Mrs Dawson **D:** £37.50–£47.50 **S:** £65.00 **Beds:** 3D **Baths:** 3 En ⚡ (14) 🅿 (30) ✄ 📺 ✕ 🆅 ▥ & cc

Capel-y-ffin
SO2531

The Grange, *Capel-y-Ffin, Abergavenny, NP7 7NP.* Small Victorian guest house situated in the beautiful Black Mountains. **Open:** Easter to Nov **Grades:** WTB 1 Star **01873 890215** Mrs Griffiths **Fax: 01873 890157** **D:** £22.50–£23.00 **S:** £22.50–£23.00 **Beds:** 1F 1D 1T 1S **Baths:** 3 En ⚡ (6) 🅿 (10) 📺 ⋔ ✕ 🆅 ▥ & ♨

Church Stoke
SO2794

The Drewin Farm, *Cwm, Church Stoke, Montgomery, Powys, SY15 6TW.* C17th farmhouse with panoramic views. Offa's Dyke footpath on doorstep. **Open:** Easter to Oct **Grades:** WTB 4 Diamond **01588 620325 (also fax)** C M E Richards *ceinwen@drewin.freeserve.co.uk* **D:** £20.00–£22.00 **S:** £25.00 **Beds:** 1F 1T **Baths:** 2 En 🅿 (6) ✄ 📺 ⋔ ✕ 🆅 ▥ ♨

Cilmery
SO0051 ⬢ *Prince Llewellyn*

Llewelyn Leisure Park, *Cilmery, Builth Wells, Powys, LD2 3NU.* Jacuzzi, snooker, views, hospitality, inn, cows, sheep; self-catering, camping. **Open:** All year **01982 552838** Mr Johnson **Fax: 01982 551090** *deejay1010@aol.com* **D:** £18.00–£22.00 **S:** £22.00–£26.00 **Beds:** 2F 1S **Baths:** 2 Sh ⚡ 🅿 📺 ⋔ ✕ 🆅 & ♨ cc

Clyro
SO2143

Tump Farm, *Clyro, Hay-on-Wye, Hereford, HR3 6JY.* Comfortable, friendly, peaceful farmhouse in outstandingly beautiful countryside. Near 'book town', Hay-on-Wye. **Open:** All year (not Xmas) **01497 820912** Mrs Francis *jafrancis20@hotmail.com* **D:** £15.00 **S:** £16.50 **Beds:** 1T 1D **Baths:** 1 Sh 🅿 (4) 📺 ▥ ♨

Baskerville Hall Hotel, *Clyro Court, Clyro, Hay-on-Wye, Hereford, HR3 5LE.* Brecon Beacons, mountainous. Indoor pool, sauna, Conan Doyle connections **Open:** All year **01497 820033** *enquiries@baskervillehall.co.uk* www.baskerville.co.uk **D:** £25.00–£37.00 **S:** £35.00–£47.00 **Beds:** 5F 10T 10D 2S **Baths:** 27 En ⚡ 🅿 (30) 📺 ⋔ ✕ 🆅 ▥ ♨ cc

Commins Coch
SH8402

Gwalia, *Commins Coch, Machynlleth, Powys, SY20 9PZ.* Peaceful, remote, small farm. Home cooked, wholefood, vegetarian meals. **Open:** All year **01650 511377** Mrs Chandler **D:** £18.00 **S:** £18.00 **Beds:** 1F 1T **Baths:** 1 Sh ⚡ 🅿 ✄ ⋔ ✕ 🆅

Crickhowell
SO2118 ⬢ *White Hart*

Glangrwyney Court, *Crickhowell, Powys, NP8 1ES.* Georgian mansion in 4 acres of established gardens surrounded by parkland. **Open:** All year **01873 811288** C R Jackson **Fax: 01873 810317** *glangrwyne@aol.com* www.walescountryhousebandb.com **D:** £22.50–£27.50 **S:** £55.00 **Beds:** 1F 2T 2D **Baths:** 4 En 1 Pr ⚡ 🅿 (10) ✄ 📺 ⋔ ✕ 🆅 ▥ ✳ ♨

National Grid References given are for villages, towns and cities – not for individual houses

Castell Corryn
Castell Corryn, *Llangenny, Crickhowell, Powys, NP8 1HE.* Above Usk Valley in Brecon Beacons NP. Outstanding views, beautiful restful gardens, homely welcome. **Open:** All year (not Xmas/New Year) **Grades:** WTB 3 Star **01873 810327 (also fax)** Mr Harris *castellcorryn@aol.com* **D:** £20.00–£25.00 **S:** £25.00–£30.00 **Beds:** 2T 1D **Baths:** 2 En 1 Pr ⚡ 🅿 (6) 📺 🆅 ▥ ♨

White Hall, *Glangrwyney, Crickhowell, Powys, NP8 1EW.* Comfortable Georgian house next to restaurant, close to Black Mountains. **Open:** All year (not Xmas) **01873 811155 & 01873 840267** Ms Llewelyn **Fax: 01873 840178** *pllewelyn@white-hall.freeserve.co.uk* **D:** £15.00–£20.00 **S:** £20.00–£25.00 **Beds:** 1F 2D 1S **Baths:** 2 En 1 Sh ⚡ 🅿 (3) ✄ 📺 ⋔ 🆅 ▥ ♨

Bell Inn, *Glangrwyney, Crickhowell, Powys, NP8 1EH.* C17th former coaching inn. Excellent food and ensuite accommodation. **Open:** All year **01873 810247** Mr Llewelyn **Fax: 01873 812155** **D:** £25.00–£35.00 **S:** £30.00 **Beds:** 1F 2D 2T 1S **Baths:** 6 En ⚡ 🅿 (20) 📺 ✕ 🆅 ▥ ♨ cc

Criggion
SJ2915

Brimford House, *Criggion, Shrewsbury, Shropshire, SY5 9AU.* Elegant Georgian farmhouse in tranquil scenic surroundings between Breidden Hills & River Severn. **Open:** All year **01938 570235** Mrs Dawson *info@brimford.co.uk* www.the-virtual-shropshire.co.uk/brimford-house **D:** £20.00–£25.00 **S:** £20.00–£30.00 **Beds:** 1T 2D **Baths:** 2 En 1 Sh ⚡ 🅿 (4) ✄ 📺 ⋔ 🆅 ▥ ♨

Crossgates
SO0864

Guidfa House, *Crossgates, Llandrindod Wells, Powys, LD1 6RF.* Stylish Georgian house offering comfort, good food and a relaxing atmosphere. **Open:** All year **01597 851241** Mr Millan **Fax: 01597 851875** *guidfa@globalnet.co.uk* **D:** £26.50 **S:** £31.50 **Beds:** 2D 3T 1S **Baths:** 5 Pr 2 Sh 🅿 (10) ✄ 📺 ✕ 🆅 ▥ ♨ cc

Cwm
SO2590

The Drewin Farm, *Cwm, Church Stoke, Montgomery, Powys, SY15 6TW.* C17th farmhouse with panoramic views. Offa's Dyke footpath on doorstep. **Open:** Easter to Oct **Grades:** WTB 4 Diamond **01588 620325 (also fax)** C M E Richards *ceinwen@drewin.freeserve.co.uk* **D:** £20.00–£22.00 **S:** £25.00 **Beds:** 1F 1T **Baths:** 2 En 🅿 (6) ✄ 📺 ⋔ ✕ 🆅 ▥ ♨

Darowen

SH8201

Cefn Farm, Darowen, Machynlleth, Powys, SY20 8NS. Unsurpassable views, good walking. Half-hour drive seaside. Open fire, personal service. **Open:** All year
01650 511336 Mr Lloyd **D:** £20.00 **S:** £20.00 **Beds:** 1F 1D ⌂ 🖪 ⊀ 🛏 ▥ ♨

Erwood

SO0942

Trericket Mill Vegetarian Guesthouse, Erwood, Builth Wells, Powys, LD2 3TQ. Listed C19th watermill in Wye Valley, friendly and informal.
Open: All year (not Xmas) **Grades:** WTB 2 Star
01982 560312 Mr Legge **Fax:** 01982 560768
mail@trericket.co.uk www.trericket.co.uk
D: £21.00–£24.00 **S:** £31.00–£34.00 **Beds:** 2D 1T **Baths:** 3 En ⌂ 🖪 (8) 🖻 ✕ 🖤 ▥ ♨

Hafod-y-Gareg, Erwood, Builth Wells, Powys, LD2 3TQ. Secluded medieval farmhouse in idyllic Welsh hillside locality. Rooms overlooking pasture & woodland.
Open: All year (not Xmas)
01982 560400 Mrs McKay **D:** £13.50–£17.50 **S:** £13.50–£17.50 **Beds:** 1F 2D 1T **Baths:** 3 En ⌂ 🖪 (6) 🖻 🛏 ✕ 🖤 ▥ ♨

Felindre

SO1681

Trevland, Felindre, Knighton, Powys, LD7 1YL. Quiet border village. Warm welcome offered to all. **Open:** All year
01547 510211 Mrs Edwards *marion@ trevland.freeserve.co.uk* **D:** £16.50–£17.50 **S:** £16.50–£17.50 **Beds:** 1F 1D 1T **Baths:** 3 En ⌂ 🖪 (5) 🖻 🛏 ✕ 🖤 ▥ ♨ ❄ ♨

Felinfach

SO0933   ◁ Griffin Inn

Llwyncynog Farm, Felinfach, Brecon, Powys, LD3 0UG. Peaceful location commanding splendid views of Brecons and Black mountains. **Open:** Easter to Oct
01874 623475 Mrs Phillips **D:** £18.00–£20.00 **S:** £20.00–£25.00 **Beds:** 1F 1T 1D **Baths:** 2 En 1 Pr 🖪 (2) 🛏 🖤 ♨

Forden

SJ2200

Church House, Forden, Welshpool, Powys, SY21 8NE. Georgian house, near Powis Castle & Welshpool Light Railway. Large garden. **Open:** All year (not Xmas/ New Year)
01938 580353 Mrs Bright **D:** £17.50 **S:** £17.50 **Beds:** 1F 1D 1T **Baths:** 1 Pr 1 Sh ⌂ 🖪 🖻 ♨

Meithrinfa, Forden, Welshpool, Powys, SY21 8RT. Large bungalow set in own grounds, elevated position, overlooking Severn Valley. **Open:** Easter to Nov
01938 580458 Mrs Hughes **D:** £18.00–£20.00 **S:** £20.00–£22.00 **Beds:** 1F 1T **Baths:** 2 En ⌂ 🖪 (3) ✄ 🖤 ▥ ♨ ♨

Gladestry

SO2355

Offa's Dyke Lodge, Gladestry, Kington, Herefordshire, HR5 3NR. Luxury accommodation, spectacular views, fine cooking, the perfect relaxing break.
Open: All year
01544 370341 Steve Wright **Fax:** 01544 370342 *odl@offtec.ltd.uk* www.offas-dyke-lodge. co.uk **D:** £25.00–£27.00 **S:** £33.00–£35.00 **Beds:** 1D 2T **Baths:** 2 En 1 Pr ⌂ 🖪 (10) ✄ 🖤 ✕ 🖤 ▥ ♨ 3 ♨

Glyntawe

SN8416   ◁ Tafarn-y-Garreg, Gwyn Arms

Dderi Farm, Glyntawe, Penycae, Swansea, W Glam, SA9 1GT. Modernised C15th farmhouse. Lovely setting. Good walks. Good welcome. **Open:** All year (not Xmas/New Year) **Grades:** WTB 3 Star
01639 730458 Mrs Williams **D:** £20.00 **S:** £22.00 **Beds:** 1T 1D **Baths:** 2 En ⌂ (6) 🖪 (3) ✄ 🖤 ▥ ♨

Hay-on-Wye

SO2242   ◁ Radnor Arms, Seven Stars, Wheelwrights' Arms, Erwood Inn, Rhydspence Inn, Kilvert Court Hotel, Pandy Inn, Red Lion

Tinto House, Broad Street, Hay-on-Wye, Hereford, HR3 5DB. **Open:** All year (not Xmas) **Grades:** WTB 3 Star, AA 4 Diamond
01497 820590 Mr Evans **Fax:** 01497 821058
tinto@haydesign.co.uk www.hay-on-wye.co. uk/tinto **D:** £22.50–£27.50 **S:** £30.00
Beds: 1F 2D 1T **Baths:** 4 En ⌂ 🖪 (2) ✄ 🖤 🛏 🖤 ▥ ♨
Comfortable Grade II Listed Georgian town house in the centre of famous book town of Hay-on-Wye, which has a large garden overlooking the River Wye and Radnorshire Hills.

Lansdowne, Cusop, Hay-on-Wye, Hereford, HR3 5RF. Victorian house, pretty garden, beautiful views, spacious bedrooms, quiet location.
Open: All year (not Xmas/New Year)
01497 820125 (also fax) Mr Flack
reservations@lansdowne.bb.co.uk
www.lansdowne.bb.co.uk **D:** £18.00–£20.00 **S:** £25.00–£27.00 **Beds:** 1T 1D **Baths:** 2 En 🖪 (3) ✄ 🖤 ✕ ▥ ♨

The Old Post Office, Llanigon, Hay-on-Wye, Hereford, HR3 5QA. A very special find in Black Mountains, superb vegetarian breakfast.
Open: All year
01497 820008 Mrs Webb www.oldpost-office. co.uk **D:** £18.00–£28.00 **S:** £20.00–£35.00 **Beds:** 1F 1D 1T **Baths:** 2 En 1 Sh ⌂ 🖪 (3) ✄ 🖤 🛏 🖤 ▥ ♨

Tump Farm, Clyro, Hay-on-Wye, Hereford, HR3 6JY. Comfortable, friendly, peaceful farmhouse in outstandingly beautiful countryside. Near the small, interesting 'book town' of Hay-on-Wye.
Open: All year (not Xmas)
01497 820912 Mrs Francis *jafrancis20@ hotmail.com* **D:** £15.00 **S:** £16.50 **Beds:** 1T 1D **Baths:** 1 Sh 🖪 (4) 🖤 ▥ ♨

Fernleigh, Hardwick Road, Cusop, Hay-on-Wye, Hereford, HR3 5QX. Quiet location walking distance of the famous book town of Hay-on-Wye. **Open:** Easter to Oct
01497 820459 Mr Hughes **D:** £16.00–£20.00 **S:** £19.00 **Beds:** 2D 1S **Baths:** 1 En 1 Sh ⌂ 🖪 (4) ✄ 🖤 ✕ 🖤 ▥ ♨

Hendomen

SO2198

Hendomen Farmhouse, Hendomen, Montgomery, Powys, *SY15 6HB.* **Open:** All year (not Xmas/New Year)
01686 668004 Miss Wilson **Fax:** 01686 668319 *bruce.lawson@btinternet.com* **D:** £18.00–£22.00 **S:** £18.00–£22.00 **Beds:** 1T 1D 1S **Baths:** 1 En 1 Sh ⊃ (9) ▣ (2) ⊬ ⊠ ✕ ▽ ▥ ⚓ **cc**
Welcome to Montgomery - an undiscovered Georgian gem. 1 mile from Offa's Dyke. Walkers our speciality. Transport (people and luggage) arranged. 1 mile from 5 pubs, hotel, museum and castle (Montgomery) Powis Castle 5 miles. Superb views and breakfasts.

Heol Senni

SN9223

Maeswalter, Heol Senni, Brecon, Powys, *LD3 8SU.* 300-year-old farmhouse situated in the picturesque Senni valley. **Open:** All year **Grades:** AA 3 Diamond, RAC 3 Diamond
01874 636629 Mrs Mayo *maeswalter@ talk21.com* **D:** £18.75–£20.00 **S:** £20.00–£25.00 **Beds:** 1F 1D 1T **Baths:** 1 En 2 Sh ⊃ (1) ▣ (8) ⊬ ⊠ ▽ ▥ ⚓

Howey

SO0558

Holly Farm, Howey, Llandrindod Wells, Powys, *LD1 5PP.* Comfortable old farmhouse, dates back to Tudor times, bedrooms have lovely views of countryside. **Open:** All year (not Xmas)
01597 822402 Mrs Jones www.smoothhound.co.uk/hotels/hollyfm. html **D:** £20.00–£25.00 **S:** £24.00–£26.00 **Beds:** 1F 2D 2T **Baths:** 3 En 2 Sh ⊃ ▣ (6) ▽ ✕ ▥ ⚓

Hundred House

SO1154

Gaer Farm, Hundred House, Llandrindod Wells, Powys, *LD1 5RU.* Converted stone timber barn with panoramic views of surrounding mountains. **Open:** All year (not Xmas) **Grades:** WTB 2 Star
01982 570208 (also fax) Mrs Harley *relax@ gaerfarm.co.uk* www.gaerfarm.co.uk **D:** £18.00–£25.00 **S:** £20.00 **Beds:** 2F 1S **Baths:** 3 En ⊃ ▣ ⊬ ⊠ ✕ ▽ ▥ ♿3 ⚓

Kerry

SO1489 ⚓ *Dolfor Inn*

Greenfields, Kerry, Newtown, Powys, *SY16 4LH.* Comfortable guest house, good food, warm welcome. **Open:** All year (not Xmas) **Grades:** WTB 2 Star
01686 670596 Mrs Madeley **Fax:** 01686 670354 **D:** £18.00–£20.00 **S:** £18.00–£22.00 **Beds:** 1F 1D 1T 1S **Baths:** 3 En ⊃ (4) ▣ (6) ⊬ ▽ ✕ ▽ ▥ ⚓ **cc**

Knighton

SO2872 ⚓ *Horse & Jockey*

9 West Street, Knighton, Powys, *LD7 1EN.* **Open:** All year (not Xmas/New Year)
01547 529021
Mrs Maslen-Jones *maslenjones@ btinternet.com.uk* **D:** £18.00 **S:** £20.00 **Beds:** 1T 1D **Baths:** 1 Sh ⊃ (6) ▣ (2) ⊬ ▽ ✕ ▥ ⚓
A warm welcome to The Gateway to Mid Wales, perfect for exploring the beautiful Welsh Marches & walking in the foothills. Visit the Offa's Dyke Centre, Elan Valley (Red Kite Country), Shropshire Hills Discovery Centre & other attractions within easy travelling distance.

The Fleece House, Market Street, Knighton, Powys, *LD7 1BB.* Attractive decorated quality accommodation in converted C18th coaching inn. **Open:** All year **Grades:** WTB 3 Star
01547 520168 Mrs Simmons *info@ fleecehouse.co.uk* www.fleecehouse.co.uk **D:** £20.00–£28.00 **S:** £25.00–£36.00 **Beds:** 3T **Baths:** 2 En 1 Pr ⊬ ▽ ▥ ⚓

Westwood, Presteigne Road, Knighton, Powys, *LD7 1HY.* Spacious Victorian house in quiet town location. Warm, friendly welcome. **Open:** All year
01547 520317 Mrs Sharratt *sharratt@ westwoode.freeserve.co.uk* **D:** £18.00 **S:** £18.00 **Beds:** 1F 1D 1S **Baths:** 1 En 1 Sh ⊃ ▣ (4) ⊬ ▽ ✕ ▽ ▥ ⚓

Offa's Dyke House, 4 High Street, Knighton , Powys, *LD7 1AT.* Warm friendly B&B situated in the heart of Knighton. **Open:** All year
01547 528634 (also fax) S Ashe **D:** £16.00 **S:** £16.00 **Beds:** 2T 3D 1S **Baths:** 3 Sh ⊃ ▣ (4) ⊬ ▽ ✕ ✕ ▥ ⚓

Leighton

SJ2305 ⚓ *Green Dragon*

Sycamore Cottage, Leighton, Welshpool, Powys, *SY21 8HR.* Perfectly situated for exploring Mid Wales, warm welcome, farmhouse breakfast. **Open:** All year (not Xmas/New Year)
01938 553899 Mr & Mrs Jones **D:** £17.00–£20.00 **S:** £18.00–£22.00 **Beds:** 2F 2D **Baths:** 2 Sh ⊃ ▣ ⊬ ▽ ▽ ✕ ▥ ⚓

Orchard House, Leighton, Welshpool, Powys, *SY21 8HN.* Comfortable, lovely, quiet location, yet close to Welshpool. **Open:** All year **Grades:** WTB 3 Star
01938 553624 (also fax) Mrs Pearce *pearce@ orchardhouse.softnet.co.uk* **D:** £22.00–£23.00 **S:** £22.00–£25.00 **Beds:** 1T 2D **Baths:** 2 En 1 Pr ▣ ⊬ ▽ ▽ ▽ ▥ ♿ ⚓ **cc**

Llanbadarn Fynydd

SO0977

Hillside Lodge Guesthouse, Llanbadarn Fynydd, Llandrindod Wells, Powys, *LD1 6TU.* Half mile main road, on hillside in private gardens overlooking Ithon Valley. **Open:** Jan to Dec
01597 840364 Mr & Mrs Ainsworth **D:** £20.00 **S:** £25.00 **Beds:** 2F 1T **Baths:** 3 En ⊃ ▣ (6) ⊬ ▽ ▽ ✕ ▽ ▥ ⚓

Llanbister

SO1073

The Lion, Llanbister, Llandrindod Wells, Powys, *LD1 6TN.* Small country pub set in beautiful countryside overlooking river. **Open:** All year
01597 840244 J E Thomas **Fax:** 01597 840601 *lion@llanbister@virgin.net* **D:** £20.00 **S:** £25.00 **Beds:** 3F 1D 1S **Baths:** 5 En ⊃ ▣ (5) ▽ ▽ ✕ ▽ ▥ ⚓

Llanddew

SO0530 ⚓ *The Oak, Castle Hotel, George Hotel*

The Gables, 23 Alexandra Road, Llanddew, Brecon, Powys, *LD3 9SS.* Edwardian house, magnificent view of Brecon Beacons, private parking. **Open:** All year (not Xmas/New Year)
01874 622058 Mrs Williams **D:** £22.00 **S:** £26.00 **Beds:** 1T 2D 1S **Baths:** 1 En 2 Sh ⊬ ▽ ▥ ⚓

Llandinam

SO0288

Trewythen, Llandinam, Powys, *SY17 5BQ.* Situated in scenic surroundings and ideal for touring Lakes & Wales. **Open:** Easter to Nov
01686 688444 (also fax) Mrs Davies **D:** £22.00–£24.00 **S:** £25.00–£30.00 **Beds:** 1F 1D **Baths:** 2 En ⊃ ▣ ⊬ ▥ ⚓

Llandrindod Wells

SO0561

Greylands, *High Street, Llandrindod Wells, Powys, LD1 6AG.* Handsome Victorian townhouse. Surrounded by beautiful countryside. Secure cycle storage. **Open:** All year
01597 822253 Mrs MacDonald *greylands@csma-netlink.co.uk* **D:** £16.00–£19.00 **S:** £17.00–£20.00 **Beds:** 1F 2D 1T 3S **Baths:** 6 En 1 Sh (5) cc

Llandrinio

SJ2817

Haimwood, *Llandrinio, Llanymynech, Powys, SY22 6SQ.* C18th guest house. Beautiful rural situation and views. River Severn. **Open:** All year
01691 830764 (also fax) Mrs Nixon **D:** £18.00–£23.00 **S:** £18.00–£28.00 **Beds:** 1D 2T **Baths:** 1 En 1 Sh (6)

Llandyssil

SO1995

The Dingle, *Cwminkin, Llandyssil, Montgomery, Powys, SY15 6HH.* Converted barn. Private, peaceful valley, running stream, wildlife. Garaging. **Open:** All year
01686 668838 (also fax) Mrs Nicholson *kaybuzzards@altavista.com* **D:** £15.00 **S:** £15.00 **Beds:** 1F 1D 1S **Baths:** 1 Sh (8) (6)

Llanfair Caereinion

SJ1006

Cwm Llwynog, *Llanfair Caereinion, Welshpool, Powys, SY21 0HF.* Easy reach Powis Castle, steam railway, garden with unusual plants. **Open:** All year (not Xmas)
01938 810791 (also fax) Ms Cornes **D:** £20.00 **S:** £20.00 **Beds:** 2D 1T **Baths:** 2 Pr 1 Sh

Madogs Wells, *Llanfair Caereinion, Welshpool, Powys, SY21 0DE.* Beautiful valley, watch bird life from your breakfast table. Astronomy holidays. **Open:** All year (not Xmas)
01938 810446 (also fax) Mrs Reed **D:** £17.00 **S:** £17.00 **Beds:** 1F 1D **Baths:** 1 Sh (5)

Llanfihangel-nant-Melan

SO1858

Summergill, *Llanfihangel-nant-Melan, Presteigne, Powys, LD8 2TN.* Surrounded by farm land. Ideal for walking and touring. **Open:** All year
01544 350247 Mrs Griffiths **D:** £15.00–£16.00 **S:** £15.00–£16.00 **Beds:** 1F 1T 1D **Baths:** 2 En 1 Sh (4)

Llanfrynach

SO0725

Llanbrynean Farm, *Llanfrynach, Brecon, Powys, LD3 7BQ.* Beautiful countryside, traditional family farmhouse, ideal location for Brecon Beacons. **Open:** Easter to Nov
01874 665222 Mrs Harpur **D:** £19.00–£21.00 **S:** £20.00–£25.00 **Beds:** 1F 1D 1T **Baths:** 2 En 1 Pr (8)

Llangorse

SO1327 *Castle Inn, Red Lion*

Trefeinon Farm, *Llangorse, Brecon, Powys, LD3 0PS.* Delightful area for exploring. Activities in the National Park. **Open:** Easter to Oct
01874 658607 Mrs Sheppard **D:** £20.00–£25.00 **S:** £20.00–£25.00 **Beds:** 1D 1S **Baths:** 2 Pr

Llangunllo

SO2171

Cefnsuran Farm, *Llangunllo, Knighton, Powys, LD7 1SL.* Set in beautiful location for a peaceful, interesting & private holiday. **Open:** All year (not Xmas/New Year)
01547 550219 Mrs Morgan **Fax: 01547 550348** *cefn@suran.freeserve.co.uk* farmbeaks.org.uk. **D:** £20.00–£22.50 **S:** £20.00–£25.00 **Beds:** 1F 1D 1T **Baths:** 1 En 1 Pr (10)

Llangurig

SN9079

The Old Vicarage Guest House, *Llangurig, Llanidloes, Powys, SY18 6RN.* Charming Victorian house in Llangurig, 1000ft above sea level, highest village in Wales. **Open:** Mar to Nov
01686 440280 (also fax) M Hartley *a0048805@infotrade.co.uk* **D:** £18.00–£22.00 **S:** £25.00 **Beds:** 1F 2D 1T **Baths:** 4 En (5) (6)

Llanidloes

SN9584 *Red Lion, Unicorn, Mount Inn*

Esgairmaen, *Van, Llanidloes, Powys, SY18 6NT.* Comfortable farmhouse in unspoilt countryside, ideal for waking & bird watching. **Open:** Easter to Oct
01686 430272 **D:** £17.00–£19.00 **S:** £17.00–£19.00 **Beds:** 1F 1D **Baths:** 2 En (1) (4)

Lloyds, *Cambrian Place, Llanidloes, Powys, SY18 6BX.* Small, informal country town hotel with high standards of hospitality. **Open:** Mar to Jan
01686 412284 Mr Lines **Fax: 01686 412666** **D:** £25.00 **S:** £19.00–£33.00 **Beds:** 3D 2T 4S **Baths:** 6 En 1 Sh

Llanigon

SO2139

The Old Post Office, *Llanigon, Hay-on-Wye, Hereford, HR3 5QA.* A very special find in Black Mountains, superb vegetarian breakfast. **Open:** All year
01497 820008 Mrs Webb www.oldpost-office.co.uk **D:** £18.00–£28.00 **S:** £20.00–£35.00 **Beds:** 1F 1D 1T **Baths:** 2 En 1 Sh (3)

Llanrhaeadr-ym-Mochnant

SJ1226

Eirianfa, *Waterfall Road, Llanrhaeadr-ym-Mochnant, Oswestry, Shropshire, SY10 0JX.* Overlooking the village and the Tanat Valley, we offer comfortable warm accommodation. **Open:** All year (not Xmas)
01691 780507 Phil Common & Cathy Laceby *eirianfa@yahoo.com* **D:** £17.50–£20.00 **S:** £25.00–£35.00 **Beds:** 1F 1D **Baths:** 1 Sh (3)

Llansilin

SJ2028 *Green Inn, Wynnstay Inn*

The Old Vicarage, *Llansilin, Oswestry, Shropshire, SY10 7PX.* Peaceful rural location. Spacious, comfortable rooms with views. Guest lounge. **Open:** All year (not Xmas/New Year)
01691 791345 (also fax) Mrs Johnson *pam@vicarage-guests.co.uk* www.vicarage-guests.co.uk **D:** £22.00–£25.00 **S:** £30.00–£35.00 **Beds:** 1T 2D **Baths:** 2 En 1 Pr (13) (4)

Lloran Ganol, *Llansilin, Oswestry, Shropshire, SY10 7QX.* Dairy and sheep working farm set in its own Welsh valley. **Open:** All year
01691 791287 Mrs Jones **D:** £15.00 **S:** £15.00 **Beds:** 1D 1T 1S **Baths:** 2 Sh

Llanspyddid

SO0028

Ashgrove, *Llanspyddid, Brecon, Powys, LD3 8PB.* This spacious old dower house is situated 2 miles from Brecon. **Open:** Mar to Sept
01874 622833 Mr Wakeham *ashgrove@btclick.com* **D:** £15.00–£16.00 **S:** £15.00–£16.00 **Beds:** 1D 2T **Baths:** 2 Sh (5)

National Grid References given are for villages, towns and cities – not for individual houses

Llanwrin

SH7803 🔹 *Penrhos Arms, Black Lion*

Mathafarn, *Llanwrin, Machynlleth, Powys, SY20 8QJ.* Historic farmhouse in beautiful Dovey Valley. Near Centre for Alternative Technology. **Open:** All year (not Xmas/New Year) **Grades:** WTB 4 Star **01650 511226 (also fax)** Mrs Hughes **D:** £20.00–£25.00 **S:** £25.00 **Beds:** 1T 1S **Baths:** 1 En 1 Pr 🛇 🄿 🄫 🛏 🅅 🖿 🚾

Llanwrthwl

SN9763 🔹 *Vulcan Arms*

Dyffryn Farm, *Llanwrthwl, Llandrindod Wells, Powys, LD1 6NU.* C17th home. Warm and friendly atmosphere. **Open:** Nov to Feb **Grades:** WTB 3 Star **01597 811017** Mrs Tyler **Fax: 01597 810609** *dyffrymfm@cs.com* **D:** £20.00–£22.00 **S:** £20.00–£22.00 **Beds:** 2D 1S 🛇 (15) 🄿 (6) 🗝 🄫 🗙 🖿 🚾

Llanwrtyd Wells

SN8746 🔹 *Stonecroft Inn, Drovers' Rest*

Kilsby Country House, *Llanwrtyd Wells, Powys, LD5 4TL.* Breathtaking views, peaceful surroundings, walkers/cyclists/ birdwatchers paradise. Friendly atmosphere. **Open:** All year (not Xmas/New Year) **Grades:** WTB 3 Star **01591 610281** Ms Cooper **Fax: 01591 610873** *kilsbyBB@aol.com* www.kilsbybb.co.uk **D:** £20.00–£22.00 **S:** £22.00–£28.00 **Beds:** 1F 1T 1D **Baths:** 1 Pr 2 Sh 🛇 🄿 (4) 🗝 🄫 🖿 🚾

Llanyre

SO0462

Highbury Farm, *Llanyre, Llandrindod Wells, Powys, LD1 6EA.* Peaceful location with short farm trail. Laundry room. Excellent food. **Open:** Mar to Nov **01597 822716 (also fax)** Mrs Evans www.farmbreaks.org.uk **D:** £18.00–£21.00 **S:** £21.00–£24.00 **Beds:** 1F 2D **Baths:** 2 En 1 Pr 🛇 (1) 🄿 (3) 🗝 🄫 🗙 🅅 🖿 🚾

Greenglades, *Llanyre, Llandrindod Wells, Powys, LD1 6EA.* Beautiful country house in tranquil setting near village inn. **Open:** All year (not Xmas) **01597 822950** E J Jones **D:** £18.00–£22.00 **S:** £20.00–£24.00 **Beds:** 1F 1D 1T **Baths:** 2 En 🛇 🄿 (3) 🗝 🄫 🛏 🅅 🖿 🚾

Llowes

SO1942

Ty-Bach, *Llowes, Glasbury, HR3 5JE.* Ornamental ponds, woodland garden, breathtaking views, abundant wildlife, birds. Friendly. **Open:** All year (not Xmas/New Year) **01497 847759** J M Bradfield **Fax: 01497 847940** *charles.bradfield@farmline.com* www.hay-on-wye.co.uk/tybach **D:** £22.50–£25.00 **S:** £30.00–£40.00 **Beds:** 1T 1D **Baths:** 2 Pr 🛇 (5) 🄿 (5) 🄫 🗙 🖿 🚾

Llyswen

SO1337 🔹 *Bridge End*

Lower Rhydness Bungalow, *Llyswen, Brecon, Powys, LD3 0AZ.* Upper Wye Valley. Wonderful view. Warm welcome. Farm house breakfast. **Open:** All year **01874 754264** Mrs Williams **D:** £18.00 **S:** £18.00 **Beds:** 1F 1D **Baths:** 2 Sh 🄿 (2) 🗝 🄫 🖿 🔳

Machynlleth

SH7400 🔹 *Black Lion, The Wildfowler*

Maenllwyd, *Newtown Road, Machynlleth, Powys, SY20 8EY.* Home from home, within walking distance all amenities, safe parking. **Open:** All year (not Xmas) **Grades:** WTB 3 Star **01654 702928 (also fax)** Mr Vince *nigel@ maenllwyd.co.uk* www.maenllwyd.co.uk **D:** £21.00–£22.50 **S:** £25.00 **Beds:** 1F 4D 3T **Baths:** 8 En 🛇 🄿 (10) 🗝 🄫 🛏 🅅 🖿 🚾 cc

Gwelfryn, *6 Green Fields, Machynlleth, Powys, SY20 8DR.* Quiet but central, fantastic breakfasts, near all tourist attractions. **Open:** Easter to Oct **01654 702532** *bb@gwelfryn.co.uk* www.gwelfryn.co.uk **D:** £18.00–£21.00 **S:** £18.00 **Beds:** 1D 1T 1S **Baths:** 1 En 1 Pr 🛇 🗝 🄫 🛏 🅅 🖿 🚾

Talbontdrain, *Uwchygarreg, Machynlleth, Powys, SY20 8RR.* Friendly family B&B. Rivers, mountains, seaside. Safe playing space, fantastic food. **Open:** All year (not Xmas/New Year) **01654 702192** Ms Matthews *talbontdrain@ btclick.com* home.btclick/talbontdrain. **D:** £19.00–£21.00 **S:** £16.00–£19.00 **Beds:** 1D 1T 2S **Baths:** 1 Pr 1 Sh 🛇 🄿 (4) 🗝 🛏 🗙 🅅 🖿 🚾

Milebrook

SO3072

Milebrook House Hotel, *Milebrook, Knighton, Powys., LD7 1LT.* Dower House, once the retreat of Emperor Haile Selassie. **Open:** All year **01547 528632 Fax: 01547 520509** *hotel@ milebrook.kc3* **D:** £37.75–£41.75 **S:** £51.00–£55.00 **Beds:** 3T 7D **Baths:** 10 En 🛇 (8) 🄿 (30) 🗝 🄫 🗙 🅅 🖿 🕹 🚾 cc

Mochdre

SO0788

Llettyderyn, *Mochdre, Newtown, Powys, SY16 4JY.* Traditional hospitality in a restored farmhouse, one ground floor room. **Open:** All year **Grades:** WTB 3 Star Farm **01686 626131** Mrs Jandrell **D:** £20.00–£22.00 **S:** £25.00–£27.00 **Beds:** 2D 1T **Baths:** 3 En 🛇 🄿 🄫 🗙 🅅 🖿 🚾

Montgomery

SO2296

The Dingle, *Cwminkin, Llandyssil, Montgomery, Powys, SY15 6HH.* Converted barn. Private, peaceful valley, running stream, wildlife. Garaging. **Open:** All year **01686 668838 (also fax)** Mrs Nicholson *kaybuzzards@altavista.com* **D:** £15.00 **S:** £15.00 **Beds:** 1F 1D 1S **Baths:** 1 Sh 🛇 (8) 🄿 (6) 🗝 🄫 🅅 🖿 🕹 🚾

Little Brompton Farm, *Montgomery, Powys, SY15 6HY.* C17th farmhouse on working farm. Superior quality for discerning visitors. **Open:** All year **Grades:** WTB 4 Star, AA 4 Diamond **01686 668371 (also fax)** G Bright *gaynor.brompton@virgin.net* www.littlebrompton.co.uk **D:** £21.00–£23.00 **S:** £25.00 **Beds:** 1F 1T 1D **Baths:** 3 En 🛇 🄿 🗝 🄫 🛏 🗙 🅅 🖿 🚾

The Manor House, *Pool Road, Montgomery, Powys, SY15 6QY.* Former house of correction, friendly welcome, private house. **Open:** All year **01686 668736** Mrs Williams **D:** £16.00 **S:** £16.00 **Beds:** 1D 1T 1S **Baths:** 1 En 1 Pr 🛇 🄿 (2) 🗝 🛏 🅅 🖿 🚾

New Radnor

SO2160

Bache Farm, *New Radnor, Presteigne, Powys, LD8 2TG.* C17th farmhouse in beautiful unspoilt countryside amidst the Welsh Marches. **Open:** All year (not Xmas) **01544 350680** Mrs Hardwick **D:** £18.00–£19.50 **S:** £22.00–£25.00 **Beds:** 2D 1T **Baths:** 1 Sh 🛇 🄿 🗝 🄫 🛏 🗙 🅅 🖿 🚾

Newbridge on Wye

SO0158

Lluest Newydd, *Llysdinam, Newbridge on Wye, Llandrindod Wells, Powys, LD1 6ND.* Luxury remote farmhouse. Ideal for walking & birdwatching. Elan Valley closeby. **Open:** All year **01597 860435 (also fax)** Mrs Burton *lluestnewydd@talk21.com* wiz.to/zzz **D:** £18.00–£22.00 **S:** £22.00–£26.00 **Beds:** 1F 1T 2D **Baths:** 2 En 1 Pr 🛇 🄿 (6) 🗝 🄫 🗙 🅅 🖿 🕹 🚾

Newtown

SO1191

Plas Canol Guest House, New Road, Newtown, Powys, SY16 1AS. Quiet, comfortable, friendly accommodation. Cotton sheets, fresh flowers, brochure available. **Open:** All year **Grades:** WTB 3 Star
01686 625598 Mrs Burd **D:** £18.00–£20.00 **S:** £18.00–£26.00 **Beds:** 2T 1D **Baths:** 3 En 🄿 (3) 🖥 🖩 ✕ 🔲 🛀 ☕

Greenfields, Kerry, Newtown, Powys, SY16 4LH. Comfortable guest house, good food, warm welcome. **Open:** All year (not Xmas) **Grades:** WTB 2 Star
01686 670596 Mrs Madeley **Fax:** 01686 670354 **D:** £18.00–£20.00 **S:** £18.00–£22.00 **Beds:** 1F 1D 1T 1S **Baths:** 3 En ➹ (4) 🄿 (6) ⅄ 🖩 🛏 ✕ 🔲 🛀 ☕ cc

Old Radnor

SO2459   🍺 Harp Inn

Trewern Farm, Old Radnor, Presteigne, Powys, LD8 2RP. Georgian farmhouse accommodation in unspoilt countryside. Lovely views and bird watching area. **Open:** All year
01544 350255 Mrs Lewis **D:** £22.00–£25.00 **S:** £18.00–£22.00 **Beds:** 1F 1T 2D 2S **Baths:** 1 En 1 Sh ➹ ⅄ 🖩 ✕ 🔲 ❄ 🛀

Pontsticill

SO0611   🍺 Butchers' Arms

Station House, Pontsticill, Merthyr Tydfil, CF48 2UP. **Open:** All year
01685 377798 Mrs Hills **Fax:** 01685 384854 **D:** £22.50–£25.50 **S:** £22.50–£25.50 **Beds:** 1F **Baths:** 1 Pr ➹ 🄿 (3) ⅄ 🖥 🖩 🛀
Comfortable and carefully converted former railway signal box. The property is on the edge of a reservoir with spectacular views across the water to the Brecon Beacons. The Brecon Mountain Railway and Taff Cycle Trail are adjacent.

Presteigne

SO3164   🍺 The Stagg, New Inn, Radnorshire Hotel

Willey Lodge Farm, Presteigne, Powys, LD8 2NB. Comfortable accommodation, C16th house, working farm amidst Welsh Marches - welcome. **Open:** All year (not Xmas/New Year)
01544 267341 Mrs Davies **D:** £18.00–£20.00 **S:** £18.00–£20.00 **Beds:** 1T 1D **Baths:** 1 Pr ➹ 🄿 🖥 🛏 ✕ 🖩 🛀

Planning a longer stay? Always ask for any special rates

Rhayader

SN9768   🍺 The Crown

Brynafon Country House Hotel, South Street, Rhayader, Powys, LD6 5BL. **Open:** All year **Grades:** WTB 3 Star
01597 810735 Mrs Collins **Fax:** 01597 810111 *info@brynafon.co.uk.* www.brynafon.co.uk.
D: £18.00–£40.00 **S:** £35.00 **Beds:** 1F 11D 4T **Baths:** 16 En ➹ 🄿 ⅄ 🖩 🛏 ✕ 🖥 🛀 🔲 ☕
A former Victorian workhouse built in 1876, this impressive building is now a comfortable, relaxed, family-run hotel. Set amid glorious hills and mountains near Rhayader and the beautiful Elan Valley with a rare Red Kite feeding centre next door.

Gigrin Farm, South Street, Rhayader, Powys, LD6 5BL. Working farm, spectacular daily feeding Red Kites. Beautiful location. **Open:** All year **Grades:** WTB 2 Star
01597 810243 Mrs Powell **Fax:** 01597 810357 *accomm@gigrin.co.uk* www.gigvin.co.uk.
D: £17.50–£20.00 **S:** £20.00–£22.50 **Beds:** 2D **Baths:** 1 Sh 🄿 (4) ⅄ 🖩 🛀

Crown Inn, North Street, Rhayader, Powys, LD6 5AB. C16th oak-beamed inn, ideally located for discovering lakeland Wales. Friendly atmosphere. Home-made meals. Cask ales. **Open:** All year
01597 811099 Mrs Giles **D:** £18.00–£20.00 **S:** £18.00–£20.00 **Beds:** 3T **Baths:** 3 En ➹ 🄿 (3) 🖥 🛏 🖩 🛀

Brynteg, East Street, Rhayader, Powys, LD6 5EA. Comfortable Edwardian guest house, overlooking hills and gardens. **Open:** All year (not Xmas) **Grades:** WTB 3 Star B&B
01597 810052 Mrs Lawrence *brynteg@ hotmail.com* **D:** £17.00 **S:** £17.00 **Beds:** 2D 1T 1S **Baths:** 3 En 1 Pr ➹ 🄿 (4) 🖥 🖩 🛀

Beili Neuadd, Rhayader, Powys, LD6 5NS. Award-winning accommodation in farmhouse - secluded position with stunning views. **Open:** All year (not Xmas)
01597 810211 (also fax) Mrs Edwards *ann-carl@thebeili.freeserve.co.uk* www.midwalesfarmstay.co.uk **D:** £23.00 **S:** £23.00 **Beds:** 2D 1T 1S **Baths:** 2 En 2 Pr ➹ (8) 🄿 🖥 🛏 🖩 🛀 ☕ 🛀

Liverpool House, East House, Rhayader, Powys, LD6 5EA. Excellent accommodation, very close to beautiful Elan Valley Reservoirs. **Open:** All year (not Xmas)
01597 810706 Mrs Griffiths **Fax:** 01597 810964 *ann@liverpoolhouse.net* www.liverpoolhouse.net **D:** £15.50–£17.00 **S:** £18.00–£22.00 **Beds:** 2F 5D 1S **Baths:** 7 En 1 Sh ➹ 🄿 (8) 🖥 🛏 🖩 🔲 🛀 cc

Staylittle

SN8892

Maesmedrisiol Farm, Staylittle, Llanbrynmair, Powys, SY19 7BN. Quiet stone-built farm house. Home cooking a speciality. Good walking. **Open:** Easter to Nov
01650 521494 P Anwyl **D:** £16.00 **S:** £16.00 **Beds:** 1F 2T 2D 1S **Baths:** 1 En 1Sh ➹ 🄿 ⅄ 🖥 ✕ 🔲 🛀

Talgarth

SO1533

The Olde Masons Arms Hotel, Hay Road, Talgarth, Brecon, Powys, LD3 0BB. C16th hotel with country cottage ambience. Ideal for walking amidst Black Mountains & Brecon Beacons. **Open:** All year
01874 711688 C J Evans **D:** £26.50–£29.50 **S:** £29.50–£32.50 **Beds:** 2F 2D 1T 2S **Baths:** 7 En ➹ 🄿 (10) 🖥 ✕ 🔲 🛀 cc

Talybont-on-Usk

SO1122

Llanddety Hall Farm, Talybont-on-Usk, Brecon, Powys, LD3 7YR. C17th Listed farmhouse in Brecon Beacons National Park, beautiful views. **Open:** All year (not Xmas)
01874 676415 Mrs Atkins **D:** £22.00–£26.00 **S:** £25.00–£26.00 **Beds:** 2D 1T **Baths:** 2 En 1 Pr ➹ (12) 🄿 (5) ⅄ 🖥 ✕ 🛀

Talyllyn

SO1027

Glascwm, Talyllyn, Brecon, LD3 7SY. Tranquil rural setting, close to the Brecon Beacons & Llangorse Lake. **Open:** All year (not Xmas)
01874 658659 J C King **Fax:** 01874 658649 *cathkin@lineone.net* **D:** £22.00 **Beds:** 1F 1D 1T **Baths:** 3 En ➹ 🄿 (4) ⅄ 🖥 🖩 🛀

Tretower

SO1821

The Firs, Tretower, Crickhowell, Powys, NP8 1RF. Charming country house situated in a secluded position of Tretower village. **Open:** All year
01874 730780 (also fax) Mrs Eckley **D:** £19.00–£23.00 **S:** £25.00 **Beds:** 1F 3D 1T **Baths:** 2 En 2 Pr 2 Sh ➹ 🄿 (10) 🖥 🛏 🖩 🛀 ❅ 🛀

Trewern

SJ2711

Greenbank, *Criggan Lane, Trewern, Welshpool, Powys, SY21 8EE.* Peaceful, rural, central for Wales and Borders. Welshpool 5 miles. **Open:** All year
01938 570319 Mrs Hamer **Fax: 01938 570719**
D: £17.00–£19.00 **S:** £17.00–£19.00 **Beds:** 1F 1T 1D **Baths:** 1 En 1 Sh ⥂ 🅿 (3) 📺 ⼻ ✕ 🖿 ⚑

Van

SN9587

Esgairmaen, *Van, Llanidloes, Powys, SY18 6NT.* Comfortable farmhouse in unspoilt countryside, ideal for waking & bird watching. **Open:** Easter to Oct
01686 430272 D: £17.00–£19.00 **S:** £17.00–£19.00 **Beds:** 1F 1D **Baths:** 2 En ⥂ (1) 🅿 (4) ⼻ 📺 ⼻ ✕ 🖿 ⚑

Welshpool

SJ2207 🍽 *King's Head, The Raven*

Tynllwyn Farm, *Welshpool, Powys, SY21 9BW.* Visitor's remark - 'Nearest place to Heaven'. Friendly, quiet, wonderful views. **Open:** All year (not Xmas)
01938 553175 Mrs Emberton *caroline@ tynllwyn.fsnet.co.uk* tynllwynfarm.co.uk
D: £18.00–£20.00 **S:** £20.00–£25.00 **Beds:** 3F 1D 1T 1S **Baths:** 3 En 2 Sh ⥂ 🅿 (10) 📺 ⼻ 🖿 ⚑

Planning a longer stay? Always ask for any special rates

Orchard House, *Leighton, Welshpool, Powys, SY21 8HN.* Comfortable, lovely, quiet location, yet close to Welshpool. **Open:** All year **Grades:** WTB 3 Star
01938 553624 (also fax) Mrs Pearce *pearce@ orchardhouse.softnet.co.uk* **D:** £22.00–£23.00 **S:** £22.00–£25.00 **Beds:** 1T 2D **Baths:** 2 En 1 Pr 🅿 ⼻ 📺 ⼻ 🅅 🖿 ⅃ ⚑ cc

Whitton

SO2767

Pilleth Court, *Whitton, Knighton, Powys, LD7 1NP.* C16th house in historic location offering quality accommodation. **Open:** All year (not Xmas)
01547 560272 (also fax) Mrs Hood **D:** £18.00 **S:** £20.00 **Beds:** 1F 2D 1T **Baths:** 1 En 1 Sh ⥂ (9) 🅿 (6) 📺 ✕ 🖿 ⚑

Location Index

The cities, towns, villages and hamlets listed in this index all have entries in STILWELL'S: BRITAIN BED & BREAKFAST under their respective regional heading. If there is no listing for the place you wish to stay in, the section map for that particular region will show you somewhere else to stay close by.

ORDER A COPY FOR A FRIEND OR COLLEAGUE

Yes, I wish to order the following title/s:

___ **Stilwell's Britain: Bed & Breakfast 2002**
@ £12.95 (inc. £2 p&p)

___ **Stilwell's Ireland: Bed & Breakfast 2002**
@ £8.95 (inc. £1 p&p)

___ **Stilwell's Britain & Ireland: Hostels & Camping 2002**
@ £7.95 (inc. £1 p&p)

___ **Stilwell's National Trail Companion**
@ £10.95 (inc. £1 p&p)

___ **Stilwell's Cycleway Companion**
@ £10.95 (inc. £1 p&p)

Sterling or EC currency cheques only please, made payable to Stilwell Publishing Ltd. Please send me my copy within 21 days of receipt of this order.

Name . . . .

Address . . . .

. . . .

Postcode . . . .

Tel No . . . .

Please send this order form, accompanied by your payment, to:
Copy Sales, Stilwell Publishing Ltd, The Courtyard, 59 Charlotte Road, Shoreditch, London, EC2A 3QW.

Please debit my credit/payment card (Visa/Mastercard only).

Card No . . . .   Expiry date ___ / ___ / ___

Signature . . . .

If different from above please state card-holder name exactly as it appears on the card, followed by card-holder address.